JG

8 95

MAINTENANCE ENGINEERING HANDBOOK

OTHER McGRAW-HILL HANDBOOKS OF INTEREST

AMERICAN SOCIETY OF MECHANICAL ENGINEERS · ASME Handbooks:
    Engineering Tables   Metals Engineering—Processes
    Metals Engineering—Design   Metals Properties

AMERICAN SOCIETY OF TOOL AND MANUFACTURING ENGINEERS:
    Die Design Handbook   Manufacturing Planning and
    Handbook of Fixture Design   Estimating Handbook
                                  Tool Engineers Handbook

ARCHITECTURAL RECORD · Time-Saver Standards
BAUMEISTER · Marks' Mechanical Engineers' Handbook
BEEMAN · Industrial Power Systems Handbook
BRADY · Materials Handbook
CARROLL · Industrial Instrument Servicing Handbook
CONSIDINE · Process Instruments and Controls Handbook
CONSIDINE AND ROSS · Handbook of Applied Instrumentation
CROCKER · Piping Handbook
DUDLEY · Gear Handbook
EMERICK · Heating Handbook
FACTORY MUTUAL ENGINEERING DIVISION · Handbook of Industrial Loss
    Prevention
FLUGGE · Handbook of Engineering Mechanics
HARRIS · Handbook of Noise Control
HARRIS AND CREDE · Shock and Vibration Handbook
HEYEL · The Foreman's Handbook
KALLEN · Handbook of Instrumentation and Controls
KING AND BRATER · Handbook of Hydraulics
KNOWLTON · Standard Handbook for Electrical Engineers
KOELLE · Handbook of Astronautical Engineering
KORN AND KORN · Mathematical Handbook for Scientists and Engineers
LEGRAND · The New American Machinist's Handbook
MAGILL, HOLDEN, AND ACKLEY · Air Pollution Handbook
MANAS · National Plumbing Code Handbook
MANTELL · Engineering Materials Handbook
MAYNARD · Industrial Engineering Handbook
PERRY · Chemical Engineers' Handbook
PERRY · Engineering Manual
ROSSNAGEL · Handbook of Rigging
ROTHBART · Mechanical Design and Systems Handbook
SHAND · Glass Engineering Handbook
STANIAR · Plant Engineering Handbook
STREETER · Handbook of Fluid Dynamics
TOULOUKIAN · Retrieval Guide to Thermophysical Properties Research Literature
TRUXAL · Control Engineers' Handbook

MAINTENANCE ENGINEERING HANDBOOK

L. C. MORROW, Editor

Consulting Editor and formerly Chief Editor, "Factory"
General Administrator, National Plant Engineering and Maintenance Conferences
Formerly Director, Special Editorial Services, McGraw-Hill Publications

SECOND EDITION

McGRAW-HILL BOOK COMPANY

New York   San Francisco   Toronto   London   Sydney

MAINTENANCE ENGINEERING HANDBOOK

43201

1234567890(MP)721069876

CONTRIBUTORS

Allard, Harold F., Maintenance Staff Consultant, Albert Ramond and Associates, Inc., Chicago, Ill.

Anderson, Elmer, Service Manager—Domestic and International, The Timken Roller Bearing Co., Canton, Ohio.

Anderson, F. C., Research and Development Laboratory, Gould-National Batteries, Inc., Minneapolis, Minn.

Austin, R. S., Maintenance Consultant. Formerly Head, Mechanical Department, American Cyanamid Co., Warner's Plant, Linden, N.J.

Baecker, M. F., Engineering Department, Gardner-Denver Co., Quincy, Ill.

Ball, Russell C., Jr., President, Philadelphia Gear Corp., King of Prussia, Pa.

Balzano, Edmund, Mechanical Engineer, Akron, Ohio.

Barkle, J. E., Chief Electrical Engineer, Power and Industrial Div., Bechtel Corp., San Francisco, Calif.

Bartlett, Robert, Service Training Instructor, Industrial Truck Div., Clark Equipment Co., Battle Creek, Mich.

Beebee, A. M., Jr., Plant Engineer, Rochester Products Div. of General Motors Corp., Rochester, N.Y.

Bennett, J. L., Technical Research Manager, The Black & Decker Manufacturing Co., Towson, Md.

Bernhard, D. L., International Research and Development Corp., Worthington, Ohio.

Black, Warren M., Marketing Manager, The Rotor Tool Co., Cleveland, Ohio.

Bodle, Alex T., Chief Engineer, Dodge Manufacturing Corp., Mishawaka, Ind. (retired)

Bonn, David E., Manager, Dust Control Department, American Air Filter Co., Inc., Louisville, Ky.

Bradley, Frank L., Assistant to Engineering Manager, Stone & Webster Engineering Corp., Boston, Mass.

Brewer, Allen F., Consultant in Lubrication, Eden, Fla.

Brinker, C. S., Assistant Manager, Generator Service, Westinghouse Electric Corp., East Pittsburgh, Pa.

Cannon, Arthur R., President, Oliver B. Cannon & Son, Inc., Philadelphia, Pa.

Cary, A. E., Exide Industrial Div., The Electric Storage Battery Co., Philadelphia, Pa.

Cooling, W. C., Corporate Staff Industrial Engineer, American Standard, American Radiator & Standard Sanitary Corp., New York, N.Y.

Cooper, Berlon C., Associate Editor, *Electrical Construction and Maintenance*, McGraw-Hill, Inc., New York, N.Y.

Cotesworth, A., Service Manager, Columbus McKinnon Chain Div., Columbus McKinnon Corp., Tonawanda, N.Y.

Crofoot, W. A., Field Service Supervisor, Industrial Truck Div., Clark Equipment Co., Battle Creek, Mich.

Davis, Alan R., Vice President and Chief Engineer, Time-Trol, Inc., Van Nuys, Calif.

Docter, Stewart, Editor, Editorial and Writing Services, Carrier Air Conditioning Co., Syracuse, N.Y.

Englert, E. C., Vice President—Sales, Hartzell Propeller Fan Co., Div. of Castle Hills Corp., Piqua, Ohio

Flesch, Robert W., Senior Management Systems Analyst, Space and Information Systems Div., North American Aviation, Inc., Downey, Calif.

Fohl, H. A., Maintenance Consultant, Parkesburg, Pa. Formerly Manager, Maintenance and Construction, Lukens Steel Co., Coatesville, Pa.

Gess, Louis, Technical Services Consultant, Philadelphia Div., Honeywell, Inc., Philadelphia, Pa.

Goldenbogen, W. N., Manager, Material Quality, Cleveland Graphite Bronze, Div. of Clevite Corp., Cleveland, Ohio.

Graveley, Oscar W., formerly Director of Maintenance, Electro-Metallurgical Co., Div. of Union Carbide Corp., Niagara Falls, N.Y.

Heisman, Fred, Manager of Supervisory Development, The Dow Chemical Co., Midland, Mich.

Herrman, D. D., Vice President—Engineering, Hartzell Propeller Fan Co., Div. of Castle Hills Corp., Piqua, Ohio.

Hicks, Tyler G., Mechanical Engineer, Hicksville, L.I., N.Y.

Honnaker, L. R., Engineering Department, Engineering Services Div., E. I. du Pont de Nemours & Co., Inc., Wilmington, Del.

Huntsberger, J. D., Manager, Application Engineering, Industrial Div., Gould-National Batteries, Inc., Trenton, N.J.

Hutchison, J. S., Chief Engineer, Lemon Products Div., Sunkist Growers, Corona, Calif.

Jakobi, William W., Medtronic, Inc., Minneapolis, Minn.

Johns, Frederick C., Professional Engineer, Buffalo Forge Co., Buffalo, N.Y.

Johnson, Glen R., Director, Material Handling Development Center, Industrial Truck Div., Clark Equipment Co., Battle Creek, Mich.

Johnson, R. M., Instructor in Maintenance Education, The Dow Chemical Co., Midland, Mich.

Kayse, James R., Staff Analyst, Dust Control Department, American Air Filter Co., Inc., Louisville, Ky.

Kelly, Robert M., Associate Editor, Editorial and Writing Services, Carrier Air Conditioning Co., Syracuse, N.Y.

Kennedy, William H., Construction Consultants, Inc., Detroit, Mich.

Klingenmeier, Jack, Application Engineer, The Gates Rubber Co., Denver, Col.

Knight, Charles E., General Superintendent of Engineering and Manufacturing Services, Monsanto Co., Plastics Div., Springfield, Mass.

Koonce, John H., Manager, Parts and Service Operations, Carrier Air Conditioning Co., Syracuse, N.Y.

Langford, R. C., Director of Research, General Precision, Inc., Aerospace Group, Research Center, Little Falls, N.J.

Lashar, W. B., Jr., Manager, Technical Sales, American Chain & Cable Co., Inc., York, Pa.

Layton, C. H., Chief Engineer, Wire Rope Divisions, American Chain & Cable Co., Inc., Wilkes-Barre, Pa.

Lennox, Frederick E., Commander, CEC, USN, Bureau of Yards and Docks, U.S. Navy, Washington, D.C.

Linneman, H. W., Administrative Assistant to Chief Engineer, Gardner-Denver Co., Quincy, Ill.

Loucks, Charles M., Consulting Chemist, Cleveland, Ohio.

Lutz, H. W., Application and Development Department, Machinery Div., Dravo Corp., Pittsburgh, Pa.

Martin, G. J., President, Industrial Management Consultants, Baltimore, Md.

Martin, John C., Staff Assistant, Headquarters Manufacturing Controls Dept., Westinghouse Electric Corp., Pittsburgh, Pa.

McPartland, J. F., Associate Editor, *Electrical Construction and Maintenance,* McGraw-Hill, Inc., New York, N.Y.

Mehler, J. J., Jr., Application and Development Department, Machinery Div., Dravo Corp., Pittsburgh, Pa.

Meng, V. W., President, Patent Scaffolding Co., Div. of Harsco Corp., Long Island City, N.Y.

Meyers, George E., Management Consultant—Maintenance Specialist, Waban, Mass.

Michal, Frank W., Consulting Engineer, Maplewood, N.J.

Mitchell, G. A., Manning, Maxwell & Moore, Inc., Crane & Hoist Div., Muskegon, Mich. (retired)

Moore, Victor K., General Foreman, Mechanical Div., American Oil Co., Whiting, Ind.

Mossor, Henry C., formerly General Zone Foreman, The Atlantic Refining Co., Philadelphia, Pa.

Moynes, John V., Vice President and General Sales Manager, Morse Chain Co., Div. of Borg-Warner Corp., Ithaca, N.Y.

National Fire Protection Association, Boston, Mass.

O'Donnell, L. H., Consultant, Maintenance Engineering Group, E. I. du Pont de Nemours & Co., Inc., Wilmington, Del.

Otto, H. R., General Service Superintendent, Otis Elevator Co., New York N.Y. (retired)

Peach, Norman, Associate Editor, *Power,* McGraw-Hill, Inc., New York, N.Y.

Pierson, Frank O., Consultant and Engineer, Cherry Hill, N.J.

Portland Cement Association, Chicago, Ill.

Pyle, Theodore H., The Lunkenheimer Co., Cincinnati, Ohio.

Quinn, Gerald C., Senior Editor—Plant Electrical and Utilities Services, *Factory,* McGraw-Hill, Inc., New York, N.Y.

Reul, Raymond I., Coordinator of Industrial Engineering, Chemical Divisions Management, FMC Corp., New York, N.Y.

Rush, D. B., Manager, Application Engineering, Reeves Pulley Co. Div., Reliance Electric & Engineering Co., Columbus, Ind. (deceased)

Sargent, James H., Manager—Product and Service Planning, Utility and Marine Industries, General Electric Co., Schenectady, N.Y.

Schmid, C. E., Director, Plant Engineering and Facilities, General Precision, Inc., Aerospace Group, Little Falls, N.J.

Schreiber, Edward T., Construction Consultants, Inc., Detroit, Mich.

Shaw, Edward T., Technical Service Section, Electric Service Div., Westinghouse Electric Corp., Pittsburgh, Pa.

Shockley, H. W., Management Specialist, Wilmington, Del.

Sinclair, Carter, Development Engineer, Specialty Control Department, General Electric Co., Waynesboro, Va.

Skala, J. J., Manager—Chemical Research, G. H. Tennant Co., Minneapolis, Minn.

Smith, Harold E. P., President, Construction Consultants, Inc., Detroit, Mich.

Smith, William J., Project Engineer, Plant Facilities, General Electric Co., Computer Department, Phoenix, Ariz.

Solworth, Mohe H., President, Industrial Sanitation Counselors, Louisville, Ky.

St. Andre, Joseph W., Chief Electrical Engineer, Kaiser Aluminum & Chemical Corp., Newark, Ohio.   (deceased)

Staniar, William, formerly Mechanical Power Engineer, E. I. du Pont de Nemours & Co., Inc., Wilmington, Del.   (deceased)

Starr, Albert R., Plant Engineer, Caterpillar Tractor Co., Mossville Plant, East Peoria, Ill.

Sterzinger, Gorman, Grounds and Services Manager, Caterpillar Tractor Co., Peoria Plant, Peoria, Ill.

Stewart, Oswald, Communications Coordinator, Sales Engineering Div., Bethlehem Steel Co., Bethlehem, Pa.

Structural Clay Products Institute, Washington, D.C.

Sutton, Edward W., Maintenance Superintendent, FMC Corp., Inorganic Chemicals Div., South Charleston, W. Va.

Swanson, E. J., Product Service Manager, Baker Div., Otis Elevator Co., Cleveland, Ohio.

Thompson, James E., Consulting Engineer, Lake Havasu Irrigation and Drainage District, Lake Havasu City, Ariz.

Thornton, Jack F., District Engineer—Oklahoma District, Exploration and Production Department, Phillips Petroleum Co., Oklahoma City, Okla.

Union Carbide Corp., Linde Div., New York, N.Y.

Wellons, Frank W., Chief Engineer, SKF Industries, Inc., King of Prussia, Pa.

Wendt, John S., Senior Development Engineer, Engineering and Construction Department, Ore Processing, Dravo Corp., Pittsburgh, Pa.

Werner, G. C., Manager of Engineering, Thomas Coupling Div., Rex Chainbelt, Inc., Warren, Pa.

Wilson, Robert, Vice President, Director of Application Engineering, The Lincoln Electric Co., Cleveland, Ohio.

Winston, Charles C., Vice President, United States Tobacco Co., New York, N.Y.

Wohlgemuth, M. J., Consultant, Swindell-Dressler Co., Pittsburgh, Pa. (deceased)

Wright, William D., Construction Consultants, Inc., Detroit, Mich.

Wyder, Carl G., Senior Editor—Maintenance, *Factory*, McGraw-Hill, Inc., New York, N.Y.   (retired)

Ytterberg, R. F., Vice President, Kalman Floor Co., New York, N.Y.

PREFACE TO FIRST EDITION

"Maintenance Engineering Handbook" is compiled for use by those people in industry who carry on the function of maintenance. For the most part, industry confers "maintenance" titles on such people. However, the title "plant engineer" many times is carried by men responsible for the upkeep of plant, equipment, and services, as well as the engineering required in plant operation. And, at times, men with production responsibilities and titles also have the responsibility for maintenance. The book has been prepared to serve the *function* rather than the title.

Moreover, this handbook will be found to be of service to management personnel. It contains treatment of the *management* phases of maintenance to an extent found nowhere else. Because of the necessarily close cooperative relationship between the maintenance and management forces, *both* maintenance and management must understand the problems in management which must be solved by the maintenance forces. There are five sections devoted to matters of management: Organization and Administration of the Maintenance Forces; Maintenance Personnel Administration; Planning and Scheduling Maintenance Work; Project Control; Costs and Budgets for Maintenance Operations. The twenty-three chapters in these five sections make this book unique.

The remainder of the book is devoted to information relative to the selection, installation, and upkeep of the kinds of equipment and services that *every* plant must deal with: buildings, electrical equipment, mechanical equipment, service equipment, transportation equipment, maintenance stores, lubricants and lubrication, instruments, sanitation, welding, corrosion control. Production equipment is treated to the extent that units entering into its design and construction are covered, such as bearings, clutches, chains, drives, gears, valves, and instruments. The chapters devoted to these units, in combination with the service manuals of equipment manufacturers, extensively supplied with the equipment, will afford a well-rounded source of instructions for the upkeep of production machines, no matter what the industry.

More than eighty men, specialists in their fields, and whose names, for the most part, appear at the heads of the chapters they have written, have contributed to the handbook. They have given of their time and knowledge, with objective self-interest, to be sure, but with far greater ambition to serve. I acknowledge my gratitude and admiration for the work they have done, and I know they will have the heartfelt thanks of the men in industry who will profit by their contributions.

In presenting "Maintenance Engineering Handbook," may I wish for the vast army of people engaged in the maintenance function the great measure of success which they deserve. Without their work, production would be but a halting thing.

L. C. MORROW

PREFACE TO SECOND EDITION

The second edition contains most of the chapters of the first edition, brought up to date where necessary. There are added chapters to cover advances in the profession of maintenance engineering that have taken place since the first edition was published. The new subjects include: programed instruction; maintenance manuals; critical path scheduling; work simplification; data processing; reliability indexes; solid state and semiconductor electronics; effective use of plant facilities; diagnostic instruments; numerical control; vibration analysis and correction; clean room construction and maintenance; chemical cleaning of equipment; maintenance and cleaning of clay products masonry; reports to management and interdepartmental reports.

L. C. MORROW

CONTENTS

Section 1

ORGANIZATION AND ADMINISTRATION OF THE MAINTENANCE FORCES

Chapter 1

GENERAL CONSIDERATIONS AND EXAMPLES

By Charles E. Knight

General Superintendent of Engineering and Manufacturing Services

Monsanto Company, Plastics Division

Springfield, Mass.

GENERAL

Why does a factory need a maintenance department? The answer to this question is the basis for developing the general concepts and basic philosophy of a maintenance engineering organization, and although the answer seems obvious, it is often lost sight of in actual practice.

The justification for a maintenance engineering group lies in its use to ensure availability of the machines, buildings, and services needed by other parts of the organization for the performance of their functions at optimum return on investment, whether this investment be in machinery, material, or people. The maintenance function should be considered an integral, important part of the organization, handling one phase of operations.

Dependence of operating personnel on maintenance engineering is ever-increasing with the complexity of the equipment used in modern industry. The cost of maintenance has become a greater part of the total cost of manufacturing and the maintenance engineering group a major unit of the company. Regardless of this tremendous growth in importance, cost, and complexity of the maintenance function, it is important to remember that the function exists because it is a necessary facet of the whole plant operation, not a self-sufficient unit. It is one part of a team which can be successful only when functioning cooperatively. It cannot be an individual star shining for its own glory.

The maintenance function and the group charged with this responsibility are called by various names. That there may be a clear understanding of the field to be covered in subsequent discussion, a definition of maintenance engineering is necessary. Engineering other than that normally found in research can be divided into four categories—development engineering, design engineering, construction engineering, and maintenance engineering. Development engineering covers the exploratory phase of materials processing. Design engineering implies the transfer of new processes or new developments into completed drawings and specifications, suitable for erection of equipment. Construction engineering employs these drawings and specifications to construct and install the equipment and its attendant buildings and services. *Maintenance engineering* is concerned with the day-by-day problems of keeping the physical plant in good operating condition. Frequently the actual activity of the maintenance engineering group will extend into the other categories, but in subsequent discussion of functions and organization maintenance engineering will be considered in the perspective just outlined.

SCOPE

Although in practice the scope of the activities of a maintenance engineering department is different in each plant and is influenced by plant size, type, company policy, and industry-wide and sectional precedent, it is possible to group these activities into two general classifications: Primary functions, most of which are included in the justification for the maintenance engineering department, and secondary functions which, because of expediency, know-how, precedent, or because there is no other logical division of the plant to which the responsibility can be assigned, are delegated to the maintenance engineering group. (Not all maintenance engineering organizations include all these primary functions, particularly where one of these assumes such major importance as to warrant a separate organization reporting directly to top management.)

Primary functions:
1. Maintenance of existing plant equipment.
2. Maintenance of existing plant buildings and grounds.
3. Equipment inspection and lubrication.
4. Utilities generation and distribution.
5. Alterations to existing equipment and buildings.
6. New installations of equipment and buildings.

Secondary functions:
1. Storeskeeping.
2. Plant protection, including fire protection.
3. Waste disposal.
4. Salvage.
5. Insurance administration.
6. Janitorial service.
7. Property accounting.
8. Pollution and noise abatement.
9. Any other service delegated to maintenance engineering by plant management.

Note. The list of secondary functions is not intended to be complete but is merely indicative of the type of service rendered by some maintenance organizations. There are many others, ranging from purchasing to vermin control. Some enlargement on these functions follows:

Primary Functions. *Maintenance of Existing Plant Equipment.* This activity requires very little definition, being an axiomatic major function of all maintenance engineering groups. It is the principal reason for the existence of the maintenance group. The responsibility attached to this activity is one of making the necessary repairs to the machinery involved in the production processes, expeditiously and economically; anticipation of the need for these repairs and taking preventive action, where possible; maintenance of a group of skilled craftsmen capable of performing these duties; minimizing of the time during which machinery and equipment are unavailable for production; keeping adequate records for proper distribution of charges accrued in the performance of this work.

Buildings and Grounds. The repairs to buildings and to the external property of a plant, such as roads, tracks, sewers, and water systems, are generally assigned to the maintenance engineering group. There are, however, many other ramifications of the maintenance of buildings and grounds for which the responsibility varies considerably in different plants. Such items as janitor service, including window washing, floor washing, and general cleaning, often are separated and handled by an employee service group. Frequently road maintenance, including snow removal, is a function of a materials-handling group. A plant having extensive office facilities and a major building-maintenance program may divorce all building maintenance from the maintenance engineering group. In some plants (such as an explosives plant) where a large number of buildings are located over a considerable area, the care and maintenance of this extremely large acreage of land warrants a special organization.

Repairs and minor alterations to buildings (roofing, painting, glass replacement) and the care of electrical, plumbing, and other items normally a part of the building can logically be handled by maintenance engineering. Road repairs and the maintenance of tracks and switches, fences, and outlying structures can also be so assigned.

The justification for the omission of the items mentioned above should be based either on the fact that the job per se is of such magnitude as to warrant a special organization, or on the existence of some other department which by its nature can more logically and adequately supervise the work. From a cost-accounting point of view, better control can be realized if the items of true maintenance of buildings and grounds can be separated from the items of routine clean-up which are affected to a much greater extent by the type of occupancy.

Lubrication and Inspection. These functions can be handled either by the production department or by the maintenance engineering group. In medium-sized or large plants, delegation of this work to the maintenance engineering group results in a more standardized procedure and an impartial follow-up. Frequently production groups are swayed by expediency and production goals in their interpretation of equipment inspection results.

In plants where most of the time of production operators is spent in attendance of machines, with adequate time to handle lubrication, it is economically unsound to provide a separate group for this service. Even when this is the case, lubricant specifications, procedure, and record inspection should be provided by the maintenance engineering group. In plants such as steel and paper mills, where operation of the equipment requires a thorough knowledge of its construction, and where most inspections must be conducted during outages which idle the operators, the inspection function is most economically handled by them; but again, the interpretation of inspection results and the responsibility for taking necessary corrective action should be with maintenance engineering.

In the average plant where most production personnel are engaged entirely in superficial operation of the equipment, the responsibility for both lubrication and inspection is best delegated to one group administered by the maintenance engineering department. Deviations should be carefully scrutinized and require sound economic justification.

Utilities. Whether to include generation and distribution of utilities with the maintenance engineering department should be determined by consideration of the relative size of the two activities. In a plant with huge electric-power consumption, such as a reduction plant, the electrical group assumes tremendous importance and has a large supervisory and hourly staff. The major utilities problem is one of generation of electricity and may be handled by an electrical engineering department, divorced from other maintenance activity. In a large plant generating its own electricity and providing its own process steam, the powerhouse could assume the proportions of a small public-utilities company and justify an operating department of its own, reporting to plant management. However, in the average plant, where the number of personnel involved in the distribution of utilities is small compared with the total maintenance force, this activity logically falls in the maintenance engineering group. It can be administered either as a separate function or as part of some other function, depending upon the supervisory requirements.

Alterations and New Installations. This is probably the most controversial and nebulous area of operation for the maintenance engineering department. The three factors that seem to determine to what extent this area concerns maintenance engineering are:

1. Plant size.
2. Multiplant company size.
3. Company policy.

In a small plant of a one-plant company it is logical that, though this type of work may be handled by outside contractors, its administration and that of the maintenance force should be handled by the same department. In a small plant of a multiplant company the majority of new installations and major alterations may be handled by a central, company-wide engineering department.

In a large plant it is logical for a separate organization to handle the major portion of this work, engineering at plant or company level. Where a separate department to handle the new installation or major alteration activity exists, the problem of where to draw the line presents itself. It would be foolish to require that all new work (a new unit heater, for instance) be handled by an engineering group divorced from maintenance. There are many criteria for establishing this line of demarcation, the most common being the amount of money involved. This, however, is a rather arbitrary ground rule and sometimes impractical if followed to the letter. Other criteria frequently used are the amount of labor involved, the type of work, the amount of engineering that must precede the work, the amount of coordination with production necessary to perform the work, the relation of the work to existing installations, etc. In general, although some pretty specific rules can and should be established for the allocation of this type of work, the final decision concerning each project should be based on logic and on a mutual agreement between the two engineering groups.

Secondary Functions. *Storeskeeping.* In some plants there is a differentiation between mechanical stores and general stores. In such instances the administration of mechanical stores normally falls in the maintenance engineering group because of the close relationship of this activity with other maintenance operations. General stores, on the other hand, can be assigned to some other department such as purchasing, or if sufficiently large to warrant the expense, it may be set up as a separate department reporting to top management.

In other plants where all types of stores and storeskeeping, including receiving and distribution, are in one group, the assignment of the responsibility for this operation will depend on plant policy. Frequently this may be assigned to the maintenance engineering department for administration on the grounds that the major activity is in mechanical supplies. There is no clear-cut rule that can be followed. The decision should be based on a logical and expeditious allocation of responsibility within the over-all plant organization.

Plant Protection. Plant protection may include two categories—the guard force and the fire department. Incorporation of these functions with maintenance engineering is not general. The guard force in most plants reports through the personnel department, and only in small plants or where some special problem makes it preferable is the guard force assigned to the maintenance engineering department.

The fire department, on the other hand, is more frequently included in the maintenance engineering function, since in many plants the majority of its members are drawn from the crafts groups. Here again, however, local conditions control the organization, and present practice divides plants about evenly in preference for safety-department or maintenance-department control of the fire department.

Waste Disposal. This function is normally combined with that of yard maintenance, particularly where a disposal plant is involved, since the labor used in waste pickup and disposal is of a type similar to that used in yard maintenance. If yard maintenance is apart from the maintenance engineering department, waste disposal in all probability will be handled by the former. In instances where the salvage operation is of such magnitude as to be apart from maintenance, waste disposal is assigned to it.

Salvage. The operation of a salvage group and the organization to which it belongs depend on the type of material being handled and the magnitude of the operation. If a large part of the activity is with off-grade products, the salvage department should be set up as a separate production unit. If, on the other hand, the salvage operation primarily involves mechanical equipment, scrap lumber, paper, containers, etc., it may be assigned to the maintenance function. Frequently, where much of this reclaimed material can be reused, the salvage department can function under the administration of stores, and the reclaimed material can be routed through stores for reuse.

Insurance Administration. This category may include claims, process-equipment and pressure-vessel inspection, liaison with underwriters' representatives, and handling of insurance recommendations. These functions are frequently included with maintenance, since most of the information has to be gathered through this group. On the other hand, company policy or local conditions may require assignment of this function to some other department, such as accounting, or decentralization to the various production units.

Other Services. Unfortunately (or fortunately) the maintenance engineering department seems to be a catch-all for many other odd activities that no other single department can or wants to handle. The administration of the maintenance engineering department should be careful in accepting responsibility for these "cats and dogs" since the attention required can tend to dilute the main effort. It is human nature to welcome any activity that may increase the scope of one's department, but careful consideration should be given to the effect of such empire building on the effectiveness of the main functions of the maintenance group. Too often the maintenance superintendent is placed in the role of a "good Joe" who will do an irrelevant, spur-of-the-moment job, possibly at the expense of his primary mission, that of providing adequate plant maintenance in a satisfactory manner.

Whatever the responsibilities assigned to the maintenance engineering department, it is important that they be clearly defined and the limits of authority and responsibility established and agreed to by all concerned. Too frequently shadowy areas exist with subsequent misunderstanding and confusion which can do much to undermine smooth functioning and satisfactory relationships with other plant groups. The limits of authority and responsibility should be placed in writing and issued over management's signature to serve as a basis of operations for the maintenance engineering department. It actually becomes a charter under which the maintenance engineering group functions.

Following is one such bulletin defining the authority and responsibility of a maintenance engineering department in a medium-sized plant:

SUBJECT: MAINTENANCE ENGINEERING

SCOPE: The scope of the maintenance engineering department encompasses the maintenance, construction, utilities generation and distribution, and miscellaneous servicing phase of plant operations.

FUNCTION: The function of the maintenance engineering department is to provide the engineering and craft service required for the safe and efficient operation of the plant.

RESPONSIBILITY: The maintenance engineering department is responsible for:
1. Engineering and execution of planned maintenance, repairs, minor installations, and replacements.
2. Generation and distribution of power and other utilities.
3. Administration and supervision of crafts groups.
4. Engineering and supervision of construction projects within the scope of the group.
5. Administration of various other service facilities delegated to the group.
6. Technical consultation on mechanical problems with production supervision.
7. Providing adequate plant fire protection, including contacts with fire insurance company representatives.
8. Establishing and maintaining adequate property and accounting records covering plant equipment and property.
9. Performing all these functions in a safe and efficient manner.

DESCRIPTION OF RESPONSIBILITIES:
1. *Engineering of Planned Maintenance, Repairs, Minor Installations and Replacements*
The main objectives of maintenance engineering are:
a. To provide freedom from breakdowns during manufacturing operations.
b. To maintain equipment in a satisfactory condition for safe operation.

c. To maintain equipment at its maximum operating efficiency.

d. To reduce to a minimum the downtime resulting from breakdowns.

e. To reduce to a minimum the cost of this maintenance consistent with the above items.

f. To maintain a high level of engineering practice in the performance of the work handled by the department.

Attaining these ends necessitates:

1. Provision of an adequately staffed and supervised engineering group.
2. A sound preventive maintenance program.
3. The maintenance of adequate spare parts consistent with current conditions.
4. Continuous investigation into the causes for and remedies of emergency breakdowns.
5. Keeping abreast of industry practice, technological advancement, new methods, equipment, and materials.
6. Close cooperation with operating supervision in order to meet equipment and schedule requirements.

The responsibility for the continued economical use of production equipment lies with operating supervision. It is, however, the responsibility of the engineering group of the maintenance engineering department, in cooperation with operating supervision, to organize preventive maintenance programs, to improve the efficiency of equipment, and to develop equipment necessary to meet production schedule requirements.

To provide these services, engineers are assigned to insure that the work is done in an economical and expeditious manner at the convenience of production schedules and consistent with a high level of engineering and safety practices.

2. *Generation and Distribution of Power and Other Utilities*

The provision of economical and reliable utilities—steam, electricity, compressed air, hydraulic power, water, and sewers—is the function of the power group of the maintenance engineering department.

The power engineer is responsible for the generation and distribution of steam, the purchase and distribution of electrical power and water, the provision and distribution of the other utilities . . . to produce an adequate supply of steam of suitable quality at minimum cost.

3. *Administration and Supervision of Crafts Groups*

In order to handle the mechanical work involved in carrying out the functions of the maintenance engineering department, an adequate, skilled labor force provided with suitable equipment and facilities and properly supervised is necessary. This labor force consists of several central craft groups and a number of area groups, each with its own facilities and supervision. The over-all responsibility for the proper administration of this labor force rests with the master mechanic. The master mechanic and his assistant shall:

1. Provide the type and size of groups required as determined on the basis of a balance between the cost of establishing and maintaining the group versus cost of contracting for the work by outside firms, considering the factor of immediate around-the-clock service.
2. Plan and coordinate work distribution among crafts.
3. Provide and maintain shop equiment required.
4. Organize and carry out programs for the training of both the supervisory and hourly personnel.
5. Maintain liaison with other branches of the department.

Supervision of the individual groups is the responsibility of area or craft foremen reporting to the master mechanic. They shall direct their groups in carrying out assigned work so that the work is performed in a safe and efficient manner consistent with established quality requirements. They are also responsible for the housekeeping of their areas, training of their personnel, cooperation with operating supervision and area engineers, and other normal supervisory duties.

4. *Engineering and Supervision of Construction Projects within the Scope of This Group*

Maintenance engineering is a definite part of preliminary and final design. It is the responsibility of the maintenance engineering group to be familiar with all projects under consideration or execution that will eventually become part of the plant. Through an assigned engineer, the maintenance engineering group may handle major construction projects. In carrying out projects of this type, complete cooperation with division engineering covering work progress and necessary field changes is essential. Such accounting and property records as are necessary so that records of the final project are in keeping with the procedures established for this purpose must be maintained.

The primary responsibility for major construction projects rests with division engineering; the responsibility of maintenance engineering will vary according to the nature of the project.

It is the responsibility of the maintenance engineering department to maintain all buildings in good condition. This includes walls, roofs, windows, foundations, stairwells, as well as lighting and wiring, sprinkler systems, plumbing, lavatory and service facilities, service piping, heating and ventilating equipment, and elevators. The building maintenance engineer annually prepares a budget with adequate justification covering the cost of the above. He is responsible for the performance of the necessary work within the allocated money.

5. *Administration of Various Other Service Facilities Delegated to the Group*

These are as follows:

a. *Central Stores*

The maintenance engineering department is responsible for maintaining and administering a central stores.

The type and quantity of items carried are determined by considering the economics of quantity buying, frequency of use, delivery time, and availability. The ultimate responsibility of stores inventory control rests with the plant engineer.

b. *Yards, Roadways, Parking Lots, Switch Tracks, Fences, and Sewers*

It is the responsibility of the maintenance engineering department to maintain all existing yards, roadways, parking lots, switch tracks, fences, and sewers in good condition, to provide the necessary policing, sweeping, etc., so that the plant yard, walkway, platforms and roads are at all times clean, safe and neat. The yard foreman, reporting to the master mechanic, is responsible for the above. He is further responsible for snow removal and sanding in order that the roads and walkways are in a safe, usable condition. These operations are to be performed within a budget established for this purpose.

c. *Waste Pickup and Disposal and Salvage Department*

It is the responsibility of the maintenance engineering department to provide adequate waste pickup on a routine scheduled basis, to avoid undue accumulation of waste in designated pick-up locations, and to maintain a salvage department, dump, and burning pit for the disposal of all rubbish, scrap, and discarded material or equipment in a manner to secure maximum revenue and avoid dangerous, obnoxious, or unsightly conditions.

All sales to employees of these types of material are handled through the salvage department.

    d. Employee Welfare Service and Office Janitorial Service

        Where practical, the maintenance engineering department shall provide the necessary janitorial and other services . . .

    e. River and Air Pollution . . .

    f. Sewing Room and Laundry . . .

    g. Lift Truck Repair Service . . .

  6. *Engineering and Consulting Service to Production Supervision* . . .

  7. *Fire Protection*

    The responsibility for all fire protection, fire-fighting activities, and liaison with fire insurance carriers rests with the maintenance engineering department.

    The fire chief is responsible for establishing and maintaining an adequate routine fire-equipment inspection, an organized, trained, properly equipped volunteer fire department, providing 24-hr, 7-day coverage, and close contact with the local municipal fire department.

    Contacts with fire insurance carriers including semiannual inspections, carrying out of recommendations, approvals of changes or additions and discussion concerning losses or claims are the responsibility of the building maintenance engineer. He also handles all contacts with the main office of the company on fire insurance recommendations and cooperates with the accounting department in matters relating to claims resulting from fires.

  8. *Property Accounting*

    The maintenance engineering department establishes and maintains records and reports on all equipment, work in progress and completed work necessary to provide the accounting department with the information needed for accounting, in accordance with company practice.

    The above records and reports are the responsibility of the property engineer. He also functions as the liaison with the accounting department, assists other engineers in job accounting, provides control information on the performance of the maintenance engineering department and functions as office manager of the engineering office.

ORGANIZATION

In developing an organization to handle maintenance engineering it should be remembered that there is no one "best" organization that can be used in all cases. The organization must be one tailored to fit the particular technical, geographical, and personnel situations involved. There are, however, some basic rules to be used in establishing any organization for effective group action. In addition, there are various factors of the local maintenance problem that must be taken into consideration in developing the optimum organization. It is particularly important that the formally established structure should not result in an artificial bureaucratic relationship which might hinder the smooth operation of the department. It is equally important that some recognized, formal relationship exist, specifying lines of authority and responsibility. A clearly defined organization, based on some universal truths and modified for the local situation, staffed by people who understand and appreciate each other's problems, is the one most likely to succeed.

Some of the basic concepts of good organization that should be borne in mind are:

1. *A reasonably clear division of authority with little or no overlap.* The division of authority can be functional, geographic, or based on expediency, or a combination of all three. However, there must always be a clear definition of the line of demarcation to avoid confusion and possible conflict that can result from over-

lapping authority.   This is particularly important in the case of staff assistants.

2. *The vertical lines of authority and responsibility should be kept as short as possible.*
"Stacking," or the use of assistants, should be minimized unless a clear division
of duties can be made between assistant and assisted.   It is in the interests of
efficient organization to avoid using any level merely as a medium for transmitting
information up and instructions down.

3. *Maintain optimum number of people reporting to one individual.*   This is a subject
that has been treated at considerable length by various experts in the field of
organization.   The consensus appears to be that most effective organizations limit
the number of people reporting to one supervisory individual to between three
and six.   This is accepted as being "the average number of human brains one
human brain can effectively handle."[1]   There are, of course, many factors which
can affect this limitation, and frequently where the amount of supervision necessary
is small and where the type of work supervised follows the same general pattern,
this number can be increased, sometimes to ten or twelve.   In developing an
organization to fit a particular maintenance department, it is well to consider this
ratio carefully.   Too few people reporting to an individual can result in a waste of
supervisory talent, and too many people can result in inadequate supervision.

4. *Fit the organization to the personalities involved.*   Another principle of good organization is to consider the personalities of the individuals involved.   Theoretically, of
course, an organization should be established that is technically correct and
individuals should adapt themselves to it.   However, acceptance of the thesis
that its organization should be a means toward the end of smooth functioning
of the maintenance department requires consideration of personalities making up
the organization.   This implies a flexible organization structure which is revised
periodically to fit changing personnel and conditions.

There may be several other basic factors to be considered in developing an organizational structure, but those above have been proved by experience to be of paramount
importance.

Consideration of the basic features of good maintenance engineering organization
must be accompanied by allowance for a number of local problems.   No two plants
are alike, and their differences will necessitate modifications in emphasis within the
same basic organizational structure from one plant to the next.

1. *Type of Operation.*   Maintenance may be predominantly in one field (buildings,
machines, process piping, or electrical equipment, for examples).   To the extent
that one of these fields predominates, the character of the work and the amount
and type of supervision will be affected.   Predominance of one of these categories
may also indicate the use of staff assistants.

2. *Continuity of Operations.*   Five-day, one-shift operations vs. round-the-clock, 7-day
operations will affect the size of the maintenance force and the structure of the
supervisory organization.   Night supervision introduces a problem of over-all
coordination.   Planning and preventive maintenance in the two cases assume
entirely different aspects which may require organizational recognition.   For
instance, in a one-shift, 5-day plant the entire preventive-maintenance program
can be carried out with a staff of inspectors reporting to one individual.   In a
continuous operation, where these functions can be performed only while equipment is down, this responsibility must be divided at a level where it can be exercised when the occasion arises.

3. *Geographical Situation.*   The type of maintenance organization most effective in a
compact plant, where the maintenance force can operate from a central location,
must be modified considerably to handle a dispersed plant.   A plant that occupies
a considerable area requires decentralization and may result in several parallel
organizations performing the same type of work at different locations.

4. *Size of Plant.*   The size of the plant, as it affects the number of maintenance
employees involved, must be taken into consideration in any maintenance organiza-

[1] General Sir Ian Hamilton, "The Soul and Body of an Army," p. 229, Edward Arnold & Co., London,
1921.

tion. The effect is not so much on the structure of the organization as on determination of the number of supervisory employees needed. This, in turn, affects the number of levels of supervision necessary for effective management. In a plant with a large number of maintenance employees supervision density may be increased considerably at the lowest level to provide for a high degree of specialization. Many more subdivisions, in both line and staff supervisory personnel, can be justified since this overhead is distributed over a large number of people. In the small plant, however, it is frequently necessary to double up on responsibility, resulting in an organization composed of fewer, but more versatile people.

There are no specific rules for the exact relationship between the size of the maintenance force and the organization necessary to administer it properly. This relationship can be grossly affected by other factors but, in general, the smaller the plant the greater is the relative cost of supervision required for adequate maintenance.

5. *Scope of the Plant Maintenance Department.* Referring to the introduction, it is apparent that plant policy, as it determines the activities of the plant maintenance group, must be considered in tailoring the organization of this department. Although many of these activities can be handled by additional supervision at lower levels, such differences as the inclusion of utilities or emphasis on design and construction, as well as maintenance, in one organization must be recognized at all levels. In a maintenance engineering department whose responsibility is limited to strict maintenance of machinery and buildings, the depth of the organization can and should be a great deal less than when it is necessary to provide an organization for handling more varied activities.

6. *State of Training and Reliability of Work Force.* The state of training and reliability of the work force will vary from one location to another and must be considered in constructing an organization because of the effect on supervision density and provisions for training. Where the machine-tool industry predominates, the availability of skilled craftsmen and competent supervision will result in the need for a much smaller supervisory organization, all other factors being equal. However, in a rural area, or other areas where skilled craftsmen are scarce, closer supervision is necessary at all levels, and a more comprehensive training program will be required. Another factor is the extent to which an unskilled group can be effectively decentralized. With the need for closer technical supervision, the overhead cost of decentralization can become prohibitive.

All these points must be considered in developing the optimum maintenance engineering organization. It is often necessary to compromise in some areas so that the resultant structure will be one that results in orderly, initial operation of the department, yet flexible enough for modifications to cover changing conditions such as plant growth, production modification, personnel development, and activity fluctuation. Following are several basic organization charts which demonstrate modifications dictated by some of the factors just discussed. To some extent each is a compromise with the ideal.

Figure 1-1 shows medium-sized Company A, geographically dispersed over 100 acres, employing 300 maintenance workers. The maintenance engineering group is charged with responsibility for maintaining the plant (including machinery, buildings, and grounds), generation and distribution of utilities, handling of some new construction, keeping all property records, and many other services, such as fire protection, stores, and insurance.

Figure 1-2 shows plant of Company B, of similar size and area, but one where the maintenance engineering department handles only the maintenance function. All other activities are covered by other departments.

Figure 1-3 shows the organization of Company C, a small plant of 25 to 30 maintenance employees where the person in charge of maintenance is responsible for all types of work not included with production, sales, or accounting.

Company D (Fig. 1-4) is a large plant, with a working force in excess of 15,000 people and a maintenance force of 3,000. The maintenance function is limited to the

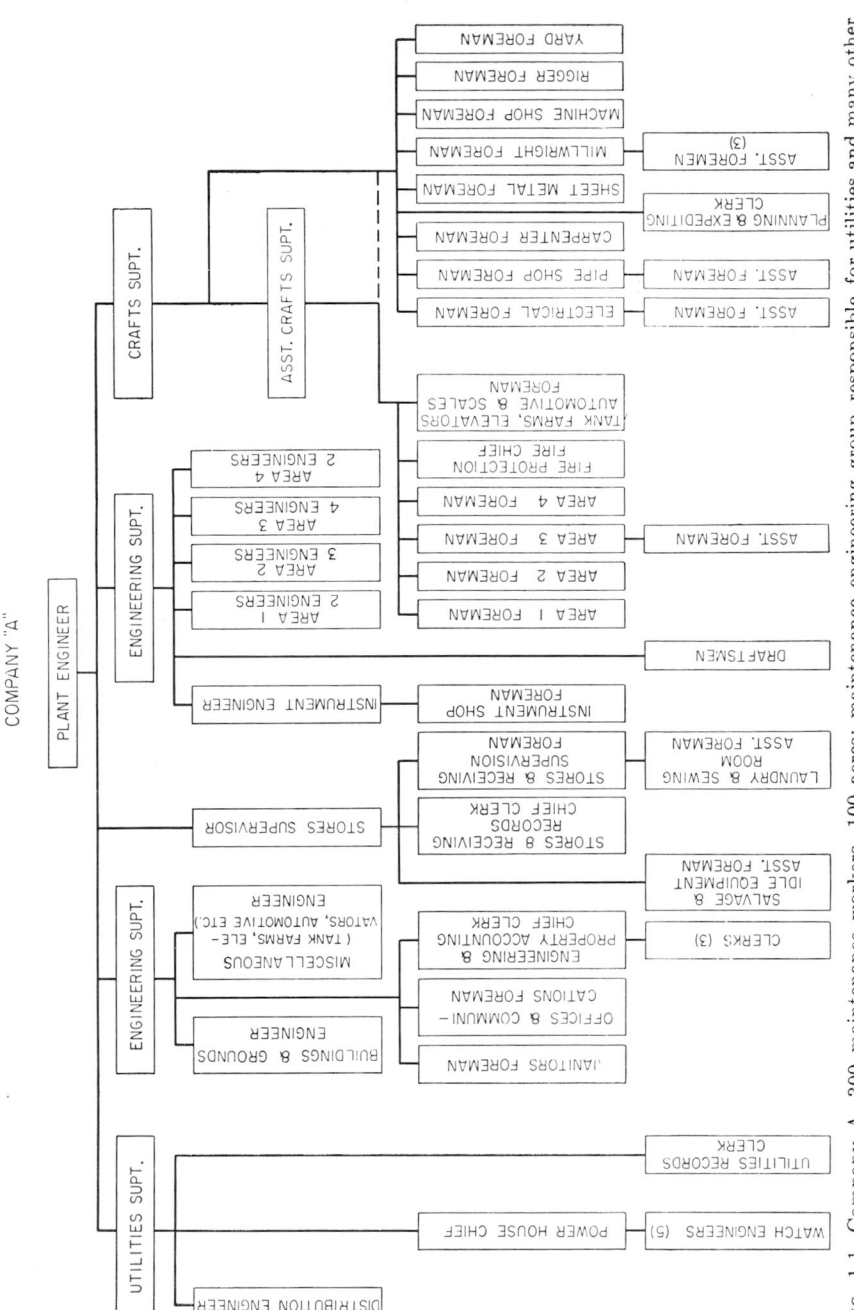

COMPANY "A"

Fig. 1-1. Company A, 300 maintenance workers, 100 acres; maintenance engineering group responsible for utilities and many other services.

1–13

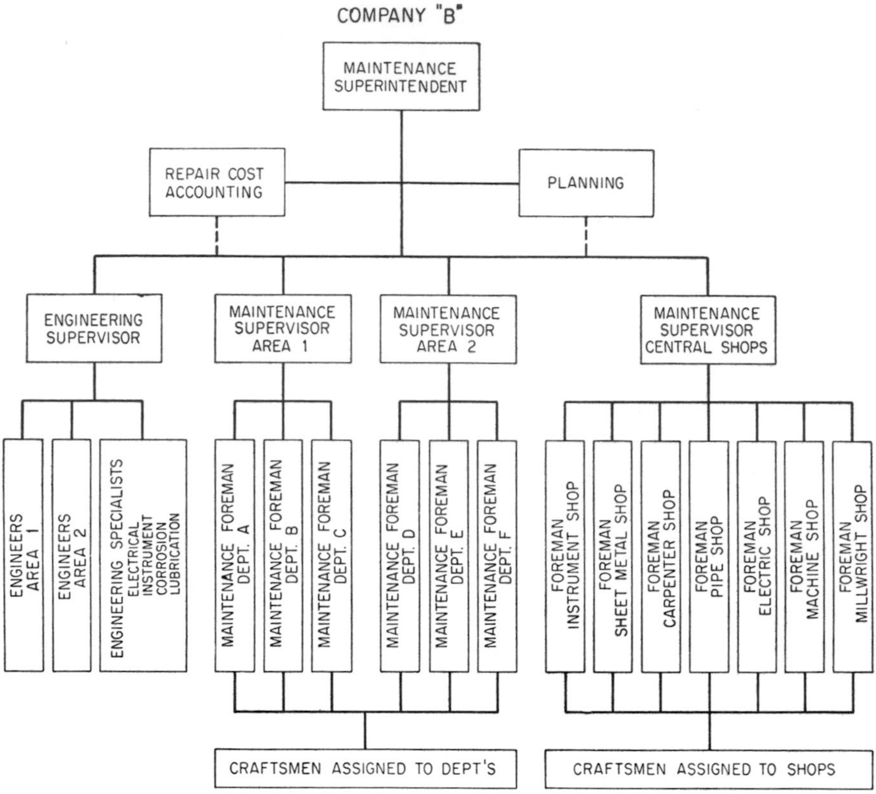

COMPANY "B"

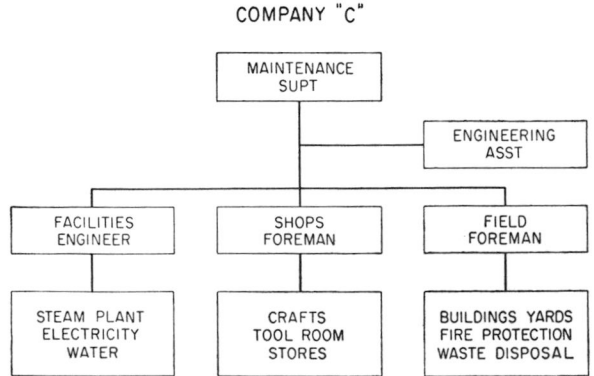

FIG. 1-2. Company B, similar to A, except maintenance engineering group handles only the maintenance function.

COMPANY "C"

FIG. 1-3. Company C, 25 to 30 maintenance employees; maintenance responsible for all types of work not included with production, sales, or accounting.

COMPANY "D"

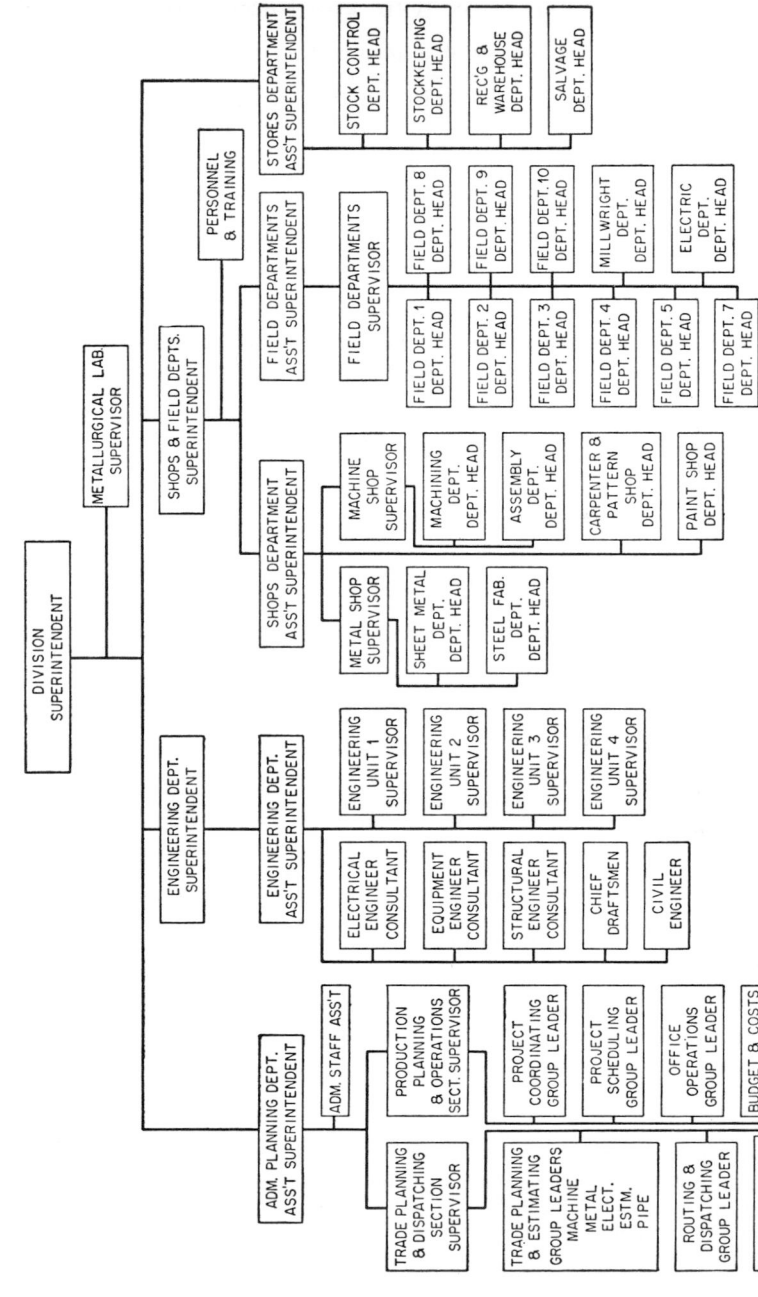

Fig. 1-4. Company D, maintenance force 3,000, total force 15,000. Maintenance limited to equipment and record keeping.

maintenance of equipment and record keeping necessary to satisfy accounting requirements. Most operations are of a one-shift, 5-day nature.

This entire section could be devoted to the variations that will be found in well-organized maintenance departments as a result of the variables covered earlier. The illustrations given indicate a few of these modifications.

To Whom Does Maintenance Engineering Report?   The proper level of reporting for the maintenance engineering department is a subject for discussion. Some feel that maximum effectiveness can be obtained only if the department reports to top levels of management. There have been numerous articles written which contend that only in this way does it have the authority to act independently of other plant organizations and thus function effectively. Similarly, there have been many presentations indicating that the same is true of practically any group that is not a direct function of the production line. This philosophy includes preference for such departments as safety, personnel, inspection, control, and others, reporting to a level permitting them to act independent of the production department they service.

Under certain circumstances this independence may be necessary for proper performance of the maintenance engineering function. On the other hand, there are many plants in which the level of reporting for the individual in charge of the maintenance engineering group has little or no bearing on its effectiveness. If the proper relationships exist between maintenance personnel and other departments, this need for high authority does not exist. If maintenance supervision considers itself in the proper perspective as part of the production team, and its performance is evaluated in the same light, they should report at plant level to the authority responsible for the rest of plant operations.

The need for sharply defined authority is often overemphasized for service or staff groups. Performance based on use of authority alone is not and cannot be so effective as performance based on cooperative effort. If the energy expended to secure this sacred authority were used instead in establishing the proper interdepartmental relationships and resultant cooperation, the over-all effectiveness of the maintenance engineering department as a member of the production team would be improved. In addition the entire atmosphere of the group, including the morale of the men and the attitude of the rest of the plant toward the department, is more desirable.

Naturally it is impractical to have a maintenance engineering group report to an individual who does not have full authority over the majority of the operations that must be served by the group. The area in which a lack of such authority can be most troublesome is in the assignment of priorities for work performance. Where the ultimate authority is also responsible for the performance of the production or other units being served, the assignment of priority is more likely to consider total effect on the plant, free of influence from advantage that might accrue to any particular phase of operations.

In summary, maintenance engineering should report to a level that is responsible for most other plant groups which the maintenance engineering department serves. This may be the plant manager, production superintendent, or manager of manufacturing, depending on the organization. The necessity for reporting to higher management, or through a centralized engineering organization, or directly to a vice-president should not exist if proper intraplant relationships have been established.

Comments on Organization.   *The Role of the Technically Trained Engineer.*   There are two schools of thought on the use of the technically trained engineer in the maintenance organization. One holds that the engineer should be utilized only where maximum advantage is taken of his professional training and experience, and that his effort should not be diluted by supervisory duties. The other feels that a technical man must be in the line to be effective and that the functions of professional engineering and crafts supervision should be combined. Much can be said in favor of both approaches to the use of engineers in the maintenance department. The former arrangement results in:

1. Maximum utility of the engineer's technical background.
2. Maintaining a professional approach to maintenance problems.

3. Higher probability of a long-range approach to maintenance problems, contrasted with major concern with breakdowns—thinking in terms of preventing fires as well as of putting them out.
4. Better handling of crafts' problems by using up-from-the-ranks supervision.
5. Opportunity for developing nontechnical men for positions of higher responsibility.

On the other hand, advantages of combining engineering and supervision are:

1. Quicker maturing of new graduates by intimate association with personnel problems.
2. More expeditious work performance because of shorter lines of communication.
3. Possible reduction in the supervisory organization or an increase in supervision density as a result of more people in first-line capacity.
4. Early intensive training in the art of handling men to prepare technical personnel more quickly for use as production supervision.
5. Less resistance to new ideas since the craft heritage is reduced.

Summarizing, it would seem that the former has long-range advantages while the latter has more immediate benefits.

The Use of Specialists.   The use and number of staff specialists, such as electrical engineers, instrument engineers, metallurgists, corrosion specialists, etc., depends on:

1. Availability of such specialists elsewhere in the organization.
2. The amount of emphasis that must be placed on the particular field in question.
3. An economic balance of the cost of a consulting service against retaining a specialist in the maintenance organization.

It is not unusual to have specialists in the maintenance organization, but in each instance the choice should be governed by the above factors.

Inspection and Control Function.   Some large maintenance organizations separate the inspection phase of preventive maintenance and the control function (estimating, setting budgets) from line engineering and crafts supervision.   This separation, if improperly emphasized, can connote a policing activity which may antagonize line personnel and result in a lack of complete cooperation.   The particular situation in any plant should be scrutinized carefully in considering such a move.   If at all possible, the responsibility for inspection and control should be placed directly with the people performing the work.   This will result in better morale and in acceptance of over-all responsibility, which is most beneficial.   However, if the problems of inspection or control are so complex as to detract from the primary effort of line engineering and supervision, one or more centralized groups to handle this function should be considered.   Theirs should be, however, an approach of providing service to the line functions rather than that of a policing unit.

Clerical Staff.   In reviewing the existing clerical staff or in establishment of a new organization, there are two primary considerations.   First, paper work should be minimized consistent with good operations and adequate control.   Second, the clerical staff should be designed to relieve supervisory personnel of routine paper work that can be adequately handled by clerical personnel.   Most record keeping is required for accounting and flow of information to higher management plus those basic records necessary for the efficient administration of the maintenance department.   Caution should be exercised in accumulating and recording information that is not used productively.   The actual ratio of clerks to other personnel can have a wide range.   The availability of mechanical accounting equipment is an important factor, as well as the use of job standards, incentives, or work measurement.

The number of clerks used will vary from 1 clerk per 100 employees to 1 clerk for 20 to 25 employees.   Clerical groups can report at practically any level of the organization or may be gathered into one central unit.   Here again, factors of geography, company policy, and type of activity must be considered but, in general, clerks should report at the level to which they are of the greatest service.

TITLES

There is as much variation in the titles used to designate the positions in the organization chart as there are organizations. Often too much emphasis is placed on the exact title. One of the most important things to be considered in designation of a title is its connotation relative to titles in other phases of company activity. If the man in charge of a small production unit is called a superintendent, then the man in charge of a shop group should also be designated a superintendent. In other words, for the same levels, in production or maintenance, the connotation should be the same. This is also true with respect to staff and other technical personnel, where the significance of the title should be comparable with those of similar responsibilities in design engineering, construction engineering, research, and production.

The individual in charge of the maintenance engineering department is usually called a plant engineer, but other titles such as maintenance superintendent, superintendent of maintenance, maintenance supervisor, and engineering superintendent also are used. Some companies use the "director" or "manager" prefix but 80 to 85 per cent of plants that recognize maintenance as a primary department use the term plant engineer for designating the person in charge.

The next level of supervision normally consists of superintendents, supervisors, or engineers, depending on company custom. At this level there may be such titles as superintendent of power, superintendent of grounds, and superintendent of shops. Sometimes there are engineers supervising other engineers. In small plants where there are few intermediate levels of supervision the title of general foreman may be used. For the lower levels "engineer" or "foreman" titles are common, with prefixes indicating specialty, i.e., instrument engineer, electrical engineer, area engineer, yard foreman, salvage foreman. Men in the first line of supervision (to whom the crafts report) are pretty generally designated foremen or assistant foremen. If technical personnel are used in this capacity, some companies designate these people as "engineers."

The use of the term master mechanic, although still prevalent in some older organizations, is gradually becoming extinct, being replaced by some title including superintendent or supervisor. In a strictly crafts organization the term master mechanic is still used to designate the individual responsible for the crafts activity.

It is difficult to give rules for the designation of titles in a maintenance organization, since the emphasis placed on titles varies considerably with different companies. It is important, however, for the sake of morale and prestige, to establish titles in the maintenance engineering department consistent with those for similar levels elsewhere in the plant.

MANPOWER REQUIREMENTS

In determining the number of men, both labor and supervision, adequate for maintenance coverage of a plant, many factors must be considered. Each plant should be treated as a separate problem, considering all its peculiar aspects.

Hourly Personnel. *Relation of the Number of Men to the Total Operating Personnel.* The ratio of maintenance personnel to production personnel is too often considered the measure for adequacy and relative efficiency of the department. Consideration of two extremes in plant types indicates the fallacy of this approach. A completely instrumented plant, where a minimum of production personnel control a large investment in complex equipment, may require a maintenance force several times the size of the production group. On the other hand, a plant employing a large number of people engaged in handwork, with a minimum of machinery, can get along with a maintenance force that numbers a small fraction of the production personnel. It can be said that the ratio of maintenance to production employees varies directly with the machinery and equipment investment per operating employee. Here again, the type of machinery and equipment involved can have a profound influence.

In making a preliminary estimate of the number of maintenance employees necessary to maintain a plant properly, an approach based on the estimated size of the maintenance bill and the percentage of this bill that will be labor has been found to be a more realistic one.   Here again there are many variables and a broad spread in practice.   There are, however, experience factors in many industries which can be used to estimate maintenance cost as a percentage of investment in machinery and equipment.   Before building a plant most companies determine the approximate return on investment that can be expected.   One of the factors to be considered in this estimate is the cost of maintenance which, in turn, is a logical point for setting up maintenance manpower requirements.   Considering the value of the equipment at today's prices, the annual cost of maintenance should run between 7 and 15 per cent of the investment in the average plant.   Building maintenance should run between 1½ and 3 per cent of the investment per year.   The cost of labor alone, exclusive of overhead, will run between 30 and 50 per cent of the total maintenance bill.

No attempt will be made to tabulate any of these values by industry, company size, or location, since the available information is unreliable.   There is considerable variation in accounting procedures and in those items which are included as part of the maintenance bill.   The basis for the calculation of the investment and the correction for charging replacement values also varies.

In addition to the manpower necessary to maintain equipment and buildings, the other duties of the maintenance department must be considered and allowances made for manpower to handle these.   To some extent this area can serve as a cushion for fluctuations in the strictly maintenance work load.   By adding 10 to 20 per cent to the size of the maintenance force estimated to be necessary under normal conditions, some crafts will usually be available for construction and alterations, yet can be diverted to give immediate maintenance service.

These criteria can be used only for a preliminary study.   Actual manpower requirements must be controlled by a continuous review of work to be performed.   Backlog-of-work records are a help here, and the trends of the backlog for each craft enable maintenance supervision to increase or reduce employees to maintain the proper individual craft strength and total work force.

Crafts That Should Be Included in a Maintenance Organization.   The crafts and shops that should exist in any good maintenance organization are determined by the nature of the activity of the department and the amount of work involved.   This, of course, connotes a close relationship between the size of the plant and the number of separate shops that can be justified.

Another factor that must be taken into consideration is the local availability of adequately skilled contractors to perform the various types of work.   In small plants a few maintenance men who are Jacks-of-all-trades can be combined in one shop with no particular problem.   However, in spite of the problems in recognizing craft lines in scheduling, there is a real advantage in larger plants to segregating various skills with their attendant equipment into shops.   Considering the present strength of organized labor, the advantages of ignoring craft lines are usually nullified by the other problems involved.   This subject will be discussed at greater length in the chapter on Operating Policies and Procedures.   In general, however, it is difficult to justify a separate crafts group with its own shop and supervision for less than 10 men.   Reference to the organization charts will give some indication of actual practice in several plants.

Numerical Relations between Crafts.   It is difficult to present any preliminary basis for determination of the size of each craft group necessary in a given plant.   In practice it is important to keep this relationship under continuous study in order to maintain an optimum condition, avoiding a surplus in one craft and shortages in another.   Most jobs require coordination of several crafts, and although temporary imbalances are inevitable, long-range planning should include provision for maintaining relative craft strength appropriate to the anticipated work load.   A record of the backlog of work by crafts is therefore an effective planning tool.

In the interests of morale and work quality it is preferable to stabilize the maintenance force by adjustment of the work load rather than the number of employees.   Every effort should be made to maintain a stable group by deferring work for which there is not an immediate need during periods of high loads and by using local contractors, if necessary, for the balance of the immediate work. During a slack period, emphasis should be placed on handling installations, revisions, and deferred work.

Supervision. *Supervision Density.* The number of men per supervisor, or "supervision density," is a generally accepted measure for determining the number of first-line supervisors needed to handle a maintenance force adequately. Although densities as low as 8 and as high as 25 are sometimes encountered, the norm seems to lie between 12 and 14. Where a large group of highly skilled men in one craft is doing routine work, a higher ratio will be found. If, on the other hand, the work requires close supervision or is dispersed geographically, a lower ratio is more common. In the average shop, with conventional crafts such as millwrights, steam fitters, sheet-metal men, and carpenters, one foreman or assistant foreman can effectively supervise the activities of from 12 to 15 men. This assumes average skills on the part of the men and some degree of centralized planning to aid work distribution. In any event, supervision density should be such that the foreman is not burdened with on-the-job supervision at the expense of time for planning improvement of his shop, training of his men, and the necessary personal contacts that result in good morale.

Cross-crafts Supervision. The use of a member of first-line supervision to supervise more than one craft should be considered carefully. There are many circumstances in which, because of the small number of men involved, this arrangement is economically preferable. When this is the case, consideration must be given to similarity of the crafts involved. An electrical foreman in charge of carpenters could cause a serious problem, while painters and carpenters can frequently be combined. Machinists and millwrights can be associated in the same way. For the most effective use of the particular skills of any craft, however, experience indicates that each should have its own supervision if possible.

From this it may appear that several foremen would share the responsibility for a large job requiring the services of several crafts. Obviously this could result in confusion and added cost. In many plants this has been successfully offset by evolution of a working agreement, between both members of supervision and the craftsmen involved, which differentiates between on-the-job supervision and craft-administrative supervision. In this way it is possible to assign one foreman the primary responsibility for completion of a job, issuing work assignments to all crafts involved. The quality of the work of any one craft and its administrative supervision remain with the craft foreman.

SELECTION AND TRAINING

General. The selection and training of supervisory and crafts personnel in a maintenance engineering department is of extreme importance. While it is not intended in this chapter to cover selection or training programs in detail, some general comments are in order.

Selection—Crafts Personnel. In unionized plants the selection of applicants for maintenance work from outside the department is usually controlled by the labor contract, varying from strict adherence to seniority to a liberal, mutually agreeable method based on personal qualifications. In nonunionized plants it is possible to use more definitive methods of selection. The bases for selection should be education, general intelligence, mechanical aptitude, and past experience. In many localities it is possible to hire men with prior craft experience and, in general, this is the easiest and most satisfactory method of staffing a maintenance engineering department, particularly in smaller companies where formal training programs cannot be justified. If trained craftsmen are not available outside, and no formal training program exists, the factors mentioned above, as well as the age of the candidates, should be considered in making selections from either new employees or those employed elsewhere in the plant. It is easier to develop a craftsman from a man in his early twenties, than from one who is over forty.

Training. Training of crafts personnel can be divided into two types—formal instruction and informal on-the-job training. The extent of training should be governed by department size, need for training, and facilities available.

Formal Instruction (see, also, the chapter on Training).   Several formalized training plans are in use in maintenance engineering departments.   The most common is an apprentice-training program that conforms to the National Apprenticeship System of the U.S. Department of Labor, Bureau of Apprenticeships.   Considerable aid in establishing this program can be obtained from the local Labor Department representative and, since it is in widespread use throughout the country and accepted by most unions, its introduction is usually less difficult than some other programs.   Successful completion of this program is recognized by the award of certificates bearing signatures of both Federal and state representatives.   In addition to providing the plant with better-trained craftsmen, it equips the craftsman with training that is recognized nationwide.   The administration of such a system constitutes an expense which must be seriously considered.

Most other formalized training plans are those developed by some of the larger companies for their own use or those available from industrial engineering firms. For specialized or limited training these have advantages over the Federal program in that they can be tailored to the individual needs of personnel.   On the other hand, they can be costly to develop or purchase and do not have such universal recognition.

Informal Training Programs.   Most informal training programs consist of spot exposures of personnel to intensive instruction in some phase of their activities. These may take the form of lectures, sound slide films, movies, or trips to suppliers who provide instruction concerning their products.   In most cases programs of this type are aimed more at developing advanced skills rather than the basic and intermediate training incorporated in most formalized programs.

On-the-job Coaching.   On-the-job coaching is the most prevalent form of training maintenance personnel.   Although the short-range effectiveness of this sort of training is difficult to measure, a great many excellent craftsmen have acquired their skills in this manner.   The usual procedure is to assign a new man to an experienced craftsman as a helper, who then learns by exposure to the job and instructions given him by the experienced man.   The effectiveness of such training is improved if it is supplemented by routine rotation of the novice among several experienced craftsmen, and personal interviews by the foreman to check progress.

Selection—Supervisory Personnel.   Only general rules can be laid down for the selection of supervisory personnel for the maintenance engineering group.   Considering the first and second levels of supervision, those directly in charge of crafts personnel performing mechanical work, the candidates should have better than average mechanical comprehension and should be the type who can juggle several problems at once without confusion.   Further, they should be buoyant and enthusiastic and should have qualities of leadership and a sincere liking for people.   While they should have training and skill in the craft for which they are being considered, this qualification should not be the sole basis for selection.   Unfortunately the other requisites of a successful foreman do not necessarily go hand in hand with craft skill.   Consequently, although a foreman may be above reproach with respect to his technical ability, his effectiveness as a member of supervision will be limited if he lacks personality traits required for good leadership.   There is more chance of developing a satisfactory foreman from an individual having all traits except craft skill than of developing these other characteristics in a man having only the crafts training.

If there is an established foreman-selection program in the production areas of a plant, the candidate for maintenance supervision should be processed in the same way.   Although there are advantages in selecting these men entirely from the maintenance employees, people elsewhere in the plant who indicate proper leadership potential should be considered before going outside the plant.   Again, it is suggested that too much importance attached to long years of experience and technical skill can result in poor selection of first- and second-level supervision.

Aside from the accepted standards of education, serious consideration should be given to the temperament of technically trained men when selecting them for the maintenance department.   For best performance the candidate should be slightly on the extrovert side, and one who tends to take the broad rather than the narrow view of his professional utilization.   He should enjoy working with people and mixing freely. He should be able to temper professional perfectionism with expediency. He should have enthusiasm and buoyancy. It is important that an engineer in the maintenance department be able to cope with crises enthusiastically and not be easily discouraged. Since the effectiveness of the maintenance engineering department depends in great part on the relationships that exist with other plant units, as well as on the expediency and effectiveness of the work performed, the technical man in this field must have some of the attributes of a salesman.

Great care should be exercised in the selection of these individuals and, if possible, aptitude testing and comprehensive interviews should be employed. The use of comprehensive interviews in the selection of all supervisory employees is of inestimable value. This service can be obtained from professional sources, or the technique can be developed within an organization by training of key individuals. Comprehensive interviews afford the person charged with selection good basic information on inherent personal characteristics of the candidate.

Training—Supervisory Personnel. The training of supervisory personnel should consist of initial orientation, a formalized, sustained program of leadership training, and on-the-job coaching and consultation.

Orientation should provide the candidate with basic information on the management team he is joining, and company policy, as well as specific information on the broad policies of the maintenance engineering department. He should be completely informed in the scope of his personal responsibilities and authority delegated to him. He should be instructed concerning his relations with his superiors and other members of supervision with whom he will come in contact.

The same program that is used for ensuring continued effectiveness and improved performance of production supervision should be applied to supervision in a maintenance engineering department. This training should include such subjects as human relations, conduct of interviews, instruction on teaching methods, safety instruction, and many others. Goals for such a program should be increased effectiveness of the individual as a supervisor, a feeling of unity with the management team, and assistance in his personal development.

With a supervisor as with any other individual, on-the-job coaching is essential. There is no substitute for frequent, informal, personal contact with a superior concerning current technical, personnel, and personal problems. This type of development heads the list as a force for high morale and job satisfaction. It should include praise as well as criticism. When criticism is needed, it should be constructive, and praise should be sincere. Too often lower levels of supervision are either funneled into a formalized program and forgotten or are placed on a lone job and left to themselves, with contacts by superiors limited to those required for instruction or criticism for poor work performance.

Chapter 2

PRINCIPLES OF ORGANIZATION

By H. W. Shockley
Chief Maintenance Consultant
Engineering Department
E. I. du Pont de Nemours & Co., Inc.
Wilmington, Del.

Definition, purpose, scope, and expected results of organization are indicated in Table 2-1. In establishing a maintenance organization, it is essential to recognize:

1. That the basic necessity is to maintain a plant at a level consistent with low cost and high productivity.
2. That all supervisory personnel should be selected according to the duties and responsibilities involved.
3. That equal consideration should be given to the skills of wage-roll personnel.
4. That the approach of the automatic and the atomic ages indicates greater need of modern engineering techniques and skills.

An organization chart is shown as Fig. 2-1. The manager or engineer of the small plant may conclude that it is not applicable to his plant. However, the same duties and responsibilities exist in the small plant as in the large one, except that some phases of engineering may not be included or some conditions of operation do not exist. The problems of one plant may be chiefly wear and abrasion; in another they may be

Table 2-1

1. TITLE: Organization.
2. DEFINITION: Organization establishes the authority, responsibility, and relationships to effectively attain the objectives of the organization.
3. PURPOSE: To establish:
    a. The administrative structure required.
    b. The duties and responsibilities of all supervisory levels.
    c. Work engineering requests to meet all production levels.
4. SCOPE: Organization applies to plant, departments, company—line and staff groups—clerical personnel.
    To each level of supervision must be assigned the authority and responsibility which will enable it to fulfill its function without needless or duplicated activities.
    In all cases the functions of the position must be established with due regard for and cognizance of local conditions as rigid standardization is neither feasible nor desirable.
5. RESULTS: Organization may be expected to:
    a. Promote improvement and uniformity in operating practices and procedures.
    b. Eliminate duplication of effort and overlapping of functions.
    c. Stimulate more economical business practices.
    d. Utilize all available means for improved performance.

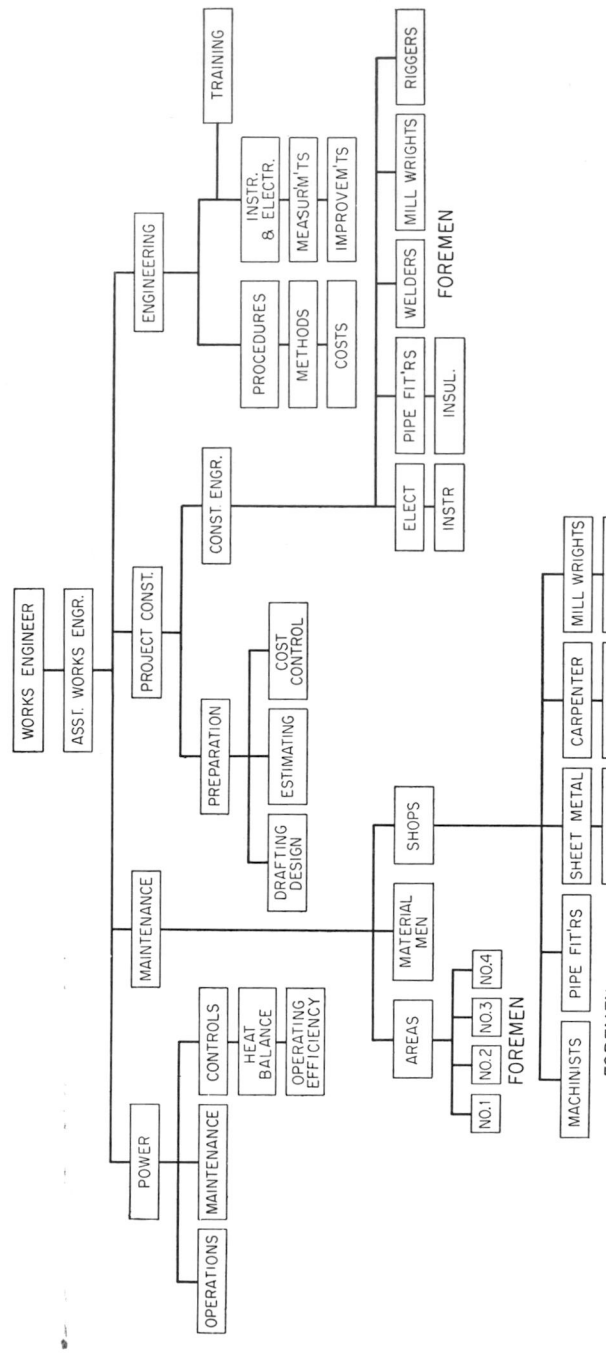

Fig. 2-1. Organization proposed as basic, to which can be added and from which can be taken, according to size of plant.

duties and responsibilities exist in the small plant as in the large one, except that some phases of engineering may not be included or some conditions of operation do not exist. The problems of one plant may be chiefly wear and abrasion; in another they may be mostly corrosion. This means that such things as protective coatings, engineering materials for resisting corrosion, and the effect of operation on oils and greases may be different in any two plants. So are matters of stress, design, wear, and tolerance. But all plants have maintenance problems and need a maintenance organization to handle them. Such organization must be properly organized and administered.

The organization charted provides for a works engineer and assistant. The committee type of plant operation employed in today's industrial plants requires that the works engineer spend considerable time in analyzing problems of cost, production, and other engineering aspects for improvement. The services of an assistant are needed to administer the performance and personnel aspects of the organization.

The chart shows that the power engineer is responsible for operation, maintenance, and control of the power plant. Fuel is the high-cost item, and the power engineer must establish controls, usually based on heat balance and cost efficiency, to operate the minimum of equipment at a maximum of efficiency. To maintain his plant properly, he must utilize the same procedures, methods, and controls used in maintaining the process equipment and facilities. In some plants there is a power maintenance group responsible to the power engineer. In other cases, maintenance of power-plant equipment is a responsibility of the plant maintenance organization. In either case, major shop- and toolwork is a function of the plant maintenance organization in the interest of minimum investment. The same rules apply relative to projects, construction, and engineering assistance.

The next major department shown on the chart is "Maintenance," headed by a graduate engineer and divided into two phases, areas and shops. Engineers serve each in a supervisory capacity.

The area engineer is responsible for procedures, controls, costs, improvements, training, and skills. It is his function to work with the operating supervisory personnel, assist in the training of his foremen, analyze costs and conditions for both reduction of downtime and equipment improvement, stress safety and good employee relations, and utilize engineering assistance whenever possible.

In the operation of the shops, service to the areas, including power, is the principal function. This group occupies a secondary station in that work either originates in the areas or is supplied by minor construction. In large operations, the shopwork may be the major function of the minor construction group, leaving the central shops entirely dependent on the areas for their work load. However, investments in machine tools and equipment are of such magnitude today that maximum service to the operations must be a first consideration.

At this point consider backlog or control of maintenance personnel to meet maximum requirements. Experience in many plants indicates that, whenever current backlog is over 2 weeks in most kinds of shopwork, it affects the area groups to a major extent. This same condition may be reflected if the routine or service-to-operations jobs in an area have a current backlog of more than 2 weeks, sometimes of more than 1. Conversely, in certain crafts or construction skills, it may be possible to work with a backlog of 4 to 6 weeks without undue interference and without causing emergencies. It must be remembered that the larger the backlog that may be utilized the smaller the maintenance group required, as long as operations are not affected.

In backlog control, keep in mind that the application of better methods, better tools (both hand and machine), the use of motion and methods analysis, and the constant training and retraining of maintenance and minor construction personnel are of the utmost importance in reducing both maintenance and minor construction costs.

Maintenance skills are used in every aspect of any business; a business which keeps these skills properly developed will meet with the greatest success in its competitive field. Keep in mind that before automation the ratio of operating to maintenance personnel was as high as 5 to 1. Today, in many instances, the ratio is reversed; hence the much greater maintenance and minor construction costs must be overcome by greater efficiency.

In the operation of shops, it is essential that the shops engineer be familiar with the latest techniques in equipment maintenance. This includes piping, welding, sheet-metal work, machining, assembly, handling, and others.

The automatic-control equipment of an area may involve instrumentation, electronics, and other types of specialized knowledge or skills. It calls for the training of skilled mechanics, establishing inspections, and scheduled patrolling based on operating conditions.

In the areas, foreman-mechanic ratios may vary from 1 to 10 to 1 to 15. In shops, they may vary from 1 to 15 to 1 to 25, depending upon conditions. The advent of special techniques, methods, and tools in all skills, plus the use of planned and measured work, has indicated the need for more competent supervision if modern engineering and standard practices are to be a part of maintenance work.

Project construction, shown on the chart as the third major function, is one of the main phases of a works engineering organization. It deals with process control, plant increase, plant improvement, and execution of the work involved in these services. It is particularly important that plant engineers be familiar with plant costs relative to obsolescence, depreciation, operations, and capital equipment. In project construction, costs chargeable to operations are maintenance costs. Many times, in evaluating a works engineering organization as to plant need, both labor and material costs chargeable to plant investment and those involved in operations or maintenance are lost sight of.

The minor construction work in many plants usually is separated from maintenance as to physical forces involved. This is so even in small plants where it may be confined to 1 foreman and 10 or 15 mechanics. The reasons are obvious: The work is mostly new; it involves a major overhaul or change; or the group represents a pool that can be added to or reduced as this type of work contracts or expands. Because of this condition, union reaction in many plants favors having this group tied in with maintenance. However, it is to the plant's advantage to keep it separate.

In some plants, to avoid the increased investment in buildings, tools, and facilities, certain types of shopwork are confined to either maintenance or minor construction for total plant requirements. This involves closer coordination of the groups in the planning and scheduling of all work.

An important activity of this group is cost control. Project costs are maintained on a daily basis. This is necessary to discourage overruns and underruns. Cost estimates, based on proper planning and measurement of work, will do much to improve this condition, if it exists.

Another very important phase of project application is not only cost, but whether or not the objectives have been met. This is particularly so today because of the use of arrow-diagram planning, or critical path scheduling, described in another chapter.

The engineering group, shown fourth on the chart, is one of the most important in modern plants. Staff functions, of which it is one, represent overhead and often have been without favor in the view of plant management on grounds of cost alone. This is a shortsighted policy. Line organization is fully occupied in keeping operating equipment functioning with a minimum of downtime and with a high level of maintenance. This requires that services pertaining to the improvement function, such as preventive and corrective procedures, must be supplied by other groups. In small plants, these services may be combined under an individual, known as a planning and scheduling engineer. In the large plant, they may involve methods engineers, planning and measurement applicators, and specialists in tooling, welding, engineering materials, instrumentation, electronics, and so on.

As a measure of the importance of a maintenance function, we have only to look at a comparison of the operating forces with maintenance forces 15 years ago and today. In chemical plants, where the ratio of operating personnel to maintenance personnel was as high as 8 to 1, today it is as low as 1 to 1, and in some cases 1 to 3.

As an indication of the need for higher-class skills, we have only to look at the capital investment of our plants excluding real estate, where instrumentation, electronics, and special facilities previously represented a very small per cent. Today they represent as high as 10 per cent and are increasing. It therefore becomes a function of this engineering group to supply staff services to the other groups of the works engineering organization, whether they involve methods studies, cost analyses, planning, or any kind of engineering technique.

Thus far we have dealt with the supervisory phases of a plant works engineering organization. Let us look at the wage-roll phases and observe what changes have taken place in this group. We have stated previously that the number of mechanics in the areas may vary from 10 to 15 per foreman while in the shops it may be as high as 1 foreman to as many as 25 men. At the same time, we are attempting to have mechanics in the areas and have them utilize more than one skill. In the shops it may be necessary to hold to one skill. Our problem, therefore, is to ascertain the types of jobs covered by the plant work load, and determine:

1. What are the tools required, whether hand, hand-powered, or machine, as well as equipment and facilities?
2. What do repairs entail as to materials, methods, and techniques?
3. To what extent can shop fabrication reduce field work?
4. To what extent should outside contractors be used?
5. To what extent should mechanics be trained?
6. The importance of the use of small tools as covered by tool-crib control.

By means of this analysis we may find that there is a definite segregation of the work into the following classifications:

1. Small jobs, where frequency is regular and standardization can be definitely established. This might be known as standard tasks and service to operations. Such work covers inspections, patrols, lubrication, etc. It can be assigned to specific groups with definite instructions.
2. Jobs of medium size, requiring a minimum of 8 hr or a maximum of 24 hr (16 might be preferred under some conditions). These may cover the replacement of tubes in a condenser, the cleaning of strainers, replacement of a shaft in a pump, and the like. Various skills are required, as is shop fabrication.
3. Major overhauls, requiring from a day to several days, where continuous work by shift is involved, where each phase of the work is studied, and close schedules are maintained. Again, various skills and shop fabrication are likely to be required.
4. Work requirements covering large or small jobs involving skills not necessary to the plant except on an irregular basis. These are the ones usually assigned to outside contractors.

It is obvious that to know of the conditions described, and be prepared to do something about them, knowledge of plant work-load conditions is essential. So it is a function of the service engineering group to assist in:

1. Developing the information called for in the preceding paragraphs.
2. Planning and scheduling the work.
3. Establishing preventive-maintenance schedules.
4. Establishing the records for corrective services.
5. Following such records for engineering improvements.
6. Analyzing cost results.
7. Establishing charts and data to show management where the plant stands maintenancewise, and what must be done for improvement and correction.

Figure 2-2 shows a chart for evaluating the levels of supervision and control in relation to the top job of works engineer, mechanical superintendent, or plant engineer. Points can be assigned to the duties and responsibilities and a basis for salary distribution indicated.

Having discussed the basis for a works engineering and maintenance organization, let us define the duties and responsibilities of line and staff functions. Tables 2-2 to 2-25 show the primary functions, also duties and responsibilities. Some of the terms expressed in these tables are defined in Chap. 4.

WORKS ENGINEERING ORGANIZATION

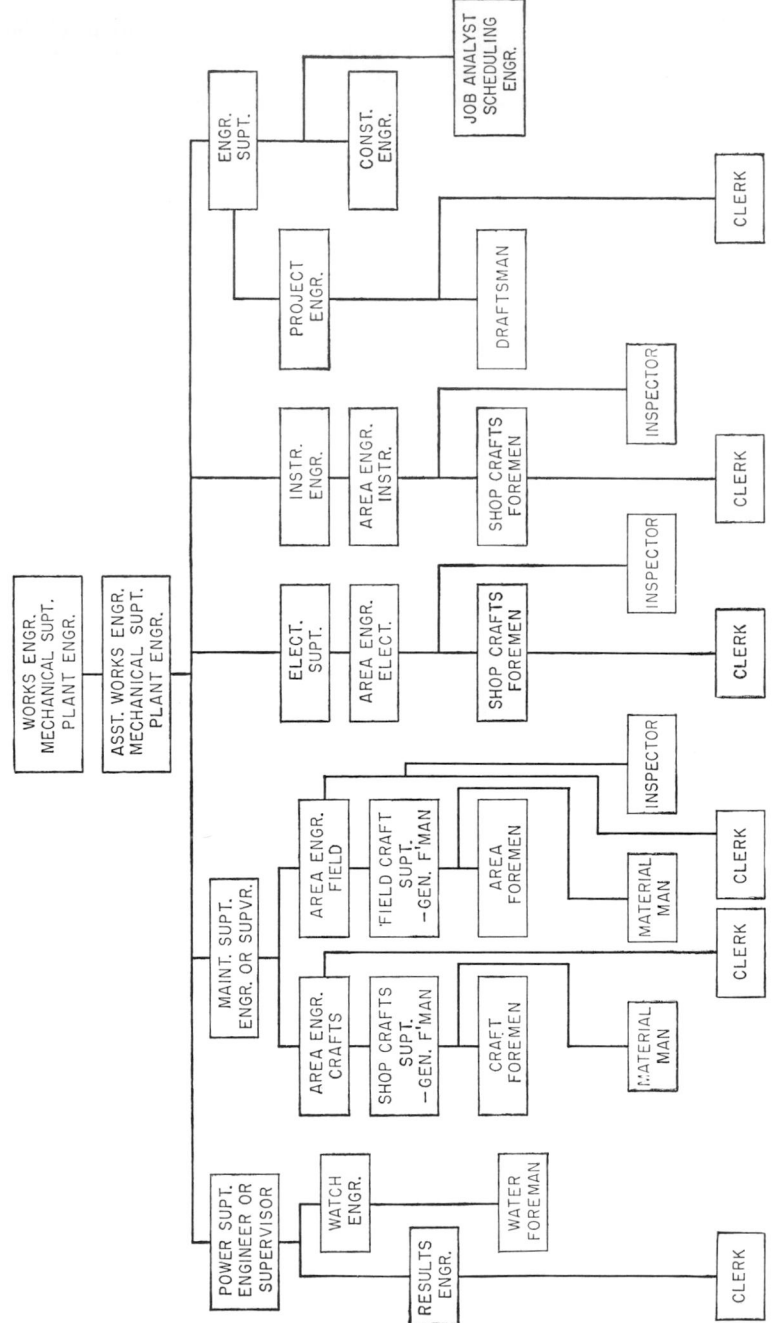

Fig. 2-2. Relative values of jobs.

Table 2-2

POSITION: Works engineer, plant engineer, or mechanical superintendent.
DEPARTMENT: Mechanical and electrical.
PRIMARY FUNCTION: To administer the works engineering department.

DUTIES AND RESPONSIBILITIES
1. Responsible for the organization of the works engineering department: The selection of supervisory personnel, salary administration, promotion approval, and performance standards.
2. Select and direct installation of adequate controls necessary to secure minimum maintenance costs for maximum operating efficiency.
3. Promote and approve all training programs.
4. Interpret all management policies to the organization in order to promote sound labor-management relations.
5. Promote an effective safety program designed to ensure safe working conditions.
6. Maintain active contact with operations and management relative to the functions of the works engineering department and its relationship to other departments.
7. Review all plant additions or changes in order to promote the application of best engineering practices in relation to plant operations.

Table 2-3

POSITION: Assistant works engineer, assistant plant engineer, or assistant mechanical superintendent.
DEPARTMENT: Mechanical and electrical.
PRIMARY FUNCTION: To assist the works engineer, mechanical superintendent, and plant engineer in the administration of the works engineering department.

DUTIES AND RESPONSIBILITIES
1. Responsible for the organization and functioning of the works engineering organization.
2. Review both cost and work summaries in order to determine that maximum efficiency is being obtained by supervisory personnel through the proper use of standard controls and facilities and take necessary corrective measures when results do not meet standards.
3. Review the application of work and crew classification by supervision in order to control the proper distribution of wage-roll personnel.
4. Promote effective application of all departmental training programs.
5. Instruct supervisory personnel in industrial relations in order to promote good morale, and assist in disposing unsettled grievances.
6. Actively follow all safety programs, review all safety reports in order to secure maximum safety.

Table 2-4

POSITION: Power engineer.
DEPARTMENT: Power area.
PRIMARY FUNCTION: To administer the production and distribution of utilities.

DUTIES AND RESPONSIBILITIES
1. Responsible for the proper organization and functioning of the power area.
2. Through informative data determine power operating efficiencies and take necessary corrective measures where results are below standards.
3. Control the distribution of operating wage-roll personnel and others, actively guide and make necessary corrections in conjunction with:
   a. Inventory control of essential materials and supplies.
   b. Distribution of utilities.
   c. Forecasts of major repairs.
   d. Control of waste.
4. Assist in the formulation of and apply training and upgrading programs.
5. Interpret labor relations policies for supervisory personnel, and assist in disposing of unsettled grievances.
6. Actively assist in the establishment, review, and application of all safety programs.
7. Actively support and initiate programs for the improvement of methods and the reduction of costs.
8. Responsible for inspection of all power facilities.

Table 2-5

POSITION: Maintenance engineer, maintenance supervisor, or maintenance superintendent.

DEPARTMENT: Mechanical.

PRIMARY FUNCTION: To administer and coordinate all activities in conjunction with the general maintenance work.

DUTIES AND RESPONSIBILITIES

1. Responsible for the organization and functioning of the general maintenance organization and the coordination of shop and field activities.
2. Through informative data, control the application of direct, indirect, and general maintenance costs, budgetary control systems, and departmental and unit costs.
3. By means of work and crew classification, control the distribution of maintenance wageroll personnel.
4. Through reports, contact with supervisory personnel and others, actively guide and make necessary corrections in conjunction with:
   a. Shop layout, tool, and equipment requirements.
   b. Central prefabrication and assembly.
   c. Inventory control of maintenance materials.
   d. Forecast repairs.
   e. Control waste.
   f. Quality of work.
5. Assist in the formulation and application of training and upgrading programs.
6. Interpret labor-relations policies for supervisory personnel and assist in disposing of unsettled grievances.
7. Actively assist in the establishment, review, and application of all safety programs and review all safety reports.
8. Actively support and initiate programs for the improvement of methods and costs of maintenance work.
9. Maintain active contacts with operations and his supervisory personnel through meetings or otherwise.

Table 2-6

POSITION: Instrument engineer.

DEPARTMENT: Mechanical and electrical.

PRIMARY FUNCTION: To administer and coordinate all activities in conjunction with plant instrumentation.

DUTIES AND RESPONSIBILITIES

1. Responsible for the organization and functioning of the instrument division.
2. Through informative data, control the application of direct and indirect maintenance costs, budgets, departmental and unit costs.
3. Through the application of work and crew classification control the distribution of personnel within the division.
4. Through reports, contacts with supervisory personnel and others, actively guide and make necessary corrections in conjunction with:
   a. Shop layout, tool, and equipment requirements.
   b. Inventory control of maintenance materials and spare parts.
   c. Forecast repairs.
   d. Control of waste.
   e. Quality of work.
5. Assist in the formulation and application of training and upgrading programs.
6. Establish test and calibration procedures, and maintenance standard practices.
7. Interpret labor-relations policies for supervisory personnel and assist in disposing of unsettled grievances.
8. Actively assist in the establishment, review, and application of all safety programs, and review all major and submajor injury reports.
9. Actively support and initiate programs for the improvement of methods and the reduction of maintenance costs.

Table 2-7

POSITION: Area engineer—shops and crafts.

DEPARTMENT: Mechanical.

PRIMARY FUNCTION: To supervise and coordinate shop operating maintenance practices in the promotion of a higher standard of maintenance through better methods and corrective measures.

Table 2-7 (*Continued*)

DUTIES AND RESPONSIBILITIES

1. Responsible for the proper functioning and allocation of personnel in the shops and crafts.
2. Review direct, indirect, and general maintenance costs for control purposes.
3. Coordinate the work of a planning and scheduling engineer in establishing a job-standardization program, currently review improvement and cost-reduction programs, and approve standard maintenance practices.
4. Coordinate the work of the planning and scheduling engineer in interpreting studies of standardized jobs and in recommending improvements in job methods, building, and equipment for cost reduction.
5. Conduct orientation, job training, and refresher courses for supervisory personnel and obtain assistance from the planning and scheduling engineer in promoting better use of maintenance controls.
6. Review periodically all maintenance stores items for the purpose of balancing stores inventory.
7. Assist supervisory personnel in the formulation of policies, the promotion of sound labor relations, and the disposition of unsettled grievances.
8. Assist supervisory personnel in the application of all safety regulations and programs.
9. Be responsible for all general inspections not covered by areas.

Table 2-8

POSITION: Project engineer.
DEPARTMENT: Mechanical and electrical.
PRIMARY FUNCTION: To prepare projects for construction work.

DUTIES AND RESPONSIBILITIES

1. Responsible for the organization and functioning of the project engineering section.
2. Supervise and assist in the preparation of projects for plant rearrangement, replacements, and additions which include necessary estimates, drawings, design, schedules, bills of material, cost summaries, and equipment and material specifications.
3. Provide and supervise drafting and design service for the plant.
4. Receive periodically cost summaries covering the status of all active projects and use as a control of expenditures.
5. Supervise the preparation of all revisions to active projects and explain all underruns or overruns not within the allowable limit.
6. Approve all orders issued to the maintenance division covering project work.
7. Interpret labor-relations policies for group and assist in disposing of unsettled grievances.
8. Support all safety programs.
9. Have working knowledge of accounting policies affecting projects.
10. Be familiar with the method of preparing plant construction forecast.

Table 2-9

POSITION: Electrical engineer or electrical superintendent.
DEPARTMENT: Electrical.
PRIMARY FUNCTION: To administer and coordinate all activities in conjunction with the maintenance of plant electrical facilities.

DUTIES AND RESPONSIBILITIES

1. Responsible for the organization and functioning of the electrical division.
2. Through informative data, control the application of direct, indirect, and general maintenance costs and budgetary control systems as well as departmental and unit costs.
3. Through the application of work and crew classification control the distribution of wage-roll personnel in the division.
4. Through reports, contacts with supervisory personnel, and others, actively guide and make necessary corrections in conjunction with:
   a. Central prefabrication and assembly.
   b. Inventory control of electrical maintenance materials and spare parts.
   c. Forecast of repairs.
   d. Control of waste.
   e. Quality control.
   f. Shop layout, tools, and equipment requirements.
5. Assist in the formulation and application of training and upgrading programs.

Table 2-9 (*Continued*)

6. Interpret labor-relations policies for supervisory personnel and assist in disposing of unsettled grievances.
7. Actively assist in the establishment, review, and application of all safety programs and review all major and submajor injuries and reports.
8. Actively support and initiate programs for the improvement of methods and costs of maintenance work.
9. Advise on all electrical problems involving either repairs or new work.
10. Initiate latest techniques relating to electronics or latest types of electrical control.

Table 2-10

POSITION: Shop crafts superintendent or shops engineer.
DEPARTMENT: Mechanical.
PRIMARY FUNCTION: To coordinate the activities of the foremen under his supervision in completing maintenance and construction work schedules.

DUTIES AND RESPONSIBILITIES
1. Responsible for the proper organization and functioning of personnel in his group.
2. Review foreman's repair orders for proper control of unpredictable and current work.
3. Approve and initial all daily schedule sheets. Any jobs added after this approval become emergency jobs and must be investigated and explained as to cause.
4. Review with foreman the information supplied with repair orders to determine inspection control.
5. Review and approve all training programs for employees and foremen under his supervision.
6. Assist in the preparation and use by the foremen of budgetary control and the segregation of the three classes of maintenance by direct, indirect, and general.
7. Assist supervisory personnel in the formulation of policies, promotion of good labor relations, and handling of unsettled grievances.
8. Attend supervisory safety meetings—actively support foremen's safety programs, and keep currently informed regarding their safety records.
9. Assist foremen in determining the amount of prefabrication to be used in completing maintenance and construction work.
10. Review any maintenance job that has been studied, for the purpose of establishing a standard maintenance practice, in order to assist in its improvement.

Table 2-11

POSITION: Area engineer—areas.
DEPARTMENT: Mechanical.
PRIMARY FUNCTION: To supervise and coordinate field operating and maintenance practice through preventive and corrective measures.

DUTIES AND RESPONSIBILITIES
1. Responsible for the proper functioning and allocation of maintenance personnel in the operating areas.
2. Review direct, indirect, and general maintenance costs for control. Approve indirect orders for all work in this area.
3. Review equipment cost cards to effect maintenance cost improvement.
4. Coordinate the work of the planning and scheduling engineer in establishing a job-standardization program. Currently review progress of cost-reduction programs and approve standard maintenance practices.
5. Conduct orientation, job training, and refresher courses for supervisory personnel and coordinate the planning and scheduling engineer in promoting better use of maintenance controls.
6. Review with both the area foreman and the planning and scheduling engineer the shutdown schedule affecting operating and maintenance conditions as well as the economical use of labor and material.
7. Review reports for all emergency jobs and discuss cause and possible improvements with the area supervisor, planning and scheduling engineer, and operating supervision.
8. Review periodically all maintenance stores items for the purpose of establishing a correct stores inventory.
9. Assist supervision in the interpretation of policies and promotion of sound labor relations and in disposing of unsettled grievances.
10. Assist supervisory personnel in the application of all safety regulations and programs.
11. Responsible for the carrying out of inspections in their areas.

Table 2-12

POSITION: Area instrument engineer.

DEPARTMENT: Mechanical.

PRIMARY FUNCTION: To assist in the correct operation of all instruments and to supervise craft foremen in their maintenance.

DUTIES AND RESPONSIBILITIES

1. Responsible for the proper functioning of work and crew classification and the control of maintenance personnel.
2. Review direct, indirect, and general maintenance costs and be responsible for the maintenance of budgetary control. Approve indirect orders.
3. Review instrument maintenance records to determine the possibility of improvement and replacement.
4. Assist the planning and scheduling engineer in establishing standard practices and currently review improvements and cost-reduction programs.
5. Conduct orientation, job training, and refresher courses for supervisory personnel; and assist the planning and scheduling engineer in promoting better use of maintenance controls.
6. Review reports of all emergency jobs and discuss causes and possible improvements with both the planning-scheduling engineer and operating supervision.
7. Review periodically all stores items for establishing correct stores inventory.
8. Assist supervision in the formulation of policies, the promotion of sound labor relations, and the handling of unsettled grievances.
9. Assist supervision in the application of all safety regulations and programs.

Table 2-13

POSITION: Engineering superintendent.

DEPARTMENT: Mechanical and electrical.

PRIMARY FUNCTION: To supply all engineering staff functions required to (1) maintain a plant at a high level of maintenance, (2) provide the preventive and corrective services necessary for effective performance and minimum downtime.

DUTIES AND RESPONSIBILITIES

1. To supply the necessary services in order to assist maintenance supervision in applying good business methods in operating the plant.
2. Promote necessary procedures and controls to measure plant performance.
3. Instigate improvement programs to meet plant weaknesses.
4. Keep abreast in all fields of engineering as required by plant requirements.
5. Evaluate data secured and indicate corrective measures required.
6. Utilize equipment record data for preventive-maintenance improvement.
7. Promote standardization programs for better job practices.
8. Institute latest tooling methods and procurement of listed shop equipment and facilities.
9. Assist all maintenance groups in the use of latest engineering techniques, materials, and equipment.
10. Analyze shops-layout conditions and make necessary improvements for both fabrication and handling.

Table 2-14

POSITION: Field crafts superintendent or general foreman.

DEPARTMENT: Mechanical and electrical.

PRIMARY FUNCTION: To coordinate all maintenance activities of the foremen under his supervision in completing maintenance work schedules to meet operating requirements.

DUTIES AND RESPONSIBILITIES

1. Responsible for the proper organization and functioning of personnel in his group.
2. Review foremen's normal repair orders for proper control of unpredictable and current work.
3. Review with the planning and scheduling engineer summaries of blanket and patrol repair orders for control of area maintenance personnel and the possibility of establishing additional blanket orders.
4. Approve daily allocation of all area maintenance personnel.
5. Review inspection schedules as to completion dates, the necessity and amount of work to be done; and approve necessary revisions.
6. Review and approve all training and upgrading programs for employees and foremen under his supervision.

Table 2-14 (*Continued*)

7. Assist in preparation and use by the foremen of budgetary control and the interpretation of direct, indirect, and general classes of maintenance work.
8. Assist supervisory personnel in the formulation of labor policies, promotion of good labor relations, and handling unsettled grievances.
9. Attend supervisory safety meetings; actively support foremen's safety programs; and keep currently informed regarding their safety record.
10. Review any maintenance job that has been studied for the purpose of establishing a "standard maintenance practice" for the work, in order to assist in its improvement.

Table 2-15

POSITION: Planning and scheduling engineer.
DEPARTMENT: Mechanical and electrical.
PRIMARY FUNCTION: To assist in (1) the application and use of the most effective procedures for the execution of maintenance and construction work; (2) the application of improvements in methods, tools, and preventive maintenance; and (3) the establishment of records and making necessary analyses for indicating what corrective measures are necessary.

DUTIES AND RESPONSIBILITIES

1. Assist in the application of a work-order system covering normal, patrol, blanket, and cross orders to suit plant conditions.
2. Establish a means of backlog control covering both over-all and current conditions.
3. Daily scheduling and weekly forecasting of all maintenance and minor construction.
4. Investigate all emergency, service-to-operations, and indirect jobs.
5. Establish a preventive-maintenance program covering all operating equipment, buildings, and facilities.
6. Establish an equipment record system for the plant.
7. Establish direct, indirect, and general costs, and a budgetary control using such costs.
8. Carry out a job methods and preplanning program covering all work requests.
9. Carry out an improvement program covering tools and shop facilities.
10. Carry out a program for standardizing jobs covering methods, tools, materials, skills.
11. Analyze all maintenance costs by operating departments, and establish graphic relationships among production, direct, indirect, and general maintenance costs.
12. Assist in establishment and application of all training programs for both supervisory and wage-roll personnel.

Table 2-16

POSITION: Watch engineer.
DEPARTMENT: Power.
PRIMARY FUNCTION: To supervise operating and coordinate maintenance functions of the powerhouse and related property.

DUTIES AND RESPONSIBILITIES

1. Supervise all activities in conjunction with the generation and supply of utilities. The equipment and facilities include:
   a. Boilers and auxiliaries.
   b. Turbines and auxiliaries.
   c. Switchboard.
   d. Filter plant.
   e. Pumps.
   f. Refrigeration and auxiliaries.
   g. Vacuum and air.
2. Accountable for time distribution of powerhouse wage-roll personnel under his supervision.
3. Responsible for instructing personnel in duties of operation under his supervision.
4. Assist supervisory personnel in the formulation of labor policies and promotion of good labor relations; and assist in the handling of unsettled grievances.
5. Conduct safety meetings for own personnel, promote use of all applicable safety regulations, investigate injuries affecting own group.

Table 2-17

POSITION: Craft foreman.
DEPARTMENT: Mechanical.
PRIMARY FUNCTION: To supervise the execution of work performed by his craft.

Table 2-17 (*Continued*)

DUTIES AND RESPONSIBILITIES
1. Analyze repair orders as to skill, material, tools, methods; and prepare estimate of time and manpower requirements.
2. Requisition materials.
3. Fit analyzed jobs into a daily schedule according to operating conditions, manpower, and availability of material.
4. Responsible for completion of all work.
5. Responsible for quantity and quality of all work performed by his group.
6. Accountable for time and proper charge covering personnel supervised.
7. Responsible for training of personnel supervised covering:
   a. Orientation.
   b. Proper use of tools and equipment and standard maintenance practices.
8. Control costs through: budgets–direct, indirect, and general classification of maintenance; other cost methods.
9. Assist in the formulation of policies and the promotion of good labor relations; also in settling of grievances.
10. Conduct meetings for own group—enforce use of all applicable safety regulations, investigate injuries affecting own group and prepare injury reports.
11. Establish backlog covering all work for personnel control.
12. Establish forecasts covering 1 week's work for his personnel.
13. Assist other foremen in meeting schedules for work in which he is the prime foreman.
14. If preplanning and measurement are in effect, assist applicators in applying better methods, tools, and facilities.

Table 2-18

POSITION: Area foreman.
DEPARTMENT: Mechanical.
PRIMARY FUNCTION: To supervise the execution of maintenance work in the field.

DUTIES AND RESPONSIBILITIES
1. Analyze repair orders as to skill, material, tools, methods; and prepare estimate of time and manpower requirements.
2. Requisition materials.
3. Fit analyzed jobs into a daily schedule according to operating conditions, manpower, and availability of material.
4. Responsible for completion of all work.
5. Responsible for quantity and quality of all work performed both by his and other crafts in area on which he is the key foreman (originator of cross orders).
6. Account for time and proper charge covering personnel under his supervision.
7. Responsible for training of personnel supervised which includes:
   a. Orientation.
   b. Proper use of tools and equipment.
   c. Standard maintenance practices.
8. Control cost through: budgets–direct, indirect, and general classification of maintenance; other cost methods.
9. Assist in the formulation of policies, the promotion of sound labor relations, and in settling of grievances. Attend meetings.
10. Conduct meetings for own personnel—enforce use of all applicable safety regulations. Investigate any injuries affecting own group and prepare injury reports.
11. Establish backlog covering all work for personnel control.
12. Establish priorities for all work done by other maintenance groups in his area.
13. Assist other foremen in meeting schedules for work in which he is the prime foreman.
14. If preplanning and measurement are in effect, assist applicators in applying better methods, tools, and facilities.

Table 2-19

POSITION: Results engineer.
DEPARTMENT: Power.
PRIMARY FUNCTION: Through the use of established standards to secure greatest effectiveness of powerhouse operating equipment as it concerns the production and distribution of utilities.

DUTIES AND RESPONSIBILITIES
1. Secure all instrument readings through reports or meter charts and translate the records into work loads. Compare with standards to determine the degree of efficiency of powerhouse operating equipment.

Table 2-19 (*Continued*)

2. Make efficiency tests and check instruments on powerhouse equipment for accuracy.
3. Issue periodic reports (at such frequency as is found necessary) showing actual operating results vs. standards for all operating equipment in the powerhouse.
4. Review power equipment cost cards and summarize the results periodically for corrective maintenance purposes.
5. Assist in establishing inspection systems covering all powerhouse equipment and outside lines or other utility equipment.
6. Furnish information on powerhouse operation and maintenance for monthly summary.
7. Assist in the purchase of spare parts and extra machinery.
8. Follow up inspection procedures.

Table 2-20

POSITION: Draftsman.
DEPARTMENT: Mechanical and development.
PRIMARY FUNCTION: To perform drafting and related duties for the works engineering department.

DUTIES AND RESPONSIBILITIES
Under direction of the project engineer:
1. Prepare and revise designs, drawings, tracings, sketches, bills of material, estimates, and equipment specifications.
2. Check designs, drawings, tracings as required.
3. Use standard technical and reference books in performance of work.
4. Comply with existing safety regulations.

Table 2-21

POSITION: Material man.
DEPARTMENT: Mechanical.
PRIMARY FUNCTION: To assist in the procurement and distribution of all maintenance materials.

DUTIES AND RESPONSIBILITIES
1. Prepare requisitions, with adequate specifications, for:
   a. Nonstores materials.
   b. New items to be added to stores stock.
   c. Items required in excess of stores stock.
   d. Work to be done by outside vendors.
2. Contact purchasing section relative to delivery dates, convey information to parties concerned, and arrange delivery of material to location for use.
3. Review periodically all outside purchases for inclusion as spare parts or extra machinery.
4. Assist supervision in the preparation of budgets through a review and submission of material costs.
5. Prepare papers for any maintenance materials to outside concerns.
6. Assist in maintaining adequate stores stock by:
   a. Monthly forecast of maintenance materials.
   b. Estimated consumption of new stock items.
   c. Contacting foremen relative to acceptability of write-downs and write-offs.
7. Take steps to correct variations in material dimensions, tolerances, quality, etc., as evidenced by inspection.
8. Assist in reducing material costs through substitution of materials and parts.

Table 2-22

POSITION: Clerk.
DEPARTMENT: Mechanical.
PRIMARY FUNCTION: To perform clerical duties in conjunction with the activities of the works engineering department.

DUTIES AND RESPONSIBILITIES
Under direction, perform duties as follows:
1. Post and maintain records.
2. Calculate efficiencies, loads, material and labor costs.
3. Prepare tabulations, charts, logs, reports, and requisitions.
4. Perform clerical work in connection with repair order control, scheduling and equipment cost-card procedure, time distribution, and backlog control (maintenance clerk).

Table 2-22 (*Continued*)

5. Assist in preparation of projects (project clerk).
6. Prepare monthly distributions of water, steam, and electric power (power and electrical division clerks).
7. Maintain essential material usage records (power clerk).
8. Stamp, record, integrate, and change instrument charts (instrument division clerk).
9. Operate the photostat and blueprinting machine (project clerk).
10. Answer telephone.
11. Maintain files.
12. Take notes and summarize minutes of meetings.
13. Perform clerical work as directed by supervision.

Table 2-23

POSITION: Construction engineer.
DEPARTMENT: Mechanical and electrical.
PRIMARY FUNCTION: To administer and coordinate all activities in conjunction with plant construction work.

DUTIES AND RESPONSIBILITIES
1. Responsible for the organization and functioning of the plant construction organization and by coordination of shop and field activities·
2. By work and crew classification, control the distribution of wage-roll personnel.
3. Through informative data control all expenditures and advise of any conditions requiring addition or subtraction of work or costs.
4. Review periodically the status of all projects and advise of any conditions where either overruns or underruns may be expected.
5. Actively support and initiate programs for improvements in methods and costs of plant construction work.
6. Through reports, contact with supervisory personnel and others, actively guide and make necessary correction in conjunction with:
   a. Tool and equipment requirements.
   b. Prefabrication and assembly.
   c. Bills of materials.
   d. Control of waste.
   e. Quality of work.
7. Assist in the formulation and application of training programs.
8. Interpret labor-relations policies for supervisory personnel and assist in disposing of unsettled grievances.
9. Assist supervisory personnel in the application of all safety regulations and programs.
10. Have contacts with outside contractors relative to securing estimates of work and coordination of these activities with plant operating and maintenance conditions.

Table 2-24

POSITION: Inspector.
DEPARTMENT: Mechanical and electrical.
PRIMARY FUNCTION: To determine through inspection the necessity for all maintenance repairs or replacements.

DUTIES AND RESPONSIBILITIES
1. List all equipment and facilities needing inspection and establish schedule and frequency subject to the approval of the planning-scheduling engineer and area engineer.
2. Determine what part of the equipment or facilities is to be inspected and what is to be looked for.
3. Establish a method of recording conditions found and what repairs are to be made.
4. Make repairs of a minor nature.
5. Issue repair orders calling for major repairs and turn over to area engineer for execution.
6. Maintain close contact with schedule clerk for keeping schedule up to date.

Table 2-25

POSITION: Area electrical engineer.
DEPARTMENT: Electrical.
PRIMARY FUNCTION: To supervise craft foremen in the maintenance of electrical facilities.

DUTIES AND RESPONSIBILITIES
1. Responsible for the proper functioning of work and crew classification and meeting the needs and the control of maintenance personnel.

Table 2-25 (*Continued*)

2. Review direct, indirect, and general maintenance costs and be responsible for the maintenance of budgetary control. Approve indirect orders.
3. Review equipment record cards to determine the possibility of electrical maintenance cost improvement.
4. Assist the planning and scheduling engineer in establishing job standardization; currently review improvements and cost-reduction programs; and approve standard maintenance practices.
5. Assist the planning and scheduling engineer in interpreting studies of standardized jobs and in recommending improvements to shops, buildings, and equipment.
6. Conduct orientation, job training, and refresher courses for supervisory personnel and assist the planning and scheduling engineer in promoting better use of controls.
7. Review with the planning and scheduling engineer shutdown schedules for most economical operating and maintenance conditions.
8. Review reports of all emergency jobs and discuss causes and possible improvements with both the planning and scheduling engineer and operating supervision.
9. Review periodically all stores items for establishing correct electrical stores inventory.
10. Review equipment record cards to effect maintenance cost improvement.
11. Assist supervision in the formulation of policies, the promotion of sound labor relations, and in handling unsettled grievances.
12. Assist supervision in the application of all safety regulations and programs.

Chapter **3**

OPERATING POLICIES BY WHICH MANAGEMENT SHOULD BE GUIDED

By CHARLES E. KNIGHT
General Superintendent of Engineering and Manufacturing Services
Monsanto Company, Plastics Division
Springfield, Mass.

This chapter covers basic policies for the operation of a maintenance engineering department. While many of these policies overlap and are interdependent, they may be grouped in four general categories:

Policies with respect to *work allocation.*
Policies with respect to the *work force.*
Policies with respect to *intraplant relations.*
Policies with respect to *control.*

POLICIES WITH RESPECT TO WORK ALLOCATION

To Schedule or Not to Schedule? Work scheduling is one of the most effective tools that can be used in improving the efficiency of any maintenance department. The form of scheduling may range from the planning a foreman does in assignment of his men to the day's work to an elaborate, centralized planning system, employing specialists who allocate all the time of each craftsman to specific jobs. The position for any one maintenance engineering department should be determined at a point in this range where optimum utilization of manpower results. There should be as much planning as necessary for maximum over-all efficiency so long as the system costs less than the cost of operating without it.

It is generally accepted that, in any maintenance department where there are more than 10 men and more than two or three crafts, some planning, other than day-to-day allocation of work by foremen, can result in improved efficiency. As the size of the maintenance organization increases, the extent to which work planning can be formalized and the amount of time that should be spent on this activity are increased.

How Much Scheduling? There are practical limitations to the comprehensiveness of any scheduling system. A very detailed schedule which becomes obsolete after the first hour or two of use because of emergencies is of little value. If, however, actual performance indicates from 60 to 80 per cent adherence during normal operation, the value of the schedule is real. Justification of any scheduling system requires determination of its effectiveness in terms of efficiency improvement, i.e., dollars saved. Where some form of incentive system or work measurement exists, the answer is readily available, but in most maintenance departments no such definitive method is available and the only criteria are over-all trends in maintenance costs and quality of service. Some aspects to be considered in arriving at a sound work-scheduling procedure are:

Work Unit. Most detailed schedules are laid out in terms of man-hours or, if standard times are used, to fractions of hours. Other scheduling systems use a half man-day as a minimum work unit. Others may use a man-day or even a man-week as a basis.

Size of Jobs Scheduled. Some work-scheduling systems handle small jobs as well as large ones. Others schedule only major work where the number of men and the length of time involved are appreciable.

Per Cent of Total Work Load Scheduled. Although in some cases all work may be scheduled, the most effective systems recognize the inability of any maintenance engineering department to anticipate all jobs, especially those of an emergency nature, and do not attempt scheduling for the entire work force. A portion of the available work force is left free for quick assignment to emergency jobs or other priority work not anticipated at the time of scheduling.

Lead Time for Scheduling. Lead time for scheduling, or the length of time covered by the schedule, is another variable to be considered. Some scheduling systems do not attempt to cover breakdown repairs and are limited to the routine preventive maintenance and to major work that can be anticipated and scheduled well in advance. In these cases a monthly or biweekly allocation of manpower suffices. In most instances, however, a weekly schedule with a 2- or 3-day lead time results in good performance, yet is sufficiently flexible to handle most unexpected work. In extreme situations a daily schedule with 16 to 18 hr lead time may be necessary to provide the necessary control. A more workable solution for this situation, however, involves use of a master schedule for a minimum of 1 week with provision for modifying it daily.

Selection and Implementation of a Scheduling System. *Flow of Work Requests.* Before any formalized scheduling program can be initiated the method of requesting work from the maintenance department should be formalized. This request may take the form of a work description or job ticket, listing manpower or equipment requirement, or it can be in the form of a work sheet on which the same type of information is accumulated by either verbal or written communication. Regardless of the form this information takes it must be routed to one central point if a scheduling system is to be used. In a small plant this can be the shop foreman, the maintenance superintendent, or the plant engineer. In a larger maintenance department it should be through a staff individual or group.

The amount of information on the work request depends considerably upon the type of talent used in the scheduling group. If the individual charged with planning is completely familiar with the job requirements and can determine the craft manpower involved, the necessary equipment, and any other information required for scheduling, a summary of the jobs will suffice. On the other hand, where complexity of work is such that it is practically impossible for any individual to have this information, or if the person charged with scheduling does not have the training necessary to analyze the work, then the information on the work request must be presented in more detail. The number of man-hours required, by craft, the timing, the relation between crafts, the location and availability of parts and equipment, and any special requirements concerning coordination with production schedules or personnel should be included. The method by which this information is procured and transmitted to the scheduling center will be controlled by the work-request system either in effect or selected for use prior to formalized scheduling.

In addition to job information required for planning, it is equally important to have a feedback on actual performance in terms of notification of completion and actual time consumed, by craft. This may be incorporated in the work-request system but provision must be made for channeling this information back to the scheduling center. The scheduling system should also provide for work scheduled but not completed becoming a part of the work backlog. As such, it is considered, along with new work, for new scheduling.

Coordinating and Dispatching.   In the execution of an effective scheduling system it is necessary to compromise with the practical considerations of getting the work done, and done economically.   If a foreman guided his craftsmen and himself on the assumption that the job must be completed at the exact time he had estimated and then continued to assign work on the basis of his estimate of the time necessary, it is obvious that confusion, incomplete work, and idle craft time would result.   A formal schedule, issued weekly and followed blindly, would have the same effects. A central dispatch, or work-assignment center, is required which uses the formalized schedule as a basis, modifying it continually to correct for errors in estimating time and unforeseen job difficulties, and coordinating changes among various crafts, production, and equipment.   Here again, if only one or two foremen are involved, this can be an informal, discussion-type adjustment.   But if there are many crafts and a large number of people in the department, a dispatch center to adjust work assignments will increase the efficiency of the work force and the effectiveness of a formal work schedule.   This dispatch center must have sufficient know-how to understand craft relationships and the proper division of work among crafts.   It must have the confidence of the men who supervise the work force and must have the authority to alter work assignments for the most effective accomplishment of the work to be done. Communications between this center and the field crews must be such that the dispatch center is constantly aware of the dispersion of men, availability of equipment, and progress of the work.

It is also essential that any changes or unexpected work for which provision has not been made in the schedule be funneled through the dispatch center.   Usually the dispatch center can incorporate this type of work more efficiently than is possible by random selection of the nearest craftsmen or injection of higher authority into the picture.

Determination of Priority.   In any maintenance organization which is efficiently manned the work load, in terms of quantity or timing, exceeds the availability of men and/or equipment.   A department staffed for maximum demand would encounter frequent intervals of inactivity and subsequent loss of efficiency.   For this reason the problem of defining the order in which the work is to be carried out, or establishing priority, exists and is an important factor in scheduling.   In a small plant with one operating department and a small maintenance organization, establishment of priorities may amount to casual discussion between maintenance and production. However, as the plant grows and the maintenance department is called upon to provide service to more than one production department, the problem of equitable and efficient priority assignment becomes more involved.   One of the most serious problems in maintaining good relations between maintenance and production departments is in this sphere.   Too frequently personalities, working conditions, accessibility, or geographic location with respect to central shops influence the order of work assignment.   This may decrease the over-all efficiency of the plant.

The means for determining work priority figures most importantly in the establishment of a work-scheduling system.   On the surface a solution to this problem would reserve decisions concerning priorities to an individual who is in position to judge the effect on over-all plant performance.   In a plant of any size, however, this becomes impractical because of the large number of priority decisions that must be made and the difficulty in evaluating the results.   Naturally the plant manager, or other individual to whom both production and maintenance report, has the final say if the matter cannot be settled at a lower level.   More effective service results if such things can be handled at a lower level.   If maintenance personnel alone establish the priorities, using only their opinion of the importance of the work, relations with production supervision usually will be strained.   Some cooperative means of determining priorities should be negotiated and agreed to by production and maintenance to avoid friction and expedite efficient scheduling.

A method which has proved satisfactory in many instances has been to assign a rough allocation of craft manpower to each production department, then to establish the priority of work within each department by consultation with its supervision. When it is necessary to vary the allocation of men this should be done by negotiation between production departments to arrange a mutually agreeable exchange. If such a reallocation cannot be concluded, as a last resort the plant manager must make the decision. In such a system nearly all decisions are made at the lowest possible level, based on a mutual understanding of each other's problems by maintenance and production.

Preventive vs. Breakdown Maintenance. Preventive maintenance has long been recognized as extremely important in the reduction of maintenance costs and improvement of equipment reliability. In practice it takes many forms. There are exhaustive programs which cover every piece of equipment with periodic inspections which include recording wear or other deterioration of parts. These records are a basis for maintaining equipment in good condition while operating and will point to the need for major overhaul and replacements before breakdown. Other preventive-maintenance programs may consist simply of a good lubrication program, accompanied by superficial examination for major defects. It is not intended here to discuss these systems in detail but rather to point out some factors that should be considered in establishing the scope of a preventive-maintenance program and some other devices which can be used for the same purpose, i.e., reduction of maintenance cost and downtime.

Two major factors that should control the extent of a preventive program are first, the cost of the program compared with the carefully measured reduction in total repair costs and improved equipment performance; second, the per cent utilization of the equipment maintained. Establishment of a comprehensive preventive-maintenance program for its own sake should be approached with caution. It is possible for the cost of the program to exceed the total maintenance cost, using the breakdown maintenance approach. A shutdown of some equipment for no other reason then periodic inspection and adjustment may be intolerable from a production point of view. Even if there is adequate schedule time available on the equipment for inspections, the program can still be justified only if maintenance costs are reduced. In this case it is fair to add the cost of breakdown time only where it would have been impossible to reschedule production on other equipment. If the cost of preparation for a preventive-maintenance inspection is essentially the same as the cost of repair after a failure accompanied by preventive inspections, the justification is small. If, on the other hand, breakdown could result in severe damage to the equipment and a far more costly repair, the scheduled inspection time should be considered. Furthermore, in the average plant preventive maintenance should be tailored to fit the function of different items of equipment rather than applied in the same manner to all equipment. In a chemical plant, for instance, a great deal more preventive maintenance can be justified for instruments and for other equipment because of their general availability and ease of access. Such a program will avoid costly delays for a much higher investment in productive capacity than is represented by the instrument itself. Key pieces of equipment in many other integrated manufacturing lines are in the same category. Conversely, periodic inspections of small electric motors and power transmissions can easily exceed the cost of unit replacement at the time of failure.

Indeed, a program of unit replacements can result in considerably lower maintenance costs where complete preventive maintenance is impractical. In a plant using many pumps, for instance, a program of standardization, coupled with an inventory of complete units of pumps most widely used, may provide a very satisfactory program for this equipment. This "spare-tire" philosophy can be extended to many other components or subassemblies with gratifying results.

Sometimes, instead of using a centrally administered formal preventive program, qualified mechanics are assigned to individual pieces of equipment, or equipment groups, as mechanical custodians. Operating without clerical assistance and with a minimum of paper work these men, because of familiarity with equipment and ability to sense mechanical difficulties in advance, can effectively reduce maintenance costs and breakdowns. These compromise devices can frequently be used to greater advantage, even in plants where equipment is not in continuous operation and a more comprehensive preventive program might be set up.

Periodic shutdown for complete overhaul of a whole production unit, similar to the turn-around period in oil refineries, is another method of minimizing breakdowns and performing maintenance most efficiently.   Unfortunately, this is a difficult approach to sell to management of a 7-day, around-the-clock manufacturing plant not accustomed to this method.

One of the most effective methods of tempering ideal preventive maintenance with practical considerations of a continuous operation is that of taking advantage of a breakdown in some component of the line to perform vital inspections and replacements which can be accomplished in about the same time as the primary repair.   This requires recording of deficiencies observed during operating inspections and moving in quickly with craftsmen and supervision prepared to work until the job is done. Production supervision usually can be sold the need for a few more hours' time for additional work with repair of a breakdown much more easily than they can be convinced of its necessity when things are apparently running smoothly.

In spite of the undisputed advantages of a sound preventive-maintenance program, the plant engineer must face the fact that it is sometimes more profitable to the company as a whole to run a piece of equipment until it breaks down rather than take a deliberate shutdown during a crowded production schedule.   While this may be hard for maintenance personnel on the scene to accept, it is something to be included in consideration of any preventive program so long as no threat to the safety of personnel or adjacent equipment is implied in the unexpected failure.

Preventive Engineering.   One of the most important tools in minimizing downtime, whether or not a conventional preventive-maintenance program is possible, is called "preventive engineering."   Although this would appear to be the application of common sense to equipment design maintenance engineering, it is a field which is often neglected.   Too often maintenance engineers are so busy handling emergency repairs or in other day-to-day activities that they find no opportunity to analyze the causes for breakdowns which keep them so fully occupied.   While most engineers keep their eyes open to details such as better packings, longer-wearing bearings, improved lubrication systems, true preventive engineering goes further than this and consists of actually setting aside a specific amount of technical manpower to analyze incidents of breakdown and determine where the real effort is needed; then through redesign, substitution, changes, and specifications, or other similar means, reduce the frequency of failure and the cost of repair.

This can be handled by a special group acting as a cost-reduction unit or it can be included as one of the functions of the maintenance engineer.   Some companies can support groups that actually develop and test equipment to promote more maintenance-free operation.   The aid of equipment suppliers can be solicited in this same effort.   It should be emphasized, however, that this type of program requires intelligent direction to ensure that time and money are expended in the areas where the most return is likely.   A particular pump, operating under unusual conditions, shows a high incidence of failure but because of the simplicity of repair has a low total maintenance cost, and if it were the only one of its type in the plant, an intensive investigation for maintenance-cost reduction would be difficult to justify.   On the other hand, a simple component, such as a capstan bearing on a spinning machine, which, although having a low unit-replacement cost, can fail so often and on so many machines that the total cost per year would run to many thousands of dollars.   Here an investigation concentrated on the reason for failure of one unit could be extremely profitable. Effective preventive engineering can result only when it is recognized as an independent activity of a research nature that cannot be effectively sandwiched into the schedule of a man who is occupied with "putting out fires."

POLICIES WITH RESPECT TO WORK FORCE

Own Work Force or Outside Contractors?   In discussing the general subject of assignment of work to contractors it is assumed that some form of maintenance organization does exist within the plant.   The basic consideration in establishing a policy with respect to the use of outside contractors should be of their employment as an aid in establishing the types and sizes of craft groups in the maintenance department. The primary factor in determining this policy must be that of cost. Is it cheaper to staff *internally* for the performance of

1. The type of work involved,
2. The amount of work involved, and
3. The expediency with which this work must be accomplished?

In studying these relative costs it is not sufficient to consider the maintenance cost alone. The cost to the company, including downtime and quality of performance, must also be considered.

To establish, supervise, and maintain a group of men in any specific craft means a continuing expense over the wages paid the men. In general, this total cost must be balanced against the estimated cost for the same work performed by an outside contractor who must, in all probability, pay higher wages, carry the overhead of his operations, and realize a profit. By analysis of the work load and evaluation of the relative costs of its performance by plant maintenance or outside contractors, criteria for this division of work can be evolved. This analysis must include other factors such as time required, availability of the proper skills with outside contractors and in some instances, the possibility of process know-how leakage if contractors are employed. In deciding whether to set up your own shop or rely on contractors the degree of skill required in the particular craft is important. If this requirement is relatively low, and supervision and facilities of some other craft can be expanded to include it, this step can often be profitable. If, on the other hand, the degree of skill is high or the necessary equipment complex or costly, there must be a much greater amount of work for this craft before such a shop can be justified.

Once the basic craft types have been established for the maintenance organization, the question of the personnel strength of these crafts is also a function of the amount of work assigned to outside contractors. For optimum operation it is essential that the in-plant work force be always occupied. Most maintenance loads fluctuate considerably and it is impractical to staff for the highest peaks. Where the nature of work during peak periods is such that not enough can be deferred to level the valleys, outside contracting should be considered. The same consideration applies to construction projects which may become the responsibility of the maintenance department. Smooth operation and improved efficiency can result from maintaining a relatively stable in-plant work force. Outside contractors can be used as a labor reservoir to be tapped when the work load exceeds the capacity of the in-plant force. In general it is wise to staff the in-plant force so that it can handle a work load slightly above the valleys in anticipation that some of the peaks can be deferred. Outside contractors may then be used for the normal peaks and for the unusually high loads resulting from major construction or revision projects.

The preceding discussion has omitted two elements which may have an arbitrary effect on the practical distribution of work between inside and outside labor. The first of these is the availability in the area of properly trained craftsmen with adequate skill, and reliable contractors who can supply and supervise them. In some areas this is not the case and the economically optimum distribution of work between inside and outside crafts cannot be realized. Where the use of outside contractors involves the importation of both the contractor and the required craftsmen, expeditious work performance often dictates maintaining a much larger and more diversified maintenance group. The use of outside contractors may then be limited to major projects where it is feasible to use imported labor for an extended time, or to highly specialized work performed by a factory representative or a contractor specializing in this work as a job unit.

The other factor which may interfere with the optimum formula is the attitude of the labor organizations involved. This is a problem which varies not only among geographical areas, but frequently among plants in the same area. In some instances the plant union is militant at the prospect of any work being performed within the plant by nonunion workers or by members of another union. In other plants an understanding is reached, generally limiting contractor participation to construction or major revisions. Other plant unions recognize factors which permit considerable latitude in the use of outside contractors. For instance, the union may recognize that the amount of concrete and masonry work will not justify more than a minimum repair crew and that any new work or major repair in this line would be more economically handled by an outside contractor. Many unions recognize the need for employment of contractors in such fields as refrigeration, window washing, and steeple-jack services. An optimum solution for this problem is more likely to result if the union and maintenance supervision arrive at a mutual understanding of the problem in advance. However, this is often difficult, and failure may occasionally necessitate establishment of uneconomical crafts and work allocation for the in-plant work force.

On the other hand, the situation may be reversed, with outside craft unions refusing to perform in-plant work unless granted exclusive rights to all the work or at least to certain clearly defined portions of the work. This presents an entirely different problem and generally favors the expansion of the in-plant group, with respect to both numbers and crafts involved, so as to minimize the use of contract labor, limiting its use to major new construction. The availability of outside contractors, the union sentiment (both external and internal), and the nature and amount of work to be performed have a profound influence on the size and make-up of the work force in a maintenance department, and all factors should be thoroughly explored and evaluated in establishing the department.

Shift Coverage. The problem of providing adequate maintenance coverage on a one-shift, 5-day operation is relatively simple, since most of the breakdown maintenance can be done during the normal working hours, with plenty of time available to execute a thorough preventive program without interfering with production. As the number of hours a plant operates increases over 40, by use of two or three shifts or extension to a sixth or seventh day, provision of adequate maintenance coverage, particularly for breakdowns, becomes involved.

Even in the process industries, where plants frequently operate continuously—three shifts, 7 days a week—some of the maintenance load can be separated and handled simply. Maintenance of buildings and grounds, for instance, is the same for three-shift operations as with one shift. For the rest, however, special consideration is required to provide the service necessary for optimum production. Not only will lubrication and breakdown repairs continue around the clock, but other items such as waste collection, janitor service, elevator maintenance, and fork-truck maintenance must be considered in a different light from the same services in a plant on a one-shift basis. The two extremes in providing maintenance for continuous operation are to provide full coverage during all hours that the plant is in operation or to maintain day coverage only, letting the plant shift for itself during other periods or to accept minimum essential service on call-in, overtime basis. The optimum arrangement is something in between, depending a great deal upon circumstances in an individual plant.

In considering the staffing of a maintenance department to cover more than one-shift operation, many factors are involved.

Efficiency of the Worker. Although exception may be taken to this statement, it is generally conceded that a man who is not paced, by either the equipment he operates or the performance of a large group of individuals, is not so efficient on the off shifts as during the day. This loss of efficiency can be attributed to many causes. First, a man is normally happier living a normal life which, in most communities, includes sleeping at night and working days. Most of his out-of-plant relationships are with people living this sort of life. The activities of his wife and children are normally concentrated in the daylight hours. All these factors make for conflict in an attempt to reconcile the schedule of the shift worker with that of his family and friends. This situation seems to be more acute among the personnel of maintenance craft groups than with those of similar skills and backgrounds employed in the building trades.

Another cause for a loss in efficiency is the fact that usually the work of a maintenance man must be coordinated with production activity. Even though every attempt is made to plan this activity, unexpected variances occur which call for changes in coordination with production. Since most of these require decisions at supervisory levels normally at work during the day, delays frequently occur, resulting in a loss of efficiency.

While some types of operations may justify both production and maintenance supervision on the scene at full strength around the clock, usually only the supervision necessary to maintain operations on an essentially static basis is available during the off shifts. Around-the-clock maintenance must be weighed against the reduction in efficiency resulting from the absence of adequate authority. Efficiency may also be reduced by the need for unexpected supplies, tools, or equipment which can be procured only from outside suppliers during regular working hours. The alternative may be improper substitutions or costly on-the-spot fabrication, either of which will reduce maintenance efficiency.

There are other factors which argue for around-the-clock maintenance, such as the location of a plant with respect to the homes of the craftsmen, which may make call-in impractical. In other cases a particular production unit may be so critical as to make any maintenance delay intolerable, or a breakdown may create a safety hazard so grave that maintenance coverage must be provided, regardless of its economic justification.

Experience indicates that minimum downtime and lowest maintenance cost result from using the least coverage on the off shifts that can be tolerated from the standpoint of safety and lost production time. Adequate craft supervision should be provided where justified, or this responsibility should be transferred to some other member of supervision. As much work as possible should be handled on the day shift. The cost of call-in overtime should be compared with the cost of scheduled coverage, including the cost of delays resulting from call-in. The cost of finishing jobs of more than 8 hr duration should include comparison of cost of holdover overtime with that of a second or third shift. The amount of routine work that can be assigned to fill out the time of men on off shifts and the amount of application of the men to this work that can be reasonably expected is another factor. Where both centralized and decentralized maintenance groups are available, men on the off shifts, with the possible exception of such specialized crafts as electricians and instrument men, should be from the decentralized group.

It is sometimes possible to use a split-day-shift schedule with one crew working Monday through Friday and another on a Wednesday through Sunday schedule to extend day coverage over a 7-day period. In some instances it may be more economical to have a large day crew, an intermediate afternoon and evening shift, and a skeleton midnight shift.

The best plan for any plant can be determined only after due consideration of all the factors mentioned above and any other special considerations peculiar to the plant. This plan may have seasonal variation or may change with the plant's economic situation.

Centralization vs. Decentralization. The subject of centralized vs. decentralized maintenance has elicited a great deal of discussion over the past few years, with strong proponents and good arguments on each side. Advantages of a centralized maintenance shop are:

1. Easier dispatching from a more diversified craft group.
2. The justification of more and higher-quality equipment.
3. Better interlocking of craft effort.
4. More specialized supervision.
5. Improved training facilities.

The advantages of decentralized maintenance are:

1. Reduced travel time to and from job.
2. More intimate equipment knowledge through repeated experience.
3. Improved application to job due to closer alliance with the objectives of a smaller unit—"Production-mindedness."

4. Better preventive maintenance due to greater interest.
5. Improved maintenance-production relationship.

In practice, however, it has been found that neither one alone is the panacea for difficulties in work distribution. Often a compromise system in which both centralized and decentralized maintenance coexist has proved most effective. For handling major work requiring a large number of craftsmen, the centralized maintenance group provides a pool which can be deployed where needed. To provide the same availability in a completely decentralized setup would mean staffing at dispersed locations far in excess of optimum needs for each area, plus difficulty in coordinating on the big job. The installation of some of the costly and specialized equipment that is needed for some of the crafts can seldom be justified at other than a central location. On the other hand, a great deal can be accomplished in minimizing downtime by having a decentralized group which can function "Johnny-on-the-spot" and give immediate attention to minor maintenance problems. Familiarity with a smaller sphere of production equipment through experience is almost certain to improve the performance of craftsmen. In general, good over-all efficiency will result from the decentralization of a specific number of the less specialized crafts in area shops, augmented by minimum personnel of specialized crafts to provide emergency service in their field. An improvement over this would be the utilization of a general craftsman who can perform the work of many crafts in a decentralized group. This, of course, presents a problem with organized labor and will normally require agreement from the union. It also limits the skill that can be expected of such men, since there are few men who can become experts in all the crafts.

It is suggested that, rather than assign an arbitrary number of people to a decentralized facility, a comprehensive study be made of the type of service required to sustain production in the area under consideration, and that from this service be separated that which can be performed by a general area mechanic. The incidence of this type of work and the resulting area mechanic work load should then be determined from some factual records, and a sufficient number of men assigned to handle this work load. The preventive-maintenance program can provide a reservoir of work for the maximum utilization of this decentralized group during periods of low breakdown or modification maintenance activity.

Recruitment. Unfortunately policies for recruitment of personnel for the maintenance department are controlled a great deal more by local conditions and expediency than by the ideal approach. This in itself is a major argument for maintaining as stable a work force as is economically practical.

Where the union contract makes job posting mandatory the problem of getting men who are or will eventually be satisfactory craftsmen can be difficult. All too often, since this particular problem is only a small part of the over-all management-union relationship, little effort is made to arrive at a better method of filling vacancies among the crafts. Many maintenance departments in union plants have become resigned and make the best of the candidates turned up through the bidding procedure usually selected on a seniority basis. With good union-maintenance supervision relationships supplementary agreements or understandings may be reached which will considerably improve the type of candidate considered. Age, aptitude, past experience, educational background, and general level of intelligence are frequently considered in some mutually acceptable screening technique. An accepted apprentice-training program with recognized entrance qualifications will generally create a source of competent personnel.

In plants where there is no problem of union resistance, local conditions and the make-up of the production work force are the major factors in recruitment of maintenance personnel. Where many of the operations being performed on the production line are of a mechanical nature the probability of securing competent recruits from production is greater than in the process industries which do not generally attract the type of individual suited for maintenance. Availability of trained prospects outside the plant is naturally better in highly industrialized communities. A detailed discussion of the qualifications of candidates for maintenance work and methods for evaluation of applicants is a subject in itself. However, a few generalities can be made concerning the two types which make up the craft groups of a maintenance department. These two types are the untrained candidate, who enters at the bottom of the scale and receives his training while employed in the maintenance department, and the completely trained, skilled mechanic. In evaluating the untrained candidate, primary considerations should be age, mechanical aptitude, manual dexterity, and analytical ability. Some degree of self-assurance and stability of character is important. Also, the candidate's motivation for entering the crafts field should be thoroughly explored during interviews. It is preferable that this motivation be a real liking for the type of work rather than a desire for more money, security, prestige, or some other factor. In selecting trained applicants, age and education should carry less weight. Experience is most important in this case, as well as attitude and motivation. Experience should be explored not only with respect to the nature and type of work he has done, but also regarding the quality of performance, teamwork potential, ability to carry out assignments without constant supervision, and his personal stability. Summarizing, policies with respect to the recruitment of maintenance personnel are controlled largely by the conditions existing at a specific plant. Every device for the best selection of the available personnel should be employed, and the use of advanced techniques in testing, interviewing, and screening is recommended.

Training. There are several methods for training personnel in a maintenance department. The simplest and most effective is an established and recognized apprentice-training program. The details of such a program are available from many sources, but the most widely used is the apprentice-training program sponsored by the U.S. Department of Labor, Bureau of Apprentice Training. Usually the administration of this program is handled by a state organization which will provide all the necessary information, as well as assistance in adapting the program to an individual plant.

Many companies establish their own apprentice-training programs which are similar to this nationally recognized one. This requires considerably more preparatory work by the company but is not so widely recognized and therefore does not have the same appeal to the craftsmen as the national program. Administration of both systems requires about the same attention.

On the other hand, many plants have no formalized training for their craftsmen and depend entirely upon exposure, supervisory job coaching, and association with experienced workmen for their training. In between there is a whole range of possibilities, including such variations as "short-course" on-the-job programs, qualification and skill-development evaluation tests, promotional programs based on either formal or informal evaluations, and less detailed apprentice programs.

The factors that should influence the degree of formality of the training program are similar to those used to determine many other aspects of maintenance operations, i.e., size of the plant, attitude of the labor group, availability of skilled craftsmen, and the over-all policy of management. A large plant can obviously afford to initiate and maintain a more elaborate training program than can a small plant. The lack of availability of skilled craftsmen increases the need and justification for better training.

Training programs have been installed with and without the support of organized labor but, in general, they are more effective with the wholehearted support of the crafts group, particularly if it is jointly administered by the company and the union. Of course there are exceptions to this rule, and some excellent programs are in effect that are unilaterally administered by the company. Before any decision is made regarding the initiation of such a program, the effect on labor attitude should be seriously explored.

Above all, the amount of formal training to be used must be based upon the value of the results. It is not good management to have a training program for the sake of having a training program. A training program should result either in improved maintenance performance or in proper staffing of a maintenance department. The availability of some craft skills in certain areas or a change in methods and techniques may be such that the only means of providing the necessary skills is through a training program. Frequently, although a comprehensive program cannot be justified for all crafts, programs for individual skills are a necessity. These can be handled internally or in cooperation with an educational institution or an equipment supplier. Excellent examples of this treatment are the courses run by the suppliers of welding equipment which make it possible to provide men with up-to-the minute instructions on developments in welding techniques.

In summary, the policy of a maintenance department with respect to training should be based entirely upon the special circumstances and requirements of each plant, and the program selected should be the one which will result in the highest return for the cost of its establishment and operation.

POLICIES WITH RESPECT TO INTRAPLANT RELATIONS

Participation by Maintenance Personnel in Selection of Production Equipment. In some plants one engineering department handles all phases of engineering activity from design through construction and maintenance. In the majority of plants, however, the construction of major facilities or addition of major equipment is engineered by a separate organization, reporting at a higher level, or by outside engineering contractors. The primary mission of these activities is to project pilot-plant operations to production-scale facilities or to expand existing installations to meet increased production goals. Built-in ease of maintenance does not normally receive the same emphasis that would result from the same work done by people who are to be responsible for maintenance. Most progressive companies provide for representation from the maintenance group as well as from the production group in design and selection of new facilities. A trained maintenance engineer can draw upon his experience or that of his department in suggesting modifications or brands of equipment that will result in reduced maintenance cost after it is placed in operation. Good equipment histories on performance of existing facilities are invaluable in assisting this contribution to design and construction.

It is not meant to suggest that the maintenance engineer should attempt to control the design of new equipment. He should, however, be offered the opportunity to review designs and specifications carefully in order to predict maintenance problems and suggest modifications for reduced repair costs. If his recommendations are logical and well presented, they will usually be accepted, particularly when real savings can be demonstrated. All too often the maintenance department is handed a surprise package which can be a nightmare to maintain and quickly requires revision to make maintenance at all practical. This not only results in high maintenance costs but is extremely damaging to the morale of the department. In summary, the maintenance engineer can be of inestimable value to a design group, first, because of the performance records at his disposal and second, because of his ability to suggest changes reducing the maintenance problem.

Standardization of equipment, whether centralized for a multiplant company or delegated to the maintenance department in a single plant, is another factor to be considered in specifying equipment. In this case, also, the maintenance engineering department should play a major part in policy formulation. A considerable reduction in maintenance costs can result from a sound standardization program by

1. Simplifying training of both operating and maintenance personnel.
2. Increasing interchangeability of equipment.
3. Decreasing capital tied up in spare-parts inventory.

As with preventive maintenance, a poorly established or inflexible program of standardization can be an obstacle and can be obstructive and costly. Any program of standardization should provide for transition to improved equipment types as they are available and should take local vendor relationships into account.

Design and construction groups should provide the maintenance department with recommendations concerning spare-parts and preventive-maintenance programs received from equipment suppliers. The former group can transfer their contact with the supplier to the maintenance department with much better effect than is possible when the maintenance department is required to make the contact independent of the work that has gone before.

The use of a group called the "project board" has proved extremely successful in smoothing the way for any new engineering venture. This group functions as a clearinghouse for progress of the work and brings together all the activities that can be expected to have contact with the work during and after installation. The project board consists of a qualified member from each of the departments involved. For example, in an expansion of existing facilities this board might consist of a representative from production, two or more from design engineering, one from maintenance engineering, and a representative from the safety department. If, on the other hand, the project is one involving a new process recently developed by a research group, a member of this organization should be included on the board. In this way the transition to an operating production unit is much easier since the project board normally is in existence until a successful plant demonstration has been made and tentative operating procedures established. This approach gives the maintenance department, as well as production, the opportunity to grow with the job and to suggest the modifications which familiarity with similar equipment makes possible and which make the final operation so much more satisfactory.

Authority to Shut Down Equipment for Maintenance. The authority of a maintenance department to dictate shutdown of production equipment for needed repairs is controversial and has contributed a good deal to the friction that sometimes exists between maintenance and production departments. In some plants the maintenance department does have this authority and it is generally recognized. In others there is no such prerogative and the decision rests entirely with production. Usually, and preferably, the decision is reached jointly.

It is not practical to form any ground rules for the selection of the proper course for a particular plant. This implies that there are two conflicting interests in the plant and that rules must be laid down to permit them to work harmoniously. Ideally, of course, the goal of both groups is the same and the question of shutting down equipment for maintenance should be resolved on its merits with respect to the accomplishment of this goal, i.e., maximum production at lowest cost in a safe working environment. In a well-ordered company where the proper relationship exists between production and maintenance departments the question of authority to shut down for maintenance should seldom, if ever, arise. Production should have sufficient confidence in the maintenance department to realize that a recommendation for shutdown should be considered, and conversely, maintenance will appreciate the production viewpoint and understand its problems of availability of equipment and scheduling. In this relationship the authority to shut down is a mutual one, taking into account an objective evaluation of all the facts.

If, on the other hand, this relationship does not or cannot exist, then the authority to shut down clearly rests with the department management holds accountable for repairs costs, safety, and equipment availability. If this accountability rests with the maintenance department, naturally it should also have the authority to shut down equipment for repairs. Where management holds the operating departments responsible for all these elements, the authority rests there. If, however, management holds maintenance accountable for repair costs and production responsible for equipment availability, this management must be ready to step in when the separate courses for each group seem incompatible.

Naturally, there are many areas in which the maintenance department has essentially unilateral authority, particularly in building repair, yard maintenance, upkeep of shops, etc. However, the primary responsibility for total manufacturing costs is usually that of a production department and so, therefore, is the ultimate control of production equipment availability. The maintenance department should have the complete confidence of production so that a recommendation for shutdown results in immediate consideration. A doctor has no authority to order medication or treatment for a patient if the patient refuses. However, the doctor's specialized training and knowledge are generally recognized, and once we retain him, it would be well to follow his advice.   The same philosophy is applicable in the maintenance-production relationship.

Responsibility for Safety.   Safety is one of the most important aspects of industrial management today.   The maintenance department should play a large part in making its plant a safe one in which to work.   Although general administration of the safety effort is usually delegated to a specialist group, the maintenance department is often the key to success of the program.   Not only is it responsible for the safety of its own personnel, but by definition it also is responsible for providing mechanical safeguards and for maintaining equipment and services in safe operating condition. Because of this collateral responsibility, the safety function is often combined with maintenance in a small plant.   In a larger plant there is a definite need for a separate staff group.

The problem of safety of personnel in the maintenance department is somewhat different from that of safety of production personnel.   Although mechanical guarding and safe operating conditions can be maintained in the shops, most of the work performed outside the shop is of a nonrepetitive nature, frequently requiring operation of equipment with guards or other safety devices removed.   Safety in maintenance department activity, therefore, depends to a much larger extent on the individual safety performance of its men.   In a production department where obvious hazards can be kept guarded and personnel instructed in performing a routine operation, programs and specific safety instructions are most effective.   In the maintenance department, however, the craftsman must be taught to think safety and translate his thoughts into a multitude of situations without much help from prescribed rules.

Although it is generally recognized that exposure to hazards is greater in the maintenance department than in production and the incidence of accidents is usually higher, it is still possible and, indeed, has been demonstrated that maintenance work can be performed as safely as work in production.   The important thing is that the safety attitude of maintenance supervision match the increased exposure and that this attitude be projected to their men.   They should be led to understand that their safety is of paramount importance to the company and that, with proper instruction in safe practices and eternal vigilance, an excellent safety record is possible.

Whether the responsibility for the safety program rests with a staff safety department or with the maintenance department, the work to be done must be performed by the maintenance group.   Standards for guards, grounding, bumping- and tripping-hazard elimination, warning signals, and safety devices must be closely followed. Installations of this type must be maintained in perfect operating condition.   A maintenance department should not presume to ignore requests for work of a safety nature and must find the means for giving top priority to these jobs.   Often the actual inspection of safety devices rests with the maintenance department.   Where this inspection is a function of the safety department or production department, close liaison must be maintained with maintenance for the immediate correction of deficiencies.

During repair of equipment in production areas maintenance personnel must be continuously alert to the hazards they may be creating for themselves and less experienced personnel in the immediate area.   Fire permits, lockout procedures, and warning signs must be used in this connection.   Possibility of tools or pieces of equipment falling and injuring others is always present.   Protection must be provided from exposure to welding, sandblasting, and oil spillage.   Electrical work is always accompanied by potential hazards and deserves special attention.

In conclusion, while the staff responsibility for safety may be part of the maintenance function in a small plant, usually it is preferable to have an independent safety department either reporting to top management or incorporated in the personnel department.   Regardless of its staff responsibility for safety, the maintenance department in any plant has a direct responsibility for implementation of the safety program, and its supervision must recognize this and provide the means for its accomplishment.

Instrumentation.   The question of responsibility of the maintenance department for instruments can best be answered by practical consideration of the problems peculiar to the plant involved. Instrument installation and maintenance theoretically should be considered in the same light as the addition of any other equipment. There are, however, several factors which make some other arrangement expedient, such as a separate department or assignment of this responsibility to the production department.

In a plant using relatively simple types of instruments their selection and maintenance is frequently a function of the electrical group. On the other hand, in some industries where instrumentation has been carried much farther and includes knowledge of complex electronic components, particularly in fields of automation, instrumentation may be a separate plant department. In some industries instruments are the major tools of production personnel and smooth operation requires their intimate knowledge of the instruments involved. In this situation, except for major changes, the responsibility for instrument care is with the production department.

With the increased use and complexity of instruments the problem of providing trained personnel for selection and maintenance has also increased. Technical men must frequently be used in a maintenance capacity for effective service. Unless there are enough instruments to warrant staffing the maintenance department with this caliber of personnel, the responsibility may be best transferred to those technical personnel operating the plant.

POLICIES WITH RESPECT TO CONTROL

Communications. Rapidly changing activities and need for integration of a diverse group in a complex effort make good communications a vital necessity in the maintenance engineering department. This includes not only rapid transmission of instructions and information but also the intimate working relationships developed by frequent informal contacts that can make a maintenance department a close-knit operating unit.

Most of the conventional forms of intraplant communication are useful to a maintenance engineering department. The extent to which the more costly and complex communications systems can be employed depends a great deal on the size and geographic layout of a plant. There are maintenance departments in large plants which utilize effectively a wide range of devices, from word of mouth, written notes, and telephone, to two-way radio and television. In addition to these tactical methods, meetings of individuals, either formal or informal, are a valuable means of transmitting instructions and information and developing a unified approach to problems.

The investment in improved communication can definitely be justified in terms of improved performance of the department. Cost of meetings, however, is more difficult to establish, and their true value more difficult to determine. Prepared agenda with provision for discussion or question-and-answer periods will help keep meetings on the track and pertinent to the business at hand.

A starting point in analyzing the problem of communications and the types to be used is a study of the sort of information to be transmitted and the amount of detail involved through these three major channels:

1. Up through the supervisory organization.
2. Down through the supervisory organization.
3. Laterally across the same level of organization.

Generally, all communications should be reduced to a minimum consistent with effective operation. It is also accepted that information should flow upward only as far as is necessary for effective action. Slower response frequently nullifies the value of higher-level judgment that might result from a flow of the information upward beyond this point. In addition, communication upward should be so handled that each level passes on only that information which is of *value* to the next level. Horizontal channels of communication should also be controlled to limit information to that necessary for effective cooperation between various sections of the maintenance group. In a small plant having only two or three levels between first-line supervision and the department head, and where most transactions can be handled by telephone or word of mouth, there is little problem. As the plant gets larger, with more intermediate levels of supervision, more procedural formality and greater specialization of duties develop. This evolution should be accompanied by clearly defined limits of authority for independent action at each level, with "action" communication up from any level limited to that on decisions outside its authority. If a foreman has a question concerning his work that can be answered by his supervisor, there is no need to involve the superintendent or plant engineer in the transaction.

Copies of order or performance reports are too often distributed to people who ignore them or at best scan them briefly, with no thought of retention. Detailed information is frequently passed to top levels where it is meaningless unless summarized. It would have been better to transmit only the summary. Indiscriminate requirement for approvals of instruction sheets, order blanks, requisitions, and correspondence can also clutter channels of communication and delay action. This problem is characteristic of fast-growing organizations and should be reviewed periodically. Flow diagrams for all written instructions, reports, and approval systems are helpful in focusing attention on unnecessary steps which increase the work load on the supervisory and clerical organization and delay execution of the work.

This "minimum flow" should naturally be tempered by recognition of the natural desire of people to know what is going on around them, with respect to their own work, that of other departments, and the company as a whole. For this reason it is important to include provision for passing this type of information to the satisfaction of the personnel involved. In most attitude surveys among first- and second-level supervision more dissatisfaction is evident with the amount of this type of information than with that required for performance of their work. The morale of supervision, which in turn is frequently reflected in the morale of the hourly group, can be considerably improved by the proper dissemination of general information for its own sake, making them feel as though they "belong."

There are at least two areas in the activities of a maintenance organization where effective use can be made of special advanced aids to communication. These are the transmission of work requests and job instructions from various sections of the plant to the proper coordinating group or work area, and the quick contact with personnel dispersed throughout a plant.

It is important that requests for maintenance work be promptly and accurately received at the dispatch center or at the individual shops. The advantages of written work requests should be thoroughly explored since they can be justified at much lower levels of operation than is evident at first glance. When used, these written requests can be transmitted by courier or plant mail service. Telephone orders are frequently used to initiate the work with a written confirmation following. This introduces considerable chance for error in word-of-mouth instructions, and there is a tendency to neglect confirmation once the work is performed. This in turn results in difficulty in accounting and repair cost analysis.

While more elaborate methods of work-request transmission may not be justifiable in small plants, their use has many advantages where the extent of operations warrants their installation. Two of these are message conveyor tubes running from suitable locations in the operating areas to a central dispatch center in the maintenance headquarters, and some type of remote-writing equipment such as the Telautograph or Western Union's "Intrafax," again with transmitting stations dispersed through the operating areas and the receiving station at the shops. The former, particularly over large areas, is an extremely costly installation, while the latter can be extended over considerably dispersed facilities at very little expense after the initial investment.

The use of written job instructions for all work, while it may seem troublesome, is basic to the development of many other control devices, particularly those for accumulation of information used to assist in improving operations and in accurate distribution of the resulting costs. General, or blanket authorizations are frequently sufficient for repetitive small items such as light-bulb replacement, routine lubrication, and miscellaneous valve packing, but even here, handling of these requests by operating departments will direct attention to trouble spots and allow more equitable distribution of accumulated charges.

A major problem in some maintenance organizations is that of keeping in touch with members of supervision and craftsmen dispersed over a wide area. The perfect solution to this problem has not yet been put in production. This would appear to be a lightweight, pocket-size, continuously operating two-way radio in the hands of every member of the maintenance department, but until this "Dick Tracy" two-way wrist radio is perfected, other means must suffice. The most common means of locating dispersed supervision is through a plant auto-call system. In a small plant this may be adequate, but as a plant grows and the system becomes more and more complex with blacked-out areas developing, this method becomes slow and unreliable. If each member of supervision checks out of a central point to a predetermined area, the auto-call system can be augmented by other telephone, but maintenance problems are usually such that a foreman may go from one area to another on a route that is impossible to predetermine. Two-way radio on maintenance vehicles has been very successful for groups working in the open or in areas that are within sound of a parked vehicle. Radio becomes less effective where craftsmen are occupied inside a building, out of hearing from a vehicle-borne receiving unit. An individual paging unit about the size of a package of cigarettes which can be carried on the person at all times is available today. In its present stage of development, however, this device depends upon an induced current necessitating special installations in each building covered. It has considerable value in compact, multistory plants, but where there are many smaller buildings through which the call system must operate the installation expense is rather high. Any maintenance department should consider the increase in supervisory efficiency that can be realized from quick contact with dispersed personnel and provide the best means that can be justified economically.

Use of Standard-practice Sheets and Manuals. There are many forms of standard-practice sheets, or standard job-instruction sheets, and instruction manuals used in maintenance departments. They are excellent devices for planning work, ordering materials, improving estimating accuracy, and training crafts personnel. Justification of cost of preparation and their ultimate effectiveness depend entirely on the particular problems of an individual plant.

A plant having a large number of identical machines or of machines having identical components which require a repetitive type of repair can justify more detailed standard-practice sheets than a plant with very little duplication of equipment or maintenance jobs. The need for standard-practice sheets also varies with the complexity of the repair and with the degree of skill and the experience of the men performing the work. Most equipment suppliers will provide excellent manuals which, although they do not cover all the detail found in a standard-practice sheet, cost little and provide much assistance for maintenance of the equipment. Every effort should be made to maintain a complete supply of these manuals available to the men directly involved in the maintenance of the equipment. These may be reproduced and divided to provide each craftsman with a copy if this seems advisable. A work measurement or incentive system based on summarized elemental standards makes some sort of standard-practice sheet a "must."

Most repetitive repairs can be profitably studied for the best approach, and a standard procedure developed. A typical standard-practice sheet should include specifications for the tools required, the necessary parts and supplies, a sufficiently detailed print of the equipment, indicating the components with sufficient clarity for the craftsman to follow the instructions, a step-by-step procedure with complete notes to cover any unusual or critical steps, and a close approximation of the time required. The development of these sheets is time-consuming and expensive and rapidly changing conditions and equipment may make them obsolete quickly.

Electrical- and piping-layout drawings for the plant should be available to craftsmen and their supervision for quick appraisal in execution of their work. These should be kept up to date and new work or changes in the field should be recorded by supervision in charge of the change on the master copy of the appropriate print. A great deal of time and expense can be saved by the availability of clear up-to-date drawings for use in planning repair, replacement, or modification of existing installations. This is particularly true of underground systems which cannot be easily traced.

Cost Control. The subject of cost control in the maintenance department is a complex and controversial subject. While it is not intended in this chapter to go into details of cost-control systems or budgets, some generalizations can be made regarding cost-control techniques, cost indexes, and performance checks which may be found useful in establishing the over-all cost policy of a maintenance organization.

Although many attempts have been made to arrive at a universal yardstick for financial performance of a maintenance department, it is generally accepted that there is no one index that can be used for this purpose. Each method of measurement has its exponents, but a close inspection reveals most of them to be tailored to the needs of a specific plant or company, or to be so indefinite as to be of little real value. In either case they are of little use as bases for comparison with other organizations. One of the major problems in establishing means of evaluation and comparison of performance for internal historical purposes or for comparison with other maintenance departments is the effect of company policy variables outside the control of the maintenance department. Differences in use of these and similar variables enter into maintenance-cost measurement, whether it is presented as a function of capital invested, pounds produced, dollars of manufacturing cost, power consumed, or per cent of total sales.

Any indexes used for internal control should incorporate factors within the control of those people held accountable for performance. For instance, for the lower levels of supervision, man-hours per unit of work, per job, or per department maintained can be directly influenced by the efficiency of the men performing the work and are therefore good measures of performance at this level. At the maintenance superintendent level the over-all cost of maintaining the plant in terms of the value of equipment maintained, or in terms of the goods produced or per cent of operating time available, can be influenced by good planning, good engineering, and good management, and these broader indexes may be applicable.

Top management, on the other hand, is generally interested only in that part of the total cost to manufacture that is chargeable to the maintenance department. They are not interested in high worker efficiency if poor engineering and poor planning result in higher over-all cost, nor are they interested in an extremely low maintenance cost with respect to the value of installed equipment if, as a result, the total cost of manufacturing is increased. Good management in a maintenance department should provide such indexes as are needed to permit evaluation of the performance of the department internally and provide top management with the information they need to assess maintenance performance of this function as part of the "big picture."

Some of the indexes that are commonly used are maintenance cost as a function of:

1. Value of the equipment maintained.
2. Pounds produced.
3. Total manufacturing cost.
4. Total conversion cost.
5. Power consumed.

Some other useful presentations are:

The ratio of labor cost to material cost in maintenance work.
The comparison of man-hours used to the level of the activity of the plant.
Downtime of equipment expressed as a per cent of total scheduled operating time.

Sometimes a formula, expressing a combination of two or more of the above relationships, is developed and accepted by a company as a more usable composite index. Some of these formulas take into consideration the value of the equipment, the rate of its utilization, and downtime chargeable to repairs.

A few companies have established work-measurement programs where it is theoretically possible to set a definite standard for maintenance costs at varying levels of activity and then compare actual performance against this standard. This type of comparison can frequently be misleading if carelessly set up. It is possible for it to indicate excellent performance in spite of excessive over-all maintenance costs. If properly administered and used for the purpose intended, such a standard can be extremely useful in maintenance management. Unfortunately, the overhead cost of most work-measurement programs detailed enough to be useful for this purpose is high and can be justified only by a large plant or by an industry having many similar plant operations. In this case a study by an independent industrial engineering firm may be practical.

In general, maintenance-cost trends are more important than the cost for any one short length of time. Although high and low peaks may occur monthly, for instance, if the trend of an index is downward, this change is more significant than the month-to-month variation. Most maintenance departments will find that no single index will be sufficient to evaluate their performance completely. A study of the trend of several indexes is more satisfactory.

Cost-control Systems. In selecting its cost-control system maintenance engineering should conform to the system that is in use in the plant it serves. It may be expedient to adapt this system to the particular needs of the maintenance department, but the plant-wide format should be used.

The purposes of a cost-control system include:

1. Equitable distribution of repair costs over the departments serviced.
2. A source of information necessary for sound administration of the maintenance department.
3. Compliance with legal requirements for taxes and earnings.
4. A source of information for the plant accounting group in its function of recording and reporting the financial position of the plant.

In establishing its cost-control system the maintenance group should keep these purposes in mind and solicit the cooperation of the accounting group in adapting the plant-wide program to maintenance needs, eliminating as much detail and duplication of effort as possible. Hand data processing should be minimized by the use of modern business machines whenever this can be justified.

One of the most effective cost-control systems is the conventional job-cost method which accumulates expense items for labor, supplies, and services on a specific job number which, in turn, is the liability of a specific department. This accumulated charge, together with overhead and fixed charges, then provides the basis for distribution of cost by the accounting department.

In cost control, as with all performance records, it is well to remember that the actual cost of recording information at its source is small compared with the cost of further processing and analysis of the information. For this reason it is well to record information in considerable detail at the source but to scrutinize its further use and analysis carefully to ensure the most economical data-processing system required for the cost-control plan in use. It is then possible to rearrange the processing to fit changes in cost-control systems without affecting the data-accumulation habits at the level of origin.

The subject of cost control is covered in more detail in another section. Regardless of the system selected it should be flexible enough to provide additional information that might be useful in resolving specific cost problems and should operate at minimum overhead cost.

Consideration of any policy for the operation of a maintenance department should be governed primarily by the effect the policy has on the mission of the maintenance department. This mission may be said to consist of provision for production of goods and/or services at minimum cost through minimum deterioration in value of its capital assets. A maintenance department can be justified only if it continually operates to assist the plant in attaining these over-all objectives.

Chapter 4

OPERATING PRACTICES MAINTENANCE CAN FOLLOW

By H. W. SHOCKLEY[1]
Chief Maintenance Consultant
Engineering Department
E. I. du Pont de Nemours & Co., Inc.
Wilmington, Del.

In this chapter, operating practices are discussed for the "existing plant," and for the "new, or added, plant."

EXISTING PLANT

A discussion of operating practices for the existing plant must deal with many items which, taken together, cover principles of work execution; cost control; engineered maintenance and standard practices; corrective maintenance, involving improved design and better materials of construction; and preplanning and measurement. The relationship of the individual items to the whole will be apparent.

Work Load. In adopting operating practices, it is necessary to determine the work load. It is calculated from records covering maintenance work, both major and minor, performed on all operating equipment and facilities for a considerable time and on service-to-operation jobs as well. In plants where minor construction is a function of the maintenance department, work load is also important because it involves personnel, equipment, tools, methods, and scheduling. In plants where capitalization cost per employee is high, it is in the interest of economy that central shops fabricate as much as possible of total requirements of maintenance and minor construction. So doing allows the use of better tools and methods as well as the better utilization of manpower.

Work-order Control. Work-order control, to bring about orderly execution of the work load—an essential of effective operating practice—presupposes: the use of a work- or repair-order system; that all work, major and minor, is covered; that such work is properly described; and that cross-order work affecting areas, shops, craft skills, and minor construction is covered by a cross order. (A cross order is the same as a regular order to any group receiving it.)

When these conditions are met, labor requirements to meet all demands of repair can be determined. The backlog requirements, both current and over-all, are indicated. Equipment requiring the greatest and costliest service is revealed. Indexes for improving work performance can be adopted.

[1] The author is now Management Specialist, Wilmington, Del.

Description of a work-order control is shown as Table 4-1. The work-order form (not shown) should provide space to cover job description, tools required, materials required, pertinent safety instructions, and number and amount of skills. So should the cross-order form. In those plants where preplanning of work is done by persons other than foremen, a separate form may be used to record this information. In either case the records of the work done must be sufficient for development and record purposes. The work-order form must also show charges, equipment records, and spaces for approval by operating and maintenance supervision based on plant requirements.

Blanket orders are permissible for some kinds of work. They are usually issued on a monthly or annual basis. As the coverage by preventive maintenance increases, the greater becomes the number of blanket orders. The greater the coverage of jobs by standard practices, the less the need for repetitious writing of formal orders.

Table 4-1. Standard Practice in Handling Work Orders

1. TITLE: Work-order control.
2. DEFINITION: Work-order control is a means whereby every type of maintenance job done, whether minor or major in scope, is definitely covered by a standard written form which shows that the work is needed, is adequately described, is properly approved, is issued by proper authority, and provides a record.
3. PURPOSE: To enable a maintenance foreman to analyze and schedule his work; to provide a means of scrutinizing jobs as to cost, necessity, size, etc., both before and after they are done. To assist the operating supervision in determining the necessity of the job and to give maintenance supervision the means to estimate and schedule the job according to best plant requirements.
4. SCOPE: Work-order control is secured through the use of four types of orders:
    a. A normal order uses a standard form. It is issued to cover nonrepetitive jobs requiring more than 4 man-hours. The responsibility for completion of the work rests with the foreman of the key craft involved.
    b. A cross order is a normal order issued by the responsible craft foreman to another.
    c. A blanket order is a standard or monthly order issued by the works engineering department and approved by operations, to cover a series of regular repetitive scheduled jobs.
    d. A patrol order is prepared on a separate form by an operating foreman and issued to an area-maintenance foreman, to cover substantially nonrepetitive jobs requiring less than 4 man-hours. It can also be used by craft foremen for small fill-in jobs.
5. RESULTS
    a. Provides a written contract to spend money or do work.
    b. Establishes a procedure where definite approvals are necessary.
    c. Offers a follow-up for progress and completion of the work.
    d. Utilizes records available of all work done as to labor and materials cost.

The patrol order, representing a record of work, was developed initially to be used within an area with a minimum of signatures. Usually it covered jobs with up to 4 man-hours of labor. The patrol order also has been found to be quite useful for work covering the craft skills. There are many small jobs which can be done on patrol orders, especially to fill in toward the end of the day in meeting a full day's schedule of work and keeping all personnel properly employed.

Having determined work-load requirements, and having developed a means for controlling work, it is essential that all lost-time factors be eliminated to ensure proper work execution. This is accomplished by daily scheduling as shown in Table 4-2 and weekly forecasting as shown in Table 4-3.

Scheduling and Forecasting. The initial approach to work scheduling is on a daily basis. By scheduling, supervision learns how close its estimated work in hours is to actual; the number of jobs to apply against manpower requirements; and the kinds and types of interruptions and their influence on scheduling effectiveness. On his schedule the foreman has a record of each day's work, which can be used as a basis for improvement and correction.

Weekly forecasting comprises full work quotas for all personnel in all crafts or groups. Many jobs affect a number of crafts; so it is essential that the work be properly coordinated. This coordination is established at a weekly meeting, usually presided over by a planning and scheduling engineer. Each maintenance foreman, both craft and area, comes to the meeting with work requirements for a full week's period for his personnel. Both operating and technical supervision also attend. At this meeting each foreman is concerned only with those jobs requiring assistance of other crafts for coordination and with priorities required for the jobs, as indicated by

Table 4-2. Standard Practice in Scheduling Maintenance Work

1. TITLE: Scheduling maintenance work.
2. DEFINITION: Fitting analyzed jobs into a daily schedule according to operating conditions, production schedules, manpower available, and availability of materials.
3. PURPOSE: To have available, for every person in each craft or group sufficient jobs to cover a day's work according to priority and analyzed as to labor, material, and tools required, and so arranged that on the completion of one job another is available.
4. SCOPE: The scheduling of maintenance work is done by the maintenance foreman assisted by a work-order control and scheduling clerk. Analyzed jobs are scheduled according to the personnel available and recorded on a daily schedule sheet made out in duplicate, which sheets are prepared for the following day's work by a fixed time of the previous afternoon. They are then approved by the general foreman. A red line is drawn under the last job recorded. Any job added to this sheet after general approval becomes an emergency job and is investigated as to cause by the planning and scheduling engineer.
5. RESULTS
    a. To minimize lost time in the doing of any maintenance job.
    b. To have available, for direct use, a daily record of each foreman's activities.
    c. To have a knowledge of causes of bad scheduling.
    d. To list all emergency jobs as to cause.
    e. To provide a means of training foremen relative to the duties and responsibilities of their jobs.
    f. To enable correlation of operating and maintenance activities.

Table 4-3. Standard Practice in Forecasting Maintenance Work and Minor Construction Jobs

1. TITLE: Forecasting maintenance or minor construction work.
2. DEFINITION: To plan major maintenance and minor construction jobs which have been preanalyzed for execution over a 1-week period based on work priorities, operating conditions, and available labor and material supply.
3. PURPOSE: To provide supervision with a comprehensive picture of work requirements greater than 1 day, thus enabling them to distribute their personnel for maximum results.
4. SCOPE: Preanalyzed maintenance and minor construction jobs of major importance are integrated into a single master schedule. This schedule is developed at a weekly meeting of maintenance, engineering, and operating supervision.
    At this meeting discussion centers on priorities, operating conditions, available mechanics, and job coordination where more than one craft is involved.
    The maintenance supervisor acts as the chairman and the master schedule is coordinated and distributed by the planning and scheduling engineer.
5. RESULTS
    a. Is a record of work for use in daily scheduling.
    b. Permits longer-term planning.
    c. Permits complete jobs, involving a number of crafts or groups to be properly planned.
    d. Permits better control of maintenance materials.
    e. Permits a more even distribution of maintenance work according to plant requirements.
    Each maintenance foreman establishes a week's schedule of preanalyzed major maintenance and minor construction jobs based on his total labor supply and considering minor and emergency labor requirements.

operating and technical supervision. Schedules are then determined, typed, and given to all concerned. These weekly schedules serve as a basis for daily scheduling for the following week for each foreman. To operating and technical supervision it is a schedule of when their work is to be done. At the end of each week any unfinished work is added to the next week's schedule, and the reason for its not being done is given.

Need for Outside Contractors. The need for outside contractors is based on the type of work undertaken, the extent of existing backlog requirements, and facilities or lack of them in the plant.   Painters, bricklayers, elevator inspectors, machine-tool repair men, sewer constructors, and the like, from the outside, are used to some extent in most plants.   As the backlog of work declines, or production schedules are reduced, it may be necessary to reduce the amount of this outside work.   Emphasis on service and seniority also prompts many plants to do a large portion of such work by their

Table 4-4. Duties and Responsibilities of the Planning-Scheduling Engineer

1. TITLE: Planning-scheduling engineer.
2. DEFINITION: A qualified engineer to assist in applying preventive and corrective maintenance and the use of the most effective procedures for the execution of maintenance and construction work.
3. PURPOSE: To institute, coordinate, and follow up procedures and methods required by a works engineering organization for optimum conditions of performance and cost.
4. SCOPE: The application and use of maintenance procedures, the most important of which are:
   a. Work-order procedure.
   b. Planning and scheduling.
   c. Equipment cost-card procedure.
   d. Job standardization.
   e. Budgetary control by direct, indirect, and general maintenance.
   f. Organization.
   g. Preventive maintenance.
   h. Corrective maintenance.
   i. Annual cost-reduction programs.
   j. The application of arrow-diagram planning.
   k. The classification of skills.
5. RESULTS: Assumes full responsibility for the use of maintenance procedures as outlined in the program for preventive and corrective maintenance and job standardization.

Table 4-5. Objectives and Procedures in Job Analysis

1. TITLE: Job analysis.
2. DEFINITION: The analysis of each maintenance job as to craft, material, tools, and methods, and the preparation of a workable estimate of time and manpower requirements.
3. PURPOSE: To train maintenance supervision in the various factors that affect proper job execution.   To have available for personnel doing the work the means of working effectively.   To have available for computing backlog, the estimated man-hours for completion of all approved jobs.
4. SCOPE: A maintenance foreman receiving a normal work order visits the location of the proposed work.   He analyzes the job as to the man-hours required by his own craft or group and enters this on the face of the order, noting also the work to be done by other crafts and groups to whom he issues a cross order.   In addition, he notes on the back of the second copy of the order form, the following: any additional description that will assist the person or persons doing the job; the general materials necessary; tools, either regular or special, that are not part of a standard tool kit; and any safety precautions.   If the material required to do his part of the job is not stores stock, it is his responsibility to see that it is ordered.   Cross orders are treated the same as normal orders by the foremen receiving them.   Blanket orders, being repetitive jobs, have been analyzed at the time of origin.   Patrol orders, because of the type of work involved, require no analysis by the foreman.
5. RESULTS
   a. To assist in the performance of maintenance work in a safe and accurate manner, with a minimum of classified personnel.
   b. To furnish proper tools, equipment, and materials.
   c. To utilize crafts and groups for optimum skill and proper scheduling.

own crews.   However, there probably will always be certain types of work that can be done much more quickly and cheaply by outside contractors.   It also must be kept in mind that fringe benefits increase overhead in the plant for each person employed.

The Planning and Scheduling Engineer.   It is difficult to overemphasize the importance of this individual in the control of maintenance work.   Table 4-4 gives the definition, purpose, scope, and results of the work of his job.

Job Analysis.   There are two approaches to job planning.   One, job analysis, is outlined in Table 4-5.   The definition shows that the analysis covers skills, materials, tools, methods, and the workable estimate of time required.   It is this type of analysis that reduces the lost-time factors in following a schedule of work.   It is obvious that this is a means to reduce lost time by having mechanics go to each job with full work requirements.   It does provide, however, that each foreman see each job; that he cover the requirements; and that he issue any cross orders required.   This is also essential for total and current backlog purposes.

Engineering Analysis.   The second phase of job planning is engineering analysis (see Table 4-6).   The difference between the two methods is "eliminating lost-time factors" vs. "applying the one best method of performance."   Preanalysis and some form of measurement may be added if desired.   Persons other than foremen must establish the job standard practices.   Practices are based on job study and include any factor of improvement that can be determined.

In applying engineering analysis to maintenance work, three important functions should be considered: who is to do it, how it is to be done, and what is necessary in the way of control before the work should be started.   Two of the weakest links in maintenance job performance are lack of methods and time measurement.   Simply studying a job and establishing its rate of performance based on present method represents

Table 4-6. Objectives and Procedures in Engineering Analysis

1. TITLE: Engineering analysis.
2. DEFINITION: The arrangement of the component parts of the job and the selection of correct materials, tools, equipment, supplies, and labor to determine the one best method of performance.
3. PURPOSE: To break down a job into its elemental operations in order to determine the possibilities of improvement relative to use, design, and methods, and to utilize the information secured to establish a standard of performance for practical use.
4. SCOPE: Jobs should be studied by individuals who understand how such an analysis can be made.   A process chart should be made of the resulting operations and studied from the standpoint of the use of the equipment, the cause of the repairs, the methods used and tools required.   From this a revised chart is made and discussed with operating and maintenance supervision.   Any development work required should be turned over to persons giving that service.   After all corrections or improvements have been made, it is issued as a standard operation sheet.
   Once engineering analysis is accomplished, very little job analysis is necessary.
5. RESULTS
   a. Permits the best known method of doing a job to be developed and utilized.
   b. Is a necessary step for maintenance measurement.
   c. Serves as a basis for training maintenance supervision in job improvement.   Is a basis for corrective maintenance.

but a small savings.   If time values are established by persons whose only training is time study, again the engineering approach is neglected.   The combination of job-methods engineers, trained in both engineering techniques and time study, is rare.   However, such a combination is necessary if real results are to be secured.   It must be remembered that all the improvement, independent of kind, is finally expressed in the time values.   Establishing such time values takes time and money.   Once established they will pay for themselves many times.

Arrow Diagramming.   The techniques of Arrow Diagramming, or critical path scheduling, as applied to planning, scheduling, and evaluating programs, are particularly applicable where projects are being developed.   There are eight steps to be considered in application:

1. The objectives in terms of ranges of quantity, quality, and timing.
2. The best course of action leading to the objectives in time and money.
3. External factors that might restrain the progress.
4. Feasible alternatives in terms of timing, manpower, and costs.
5. Elements that are most important in reaching objectives.
6. Ways to obtain assurance that resources are being assigned effectively at any time.
7. The evaluation of progress.
8. Effects this program has on other current work.

There are three important factors that govern the use of this technique:

1. It requires a thorough knowledge of maintenance and construction engineering, of their types of jobs and latest equipment and methods, and an ability to make correct estimates of the time required for doing jobs.
2. It is a means of scheduling by computer, which is becoming more necessary in all types of engineering work.
3. It allows a means whereby time and money can be evaluated in selecting what is best for the job in mind.

(*Note:* Critical path scheduling [arrow diagramming] is the subject of another chapter.)

Material Control. There are many good material-control systems available. The plant should make certain that any plan for good maintenance is not blocked by poor

Table 4-7. Objectives and Procedures in Maintenance Inspection

1. TITLE: Maintenance inspection.
2. DEFINITION: Inspection of plant equipment, buildings, and facilities is a procedure to determine the necessity for repair, either minor or major.
3. PURPOSE: To prevent unscheduled interruptions to operating equipment and undue deterioration of buildings and facilities due to any cause.
4. SCOPE: An inspection procedure operates in two ways:
    a. Visual inspection—observing equipment in operation to determine potential breakdowns.
    b. Shutdown inspection—to determine the wear and general condition when equipment is not operating.
    In addition, inspection is necessary for all parts of an industrial plant, such as buildings, roofs, and lines, and might also be called visual inspection, although it may be done at less frequent intervals. In establishing an inspection procedure, all buildings and equipment should be listed and analyzed as to whether they should be inspected on a visual or shutdown basis and the frequency established.
5 RESULTS
    a. Establishes a basis for a high standard of maintenance.
    b. Determines needed repairs to plant buildings and equipment.
    c. Prevents exorbitant job costs. Contributes to the job consciousness of operating and maintenance supervision.
    d. Permits more continuous production.
    e. Reveals quality of maintenance work.
    f. Permits forecasting of normal maintenance jobs.
    g. Contributes to a balanced scheduling of maintenance work and leveling of maintenance costs.
    h. Forestalls breakdown of equipment.

material control. There are a few policies that can be followed to assist in control: (1) Both maintenance and minor construction groups should draw materials from plant stores. (2) For both large maintenance and minor construction jobs, separate purchasing lists should be made up. (3) If both area and central stores exist, all should be controlled by one group. (4) Special purchases by operating-area supervisors should be discouraged. (5) Physical inventories of all materials should be made at least once a year for both central and area locations. (6) If more than one plant uses similar pieces of equipment, at least annual comparisons for minimum stores requirements should be made.

Related to stores is salvage. A study should be made of actual cost of reworking parts. In many cases, reworking will cost many times as much as a new item.

Inspection. Inspection, covered by Table 4-7, is a responsibility of each member of maintenance supervision. Whether it covers an industrial job that is completed, a major overhaul to be made, or preparation for routine tasks, proper inspection is essential to quality control. Preventive maintenance, also, is concerned with inspection, as will be seen later.

Visual inspections are made while the equipment is operating. They have for their purpose the uncovering of such potential breakdown conditions as failure of small parts, faulty lubrication, and improper operation. Some repair conditions can be found by simply observing, listening to, and feeling the equipment at frequent intervals for such obvious faults as change in operating speed, or overheating. Shutdown inspections are those requiring that equipment be taken out of service and disassembled to the extent necessary to make a thorough inspection. Shutdown inspection intervals are based on accurate records of repair costs and production losses.

In establishing either class of inspection, definite schedules should be established.

Inspection also determines what work can or should be done during the day, whether shift work is required, and how much.

Shift Requirements. While it is obvious that plants working on a 24-hr, 7-day-week basis can tolerate little downtime, experience has shown that, if maintenance jobs are properly planned and scheduled, or preplanned and measured, a minimum of shift work will be necessary. Studies have indicated that:

1. It has been to the plant's advantage to have a minimum of all-around mechanics on shifts.
2. It has been found economical in some plants to eliminate all maintenance shift workers even though a premium must be paid to mechanics brought in during shift periods if breakdowns occur.

It is uneconomical to work on a breakdown maintenance basis.

Costs—Direct, Indirect, General. The preferred maintenance-cost plan is one that involves direct, indirect, and general charges. Budgets established on this basis are more reliable then those based on other plans.

Direct costs are those incurred in the maintenance of operating equipment and auxiliaries. They therefore have some relation to production schedules and are proportioned as such to some extent.

Indirect maintenance costs cover:

1. Rearrangements when improvement is indicated, whether in process or better handling.
2. Replacements when redesign, different materials of construction, etc., are involved.
3. New work when not capitalized.
4. Service to operations or other items affecting the maintenance department over which it has little or no control.

General maintenance costs include those for buildings, roads, facilities, air conditioning, etc.—in fact, any maintenance that does not directly affect process operations.

While the ratios of maintenance costs vary, they will be, approximately: direct, 70 to 75 per cent; indirect, 15 to 35 per cent; general, 5 to 15 per cent. Indirect has the greatest variation. Therefore, it is of great benefit to:

1. Review need and estimated costs for such work.
2. Have the orders closely scrutinized.
3. Have high levels of supervision responsible for approvals.

A plant making corrective improvement might have a justifiable high percentage of indirect work.

Once the definitions of direct, indirect, and general maintenance costs have been established, all maintenance work, regardless of kind, degree, or amount, is covered by the proper type of order. When it is costed, the per cent of each class of maintenance work is easily found.

Complete records of the three types of costs, as well as nature of jobs, must be maintained for proper corrective analysis. If a worthwhile budget is to be established, these costs are essential.

Budgetary Control. In budgeting, a review of the work covered by specific costs is necessary. It should be a simple matter to determine the feasibility of spending maintenance money, once production and maintenance conditions have been established and are reviewed at proper intervals.

Preventive Maintenance. There should always be a preventive-maintenance program. In a single-shift plant it can be carried out easily. When a plant is operating 24 hr, 7 days a week, it is up to the maintenance organization to utilize all its knowledge, ingenuity, and skill to take advantage of any process shutdowns.

A study should be made of the production cycle for scheduled interruptions, even though short. Small jobs may be done.

Whether continuous or batch process is used, downtime should be taken advantage of for inspection and upkeep of process equipment.

Table 4-8. Procedures in Practice

1. Capitalization
   Number of employees in maintenance
   Number of normal repair orders per month
   Causes of need for maintenance (corrosion or abrasion)
   Products manufactured
   Type of operation
   Total plant personnel
2. Crew Classification
   Application
   Maintenance
   Job evaluation
3. Work Order Procedure
   Normal
   Patrol
   Blanket
4. Control of Maintenance Man-hours
   Normal orders estimated
   Backlog chart
   Five-point method of control
   Defined patrol for foremen
   Measurement of estimating
5. Planning and Scheduling
   Daily schedule sheets
   Workman's racks
   Clocks
   Log sheets
   Job analysis—tools—materials
   Standard operation sheets
   Emergency investigations
   Emergency classification
   Efficiency of scheduling
   Tabulation equipment
   Weekly forecasting
   Arrow diagram planning
6. Organization
   Areas
   Crafts
   Minor construction
   Job analysis
   Methods engineer

Project engineer
Foreman-mechanic ratio
7. Equipment Cost Card Procedure
   Breakdown of costs by departments and accounts
   Building segregation
   Machine segregation
   Cards by buildings and facilities
   Cards by mechanical equipment
   Cost segregation by direct, indirect
   Periodic summary of results
8. Inspection
   Visual
   Shutdown
   Master sheet of shutdowns
   Standard patrol of visual
   Repair order by inspection
9. Direct, Indirect, and General Costs
   Definition
   Application
   Use
10. Budgetary Control
    Normal
    Direct, indirect, general
11. Materials Control
    Inventory control of stores
    Disbursement
    Purchasing
    Work-order control (costing)
    Delivery to maintenance (control)
12. Forecasting
    Normal orders
    Blanket orders
    Painting
    Roofing repairs
    Shutdown inspections
13. Improvements
    Job methods
    Tools and equipment
    Training (formal plan)
    Corrective maintenance
    Costs

Stocking a greater number of spare parts as insurance items should be considered.

The application of an intensive improvement program involving replacement, redesign, better materials of construction, and better methods of making necessary repairs should be studied; the program should be placed in operation on an annual basis under the supervision of a competent engineer.

Experience indicates that only in highly corrosive operations are services or equipment actually used until failure necessitates their repair or replacement. When so used, it is only because methods or materials of construction are not available to give greater operating life.

Similar considerations are given to the use of personnel on shift. In operations requiring continuity, there are types of maintenance or service-to-operation work that must be done to keep process equipment functioning over a 24-hr period. In many cases these service-to-operation jobs require special skills.

In other cases shift mechanics are used to make unnecessary the acquisition of more shop space, machine tools, or other equipment, which would be necessary if all work were done on the regular day shift.

In cases where maintenance work is properly controlled, shift requirements are minor, having been eliminated entirely in some instances.

Power-plant Maintenance. Usually, the responsibility for maintenance as a power-plant function is in large power plants. This is because of the number of mechanics, the skills involved, and the type of operating equipment. In small plants only two or three mechanics are required. They may be part of the regular maintenance group reporting to the maintenance organization. This arrangement allows for greater flexibility in the use of skills. In the power plant, repairs are either routine or overhaul. Methods studies can be made of most jobs. Preplanning and measurement easily fit in.

Table 4-8 is a check list by which to determine whether all engineering requirements are in use. If also affords an excellent means of comparing plants within the same company.

NEW, OR ADDED, PLANT

Because information concerning application of maintenance principles has been given in the first part of the chapter, the discussion of new, or added, plant involves basic data requirements only.

Recommendations. Recommendations covering tools, equipment, service facilities, organization, lubrication, and gasket and piping specification are made in the form of predesigned data and sketches, specifications, and memoranda. They should provide the new plant with adequate equipment and facilities to maintain if effectively.

Investigation. *Orientation.* Become familiar with the processes and equipment. Make lists of equipment to be served, based on process and productive capacity.

Developing Work Load. Tabulate the number, type, location, and cost of operating equipment, buildings, and facilities, taking the information from the project estimate. Reuse these data as a basis for equipment records. Determine the probable kind and frequency of repairs for equipment, basing conclusions on past maintenance experiences at similar plants. If new processes, put down arbitrary frequencies and kinds of repair.

Use maintenance cost as per cent of capital investment from previous experience to forecast probable annual maintenance costs for the new plant. Translate these costs into labor and material, and the labor cost into required personnel. If data from plants having similar processes are not available, maintenance costs will have to be developed from scratch.

Divide the maintenance work load of the plant into area and shop requirements. Usually a large amount of the work, particularly fabrication, for all areas can be done at a common location.

The principle of having one combined shops building, located centrally among the areas, with area-maintenance shops located as required, may be most effective and economical. The combined shop handles the large and expensive maintenance jobs. The area shops handle the small repetitive jobs peculiar to their areas. As much work as possible is done in the areas.

Make a survey of commercial shop facilities and industrial supply houses in the proposed plant area. Show how extensive supplies stored at the plant must be and what outside shop facilities are available. This information can be taken into consideration in the development of storage space and plant facilities.

Developing a Maintenance Organization. An organization is planned to provide the number of wage-roll and supervisory personnel required to maintain the plant effectively. Organization charts for similar plants are used as guides for establishing responsibilities, functions, and classes of personnel. The classes and number of wage-roll personnel are determined from the indicated work load, and estimated annual maintenance costs.

Developing Major Machine-tool Requirements. (1) Combined shops. Machine-tool shop equipment and cutting-tool recommendations are based upon a review of work-load conditions and plant requirements, the facilities available in the new plant area, and the latest methods and techniques for maintaining plant equipment. (2) Area shops. Machine-tool equipment, and hand-power-tool recommendations are made for area shops based on the kinds of jobs to be done in each area. The extent to which disassembly and assembly of major equipment can be done in the areas has an important bearing on tool requirements.

Developing Space Requirements. 1. Combined shops and stores. Space requirements for maintenance shops are dependent upon the amount and size of equipment and facilities to be housed, the type of work to be done, and the number of personnel that will work on them. Adequate space for proper handling, work storage, and material storage must be included.

Certain crafts perform a high percentage of their work in locations other than their shops. For example, riggers, electricians, instrument mechanics, millwrights, and welders have many jobs which can or must be done in the field. When the approximate space for crafts has been determined, the shops are arranged functionally in the combined shops and stores building. The shops which assist each other most frequently in the execution of maintenance work are located as near each other as possible.

The combined shops building usually is divided into bays. An overhead crane services the entire width and length of shops working area. Shops such as machine, sheet metal, assembly and disassembly, which have the greatest use for a crane are located in the crane bay. Other shops can be arranged functionally in the remaining space along with the tool crib, shop offices, and service facilities. Aisles should be provided giving access to each shop from the inside. Building design gives them accessibility from the outside.

Templets and three-dimensional scale models of machine tools and equipment may be used to make a scale layout and arrangement of combined shops and stores. It should give most convenient service to and from the stores area.

Placing carpenter, paint, and sandblast shops at the end of the combined shops and stores building, or at another location entirely, keeps the main shops cleaner, thereby prolonging the life of many tools and permitting better housekeeping.

Good planning permits bulk materials such as pipe, sheet metal, and bar stock, to be stored in the main stores area near the shops they serve. Remaining stores stock items, including spare parts and extra machinery, also can be kept in the main stores area. Lumber storage or bulk articles can be stored adjacent to the areas they serve.

2. Area shops. Space requirements for any area shop should provide adequate space for the proposed number of mechanics, necessary facilities and equipment, offices, tool crib, and material and oil storage. Service facilities should be provided. A monorail with a hoist running full length of the shop may be beneficial.

Space and facilities for a small electrical test bench should be provided in one corner of the area shop. This may apply also to instrument testing and repairing.

It may prove beneficial to locate concrete pads with all service requirements on the outside, adjacent to each area shop. These pads can be used for cleaning equipment before it is transported within the shop. Housekeeping in the shops will be greatly improved by having equipment precleaned. Cleaning services such as steam, air, and water, as well as a drain, can be provided at each pad.

Lubrication Specifications. When 90 per cent of the equipment has been selected, and blueprints are available, lubrication charts should be drawn up. They include a list of equipment requiring lubrication by unit number, manufacturer, and lubricant. The charts provide implicit instruction as to what lubricant to use; and they provide a means for the plant maintenance department to establish its lubrication schedule.

Packing and Gasket Specifications. Most original drawings indicate the gasketing or packing required. The packing-gasket specifications prepared during construction or immediately thereafter provide the maintenance personnel with proper material as well as sizes. Store stock can be established, and flanges or stuffing boxes do not have to be measured.

Garage, Ground, and Labor. Space requirements can cover automotive repair shop; fire-truck storage; safety-equipment issue and storage, grounds, and labor equipment storage; office; conference room; services; and car-wash stall.

Powerhouse Maintenance Shop. Space should be provided during the design stages of the building, allowing ample space for major tools, power tools, hand tools, small parts, and special spare parts.

Developing Specifications for Machine Tools and Equipment. Specifications, prepared by competent individuals, should be sufficiently general to permit vendors to submit quotations on comparable equipment. The particular make and model of tool described in the specification usually correspond to the current plant's preference. However, price and availability must be considered.

Specifications for electrical equipment should be reviewed and approved by the electrical section.

Quotations are received and decisions are made by procurement personnel and the plant engineering group. Purchase orders are executed according to the normal procedure.

Procurement of storage equipment, such as shelving and cabinets, can be facilitated by sales representatives who will advise as to amount and type required. Specifications are prepared and quotations requested. Selection is made in the manner described for machine tools.

When the specifications for major tools have been completed, specifications for tool-crib requirements can be drawn up, and purchases made.

Developing Spare-parts and Extra-machinery Requirements. Recommendations for spare parts and extra machinery are made for the entire plant, area by area. Electrical equipment and instruments can be handled by electrical and instrument design groups. Power-plant spares can be a responsibility of the power group. After a thorough review and consolidation of recommendations, lists are transformed into purchase requisitions, spare-part drawings are requested from manufacturers, and orders are placed.

The Use of Technical Assistance. The maintenance organization requires staff technical assistance, if the plant is to have continuous operation at low maintenance cost and improve its processes at the same time. In operations, the field of technical assistance lies in quality and yield improvement; development of better operating techniques; and coordination of sales, production, and operating standards.

As a comparison, in maintenance we utilize the same approach by determining through inspections the need for repairs, and a basis for establishing standards of quality for completed work. By coordinating many smaller jobs into one major overhaul, downtime is reduced and better maintenance performance secured by most effective methods, tools, and skills. Through the utilization of maintenance repair costs, a basis is secured for both machine development and improvement of maintenance materials. All this work can be coordinated into an engineering planning and scheduling section.

Use of Cost Indexes. When the maintenance labor and material rose 500 per cent from 1913 to 1954, it became obvious that there was advantage in using cost indexes. Each plant can prepare its own. However, for comparison on an annual basis, the *Engineering News-Record* Construction Index will be helpful.

Maintenance Engineering. Experience indicates that the duties and responsibilities of line supervision are exacting. If preplanning of jobs, investigations of emergency conditions for correction, establishing inspection and overhaul schedules, studying equipment overhauls for improvement and materials betterment, and the remaining phases of improved maintenance conditions and costs are also to be their responsibilities, either repairs or improvement will suffer. It therefore becomes necessary that additional technical assistance be made available.

Selection of Engineers. Engineers who perform the staff functions suggested should be graduate engineers or have equivalent technical education, have a minimum of

2 years' plant experience, and have an open mind and be willing to work with others and share their thoughts and opinions.

Use of Methods Engineers and Work Covered. Equipment-cost records are a means of recording repairs according to building, equipment, and facilities. They are numbered for simplification. They represent all types of maintenance costs applied against these numbers. Analysis of these costs can be used for both preventive and corrective purposes. Preventively, they indicate when frequencies of inspection and overhaul schedules can be established. Correctively, analysis by maintenance cost per cent of investment, and by labor and material ratio, indicates whether correction or replacement should be made, either in whole or in part, and whether correction should be in the form of methods, materials of construction, or design.

In order to operate a plant with a minimum of personnel, it is necessary that: (1) Electrical controls and mechanical improvements be coordinated under a central control. (2) Both craft skills and technical assistance be available if production goals and yields are to be secured.

Chapter 5

REPORTS FROM MAINTENANCE—
TO MANAGEMENT
AND INTERDEPARTMENTAL

By Jack F. Thornton
District Engineer—Oklahoma District
Exploration and Production Department
Phillips Petroleum Company
Oklahoma City, Oklahoma

Reports to management are intended to keep management so well informed that it can carry out its assigned task of coordinating and controlling all plant activities toward maximum over-all effectiveness. The importance and variety of reports from maintenance to management, and to other departments and services, depend upon their value as contributions to the objective of transmitting worthwhile information.

The term "maintenance" is intended to include, specifically:

1. The line maintenance organization engaged in maintenance inspection, preventive maintenance, repair, overhaul, minor construction, and salvage. (The generation and distribution of plant utilities are maintenance responsibilities in many plants.)
2. The maintenance engineering section, whose activity is limited, essentially, to maintaining the equipment in optimum economic condition. (Process design, mechanical design, and construction involved in any but minor capital expenditures are excluded.)
3. The industrial engineering function.
4. The planning and scheduling section, along with those staff services usually set up as an integral part of the maintenance organization.

Based on this definition, the departments and other services with a significant relationship to maintenance are operating, accounting, and stores-purchasing.

The objective of any maintenance activity is to minimize the manufacturing cost of the product without sacrificing quality or worker safety by the economical application of men, tools, and materials to protect facilities and increase productivity. But the measure of attainment of such an objective necessarily is affected by factors beyond maintenance control. For this reason, the operations-maintenance relationship is of prime importance. Plant management must clearly define and assign the related responsibilities.

The maintenance department must be responsible for maintaining the facilities in good operating condition at the lowest unit cost; must assist and guide operations in establishing an economic level of repair; must make repairs at intervals required for the most efficient operation and in a manner which presents minimum interference with operations; and must ensure that emergency work is converted to planned work by anticipating it.

The operating department must realize the profit potential of its contribution to good maintenance service by knowing the performance and condition of facilities to anticipate work in advance, scheduling shutdowns and overhauls a long time in advance, authorizing repairs and describing them clearly in writing, and establishing realistic priorities and reasonable completion requirements by watching operations closely to detect and anticipate unsatisfactory conditions.

PRIORITY (EMERGENCY WORK) REPORT

FOR WEEK ENDING _____ 8-20

ITEM	DATE	W. O. NO.	DESCRIPTION	WRITTEN BY	MANHOURS	OVERTIME
46	8-13-64	12708	Repair B. F. Pump	F. P. J.	20	8
46	8-15-64	12722	Replace Cplg. #2 Turbine	F. P. J.	2	0
52	8-17-64	12844	Replace Bad Valve	O. N. G.	4	0
55	8-15-64	12803	Motor Starter #1262	O. G. E.	2	2
55	8-18-64	12817	Repair M. V. #10 Feed	E. G. O.	8	0

TOTAL MANHOURS AVAILABLE	840
MANHOURS ON EMERGENCY WORK	36 4. 3%

FIG. 5-1. Priority report.

The following reports from maintenance to management and to the other departments are important only to the extent that assigned duties are understood and responsibility is assumed for successful completion. Any report should be primarily the tool of the department which originates it. So the primary purpose of these reports is for the maintenance manager to control the portion of the business for which he is responsible. The objective in compiling the data is to search out areas needing corrective action and to facilitate control by the transmission of information.

PRIORITY REPORT

To: Plant Management and Operations

OBJECTIVE: To improve the effectiveness of scheduling maintenance work.

The priority report, Fig. 5-1, shows the number of work orders received weekly (or monthly if the emergency and overtime work situation is respectable) broken down by operating units into priority classifications. The term "operating unit" is used here to indicate the extent of responsibility of operating supervisors. The intent is to show (1) who is responsible for emergency work, (2) whether the emergency demands are realistic and justified, and (3) to show the corrective action required. Usually, work is separated into three degrees of urgency:

1. Emergency: Work that must be done immediately to
   a. Prevent loss of production.
   b. Prevent serious damage to equipment.
   c. Correct an extreme safety hazard.   (Work in this classification takes precedence over all other work.)
2. Urgent: Work that must be completed as soon as possible with normal planning and scheduling.   Such work usually is scheduled to start within 24 to 48 hr after receipt of the order.   It can be defined as nonemergency work which shows a requested completion date of not more than 3 days after date of the work order.
3. Normal: The bulk of maintenance work.   It may be delayed for more than 48 hr. It is scheduled in the light of other operating requirements and the availability of maintenance manpower for maximum utilization.

The priority report often includes data on maintenance overtime.   Emergency work is not always overtime, but the analysis of priorities should assist in the establishment of a consistent policy to guide the use of emergency on No. 1 priority work orders.   It is customary that anyone originating an emergency work order should be prepared to justify overtime.   This definition of emergency work, when enforced, goes a long way in controlling unrealistic use of No. 1 priority work orders.

Emergency work is costly work done without benefit of planning and scheduling. It is important to know the hours involved or the percentage of hours unplanned, which will vary from plant to plant.   What it should be for a specific plant is strictly a matter of economics.   The purpose is to control, in the interest of least unit cost. No control should cost more than it saves.   If it costs more to reduce the emergency work-order man-hours than to sustain the losses due to emergency work, a negative profit contribution has been made.   Only realistic analysis can tell what the optimum amount of emergency work is for a specific plant or unit.

Emergency work expressed as a percentage of total man-hours from week to week will indicate gains or losses in maintenance effectiveness.   The control of emergency work is a joint responsibility of maintenance and operation.   Priority reports are furnished to plant management to advise how well the joint task is being accomplished, to coordinate efforts when required, and to see that desired results are achieved.

SCHEDULE COMPLIANCE REPORT

To: Plant Management and Operating Departments
OBJECTIVE: To measure effectiveness of planning and scheduling.

This report (Fig. 5-2) shows two measurements:

1. The man-hours scheduled, by crafts, as a whole number and as a percentage of the available man-hours.   This measurement, primarily, is maintenance control information.   To be totally effective, planning and scheduling maintenance work must be applied to all maintenance people.   It is easy to cheat and procrastinate on this report.   Resorting to blanket work orders and the assumption that work is planned and scheduled under a term such as "miscellaneous clean-up" or "minor repairs in the boiler house" can make the per cent of scheduled work appear to be much higher than it actually is.   Considerable preventive maintenance is done on blanket or continuous work orders.   This is the common solution for handling numerous small operating inspections.   The use of check lists for this type of work is assurance that the inspecting mechanic is being assigned a full day's work.
2. The man-hours scheduled, by crafts or units, compared to the man-hours actually worked as scheduled.   This report answers the question, "How realistic is the

schedule, and to what extent is it adhered to?" The daily data become evident in the late afternoon meeting of the foremen and the planner. Emergency work, poor estimates, and unforeseen circumstances reduce the per cent of compliance.

SCHEDULE COMPLIANCE REPORT

The following summarizes how the work schedule was followed by the Electrical Section on Wednesday, August 19.

W. O. NO.	UNIT	TOTAL HRS. SCHED.	HRS. WKD.	HOURS IN COMPLIANCE	HOURS NOT IN COMPLIANCE
32519	22	8	1	1	- 7
33470	66	5	0	0	- 5
36490	28	4	2	2	- 2
36997	53	1	0	0	- 1
34895	66	2	0	0	- 2
36981	66	14	16	14	+ 2
36738	10	8	0	0	- 8
37199	68	16	24	16	+ 8
37176	29	16	16	16	0
37068	29	16	0	0	-16
36832	68	2	8	2	+ 6

JOBS WORKED NOT ON SCHEDULE

W. O. NO.	UNIT		HRS. WKD.	HOURS IN COMPLIANCE	HOURS NOT IN COMPLIANCE
70710	71 (Clean Shop)	-	5	0	+ 5
33635	29	-	8	0	+ 8
TOTALS		**92**	**80**	**51**	

PERCENT COMPLIANCE WITH SCHEDULE—63.7%

SCHEDULED JOBS NOT WORKED ON

W. O. NO.	UNIT	DESCRIPTION OF WORK	REASON NOT WORKED
33470	66	Training Program	Did not attend— Program called off.
36997	53	Smith Meters at Truck L. R.	Electrician to be used on call only— was not called.
34895	66	Check Batteries	Did not do. This is a routine job to be done as time allows.
36738	10	Revision to Shutdown System	Work order was not clear as to what was to be done— spent most of day getting lined out on job and determining material requirements.
37068	29	Shutdown Work	One man was off that was supposed to work on this job, the other man was sent to assist on W. O. #37199.

Fig. 5-2. Schedule compliance report.

It never will be 100 per cent; 85 to 90 per cent is respectable. The importance of this percentage lies in the corrective action. Corrective action, in turn, depends on the causes of noncompliance on an individual work-order basis.

Some plants add another feature to this report, of great interest to the operating department. All normal (excluding emergency) work orders show a required completion date.   The daily work schedule shows a letter L (meaning "late") after each work order which is running late.   The number and percentage of work orders not meeting the required or requested completion time are periodically reported. Obviously, this puts maintenance on the spot, but the greatest benefit from the information is the consideration of time requirements by operations and much more realistic completion requests.

BACKLOG REPORT

To: Plant Management and Operating Departments
OBJECTIVE: To summarize the backlog of work available to the maintenance forces to level out the work load and best utilize manpower.

The backlog report (Fig. 5-3) is based on an accumulation of authorized low-priority work orders matched with manpower requirements.   By comparing the manpower

WEEKLY FORCE AND BACKLOG REPORT							
PREPARED_____ FOR WEEK OF_____ THROUGH_____	TOTAL	LABORERS	MECHANICS	ELECT.	INST.	CARPENTERS	PAINTERS
A. TOTAL HOURLY MEN IN SECTION							
B. EXPECTED ABSENCES AND SCHEDULED VACATIONS							
C. ASSIGNED TO NONSCHEDULED WORK							
D. MAN-DAYS AVAILABLE (A-B-C) X 5							
AUTHORIZED WORK BACKLOG AVAILABLE FOR SCHEDULING (MAN-DAYS)							
E. WORK ORDERS DATED FOR THIS WEEK							
F. EST. NEW WORK ORDERS DATED FOR THIS WEEK							
G. TOTAL WORK DATED FOR COMPLETION THIS WEEK							
H. WORK ORDER NOT DATED THIS WEEK– CAN BE SCHEDULED							
I. TOTAL AUTHORIZED AVAILABLE WORK FOR WEEK (G & H)							
J. BACKLOG–WEEKS (J/D)							

FIG. 5-3. Backlog report.

requirement with the manpower available, one can arrive at a backlog expressed in days or weeks.   Obviously, the backlog must be broken down by crafts if it is going to mean anything.   Ideally, the backlog in each craft should be about 4 to 6 weeks in order most effectively to level out the work and best utilize manpower.   However, any arbitrary figure for the size of a backlog must be considered in view of the attendant circumstances.

A small backlog can indicate that needed maintenance and repair work is not being recorded by operations and the information transmitted to maintenance.   Or it could mean that the facilities are in good condition, maintenance is not needed, and maintenance manpower is at too high a level.   The trend of the backlog information is more significant than any single weekly figure.

Backlog information must be coupled with periodic tours of all plant facilities by responsible maintenance and operating supervisors.   The experienced eye can pretty well determine general condition of equipment and quality of housekeeping.

The extent of preventive maintenance bears significantly in backlog analysis. Future, scheduled PM should be included in the backlog only to the extent of that portion which can be done within the backlog period.   A month's schedule of 160 hr of PM inspection for one inspector is really a backlog of only 2 man-weeks, when the particular craft backlog is about 2 weeks.   Similarly, construction work that cannot be scheduled until the following month, when material will arrive, has no business in a short-term backlog report.

To: MANPOWER FORECAST REPORT
               Plant Management and Operating Departments
OBJECTIVE: To permit future manpower planning by comparing known and estimated
               work load with available manpower.

The manpower forecast (Fig. 5-4) is maintenance management's over-all control tool.   It is through this report that maintenance accomplishes the most important

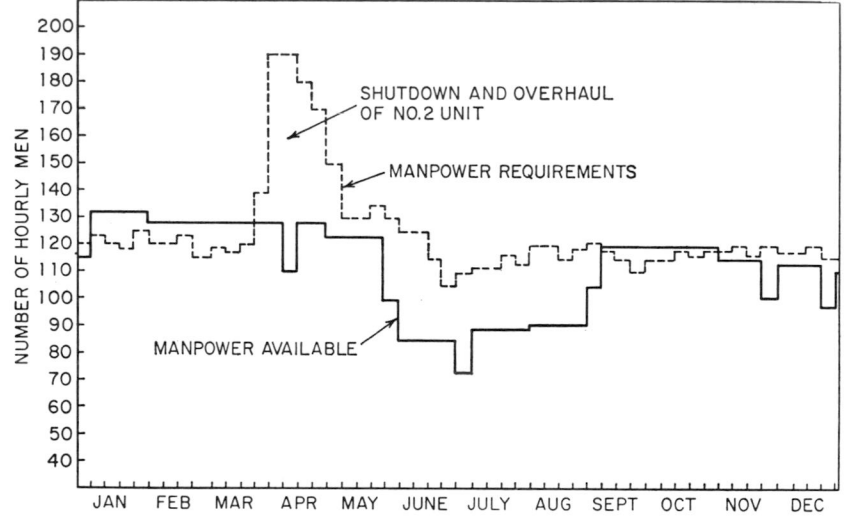

FIG. 5-4. Manpower forecast report.

part of its own administration, the continual balancing of work force and work load. The data are a combination of the backlog and a projection of the weekly manpower force report.   The manpower force report is not a report to plant management, but is a maintenance control device.   It is supplied weekly for information only, and reports manpower quotas, total manpower, manpower available for scheduling, and man-hours actually scheduled.   It also breaks down the man-hours scheduled into the types of work being done, which provides an indication of the PM progress.   It also shows the amount of construction and special work, such as turnarounds.

The manpower forecast is a chart or graph with a continuous calendar by weeks as the "X" axis and numbers of men as the "Y" axis.   It is compiled weekly and extended on tracing paper.   It is reproduced periodically (usually every 4 weeks) and released as a current report.   Thus the manpower forecast, so far as the past is concerned, is merely a graphic compilation of the weekly force reports.   But the purpose is to enable maintenance management to look into and plan for the future.

The recorded past history, along with known probable future plans by management and operations, is the basis on which situations requiring corrective action can be planned for before they happen.   It enables foreseeing graphically the future man-power requirements compared with the manpower available.   The planner's experi-ence and judgment play a most important part in the accuracy of the manpower forecast.

The forecast usually is drawn up for a year in advance.   With some experience, the accuracy of the forecast becomes almost unbelievable.   Nevertheless, it is still an estimate and is subject to revision every few weeks.   Such a forecast is the basis for vacation scheduling, turnaround timing, and other long-range planning.

The successful manpower forecast makes use of the fact that a known percentage of maintenance work can be flexibly scheduled.   It enables maintenance to advise management concerning such facts as the need for additional men several months in advance.   By the same token, it gives notice far in advance of any surplus manpower.

In addition to the regular, scheduled reports described, several other reports usually are necessary at irregular intervals to manage the maintenance function properly. The ones described are the basic control reports, intended to make planning and scheduling routinely effective.   When this interim goal is reached, additional steps to improve maintenance are in order.   When a day's work for every man is being scheduled, the productivity of the work force and methods for measuring and improv-ing work performance should be looked into.   This leads to investigation of work methods, work simplification, work sampling, and similar techniques which are described in other chapters.

Reports are essential in maintaining a plant at its optimum level.   The most commonly needed in the average plant have been mentioned.   This does not imply that all are justified in all plants.   Reports have a way of multiplying toward the point where maintenance supervisors and their personnel spend so much time in a blizzard of paper that they lose sight of the real purpose of their jobs.   Often it appears that maintenance reports are written on subjects of minor importance and distributed in numerous copies to various people who are not in position to do anything about changing the conditions the reports describe.   Reports have a tendency to deteriorate into what might be called "alibi files," to prove that the job is being done.   In the complexity of any plant organization, where the final result is due to the combined efforts of many, it is really not much of a trick to prepare reports that make a sorry maintenance department look good losing.   There is a serious danger in that main-tenance may be reporting the winning of battles to management while the accounting cost data indicate that maintenance is losing the war.

THE MAINTENANCE–ACCOUNTING DEPARTMENT RELATIONSHIP

The accumulation of maintenance cost data is usually done by the accounting department as a service to the maintenance department, and reports are made. From the maintenance viewpoint, there are two kinds of maintenance cost information reports:

1. Reports to plant management.
2. Cost information reports for cost control purposes within the maintenance depart-ment.

Maintenance Cost Reports to Management.   The objective of this type of report is to furnish plant management with cost information to permit management to judge maintenance performance as a plant service.   Over-all maintenance cost, and spe-cifically the trend in maintenance cost per unit of product, is the only true measure of maintenance performance.   Ideally, maintenance costs would be defined as those expenditures controllable by the maintenance department.   But the difficulty is the definition of those costs for which maintenance can be held accountable.   If produc-tion people authorize maintenance work, they certainly play a part in the control of maintenance costs.   However, control of maintenance costs by production people is of minor importance.   A maintenance department that is progressive, effective, and trusted by the production people is usually very much in control.

So a summation of maintenance labor, material, contracts, transportation, supplies, and all other costs defined as maintenance is controllable essentially by the maintenance department and is a realistic measure of maintenance performance. Responsibility for the control is rightly assignable to the maintenance department by plant management. Such a yardstick is the basis of budgetary control on a total monthly cost basis. Objectives expressed in improved maintenance cost per unit of product are readily compared with monthly progress.

Cost Information for Cost Control Purposes within the Maintenance Department. This is the cost information that maintenance receives from accounting to control maintenance costs. These figures would be compiled by maintenance if it were not that accounting can data process them at much less expense. This cost information should not be what the accounting department thinks maintenance needs to run the business; maintenance cost control should be designed by maintenance and administered by maintenance.

Any respectable maintenance supervisor is concerned with costs and cost reports. But only when he is held accountable for those costs that he substantially controls will he be motivated to make costs his prime concern. When they become "his" costs, he thinks in terms of dollars even though he may be talking about man-hours, pounds, or barrels.

MAINTENANCE-STORES AND PURCHASING RELATIONSHIP

The objective of the stores and purchasing department is to contribute to the profit objective by controlling the investment in spare parts and repair material at the lowest point consistent with operation and maintenance requirements. It strives to have the necessary spare parts and repair material on hand, at the right location, in the right quantity, at the minimum cost. The importance of the relationship between maintenance and stores is obvious because of the major contribution the stores or purchasing department can make to the effectiveness of the maintenance department. Some organizations include stores as a part of maintenance, but, to review the interchange between the two functions, they are considered here as separate departments.

The control of general maintenance material (sometimes called active stock) is essentially a stores department activity employing usage data, stock-outs, and inventory records to maintain the optimum economic stock. Maintenance can assist greatly in this problem by foreseeing future plans which will change the requirement of particular items and making the necessary reports to stores.

Maintenance can make a significant contribution to economic inventory control of spare parts or protective stock. The familiarity of maintenance with the equipment is the key to maximum standardization and elimination of duplicate stocks. The effectiveness of preventive maintenance is an important contributing factor to the control of spare parts, provided there is close association and PM data are furnished to the stores department in planned reports.

A report to be used within the maintenance department is a recorded history of failure and repair cost. It should be used to justify a specified selection of equipment. The data are gathered in the PM files. An equipment selection, backed up by efficiencies that justify added power costs, seldom is questioned.

REQUESTS AND PROPOSALS TO MANAGEMENT

Effective Writing. Consideration of reports and communications originating in the maintenance department is not complete unless it includes reference to uncalendared or infrequent correspondence, in addition to scheduled reports. Maintenance managers and supervisors in any plant expend considerable time and effort preparing requests, proposals, and justifications to plant management. These communications should be written effectively. Also, maintenance communicates with all other agencies in the plant organization. Improvement in transmitting ideas will by no means replace basic formation of ideas, but as far as most technically trained people are concerned, it is a much neglected supplement. Here are points that will help in communication.

1. Prepare and plan.   Consider what ideas you want to transmit and what you want to accomplish.   Adapt language, approach, and pitch to best serve those objectives. Some letters deserve an outline; writing or not writing one is a matter of choice. If there is time, let your subconscious help; often a scribbled listing of thoughts in the evening becomes a well-arranged presentation after a night's sleep.

2. Consider the reader.   Remember that your purpose is to motivate the reader to take the action you are proposing and that he is emotional as well as logical. His understanding of your information will be influenced by his background and experience, also by his emotions.   Try to make sure he will see the same thing you see.   Temper your presentation to his viewpoint.   Remember that his interest is in personal goals as well as in the plant's profit objective.   "What's in it for me" is a heavy factor in every action men decide upon.

3. Get the message through.   Secure favorable attention by opening with the anticipated benefits (to him) when your proposal is approved.   Follow with a brief statement of what you propose to do.   Avoid making him read a whole page or two to find out what you are writing about.   Certain supporting details need to be included, but don't clutter up his thinking with them before you tell him what you intend to accomplish and how you intend to do it.   Express the pertinent facts.   Avoid the natural tendency to impress him with how much you know. Your job is to remove all the chaff, hand him only the wheat.   The perfect presentation is one that can be answered simply by yes or no.   When it is necessary to explain something complex, feed the reader small bites in an orderly manner. There is a danger of being too verbose, yet authorities advocate some redundancy, the actual repeating of an important thought to insure getting it through.   A paraphrased restatement or an interesting illustration is often necessary to overcome inattention and misunderstanding.

The basic engineering school design of a report consists of:

a. Objective.   What you are trying to accomplish.
b. Procedure.   What you did about it.
c. Findings.   What you observed.
d. Recommendation.   What you propose to do.

The logical opening is a brief statement or summary of what the reader will derive from the proposal.   The plant manager's personal objective is increased plant profit, so the first thing to mention in a proposal addressed to him is how much it will increase profits, decrease costs, or show a rate of return on the proposed expenditure.   The "procedure" and "findings" items of a basic report usually are combined and simplified.   A complex proposal will require development by steps to convey the necessary picture.   Since proposals are read by many people, it is common practice to transmit the long proposal with a cover letter.   The manager's staff is concerned with the details of the proposal; the manager himself need not go further than the cover letter, which states what, how much, and the economic justification.   The "recommendation" portion of the engineering report becomes only a few words or even only an implication in a proposal or request. "What to do" and "how to do it" are included in the summary in the opening and elaborated in the supporting paragraphs.

4. Provide interest and readability.   Authorities agree that the key to effective writing is a matter of the reader's interest and the readability of the writing.   As writers of specific requests, maintenance executives have to appeal to the interest of only a few—usually only an individual.   Interest is generated by the use of personal words and phrases that are people-oriented.   True, the plant engineer doesn't include a phrase like "you can't afford not to" when writing to the plant manager.   But he can avoid the unnecessarily impersonal passive-voice phrases. "I recommend" or "we recommend" not only adds interest but hits much harder than "it is recommended."   Readability is increased by short, common words and short, simple sentences.   The best example is the news magazine style that manages to convey quite complex ideas with minimum effort on the part of the reader.

Chapter 6

AREA AND
CENTRALIZED MAINTENANCE CONTRASTED

By H. A. FOHL
Maintenance Consultant
Parkesburg, Pa.
Formerly Manager, Maintenance and Construction
Lukens Steel Company
Coatesville, Pa.

Area Maintenance. Area maintenance means just what the name implies, namely, the division of the plant into areas, each with its own maintenance crew. It makes for high efficiency and economy, because area-maintenance headquarters and shops are located near the production departments they serve. This type of organization usually is controlled by top-level production supervision and often makes use of production employees as reinforcements for maintenance forces in emergencies. The personnel become efficient in the upkeep of facilities within their own areas but when used in other areas, where they are not familiar with the equipment, are likely to cause maintenance costs to increase.

The well-planned area setup often includes repair shops, but for reasons of economy these shops have limited capacity and can take care of only certain types and amounts of repair work, the balance being sent to the regular shops which usually are controlled by supervision outside the direct production sphere. With this type of maintenance, many complex problems arise, such as priorities, transportation, ordering, purchasing, spares, engineering, emergencies, and cost control. Unless rigid controls are in force, programs break down and red tape causes unnecessary cost.

When the area system is properly organized, it provides for a work order originated within the area, by either maintenance or production, and issued direct from the office of the production superintendent to the departments which will perform the work. Work performed within production areas, as supporting shops, usually is authorized by written requisition signed by the foreman or supervisor requiring the work, who designates a charge number for cost purposes.

The area superintendent, under this setup, must decide on priorities. If the work is sent outside his area, responsibility for priorities then becomes a problem of the supervisors who must perform the work. If several areas call for emergency work at the same time, the question of priorities may have to be referred to management at top level.

The office of each area superintendent should have its schedule boards and should be notified of work-completion dates. Such information having to do with work done outside the area should be passed on to maintenance supervision within the area.

Supporting departments, such as cost, time, and stores, usually receive their notification direct from the departments performing the work.

The working force required in an area setup usually is greater than in centralized maintenance, because of the difficulty of moving workmen from one area to another. The greater force increases the chances of having maintenance workers idle when all equipment in a given area is in good operating condition.

In area maintenance, the organization (Fig. 6-1) receives its authority from production management, which has received its authority from the general manager or superintendent's office. Production management directs its authority to the various maintenance-foreman levels and to the various supporting shops included in their setup. The supporting shops, not parts of the maintenance organization, usually

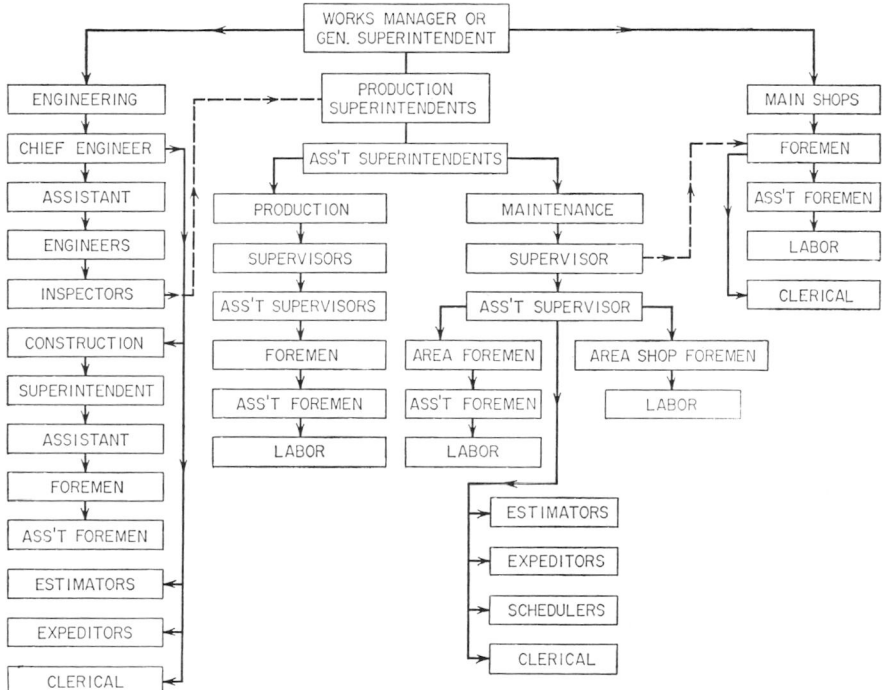

FIG. 6-1. Organization chart showing direction of lines of authority, area maintenance.

receive their authority from the general manager's office. When maintenance depends upon these shops for work to fulfill its assignments, it will find itself facing delays unless a clearance center has been established to control priorities in these shops. Because a number of areas contend for the services of supporting shops, lines of authority must be definite, or the system will break down.

Area maintenance being subject to production control, inspection ordinarily is a function of the maintenance personnel. If trouble is discovered, or failures are expected, decision as to what procedure to follow is made, as a rule, at top production level. Many times, to keep production going on, maintenance is ordered to make minor repairs rather than the major repairs called for by the condition of equipment. The final result can be a costly breakdown. Preventive maintenance in this type of setup can be an effective tool, provided close cooperation exists among maintenance, production supervision, engineering, and inspection. Engineering is a separate department, taking its authority from the general-manager level.

Costs, under area maintenance, are not so likely to get out of control as in centralized maintenance, because of the type of organization and the close contact of the area supervision with its equipment and the maintenance crews that are part of the area personnel.

Centralized Maintenance. Centralized maintenance means that all maintenance is directed from a central location. Personnel are transferred from one area or trouble spot to another. Shops are centrally located. Engineering and cost control are parts of the setup. The whole organization is headed by a maintenance manager, reporting, as a rule, to the same top-level management as do the production managers. Maintenance of this type must work in close harmony with production, by which it must be guided as to the removal of equipment from production.

This type of setup, if well organized, streamlines maintenance. It provides well-trained personnel familiar with all types of equipment within the plant, holds down transportation and handling costs, and lends itself to simple and practical procedures

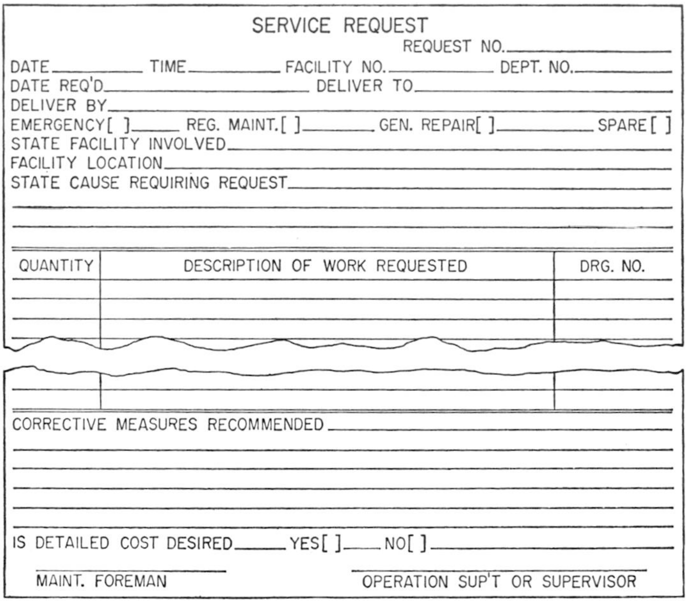

```
                        SERVICE  REQUEST
                              REQUEST NO._____
DATE_____ TIME_____ FACILITY NO._____ DEPT. NO._____
DATE REQ'D._____ DELIVER TO_____
DELIVER BY_____
EMERGENCY[ ]_____ REG. MAINT.[ ]_____ GEN. REPAIR[ ]_____ SPARE[ ]
STATE FACILITY INVOLVED_____
FACILITY LOCATION_____
STATE CAUSE REQUIRING REQUEST_____
_____
_____

QUANTITY |    DESCRIPTION OF WORK REQUESTED    | DRG. NO.

CORRECTIVE MEASURES RECOMMENDED_____
_____
_____
_____

IS DETAILED COST DESIRED_____ YES[ ]____ NO[ ]_____
   MAINT. FOREMAN              | OPERATION SUP'T OR SUPERVISOR
```

FIG. 6-2. Service-request sheet, originating in department requesting maintenance work performed.

for priorities, ordering, purchasing, spares, engineering, and cost controls. It minimizes red tape. When an emergency arises, there is always a full complement of well-trained personnel available. During slack periods, the men can work at preparing spares, building new equipment, or rebuilding the old.

The procedure used in the centralized system begins with a request for labor and material, signed by a supervisor. This request (Fig. 6-2) must carry request number, identification of the facility, department in which located, date issued, date required, and a description of work wanted. The request is cleared through a control center, preferably a cost-control center, where it is approved or rejected. If accepted, a written order is issued to the departments which will perform the work. The control center schedules all orders according to their emergency demands and priorities. Thus decisions are made at the central point and departmental supervision performing the work is relieved of that responsibility.

All orders and requisitions, including those to the purchasing department, must carry request number, order number, facility identification, and delivery point of the finished work, as shown by Fig. 6-3 and 6-3a. Copies of all orders must go to supporting departments, such as cost, time, and stores, for accumulating cost data. Schedule boards under direct supervision of cost control should be maintained in either the control center or departmental offices for control of orders.

When an order has been completed in a department, notification must be sent to the control center, making use of a completion stub (not illustrated) attached to the order.

WORK ORDER

ORD. NO.	
DATE	
CHARGE	
EMERGENCY	
REGULAR	
SPARES	

DEP'T REQUESTING WORK ______
FACILITY NO. ______ DESCRIPTION ______
REASON FOR REPAIR ______
DESCRIPTION OF REPAIR ______
REPAIR INSTRUCTIONS ______
ESTIMATED HRS. ______ REQUESTED BY ______
SHEET NO. ______

ITEM NO.	DEP'T	DESCRIPTION OF WORK TO BE PERFORMED	OPERATION	DATE		EST. HRS.	
				IN	OUT	MACH.	MAN

FINISHED WORK APPROVED ______ INSPECTOR ______
DISPATCHER ______ ORDER APPROVED BY ______

FIG. 6-3. First copy, maintenance work-order sheet.

Control center then notifies all supporting departments, so that all costs can be accumulated. Cost reports are sent to the control center for checking against estimates and contracts and posting for the maintenance manager's office.

The centralized maintenance organization (Fig. 6-4) receives its authority direct from the general manager, or superintendent's office. The manager of the maintenance division delegates authority to the maintenance departmental supervision,

WORK ORDER
SUPPLEMENTARY SHEET

ORDER NO. ______
SHEET NO. ______ DATE ______

ITEM NO.	DEP'T	DESCRIPTION OF WORK TO BE PERFORMED	OPERATION	DATE		EST. HRS.	
				IN	OUT	MACH.	MAN

FIG. 6-3a. Supplementary copy, maintenance work-order sheet.

including that of all supporting departments and shops, as shown on the chart. The flow of authority becomes a simple procedure with chances of breakdown remote. Engineering and inspection receive their authority through the office of top maintenance management, thus relieving the maintenance personnel in the field of the responsibility for inspection. This arrangement places the maintenance forces in a good position to carry on preventive maintenance.

In the centralized system, inspection is a three-way program, involving maintenance and engineering as well as inspection. Thus there is a double check, without adding extra duties to maintenance personnel. This program eliminates any chance for a department to overemphasize its authority or not follow the instructions issued by inspection. Figure 6-5 shows the inspection chart used.

Because, under centralized maintenance, with its over-all coverage and its own organization, and with no direct tie-in with any specific department, costs can mount quickly to the danger point, the controls must be very tight. However, the system for keeping track of them can be about the same as for area maintenance.

Common Ground for Both Area and Centralized Maintenance. An effective preventive-maintenance program for both area and centralized maintenance must be simple, systematic, and well defined. Inspection information, recorded on log sheets, should be transferred to permanent records and filed according to facility identification. Maintenance supervision should check the log sheets weekly. By comparing the notations with the permanent records, the checker should be able to detect deterioration and approaching failures, and prevent costly breakdowns by planning in

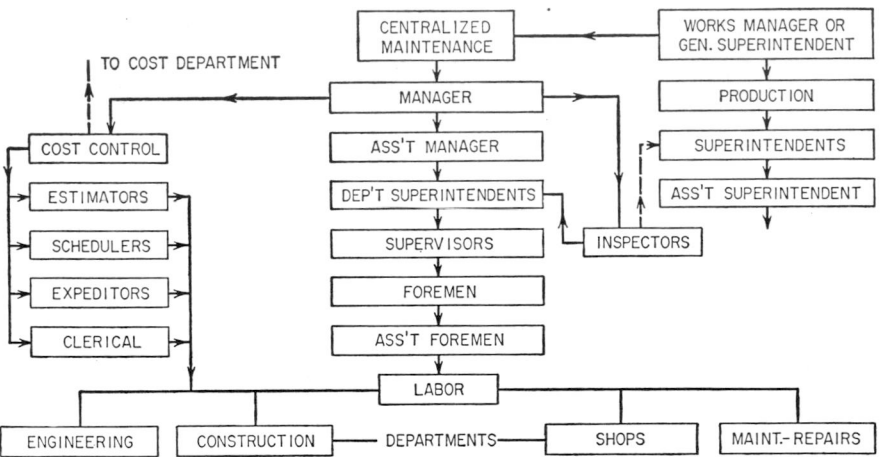

Fig. 6-4. Organization chart, showing direction of lines of authority, centralized maintenance.

advance for repairs and replacements, to be taken care of, in many cases, during regular scheduled downtime. Should the failures require emergency measures, management can be informed, and a date can be set for taking the equipment out of service.

The daily log sheet should be large enough to accommodate all the facilities in a given area or department. Equipment composed of subassemblies, where failures might occur which would be instrumental in shutting the whole unit down, should be listed along with the unit. When one facility is dependent on another, both should be listed. Example: A rotary shear driven by a motor through a gear reduction unit. The shear is listed. So is the motor and gear reduction unit.

The code taken from the daily inspection sheet (Fig. 6-6) should be entered by someone in the supervisor's office, preferably the supervisor himself, because this will keep him aware daily as to just what is taking place with each facility under his care. The illustration of a daily inspection sheet is self-explanatory.

Each week a designated inspector should consult the log sheet, noting entries out of the ordinary, or an increased number of minor delays or repairs, which are always the symptoms of approaching failure. This inspector should have the authority to shut the equipment down if, in his judgment, further examination is necessary, or engineering should be consulted.

A permanent record, in the form of a card file, should be set up. One of the cards is shown in Fig. 6-7. There should be entered on this card all information concerning emergency repairs, overhauling, or rebuilding, including the length of time the equip-

MAINTENANCE INSPECTION LOG SHEET

NO.	EQUIPMENT	TIME CYC.	1	2	3	4	5	6	7	8	9	10	11	12	13	14	15	16	17	18	19	20	21	22	23	24	25	26	27	28	29	30	31	NOTATIONS	NO.
1	STIFF LEG																																		
	MECHANICAL	3					A	A	A						A							A							B				B		
	ELECTRICAL	3					A	A	A						A							C							B				B		
	LUBRICATION	3					A	A	A						A							E							A				A	Broken connection	
2	PIT COVERS																																		
	MECHANICAL	3							C						C							A							A				A		
	ELECTRICAL	3					A	A	A						A							A							A				A		
	LUBRICATION	2	A	A	A	A	A	A	A	A	A	A	A	A	A	A	A	A	A	A	A	A	A	A	A	A	A	A	A	A	A	A	A		
3	P. C. CRANE																																		
	MECHANICAL	3					A	A	A						A							A							A				A		
	ELECTRICAL	3					A	A	A						E							A							A				A		
	LUBRICATION	2	A	A	A	A	A	A	A	A	A	A	A	A	A	A	A	A	A	A	A	A	A	A	A	A	A	A	A	A	A	A	B		
4	FANS	3					A	A	A						A							A							A						
5	FUEL OIL PUMP	3					A	A	A						A							A							A						
6	INGOT BUGGY	2	A	A	B	B	A	B	C	C	A	A	A	A	B	A	A	A	A	C	B	B	A	A	A	A	A	A	A				A	Bearings	
	MECHANICAL	2	A	A	A	A	A	A	A	A	A	A	A	A	A	A	A	A	A	A	A	A	A	A	A	A	A	A	A				A		
	ELECTRICAL	2	C	A	A	A	A	A	A	A	A	A	A	A	A	A	A	A	A	C	A	A	A	A	A	A	A	A	A				A		
7	CHARGE CRANE																																		
	MECHANICAL	4							A						A							A							A						
	ELECTRICAL	3							A						B							B							A						
	LUBRICATION	3							B																				B						
8	F & B TABLES																																		
	MECHANICAL	1	A	A	A	A	A	A	A	A	A	A	A	A	A	A	A	A	A	A	A	A	A	A	A	A	A	A	A	A	A	A	A		
	ELECTRICAL	3					A	A	A						A							A							A				A		
	LUBRICATION	1	A	A	A	A	A	A	A	A	A	A	A	A	A	A	A	A	A	A	A	A	A	A	A	A	A	A	A	A	A	A	A		
	HYDRAULIC	2	A	B	A	A	A	A	A	A	A	A	A	A	C	A	A	C	C	A	A	C	A	A	C	A	C	A	A				A		
9	R. MILL PROP.																																		
	HOUSING SHOE P.	4													A							A							A						
	CHUCKS	3							A						A							A							A				A		
	SCREWDOWN	1	A	A	A	A	A	A	A	A	A	A	A	A	A	C	A	C	C	A	A	B	A	B	B	A	B	A	A	A	A	A	A	Replace screw	
	SPINDLES	2	A	A	A	A	A	A	A	A	A	A	A	A	A	A	A	A	A	A	A	A	A	A	A	A	A	A	A				A		

TIME CYCLE: 1-EVERY 8 HOURS; 2-EVERY 24 HOURS; 3-EVERY 7 DAYS; 4 EVERY 28 DAYS

SYMBOL SCHEDULE: A-NO REPAIRS; B-MINOR REPAIRS; C-ROUTINE REPAIRS; E-EMERGENCY REPAIRS

FIG. 6-5. Daily log sheet. One sheet each month.

DAILY INSPECTION SHEET

DEP'T _120"mill_   DATE _8-7_

INSPECTOR _John Doe_

TURN _2_   MECH.   ELECT.   LUBR. ✓   HYDR.   PNEUM.   MISC.

NO.	EQUIPMENT	SYM. SCH.	REMARKS	NO.	EQUIPMENT	SYM. SCH.	REMARKS	REASON FOR REPAIRS
1	STIFF LEG	A		26				1.Lub. lines
2	PIT COVERS	A		27	#1 SHEAR TABLE	A		broken
3	P. C. CRANES	E	1	28				
4	FANS	A		29				2. Lub. lines
5	FUEL OIL PUMP	A		30	R. S. APP. TABLE	B	3	off on 4 lead
6	INGOT BUGGY	B		31				rollers
7	CHARGE CRANE	A		32				
8	F & B TABLES	E	2	33				3.grease connection
9	ROUGH MILL	A		34	R. S. SCRAP CUTT.	C		broken off
10				35				
11				36				
12				37				
13				38				
14				39				
15				40				
16				41				

| 25 | NO.1 SHEAR | A | | 50 | NO.2 PILER | A | | John Doe |
| | | | | | | | | SIGNATURE INSPECTOR |

FIG. 6-6. Daily inspection sheet. One sheet each turn for type of inspection.

FACILITY RECORD

DEPT._____ NO._____ FACILITY CLASS NO._____ FACILITY NO._____

FACILITY LOCATION_____

FACILITY DESCRIPTION_____

MANUFACTURER NAME _____ NO. _____

SERIAL NO. _____ PURCHASE ORDER NO. _____ DATE _____

DATE REC'D _____ DATE IN OPERATION _____

INSTALLED BY _____ WORKS ORDER NO._____

PURCHASE PRICE_____INSTALLATION COST_____

DISPOSITION: SOLD_____ TRANSFERRED_____ SCRAPPED _____

ELECTRICAL EQUIPMENT: COMPLETE DATA_____

MECHANICAL EQUIPMENT: COMPLETE DATA_____

MISCELLANEOUS EQUIPMENT_____

			REPAIR	RECORD							
DATE	ORDER NO.	REASON FOR REPAIR DESCRIPTION	DATE OFF	ON	REPAIR COST	DATE	ORDER NO.	REASON FOR REPAIR DESCRIPTION	DATE OFF	ON	ORDER NO.

FIG. 6-7. Facility record card. Back of card to be used entirely for repair record entries.

ment was out of use.   This file should include cards for machinery, buildings, bridges, roads, fences, land, streams—in fact, every piece of property or equipment.   This permanent record file should be kept in the office or top production management if in an area system, or top maintenance management if the centralized system is in use.

With the aid of the records and forms described, a preventive-maintenance program can be an effective tool for the protection of a company's assets.

Checking of work done should follow the same prescribed lines of procedure in both area and centralized maintenance. Working from the completion data established on the original order, all subsequent orders issued for the job should carry completion dates based on the original date and then placed on regular schedule boards in either departmental or central offices. Copies of the orders should be sent to all departments connected in any way with the project, such as purchasing, engineering, supporting shops, construction, maintenance, cost; and copies should go to the inspectors and expediters.

Cost controls for both area and centralized maintenance should be about the same and the systems for keeping track of them should be similar. The most efficient approach is through the medium of a cost-control center, or department. In area maintenance, it can be part of the area management's office. In centralized maintenance, it should be a supporting department of the office of the maintenance division manager, responsible only to that office. In this center, estimates are made, requests for work are received and screened, orders to perform the work are issued, and costs are recorded against the orders. This department does not assemble the costs, but receives them already assembled from the cost department. The center also prepares daily, weekly, and monthly charts for management's consumption, and is in position to point out the danger spots in rising costs before they get out of control. If operated properly, the center can become the library for all maintenance information, data, and records.

Editor's Note: It is impossible to set up hard-and-fast rules by which to choose and carry out area or centralized maintenance. In the preceding pages the differences and similarities of the two systems have been pointed out, likewise the advantages and disadvantages. The obvious conclusion is that the division of maintenance work between the two systems must depend upon the conditions existing in the specific plant. This is well illustrated by examination of the following details of two plants, one the plant, before his retirement, of the author of the preceding pages, and the other the plant of the Aircraft Turbine Division of the General Electric Company, at Evendale, Ohio, as described by J. Gibbons, Plant Engineer, at the Fifth National Plant Maintenance and Engineering Conference, in 1954.*

Plant 1. The manager of maintenance reports to the general works manager on the same level as the eight other managers in the plant, who include director of research, manager of production control, manager of the steel plants, managers of fabricating, and manager of industrial engineering.

Directly under the manager of maintenance are the chief engineer for engineering and construction and five superintendents: of electrical department; mechanical department; machine, forge, grinding, pattern, and carpenter shops; refractories and fuel department; cost control (a staff man); also a facility engineer, a staff man.

There are 6,000 employees in the plant. Total force for construction, repair, and inspection is 1,300. Of these, 50 are lubrication men, and 110 are general repair men. There are 40 in the forge and smith shops (part maintenance and part sales), 40 in the carpenter shop, 10 in the pattern shop, 300 in five machine shops, 250 in the electrical shop or working on electrical repairs, while the staff cost-control man has 20 to 30 people working under him. There are 134 supervisors for the 1,300 men.

Included in the maintenance division are pipe shops, welding shops, safety shops, specialty shops, pumping plants, substations, motor rooms, hot-top department, outside contracting, and personnel to handle general labor, automotive, locomotive, and car repair, masonry, sheet-tin work, painting, boiler rooms, crane running.

There are also skeleton crews in the areas, with maintenance supervisors, but the larger part of the work force constitutes a pool from which men may be drawn for work in any area, and the planning and scheduling are centralized under the cost-control superintendent.

Inspectors are divided into four groups: mechanical, electrical, structural, and pipeline. Chief inspectors report to engineering.

The plant covers 650 acres, of which two-thirds is in building floor space, the rest in yards and grounds. Maintenance men use scooters.

The work-order system is under the direction of the cost-control superintendent.

* Techniques of Plant Maintenance and Engineering, 1954 (Clapp & Poliak, New York, N.Y.)

A service request is initiated by a foreman in an operating department and is signed by the superintendent of the area operating group, and by the manager of the operating department.   It flows into the cost-control office and is immediately checked to ascertain the shops involved in the work and the materials necessary, including fabricated parts.   Upon approval of the request, the necessary work orders are issued.

The cost-control office has a corps of expediters who maintain a master control book for the orders issued to them in the zones which they expedite, not only from the standpoint of materials but also from the standpoint of coordinating the shops involved.   When the request comes into the office and the order is issued on it, the order is immediately recorded against a specific facilities card maintained in the office. There is a card for each facility in the plant.

The work order is issued to the shops and expediters follow it through the completion stage.   As the reports come in, they are correlated and tabulated against costs. They are sent to the tabulating division, which maintains a master card on each work order issued out of the cost-control office.

The tabulating department collects the labor cost, and the auditing department applies the burden rates and side material costs from the stores and purchasing departments.   The cost-control superintendent gets a weekly report of all maintenance department costs.   In most cases tabulations are detailed; but simplified reports of all their costs are sent to the superintendents weekly.   Every 3 months they get a report on the cost of the facilities.

Orders are divided two ways: blanket for routine work, individual for repair work. Costs can be picked up on a weekly basis.   On daytime emergencies and breakdowns, superintendents can call in at any time to cost control.   A work order can be issued in 2 minutes, and crews put to work at once.   On night emergencies, the work is charged against special blocks of work-order numbers already issued.   The time of the repair men is charged against blanket orders for routine, and specific orders on repair jobs, emergencies, and breakdowns issued once each 4-week period.

The manager of maintenance has authority to shut down equipment for repair. However, the nine major managers of the company, including the manager of maintenance, meet once a week to discuss schedules and over-all problems.   In another weekly meeting production superintendents meet with lower-level maintenance supervision to set up regular weekly schedules with due regard for production schedules.   As much work as is possible is scheduled for Saturdays, Sundays, and holidays.

Detail scheduling is done by the cost-control group, and in each of the machine shops there is a supervisor of planning and scheduling who schedules the craft work. The plan is to use a control board and schedule 5 weeks in advance.

Plant 2.   The plant consists of 13 buildings, with 3,761,000 sq ft of floor space. It is more than 1 mile long and $\frac{1}{2}$ mile wide.   It is devoted to the planning, development, manufacture, and assembly of jet engines.   It is an integrated plant, supplying its own steam and softened water and having control, from its own substation, of its electrical supply.   The 13 buildings are occupied by three operating departments. Each of these departments is a business, completely responsible for its own profit and loss.   Therefore each is given, along with the responsibility, the authority to organize and operate as it wishes within the framework of the General Electric Company's over-all policy.

Each department handles the maintenance of its own production facilities—machine tools, stockrooms, materials-handling systems, etc., that are tied directly into producing the product for which the department is responsible.   Having decentralized maintenance specialists in the areas where the problems occur permits quick action, simplifies paper work, and enables the operating departments to keep their own records on their own equipment.

On the other hand, there are utilities and maintenance functions which are common to the departments and which it would be difficult to divide into three pieces.   These are the responsibility of the central maintenance group.   Responsibilities of the central maintenance group include steam plant, air-supply system, water-softening plant, substation, gas-reducing station; also main utility services in the buildings; also grounds and building structures, including parking lots and roadways.

Operating departments are responsible for maintaining the utilities from the main distribution lines to the equipment, and the equipment itself. They are responsible for internal building services—cleaning, replacement of lights, rest-room upkeep. Thus operating departments are staffed to do the day-to-day routine maintenance of productive equipment and its related services, but not to take care of emergencies.

The central maintenance group staffs itself for the day-to-day maintenance of the grounds and buildings, and also maintains a work force of specialized trades which the operating departments would not ordinarily carry, such as carpenters, millwrights iron workers, and painters. These people serve as a pool of talent for emergencies which cannot be handled by the operating departments' routine maintenance personnel.

Work orders for routine maintenance are handled on a standing-order basis providing for immediate action, and the labor vouchers are made out as the maintenance is done and are charged to the standing-order number. When other than routine maintenance is to be handled by the central maintenance group, work orders are issued directly to the central maintenance group. For items costing less than $100, no formal estimate is required. On items costing more than $100, central maintenance provides a cost estimate of time, material, and overhead to the operating department.

After the work order is issued, control of the cost of the job is exercised by a job cost and control section. A job-control card is issued, allocating the amount of money available according to the craft involved. Clerks keep a record on the cost of all jobs; and when 80 per cent of the allocated funds for a job have been expended, a review is made to see if it can be completed within the allocated funds. If not, the job- and cost-control section informs the customer and, if need be, stops the job until more funds are made available. These clerks report directly to the supervisor of job and cost control and maintain a backlog report according to crafts, summarizing the work in prospect. It is their goal to keep the backlog down to a maximum of 4 weeks; when the backlog exceeds this limit, the work is contracted. After a job has been completed by the central maintenance group, a complete accounting and billing is rendered to the operating department.

Chapter 7

USING OUTSIDE CONTRACTORS

By Albert R. Starr
Plant Engineer
Caterpillar Tractor Co., Mossville Plant
East Peoria, Ill.

Many industries are employing contractors for all or certain phases of construction and maintenance work necessary in a plant, and are finding it advantageous to do so. Contractors are used to varying degrees, depending upon the needs of the plant being served. In some plants which do not employ their own craftsmen, all construction and maintenance work is performed on a routine basis by contract. In other plants which have their own craftsmen, contractors may be used only during peak loads of work, on jobs which are not repetitive in nature and are in the one-time-only category, and/or on an emergency basis. In the latter categories, the contractor's force may be considered as supplemental to a plant work force.

Routine Basis. When a contractor is used on a routine basis, administration of the work force, so far as the company is concerned, is minimized. This function becomes the responsibility of the contractor. All matters pertaining to personnel, supervision, payment, and obtaining and releasing of employees are performed by the contractor. A company needs only to employ a skeleton technical supervisory force to plan and coordinate the work with a contractor and to assure good workmanship. This does not necessarily indicate economy of operation, however, since the lessened company labor and overhead costs may be offset by the higher labor and overhead costs required by the contractor.

Routine work is generally, though not necessarily always, performed on a cost-plus form of contract. Estimates, where possible, should be given for work to be so performed. The use of a cost-plus form of contract could lead to increased cost in maintenance and construction work through lack of incentive and efficiency on the part of the contractor and his work force unless continuous direction is given the contractor in scheduling and execution of work.

Depending on location, economic conditions, and past practice in any given area, more favorable rates for contract labor used on a routine basis can usually be negotiated with various craft unions. While these rates are generally higher than those paid plant craftsmen, they are less than is demanded when a contractor employs his labor intermittently.

Intermittent Basis. When a contractor is used on an intermittent basis, a means is provided for stabilizing the employment of a fixed number of plant craftsmen while yet retaining flexibility of operation, and the capability of handling peak work loads or emergency work loads. Normally a plant construction and maintenance organization is developed to provide employment for a fixed number of employees capable of handling all routine work on a continuous repetitive basis. During periods of fluctuating or peak work burden or in emergency situations, unless a contractor's force is employed, more plant employees would be required to handle the work capably. Some difficulty may be experienced in obtaining sufficient skilled personnel when necessary to expand a plant force as required, as well as in the subsequent reduction of force that necessarily follows when the work load is completed. Employment of a contractor as necessary will help alleviate these problems and provide a means of accomplishing the work without sacrificing routine service.

General. The skill in comparable crafts of the plant craftsmen is generally equal to that of the outside craftsmen. In some cases, a greater degree of skill for certain classes of work may be found in the outside craftsmen, whereas, for specialized work of the type found in an industrial plant, the proficiency may be greater with the plant craftsmen. For example, in architectural-trades work, better workmanship may be found in the outside craftsmen vs. the plant craftsmen, since less such type of work by volume may be performed by plant craftsmen. The same may be true of cement finishing, plastering, and other specialties.

While a contractor tries to provide steady employment for a fixed number of men whom he has found reliable, he does have in reserve a large reservoir of readily available manpower upon which he can call, on short notice as necessary, to meet heavy work demands. His arrangements are such with this manpower pool that he is also able to release men on short notice as a given job nears completion.

Some jobs in plants require special equipment and special skill for a limited period of time. A contractor, in his operations, is a little more flexible in being able to obtain such special skill and equipment, whereas such facilities may not normally be required or be available for use in the plant otherwise.

Qualification of Contractors. If the use of contractors is contemplated, first consideration should be given to the needs of the plant as to the types of work, skills, and capabilities required of contractors. With this in mind, a survey should be made of all potentially eligible contractors in the area of the plant to be served. Contractors should be classified as to availability, organization, character, experience, and financial condition.

Availability. Contractors must be available when needed if they are to be of any value or service to a plant. This means that each contractor should be flexible in his operations so that he can effectively man plant jobs on short notice in spite of any other commitments that he may have.

Organization. The secret of success in any endeavor has been defined as organization. Certainly, this is true in the case of a contractor. He is only as effective as the organization he directs. The contractor, his supervisors, and his staff should be cooperative and well qualified for their positions by reason of education, experience, and demonstrated ability. The contractor's supervisory organization should be composed of people with a background of experience in their particular fields, and capable of handling, directing, and organizing men to accomplish jobs in minimum time with quality workmanship.

Character. Contractors should be reputable businessmen of high integrity. They should be dependable and reliable so that jobs may be started and completed on a prearranged schedule. This reputation should be founded on consistent performance.

Experience. One of the most important factors to be considered in qualifying contractors is experience in the kind of work contemplated. Each contractor should provide a résumé of completed jobs including the organizations for whom work has been accomplished, a list of the experience of the principal individuals of the contractor's firm, and a list of equipment the contractor has available. The contractor should have a clean record of past jobs successfully completed. With this information at hand, each contractor can then be classed according to his capabilities. Such a classification may include the following:

1. General contractors capable of handling all trades in large jobs. This type of work requires the contractor to have extensive personnel, heavy equipment, and the technical staff necessary for such work.
2. General contractors capable of handling all trades, but limited to small-volume

work. In this group should be placed those who are efficient but have smaller organizations and past experience limited to lesser jobs.

3. General contractors specializing in architectural-trades work.
4. General contractors specializing in mechanical-trades work.
5. Prime contractors capable of highly specialized work such as excavating, grading, earth moving, and landscaping.
6. Contractors whose work has been generally limited to subcontracts.

Financial. A contractor should be able to carry the financial obligations of a job. This will protect the owner from necessary liens and work stoppages. Each contractor should have a net worth of sound and liquid assets equal to approximately 25 per cent of all the work he has in progress, including the work for which he is being considered. Information relative to a contractor's financial status can be obtained from the contractor or by investigation through independent mercantile agencies, which are organized for this purpose. Such an investigation will reveal how well a contractor has discharged his financial responsibilities, and will further verify and clarify other related qualifications.

Administrative Considerations. No analysis of a contractor is complete unless his administrative capabilities are also considered. The study should include contractor methods of estimating, keeping time, charges, labor relations, insurance, and other items at times.

Estimating. All plant engineers and other top-management people are interested in accurate cost estimates. These are generally the basis for approval or disapproval of proposed projects. The pet peeve of many plant managers is the inaccuracy of an estimate as compared with the final cost of the project. Where a contractor is to be engaged in work to be performed on a cost-plus basis, it is important that his method of estimating be realistic and accurate. Basically, the total cost of any job equals the cost of material, labor, overhead, and profit. Strictly speaking, all estimates are approximations; however, detailed estimates will provide more accurate costs. Detailed estimates are based upon quantity estimates for contemplated jobs. Unit costs are applied to these quantity estimates, extended and totalized to complete a detailed estimate. This method is commonly used by contractors in preparing bids.

An estimator actually plans how a job is to be accomplished, taking into account all pertinent factors. It is not too much to expect that an estimate be within 10 per cent of the final cost of the job. A record of past jobs can be a source of obtaining information as to the contractor's ability in this respect. If not available from this source, it is beneficial to develop experience with each contractor as he works in the plant.

Keeping Time. The contractor's timekeeping methods are of importance since charges will be based on these records on any job let on a cost-plus form of contract. Each contractor should have adequate office and field forces to record accurately time and material used on all operations being performed. On minor jobs, to lessen overhead, this may be satisfactorily performed by the contractor's job foreman. In the case of larger jobs, a separate timekeeper or field clerk should be required to assure sufficient checks daily for purposes of accurate records and control.

Charges. The charges made by a contractor generally should be standardized and equal to those of other contractors in the area. If a contractor is used on a cost-plus basis, it is well to know labor rates per hour of the various crafts, equipment rental rates, and insurance, overhead, and profit fees of each contractor. For other forms of contracts, competitive bidding is usually in order.

Labor Relations. Previously mentioned is the fact that a contractor's supervisory force should have ability to handle and direct people. Nowhere does this ability stand out more than in the labor-relations field. Past jobs will generally indicate the proficiency of the contractor's organization in this respect. Certainly, each foreman should have a working knowledge of the limits of craft responsibility, and to be able, effectively yet wisely, to apply these to jobs under his control. This proficiency, on the part of the contractor, is very important to a plant engineer employing a contractor on a routine or other basis. When plant craftsmen are also involved, this proficiency assumes an even greater degree of importance since disputes resulting in costly delays in completion of required work can readily develop between plant craftsmen and outside craftsmen.   Before employment of contractors, a thorough study should be made of the plant's contract with its own forces and of the union contract with which the contractor is bound.   These should be compatible; one cannot outlaw the other.   A frank discussion with prospective contractors will help decide whether or not outside craftsmen are cooperative and will work in a plant without disputing work performed by plant forces.   If construction work in the area of the plant is scarce and outside craftsmen have been unemployed for a time, disputes over work performed by plant forces can be expected.   The responsibility for handling these disputes on the part of outside craftsmen rests with the contractor who hires them.

Plant management people are tempted, on occasion, to settle such disputes by dealing with contractor's union business agents.   Hiring a reputable conscientious contractor is one of the best means of avoiding disputes.   The contractor, knowing that questions could arise involving work by plant craftsmen, can exercise care in selection of people.   He usually has craftsmen available who are not union radicals and are interested in doing a good job, as well as in being employed.

When using a contractor, it is of prime importance to define his scope of work clearly so that he knows where to stop.   This also will help in preventing many disputes.   Once this scope is defined, it is advisable to adhere to it; otherwise again disputes may develop.

In analyzing whether or not a contractor can be used in a plant, the greater problem may arise from the plant forces.   With employment of a contractor, plant craftsmen feel that a contractor is performing their work.   The use of a contractor is resented because it is believed this results, directly or indirectly, in less overtime, money, and job security for individual plant craftsmen.   Overtime is particularly a strong issue, and its use by contractor forces should be minimized.

High rates paid to outside craftsmen are also a point of contention.   Rest assured, by some means or other, plant craftsmen will learn of the rates paid to outside craftsmen.   The wage of the outside craftsmen has been built up by demand because of the fact that their employment is generally less stable.   In discussions with plant people involving these rates, it is helpful to point out the advantages enjoyed by industrial employees as compared with outside craftsmen.

In some cases contractor's people have been successfully integrated with plant forces to accomplish jobs; however, it is generally good practice to keep plant craftsmen and the contractor's as far apart as possible.   No point in inviting trouble. In dealing with your own people, it is advisable to notify the plant union committee what work is to be performed and why.   Telling them ahead of time is an excellent way of determining their attitude, and while they may not like it, usually they can be made to understand the value of employing a fixed number of people vs. a fluctuating one, the need for special equipment or skill, or the need to complete a task within a specified time limit.   Telling them ahead also makes them feel that they are being taken into a confidence and that their opinions are weighed and considered as they should be.

Insurance.   Contractors should carry or be willing to carry ample insurance to protect the owner while employed in a plant.   The kinds of insurance and amounts of coverage are influenced by the job, its location, and the laws of the state in which work is to be done.   Adequate coverage can usually be obtained if the following insurances with proper limits are included: workmen's compensation, public liability, employer's liability, property damage, owner's contingent insurance, fire insurance, automobile liability, and automobile property damage.

Prior to employment of any contractors, certificates of insurance should be provided for approval by the owner.   These certificates can be readily furnished by the contractor through his insurance agency.

Selection of Contractors.   Once all information on potential contractors is obtained, a final analysis and comparison of over-all qualifications should be made, keeping in mind the minimum qualifications necessary for the contemplated work.   To meet those minimum requirements a contractor should:

1. Be available for the job.
2. Have ample and suitable equipment available.
3. Have previous experience in executing a similar contract of approximately the same size.
4. Have a clean record of past jobs successfully completed.
5. Have an effective organization with a good reputation based on past performance and character.
6. Be financially sound.

If a contractor is to be selected for routine work, the one best suited for the contemplated work should be interviewed and awarded the job unless something detrimental develops during the interview.   The remainder should be listed for future use. Listing the contractors, their capabilities, and equipment available is very desirable for future reference of the plant engineer; particularly is this true should emergencies arise.   If any bid work is contemplated, qualified contractors can be listed on a preferred bidding list, each according to his capabilities.   When such work is scheduled, at least three contractors should be invited to bid competitively.

Types of Contracts.   Work performed by contractors can be accomplished by three general types of contracts: the lump-sum, the unit-price, and the cost-plus forms.   There are several variations of the cost-plus form that can be used.   The form of contract used is dependent upon the type of work, the flexibility required on a job, and the advantage one has over the other in a given situation with respect to the owner.

General vs. Separate Contracts.   If, in the contemplated work, the functions of all crafts are required to complete the job successfully, some consideration must be given as to whether a single prime contractor is to be retained as a general contractor and have him administer, as subcontracts, the work of trades not performed by his own forces, or contract the work of various trades separately as prime contracts.   The manner in which a job is let is dependent upon its size, complexity, and the abilities of the plant engineer's representatives.   If a job is let to a general contractor who administers other trades than his own by subcontract, the general contractor is responsible for over-all administration and coordination of the subcontractors.   While the cost of a job so awarded is higher because of the general contractor's fee for each subcontract administered, certainly, on some large jobs this arrangement may be desirable.   One compensating factor is that the general contractor usually sublets those parts of the work not performed by his own forces to subcontractors with whom he is familiar.   As a result, each subcontractor is more likely to integrate his work force better with that of the other subcontracts, thereby bettering the performance and quality of work.

Should the work of the various trades be let as separate prime contracts, the burden of administration and coordination of the work falls entirely upon the plant engineer's representatives.   On relatively small jobs this can be done, and a savings equal to the amount of a general contractor's fee can be realized.   On larger jobs, however, difficulty may be encountered unless the plant engineer's representative group is well organized.   Many jobs can be performed advantageously by means of a combination of the two methods described.   Some parts of a larger contract, for example, the architectural trades, may be handled by a general contract; whereas all special skills, such as excavation, piling, and mechanical trades may be handled as separate prime contracts.

Control of Contractors.   Prior to employing a contractor, an administrative procedure should be adopted to handle all the documents that are a part of contractual procedure.   Such items as correspondence, specifications, bulletins, change orders, invoices, payments, requisitions, and contracts play an important part in the execution of a contract job.   Procedures should be set up so that these documents may flow through prescribed channels for proper consideration and approval by top-management people.

On the job, the plant engineer's representative plays a vital part in control of the contractor. He may begin by examining engineering drawings for completeness and correctness, and then assemble such specifications as are necessary to define the scope of work. If the work is to be let on a cost-plus basis, he may deal directly with approved contractors as the resident engineer on the job. If the work is to be let for bidding he may prepare sufficient copies of specifications and drawings, meet prospective bidders, visit the job with them, and receive and tabulate bids for approval of the plant engineer and other top management. When work actually begins, again he may act as the resident engineer on the job, interpreting drawings and specifications when necessary, and directing and coordinating the activities of the contractor with plant operations and the plant engineer's staff. In close contact with the job, he is able to determine necessary changes in the work not covered by contract and make rapid recommendations for approval of change orders before the contractor's work is interrupted because of the required change. One of the most important benefits derived by the use of a field representative is that of assuring quality workmanship by the contractor.

Since this representative is so closely involved with the job, it is then natural to expect that he should have a hand in examining and approving contractor's invoices and any supporting papers such as daily time sheets, vendor's material bills, and equipment-rental bills. These documents supporting contractor's invoices should be required only when a cost-plus type of contract is used.

Upon completion of a job and before final payment, a final acceptance inspection should be made in the presence of the contractor to assure satisfaction and correction of minor details in work, if any are required. A contractor, knowing this inspection is to take place, will make sure that good workmanship is exercised by his people to prevent undue costs at the end of the job.

Guarantees and Penalties. Where possible guarantees should be established in the specifications to cover failures in any installation due to defective workmanship or material furnished by the contractor. The guarantee period varies with the materials used; for example, roofs may be guaranteed for 10 to 20 years after completion, structural-steel work and mechanical-trades work may be guaranteed for 1 year, and other phases such as architectural trades may carry no guarantee. Where applicable however, it is advisable that a contractor be required to execute a written guarantee for the protection of the owner.

Penalties may be used under certain conditions. If time is of the essence and failure to complete an installation on a given date is critical and will cost the owner financially, a penalty may be used at the owner's discretion to provide protection for the owner and additional incentive for the contractor to complete the work on schedule. However, the use of a penalty may well lead to poorer workmanship in order to assure completion on schedule. In general, so far as employment of a reputable contractor in industry is concerned, penalties are not deemed necessary.

Chapter 8

PREVENTIVE MAINTENANCE

By CARL G. WYDER[1]
Senior Maintenance Editor
Factory
New York, N.Y.

WHAT PREVENTIVE MAINTENANCE IS

Ask any 10 plant operating executives to define preventive maintenance, and you'll probably get 10 different meanings. Because preventive maintenance—PM for short—varies widely in scope and intensity of application.

Many executives think of PM only in terms of periodic inspection of plant and equipment to prevent breakdowns before they occur. To this limited view some add repetitive servicing, upkeep, and overhaul. In a more advanced stage are those who include other repetitive maintenance functions such as lubrication, painting, and cleaning. Still others include the use of plant and worker protective equipment. Further along the way are those who also study materials and finishes of the equipment (or building, or facility) before it is purchased and installed. Good PM, they say, begins with proper design and installation. Instead of setting up routines to keep motors clean in dusty areas, for example, they specify T.E.F.C. (totally enclosed, fan-cooled) motors to eliminate this continuing expense.

Then we progress to a few people who broadly apply the PM philosophy to any activity that not only will prevent breakdowns or cut operating costs but also will improve output or quality of product. In one plant, a control automatically shuts down a machine tool when any particular cutting tool has worked on a predetermined number of pieces. The worn tool is replaced. This is PM of a highly developed character—a far cry from the purely inspection-adjustment routine of the majority of PM programs; but it is typical of a trend in highly mechanized industries that will accelerate as automation gradually takes over.

Basic Definition. No matter to what degree of refinement a PM program is developed, all of them contain these basic activities:

1. Periodic inspection of plant assets and equipment to uncover conditions leading to production breakdowns or harmful depreciation.
2. Upkeep of plant to sterilize such conditions, or to adjust or repair such conditions while they are still in a minor stage.

Size of the activity is immaterial. To an electrical engineer, PM may mean the proper choice and setting of delicate relays in controls to avoid unnecessary downtime. To a mechanical engineer, it may mean a complete tear-down and overhaul of a process pump or rolling mill.

This basic concept will be the definition in most of the discussion in this chapter.

[1] The author is now retired.

At the close, however, finer techniques which might be added to any basic program if the extra costs justify will be reviewed. Lubrication is not discussed because it is covered elsewhere in this book. There is no discussion of the rudiments of job planning, scheduling, and work orders for the same reason.

"Planned maintenance" often is misused as a synonym for preventive maintenance, as also are "scheduled," "controlled," and "productive" maintenance. The fact is, PM should be an important part of all these functions, but not the only constituent. There are many activities other than PM which should be planned, scheduled, controlled, and made productive. Among them is "corrective" maintenance, which some define as the activity of repair after breakdown, others as the study of better materials and design to minimize breakdowns.

Obviously, PM reduces the corrective-maintenance work load. As PM takes over, in effect the timing of the corrective work load is shifted from when you *have* to do it to when you *want* to do it. Thus the work can be done more efficiently and at lower cost.

WHY INDUSTRY NEEDS PM

Any well-designed PM program will yield benefits far in excess of its cost. I still have to find someone practicing PM who says it doesn't pay. Many men have had some doubts before adopting it, but none thereafter.

Not every plant can expect to derive equal benefits. The product, the process and the method of manufacture are factors in amount and scope of results. The more highly mechanized an industry gets, the more it needs the advantages of PM. Costs of maintenance of modern equipment are higher. And cost of downtime, too. One large automobile plant estimates a penalty of $3,000 for every minute the main-assembly conveyor line is down. In any plant where downtime is important, PM will reduce it. There is no question that downtime will be less with PM than without it. To what extent, depends on what you aim for. In this auto plant, for instance, 1 per cent downtime can be critical.

Preventive maintenance is not a cure-all for excessive downtime or high maintenance costs. There are other maintenance functions with which PM must be integrated to achieve an efficient plant-maintenance program—a good paper-work system, work planning and scheduling, training, work measurement, control reports, and good shop and tools. Here are the major returns with which PM has rewarded its users:

1. Less production downtime, with all its related savings and customer benefits, because of fewer breakdowns.
2. Less overtime pay for maintenance men on ordinary adjustments and repairs than for breakdown repairs.
3. Fewer large-scale repairs, and fewer repetitive repairs, hence less crowding of maintenance manpower and facilities.
4. Lower repair costs for simple repairs made before breakdowns, because less manpower, fewer skills, and fewer parts are needed for planned shutdowns than for breakdowns.
5. Fewer product rejects, less spoilage, better quality control, because of properly adjusted equipment.
6. Postponement or elimination of cash outlays for premature replacement of plant or equipment, because of better conservation of assets and increased life expectancy.
7. Less standby equipment needed, thus reducing capital investment.
8. Decline of maintenance costs—labor and material—on asset items in the program.
9. Identification of items with high maintenance costs, leading to investigation and correction of causes such as (1) misapplication, (2) operator abuse, and (3) obsolescence.
10. Shift from inefficient "breakdown" maintenance to less costly scheduled maintenance, hence better work control.
11. Better spare-parts control, leading to minimum inventory.

12. Better industrial relations because production workers don't suffer involuntary layoffs or loss of incentive bonus from breakdowns.
13. Greater safety for workers, and improved protection for plant, leading to lower compensation and insurance costs.
14. Lower unit cost of manufacture.

These are all realistic benefits that apply in any industrial economy—peace or war, expanding, stable, or contracting. To sum up, the benefits of PM are the same as those accruing to any well-maintained plant, plus the economies it provides in greater plant efficiency and lower over-all manufacturing costs.

Is there any industry where PM doesn't pay? Not that I know of. It is being applied successfully to all types of operations, large and small. One maintenance executive of a multiplant setup applies PM to his smallest operation of 3 maintenance men as well as to his larger plants of 250 men. There is no upper manpower limit. PM works in process industries—in either batch or continuous round-the-clock operations. It works in job-shop or production-line or continuous-flow operations. None is exempt from its benefits.

BEFORE YOU START A PM PROGRAM

Whether or not the plant maintenance executive is the one who starts the idea of a PM program, he usually has to run it. But unless he is careful to erect some firm foundations of company understanding and policy before applying the program, he will find it tough going afterward. And the program may fail, not because unworthy but because it wasn't given a fair chance.

How to Sell PM. The success of a PM program hinges largely on how well everybody in the plant is sold on PM—higher management, production executives and supervisors, and plant-maintenance supervisors and craftsmen. Time spent in winning management support will spare you many headaches later on.

Most logically, start selling with higher management. This immediately raises the question: What will a PM program cost? So maintenance men clamor for a proved formula for dollars-and-cents savings.

There are several ways of satisfying management's understandable demand for cost figures. I have for some time suggested the following approach: Check over records for the past year or more for all machine breakdowns. List the total cost of breakdown repairs—labor, material, overtime, any other charges. List what each breakdown has cost in idle time of operators, spoilage, and rework. To these you might add cost of operating overhead, and other possible losses such as cost of injuries. Next, estimate what the repairs would have cost if made before the breakdowns—if there had been time for planning, getting materials, and making productive use of operators. The difference is what might be spent on a preventive-maintenance program.

In drawing up any cost vs. savings comparison, there is a possibility (at least at the start) that direct maintenance costs will rise. Management must realize PM is an investment that needs extra cash as does any new plant or equipment. In the case of PM, the return is highly promising. A good way to document the gross return is to check the list of benefits given under Why Industry Needs PM, and evaluate them as best you can. The summation is always impressive. The secret of selling management on PM is to show PM in its over-all results of lower unit cost of manufacture of the product. Don't fail to show its effect on higher output, better quality, and lower capital-investment needs.

The next step is to win production men to the idea. In selling them the appeal is somewhat the same as for higher management. Don't try to sell better maintenance—sell better production. This is the advice of those who have ventured and won. Unless the production executive sees definite gains for his own interests, he will stall or balk whenever it's time to shut down a machine for a scheduled inspection or overhaul. But if he knows that the downtime for PM will be less in the long run than total outages from breakdowns, he will cooperate. Biggest objections to PM might come from continuous-process departments where a whole line instead of a single unit is involved in a shutdown. In this case your strong argument is that you are servicing all units in that line simultaneously and at one predetermined time rather than single units at separate breakdowns for a greater total of downtime.

"But you can't always prove these benefits in advance," is the wail of many maintenance executives. "Without decisive proof we can't get to first base with either management or production people." In such case, you're not necessarily lost. Show them articles on how other plants have profited from PM. Send them a report on defects you have discovered by inspections, and corrected, and show what "might have been" if not discovered. If they won't buy that, you can do as many others have already done—quietly install PM in one or two departments where it should prove most effective. Or find one sympathetic production department head willing to give PM a trial, and use this successful case as a wedge to break down stubborn resistance. In that case be sure to keep a record of rejects, downtime, overtime, and similar penalties. The results always have spoken for themselves.

The selling job isn't completed with selling the idea to management and production. After the program is prepared, it is best to explain it in detail to all departments affected. An ideal way is for management to arrange for briefing sessions with production or operating heads and supervisors. Use the first session to introduce the program, others as needed to smooth out the wrinkles. It's a mistake ever to give the impression that PM is strictly a maintenance responsibility. Make it clear that it's everybody's job.

Should the union be advised? By all means, say those who have learned the hard way. By acquainting the union with the program, you gain its confidence, also forestall possible complaints and grievances by first clearing up misunderstandings. Show the union that men will not suffer from PM. As a rule the time saved by PM can be directed to better maintenance of existing plant and to take care of added work load of a growing plant.

Finally, all maintenance supervisors and craftsmen must be briefed. Because these are the men who are most intimately involved, they need more administrative details than other departments. Craftsmen long schooled in the old order of "standby" or "breakdown" maintenance also need help in making a mental about-face under a new regime of PM. It may take some time for die-hards to come around to the PM approach, but experience has proved they can be brought in line by proper indoctrination, training, and (later on) by pointing to the results of the program itself. The men will soon realize that PM has made their jobs easier, and often safer.

Program Takes Time. Anybody who expects the full benefits of PM quickly will be disappointed. All the experts agree it takes several years to get rolling in high. You will see some progress after several months. And it will keep snowballing.

Will a consultant speed things up? Or is this a do-it-yourself job? Obviously a consultant will speed up the period of planning the program and its installation. But this is not always the only determinant. In many cases where PM is not a habit, the maintenance executive is already up to his ears in responsibilities. He doesn't have time to work out the best PM program. He has to start from the ground up. Unless he can delegate much of the leg work of accumulating records and directing the moves, he can't handle the mass of details involved at the start. It isn't therefore a question so much of whether the maintenance executive is capable of organizing an effective PM program, but of whether he has the time.

There are other factors in the time picture—size of plant, type of operations, educational qualifications of the maintenance executive and his assistants, proper clerical help, and the present condition of plant and equipment. As a rule, larger plants require more study and need more highly refined PM programs and methods of administration.

Conditions Inventory. If a plant has been plugging along, say, on an 80 per cent breakdown basis (80 per cent of its maintenance man-hours on breakdown repairs), the time of conversion to a satisfactory PM basis (it may range from 30 to 80 per cent man-hours on PM) will be delayed. Before the maintenance executive can apply PM to any plant or equipment, he must put it into good shape. It may take him 6,

12, or more months to do it. And he must have an equipment record, one of which is shown in Fig. 8-1.

The maintenance head should not fail to point out this fact when he's got the green light from management for a PM program. Otherwise the time and cost of reconditioning gets charged against PM, gives it a black eye right at the start. It is therefore a good plan to take a "conditions inventory" to size up the cost of reconditioning and time needed. Such a survey often leads to disposal of high-repair-cost items that should have been junked long ago.

EQUIPMENT RECORD   Our No. 3206

Description	Model TG-636 Automatic Thread Grinder				Maker			Serial No. 110564	

Vendor						Address			

Date	Ordered	9-1-52	Width	10'	Weight	11,000 Lbs.		Water	No
	Received	12-8-52	Depth	6'	Exhaust	2-6" sq. exhaust ducts		Gas	No
	Installed	12-14-52	Height	6'	Air	Air gun by machine		Steam	No

Details   Uses refrigerating unit to cool grinding oil

Location Now in Dept.	T. Gage #38	Transfers	Date 11/27	To Dept. 40	Date	To	Date	To

Lubrication		Bearing and Belt Data

Spindle bearings   3 Drip feed-daily
Base   1 Reservoir-(W) 4 mos.
Gear change box   1 Reservoir-(W) 4 mos.
Grinding   5 Reservoir-(W) 3 mos.
Elec. motor bear.   12 Grease gun-4 mos.
		Ball thrust bearings used
		   5207K
		   3207 Internal attachment bearings
		
		1-2" x 28" lg. endless flat belt

MOTOR RECORD

Mfg.	HP	RPM.	Type	Frame	Style	Serial No.	Model No.	Volts	Amps .
	1.5	1135	K	224		XK6588	5K224D932	220/440	4.98/2.49
	5	1150/3450	B	284		PK217	58284A154	220	10.8
	1/8	1725	DM	2912		PA9569		230	.7

Phase	Cycle	Control Equip.	Drives	Belts	Type Bearing	Bearing Data	Our No.
3	60	Main cont. bx.	Direct		Ball bearing	1305W	4224
DC	DC	Main cont. bx.	Direct	B-85		207MF	5152
DC	DC	Main cont. bx.	Direct		Ball bearing	202	5148

FIG. 8-1. Equipment record. Typical equipment record of plant machinery and equipment includes all data needed by maintenance executive to set up a PM program.

As a result of this inventory some plants have to add craftsmen to their maintenance forces to catch up with the bigger repair load. Outside manufacturers' shops or local repair shops can lighten the burden and are sometimes better equipped to do a cheaper and better job. Often this backlog of repairs stems from an inadequate maintenance force. If so, force enlargement should be made permanent. Enlightened management must realize the added labor cost is more than offset by production benefits. Case after case has proved it.

HOW TO START A PM PROGRAM

To many of the uninitiated, PM is a system, nothing more. They think all they have to do is set up forms, inspection schedules, and a corps of inspectors, and let the calendar do the rest. They ask for hard-and-fast rules of conduct to use like dimensional blueprints for building and running the program.

That is not the way to start a PM program. This concept loses sight of the true goal of PM, and of all plant-maintenance functions—maintenance for low-cost production of a quality product. This same element of cost dominates every phase of a good PM program, and determines what to do. The right and economic PM plan for one plant might be wrong and uneconomic for another. Take the case of a company that erected a building solely for housing experiments calculated to run 1 year. It maintained this building on that basis. Shortly after the conclusion of experiments, the building practically fell apart. But it had served the purpose. Poor maintenance, but economically justified. And therefore good PM.

If a PM program is to succeed, the administrator must learn to let economic considerations guide and even overrule his engineering dictates. Any good engineer can set up an airtight PM program aimed solely to conserve plant and equipment. And he might do this at minimum maintenance cost. But he's got to learn, right from the start, to examine the effect of all facets of the PM program on manufacturing costs. It might seem engineering folly to let a $500 motor go to ruin to keep a production line going. But when balanced against a loss of $2,000 in work in process because of a shutdown, it makes common sense.

This emphasis on economics may seem a strange approach to what appears to be strictly an engineering problem. But as we get into the mechanics of a PM program, we are faced at every turn with economic decisions on where to draw the line. This is another reason why the administrator needs the understanding and cooperation of higher management and all operating heads.

Master the Principles. There is no ready-made, on-the-shelf PM program for any plant. It must be tailor-made—measured and cut to fit individual requirements. I have studied hundreds of PM programs, and never found two exactly the same.

The reason should be clear. There are no two plants identical in size, age, location, construction, equipment, services, or layout. They differ in organization, operating policies, and personnel. Problems of maintenance differ. A chemical plant may justify the services of a corrosion engineer on its maintenance staff. Or a food plant may need a sanitation engineer. That's no reason a clothing manufacturer should have either. Similarly, the problems of PM are different, don't respond to the same treatment.

That is not to say that there is no resemblance between any two PM systems. There is, in objectives and basic principles, not in engineering or paper work. To anyone seeking a ready-made program—and the majority of beginners seem to pursue this will-o'-the-wisp—I can give only this advice: Learn the PM principles first, and let the paper work follow. Paper work is important. But it can cost more than it should if it's the wrong kind. In short, don't adopt paper work successfully used elsewhere prior to a study of your own problem. Such a mistake can lead to costly misapplication of unsuitable forms and procedures.

Where to Start PM. Consensus is that it's too big a bite to apply PM to the entire plant at once. It's best to build up the program in pieces. How fast you must do it isn't significant. When one piece is finished, start the next.

Is it best to tackle one department at a time, or one type of equipment over the entire plant? Opinion seems divided. So why not decide on the easier? Local conditions probably rule which approach is best. Another factor is how well PM has been sold. If you have to show proof fast of the value of PM, start where you think it's needed most, and therefore will pay the biggest dividend more quickly.

Basic Problem. For the sake of simplicity, view PM primarily as the function of minimizing breakdowns or harmful depreciation of plant and equipment through periodic inspections to discover and correct unfavorable conditions. The entire program hangs on inspections and their related duties of adjustment and repair.

Inspections are costly in labor, and sometimes in equipment downtime. They are the key point in the control of the cost of a PM program. The fewer the inspections needed, the lower the cost. The problem, therefore, is to strike a favorable balance between this cost and the cost of not utilizing PM. The inspection cost can be directly measured. The cost of not using PM includes not only direct repair costs, but also indirect charges—productive downtime, spoilage, lower depreciation, and many others—which enter into the manufacturing cost of the product. Arm yourself with all these historical data for several years back. They will guide your inspection policies. Moreover, should higher management look askance at the mounting cost of a growing PM program, you can demonstrate with cold facts how the cost balance lies.

WHAT TO INSPECT IN PM

By far the most wanted information from those starting a PM program has been: "Can you give me a list of what items to include and how often to inspect?" It would be nice if we could, but it isn't that easy.

In fact it can't be done. This part of the tailor-made process everyone has to do for himself. There are general principles, however, to guide the development. There are do's and don't's to keep you on the right track. We'll examine first the "what to include" part, and attack the "how often" angle in a subsequent portion.

Here is an indication of how industry is applying PM to its various properties: In 1953, *Factory Management and Maintenance* published the results of a survey of 542 plants on maintenance practices. Replies indicated the following percentages for PM in these general categories: motors, 78.4 per cent; production machinery, 65.9 per cent; controls, 63.6 per cent; buildings, 61.9 per cent; materials-handling equipment, 58.9 per cent; process equipment, 51.8 per cent; plant services, 50.5 per cent; lighting, 48.8 per cent.

What should the individual plant decide to include? The answer depends largely on local conditions. A good program will include most of the plant's physical property. One maintenance executive sums it up this way: "We've found it pays to inspect buildings, tanks, fences, roof, elevators, cranes, sanitary facilities, lighting, and mobile equipment."

A process plant summarizes its PM coverage in somewhat more detail to include:

1. Process equipment—furnaces, heat exchangers, piping, pumps, compressors, motors, stills, instruments.
2. Safety equipment—vacuum and pressure-relief valves, flashback or flame arrestors, breathing and emergency-relief equipment.
3. Utility equipment—main boilers, electric generators, supply, storage, and distribution systems for water, steam, and compressed-air pipelines.
4. Tanks and auxiliary equipment—storage tanks, pipelines, dikes, drains, gages, and measuring instruments.
5. Plant buildings—includes shipping and storage areas, also transportation equipment such as tank cars and transfer pumps.
6. Fire-protection equipment—water supply and pipelines, pumps, permanent fire-extinguishing installations of foam, fog, gas, spray, or dry powder, first-aid extinguishers, fire trucks, alarm systems.

A good PM program makes sure to include seasonal functions of equipment as well as care of equipment itself. For example, it will include one-shot duties such as the pumping down of a refrigeration system not used in winter months, or protection of valuable shrubbery against cold, or making ready the snowplow. And it will include special measures for preservation of machinery and plant during shutdowns for off-season layups, scheduled vacations, unexpected labor troubles, or weather catastrophes.

What Not to Inspect. Up to this point the approach to what to inspect has been made purely for good maintenance of physical or operating conditions. On that basis alone an engineer would be inclined to include everything in the plant that wears out or is likely to cause downtime. This is where the economics of PM must step in to sift out unprofitable activities. No need to inspect everything.

Where draw the line? Only an itemized appraisal of your own equipment will tell. "Is it necessary and is it worth the cost?" is the focal question. One plant which covers about 80 per cent of its major equipment in PM, and expects to add more, uses this guide: "We include a piece of equipment if the program saves money over casual maintenance methods. We don't inspect about 400 noncritical fractional-horsepower motors. Outages run 5 to 10 such motors a year. Most failures are the hard-to-detect winding faults. Inspection costs would far exceed the $200 annual replacement costs."

Another plant reports: "We arbitrarily limit our inspections to items costing above $500." Many plants apply such arbitrary dollar limits, ranging from $50 up.

Sometimes the dollar limit varies for different types of equipment or parts of equipment, depending on factors such as ease and speed of repair, or effect of failure on employee safety.

There is one process plant that does not inspect its process pipelines. The reason makes good sense; it doesn't waste money inspecting the obvious but depends on all operating and maintenance personnel to report defects or suspicious conditions on that type of equipment. Another plant inspects only its very large motors. It found that inspections of lesser motors cost more than keeping spares on hand and replacing them as required. It does the same for its starters and controllers. A third plant spends $1,500 monthly for a weekly checkup of 5,000 motors.

How decide? An over-all analysis along the lines of these questions will help:

1. Is this a critical item? If failure will cause a major shutdown, or costly damage, or harm to an employee, need for PM is almost certain.
2. Is standby equipment available in case of failure? You can rent air compressors or package boilers on short notice. If the load or duty can be easily shifted to other equipment, need for PM is contingent on other factors, such as cost of "breakdown" maintenance.
3. Does cost of PM exceed expense of downtime and cost of repair or replacement? If it costs no less to tear down a machine to repair a repetitive wear point than the over-all cost of the repair itself, the value of PM is highly questionable.
4. Does the normal life of the equipment without PM exceed manufacturing needs? If obsolescence is expected sooner than decay, PM may be a waste of money.

In the case of nonoperating equipment, the decision of what to include can be guided by this simple philosophy: If failure in upkeep or adjustment of the element harms either production or the employee, or wastes plant assets, think hard before you exclude it from PM. To wit, if poor lighting hampers production, or holes in the floor harm the worker, they may rate PM. If failure to clean air filters causes dirt and grit that is harmful to plant, people, or product, PM seems justified. That is why some plants include machine guards, hand tools, and similar accessory equipment that needs periodic checking to assure efficient and safe plant operations.

WHAT TO INSPECT FOR

When drawing up a list of items for PM you must have given thought as to why you need to inspect them. Now comes the job of determining what physical parts of each piece of equipment need attention. This is not an academic suggestion. For in this study you bridge the gap between theory of PM and practice. Unless a man is told what parts to inspect he may defeat your plans for proper surveillance.

Many of these inspection points can be worked out by the collaborative efforts of the maintenance force. Don't overlook the craftsman who regularly maintains the equipment—he often pin-points an item liable to wear or maladjustment under local conditions that even the manufacturer might overlook.

But plant experience isn't enough to draw on. One of the best sources is the service manual issued by the equipment manufacturer. It's an invaluable guide to what and when to inspect, as well as how to install, service, and maintain the equipment. In appreciation of their value, many plants accumulate and file service manuals. Purchase orders specify two or more copies. One goes to the central file, another to the craft foreman, and often a third to an area file for craftsmen. This growing demand for service manuals—incidentally the government insists on them—has put so much pressure on manufacturers that rarely is one not available for new equipment.

Check Lists. After going to all the trouble of developing a list of machines and their inspection points, how do you make sure they are not overlooked? This is done by the check list. In the afore-mentioned 542-plant survey, some 70 per cent reported they use check lists. In principle, a check list itemizes for the inspector all the points to be checked on any one piece or type of equipment or property. It provides spaces for dates and initials to show when inspected, and by whom. Nothing is left to memory.

Check lists have other advantages. They assume uniform and complete inspections regardless of who does the job. They are invaluable when new inspectors or substitutes are needed, or where rotation of inspectors is practiced.

A simple form is shown in Fig. 8-2. Here again, the layout is not important. The problem is more what to put on it. The goal should always be simplicity and a minimum of paper work. Make sure no machine part or item is omitted that needs attention. But also see that inspection costs are not inflated by needless checks and tests.

CHECKLIST FOR MACHINE INSPECTION
INSPECT AND CHECK OFF FOLLOWING ITEMS
SHOW ALL DEFECTIVE ITEMS WITH X MARK

TO BE CHECKED	DEF.	OK	DEF.	OK	DEF.	OK	DEF.	OK	DEF.	OK
Motor		✓		✓		✓		✓		✓
Bearings	X			✓		✓		✓	X	
Gears	X		X		X		X		X	
Clutch		✓		✓		✓	X			✓
Brake		✓	X			✓		✓		✓
Piping		✓		✓		✓		✓		✓
Guards		✓		✓	X			✓		✓
Lubrication	X		X		X			✓		✓
Rolls		✓		✓		✓		✓		✓
Cutter		✓		✓		✓		✓		✓
INSPECTED BY DATE	H.V. 6-1		H.V. 7-1		H.V. 8-1		H.V. 9-1		H.V. 10-2	

FIG. 8-2. PM check list. Simple check list can be used for different types of machinery. Items in "to-be-checked" column are set up permanently for each type, revised when necessary.

One West Coast airplane company has devised a unique two-part inspection form that minimizes paper work. The first part is a light cardboard strip, 4½ by 11 in., which overlays the left half of the second part, a yellow paper sheet 8½ by 11 in. The first part, the instruction card, lists the items to be checked. The second part serves as the report form, on which the inspector notes the date and results of the inspection. It has 13 columns for weekly inspections. When the yellow sheet is filled at the end of each quarter it is permanently filed. The cardboard overlay is reused until it wears out or is replaced by a revision.

There is some danger that a check list will make an inspector feel it lists everything he needs to inspect, no more. To avoid discouraging his ability or imagination, you can provide a space on the form for extra comments. Don't just label it "Comments," or "Suggestions." Instead, challenge the inspector's pride with a question such as "Do we need to include anything else in the next inspection?" Like PM inspection lists, check lists need continual refining and updating. Experience usually cues the need for checking overlooked items.

How many check lists does a plant need? It's impossible to tell. One metalworking plant employing 40 maintenance craftsmen has developed about 50 check lists. A cable manufacturer with 500 machine units developed almost 400. All observations point to their increased use in industry as mechanization grows.

Sometimes check lists can be combined with other forms to minimize paper work. Some plants combine them with inspection schedules, or use them as blanket work orders. One maintenance executive gets more mileage out of his check list for buildings by using it as a periodic "conditions survey." He provides columns for 3 years ahead, laid out in 6-month intervals. Besides checking current conditions, his inspector marks whatever date he estimates repairs will be needed. This gives the maintenance executive a reliable picture of future needs for long-range planning and budgeting.

HOW OFTEN TO INSPECT—FREQUENCY

Other than what to inspect, more people ask for a ready-made list of how often to inspect than anything else. The decision of how often to inspect probably has the most bearing on costs and savings of a PM program. Overinspection is a needless expense and may involve more productive downtime than an emergency breakdown. Underinspection results in more breakdowns, earlier replacements. Good balance is needed to bring optimum savings.

No ready-made list is available. You must work out your own values—no one else can do it for you. Age of plant, kind of equipment, environment, types of operation, and similar factors must be considered. No two plants are alike.

But you can get helpful timetables from many equipment and materials manufacturers. Even they avoid being dogmatic. They are careful to qualify their recommendations by saying the tables apply to normal conditions. They may describe what these normal conditions are. And they suggest you trim the normal figures by various percentages for special exposures or types of service.

Here are other sources of timetables:

National Electric Manufacturers Association, New York City, and similar trade organizations for mechanical and building items.
Factory Insurance Association, Hartford, Conn.
Factory Mutual Engineering Division, Norwood, Mass.
National Safety Council, Inc., Chicago, Ill.
Your own insurance carrier.

At this point let's be sure we distinguish frequencies from schedules. These two words are often misused for each other. Frequency is the period or interval which is determined from an engineering and economic viewpoint as most desirable for servicing. A schedule shows the calendar time or date chosen to do the job. Frequency is "how often"—schedule is "when."

Remember, too, that one piece of equipment may have several frequencies for servicing, such as once daily for cleaning, once weekly for adjustment, once monthly for functional inspection, and once yearly for overhaul. So when we speak of inspection frequency in this section, we are actually thinking of all types of maintenance services as epitomized by the inspection function. They include lubrication, sanitation, painting, testing, and the like, but exclude repairs.

Start with Engineering Analysis. There is no dearth of data on inspection frequencies for any type of equipment. The big job is to assemble them, weed out what you need, then temper to your plant conditions.

First step in gaging the best frequency cycle is an engineering analysis of equipment from these viewpoints:

1. Age, condition, and value. Older and poorer equipment needs more frequent services. But if ready for the junkpile, or soon to be obsolete, may be cheaper to inspect on a skeleton basis or not at all.
2. Severity of service. More severe applications of identical equipment require shorter cycles. In a process plant you might need to inspect a critical pump every day—the same type of pump in a metal-working plant only once a month.
3. Safety requirements. Allow a wide margin for safety. For example, one plant inspects the solenoids operating the clutches on presses every 2 weeks.
4. Hours of operation. Many manufacturers suggest frequency cycles based on an 8-hr day, others on usage (such as mileage). Buildings and seasonal services operate on a calendar basis. Sometimes two bases are used, whichever comes first. For example, sump cleaning may be needed when changing operations, or at least every 30 days.

5. Susceptibility to wear. What is exposure to dirt, friction, fatigue, stress, corrosion? What is life expectancy?
6. Susceptibility to damage. Is it subject to vibration, overloading, abuse?
7. Susceptibility to losing adjustment. How will maladjustment or misalignment affect it? Where manufacturing tolerances are tight, shorter inspection cycle is needed.

In this process of revising manufacturers' recommendations to suit your own plant conditions, it is best to follow those recommendations until you have good reason to alter them. If in doubt, err on the safe side. Seek the data involved in carrying out the following procedures:

1. Service records. Dig out whatever data on costs and performance you have— equipment records, downtime reports, routine maintenance schedules. They are excellent clues not only as to what to inspect for, but also how often.
2. Maintenance work orders. Sort out completed orders by individual machines or functions, if you don't already have an equipment record. Then analyze nature of repairs.
3. Craftsmen. Get the benefit of their close experience, including lube men.
4. Operating heads. Ask them how often they think service is needed.
5. Quality-control charts. Product inspectors can point to main causes of rejects and spoilage.
6. Other plants. Review lists of those preferably in the same industry, but merely as a guide. To quote from the experience of one maintenance executive who supervises over 50 plants in his multiplant setup, and all in the same industry: "It's necessary to inspect some equipment more frequently, other equipment less frequently, in one plant than another."

Gradual Refinement Needed. Once you've decided on frequency cycles, you've only begun. This is not a static thing either. You can't sit back and watch the program run. You have to check the results continually and be willing to modify cycles to meet operating requirements. This is true of all facets of the PM program— beginning with what to inspect, and what to inspect for, right down the line. You have to add or subtract, even rightabout-face. When you find yourself replacing parts that are still good, you may be playing too safe. Cost of discarding good parts adds to the cost of PM. The only instance I've heard of failure of a PM program was directly attributed to failure of the maintenance executive to update frequencies and adjust them to better economy.

If you're lucky, it may take only a year to stabilize the inspection program. But a periodic appraisal is still necessary to keep it on an even keel. Many plants, especially larger ones, have been refining and tightening up their program for several years or more. Frequency cycles are the chief targets.

To ensure a continuing attack on the validity of a cycle, some plants use these methods:

1. Cut and try. Whenever a unit is inspected or repaired, they decide when next to inspect.
2. Check new equipment more frequently until run in. In one case a new compressor was checked every day, then every week, and now every 4 months.
3. Require inspectors to indicate on check lists or inspection reports whether frequency cycle needs a boost or can take a cut.

Statistical Checks. How can one know whether he is overmaintaining, or undermaintaining, or doing just the right amount? Obviously it's a matter of individual analyses of actual results. On one side of the ledger are number and costs of inspections and services. On the other side, number and over-all costs of repairs and breakdowns. If there are no repairs, chances are you're overmaintaining. If too many repairs, the inspections aren't getting at the root of the trouble. The dollar-wise appraisal always helps you arrive at a good balance.

Another way to evaluate the success of PM is by a comparison of scheduled maintenance (PM or routine repairs) with unscheduled maintenance (emergency repairs). Good maintenance executives insist on a monthly report of these types of work in maintenance man-hours. Too much unscheduled work points to lack of PM. This may mean too few units inspected or too low an inspection frequency. No unscheduled work is the other extreme. What is a good ratio? Some plants boast of 80 to 90 per cent man-hours on scheduled work, including repairs turned up by PM inspections.

WHEN TO INSPECT—SCHEDULES

Up to this point we've decided on what to inspect, and how often. The next step is making up a work schedule to include each PM item (see Figs. 8-3A and 8-3B).

Theoretically a schedule must be perfect in coverage. If it overlooks a single item, some kind of trouble will pop up later. Failure to check an alarm, for example, might invoke costly penalties if it doesn't function when it should.

Ordinarily, scheduling involves a determination of calendar inspection dates that will fulfill the frequency requirements in the most efficient way. This is not always possible, particularly in the case of production machinery and equipment. There's where the headaches usually are, unless everybody—maintenance and production forces—will cooperate. The maintenance executive himself can eliminate many of those headaches. In setting up schedules he must be continually conscious of his responsibility to keep production going at lowest over-all cost. He must arrange schedules to be adaptable to production needs.

But this is getting the cart before the horse. We ought first to examine the problems in the mechanics of setting up schedules, then the problems of their application. Practically every plant can divide its PM inspection and service functions into **three** groups:

1. Routine upkeep. This type of work is done at regular short intervals—adjusting, lubricating, cleaning—while equipment is operating or productively idle. This also includes care of nonproductive items such as lighting, heating, filters.
2. Periodic inspections. Covers work at prescribed intervals on equipment that is running or shut down—visual inspections, teardown inspections, overhauls, scheduled replacement of parts.
3. Contingent work. Includes work at indefinite intervals when equipment is down for other reasons. Example, inspection of gas burners when relining a furnace.

Obviously, the more PM work you can squeeze into the contingent category, the less costly it will be. To ensure that the work will be done, you can schedule such items on a "which-comes-first" basis. This you do (1) by listing these PM items on your work-planning sheet kept for repetitive maintenance jobs (such as relining a furnace), and (2) by protecting yourself by a "tickler" item timed for the maximum allowable period between inspections. Along the same lines, you can pile up a list of repair jobs that have been uncovered by running inspections and which can be deferred until the next shutdown.

In scheduling PM of the nature of routine upkeep or periodic inspections, these are good goals:

1. Handle them on the day shift, preferably, to minimize overtime. But don't overlook the possibility of greater worker effectiveness on overtime basis overbalancing the greater labor cost.
2. Distribute them over the year to even up the total maintenance work load. But remember to schedule PM work for slack seasons whenever possible, like service refrigeration units or air-conditioning units in winter when not operating.
3. Shoot for least productive downtime. You might do this by scheduling PM during setup time, or even shifting the job to an off shift.

DEPARTMENT 23		WEEKLY MAINTENANCE SCHEDULE PRODUCTION MACHINERY

Ⓒ CLEAN　-⊙-OVERHAUL　● FUNCTIONAL CHECK

MACH. NO.	DESCRIPTION OF MACH.	1	2	3	4	5	6	7	8	9	10	11	12	13
2233	Surface Grinder						Ⓒ							
2201	Surface Grinder			Ⓒ								-⊙-		
1216	#2 Horizontal Mill				-Ⓒ-									Ⓒ
131	#2 Horizontal Mill	●							●					
132	%8 Horizontal Mill		●											
134	%8 Horizontal Mill		●											

A

WEEKLY MAINTENANCE SCHEDULE
AIR CONDITIONING SYSTEMS

Ⓧ CLEAN　　-⊙- OVERHAUL　　● FUNCTIONAL CHECK

		1	2	3	4	5	6	7	8	9	10	11	12	13	14	15	46	47	48	49	50	51	52
NORTH BUILDING	UNIT	Ⓧ	-⊙-		Ⓧ				Ⓧ●			Ⓧ			Ⓧ		●	Ⓧ			Ⓧ		
	FILTERS		Ⓧ						Ⓧ							Ⓧ							
	FANS		Ⓧ●													Ⓧ							
	CONTROL		Ⓧ		●	Ⓧ			Ⓧ●			Ⓧ	●		Ⓧ		●	Ⓧ			Ⓧ●		
GAGE LAB.	UNIT					●		Ⓧ-⊙-			●					Ⓧ●					●		
	FILTERS	Ⓧ	Ⓧ	Ⓧ	Ⓧ	Ⓧ	Ⓧ	Ⓧ	Ⓧ	Ⓧ	Ⓧ	Ⓧ	Ⓧ	Ⓧ	Ⓧ	Ⓧ	Ⓧ	Ⓧ	Ⓧ	Ⓧ	Ⓧ	Ⓧ	Ⓧ
	FANS			Ⓧ						Ⓧ						Ⓧ							
	CONTROL				Ⓧ●				Ⓧ				Ⓧ			●							
CAFETERIA	UNIT					-⊙-															●		
	FILTERS	Ⓧ			Ⓧ			Ⓧ			Ⓧ				Ⓧ			Ⓧ					
	FANS																						
	CONTROL	●						●							●								
EXECUTIVE	UNIT				●		Ⓧ●			●					Ⓧ●						●		

B

FIG. 8-3. Inspection schedules.　Typical weekly flexible schedules: (*A*) for production and (*B*) for service equipment.　They also serve as standing orders for PM inspections and services.　Work is staggered to minimize production downtime and spread the work load.

Types of Schedules.　There are many designs and layouts, but schedules generally are of two main types:

1. Over-all charts.　These list on one large sheet every piece of equipment in a plant, department, class of machine, or service function.
2. Individual cards.　There is usually a separate card for each piece of equipment, machine, or service function. .

The over-all chart is the simpler approach and gives a quick picture of the PM work load.   A typical schedule lists days or months across the top, and itemizes equipment down the left side.   Date for inspections is shown by a check mark or cross in the appropriate columns all across the chart.   A differing symbol can be used to show cleaning, adjustment, overhaul, and so on.   The chart can be used merely as a master list to originate PM work orders, or also as a blanket order for the whole year.   One plant, for example, uses separate charts as blanket orders for PM servicing of ventilating equipment, production machinery, interior building, decorating, lighting, and heating.   Another plant uses a chart for a painting schedule covering 15 years. For that type of projection a chart has no equal.   Charts are generally too unwieldy for scheduling PM functions on machines or equipment in large plants.

Many small and large plants are using card schedules.   They have the advantages of holding more details on PM requirements, and are often combined with equipment records.   In this case the card bears a series of dates along one edge for a movable tag which acts as a visual signal when the next inspection is due.

Don't overlook time meters or totalizers as a basis for scheduling.   Because they show running time in hours or rpm, they are useful on equipment that is run irregularly—pumps, presses, conveyors—as are mileage readings on vehicles.

More will be said on this later.   The whole point is that schedule dates must be set down somewhere—on paper, or punched card, or recording tape—to control the PM inspection program.

Job Scheduling.   In the true sense the date scheduling by chart or card is actually only preliminary programing.   The real scheduling takes place when a definite day has been set, and the job has been planned as to method, tools, equipment, and so on. Whoever does the final scheduling—be he dispatcher, area-maintenance engineer, or craft foreman—must analyze the job for the skills needed and the time required. Other chapters in this handbook tell you how.   Some plants have established "task limits" by an easy historical analysis of past performances, others by time study.

Application of good scheduling practices to PM raises some popular questions:

Should every item be scheduled, no matter how small?   Consensus is yes.   If an inspection is worth making, it's worth scheduling in some way or another.   Small details can often be covered on the check list used on a larger assignment.
What should be done when a schedule is not completed on time?   Assuming the inspection should be made, there's only one thing to do—carry it over to the next period if the delay isn't harmful.   But if delay is bad, issue a special work order that gets priority.   Experience indicates you can expect to fall behind sometimes, catch up other times.   Some plants prefer a 110 to 120 per cent schedule in case work goes faster than expected.
What should be done when level of plant activity changes?   Depends on whether temporary or permanent.   If permanent, revise the schedule up or down as needed. If temporary, ignore the schedule when activity drops, or slot in a special inspection when it jumps (if length of usage is an important factor).   If you go from one to two shifts, building inspections will be least affected, if at all.   But machine inspections may have to be doubled.
How can work be scheduled in a plant on 24-hr, 7-day operation?   Since you've decided you have to inspect, there is no way out but to arrange for the most convenient shutdown.   This may seem impossible, but you have a good case, according to plants that have licked this problem.   Many plants report that the loss in production hours is more than made up by fewer breakdowns and decreasing inspection time.   One process plant says: "We don't have trouble getting production to allow downtime.   We proved it pays.   Before, 75 per cent of our work was on breakdowns—now 95 per cent is scheduled."   If production people won't listen, you'll have to take the case to higher management.   It's safe to argue it will have a minimum of downtime if you can preplan shutdowns.
How handle equipment that needs PM servicing more than once a day?   Arrange for an area craftsman to service on a standing order.   Otherwise, reroute your PM inspector or serviceman.

Problem of Production Equipment. This is a sticky problem, particularly for novices in PM. How schedule a downtime inspection of production equipment? Who is responsible? Who has the final say? How get production people to release equipment?

One way is by "flexible" scheduling. Many schedules give a leeway of 30 days on PM assignments. (Critical equipment, of course, needs more rigid adherence to a schedule.) The craft foreman or dispatcher then fits PM in whenever a machine is down. Production people who are sold on PM will help squeeze out some free time.

Another way is by higher-management dictum, if you can get it, giving the maintenance executive the deciding vote. In one metalworking plant with many types of heavy presses, the maintenance head and safety department have the authority to shut down any machine if continued operation is harmful to equipment or personnel.

Best way, however, is for maintenance men to encourage good coordination with production people. Where organizations have an area-maintenance engineer the problem seldom exists. Somebody from maintenance has to dicker with production, convince it maintenance has only production interests at heart. Here are ways that plants are doing this:

1. Operating foremen agree on suggested schedules. They are not *told*, they are *consulted* on dates. They know cooperation pays.
2. Maintenance executive sets up a tentative schedule for a year, circulates it to production heads for correction and approval.
3. Maintenance department sends advance notice to production as each item comes up, showing reason for need of PM and estimated downtime.
4. Maintenance central planning group sends a weekly report summarizing all units due for maintenance shutdown the following week. List shows downtime expected on each item, also degree of urgency, and what may happen if work cannot be done as scheduled. Later both interests agree on schedule at a weekly meeting.

Revisions in Schedules. As in the case of frequencies, schedules should not be considered static. Give them a periodic review. Changes in frequency will automatically affect schedules. But plant conditions also change. Layouts change. Products change. Equipment and services are constantly improving. New varieties of the same functional equipment appear that require either more or less maintenance. New materials, new methods, new tools all affect scheduling.

WHO INSPECTS—ORGANIZATION

Nobody has to upend his maintenance organization chart to install a PM program. It can be made to fit any type of setup with minor changes. For PM is more a philosophy of operation than a method. Other than the possible addition of one or more clerks and engineers, the same personnel as a rule will be able to execute the program. Should you have to add more people later, it only proves you were not doing the right kind of maintenance job.

Some plants like to handle PM by a separate division of inspectors, crafts, and supervisors. They say it protects PM against domination by other maintenance functions. Others prefer all maintenance work—routine and PM—to be done by the same force. But they avoid neglect of PM by giving it priority. One plant sets up a separate budget for PM manpower. In either case, both views agree on these principles:

1. Don't allow PM work to be interrupted by other maintenance work. It's a great temptation to relax at the start to keep repairs moving. But if you stick to your guns, eventually decrease in breakdowns will release enough men from repairs to keep on top of everything.
2. Routine of work generated by PM should follow same administrative principles as regular maintenance for authorization, accumulation of labor and material costs, and reports. To keep out special forms, one company simply stamps "PM" on regular forms to differentiate.

3. The PM function should head up to the same executive who directs all other plant maintenance. He may need assistance, but PM needs his direction.

If you have a maintenance force of 100 or more men, you'll probably need a full-time PM administrator. His title in some plants is "PM engineer." In one typical company he reports only to the plant engineer. He plans and schedules all necessary inspections, overhauls, services, and repairs. He issues PM work orders for supervisory approval. He follows up all PM jobs to completion. Another plant uses a "maintenance methods" man as staff to the executive. He prepares operation sheets, schedules, and time standards. In smaller plants the maintenance executive usually can supervise the program himself, provided he has the clerical help to process the paper-work details.

What Type Inspector? In the switch from "breakdown" maintenance to PM the new role of inspector raises some questions. What makes a good inspector? Should he be a specialist? Should he inspect full time, do no repairs? Should the job be rotated among qualified craftsmen?

Consensus is that a good PM inspector is generally a craftsman with top skills, who has the ability to test, adjust, and repair the unit he inspects. It helps if he's a trained trouble shooter. Oilers or lubrication men, say many, cannot always diagnose trouble.

Where do you get inspectors? Right from your own force. All you need do is train a competent craftsman in the philosophy of PM, and show him the few paper-work requirements—he'll catch on.

As to developing specialists, opinion seems about evenly divided. And both sides claim advantages. Those in favor of full-time men say they get better inspections. They disapprove of men inspecting their own work. Besides, they say, only trained specialists should be used on hydraulic or electronic equipment. In this belief one company will let only one man inspect press safety equipment, both to ensure proper inspection and to avoid divided responsibility.

Those in favor of rotating the inspection duties among qualified craftsmen present these views: Inspectors do a better job because they know someone else will follow. Such men have a fresh viewpoint, and if they don't see the previous report they can be more impartial in checking each other. They don't develop into prima donna specialists. There is no need to set up a new classification or argue about special pay. They steer clear of jurisdictional disputes by assigning the proper crafts. Also, they have substitutes for illness and vacation absences.

Along these lines one plant rotates its men twice a week. Another plant rotates only for mechanical and electrical inspections, not for building-maintenance functions. Here it employs a structural engineer. A third plant—a small one—delegates daily inspections and lube chores to machine operators but has craftsmen make weekly or longer checks. A fourth plant, which can't find one man singly qualified for mechanical, electrical, and hydraulic inspections, assigns a mixed crew—millwright, electrician, and pipe fitter—to work on a machine all at the same time. Its check lists are broken down into parts for each craft. This cuts down on inspection time, too.

In all cases, pro and con, the practice is fairly unanimous to make simple adjustments during inspections but to avoid lengthy repairs. Some plants set arbitrary time limits for repairs of 15 min up to 2 hr, to enable the inspector to complete his inspection schedule.

Should inspectors be line or staff? Either way seems to work. Tendency is for rotating inspectors to be line, and for full-time inspectors to be staff to the maintenance engineer or in a separate department under him. Some plants use "area" inspectors to handle all types of equipment in a single department. Others prefer to draw inspectors from a central pool. Which is better? The "area" scheme is probably better in a large plant where distances are great and a competent man is there anyhow for operating adjustments, such as in a packaging room. In the central pool, the supervisor can draw on special skills, lay out a fair-day's-work route, and control inspections.

What about pay? There's only a general pattern to guide you. If craftsmen are rotated through inspection assignments, usually they earn their regular rate. Full-time inspectors may be on hourly wage or salary, depending on the level at which they operate. If the inspector is at the foreman's level in job classification, he should get foreman's pay. In short, qualifications and rank should decide.

Unofficial Inspectors. It's a mistake ever to create the impression in a plant that PM inspectors alone are responsible for sleuthing trouble. In a good PM program, everybody from the big boss down gets inoculated with the PM spirit. These include production supervisors, watchmen, all craftsmen, and particularly lube men. In one plant production supervisors are encouraged to recognize bad symptoms by a special check list attached to production units. Another plant has trained its lube men to report unusual vibration, overheating, leaks, and noise. A steel plant boasting of its safe crane operations has inspections made by the crane operator, also a regular maintenance man, a department inspector, and a central plant inspector. It also expects operating foremen, maintenance foremen, cleaners, and oilers to be alert for defects.

There are inspections, of course, which must be certified by outside agencies for insurance or state regulations—boilers, pressure vessels, fire apparatus, and so on. And usually outside agencies can inspect elevators and similar equipment at lower costs. But there may be occasions when outside contractors can also be used to advantage for regular inspections and servicing of equipment such as air conditioning, office machines, communications equipment, electronic equipment, and plant lighting. If you have nobody to inspect production equipment, you can arrange for expert help from the machine manufacturer. This might pay on all complicated equipment regardless of the quality of your staff. Also, you might save in a more skillful appraisal without any investment in special inspection tools.

Size of PM Force. In the previously mentioned 542-plant maintenance survey, *Factory* derived some interesting statistics as to the manpower used for PM as compared with total maintenance manpower. Obviously, the ratio varied for different industries. It ranged from 1 to 2.37 men (primary-metal industries) to 1 to 2.69 men (machinery manufacturers) to 1 to 10.00 men (general manufacturing).

Breaking these data down as to the amount of their daily time men actually doing PM spent at it, the reports ranged from 17.9 to 68.2 per cent doing full time, 6.5 to 71.4 per cent doing more than half time, and 7.0 to 74.1 per cent doing less than half time. If nothing else, these figures prove how necessary it is to tailor PM to your own needs.

How much of PM is pure inspection time? One plant reports it uses 1 inspector to each 10 craftsmen; two others report 5 out of 100. A fourth cites a range of 5 to 12 per cent. Here again, local conditions undoubtedly prescribe, such as degree of mechanization and type of equipment.

Inspection Reports. They are indispensable. Your aim is to cut field paper work to a minimum, but not to the point where it doesn't tell the full story. So don't abbreviate inspection reports just to save writing time, lest you lose out on full benefits of the cost of inspection.

Simplest report form is one which can be universally applied. A typical form has headlines for spaces for filling in general data on department, date, machine, and so on. Below this there are ruled lines for filling in items that need attention. It can be used for all types of equipment. When using such a form a separate reusable check list for each type of equipment is needed.

In many cases the check list and report form are combined. The data are all pre-printed. The inspector merely checks or OK's each item on the list and explains in a "remarks" column whatever items need attention, and how soon (see Fig. 8-4).

There are many variations of either type, again an evidence of the tailored-to-meet-the-need approach. Three important questions can go on any form: (1) What is the cause of the failure or defect? (2) What is the remedy? (3) Have you any ideas for improvement in machine, equipment, inspection methods, or tools?

Routing Inspection Reports. Completed inspection reports become the basis for maintenance work orders in the same way that requests originate from regular production or maintenance people. Many ask as to who should request a work order for repairs found necessary by a PM inspector. The answer is, whoever normally has to authorize that type of work in the organizational setup. The essential aim in routing inspection reports is to get action geared to the need.

In some plants the reports are screened through maintenance foremen, (1) to be kept updated on conditions, (2) to check the need when severe or urgent, (3) to coordinate with production people for repair, and (4) to decide which one should generate the request for a work order. Other plants route all inspection reports to a maintenance clerk or dispatcher who automatically issues work orders on minor jobs and refers major jobs to the maintenance executive for decision. In one large plant the inspectors themselves prepare work-order requests at the close of each day for approval by executives up the line according to the estimated cost of repair.

INSPECTION ENGINEER'S REPORT TO DEPT. HEAD			TO DEPARTMENT HEAD E. Whitten	DEPT. 37
1. Machine condition			MACHINE & NO. ▓▓ wire drawing	EQUIP. NO. 13041
2. Recommendation for repair			SIGNED, INSPECTION ENGINEER *H. After*	DATE *10-6*

ITEM NO.	MACHINE CONDITION REPORT	CORRECTION	SAFETY	EMERGENCY REPAIR	ENGR REC-OMMENDN
1	Main roll bearings worn - all shims removed at last overhaul	Replace bearings on all four roll shafts			✓
2	Oil pump shaft scored and worn	Install new oil pump - rework damaged pump for spare		✓	✓
3	Capstan bearing worn and housing damaged	Rebore casting and fabricate sleeve to adapt new bearing			✓
4	Belt guard damaged	Repair guard and paint	✓		✓
5	Noisy drawing roll drive gears	Replace gears			

ITEM CLASSIFICATION (header over last three columns)

ESTIMATED REPAIR COSTS			ENGINEER'S REMARKS	DEPARTMENT HEAD DISPOSITION	
COST DISTRIBUTION	TOTAL ITEM COSTS		Item 5 - Gear play not serious enough to warrant replacement at this time	APPROVED ITEM REPAIRS	REMARKS
	ALL LISTED	RECOMMENDED		ALL	*TAKE CARE OF SAFETY*
				SAFETY	*AND EMERGENCY*
MATERIAL	262 00	152 00		EMERGENCY REPAIR	*REPAIR ITEMS*
				ENGINEER'S RECOMMENDATIONS ✓	*IMMEDIATELY-BALANCE*
LABOR	167 00	120 00		OTHER (SEE REMARKS)	*OVER WEEK END OF*
OVERHEAD	143 60	103 20		NONE (SEE REMARKS)	*10-29*
TOTAL	572 60	375 20		REPAIR ORDER ISSUED ✓	SIGNATURE *E. Witten* DATE *10/7*

Fig. 8-4. Inspector's report. Formalized report is sometimes used in conjunction with a permanent check list to report unsatisfactory conditions found by a PM inspector. In this case, report is sent to department head with cost estimate of recommended repairs for approval.

A good rule is that unsafe conditions or major defects deserve special routing immediately when discovered. To avoid arguments between production and maintenance heads about shutdowns, policy in one plant is for the plant manager to rule in all such cases.

Checking Inspections. What evidence has a maintenance executive that his inspectors are doing a thorough job, and that PM repairs are not being neglected? I know of one executive who makes a practice of spot checks to see that firmly established inspection procedures are being followed. Any plant that has too many breakdowns on equipment covered by the inspection schedule has good reason to suspect the quality of inspections is not up to snuff. But first see whether the item is on the check list, and how inspectors reported it. Was an urgent recommendation postponed? Perhaps the failure needed a shutdown (exterior) or teardown (inside) inspection when only a visual or running inspection was made. One food plant calls for a shutdown for every third inspection. A chemical-process plant averages 25 per cent in teardowns, and says they are justified.

As to neglect of repairs, usually a good work-order system will ensure timely completion of work orders arising out of PM. That is one advantage of integrating a PM program with normal paper-work procedures. Anyone who doesn't have this centralized control of all maintenance work certainly needs some kind of separate watchdog on PM jobs. For foremen who schedule their own work without master control are often prone to let the PM work slide. One way to keep tabs on PM repairs is to hold inspection reports in a tickler file until repair orders are completed. In one plant the maintenance executive lists all operating machinery on a large wall chart, and highlights the status of inspections and repairs by colored pins—red for emergency repair, and white, blue, and yellow for good, fair, and poor condition.

Inspection Methods. Because PM inspections are highly repetitive, good methods and procedures will pay big dividends. In other words, the rules espoused in this handbook for planning also apply to PM, only more so. Planning (as contrasted with scheduling) is the development of step-by-step procedures needed to do the work. Time studies help effectiveness. An industrial engineer can contribute much in these studies.

Here are some avenues particularly worth exploring:

1. Study of methods of inspection and servicing to do a better or faster job, or cut costs. Perhaps inspections can be combined with other maintenance work. How about centralized lubrication? Why clean a cooler mechanically when a chemical solution may do it cheaper and faster?
2. Planning of methods of inspection, also of routes to cut walking time. Give the men job write-ups for each piece of equipment inspected in any quantity or at great frequency. Sometimes it is possible to arrange check lists in sequence of operations. Also include safety precautions, safety equipment needed.
3. Planning of overhauls, similar to inspections, to cut downtime. Involves best utilization of crafts, also timesaving coordination. Often replacement parts can be prefabricated, made ready to shove in fast.
4. Review of major repetitive overhauls after completion to see where planning for next one can be improved.
5. Provision of better tools and test instruments. How about a work cart, scooter, or mobile unit to carry equipment and spare parts? Will torque wrenches or power tools speed up inspections? Some plants use high-lift trucks for servicing lighting and overhead facilities. Can you use an anemometer for testing air flow in ductwork, or indicating and measuring instruments to check loads, or a lightmeter to check illumination? Ask the men themselves for suggestions on better tools—they'll surprise you with good ideas.
6. Redesign of equipment to speed up inspections. Perhaps you can substitute quick-detachable fasteners for screws or bolts on guards, panels, access plates, or handholes. There are quick-opening hatch covers for tanks and pressure vessels. One company installed a hydraulic lift on a small underfloor furnace to facilitate relining. A swing-out chassis makes inspection and adjustment easier. A plug-in or modular unit can be taken back to the bench for complex tests and trouble shooting.

Inspection Manuals. Judging by the reports from plants using written PM instructions of one kind or another, manuals are almost a must. A manual goes beyond the check-list stage in that it gives detailed practices and procedures on maintenance of all important equipment.

A typical manual tells how to install, operate, and service physical properties, what materials and tools to use, and what safety measures to take. It devotes a single page to each kind or type of equipment, is well indexed for easy and quick reference. Everybody in maintenance can use it—foremen, planners, inspectors, and craftsmen.

Manuals take long to come by—it's often several years' work to assemble one. Sources of information are manufacturers' catalogs and instructions, plant records, and maintenance experience and know-how. A good way to start is gradually to build up a file of procedure sheets on items where simple instructions won't do. Make them as brief in words as possible and talk the user's language, or they won't be used.

Use lots of close-up pictures or diagrams for arrangements of parts and hookups, where words will never do.

Standard procedures are also helpful for trouble shooting. An inspector may use know-how to check, adjust, service, or repair equipment, and still not be able to trouble-shoot. In complex equipment, such as highly specialized hydraulic or electronic equipment, he must put his finger on the trouble. More and more companies are already issuing procedures for equipment such as motors, starters, and pumps on a symptoms-cause-cure basis. But these won't always work in hydraulics or electronics. In such case you can get the maker to devise a trouble-shooting sequence of testing, where the next step is dictated by the results of the previous one. Uncle Sam had many men using this technique successfully in the last war on complicated equipment whose principles were only vaguely understood, if at all, by the servicemen.

PAPER WORK FOR PM

Biggest obstacle in the adoption of a PM program seems to be paper work. The inexperienced maintenance executive envisions a mountain of details, and wants none of it. And even if he overcomes that fear, higher management often balks at the clerical expense.

There is no need for paper work to be top-heavy or burdensome. But both the maintenance executive and higher management must realize that the cost of good paper work is justified by the results. Does management frown on production reports on output and quality? In equal vein it must reconcile itself to the truism that no good PM program can do without facts to tell where you are and where you're going. The administrator must have good records, adequate filing equipment, and adequate clerical help. Also, he must view PM as an everyday job, not just a "fill-in." Records must be kept up to date, not just when he has the time. Postponing clerical PM duties is a sure way to paralyze and kill the whole program.

How many clerks does PM need? It's hard to say—depends much on the type of records you choose and the amount of details you need. There are purely manual record systems in which all work is done by pencil or typewriter. There are punched-card systems which rely on business accounting machines for preparing inspection orders, processing cost and performance data, and issuing control reports. A handful of progressive companies where maintenance costs are a big item of expense are applying electronic data-processing machines to obtain up-to-the-day repair and maintenance costs of operating units. Some plants use a combination of clerical and machine methods in varying degrees. In one of the latter, the maintenance executive reports that his system processes some 2,500 work orders (including regular maintenance and repair work) for 400 men per month. His setup uses four clerks.

As a rule the PM clerical staff is involved in handling maintenance work other than PM as well. There's no way to tell how the time is divided. Consensus is that you need 1 to 2 clerks for all clerical work—PM and regular—for every 100 maintenance men. Exponents warn against stinting at the start, because it takes time to make out the forms and start them going. In a small plant the PM chores may take only 1 to 2 hr each day. In such case a storeroom clerk or dispatcher can be trained to handle them.

No matter what paper-work system you select—and there are many good ones—there are some basic guides to follow:

1. Minimize the number of forms and entries. Don't try to record information just because it's nice to have. But don't eliminate data to the point where records cannot be interpreted and thus lose their usefulness. One large metalworking plant says it pays to show monthly totals of maintenance costs and running hours on all its machine-equipment records. Such data may be valueless to you. But omission of small costs because they are a bother might mislead one in appraising machine performance. Most plants include total labor and material costs on an equipment record for every job, and note nature of job, and number. If more details are wanted, they can refer to the "completed-order" file.

2. Integrate the PM system with other maintenance paper-work procedures. A good PM program won't stand alone. It has to be meshed with regular plant maintenance and engineering. This is particularly true in paper-work flow. Methods and routes for PM work orders, time reports, material requisitions, and cost accumulations should coincide with regular maintenance procedures. Don't set up a separate routine for dispatching, planning, scheduling, and following through. You can, but you will boost your administrative costs.

3. Make sure costs of all primary PM inspection activities are accounted for. Only this way can you prove to yourself and higher management what the exact costs are, and how well you are doing. The degree of breakdown depends on plant operations. In a plant requiring full-time inspectors for single functions—such as cranes, buildings, and corrosion—separate accounting is a foregone conclusion. Where rotating inspectors are used, labor hours in lump sums for major inspection categories such as machinery, electrical utilities, and buildings may do. Repairs originating from PM should follow normal work-order routine. If these costs are ever needed to prove your program, you can earmark each such order with a prefix or suffix (PM, for example) for quick extraction from the whole pile. Or use a similar code in the "requested by" column on the work order.

4. Arrange for a periodic control report, say once a week or month, to check on PM performance. Such a report might summarize the number of inspections scheduled, completed, uncompleted (and why), and number of work orders originated by PM, and number completed. As the program gets going the number of work orders will slowly drop and smooth out to a fairly even flow. Also consider using this same control report as the basis for keeping management posted on PM. Include it in a regular report that is good practice to send to higher management on all maintenance activities.

What System to Use. No amount of exhibits of the hundreds of forms in use will help that decision. All along the emphasis has been on mastery of the principles. Moreover, it's impossible to cover in this handbook even to a small degree the many types of maintenance organizations and their variety of paper-work procedures to which the PM paper work must be tailored.

In general there is a choice between manual systems or business-machine-operated. The plant that is already equipped with business machines would do well to explore that avenue. But first check whether the working schedule of these machines is already so loaded as to preclude reliable service to maintenance. Also, does the PM program justify use of punched-card methods? One punched-card user says: "We can quickly trace any type of equipment, or any type of failure." Another reports: "We used to do it clerically, but now our tabulating department gives us the daily score. But we still do some parts manually." In theory a manual system can give you just as much data and selectivity as the punched-card system. But when the number of combinations and permutations runs high, punched cards excel in speed, accuracy, and cost of administration. Manual systems have their place, however, where PM operations are on a limited scale.

Some systems combine elements of both manual and mechanical tabulation. Also, there is the hand-sort punched-card system (McBee) which uses a steel rod manually to separate any chosen categories quickly from a file of completed, coded cards. And there is the embossed-plate method (Addressograph) of producing inspection orders mechanically on a printing machine. Any one of those may be the best method for your specific needs. Anyone designing a PM paper-work setup would be wise to study all the various systems in vogue, whether or not he has preconceived ideas as to which system—perhaps his own—he expects to adopt. I've seen many changes made in methods later on because of failure to look the field over at the start.

Here are some of the leading manufacturers of proprietary forms and equipment that have been used in industrial PM programs. They can furnish exhibits of many types of applications, one or more of which may fit or come close to your needs:

Acme Visible Records, Inc., Crozet, Va.
Addressograph-Multigraph Corp., Cleveland 17, Ohio.

International Business Machines Corp., 590 Madison Ave., New York 22, N.Y.
Remington Rand, 315 Fourth Ave., New York 10, N.Y.
The McBee Company, Athens, Ohio.
The Electrofile Corp., 420 Lexington Ave., New York 17, N.Y.
Visirecord, Inc., Copiague, L.I., New York.

In addition, purveyors of many types of card-filing equipment can suggest how the various methods of filing in drawers, trays, circular drum files, and so on might fit into a self-designed paper-work setup.

Five Forms. Any PM program adds a maximum of five basic forms to conventional maintenance paper work: equipment record, check list, inspection schedule, inspection report, and equipment- and maintenance-cost record. All are illustrated. In most cases some of these are conveniently combined—such as equipment inventory, inspection schedule, and equipment cost record on one form, Fig. 8-5, or check list and inspection order on another—leaving only two to three forms to cope with at most. By now the function of each form should be clear enough to enable anyone to interpret these forms and design a set for himself.

The bigger problem in designing paper work, as already hinted at, is in the choice of type of paper work and flow rather than content of forms. Several systems may fill the bill as to requirements, but what about operating cost? The simplest card system will work in a large plant as well as a small, but at tremendous if not prohibitive administrative expense. The latest machine-operated system is obviously too costly and complicated for the small plants, but just what the doctor ordered for a large one. Size of plant and operations, also the amount of details wanted, largely govern the best methodology. To illustrate, a novice sooner or later discovers that much of the continuing clerical cost is tied up in issuing inspection orders and posting results to equipment-cost records. Any way to simplify either function is all to the good. Machine operations are not the only answer, and sometimes can be the wrong answer.

There's one way to get the right answer: the flow sheet for all paper work. This is the method used by trained industrial engineers and office-methods engineers. The idea is to develop a basic flow sheet of what you want. Then look for all possible combinations or short cuts that will eliminate work and travel. No PM system, however simple, should be installed without a flow-sheet study. It shows the route of every form from start to finish, and how each person uses them. Equivalent to a working model, it eliminates the "bugs" in the design stage, will save you many revisions later on.

Watch out for false economies! Because inspection orders are a major cost factor, system designers are tempted to combine them on one blanket order without realizing they lose the benefit of itemized costs on single machines or types of work. On the other hand, detailed costs are not needed for continuing operations such as cleaning filters, repairing floors, checking motors. Here a monthly or even an annual standing order will do. And if details ever are needed, a special study can get them for you.

In the *Factory Management and Maintenance* survey, the 542 plants reported how they order PM inspections, as follows:

	Per Cent
Separate order for each machine each time inspected	38.6
One order for a group of machines or department each time ordered	26.1
One order for a group or type of work by annual schedule	35.1
Informal schedules or standing orders	9.2
Miscellaneous	11.6

Some plants reported several methods in use, which accounts for the total of 120.6 per cent. If nothing else, this scattering of votes shows the desirability of examining all types of paper work and avoiding commitment to just one approach.

Systems in Use. It is now my purpose to summarize briefly some PM paper-work systems in actual use. The descriptions must necessarily be bare and are not intended as perfect patterns for any plant. And they are not a complete roundup, nor does space permit showing paper-work flow. But they do represent a range of possibilities

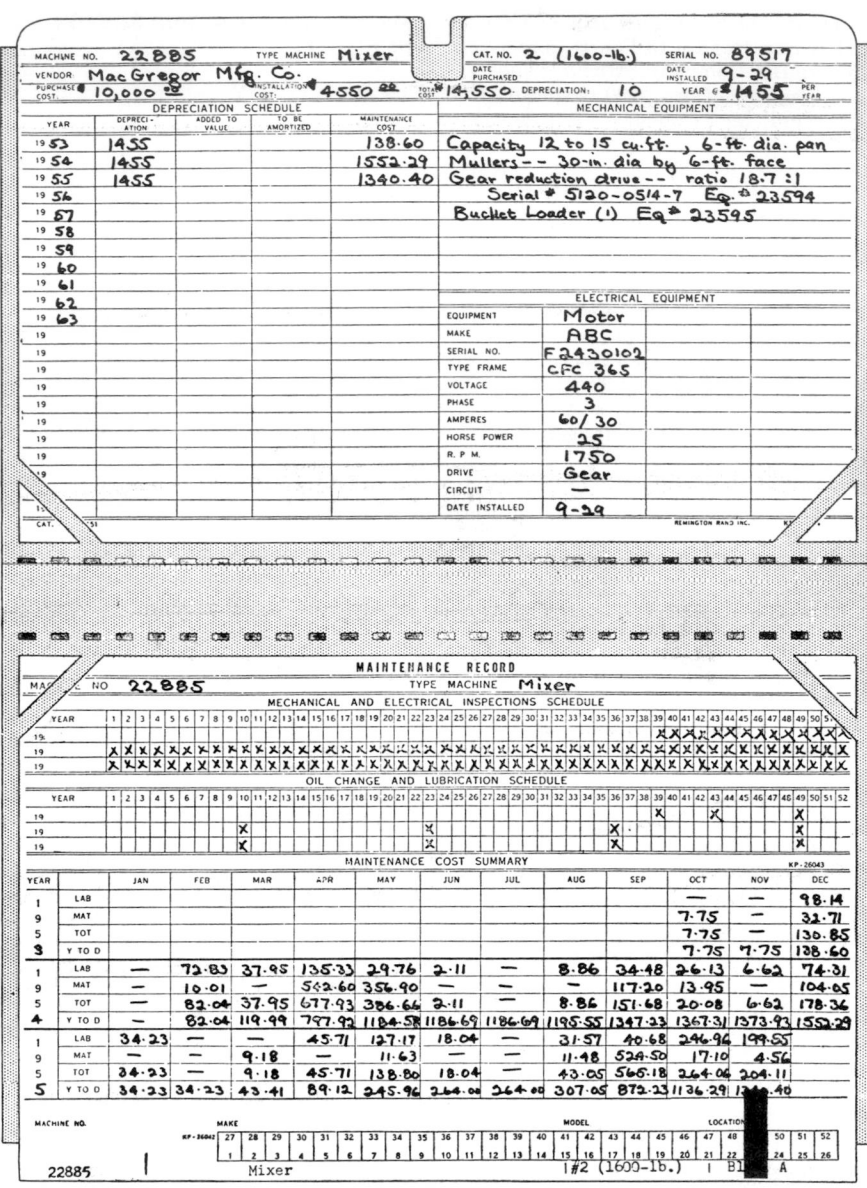

Fig. 8-5. Maintenance-cost record. Many plants use a manually posted record of maintenance costs in combination with an equipment record and inspection schedule. The setup consists of two forms for each item, kept in one of some 75 hinged card holders in a flat metal tray. As leaves are flipped over, top card shows equipment data, bottom card shows schedule and costs. Tab at bottom is moved to next inspection date. When bottom card is completely filled, it may be retained as a permanent record in the leaf, and superimposed by a fresh card. In such case the lower part showing machine number and schedule positions can be trimmed off.

of physical equipment from the simple manual setup to the highly mechanized type.

Plant A. Small plant, 15 maintenance men. The maintenance executive administers the paper work, with some help from an office clerk. PM schedules for general plant services such as lighting, heating, and ventilating are set up for each category on a separate, large annual chart. Equipment record (equipment inventory on one side, and original and accumulated maintenance costs on reverse side) is set up on 5- by 8-in. cards for all machinery and service equipment. These cards are filed (by plant location) in a box file. PM schedules for each of these items are set up on individual 4- by 6-in. cards. Those cards are kept in another box file equipped with weekly calendar tab separators. That file is used as a tickler.

Early each week the tickler file and charts are consulted for PM work due the following week. Clerk issues orders for PM jobs on regular work-order form, and holds tickler cards in an "Inspection Due" section of tickler file until order is completed. No check lists are used. Completed inspection reports are reviewed by the maintenance executive, who prepares necessary repair orders. Clerk signs off PM completion dates on chart or schedule cards, refiles cards in tickler according to next due date. Repair orders get normal follow-up geared to importance of job. Costs of all completed repair orders—whether for PM or breakdown—are hand-posted to the equipment record.

Plant B. Medium-sized plant, 40 maintenance men. A clerk who takes care of all paper-work routine for regular maintenance procedures on a part-time basis also handles all PM paper work. For this added bit he averages about one-half day extra time each week. The PM system uses a 13-tier steel tray-type cabinet file for combined equipment records and cost data. Each tray holds about 75 overlapping flip-over leaves, into which are inserted a 5- by 8-in. equipment record (on underside) and a cost record (on top). Each piece of equipment requires one leaf. When needed, a smaller motor record card is placed under the equipment card.

A section along the bottom edge of each equipment card is printed with consecutive spaces to indicate the months of the year, subdivided into four weekly periods. This section alone is visible when all the cards lie in flat overlapping position. Purpose is for easy and quick identification of PM due dates and appraisal of progress of inspection. Each date is shown by moving a colored sliding tab along the bottom edge to the date the next inspection is due. At the time each card is set up and the PM frequency is decided on, the calendar strip is checkmarked all across the year accordingly. Lubrication schedules are covered by separate master sheets. Motors and electrical controls get a routine periodic inspection.

Each week the clerk scans all the trays for inspections due the following week, as indicated by the colored tab positions. For each item due he pulls out from a file folder one of a series of inspection check lists specially prepared for each type of equipment. This folder contains one or more previous reports as well as blanks. The clerk turns over the "due" check lists to the maintenance foreman, who arranges with the production foremen for the exact time of inspection. During the inspection the inspector marks the conditions reviewed, whether OK or defective. If he adjusts a minor defect, he also notes that item. The completed check list now goes back to the clerk. If there were any uncorrected defects, he routes it to the maintenance foreman. He prepares work orders for repairs as instructed by the foreman.

All completed check lists are compared with previous reports. If the latest report discloses repetitions of the same defects, or bears significant notations by inspector, it goes to the maintenance foreman for study and action before filing. Final step is to move the scheduling marker in the tray file to the next due date. But whenever an inspection requires a work order, a second and taller marker is temporarily inserted at the current inspection date. This shows there is repair work outstanding. It remains there until that repair job has been completed. Costs of all repairs (PM or otherwise) are hand-posted to the PM file from completed work orders. Inordinate or repetitious costs are cause for study to minimize or eliminate them.

Plant C. Medium-sized plant, 50 maintenance men. This plant uses cards and a box file (similar to that described for plant A) for its equipment record. History and costs of maintenance are hand-posted thereto. But PM requirements of machines are scheduled on an actual running-time basis. Purpose is to service machines that vary in usage from one to three shifts daily only when they need it.

This is done by means of a Gantt chart kept on a letter-size sheet—one for each machine—by a maintenance clerk. The chart is blanked off in increments of 10 hr for each space, runs in horizontal lines of 400 hr each successively down the page to a total of 10,000 hr. PM frequencies for need for a running inspection, shutdown inspection, and teardown inspection are predetermined for each type of equipment and marked at the head of each sheet.

Each week the maintenance clerk extends the Gantt line with crayon on each chart by the number of hours of operation reported to him by the production department. As each line reaches a predetermined PM point, the clerk notes the machines due for attention. Thereupon he lines up and delivers to the maintenance foreman the specific check lists prepared for each type of equipment, one for each item due. Machine repairmen who are familiar with the equipment are assigned to the PM job. If the repairman discovers any serious condition calling for an extensive overhaul, he immediately confers with the maintenance foreman before signing his report. In such case the report bears a full recommendation of action needed. In all cases each completed report is cleared through the maintenance foreman and returned to the maintenance clerk before the end of the week it was scheduled.

The clerk posts data from each report to the equipment record, such as date, inspector, and results. If no maintenance work is called for, the card stays in its proper place in the box file. If work is recommended, the foreman dictates whatever is needed. In case of a teardown job, he fills in details later. Whenever any equipment needs repair, the clerk attaches a blue flag to the record card and shifts it to a special section in the front of the box file. For emergency repairs a red flag is attached. When the repair work is completed, the tab is removed and the card refiled in proper order. Every time a PM inspection is completed and entered on the equipment record, the clerk marks on the Gantt chart the spot where the next inspection is due. All repair costs not originated by PM also are posted to the equipment record cards. This ensures a complete history of maintenance required for each item.

Plant D. Large plant, about 250 maintenance men. Aim of the PM system installed in this plant was simplicity and economy of administration without sacrifice of effectiveness. It relies on only two conventional PM forms—an equipment record and a check list. The check list also serves as a tickler and inspection order. Three full-time clerks handle all maintenance paper work, including the PM routine, to cover several thousand pieces of equipment.

The equipment record is a letter-size paper form. Front side contains customary equipment data and specifications, also spare parts stock list. Along right margin, from top to bottom, is a blank frequency schedule of 14 spaces. The first two spaces are reserved for daily and weekly notations—the balance of 12 are monthly spaces from January to December. Thus this entire margin can be tabbed for any and all frequencies desired. This form is intended for a loose-leaf binder. Separate binders are kept for different types of equipment—or different departments or buildings—earmarked by a code letter used as the prefix to the equipment inventory number for easy reference. Reverse side of equipment record is arranged in columnar form for tabulation of nature and costs of maintenance repairs and changes.

Check lists are designed for each specific class of equipment. They are set up for repeated usage up to six times, cover both running and shutdown inspections. This is done by noting the due date of inspection in one of six spaces in upper right corner marked "tickler date." One check list can serve for as many as 15 identical pieces of equipment because of the arrangement of the checkpoints—as many as 20 points on packaging machines—in a horizontal cross-index to the tabulation of equipment checked. Routine repetitive work (adjustments, lubrication, etc.) is controlled by standing orders covering long-term schedules. Buildings and plant services, for examples, are inspected twice yearly.

Each week a maintenance clerk issues the scheduled quota of check lists to various maintenance foremen, who assign the inspections to rotating inspectors. Inspectors are expected to perform minor repairs or adjustments as well. Where necessary, standard procedure instructions have been set up to ensure efficient methods and workmanship. Completed check lists are screened by the foremen to keep them acquainted with plant conditions. All reports flow back to the maintenance office. If repairs are needed, they are handled through the regular maintenance work order system. Eventually labor and material costs are posted to the equipment records. In all cases, a clerk marks the next date of inspection in "tickler date" space and reslots each check list in the tickler file accordingly.

Each month a maintenance clerk prepares a formal report on the PM inspection program. For each type of equipment it shows number of inspections scheduled, numbers completed and incompleted, critical cases found, number of jobs required, and number completed. The success of the program is measured by a gradual decrease in jobs that need to be done.

Plant E. Large plant, about 400 maintenance men. This maintenance organization operates on an area basis both for regular maintenance duties and PM. The PM program is in charge of a PM administrator, located in a central office, who reports to the maintenance executive. He has four clerks who handle the basic PM paper work manually. His duties cover the entire administration of the PM function to guarantee efficient execution of work and accumulation of reliable records. He sets up all PM procedures, agrees on PM schedules with operating departments, issues schedules and expedites their completion. He keeps and analyzes cost records, takes part in repair parts control, checks effectiveness of the program. He coordinates wherever PM is involved.

Accumulation and analysis of maintenance labor and material costs are done by punched-card procedures using IBM equipment. Purpose is to get daily status of work, which this plant found it could not do by hand-posting of costs. A complete equipment record of some 7,500 items is kept in the central PM office. Cards are filed according to an equipment charge number given each major piece of equipment or building. This permits segregation of costs to a narrow and analytical degree.

Each operating department also has copies of equipment cards for its own area, kept in a loose-leaf binder. Repair costs are not posted to any equipment cards, but made available on monthly tabulating reports. Inspection frequencies are marked on equipment cards. Lubrication is handled by a subsidiary program headed by a lube specialist. Buildings are inspected on an annual basis under the control of the PM administrator.

Each week the PM office prepares and sends out tickler sheets to all operating areas. They list all inspections due, major repairs, and overhauls. Scheduling of this work is done by area foremen in conference with operating men. Foremen assign inspections to craftsmen available and qualified to make them. There are no full-time inspectors as such. The same supervision handles PM assignments who directs regular maintenance work. Inspectors are given check lists, on which they report current conditions and recommendations for repairs. They are permitted to make only minor adjustments. All inspection time is charged to a standing order, thus reveals PM inspection cost.

Completed check lists are routed through both operating and maintenance foremen for action. At this point the regular work order system for necessary repairs takes over. When all inspections on any single tickler sheet are completed, the sheet is returned to the PM office for signing off. Maintenance labor and material charges enter daily into the punched-card routine, are handled by the tabulating department. Tabulated reports are sent monthly to the maintenance executive on completed orders, subdivided by charge numbers and departments. They show estimated time for each job, actual time, percentage variance, dollar labor costs. Costs are also reported by hours and dollars spent for each operating department for each craft and job. Other reports cover uncompleted work in similar detail.

Plant F. Large plant, about 500 maintenance men. A central "control" group acts as staff to the maintenance executive. It consists of one maintenance planner and two clerks, who handle all administrative paper work for five maintenance areas. A foreman in each area reports to the maintenance head. This head is assisted by a maintenance engineer.

The PM load averages 50 per cent of total maintenance needs. The PM program includes some 1,800 machine tool and auxiliary items that cost over $500 each (minimum limit) or otherwise are critical to operations. There are three basic records for each machine tool: (1) a permanent history folder which holds manufacturer's information, including original papers, guarantee, specifications, and costs, (2) a 5- by 8-in. data card which spells out PM requirements, and (3) an 8- by 8-in. tub-file card for accumulation of all maintenance costs. These records are originated by the control group. Entries on the cost record are hand-posted after each repair.

But PM itself is machine scheduled, to minimize clerical costs of issuing inspection orders. This is done by use of Addressograph equipment for making plates and printing orders. Permanent inspection orders are prepared for each unit on embossed plates. Each plate defines the machine tool, tells what parts to inspect (check list), and time allowed for the job. These facts are taken from the PM data card. Inspection frequency is based on cycles of 2, 4, 8, 16, and 24 weeks and up. A master schedule has been worked out for fairly even distribution of PM assignments over the month and year.

Each week inspection orders are produced mechanically by running banks of plates through the Addressograph printing machine. Each plate bears a metal tab positioned according to frequency, so that the printer can be set to print only those inspections due any particular week. The printer also produces a summary inspection schedule for each craft group for each week. This serves as a control sheet for craft foremen to check progress of work. Totals of these schedules show number of man-hours needed for each craft, thus serve to determine PM manpower needs.

Craftsmen make inspections as they are assigned by maintenance supervision. At the finish, they pencil in their findings on each inspection order, also time data, and attach copies of material requisitions. Completed PM orders flow back to the foremen for checking work done and preparing whatever repair orders are needed. The foremen send completed orders, plus the control sheet, to the control group each Monday morning. This group posts the cost data (labor and materials) onto the tub-file card, and files completed orders in the history folders. It also prepares a weekly PM report showing number of machines serviced, estimated labor hours, actual labor hours, hours behind schedule, and hours scheduled for the following week.

Plant G. Large plant, over 800 maintenance men. This plant uses business accounting machines to handle all but a negligible part of its maintenance paper work. Once the engineering data have been fed into the system at the start, paper-work routine is practically entirely machine controlled except for corrections when adding new equipment or adopting new methods that change job time values. The system serves over 4,500 machine tools plus many other types of plant service equipment. It requires only 12 people (including tabulating clerks) to operate it. The company says it would take over 300 clerks to do the same job manually and even then not as accurately or as fast.

Groundwork of organization and of preparation of details to build the system took several years. It involved development of an equipment inventory, an analysis of PM requirements of every piece of equipment, and establishment of frequencies, schedules, and time allowances for each job. Procedures manuals had to be set up for every job. The system handles all types of maintenance—scheduled, routine, repair, and large projects—with hardly an iota of pencil work. Every machine is listed on a separate property location tab card, the sum of which serves as an up-to-the-minute equipment record. Another machinery and equipment maintenance record (12- by 12 ledger card) provides an accurate up-to-date summary of maintenance costs for each item of equipment.

From the reservoir of basic tab card records the tabulating machines prepare monthly PM inspection schedules. These schedules itemize the workload for each craft, and estimated cost. Machines also prepare prepunched tab cards that serve as inspection orders. Each card tells the worker, by code reference to standard procedures manuals, exactly what to do. Check lists are supplied separately when needed. Workers need only to clock-stamp their time.

Punched-card forms are used for material requisitions. Labor and materials on special repair orders and other nonroutine work are included in the system by issuing properly coded prepunched tab cards.

Accurate costs of maintenance are assembled by the accounting machines separately for each piece of equipment.   These job costs are machine-posted daily onto the proper machine cost record.   For control, the maintenance executive gets a full report each Monday of the maintenance costs—by order number and machine number—for the previous week.   He also gets a monthly report, by craft breakdown, showing manpower effectiveness, and a monthly list of all equipment for which maintenance costs exceed predetermined limits.   This system can quickly prepare any special type of report or analysis wanted, provided the necessary basic data have been stored on tab cards.

AIDS TO GOOD PM

There are many ways other than just regular inspections by which to effectuate a good PM program.   They involve the finer techniques which might be added to any basic program if the extra costs justify.   Let's review them briefly as to principles, solely to point out their value.   You will have to judge for yourself which ones deserve application in your plant.   These techniques are not arranged in order of importance; so be sure to examine them all.   They represent actual practice in one or more plants.

Materials Research.   Aim is to avoid repetitive service calls by use of better materials.   For example, a large steel plant has set up a program for investigation of all material failures and elimination of causes.   As a result it has reduced frequency of failures, cut maintenance costs, and improved safety of personnel.   A full-time materials engineer studies each failure as it is reported by maintenance foremen. He looks for faulty design, faulty manufacture, operation beyond limits, abuse, inferior maintenance, or misapplication.   He reports his findings to an executive committee for action, and it decides on PM measures.   He also lists the decisions in a materials manual to guide future installations.   This principle can be enlarged to include periodic reports on building materials or other long-lived equipment to see how they are standing up.

Design Changes.   These may involve using the same or better materials.   In the case of a machine don't start redesigning, however, before you check load and capacity, and consult with manufacturer.   Perhaps failure was due to reasons other than design weaknesses, such as overload or misapplication.

Maintenance Training.   Both supervisors and hourly paid workers need brief but solid indoctrination into the philosophy of PM to win intelligent cooperation.   They need to know over-all objectives and general procedures.   You can use films available from equipment manufacturers for both purposes.   After laying this groundwork one plant uses a permanent exhibit of broken or worn parts with place cards describing how PM could have avoided them.   It feels a continuing education is needed.

Special training often is required for inspectors and repairmen.   A good trick is to let such people help in the erection of new equipment—it speeds up PM services later on.   And if the outside erector is teaching the men in operation and repair, take a tape recording for later reference in compiling a manual.   A growing practice is for the machine builder or equipment maker to offer a course in PM at his own plant.

Operator Training.   Abuse of equipment by operators is a major complaint of maintenance men.   The same techniques as for maintenance training can be used here.   It's a good idea always to assign operators to the same machines or vehicles. This highlights the careless or destroyer type, tips you off to those who need more training.

Equipment Study.   Today's good tools may be obsolete tomorrow.   New products are appearing on the market continually to cut down on PM inspection time.   Non-destructive methods—X-ray and ultrasonic for hidden flaws, or magnetic particle or black light and dye inspection of surface fatigue cracks—now catch defects before breakdown.   Welding hastens repairs.

Standard-practice Manuals.   These go beyond the standard-procedure sheets already mentioned for installation and servicing of specific items of equipment. They include organizational responsibilities and administrative procedures, flow of paper work, and so on. Both production and maintenance supervisors know what to expect of each other.

Standardization. One large auto plant achieves simplification of its PM problem by standardization of tools, methods and specifications, process standards, industrial equipment, and materials. This simplifies spare-parts procurement and storage.

Adherence to standards also speeds PM inspections and upkeep service. More and more plants are adopting JIC (Joint Industry Council) standards as a part of purchase specifications for equipment involving electrical, hydraulic, or pneumatic units. These standards aim for uniform specifications for parts, accessibility for inspection or repair, protection from physical damage or harmful elements, and safety of operation.

Special Reports. These aim to control PM by the "rule of exception." For example, many maintenance executives look to a breakdown report for guidance in administering their PM program. It is a good measure of the effectiveness of the program. It points to weaknesses or need for overhaul, and helps justify shorter inspection frequencies. Such a report usually contains name, number, and location of machine, actual time lost, and what repairs were needed.

Here are other helpful reports. One company submits a monthly report to the maintenance executive that lists all machinery producing work outside of tolerances. Another plant uses a report of accidents to equipment and machine tools, to minimize damage. This report is made out by the operating foreman, and checked by the maintenance head, then submitted to a committee for recommendations. As a result, all workers and supervisors are more alert to trouble, and there are fewer breakdowns from abuse or carelessness.

Protective Methods. Aim is to prolong equipment life by special barriers to deterioration. Most common among these are protective surface coatings, or cathodic protection against corrosion, or hard facing—by welding or plating—against wear. Abrasion can be minimized by surfacing with plastic or rubber. By inserting nylon wear strips on the U channel of its bottle-conveyor line one plant stretched chain life from $\frac{1}{2}$ to 3 years.

The scope of good protective methods is indefinite. For example, dust-filtered air is a boon in rooms making high-tolerance products. Lubrication caps on grease nipples will keep lubricant clean. Vibration mounts will extend equipment and building life. Electronic devices can stop unattended automatic metalworking machines at the slightest cause for overload. Alarms can signal dangerous temperatures. pressures, or liquid levels. Clutches can release the drive automatically when machine is overloaded.

Maintenance Storeroom. A well-organized storeroom is indispensable to a successful PM program. If you don't have the parts or supplies when your inspectors find you need them, you might just as well have done without the inspection. Some plants even store critical parts in production areas to minimize downtime.

The requirements of a storeroom are fully described elsewhere in this handbook; so I offer only a few comments on what parts to store. As a rule past experience and plant activity influence the selection of spare parts and the choice of maximum and minimum quantities. Many maintenance executives analyze the manufacturers' recommendations, and with the help of foremen they set up requirements for each type of machine or equipment. Often these parts are noted on equipment records under "Spare Parts Needed." The plan for assignment of company serial or code numbers—called commodity classification—minimizes duplications and helps to identify needed parts accurately and quickly.

Sometimes the cost of a spare part on critical equipment may run into thousands of dollars. In such cases decision whether or not to store it should consider the cost of failure (including lost production) both ways. In this calculation delivery time from vendor is the critical factor; so check it carefully. Of course, if you can rely on the vendor for fast delivery you not only keep your own inventory down but also eliminate the chances of being stuck with an obsolete part.

Records Analysis. Many companies which are maintaining excellent equipment records are not getting much out of them because they don't analyze them periodically. They refer to these records only when some question of maintenance cost comes up on a single machine.

So they might as well dispense with equipment records, because they can make cost studies of completed work orders on the machine in question, and get the same answer. Why keep a record you don't use?

But the point is that you can make equipment records more than pay their way. From plant-maintenance executives who are regularly analyzing their equipment records come statements like these: "We have saved money by examining high-cost items." "We found we weren't taking full advantage of entries without a systematic review." "Until we analyzed our records we were spending money in continual repair of repetitive failures." The moral is this: Periodic analysis of equipment records for machinery, equipment, and buildings will reveal classes or types or makes of items that (1) have high maintenance costs, (2) cause excessive downtime, and (3) suffer repetitive failures. These data are the clues to what action to take along any of the following lines:

1. Revise frequency of inspection.
2. Redesign the weak part.
3. Substitute better materials.
4. Change method of operation.
5. Use a better unit.

In one company an analysis showed a high frequency of repair of shear pins at an annual cost of $2,000. As a result the company developed a spring release which eliminated the trouble. Another company cleared up repetitive bearing trouble revealed by equipment records by substitution of a different design.

The big reason for failure to analyze equipment records, I find, is lack of time by the maintenance executive. Can he delegate this analysis to anyone? I admit it takes a qualified maintenance engineer to interpret the records and draw conclusions that a junior or clerk might easily miss. A good compromise is to train the records clerk to scan each record as he makes an entry, and to pull out all suspicious cases for engineering review. If the maintenance executive supplements this with at least an annual review of his own, very few if any noteworthy cases will get by.

In a large plant with thousands of record cards the time for executive analysis becomes more of a problem. This is also true where machine accounting or hand-sort punched-card systems are used. Several plants are setting maximum annual maintenance-cost limits on single units, which if exceeded are earmarked on the monthly tabulating report of maintenance costs for executive attention. One government agency codes every type of repair on vehicles on hand-sort cards to get a periodic analysis of types of breakdown. This sets the pattern for service requirements.

The smart maintenance executive will not ignore the benefits of record analysis. With so many vendors of good proprietary systems willing to help him develop suitable and timesaving systems, he is sure to find one or more profitable methods.

A word about statistical-analysis methods: Production is using them successfully in quality control. A few farsighted maintenance executives are experimenting with them in various directions, such as establishing inspection or overhaul frequencies, or checking maintenance performance and quality. One plant is exploring the possibility of elimination of PM inspections on machinery by resorting to a statistical analysis of the frequency and severity of adjustments and repairs. The time that either of these maintenance services requires to reach predetermined limits, it hopes to prove, will be the optimum economic time for an overhaul.

These facts are sure: PM, with all its complexities, is here to stay. Developments to date are gradually making its administration easier. The maintenance executive of the future must be familiar with modern administrative procedures, as well as technically trained, to prosecute the plant preventive-maintenance function successfully.

POLISHING THE PM PROGRAM

No PM program, however carefully planned, can remain static if it is to be effective. New manufacturing concepts, new management techniques, and new tools require the periodic checking and updating of its operation. Here are pointers for refining a PM program.

Avoid Overmaintenance. A good PM program is not rated by the percentage of equipment it covers. In fact, repairs as needed (instead of PM) are usually less costly for equipment that operates at a low hourly capacity. To find the optimum level of application, chart the costs of PM, repairs, and production losses at various levels of PM activity. The optimum level is at the point of the lowest sum total of these three costs. This level should be ascertainable for a single machine, a cost center, or an entire plant.

Get Accurate Costs. To arrive at the optimum level, the maintenance engineer must have true costs. They must be segregated for regular repairs, PM activities, operating maintenance, downtime losses, improvements, and new work. And they must permit cost breakdowns by machine units and single jobs. Without such detailed costs, it is impossible to appraise the value and extent of PM application. To this end, if possible, get a leg on any available time on the company's mechanical or data processing equipment to produce detailed cost analyses otherwise difficult or impossible to get. Failing that, consider the services of a local data-processing organization.

Check Inspection Frequencies. At the start of a PM program, the rule is to over-inspect to play safe. If a machine record shows no maintenance cost other than PM inspections, consider extending the interval. Moreover, changes in operating conditions and equipment, also improvements in inspection measures, may justify a stretch-out. Check the frequency of all inspections requiring shutdown or dismantling, and explore for an easier way to inspect. One plant tore down a turbo-generator every year. After a series of vibration and tolerance studies without teardown, the overhaul interval was safely extended to from 3 to 4 years.

Provide Specific Craft Instructions. And be sure to keep them updated. They ease the load of supervision. Secure from vendors complete parts and service manuals for each piece of equipment. Develop procedure sheets to describe how to handle all ticklish or complex PM jobs. Insist that craftsmen read these sheets at the start of every job. Develop check lists for each type of equipment; show inspection tools needed. Review the check lists periodically for omissions. Encourage corrections by craftsmen and operators. Check these lists against all breakdowns for possible improvement.

Adopt Repair Codes. These are usually 4- to 6-digit accounting codes that show on each maintenance order (PM or repair) the machine and part worked on, nature of the repair, probable cause, craft time, and material and labor costs. They are invaluable for discovery and analysis of maintenance trouble. Periodic review of repair costs will highlight high-cost items and show need for PM changes or CM (corrective maintenance) redesign.

Use Modern Diagnostic Tools. Inspections can be simplified and speeded up with special tools such as stethoscopes, dial indicators, vibration analyzers, and non-destructive ultrasonic and X-ray apparatus. Operating equipment can be continuously monitored by malfunction detectors, with alarms or cutoffs, for pressure, temperature, and wear limits. Paint and wall thicknesses can be accurately measured ultrasonically, and erosion detected by corrosimeters. Scores of automatic sensing, measuring, or control devices are finding wide PM application.

Apply Industrial Engineering Techniques. Set time standards for repetitive jobs. Develop procedures for inspections and overhauls that show work methods, work sequence, tools, materials, and accessory equipment. In a teardown, do only what is necessary at standstill, to minimize downtime. Use the critical path method for scheduling jobs over 30 to 50 hr. Coordinate inspections to minimize the number of visits and travel time. Preinspect new parts when received to avoid delays from missing or defective elements. Apply work simplification principles to all jobs.

Utilize Statistical Aids. Learn the types of equipment failure curves (wear-out, random) and how they influence the PM program. For example, parts without definite wear-out characteristics or those in the random failure category do not profit from PM. Study wear patterns of equipment; keep logs that help determine the fewest inspection or overhaul cycles for adjustment or replacement.

Design for Low-cost Maintenance. This is the first step in minimizing the PM work load. Designed reliability (mean time to point of failure) reduces frequency of failure. Designed maintainability (mean time needed to repair) improves equipment availability. Policy of MP (maintenance prevention) requires examination of maintenance cost in purchase-cost justification. All new equipment and alterations are checked for excessive maintenance needs. Items more likely to fail must be made accessible, easy to repair or replace, as by modules or plug-in units. This MP policy may well prove the best way to achieve high equipment availability in integrated or automated production lines.

Chapter 9

PROCEDURES IN ORGANIZATION

By JAMES E. THOMPSON[1]
Stanford Research Institute
Southern California Laboratories
South Pasadena, Calif.

Two prime considerations are involved in the organization of a maintenance department: (1) Maintenance's place in the general organization structure; and (2) the proper internal organization for the department. Each consideration can best be resolved by examining the basic functions to be executed by Maintenance. Examination of the functional structure of any activity always permits logical assignment of responsibility and authority to create a sound, workable organization.

MAINTENANCE'S PLACE IN THE COMPANY ORGANIZATION

Maintenance's basic objective can be defined as efficient accomplishment of all inspection, repair, overhaul, and construction necessary to establish and maintain a facility and its equipment in a condition to meet operating requirements.

It is apparent that this objective is primarily an operating or *doing* function, and that satisfactory accomplishment of certain aspects of Maintenance's objective will require instructions and direction from a *design and planning* function. This is particularly true of activities involving alteration, installation, or construction of facilities and equipment. This design and planning function necessary for the direction of Maintenance must always exist in some form. The only possible exception would be an operation so completely static that nothing is undertaken or contemplated in the nature of alteration or addition to the facility or its equipment.

It appears logical that Maintenance, basically being an operating function, should be a portion of the production or operating division of the company and should report to a level of management that is high enough to direct both the doing and the design-and-planning activities necessary for satisfactory accomplishment of the total maintenance function. Many terms have been used to identify this over-all function, of which Maintenance is a part, but the one generally accepted as most descriptive is *plant engineering*.

Maintenance and Plant Engineering. Plant Engineering, as an over-all function, logically should report to the executive in charge of operations[2] in order that it may be on sufficiently high level within the company organization to carry out its responsibilities effectively. The basic responsibilities of Plant Engineering can be divided into two basic functions of *facilities engineering* and *maintenance*. If it is granted that the objective of Maintenance is maintaining the facility in a condition to meet

---

[1] The author now is Consulting Engineer, Lake Havasu Irrigation and Drainage District, Lake Havasu City, Arizona.

[2] *Operations* as used herein identifies the "producing" segment of a company. This signifies the manufacturing departments in the case of a production plant, or the operating departments in the case of a transport activity.

operating requirements, the Facilities Engineering must have as its objective all *make-ready* activities necessary for Maintenance to accomplish its task. These activities logically include budgeting, planning, and design functions necessary to establish properly and maintain the facility and its equipment.

On this premise Maintenance activities are, in a large measure, the implementation of planning and design work accomplished by Facilities Engineering. This does not mean that Maintenance must be subordinate to Facilities Engineering, but rather it indicates the desirability of both these functions reporting to the same executive. When establishing Maintenance's place in the over-all company organization it should always be taken into account that the total task of planning, establishing, and maintaining a facility and its equipment is clearly divisible into the two segments—of planning and of doing. Unless both these functions report to the same executive there may well be opportunity for needless inefficiency.

BASIC FUNCTIONS OF MAINTENANCE

It was stated earlier that the basic function of Maintenance can be summarized as the accomplishment of all work necessary to establish and maintain the facility and its equipment in a condition to meet normal operating requirements. This broad function can be grouped into subdivisions of (1) inspection (2) preventive maintenance (3) repair, (4) overhaul, (5) construction, and (6) salvage. All normal work activities of Maintenance can be classified as belonging in one of these six groupings. A seventh function of *administration* is necessary for the actual direction and supervision of the work functions.

Maintenance Inspection. Primary functions of maintenance *inspection* involve (1) periodic inspection of machinery and equipment to ensure safe efficient operation, (2) making certain that equipment requiring work at specified periods receives proper attention, (3) examination of items removed during maintenance and overhaul operations, to determine feasibility of repair, (4) inspection of maintenance items received from vendors, and (5) control of the quality of work accomplished by maintenance groups.

Inspection's function in this case is not greatly different from that required for a production operation. Greater emphasis is placed upon salvage determination, as often a large portion of maintenance inspection work involves examination of used items removed during maintenance or overhaul work to determine the feasibility of their repair. In addition, Inspection has the responsibility of making certain that all equipment requiring periodic maintenance or overhaul receives attention at the required times. This function assumes major importance in the case of an activity such as an airline, where government regulations stipulate certain maintenance operations at designated periods. In such cases maintenance inspection has the clearly defined responsibility of maintaining accurate records of the location and usage of a variety of equipment, and the issuance of orders to withdraw each from service for maintenance or overhaul at the proper time.

Preventive Maintenance. Properly defined, true maintenance work is confined to the checking, adjustment, routine replacement, lubrication, and clean-up necessary to make certain that the facility and its equipment are in proper condition and ready for use. This maintenance work is predictable, readily adaptable to accurate planning and scheduling, and can be placed on a standard time basis for cost-control purposes. It is largely classifiable as *preventive maintenance* and should not be confused with the unpredictable work load generated by breakdowns and trouble calls.

Preventive maintenance is the area in which Maintenance can effect the greatest savings in over-all manufacturing or operating costs. Downtime, the period in which a machine or vehicle is out of service and not producing a profit, is a large factor in unit operating cost—whether this be measured in cost per pound, piece, or ton-miles. Equipment suddenly rendered unserviceable because of breakdown is not only costly in terms of lost production or available ton-miles, but the total cost may be much greater than the apparent loss—because of effect upon schedules, with resultant customer dissatisfaction, and possible cancellation of orders.

It is the task of **preventive maintenance**, through planned, scheduled inspection, maintenance, and overhaul to ensure that equipment failures should not occur. Obviously it is impossible to establish a plan that will provide preventive maintenance that will reduce the occurrence of failures to zero through early detection and application of corrective measures.

Repair. Corrective repair to alleviate unsatisfactory conditions found during preventive-maintenance inspections is considered a portion of that operation. *Repair,* as considered here, is that unscheduled work, often of an emergency nature, necessary to correct breakdowns; and it includes trouble calls. With an adequate preventive-maintenance program there should be little of this work—as the effectiveness of the preventive maintenance is inversely proportional to the effort that must be devoted to unscheduled repair.

In a well-maintained plant a large portion of repair work will be confined to routine trouble calls. A few electrical and mechanical trouble shooters stationed in factory production areas can provide immediate service on most of these. In a transport operation most of the repair work can be accomplished by line-maintenance mechanics in addition to their scheduled preventive-maintenance work. In the case of a major failure, beyond the manpower of skills available from the trouble-shooting or line-maintenance crews, it becomes necessary to pull men from some scheduled job to accomplish the required work.

Overhaul. Overhaul is considered as the planned, scheduled reconditioning of facilities and equipment. This work will always involve one or more of the elements of teardown, examination, replacement, reconditioning, reassembly, and testing. While primarily relating to machinery and transport equipment, it is also applicable to the facility and its fixed equipment—such as heating and ventilating installations. It is quite different from preventive maintenance, which essentially involves inspection and testing of various items in accordance with a prescribed plan to ensure serviceability.

All planned overhaul should be handled by a maintenance inspector who reviews the job and determines the complete bill of material. The material should then be ordered, for delivery prior to the scheduled time of the overhaul. When the material is available in its entirety the equipment to be overhauled should be withdrawn from service at the scheduled time, and the work undertaken without delay.

Construction. At some companies it is basic policy that Maintenance undertake all possible construction jobs and be provided with personnel and equipment for handling wood and steel construction, cement and asphalt paving, plumbing and electrical installations, and the like. At others the policy is modified to contract all construction jobs whose nature is such that the work can be separated from, and avoid interference with, normal company maintenance and production activities.

In all cases, the exact magnitude of contracted construction work will vary, but policy should be established to contract sufficient work to reduce maintenance backlogs to a reasonable value. When this policy is followed Maintenance will not only be able to provide better service, but it will also be practicable to avoid undesirable employment peaks.

Often it is economical to accomplish construction work with Maintenance personnel. In some areas maintenance labor rates are lower than those paid by the building trades. Also, there may be less probability of industrial-relations problems arising when construction jobs are handled by Maintenance employees.

Salvage. Salvage, or the reclamation and disposition of scrap or surplus material, can be a very profitable Maintenance procedure. This activity involves segregation, reclamation, and disposition of production scrap, and the collection and disposition of surplus materials, equipment, and supplies. The handling of scrap is closely related to the Maintenance clean-up and housekeeping function. Handling of surplus items is closely allied with maintenance inspection, for often the decision to declare an item surplus is based upon the expense of restoring or modernizing the item in comparison with its replacement cost or possible future use.

Salvage items usually are disposed of through sale to company employees and outside scrap dealers. In some of the most profitable salvage operations a company salvage store, available to both employees and the general public, is maintained. Comparatively few surplus items, except scrap metal, are sold to scrap and junk dealers. Salvage may be considered a basic Maintenance function, as a substantial portion of the work required can best be accomplished by Maintenance.

BASIC TYPES OF MAINTENANCE OPERATIONS

Before plunging into the details of maintenance organization it appears prudent to first examine the basic types of maintenance operations, and then separately consider the organizational problems peculiar to each of these.

It would appear possible to subdivide maintenance operations into many types, not only for each industry, but possibly for different companies within an industry. However, when these apparent types are analyzed, it becomes obvious that rather than many types there are only many *variations*. Actually, there are only *two* basic types of maintenance operations: *facility maintenance*, and *transport maintenance*. The problems and responsibilities of each are sufficiently different to justify two broad groupings, which in turn establishes two basic maintenance organization patterns. The maintenance activities of any company can be fitted into one of these two patterns.

Facility Maintenance. The most frequently encountered maintenance is that relating to a manufacturing or processing plant, which can be broadly termed *facility maintenance*. This involves construction, alteration, installation, maintenance, and repair work necessary to maintain the facility[1] and its equipment[2] in proper condition.

During the normal operations of a facility maintenance department it is usual for scheduled maintenance, repair, and overhaul work to consume only a portion of the total maintenance task. A majority of Maintenance's task often is involved with construction, alteration, and installation work; trouble calls; and clean-up and salvage activities.

Transport Maintenance. Transport maintenance, whether it be of a truck fleet or an airline, is tightly bound to schedules. Also, extensive preventive maintenance is mandatory to ensure high utilization of equipment and maintain safety.

Inspection, repair, and overhaul form the majority of transport maintenance work. The administrative problems of transport maintenance often are more complex than those encountered with facilities maintenance, because of requirements for maintenance services throughout the transport system. This results in some decentralization and introduces unique problems of administrative and functional control over maintenance personnel stationed hundreds or even thousands of miles from the maintenance center or base.

BASIC ORGANIZATIONAL PRINCIPLES

The organization plans considered in this section are based upon not more than four supervisors reporting to a superintendent of maintenance. The number of supervisors reporting to the maintenance head should be kept to the absolute minimum in all cases to avoid his becoming so enmeshed in details that he is unable to devote sufficient time to major issues.

The basic objective of organizing any activity revolves around the establishment of a staff of general supervisors who carry out the operations and are directly responsible to the management. Maintenance Management is represented in this case by the superintendent of maintenance, and as long as the department is small it is possible for the superintendent to direct personally the operations of all functions; but, when the department increases in size, a point is reached where this is no longer feasible,

---

[1] *Facility.* For the purpose of this text the term *facility* is defined to include all buildings and fixed equipment (such as heating and ventilating, or monorail installations), but excluding all productive and nonproductive equipment.

[2] *Equipment.* For the purpose of this text equipment is defined as all production machinery and equipment, and nonproductive equipment (material-handling equipment, office equipment, and the like) necessary to permit operation of the facility.

the growth resulting in too much responsibility for one person, too many details, too many decisions. The superintendent who still insists upon carrying the entire load will soon find that it is increasingly difficult to concentrate on the matters at hand, difficult to make even simple decisions. The superintendent will become uncertain of himself and correspondingly irritable. This mood will infect those in contact with him and will spread throughout the department or division, resulting in general deterioration of morale.

Line Organization. The solution, which is not difficult, involves simply the application of the military principle of line organization with a staff command. Instead of Maintenance operating as a one-man organization, it then functions as a group of coordinated functional sections, each managed by a general foreman, who acts with the authority of the superintendent of maintenance on certain delegated functions.

These general foremen are selected and retained for their ability to apply the superintendent's policies to each situation and to arrive at substantially the same decision that he himself might have made. The superintendent of maintenance is then free to devote undivided attention to developing and perfecting policy and to dealing thoroughly with new problems that have been referred to him for solution by the general foremen. The same general policy should be followed with detail foremen responsible to the general foremen.

Application of the principle of staff command to a maintenance department not only is important from the viewpoint of the superintendent of maintenance but also is vitally important to the company as a whole. For with this type of organization, the company may feel secure in the knowledge that, should the department head be incapacitated, the general foremen would be qualified to carry on until a suitable replacement for the department head could be selected.

After a staff has been established to operate a maintenance department, it is desirable to inaugurate the practice of regular scheduled meetings of the superintendent of maintenance and his staff. At these meetings progress reports can be reviewed, budgetary matters discussed, policy corrected, and special problems studied and solved. These procedures avoid the re-evolution of a dictatorial organization, in which orders and decisions are arbitrarily handed down by the department head, and ensure the workability of a staff-command organization. A similar practice should prevail of regular meetings of each general foreman with his foremen, to precede the staff meetings. This should not be interpreted as a recommendation for "Committee Management" but rather for staff reviews of progress and problems.

BASIC ORGANIZATION FOR TRANSPORT MAINTENANCE

The basic functions of Maintenance outlined earlier in this section and shown in Fig. 9-1 can readily be converted into a basic maintenance-organization chart for a transport activity. This is shown in Fig. 9-2, where an organizational structure suitable for an airline is arranged on a *functional* basis. Transport maintenance, in contrast to facilities maintenance, usually is concerned with the maintenance of a specific kind of equipment and should be organized on a basis of the functions necessary to maintain this equipment. Facilities maintenance, on the other hand, is concerned with a vast variety of kind and type of equipment and is suited to an entirely different organizational structure.

With the arrangement shown in Fig. 9-2 it will be observed that the prime functions of inspection, overhaul, and administration (identified as *work control*) retain their basic functional identity. Preventive maintenance is an integral part of inspection in this grouping. Construction of facilities is considered to be a minor part of the total task and is combined with repair in the facilities maintenance group of the *service* section. Salvage, in this case, usually will pertain principally to the reclaiming or disposal of scrapped transport-equipment components and has been assigned to work control on the premise of its being closely allied to material control and stockroom functions.

Station Organization. The very basis of a transport activity is a system over which vehicles are operated. Such a system usually involves a quantity of *outlying stations*, remote from the home base and serving as the points of origin and destination for vehicles traveling the system.   Each of these stations is somewhat analogous to an operating division of a large manufacturing enterprise.   At each station will be found practically every function necessary to operate the transport activity.   One employee may be responsible for a variety of these at a small station.   At large stations a super-

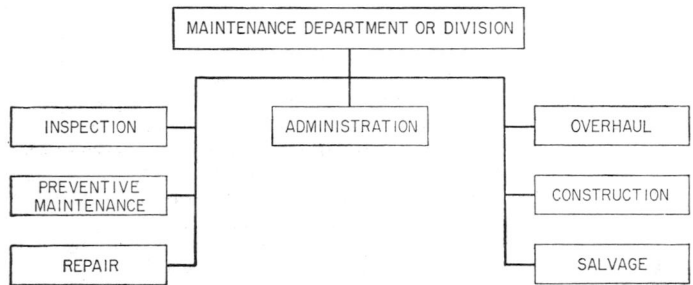

FIG. 9-1. Basic functions of maintenance.

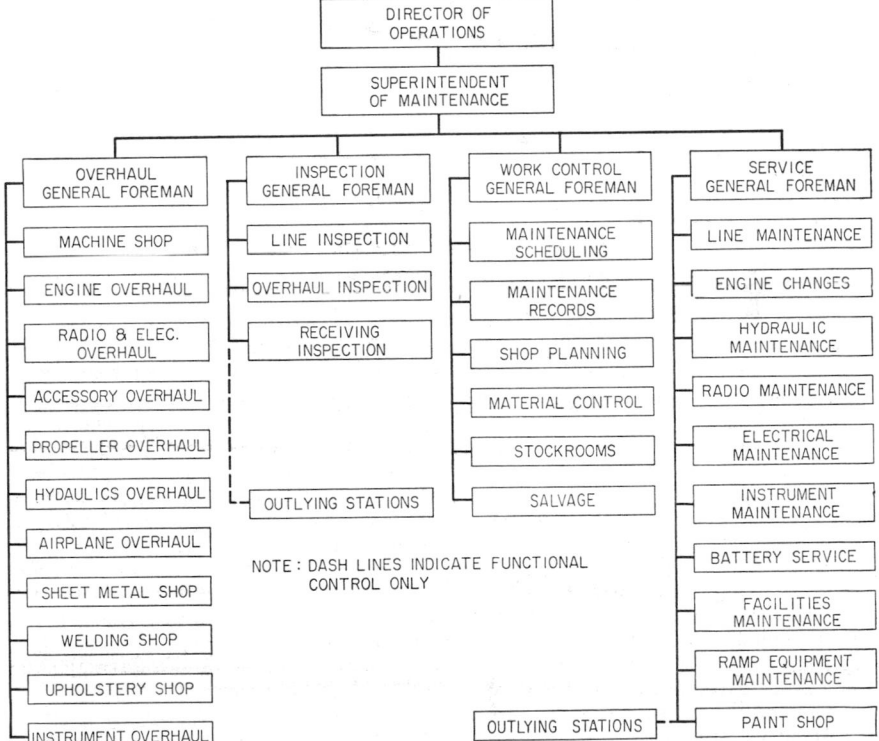

FIG. 9-2. Functional plan for transport maintenance organization (airline).

visor and a group of employees may be required to handle a single function—such as maintenance.

On this basis the position of station manager becomes comparable with that of division manager for a manufacturing enterprise.   The station manager is responsible for successful functioning of every phase of operating the station.   It follows logically that if the station manager is *responsible* for the station it will be necessary for him to have full authority over all station personnel.

This organizational relationship is shown in Fig. 9-2, where control by a general foreman at the main base is limited to policy or *functional control*, which involves only establishing methods to be followed in accomplishing necessary maintenance work at outlying stations. The station manager is responsible for proper execution of these policies and has complete administrative control over all maintenance personnel assigned to his station.

BASIC ORGANIZATION FOR FACILITIES MAINTENANCE

Facilities maintenance, also, can be contained within the six basic functions discussed earlier in this section. However, in the case of this type of maintenance department, each of the six basic functions must be applied to a variety of things, rather than to one basic type of equipment as is usually the case with transport maintenance. A somewhat different type of functional organization is indicated for facilities maintenance, in order to avoid unnecessary duplication of maintenance skills in each section of Maintenance. It appears logical that facilities maintenance should be organized on a basis of the type of work to be done, as shown in Fig. 9-3, where the *work functions* are established as *buildings, electrical,* and *mechanical.*

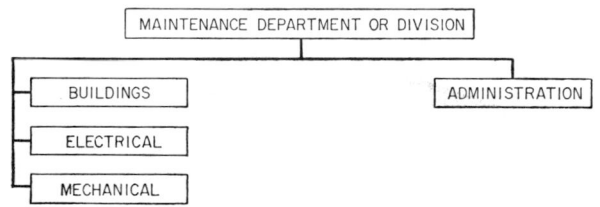

Fig. 9-3. Basic functional organization for facilities maintenance.

With the arrangement shown in Fig. 9-3, each of the work sections of buildings, electrical, and mechanical carries out the inspection, preventive maintenance, repair, overhaul, and construction functions relating to its kind of work. When a construction job involves work by two or more sections (as usually is the case), then the section having the larger share of the job is responsible for the total task and for carrying out necessary coordination with the other sections and with facilities engineering.

The facilities maintenance functions shown in Fig. 9-3 can readily be converted into a basic organization chart. This is shown in Fig. 9-4, where a facilities maintenance department is organized on the basis of four general foremen reporting to a superintendent of maintenance.

In the plan shown in Fig. 9-4, certain arbitrary assignments of work have been made. On the premise that *buildings* should include not only the physical facility and its roads and grounds but also all *fixed equipment* permanently attached to the buildings, it appears logical that all work relating to air conditioning, refrigeration, ventilation, monorails, and conveyors should be assigned to this work section. Similarly, the premise that the most complex work of business-machine maintenance is that relating to electrical components makes it logical to assign this work to *electrical*. Clock and instrument maintenance also is assigned to *electrical* on the premise that the types of skills needed for this work are more likely to be found in that section.

Preventive maintenance is a responsibility of all three work sections—each being responsible for inspection and necessary repair and replacements relating to the items and equipment assigned to its section. The *planning and scheduling* of preventive maintenance, however, are considered to be a proper function of *work control*, which should handle this responsibility for all three of the work sections.

Application of the plan shown in Fig. 9-4 to the organizational needs of a particular maintenance department may require some deletion and addition of functions in the work sections, because of the particular needs of a given plant. Ordinarily this should present little difficulty, if it is kept in mind that there can be no need for additional work sections beyond the three shown. These are basic; additions would simply be subdivision without logical reason and would only increase the superintendent's work load by creating additional jobs reporting directly to him.

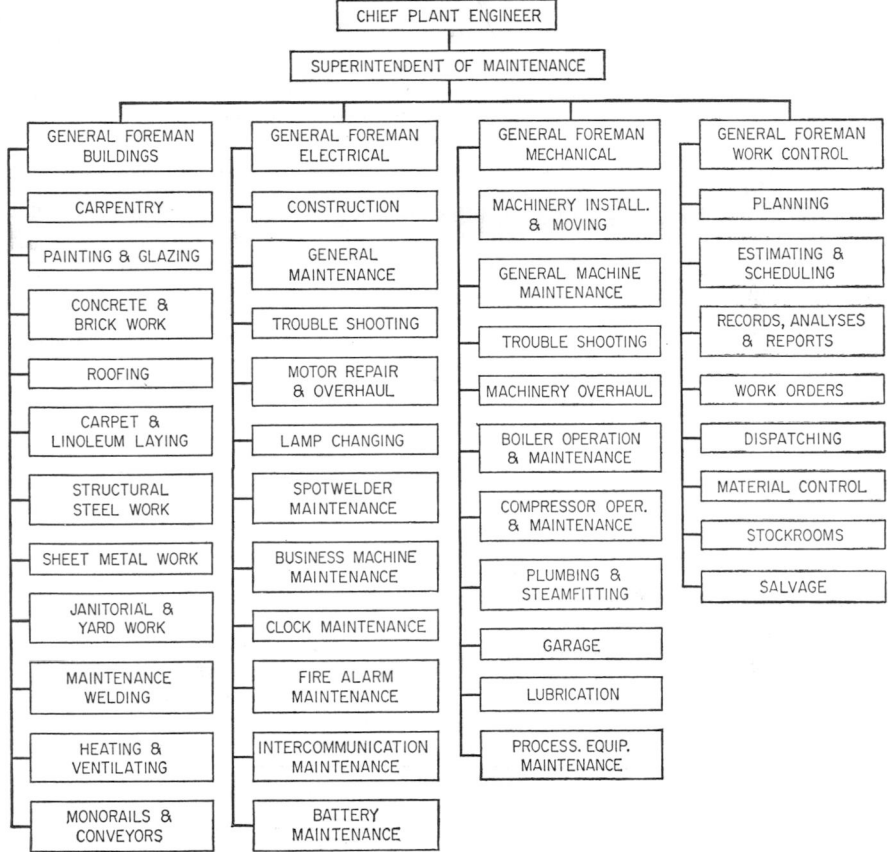

Fig. 9-4. Functional plan for facilities maintenance organization (heavy manufacturing plant).

DETAIL ORGANIZATION

Expanding the basic functional organization plans shown in Figs. 9-2 and 9-4 into detail organizational structures for a particular company is simply a matter of assigning foremen to various functions or groups of related functions. Because an endless variety of such detail organizational structures is possible, it is not considered practical to attempt such detail presentations in this section but rather to concentrate on principles of good organization.

The two functional plans shown here are applicable to any maintenance activity regardless of its size, but the job titles used are those suitable to a medium-sized organization. Maintenance is shown as being headed by a *superintendent of maintenance* and supported by major subordinates designated as *general foremen*. Each general foreman, in turn, is considered to have one or more subordinates designated as *foremen*—with each of these responsible for a group handling a certain kind or kinds of work.

In the case of a small maintenance department, the superintendent might become a general foreman from the viewpoint of job titles, and be supported by foremen. In an even smaller operation the head of Maintenance might be a foreman, supported by assistant foremen, or even by *leadmen* only. In any event the identical principles of functional organization will apply, regardless of the size of the maintenance activity.

MULTISHIFT RESPONSIBILITY

In many cases the maintenance department maintains a second shift and it often operates on an around-the-clock, three-shift basis. In each such case it is necessary to establish lines of authority between the first-shift foreman of each section or group and his second- and third-shift counterparts. Experience with this organizational problem indicates that the best solution is to assign to each first-shift foreman *functional control* over second- and third-shift foremen of his section. Under such an arrangement the second- and third-shift foremen are responsible for operating in accordance with policy, methods, procedures, and schedules established by the first-shift foreman.

On the other hand, complete authority for *administrative control* of each section or group should be vested in the foreman of each shift. In this manner each foreman retains full responsibility (and has all normal authority) for matters of discipline, changes of status, quality of workmanship, and the like, relating to his section and on his shift.

LINE AUTHORITY

After a maintenance detail organization has been established, certain basic principles of management must be followed, to ensure its proper operation. Again we may borrow from a military expression to illustrate the point and say that it is necessary for all instructions and requests to "go through channels." All must flow along established lines of authority, and in no case should any member of the maintenance department pass over a superior or a subordinate when transmitting instructions, complaints, requests, or assignments.

Unless this policy is scrupulously observed on the part of all supervision and enforced on the part of employees, it is difficult to maintain morale and discipline within the department. The employee must first take all problems to his foreman and must in all cases receive his instructions from the same person if he is to have proper respect for the foreman.

Employees should not receive from a general foreman decisions on matters that are under the jurisdiction of foremen; instead, they should be referred back to their foreman. On the other hand, the general foreman (or department head, for that matter) who issues instructions directly to employees of a foreman (even though subordinate to the general foreman) is guilty of a cardinal error. Such practices destroy the foreman's prestige, with resultant deterioration of departmental morale.

ORGANIZATION CHARTS

It may seem that issuance of an actual, physical organization chart of the maintenance department is relatively unimportant. This is not true. In fact, one of the most important steps in establishing a smoothly functioning department is the issuance of an organization chart, followed by immediate revision and reissue whenever personnel or functional changes become necessary. When this is done, there can be no misunderstanding regarding authority and responsibilities of the various foremen. The department morale is greatly strengthened by the public announcement of the status of each person in the department.

Concurrent with issuance of an organization chart, there should be distributed a brief statement defining the responsibility of each supervisor shown thereon. This can be similar to the example for a Maintenance Mechanical Section shown in Table 9-1 and will clarify the duties of each person beyond the possibility of misunderstanding. The importance of these simple steps must not be underestimated. Nothing is more deleterious to departmental morale than uncertainty regarding responsibility or authority.

In conclusion, the essence of Maintenance organization involves determination of the functions involved; allocation of these to a *small* staff of general foremen, each of whom directs a group of foremen; followed by a clear-cut detail organizational scheme based upon positively defined duties and authorities.

Table 9-1. Responsibilities of Mechanical Section

Responsible for:

Inspection, maintenance, repair, overhaul, installation and/or operation of the following items. Makes "repair or overhaul" decision whenever required.

1. Machinery-maintenance and Trouble-shooting Group

    All production machinery, and other equipment as designated by general foreman. Includes inspection, repair, and replacement of grinding wheels; and grinder dust-collector cleaning.

2. Maintenance Machine and Welding-shop Group

    a. Machine and welding work required for maintenance activities, except welding done by steel-construction section on their work.

    b. Manufacture all spot-welder tips required by the company.

3. Machinery-oiling Group

    All oiling and cleaning of production and other equipment requiring lubrication. Includes such items as doors and filing cabinets, but excludes business machines and clocks.

4. Hydraulics Group

    Hydraulic test stands, including construction of these units. Install all hydraulic apparatus relating to production equipment.

5. Processing-equipment Group

    a. Processing equipment, such as anodic, plating, heat-treating, sandblasting, foundry furnaces, pots, steam-cleaning equipment, and the like—including pumps and emergency equipment.

    b. Trouble shooting and repair on items not handled by machinery-maintenance groups, including such items as hydraulic elevators, vacuum pumps, mechanized doors, and compressors.

    c. Operation of compressors and vacuum pumps.

    Note. Workmen are available on a 24-hr, 7-day basis.

6. Machinery-moving Group

    a. Moving heavy equipment required for repair and construction work. Includes disassembly for moving, reassembly, leveling, and bolting down. Difficult or extensive moving may be contracted.

    b. Moving benches and cabinets in production areas, and heavy office equipment.

    c. Delivering heavy production supplies, such as paint and chemical drums.

    Note. Light office equipment is moved by janitors.

7. Heating, Ventilating, Air-conditioning, and Refrigeration Group

    a. Air-conditioning and ventilating equipment, including filters and dust collectors (but excluding cleaning and oiling of filters).

    b. Refrigeration equipment.

    c. Heaters.

    Note. Workmen are available on a 24-hr, 7-day basis.

8. Plumbing Group

    Sewer, water, and gas lines, including new construction of these services.

    Note. Plumbers are available on a 24-hr, 7-day basis.

9. Pipe-fitting Group

    a. Steam, air, and vacuum lines, including new construction of these services.

    b. Steam boilers, including operation thereof; with certain boilers operated on a 24-hr, 7-day basis.

Section 2

MAINTENANCE PERSONNEL
ADMINISTRATION

Chapter 1

MAINTENANCE TRADES
AND SUPERVISORY TRAINING

Part 1. Maintenance Trades Training

By ROBERT M. JOHNSON
Instructor in Maintenance Education
The Dow Chemical Company
Midland, Mich.

Part 2. Supervisory Training

By G. FRED HEISMAN
Manager of Supervisory Development
The Dow Chemical Company
Midland, Mich.

PART 1

MAINTENANCE TRADES TRAINING

Needs and Basic Provisions for Training

Need for Training. Your company may be one of the many companies who are considering, or will be considering, training programs for your maintenance men. Perhaps the main reason for this consideration is that you are unable to hire qualified men to carry out daily plant maintenance requirements. Other reasons for establishing training programs in your plant may be that maintenance work is becoming increasingly complex due to technological advancements in equipment, your maintenance men may not be properly trained in the fundamentals involving a particular trade, or maybe they have never received any formal training. Whatever the reason, it is important that you identify the need for establishing a training program in your plant. A well-defined need is essential at the onset. If the need for training cannot be identified, there is little reason for planning further. If you are able to unmistakably identify the need for establishing a training program, your next move is to convince your management. Be absolutely sure they are sold on this venture. This procedure applies to any kind of craft training.

Basic Provisions. After you have identified the need for training, make a list of general provisions for your program. Consideration should be given to the following:

1. A provision for selecting qualified men to be trained.
2. A provision for determining standards of performance for the trainees.
3. A provision for measuring the performance of trainees against standards of performance.
4. A job-progression schedule, showing job classification and wages related to a training schedule.
5. A job description for each classification.
6. A means of settling individual trainee problems, such as what to do when a trainee is doing failing work and what happens to the trainee who misses work due to illness.
7. A means of determining number of men to be trained.
8. A means of determining how, when, and where training is to be given.
9. A delegation of responsibility for carrying out the training program.
10. A means of correlating classroom training with shop and/or field training.
11. A means of rotating trainees to provide them with varied shop and/or field experiences.
12. A means of evaluating training to insure that it is always kept current.
13. A means of determining what happens to the trainee who fails the program.
14. A means of determining who is going to buy supplies used in the program—the trainee or the company.
15. A concise definition of the skills which the trainee is required to be able to perform upon completion of training.

Training Agreements

Negotiate Training Agreements. A practice that works effectively is to include in your company-union contract only general provisions such as (1) age requirements and (2) the privilege to conduct training as required. Included in these general provisions is a statement to the effect that training agreements for each trade may be drawn up between the company and union provided that the training agreements contain nothing contrary to the terms of the company-union contract. Using this approach, both you (the company) and the shop stewards are free to prepare a training agreement for each trade and tailor it to specific needs. Revisions can be made with a minimum of negotiating.

Writing Training Agreements. The training agreement covers the detailed wording of the basic provisions which have been stated. After you have established the need for training and have carefully analyzed the basic provisions to be included in your program, the instructor or shop supervisor is confronted with the task of writing the training agreement. Whoever has this task should prepare a rough draft. As soon as the rough draft has been completed and reviewed, have the shop stewards thoroughly review it. They can be extremely helpful in bringing the rough draft into its final form. This technique will result in saving a great deal of time. After you and the shop stewards have agreed to the contents of the agreement, have the company and union bargaining committees carefully examine the proposal, at this point usually in its final form. This review acts as a double check to prevent violation of the plant company-union contract.

Bureau of Apprenticeship and Training. A number of companies are using the services of the Bureau of Apprenticeship and Training, U.S. Department of Labor, Washington, D.C., to set up apprenticeship programs. Their fundamentals for a good apprenticeship program are:

1. The starting age of an apprentice to be not less than 16.
2. A schedule of work processes in which an apprentice is to receive training and experience on the job.
3. Organized instruction designed to provide the apprentice with knowledge in technical subjects related to his trade (a minimum of 144 hr per year is normally considered necessary).
4. A progressively increasing schedule of wages.

5. Proper supervision of on-the-job training with adequate facilities to train apprentices.
6. Periodic evaluation of the apprentice's progress, both in job performance and related instruction, and the maintenance of appropriate records.
7. Employee-employer cooperation.
8. Recognition for successful completions.
9. Selection of men and women for apprenticeships without regard to race, creed, color, national origin, or physical handicaps.

Information regarding services of the Bureau's field representatives may be obtained from the Regional Office of the Bureau of Apprenticeship and Training covering the state in which your company is located or from the field office nearest you.

Selecting Qualified Men

Need for Selection. You cannot afford to overlook a sound selection program for men entering your maintenance training programs. Always keep in mind that each man entering any maintenance training program is a potential maintenance foreman. By the time a man completes a training program for a particular trade you are going to have a sizable monetary investment. A good selection program will aid in hiring a high-caliber tradesman, and this man will be able to grow as maintenance work becomes more complex. A sound selection program will result in lower maintenance costs. It will lower the turnover of manpower, lower the cost of maintenance training, eliminate the chance of lowering the standards of a particular trade, and improve employee morale. And it will result in more and better work accomplished.

Many companies are using a series of tests which aid them in their selection of maintenance tradesmen. Frequently, a series of tests has been used in the selection of men at the point of hire. In addition, a group of tests can be selected which will indicate the man's ability to achieve in a particular maintenance trade. In general, it should be remembered that the reason for using a test battery in selecting maintenance men is that it serves as an aid in attempting to see the man as he actually is. As a result, you will have a better understanding of this man's potential relative to the job he is seeking.

Negotiate Tests and Test Scores. You may believe that the union would object to the use of a test battery for the selection of maintenance men. However, many companies have installed test batteries and in many cases have accomplished this through the help of the union. While you are considering a training agreement for a particular maintenance trade, work with your union in developing the selection program. If the union steward is unfamiliar with tests and testing procedure, have him take the test you are thinking of using and have a qualified man explain the results. This is one of the better ways to achieve union acceptance of a testing program.

It may also be helpful to have the men who are already tradesmen take your proposed test or test battery. This approach will enable you to evaluate the test better and will be helpful in establishing minimum test scores. Your job of selling the union on a test selection program will be much easier if members of the union have a part in its development. Also, minimum time will be required for negotiations.

Types of Tests. There are several types of tests which have been found to be useful in the selection of maintenance trainees. Examples are:

General Ability Tests. Measure how well a man can perform in the area of general ability or his ability to learn.

Interest Tests. Indicate areas of activities in which a man shows an interest. In general, individuals are likely to be motivated to achieve levels of satisfactory performance in areas which are of interest to them.

Personality Tests. Measure the pressures that produce behavior and may possibly help predicting behavior. Certain things about behavior either support the general activity or retard its success. Professional interpretation of personality tests will provide this kind of information.

Achievement Tests (Equivalency Tests). Indicate the degree of mastery or retention of a subject field as compared with what other people have retained in the same subject field.

Aptitude Tests. Attempt to measure special individual abilities which will indicate if the man is likely to perform a given job satisfactorily.

Test Battery. Aids you in the selection of maintenance men for a particular trade. One test battery which you might consider may contain any combination or all of the following tests:

Wonderlic Personnel Test.
Bennett Mechanical Comprehension.
Revised Minnesota Paper Form Board Test.
Purdue Industrial Mathematics.
Small Parts Dexterity Test.

It should be remembered that there are other tests or combinations of tests that will do an equal job, but here is a testing program used by one of the large chemical companies.

Department	Tests
Boiler Shop	
Boilermaker helper	
Blacksmith helper	Wonderlic
Flanger helper	Revised Minnesota Paper Form Board
Welder apprentice	
	Army General Classification Test Form AH
Senior apprentice layoutman	Revised Minnesota Paper Form Board (Must have attained journeyman boilermaker classification)
Construction	
Construction maintenance helper	
Millwright helper	Construction Test Form B-10-51
Riggers	
Crane operators	
Electric	
	Wonderlic
Electrician helper	Bennett Mechanical Comprehension
	Purdue Industrial Mathematics
	Elec. Dept. N. 4
Fire	
	Wonderlic
Fireman	Bennett Mechanical Comprehension
	Revised Minnesota Paper Form Board
Garage	
	Wonderlic
Auto-mechanic apprentice	Bennett Mechanical Comprehension
Body repairman helper	Revised Minnesota Paper Form Board
	Purdue Mechanical
	Wonderlic
	Bennett Mechanical Comprehension
Stock clerk	Dow Industrial Math
	Minnesota Clerical—Part I Numbers Part II Names
Journeyman auto mechanic	Garage Department Mechanics Employment Examination
Journeyman body repairman	Work Experience Test for Body Repairman Form A-7-31-52

Department	*Tests*
Instrument	
Instrument helper	Instrument Department Aptitude Test Purdue Industrial Mathematics Wonderlic Personnel Test Small Parts Dexterity Test
Lead Shop	
Leadburner helper Lead shop apprentice machinist	Wonderlic Revised Minnesota Paper Form Board Bennett Mechanical Comprehension
Machine Shop	
Machinist apprentice	Wonderlic Bennett Mechanical Comprehension Revised Minnesota Paper Form Board Purdue Industrial Mathematics
Machinist helper— (Outside and bench repair) Scale repair helper Tinsmith apprentice	Wonderlic Bennett Mechanical Comprehension Revised Minnesota Paper Form Board
Mechanical Fabrication and Development	
Tool and die maker (All classifications that require training)	Wonderlic Bennett Mechanical Comprehension Revised Minnesota Paper Form Board Purdue Industrial Mathematics
Pipe Shop	
Fitter helper	Wonderlic Bennett Mechanical Comprehension Revised Minnesota Paper Form Board
Coverer apprentice Class B machine man	Wonderlic Bennett Mechanical Comprehension Pipe Shop Exam—Form A-3-55
Set-up man	Wonderlic Bennett Mechanical Comprehension Revised Minnesota Paper Form Board
Welder apprentice Apprentice torch repairman	Wonderlic Revised Minnesota Paper Form Board Pipe Shop Welder Exam—Form A-3-55
Power Department	
Instrument man	Instrument Department Aptitude Test Wonderlic Bennett Mechanical Comprehension Purdue Industrial Mathematics Small Parts Dexterity Test
Refrigeration	
Refrigeration helper	Wonderlic Bennett Mechanical Comprehension Purdue Industrial Mathematics
Steam Trap and Valve Repair	
Sprinkler fitter helper	Wonderlic Bennett Mechanical Comprehension Revised Minnesota Paper Form Board
Trapman helper	Wonderlic Bennett Mechanical Comprehension Revised Minnesota Paper Form Board

Retesting Procedure. A basic question you may have to resolve when setting up a training program is "What happens to the man if he fails the series of tests you are using for selection?" Resolving this question should be a joint effort of the company-union bargaining committees. This will result in establishing a uniform retesting procedure. You might want to develop a retesting procedure similar to the following:

1. A second test will be given to those who fail a test for the first time, provided the score on the first test is at least 75 per cent of the minimum required score. The second test will be given not less than 6 months after the first test.
2. If the score on the first test is less than 75 per cent of the minimum required score, the man will be considered for a second test after 6 months only if he successfully completes a recognized educational course.
3. The second test will be an alternate form of the first test whenever possible.

References on Selection Tests

Albright, L. E., J. R. Glennon, and W. J. Smith: "The Use of Psychological Tests in Industry," Howard Allen Inc., Cleveland, 1963.
Bellows, R. M.: "Psychology of Personnel in Business and Industry," Prentice-Hall, Inc., Englewood Cliffs, N.J., 1961.
Buros, O. K.: "The Fifth Mental Measurements Yearbook," The Gryphon Press, Highland Park, N.J., 1959.
Cornbach, L. J.: "Essentials of Psychological Testing," Harper & Row, Publishers, Incorporated, New York, 1960.
Ghiselli, E. E., and C. W. Brown: "Personnel and Industrial Psychology," 2d ed., McGraw-Hill Book Company, New York, 1955.
Stone, C. H., and W. E. Kendall: "Effective Personnel Selection Procedures," Prentice-Hall, Inc., Englewood Cliffs, N.J., 1959.
Thorndike, R. L.: "Personnel Selection-Test and Measurement Techniques," John Wiley & Sons, Inc., New York, 1950.
Tiffin, J., and E. J. McCormick: "Industrial Psychology," Prentice-Hall, Inc., Englewood Cliffs, N.J., 1961.

Conducting Training

Instructors. The practice among companies varies greatly. Most maintenance training programs have one or a combination of the following people do the actual classroom instructing:

1. Shop supervisors.
2. Engineering department personnel.
3. Outside educational institutions.
4. Vendor representatives.
5. Training department personnel.

Using the shop foremen or shop superintendents to do the actual instructing has the advantage of making it possible to carry out the important principle that the responsibility for training must rest with maintenance supervision. It affords opportunities for supervisor and men to get to know each other as individual personalities, which is important for shop morale. It gives added insurance that the men will be taught the practical things they need to know on the job. However, it has two major disadvantages (and they are mighty big disadvantages): (1) it is difficult to train most foremen or superintendents to be good instructors; (2) they usually cannot take enough time from their other duties to prepare for their classes.

Engineers usually have the technical know-how that is required for maintenance instruction, but it is difficult to make a good instructor out of an engineer, especially if he does it only part time.

If you do use foremen, shop superintendents, engineers, or other technical men as instructors, give them an intensive instructor-training course with plenty of opportunity to practice teaching techniques before you turn them loose on trainees. It will pay big dividends.

Many vendors offer excellent instruction service whereby a well-qualified representative will come to your plant or you can send your men to the vendor's plant. They furnish the required equipment and put on a short course covering the maintenance and operation of the equipment you purchase from them. If the vendor brings the course to your plant, he will usually tailor the course to fit your specific needs, if you so request.

The author believes that instruction should be given by a full-time man with a degree in vocational education and some teaching experience in shopwork in public schools, night schools, or trade schools. This person could be a member of the maintenance organization or training department. In addition, a shop supervisor should be available to supplement his work. Thus you have a two-man instruction team with the training man carrying the responsibility for calling in the shop supervisor.

Some of the major advantages of this team approach are:

1. The training man knows how to teach—how to get the materials across to the men.
2. The shop supervisor furnishes the "expert" knowledge on specialized subjects.
3. The shop supervisor knows what is going on in the training program and can thus help keep it geared to the shop's needs.
4. The training man can assist the shop supervisor in planning and organizing the sessions which the supervisor will teach. He can help secure material, visual aids, and demonstrations, as well as sit in the session with the shop supervisor to help get the points across to the men.
5. The shop supervisor is not overburdened with classroom instructing duties.

Trade Curriculums. The combination of courses which constitute a curriculum for a specific trade in maintenance training programs will vary. Include only the material necessary to enable the man to know how to do the job for which he is in training. The job description or job-evaluation study of each trade is the best criterion upon which to base the content.

Blueprint reading and mathematics are standard courses in most maintenance training programs. Some companies use the same blueprint-reading course and mathematics course for all the trades; others have a different blueprint-reading course and different mathematics course for each trade.

Examples of courses taught for a sampling of maintenance trades are listed below:

Auto Mechanic

Apprentice Training	Hours	Senior Apprentice Training	Hours
Shop mathematics	30	Burning and cutting practices	10
Blueprint reading and sketching	25	Automotive chassis and body	40
Use and care of general repair tools	30	Automotive transmissions and power trains	40
		Automotive engines	36
		Automotive fuel, lubrication, and cooling	28
		Automotive electrical equipment and tune up	100

Electrician

Senior Helper Training	Hours	Journeyman Training	Hours
Electrical math	72	Electronics I	60
Electrical blueprint reading	24	Electronics II	72
National Electrical Code	24	Electronics in solid state	144
D-c theory	86		
A-c theory	108		

Grinder

Apprentice Training	Hours	Senior Apprentice Training	Hours
Grinding theory	45	Shop mathematics	60
Metallurgy	45	Blueprint reading	30

Work Experiences

	Hours		Hours
Blanchard No. 18	200	Abrasive surface	250
Foulmer hone	250	Knife grinder	200
No. 13 B and S univ. tool and cutter	700	Heald internal	300
Landis O. D.	600	Lap master	250
Cincinnati universal	800	Small tool and cutter grinders	200
Grand Rapids surface	250		

Instrument Man

Class B Instrument	Hours	Class B (Electrical) Instrument	Hours
Mathematics review	72	Mathematics review	72
Physics review	30	Physics review	30
Blueprint reading review	24	Blueprint reading review	24
Instrumentation I	80	D-c theory	86
Instrumentation II	108	A-c theory	108
A-c and d-c theory	72	National Electrical Code	24
Electronics	160	Electronics I	72
		Electronics II	72

Refrigeration Man

Helper Training	Hours	Senior Helper Training	Hours
Shop mathematics	60	Refrigeration and air conditioning	
Physics	18	course	120
		Blueprint reading	22
		Reading refrigeration shop and field	
		prints	22
		Refrigeration code	11

Tool and Die Maker

Apprentice Training	Hours	Work Experiences	Hours
Shop theory	26	Shaper	480
Blueprint reading, shop prints, and		Drill press	480
sketching	80	Lathe	1200
Mathematics	160	Milling machine	1600
Metallurgy	80	Grinders	800
		Do-all contour saw	400
		Die sinker	400
		Filing machine	120
		Super finishing	120
		Heat treating	120

Classrooms and Laboratories. Give a great deal of thought to where you are going to hold your classes. Consideration should be given to the classroom regarding air conditioning, lighting, space, size of classes, noise, location, and equipment. Too often classes are conducted where the proper environmental conditions do not exist. It is obvious that poor classroom facilities are not conducive to learning.

When laboratories can be planned so that laboratory work is correlated with the classroom training, you have the ideal training situation. Many times practical work experiences are assumed to be provided in the shop or field when in fact they have not actually happened. Sometimes proper instruction is not provided, or classroom instruction and work experiences do not have the proper timing. One sure way that you can solve this problem is to provide a laboratory with the classroom.

Evaluating Classroom Training. It is difficult to put teeth into your maintenance training or to hold to the standards you expect of your men unless you have a strong in-training testing program in all three of the following areas:

1. Periodic quizzes throughout the progress of each course.
2. Final examinations covering each course or covering a prescribed period of time.
3. Qualification tests on practical phases of the work.

A periodic quiz (10-min) can be given at the beginning of each class session. A more common practice is to devote every fourth or fifth class session to a quiz. The latter method is preferable, since the time element is not so critical. Of course, the frequency may vary considerably because of changing conditions, but in general it is wise to have at least four or five periodic quizzes in each course. There are three main advantages to this procedure:

1. You have a measuring stick which tells you how much each trainee is learning during the progress of the course.
2. The trainee knows where he stands and has an opportunity to improve before it is too late. If he fails even one quiz, call him in together with the steward and instructor and discuss his progress. You may not find out what his real trouble is, but it is almost a sure bet that he will show marked improvement after such a discussion. Should it happen that the trainee continues to fail his quizzes and you have held several meetings with the steward, trainee, and instructor, you have a good case built up to take him out of the trade if you feel that should be done.
3. A quiz is an excellent learning device. Reviewing a quiz, pointing out errors, emphasizing key points all help to fix the knowledge in the mind of the trainee.

Final exams for the course should be comprehensive and cover only material that the trainee has been taught in the class, field, or shop. Reviewing the final exam with the steward before it is administered is a good practice to help prevent a future grievance. Have the steward sign his approval on the exam sheet which is given to the trainee. Sometimes it is advisable to let the steward help the instructor grade the examination.

Qualification Tests on Maintenance Skills. Practical qualification exams or tests administered by the foreman in the shop are invaluable tools in an effective maintenance training program. They need not be any more time-consuming than written tests. If well planned and properly administered, a qualification test will give conclusive evidence of the trainee's ability on certain jobs. Two key points to keep in mind: (1) the test should cover those operations which occur frequently in the daily maintenance work; (2) previous training must have been given the trainee on the skills required in the performance of the test.

Shop and/or Field Training. The trainee usually spends no more than 4 hr per week in class, except in those companies which have the vestibule type of training shop. (In the vestibule the maintenance shop facilities are duplicated in a separate training shop or as part of a central company school.) In the majority of companies the trainee works in the maintenance shop and field at least 90 per cent of the time. Therefore, it is important that considerable planning be devoted to seeing that the trainee gets a well-rounded work experience in the shop and field.

The training schedule in the shop is fairly easy to set up. You can determine how many hours should be spent on each machine or piece of equipment and on repair work coming into the shop. Then set up a schedule of rotation, and have the shop foreman responsible for carrying out the schedule as planned. Perhaps the greatest difficulty is in trying to carry out the rotation schedule in the face of varying work loads and kinds of repair work being done in the shop. It is virtually impossible to follow the schedule exactly.

A rotation schedule in the field is much more difficult to carry out. However, it is essential that this be done, so that the trainee has an opportunity to perform all phases of the field work required of his trade. Rotating the trainee among all the foremen and journeymen is the most common method of accomplishing this. Some companies specify the number of hours to be spent on each phase of field work. The important thing is to see that the schedule is practical and is followed as closely as possible. A great deal of cooperation is required to assure that the trainee gets well-rounded field experience.

Evaluating Shop and/or Field Training. Examinations are, in themselves, a form of rating your trainee, but certainly only a small part of the total evaluation of your maintenance man. Additional forms of written ratings are necessary to enable you to guide and develop the trainee to the stage where he is a highly skilled man in his trade. Yet, before plunging into this rating business with both feet, consider a few basic fundamentals and major difficulties that will be encountered:

1. The rater must be willing and able to justify every mark or statement he puts on a rating sheet. The problems encountered in trying to stick to this principle have often caused the entire rating system either to be thrown out entirely or to degenerate into a meaningless routine of periodically checking rating sheets to make the record look good. Unless supervisors conscientiously and honestly try to carry out this principle of going to bat for every item they rate, it is better not to have a formal rating system.
2. Each trainee should have two or more independent ratings from different foremen. Rotating the trainee among several foremen solves this problem. A common practice is to rate the trainee monthly until he completes training, then semi-annually or annually.
3. The rater should discuss the rating with the trainee. Since the primary purpose of the rating is to bring to light areas wherein the trainee needs improvement and then take proper action to bring about the necessary improvement, frequent counseling between the rater and trainee is essential. Admittedly, it is difficult to do this, but important that it be done.
4. Ratings should be treated as confidential matter by the supervisors and the stewards. Embarrassing situations can arise unless considerable caution is exercised.
5. The make-up or content of the rating form itself is not as important as the use or administration of the rating procedure. A smoothly operating rating procedure is not easily attained; in fact, at times the whole procedure may look downright discouraging. But even if you only occasionally spot a difficulty and are able to correct it, the effort is rewarding and worthwhile.

The subject of rating is controversial. There is no one best rating form, no one best rating procedure.

Training-material Sources. Experience has proved that the best practice is to prepare and develop training material within your own organization. Sometimes a textbook is available which will cover general theory courses for a great many maintenance trades. However, you may find that you have to use several textbooks. Using several textbooks is costly, but developing training material is even more costly. In many instances the development of training materials is the only way out. Be prepared for this to happen.

Investigate various textbook companies for new materials. Each year many of these companies revise their training materials, and in many cases new ones are added. It is absolutely essential for the instructor to evaluate new training materials periodically. This effort can result in a tremendous amount of time saved developing training programs.

Today, many companies have organized and developed maintenance training programs. These companies, in many instances, will provide you with valuable training materials just for the asking. If you are contemplating training programs, send your instructors to other companies to see what kinds of training materials are available and discuss training problems with experienced people This is a very sound practice.

Manufacturers of equipment on which you will be conducting training will be extremely helpful. They often will send a representative to your plant and provide you with training material and even help conduct classes. Manufacturers have training films on their equipment which can be loaned to you. I strongly suggest that you always include the manufacturer in your investigation of training materials.

Programmed Instruction. The programmed learning technique, as it is sometimes referred to, is a relatively new teaching method, described in the next chapter. Programmed instruction has now been developed to apply in a great many teaching situations which include public schools, universities, business, and industry. Many subjects have been programmed and are commercially available.

Such subjects as blueprint reading, mathematics, various physical and chemical principles common to several training programs will merit your consideration. It is worthwhile to become familiar with programmed instruction and tailor it to fit your training program. It could prove to be an excellent way for reviewing and reinforcing fundamental principles in the subject fields stated. Using programmed instruction will provide the instructor with more free time which can be devoted to other job functions.

Audio-visual Aids. Include audio-visual aids in your training programs. There is a tremendous amount of audio-visual aid equipment and material available. Evaluate the application of chalkboards, display materials, models, objects, film strips, slides, transparencies, films, charts, posters, records, tape recorders, and possibly closed circuit television to your training situation. Good audio-visual aids will help the trainees learn more efficiently, with greater retention of the material presented.

It is not necessary to spend a great deal of money to have good visual aids in your training. Excellent movies, film strips, and slides can be rented at nominal fees or secured on a free loan basis. Many times you can make your own visual aids. If this is done, keep in mind it can be time-consuming, especially if you are a novice. Often, the best visual aid of all is overlooked—the piece of equipment itself. Bring it into the classroom for a demonstration and discussion. Trips to equipment sites should always be considered, and you will find they are extremely beneficial to the trainee.

Many public school systems, colleges, universities, and companies have organized audio-visual aid departments. In addition to this, a lot of companies are producing audio-visual aids in conjunction with their products. Some companies are in the audio-visual aid business. You should consult all these sources. Regarding this, you should be able to obtain help from your purchasing agent.

College and University Audio-visual Aid References

Brigham Young University, Audio-Visual Center, Provo, Utah.
Brown University, Brown Photo Laboratory, Providence 12, R.I.
Cornell University, Visual Aids Office, Roberts Hall, Ithaca, N.Y.
Dartmouth College Films, Fairbanks Hall, Hanover, N.H.
University of Florida, Department of Visual Instruction, General Extension Division, Gainesville, Fla.
University of Illinois, Visual Aids Service, Division of University Extension, Champaign, Ill.
Indiana University, Audio-Visual Center, Bloomington, Ind.
University of Michigan, Audio-Visual Education Center, 4028 Administration Building, Ann Arbor, Mich.
University of Minnesota, Audio-Visual Education Service, Westbrook Hall, Minneapolis 14, Minn.
University of Mississippi, Department of TV, Film and Audio, University, Miss.
New York University Film Library, 26 Washington Pl., New York, 3, N.Y.
Ohio State University, Department of Photography, Brown Hall, Room 4, Columbus 10, Ohio.
University of Southern California, Audio-Visual Services, Department of Cinema, University Park, Los Angeles 7, Calif.

There are many other colleges, universities, and public schools which have audio-visual aid departments and are located near you. Obtain their publications to see what they have available.

Company Audio-visual Aid Department References

Air Reduction Sales Company, 205 West Monroe St., Chicago 6, Ill.

Allegheny Ludlum Steel Corporation, Sales Promotion, 2020 Oliver Building, Pittsburgh 22, Pa.

Allis-Chalmers Manufacturing Company, Tractor Photographic Group, Milwaukee 1, Wis.

Aluminum Company of America, Motion Picture Section, 1501 Alcoa Building, Pittsburgh 19, Pa.

American-Standard Plumbing and Heating Division, Princeton Training Center, 16 John St., Princeton, N.J.

Brown and Sharpe Manufacturing Company, 235 Promenade St., Providence, R.I.

California Redwood Association, Service Library, 576 Sacramento St., San Francisco 11, Calif.

Carborundum Company, The, Niagara Falls, N.Y.

Cincinnati Milling Machine Company, The, Advertising Department, 4701 Marburg Ave., Cincinnati 9, Ohio.

Clark Equipment Company, Advertising and Sales Promotion Department, Battle Creek, Mich.

Cleveland Twist Drill Company, The, 1242 East 49th St., Cleveland 14, Ohio.

Do All Company, The, Film Library, 254 North Laurel Ave., Des Plaines, Ill.

Dow Chemical Company, The, Audio-Visual Center, Film Library, ARB, Midland, Mich.

du Pont de Nemours and Company, Inc., E. I., Motion Picture Section, Advertising Department, Wilmington 98, Del.

Ford Motor Company, Ford Film Library, Ann Arbor, Mich.

General Motors Corporation, Public Relations Staff, Film Library, General Motors Building, Detroit 2, Mich.

Goodyear Tire and Rubber Company, The, Audio-Visual Department, Akron 16, Ohio.

Jam Handy Organization, Film Distribution Department, 2821 East Grand Blvd., Detroit 11, Mich.

Norton Company, Advertising Department, Worcester 6, Mass.

Republic Steel Corporation, Steel and Tube Division, Products Engineering Department, 224 East 131st St., Cleveland 8, Ohio.

Reynolds Metals Company, Motion Picture Department, P.O. Box 2346, Richmond 18, Va.

Shell Oil Company, Film Library, Flushing 54, N.Y.

Smith Corporation, A. O., Audio-Visual Section, Department 0162, P.O. Box 584, Milwaukee 1, Wis.

Standard Oil Company of California, Public Relations Department, 225 Bush St., San Francisco 20, Calif.

Wickers Incorporated, Advertising and Public Relations Department, P.O. Box 302, Detroit 32, Mich.

Film Library References

Bailey Films, Inc., 6509 DeLongpre Ave., Hollywood 28, Calif.

Cornet Instructional Films, 65 E. South Water St., Chicago 1, Ill.

Educators Guide to Free Films, 23rd Annual Edition, Educators Progress Service, Randolph, Wis.

Encylopaedia Britannica Films, Inc., 1150 Wilmette Ave., Wilmette, Ill.

McGraw-Hill Book Co., Text-Film Department, 330 W. 42nd St., New York 36, N.Y.

Teaching Aids, Inc., P.O. Box 3527, Long Beach 3, Calif.

All of the above companies issue catalogs or brochures covering a wide range of films and filmstrips. Take time to send for their publications.

Audio-visual Aid Equipment Reference

The Audio-Visual Equipment Directory, 1964, National Audio-Visual Association, Inc., 1201 Spring St., Fairfax, Va. This is a fully illustrated guide to some 2,000 current models of projectors, recorders, and all other types of audio-visual equipment. I believe this to be one of the best references for audio-visual aid equipment.

Union Participation in Training

Since there are no two unions alike any more than there are two companies alike, the part that the union plays in the training program will probably vary as much as the plants and industries themselves. However, the success of your training program will be in direct proportion to the cooperation and support your union gives all phases of the program from the selection of the trainee on through graduation day. And how well the union cooperates depends largely on how well you cooperate with the union. It may seem that additional time will be required to consult the union as much as is implied, but actually you will save time by reducing the number of grievances, misunderstandings, and gripe sessions between stewards and trainees. Morale, efficiency, and output will be higher. And you'll get some good ideas from the union if you're willing to listen. Sure, you'll get some bad ones, too.

Union participation should be achieved in the following way:

1. Training agreements. A proposed training agreement is prepared after consultation with shop supervision and perhaps the labor-relations representative of the shops. The proposed agreement is then given to the union and discussed in the shop by the shop stewards and the men in the trade. The labor-relations man then calls a meeting of shop supervision, union shop committee, shop stewards, and training representative for final approval. The company-union bargaining committees then sign the training agreement.
2. Tests and test scores. Proposed tests and test scores should be discussed with the shop supervision, shop stewards, and training representative before they are used.
3. Counseling with the trainee. Whenever the trainee is doing poorly, it is wise to correct the situation before he fails. A meeting with the trainee, shop stewards, shop supervisor, and instructor should be held to determine ways to improve the situation.
4. Reviewing final examinations. In some shops, you might want the shop steward to approve the final examination before it is administered.
5. Suggestions. The shop stewards should be at liberty to examine the training program at any time and suggest constructive changes. Considerable improvement can result from this practice.
6. Awarding certificates. Ask the union officials to attend certificate presentations. If a graduation ceremony is held, ask the union to participate.

Trainee Recognition

Companies vary in their method of giving recognition to trainees who have completed their respective training programs. The method is not so important as the fact that some form of recognition is given. When a trainee completes his training program, which includes both classroom and field instruction, he then becomes eligible to enter the journeyman classification. Upon satisfactory completion of training requirements, I believe it extremely worthwhile to present to each trainee a certificate of achievement. Certificates should include signatures of the plant general manager, shop supervisor, training director, and perhaps the instructor. This will certainly indicate to the trainee there are others who are aware of his efforts in becoming a tradesman.

Your company might be interested in holding a graduation ceremony on company time for your tradesmen. At this ceremony have several speakers from top management and the union give talks on the importance of training and make certificate presentations to the tradesmen. This is a very fine way of highlighting the end of the training program.

General References

Dow Chemical Company, The, Education Department, Midland, Mich.
Smith, R. G.: "Training Workers and Supervisors," in L. C. Morrow (ed.), *Maintenance Engineering Handbook*, sec. 2, chap. 1, McGraw-Hill Book Company, New York, 1957.

PART 2

SUPERVISORY TRAINING

Why Train Supervisors?

In today's dynamic industrial world the supervisor who does not keep up his training and development runs the risk of becoming as ineffective as obsolescent equipment. This does not mean that supervisors and managers must spend excessive time and effort on training and self-development. The manager or supervisor who is not learning is not growing. And growth is imperative today to enable supervisors to provide effective leadership for their employees. Various forms of automation and semiautomated industrial processes are requiring many semiskilled tradesmen and operators to become skilled technicians. Supervising employees who are contributing to space age operations will require the competent supervisor to work on his own development as a continuing open-end process. It will be helpful for the effective supervisor to integrate his formal training with his informal training experiences, such as special assignments, job rotation, and coaching by his manager.

Very often the reason given for training supervisors is that some fault or deficiency is to be corrected. Certainly proper training can help supervisors improve faulty skills and acquire new ones as well. However, the emphasis should be more forward looking. The supervisor's training and development should be implemented as a series of integrated experiences aimed at not only improving his present performance but also preparing him for the demands of the future. The training we plan now should be an appropriate risk investment in better supervisors and managers 2 to 5 years from now. In industry we invest large sums of money in equipment and process expansions aimed at profitable long-term returns. This is forward looking, as it must be. We also need to invest in a supervisor's training and development with long-term returns as the objective.

An informed, understanding, and skillful body of supervisors can well prove to be one of the strongest assets of any company. It has been commonly said that all development is a personal, self-development process. Although nobody can be effectively trained or developed against his will, it is negligent to say, therefore, that we will place the entire burden for his own training and self-improvement on each individual supervisor. The climate to motivate supervisors to perform better today and in the future includes the sharing of responsibility for the supervisor's continuing development by the supervisor and his manager.

Actually, in the absence of a well-planned and integrated training program in which the supervisor and his manager have a dominant voice, some training still happens. What happens is sometimes not only undesirable but disastrous. If the larger climate does not stimulate the manager to help his supervisors develop, then the supervisors become indifferent about the training of their employees. The hit-and-miss training that is occurring has started a chain reaction of poor examples. Disinterest at the manager level causes the supervisor to be indifferent about his own development and less concerned about the improved performance of his employees. This can lead only to marginal mediocrity in employee performance. You can ill afford not to plan effective training now for better supervisors in the future.

Determining the Training Needs of Supervisors

If you accept the premise that effective training can be profitable for both the company and the individual supervisor, then the question of what the training needs are must be answered. Training without investigating needs is at best hit-and-miss, and can be very wasteful of time and money. Determining the training needs of supervisors requires that we find out not only what is needed, but why it is needed, and what are the long- and short-term results expected of the training. Various approaches have been taken to identify supervisory development needs. They include examining performance records of productivity, costs, quality, safety, turn-over, and grievances; conducting attitude surveys; examining performance ratings of supervisors; using questionnaires which encourage the supervisors to indicate areas where they need training; consulting various levels of management; conducting depth interviews with supervisors; using appropriate tests to determine capabilities.

The climate and operations will differ from one company to another and possibly from plant to plant and department to department within a company. Possibly no single one of the previously mentioned approaches to identifying supervisory training needs will do the job completely. You may find it helpful to use a combination of several approaches to verify training needs. The important thing to consider is that just as a supervisor's training and development is a continuing process, so is the requirement to continue assessing his training needs and measuring progress in achieving them. If you recognize that the two persons most responsible for a supervisor's development are the supervisor and his immediate boss, then here is the place to start identifying supervisory training needs. A working example of depth interviews with line supervisors and their managers combined with examining the performance ratings of the supervisors will be described more in detail later in this section.

Setting Objectives and Goals for Supervisory Training

A long-term objective of supervisory training should be to improve supervisory performance by helping supervisors to increase their knowledge, motivation, and skills. However, to be effective, the broad objective should be broken down into more concrete and measurable goals related to the identified needs. Wherever possible the training goals should be stated in terms of desired trainee behavior. Stating training goals behaviorally facilitates evaluating the effectiveness of the training against improved trainee performance. It is not enough just to help the supervisor increase his knowledge. He may absorb all the information given him and still show no improvement in performance. Effective training should motivate the supervisor to apply what he has learned in the form of more skillful behavior on the job. For example here are two statements of the same training goal: (1) train the supervisor in the effective principles of cost control; (2) train the supervisor to control costs for which he is accountable. The second statement describes what the supervisor should be able to do as a result of training. Here is where supervisory training frequently falls short of success. The failure to state training goals in terms of what the learner should do as a result of the training leads to little or no follow-up measurement of performance after training. This is a very crucial step in the planning of supervisory training. The more you can define training objectives and goals in terms of desired terminal behavior, the more readily you can evaluate the effectiveness of the training in terms of performance back on the job.

Subject Areas to Include in Supervisory Training

Because there can be such a wide variety of supervisory training needs in a wide variety of companies, it would be presumptuous to prescribe what subjects should be included. Certainly the supervisory training needs which you identify through thorough investigation will determine the subject areas to be covered. If you see supervisory training as open-ended and you continue carefully to diagnose needs based on continuing evaluation, there will undoubtedly be new areas of training needs emerging.

The author will make no attempt to assemble an all-inclusive bibliography on supervisory training. Source materials and practices are very numerous. However, the "AMA Encyclopedia of Supervisory Training" represents a broad cross section of supervisory training from many companies in various industries. It was published in 1961 by the American Management Association, New York, N.Y. Thirty-eight subject areas are included in the Subject Guide which follows.

Subject Guide to the AMA Encyclopedia of Supervisory Training

1. Industry and Company Background.
2. Management Philosophy.
3. Organization Structure—The Management Team.
4. Economics and the Free Enterprise System.
5. Union-Management Relations.
6. Supervisory Responsibility and Authority.
7. Leadership Concepts.
8. Principles of Human Behavior.
9. Order Giving and Worker Morale.
10. Common Sense About Discipline.
11. Basic Guides to Communication.
12. Effective Writing and Speaking.
13. Rules to Personal Contacts.
14. Selection Methods and Procedures.
15. Wage Administration.
16. Orientation of New Employees.
17. Job Instruction.
18. Performance Evaluation.
19. Discussion of Appraisal Results.
20. The Case for Firing.
21. Work Planning and Organization.
22. Delegation of Authority.
23. Problem Solving and Decision Making.
24. The Art of Holding a Meeting.
25. Group Thinking and Creativity.
26. Responsibility for Costs and Profits.
27. Corporate Finances.
28. Methods Improvement and Work Simplification.
29. Quality Control.
30. The Maintenance Function.
31. Safety and Accident Prevention.
32. Good Housekeeping.
33. The Grievance Procedure in Action.
34. Induction Schedules.
35. Conferences for New Supervisors.
36. Sharing in the Training Process.
37. Case Studies and Problem Situations.
38. Development of Self and Others.

Methods of Training Supervisors

When you have identified valid training needs and the consequent subject areas and have set training goals in terms of expected supervisory behavior, it is time to select the appropriate method or methods for reaching the goals.

Programmed Learning. We shall not go into detailed explanation of this methodology since it is covered in the next chapter. Programmed learning can be a very useful and powerful method of self-instruction if it is well designed. It is particularly useful to teach principles and theory which can be followed up with group discussion and skill seminars. Programmed instruction has the advantage of allowing supervisors to cover subject areas at their own individual pace. The rapid learner is not held back by the slow learner, nor is the slow learner discouraged by the more rapid progress of others. Programmed learning permits the flexibility of tailoring training to the individual supervisor's needs. However, unless followed up with group discussion or seminars, it does not give the supervisor the opportunity to interact with fellow supervisors to gain further ideas and motivation for application back on the job. Some supervisory training topics are being published currently in the form of programmed instruction. If you do not find appropriate programmed subject areas, you may wish to contract with a program-designing firm to design programs to meet your own needs.

Group Discussion or Conference. This is the most common and still popular method of conducting training for supervisors. The philosophy of the group discussion type of training conference is aimed at getting participants involved in contributing ideas, exchanging experiences, asking questions, and at times drawing their own conclusions concerning application. The trainer or conference leader may lecture briefly to present theory or a framework of basic principles. But to insure an effective group discussion the participants should be encouraged to disagree or bring up negative feelings or counterarguments to ideas presented. Unless a participant is free to express his disagreement with the trainer or other participants, he may resist the learning completely. Freewheeling interaction in the learning experience optimizes the opportunities for the participant to consolidate the learning. Consequently the supervisory trainee is much better prepared to apply his learning on the job.

Role Taking—Action Training. Role taking, which is more commonly known as role playing, can be a powerful learning tool for supervisors if it is not used as phony play acting. The author has experienced considerable success in having supervisors role play actual cases which the supervisors prepare from their own experience. An example of effective use of role taking can be taken from the author's experience in training supervisors to conduct job performance reviews. During the course each supervisory trainee is assigned the task of writing up a performance review case involving one of his subordinates. He is asked to provide fairly complete information concerning his employee's performance. Then after briefing another supervisory trainee on the case, he assumes the role of his subordinate during the role-taking or skill practice session. The supervisory trainee who has been briefed on the case takes the role of the supervisor. Other trainees are briefed to serve as analytical observers. The trainees taking the roles of the supervisor and the subordinate interact during the skill practice session as their feelings about the case prompt them. After the role-taking session is completed, the observers report their analyses of objectives accomplished and impressions of techniques used to accomplish the objectives. The supervisory trainee who has taken the role of the supervisor gets feedback concerning the effectiveness of the way he handled the situation. The supervisory trainee who served as the subordinate gets the full impact of how it feels to be in his employee's shoes.

By using multiples of three, the role-taking practice involving a supervisor, a subordinate, and an observer can be conducted by handling a number of cases simultaneously. This is a variation of multirole playing.

The analysis and general follow-up discussion of any role taking should examine possible discoveries in trying out different skills and techniques and in gaining greater insight into the problems of the people involved.

Case Studies. A case study used to implement supervisory training is usually the story of a problem situation without an ending. The case study of the problem situation is described as interestingly and concretely as possible. However, no solution is included in the written case. Participants are challenged to analyze the case and find possible solutions. A thorough and general discussion of the case problem will usually bring out a number of plausible solutions. There should be no official or perfect solution to any case problem. Trainees should learn to develop several effective solutions to a problem situation. Frequently the most meaningful case studies can be supplied by the supervisory trainees from their own experiences. There are numerous published books containing prepared case studies if you wish to supplement your supervisors' experiences.

Perceptivity or Sensitivity Training. Perceptivity or sensitivity training is a form of action learning which is extremely different from most conventional approaches to training. Major objectives for this training include establishing a laboratory climate where the participant may examine his own behavior, the behavior of other participants, and the processes occurring in the group. The participant may gain greater insight concerning the way his behavior affects others and how others affect him.   He may also learn from studying the events in the training group more about processes which influence the productivity of groups.

Most of the sessions in this type of training are unstructured.   The trainer may present a minimum of relevant theory but refrain from the usual didactic instructions. His aim is to help the participants learn for themselves by providing a participative model of shared inquiry.   This seemingly passive role of the trainer calls for much greater skill than most other types of training.

If you are considering this type of training you may wish to contact the National Training Laboratories in Washington, D.C.   The N.T.L. offices can provide you with a list of N.T.L. Fellows and Associates who would be competent to help you set up a sensitivity training program for your supervisors.

On-the-job Coaching.   Some of the best supervisory training can take place when a supervisor and his manager work together on the supervisor's development.   This process involves day-to-day contacts and planned periodic progress reviews.   The success of the coaching process depends primarily upon the motivation of the subordinate supervisor, the manager's skill as a coach, and the actual example set by the manager in his own supervisory practices.

Most supervisors want to grow and improve their performance on their present jobs.   A person can best improve his performance when he knows what his responsibilities are, what yardsticks will be used to measure his performance, and what the goals are for the areas in which he is responsible.   A subordinate supervisor has the greatest commitment to his improvement when he has a part in setting his performance goals.

Dr. Walter R. Mahler of Mahler Associates in Wyckoff, New Jersey, has designed an approach which helps to implement the coaching process effectively.   The first step in the approach involves the identification of responsibilities which define the areas in which the subordinate is accountable for achieving results.   The second step requires the determination of performance indicators which provide yardsticks for measuring progress in achieving the responsibilities.   The third step requires setting performance goals which are statements of desired end results within a given period of time.   Performance indicators provide a bridge between the responsibilities and goals; indicators also provide a common source of evidence for the manager and his subordinate in deciding how well responsibilities have been performed.

Using this three-step approach facilitates making coaching a two-way process. When the manager and his subordinate supervisor jointly work out the responsibilities, indicators, and goals for the subordinate, both experience additional development. Periodic progress reviews and resetting of goals where appropriate further implement the effectiveness of coaching.

Miscellaneous Supplementary Training Methods.   *Special Meetings with Top Management.*   These meetings may allow line supervisors to submit questions in advance, so that top management may give timely answers concerning policy problems, current business trends, and the long range goals of the company.

Meetings with Functional Management.   Periodic meetings of line supervisors with the managers of various functions provide a broader understanding for all supervisors of the activities performed in all the functions of the company.

Job Rotation.   Some companies provide supervisors the opportunity to rotate from one supervisory job to another.   This rotation can give the supervisor broader understanding and skills in different areas of operation.   It can help prepare him for greater responsibility at a higher supervisory level.

Outside Courses and Seminars.   Many companies supplement their own supervisory training by sending selected supervisors to various outside training experiences.   The American Management Association offers many seminars and workshops.   Universities and colleges offer courses and seminars in supervisory training.

Evaluating the Effectiveness of Supervisory Training

There is much talk but little action in this area in many companies.   The inactivity usually stems from looking for the perfect evaluation yardstick to measure training effectiveness. A combination of evaluative approaches offers many possibilities to measure training.

The simplest method for evaluating supervisory training is to ask participants for anonymous but critical comments. Although this approach will evoke some helpful suggestions for improving training, the preponderance of responses are usually very favorable. Consequently, as an evaluative method it does not tell very much about improved participant performance.

A second evaluative approach is to give tests before and after training. Generally this will help to measure what the supervisor has learned. Although increasing his knowledge is helpful and desirable, knowing is not enough. The participant who writes brilliant answers on the test will not necessarily apply his knowledge to improve performance.

A third approach is to measure performance factors before and after training. Performance factors might include such results areas as controllable costs, number of process and methods improvements, number of safety improvements, safety record, number of complaints and grievances. Examining measurable results is an effective way to evaluate the short-term effectiveness of training. However, there are desirable intangibles such as improved problem solving, decision making, planning, communicating, and motivating which lead to the long-term growth of the supervisor but are not readily measured in short-term results.

A fourth approach consists of using a before and after questionnaire with the supervisor's boss and/or his subordinates. If the questionnaire is well designed, the evaluation can show changes in the supervisor's behavior and also reflect improved operating results.

Some gains made through training probably never can be accurately measured with evaluative yardsticks. Improved supervisory performance and operating results are often influenced by other factors in the environment besides training. However, the more we seek to improve the evaluation of training, the more effective the training can become.

Supervisory training never takes place in a vacuum. The supervisor's training experiences should be integrated with the total climate of which he is a part. Goals for his training must be integrated with the demands of the supervisor's job and the goals of the company. If we are dynamic in assessing the supervisor's needs, then his training is a process which never ends.

Chapter 2

PROGRAMMED INSTRUCTION

By L. H. O'Donnell
Consultant, Maintenance Engineering Group
E. I. du Pont de Nemours & Co., Inc.
Wilmington, Del.

The phrase "programmed instruction" refers to the use of a self-instructional course to achieve an instructional objective. Such a course provides conditions under which a student learns efficiently with little or no outside help. In some cases the course is presented by a device called a "teaching machine"; in other cases it is presented by a specially designed form of book called a "programmed textbook."

THE PROCESS OF PROGRAMMED INSTRUCTION

The process has these distinguishing characteristics:

1. Each student receives instruction individually, at his own pace.
2. Each student responds continuously as he receives instruction. His responses may be either covert or overt, but instruction proceeds only as the student responds.
3. Each student receives rapid feedback for each response. The feedback consists of either confirmation or correction of his response.

The results of extensive experimentation with programmed instruction in industrial, military, and educational organizations indicate that good programmed instruction courses, properly used, can significantly improve both the quality and the economy of instruction.

CHARACTERISTIC OF PROGRAMMED INSTRUCTION COURSES

Programmed instruction courses are designed on the basis of scientific knowledge of the learning process. They vary in appearance and format, depending on the nature of what is to be learned and on how the author wishes to apply his knowledge of that process. Most courses, however, have these distinctive characteristics:

1. A large number of small discrete units, with each unit presented to the student in a prearranged sequence. Each unit is called a frame.
2. An inducement for the student to respond actively to each frame. Typical inducements include: a blank to be filled in, an incomplete sketch or equation to be completed, an inquiry or question, a direct request that the student do something.
3. A correct response for each frame. The correct response is hidden from the student when he makes his response but is available to him after he makes his response.

4. A design which insures that almost all the student's responses will agree with the correct response.
5. A sequence which leads the student to mastery of the subject matter with little or no outside help.

Figure 2-1 illustrates a part of a sequence of frames from a programmed instruction course. The correct response for each frame is printed in the response space to the left; the student's response is to be written in the response space on the right. The correct response is masked until after the student has made his response. The course contains hundreds of frames in a sequence which progressively becomes more complex and more significant. Each frame can be completed rapidly by the student, and the

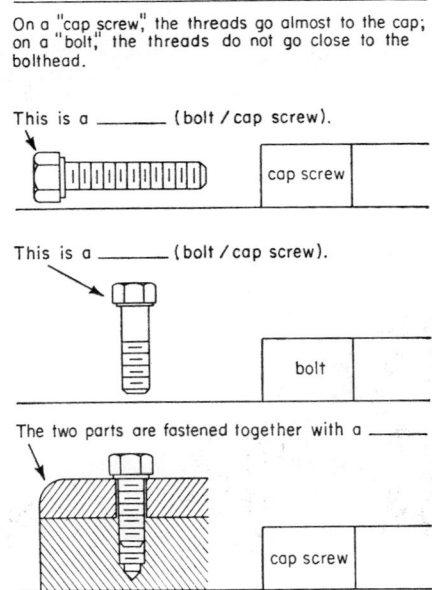

FIG. 2-1. A part of a sequence of frames from a program entitled "Reading Engineering Drawings," copyright 1962, Basic Systems, Inc.

cumulative effect of all the frames is mastery of the instructional objectives of the course.

CHARACTERISTICS OF PRESENTATION DEVICES

Teaching machines and programmed textbooks are the two types of presentation devices for programmed instruction courses. Each type has these characteristics in common:

1. Presents the programmed instruction course to the student.
2. Provides for suitable responses from the student.
3. Permits each student to make individual responses at his own pace.
4. Provides feedback to the student for each of his responses.

Programmed Textbook. Figure 2-2 illustrates a programmed textbook. Each frame is set apart from the other frames, and each contains space for the student's response. This format is known as "page-to-page." The student turns the page after each frame, finding the correct response and the next frame on the following page. The frames are arranged in levels. The student goes through the text doing all the frames on one level, then repeats the procedure for each successive level.

A different format known as "down-the-page" is also common. With this format the student masks the correct response space for the frame that he is working on. He moves the mask to expose the correct response and the next frame as he progresses frame by frame down the page.

Programmed Textbooks as Compared with Conventional Textbooks. A programmed textbook is somewhat similar in appearance to a conventional textbook. Both are bound books, with hard or soft covers. Both contain specific subject matters, and both give emphasis to specific topics. They differ, however, in several

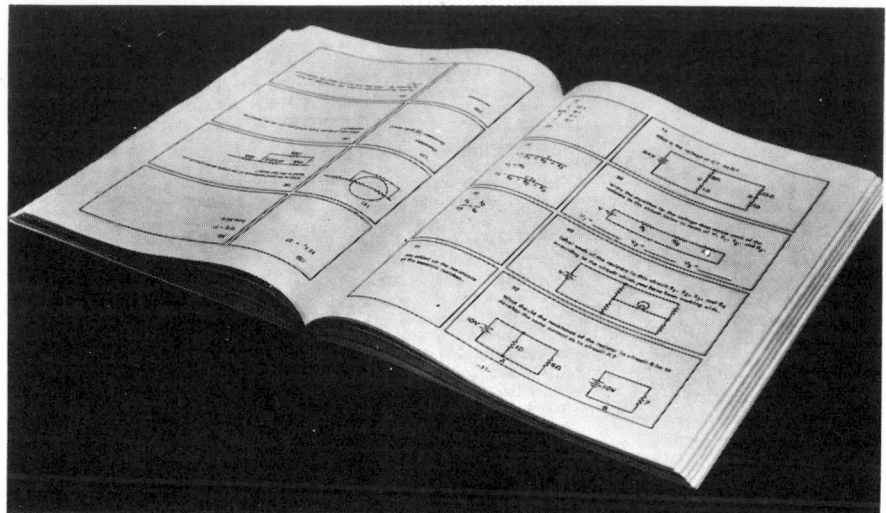

Fig. 2-2. A programmed textbook.   (*Courtesy of Basic Systems, Inc.*)

significant ways. The conventional textbook has the general purpose of serving as a reference source for information. The programmed textbook has the specialized purpose of establishing a predictable pattern of student behavior. The conventional textbook usually contains complete coverage of the subject matter; the programmed textbook is sharply focused toward specific effects on the student.

Teaching Machines. In addition to the characteristics common to programmed textbooks, machine devices also house and display the programmed instruction course.

Specific designs vary as to type of display, mode of response required of the student, and type of feedback to the student. The display may be printed sheets of paper, filmstrips, audio material, printed cards, or similar materials. The student may respond by writing an answer, typing an answer, pulling a tab, marking with special ink, and talking into a microphone. The type of feedback may be colored lights, a reply typed by an electric typewriter, visual display of the correct answer, and audio recording of the correct answer.

Figure 2-3 illustrates one type of simple mechanical teaching machine. The programmed instruction course, printed on loose sheets of paper, is inserted into this machine. The student operates a knob to move a frame under the clear plastic window, writes his response through the opening in the window, and then again operates a knob to expose the correct response and the next frame. The teaching machine is not simply a machine used in teaching—such as a projector or a simulator. Each teaching machine provides for active responses from the student and feedback for those responses. The machine itself, however, does not teach. Instruction depends primarily on the programmed instruction course presented by the machine.

Teaching Machines as Compared with Programmed Textbooks. The comparative merits of these presentation devices are yet to be resolved. Any advantage for one over the other will depend on the characteristics of the specific device in question and the conditions under which it is to be used.

Some machines are designed so that a course can be reused indefinitely; others require a new course for each student. Programmed textbooks may also be used by many students, assuming that each student writes his response on a separate pad rather than in the textbook. The programmed textbook is readily transported; yet many of the teaching machines are small and require no utility services. In use, the

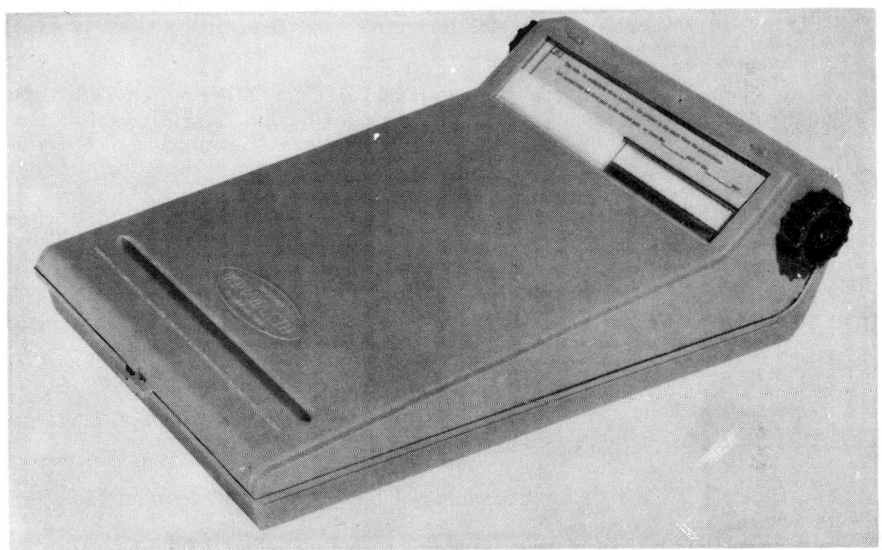

Fig. 2-3. A teaching machine.   (*Courtesy of Teaching Materials Corporation.*)

teaching machine exerts external control over the behavior of the student as he works on his programmed instruction course; experimental evidence indicates, however, that external control often has no effect on the student and may be unnecessary. The teaching machine may require periodic maintenance; the programmed textbook becomes worn with reuse.

Some programmed instruction courses require a machine for their presentation, some are available only in the form of a programmed textbook, and some are available in two separate versions for either type of presentation. In the last case, the choice of type of presentation will be decided on the basis of use requirements.

AVAILABILITY OF COURSES AND PRESENTATION DEVICES

A large number of programmed instruction courses and presentation devices are commercially available. The courses range from elementary to college level curriculum and cover a wide variety of subject matters, including mathematics, English grammar and punctuation, physical science and technology, vocational education, and business education.

Each of the following publications contains descriptive information on available programmed instruction courses:

"Programs '63—A guide to Programmed Instructional Materials Available to Educators by September, 1963—OE34015-63," U.S. Government Printing Office, Washington, D.C., 1963. Although addressed to educators, this text describes many courses designed primarily for business and industrial education.

Hendershot, Carl H.: "Programmed Learning: A Bibliography of Programs and Presentation Devices," 1963. Author, 4114 Ridgewood Drive, Bay City, Mich.

Descriptive information on presentation devices with illustrations is contained in the following publications:

"Teaching Machines and Programmed Learning, 1962: A Survey of the Industry— OE34019," U.S. Government Printing Office, Washington, D.C., 1962.

Hughes, J. L.: "Programmed Instruction for Schools and Industry," Science Research Associates, Inc., Chicago, 1962.

New developments in the field of programmed instruction occur frequently, and the information in the above references may lag far behind the current situation. Publishers and manufacturers of courses and devices can be contacted directly for up-to-date information on their materials.   A directory of some of these organizations is given in Table 2-1.

Mere availability of a programmed instruction course is no guarantee of its effectiveness.   One course may be enthusiastically accepted by instructors and students, whereas another course, from the same publisher, may be severely criticized.   In addition, a course may be announced long before it is actually available.   Thus, announced availability is not the only criterion for a selection decision.

SELECTION OF PROGRAMMED INSTRUCTION COURSES

In industry, programmed instruction courses are usually selected to accomplish one or more of the following tasks:

1. To teach basic academic subject matters which are prerequisite to industrial training courses.
2. To meet some or all of the instructional objectives of industrial training requirements.
3. To encourage employees to broaden their knowledge beyond their current training needs.

To aid in determining the suitability of an available course for an educational or training situation, publishers will supply most, if not all, of the following items of information for each of their courses:

1. Content and scope.   An abstract of the subject matters contained in the course, the instructional objectives, the prerequisites for the course, and the characteristics of the intended students.
2. Content authority.   The course for the instructional content.
3. Estimated length of time for a typical student to complete the course.
4. Mode of presentation.   Either teaching machine or programmed textbook.   If machine presentation, the characteristics of the machine device, its dependability, and the availability of courses for that particular device.
5. Accessory materials and equipment.   Materials and equipment, if any, needed to accomplish the programmed instruction.
6. Tests.   The tests that accompany the programmed instruction course.   Whether diagnostic or achievement type.
7. Development and validation data.   The conditions of pretesting, post-testing,

and revising used during the development of the course, and information pertinent to validation of the course.
8. Cost.

With this information, the potential value of a programmed instruction course can be accurately identified and copies of the course obtained for evaluation.

EVALUATION OF PROGRAMMED INSTRUCTION COURSES

Each course has certain characteristics upon which a useful evaluation can be based. To aid in this evaluation, a distinction is made between the internal and the external characteristics of a course. Internal characteristics refer to features which can be observed by careful inspection and review. External characteristics refer to the effectiveness and efficiency of the instruction. Rigid standards for these characteristics are not available because of the newness of programming technology. The criteria suggested here are generalizations, and will allow for flexibility in evaluation.

Criteria for internal characteristics

1. The subject matter is up-to-date and factually correct.
2. The more significant topics are given greater emphasis than the less significant.
3. A pattern of repetition and review exists to aid retention.
4. The nature and frequency of prompts for the student's responses are not excessive.
5. The sequence of frames is such that the student will progress to more significant behaviors as he proceeds through the course.
6. The content and scope of the course are compatible with the level of the students who are to take the course.
7. The physical arrangement and appearance of the course will not distract the student as he uses it.

After the internal characteristics of a course have been evaluated and the course meets the criteria, the course can be given to a number of typical students to assess its external characteristics.

Criteria for external characteristics

1. Students achieve the instructional objectives. The United States Air Force, for example, requires that 90 per cent or more of the students in the target population score 90 per cent or better on a comprehensive achievement test.
2. The major portion of the instruction is achieved without the intervention of an instructor.
3. Students maintain an interest in the instruction as they progress in the course.
4. Each student can proceed through the course at his own pace.
5. The average time expended by the students in relation to their instructional achievement is reasonable.

Programmed instruction courses which meet these criteria can be obtained and used on a large scale to achieve instructional objectives.

Note that the evaluation of a particular programmed instruction course is not an assessment of the usefulness of programmed instruction in general. Outstanding success with one course may be followed by evident failure with another. The technology of programmed instruction is relatively new, and the applications of the science of learning may not be successful in every instance. Thus, there exists a need for thoughtful selection and thorough evaluation of each candidate course.

Additional information on evaluation concepts is contained in "1962 Interim Report of the Joint Committee on Programmed Instruction and Teaching Machines," U.S. Office of

Education, Educational Media Branch, Washington, D.C., 1962. The joint committee is composed of representatives from the American Educational Research Association, The American Psychological Association, and the National Educational Association, Department of Audio-Visual Instruction.

USE OF PROGRAMMED INSTRUCTION COURSES

In programmed instruction, each student proceeds independently at his own pace with his individual course. These features provide great flexibility in achieving instructional objectives. If desired, just one student can receive instruction at any one time. On the other hand, many students can receive instruction at the same time, subject to the availability of courses and presentation devices. Instruction can proceed at any physical location, subject only to the requirements of the presentation device. The availability of a competent instructor is not a requirement during programmed instruction, although he may be needed for follow-up.

Despite the flexibility of programmed instruction there are certain requirements for preparation, presentation, and follow-up. Programmed instruction is self-instructional by design, but maximum benefits can be derived by meeting these requirements.

Preparation for programmed instruction

1. Insure that each student has the necessary prerequisites for the course. These prerequisites may be stated explicitly by the publisher, or they may be implicit in the stated level for intended students.
2. Provide for individual course use. Courses are not shared by students concurrently. When a single course is to be used by more than one student, student time can be scheduled.
3. Provide for accessory materials and equipment as needed. The needs will be stated in the course.
4. Provide for adequate space and facilities, free of distractions. If a student is to receive programmed instruction away from the company location, caution the student to avoid a distracting environment.
5. When programmed instruction is an interruption of a work schedule, provide for individual student assignments after completion of the course. Each student will progress at his own pace, and the time-to-complete may be different for each student.
6. When several students are receiving programmed instruction on the same subject in the same room at the same time, insure that the progress of each student is not evident to the others.
7. Before a student starts on his programmed instruction course, demonstrate the procedure which is to be followed. The procedure will be stated in the course.
8. Explain to the student that the programmed instruction course is not a test. A course has a superficial similarity to a test, since active responses are called for in both situations.
9. Establish a schedule for receiving programmed instruction. The schedule may be based on time alone, such as 2 hr per day, or it may be based on completion of logical portions of the programmed instruction course irrespective of time.

Excessive time in programmed instruction is fatiguing to the student and detracts from the effectiveness of the course. Too short a time also detracts from the effectiveness since the cumulative effect of many responses is lost.

Presentation

1. During programmed instruction an instructor or administrator need be available only for infrequent consultation or guidance, if at all. He may occasionally monitor the activity and administer achievement tests if used.

Follow-up for programmed instruction

1. A post-test can be administered shortly after completion of the course to obtain an objective measure of achievement.
2. A post-test can be administered at some future date to obtain an indication of retention, but the intervening activities of the students may destroy the usefulness of the data.
3. The conceptual behaviors acquired by a student through programmed instruction can be related to his practical situation through an individual or small group discussion session.

DEVELOPING PROGRAMMED INSTRUCTION COURSES

Scientific principles of program development are yet to be established. Evidence has shown that courses developed according to a few basic principles of behavioral science have been effective, but the relative merits of the various techniques of development have not been resolved. In general, however, a course is usually developed by a two- or three-man team which accomplishes each of the following development tasks:

1. Identifies the new behaviors desired of the students in the target population. These behaviors constitute the evidence that the student possesses the intended knowledge or ability.
2. Analyzes the desired behaviors to identify their characteristics. Behaviors usually consist of discriminations, generalizations, conceptualizations, and sequential chains.
3. Designs the frames which will induce the students to emit these behaviors under appropriate conditions.
4. Tries out the design on typical students; modifies and revises as necessary until the course accomplishes the instructional objectives.

The development of an effective program instruction course involves considerable effort and expense. Estimates of total direct development cost range from $1,000 to $3,000 per hour of student time expended on the completed course. A programmed instruction course which requires an average of 20 hr for a student to complete may require an investment of $60,000 for its development. This investment can be recovered, however, through: (1) reduction in student time spent in programmed instruction as compared with time spent in conventional instruction, (2) reduction in requirements for competent instructors to present the subject matters, and (3) more effective instruction.

The development of a programmed instruction course program requires a variety of skills. Task analysis, behavioral analysis, and effective writing skills predominate. And like other skills, they require guided practice for proper development. Many organizations and individual consultants conduct seminars, workshops, and training classes in programmed instruction. Many others will develop individual programmed instruction courses to their specifications. The names of the organizations and consultants which provide these services can be identified through the reference materials contained in the selected bibliography.

SELECTED BIBLIOGRAPHY

Whether or not a company decides to develop its own program development capability or to contract a program development, these materials will serve as valuable references for skillful selection, evaluation, and use of programmed instruction courses and presentation devices.

Films

1. "One Step At a Time" (30 min, sound, color, 16 mm). American Institute for Research, 410 Amberson Avenue, Pittsburgh 32, Pa.

2. "Teaching Machines and Programmed Learning" (29 min, sound, b-w, 16 mm). National Educational Association, Department of Audio-Visual Instruction, Washington, D.C.

Books

1. Deterline, William A.: "An Introduction to Programmed Instruction," Prentice-Hall, Inc., Englewood Cliffs, N.J., 1962.
2. Fry, Edward B.: "Teaching Machines and Programmed Learning, An Introduction to Auto Instruction," McGraw-Hill Book Company, New York, 1963.
3. Galenter, Eugene H. (ed.): "Automatic Teaching: The State of the Art," John Wiley & Sons, Inc., New York, 1959.
4. Keller, F. S.: "Learning-Reinforcement Theory," Random House, Inc., New York, 1962.
5. Lumsdaine, Arthur A., and Robert Glaser (eds.): "Teaching Machines and Programmed Learning: A Source Book," National Education Association, Department of Audio-Visual Instruction, Washington, D.C., 1960.
6. Stolurow, Lawrence M.: "Teaching by Machine," U.S. Department of Health, Education, and Welfare, Office of Education, Washington, D.C., 1961.
7. Teal, Gilbert E. (ed.): "Programmed Instruction in Industry and Education," Public Service Research, Inc., 65 South St., Stamford, Conn., 1963.

Periodicals

1. *Journal of National Society for Programmed Instruction*, monthly, National Society for Programmed Instruction, Trinity University, San Antonio, Tex.
2. *Journal of Programmed Instruction*, quarterly, Center for Programmed Instruction, New York 24, N.Y.
3. *Programmed Instruction Bulletin*, monthly, Center for Programmed Instruction, New York 24, N.Y.

Table 2-1. Directory of Some of the Publishers and Manufacturers of Programs and Devices

Company	*Address*
Addison-Wesley Publishing Company, Inc.	703 Welch Rd., Palo Alto Calif.
American Institute for Research	410 Amberson Ave., Pittsburgh 32, Pa.
American Management Association	135 West 50th St., New York, N.Y. 10020.
Appleton-Century-Crofts	440 Park Ave. South, New York, N.Y.
Basic Systems, Inc.	2900 Broadway, New York 25, N.Y.
Center for Programmed Instruction	525 West 120 St., New York, N.Y.
Central Scientific Co.	1700 Irving Park Rd., Chicago 13, Ill.
Coronet Instructural Films	65 E. South Water St., Chicago 1, Ill.
Encyclopaedia Britannica Films	425 North Michigan Ave., Chicago 11, Ill.
Entelek, Inc.	42 Pleasent St., Newburyport, Mass.
General Programmed Teaching Corporation	1719 Girard North East, Albuquerque, N.M.
Graflex, Inc.	1408 Division Ave. South, Grand Rapids, Mich.
Harcourt, Brace & World, Inc.	750 Third Ave., New York 17, N.Y.
Harper & Row, Publishers, Incorporated	Evanston, Ill.
Holt, Rinehart and Winston, Inc.	750 Third Ave., New York 17, N.Y.
Honor Products	19 Belmont St., Cambridge 28, Mass.
The Macmillan Company	60 Fifth Ave., New York 11, N.Y.
Mast Development Co., Inc.	2212 East 12th St., Davenport, Iowa
McGraw-Hill Book Company	4655 Chase Ave., Lincolnwood, Chicago 46, Ill.
Prentice-Hall, Inc.	Englewood Cliffs, N.J.
RCA Educational Services	Camden 8, N.J.
Science Research Associates Inc.	259 East Erie St., Chicago 11, Ill.
Teaching Materials Corp.	575 Lexington Ave., New York 22, N.Y.
Varian Associates	611 Hudson Way, Palo Alto, Calif.
John Wiley & Sons, Inc.	605 Third Ave., New York, N.Y.

Chapter 3

RATING AND EVALUATING MAINTENANCE JOBS

By GEORGE E. MEYERS
Management Consultant—Maintenance Specialist
Waban, Mass.

Salaries and wages and the administration policies pertaining to them have been more important since 1942 than at any other time in our industrial history. This has been true not only because of the supply of and demand for labor during emergencies, but also because of employee and bargaining-agency demands over this period. The salary or wage of a worker often is the most important material thing in his life. It is imperative, therefore, that employers should take the steps necessary to establish salary and wage structures within their organizations which properly, adequately, and equitably compensate their employees. Yet it is also necessary to keep the general level of compensation in line with that of competition and the geographical area in which their businesses are located.

The initial approach to these seemingly perplexing problems should be to develop a means of classifying jobs. It must be based on exact knowledge concerning the relationship between job content and characteristics and compensation therefor, so wage and salary structure may rest on a solid foundation. A sound and defensible basis for determining rates of pay is particularly important when negotiating with employees or bargaining units in regard to both wage increases and alleged inequities. Increases and adjustments in pay affect basic job rates, and intelligent discussions of these rates must be predicated upon mutual agreement between employer and employees regarding the relative value of various types of jobs. Such mutual agreement is in turn dependent upon mutual understanding regarding job content and its relation to other jobs as determined by the use of a common barometer.

This measuring device and ultimate meeting of minds with respect to wages and salaries comes as a result of job evaluation. It determines the demand of jobs upon the employees performing them and the relative value of these jobs to the employer. It is not a program for increasing or lowering wages but is concerned with the establishment of a properly graduated wage or salary scale based upon the judgment of not one but a number of responsible and qualified persons. Job evaluation has proved to be an effective aid in providing an equitable and supportable basis for this distribution of payroll dollars.

THE BASIC PRINCIPLE OF JOB EVALUATION

The basic principle of job and salary evaluation is to establish a relationship among jobs, first as to their relative value from the standpoint of job content, and second, to translate this job-to-job relationship into a wage-rate structure. Individuals or personalities are not taken into consideration. Job and salary evaluation, as such, pertains only to the ultimate monetary value of a job regardless of the individual performing the task.   (Merit rating, which can be an added part of job evaluation, and the adoption of which becomes a part of wage- and salary-administration policy, is a means of rewarding employees for length of service, quality of workmanship, and other factors having to do with individual performance.)

Not only should wages and salaries be administered properly, all employees should be acquainted with the long-range program of the company as to increases, opportunities and requirements for promotion, and all other matters pertaining to compensation and policies governing it.

There are, ordinarily, three phases of wage and salary evaluation as follows:

1. The evaluation of a job, applying some form of point rating.
2. The establishment of a sound and satisfactory wage and salary structure to apply to all jobs.
3. The preparation of a manual which will incorporate job descriptions, the point values of the jobs and how these values were determined, the wage and salary structure, and a complete outline of all company policies dealing with employee compensation.

ESTABLISHMENT OF AN EVALUATION COMMITTEE

A sound and popular method of establishing the proper relationship of one job with another is through the use of an evaluating committee.   The committee is composed, ordinarily, of five members of the organization being evaluated.   Three should be permanent members of the committee, and two should be selected from each department as it is being evaluated to assist the permanent committee members.   It is not necessary that the committee be composed of five members; in some instances three are sufficient, and in other instances more than five may be required.   The first obligation of this committee is to obtain a thorough background in job evaluation and the particular plan to be used.   It should then proceed to secure a list of all the job titles within the organization.

It is generally conceded that in each and every job certain variable factors are inherent, such as skill, responsibility, application, and working conditions.   Evaluating plans use from 4 to 20 factors.   So as to thoroughly understand what is meant by factors, two of them are described—skill and application.

Skill is composed of three subfactors—training, experience, and judgment.   Training usually is the amount and type of education needed to perform a given job satisfactorily.   Some jobs require only a grammar-school education, others high school, and still others may require a college background.   There are jobs which may not require a college degree but may call for a specialized training or business course.   It is necessary to have some means of determining, by pooled judgment, just how much training a person should have to perform a specific task.   By experience is meant the time it has taken to learn a job satisfactorily.   Some jobs can be learned in a matter of weeks while others may take up to several years to master.   Judgment is a part of the skill of a job, and this factor is present in practically every job in varying degrees.

The factor of application has to do with the mental and/or visual as well as the physical aspects of a job.   The extent and continuity of mental and/or visual application must be taken into consideration; so must the degree and continuity of physical effort.

In order for the evaluating committee to decide intelligently the degree with which the factors of skill and application as well as the remaining factors exist in each job, they must have adequate information as to job content and requirement.

After the committee members have become acquainted with the plan to be used and have secured a complete list of job titles to be evaluated, they should select a key list of representative jobs numbering between 5 and 10.   These key jobs should be selected so as to include tasks which have a wide range in the requirements of skill, responsibility, and other factors important in all the jobs.   By this is meant that jobs requiring very little training and very little experience as well as those requiring a high degree of these two factors should be chosen.   Other jobs should be chosen having high and low degrees of responsibility, mental effort, physical effort, and with varying working conditions.   The principal idea of this selection of key jobs is to use them after they are evaluated as a guide and barometer for all other jobs.

THE PREPARATION OF JOB DESCRIPTIONS

The next step is to secure the descriptions of the key jobs.   These descriptions should be so written as to enable the evaluating committee to extract from the description the degree to which the various factors such as education, experience, judgment, and leadership are involved in each particular job.   For example, as to experience, the job descriptions should be so written that it is rather easy to decide whether it takes 6 months, 1, 2, 3, or 5 years of experience to do satisfactorily the job which is under consideration.   It is imperative, particularly in negotiating with unions or bargaining agencies where job and salary evaluation is involved, that the detail involved in writing descriptions should be given serious consideration. Descriptions should not be too general or the committee would not be able to evaluate adequately and fairly.   If too greatly detailed, and minor requirements are omitted, in evaluation, argument and possible upgrading of the job, as to both point and monetary evaluation, might result.

THE POINT SYSTEM OF JOB EVALUATION

The procedure described here (the point system) for establishing job relationships for hourly paid jobs within the manufacturing units calls for the assignment of

Table 3-1. Comparison of the Four Basic Systems of Job Evaluation

Ranking system	Classification system	Point system	Factor-commission system
The job analysis. A narrative description of the job with the duties, responsibilities, degree of difficulty, and required qualifications clearly brought out.		*The job analysis.* A narrative statement of duties and qualifications. In addition, the job is broken down into the important compensable factors, such as required experience and training, mental effort, and physical effort. The amount to which each factor is present in the job is indicated by a short narrative statement.	
Method of relating jobs			
Jobs are ranked in their order of relative difficulty or value to the company, and grade levels are sometimes defined after the jobs have been ranked.	Jobs are allocated to grade levels which are defined arbitrarily prior to evaluating jobs.	Jobs are related by factorial analysis. A restricted number of fairly specific factors are selected for application to a limited number of types of work. The point values are predetermined before analysis of jobs and are decided arbitrarily, and the degree of each factor is expressed by a definition.	Jobs are related by factorial comparison. The factors used are assumed to be fundamental to all jobs and of universal application, the point values are set after analysis of jobs from existing rates of key jobs, and the degrees of each factor are expressed by sample jobs.

weighted point values to the various factors used. Other methods in general use are the factor-comparison system, the job-ranking system, and the job-classification system. In Table 3-1 is shown a comparison of these methods with the point system described here. This chart was developed by the War Manpower Commission, now the U.S. Employment Service. Within these factors are "stage" values for the various degrees of factor requirements. For example, when considering the factor of training or education, the first stage would be the need of a grammar-school education which, being the minimum training requirement, would call for the minimum number of points being assigned. The next stage might be a high-school education calling for a greater number of points. Third, a high-school education plus a special course. The last and highest stage would be a college-education requirement with the greatest number of points being assigned. The same principle applies to the experience factor with the lowest point assignment being for a job requiring a few weeks to learn and moving up through five or six stages to include jobs needing 1, 2, 3, and 5 years.

The responsibility factor has subfactors, all with varying stages, such as responsibility for equipment, waste, safety, and quality. The stages of these subfactors could be first, no responsibility, then minor responsibility, the third stage medium, and the last stages high responsibility. These same degrees or stages might apply to the factors of mental or visual application and to the factor of physical effort. In the factor of working conditions, the stages could be excellent, good, fair, poor, and hazardous, the last being the stage to which the highest number of points is assigned.

Ordinarily an employer considers the skill of a person to be most important when hiring people; so naturally the factor of skill is allotted the largest percentage of total points, usually between 50 and 70 per cent. Responsibility is next with from 15 to 25 per cent; mental and physical application third, with from 3 to 7 per cent; and the working-condition factor last, getting about 3 to 7 per cent of the total. A schedule showing a typical distribution of points is as follows:

Factors	Stages and points				
	1	2	3	4	5
Skill:					
Training................	60	120	180	240	300
Experience..............	80	160	240	320	400
Judgment...............	60	120	180	240	300
Responsibility:					
Equipment..............	20	40	60	80	100
Waste..................	20	40	60	80	100
Safety..................	20	40	60	80	100
Quality.................	20	40	60	80	100
Application:					
Mental.................	40	80	120	160	200
Physical...............	40	80	120	160	200
Working conditions.........	40	80	120	160	200

THE DETERMINATION OF JOB POINTS

When adequate job descriptions have been submitted to the evaluating committee, the procedure of point evaluation then takes place. If the key-job procedure is to be followed it has been found advisable, from experience, to consider the same factor for all the key jobs at one time. This means that the factor of education or training should be considered for all the key jobs before either experience or any of the other factors is given attention. The committee can direct its attention to deciding upon the education required to perform the various key jobs and the relationship and comparison of one job with another can be decided upon more intelligently.

It may be appropriate to note at this point that there is very little opportunity, if any, for the evaluating committee to be biased in arriving at their ultimate evaluations. This is particularly so when each factor is considered for all jobs before a second or third factor is evaluated. The absence of bias in this connection means that there are no predetermined total point values for any particular job. The procedure described here tends to eliminate this kind of bias, whether conscious or not.

After the various factors are considered, and points are allotted for each, again in accordance with the degree to which they are inherent in the job, the total points for each job are secured. If the evaluating committee has been conscientious and sound in its judgment, there should be a relationship, as indicated by total points, established between these key jobs. For example, the simplest job will normally have the lowest number of total points and another for which the job content requires top skill, high responsibility, etc., will have the highest total points. The remaining key jobs will fall in their proper slots between these two extremes. This is what is known as relativity or the relationship of one job to the others.

Following the key-job evaluation, descriptions of all remaining jobs within the maintenance department are secured and in like manner evaluated. The key-job list is used as a guide or as a barometer whenever necessary in establishing the true point values of all other jobs. When all the jobs have been evaluated, they are put in sequence of their point value with the top job at the head of the list and the job with the lowest number of points at the bottom. In the maintenance department this top job could be that of a first-class toolmaker while the job with the lowest points could be a janitor or laborer. In order to fit all the maintenance jobs into their proper slots and establish their relationship with the other jobs in the entire plant it is necessary at this point to discuss job relationships and the establishment of an hourly wage structure for the plant as a whole.

When all jobs have been evaluated and relationships, one with another, have been set up, the next step is to formulate a wage-rate structure so that each job can be given an hourly monetary value. This means that the evaluating committee should decide the following:

1. A minimum and maximum hourly rate of pay for the plant.
2. The number of different rates of pay that should exist between the minimum and the maximum (these various rates are also known as labor-grade rates of pay and will be described later).
3. Whether a single rate of pay or a rate range should apply to each labor grade.

In establishing the minimum and maximum hourly rates for the plant the committee will have to take into account many important factors, including the following:

1. The present wage-rate structure.
2. Any desired revision of either the minimum hourly rate that is in existence, or the maximum, or both.
3. The going rates of pay in the geographical area where the organization is located.
4. The wage structure of competitive businesses.
5. The requests, or demands, if any, of employees or their representatives.

After due consideration of these factors it may be the consensus of the evaluating committee that they should raise the existing minimum and leave the maximum at its present level, or just the reverse may be desirable (the specific determination of wage plans in union and nonunion shops will be treated later). Let us assume for purposes of illustration, that a new wage scale has been set up, the minimum being $1.20 per hour and the top rate $2.40 per hour.

In order to complete the wage structure it is now necessary to decide upon the number of wage-rate brackets or labor grades which would constitute a sound and equitable pay plan. Ordinarily this is determined by taking into consideration the differential between the minimum and maximum hourly wage to be paid as well as the point differential between the lowest-rated job and the highest. Normally from

10 to 18 grades are sufficient but some companies have in excess of 30 grades.   Let us assume, for example, that 15 grades are adequate and that the lowest-rated job carries 500 points and the highest-rated job 1,700 points.   This leaves a differential of 1,200 points which, if divided by 15 grades, equals 80 points per grade.   Therefore, all jobs from 500 to 579 points will fall in the first grade and all jobs from 580 to 659 points will be in the second grade, etc., the top grade being 1,620 to 1,700.   Also with 15 labor grades and a monetary rate range of from \$1.20 to \$2.40 the differential in pay between each two labor grades would be \$0.08 per hour, as shown in Fig. 3-1 where an \$0.08 range has been set up for each grade.

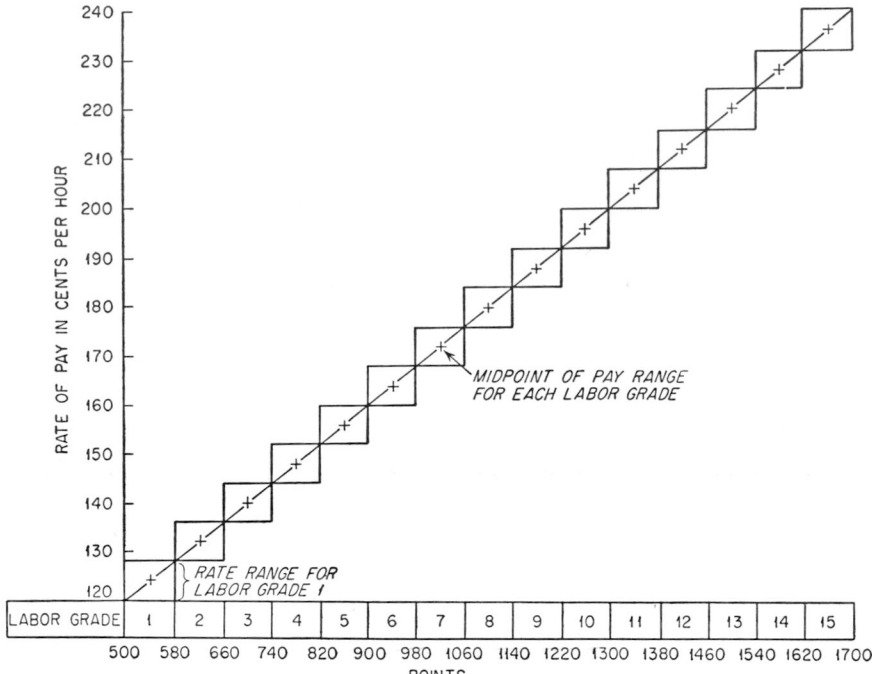

FIG. 3-1. Hourly pay range from \$1.20 to \$1.28 per hour.

Next, the committee must give thought as to whether or not they wish to have a single wage rate for each grade or whether within each grade they will have a minimum and a maximum rate of pay.   If the minimum hourly rate for labor grade 1 is \$1.20, this can either be a single rate for all jobs with a point rating of 500 to 579, or one can have an hourly pay range for these jobs from \$1.20 to \$1.28 as shown in Fig. 3-1.   This rate range would be used to give wage increases to employees while they are performing the same job.   Increases within the range would come about automatically over a period of time or by merit rating or by a combination of both.

So far the following has been accomplished:

1. Point values have been allocated to all jobs.
2. The relationships between jobs have been determined.
3. A wage-rate structure has been constructed.
4. Either a single rate or a range of rates for each labor grade has been established.

It is necessary at this point to set forth clearly the effect of these developments on the current wage structure so that management may understand clearly the company position if the new plans are adopted.

EFFECT OF RATING ON EXISTING WAGE STRUCTURE

In order to determine the effect of the new evaluated jobs and their new respective rates of pay on the existing hourly rates, it is well to develop a scatter chart as shown in Fig. 3-2. This chart will show across the bottom each job title within the labor grade into which it falls. The title of each job in labor grade 1 (jobs with point values 500 to 579) should be written perpendicularly starting at the left of the bottom of the chart and continuing with job titles in each of the 15 labor grades across the bottom of the chart. Heavy lines should be drawn perpendicularly between the labor grades to distinguish them. Along the left-hand side of the chart starting at the bottom and working up should be shown the rates of pay starting with $1.20 per hour and continuing to the top rate of $2.40. The rate range applicable to each labor grade is shown by horizontal lines marking off the pay appropriate to each.

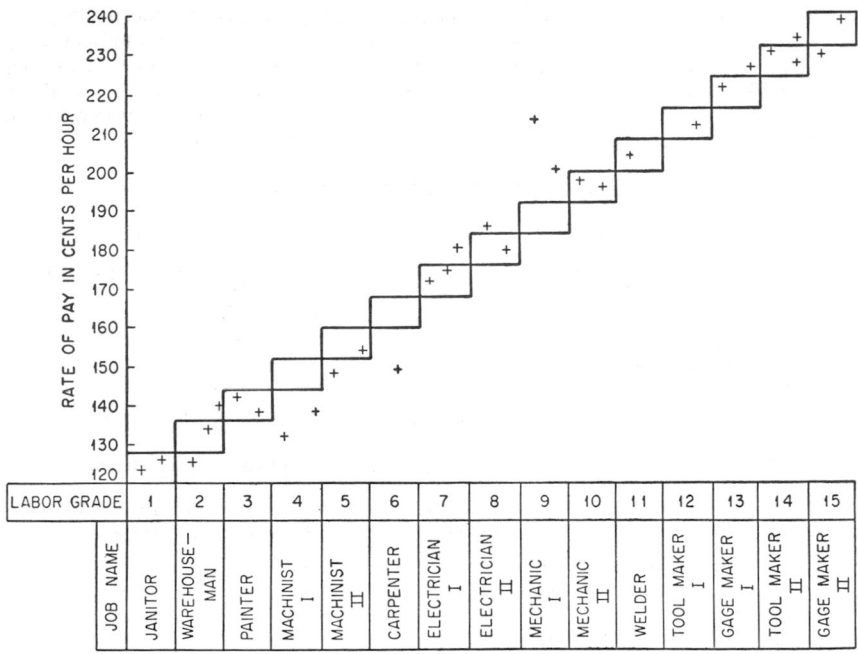

FIG. 3-2. Scatter chart to help in determining effect of new evaluation on existing rates.

This chart will indicate clearly the new evaluated rates for each job title and then the existing rates of pay (marked with a +) can be entered as shown. Reference to the chart will show the comparison of new and old rates, and some will be found to be the same while others will be either higher or lower. At this point it is suggested that the number of employees working under each job title be shown either immediately before or after the job-title name at the bottom of the chart. The net effect on the total payroll cost per hour can be determined by multiplying the number of employees on each job by the amount of the job-rate change. For example, if only two job rates are changed and one is increased $0.10 per hour and one is decreased by $0.05 per hour and each job has 50 employees working thereon, the net effect on the total hourly payroll cost will be an increase of $2.50.

Usually, as a result of job evaluation, some job rates are increased, some lowered, and some remain the same. In those cases where rates are evaluated higher than existing rates, employees on these jobs enjoy the immediate benefit of an hourly pay increase. However, in instances where the new rate is lower than the current rate, the incumbents on these jobs must suffer no adverse change in their hourly rates of pay. These latter job rates are commonly known as red-circle rates and, although the incumbents on these jobs have no rate changes, all new employees are hired at the newly evaluated rate. By the same token, employees on red-circle rates do not usually benefit by general wage-rate increases until the extent of these upward adjustments exceeds the red-circle rate.

Because of this rather common method of adopting job evaluation, the immediate cost to the company is the amount of the increases resulting from the evaluation. As incumbents leave those jobs on which they are protected by red-circle rates, the company benefits by the change from the incumbents' higher rate to the decreased rate of their replacements. Eventually, when all such red-circle rates have been eliminated, the original cost of the job evaluation will be reduced. Ultimate payroll costs, when all evaluated rates are in effect, can be higher, lower, or about equal to the cost before job evaluation was applied.

The next step is to formulate and prepare a manual governing the policies pertaining to the administration of the job-evaluation program. This should contain a complete explanation of the plan, how increases or promotions from one job to another can be obtained, an outline of all policies pertaining to sick leave, vacations, holidays, and other fringe benefits. It should constitute a continuing and complete record of the entire job-evaluation program and its effects on maintenance operations.

THE COST OF JOB EVALUATION

The cost of the job-evaluation program will be the sum of the following costs:

1. The cost of those technical and clerical personnel necessary to prepare the job analyses.
2. The cost of workers' time in answering questions both written and oral necessary to the preparation of the job analyses.
3. The cost of any increases in pay rates which result from the installation of the wage structure developed.
4. The cost of administering and maintaining the program on a continuing basis.

THE BENEFITS OF A SOUND JOB-EVALUATION PROGRAM

The benefits which will result from investment in a job-evaluation program for maintenance employees may be considerable. Some of these are as follows:

1. A clear and equitable wage-rate structure is developed.
2. A measure and evaluation of the relative worth of all jobs is obtained.
3. It enables the organization to maintain a balanced compensation structure which can be defended on a factual basis.
4. Tends to remove suspicion of favoritism from employees' minds.
5. Minimizes controversies over job rates and is a tremendous aid to management and department heads in their wage-administration problems.
6. Sets forth a promotional pattern as a guide in upgrading employees.
7. Differing viewpoints between the employer and the employee with respect to wage rates can be discussed intelligently, because the over-all pattern is not an additional variable to confuse either party.
8. Advancement opportunities for employees can be publicized because requirements for promotion become standard for all employees.
9. Over-all adjustments in the level of wage rates due to economic conditions can be made readily by raising or lowering the rate curves. Job relationships need not be disturbed.
10. The personnel department will have a complete outline of the requirements of every job which will greatly aid it in securing proper personnel for available positions.

As can be seen, the benefits to be obtained from a sound job-evaluation program for maintenance workers will usually far outweigh the costs of the program. However, it must be remembered that these benefits result not from the installation of the job-evaluation program, but from its operation on a sound and continuing basis.

SALARY EVALUATION

Salary evaluation has the same objectives as wage evaluation, that is, to formulate and make effective salaries which are fair and equitable for the various jobs covered. Within the maintenance department, the foremen and maintenance heads usually are paid on a salary basis; therefore, wherever salary evaluation is a policy of management, the incomes of supervisory maintenance personnel are affected. Earlier in this chapter the history and principle of job evaluation was outlined. Also the procedures covering the selection and functions of the evaluating committee as well as the manner of securing job descriptions were described.

Basically, the factors of skill, responsibility, application, and working conditions are inherent in salaried jobs as well as hourly paid jobs. However, the subfactors under the four major factors differ considerably. For example, responsibility as related to a salaried job may involve responsibility for costs, good will, integrity, schedules, and the like, while the skill factor may include such subfactors as intuitiveness, analytical ability, and personality, which factors ordinarily are not so important in hourly paid jobs. A typical scale of points is shown in Table 3-2.

Table 3-2. Typical Scale of Points

Factors	Points and stages						% of total
	1	2	3	4	5	6	
Education..........................	80	160	240	320	400		20
Experience..........................	100	200	300	400	500	600	30
Complexity of duties.................	80	160	240	320			16
Monetary responsibility..............	40	80	120	160			8
Contacts............................	40	80	120	160			8
Working conditions..................	40	80	120	160			8
Supervisory responsibility............	40	80	120	160	200		10
Total points.......................						2,000	100

The corresponding point ranges if 12 salary grades is deemed sufficient would be as follows:

Salary Grade	Point Range
A	Up to 600
B	601– 700
C	701– 800
D	801– 900
E	901–1,000
F	1,001–1,100
G	1,101–1,200
H	1,201–1,300
J	1,301–1,400
K	1,401–1,500
L	1,501–1,600
M	1,601–1,700

The preparation of job descriptions in such manner as to permit the evaluating committee to judge the degree to which the above factors are present in each job is much the same as for hourly paid jobs. The evaluating and allocating of point values will, of course, result in all the salaried jobs being placed in their proper relationship one with another. Building the salary structure considers the following:

1. The number of salary grades best suited to an equitable structure.
2. The existing minimum and maximum salaries paid for the jobs being evaluated.
3. Area salaries paid for the same type of jobs.
4. Revisions in the minimum and maximum salaries currently paid as a result of employee demands or dissatisfaction.
5. Establishment of salary ranges within each salary grade to provide for pay increases to employees while on the same job.

Table 3-3. Salary Schedule—Monthly Rates
(20 % × 12½ % rate range)

Grade	Min	Mid-point	Max	Range
A	$250	$268	$285	$35
B	265	285	305	40
C	285	305	325	40
D	305	328	350	45
E	325	350	375	50
F	350	375	400	50
G	375	403	430	55
H	400	430	460	60
J	430	463	495	65
K	460	495	530	70
L	495	533	570	75
M	530	570	610	80

In addition to the above, important consideration must be given to the possibility of hourly paid employees being paid as much as or more than their supervisors. This condition is brought about primarily when the overtime pay earned by hourly workers and, in certain isolated cases, where the straight-time hourly rates of employees for regular-time work, exceeds the salary of their supervisors. With specific reference to the salaries of maintenance supervisors, it is well to have their compensation at least 25 per cent above the average take-home pay of the highest-paid workers under their jurisdiction.

Regarding the salary ranges within each salary grade, the spread from the minimum to the maximum is generally in the neighborhood of 15 per cent. If the lowest salary to be paid is $250 per month, then the maximum of Grade A would be $285. An example of a salary schedule in monthly rates is given in Table 3-3. It is important to note here that higher salary grades signified increased responsibility and that a constant percentage rather than absolute differential is maintained between grades. This geometric progression of salaries according to increased responsibility is illustrated by the plot of Table 3-3 shown in Fig. 3-3.

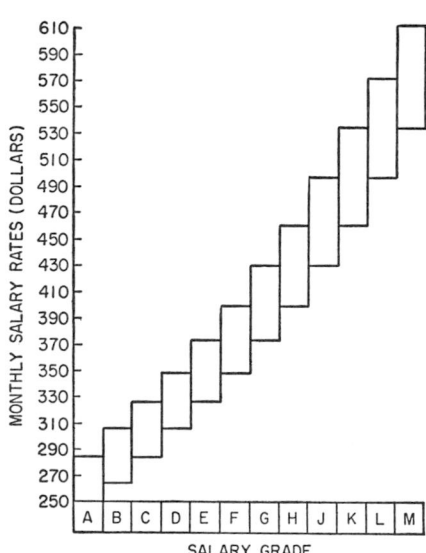

FIG. 3-3. Geometric progression of salaries according to increased responsibilities.

Salary evaluation is not nearly so generally used as is evaluation for hourly paid jobs. Furthermore, its application has more or less been restricted to jobs under the

$8,000 to $9,000 level.   If proper care and exceedingly good judgment are exercised by the evaluating committee, a sound and equitable salary structure can be developed with benefits comparable with a well-designed wage-evaluation program.

It is quite important to note in this connection that, if applied properly, a salary-evaluation program will tend to eliminate any inequities which might exist between salaries paid to maintenance supervisors and executives and production line and staff management.   This is often one of the most important benefits of such a program.

HOW UNION AGREEMENTS CONTROL RATES OF WORKERS

Unions control the rates and wages of workers by means of written agreements called contracts.   These contracts are the result of negotiations between company and union representatives.   Usually these contracts are of 1 year's duration, although some are written to be in effect for 2 or more years.   The major portion of such contracts is devoted either directly or indirectly to rates of pay and/or wages of employees. Most contracts begin in somewhat the following manner: "This agreement dated the _____ day of _____, 19____, is entered into by and between the Company and the Union to *govern* rates of pay and working conditions for production and maintenance employees of the company."   The first section of the contract sets forth the purpose of the agreement and typically reads in part as follows: "The purpose of the Company and the Union in entering into this labor contract is to set forth their agreement on rates of pay," etc.   This union control over rates of pay and wages emphasizes the third sentence of this article wherein it states "the salary or wage of a worker most often is the most important material thing in his life."   Most company-union contracts provide for a wage-reopening clause which permits either party at specified times to reopen the agreement on the subject of wage rates only.

The section of the contract pertaining to "rates of pay" ordinarily covers the following:

1. Standard hourly rates of pay for the various jobs or job labor grades.
2. A schedule of apprentice rates for the respective apprentice-training periods.
3. Shift differential rates of pay.
4. New and changed incentives and their effect on rates of pay.
5. Overtime and overtime pay.

Job evaluation and wage administration may not affect the minimum and maximum wages to be paid under collective bargaining, but within this framework it can assure equitable payment according to an objective determination of labor grade and rate. Thus not only will bargaining over individual rates be eliminated, but many grievances arising over alleged inequities in wages will be avoided.   Further, those grievances which arise can usually be settled much more easily within the framework of a sound job-evaluation program.

DETERMINATION OF WAGE RATES IN NONUNION SHOPS

Here it is important to state as a first principle that wage rates set in nonunion shops should not be less than those in corresponding union shops.   A wise employer will always make sure that his employees are not worse off and preferably are better off than those under union-bargained agreements.

The specific determination of wage rates is, of course, exactly like the determination of the price of all other factors of production, that is, based on the supply of and demand for labor which exists at the time rates are set.   Through job evaluation, the employer recognizes the many factors which determine relative differences in pay within his plant.   It is only through market surveys that he may determine the position of his over-all wage structure.   Because of the importance of the market as a determinant of wages, adequate and timely wage statistics are essential.   Two important sources of such data are the "Wage Chronology Series" of the Bureau of Labor Statistics of the U.S. Department of Labor and the "Occupational Wage Rate

Surveys" of the National Industrial Conference Board. Many state agencies also compile and publish wage statistics. These sources provide accurate and up-to-date wage statistics so necessary to rate determination.

It is also essential that a local survey of wage rates be undertaken so that local economic factors and their influence on wage rates may be assessed properly. These surveys should be done on a continuing basis so that effective control over wages may be maintained.

Job evaluation is a considerable help in wage determination, also, as it provides the necessary job standardization so that wage rates may be compared between companies and industries. Without this kind of objective standardization of jobs on the basis of content, the determination of wages would be imperfect indeed.

Chapter 4

INCENTIVE PAYMENT OF
MAINTENANCE WORKERS

By W. C. COOLING[1]
Manager, Methods and Standards Department
International Resistance Company
Philadelphia, Pa.

Kinds of Incentive Ordinarily Used. Many applications of incentive bonus payments have been made other than those based on direct measured standard times for the work involved. An incentive plan based on measured standards requires the highest management ability in the development and installation of all cost-control functions: methods, planning and scheduling (equipment, materials, and workers), work-measurement standards, and accounting procedures. It also requires the highest management ability in the administration of these control functions from the time the work is authorized until incentive bonus is paid for the efficient completion of the work. These cost-control functions are essential to good management and are necessary with or without incentive payment. The addition of incentive pay on top of cost-control functions might truly be considered as a "fringe" benefit in the reduction of maintenance costs. Wage incentives are not a cost-control function, but a method of rewarding worker efficiency and management efficiency. The direct-measurement-type plan is discussed in further detail in this chapter and in Sec. 3, Chap. 3.

Other applications of bonus payments include:

1. Ratio plans—maintenance hours (or dollars) to items such as manufacturing labor hours (or dollars), net sales dollars, and factory cost dollars.
2. Ratio plans—equipment-operating hours to downtime hours.
3. Bonus to maintenance workers based on production efficiency.
4. Work-load-type bonus plan; established primarily for assigned maintenance personnel in areas or on specific equipment. This type of plan will be discussed in detail under Kinds of Maintenance Work for Which Appropriate.

A typical *ratio plan* could be developed and administered in the following manner, using the ratio of maintenance-labor dollars to total manufacturing-labor dollars as an example:

Development of Plan	*Example*
1. Select a base period to establish ratio.	Approx 2 years
2. Determine from cost data the ratio of maintenance-labor dollars to manufacturing-labor dollars.	Maintenance 12%, manufacturing labor 88%
3. Determine share of gains maintenance labor is to receive.	50%
4. Determine pay method.	On an accounting-period basis, 75% of bonus paid immediately, 25% held for deficit periods.

[1] Author is now Corporate Staff Industrial Engineer, American-Standard, American Radiator & Standard Sanitary Corporation, New York, N.Y.

Payment of Plan.   Using the examples as listed under items 2, 3, and 4 under Development of Plan, the following hypothetical figures show the basic concept of payment method for a ratio plan.

	Second accounting period	Year to date
A. Total cost of manufacturing and maintenance labor......	$333,000	$623,000
B. Standard maintenance cost (A × 0.12 = B)............	39,960	74,760
C. Actual maintenance cost........................	35,640	66,410
D. Variance (B − C = D)............................	4,320	8,350
E. Incentive earnings (D × 0.50 = E).................	2,160	4,175
F. Amount to deficit fund (E × 0.25 = F)..............	540	1,044
G. Available for distribution (E − F = G).............	1,620	3,131

The comments made here in regard to the development of, and plan of payment for, a ratio incentive plan are by necessity general.   There can be no "store-bought" ratio plan.   Each one must be tailored to the individual specifications of the organization concerned.   The apparent simplicity of such a plan is deceiving.   Each step in the development and administration of this type of plan depends on the validity of the previous step upon which it is based.   The following points are particularly critical:

1. Be certain that a *valid* ratio exists upon which incentive payments can be based.   A good rule—the longer the length of time for which the ratio has existed, the more probable its accuracy.
2. Take care in determining the percentage of realized savings to be made available as incentive payments.   Such payments should be made only to the extent that the recipients can control the variable factors involved.   But they must also be inviting enough to furnish the desired pull.
3. Do not install any such plan without including in the basic agreement the machinery to adjust the base ratio for changes, such as technological improvements which will occur.   It is advisable, in order to keep such adjustments to a minimum, that no changes less than 5 per cent (which may be cumulative) be cause to adjust the base ratio.
4. Foresee the possibility of deficit periods existing and provide a means to fill these gaps.

These ratio plans have the following advantages:

1. They are not profit sharing.   There is some basis for measurement.
2. There are no time studies involved.
3. There is no added administration cost beyond good cost-accounting procedures.
4. Not all the gains go to the employees, since there are also management contributions.
5. In those instances where the plan is accepted and functioning, management is forced into efficient cost-control functions such as planning and scheduling, material control, and improved methods, by worker pressure.
6. There is an incentive to the workers to use all the ingenuity and resourcefulness available to complete the job efficiently.   Under the individual incentive system this is not usually the case as a change of standard is the end result.
7. This type of plan encourages group participation and has in some cases broken through craft barriers.
8. It tends to control waste and scrap which result in excess labor costs.
9. It provides an opportunity for maintenance workers to increase their earnings.

This plan has disadvantages that require careful administration to preserve the incentive aspects:

1. If the base of this plan is not quickly and accurately adjusted for outside influences that are beyond the worker's control, such as the effect of capital improvements, product mixes, number of shifts in operation, the production rate, sales price, or other changes not included in the base calculations, the plan will fail. If the union has shared in developing the base and the administration of the plan, these adjustments to the base could create the same problems as wage reopeners, a wage-negotiation session every time there is a change in the base ratio.
2 There are also disadvantages as far as employee relations are concerned. An incentive plan to be effective must pay off. Since the base consists of averages, there could be accounting periods when bonus would not be earned. There is no direct relationship between effort and bonus, and the same amount of effort, or more, could have been used during the period which did *not* pay off as during the period which *did* pay off. This situation is difficult to explain to the workers and makes necessary a continual selling program on the worth of the plan. This selling program does not exist to such a degree with direct measured standards, where good administration and the relation of effort to pay are the items that do the selling.
3. The computations required to adjust base ratios for the effect of major capital improvements, new products, or new sales prices (depending on type ratio) will of necessity be based on estimates and projections. The degree of accuracy of these estimates to future maintenance cost experience will be questionable.
4. Unless this ratio plan is supplemented by some basic manning or work standards, there will still be considerable loss of maintenance labor.
5. If this plan is installed in a plant with low maintenance efficiency, bonus payments could be made on substandard performance that could be completely out of line with effort output and bonus paid production workers, creating problems with production incentive pay.

It is evident that the chance of success of a ratio plan is more favorable in a plant that has a relatively stable volume, a fairly constant product mix, few process changes, and fairly well established maintenance cost-control measures already in effect.

Plans based on operating to downtime ratios are usually based on historical records of lost time due to machine delays caused by defective maintenance and paid to assigned or preventive-maintenance crews. A bonus payment of 20 to 30 per cent is usually added to the hourly wage rate of maintenance men. When machine delays occur, a predetermined bonus penalty is deducted from the 20 to 30 per cent bonus possibility. This is a very difficult type of plan to administer because of the necessity to provide effective maintenance. The only working relationship it could lead to between management and maintenance workers would be one of constant friction. This method of paying bonus is also very poor from a psychological viewpoint. It is virtually impossible to give a promise of 20 to 30 per cent bonus and then deduct from it without tangible proof of negligence.

This type of plan is normally used as a supplement to other kinds of incentive plans that cover shop and plant standard maintenance work. It lacks any type of measurement that could determine the number of maintenance hours required to perform the work.

A bonus based on production efficiency is nothing more than a method of adjusting pay. While it may be true that there is a relationship between the efficiency of direct labor and maintenance, in most cases the entire control of maintenance bonus is in the hands of production operators. There will be no incentive pull of maintenance workers. From a practical viewpoint the only advantage would be in the adjustment of maintenance wages, keeping them in line with production wages. In addition to applying the method of pay to the entire maintenance group, this type of bonus payment is used as a supplement to other types of incentive plans covering shop and plant maintenance work   Without a method of work measurement, there is no value

PRODUCTION STANDARD

J. H. Thomas	DEPT. NUMBER 5	OPER. NO. 0500XX911
METHODS AND STANDARDS ENGR.	DEPT. NAME Assembly	PAGE 1 OF 3
W. C. Cooling	ISSUED DATE	EFFECTIVE DATE
METHODS AND STANDARDS SUPT.	CHANGE	

Indirect Bonus Plan

Operators.   Machine Adjustors—Department 5—Equipment All Assembly Machines

Type of Plan.   Group Incentive

Duties of Machine Adjustor

A. Adjustments as required to wire machines and assembly units.

B. Clear jams occurring in wire machines, assembly units or along length of machine.

C. Repair or replace parts as required.

D. Routine assigned duties
1. Change emory on hold down weights.
2. Scrape paint off inker.
3. Add graphite to lead tracks.
4. Mix and add CP paint to tanks.
5. Add alox to reservoirs.
6. Clean lead screw.
7. Oil machines.
8. Scrape and clean felts.
9. Clean pump (once per week per side).
10. Clean harmonicas.
11. Clean paint filter.
12. Clean solvent tank (once per·day).
13. Clear out overflow chutes (as required).

E. Necessary attention to prevent or diagnose trouble.

F. Repair set bars and make necessary clips.   Repair shaker box if required.

G. Necessary conversation with foreman, other adjustors, crew operators, or spot checkers.

H. Wipe off excess grease or dirt from machines.

Base Work Load (zero bonus) of the machine adjustor in Department 5 equals 5.0 sides per machine adjustor.

Administration.   The timekeeper will be informed daily by departmental supervisor as to the number of sides allowed the group of adjustors.

Per cent bonus is determined by reference to Chart A.

Conditions.   The application of the above standard is contingent on the following conditions:

1. Standard applies to the machine adjustor function in Department 5 under the existing plant layout, machines and equipment only.
2. These standards will be adjusted should the plant layout, machines, or equipment change.
3. Machine crews on average earnings will not affect the bonus computation of the machine adjustor unless the average earnings is due to his failure to adjust or service.
4. The machine adjustor must perform his function so that no crew will have excess waiting time due to his failure to adjust or service.   Should excess waiting on the assembly machines be charged to the machine adjustor, the number of sides involved will be deducted from the total daily sides.
5. No average earnings will be paid to the machine adjustor.   His daily method of pay is based on the number of sides as determined by the production equipment in operation.
6. In the event machine adjustor or adjustors fail to service the number of machines assigned (assembly operators frequently charging waiting time to machine adjustors), departmental supervision may assign additional adjustors.   In determining point at which additional adjustor should be assigned, foreman will use following as a guide: Time charged to account 984 and 973 (machine breakdown and nonstandard due to faulty equipment), has not exceeded 2.5% of total machine time operated during any period of time checked in past.   This percentage should be calculated daily and results plotted on a graph.   When the trend is upward, it would be a signal to review and assignment.
7. If a trainee enters the group of machine adjustors, the trainee will not participate in

beyond solving a pay-discrimination problem that might arise from unskilled take-out pay exceeding that of the skilled take-out pay.

Kinds of Maintenance Work for Which Incentive Pay is Appropriate. There are three broad classifications of work in maintenance:

1. Direct craft workers in shop or plant.
2. Assigned maintenance workers who are mainly trouble shooters and work on numerous small repair jobs within specific areas or on specific equipment.
3. Service personnel, such as storekeepers and toolroom attendants, where people are required for constant attendance, but the work requirements are intermittent and certainly beyond the control of the worker filling the job.

If the majority of maintenance workers are covered by direct maintenance-work measurement, and are receiving incentive pay, some provision must be made to avoid pay-differential problems among assigned maintenance personnel, service personnel, and the scheduled direct maintenance personnel. In some instances, the assigned personnel could be the better craftsmen and yet receive less pay. The same problem exists with service personnel. If other maintenance workers receive incentive bonus, it is necessary to provide a method to increase their earnings with incentive pay. There have been various plans to measure storeroom work, toolroom work, etc., but because of the intermittent work requirements, none of which is within the control of the service personnel, the most satisfactory arrangement, and purely for the purpose of avoiding pay discrimination, is to pay bonus based on the efficiency of the maintenance workers serviced. The assumption is that the stores attendant will give prompt service to avoid dilution of maintenance-worker efficiency through delays caused by careless servicing.

The kind of incentive that could be applied to the three work classifications is illustrated as follows:

Maintenance Work Classification	*Kind of Incentive Plan*
1. Direct craft work	Plan based on measured standard times. Ratio plan—maintenance dollars to manufacturing-labor dollars, etc. Bonus based on production efficiency
2. Assigned maintenance work	Work load bonus plan. Ratio plan—maintenance dollars to manufacturing-labor dollars, etc. Ratio plan—equipment-operating hours to downtime hours. Bonus based on efficiency of area or group serviced
3. Service personnel	Ratio plan—maintenance dollars to manufacturing-labor dollars, etc. Bonus based on efficiency of area or group serviced

The principles and techniques of direct measurement have been presented in detail

---

    the bonus until he has completed the specified training period. Bonus for qualified operators of a group in which there is a trainee will be calculated as follows:
    a. Subtract 5 sides per trainee from total sides.
    b. Using the remaining number of sides, refer to chart *a* to determine per cent bonus earned by adjustors (excluding trainee).
  8. In converting to incentive classification from nonincentive, a minimum bonus of 8.7 % (rounded off to 9 % on chart *a* will be paid to guarantee minimum of present hourly earnings.
  9. If number of sides operated is <u>decreased</u> during the shift, per cent bonus will be determined from most number of sides operated and applied to total time worked by adjustor.
 10. If number of sides operated is <u>increased</u> during the shift, per cent bonus will be determined separately for each portion of shift during which different number of machines operated and applied to portion of time adjustor worked under different assignments.

FIG. 4-1. The write-up of the indirect bonus plan. It defines who is covered, the type of incentive, the duties of the job, incentive base, administration, and condition upon which application of standard is contingent.

PRODUCTION STANDARD

J. H. Thomas	DEPT. NUMBER	5		OPER. NO. **0500XX911**
METHODS AND STANDARDS ENGR.	DEPT. NAME	Assembly		PAGE 3 OF 3
W. C. Cooling	ISSUED DATE			EFFECTIVE DATE
METHODS AND STANDARDS SUPV.	CHANGE			

Chart A.   Per Cent Bonus Earned

No. of Mach. Sides	Number of Adjustors (Exclude Trainees)						Operation Numbers	
	1	2	3	4	5		XX	% Bonus
	% Bonus							
1........	109						01	109
2........	109						02	111
3........	109						03	112
4........	109						04	113
5........	109						05	114
6........	120						06	115
7........	140	109					07	116
8........		109					08	117
9........		109					09	118
10........		109					10	120
11........		115					11	125
12........		120					12	127
13........		130					13	130
14........		140	109				14	133
15........			109				15	135
16........			113				16	140
17........			117					
18........			120					
19........			127					
20........			133	109				
21........			140	112				
22........				115				
23........				118				
24........				120				
25........				125	109			
26........				130	111			
27........				135	114			
28........				140	116			

Notes. (1) There is no top limit on earnings, but an assignment beyond 7 sides per adjustor should be for a temporary period at the discretion of the foreman.

(2) If an assignment beyond 7 sides per adjustor should be necessary, foreman will notify methods and standards before assignment (or as near after as possible). Methods and standards will then inform timekeeping of per cent bonus to be paid.

FIG. 4-2. From this chart the per cent bonus is determined. The term "per cent bonus" conforms to the plant terminology. Actual per cent bonus may be determined by subtracting 100 from bonus figures on chart.

in the remainder of this chapter and in Sec. 3, Chap. 3. With the exception of the work load bonus plan, the other types of plans have been discussed under Kinds of Incentives Ordinarily Used.

The work of machine adjusters (maintenance-personnel-assigned production units or areas) can be effectively measured on work-load-manning requirements and the net results attained by the mechanics. The following procedure, illustrated by Figs. 4-1 and 4-2, has been used effectively to pay incentive for an incentive work load.

Steps in the Development of Work Load Bonus Standards for Assigned Maintenance Personnel

1. Discuss operation in detail with foreman to:
   _a._ Supply him with background for discussion with union and/or workers involved.

    b. Orient the study observer as to plant nomenclature of equipment involved and necessary work duties.
2. Study observer makes preliminary observations to introduce himself to equipment and personnel.
    a. Since this type of study does not permit a prepared list of cyclical elements, observer must make mental note of the time-study breakdown of the job into constant and variable elements.
3. Take a series of all-day studies. Number of studies may vary but must include the complete range of probabilities and should be on several different workers if available.
4. Analyze study—elements and occurrences; accumulate times.
5. Discuss (the elements observed) with foreman to avoid possible inclusion of unnecessary work.
6. Determine for each element total time and number of occurrences.
7. Determine time per occurrence for each element.
8. Determine frequency of elements.
9. Discuss final summary of elements with foreman. The foreman might recall work which was not observed because it occurs infrequently. The foreman may indicate that elements were performed too often by adjuster during study. Adjust frequencies of occurrence if necessary.
10. Determine unit of measurement (in this case, per machine) and total minutes per unit.
11. Add allowances for rest and delay, miscellaneous work, interference, etc.
12. Express number of machines per shift to be serviced by adjuster at base and compute incentive work loads.
13. Write up duties, standards, and conditions under which incentive will be applied.
14. Review write-up with foreman; discuss in complete detail to prepare foreman for explanation to workers.
15. Allow foreman time to explain plan to steward and/or workers involved.
16. Brief timekeeper on operation of incentive.
17. Issue plan.

Economical Limits to the Application of Incentives. When investigating the economic possibilities of an incentive system, many companies think in terms of number of maintenance employees. This is the wrong approach. Evaluate the installation cost and maintenance cost of an incentive plan in the same manner as any evaluation for proposed changes: new equipment, revised methods, layout changes, as examples. The problem is to determine old costs, without incentives, estimate new costs, with incentives, and arrive at potential savings. Use the approach outlined in Sec. 3, Chap. 3 for determining maintenance efficiencies. From this determination, a dollar figure can be arrived at, and this savings potential evaluated against the cost of the initial installation and continued administration of an incentive plan.

    Forget maintenance ratios, such as the ratio of maintenance labor to production, total plant labor, the ratio of maintenance expense to operating costs or net sales dollar. There are many factors that influence ratios: the trend toward more complicated equipment, the age of equipment, the number of shifts operating, and product mixes. These all have an effect on maintenance costs and will change the ratio. The ratio can rise with a decrease in direct-labor costs while at the same time your maintenance efficiency has not changed, giving a false picture.

    The administration of a maintenance plan is about 3 to 12 per cent in additional costs. This is a small factor when most companies can reasonably expect a decrease in maintenance costs from 10 to 50 per cent. In a survey by *Factory Management and Maintenance*, covering eight companies of different industries, the additional administrative personnel required for a wage-incentive system amounted to 2.4 to 10 per cent of the number of direct workers.[1]

    Most of the administrative work required to facilitate wage incentives should be

[1] Incentives Work Fine in Maintenance, *Factory Management and Maintenance*, February, 1955.

performed as staff services to maintenance foremen whether an incentive system is installed or not.   The administrative work required for a wage-incentive program consists of these functions: methods, planning and scheduling, material control, work measurement, and timekeeping.   To run an efficient maintenance organization, these functions must be performed with or without wage incentives to maintain proper cost control.   Adding incentive pay, in areas where these functions are under control, gives a final push to maintenance productivity.

Low-cost Administrative Standards for Plant Maintenance.   Methods Engineering Council has adopted a unique approach to low-cost administration of plant standards (nonshop work).   It is based on their findings that, in plant work, "80% of the total jobs required less than 8 hours to perform."   It was also found that, "although these short jobs cause the bulk of standard-setting problems, they represent only about 20% of the total time worked in a typical maintenance operation."[1]

From these facts, it was evident that a method of establishing quick standards on small jobs, to leave the planning and standards groups more time to concentrate on the majority of maintenance hours and material, would reduce administrative hours.

Methods Engineering Council used this approach:

1. A large number of maintenance jobs were studied as they occurred.   These jobs were selected to match the types of work that occur in normal day-to-day operations.
2. Jobs requiring about the same amount of working time were grouped (standard work groupings), each group representing a range of time (see Table 4-1).
3. The standards applicator determines the standard work grouping and applies the corresponding time to each job.
4. With performance completed on a weekly or biweekly basis, measurement is sufficiently accurate for incentive-wage purposes on this 20 per cent portion of maintenance hours.

The above approach is a combination of two methods for applying standards discussed in Sec. 3, Chap. 3, standard data (80 per cent of the hours), and historical data or planner's estimate (20 per cent of the hours).   This type of application has been termed universal maintenance standards by Methods Engineering Council and does substantially reduce administrative costs.   For each incentive installation, it would be necessary to determine the work groupings, then apply standards to various jobs with both methods (standard data and standard work groupings), and determine if the time difference between the two types of standards is acceptable.

Reduction of Administrative Costs.   Administrative costs can be reduced after careful study just as labor costs can.   When thinking of maintenance wage incentives most people visualize a group of planners working with calculating machines determining work standards.   Hand calculation of incentive standards from standard data is obsolete.   The use of punched-card data to develop standards removes the hand labor and places data in a more usable form.   After standards are placed on punched cards, the cards can be used for a number of administrative aids beyond the payroll function, particularly in planning and scheduling.

1. Before work commences, tab runs with punched-card data coded in various ways will give for any period of time:
   a. Standard man-hours required per craft.
   b. Standard man-hours required by craft by area.
   c. Total standard man-hours required.
2. After the work is completed, for any period of time:
   a. Individual worker efficiency.
   b. Craft efficiency.
   c. Area efficiencies.
   d. Job efficiencies.

[1] "Maintenance Cost Reduction through New Control Procedures," Methods Engineering Council, Pittsburgh, Pa., 1955.

Table 4-1. Standard Groupings for Maintenance Standards

Group	A	B	C	D	E	F	G	H	I	J
Man-minutes allowed	30	50	75	105	140	180	230	290	360	440
Range	20 40 60 90 120 160 200 260 320 400 480									

Job area Cab cranes						
E-3 Replace or repair fuse E-4 Visual check and adjustment of one controller E-5 Adjust limit switch	E-6 Small repair and adjustment to limit switch E-7 Replace brushes and 3 or 4 contacts in one controller E-10 Check and adjust magnet brake	E-8 Replace contacts and brushes in 3 or more controllers E-13 Check and alleviate hot bearing of motor	E-11 Check motor and sand commutator E-12 Check crane out for ground		E-9 Reline brake shoes E-14 Replace small armature (trolley, etc.)	E-1 Preventive maintenance (oil and inspect 19 cranes) E-2 Remove and replace bridge or large armature

Courtesy of Methods Engineering Council.

This chart is a typical example of how standard groupings for maintenance standards are set up for purposes of administration.   In Cab Cranes (above), Example E-3, it will be noted that to "replace or repair fuse" is under Group A and will take between 20 and 40 man-minutes—but actually 30 man-minutes are allowed.   In the next column to the right, Example E-6, it will be noted that this belongs to Standard Grouping B, and that 50 man-minutes are allowed for small repair and adjustment to limit switch—though it may actually take from 40 to 60 min.   This, and all above standards will remain constant in the plant where they are set up.

Punched-card Procedure for Applying Elemental Standard Data.   This system is used at International Resistance Company with indirect jobs that require the development of elemental standard times (see Fig. 4-3).

Methods and standards:

1. Standard elemental time tables are developed for all work.   Individual elemental times are coded.
2. Standard-data tables sent to tabulating department to prepare prepunched elemental standard data cards, which include code number and standard time.

Tabulating department:

3. A master time-ticket card is punched for each standard time (operation code and standard time).
4. Master time-ticket cards are verified.
5. Master time-ticket cards are sent to reproducing machine where required volume of time-ticket cards are prepunched for standards applicators.

Standards applicators:

6. Standards applicators receive prepunched cards along with master time tickets which are used for reordering of cards.

7. Standards applicator develops job standard from print, inspection of work to be done, etc. Pulls corresponding standard-data punched card for each standard-data time. Mark senses number of occurrences of each standard-data time on the time ticket. Prepares a job card which is mark sensed for job number.
8. Applicator places job card on top with standard-data time tickets following. Files job until work is scheduled.

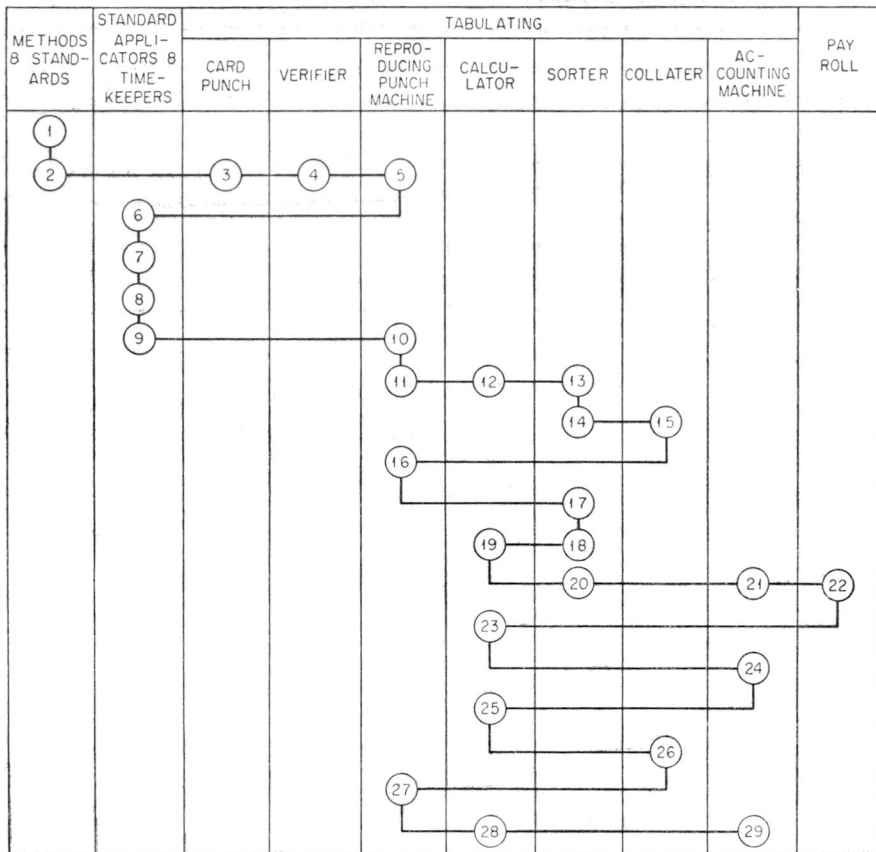

Fig. 4-3. Punched-card procedure for applying elemental standard data.

9. Job is scheduled. Applicator pulls job standard (job card and standard-data time tickets), mark senses clock number of workers and work code (incentive or a nonincentive category) on job card. Applicator keeps time record and at completion of job mark senses actual hours on job card. Standard-data cards are placed on top of the job card and forwarded to tabulating.

Tabulating:

10. Cards are fed to reproducing punch machine which punches out all mark sensed areas. Cards are verified on same machine.
11. Punched standard-data cards are put through reproducing punch machine again which rearranges and punches same information in step 10 on a labor-detail distribution card to facilitate calculation of earned hours and clock hours. Standard-data cards are filed for reference.

12. Labor-detail distribution cards are fed into a calculator which computes earned hours on each trailer card and punches total earned hours on one operation master card.
13. Cards from step 12 are fed into sorter.   Obtain two groups of cards: (1) labor-detail distribution cards and (2) master job cards with total earned hours.   File labor-detail distribution cards.
14. Master job cards from step 13 are added to other master job cards, fed into sorter, and sorted by clock number in sequence.
15. Cards from step 14 are fed into a collator to match up and merge with a master labor-rate card for each clock number.
16. The merged group of cards from step 15 are fed into reproducing punch machine which punches information from master labor-rate card on operation master cards.
17. Cards from step 16 are fed into sorter to separate master labor-rate cards from operation master cards.
18. Cards from step 17 are fed into sorter again to separate daywork from incentive cards.
19. Incentive cards are fed into calculator which gives total amount spent on lost hours and earned hours and gives a first gross total of lost earned hours.   Cards are run through calculator again and checked using different storage units in the machine.
20. Incentive cards are combined again with daywork cards and fed into sorter, sorted by department, clock number, and date.
21. Sorted cards go to accounting; machine transfers punched information from operation master cards to a gross-pay summary card for each clock number. Accounting machine also prints detail-labor efficiency report at this time.
22. Detail-labor efficiency reports are sent to payroll for checking.   Corrections are made if required, sent back to tabulation, and gross-pay summary cards corrected.
23. Gross-pay cards are fed into calculator where payroll adds other premiums and overtime if any is calculated and final gross pay punched.
24. Cards are run from step 23 on accounting machine and final gross-pay report is printed.
25. Cards from step 23 are run through reproducing punch machine and transfer punches date, department number, clock number, clock hours, pay hours, tax class, base rate, and gross pay on a net-pay card.
26. Net-pay cards from step 25 are sent to collator which matches cards with master punched cards having deductions by clock number.
27. Collated cards from step 26 are sent to reproducing punch machine and deduction information is punched on net-pay card.   Master punched deduction cards are filed.
28. Net-pay cards from step 27 are fed into calculator which calculates and punches withholding tax, city tax, old age security tax.   Cards are run through again and checked using different storage units.   They are sent through for third time and net-pay information is punched.
29. Net-pay cards from step 28 are matched with master name-file cards and fed into accounting machine, which prints check.

The above procedure looks like a large number of steps.   However, the great majority of these steps are machine operations.   Another consideration is that steps 9 to 16, with the exception of steps 11 to 13, are a part of the pay procedure and must be performed with or without incentives.

Another part of this handbook describes a procedure for compiling labor and material charges by various classifications to control maintenance costs.   The two systems can be integrated for the wage-incentive purposes and material- and labor-distribution control and charges.

Preset Standards vs. Postset Standards.   With the preset (analyst) method of applying standards, standard times for the work involved are applied before the actual work starts.   The postset (checker) method of applying standards refers to the establishment of standard times for the work involved after the work is completed or is in process.

Based solely on administrative costs, the more expensive method of applying standards to maintenance work usually is the preset method. In a chemical plant, a study made of the two methods demonstrated that the preset method was approximately double the cost of the postset method for the same number of craft maintenance hours involved. The cost ratio of craft hours to checker hours (postset) was 1.75 per cent and the ratio of craft hours to analyst hours (preset) was 3.60 per cent.[1]

The above costs should not be taken at face value. There are many intangible savings to be realized through preset standards. Among these items are the planning and control of labor, materials, and equipment. Preset standards force more effective controls. Through the clear definition of work to be done, equipment to be used, and material to be used, costs are effectively controlled. With a postset system, it is possible for most crafts, painters, carpenters, etc., to do more work than is actually required, by less efficient methods, and receive incentive pay, at the same time wasting labor hours and materials. The preset method requires the best management tactics and contributes the most to effective cost control. The last statement has no reflection upon earnings potentials of maintenance workers. It does mean that the money is well spent. The additional cost of preset standards will be more than recovered by tighter management controls.

Amount of Incentive Pay. In the past, there were incentive plans where the employee shared incentive earnings with management. This concept has disappeared with current management thinking and union pressure.

The current thinking is to pay the incentive worker a 1 per cent increase in the incentive base wage rate for each 1 per cent increase in output. With shopwork where handling methods, machine speeds, and other working conditions make possible a high degree of work standardization, this payment is practical, fair, and easily understood by the employees.

For field (in-plant) work, because of the impossibility of standardizing working conditions as effectively as for shopwork areas, a payment curve is usually established. Figure 4-4 illustrates such a curve. Incentive pay usually starts at a lower level than shopwork and increases at a higher rate. This is to avoid the abrupt jump from a daywork pace to an incentive pace and encourage the incentive workers to extend their production and earnings. The bonus curve begins to level out between 95 and 105 per cent worker-efficiency level. Note that at 100 per cent the field incentive worker receives the same bonus as a shopworker. Above the 105 per cent level the payments begin to ease off. This curve also attempts to compensate in part for work at the extremes of the averages, the greater than 1 for 1 pay rise from 65 to 95 per cent efficiencies compensating for those extremes of the averages unfavorable to the employee, and the easing off of incentive pay above 105 per cent to compensate for the extremes in the averages unfavorable to management.

To place a value on the 100 per cent operator-performance level, consider this point comparable in worker output to a man walking 3 mph on smooth level ground without carrying a load. With this as a standard, the average shop- and field-efficiency level should equal a payoff of 25 to 30 per cent incentive bonus.

Methods of Payment—Group vs. Individual. The various plans which have been outlined can operate with either group or individual payments, which do not concern the basic plan. They are simply methods of distributing incentive earnings.

At a management conference, the following points were advanced as being in favor of *group-incentive* payments:

1. Group payment averages earnings so that each job classification maintains the same pay position.
2. Group payment averages earnings so that each employee in the same craft receives the same incentive pay.
3. Group payment averages difficult work with easy work.

[1] W. C. Cooling, "Pre-determined Job Standards for Maintenance in Chemical Process Industries," Master's Thesis, Temple University, Philadelphia, 1949.

4. Group payment may be extended to cover all hours—even those without standards (nonrated productive work, sweepers, toolroom attendants, etc.)
5. Group payment simplifies the administration of the plan.

While these advantages of group payment appear to be valid, each one is a compensation for potential errors or inefficient management. With high coverage and good standards, incentive payments between individuals and wage differentials among varied skills should not be a problem. It is only with low coverage and inadequate standards that individual earnings and wage differentials among skills go out of line. With adequate standards as the base for a well-administered wage-

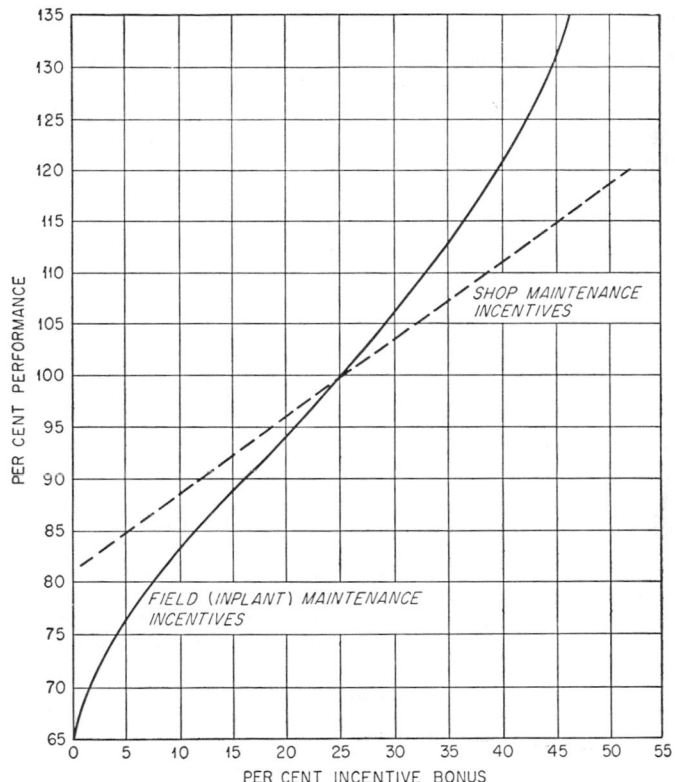

FIG. 4-4. With the degree of standardization of shop working areas, a pay curve providing a 1 per cent pay increase for each 1 per cent increase in output is desirable and practical. Field (in-plant) standards, which are based on work areas that cannot be standardized to the degree of shop work areas, should pay on a curve with bonus payments starting at a low level (67 per cent), leveling out in the areas of normal worker efficiency (95 to 100 per cent) and tapering off above that level.

incentive system, there is no "difficult" or "easy" work. Most jobs are equitable as long as the basis for the standard data does not change and the standard data are applied correctly to each job. Item 4 above compensates for low coverage and jobs that cannot be placed on standards. As mentioned at the beginning of this chapter, there are jobs that cannot be placed on incentive with standard data, but a catch-all group plan is not the way to erase pay discrimination caused by the lack of opportunity to earn incentive pay. With item 5, simplified administration, it is implied that basic management controls such as material control and planning and scheduling do not have to be so efficient. Standards and the timekeeping function do not have to be so accurate. If a group plan is installed solely for the purpose of controlling pay scales and allowing for management's faults in establishing and operating basic cost-control measures, the principles of wage-incentive administration have been violated.

The most important *advantage* of *group* payment is in promoting teamwork, to maintain a level of quality and to stimulate mutual assistance on jobs. If group-incentive payment is installed with the above in mind rather than the five preceding so-called advantages, together with well-developed control functions and accurate, properly maintained standard data as the basis of the incentive standards, a group plan should achieve about the same results as an individual incentive plan.

The loosely administered group-payment system will be a failure when:

1. Individuals or small groups feel they are "carrying" less efficient fellow workers.
2. Individuals or small groups feel they contributed more incentive earnings to the common "pot" than toolroom attendants, crane operators and helpers, sweepers, etc., who are included in the same plan, and begin to "peg" their production. Poor administration of old standards and careless development of new standards, on the basis that everything will average out, will also destroy the group-payment system.

On a group-incentive basis, group performance would be measured by comparing total standard hours with total actual hours. This does not provide for a job efficiency or individual efficiency or any means to measure individual output for cost-control purposes. If the group includes the workers under more than one supervisor, a group plan does not provide a measure of individual supervisory efficiency.

The following points are advanced in favor of individual incentive payments:

1. Individual incentive can be a basis for the foreman to appraise the production of each employee.
2. Each employee receives pay in direct proportion to what he produces; high producers tend to produce more, and low producers have the incentive to continually improve.
3. High producers receive high earnings which are not shared with low producers.

With these qualities, the individual-incentive plan tends to promote a higher individual production level than the group plan.

With maintenance work, where a number of craftsmen work on each job, it is not possible to pay on individual accomplishments. A combination of group and individual measurements must be used.

Each job may be considered a measuring point. The efficiency on each job can be determined by dividing the total standard hours allowed by the actual hours worked. This is group efficiency for the job. The worker's earned hours may be determined by multiplying the number of hours spent on the job by the group job efficiency to determine the total standard hours to be credited to the worker for that job; thus he will share group earnings for that job. However, if he should be in another group on the next job, he receives the same incentive efficiency as each member of that group. At the end of the worker's pay period, his total actual hours from all jobs divided by his total standard hours from all jobs will determine his efficiency for pay purposes. If he should work as an individual during this period, his individual hours would be treated as a job and be included in the total standard hours for pay purposes.

Incentive Pay Periods.[1]   The elemental data used for standard-data development are based on normal times under normal working conditions. The time studies are made over a lengthy period to obtain these average times under average operating conditions. The allowances that cover unavoidable delays and miscellaneous work are also established over a lengthy period and on average working conditions. There-fore, the incentive pay period must be long enough to be representative of the averages

[1] W. C. Cooling, Work Measurement, Work Standards, and Incentives, in "Techniques of Plant Maintenance and Engineering," p. 108, Clapp and Poliak, Inc., New York, 1954.

on which the standards are based.   A biweekly pay period is normally sufficient to meet these requirements.

There will always be jobs that are not completed by the end of the pay period. A method must be established to pay job base-wage rates for unfinished jobs at the end of the pay period.   Incentive payments must be delayed until the job is complete and this portion of total pay can be determined.   In some instances, it will be possible to establish incentive-pay breaking points in a lengthy job, so that incentive pay can be paid at a time more closely related to the work.

Table 4-2. Time Allowances

Lift, ft	Select time, min	Add delay, misc. 16.8%	Add personal 5%
20	1.08	1.26	1.32
40	1.60	1.87	1.96
60	2.10	2.45	2.57
80	2.55	2.98	3.13
100	3.00	3.50	3.68
120	3.25	3.80	3.99
140	4.10	4.79	5.03
160	4.90	5.72	6.01
180	6.20	7.24	7.60
200	7.15	8.35	8.77
220	7.95	9.29	9.75

Allowances are added to select times (from figure lift and move in equipment with air tugger) to establish standard time to complete work element.   The 5% personal allowance is not totaled with delay and miscellaneous work allowances as these work allowances require 5% personal allowance also.

Allowances. In addition to the select time to perform standard work elements, there are other events in the course of a workday, necessary for successful completion of tasks, that require a time allowance (see Table 4-2).   Time must be provided for:

1. Personal needs.   Some time must be allowed to provide for necessary events such as visiting the washroom, adjusting clothing, and other personal needs.   This is not a measured allowance, but a negotiated or agreed allowance depending on the type of product, nature of work, etc.   This allowance varies from 2.5 to 15 per cent of total standard time in current practice, with the majority of incentive plans using 5 per cent.

2. Delays and miscellaneous work.   With maintenance work, there are certain delays that may be minimized, but not avoided.   There will be a lower percentage delay time allowed in shopwork than in plant work.   Shopwork areas are planned and arranged to reduce delays and miscellaneous work.   This is not always practical for field (in-plant maintenance work).   Time must be provided for these unavoidable delays.

   a. Miscellaneous work.   In most jobs, there exist some nonrepetitive or irregularly occurring items which must be performed in connection with the regular job. These items are usually different in character and not of sufficient duration to justify their coverage by individual standards.   Such jobs as removing equipment obstacles and adjusting and sharpening tools fall into this category.

   b. Interference.   Inherent factors are to be found in every job which interfere with the normal flow of work, such as waiting for other crafts and delays due to cranes, trucks, etc., that are on other jobs.

   c. Crew balance.   In some classes of work, where more labor within a craft is needed on some portions of a job than can effectively be used on the entire job, a condition of enforced idle time exists.   An example might be riggers waiting for a tugger load to be raised into position.

Where crew size can be scheduled for positions of a job, this allowance is not required.

d. Abnormal work. Direct or supplementary work that is encountered at the time of the study which cannot be considered as a normal function in the completion of the job. An example of this would be the fitting of safety boots on a high power line by the riggers while hanging a boilermaker's chair near the line.

These allowances may be determined through a series of 8-hr time studies or through the ratio-delay procedure outlined in Sec. 3, Chap. 3. The computation of these allowances is illustrated by Fig. 4-5. In some instances, the allowance would

COMPUTATION OF ALLOWANCES FOR RIGGING

Time study No.	Normal minutes			
	Work measured by basic time standards	Miscellaneous work	Crew balance	Inter-ference
R- 2	153.86	1.20	8.53	6.50
R-23	14.53	. . . . . .	2.53	.90
R-54	452.96	7.86	60.38	6.51
R-55	395.51	2.35	24.41	7.60
R-57	452.59	4.26	53.22	6.38
R-58	526.10	1.98	25.05	14.42
R-59	171.55	1.65	18.57	2.61
R-60	114.17	4.38	36.34	9.17
R-62	266.14	1.07	22.82	38.90
R-70	96.50	. . . . . .	18.25	11.20
R-71	394.25	11.00	49.95	12.62
R-75	463.20	29.75	43.32	45.50
R-77	327.57	14.25	27.16	4.25
R-82	201.59	8.36	8.60	.45
R-84	190.30	3.74	7.00	11.58
R-85	236.79	9.90	33.76	15.97
R-86	204.22	6.20	25.18	14.22
Total	4661.83	107.95	465.07	208.78

$$\text{Allowances: Miscellaneous work} = \frac{107.95 \text{ min}}{4661.83 \text{ min}} \times 100 = 2.3\%$$

$$\text{Crew balance} = \frac{465.07 \text{ min}}{4661.83 \text{ min}} \times 100 = 10.0\%$$

$$\text{Interference} = \frac{208.78 \text{ min}}{4661.83 \text{ min}} \times 100 = 5.4\%$$

FIG. 4-5. The computation of allowances that are necessary to provide time for other necessary events in the work day. These allowances, totaling 16.8 per cent, plus the addition of a personal allowance of 5 per cent, are applied to the select time for work elements (see Table 4-2). (*Courtesy of Factory Management and Maintenance.*)

be applied only to specific categories of work. With riggers using a tugger hoist (Fig. 4-6) there is a higher crew balance time necessary than with other classes of rigging work, because of alternate waiting time by the hoist operator and helpers while raising loads. A specific crew balance allowance could be determined and applied only to this class of rigging work.

3. Machine allowance. This allowance usually enters the picture in shopwork where an operation is machine-controlled and an operator cannot earn incentive pay with extended effort. In order to avoid discrimination and inequities in

pay, it is a practice in many shops to allow an incentive factor on the machine elements of the job.   Where it is possible to schedule work during machine time or utilize operator time during machine periods by adding other machines this allowance can be avoided.   If it is not possible to find a useful activity during machine time, this type of allowance should be considered to enable an operator to earn incentive pay that will approximate the earnings of the other people in the shop.   The allowance might be applied in this manner: 5 per cent machine allowance for jobs that are under 50 per cent machine-controlled and 15 per cent

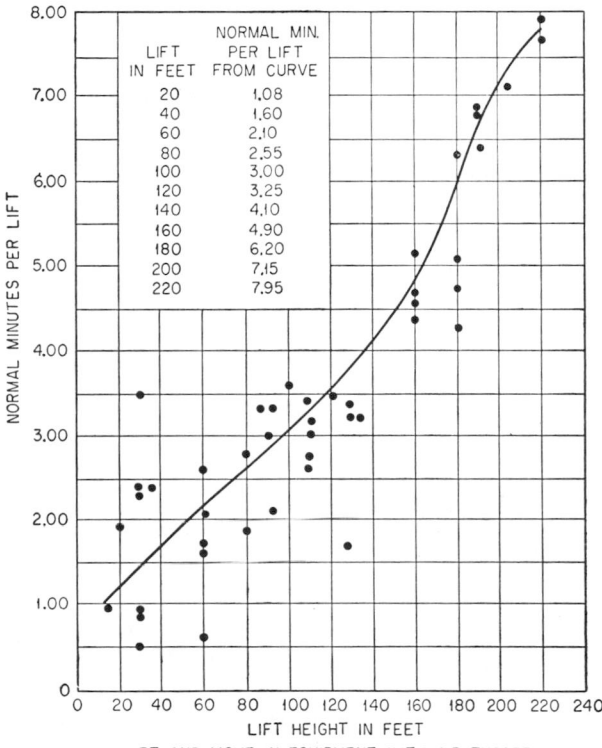

LIFT IN FEET	NORMAL MIN. PER LIFT FROM CURVE
20	1.08
40	1.60
60	2.10
80	2.55
100	3.00
120	3.25
140	4.10
160	4.90
180	6.20
200	7.15
220	7.95

LIFT AND MOVE IN EQUIPMENT WITH AIR TUGGER

FIG. 4-6. Select times for one element—lifting and moving equipment with air tugger. Line is drawn through average of time-study data to represent selected standard times. Allowances must be added to these select times to obtain elemental standard-time data.

machine allowance for jobs over 50 per cent machine-controlled.   The potential pay of nonmachine operators will have to be considered in each individual case in establishing machine allowances.   This is not a time-studied allowance and must be used only when there is a true need.

4. Specific conditions.   Examples will follow to outline the need for this allowance, but each plant has specific problems and must determine its own allowance based on the individual need.   Working inside a closed vessel, such as a tank, requires an allowance for conditions such as inadequate ventilation and restricted movements in the working area.   Work areas with extreme temperature conditions, hot or cold, would require this type of allowance.   It can be determined only by job experience, past working practices, or agreement.   Allowances for specific conditions that run as high as 50 per cent are not unusual.   An allowance of this type is not built into the elemental time standards but is applied to those portions of the job standard where the need arises.

5. Job allowances. Preparation and clean-up allowances must be developed and applied on a job basis since it is impossible to prorate this time in the elemental standard data with the number of jobs varying from day to day. There are also specific job allowances that can be encountered. For example, in a plant processing selenium rectifier plates, exposure to this type of metal requires frequent washing of hands to avoid swallowing the selenium particles. Maintenance work in this area requires an allowance, beyond that of the normal personal allowance, to provide for clean-up time. This allowance would not be included in the standard times but would be issued as a time value in the form of a job allowance for work in that specific area.

In the process of developing standards, avoid placing any allowance in the elemental standards for conditions that are not present in the average 8-hr day. For example, use job allowances for such items as clocking in and out, job preparation, and clean-up. This time will then be charged to the specific jobs where the time was required. Use a daily allowance for instruction and preparation time at the start of the day and clean-up at the end of the day, if these items are completed on company time. For cost purposes, the daily allowance (nonproductive) can be charged to maintenance overhead for proper prorating to individual jobs.

When Adopting Incentives, Recognize These Facts

1. The same controls are needed for efficient cost administration with or without wage incentives. A wage-incentive program will not be a success without successful administrative controls.
2. A wage-incentive program requires a higher degree of management administrative skill than a daywork program. A wage-incentive system does not control costs, the people who run the system do. Therefore management control functions, such as planning and scheduling, and cost accounting must be functioning at a high efficiency level. All a wage-incentive system can accomplish is to pay a worker more for supervising himself as to (1) work time and (2) the skill and effort that he applies to his job.
3. Supervision and the workers play major roles in a successful wage-incentive plan. Both supervision and representatives of the employees should have an appreciation course in methods and time study and a training course in the administration of wage-incentive standards and policies. All employees should have a general idea of how standards are set, how they are administered, incentive-pay policies, and how to compute their pay.
4. Every phase of management will be affected by a wage-incentive program: engineering, production, industrial relations, and accounting. All these functions must be oriented with respect to their responsibilities and contributions.
5. A wage-incentive policy is necessary with or without a union. Individual practices or interdepartmental practices should not establish policies.
6. An incentive program must be established only when a firm base-wage-rate standard exists.
7. Extreme care and study must be used in the selection of an incentive-payment plan. More than one payment plan may be instituted to take care of specific work circumstances (i.e., shop or field). Each plan must be tailored to the type work that is to be measured.
8. Plan a payment curve that avoids an abrupt jump from a daywork pace to an incentive pace. Tailor payment curves to the degree of reproducibility of working conditions.
9. The choice of payment (group vs. individual) under the incentive plan must be final. Figure 4-7 shows an efficiency distribution of a group of workers. In changing the payment method from group to individual, the worker performing at below-average efficiency would take a pay cut. Should the change be the reverse, from individual to group, the workers performing at the above-average level would receive a decrease in earnings. It is obvious that such a change in

the method of incentive payment will leave about half the workers dissatisfied and would not be acceptable.

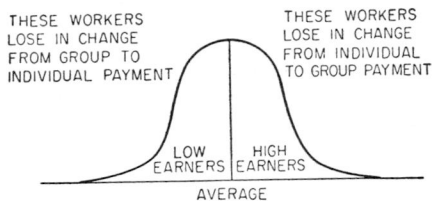

FIG. 4-7. Efficiency distribution of a group of workers.

10. If an incentive plan is to reach the maximum point of effectiveness, the basis for incentive earnings must be directly related to the output of skill and effort of the workers. A ratio plan that can be influenced by factors beyond the control of the workers can be more difficult to administer successfully than a direct measurement plan.

When Adopting Incentives, Don't

1. Install incentives where management is not wholeheartedly behind the program.
2. Allow the imagination of supervision or the workers to run loose with any phase or problem of the incentive system. (Pay is involved; keep them informed.)
3. Underhire. (Pay for capable industrial engineering personnel.) As for supervision, don't keep any supervisor unless he can be trained in wage-incentive administration and is willing to accept his new responsibilities. (If personnel are selected from within to function as industrial engineers, supervisors, or timekeepers, make sure they are formally trained. This can't be done overnight.)
4. Place industrial engineering in the role of time study and rate setting. (The standardization of working area, working conditions, and working methods requires competent personnel operating above the level of time study and rate setting.)
5. Install an incentive plan without prior consideration of what to do with excess working hours that are going to be available. (A consideration of work load and number of people involved is most important.)
6. Install a piece rate or any dollar system. (In an era of wage increases, the maintenance of this type of standard is impractical. A standard-hour system requires no change in incentive standards, when an increase occurs. The only changes required occur in the accounting function.)
7. Adjust standards, through increased bonus allowances, to give pay increases. (Provide for pay increases in the base wage rates.)
8. Attempt to eliminate pay inequities through incentive payments.

When Developing Incentive Standards

1. Standardize **work** methods. It is not always essential to install the best method if this will require a long period of time. When work is standardized, it may be studied, the standards issued, with the employee earning incentive pay and management enjoying lower costs. Delay while waiting for a new method to be approved and installed will result in lost pay to the employee and lost efficiency to management. The new method may be installed at a later date after it has been perfected and approved by management and any additional equipment procured. An incentive system must provide the opportunity for incentive earnings to satisfy the incentive workers. Don't hold up incentive standards.
2. Study standard work methods and train workers in them.
3. Make some provision for machine-paced operators to earn incentive pay. Attempt to provide work for operators during machine running time or plan for multiple machine operations. If these are not possible, it may be necessary to add an allowance for machine running time to avoid incentive-pay discrimination.

4. Keep the workers involved informed of the progress in developing standards.
5. Review in detail the results of time studies and the build-up of standard data with supervision and employees' representative.
6. Use sound industrial engineering techniques to develop a standard; workers' pay is involved.
7. Train supervision in the method of introducing a standard to the workers. This is a major part of the supervisory administrative function.
8. Standard data must be based on a large number of elemental times for each work element to obtain a select time that will be representative of average working conditions.
9. Include allowances to cover delays and miscellaneous work that are unavoidable in maintenance work.

When Developing Incentive Standards, Don't

1. Study an untrained worker and attempt to adjust for lack of training by leveling.
2. Study an operator using a poor method and attempt to adjust by leveling. (Have the foreman instruct the operator in the proper method; then study.)
3. Study a job under conditions other than those normally experienced.
4. Study an operator who is not giving an honest performance. (Inform supervision when this condition occurs for correction.)
5. Pay a supervisor bonus based on the working efficiency of his people. (When his pay is based on working efficiency alone, there is a conflict of interests, which usually results in poor wage-incentive administration by the foreman. This practice can encourage supervision to make methods changes without calling for adjusted standards, create improper timekeeping practices, and in general result in the failure of supervision to give management leadership to the job of wage-incentive administration.)
6. Use temporary standards. (A short-term standard should be established on reproducible conditions, and the term temporary avoided. A new standard can replace the short-term standard when a change is made that affects time.)

Administration of Wage Incentives Calls for

1. An aggressive but fair approach to all problems regarding them. Treat every wage-incentive problem as a major problem because pay is involved. Immediate action is necessary on every question or complaint; retroactive pay might be involved to complicate the issue further. Publicize the fact that action is taking place and keep the workers informed as to progress.
2. A procedure to handle all questions concerning wage incentives, with or without a union.
3. Making all data available to anyone who has questions concerning the development of incentive standards.
4. Constant review of incentive payments, searching for possible wage inequities. Be constantly aware of the amount of incentive coverage. Keep coverage high so that incentive payments can be maintained through productivity and not guarantees.
5. Establishing a long enough pay period to cover average working conditions (biweekly).
6. Guaranteeing incentive standards against changes. When change is made because of a methods change or any other change that adds or removes work from the job, take the necessary time to review with the workers involved that change and its effect on time. Review comparisons of the old and new elemental times and the development of the standard. Supervision should be the leader in this presentation to the workers.
7. Accepting the maintenance of existing standards as the primary function of the standards department. Accept this as a necessary cost to manage an effective wage-incentive system. Immediate action is necessary when a change of work methods occurs to continue the earnings opportunities of the workers involved.

It is a problem to effect a smooth methods change.   Loss of incentive pay after the new method is installed will further complicate the problem.

8. Paying bonus only on the method used to complete tasks.
9. A high degree of standards control by rate setters or applicators who are highly skilled individuals in craft-work methods, use of standard data, and timekeeping procedures.
10. The availability of complete, accurate data to substantiate existing standards and compare the effect of old vs. new methods.

When Administering Wage Incentives, Don't

1. Establish a ceiling on wage-incentive earnings.
2. Neglect to judge the quality of in-process or finished work.   (Incentive standards are based on the necessary time for a normal operator to complete acceptable work.   Supervision must accept the responsibility for obtaining acceptable work.)
3. Apply standards to any job unless working conditions, material, equipment, and work methods are standard.
4. Allow delay in the settlement of grievances.   (Every problem, large or small, must be settled within the shortest possible time.)
5. Bargain incentive standards.   (Confine bargaining to base wage rates.)
6. Allow lengthy jobs to exceed pay periods.   (Whenever possible on large jobs, attempt to establish breaking points to pay incentive wages as close to the actual work date as possible.)
7. Allow the evaluation of the effect of any change of work methods to be made by anyone outside the standards department.   (No matter how large or how small the change may be, it is a supervisory responsibility to report this change for proper evaluation.)
8. Allow money to replace worker satisfaction in his contribution to completed jobs. (Management must be capable of creating and continuing high worker morale for individual and group accomplishments.)
9. Allow industrial engineers to deal directly with workers or their representatives regarding wage-incentive problems.   (This is transferring the leadership of wage-incentive administration from supervision to a staff function.   Supervision always requires competent assistance in administration of wage incentives, but only as a staff function.)
10. Use methods changes as an attempt to correct out-of-control standards.   (An incentive worker should have the same incentive earnings potential with the application of the same amount of skill and effort under the old and new standards. Loose standards must be adjusted by the collective-bargaining process.   Failure to comply with this principle will jeopardize the acceptance of methods changes. This acceptance of methods changes and new standards is far more important than picking up a few cents here and there under the subterfuge of a methods change.)

Chapter 5

GETTING ALONG WITH UNION LABOR

By EDMUND BALZANO
Mechanical Engineer
Akron, Ohio

Grievances. When an employee is dissatisfied with some action of management, he will complain to his union representative. This is the first stage of a grievance procedure. This, and the other stages to be followed, are stipulated in most union contracts. Management recognizes the union's right to file and process grievances. Usually a clause is contained in the contract to limit the time a union representative may devote to this work.

Most companies pay union representatives for time spent in processing grievances. They are required to check in and out with their foremen. The contract should specify the activities permitted. A grievance procedure is necessary for good employer-employee relations. To stifle such a program with unreasonable restrictions on time spent by union representatives is to ask for trouble.

Seniority of Union Officials. Most union contracts contain provisions giving union officials special seniority rights. These provisions usually apply to layoffs and recalls, to ensure that union officials are laid off last and recalled first. Where plant-wide seniority is provided for, the union representative of one department can bump a man with less seniority in another department. This employee may claim the job of another, and so on. A chain reaction of job shuffling can upset the entire production schedule. When the union official regains his old job and department, the same disruption is created by a rearrangement of employees. Limiting the top-seniority status of union officials to the departments in which they worked when elected may prevent an occurrence of this kind.

No matter how clearly the bumping procedure is spelled out in the contract, its application means trouble. Does the senior employee have the ability to perform the job held by the junior employee? Management has the right to question the ability and to determine the capability of the employee to handle the job. The union can counter with a grievance if it does not agree with the decision. Some union contracts specify a trial period with a limited time for breaking in on new jobs, usually from a week to a month. If an employee fails to qualify on the first job, the union may want him to be given a chance at another. However, most arbitrators will rule against such action, on the basis that it is not management's responsibility to see that the employee picks the right job.

Disciplining Employees. The job of disciplining an employee can be tough when a union contract is involved. The union invariably will scrutinize the misdemeanor and the punishment. The supervisor will be called upon to state the case and justify his action. If a lack of consistency in disciplining is found, the supervisor may be overruled.

To deal with disciplinary problems, the supervisor should follow a set practice or system. He should warn an employee for first offense, penalize him with days off on second offense, and discharge him if the offense is repeated.

The course of action elected becomes the company policy and establishes a practice. An increase in the frequency of disciplinary problems does not give the right to alter the policy, unless employees are first informed of the change. Employees have a right to expect consistency in treatment.

Rest Periods. A relief or rest period is provided in most union contracts. Even if rest periods are not regulated by contract, they should not be changed without negotiation, once they have been established as a working condition. An employee taking more than the scheduled amount of rest is subject to discipline. Unless action is taken, precedent may be established, with probable future trouble.

Classification. Some unions are opposed, in theory, to classification of members on the basis of the work they are qualified to handle. But they have been forced to recognize some classifications and qualifications because they claim that the accomplishment of a specific job assignment is proof of the qualifications of an employee, who should be rated accordingly. If classification for pay rating on a time-trial basis is not opposed by the union, and time-trial arrangements are established, no employee should be allowed to overrun the period set without notice, or a precedent will be established and the pay rate will become a new classification.

The reason for job classification is to assure employees of equitable wage treatment. Such systems are based upon job analyses and descriptions which give comparisons of jobs and permit pay ratings. It is important that jobs should be placed in the proper labor classifications. Job titles alone are misleading. If the job description should prove to be inaccurate, or the job content is changed, a new study is in order. Changes in materials, processes, tools, and equipment will be made from time to time. Any job affected should be restudied and a standard established to reflect such changes.

Use of Outside Contractors. The use, on a part-time basis, of the labor forces of outside contractors, to supplement or work with maintenance employees, sometimes is debated by the union, even though the contract contains no provisions prohibiting the practice. Certainly the employer has the right to have work done on contract, so long as the contractor does not perform the work on company premises. No such certainty exists as to contracting week-end work that is regularly executed by plant employees, unless the employees are scheduled for the week end and have worked a full week. If those conditions pertain, the company is under no obligation to hold up a job until regular employees are available or to upgrade lower-rated employees to perform the work.

The time element and magnitude of the job are factors involved when using outside labor to do the work that could be done by the regular employees. The union, as well as the individual, realizes that there are times when it is necessary to contract work to outside firms. With some planning, an agreement often can be reached where the work to be done can be coordinated between the contractor and the employees.

Labor's Attitude toward Incentives. Some unions believe that an effective incentive plan for maintenance employees cannot be established, on the basis that the variety of jobs involved makes it impossible to establish fair and just rates. They point to the confusion that would take place when several crafts were required for the same job. Other unions endorse the use of incentive plans. Whether or not an incentive plan is to be used in a given plant must depend upon existing management-union relationships. When a plan is in operation, the union must be fully conversant with its provisions and operation, and must have the privilege of appeal in connection with details of its application.

Absenteeism. Absenteeism may be a persistent problem. It does not always decrease when jobs are few and applicants plentiful. It is a symptom of personal maladjustment or improper working conditions. Habitual or excessive absence may be ground for discharge, regardless of how good the excuse. Most arbitrators feel that the economic welfare of fellow workers, as well as that of the company management and stockholders, is jeopardized by excessive absence. There is no provision under contract, or company rules, that obligates the company to retain any employee who is habitually absent.

Genuine illness justifies an occasional absence. Where an employee is habitually ill or is suffering from some injury that causes his absence to make his services of no value to the company, the company is under no obligation to retain him.

It can be established that excessive absence may be cause for discharge. What is excessive absence? Many cases that go to arbitration have an absurdly high rate. These should not be taken as a standard. If management permits an employee's absence frequency to continue for long periods, the arbitrator may hold that the absence has been condoned by management.

Management, in presenting its case, may offer the following facts: How often the employee has been absent. Over how long a period. Over-all rate of absence in the company. What management considers excessive absence. Records of employees having the most absences. The company may have to define what is meant by absence. A good definition of absenteeism offered by the Bureau of Labor Statistics is "Absenteeism is the failure of workers to report on the job when they are scheduled to work. An employee is to be considered scheduled to work when the employer has work available and the employee is aware of it."

The arbitrator will seek to know if management has established a standard that is consistently and fairly applied in judging what amount of absence is excessive. A statistical standard is not sufficient, because absence must be judged in each individual's circumstances. One has to weigh the method by which all employees with normal absence records are treated and the circumstances warranting or not warranting the acknowledgment of excessive absence in any particular case. The union's strongest argument against discharge for absenteeism is "discrimination," and arbitrators are vigilant with regard to evidence on this matter.

While the burden of proof of absenteeism rests with the employer, arbitrators do not overlook the employee's responsibility to correct his excessive or habitual absenteeism. In upholding the discharge of a chronically ill employee, the arbitrator feels that such a person should try to correct his record by telling management of his illness, giving proof of obtaining regular treatments for it, and requesting leave of absence for lengthy periods when needed for treatments.

Second only to discrimination, the strongest defense against discharge for excessive absenteeism is failure of management to give ample warning to an employee of the consequences if his absence record continues to be high. The penalty of discharge for absenteeism must not come as a surprise. Discharge should not be used as a poor substitute for the failure of management to exercise more constructive efforts to control absenteeism.

Importance of Supervisor Conduct. Good supervision must have high intelligence and great capacity for learning. These qualities often are adhered to by management when selecting a foreman, but the results remain with the selectee. Management cannot perform miracles. It cannot bestow upon this man the skill of managing. That must be acquired through special training and practice.

The supervisor who succeeds will bone up on labor relations. He may unlock the door of substantial increases in worker performance if he will put forth every effort to win over the employees' support and cooperation.

A good supervisor should know his employees, not only by last name and clock number, but by the names they would like to be called. He should know each employee's background and experience. Each employee is an individual and should be handled as such. The supervisor should know the best personal approach to use with each employee when giving him information, correction, praise, and encouragement. The employee looks to his foreman for leadership and should receive it. Supervisors with good labor relations will explain the reasons behind decisions that affect the individual employee.

The supervisor should know his communications. Giving instructions, interviewing, reviewing a man's performance, discussing an idea, or telephoning are methods of oral communication. Some of the written forms are bulletin-board notices, letters, schedule announcements, posters, and work-schedule instructions.

Stumbling blocks in communication are wrong attitude, lack of understanding, poor planning, wrong means, and closed mind.

Wrong attitude is typified by the policy, "Why tell them? What they don't know won't hurt them." The failure to realize that employees really want to know is lack of understanding. When a foreman is too busy to keep his people properly informed, or to exchange ideas with them, he is engaging in poor planning. Wrong means of communication consists of using words that are hard to understand and that often arouse resentment; also posting a notice without a message of explanation. The closed-mind attitude exists when a foreman fails to listen to and consider someone else's idea.

The employee always looks to the supervisor for information. Higher management depends upon the supervisor to sell ideas, get employee reactions, and pass along information. Communication should flow in both directions, through the supervisor.

Everyone makes mistakes. Supervisors are no exception. It is hard to believe, but sometimes foremen proficient in production are great bunglers when it comes to handling the employee and discussing his weak points with him. To do this successfully requires tact, with a sincere interest in helping the person involved. Most people are sensitive to criticism, and resist correction in any form. They often defend their methods and ideas loudly.

When an employee finally attains the peak in his career, when he is boss, he naturally develops pride in his own importance. This pride can flare up into anger when someone who should know better goes over his head and neglects to clear through him matters that are rightfully his for decision. Much of this trouble can be avoided by a careful plan describing detailed lines of authority. This information can be conveyed to the employees by means of organization charts. The charts should show rank, divisional relationship, and departmental relationship.

Tact and drive are leadership concepts which have a double edge in that a supervisor can measure his own ability by them. He can easily and effectively discuss leadership with others in these terms.

Tact is the ability to say and do what is best in a given situation, with the objective of avoiding offense. It is necessary to recognize that all people—workers, supervisors, bosses—have their prides and ambitions, their hopes and fears, thoughts, ideas, interests, and nerves. What is on the other fellow's mind is important. There is just one way to deal with employees tactfully—consider in advance the effects your words and actions are likely to have. Then choose those words carefully and act considerately.

Drive is the ability to get things done, to keep moving forward to satisfactory completion of whatever job is undertaken. Drive does not consist of putting the pressure on employees. It consists of following up work, keeping on top of his own job at all times, spending his own mental and physical energy in getting things done. The one person a supervisor can afford to go after hammer and tongs, day after day, is himself.

Persuasion is a form of drive. The supervisor must know how and when to be persuasive. Employees do best the things they do willingly. The purpose of persuasion is to obtain a willing action on the part of the employee. The supervisor who has drive, without the use of persuasive methods, invites trouble.

The supervisor must be cooperative. Supervision, like any other type of human relationship, has to be a give-and-take proposition. This above all is the keynote to success in leadership.

Here are some of the pitfalls in supervisory conduct that lead to union complaints and grievances: (1) failure to keep promises, (2) taking credit for employees' ideas, (3) showing personal favoritism, (4) failing to admit mistakes, (5) fear of responsibility, (6) neglecting to praise when praise is due, (7) losing control of emotions, and (8) being disloyal to employees.

Basic Data about Unions for Reference. Specific aims may vary, but the over-all activities of unions are directed toward regulation of working conditions, the establishment of standards of efficiency, the training of apprentices, and the promotion of the general and material welfare of the members. Rate of pay, working conditions, and fringe benefits are primary objectives.

Craft Union. A craft union consists of a group of skilled workers in a particular craft, organized for the common welfare and benefits to be derived from actual or threatened concerted action. The members of a craft union are well trained in their field of endeavor. In accepting its members, the union adheres to specific minimum qualifications. The union member must be fully qualified in his particular craft, if he is to rate top pay. The bartering agent, or representative of such a group, invariably is a qualified worker, who is well versed in the problems of the workers he represents. There is no division of classification in a craft union. The member is either a journeyman or an apprentice.

Industrial Union. An industrial union is a labor organization, local or national, which admits to membership all workers of an industry, regardless of occupation or craft. The master contract between an industrial union and management, with its rules, regulations, and restrictions, attempts to cover all job classifications, from common labor to the most highly skilled worker in the plant.

Kinds of Union Shops. A union may have any of the following arrangements with management, established through contract negotiations:

1. *Open Shop.* Anyone can be employed and hold a job, whether he belongs to a union or not.

2. *Union Representative Shop.* The union is recognized by management as the sole bargaining agent for all the employees, union and nonunion. Employees are not required to join the union. The union is expected to treat all employees alike.

3. *Preferential Shop.* The employer agrees to give union members preference treatment under specified conditions. In case of layoff, nonunion employees go first. Promotion is to be given union members before nonunion members. Union members are to be hired when available.

4. *Percentage Shop.* Employers are required to keep a specified percentage of union members on the payroll. Nonunion people can be employed so long as the percentage ratio of union to nonunion members is maintained. Some percentage-shop agreements provide that only union members, or applicants willing to join the union, can be hired.

5. *Closed Shop.* Only members in good standing can be employed or hold jobs. Employers hire only through the union, calling upon it for employees as they are needed. Under the Taft-Hartley Law, the closed shop is illegal. The contracts do not mention union security, but employers and union have an understanding that, as long as they are available, union members will be given preference.

6. *Union Shop.* Anyone, union or nonunion, can be employed, but all employees must join the union after a specified time on the payroll. The union must accept all applicants. Any employee refusing to join the union after the time limit must be discharged, if the union so demands. Any employee ousted from the union for any reason other than nonpayment of dues retains a right to work, exempt under the Taft-Hartley law from compulsory union membership. There are modifications of the union shop, worked out as compromises in labor-management bargaining.

Section 3

PLANNING AND SCHEDULING MAINTENANCE WORK

Chapter 1

WORK AUTHORIZATION AND CONTROL

By James E. Thompson[1]
Stanford Research Institute
Southern California Laboratories
South Pasadena, Calif.

Maintenance *Work Authorization and Control* is a technique for forecasting and controlling maintenance department costs. Its purpose is to *plan* and *control* the work accomplished by Maintenance. It is an evolution of the function that has often been referred to as "planning and scheduling."

This section presents a basic methodology which can be used to develop a Maintenance Work Control function to fit the needs of any maintenance department. The plan presented is not a cut-and-dried procedure, complete with forms and estimating values, but rather a basic approach to the subject which can be tailored to suit conditions in individual companies.

It would be futile to present the plan actually in use at a particular company and imply that this represented the optimum and that it could be directly applied to another maintenance department. Such a step would not be wise even if the same product was being manufactured in both cases, for it is unlikely that every controlling condition would be identical within the two companies.

BASIC ELEMENTS OF WORK AUTHORIZATION AND CONTROL

The basic elements in the approximate order of their application, of maintenance work authorization and control are:

1. A *work-planning function* to chart a course for Maintenance.
2. A *work-order system* for job delineation and authorization.
3. A *work-priority system*, to control work sequence.
4. An *estimating procedure*, to determine the magnitude of tasks.
5. A *master schedule*, to relate total authorized tasks to time and available manpower.
6. A *detail-scheduling procedure*, to establish work sequencing for each major task shown on the master schedule.
7. An *hours-control procedure*, to collect actual costs for comparison with estimates.
8. A basis for *work measurement*, to permit comparing progress with expenditures.
9. An adequate *reporting system*, for recording accomplishment, effectiveness, and variances.
10. *Work standards*, to ensure common bases for estimates.

In a small maintenance department the Work Control function may be the part-time responsibility of one man—while in a large maintenance operation this function

[1] The author is now Consulting Engineer, Lake Havasu Irrigation and Drainage District, Lake Havasu City, Ariz.

may require the full-time attention of several people.   In all cases the identical basic elements will be involved.

WORK PLANNING

The first step in Maintenance Work Authorization and Control is *work planning*. This function, working in close coordination with the facilities engineers (or the equivalent Plant Engineering function), must establish and maintain a *master plan* for Maintenance's operations.   As part of this responsibility Work Planning should be the point of issuance for all work authorization, referred to herein as *Maintenance Work Orders* (MWO).

Work planning should analyze all contracts, incoming requests (other than routine "squawks"), new specifications, and like items which may generate additional maintenance work.   Once all facts are determined in each instance it is possible to advise Maintenance management, in the case of major items, of the responsibilities of each group or unit, the estimated man-hours required by each, the work priority considered advisable, and the in-work and completion dates possible of accomplishment without either rescheduling existing work or obtaining more manpower.   In the case of minor jobs, either new work or changes to existing .tasks, Work Planning should be able to issue new or revised work authorizations on its own authority.

To keep Maintenance management informed of the over-all work load and the plan necessary to complete successfully the tasks making up this work load it is necessary that Work Planning have full, current knowledge of: (1) management thinking regarding new projects as soon as these are even considered in the most preliminary form, (2) each incoming or intradepartmental item that may generate new work or affect scheduled work, (3) available maintenance manpower, and estimated future manpower, (4) manpower allocations within Maintenance, (5) relationship of estimated to actual manpower expended on each active task, (6) current progress of each active task, (7) relative efficiencies and abilities of the various Maintenance sections and groups, (8) relative importance of all active tasks, and (9) probable effect of changes in the maintenance schedule upon other departments of the company.

With these facts at hand it should be possible for Work Planning to advise Maintenance management accurately of the effect of major new tasks (or significant changes in existing tasks), and on its own initiative to handle minor new tasks or changes.

In summation, the work-planning function of Maintenance Work Control has the responsibility for ensuring that: (1) only necessary work will be done, and (2) this work is accomplished in the most effective fashion.

WORK-ORDER SYSTEM

A work-order system to define the nature of approved maintenance jobs is the next step.   This involves, first, establishing a system of time charges to provide positive identity for every item of work accomplished by Maintenance.   A satisfactory time-charge system must permit a daily cost accumulation of maintenance labor and materials by charging every labor hour and material dollar against a designated *job number*.   These job numbers not only should provide for charging time and materials against each maintenance project, but should provide sufficient detail breakdown to show exactly how costs are distributed within each project—by kind of labor and material.   This will permit compilation of cost data that can indicate why estimates are exceeded or decreased.

It should be made a hard-and-fast rule that every hour of maintenance time (and every dollar of materials) expended must be charged against a valid, active maintenance job.   Each Maintenance foreman should furnish Work Control with a daily report showing the distribution of the work of his men, with the proper quantity of hours allocated to each job on which his men applied effort during the day.   A similar report of materials disbursed should be supplied by each maintenance stock room.   The daily reports can then first be posted to their proper work orders as

MAINTENANCE WORK ORDER

			JOB NO. 2-1-137

TITLE Equipment for Tool Control Station
PURPOSE Needed to Complete Job Improvement Request

JOB NO. ___2-1-137___
REVISION: _____ DATE: 12 Dec
ENG REL NO _____
DELIVER TO DEPT. ___14-10___
REQ COMPLETE DATE: ___30 Dec___

	SIGNATURE	DATE		ESTIMATED COST
REQUESTED	C W Jones	5 Dec	LABOR	168.05
PREPARED	S Green	7 Dec	BURDEN	32.65
APPROVED	J E Thompson	12 Dec	MATL ON HAND	90.56
APPROVED			MATL TO PURCHASE	—
APPROVED			FREIGHT	—
EXPENSE	x		TAX	—
CAPITAL			OUTSIDE CONTRACT	—
CHARGE TO ACCOUNT: MJO5206 CC04			TOTAL	$291.26

ITEM	DESCRIPTION	LABOR	MATL
1.	Dept 19-31 Construct one (1) foreman's desk per Std Dwg 160-322C (18 hours @ $1.85)	33.30	15.16
2.	Dept 19-34 Fabricate two (2) steel racks per Std Dwg 160-767-9 (68 hours @ $1.90)	129.20	72.32
3.	Dept 19-32 Paint the above described desk and steel racks std colors (3 hours @ $1.85)	5.55	3.08
4.	Dept 23-10 Deliver the above desk and steel racks to Dept 14-10, near column G-5. Attention J A Jones, foreman.		

BILL OF MATERIAL PREPARED   PAGE 1 OF 1
FOR THIS WO: YES ☐ NO ☒

Priority 2

FIG. 1-1. Maintenance work order, issued to describe and authorize nonroutine maintenance tasks.

detail cost records, and finally be summarized to show cost allocations and total expenditures against each work order.

Job-numbering System. The job-number system employed should provide ready identification of the work to which each job relates. One rather simple system uses a three-part coded number. The first part indicates work priority, the second the Maintenance group having prime responsibility for the job, and the last number a serial number indicating sequence of issue. Thus job number 1-2-53 might indicate a job having the highest (or "1st") work priority, with 2 indicating that the Mechanical section of Maintenance has prime responsibility for ensuring completion of the job; and the final number 53 indicating that this is the fifty-third "1" priority job assigned to Mechanical.

The Maintenance Work Order. The second important aspect of a work-order system is establishment of formal "paper" to authorize maintenance work. The basic document used for this purpose is often referred to as a Maintenance Work Order or MWO. Each MWO should define the general nature of the job and show the responsibilities of the various groups accountable for completion of the task described by the order (see Fig. 1-1), with notations of man-hours and materials dollars allotted to each group for their part of the task, and a statement of the required completion date of the job.

Individual work orders should be issued to define tasks which are specific in nature, and of sufficient magnitude to justify formalization. The determination of this "point of diminishing returns" (where the cost of authorization equals or exceeds the probable savings to be realized through control of the expenditure), is difficult to assign arbitrarily and can be established only through study of actual conditions in a given maintenance department. Some organizations allow up to 40 man-hours to be expended for *maintenance* against an "open work order," without need for issuance of a specific MWO. Regardless of the value selected, it is wise to be quite strict in

LABOR RECORD JOB NO. ____________

FAILURE TO MAKE ENTRY OR INACCURATE ENTRY IS CAUSE FOR DISMISSAL

ORDER RECEIVED ________ (DATE) ASSIGNED TO ________ (FOREMAN) PLACED IN WORK ________ (DATE)

DATE	CLOCK NO.	NAME	TOTAL HOURS	INC. HOURS	DATE	CLOCK NO.	NAME	TOTAL HOURS	INC. HOURS

JOB COMPLETION REPORT

DATE COMPLETE	FOREMAN'S SIGNATURE	TOTAL HOURS	REMARKS

COMPLETION REPORTS AND HOURS CHARGES VERIFIED BY: ____________ (GENERAL FOREMAN) ____________ (DATE)

FIG. 1-2. Labor record, maintained for each Maintenance work order by the maintenance work-control function. Usually printed on the back of the Maintenance work-order form.

the amount of *construction* work that can be accomplished without issuance of a specific MWO, and many companies limit this type of expenditure against open work orders to a maximum of 8 man-hours.

Open Work Orders. A certain number of "open work orders" will be required to describe tasks which will continue indefinitely, and where the prime concern is controlling the *rate of expenditure of manpower*, by establishing a maximum allowance of hours per week or month for each of these tasks. Instances of such open MWO are routine maintenance "squawks," and the Work Control operation itself.

General MWO also are necessary to establish accounts for accumulating time charges against such items as illness and leaves of absence.

It is important that MWO should be established, and time-charge numbers thereby exist, to cover every man-hour charged against the maintenance department. Unless this condition prevails it becomes very difficult to maintain complete control over the expenditure of maintenance manpower (see Fig. 1-2).

Controlling Materials Expense. Expenditures for maintenance materials also may be authorized and controlled through the medium of the MWO, by issuance of a detail, priced Bill of Material to accompany all jobs where materials cost is a significant item (see Fig. 1-3). Maintenance foremen then may be required to explain all significant variations between estimated and actual materials costs on jobs. It will be noted that the specimen MWO shown as Fig. 1-1 provides for indicating whether a Bill of Material has been prepared for the job described by the order. In the instance shown a materials list was not prepared, as the items called out on the

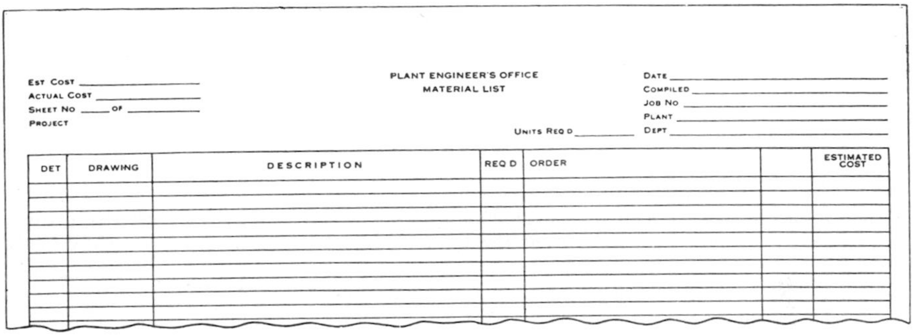
EST COST
ACTUAL COST
SHEET NO ___ OF ___
PROJECT
PLANT ENGINEER'S OFFICE
MATERIAL LIST
UNITS REQ'D
DATE
COMPILED
JOB NO
PLANT
DEPT

DET	DRAWING	DESCRIPTION	REQ'D	ORDER		ESTIMATED COST

FIG. 1-3. Material list, issued to itemize and price materials required to complete a specific maintenance job.

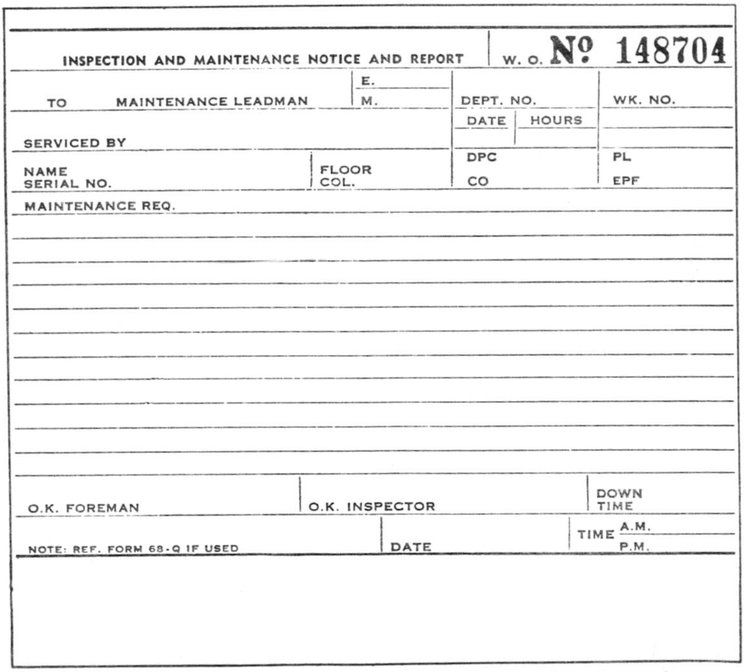
INSPECTION AND MAINTENANCE NOTICE AND REPORT
W. O. Nº 148704
TO MAINTENANCE LEADMAN
E.
M.
DEPT. NO.
WK. NO.
DATE
HOURS
SERVICED BY
NAME
SERIAL NO.
FLOOR
COL.
DPC
CO
PL
EPF
MAINTENANCE REQ.
O.K. FOREMAN
O.K. INSPECTOR
DOWN TIME
NOTE: REF. FORM 68-Q IF USED
DATE
TIME A.M. P.M.

FIG. 1-4. Maintenance notice and report, used to authorize and describe work accomplished on squawks.

MWO are to be made in accordance with Maintenance Standards drawings which show detail materials requirements. However, in this case the materials requirements *are* priced on the order.

Authorizing Work on Maintenance Squawks. Routine maintenance jobs of simple nature, often referred to as "squawks," also should be recorded to ensure prompt handling, and to control time and materials expense. These squawks usually originate as a telephone call to the maintenance department, and often are handled by a clerk who also acts as a dispatcher.

Upon receipt of such a call the clerk can fill out a simple two-part form, such as that shown as Fig. 1-4, with time, date, requester, nature and location of trouble, and the like. One copy of the form can be dispatched to the proper maintenance foreman for action, and the other filed for follow-up. The foreman can assign the squawk to a maintenance mechanic who, upon completing necessary work, can complete the form with a notation of work done and materials used, followed by returning the completed form to the maintenance office for posting time and materials to the proper job account.

WORK-PRIORITY ASSIGNMENT

For the Work Planning function to be certain "that only necessary work will be done" it often is necessary to establish a system of work priority, with the proper priority being assigned to each job at the time a Maintenance Work Order (MWO) is issued.

When establishing a work-priority system it is important that it be kept simple— so that its application and interpretation may readily be understood by everyone affected by its usage. For this reason, it is recommended that only three classes of work priorities be established—and that these be identified as "work priorities 1, 2, and 3." This permits of simple definitions, such as these:

Priority 1 jobs take precedence over all other maintenance work, and represent tasks which are mandatory for successful operation of the company.

Priority 2 jobs are those maintenance tasks which it is desired to complete as soon as practicable, and take precedence over all tasks except those in priority 1.

Priority 3 jobs are those maintenance tasks which are desirable, but which may be completed when convenient. In effect, these are the backlog of "convenience" work which must always be available to smooth out peaks and valleys in manpower loads.

In addition, when using a job-identification system that incorporates the work priority in the job number, it is desirable to have an "all-priority" code. The numeral "9" may be used for this purpose, and any job number showing "priority 9" then can be immediately recognized as a general time charge for service and cost-control purposes—with the actual priority varying with the priority of the job being serviced. Time spent on clerical and stenographic work in the maintenance office could be charged to a "priority 9" general MWO—with other "9" job numbers being used to accumulate such charges as illness and leaves of absence.

ESTIMATING MAINTENANCE TIME

The very keystone of a successful work-control procedure is accurate estimating of man-hours (and sometimes materials) required for each *job*. The basic philosophy of estimating is to reduce each task to its basic *job elements* and establish values for each element. The sum of the elements gives the estimate for the total task. The ultimate in estimating is establishing *standards* on a *work-unit* basis for each element. In the beginning these standards may be more like "guesstimates" than estimates, but as historical data on actual jobs are acquired and compared with estimates it is possible to refine these standards to a point where estimates of even the most complex work may realize an over-all accuracy of plus or minus 5 per cent.

The normal output of Maintenance is repair and construction work, and hours expended by mechanics and craftsmen to produce this work can be termed *direct-labor* hours required for the jobs.

The supporting services required, including supervision, by the maintenance direct worker as assistance in producing the required direct hours represent overhead or *burden* on the maintenance department. The actual value of this burden can be accumulated and prorated to each job as a percentage of the direct hours. This simplifies the estimating procedure and can be done quite accurately once sufficient historical data are collected.

Historical data on Maintenance supporting services can be analyzed to provide a per cent breakdown by type or class of service. When these data are available to Work Control it is possible to make accurate estimates of total Maintenance manpower requirements (by specific job classification, should this degree of detail be required), based upon a direct-hour work-load forecast.

In the beginning it may be necessary for Work Control to depend upon the opinions of the Maintenance foremen affected by each job, when estimating the man-hours required. Occasionally it may be found that a foreman considers estimating impossible because too little is known about the job. In such cases the foreman will have to agree that there is a certain minimum time that the job must require and a definite maximum that should not be exceeded. With this basis it is usually possible to arrive at a reasonable agreement on an intermediate value for estimating.

A definite plan of reviewing all significant variances between actual times and estimated times is necessary to ensure continuous improvement in the accuracy of estimates. One satisfactory method of accomplishing this end is to require that both the estimator and the foreman involved submit through Work Control to Maintenance top management written statements of the reason for variance in all cases where the actual was either *over* or *under* the estimate by more than 5 per cent. Review of these instances and the reasons advanced for their occurrence will usually indicate corrective actions that will tend to improve the accuracy of future estimates.

MAINTENANCE MASTER SCHEDULE

The essence of scheduling is to maintain a proper balance between work capacity and work load. A *master schedule* should be prepared and maintained as a preliminary to detail scheduling. This master schedule should show the nature and magnitude of each repair and construction task segment of Maintenance for a specified time span. Total man-hours required for each segment should be plotted against available manpower to obtain a distribution of "jobs" that will give reasonable man loadings, practicable of accomplishment.

This master schedule should be flexible, not fixed, as it is basically a projection into the future—and subject to change as anticipated conditions may vary from estimates upon becoming realities. In actual practice, it often is desirable to establish the master schedule on a *moving* basis—of either 90 days or 12 months, depending upon the probable degree of change in the over-all Maintenance task.

A moving master schedule of this type is based upon a time span divisible into thirds, with the first third (either 1 or 4 months) being firm and not subject to change except in grave emergency. The remaining two thirds (either 2 or 8 months) are tentative—being firmed up as well as possible in consideration of known facts when the master schedule is prepared. The entire schedule is reviewed at intervals of either 1 or 4 months, and the next third is firmed up in light of existing facts, with adjustments made in the remaining two-thirds as required, including projection of an additional future third.

A very important thing to remember in establishing a master schedule is that it should *never* be based upon scheduling 100 per cent of available manpower on high-priority work. A certain *cushion* should always exist of manpower allocated to "priority 3" work—otherwise the department will always be behind schedule. With a cushion (which should range between 15 and 20 per cent of total available manpower) scheduled for priority 3 work it always is possible to make periodic reallocation of manpower to correct jobs which are lagging behind schedule. Without such a cushion, adjustments to compensate for poor estimates and/or unforeseen conditions are practically impossible.

DETAIL SCHEDULING

As actual Maintenance Work Orders are issued to authorize and define specific jobs it becomes necessary to apply detail scheduling as a further breakdown of the over-all time spans allocated under the master schedule. This will establish the proper sequencing of the various phases of major jobs to ensure that each task will be accomplished in the most effective manner.

Effective scheduling requires realistic thinking based upon factual data. Advice given to management regarding Maintenance's work capacity and possibility for meeting due dates must be accurate and not colored by wishful thinking. Management, on the other hand, must be willing to accept the information as basic and not insist upon accomplishment of the impossible. Unless this mutual respect exists, then Work Control will be functioning only for statistical recording of failure to meet schedule.

Scheduling also must be flexible. The most carefully prepared detail schedules may be upset suddenly by unforeseen changes or emergencies. When this occurs, Work Control must be able to improvise or reschedule rapidly to meet the new conditions.

Detail scheduling requires records of the work capacity of each group or section within Maintenance and of the department as a whole. These records must be based upon the type of work, such as machine repair, electrical, plumbing, janitorial,

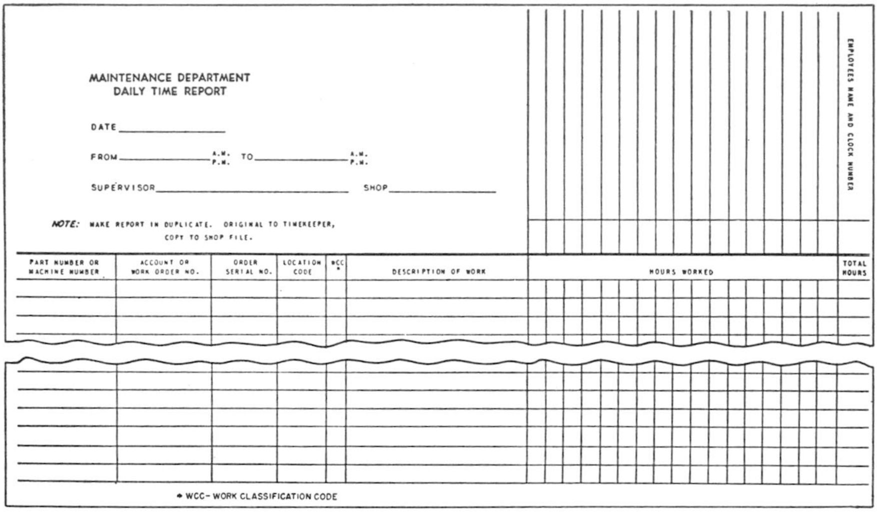

MAINTENANCE DEPARTMENT
DAILY TIME REPORT

DATE ______

FROM ______ A.M./P.M. TO ______ A.M./P.M.

SUPERVISOR ______ SHOP ______

NOTE: MAKE REPORT IN DUPLICATE. ORIGINAL TO TIMEKEEPER, COPY TO SHOP FILE.

EMPLOYEES NAME AND CLOCK NUMBER

PART NUMBER OR MACHINE NUMBER	ACCOUNT OR WORK ORDER NO.	ORDER SERIAL NO.	LOCATION CODE	WCC *	DESCRIPTION OF WORK	HOURS WORKED	TOTAL HOURS

* WCC- WORK CLASSIFICATION CODE

FIG. 1-5. Daily time distribution record, supplied by Maintenance foremen to the work-control function.

carpentry, and sheet metal. Records for all current work are also necessary, showing the work load for each maintenance employee, group, and section and for the department as a whole. Obviously the essence of detail scheduling is to maintain the proper balance between work capacity and load.

Again, as with master scheduling, it is not desirable to schedule 100 per cent of available manpower on mandatory work. When this is done there is no cushion available to absorb unexpected fluctuations in work load. Never schedule over 85 per cent of available manpower on 1 and 2 priority work. At least a 15 per cent cushion should nominally always exist, scheduled for 3 priority work.

HOURS CONTROL

An hours-control system should be established as an integral portion of Work Control to give daily cost accumulation by charging every maintenance hour against a designated job number. These job numbers not only should provide for charging time against each major project within Maintenance but should also provide sufficient detail breakdown to show exactly how hours are distributed within each project by individual Maintenance Work Order. This permits determination of when and why estimates are exceeded or decreased.

No maintenance time should be expended unless a job number is assigned to cover the work. Each maintenance foreman should furnish Work Control with a daily report showing the distribution of his employees' time, with the proper quantity of hours allocated to the jobs worked during that day (see Fig. 1-5).

MAINTENANCE HOURS REPORT
For Week Ending 9 December

DISTRIBUTION OF HOURS

(Summarized according to the kind and priority of job worked, irrespective of the job classification or group of the employees accomplishing the work)

DIRECT LABOR

Buildings Section	Actual Hours	Section Total
1 Jobs.............................	406	
2 Jobs.............................	1,110	
3 Jobs.............................	162	
		1,678
Mechanical Section		
1 Jobs.............................	390	

~~~~~~

Total direct labor...............		3,426
INDIRECT LABOR		
Supervision.........................	512	
Stenographic........................	40	
Clerical.............................	80	
Special staff assignment...............	40	
		672
OTHER CHARGES		
Premium Time......................	(77)	
Absent on Leave....................	80	
Illness.............................	140	
Vacation...........................	120	
Tardiness...........................	2	
		342
Total burden....................		1,014
TOTAL LABOR FOR WEEK...........		4,440

Per cent Burden.............. 23

Per cent Supervision........... 12

Issued: 12 December   Page 2 of 2

FIG. 1-6. Summary distribution of Maintenance hours, prepared weekly by the work-control function and distributed to all Maintenance supervision.

After expended hours are posted to the proper MWO cumulative time record (see Fig. 1-2), these daily-hours reports can be summarized each week as a weekly "operating report," showing actual time in comparison with estimated time for each direct-labor job. A separate summary of actual hours expended on burden jobs will provide a report of Maintenance overhead labor expense (see Fig. 1-6).[1] The per cent expended on each job can be compared each week with estimated per cent complete, as a check on job status.

[1] The indirect expense or *burden* referred to here and shown in Fig. 1-6 is only the *controllable* burden of maintenance and does not include the cost of services provided on a company-wide basis, such as purchasing, personnel, plant protection, and general and administrative cost. Neither does it include the cost of indirect expense chargeable to maintenance, such as utilities and stationery. To obtain a value for the total maintenance burden it is necessary to add a quantity representing maintenance's equitable share of these other indirect charges, which in the main are not controllable by maintenance management. The resultant total burden often represents, in dollar value, 100 per cent or more of the maintenance direct-labor cost.

On a highly critical job it may be desirable to prepare a distribution showing the time which *should* be expended each day in order to meet schedule, and then keep a daily check on actual time expended against the job.   In this manner it is possible to avoid poor management on the part of foremen, resulting in too little time being applied to such a job.

WORK MEASUREMENT

A requisite for successful operation of a Work Control function is a satisfactory plan of *work measurement,* to permit accurate comparison of progress with manpower (and sometimes materials) expenditures.   Obviously this requires establishment of some valid common denominator for measuring maintenance work—one that will be equally valid for both estimating and progress reporting.

Selection of a satisfactory basic unit for work measurement in a maintenance department is often a difficult problem, and one that may require considerable thought and research.   One method that has been used is the establishment of standard times for all possible elements of maintenance work.   Actual hours expended can then be compared with the *allowed or standard hours* each week to measure the apparent efficiency of Maintenance.   Comparison week by week then should reveal changes in the relative level of departmental efficiency.

OPERATING CONTROLS

A final, and very important, step in Work Control is establishment and maintenance of an adequate system of *operating controls.*   This, in essence, is a means of periodic, *current* reporting of Maintenance accomplishment and effectiveness, and of investigating all significant variances.

One method of reporting is a weekly summary of work by maintenance group—showing actual hours in comparison with estimates (allowed hours) for each group, summarized according to 1, 2, and 3 priority jobs (see Fig. 1-6).   A separate summary should be included showing actual and allowed hours expended on all overhead accounts, to provide a running record of Maintenance burden.   This report will give an over-all, or mass, impression of the manner in which maintenance time has been spent.

This type of reporting alone will not provide sufficient control, as it does not indicate what is happening to individual jobs.   Another report, which may be termed a Job Status Report, also is desirable—on a weekly basis—reporting on individual jobs.   This report should briefly note all problems existing on any job, and show actual time spent to date, allowed time to date, per cent of allowed time expended, and *estimated per cent complete of each job.*   Analysis of this report will reveal trouble spots, as obviously any job where the per cent of time expended is significantly in excess of the per cent complete may be in trouble—and should be investigated.   Also, any job where the per cent complete is considerable higher than the per cent of estimate expended should be investigated, as it may be that too much manpower is being applied to the job—manpower which could be diverted to other jobs that are in trouble.

Large wall charts may be maintained on a daily basis—showing actual time expended in comparison with allowed times and estimated per cent completion.   Often individual-group charts of this nature also are of value, particularly for internal control purposes within Work Control—as often graphic presentations are more readily interpreted than are statistical data.

A satisfactory system of operating controls for Maintenance must: (1) provide current information on progress and effectiveness, (2) indicate trouble spots and probable causes of trouble, and (3) be as near perfect in reporting as is possible.

Probably the most important thing of all is that operating reports be current.   Ideally, and this *can be done,* the reports should be issued on each Monday afternoon reflecting conditions as of the close of business on the preceding Friday.   Unless an all-out effort is maintained to keep these reports current, they simply become history and cannot be used as tools to correct troubles as soon as they occur.

MAINTENANCE STANDARDS

Work Control's task will be difficult, if not almost impossible, in the absence of standardized maintenance methods and procedures. In such cases each Maintenance group or section may be thought of as operating to a different set of ground rules— and basic functions such as estimating, for instance, become difficult of application on a consistent basis.

Standards can be established and maintained to govern construction and repair practices, maintenance methods and procedures, standard times for job elements, preventive-maintenance operations, and the like. A method of releasing this information to all concerned should be developed, together with a system to make sure that copies of revised standards promptly reach all recipients of the original information. It is logical that Work Control should control preparation, distribution, and revision of Maintenance Standards.

When standards are carefully prepared, comprehensive in nature, and faithfully observed, there will be no need for Maintenance personnel to spend time debating the proper method of accomplishing a certain job or the correct procedure for a particular condition. In order that these standards may accomplish the desired end, it is necessary for Maintenance management to require that all standards be followed without deviation, other than those changes authorized by Work Control in cases where a standard is found to be deficient.

DOES YOUR MAINTENANCE DEPARTMENT NEED WORK CONTROL?

By this time there may well be a question in the reader's mind as to whether his maintenance department needs Work Control. Perhaps it appears that Work Control is a highly complex function, requiring many people involved in "second guessing" the Maintenance foremen and mechanics. *It need not be,* and it is this writer's belief that successful management of any maintenance department is predicated upon the 10 basic principles of Work Control that were outlined in the beginning of this chapter.

In a maintenance department of up to about 50 employees the work-control function can be carried out as the part-time responsibility of one person. When a size of 75 to 100 employees is encountered it may become a full-time assignment of one man, with some assistance from a clerk to maintain and summarize the time records. When very large maintenance departments are encountered, with 500 employees or more, then several full-time employees may be required for the work-control function.

In any event it is certain that scientific planning and control of maintenance work should pay off in large values.

Chapter 2

STANDARD TIMES FOR MAINTENANCE WORK

By CHARLES C. WINSTON[1]
Assistant Manager
Management Services Division, Eastern District
Ernst & Ernst
New York, N.Y.

Some authorities argue that the work content of maintenance jobs varies so much, even on repetitive jobs, that it is silly to think in terms of accurate standards. They say if you can set fair standards on only 25 to 40 per cent of your direct work, you shouldn't even consider standard times for maintenance work.

Other authorities assert that standard times for maintenance jobs can and should be developed, that when these standards are properly used the payoff more than justifies the effort.

If you like to procrastinate, you can think up plenty of reasons for saying, "You can't get there from here." If you are progressive and you want to reduce and control maintenance costs, join the school that is setting maintenance standards and using them to good advantage.

WHAT IS A STANDARD TIME FOR MAINTENANCE?

A standard time for maintenance is the time it should take to perform any specific maintenance job. The job can be any one of an infinite number which might be performed by millwrights, carpenters, machinists, electricians, pipe fitters, painters, laborers, janitors, instrument mechanics, lead burners, sheet-metal workers, masons, etc. The maintenance standard is how long it should take to paint a wall, hang a door, replace a broken windowpane, grind the valves in a lift-truck engine, change the rolls on a calender stack, hang 100 ft of 2-in. pipe, connect a new motor and starter, etc. The combination of maintenance tasks is literally infinite in a large plant. In addition, there are many variables of location and working conditions which influence how long a job should take.

Many of these jobs will be repeated only at long intervals. Some may never be repeated. The working conditions may be the same only on rare occasions. These are the variables which make standard times for maintenance difficult to establish.

HOW ARE STANDARD TIMES FOR MAINTENANCE USED?

Maintenance standards are used for:

1. Planning and scheduling maintenance work.
2. Providing a properly sized maintenance force.

[1] The author is now Vice President, United States Tobacco Co., New York, N.Y.

3. Measuring the output or effectiveness of the maintenance crews.
4. Providing incentive earnings for maintenance personnel.

Each of these uses for standard times for maintenance will be discussed after the sections on how to establish the standards.

HOW TO SET MAINTENANCE STANDARDS

Several methods are used today to establish maintenance standards. Some of them are:

Guesstimates.
Estimates.
Statistical analyses of past performance.
Time study.
Estimates from standard data.
Methods-time measurement or work factor.
Observation or checking.

The method or combination of methods which you select should vary with the use you intend to make of the standards. Your choice will also be influenced by the data now available, the degree of development of your maintenance controls, the manpower you have available, and other considerations.

In my opinion, a combination of these methods should be used. Economic considerations should govern your selection. Ultimately, the standards developed should be accurate enough so that they may be used as a basis for incentive plans. If the maintenance standards meet this prerequisite, the standards will be more than adequate for scheduling, man assignment, and other controls.

STATISTICAL ANALYSES

By far the quickest and easiest way to develop accurate standards is the historical approach combined with guesstimating and estimating.

The first step is the design and installation of a work-order system. A work order is written for all jobs, with the exception of standing orders. The size and style of the form are unimportant, but there should be spaces for the following information:

1. Dates (issued, started, completed).
2. Department where work is performed.
3. Chargeable departments or cost center.
4. Requestor's signature.
5. Charge-account number.
6. Work-order number.
7. Signature of approval authorization.
8. Individuals assigned to the work.
9. Complete description of work required.
10. Spaces for accumulation of labor hours, labor cost, and material cost.

Specific conditions will determine the number of copies and distribution of the work order.

Accurate timekeeping is important in the development of historical standards. Every maintenance hour must be correctly reported and charged properly to work orders or to standing orders. There are various methods of accomplishing this; the most accurate and reliable is to time-stamp the start and stop time of each job on individual job cards. Man-hour totals can be accumulated manually or with tabulating equipment.

Actual hours for each type of work are accumulated for a period of time, usually covering 6 months, on work-summary sheets for each classification of work. These data are the basis for the establishment of work standards on the basis of past performance.

All maintenance work is segregated to the following work classifications:

1. Standing orders, routine jobs.
2. Repetitive jobs.
3. Miscellaneous or nonrepetitive jobs.
4. Estimated jobs.

Standing Orders, Routine Jobs.   Standing orders are issued for jobs where it is not practical to issue work orders.   A permanent number is issued for each standing order.   Standing order numbers are assigned also to work not usually connected with maintenance work so as to segregate man-hour costs from true maintenance activities. A list of a few samples of this type of standing order follows:

Storekeeping.
Attending meetings.
Clean up shop.
Visit to first aid or hospital.
Inventory taking.

Routine maintenance jobs are assigned permanent "routine" numbers, similar to standing orders.   These jobs are of a routine nature, such as routine oiling and inspection.   They include some jobs of a minor routine and repair nature, such as the replacing of electric-light bulbs.   Following is a list of samples of routine jobs:

Routine oiling.
Routine inspection.
Reading of water, gas, and power meters.
Changing electric-light bulbs.
Salvaging materials.
Motor inspection.

Repetitive Jobs.   Repetitive jobs refer to jobs which repeat at least once a month. At the end of each period, work orders covering these jobs are segregated by types and crafts.   Following are samples of repetitive jobs, by crafts:

Carpenters	*Electricians*	*Millwrights*
Sharpen saws	Repair motors	Replace belts
Repair ladders	Repair switches	Replace fire doors
Repair desks	Make extension cords	Overhaul pumps
Repair doors	Replace fuses	Repair conveyor
Repair trucks	Install switches	Repair locks
Sheet-metal Workers		*Pipe Fitters*
Make guards		Repair leaks
Make drip pans		Repair valves
Repair fire doors		Repair hose
		Repair toilets
		Repair pumps

Miscellaneous or Nonrepetitive Jobs.   All jobs performed on work orders, not considered as repetitive, and requiring less than 96 hr to complete, are included in the miscellaneous or nonrepetitive category.   Such jobs are segregated by time classifications, as follows:

Time Classification
Up to 8 hr
Over 8 to 16 hr
Over 16 to 32 hr
Over 32 to 48 hr
Over 48 to 96 hr

Estimated Jobs. All jobs requiring 96 hr or more are considered as estimated jobs.   The standards are established by a qualified estimator using a combination of standard data, discussion with foremen, good judgment, and possibly other factors.

ESTABLISHING STANDARDS

Standards for all jobs, with the exception of estimated jobs, are determined by statistical analysis of job results covering a base period, usually 6 months.   Following is a description of this procedure:

Standing Orders, Routine Jobs. The actual hours each week are posted to a work-summary sheet.   At the end of the base period the average hours per day, per week, or per unit are computed, and these become the standards.   Below is an example of standards for electrical shop, routine jobs.

Operation	Test period		Earned-hour standards
	Days or weeks	Actual hours	
Oil motors, Route A.............	127	1,714.5	13.5 per day
Oil motors, Route B.............	127	1,016.0	8.0 per day
Oil motors, Route C.............	127	317.5	2.5 per day
Replace bulbs or fuses..........	127	254.0	0.5 per unit
Check cranes............	26	104.0	4.0 per week
Check elevators................	26	67.6	2.6 per week
Clean shop....................	26	20.8	0.8 per week

Repetitive Jobs. Work orders covering all repetitive jobs are accumulated during the base period.   At the end of the base period the total actual hours expended on all jobs are computed and the average time per job becomes the standard.   A careful scrutiny of all jobs of a repetitive nature should be made at this time and all jobs, where the actual hours are excessive, should be deleted and transferred to the miscellaneous grouping.   Most repetitive jobs should have a maximum time per job established to exclude all jobs of an unusual nature.

Based on an analysis of work orders during a base period, representative standards can be established for repetitive electrical jobs similar to those shown below:

Item	Operation	No. of jobs	No. of units	Total hours	Earned-hour standards
Clocks, electric..............	Repair	20	20	23.5	1.18 per unit
Timer, electric..............	Repair	15	15	25.3	1.68 per unit
Drill, portable..............	Repair	26	26	65.0	2.50 per unit
Executone.................	Repair	11	11	14.7	1.34 per unit
Fan (office)................	Repair	12	15	24.5	1.63 per unit

Miscellaneous or Nonrepetitive Jobs. Work orders on all jobs in this category are accumulated during the base period and the average time per job is computed for each time classification.   This average becomes the standard.   For example, if 205 jobs were completed in the 0 to 8 hr classification during the base period, and 533 hr was reported, the standard then becomes 533/205 = 2.6 hr per job.

Typical Standards

Item	Description	Standard hr per unit	Max hr per unit
Garage:			
Battery	Replace and/or repair and/or check generator	1.2	4.0
Brakes	Adjust and/or check master cylinder	1.0	4.0
Gas line	Repair	1.5	2.0
Lights	Repair	1.0	4.0
Motor	Tune up	2.1	6.0
Muffler	Replace	1.5	4.0
Painters:			
Bench	Paint	0.2	1.0
Bookcase, misc	Paint	1.4	4.0
Desk, misc	Paint	1.3	2.0
Door and jamb, misc	Paint	1.8	4.0
Rack, misc	Paint	0.8	4.0
Sign	Paint and letter	0.6	4.0
Truck, lift	Paint	4.1	8.0
Welders and tinsmiths, repetitive jobs:			
Bar lock, metal for desk or cabinet	Fabricate	1.0	4.0
Basket, metal	Fabricate	1.4	6.0
Guard, machine, metal	Fabricate (up to 4.0 hr)	1.8	4.0
Guard, machine, metal	Fabricate (4.1 to 16.0 hr)	6.8	4.1 min 16.0 max
Guard, machine	Fabricate (16.0 to 36.0 hr)	22.0	16.1 min 36.0 max
Hook	Fabricate	0.4	2.0
Iron, angle	Cut to specifications	0.2	1.0
Nipple	Weld or braze	0.2	1.0
Pipe fitters, repetitive jobs:			
Air lines	Leaks, repairs, broken	2.5	8.0
Bradley fountain	Repair, leaks, unplug	2.2	4.0
Coolant lines	Repair, replace, unplug	2.3	8.0
Drain	Unplug, renew, clean	2.5	8.0
Faucet	Repair, replace	1.7	4.0
Gage	Repair, test, hook up	2.0	6.0
Pump	Pack, leak, repair	3.1	8.0
Toilet	Repair	1.9	8.0
Water sight glass	Install, change, clean	1.5	4.0

Pipe fitters, nonrepetitive jobs:

Group	Standard hr per job
Up to 4.0 hr	1.8
4.1 to 8.0 hr	6.0
8.1 to 16.0 hr	11.8
16.1 to 32.0 hr	23.1
32.1 to 48.0 hr	38.4
48.1 to 96.0 hr	62.5

Typical Standards

Item	Description	Standard hr per unit	Max hr per unit
Carpenters, repetitive jobs:			
Bench, wood.................	Fabricate to order	4.5	16.0
Bench, wood.................	Repair	4.1	16.0
Board, bulletin..............	Fabricate and install	2.2	8.0
Chair.......................	Routine cleaning and lubrication of casters, repair and minor adjustment	0.5	4.0
Desk.......................	Bolt down typewriter	1.7	4.0
Dispenser, salt, soap, paper, etc.	Install or repair	1.0	2.0
Lock.......................	Install or replace	1.7	6.0
Picture....................	Frame and mount	2.6	6.0
Saw.......................	Sharpen and set	0.5	1.0
Table......................	Repair	2.4	8.0
Venetian blind..............	Repair	1.2	4.0
Millwrights, repetitive jobs:			
Brackets...................	Make	1.2	4.0
Chain fall..................	Check and repair	4.2	12.0.
Conveyor, pallet............	Check and repair	5.9	10.0
Elevator...................	Repair, minor	6.1	12.0
Furnace, gasket.............	Change	3.6	8.0
Machine, large..............	Set-up and level	67.3	76.0
Machine, small..............	Set up and level	5.5	20.0
Rotoclone..................	Check and repair	3.3	12.0

Typical standards for nonrepetitive electrical-shop jobs based on analysis of orders during the base period might be:

Group	No. of jobs	Actual hours	Average hours per job	% of jobs to total
Up to 8 hr................	205	533.0	2.6	65
Over 8 to 16 hr............	79	908.5	11.5	25
Over 16 to 32 hr..........	16	328.0	20.5	5
Over 32 to 48 hr..........	9	345.6	38.4	3
Over 48 to 96 hr..........	6	381.0	63.5	2
Total...................	315			

Estimated Jobs. All jobs over 96 hr are estimated and the estimate becomes the standard. To accomplish this the estimated jobs should be listed on an estimate sheet, segregated to elements of work performance. Standard data are accumulated from past experience and from textbooks which contain formulas for estimating procedures. Some suggested books covering this subject are:

Walker, Frank R.: "The Building Estimators Reference Book," Frank R. Walker Company, Chicago, Ill.
Pulver, H. E.: "Construction Estimates and Costs," McGraw-Hill Book Company, Inc., New York.
Ashley, Ray: "Electrical Estimating," McGraw-Hill Book Company, Inc., New York.
Nordhoff, W. A.: "Machine Shop Estimating," McGraw-Hill Book Company, Inc., New York.
Means, R. S.: "Building Construction Cost Data—1952," P.O. Box 62, Duxbury, Mass.

To use these standards effectively for planning and scheduling, the work orders must be preclassified or guesstimated. The estimator or foreman can tell from experience the approximate hours which a job should take. He classifies each job as 0 to 8, 8 to 16, etc. If he classifies the job at 8 to 16 hr, for example, the planning time would be 11.5 hr.

For some typical standards for repetitive and nonrepetitive jobs developed by this past performance, statistical methods are as shown on pages 3-18 and 3-19.

Please keep in mind that these standards are historical averages, statistically grouped. The standards have not been leveled. They can be used for planning and scheduling and for establishing a control base. They should not be used as 100 per cent performance base for incentive wage payments. For this purpose these standards should be corrected by leveling based on time-studied samples or average effectiveness derived through work sampling or ratio and delay studies. The standards can then be reduced accordingly or the leveling can be accomplished through the pay formula. For example, instead of paying on a 1 for 1 basis, payment might be based on one-half of the improvement after a 10 per cent gain ($\frac{1}{2}$ after 10).

PUBLISHED DATA (ADJUSTED) APPROACH

Workable standard times for specific maintenance jobs can be developed by rationalizing standards published by equipment manufacturers. In a case history, garage standards for maintenance of tractors, trucks, lifts, and tow motors were derived as follows:

1. From standards books prepared by International Harvester, Towmotor, and Hyster Companies.
2. By analysis and interpolation of these data for similar but not identical jobs.
3. By historical experience on specific jobs rationalized for work method and tempo.
4. By utilizing the judgment and past experience of qualified persons to estimate a reasonable time for jobs not covered by 1, 2, or 3.

Some typical standards developed by this adjusted published data approach are:

Description of job	Earned-hour standards	
	Truck	Towmotor
Engine repairs:		
Bushing (rod and piston for O.S. pins)	1.8	1.2
Connecting rod, align one	0.3	0.3
Cylinder-head gasket, replace	3.7	3.1
Engine, remove and replace, including accessories	11.5	13.2
Manifold gasket, replace and repair	1.1	1.0
Overhaul engine, remove	27.5	20.0

USING TIME STUDY TO ESTABLISH MAINTENANCE STANDARDS

Time-study techniques have been developed and standardized over the years. There are many excellent textbooks which describe in detail how to conduct studies, how to level for performance, and what allowances to make for personal time, rest, and delay. One of the better texts on the subject is by Maynard, Stegemerten, and Schwab. Because the time-study observer should be familiar with the operations, the best time-study men are craftsmen, drawn from the trades, and trained in time study.

The time-study man should observe the job and list each operation in sequence before taking any watch readings. Any obvious defects in methods should be corrected after discussion with the mechanic and the foreman so that all three are in agreement that the proper sequence is being followed and that the most suitable tools are being used.

WORK MEASUREMENT

STUDY NO. *FRNST 9 2397*   REPETITIVE · TIME STUDY SHEET   SHEET _1_ OF _1_

OPERATION _Teardown, – (Dissassemble)_   DEPT. SYM *M001-48*
PART NAME & TYPE _Turn & Bank (Electric) Type C-5 & C-6)_   STOCK NO. *ALL*
LOCATION _Second floor   Bldg 52_   CONT.STA.NO. _2_
MACH. NO. —   OPERATOR _E. Romine_   NO. _R-2371_   OBSERVER _Pardo_
DWG.NO. —   UTLE. _____   WGHT. —   DATE _2 mar_
T.O. OR Q.C.S. NO. —   START _1305_   STOP _1348_   ELAPSED TIME _43 mn_

NO.	ELEMENT DESCRIPTION	READINGS										TOT. CYCLE	O C C	AVG. OR SEL.	LEV. FACT.	BASE MIN.
		1	2	3	4	5	6	7	8	9	10					
1.	Cut tags (10 inst)	.20	.20	–	.15	.20	–	.20	–	.12	.10	1.17 / 10	–	.117	80	.094
2.	Check glass (10 inst)		.40	.45	.40	.28	.30	.35	.30	.36	.25	.33	3.52 / 10	–	.352	80	.282
3.	Remove cannon plug screw (10 inst)	.18	.19	.18	.21	.19	.19	.21	.18	.18	.19	1.90 / 10	–	.190	80	.152
4.	Remove case (10 inst)	.25	.30	.22	.10	.18	.15	.18	.20	.15	.25	1.98 / 10	✓	.198	80	.158
5.	Set up electric screw driver + jig (10 inst)	.50										.50 / 10	–	.050	80	.040
6.	Remove dial (10 t in screws) (10 inst)	1.60	1.50	1.50	1.58	1.45	1.57	1.54	1.60	1.60	1.53	15.47 / 10	✓	1.547	80	1.238
7	Place in cabinet Rotor & Dimbul assembly (10 inst)	1.50										1.50 / 10	–	.150	80	.120
8	Place cases in box (10 inst)	.50										.50 / 10	–	.050	80	.040
9	Disassemble dial face plate	.40	.35	.41	.30	.30	.25	.27	.34	.40	.35	3.40 / 10	–	.340	80	.272
10	Remove springs from dial (10 inst)	.20	.20	.22	.15	.14	.14	.14	.32	.15	.15	1.81 / 10	–	.181	80	.145
11	Remove springs from plate placein box (10 inst)	.20	.20	.15	.15	.17	.15	.17	.17	.17	.15	1.68 / 10	–	.168	80	.134
12	Remove inclinometer (8 inst)	.35	.30	.25	.30	.22	.16	.20	.21	.27	.30	2.60 / 10	–	.260	80	.208
13	File defective inclinometers (10 inst)	.10			.20	.22		.18				1.70 / 10	✓	.070	80	.056
14	Put in boxes (10 inst)	1.00										1.00 / 10		.100	80	.080

REVIEWED BY:

Bill George   Foreman

(A)   TOTAL TIME

(B)   ADJ. TIME STUDY TIME   _80_ % LEVEL FACTOR   3.019

(C)   NORM.TIME/   _15_ % P.R.& D.ALLOW   3.472

(D)   STD.MIN/   25% TASK ALLOW   4.340

(E)   EARNED HRS. PER _instrument_ (_.072_)   .07233   SMAMA-FEB 54.5M

FIG. 2-1. Actual time study for disassembly of aircraft instrument.

In the case of highly repetitive jobs, the time study will be as complete as those taken for manufacturing operations. Several cycles should be observed and the elemental clock readings recorded. The average of each elemental time is adjusted for performance. These are then totaled and further adjustments are made for personal time, rest, and delay.   The total time then becomes the standard for the job.

An actual time study for the disassembly of an aircraft instrument is shown as Fig. 2-1.

STANDARD DATA FROM TIME STUDY

In maintenance work, highly repetitive jobs are the exception rather than the rule; so care must be taken to follow an economically sound approach.   Each job cannot be observed and time-studied.   Instead, representative jobs are studied and standards are established for various elements or operations.   Accurate estimates can then be

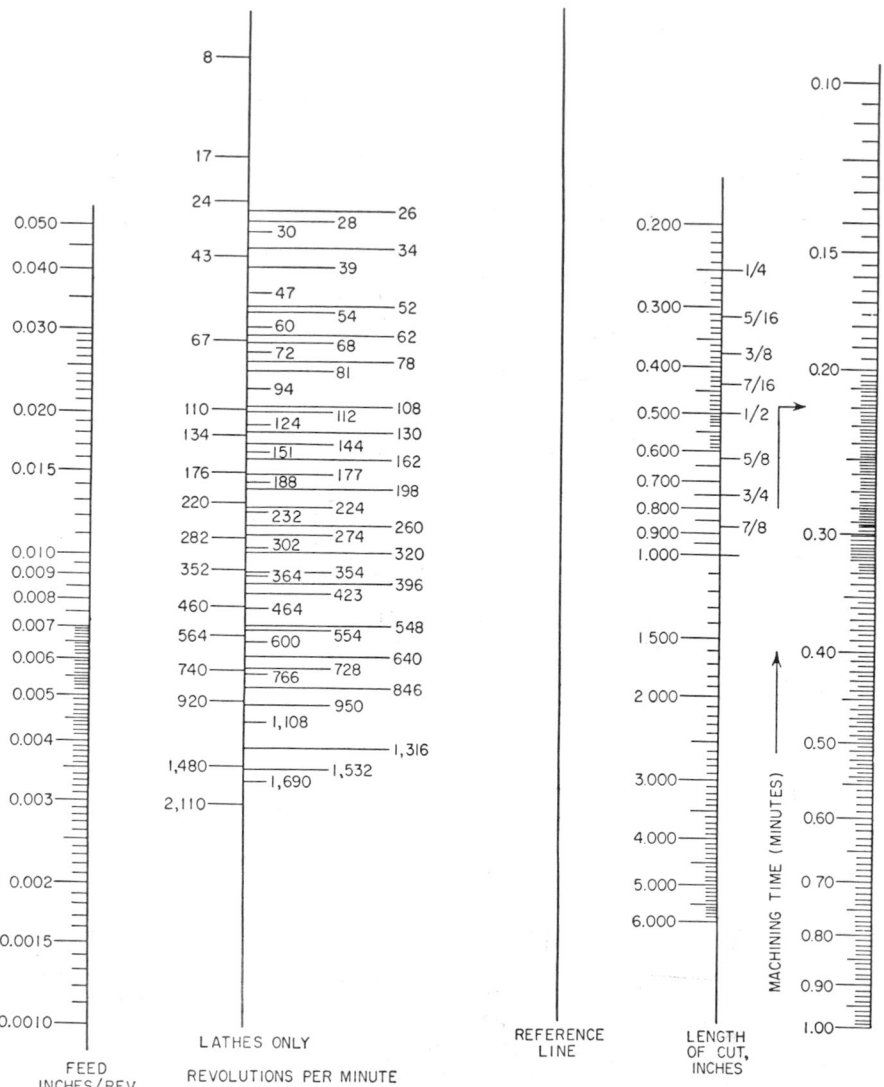

FIG. 2-2. Engine-lathe nomograph for calculating machining times for various speeds, feeds, rpm, and lengths of cut.

constructed by applying these operation standards to a wide variety of nonrepetitive jobs.   These estimates are then used as standards.

Here again, it is necessary that the estimator have sufficient craft knowledge so that he can construct an operation sequence for the job.

A standard-data computation sheet for work on engine lathes is shown in Table 2-1 and a nomograph for calculating machining times for various speeds. feeds, rpm, and lengths of cut are shown as Fig. 2-2.

Typical standard-data sheets covering power-driven crosscut and ripsaws, Do-All saws, and power shear are shown as Tables 2-2 to 2-5.

Similar data can be developed for any operations performed by maintenance mechanics—pipe fitting, welding, painting, janitor work, etc.   Data published in an article by Richard E. Deem, Lukens Steel Co.,[1] show a good example of how pipe-fitting standard data are derived:

	Elemental time standard	Frequency per 1,000 pieces	Standard man-hours
Make up 2-in. standard-screw pipe joint:			
Handle pipe horizontally (50 ft avg).......	0.012 per 2 pieces	1,000	6.0
Handle pipe vertically (7 ft avg)..........	0.009 per piece	70	.6
Handle fittings horizontally (50 ft avg)....	0.012 per 5 pieces	1,073	12.9
Handle fittings vertically (7 ft avg).......	0.005 per piece	75	.4
Measure and plan......................	0.052 per piece	1,000	52.0
Cut pipe (hacksaw).....................	0.100 per cwt	21	2.1
Cut pipe (pipe cutter)..................	0.031 per cwt	635	19.7
Thread pipe...........................	0.068 per thread	821	55.9
Make up joint (screw)..................	0.134 per joint	1,053	141.1
Total................................	....	.....	290.7
6% allowance.........................	....	.....	17.4
Standard hours per 1,000 pieces...........	....	.....	308.1
Standard hours per piece.................	....	.....	0.31

Material delivered to job site; working from ground, permanent platform, scaffold, or ladder; standard pipe fitters' tool kit, post vise, stock and die.

Summaries of studies for installing and removing pipelines of various diameters are then recorded in tabular form for easy access for the estimator when he is developing the job standards.   Here is an example:

Standard-time Data.   Pipe Fitting, Standard-screw Pipe Joint

Pipe size, in.	Standard man-hours per piece of pipe	
	Make	Break
¼–½	0.12	0.08
¾	0.17	0.11
1	0.20	0.13
1¼	0.23	0.15
1½	0.26	0.18
2	0.31	0.23

[1] *Factory Management and Maintenance*, January, 1955.

Table 2-1. Standard-data Computation Sheet for Work on Engine Lathes

W. O. _____　QUANTITY _____　NOUN _____

PART NO. _____　PLANNER _____　DATE _____

　　　　　　　　　　　　　　　　　　　　　　　　　　　　　　SHEET _____ OF _____

Approved by:　　　　Date:　　　ENGINE LATHES

　　　　　　　　　　MACHINE SHOP COMPUTATION SHEET

　　OPERATION

	Base min		Base min		Base min			Base min total	
1. Lathes	14½ by 30 in.		16½ by 45 in.		36 by 72 in.				
2. Set up and tear down—"A" Handling—"B"	A	B	A	B	A	B	O C C *	A	B
3. Turn, thread and bore with									
A. Collet chucking	28	1.72	29	1.78					
B. Three jaw chucking	31	1.91	32	1.89	55	1.89			
C. Four jaw chucking	33	3.42	35	3.39	55	3.40			
4. Drill and ream with									
A. Collet	29	2.96	30	3.02					
B. Three jaw	32	3.15	33	3.13	55	3.13			
C. Four jaw	35	4.66	35	4.63	56	4.64			
5. Using tail stock center with									
A. Collet	29	1.72	29	1.78					
B. Three jaw	33	1.91	34	1.89	47	1.89			
C. Four jaw	35	3.42	36	3.39	58	3.40			
6. Using taper attachment with									
A. Collet	31	2.02	32	2.08					
B. Three jaw	36	2.21	36	2.19	60	2.19			
C. Four jaw	38	3.72	38	3.69	61	3.70			
7. Using steady rest to turn, thread, and bore with									
A. Collet	29	1.72	31	1.78					
B. Three jaw	34	1.91	35	1.89	71	1.89			
C. Four jaw	37	3.42	37	3.39	71	3.40			
8. Using steady rest to drill and ream with									
A. Collet	29	2.96	31	3.02					
B. Three jaw	34	3.15	35	3.13	71	3.13			
C. Four jaw	37	4.66	37	4.63	71	4.64			
9. Using follower rest to turn, thread, and bore with									
A. Collet....................	32	1.72	31	1.78					
B. Three jaw	36	1.91	36	1.89	73	1.89			
C. Four jaw	39	3.42	39	3.39	74	3.40			

10. Total handling time (Col. B) _____

11. Machine time, per piece (from nomograph, Fig. 2-2) _____

12. Tool life per piece (1 % of line 11) _____

13. Check time per piece (optional) _____

14. Deburr (20 % of line 11) per piece (optional) _____

15. Total cycle time (lines 10 through 14) _____ Total _____

16. Standard hour, per piece (0.24 × line 15) _____ Total _____

17. Standard hours for _____ pieces (quantity × line 16) _____

18. Standard hour for setup (setup × 0.024) _____

19. Job standard (line 17 + line 18) _____Total_____

   * In case of new work or manufacture, the ocurrence factor is 1 and can be ignored.　On repairs to a lot size larger than 1, certain operations may be required on only 10 %, 20 %, 50 %, etc. of the pieces. In these instances, the occurrence factor is used.

Table 2-2. Typical Standard-data Sheet Covering Power-driven Crosscut Saw

Crosscut

Setup	One man	Two men	Three men
Straight cut..............	1.160	2.320	3.480
Bevel cut..............	3.444	6.888	10.332

Lengths of board up to and including, ft	One man					Two men					Three men
	Width of board cut					Width of board cut					
	4 in.	6 in.	8 in.	10 in.	12 in.	4 in.	6 in.	8 in.	10 in.	12 in.	
2	0.169	0.184			0.189	0.194	0.224			0.234	
4	0.177	0.192			0.197	0.202	0.232			0.242	150% of two-men figures
6	0.207	0.222			0.227	0.236	0.266			0.276	
8	0.229	0.244			0.249	0.254	0.288			0.298	
10	0.237	0.252			0.257	0.262	0.292			0.302	
12	0.245	0.260			0.265	0.270	0.300			0.310	
14	0.253	0.268			0.273	0.278	0.308			0.318	
16	0.275	0.290			0.295	0.300	0.330			0.340	
For each additional reposition and cut	0.060	0.075			0.080	0.120	0.150			0.160	

Table 2-3. Typical Standard-data Sheet Covering Crosscut and Ripping Saw

	One man	Two men
Setup...........	2.074	4.148

Length of board up to and including		Thickness of cut up to and including		No. men ripping	No. men crosscut
Ft	In.	2 in. Base min	3 in. Base min		
½	6	0.093	0.121	2	1
1	12	0.110	0.143	2	1
2	24	0.114	0.187	2	1
3	36	0.178	0.231	2	1
4	48	0.211	0.274	2	1
5	60	0.245	0.319	2	Use
6	72	0.278	0.361	2	ripping
7	84	0.312	0.406	2	column
8	96	0.346	0.450	2	
9	108	0.380	0.494	2	
10	120	0.414	0.538	2	
11	132	0.448	0.583	2	
12	144	0.482	0.627	2	
13	156	0.516	0.670	2	
14	168	0.547	0.711	2	
15	180	0.581	0.755	2	
16	192	0.615	0.800	2	
17	204	0.649	0.844	2	
18	216	0.682	0.887	2	
19	228	0.716	0.930	2	
20	240	0.749	0.974	2	

For thickness over 3 in. use 130% of 3-in. value.   For hardwood use 180% of corresponding thickness. For sheets of plywood 4 by 8 ft add 0.315 per cycle.

Table 2-4. Typical Standard-data Sheet Covering Do-All Saw

Sheet 1 of 2

DO-ALL SAW

Part Name _____   Job Order _____
Material _____   Part No. _____
Quantity _____   Date _____

STANDARD DATA
OPERATION SHEET

Element description*	Elem. occ.	Elem. time	Elem. total time
1. Transportation			
a. Walk with parts to bench		0.355	
b. Push cart to bench with parts		0.415	
2. Setup (external cuts)			
a. Set up Do-All for new job, change saw, change guides, etc.		5.000	
b. From flat stock to flat stock of same material		2.000	
c. Change saw		1.000	
3. Set up (internal cuts)			
a. Set up per internal cut (remove, cut, pass through work, weld, reinstall saw)		3.500	
b. Change saw		4.000	
4. Pick up, position and part aside			
a. Small part, under 5 lb from tote pan		0.210	
b. Medium part, 6–25 lb from floor		0.300	
c. Heavy part, 26–50 lb from floor		0.350	
5. "C" clamp, where necessary, per each		0.266	
6. Clean-up time		2.500	

7. Saw	Material thickness, in.								
	$\frac{1}{32}$	$\frac{1}{16}$	$\frac{1}{8}$	$\frac{1}{4}$	$\frac{1}{2}$	1	2	3	6
	Time, min, to saw 1.0 in.								
Aluminum........	0.010	0.013	0.017	0.024	0.041	0.076	0.178	0.356	0.713
Bakelite..........	0.010	0.013	0.017	0.024	0.041	0.076	0.178	0.356	0.713
Brass (soft)......	0.190	0.023	0.041	0.073	0.135	0.327	0.761	1.525	3.057
Bronze (ordinary).	0.057	0.076	0.101	0.145	0.307	0.762	1.775	3.557	7.133
Cast iron.........				0.363	0.615	1.142	2.662	5.336	10.700
Copper...........	0.028	0.038	0.051	0.073	0.123	0.229	0.533	1.067	2.140
Steel (mild)......	0.081	0.108	0.144	0.208	0.351	0.653	1.521	3.049	6.114
Steel (med.)......	0.142	0.189	0.252	0.363	0.615	1.142	2.662	5.336	10.700
Steel (hard)......	0.283	0.378	0.504	0.727	1.230	2.285	5.325	10.672	21.400

Sheet 2 of 2

DO-ALL SAW

Part Name _____   Job Order _____
Material _____   Part No. _____
Quantity _____   Date _____

MDMS-1
STANDARD DATA
OPERATION SHEET

Element description*	Elem. occ.	Elem. time	Elem. total time
8. For each minute of sawing time add following, change saw time for life of saw:			
a. Soft nonferrous metals		0.021	
b. Mild steels		0.042	
c. Hard steels		0.084	

Total time† _____

* Use applicable elements.   Standard time per piece _____
† To compute standard hours: Multiply base minutes by 0.024.   Total standard time _____

Table 2-5. Typical Standard-data Sheet Covering Power Shear

Sheet 1 of 2

POWER SHEAR
Straight or One-angle Cut

Part Name _____   Job Order _____
Material _____   Part No. _____
Quantity _____   Date _____

STANDARD DATA
OPERATION SHEET

Element description*	Elem. occ.	Elem. time	Elem. total time
1. Transportation			
a. Walk to shear with material		0.355	
b. Push cart to shear with material		0.415	
2. Set up			
a. Backstop (includes time to analyze method, make test strip)		0.660	
b. Sidestop (includes time for teardown)		0.780	
c. Front stop (includes time for teardown)		1.900	
3. Get material from cart or storage pallet, place on shear table			

Area, sq in...	0–500	1,000	1,500	2,000	2,500	3,000
Time........	0.030	0.055	0.071	0.088	0.105	0.121
Area, sq in...	3,500	4,000	4,500	5,000	5,500	6,000–7,000
Time........	0.138	0.155	0.171	0.186	0.196	0.210

4. Shear, push through, locate to stops, and hit

Backstop setting, in..............	1–2	4	6	8	10	12
Time............	0.034	0.036	0.038	0.040	0.041	0.042
Backstop setting, in..............	14	16	18	20	22	24
Time............	0.044	0.045	0.047	0.048	0.050	0.051

5. Reverse, pick up, turn piece around or over, locate to stops and hit
Use Chart 4 plus constant of 0.020

Table continued on following page.

Table 2-5. Typical Standard-data Sheet Covering Power Shear (*Continued*)

POWER SHEAR
Straight or One-angle Cut

Part Name_____   Job Order _____
Material _____   Part No. _____
Quantity _____   Date _____

STANDARD DATA
OPERATION SHEET

Element description*							Elem. occ.	Elem. time	Elem. total time
6. Pick up material from back of shear, stack for next cut or material aside									
No. of pieces......	1	2	3	4	5	10			
Time............	0.200	0.210	0.225	0.235	0.250	0.310			
No. of pieces......	20	30	40	50	60	70			
Time............	0.435	0.555	0.675	0.800	0.925	1.045			
No. of pieces......	80	90	100	110	120	130			
Time............	1.165	1.290	1.412	1.535	1.657	1.779			
No. of pieces......	140	150	160	170	180	190			
Time............	1.902	2.025	2.147	2.269	2.392	2.515			
7. Remove scrap and clean up									0.300

Total time†|_____
* Use as applicable.   Standard time per piece _____
† To change to standard hours: Multiply base minutes by 0.024.
Total standard time _____

Standard data can be developed for a wide variety of job elements performed by maintenance craftsmen. These data will prove very valuable in developing good standard times for many jobs which have been guesstimated or estimated. Again a caution: Use the best information you have at hand but continue to refine these data when you have more comprehensive knowledge of the routine and repetitive jobs which normally account for 60 per cent or more of the over-all time spent on plant maintenance.

METHODS-TIME MEASUREMENT

MTM is a method of developing standard times for any operation or job by assigning predetermined standards to elemental motions—reach or move, position, turn, grasp, disengage, kneel, sit, stand, walk, etc. These times have been established by the MTM Association for Standards and Research. Here you are dealing with elemental motions where the TMU (time-measurement unit) equals 0.00001 hr, 0.0006 min, or 0.036 sec. This unit will sound ridiculously minute to most maintenance people.   In practice, MTM has found greatest acceptance on highly repetitive jobs involving complex hand and body motions as in assembly of instruments, sewing operations, and doffing packages from spinning frames.

It is well, however, for anyone establishing standards for any types of work to be familiar with the MTM approach and at least with the simplified data which have been developed.   This method can be used to check elemental times developed through time study and will also prove of value in leveling data derived through the use of any other method of setting standards.   The following elemental standards are reproduced with the consent of the MTM Association.

Simplified Data

(All Times on This Simplified Data Table Include 15% Allowance)

Hand and arm motions	TMU		Body, leg and eye motions	TMU
Reach or move:			Simple foot motion.........	10
1 in.....................	2		Foot motion with pressure..	20
2 in.....................	4		Leg motion...............	10
3–12 in................	Length of motion + 4		Side step case 1...........	20
Over 12 in.............	Length of motion + 3		Side step case 2...........	40
Position:			Turn body case 1..........	20
Fit.....................	Symmetrical	Other	Turn body case 2..........	45
			Eye time..................	10
			Bend, stoop, or kneel on one	
Loose.................	10	15	knee.....................	35
Close.................	20	25	Arise.....................	35
Exact.................	50	55	Sit.......................	40
			Stand.....................	50
Turn, apply pressure:			Walk per pace............	17
Turn...................	6			
Apply pressure.........	20			
Grasp:				
Simple................	2			
Regrasp or transfer......	6			
Complex...............	10			
Disengage:				
Loose.................	5			
Close.................	10			
Exact.................	30			

1 TMU = 0.00001 hr
       = 0.006 min
       = 0.036 sec

For more information on MTM, its development and use, refer to Maynard, Stegemerten, and Schwab, "Methods-Time Measurement," McGraw-Hill Book Company, Inc., New York, 1948.

STANDARDS FOR JANITORS—OFFICE BUILDINGS

The cleaning of office buildings is a good example of a maintenance job which is repeated at regular intervals and consequently is an area which justifies the development of good standards for use in man-assignment and earned-hour control.

The following standards were developed for a large office building in Cleveland, 1,000,000 sq ft, where the standards for orderliness and cleanliness are high:

Area to Be Cleaned	*Standards*
1. Carpeted area..	13 min per 1,000 sq ft
2. Linoleum tile area...................................	10 min per 1,000 sq ft
3. Marble area..	10 min per 1,000 sq ft
4. Desks..	1 min per desk
5. Waste baskets..	0.75 min per basket

Area to Be Cleaned	*Standards*

6. Chairs, tables, davenports............................... 0.20 min per item
    File cabinets and safes
    Bookcases and shelving
    Counters
    Clothes trees
    Pictures
    Water coolers
    Lamps
    Thresholds
    Doors, outer, inner
    Radiators
    Drapes
7. Toilets... 1.5 min per toilet
8. Urinals.. 1.5 min per urinal
9. Washstands... 1.5 min per wash stand
10. Mirrors.. 1.0 min per mirror
11. Borrowed lights (interior glass partition panels)............ 1.0 min per light
12. Paneled walls.. 3.0 min per panel wall
13. Painted doors.. 0.5 min per door
14. Painted walls.. 2.0 min per 1,000 sq ft
15. Series of closed individual offices—opening, transporting
    equipment—closing.................................. 200 min per 100 offices
16. Personnel occupancy of zone
    a. 100 sq ft per occupant.   Add 7% to total area-cleaning minutes
    b. 140 sq ft per occupant.   Add 5% to total area-cleaning minutes
    c. 160 sq ft per occupant.   Average
    d. 175 sq ft per occupant.   Deduct 3% from total area-cleaning minutes
    e. 200 sq ft per occupant.   Deduct 5% from total area-cleaning minutes
17. Transient persons in zone area
    a. Heavy. Add 10% to total minutes
    b. Medium. 100% or normal
    c. Light. Deduct 10% from total minutes
18. Shift allowance. Add 30 min per shift

Cleaning Operations and Frequencies. *Entrances, Main Floor, Arcade, Elevator Lobbies.* Floor area power-scrubbed nightly. Rubber matting is picked up and scrubbed as needed. Stairways scrubbed by hand. Floor surfaces swept continuously during the day.

Toilet Rooms. Marble surfaces power-scrubbed twice a week, mopped nightly. Day janitors and day maids patrol toilet rooms and keep them in an orderly condition, installing toilet paper, towels, and napkins.

Stairways. Swept nightly and mopped and dusted once a week.

Zone Cleaners. All zones are cleaned nightly. Asphalt tile, rubber tile, linoleum, cork, etc., are mopped on a revolving basis. The floor areas are mopped on an average of once a week.

Polishing Metal. Bronze entrances, stainless-steel fronts, bronze revolving doors, stainless-steel doors, handrails, mailboxes, elevator stainless-steel hatchway doors, and dispatch panels are cleaned and polished nightly.

Electric signs, bronze grille work, vault doors and interior metal, directional signs, metal trim, and doors are on a schedule of 1 week to 3 months. The frequency is determined by appearance and condition.

Polishing Woodwork. The interiors of the elevator cabs are washed once a week and polished and dusted nightly. All paneled rooms are dusted down twice monthly and all borrowed light frames once a week.

Cleaning Furniture and Fixtures. Over a period of 7 to 8 months all the furniture in the building is washed, waxed, and polished.

Cleaning Marble. All public-area marble is pointed out and washed approximately twice a year.

Cleaning Glass. All entrance-door glass, borrowed lights, are on a perpetual basis of washing; some entrance-door glass is washed nightly.

Light Fixtures. All light fixtures are washed once each 6 months. This does not include fluorescent fixtures.

Waxing of Floors. Floors are waxed only at the request of the tenant and at his risk and expense.

Buffing Floors. No floors are buffed. However, a crew of full-time moppers are continuously mopping the asphalt tile, linoleum, and cork areas over a period of not less than 2 weeks.

Waste Paper and Rubbish Disposal. All waste paper and rubbish is disposed of nightly.

General Work. Sidewalk cleaning and washing, snow removal, moving of tenants, roof cleaning, handling of flags, waste paper, rubbish, supplies, equipment, equipment mainte- nance, delivery of water, paper cups, deliveries from dock, are all done as the situation warrants or when requested.

Required Maintenance Personnel. For a model building, 1,000,000 sq ft area.

Craft	*Number*
Night supervisor	1
Assistant night supervisor	1
Carpenters	4
1 specializes in metal trim door checks, also woodwork	
3 finish carpenters	
Cleaning women, day	7
2 maids, toilets	
2 laundry (rags; shades, blinds)	
1 special maid	
Cleaning women, night	102
3 foreladies	
99 cleaning, zoned	
Elevator operators*	40
Engineers	4
2 day, 6 days	
2 night, 6 days	
Glazier	1
Glazes, lays all tile	
Janitors, day	15
3 toilets	
1 services drinking fountains	
1 services main entrance, arcade, first-floor bank, sidewalks	
1 services 5 floors, annex, sweeping, dusting	
1 removes and hangs blinds and shades	
1 dusts metal trim, sweeping	
5 clean, polish bronze and stainless steel interior and exterior, general labor, deliveries	
Janitors, night	11
2 36-in. scrub machines, zoned	
8 moppers, zoned	
1 rubbish man	
Laborers, day	5
Light-bulb changer, day	1
Locksmith	1
Marble men	2
Mason	1
Painters	11
Plasterer	1
Plumbers and steamfitters	4
Watchmen	11
Window washers, zoned	5
Electricians (subcontracted)	5
Elevator electricians (subcontracted)	2
Painters, extra (subcontracted)	7
Total, all crafts	242

*Automatic elevators have been installed in this building recently.

STANDARDS BY OBSERVATION OR CHECKING

Some consulting firms claim that they have set standards for maintenance jobs involving all but highly specialized crafts, such as lead burners, for many different clients over the years.   These standards have been cataloged in the form of standard data and, according to these claims, with minor adjustments due to plant geography and due to normal workpace, can be used as standard times for maintenance jobs in any plant.

In using these standards, a checker prepares a maintenance checking sheet which breaks down the job into operations, usually while the job is in progress or after it has been completed.   Allowances are made for working conditions and any unusual operations which might have been impossible to predict in advance.   Credits are given also for trips to the storeroom, starting and stopping, etc., based on the distance from the dispatching point.

Jobs requiring less than 2 man-hours are not checked but are included in the earned-hour credit by adjusting the total actual hours by a small job credit.

As with any other type of standard, all the time of each mechanic must be accounted for and charged either to small jobs or to a work-order number assigned on the maintenance checking sheet.

An excellent article describes such a system in use with foundry operations.[1] The author inspected this installation and was well impressed with the control which had been achieved and with the force reductions.   The standard data for the various crafts included 4 volumes of about 200 pages each.   As these standards are part of the "package" provided by the consulting firm, the author was unable to secure any "samples" to include in this chapter.

GROUP STANDARDS

Some manufacturing plants have batteries of various classes of equipment and in some instances one or more crews are continuously engaged in performing routine maintenance on these batteries.   Such maintenance jobs require substantial amounts of maintenance labor and warrant detailed careful method studies to determine the optimum size crew.   Quite often the crews are too large and one or more of the crew members is "standing by" a large portion of the time.

The following tabulation shows the results of a study which resulted in reducing a three-man crew to a two-man crew in pot-line maintenance in an aluminum-reduction plant.

	% of shift	
Job elements	3-man crew	2-man crew
Contact foreman...................	1	3
Walking job to job..................	6	5
Obtaining supplies..................	7	10
Moving tools.......................	5	6
Repairs to pots.....................	28	41
Repairs to own equipment...........	2	2
Unproductive work..................	8	2
Enforced rest......................	24	16
Absolute rest......................	13	14
Delays............................	6	1
	100	100

MAINTENANCE FOR INSURANCE PURPOSES

In some industries there are large key machines whose output may well determine the profitability of the department or even the company.   The running rate in dollars per hour is high, and setup after a stop for any reason may be excessive.   Paper machines, packaging lines, certain types of airplane-line maintenance, and photographic-film machines are good examples.

It is common practice to assign one or more mechanics to these machines whenever

---

[1] Kenneth Digney, President, Oberdorfer Foundries, Inc., Syracuse, N.Y., Work Measurement for Smaller Plants, Too, *Factory Management and Maintenance*, January, 1955.

they are in operation to inspect, lubricate, and make minor adjustments continuously. Here the continuous performance of the machine rather than control of the maintenance mechanic is the important consideration. For control purposes, actual hours will equal earned hours. However, if the mechanic has long periods where he is merely "standing by" consideration should be given to providing him with some fill-in work which might not be related to his prime job. Cleaning and adjusting spark plugs from engine-overhaul shops, for example, can be assigned to line mechanics whose primary job is the "turn-around" of scheduled aircraft.

HOW STANDARD TIMES FOR MAINTENANCE ARE USED

For Planning and Scheduling. *Objectives of Shop Planning.* The primary objectives of shop planning are:

1. To provide each shop group with a planning board to be used by foremen and leadmen in assigning work to tradesmen.
2. To assure that, to the highest degree possible, one full day's work is laid out for each tradesman on the day prior to the day the work is to be performed, i.e., tomorrow's work is planned today, allowing for adequate tools, parts, and other job preparations.
3. To translate work called for on work orders into terms of man-hours, number of tradesmen required, and elapsed time.
4. To determine job priority.
5. To assign work to trades in accordance with job priority and available manpower.
6. To follow progress of jobs to completion.
7. To develop load information necessary to size the maintenance forces properly and to be used as a guide in:

Increasing or decreasing maintenance force.
Overtime assignments.
Subcontracting overload to outside shops or contractors.

It has been found through experience that maintenance work may be scheduled from day to day in the same manner that productive operations are planned. The basic requirements of a sound plan of maintenance scheduling is that all jobs have predetermined standard times established.

Scheduling of maintenance activities is segregated to two basic classifications, namely, sequence planning and formalized planning.

Sequence Planning. Sequence planning refers to the planning of jobs of a repair nature in sequence of necessity. When work orders are received by a craft foreman, they are carefully scrutinized and their order of priority determined. A planning board is furnished each craft with clips attached thereto, each clip representing a mechanic or group of mechanics. Work orders are assigned to individual workers or groups by placing them behind the proper clips, usually assigning sufficient work for at least 1 day ahead for each craftsman. This plan of scheduling assures that the most essential jobs are given priority.

In plants where the major part of the maintenance functions is devoted to minor repair jobs, the sequence plan of scheduling work will prove effective. In many plants, however, major maintenance requirements consist of work of a new-construction nature, or large repair jobs, in which case a more formalized plan of scheduling is advisable.

Formalized Planning. Each day, work orders should be selected in order of priority and a day's work should be planned for each tradesman on a work sheet. All work of a major nature should be projected on a project-planning sheet (Gantt chart), showing the sequence of operations, number of employees required by crafts, and sequence by crafts. The progress of jobs should be followed daily and per cent of completion noted on the chart.

The estimates or other standards established, as explained previously, should be utilized in determining man-hour requirements for the scheduling program. Jobs can be scheduled far in advance when they fit in with shutdowns or with available dates predicated on production schedules. Priorities of smaller jobs will change from day to day, but the work load should be reviewed periodically so that corrective action may be taken before employees are overloaded or are idle. Effective planning will minimize overtime or week-end assignments.

By referring to the planning charts the maintenance superintendent can:

1. Keep informed as to over-all progress.
2. Direct his attention to those jobs behind schedule where his help is required.
3. See clearly what effect rush jobs have on those in process, and which jobs can more conveniently be delayed, if necessary.
4. Keep operating personnel informed as to job status without requiring special field checks which are usually time-consuming and often inaccurate.

Periodic meetings of maintenance department supervisors are necessary in the scheduling and planning of work. An effective medium for the planning of major jobs can be portrayed on a planning board and their status quickly ascertained.

PROPERLY SIZING THE MAINTENANCE FORCES

All work to be performed by the maintenance department falls in the classes of routine preventive maintenance; that authorized on work orders, either for repairs or new projects; or unpredictable breakdown repairs.

With proper estimating or use of standard times for maintenance, it is possible at any time, usually at monthly intervals, to classify and total this work load and segregate this load in terms of the number of weeks' work ahead by craft. Ranges of weeks' work ahead can be developed for each plant and the force increased or decreased if the future work load falls outside these limits. The chart, Fig. 2-3 shows a range of $2\frac{1}{2}$ to 7 weeks as normal for millwrights and pipe fitters.

SUMMARY LOAD SHOWING LOAD TRENDS

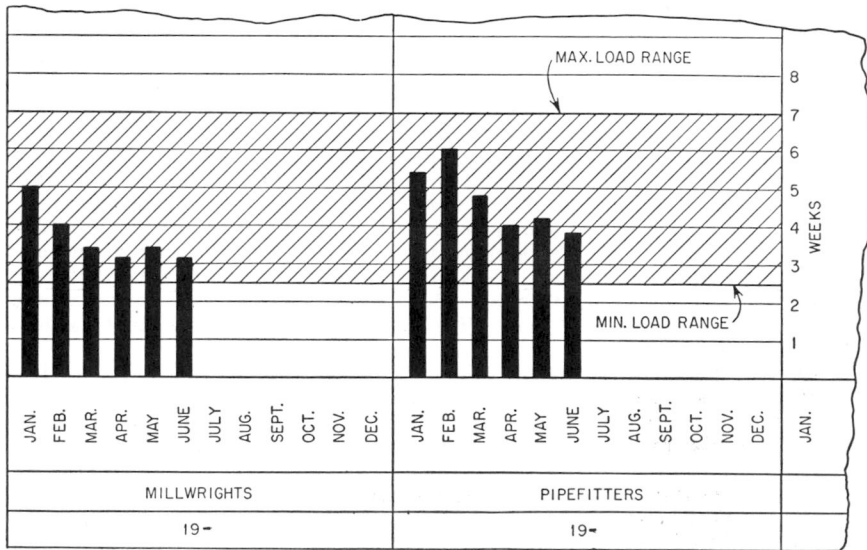

FIG. 2-3. Work-load range of $2\frac{1}{2}$ to 7 weeks as normal for millwrights and pipe fitters.

MAINTENANCE WORK CONTROL

Standard times for maintenance jobs provide a basis for establishing control of all maintenance work. This is one of the most effective uses of the standards. **Actual** times for each job are accumulated and summarized each week by craft and compared with the standard or earned hours. Normally, a 4 to 5 weeks running average is reported so that the effect of large jobs completed during any one reporting period is minimized.

		CURRENT WEEK			10 WEEK TOTALS		10 WEEK AVERAGE		
WEEK ENDED	UNITS	STANDARD HOURS	ACTUAL HOURS	%	STANDARD HOURS	ACTUAL HOURS	STANDARD HOURS	ACTUAL HOURS	%
7/11	30	120	125.1	96					
7/18	18	72	68.3	106					
7/25	17	68	67.	102					
8/1	34	132	130.5	101					
8/8	20	80	85.5	94					
8/15	25	100	92.	109					
8/22	15	60	70.2	85					
8/29	30	120	115.1	104					
9/5	12	48	62.7	77					
9/12	20	80	60.	133	880	876.4	88.	87.6	100.4
9/19	22	88	90.3	97	848	841.6	84.8	84.2	100.8
9/26	40	160	148.	108	936	921.3	93.6	92.1	101.6
10/3	18	72	77.2	94	940	931.5	94.	93.2	100.9
10/10	17	68	63.1	108	876	864.1	87.6	86.4	101.4
10/17	25	100	95.	105	896	873.6	89.6	87.4	102.5
10/24	20	80	90.5	89	876	872.1	87.6	87.2	100.4
10/31	30	120	140.5	85	936	942.4	93.6	94.2	99.3
11/7	10	40	30.5	131	856	857.8	85.6	85.8	99.8
11/14	40	160	171.5	93	968	966.6	96.8	96.7	100.1
11/21	25	100	91.2	110	988	997.8	98.8	99.8	99.
11/28	18	72	75.3	96	972	982.8	97.2	98.3	98.9
12/5	20	80	68.2	117	892	903.	89.2	90.3	98.8
12/12	17	68	60.	113	888	885.8	83.8	88.6	100.2
12/19	30	120	101.2	119	940	923.9	94.	92.4	101.7
12/26	25	100	108.5	92	940	937.4	94.	93.7	100.3

SUMMARY SHEET

CODE A

DESCRIPTION OF WORK
Miscellaneous Jobs - up to 8 Hours

DEPT.
Carpenter

FOREMAN
J. Smith

DATE 7/8   UNITS Jobs
STD. 4.0

Fig. 2-4. Earned-hour report showing effectiveness of maintenance department.

An example of an earned-hour report which shows the effectiveness of the maintenance department is shown as Fig. 2-4.

INCENTIVES

Incentives can be applied to maintenance work to secure the added cooperation of the maintenance employees. Particularly where incentives for production employees exist, a company may find it highly desirable to provide incentive opportunities to maintenance and other indirect employees. The productivity-measurement feature obtainable when standards are available will enable a company to institute a practical means of sharing cost reductions with maintenance employees.

The extent to which craft and/or departmental incentives are employed will depend largely upon the size and complexity of the maintenance department. Thus incentives may be designed to reflect the operations of individual crafts or may embrace an entire department. When multicraft participation exists, a combination of both craft and department can be used.

In developing the pay formula, care must be exercised that the standards have been developed uniformly. If they are based on standard data derived from work measurement and have been leveled to a normal pace, incentive earnings can be calculated on a 1 for 1 basis on performance in excess of 100 per cent.

However, if the standards are established on the past-performance basis they must be leveled on a work-sampling basis if the 1 for 1 formula is used. Another basis for calculating payment where historical standards are used is to agree on the per cent effectiveness and to share any improvement over the present effectiveness. The $\frac{1}{2}$ after 10 per cent formula has worked successfully in many instances. This formula, in effect, admits that standards set on past practice will be loose. Rather than to level the performance down or to spend more money to establish work-measured standards, the condition is recognized and built into the pay formula.

CONCLUSION

The gains to be derived from proper control of maintenance work with objective standards for maintenance jobs are great. The results are worth the effort.

Chapter 3

WORK MEASUREMENT

By W. C. Cooling[1]
Manager, Methods and Standards Department
International Resistance Company
Philadelphia, Pa.

Introduction. The end objective of the various techniques for work measurement is to supply standard data for determining the time required to complete specific segments of work. Whether the resulting standards are used for labor control on a straight time basis or for labor control and wage incentives, the techniques are the same. The principal techniques for establishing standards for work measurement are discussed as to principles, procedures, advantages, and disadvantages; examples of development and application are given.

Participation with Industrial Engineering in Measuring Work and Establishing Standards. Examine the positions of the foremen and industrial engineers. These two management groups, one line and the other staff, have the common goal of decreasing operating costs through various industrial management techniques. However, it is not uncommon for the two groups to be "enemies" rather than "allies."

The foreman is the front-line administrator of management methods and management policies. Assume a company is staffed with highly skilled engineers, mechanical, electrical, industrial, etc. These engineers, through engineering logic, constantly create sound improvements within the framework of their function. The improvements are of no value unless they are placed in operation. The foreman is the only man who can do that. He is on the spot where the work is being done, where labor, material, and overhead costs are realities, not just figures on paper.

With the maintenance function, there are many former craftsmen holding the position of front-line cost administrator. Many of these people carry with them the same resistance to change that they had as craftsmen. It is management's responsibility to take these courses of action:

1. If a foreman is capable of administering costs, he should be trained in every phase of management theory and management control practices; not with the objective of having him perform the control function but rather to appreciate, understand management controls, accept, and enjoy the competitive challenge of management in the cost-reduction field.
2. If the foreman is not capable of administering costs, he is not adaptable to progress, which is a necessity for every company's future. Management must find another field for him.

The industrial engineer is the staff assistant to the foreman. As such, he is in position to come in contact with people who work for the foreman. There is often a

[1] The author is now Corporate Staff Industrial Engineer, American-Standard, American Radiator & Standard Sanitary Corporation, New York, N.Y.

3–37

tendency for the industrial engineer to talk to the workers or the steward in the area about work methods, equipment, and standards.   This is not a wise course of action, if the industrial engineer is planning to work with the foreman.   The foreman, in addition to representing management in administrative matters, is also the leader of the workers.   Any staff person who bypasses the foreman in dealing with the workers concerning their jobs is infringing upon the foreman's leadership.   A foreman can be a leader only when he is not undermined by staff activities.   The industrial engineer's communication line to the workers is the foreman.

Engineers have good creative ideas, but they allow these ideas to supersede good management.   The development phase usually proceeds too far before the foreman is brought into the picture for his contributions.   In many cases, the engineers neglect to ask the foreman's assistance in the creative stages and present a finished package, expecting immediate acceptance of their work.   This method of operation does not allow the foreman to contribute his practical experience and know-how in forwarding the project.   The best approach for the industrial engineer is to call the foreman in at an early stage, ask for and use his suggestions and those of other staff people, and attempt to get him so interested in the project that it is impossible for him to be anything other than a willing participant.   A good method is to form a small committee of the people involved in launching a particular project.   Make the foreman chairman, and he immediately leads the activities.   There can be no backing out. It is a much more satisfying and easier job for a foreman to install "his project" rather than someone else's.

A successful installation of a project usually is followed by a bit of "crowing," and that's part of the job.   In order to get advanced assignments and freedom to work on future and possibly more difficult projects, the prior requisite is a history of success on the preceding projects.   A letter initiated by industrial engineering to the foreman, with a copy to his boss, thanking him for his participation and giving him an estimate of the value of the results of the first year's operation under the improvements, will put the foreman on a receptive basis for participation in future projects.

An industrial engineer is successful in his operations only when he has other management people coming to him with basic ideas or telling him of trouble spots and asking his assistance.   There is more chance of success when the industrial engineer is doing work that someone requested rather than digging up projects on his own that have to be sold to others before they are willing to participate.

In comparing the two jobs of foreman and industrial engineer, the foreman's is more difficult in the respect to completing improvement projects.   After the industrial engineer has the foreman participating in the project, he uses all the ideas he can find, his own, the foreman's, and the other staff groups', to set the job up.   He assembles a mass of data through time study, MTM, estimates, or other means.   He outlines the methods procedure, develops standards, and gives the results to the foreman. This is where the real work starts.   Initially the foreman has to orient the workers and the union in regard to this staff activity in his department.   He must coordinate and install any changes in work methods.   He must train his workers in new methods. He must man his area in balance with work-load requirements.   The industrial engineer has worked with logic and facts.   The foreman installs the results of the logic and fact procedure.   His problem is with people.   A successful installation depends upon acceptance by the majority of the workers and this is a far greater problem than getting results from logic and facts.

The foreman must deal directly with employees as work-measurement standards are introduced to remove some of the mystery from the activity.   Each new standard or standard-data series should be introduced by the foreman.   He must present the picture of the new standard in detail with a positive approach and not in a hesitant, backward fashion.   In the course of this introduction, the foreman, by his presentation, must build confidence and create in the worker the desire to give the standard a fair trial.   These are some of the impressions that he must develop in his discussion with the worker in the introduction of new standards.   That he, as foreman:[1]

[1] W. C. Cooling, "Front Line Cost Administration," p. 121, Chilton Publishing Co., Philadelphia, Pa., 1955.

1. Is positive that the job was time-studied under normal operating conditions.
2. Has determined that the standard was developed around those conditions.
3. Will guarantee that the job will continue to be performed under the same conditions or the standard will be adjusted.
4. Has thoroughly reviewed the standard and firmly believes it to be fair and attainable.
5. Is sure the standard will be given a fair trial.
6. Sincerely hopes the worker will do well on the standard.
7. Expects the worker will contact him, not the union, not another worker, and not the engineer, if there are any questions on any standard.

Without the foreman's active participation no industrial engineer would be a success. Top management must recognize this fact. They must provide the thinking and direction to impress the foreman with his responsibility and the need to operate as a "front-line administrator" rather than a "pusher." Top management must train their line and staff groups in every phase of management control in order to operate in a manner that makes active participation a habit with all improvement projects. With the line groups, the training program should not have the objective of having foremen perform all the control functions, but to have foremen:

1. Understand and appreciate controls.
2. Recognize the need for assistance from staff groups.
3. Immediately call the proper staff function when a course of action is required.
4. Be equipped to use control functions to evaluate their own performance.

With this outlook and method of operating, the most successful work-measurement program is one that calls for the most participation and responsibility on the part of the foreman. This thinking is not too common in the field of maintenance work measurement. Recently, in a comparison of advantages and disadvantages of various methods of work measurement, this sentence was noted under disadvantages: "Requires cooperation of foremen and technicians." There is a lot of revision necessary in the thinking and working of management in that particular company. Costs cannot be controlled without the active participation of the person primarily responsible for material usage and getting the work done, the foreman.

Methods. The most important contribution from method studies, with regard to maintenance, is standardization of work. Before work can be measured there must be a standard method by which the work elements are to be completed. The workers must be trained in this method. The data obtained from work measurement are based on the same method, and worker efficiencies against various jobs can be determined. Should there be a change in work methods, the standards must be reviewed to determine the time required to complete the task under the new method.

It is not a requisite to have the best method when establishing standard data. The primary goal is to establish standard methods so that the work can be measured, standard data developed, and maintenance efficiencies determined against the standards. Methods improvements usually require acceptance by management, additional equipment, training, and orientation of personnel, and other problems concerned with the installation of changes in work methods which could slow progress in work measurement. With present methods standardized, work-measurement studies can proceed. Standard data can be changed or added to in the future as improvements are made.

Figure 3-1 shows a print of a typical job for portable flame-cutting machines. Figure 3-2 is an example of standard-data development for that job. The development of the standard shows separate setup and separate machine-burning times for square and bevel cuts. This is the way the job was standardized and time-studied. Note, however, that this method contains extra operations. For square and bevel cutting, standard attachments are available for each cutting machine. The attachments consist of a mounting fixture to provide an extra torch to be mounted on the standard machine, providing the means to square and bevel-cut simultaneously. For work-measurement purposes, the present method of making each cut separately can be studied and data developed.   At a later date, with the new method of cutting installed, additional studies can be made and a standard-data table provided for change in work methods.   In the meantime the present method is standardized, measured, and worker performance can be determined on the old method.   As a

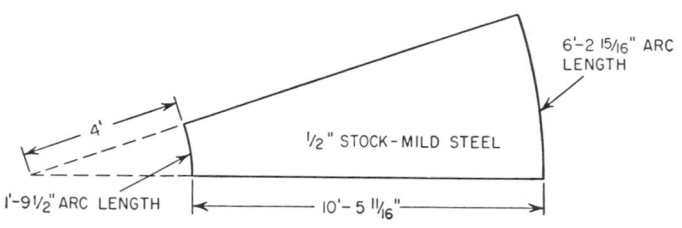

PRINT NO. 9-1738-A

ASPHALT TANK BOTTOMS

FIG. 3-1. Print of a typical job for flame-cutting machines.   (*Courtesy of Conover-Mast Publications.*)

STANDARD DEVELOPMENT SHEET

FLAME CUTTING-PORTABLE FLAME CUTTERS

DESC: *ASPHALT TANK*   PRINT NO: *9-1738-A*   MATERIAL: *MILD STEEL*
BOTTOMS (2)   DATE ISSUED: *3/20*

STANDARD DEVELOPED BY: *E. Wilmer*   DATE: *3/20*
PER SEGMENT (10 SEGMENTS/TANK)

ELEMENT	TABLE	UNIT	NO. OF UNITS	STD. MAN HRS/ UNIT	TOTAL STD. MAN HOURS
M/C BURN – SQUARE	18.02	100 IN.	3.49	.150	.523
– BEVEL	18.02	100 IN.	2.52	.180	.454
HANDLE MAT'L (WT. OF FIN. PC. APPROX. 510#)	18.05	PER PC.	1	.351	.351
SET UP CM – 16 M/C					
SHORT ARC	18.06	PER OCC.	1	.154	.154
LONG ARC	18.06	PER OCC.	1	.061	.061
SET UP CM – 30 M/C					
STRAIGHT LINES 1ˢᵗ OCC.	18.07	PER OCC.	1	.118	.118
3 ADDITIONAL OCC.	18.07	PER OCC.	3	.069	.207
PREHEATS	18.06	PER OCC. O.B.	6	.014	.084
CHIP EDGE AFTER BEVEL	18.09	100 IN.	252	.040	.101
TOTAL TIME PER PLATE					2.503
PER 20 PLATES					41.060
ADD JOB PREPARATION					.100
ADD 5 ADDITIONAL JOB PREP					41.160
					.500
					41.660

FIG. 3-2. Standard-data development for flame-cutting operation shown in Fig. 3-1. Square and bevel cuts are made independently.   (*Courtesy of Conover-Mast Publications.*)

matter of interest, Fig. 3-3 illustrates the development of the standard for the same job as Fig. 3-2 using the new operation.   There is a 21 per cent reduction in time. In this particular shop, where a large volume of plate is flame-cut for fabrication, the annual savings would be substantial.

Figures 3-13 to 3-15 illustrate the documentation of methods on a job basis.   With repetitive jobs it is imperative to be specific in all considerations with the method, that is, layout, equipment, dimensions, and work methods.

On an equipment basis such as Fig. 3-11, the documentation, as far as handling is concerned, is more general.   This is due to the fact that every job is different.   However, the work area is described in detail, setup methods are described, and the elements of the operation noted.

Figure 3-4 illustrates the procedure for standardizing methods on a craft basis. This particular example is welding pipe.   The standard practice prescribes for each size of pipe and the manner in which it is positioned, the size of electrode, and the number of passes required.   An illustration (Fig. 3-5) accompanies this to further define the standard method of welding pipes.   Similar procedures are outlined for all other work performed by the welding craft.

ELEMENT	TABLE	UNIT	NO. OF UNITS	STD. MAN HRS/ UNIT	TOTAL STD. MAN HOURS
M/C BURN - SQUARE	18.02	100 IN.	97	.150	.145
- SQ. & BEVEL	E.S.T.	100 IN.	252	.180	.454
(SIMO)					
HANDLE MATERIAL (WEIGHT FINISHED PIECE APPROX. 510 #)	18.05	PER PC.	I	.351	.351
SET UP CM-16					
M/C SHORT ARC	18.06	PER OCC.	I	.154	.154
M/C LONG ARC	18.06	PER OCC.	I	.061	.061
SET UP CM-30					
SQ. & BEVEL	E.S.T.	PER OCC.	I	.187	.187
ADDITIONAL OCC.	E.S.T.	PER ADDIT	I	.069	.069
PREHEATS					
O.B. ONE TORCH	18.06	PER OCC.	2	.014	.028
O.B. SQ. & BEVEL	E.S.T.	PER OCC.	2	.030	.060
CHIP EDGE AFTER BEVEL	18.09	100 IN.	252	.040	.101
TOTAL TIME PER PLATE					1.610
PER 20 PLATES					32.200
ADD JOB PREPARATION					.100
					32.300
ADD 5 ADDITIONAL JOB PREP.					.500
					32.800

FIG. 3-3. Standard-data development for flame-cutting operation shown in Fig. 3-1, with the improved method.   Square and bevel cuts are made simultaneously.

Methods work cannot be confined to equipment improvements or motion improvements.   A company, during the installation of incentive standards on tool- and die-makers, found that interpretation of prints and sketches delayed the start of jobs. In addition, there was quite a bit of stock spoilage.   To solve both problems, the company, with consulting engineers, developed a simplified drafting technique. This technique eliminates circles and arrowheads and all dimensions are scaled from one point.   This simplification of prints resulted in a reduction of drafting time, a reduction in interpretation time by the mechanic, and less spoilage.   Figures 3-6 and 3-7 illustrate the old and new drafting techniques.

In addition to the fact that methods studies are required for standardization, this area also provides immediate savings of maintenance dollars.   Maintenance methods should be approached in the same manner as production methods.   In most maintenance installations, maintenance methods are still in the hands of superintendents, foremen, and other management without the aid of centralized direction, which is similar to the way in which production methods were handled 30 years ago.

It has been production's experience that a staff engineering function is necessary for methods development.   A production foreman effectively administering and directing production does not have time to develop methods improvements.   This is also true of a maintenance foreman who has more mileage to cover to administer and supervise his work than the production foreman.   To expect him to keep abreast of all technological changes in maintenance equipment, to develop new methods, and at the same time do a combined supervisory and administrative job is asking too much. Set up a staff function to review all maintenance work methods and plan production.

Standard Practice—Welding

(The butt-weld tables list the electrode sizes and number of passes to be used for welding carbon-steel pipe with the approved carbon-steel electrodes)

Butt-weld Tables—Standard Practice

Size of pipe, in.		Outer circumference, in.	Rolled position				Fixed position			
			No. passes per electrode			Total passes	No. passes per electrode			Total passes
			1/8 in.	5/32 in.	3/16 in.		1/8 in.	5/32 in.	3/16 in.	
1	Std	4.2	2	...	...	2	2	...	...	2
	X Hy	4.2	2	...	...	2	2	...	...	2
	XX Hy	4.2	2	...	...	2	2	...	...	2
1½	Std	6.0	2	...	...	2	2	...	...	2
	X Hy	6.0	2	...	...	2	2	...	...	2
	XX Hy	6.0	2	...	...	2	2	...	...	2
2	Std	7.5	2	...	...	2	2	...	...	2
	X Hy	7.5	2	...	...	2	2	...	...	2
	XX Hy	7.5	2	...	...	2	2	...	...	2
2½	Std	9.0	2	...	...	2	2	...	...	2
	X Hy	9.0	2	...	...	2	2	...	...	2
	XX Hy	9.0	2	...	...	2	2	...	...	2
3	Std	11.0	1	1	...	2	1	1	...	2
	X Hy	11.0	...	2	...	2	...	2	...	2
	XX Hy	11.0	...	4	...	4	...	4	...	4
3½	Std	12.6	...	2	...	2	...	2	...	2
	X Hy	12.6	...	3	...	3	...	3	...	3
	XX Hy	12.6	...	2	2	4	...	4	...	4
4	Std	14.1	...	2	...	2	...	2	...	2
	X Hy	14.1	...	3	...	3	...	3	...	3
	XX Hy	14.1	...	1	3	4	...	4	...	4
4½	Std	15.7	...	3	...	3	...	3	...	3
	X Hy	15.7	...	3	...	3	...	3	...	3
	XX Hy	15.7	...	1	3	4	...	4	...	4
5	Std	17.3	...	3	...	3	...	3	...	3
	X Hy	17.3	...	1	2	3	...	3	...	3
	XX Hy	17.3	...	1	3	4	...	5	...	5
6	Std	20.8	...	3	...	3	...	3	...	3
	X Hy	20.8	...	1	2	3	...	3	...	3
	XX Hy	20.8	...	1	3	4	...	5	...	5
8	Std	27.1	...	1	2	3	...	3	...	3
	X Hy	27.1	...	1	3	4	...	4	...	4
	XX Hy	27.1	...	1	3	4	...	5	...	5
10	Std	33.7	...	1	2	3	...	4	...	4
	X Hy	33.7	...	1	3	4	...	5	...	5
	XX Hy	33.7	...	1	3	4				
12	Std	40.1	...	1	2	3	...	5	...	5
	X Hy	40.1	...	1	3	4	...	5	...	5

FIG. 3-4. Standard methods are necessary before work measurement can be attempted. With nonrepetitive work, methods can be standardized as illustrated. On specifications given, the work can be measured and standards applied, based on the standard method for welding specific pipe sizes and the number of butt welds required.

The methods engineer must have a staff relationship with the plant engineer and maintenance foreman. With this arrangement, maintenance foremen still are the key men in charge of setting up work methods. They review proposals with the methods engineer and accept, add to, or reject them. Out of this review will come recommendations for improved methods which will result in more efficient usage of men and equipment.

STANDARD PRACTICE – WELDING

(1) STANDARDS WILL BE BASED ON WEAVING OF THE ELECTRODE ON ALL PASSES EXCEPT THE FIRST

(2) STANDARDS ARE BASED ON THE RELATIONSHIP OF THE INCLUDED ANGLE AND THE RELATED PASS AS LISTED IN EXAMPLES BELOW

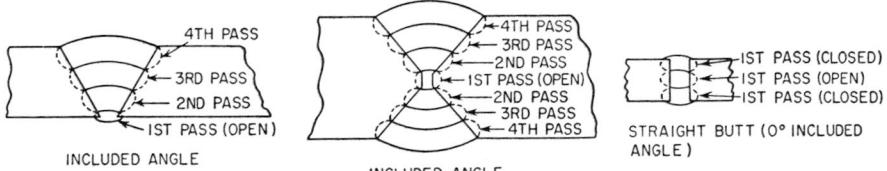

FIG. 3-5. Further definition of standard method for butt-welding pipe as illustrated by Fig. 3-4.

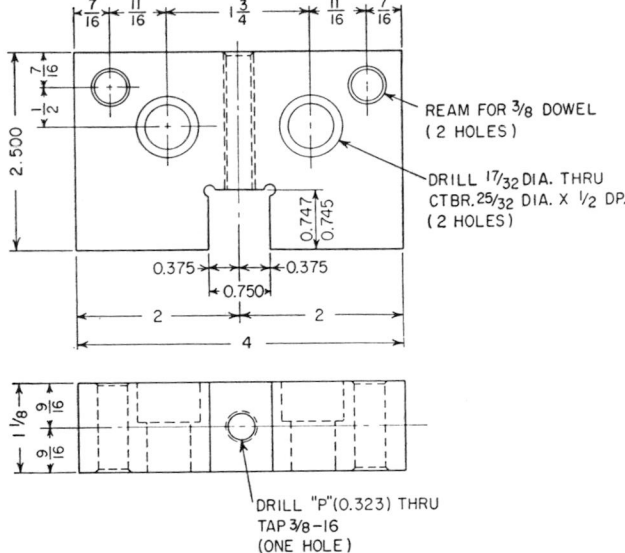

FIG. 3-6. Conventional method of drafting a part for tool-and-die work. (*Courtesy of Methods Engineering Council.*)

Providing Handling Equipment. The bulk of the improvements in maintenance work are possible through changes in handling methods. Maintenance operations still contain much of the "brute work" that has been eliminated from production jobs. Here is a typical example:

In analyzing the operation of straightening paraffin press plates a man-machine chart was developed (Fig. 3-10). This chart demonstrates that the two helpers functioned as holding fixtures to position the plates and to hold them while the operator gaged the plates.   It is evident that one man could be eliminated from the job through the substitution of some mechanical device to take his place as a holding fixture.   As illustrated in the sketch (Fig. 3-8), the simplest was a short section of roller conveyor.   Through rearrangement of operator's duties (as illustrated in Fig. 3-10), he assists the remaining helper in positioning and removing the plate and the conveyor acts as a holding fixture for the gaging operation.

It is quite possible that this method could be further improved.   A stop could be placed on the end of the conveyor to catch the plate as it is ejected from the roll, eliminating that function of the helper.   An air cylinder could be installed to push the plate into the rolls, thereby eliminating another function of the helper.   To position the plates to and from the conveyor, a chain hoist can be used, eliminating the last function of the helper.   These three modest improvements could make a one-man job out of this operation.

In addition to providing handling equipment, there is also the possibility of reducing the amount of handling involved.   Figure 3-9 is a methods proposal based on eliminating handling operations.   As illustrated in the proposal, it was felt that heat exchangers could be cleaned and tested on the pipe-still unit location rather than lowering them to the ground, moving them into position, moving them

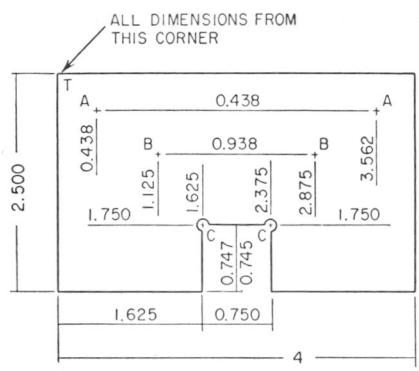

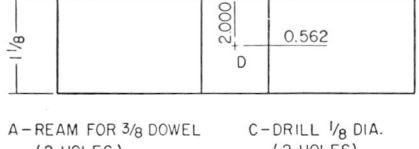

A–REAM FOR 3/8 DOWEL   C–DRILL 1/8 DIA.
    (2 HOLES)   (2 HOLES)
B–DRILL 17/32 DIA.,CT BR.   D–TAP 3/8-16 THRU
    25/32 DIA. X 1/2 DP.   (ONE HOLE)
    (2 HOLES)

Fig. 3-7.   Improved drafting technique which reduced thinking time of mechanic and material spoilage.   (*Courtesy of Methods Engineering Council.*)

again, and raising them back on the still.   Note that this eliminates from 30 to 40 man-hours per heat exchanger.   At this particular location, the savings in time amount to slightly over 1 man-year.

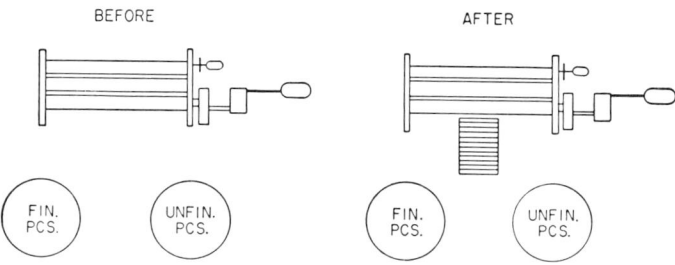

MACHINE LAYOUT

Fig. 3-8.   Before-and-after work-area sketch, showing addition of short roller conveyor that replaced one helper.   See Fig. 3-10 for elemental description of the operation.

It is difficult to separate material-handling problems from methods.   Since a large percentage of maintenance jobs consist of selecting material, getting the material to a location, removing material, installing the new material, and scrap removal, detailed studies must be made to reduce the percentage of handling time in the total working time.   An analysis must be made first on repetitive work, as illustrated by the two case histories; then an analysis must be made by craft lines.   This must be made with consideration for the size of the plant maintenance function together with the kind of materials used.   In a small plant, millwrights provide the material-handling service with an occasional boost by fork-lift trucks.   Even though on a small scale, there still are enough hours for a methods study.   In a large maintenance installation, the problem is increased according to the amount of equipment required.   This type of installation calls for a central transportation system which might include radio control with a complete dispatch system.   A project of this size will justify the assignment of a group of industrial engineers for study.   The material-handling problem in the small plant will be a consideration during job, equipment, or craft studies.

(This outline contains the results of a savings investigation regarding the discussion on bundle maintenance of all bundles on the old pipe stills.   From the discussion, the proposed changes with the savings have been outlined on these operations; lowering bundles to ground, cleaning bundles, testing bundles, and raising bundles back on still.)

Present Method	*Proposed Method*
Description:	Description
1. Lower bundles to ground level and position in alley.	1. _____
2. Clean and flange test bundles in alley.	2. Clean and flange test bundles on location.
3. Remove bundles from alley and raise to still.	3. _____
Avg No. of riggers used: 5	Avg No. of riggers used: 0
Elapsed hr for oper.:	Operation eliminated

Bundle Nos.: (0–4) (5–6) (7) (8–10)
              8   8   8   6
Bundle Nos.: (11–13) (18–22)
                6   6
Act. hr for oper.:
Bundle Nos.: (0–4) (5–6) (7) (8–10)
              40   40   40   30
Bundle Nos.: (11–13) (18–22)
               30   30
Yearly savings:

Bundle Nos.:	(0–4)	(5–6)	(7)	(8–10)	(11–13)	(18–22)
No. times pulled per year:	16	6	3	18	12	18
Hours saved per year:	640	240	120	540	360	540

Total rigger hours saved per year: 2440 (a little over 1 man-year)

Fig. 3-9. A proposal for reducing material-handling requirements.

Standardization of Crews.   One of the common complaints, with regard to the performance efficiency on maintenance jobs, is "too many men on the job."   This may be due to the old "craftsman and helper" tradition, or it may be due to poor job planning.   In either case, there is a loss in maintenance dollars.

Standardization of materials, equipment, and work methods is a must before maintenance work can be planned, scheduled, or measured.   Standardization of crew size enters the problem under the classification of work methods.   These are the normal considerations when establishing crew size: (1) physical limitations of the individual with respect to equipment and material handled, (2) individual's safety considerations on particular jobs (a standby may be necessary in areas where a craftsman is not permitted to work alone, etc.), and (3) the urgency of the job.

Crew size must be determined by work study based on the considerations listed above.   Work studies to determine crew size should be made as follows: first, on a job basis where work is repetitive; second, on handling methods of equipment that is regularly used; and third, on a craft basis where nonrepetitive type does not involve stationary equipment (millwright work, plumbing, field welding, etc.).

Figure 3-10 illustrates an example of establishing a standardization of crew size in repetitive jobs.   With the old method, three men were required, one operator and two helpers. One helper would not handle the plates without assistance, and since the operator was required at the machine controls, the crew size was standardized at three men. With small changes two helpers were no longer required. The standard crew size was changed to two men and a new standard time was established.

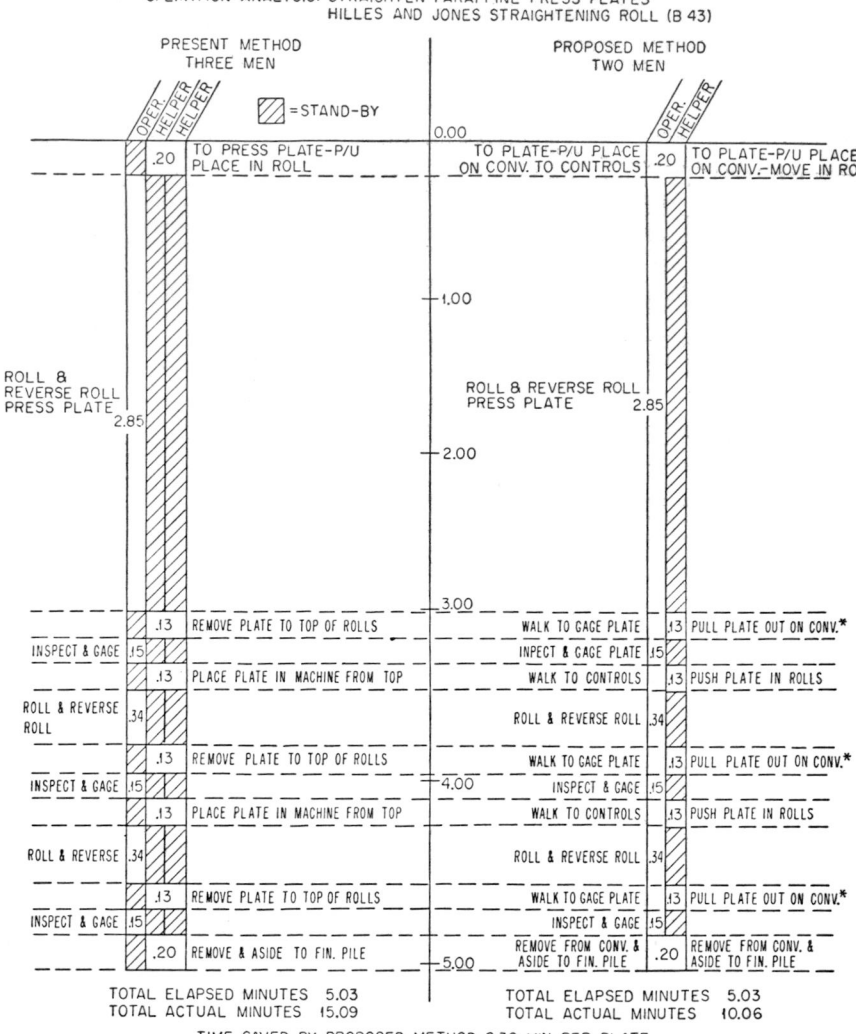

FIG. 3-10. Man-machine chart illustrating a practical method for determining crew size, analyzing handling equipment, and collecting time data prior to developing a job standard. (*Courtesy of Clapp & Poliak, Inc.*)

As pointed out previously, further improvements on the job could reduce the manning to the operator alone.

In the cases cited, the work-measurement standards were based on gang size as determined by the methods of completing the work. With the newer method (two-man gang), shop supervision scheduled the work for two men and planned the efficient disposition of the former helper who was no longer necessary for the job.

Figure 3-11 is the work area for two pieces of equipment requiring a gang. The operations, bevel shear and scarp, are performed on light plate stock prior to welding. The weight of plate handled, within equipment capabilities, determines the crew size. The work must be scheduled by crew size and the standard data developed for work measurement must tie in with crew size. With each gang size the machine speed remains the same. However, since work handling is the determining factor in gang size, extra time must be provided during machine operation for the increased gang (see Fig. 3-12). The handling elements vary with the weight of each plate and are completed accordingly with the proper gang size built into the standard. Figure 3-13 illustrates the handling elements. Note that there are two columns (Columns 1 and 2) for handling all material at the two-man gang size level. Column 1 applies to a two-man gang, and Column 2 applies to a three-man gang. This is to provide flexibility in those jobs where portions of the job require three men and other portions

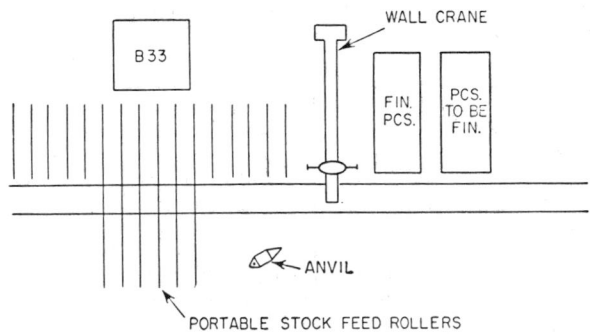

Fig. 3-11. Bevel-shear-machine work area. Within capabilities of handling equipment, the bevel-shear machine and the weight of plate handled, standard crew sizes are determined for operations performed on this equipment. At the same time work is scheduled the correct gang is scheduled, as gang size can vary between jobs.

require two men. Planning and scheduling require some flexibility, and it is not practical to separate jobs into mixed gang sizes. For those instances where various weights of plate would require a combination of two- and three-man gangs on the same job, a standard is provided for the two-man portion that will allow time for the three-man gang, avoiding mixed-gang sizes on the same job.

The determination of gang size by craft cannot be defined as clearly as the job or equipment method. However, standard methods of work must be outlined for each craft (see Fig. 3-4). It becomes the planner's or foreman's job to review the amount and type of work, consider the standard method of performing the work, and determine the most efficient gang size. The work-measurement standard for the work will be established in accordance with the standard methods of performing the work. After this standard method has been reviewed by the planner or foreman and the amount of available work has been taken into consideration together with a completion date, the proper gang size will be scheduled. The work-measurement standards will be adequate since they are also based on the standard method.

Equipment Records. For expediting control functions such as methods, planning and scheduling, and work measurement, equipment records must contain the following information:

1. Machine and parts specification numbers.
2. A breakdown history.
3. A preventive maintenance history.
4. Maximum and minimum spare-parts record.

The machine and parts specification numbers are necessary for the planning function and work-measurement function. With this information readily available, the delays in scheduling repair work and nonproductive time by maintenance crafts will be minimized since the proper parts can be located at the job before the work starts.

The breakdown history must be analyzed to determine repetitive work. The analysis of repetitive work must be made to determine if improper design or improper installation caused the breakdown. If so, this can be corrected. If either of these two is not the cause, each type of breakdown must be analyzed from the methods

Bevel Shear and Scarp

MACHINE: Hilles and Jones bevel shear (B33)
OPERATIONS: Bevel shear plate stock
Scarp plate stock corners (by hand)
GANG: The normal gang for jobs consisting of plates weighing from 51 to 100 lb each shall consist of two men.
The normal gang for jobs consisting of plates weighing over 100 lb each shall consist of three men.

CONDITIONS: The application of these standards is contingent on the following conditions:

6. The gang size shall be determined by the weight of the pieces to be processed.

Standard-time Table No. 9.2
Bevel Shear—Cutting Time Only

| Symbol | Plate thickness, in. | Man-hr per ft of bevel | |
| | | Gang size | |
		2 men	3 men
C	$\frac{1}{8}$	0.0048	0.0071
	$\frac{3}{16}$ and $\frac{1}{4}$	0.0059	0.0089
	$\frac{9}{32}$ and $\frac{5}{16}$	0.0062	0.0092
	$\frac{3}{8}$	0.0062	0.0092

FIG. 3-12. Weight of material handled with equipment available determines gang size. Standard hours for machine operations must be based on gang size.

viewpoint to see if there is a possibility of eliminating or reducing repetitive breakdowns of each type. If this is not possible, it may be necessary to plan preventive-maintenance measures which will allow this type of work to be scheduled and work-measurement standards developed based on the preventive-measurement procedure. Preventive maintenance can be planned and scheduled and job standards for work measurement can be easily applied on this type of work. Equipment records should be a source of information to point out areas for repetitive job standards.

When it is necessary to repair or make parts for equipment, the most economical method is to process this work by job lots instead of one or two parts at a time. It is more efficient to set up a job-lot method and standard quantity rather than process one or two parts. This is illustrated under Job Standards—Time Study. For a

Standard-time Table No. 9.4
Material-handling Time

Sym-bol	Description of element	Man-hr per plate					
		Weight of plate, lb					
		51-100 lb.	51-100 lb.	101-300 lb.	301-900 lb.	901-1,200 lb.	1,201-1,800 lb.
		(1)	(2)	(3)	(4)	(5)	(6)
V	Initial get and position plate to bevel only, move plate aside to finished pile, no scarping	0.037	0.054	0.221	0.250	0.362	0.362
W	Initial get and position plate to bevel and scarp, position plate for scarping after beveling, move plate to finished pile after scarping	0.064	0.094	0.259	0.297	0.399	0.458
X	Reposition plate to bevel additional edges—once per each additional edge	0.011	0.013	0.045	0.055	0.077	0.122
Y	Reposition plate for additional scarping, once per additional scarp	0.011	0.013	0.038	0.038	0.055	0.055
Z	Initial get and position plate to scarp only, move plate to finished pile after scarping	0.037	0.054	0.183	0.210	0.294	0.294

Material-handling Time—Standard-time 9.4

Column 1.   To be used on all jobs consisting only of pieces under 101 lb.   The standards in this column are based on a two-man gang.

Column 2.   To be used on all jobs consisting of pieces under 101 lb intermingled with pieces over 100 lb.   The standards in this column are based on a three-man gang and shall be applied to those pieces 100 lb or under only.

Columns 3, 4, and 5.   The Standards in these columns are based on three-man gangs.   Use Column 3 for all plates weighing 101 to 300 lb, use Column 4 for all plates weighing 301 to 900 lb, and use Column 5 for all plates weighing 901 to 1,200 lb.

FIG. 3-13. Crew size is based on weight of material handled, but there are some jobs with plate sizes that can be handled by a two-man gang intermingled with plates requiring a three-man gang.   In those jobs, since it is sometimes impractical to split crews, standard times are provided to give fair work standards to the crew.   If the job is large enough, the work can be split into two jobs at this operation, one for the two-man and one for the three-man crew.   This is a function of planning and scheduling and can result in a 33 per cent cost reduction for part of the job.

parts repair, Straightening of Paraffin Press Plates, the lot size was established at 50 plates.   This enables planning to schedule a long run of this work, normally a day's work for two men.   With a run of this type, job preparation and setup costs are spread over a large number of pieces, the most efficient crew can be scheduled, and the job becomes a production run without the delays and interference problems encountered in one or two pieces to be processed as a job.

After analyzing parts requirements, provision must be made to have as many lots of parts as necessary to provide for equipment repair, and parts maintenance. For example, one lot of parts must be in use; one lot can be in spare-parts inventory, readily available, and one lot could be in the shop in process or to be scheduled at the shop's convenience. This method of establishing repetitive jobs for parts repair will effectively reduce the cost of maintaining equipment.

Planning and Scheduling. This function is to maintenance as production control is to production. Production labor measurement is impossible without planning how, where, and when the work is to be done. Work measurement of maintenance jobs is not practical if this function is slighted.

Work must be planned ahead of time to eliminate or reduce to a minimum non-productive hours or inefficient work resulting from waiting for job assignment of instructions, wrong crafts, wrong number of men on the job, inefficient work methods, not enough material, wrong material, and performing shopwork in the field.

Work must be scheduled ahead of time to eliminate or reduce to a minimum non-productive hours or inefficient work resulting from failure to schedule equipment; excess travel time due to job chasing; failure to schedule material drops; and failure to balance manpower requirements.

There is no method to measure efficiency or pay incentive bonus on nonproductive time. The only choice is to pay base rate, and this penalizes the worker as far as the opportunity to earn incentive pay, and of course the job is credited with excess costs. For that reason, planning and scheduling are interrelated with methods and work measurement. Without a standard method, there is no way to estimate time; without time on a job, there is no basis to schedule jobs, equipment, and men.

Job Standards—Time Study. As previously discussed under Methods, there is some repetitive maintenance work. With this type of work, it is more practical to establish job standards through production-type time studies than by using the standard-data approach. The time study on a specific job supplies the data for developing a job standard based on specific elemental times and allowances for specific conditions for that job.

The method is the same as that used for establishing an ordinary production standard through time study. The processing of several complete units is observed for the purpose of determining the elements of operation. Again, the most important consideration in this mental process of breaking an operation into elements is the separation of constant times from variable times as previously discussed under Standard Data—Time Study.

After the elemental breakdown has been determined, the elements are described on the time-study observation sheet with complete definitions of the movements required for each element. During the time, the breaking points between elements are observed very closely in order to record the correct actual elemental times. Each element must be consistent within itself as far as the starting and stopping points are concerned. If the time breaks between elements are inconsistent, the resulting elemental times will mean nothing. They will have no value for building standard data to be used as a basis for other standards or for use in investigating various improvement proposals involving costs.

The number of cycles to be studied during a time study is normally decided by the time-study observer. There are statistical methods in use to determine if enough time-study readings have been taken on each element and whether they are representative of the time required for that element. However, it is more economical to employ trained time-study engineers who can adequately judge whether sufficient usable data have been obtained than to determine statistically if every elemental time has enough data to support it. The length of study varies with the type of operation, the amount of variables in the operation, the length of the operation cycle, and the performance of the operator. The important consideration is to be sure that sufficient cycles are observed in order to time, record, level the operator's performance, and document all the normal conditions of the operation. If this is an operation that has never been placed on standard, several 8-hr time studies may be taken to make sure all normal conditions have been observed. If this is a variation of a similar job that has already been placed on standard, the 8-hr studies may not be required to

OPERATION: All straightening of paraffin press plates performed on the Hilles and Jones straightening roll (B43).

STANDARD TIMES INCLUDE:

1. Change tickets, to press plate, pick up, place in roll, roll and reverse roll, remove from rolls to gage, inspect and gage, reroll when necessary, straighten with hammer when necessary, remove and aside to finished pile and stack on jig.
2. Conditional allowances: The standard-time table includes a conditional allowance for the noncyclical elements necessary to accomplish the major operation. This allowance was computed to be 3.5 % of the constant times and includes the following: starting preparation of getting tools out, oil equipment, clean tools and work area, move out of way of overhead crane, necessary interruptions by foreman, necessary conversations pertaining to work.
3. Personal allowance: A personal allowance of 7 % has been included in the standard-time table.

CONDITIONS: The application of these standards is contingent on the following conditions:

1. These standards apply to those operations performed on the below listed machine, in the boiler shop, as specified in the tables.
   Hilles and Jones straightening roll (B43)
   Manufacturer, Hilles and Jones, 1892
   Manufacturer's description, No. 1
      7-in. rolls
      Gear-driven
      No manufacturer's specifications available
      Motor, 7.5 hp, 25 cycle, 440 volts
      Motor No. 382
   Accessories
      Overhead-crane service
      Sledge hammers
      Leveling board
      5 jigs to position plates and transport
      Roller stand
2. These standards are supplementary to the Boiler Shop Standard Plan No. 1-45.
3. These standards shall apply only as long as the tools and equipment are of standard quality and the machine is in good working condition.
4. When changes in tools, equipment, machine, materials, or procedures are effected, the industrial engineering department shall be informed in writing.
5. All press plates with respect to the quality of finished plate shall be subject to the approval of the foreman.
6. The gang size consists of two men.

APPLICATION OF STANDARD: Standard time shall be applied to each job and computed on the job performance biweekly basis.

Standard-time Table: 08.01

Operation	Man-hours
Straighten paraffin press plates (per lot of 50)...........	10.00

EXPLANATION OF TABLE: Allow the standard time once for each lot of 50 plates.

FIG. 3-14. Data essential to document the conditions of work properly for a job standard.

determine if all normal conditions have been provided for in the elemental times or allowances. The variation from the existing standard might be studied for elemental times and the conditions found from the previous 8-hr studies used in combination with these new elemental times to establish the production standard.

It is possible to use the ratio-delay technique to determine allowances, but in terms of calendar days this technique takes longer. The results of 8-hr time studies can be developed and in use, with the resulting savings in effect while ratio-delay data are still being collected. The frequency of the occurrence of repetitive work (e.g., one lot every week or one lot every month) will also delay any work or allowances based on ratio delay.

During the time study it is important that a complete record be made of the conditions existing at the time of the study. An observer can hardly document enough of the pertinent facts on a job to answer all the questions that will be asked at a later date. The value of such descriptive and accurate information can best be appreciated by considering that in the past questions or disagreements with the production standard turned into grievances when this documentation was lacking.

Figure 3-10 illustrates the elemental build-up of the standard. This operation, Straighten Paraffin Press Plates, is the same operation that was previously used to illustrate a methods change. When the standard is released to the shop, it is accompanied by data for this job standard that include a definition of the work involved (see Fig. 3-14), a listing of the elements of work that are included in the standard times, and a definition of the allowances to further define the basis of the job standard. The job standard is applied only when certain conditions are met. These conditions specify the equipment and the accessories, which include handling devices and miscellaneous jigs and fixture. The gang size is also stated (Fig. 3-14) and the responsibility for quality is placed with the foreman. In this section it is specified also (items 3 and 4) that the standards are applicable only as long as equipment and working conditions remain the same. In the standard-time table it is noted that the lot size on which the standard is based is 50 plates. Under discussion of repetitive work in the section on Methods, a mention of constant lot size for repetitive jobs was made. To further define the standard, sketches of part and layout are supplied (see Fig. 3-15).

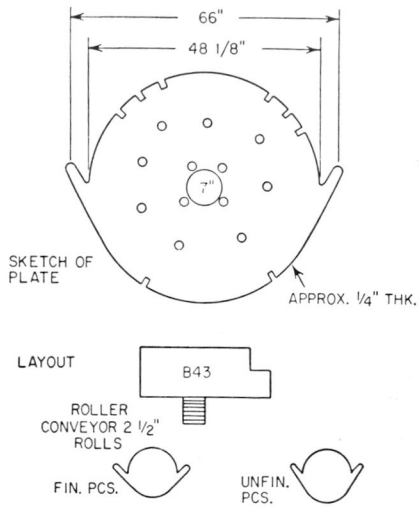

STRAIGHTEN PARAFFINE PRESS PLATES

Fig. 3-15. Parts and layout sketches serve to document the work and work methods in anticipation of future improvements in material or equipment.

For future changes of equipment or method all this documentation is necessary to demonstrate the "before" and "after" elemental times, the basis of changing standards.

Much of the same procedure would be followed if the standard had been developed through MTM data. The elemental times would have been developed through the use of MTM data rather than time study. The conditional allowances would properly be developed through continuous observation of the job or ratio-delay studies. The MTM procedure will be discussed in detail in following pages.

Standard Data—Time Study. After preliminary work has established standard methods, the next step is to take a few experimental time studies to determine standard elements. These standard elements then become the breaking points between work elements for watch readings in the process of determining elemental times.

When building standard data, the watch must be read at the same instant for every like element. After standard elements have been determined, time studies can be started to obtain elemental times for the development of standard data.

The need for elemental standard data can be explained in this manner. While the elements of work on equipment, or as performed by a craft, are the same, they vary in degree from job to job, depending upon the frequency of occurrence or amount

Flame Cutting

MACHINE CUTTING

Standard Cutting-speed Table 18.00

Size plate, in.	Size tip (Oxweld)	Fuel pressure	Oxygen pressure	Cutting speed, in. per min
1/16	4	3	30	20.4
1/8	4	3	30	18.5
3/16	4	3	30	17.3
1/4	4	3	30	16.0
5/16	4	3	30	15.0
3/8	4	3	30	14.3
7/16	4	3	30	13.8
1/2	4	3	40	13.0
9/16	4	3	40	12.3
5/8	6	3	40	11.9
1 1/16	6	3	40	11.3
3/4	6	3	40	10.8
1 3/16	6	3	40	10.5
7/8	6	3	40	10.1
1 5/16	6	3	40	9.8
1	6	3	50	9.7
1 1/8	8	3	50	9.0
1 1/4	8	3	50	8.5
1 1/2	8	3	50	8.1
1 3/4	10	3	50	7.4
2	10	3	50	6.8
2 1/2	10	3	50	6.0
3	10	4	50	5.5
4	12	4	60	5.5
4 1/2	12	4	60	5.0

Standard Job-preparation Table 18.01

Job	Man-hr per job
1. Flame cutting, CM-16 and CM-30 portable machines, tray cutting machines...	0.10

Fig. 3-16. First step in the development of standard data is to define machine specifications (standard cutting speed table). Job preparation was determined to be a series of elemental times that were constant for all flame-cutting jobs.

of work (i.e., length of cut). Another way of stating this condition is this: While each job (within the same craft) has a similar work cycle, the number of times or degree that each element is performed in the cycle varies between jobs. In order to compensate for this variance, elemental standard-data times are established to measure properly the work on each job. These elemental production standards are issued as time values for performing an element, or a degree of an element, and whenever possible extended into a group of elements (all constant times per each occurrence). When establishing a standard time for a job, the worker must be credited

Standard Cutting Table 18.02

Plate* thickness or depth of bevel, in.	Man-hr per 100 in.		Plate* thickness or depth of bevel, in.	Man-hr per 100 in.	
	Square burn	Bevel burn†		Square burn	Bevel burn†
1/16	0.10	0.16	13/16	0.19	0.27
1/8	0.11	0.17	7/8	0.20	0.28
3/16	9.11	0.17	15/16	0.20	0.28
1/4	0.12	0.19	1	0.21	0.30
5/16	0.13	0.20	1 1/8	0.22	0.31
3/8	0.15	0.22	1 1/4	0.24	0.32
7/16	0.15	0.22	1 1/2	0.25	0.34
1/2	0.15	0.22	1 3/4	0.27	0.37
9/16	0.16	0.24	2	0.29	0.39
5/8	0.17	0.25	2 1/2	0.33	0.44
11/16	0.17	0.25	3	0.36	0.48
3/4	0.19	0.27	3 1/2	0.36	0.48

* For any intermediate thickness of plate, use next higher thickness.
† Substitute the depth of bevel for plate thickness, chip edge after bevel included in standard times.

Standard Material-handling Table 18.04
CM-16 Machine

Description	Weight of finished piece, lb	Man-hr per piece
Position material to flame cut, burn scrap, scrap aside, aside finished piece.	0–25	0.02
	26–50	0.03
	51–100	0.08
	101–200	0.16
	201–300	0.23
	301–500	0.29
	501–1,000	0.35
	Over 1,000	0.37

Standard Setup Table, Tray Cutting 18.05

Description	Unit per job	Man-hr per circle
1. Prepare stock, and place machine on stock.	1st circle cut.	0.22
2. Prepare stock and reposition machine.	Each additional circle cut.	0.01

Fig. 3-17. Standard cutting times were developed from the same data that established the machine specifications. Chipping the edge of plate after beveling, a variable by length of bevel, was added to the bevel-cutting time since measurement and application of these two elements are handled in the same manner. The material-handling table was based on a curve determined by charting weight of finished piece against the time of the material-handling elements for each piece studied. From a number of studies, the time required to set up the tray-cutting machine was determined. An additional setup allowance is necessary to compensate for repositioning the machine for additional cuts in the same job.

with the number of times and the degree to which each element must be used to complete the work. To illustrate, the development of the elemental standard data for the work of Flame Cutting with Portable Cutting Machines will be used.

Since this work involved machines, standard cutting speeds and standard equipment specifications had to be determined. Through a series of experiments prior to study (a portion of the methods phase), the size of the cutting tip, fuel pressure, oxygen pressure, and cutting speeds were established (standard cutting-speed table, Fig. 3-16). The allowed cutting times (standard cutting table, Fig. 3-17) reflect these specifications.

Flame Cutting

Standard Preheat Table
Man-hr per Occurrence

Plate thickness, in.	O.B. preheat (1)	I.B. preheat (2)
Up to $\frac{1}{4}$	0.007	0.010
Over $\frac{1}{4}$ to $\frac{3}{8}$	0.013	0.019
Over $\frac{3}{8}$ to $\frac{1}{2}$	0.014	0.024
Over $\frac{1}{2}$ to $\frac{5}{8}$	0.015	0.028
Over $\frac{5}{8}$ to $\frac{3}{4}$	0.016	0.031
Over $\frac{3}{4}$ to 1	0.018	0.034
Over 1 to $1\frac{1}{2}$	0.020	0.039
Over $1\frac{1}{2}$ to 2	0.022	0.044
Over 2 to $2\frac{1}{2}$	0.024	0.048
Over $2\frac{1}{2}$ to 3	0.025	0.051
Over 3 to $3\frac{1}{2}$	0.026	0.053

Standard Table, Miscellaneous Operations 18.09

Description	Man-hr per occ.
1. Change or adjust cascade oxygen system pressure.	0.25
2. Exchange bottles in propane bank system.	0.04

FIG. 3-18. The total time of flame cutting consists of a preheat time, a constant value by thickness of plate and type of preheat (O.B. or I.B.). The above standard times for preheating were determined at the same time machine-cutting specifications were established. There are two miscellaneous operations that can occur in the burner's workday. These operations were measured and the standard established for each type of grouping the elemental time values required to perform the operation.

Before the flame cut could commence, the material had to be preheated by the fuel; then the oxygen was turned on and the machine started. In the course of obtaining machine speeds, it was also found that the preheat time was a variable, by stock thickness, and whether the cut started at the edge of the plate stock (O.B. preheat) or in from the edge of the plate (I.B. preheat). The inside preheat took longer because of the greater mass of material that had to be brought up to burning temperature. The same series of experiments that determined cutting speeds were used to establish preheat times (see standard preheat table, Fig. 3-18).

The first elements of work encountered on actual job study were preparatory elements, changing job tickets, and requisitioning material. These elements were determined to be a series of constant times for all flame-cutting jobs.

The next elements of work were those involving the positioning of material. When developing the standard data for material handling, the elements of work required in the removal of finished pieces were added to the positioning elements. These times were charted by weight of finished piece and the material-handling time of each piece. This chart was the basis for the standard material-handling table (Fig. 3-17). This charting procedure is explained in detail in Phil Carroll's book, "How to Chart Timestudy Data."[1]

The machine setup times (Fig. 3-18a) were established by grouping and totaling the elemental time values required for the various types of setup. From the large

Flame Cutting

Standard Setup Table, CM-16 Machine

Description	Man-hr per occurrence per job	
	First occur.	Each additional occur.
1. Prepare and lay out sheet stock to burn OD of circle—set up machine to burn—for square cut.	0.132	0.073
2. Prepare and lay out sheet stock to bevel OD of circle after square cut—set up machine.	0.059	0.029
3. Measure and mark landing on stock to be beveled—circles only.	0.093	0.093
4. Prepare and lay out sheet stock to burn ID of circle—set up machine to burn—for square cut.	0.067	0.040
5. Locate center of circle (underside of piece only) prior to making second bevel.	0.076	0.076
6. Prepare stock and set up to burn arc—up to 36 in. radius.	0.068	0.038
7. Prepare stock and set up to burn arc—over 36 in. radius.	0.154	0.061

Standard Setup Table, CM-30 Machine 18.07

Description	Man-hr per occurrence per piece	
	First occur. per piece	Each additional occur. per piece
1. Prepare stock and set up track and CM-30 machine to square cut or bevel up to 60 lin in. per cut.	0.044	0.044
2. Prepare stock and set up track and CM-30 machine to square cut or bevel over 60 lin in. per cut.	0.118	0.069

FIG. 3-18a. Separate setup times for each machine by type of work are necessary.

number of jobs that were studied, the necessity for the series of setup times was easily recognized.

In addition to the regular work elements, as outlined previously, additional time has been included in the standard-time tables as a conditional allowance (refer to Sec. 2, Chap. 4 for a more detailed discussion of conditional allowance). This condition allowance is to compensate for noncyclical elements necessary to supplement the previously detailed work elements. This allowance was computed to be 10 per cent of the standard time of the cyclical work elements and included the following: get tools from box or locker; notify crane of lifts to be made; clean flame-cutting tips when necessary; necessary interruptions by foreman, and other necessary conversation

[1] McGraw-Hill Book Company, Inc., New York, 1950.

pertaining to work. A personal allowance of 7 per cent was also included in the standard-time tables.

Application of these flame-cutting standards has been illustrated by Figs. 3-1 and 3-2.

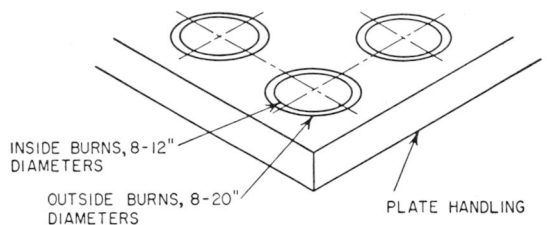

INSIDE BURNS, 8-12"
DIAMETERS

OUTSIDE BURNS, 8-20"
DIAMETERS　　　　PLATE HANDLING

Fig. 3-19. Flame-cutting blanks—ideal job for standard-data application. Diameter and plate thickness vary; however, any combination of size, within limits of the equipment used, can be worked on incentive through application of the standard data.

STANDARD TIME TABLE 18.11–FLAME CUTTING CIRCUMFERENCE

CM—16 MACHINE—JOB TABLE (CONT'D.)

DIAMETER TO BURN	PLATE THICKNESS	1 3/4"		2"		2 1/2"	
	TYPE OF CUT	I.B	O.B.	I.B	O.B	I.B	O.B.
11"	FIRST OCCURRENCE	0.204	0.247	0.208	0 251	0.229	0.270
	ADDITIONAL OCCURRENCE	0.177	0.188	0.181	0.192	0.202	0.261
12"	FIRST OCCURRENCE	0.213	0 256	0.217	0.260	0.239	0.280
	ADDITIONAL OCCURRENCE	0.186	0.197	0.190	0.201	0.212	0.221
13"	FIRST OCCURRENCE	0.221	0.264	0.225	0.268	0.250	0.291
	ADDITIONAL OCCURRENCE	0.194	0.205	0.198	0.209	0.223	0.232
14"	FIRST OCCURRENCE	0.230	0.273	0.234	0.277	0.260	0.301
	ADDITIONAL OCCURRENCE	0.203	0.214	0.207	0.218	0.233	0.242
15"	FIRST OCCURRENCE	0.238	0.281	0.243	0.286	0.270	0.311
	ADDITIONAL OCCURRENCE	0.211	0.222	0.216	0.227	0.243	0.252
16"	FIRST OCCURRENCE	0.247	0.290	0.252	0.295	0.281	0.322
	ADDITIONAL OCCURRENCE	0.220	0.231	0.225	0.236	0.254	0.263
17"	FIRST OCCURRENCE	0.255	0.298	0.261	0.304	0.291	0.332
	ADDITIONAL OCCURRENCE	0.228	0.239	0.234	0.245	0.264	0.273
18"	FIRST OCCURRENCE	0.264	0.307	0.269	0.312	0.302	0.343
	ADDITIONAL OCCURRENCE	0.237	0.248	0.242	0.253	0.275	0.284
19"	FIRST OCCURRENCE	0.272	0.315	0.278	0.321	0.312	0.353
	ADDITIONAL OCCURRENCE	0.245	0.256	0.251	0.262	0.285	0.294
20"	FIRST OCCURRENCE	0.281	0.324	0.287	0.330	0.322	0.363
	ADDITIONAL OCCURRENCE	0.254	0.265	0.260	0.271	0.295	0.304
21"	FIRST OCCURRENCE	0.289	0.332	0.296	0.339	0.333	0.374
	ADDITIONAL OCCURRENCE	0.262	0.273	0.269	0.280	0.306	0.315

Fig. 3-20. Portions of job tables for flame-cutting circumferences. Material handling and job preparation are the only additional times to be added to this table. Similar tables were developed from the elemental data tables for flame-cutting arcs and straight lines, bevel and square cuts.

Extension of Standard Data into Job or Component Standards. After mental standard data have been developed from time studies, they must in turn be developed into larger increments of time wherever possible to facilitate the application of standards. An example of this development is the common job of flame-cutting blanks prior to machine-shop operations. Using the elemental standards to determine the job standard for the job, as illustrated by Fig. 3-19, nine elemental-time calculations are necessary to develop the standard. To simplify the application of time, tables were developed combining basic times for flame-cutting circumferences with a portable

STANDARD WEIGHT TABLE 18—10
WEIGHT OF STEEL CIRCLES
POUNDS

DIAMETER		PLATE THICKNESS IN INCHES		
		1 3/4"	2"	2 1/2"
11"		47.20	53.98	67.42
12"		56.18	64.24	80.23
13"		65.93	75.40	94.17
14"		76.46	87 44	109.21
15"		87.78	100.38	125.37
16"		98	112	141
17"		112	128	160
18"		125	142	178
19"		140	160	200
20"		154	176	221
21"		170	194	243

Fig. 3-21. A table of weights is furnished the rate setter to accompany job tables for determining weight of parts. From the material-handling table, by weight of finished part, material-handling times can be determined.

FLAME CUTTING BLANKS

DATE ___5/5___   WORK ORDER NO. _870-A_

DESCRIPTION _Eight (8) Blanks – 20"O.D._
   12"I.D. – 2"steel plate stock - no bevel

BURN O.B. – 1ST PC._ _ _ _ _ _ _ _ _ _ _ _ _ _ _ _ _ _ =		.330
BURN O.B. – ADD. PCS. 7 X .271 =		1.897
BURN I.B. – 1ST PC._ _ _ _ _ _ _ _ _ _ _ _ _ _ =		.217
BURN I.B. – ADD. PCS. 7 X .190 =		1.330
MAT. HDLG. 8 X .16 =		1.280
JOB PREP. =		.100
ALLOWED HOURS		5.154

Fig. 3-22. Rate-setting form to speed development of standard times from job tables. While diameters and plate thicknesses vary among jobs, job tables provide times within the limits of the equipment used for all blank-cutting jobs.

cutting machine, reducing calculations to five, and supplying a work sheet. The machine setups, preheat times, and burn times, have all been grouped in a job table (Fig. 3-20). Since there can be a number of combinations of inside- and outside-diameter sizes, it was not practical to include material-handling time, which is based on weight of finished piece. For ease in calculating material-handling time, a basic weight table with steel circles (Fig. 3-21) is included with the job tables. A preprinted form is designed to reduce rate-setting time further on this operation. Figure 3-22 illustrates this form and the development of a standard for flame-cutting blanks.

Advantages and Disadvantages. Time Study. The development of standard data based on time study has several immediate cost considerations that must be considered as disadvantages:

1. High initial cost. A large number of elemental time studies are required. In addition to the actual studies, the development of the data is an expensive project.
2. Training costs. Maintenance management must have an application of time-study and work-measurement techniques. The industrial engineers must be trained in craft practice.
3. The payoff date is far away from the start of a complete work-measurement program. A large amount of standard coverage should be available before any work-measurement controls or incentive payments are in effect.

The advantages are:

1. Training of supervision in management's methods.
2. Application costs are reasonable once the standard data have been developed.
3. Forces tighter control over:
   a. Work methods.
   b. Material specifications.
   c. Maintaining maintenance equipment.
4. Flexibility of the system as shown by the fact that standards can be established for group or individual payment and that elements of work are reproducible.
5. A common unit of measurement is available to evaluate the performance of individual craftsmen and foremen. (Employees can relate earnings to their productivity by direct comparison of time.)
6. Audits are possible to determine if proper labor payments have been made.
7. Information is available to improve management controls in the areas of:
   a. Planning and scheduling work.
   b. Planning and scheduling equipment.
   c. Planning and scheduling manpower standards, providing an accurate means of determining excess maintenance costs in specific areas or on specific equipment or parts which would justify modifications or replacement of equipment.
8. With synthetic standard data, such as MTM, specialists in MTM are required to install and maintain the work-measurement installation. Standard data, developed by time study, require experienced time-study men; thus ease any turnover problem by reducing training costs of replacement industrial engineers.

MTM Data. Methods-time measurement data are predetermined basic-motion time values described in classifications of Reach, Move, Turn, Grasp, etc. The unit of time, a TMU, used for measurement, is 0.00001 hr. The tables (Fig. 3-23) give the number of TMU's "required by the operator of average skill working with average effort to make the designated motion under average conditions."[1]

To illustrate the use of MTM data in developing maintenance standards together with their application, examples will be presented of typical plant work. Maintenance work within plant areas was chosen over the shop maintenance work as the former might be considered by the reader to be the more difficult of the two. An example of a shop job is given in an illustration under the time-study section. The development of standards for this shopwork is quite similar to the development of standards for job-lot production work.

[1] H. B. Maynard, G. H. Stegemerten, and J. L. Schwab, Methods-time Measurement, *Factory Management and Maintenance*, New York, 1948.

TABLE I—REACH—R

Distance Moved Inches	Time TMU A	Time TMU B	Time TMU C or D	Time TMU E	Hand In Motion A	Hand In Motion B
¾ or less	2.0	2.0	2.0	2.0	1.6	1.6
1	2.5	2.5	3.6	2.4	2.3	2.3
2	4.0	4.0	5.9	3.8	3.5	2.7
3	5.3	5.3	7.3	5.3	4.5	3.6
4	6.1	6.4	8.4	6.8	4.9	4.3
5	6.5	7.8	9.4	7.4	5.3	5.0
6	7.0	8.6	10.1	8.0	5.7	5.7
7	7.4	9.3	10.8	8.7	6.1	6.5
8	7.9	10.1	11.5	9.3	6.5	7.2
9	8.3	10.8	12.2	9.9	6.9	7.9
10	8.7	11.5	12.9	10.5	7.3	8.6
12	9.6	12.9	14.2	11.8	8.1	10.1
14	10.5	14.4	15.6	13.0	8.9	11.5
16	11.4	15.8	17.0	14.2	9.7	12.9
18	12.3	17.2	18.4	15.5	10.5	14.4
20	13.1	18.6	19.8	16.7	11.3	15.8
22	14.0	20.1	21.2	18.0	12.1	17.3
24	14.9	21.5	22.5	19.2	12.9	18.8
26	15.8	22.9	23.9	20.4	13.7	20.2
28	16.7	24.4	25.3	21.7	14.5	21.7
30	17.5	25.8	26.7	22.9	15.3	23.2

CASE AND DESCRIPTION
A Reach to object in fixed location, or to object in other hand or on which other hand rests.
B Reach to single object in location which may vary slightly from cycle to cycle.
C Reach to object jumbled with other objects in a group so that search and select occur.
D Reach to a very small object or where accurate grasp is required.
E Reach to indefinite location to get hand in position for body balance or next motion or out of way.

TABLE II—MOVE—M

Distance Moved Inches	Time TMU A	Time TMU B	Time TMU C	Hand In Motion B
¾ or less	2.0	2.0	2.0	1.7
1	2.5	2.9	3.4	2.3
2	3.6	4.6	5.2	2.9
3	4.9	5.7	6.7	3.6
4	6.1	6.9	8.0	4.3
5	7.3	8.0	9.2	5.0
6	8.1	8.9	10.3	5.7
7	8.9	9.7	11.1	6.5
8	9.7	10.6	11.8	7.2
9	10.5	11.5	12.7	7.9
10	11.3	12.2	13.5	8.6
12	12.9	13.4	15.2	10.0
14	14.4	14.6	16.9	11.4
16	16.0	15.8	18.7	12.8
18	17.6	17.0	20.4	14.2
20	19.2	18.2	22.1	15.6
22	20.8	19.4	23.8	17.0
24	22.4	20.6	25.5	18.4
26	24.0	21.8	27.3	19.8
28	25.5	23.1	29.0	21.2
30	27.1	24.3	30.7	22.7

Wt. Allowance: Wt. (lb.) Up to	Factor	Constant TMU
2.5	0	0
7.5	1.06	2.2
12.5	1.11	3.9
17.5	1.17	5.6
22.5	1.22	7.4
27.5	1.28	9.1
32.5	1.33	10.8
37.5	1.39	12.5
42.5	1.44	14.3
47.5	1.50	16.0

CASE AND DESCRIPTION
A Move object to other hand or against stop.
B Move object to approximate or indefinite location.
C Move object to exact location.

TABLE III—TURN AND APPLY PRESSURE—T AND AP

Weight	30°	45°	60°	75°	90°	105°	120°	135°	150°	165°	180°
	Time TMU for Degrees Turned										
Small— 0 to 2 Pounds	2.8	3.5	4.1	4.8	5.4	6.1	6.8	7.4	8.1	8.7	9.4
Medium—2.1 to 10 Pounds	4.4	5.5	6.5	7.5	8.5	9.6	10.6	11.6	12.7	13.7	14.8
Large— 10.1 to 35 Pounds	8.4	10.5	12.3	14.4	16.2	18.3	20.4	22.2	24.3	26.1	28.2

APPLY PRESSURE CASE 1—16.2 TMU APPLY PRESSURE CASE 2—10.6 TMU

TABLE IV—GRASP—G

Case	Time TMU	DESCRIPTION
1A	2.0	**Pick Up Grasp**—Small, medium or large object by itself, easily grasped.
1B	3.5	Very small object or object lying close against a flat surface.
1C1	7.3	Interference with grasp on bottom and one side of nearly cylindrical object. Diameter larger than ½".
1C2	8.7	Interference with grasp on bottom and one side of nearly cylindrical object. Diameter ¼" to ½".
1C3	10.8	Interference with grasp on bottom and one side of nearly cylindrical object. Diameter less than ¼".
2	5.6	**Regrasp.**
3	5.6	**Transfer Grasp.**
4A	7.3	Object jumbled with other objects so search and select occur. Larger than 1" x 1" x 1".
4B	9.1	Object jumbled with other objects so search and select occur. ¼" x ¼" x ⅛" to 1" x 1" x 1".
4C	12.9	Object jumbled with other objects so search and select occur. Smaller than ¼" x ¼" x ⅛".
5	0	Contact, sliding or hook grasp.

TABLE V—POSITION*—P

CLASS OF FIT		Symmetry	Easy To Handle	Difficult To Handle
1—Loose	No pressure required	S	5.6	11.2
		SS	9.1	14.7
		NS	10.4	16.0
2—Close	Light pressure required	S	16.2	21.8
		SS	19.7	25.3
		NS	21.0	26.6
3—Exact	Heavy pressure required.	S	43.0	48.6
		SS	46.5	52.1
		NS	47.8	53.4

*Distance moved to engage—1" or less.

TABLE VI—RELEASE—RL

Case	Time TMU	DESCRIPTION
1	2.0	Normal release performed by opening fingers as independent motion.
2	0	Contact Release

TABLE VII—DISENGAGE—D

CLASS OF FIT	Easy to Handle	Difficult to Handle
1—Loose—Very slight effort, blends with subsequent move	4.0	5.7
2—Close — Normal effort, slight recoil	7.5	11.8
3—Tight — Considerable effort, hand recoils markedly	22.9	34.7

TABLE VIII—EYE TRAVEL TIME AND EYE FOCUS—ET AND EF

Eye Travel Time $= 15.2 \times \frac{T}{D}$ TMU, with a maximum value of 20 TMU.

where T = the distance between points from and to which the eye travels.
D = the perpendicular distance from the eye to the line of travel T.

Eye Focus Time = 7.3 TMU.

TABLE IX—BODY, LEG, AND FOOT MOTIONS

DESCRIPTION	SYMBOL	DISTANCE	TIME TMU
Foot Motion—Hinged at Ankle	FM	Up to 4"	8.5
With heavy pressure	FMP		19.1
Leg or Foreleg Motion.	LM —	Up to 6"	7.1
		Each add'l. inch	1.2
Sidestep—Case 1—Complete when leading leg contacts floor	SS-C1	Less than 12"	Use REACH or MOVE Time
		12"	17.0
		Each add'l. inch	.6
Case 2—Lagging leg must contact floor before next motion can be made	SS-C2	12"	34.1
		Each add'l. inch	1.1
Bend, Stoop, or Kneel on One Knee	B,S,KOK		29.0
Arise	AB,AS,AKOK		31.9
Kneel on Floor—Both Knees	KBK		69.4
Arise	AKBK		76.7
Sit	SIT		34.7
Stand from Sitting Position	STD		43.4
Turn Body 45 to 90 degrees— Case 1—Complete when leading leg contacts floor.	TBC1		18.6
Case 2—Lagging leg must contact floor before next motion can be made.	TBC2		37.2
Walk.	W-FT	Per Foot	5.3
Walk.	W-P	Per Pace	15.0

TABLE X—SIMULTANEOUS MOTIONS

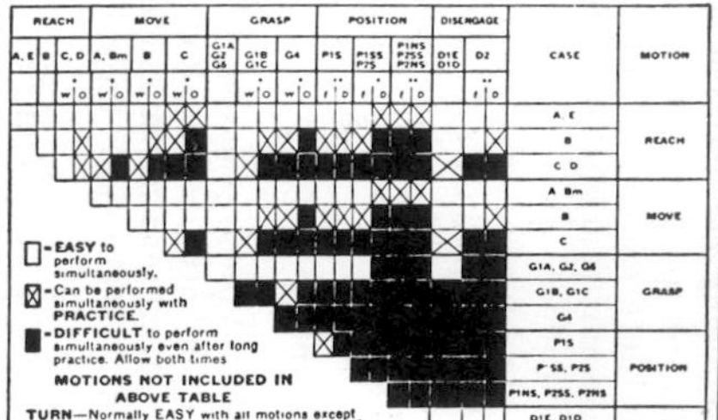

☐ = EASY to perform simultaneously.
☒ = Can be performed simultaneously with PRACTICE.
■ = DIFFICULT to perform simultaneously even after long practice. Allow both times

MOTIONS NOT INCLUDED IN ABOVE TABLE

TURN—Normally EASY with all motions except when TURN is controlled or with DISENGAGE.
APPLY PRESSURE—May be EASY, PRACTICE, or DIFFICULT. Each case must be analyzed.
POSITION—Class 3—Always DIFFICULT.
DISENGAGE—Class 3—Normally DIFFICULT.
RELEASE—Always EASY.
DISENGAGE—Any class may be DIFFICULT if care must be exercised to avoid injury or damage to object.

*W = Within the area of normal vision.
O = Outside the area of normal vision.
**E = EASY to handle.
D = DIFFICULT to handle.

1 TMU = .00001 hour = .0006 minute = .036 seconds

FIG. 3-23. MTM time tables containing basic motion-time values as classified by the type of motion. (*Courtesy of Methods Engineering Council.*)

Formulas are developed for each variation of work a craftsman encounters. For example, in the painting craft, some of these variations might be "Preparing and Brush Painting Walls, Preparing and Brush Painting Ceilings, Cleaning and Brush Painting Pipe, Cleaning and Brush Painting Machine Equipment. Figure 3-27 is "Cleaning and Brush Painting Machine Equipment," which is a common machine-maintenance job occurring in production and maintenance areas.

The first step in the development of standards, using MTM, is the collection of complete information as to the work, methods, equipment, and materials used.

METHODS ANALYSIS CHART F31-1134

PART *Machine Equipment* DEPT.____ DWG.____ SH. *1* OF *7*

DESCRIPTION—LEFT HAND	NO	L. H. SYM	T. M. U	R. H. SYM.	DESCRIPTION—RIGHT HAND
A Pick up 1" Round All-Purpose Brush - Remove excess solvent					
			14.4	R14B	Reach for Brush
			1.7	G1A	Grasp
			10.6	M8C	Brush to lip
			5.6	P1SE	Align on lip
			10.6	AP2	Press slightly to get rid of excess
			31.9	AB	
				(TBC1)	Turn
			13.4	M12B	Brush to mach. surface
			88.2		
				x .0006 = .053 Minutes	
B Dip 1" Brush into Solvent					
			29.0	B	
				(TBC1)	
			15.2	M12C	Brush into can
			5.6	P1SE	Dip Brush
			10.6	M8C	To lip of gallon can
			5.6	P1SE	Align on lip
			10.6	AP2	Pressure squeeze
			31.9	AB	Arise
			13.4	M12B	Brush to mach. surface
			121.9		
				x .0006 = .073 Minutes	
C Brush Solvent onto smooth SPASH GUARD - About one square foot area.					
			10.6	AP2	
	12		321.6	2M12B	
			332.2		
				x .0006 = .199 Minutes	
		TOTAL		T. M. U. x .0006 =	MINUTES

ELEMENT *Cleaning for Paint* SYMBOL *A, B & C*

DATE____ BY____

FIG. 3-24. The first step in developing standard data with MTM time values. MTM data (Fig. 3-23) were applied to a series of basic motions required to complete elements A, B, and C. (*Courtesy of Charles Strommenger, industrial engineer.*)

Every motion required to complete the work must be analyzed, classified, and recorded. The observer must watch the accepted methods in order to determine the sequence in which these motions occur as well as to obtain a correct mental picture of the motions required to do the entire operation.

These motions are then broken down into MTM elements and entered on a "methods-analysis chart," together with the TMU required to complete the motion. In Fig. 3-24, note Element A, "Pick up 1-in., round, all-purpose brush—remove excess solvent." The painter reaches for the brush in a can of solvent (R14B or Reach, 14 in., Case B), and takes hold of the brush (G1A or Grasp, Case 1A). He moves the

Maintenance—Plant-wide	Formula #1–54–5–6
Title: Cleaning and Painting	Sheet 2 of 15 sheets

ANALYSIS

The tools required for this job are 1- and 2-in. scrapers, a wire brush, round all-purpose paint brushes from $\frac{1}{2}$ to 2 in. in diameter, and an air hose.

The materials used are a carbon tetrachloride solvent, gray paint (Roxalin 13-494), rags, and empty gallon cans for holding the solvent.

The areas cleaned and painted are measured and figured, then classified, and then calculated for their leveled times. See Sheet 8 for a sample calculation.

PROCEDURE

The operator dips a 1-in. brush into a can of solvent, and brushes the solvent onto the machine with a rubbing back and forth motion. When necessary, the operator will also use a scraper or wire brush to remove the grime not removed by the brush and solvent. After the entire area has been cleaned in the above manner, the operator will saturate a rag with solvent and go over the cleaned area.

The operator dips his paint brush into an open can of paint, brushes off the excess paint on the lip of the can, and paints the machine. He will use several sizes of brushes ranging from a $\frac{1}{2}$-in. round to a 2-in. round brush. Where trimming is involved, it may be necessary for the operator to wipe the overlap.

TABLE OF ELEMENTS

A. Pick up 1-in. round all-purpose brush and remove excess solvent = a constant per square foot. — 0.053 min

B. Dip 1-in. brush into solvent = a constant per dip. — 0.073 min

C. Brush solvent onto a smooth surface (Example: Splash guard) about 1 sq ft in area = a constant for smooth surfaces. — 0.199 min

D. Lay brush aside = a constant per square foot. — 0.028 min

E. Pick up scraper and lay aside = a constant per square foot. — 0.059 min

F. Scrape a 1 sq ft area of smooth surface using 2-in. scraper = a constant for smooth surfaces. — 0.199 min

Date: June 30

Maintenance—Plant-wide	Formula #1–54–5–6
Title: Cleaning and Painting	Sheet 3 of 15 sheets

G. Take rag from can of solvent, and return to can = a constant per square foot. — 0.093 min

H. Clean 1 sq ft area of smooth surface with a rag saturated with solvent = a constant per square foot of smooth surface. — 0.193 min

J. Brush solvent on an irregular smooth surface = a constant per square foot of irregular surface. — 0.295 min

L. Brush solvent on very irregular surface = a constant per square foot of irregular surface. — 0.392 min

M. Scrape irregular or curved surfaces of about 1 sq ft = a constant per square foot of irregular surface. — 0.296 min

N. Scrape very irregular surfaces = a constant per square foot of very irregular surface. — 0.579 min

P. Dip brush in can of paint = a constant per dip. — 0.080 min

Q. Paint smooth machine surface of about 1 sq ft—use 2-in. round all-purpose brush = a constant per job. — 0.419 min

R. Additional painting on an irregular surface of about 1 sq ft—use $\frac{1}{2}$- to $\frac{3}{4}$-in. round all-purpose brush = a constant for irregular surfaces. — 0.418 min

S. Lay aside and pick up next size brush = a constant per brush. — 0.021 min

T. Additional painting on a very irregular surface, trimming around projections, levers, handwheels, etc. = a constant for very irregular surfaces. — 1.056 min

U. Pick up rag—lay aside = a constant for very irregular surfaces. — 0.048 min

V. Wipe paint away with rag = a constant for very irregular surfaces. — 0.109 min

Date: June 30

FIG. 3-25. Elements as developed from basic MTM values (see Fig. 3-24). These elements are outlined in the "procedure" above and are all the elements necessary to develop formulas for "cleaning and brush painting machine equipment." (*Courtesy of Charles Strommenger, industrial engineer.*)

Maintenance—Plant-wide   Formula #I–54–5–6
Title: Cleaning and Painting   Sheet 4 of 15 sheets

SYNTHESIS

The areas studied were classified into three distinct groups of work.

Class I.   Work is for smooth surfaces that are relatively easy to clean and paint. The
            surfaces are smooth and flat such as base trays and splash guards.
Class II.   Work is for irregular surfaces that are not smooth and flat such as curved chip
            guards and curved belt guards.
Class III. Work is for very irregular surfaces that have projections, piping, levers, and
            handwheels.

Class III is very difficult cleaning and painting. Examples of Class III are the complete
turret assembly, the saddle and cross slide assembly, the lathe head, and the motor.
Class I is relatively easy work, whereas Class III is very difficult with many more highly
controlled motions.
Class II primarily fits the work in between the two extremes.
Cleaning was analyzed as follows:

Leveled minutes per square foot of Class I work equals

$$\text{EL } A + C + D + E + F + G + H$$
$$= 0.053 + 0.199 + 0.028 + 0.059 + 0.199 + 0.093 + 0.193$$
$$= .82 \text{ min per square ft}$$

Leveled minutes per square foot of Class II work equals

$$\text{EL } A + J + D + E + M + G + 1\tfrac{1}{2}H$$
$$= 0.053 + 0.295 + 0.028 + 0.059 + 0.296 + 0.093 + 1\tfrac{1}{2}(0.193)$$
$$= 1.11 \text{ min per sq ft}$$

Date: June 30

Maintenance—Plant-wide   Formula #I–54–5–6
Title: Cleaning and Painting   Sheet 5 of 15 sheets

Leveled minutes per square foot of Class III work equals

$$\text{EL } A + 2B + L + D + E + N + G + 1\tfrac{1}{2} H$$
$$= 0.053 + 2(0.073) + 0.392 + 0.028 + 0.059 + 0.579 + 0.093 + 1\tfrac{1}{2}(0.193)$$
$$= 1.64 \text{ min per sq ft}$$

Painting was analyzed as follows:

Leveled minutes per square foot of Class I work equals

$$\text{EL } 2(P) + Q$$
$$= 2(0.080) + 0.419$$
$$= 0.58 \text{ min per sq ft}$$

Leveled minutes per square foot of Class II work equals

$$\text{EL } 4(P) + Q + R + 2(S)$$
$$= 4(0.080) + 0.419 + 0.418 + 2(0.021)$$
$$= 1.20 \text{ min per sq ft}$$

Leveled minutes per square foot of Class III work equals

$$\text{EL } 8(P) + Q + 3(S) + T + U + V$$
$$= 8(0.080) + 0.419 + 3(0.021) + 1.056 + 0.048 + 0.109$$
$$= 2.34 \text{ min per sq ft}$$

Combining the three classes of work, Table I (Fig. 3-27) was developed.
During time checks on painting equipment, it was found that painting the second coat
averaged about 60% of the time required for the first coat. This occurs because of the
difference of degree of coverage of the first coat. Thus, fewer brush dips and fewer brush
strokes are required. When a second coat of paint is required, apply 60% of the first coat
values. This also is incorporated in Table I.

Date: June 30

Fig. 3-26. The areas studied to develop the table of elements (Fig. 3-25) were separated
into three distinct groups of work. Formula was based on the elements required to complete work in each grouping for cleaning and painting. (*Courtesy of Charles Strommenger,
industrial engineer.*)

brush to the lip of the can (M8C or Move 8 in., Case C), and positions the brush to remove excess solvent (P1SE, position Class 1 fit, symmetrical, easy to handle). He presses brush slightly to remove excess solvent (AB2 apply pressure, part up to 2 lb) and turns body to machine (TBCL, turn body, Case 1). He moves brush to machine surface (M12B, move brush 12 in., Case B). The total time is 0.053 min for that element. In a similar manner, the same procedure is repeated for all the other elements necessary to "Clean and Brush Paint" machine equipment (B through

---

Maintenance—Plant-wide   Formula #1–54–5–6
Title: Cleaning and Painting   Sheet 7 of 15 sheets

Table 1. Leveled Minutes per Square Foot of Area

	Class I	Class II	Class III
Cleaning.....................	0.82	1.11	1.64
Painting (one coat)*.........	0.58	1.20	2.34
Total.....................	1.40	2.31	3.98

* Use 60 % for second coat.

Examples of the Different Classes of Work

Class I (smooth surfaces)	Class II (irregular surfaces)	Class III (very irregular surfaces)
	Turret Lathe	
Base or drip trays	Lathe bed	With levers, windows, handwheels
Flat splash guards	Switch boxes	Turret assembly
Flat drain covers	Curved belt guards	Turret fixtures
	Irr. shaped splash guards	Saddle assembly
	Curved chip guards	Cross slide
	Turret base (on an automatic)	Lathe head
		Motor
	Milling Machine	
	Base up to spindle	Spindle
	Knee support	
	Radial Drill	
	Column or post base	Arm
		Gearbox
	Air Conditioner	
Side panels	Side panel—close confined areas	The area around the piping (gingerbread work)

Date: June 30

Fig. 3-27. Time values developed from the application of the formulas (Fig. 3-26). These values are expressed in "leveled minutes per square foot of area" for cleaning, brush painting, and combined cleaning and brush painting of machine equipment. Examples of the different classes of work are included to clearly define the differences in the three groups of work. (*Courtesy of Charles Strommenger, industrial engineer.*)

V). These elements are shown in Fig. 3-25. At this point the MTM basic data have been converted into motions having greater time values to facilitate future formula development.

If these data were developed from stop-watch time studies, the same elements should and probably would be separated for formula application. One advantage of MTM over the stop watch is the simplicity of work in arriving at these standard times as compared with the work involved in the accumulation of a large amount of elemental time-study data and developing standard data by thorough time-study procedures.

The work observed was then analyzed and classified and the formulas developed

based on the work required (Fig. 3-26). With these formulas, time standards, based
on a square-foot unit, were established for cleaning and painting. These standard
times given in leveled minutes per square foot of area covered were then combined in
table form (Fig. 3-27) showing examples of different classes of work in order to better

Craft: Painters
Title: Machine Cleaning and Painting

Values from Formula 6

Class I.   Smooth surfaces such as flat splash guards
Class II.   Irregular surfaces such as lathe bed and switch boxes
Class III. Very irregular surfaces such as motor and turret assembly

Sq ft	Class I clean and paint	Class I paint second coat	Class II clean and paint	Class II paint second coat	Class III clean and paint	Class III paint second coat
1	1.4	.5	2.3	1.4	4.0	2.4
2	2.8	1.0	4.6	2.8	8.0	4.8
3	4.2	1.5	6.9	4.2	11.9	7.2
4	5.6	2.0	9.2	5.6	15.9	9.6
5	7.0	2.5	11.6	7.0	19.9	12.0
10	14.0	5.0	23.1	14.0	39.8	24.0
15	21.0	7.5	34.7	21.0	59.7	36.0
20	28.0	10.0	46.2	28.0	79.6	48.0
25	35.0	12.5	57.8	35.0	99.5	60.0
30	42.0	15.0	69.3	42.0	119.4	72.0
35	49.0	17.5	80.9	49.0	139.3	84.0
40	56.0	20.0	92.4	56.0	159.2	96.0
45	63.0	22.5	104.0	63.0	179.1	108.0
50	70.0	25.0	115.6	70.0	199.0	120.0
60	84.0	30.0	138.7	84.0	238.8	144.0
70	98.0	35.0	161.8	98.0	278.6	168.0
80	112.0	40.0	184.9	112.0	318.4	192.0
90	126.0	45.0	208.0	126.0	358.2	216.0
100	140.0	50.0	231.1	140.0	398.0	240.0
110	154.0	55.0	254.2	154.0	437.8	264.0
120	168.0	60.0	277.3	168.0	477.6	288.0
130	182.0	65.0	300.4	182.0	517.4	312.0
140	196.0	70.0	323.5	196.0	557.2	336.0
150	210.0	75.0	346.6	210.0	597.0	360.0

FIG. 3-28. For ease and efficiency in applying standard times to machine cleaning and brush
painting, the times from Table 1, Fig. 3-27, have been extended into square-foot areas by
the various combinations of work—Class I.   Clean and paint one coat; Class I.   Paint 2nd
coat; etc. (*Courtesy of Charles Strommenger, industrial engineer.*)

define the application limits. For handling ease, the standard times from Table 1
(Fig. 3-27) were extended into another table (Fig. 3-28), by square foot of area with
the various cleaning and painting combinations.

An example of an application of the "cleaning and brush painting machine equipment" standard is also included in the formula report. This is to further define and
illustrate the method of applying times to a typical job in a particular classification of
painter's work. Figure 3-29 illustrates the method of measuring the work required
to clean and brush-paint machine-equipment items. This is only a portion of the
total work required on a particular turret lathe (Fig. 3-30). At this point, a standard

for this piece of equipment, and all others like it can be filed for future job standard reference.

Such items as job preparation, clean-up, travel, personal time, and general allowances to cover specific job conditions (working in restricted areas, working from scaffolds, etc.), together with unavoidable-delay allowances have not been included

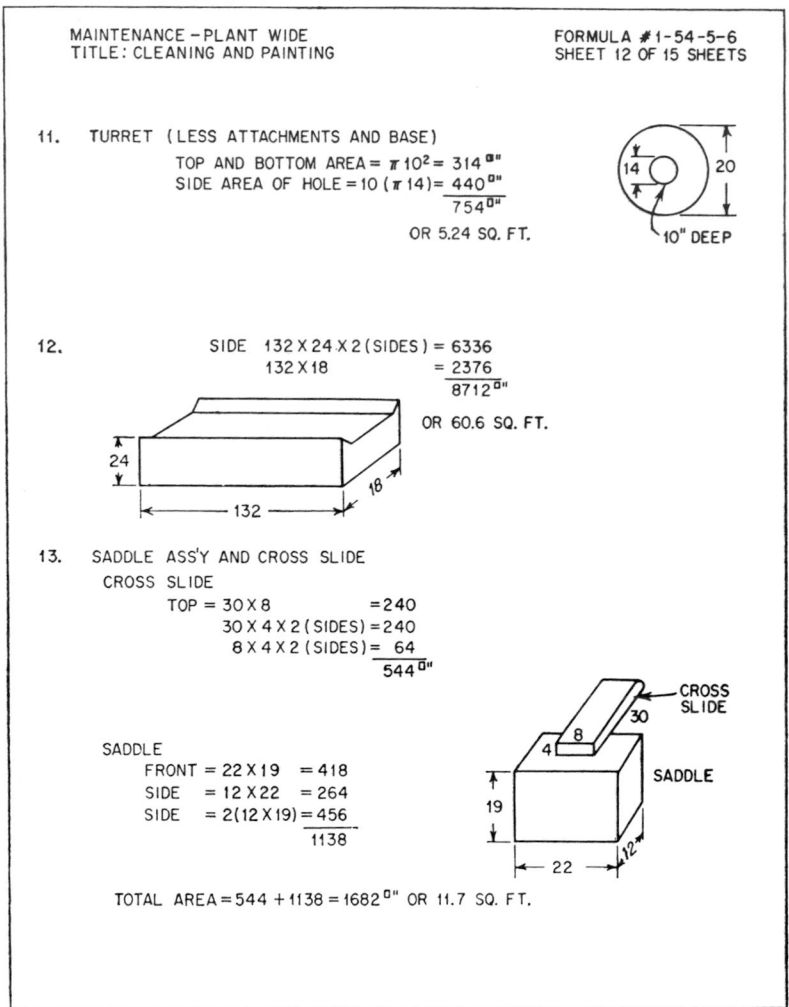

FIG. 3-29. Example of the measurement of various machine parts for application of standard times.   This is a portion of the total job of cleaning and brush-painting one coat, turret lathe 5319 (Fig. 3-30).   (*Courtesy of Charles Strommenger, industrial engineer.*)

in the basic standards for "cleaning and brush painting machine equipment."   The times are in leveled decimal man minutes and required additional times (job preparation, clean-up, travel, etc.) or allowances (personal, working in restricted areas, etc.) to complete the job standard.   This subject is treated in detail in Sec. 2, Chap. 4.

Figure 3-31 is a sketch showing another common type of maintenance work, electrical installation.   An office area must be wired for fluorescent lights and a water cooler.   MTM data (Fig. 3-32) have been developed into elements (Fig. 3-33) and then expanded further, to facilitate usage, in the development of operation standards covering the various combinations of electrical work encountered in installing junction boxes and conduit (Fig. 3-34).   Additional tables similar to Table 1 (Fig. 3-35) supply the necessary data to complete the application of standard values of time for the work involved (Fig. 3-36).   In this MTM application example, the times for "Preparation," "Clean Up," "Travel," and other "allowances" are included.

Advantages and Disadvantages.   There are several points concerning MTM applications in maintenance work that have been regarded as disadvantages, but on analyzing

---

Maintenance—Plant-wide   Formula   #I–54–5–6
Title: Cleaning and Painting   Sheet 15 of 15 sheets

Time Summary for Cleaning and Painting One Coat—Turret Lathe #5319

Item	Area, sq ft	Rate	Level. time, decimal min
Class I			
1. Base or drip tray	114.0		
2. Mounted splash guard	14.7		
4. Unmounted splash guard	26.0		
5. Drain cover	8.1		
	162.8	1.40	227.0
Class II			
3. Unmounted splash guard	10.0		
6. Chip guard	9.0		
7. Switch boxes	10.8		
8. Belt guard	15.5		
12. Bed	60.6		
	105.9	2.31	245.0
Class III			
9. Turret fixtures	19.7		
10. Turret base assembly	19.1		
11. Turret	7.3		
13. Saddle assembly and cross slide	11.7		
14. Lathe head	56.0		
	113.8	3.98	453.0
Class III			
15. Motor—painting only	11.2	2.34	26.0
			951.0

Date: June 30

Fig. 3-30.   Time summary for cleaning and brush-painting all surfaces required on turret lathe 5319.   Figure 3-29 illustrated the method of measuring various items to obtain the square-foot area.   The "rate" was taken from the values in Table 1, Fig. 3-27.   (*Courtesy of Charles Strommenger, industrial engineer.*)

these points with regard to operating costs and improved management control methods, individual plants might tend to make these so-called disadvantages appear as advantages.   They are:

1. High initial cost.   However, the MTM installation is made at such a speed that there are savings in engineering time as well as moving up the payoff period due to early increased maintenance efficiency.
2. Cost of training maintenance management personnel in work methods, equipment care, craft know-how, management control methods, and the MTM system.   While this might be regarded as a disadvantage, the cost is more than returned as experienced by progressive companies having competent trained foremen and supervisors who have become cost-conscious controllers.
3. Industrial engineering personnel must be trained in MTM.   This is a disadvantage in small industrial engineering departments if personnel turnover is a problem.   However, the cost must be compared with that involved in the accumulation of the same data through time-study procedures.

The advantages are:

1. The speed of installation which accelerates the payoff date.
2. Training of supervision in management's methods.
3. Application costs are reasonable once the standard data have been developed.
4. Forces tighter control over:
   a. Work methods.
   b. Material specifications.
   c. Maintaining maintenance equipment.
5. Flexibility of the system as shown by the fact that standards can be established for group or individual payment and that elements of work are reproducible.
6. A common unit of measurement is available to evaluate the performance of individual craftsmen and foremen. (Employees can relate earnings to their productivity by direct comparison of time.)

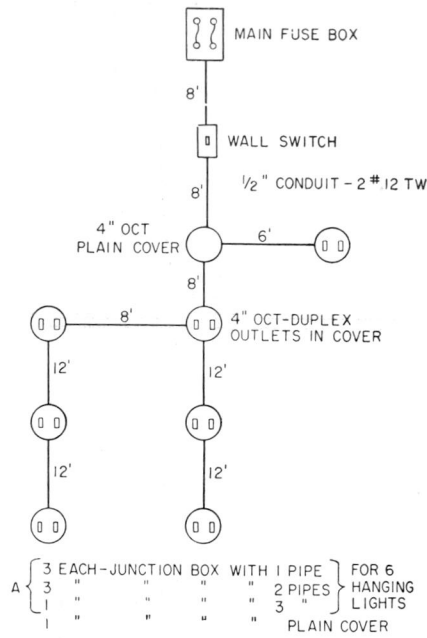

Fig. 3-31. Sketch of work involved in the installation of fluorescent lights and a water cooler. (*Courtesy of Methods Engineering Council.*)

7. Audits are possible to determine if proper labor payments have been made.
8. Information to increase management controls in the areas of:
   a. Planning and scheduling work.
   b. Planning and scheduling equipment.
   c. Planning and scheduling manpower standards, providing an accurate means of determining excess maintenance costs in specific areas or on specific equipment or parts which would justify modifications or replacement of equipment.

Statistical or Past-performance Method. A maintenance statistical plan is based on averages of past man-hours expended on jobs. While this type of plan does not give an accurate measurement and in reality is nothing more than an index, management is attracted for two reasons:

1. The minimum cost to collect data for standards.
2. The minimum control administration cost or incentive wage administration when the plan is in effect.

METHODS ANALYSIS CHART   *FORMULA 49*

PART *ELECTRICAL CONSTRUCTION*   DEPT._____   DWG._____SH. *15* OF *28*

DESCRIPTION—LEFT HAND	NO.	L.H.SYM.	T.M.U.	R.H.SYM.	NO.	DESCRIPTION—RIGHT HAND
K3 Screw nut on pipe end w/fingers						
			3.4	G1A	2	*Grasp nut*
			8.4	M2B	2	*Turn nut down*
			3.4	RL1	2	*Release nut*
			7.4	R2A	2	*Reach back*
			22.6			
				X.0006	=	*.014 mins./rev.*
B3 Get tool from belt kit						
				.044 mins. per occ. (El. C1 – formula #44)		
C3 Aside tool tool to belt kit						
				.053 mins. per occ. (El. G1 – formula #44)		
L3 Tighten nut on pipe end w/hammer and screwdriver						
Reach for screwdriver		R10A	11.3	M10A		*Screwdriver to L.H.*
Transfer to L.H.		G3	5.6			
Regrasp		G2	5.6			
Screwdriver near nut on pipe						
		M16B	15.8			
Screwdriver to slot on						
nut edge	4	M2C	16.8			
Position screwdriver	4	P1SSD	58.8			
Pressure on screwdriver	4	AP2	42.4			
			18.7	M16C		*Hammer to screwdriver*
			22.4	P1SE	4	*Pos. hammer on screwdriver*
			55.2	M4B	8	*(Hammer stroke – up*
			48.8	M4A	8	*and down*
			301.4			
				X.0006	=	*.18 mins./nut*
		TOTAL		T.M.U. × .0006 =		MINUTES

ELEMENT_____ SYMBOL_____

DATE_____ BY__*J. F.*_____

Fig. 3-32. MTM data used to develop elemental times for electrical work. (*Courtesy of Methods Engineering Council.*)

Summary of Suboperation No. 10
Tighten Two Nuts on Mounted Switch Box

Element

(K3) Screw nut on pipe end with fingers (0.014 per rev)

	Run down inside nut	$= 0.014 \times 2 - 0.028$
	Run down outside nut	$= 0.014 \times 4 - 0.056$

(B3) Get tool from belt kit (0.044 per occ.)

	Screwdriver and hammer	$= 0.044 \times 2 - 0.088$

(C3) Aside tool in kit (0.053 per occ.)

	Screwdriver and hammer	$= 0.053 \times 2 - 0.106$

(L3) Tighten nut on pipe end with hammer
       and screwdriver (0.18 per nut) $= 0.18 \times 2 - $ 0.360   *To Operation 4*

0.638

Fig. 3-33. Basic elemental times of Figure 3. 32 extended into greater portions of work termed suboperations. (*Courtesy of Methods Engineering Council.*)

Illustration of Summary Value
Junction Box with Outlet—One Pipe Box—Wood Mounting

1. Measure to determine pipe length   3.82
2. Cut off, chamfer, and thread end of pipe   4.51
3. Bend two offsets per pipe   3.64   *See Summary of Operation 4*
4. Assemble junction box and piece of pipe to wood beam   7.39
5. Assemble outlet to junction box—one pipe   5.31   *To Sub-analysis Sheet*

24.67

Summary of Operation 4
Assemble Junction Box and Piece of Pipe to Wood Beam

1. Get junction box and four nuts; knock out 2 plugs, avg.   1.106
2. Get pipe and assemble nut to each end   0.717
3. Assembly box to pipe, assemble nut and tighten   0.558
4. Get helper, wait for helper to move ladder, and give helper
   nut and pipe   1.338
5. Two men ascend ladder with pipe—helper inserts pipe into
   mounted box   0.502
6. Helper starts nut on pipe (inside box), descends ladder, and
   returns to his job   0.427
7. Position junction box to wood, drill two holes with ratchet
   hand drill   0.367
8. Finish hanging junction box   0.983
9. Descend ladder, walk to second ladder, ascend and descend
   second ladder   0.752
10. Tighten two nuts on mounted junction box   0.638

7.388

See Summary of Suboperation No. 10

To Junction Box — Outlet — One Pipe, Wood Mtg.

Fig. 3-34. Suboperations (Fig. 3-33) are extended into operations such as "assemble junction box and piece of pipe to wood beam." Operation times are grouped with each other to form combinations of work of larger time increments for ease of application (junction box with outlet, one pipe box, wood mounting). (*Courtesy of Methods Engineering Council.*)

To obtain standard times for maintenance, it first becomes necessary to make some job classifications into which all hours worked are recorded and charged to separate jobs in the various classifications. The average time clocked in on the jobs under each classification becomes the standard. There are extreme classifications where it is necessary to estimate each job.

Dept: Plant-wide—Maintenance Department　　　　　Formula #I–54–5–49
Title: Electrical Construction ½ and ¾ Conduit　　　　　Sheet 16 of 16

Table 1. Electrical Construction ½ and ¾ Electrical Conduit

	Leveled minutes No. of conduits on J. box				Variable
1. Junction box with outlet	1	2	3	4	
Wood mounted or equivalent	24.7	25.6	27.2	27.8	} Per box
Brick mounted or equivalent	33.9	34.9	36.4	37.0	
2. Junction box—cover plate					
Wood mounted or equivalent	—	21.6	24.1	24.7	} Per box
Brick mounted or equivalent	—	30.8	33.3	33.9	
3. Wall switch					
Wood mounted or equivalent				24.5	} Per switch
Brick mounted or equivalent and flush mtg.				33.7	
4. Condulet with cover				11.3	Per condulet
5. Pipe clamp					
Wood mounted or equivalent				1.8	} Per clamp
Brick mounted or equivalent				4.8	
6. Pipe coupling				0.8	Per coupling
7. Conduit bands (exclusive of box offsets)				0.9	Per band
8. Greenlee knockouts				3.3	Per knockout
9. Insert wire				0.44	Per foot of pipe

See Formula #I–54–5–31 for other pipe supports

Date: Oct. 25

Fig. 3-35. From various summary sheets, times for various combinations of work covering the "electrical construction of ½ and ¾ electrical conduit" are assembled into Table 1. (*Courtesy of Methods Engineering Council.*)

A typical statistical plan for a machine shop might follow on this procedure, commencing with the classification of completed job orders:

1. Standing orders. Permanent or perpetuating orders assigned to highly repetitive tasks. Such work as the recurring repair of paint cups for automatic color-banding equipment or the constant straightening of guide pins for specific assembly equipment.
2. Repair orders. Machine-shop orders requiring less than 24 hr labor on items such as repair, adjust, standard part replacement, etc. This order is not used in making new parts.
3. Work orders. Machine-shop orders to cover all types of work other than that covered by standing orders or repair orders, but not exceeding a specific money value, usually $400 or $500. (This amount will vary with each plan.)
4. Project orders. Machine-shop orders which apply to jobs where the total estimated cost exceeds the work-order value ($400 to $500).

The next step is to obtain hours worked against individual jobs occurring within the classifications of maintenance orders. A dispatch job-card system requiring clocking in and out is essential for the accumulation of these data.

1. A job number is issued for each job and recorded on the paper work authorizing the job.
2. The workers' time is charged on each job card (by clock rings, verbal reporting, etc.).
3. Check to see that total job times balance the total working time reported daily.
4. All hours against each job must be accumulated and totaled as the job is completed.

At this point a decision must be reached as to the length of the recording period required in order to establish standard man-hours for the various classifications of

---

Job-analysis Sheet

Job Title: Wire Office—Install ½ in. Conduit System

Location: Dept. 406—General Foreman's Office

Analyzed by: J. Frankhauser   Date: Dec. 13,

Operation	Ref.	Unit	Qty.	Lev. min Unit	Total
1. Junction box with outlet					
a. 1 Pipe box—wood mtd.	F-49	Box	3	24.7	74.1
b. 2 Pipe box—wood mtd.	F-49	Box	3	25.6	76.8
c. 3 Pipe box—wood mtd.	F-49	Box	1	27.2	27.2
2. Junction box—cover plate					
a. 3 pipe box—wood mtd.	F-49	Box	1	24.1	24.1
3. Wall switch (brick mtg.)	F-49	Sw.	1	33.7	33.7
4. Pipe clamps—wood mtg.	F-49	Clamp	4	1.8	7.2
5. Pipe coupling (over 10 ft)	F-49	Coupl.	4	0.8	3.2
6. Insert wire	F-49	Ft.	86	0.44	38.0
7. Wire to main box	F-97	Box	1	26.2	26.2
8. Wire 6 fluorescents	F-62	Fixt.	6	15.3	91.8
9. Hang 6 fluorescents	F-62	Fixt.	6	12.6	75.6
10. Preparation and cleaning					
a. Collect tools	F-28	Man	2	11.0	22.0
b. Buggy loads (load and unload)	F-28	Trip	3	14.0	42.0
					541.9
11. Travel buggy trips	F-1	Trip	2	16.0	32.0
Walk	F-1	Trip	2	8.0	16.0
				Total	589.9
				Allowance 10%	59.0
				Standard min	648.9
				Standard hr	10.8

FIG. 3-36. The development of the job standard as illustrated by the sketch (Fig. 3-31). (*Courtesy of Methods Engineering Council.*)

work. A year is usually considered a representative period of time. The base period will vary dependent upon the potential amount of data available, which is proportionate to the size of the shop (in man-hours) and the pattern of work being processed. The primary goal in gathering those statistical data is to get a good representative picture of the shop operations, or plant operations, as the case may be, and the amount of data to be collected has to be determined for each individual case.

The final step is the development of the standard data from the historical record. These data usually end up in one of four job categories:

1. Standing orders.   The total man-hours worked during the base period are accumulated and the average number of hours per working day are computed against each

standing order. This figure is then the permanent standard for this type of order. Additional allowances must be made on these jobs to compensate for any increased volume of activity due to increased production requirements. This will have to be on a ratio basis as established by production during the base period.

2. Repetitive jobs. Certain jobs will be found to be repetitive. This allows individual standards to be calculated for these jobs based on the average man-hours expended for these jobs during the base period. Duties will have to be defined so that the standard will be applied to jobs having the same content as those studied during the base period.

3. Nonrepetitive jobs.

   a. Repair orders. All hours on this type of order, as previously defined, are accumulated during the base period. This figure divided by the total number of repair-order jobs gives a standard repair-order time.

   b. Work orders. Orders are accumulated into groups according to the actual hours needed for completion, those requiring 8 hr, 8 to 24, and so on for groups 24 to 48, 48 to 100. In each of these classifications the total hours worked are accumulated against the total number of jobs and the accumulated hours are divided by the total number of jobs, giving the standard under each category. The average job time in each classification becomes the standard time in each case.

To use these standards, an estimator must judge, in advance, the category into which each nonrepetitive job will fall.

4. Estimated jobs. Any job judged as requiring more than 100 hr for completion becomes an "estimated job." All project orders are contained in this category. The allowed standards for these jobs are based on the estimate of required man-hours. In a few instances standard data which have been accumulated within the base period can be used to guide the estimator.

There will be cases where it is impossible to work an accurate estimate of time until the job has started. In such cases the estimate should be made after the job has progressed far enough to foresee all the work required for completion. If the work has commenced and the original estimate is not valid because of unforeseen work, changes in the job, etc., the estimate must be changed to conform to existing conditions.

Routine checks on all estimated jobs should be made when the actual hours reach approximately one-third of the estimate and again at approximately two-thirds of the estimate in order to establish whether or not conditions are consistent. If not, the estimate must be revised. If these four methods have been used to develop data, a means of measuring maintenance efficiency is available. By comparing actual man-hours worked in any period to corresponding standard hours as applied against the total job orders, a measure of relative performance is available. This is nothing more than a comparison of existing performance with performance during the base period. If incentive payments are made under this type of plan the incentive-pay period must obviously be a long period of time because of the way in which the standards were developed. The period of time for incentive-pay purposes would probably be in the area of 10 weeks. This type of plan is not recommended for wage-incentive purposes (see Fig. 3-37). If serious pay-differential problems exist in a plant (see items 3 and 4 under Advantages) this plan offers a reasonable method of adjustment.

There are many disadvantages to this type of plan because of the method of establishing standards.

1. The standard data developed in this manner exert no control over working methods.

2. There has been little effort to determine a normal working pace, only the pace worked during the base period is reflected.

3. The potential earnings or potential efficiency under this type of plan is unknown.

4. There is no method for adjusting standards for technological changes or change in work pattern (see Fig. 3-37).

OPERATION-ROLLING MILD STEEL-BEMENT & MILES NO.6 PLATE ROLL

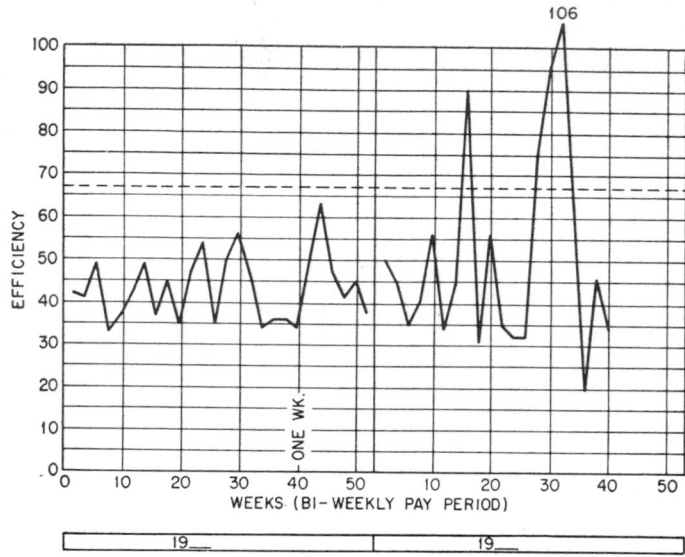

FIG. 3-37. Past average man-hours is not a sound basis on which to establish maintenance control standards. The standards that have established the above efficiencies were based on past average with separate classifications and standards for weight of stock rolled (a slight improvement over an analysis of man-hours on specific job orders). In the second year of operations with the standard, the chart reflects (1) a change of work pattern, (2) a slight equipment modification. The effect of these two items, in time, could not be calculated to allow a standards adjustment due to the broad, general averages used as a base. (*Courtesy of Factory Management and Maintenance.*)

5. Normally incentives are paid on reproduced work elements. In this instance reproducible work elements are not assured.
6. It is impossible for the employee to relate earnings to productivity.
7. There is no means to check individual employee's output, making it easier for the group to control production during peak and slow periods.
8. Without standard elemental-time data upon which to base the application of standards, no audit is possible to see if the correct standard times are allowed for various jobs.
9. Requires no management contribution from supervision.

In addition to the two *advantages* stated in the second paragraph under this topic, there are several others:

3. This type of plan adapts itself to group payment which:
    a. Averages difficult with easy work.
    b. Simplifies administration from the industrial engineering point of view.
    c. Keeps the wage differentials between various skills in line with each other.
    d. Can include everyone in the plan—including workers on standing orders such as tool-crib attendants and stock clerks.
4. This type of plan can be used successfully to eliminate wage-differential problems between production labor and maintenance labor in cases where incentive pay brings the pay of unskilled workers above that of the skilled workers.

Ratio Delay—"Work Sampling." This work-measurement technique is based on the law of probability, the basis for any other sampling procedure. The most familiar use in industry of the law-of-probability theory (as far as work elements are concerned) is quality-control sampling. The probability follows that, by observing a representative number of random occurrences of events from a total universe of events, the percentage distribution of the observed events will be representative of the same distribution in the total universe. The term "ratio delay" comes from a common use of this work-sampling technique, the determination of the ratio of a representative number of random delays to the entire mass of events.

This technique was first used by L. H. C. Tippett[1] in 1934 to determine true operating ratios of machines to properly applied burden and cost rates to spinning and weaving operations in a cotton mill. Since that time there have been many applications of this technique to measure work in production and maintenance areas.

The major applications in maintenance are:

1. The evaluation of maintenance efficiency.
2. The measurement of man-machine relationships.
3. The determination of areas for technical improvements and work simplification.
4. The evaluation of the results of improved operations (e.g., incentive installations).

To complete a work-sampling study the following procedure is recommended:

1. Define what is to be measured. The study technique will vary depending upon the end objective.
2. Determine the "elements" to be observed (e.g., adjusting machine, change belt, idle, personal, etc.).
3. Estimate the number of observations required (to determine over-all length of study period based on number of observations per day).
4. Outline a random observation plan.
5. Train the observer and other personnel involved.
6. Make the observations.
7. Develop the study data.
8. Determine level of reliability of results.
9. Make recommendations based on study results.

Obtaining a True Random Sample—Ratio Delay. Properly to ensure the absence of bias in a ratio-delay study, a mechanical method must be used to set up a study procedure and observation periods. People develop working habits. For example, the observer making a ratio-delay study might visit an acquaintance in the plant during his rounds. He might fall into the habit of doing this a specific time each day. The observer might take a coffee break with the friend, at the friend's convenience. This could be a certain time each day. The observer might tend to his own personal needs at a certain time each day. It is very easy for these types of working habits to develop which would eliminate observations during these periods and result in biased data. The procedure outlined below will eliminate bias due to habits that an observer might develop. This, or a similar type of procedure, must be used for all ratio-delay observations to ensure the collection of random data.

1. Properly define the problem and establish a list of activities for each problem (Fig. 3-39).
2. Estimate the number of observations required. The accuracy required in the answer depends on the number of observations.
3. Determine how many observations will be made per day.
4. Divide the working day into intervals and number consecutively (Fig. 3-38).
5. Use a table of random numbers[2] and proceed along the table line by line until corresponding numbers in the table appear that are the same as the numbered divisions on the chart. Check off each division as its number appears until the quantity of divisions to be observed equals the number of readings required each day. If

---

[1] L. H. C. Tippett, Statistical Methods in Textile Research, *J. Textile Inst. Trans.*, Textile Institute, England, 1935.
[2] Similar to tables in K. A. Brownlee, "Industrial Experimentation," Appendix, Chemical Publishing Company, Inc., New York, 1948.

duplicate numbers appear, pass over the duplication until the day's total is reached (Fig. 3-38). Make the ratio-delay observation during the period checked off.

6. The activity noted at first glance at the exact instance of observation must be checked. If practical, select a spot in each area where observations of specific jobs must be made. This is not practical for miscellaneous work in the plant but it is practical for observations on shopwork.

RANDOM OBSERVATION INTERVALS   DEPT. 10

WORK SAMPLING STUDY – MACHINE ADJUSTERS

TIME OF DAY	INTER VAL	1ST WEEK					2ND WEEK				
		1	2	3	4	5	1	2	3	4	5
7:45-7:59	1				×	×					
8:00-8:14	2						×		×		
8:15-8:29	3	×	×				×	×		×	
8:30-8:44	4			×						×	×
8:45-8:59	5		×					×			
9:00-9:14	6			×	×	×	×		×		
9:15-9:29	7	×	×			×	×	×	×	×	×
9:30-9:44	8							×		×	×
9:45-9:59	9			×				×			
10:00-10:14	10	×	×	×		×		×	×		
10:15-10:29	11	×						×	×		
10:30-10:44	12		×	×		×				×	×
10:45-10:59	13		×							×	×
11:00-11:14	14	×	×	×				×			
11:15-11:29	15			×		×					
11:30-11:44	16	×	×		×	×	×	×			
11:45-11:59	17				×		×			×	×
12:00-12:14	18			×			×				×
12:15-12:29	19					×	×		×		×
12:30-12:44	20	×			×			×		×	
12:45-12:59	21			×		×					×
LUNCH											
1:30-1:44	22			×	×			×			
1:45-1:59	23				×			×	×		
2:00-2:14	24	×			×		×				
2:15-2:29	25					×					×
2:30-2:44	26	×	×	×	×			×	×	×	
2:45-2:59	27	×	×					×			
3:00-3:14	28							×	×		
3:15-3:29	29					×			×		
3:30-3:44	30				×					×	×
3:45-3:59	31		×	×	×						
4:00-4:14	32	×	×	×			×	×	×		
4:15-4:30	33	×				×				×	×

FIG. 3-38. To eliminate bias in ratio-delay studies, each day is divided into time intervals and numbered. From a table of random numbers, the 12 observation periods each day are determined.

If the above steps are followed and the number of observations is consistent with the accuracy desired, the ratio-delay study will yield unbiased data.

Assigned Maintenance Manning—Ratio Delay. A common problem in measurement of maintenance hours is the determination of the number of assigned maintenance mechanics required to service a specific area containing a specific amount of production equipment. These mechanics are not concerned with parts, or machine repair, or major parts replacement, but are concerned only with making minor adjustments and keeping equipment operating.

Ratio delay is a practical method for determining the most efficient manning for a given work load. A case history of this type of operation follows.

As outlined previously, the method for obtaining a true sample was used in order to determine the proper observation intervals. Figure 3-38 illustrates the observation intervals for the first 2 weeks of the study.

The next step was to determine an activity list. This was accomplished by continuous observation in the area concerned for a sufficient period to list the activity of the maintenance personnel and the pattern of machine personnel. The activity list for this job is illustrated at the bottom of Fig. 3-39.

RATIO DELAY — MACHINE ADJUSTERS

Daily Observation Record — Dept. 10

Observations — Date: 1/3

Machine	1	2	3	4	5	6	7	8	9	10	11	12
1	A	B	A	A	A	A	A	A	A	B	A	A
		1							4			
2	A	A	A	A	B	A	A	A	A	A	B	A
					1						2	
3	A	A	A	A	A	B	A	A	A	A	B	A
						1					2	
4	B	A	B	A	A	A	A	A	A	A	A	A
	1		1									
5	A	A	B	A	A	A	A	A	A	A	A	A
			1									
6	A	A	A	A	A	A	B	B	A	A	A	A
				4			1	1				
7	A	A	B	A	A	A	A	A	A	A	B	A
			1								3	
8	A	A	A	A	C	A	A	A	A	A	C	A
					5						8	
9	A	A	A	C	A	A	B	A	A	A	A	A
		4		5			1	4				
10	B	A	A	A	A	A	A	A	B	A	A	A
	3								2			
11	A	A	B	A	A	A	B	A	A	B	A	A
			1				1			2		
12	A	A	A	A	A	A	B	A	A	A	A	A
Central *	7-7	7-7	-	7-7	7-7	7-7 / 7	-	7-7	7-7	7-7	-	9-9 / 6-8

Machine Activity
A—Machine Running.
B—Machine down—adjuster repairs.
C—Machine down—wait for adjuster.

Man Activity
A—Adjust Machine   D—Attention   G—Idle
B—Change belt   E—Walk   H—Avoidable delay
C—Clear jam   F—Misc.   I—Personal

* Central — Location for adjusters when not tending machines.

Each number represents one man

FIG. 3-39. Daily observation record of machine requirements and man activity.

Observations were made in the department and recorded on a daily observation record (Fig. 3-39). The requirements of each machine were noted and the activity of each man was noted together with the identity of the machine being serviced. Observations were made for a 20-day period and the results were summarized as shown in Fig. 3-40.

Since the actual man loading for 12 machines was 4 adjusters, a total of 960 man observations and 2,880 machine observations were recorded. Percentage figures were obtained as shown. Then a synthetic man loading for 3 adjusters tending the same

12 machines was made as follows: Each observation column was scanned with the key spot being "central" (see Fig. 3-39). This indicated whether 0, 1, 2, 3, or 4 of the adjusters were idle or nonproductive when observed. If all were occupied, then with one less adjuster a machine would be down waiting for an adjuster at this time. The daily observation record was then altered so that for each observation only 3 adjusters were considered as being present instead of 4. The new totals were obtained and listed in the column headed "Projected" on summary sheets. From this, the indication was that downtime would increase only 1.5 per cent if each man was assigned an additional machine. The cost of this increased downtime and the resulting loss in production were weighed against the potential savings reducing the number of assigned maintenance men. In this particular case, the adjusters were reduced with no appreciable increase in machine downtime.

RATIO DELAY   MACHINE ADJUSTERS DEPT. #10
Summary of Observations

Machine condition	Actual 4 adjusters		Projected 3 adjusters	
	Occs.	%	Occs.	%
A. Machine running	2,420	84.0	2,380	82.5
B. Machine down—adjuster at machine	400	14.0	400	14.0
C. Machine down—wait for adjuster	60	2.0	100	3.5
	2,880	100.0	2,880	100.0
Man activity				
1. Adjust machines	240	25.0	240	33.0
2. Change belt	28	3.0	28	4.0
3. Clear jam	48	5.0	48	7.0
4. Attention	58	6.0	58	8.0
5. Walk	38	4.0	38	5.0
6. Miscellaneous	48	5.0	48	7.0
7. Idle	384	37.0	179	25.0
8. Avoidable delay	96	10.0	45	6.0
9. Personal	48	5.0	36	5.0
Total	960	100.0	720	100.0

FIG. 3-40. Summary of actual observations and projected results of decreasing adjusting crew by one man.

Work Simplification—Ratio Delay. When used for work-simplification purposes, the study procedure as previously outlined is used. The main use of ratio delay for a work-simplification analysis is to determine the ratio of productive time to nonproductive time or delays. From the data, such items as the amount of time used for job preparation and setup, the amount of time lost by standby time or crew balance, and the amount of time waiting for material or equipment can be determined. When these losses are pin-pointed by ratio delay, detailed studies can be made of each lost-time item for reduction or elimination.

Determining Allowances—Ratio Delay. There is always additional time beyond the actual productive work elements that must be included in work standards. These times may include personal time, interference time, crew balance time, and conditional allowances that might apply to the specific craft, equipment, or jobs. These allowances can be determined by the ratio-delay technique using the same procedure as outlined previously.

This type of study is particularly useful for determining the proper allowances to include in standards based on synthetic data such as MTM. MTM data will supply select elemental times, but not allowances, which must be determined by observation of actual job conditions. Ratio delay is not practical in determining allowance if the basic standard times are based on time studies. When the time-study technique is used to develop standard data, a tremendous number of study hours are required. With continuous 8-hr studies properly documented, and enough hours of study to be representative of the working conditions, standard data and allowances can be developed from the same data, eliminating the need for separate or different types of studies for determining conditional allowances.

Accuracy of Ratio Delay—Random Sampling. With a ratio-delay or random-sampling study, there is a possibility that the results of the study will not be representative of the total universe from which the sample was drawn. There is a mathematical method of determining whether the results of a ratio-delay study are acceptable, provided acceptable tolerances can be defined. The same mathematical technique can be used to estimate the number of observations required to obtain a representative sample with random sampling.

This procedure is explained and illustrated in C. L. Brisly's article, Work Sampling.[1] Any text of statistical methods will also outline the method of testing the results of a sampling study.

Comments on Ratio-delay Studies. There have been a number of articles that emphasize the reduced cost and accuracy of ratio-delay studies as compared with time study or other methods. Ratio delay is not a practical method for determining elemental work times. It is a practical method for determining allowances, non-productive time, and manning requirements. However, the cost of ratio-delay studies can easily exceed the cost of data from continuous time studies because of the following considerations:

1. During the extended period required for ratio-delay studies, no improvements are made, and a potential loss in savings is the result. For example, a job requiring a 3-month ratio-delay analysis could possibly be completed in 2 weeks by continuous time study with two or three industrial engineers on the job. The resulting data, placed in effect, would yield actual savings $2\frac{1}{2}$ months before the same job with ratio-delay data.
2. If an engineer is required to make the ratio-delay observations, using the same illustration as above, it is not likely that he will produce any other useful work during the observation period. This is due to the constant necessity to make ratio-delay observations as scheduled. Therefore, 3 man-months are required to collect the data plus some time to summarize and install the result. With time study, assuming two men for 2 weeks, 4 weeks of engineer's time has been consumed as against 3 months of engineer's time for the ratio-delay method.
3. As for work-simplification improvements with job preparation and set-up, interference delays, conditional delays, and other items that can be uncovered through ratio delay, the same items will be uncovered with continuous time studies and corrected as fast as possible at the same time standard data are being collected.
4. For methods improvements in productive work methods (item 3 above considers nonproductive work), there is no substitute for on-the-job detailed analysis. Ratio delay should not be considered for this type of study. With assigned maintenance work, as discussed previously, ratio delay can determine high cost adjustments and studies can be initiated to reduce these adjustments through redesign of equipment or parts, or substitution of material.

Estimating Maintenance Efficiency with Ratio Delay. Ratio delay can be used to (1) estimate maintenance efficiency, when work-measurement standards are not available; and (2) to audit work-measurement standards after they have been installed. Ratio delay is a practical, accurate, and low-cost method to determine maintenance efficiency.

To make this type of study, devise an observation plan as previously outlined. However, there is a slight difference. In the case-history study of man loading, the work site was in the same area for each observation. With miscellaneous maintenance work in plant areas, there are many job sites. This requires a different approach in that the observations at a time determined by random numbers necessitate a tour of

---

[1] *Factory Management and Maintenance*, July, 1952.

all maintenance work at the many job sites.   The time necessary to make a complete tour must be estimated and the number of trips per day based on trip time and available observation hours.

For recording observations, use a chart similar to Fig. 3-41.   In the first column, enter the total crew size.   The number of men working is entered in the next column. There are an additional five columns to give the status of the men who are not working.

DATE: 9/25

LOCATION AND BRIEF DESCRIPTION OF JOB OR JOB NUMBER	NO. MEN IN CREW	WORKING (NO. OF MEN)	ESTIMATED % PERFORMANCE	IDLE (NO. OF MEN)	NUMBER WAITING FOR				CREW SIZE					TOOLS AND EQUIP.		METHOD		REMARKS
					MATERIAL	INSTRUCTION	OTHER CRAFTS	JOB ASSIGN.	UNDERMANNED	OK	OVERMANNED	RIGHT	WRONG	OK	INEFFICIENT	COULD SCHEDULE	COULDN'T SCHEDULE	
Bldg. A Replace siding	4	3	70	1						✓		✓		✓		✓		
Bldg. A Resurface roof	5	3	50	1	1					✓	✓			✓		✓		
Bldg. A Replace clutch #6 press	2			1	1					✓				✓		✓	✓	
Bldg. C Install piping for new plating tank	4	2	90	2						✓	✓			✓		✓	✓	
Bldg. B Replace	2	1	80	1				✓	✓	✓		✓				✓		

FIG. 3-41. How to estimate savings potential in applying work measurement to maintenance.   Work-sampling technique, illustrated here, provides simplified method to get data.

With the method outline above, a determination can be made of the per cent of time working, idle, or waiting.   However, to obtain a true efficiency, the work pace must be considered.   It can be estimated with a technique commonly called "eyeball" speed rating, which is nothing more than snap judgment of working pace.   An experienced time-study man can be trained in this technique through the use of leveling films.   The technique is necessary so that a speed rating can be made before the subject changes working pace as a result of the presence of the observer and to eliminate bias in the observer's judgment.

At the end of the observation period a summation of the total check marks, divided into the column totals under each category of working, idle, or waiting, will give the percentage of time spent under each of the six categories.   If the observations under working time were leveled, this time would have to be adjusted in accordance with the working efficiency.

For a more complete idea of maintenance efficiency in cases where methods, scheduling, and work-measurement techniques have been neglected or an audit is desired, columns can be added to check work methods, whether the crews are properly manned, whether the tools and equipment are proper, whether the best method is being used, and whether or not the work could be scheduled.   All these data must be recorded at an extended stay after completing the ratio-delay steps.   This type of summary with about 500 jobs should give a good picture of maintenance performance at a low cost.

In plants with standard practice as far as methods and equipment, where manning and scheduling practices are established, and where a work-measurement system is installed, the same procedure as outlined for estimating maintenance efficiency can be used as an audit of the effectiveness of management cost-control measures.

Another method that has been used to estimate maintenance efficiency is a ratio method consisting of a running index of maintenance labor dollars to direct-labor production dollars. This type of measurement would be effective in a plant where no technological improvements will be made. In a progressive plant, technological improvements tend to reduce direct-labor dollars and cause a slight increase in maintenance dollars. The over-all result amounts to cost savings, but a completely different picture will result on the running index; maintenance efficiency would appear to decrease because of the direct-labor reduction. As previously explained, this is far from reality.

Estimating Standards. The degree of accuracy required of maintenance standards depends on the ultimate use of the standard. Estimated standards usually are not accurate enough for incentive-pay purposes, but they do provide an effective base for cost-control measures.

In many plants, it is the responsibility of the foreman to review a work order, plan the job, and estimate the labor hours involved. He might also perform the scheduling function. In other plants, a planning department has been established which estimates the job and then performs the scheduling function. The foreman's estimate is based on craft know-how and past experience. The estimate from a planner is based on these two items but, in addition, the planning department probably uses a rough form of standard data developed from previous job costs.

The estimated standard usually is in the form of money, rather than standard hours, since the thinking is primarily in terms of job costs. For cost-control purposes, the estimated dollars are evaluated against the actual dollars to measure job performance. If this step is not taken, and if management does not insist on a review of jobs whose completion required money in excess of the original estimate, there is no value to estimating standards.

Advantages and Disadvantages of Estimating Standards. This type of measurement is not practical for incentive purposes since the standard is determined "by guess and by negotiation." However, it is definitely a step forward in the process of controlling maintenance costs. Many companies have made substantial cost savings through an estimating procedure tied in with the method and planning functions, and their programs may be considered successful. For maintenance departments, where the number of workers and their working efficiency will not support the cost of measured standard data, its application and administration, this type of measurement is most practical.

Advantages:

1. Low cost of determining and applying standards.
2. Can be used effectively for
   a. Methods work.
   b. Planning and scheduling.
3. Can be used as a rough measure of efficiency.

Disadvantages:

1. Accuracy of standard depends upon "educated guess" of estimator.
   a. New methods or new jobs have no past-performance history for estimator to use as a guide.
2. Poor estimates can affect the morale of the workers to the extent that they completely ignore the standard as a goal.
3. Impractical for incentive purposes.
4. Lack of reproducibility. Loss of an estimator usually means loss of data, depending on how many data are stored in the head of the estimator.

Conditions Required for the Success of Maintenance-work Measurement Programs. Certain basic conditions are necessary to ensure success in every management venture. The installation of a work-measurement system for control of maintenance hours is a difficult but rewarding job that must be completed in an environment of acceptance and participation by the entire plant where the installation is to be made.

The following conditions must have recognition and the wholehearted support by the plant to ensure success in work measurement of labor hours.

1. The need for the program must be established, based on a cost picture. Top management, middle management, line supervision, and staff executives must review the maintenance-cost picture both before and as projected after the costs of installation; and the costs of maintenance.
2. Top management should state the objectives of work measurement so completely that those in line and staff functions who are to work with and administer the program can enthusiastically support it.
3. Line supervision must be informed as to their responsibilities in completing the program. Then they must be properly trained to discharge these responsibilities.
4. The hourly worker and the union must be conditioned to the benefits of work measurement. Since this type of work has been traditionally "unratable," there will be a strong feeling of "it can't be done" in many of the workers. The line foreman can play a valuable part in orienting these people.
5. The development of standards for maintenance is not a routine time-study job. There will be considerable methods work to be done before and concurrent with the accumulation of standard data. There will be many tricky problems in frequencies of occurrences, in developing standard data, in methods of applying standard data, all of which require a good industrial engineering background and a high degree of practical judgment.
6. With or without a union, a work-measurement policy must be established. This policy should cover the usual pledges of limitation of earnings, adjustment of standards, payment of earnings, guarantee that workers will receive proper job instruction, and provision of some method of hearing and resolving differences between the workers and management.
7. Work methods and craft-working procedures must be standardized.
8. Adequate administration procedures must be installed for a work-order system, planning and scheduling, and timekeeping.
9. Decisions and their implementation, to be made at the proper level, within boundaries established by the work-measurement policy, must be encouraged.

Chapter 4

USING TABULATING-MACHINE CARDS

By OSCAR W. GRAVELEY
Formerly Director of Maintenance
Electro Metallurgical Company
Division Union Carbide & Carbon Corporation
Niagara Falls, N.Y.

Good costs for work performed depend on timely attention to details. Punched-card systems can meet these requirements through supplying details of manpower, work distribution, frequency of repair, backlog of work, and cost information for use in the management of maintenance.

The development of managed maintenance has reached the degree that justifies the use of the most advanced methods of business analysis. Punched-card and tape systems are representative of methods available that can be justified with maintenance savings. These systems offer the maintenance manager a rapid and effective means of recording, analyzing, and reporting his activities.

Punched-card systems are not new. They have been used as tools of management since World War I. All are alike in basic principles, providing a means of recording information from a source document, a method of classifying, and a medium from which to print information and at the same time perform calculations.

To take full advantage of these machine methods, it is necessary to have the basic fundamentals of a managed maintenance program in effect. Each maintenance program has to be developed to meet requirements of operational size, products, equipment, location, type of administration, and many other variables. There will be differences in detail, but the principles are the same. Thus, having the same principles, it is possible to set forth the management tools required to meet all justifiable requirements. Manual as well as machine methods require the basic components mentioned in the following paragraphs:

A Classification of Accounts. The classification of accounts is primarily designed as a method of distributing maintenance costs to the desired areas of a financial management system. It should contain the following features:

1. An index to the areas of a cost system that will aid in the management of maintenance.
2. Distribution of labor, material, services of others, and overhead. (Overhead can be distributed on an allotted basis.)
3. Be adaptable to summary at each level of management interest.

Time Distribution. A timekeeping system that distributes the amount of time by hours and crafts to the cost areas representing the location of the work performed can be achieved by using a separate distribution card issued daily and a weekly time card for payroll purposes or a daily card used for both time distribution and payroll preparation, with no weekly card.

Job-order System. A job-order system, to authorize the performance of work and to ensure that charges will be properly made to designated cost areas. The job order is the initiating document used by the tabulating department to prepare punch cards for the accumulation of costs, recording estimates, and distributed time. It is the key document of the control system.

Work Estimating. Estimating is used as the yardstick for comparing performance with ideals, also necessary for planning and scheduling. A good control system requires that estimated maintenance hours be shown by craft. Material estimates need only be shown in dollar values for maintenance cost-control purposes. Planning estimates should detail material requirements.

Craft Coding. For labor control, it is necessary to know individual craft requirements and the labor performance. To key these into the tabulating-machine system it is necessary to code the crafts.

Stores-control System. To obtain the total cost of a job, material costs must be included. A stores-control system is an absolute requirement for obtaining this information. Generally, the institution of tabulating-machine methods for stores control will justify their installation cost on the basis of stores-control savings alone.

With the maintenance management tools effected you are in a position to pose your problem to the members of the tabulating department or the representatives of machine suppliers for solution.

Machine suppliers will provide the knowledge of equipment and the technical help with experience in handling like problems. The user must know the answers required and provide the necessary background to obtain them.

Suppliers of punched-card equipment for business management are the International Business Machines Corporation, Remington Rand Division of Sperry Rand Corporation, and the Underwood Corporation. The McBee Company has a manual sorting system. Machines can be obtained on either a rental or purchase basis. Business machines are both mechanically and electronically actuated. The choice of a system or supplier should be based on individual need and preference since card areas, performance functions, and prices differ.

Punched-card systems depend on the use of cards with holes punched in predetermined positions. The areas of the cards are sectioned, and each section is coded to represent a unit of information. This may consist of figures, letters of the alphabet, or descriptive terms, or any other information that lends itself to coded form. The amount of information that can be punched into a single card is limited only by the area of the card and the size of the holes punched. A hole punched in a card and verified provides an unalterable unit record. The use of punched cards to actuate business machines provides the most versatile, economical, and effective method so far conceived.

The feasibility of the application of the card system to your problem can be understood better by having a general knowledge of the functions of some of the available equipment. This will also help develop equipment requirements and point out limitations.

Card Punching. An operator reads a source document and by pressing keys automatically converts information into punched holes. The positioning of the card in the machine can be either manual or automatic depending on the machine.

Verifying. To prove accuracy, the previously punched card is placed in another machine and the same information is fed to the machine from the source document originally used; if any difference is found, the machine alerts the operator.

Duplicating. A machine reads the card originally punched and duplicates the punching into any number of cards required.

Gang Punching. Gang punching is used to copy punched information automatically from a master card to detail cards. This operation is used to replenish stocks of punched cards and to transfer calculated results to detail cards.

Reproducing. Reproducing is used mainly as an accounting function and obtains fixed information from a set of prepunched master cards.

Interpreter. This machine senses the information punched in a card and prints the same information on it. Generally the printing is done along the top edge of the card. Printed cards are desirable when they are to be used as documents or for collection of written or marked information.

Sorter. This machine groups cards according to the holes punched in them. Any hole or combination of holes, representing either numerical or alphabetical information, can be the group control. Here cards are arranged for reports, summaries, sequences, and accounting purposes.

MAINTENANCE PUNCH CARD PROCEDURE

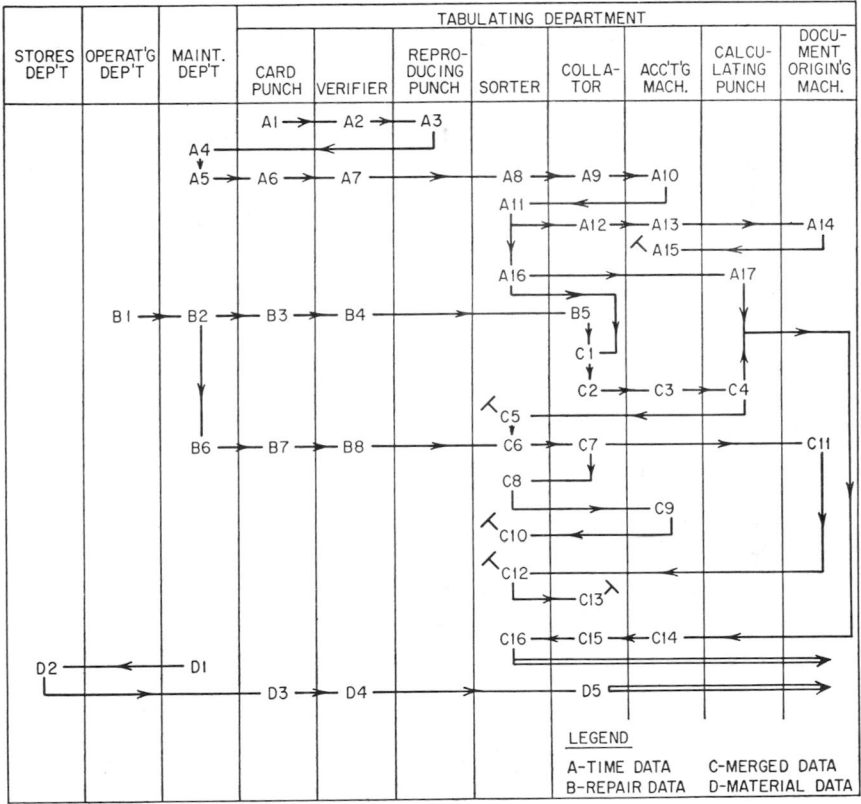

FIG. 4-1. Maintenance punch-card procedure.

Calculator. The calculator is used for computing, by multiplication, division, addition, or subtraction, basic data from cards previously punched. The results of these computations are then punched in the card or in a trailer card.

Tabulation or Accounting Machine. This provides automatic printing on report forms of all or any part of the information punched into cards. Machines can be used to add, subtract, and print combinations of the totals.

Card to Tape and Tape to Card. Equipment is also in use that transfers punched-card information to paper tape and from paper tape to punched cards. This reduces the bulk problem in mailing and storing records.

A maintenance punch-card-procedure chart is shown in Fig. 4-1; the procedure flow is symbolized and numbered for relation to the following explanations: Four alphabetical symbols have been used on the chart, each to represent the separate procedural steps.

Time Reporting. Symbol A

1. A master name card is prepared from data obtained in the fiscal office to show pay number, employee name, craft and subdivision of craft, rate of pay, and seniority date.
2. The master name card is verified.
3. A clock card is prepared from the master name card with clock number, department, name, craft code, rate, and group seniority. The clock card also serves as the labor-distribution medium.
4. The clock card is forwarded to the maintenance department where it is placed in the time-card rack.
5. The maintenance department employee punches in the time he arrives at work in the morning and the time out when he leaves at night. The craft foreman enters the time spent on specific jobs, by hours and repair-order number. The foreman checks the arrival and departure times punched on the face of the card and forwards the card to the timekeeping and tabulating department.
6. In the tabulating department, detail-job cards are punched from the daily clock card. These detail-job cards show: the decimal hours worked, the repair-order number for the work performed, amount of overtime or premium pay when occurring, the craft, the date, the employee's clock number, and the department of regular employment.
7. The information in the cards is verified.
8. The daily clock cards and the labor-distribution cards are sorted into their respective groups.
9. The daily clock cards and the labor-distribution cards are matched and merged. Any differences occurring are investigated and corrected.
10. A daily balancing report is prepared for fiscal purposes.
11. The daily clock cards and the labor-distribution cards are sorted and grouped.
12. The daily clock cards are matched with the master name file to detect any differences in names or rates. If any exist they are corrected.
13. Employee-earnings summary is prepared.
14. Employee-earnings cards are originated.
15. Normal payroll procedure is then completed.
16. Labor-distribution cards are sorted by craft, repair-order number, and charges to other than repair orders. The repair-order cards are forwarded for merging with the repair orders and held for further processing.
17. Labor distributed to other than repair orders is punched into cards and the new cards forwarded to be used in the preparation of weekly summary cards.

Repair-order Procedure. Symbol B

1. A repair order is written, generally in an operating department, the original and two copies are forwarded to the maintenance department, and one copy is retained in the operating department for reference. All copies are different colors.
2. One color copy of the repair order is prepared in the maintenance department for the tabulating department by adding the estimated man-hours and the craft designation to be used in originating the repair-order master card.
3. The tabulating department prepares a repair-order master card carrying the repair-order number, craft code, estimated hours, account to be charged, and date opened.
4. Repair-order master card is verified.
5. The new master card is merged with all other master cards on open orders.
6. The foreman's color copy of the repair order is returned to the maintenance superintendent's office signaling the completion of a job. Maintenance places the date completed on the copy and forwards to the tabulating department.
7. The tabulating department punches a card with the repair-order number and the completion date.
8. The punched data are verified and the repair-order completion card is forwarded for merging with the master cards for open orders and the weekly summary cards.

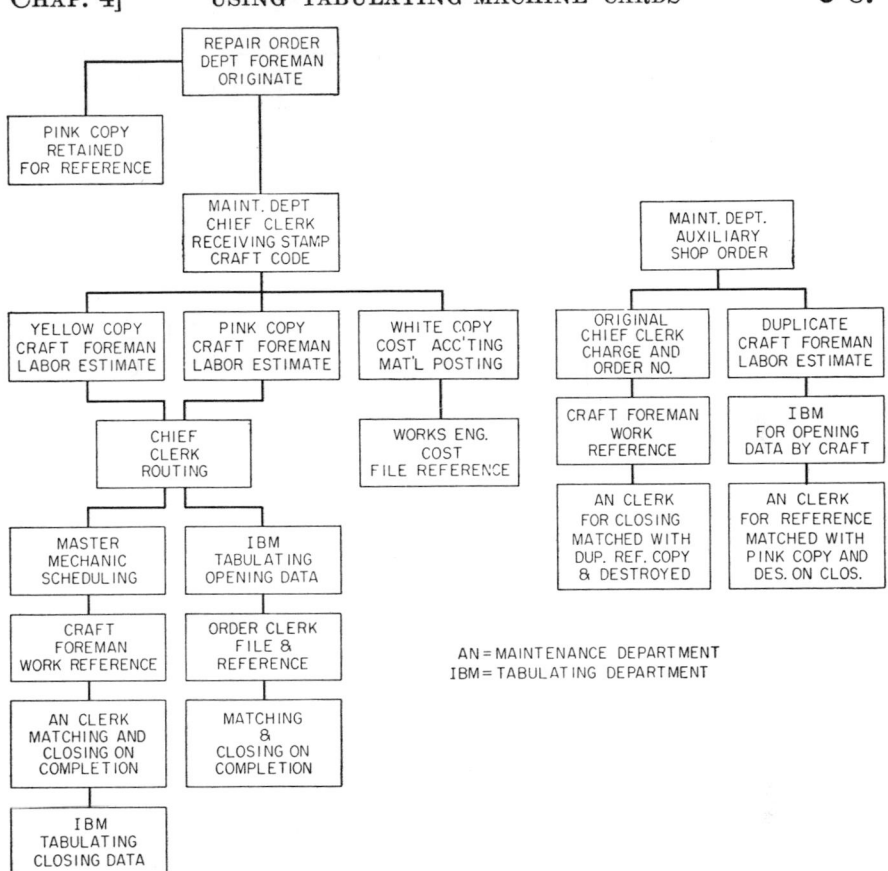

FIG. 4-2. Flow sheet of repair orders and auxiliary shop orders.

Merged-time and Repair-order Data. Symbol C

1. The master cards for open repair orders are merged with the labor charges distributed to repair-order numbers. The repair-order cards and the labor-distribution charges are compared and sorted into four groups: unmatched labor cards, unmatched repair-order cards, matched labor cards, and the matched repair-order cards.
2. The matched cards are merged and the unmatched cards are investigated. Improper charges are corrected and the unmatched cards are merged with the matched.
3. The labor is then posted to the category of accounts and a weekly summary is prepared from daily cards.
4. Weekly summary cards are punched.
5. The summary cards are sorted into two groups; one group is filed for reference, and the second group, the master cards for open repair orders, is forwarded with the posted summaries.
6. The open-order master cards and the completion cards are sorted according to repair-order number.
7. The open-order cards and the completion cards are matched, merged, and separated into two groups. One group has the remaining open orders. The other group contains the master cards of the orders completed.

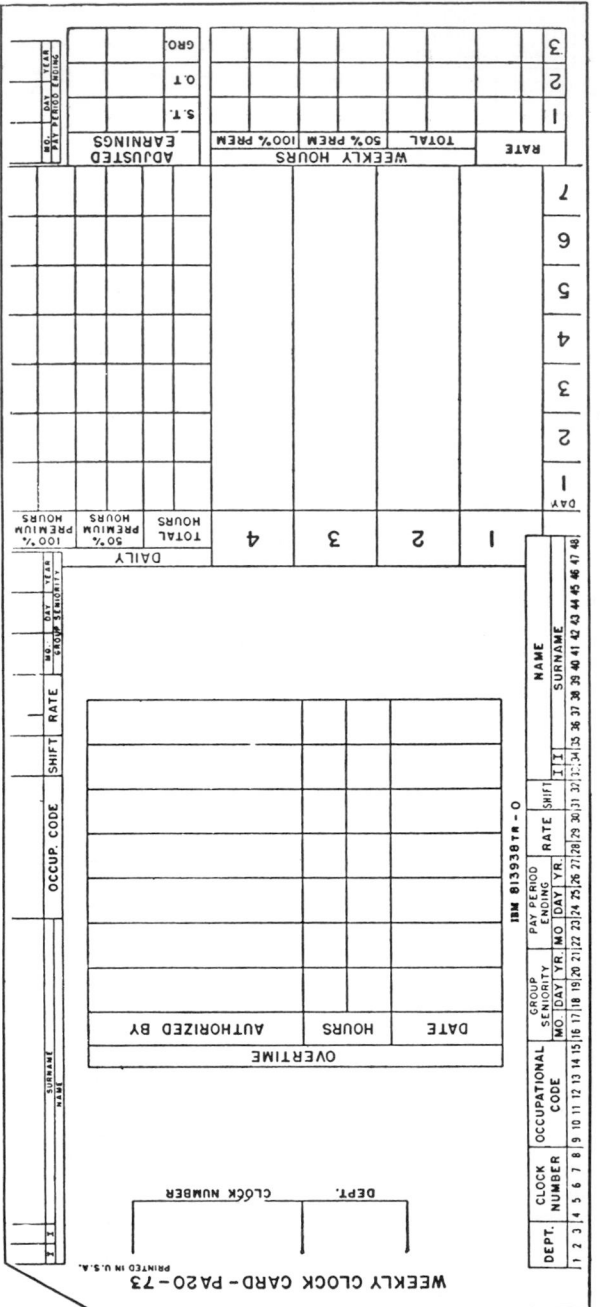

FIG. 4-3. Maintenance daily (or weekly) clock card.

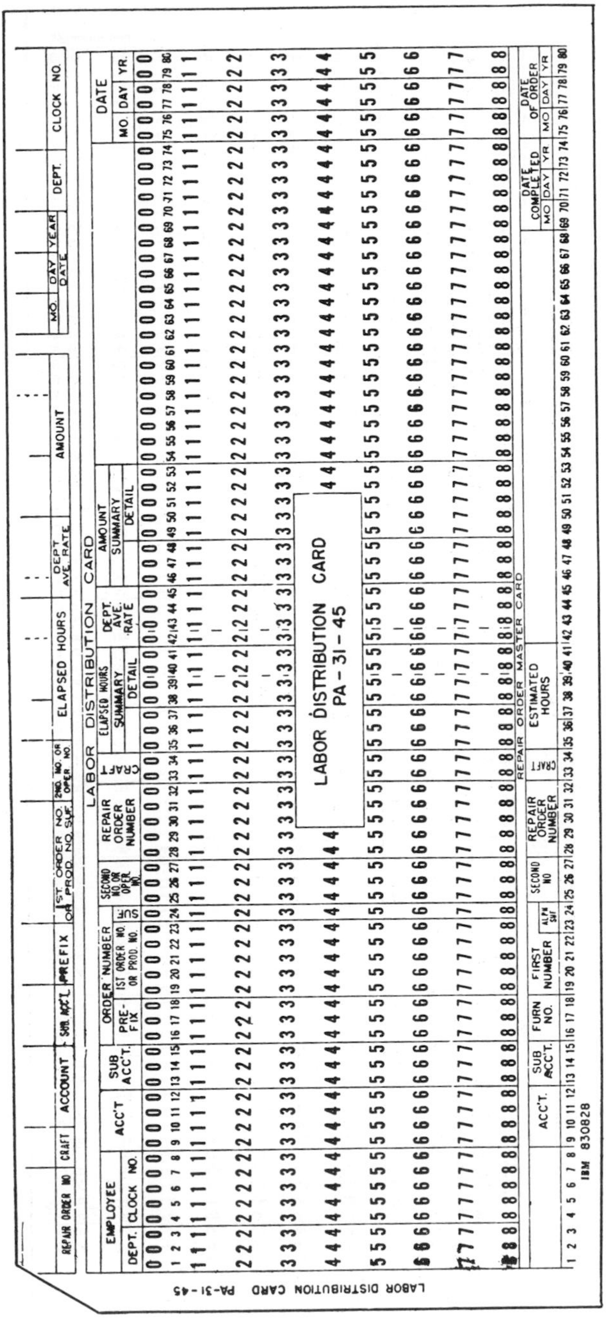

FIG. 4-4. Labor-distribution card (punched from daily clock card).

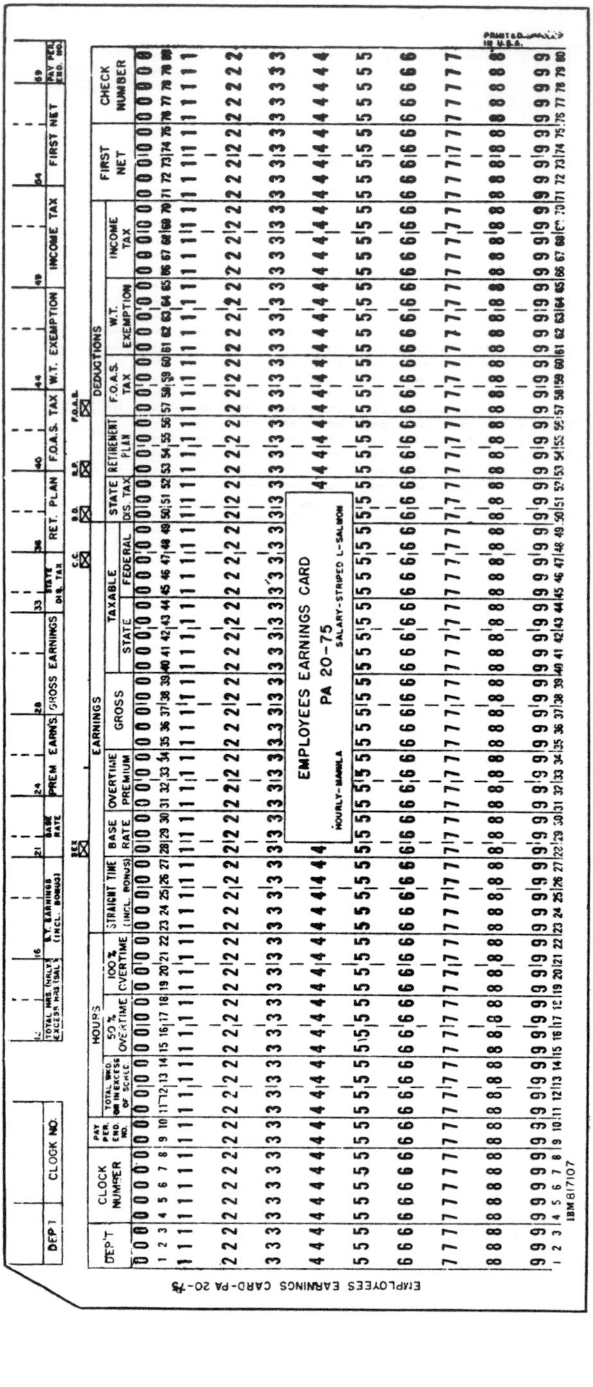

FIG. 4-5. Employee's earnings card (accumulated from clock card daily).

			REPORT OF COST OF CLOSED REPAIR ORDERS					
DEPT.	EXP. ACCT.	EQUIP. #	REPAIR ORDER #	SOURCE	LABOR $	MATERIAL $	TOTAL LABOR & MAT. $	LABOR EST. $
169	4	2700	49637	327	1330			
169	4	2700	49637	720		20345		
					1330	20345	21675	1272
169	4	2700	49644	327	443			
					443		443	424
169	4	2700	50618	327	1164			
					1164		1164	636
169	4	2700	50622	327	1330			
					1330		1330	1272
169	4	2700	50645	327	4045			
					4045		4045	1272
169	4	2700	94001	327	222			
					222		222	848
169	4	2700	94004	327	920			
					920		920	848
169	4	2700	94011	327	1149			
					1149		1149	1060
169	4	2700	94015	327	452			
169	4	2700	94015	720		2166		
					452	2166	2618	212
169	4	2700	94045	327	2875			
					2875		2875	1060
169	4	2700	94047	327	442			
					442		442	424
169	4	2700	94048	327	663			
					663		663	636
169	4	2700	94050	327	443			
					443		443	424
169	4	2700	94067	327	1149			
					1149		1149	1060
169	4	2700	94082	327	2656			
					2656		2656	1272
169	4	2700	94095	327	443			
					443		443	424
169	4	2700	94096	327	442			
					442		442	424
169	4	2700	94105	327	2655			
					2655		2655	1484

FIG. 4-6. Report of cost of closed repair orders.

8. The remaining open orders are sorted by account and craft.
9. A weekly report of the backlog of work on open orders is prepared by account number and craft.
10. The open-order master cards are sorted and arranged by repair-order number and retained for future use.
11. The master cards for the completed orders are used to prepare a completed-order report.
12. The cards are sorted and the cards originated to select the completed orders are removed and destroyed.
13. The completed-order master cards for other time periods are merged with the current cards and retained for reporting and analysis.
14. The repair-order labor-summary cards and summary cards for labor distributed to other than repair orders are used to balance payroll against distributed charges.
15. All labor-summary cards are then merged.
16. The cards are sorted to meet reporting requirements.

Material. Symbol D

1. It is to be assumed that a punch-card stores-control system exists. The material is withdrawn from the stores by a stores issue, generally originating in the maintenance department, describing the material and charged to the repair-order number.

2. The stores department places the material code number on the issue and verifies the date of issue and the quantity.
3. A card is then punched showing the information contained on the stores issue.
4. The stores-issue information is verified.
5. The issue card is then matched and merged with other stores-record cards. The materials on the issue card are priced and the value added to the card. The completed issue cards are then used to supply data for various reporting requirements.

MONTHLY LABOR DISTRIBUTION TO REPAIRS   (OPEN ORDERS)

SOURCE DEPTS.	TO DEPT.	THIRD LETTER EXPENSE	EQUIP. NO.	REPAIR ORDER NUMBER	HOURS	$
65	843	4		40217	2 00	4
					2 00 *	4 *
327	843	4	100	40238	21 00	44
327	843	4	100	44848	9 00	20
327	843	4	100	46238	2 00	4
					32 00 *	68 *
327	843	4	201	44822	2 00	4
					2 00 *	4 *
843	843	4	203		20 00	41
					20 00 *	41 *
843	843	4	205		111 00	230
327	843	4	205	44813	2 00	4
					113 00 *	234 *
843	843	4	207		6 00	13
					6 00 *	13 *
327	843	4	208	40202	93 50	198
					93 50 *	198 *
843	843	4	210		16 00	34
327	843	4	210	40204	20 50	43
					36 50 *	77 *
843	843	4	216		14 00	29
					14 00 *	29 *
843	843	4	220		68 00	141
327	843	4	220	44818	5 00	10
					73 00 *	151 *
843	843	4	225		37 00	77
327	843	4	225	40212	3 00	6
327	843	4	225	40226	78 00	165
327	843	4	225	40240	32 00	68
327	843	4	225	40248	5 00	11
					155 00 *	327 *
327	843	4	226	40262	47 00	99
					47 00 *	99 *
843	843	4	227		36 00	75
327	843	4	227	40210	16 00	34
					52 00 *	109 *
843	843	4	228		4 00	8
					4 00	8 *
843	843	4	229		27 00	56
327	843	4	229	40239	9 00	19
327	843	4	229	44844	27 50	59
					63 50 *	134 *

FIG. 4-7. Estimated outstanding labor distributed to open orders.

An orderly approach to the development or improvement of the management system is the use of a flow chart to outline existing procedure and show steps to be taken to accomplish the result. Figure 4-2 shows a flow chart of a maintenance operation that uses a repair order with three different colored copies. One copy of the repair order remains in the originating department; the original and two copies are sent to the maintenance department to initiate action. The color copies of the order signal the type of action to be taken by the tabulating department. The pink copy arriving in the tabulating department causes a data card to be punched. It is also to be noted that an auxiliary shop order is used in the maintenance department when more than one craft is involved in the work.   A copy of the auxiliary order is also sent to the tabulating department.   When all work-order copies distributed have been returned, the maintenance control officer knows that all crafts have completed their work and that the yellow copy of the repair order can be sent to the tabulating department for closing.

MAINTENANCE BACKLOG REPORT			
DEPT.	CRAFT	HOURS ROUTINE ORDERS	HOURS YEARLY ORDERS
7 9		4 0 0	
7 9	0 1	8 3 0 0	
7 9	0 7	2 3 4 0 0	4 2 0 0 0
7 9	0 8	4 0 8 0 0	
7 9	0 9	4 1 0 0	
7 9	1 0	7 7 0 0	
7 9	1 1	3 2 0 0	
7 9	1 2	1 3 6 0 0	
7 9	1 3	6 0 0	
		1 0 2 1 0 0 *	4 2 0 0 0 *
8 1		1 7 0 0	
8 1	0 1	1 3 2 0 0	8 0 0 0
8 1	0 5	6 0 0	
8 1	0 7	4 3 1 0 0	4 0 8 0 0
8 1	0 8	6 9 9 0 0	
8 1	0 9	1 5 3 0 0	
8 1	1 0	2 1 0 0 0	1 5 6 0 0 0
8 1	1 1	1 0 0	
8 1	1 2	4 0 0 0	
8 1	1 3	3 5 0 0	
		1 7 2 4 0 0 *	2 0 4 8 0 0 *
9 5		1 4 5 0	
9 5	0 1	2 5 3 0 0	5 2 0 0 0
9 5	0 3	4 0 0	1 0 0 0 0 0
9 5	0 4	6 0 0 0	2 8 0 0 0
9 5	0 5	1 7 9 5	
9 5	0 6	9 6 0 0	1 5 6 0 0
9 5	0 7	3 6 7 0 0	8 3 2 0 0
9 5	0 8	7 3 7 0 0	

Fig. 4-8. Maintenance backlog report.

Figure 4-3 shows a tabulating card for the maintenance department that can be used as a daily or weekly clock card.   When used as a daily card the back of the card has a place for entry of the jobs performed and the time required, thus acting as the medium to distribute labor to the individual repair orders.   The card is placed in the rack during the day previous to use.   It is taken from the rack and the "in" time punched on it.   The mechanic carries it with him during the day and records his jobs and the time taken to perform them. At the end of his day, he punches the "out" time on the card and drops it in a box for collection by the timekeeping department. The cycle is repeated each day.

Two other cards are required in the tabulating department to accumulate and use the information from the daily clock card; they are Fig. 4-4, a labor-distribution card, and Fig. 4-5, an employee's earnings card. The labor-distribution-card acts as the medium for collecting information to be used in charging time to a job and in preparing maintenance reports. The employee's earnings card is used in preparing the payroll.

The tabulating department needs other cards besides those shown in the exhibits; the number of cards required will depend on the detailed breakdown used and the type of report to be provided.

Reports prepared in the tabulating department are the means used to take advantage of the accumulated data for analysis and action. The increments of data can be arranged in any order desired and for any time interval. It must be remembered, though, that, unless you provide for the collection of the information to meet your requirements, the system cannot provide it for you.

Figure 4-6 is a report prepared to show the cost of closed repair orders. All repair orders completed during some stated period of time, such as a day, a week, or a month, are shown on this report. The report shows the repair-order number, the department charged for the work, the facility worked on, the cost of labor, the cost of materials, the total cost, and the labor estimated in advance of work performance. Its value is apparent from the information contained.

To keep informed concerning the status of orders that have been opened but not completed, a report (Fig. 4-7) is prepared to show the estimated outstanding labor distributed to open orders. Figure 4-8 is a maintenance backlog report that shows the estimated hours by craft and type of repair order for work to be done in each operating department. This is useful in determining maintenance work force and the department where concentration of effort is needed.

The examples of reports should be sufficient for you to decide the content that will be useful to you. It should be remembered that economic justification is required, since the collection of data and the preparation of reports cost money.

Information used in the preparation of this material has been obtained from Electro Metallurgical Company, Union Carbide and Carbon Corporation, International Business Machines Corporation, Remington Rand Division of Sperry Rand Corporation, and Underwood Samas Corporation.

Chapter 5

PAPER WORK

By G. J. MARTIN[1]
Manager, Mechanical Division
National Biscuit Company
New York, N.Y.

In deciding on the paper work to be used to obtain proper functioning and control of maintenance operations, it is essential that a thorough study be made of existing conditions, and the results desired be clearly in mind. Every form should play an important part in the control of personnel, materials, or job costs. Too little paper work will not provide the control. Elaborate paper work can be costly, decrease employee incentive, and result in a maze of red tape that will bog down the maintenance organization. Essential forms are discussed here.

Equipment Inventory. For effective planning and scheduling, it is necessary to have a complete record of the equipment to be maintained (see Fig. 5-1, the field descriptive sheet). An inventory number is assigned to each unit. It can be stamped on a metal tag and attached to the unit, or applied in some other way. Area mechanics, electricians, or trainee engineers can take the inventory. Some companies have maintenance clerks do it, to become familiar with the equipment before the program goes into operation.

To simplify inventory procedures, outline the questions and define the data required on an instruction sheet (Table 5-1). The completed field inventory sheets should be reviewed by the plant engineer or assigned members of his staff who can add additional data that may be of value on the permanent equipment record (Fig. 5-2), which is typed from the field inventory sheet.

Equipment Records. Equipment records are just as important for a plant with only 100 units as they are for plants with thousands of units. Some companies with multiplant operations maintain all equipment records in the general office for use by the plant accounting division which records depreciation and obsolescence. However, equipment records are necessary in individual plant maintenance for posting repairs, changes, and spare parts, as well as for assignment of inspection schedules. One procedure is to maintain a set of records at the branch plant and a duplicate set at the general office. Other companies retain only an inventory card file in the general office. The cards are prepared by the branches upon receipt of new equipment.

The value of these records is limitless. In case of breakdown, accurate machine and parts specifications and manufacturer's name and address can be had immediately. Whether the question refers to size, weight, lubrication, power transmission, packing, or date purchased, the information is there.

On the equipment record form, space is provided for listing the essential replacement parts which are to be stocked. This list should be checked by the person who sets the maximum and minimum quantities. When the number of parts for one unit is

---

[1] The author is now President, Industrial Management Consultants, Baltimore, Md.

large, they can be listed on a separate sheet to be attached to the equipment record (see Fig. 5-3).   The spare-parts list is a necessary aid for the supervisor who has the responsibility for keeping the equipment in operation, and the storeroom clerk for stock control.

FIELD DESCRIPTIVE SHEET

BRANCH _____

LOCATION _____

REQ. # _____

DATE PURCH _____

ITEM _____   INVENTORY NO. _____W_____
PURCHASED FROM _____   PURCHASE ORDER NO. _____
MANUFACTURER _____
HORSEPOWER _____ AMPS _____ SERIAL NO. _____ TYPE _____
SPEED (RPM) _____ OUTPUT SPEED (RPM) _____ MODEL NO. _____ SIZE _____
VOLTS _____ RATIO _____ STYLE NO. _____ CAPACITY _____
PHASE _____ FRAME _____ CAT. NO. _____ DIMENSIONS _____
CYCLES _____ JOB NO. _____ DWG. NO. _____ SHIP. WHT. _____
ADDITIONAL DESCRIPTIVE DATA AND COMMENTS _____

DRIVES W _____ ITEM _____ THROUGH TRANSMISSION/SPEED REDUCER & INV.NO. _____
DRIVEN BY _____ H.P. _____ RPM MOTOR W _____ THROUGH TRANSMISSION/SPEED REDUCER & INV.NO. _____
USED IN CONNECTION WITH W _____ ITEM _____

PACKING SPECIFICATIONS _____

BEARING DATA _____

LUBRICATION DATA _____

DRIVE SPECIFICATIONS _____

FREQUENCY OF P.M. INSPECTION _____
ITEMS FOR P.M. INSPECTION _____

INVENTORY NO'S. OF AUXILIARY EQUIPMENT _____

FIG. 5-1. Field descriptive sheet, used in recording data when taking inventory of equipment in the field.

The reverse side of the equipment record is used for recording the repairs and changes, labor and material costs.   After the records have been in use for some time, the history of repairs and changes will indicate whether the equipment is functioning properly and on an economical basis or if it is too small, too weak, or of the wrong

Table 5-1. Instructions on Field Inventory Sheets

1. The attached specimen field inventory sheet is used in connection with the installation of the preventive-maintenance program at your plant.
2. The purpose of the field inventory sheet is to compile equipment data for purpose of preparing equipment record forms at your plant.
3. Estimate your field inventory sheet requirements and arrange to mimeograph a supply of sheets accordingly. Your requirements will be based on the approximate number of pieces of equipment on hand, or anticipated in the case of new plants.
4. Field inventory sheets are to be prepared in pencil, in single copy.
5. Field inventory sheets on new equipment will be prepared as the new equipment is installed. Sheets on equipment already installed will be prepared at the time the inventory is taken.
6. It is important that all available information and data pertaining to the equipment be recorded on the field inventory sheet; the following instructions cover each of the items listed:

Plant: Indicate the name and number of the plant where inventory is being taken.
Inventory Number: Indicate the company inventory number assigned to the equipment.
Location: Indicate the building number and floor. If entire plant is in one building, use department name, such as mixing, packaging, etc.
Item: Indicate the type of equipment, such as motor, mixer, pump, conveyor.
Description: Describe the equipment in such a manner that no person will have any question about the type of equipment and what is included.
Requisition Number: Indicate requisition number when available.
Manufacturer: Indicate the name and address of the manufacturer of the equipment.
Transferred from: If the equipment was transferred from another company plant, indicate the name of the plant from which it was transferred and the date of the transfer.
Job Number, Size, Rpm, Capacity, Purchase Order Number, Type or Model, Serial Number, Weight: Show this information when it is available and when it applies to the equipment being inventoried.
Packing Specifications: If equipment is a pump, give data on make and type of packing used. If equipment is a machine unit with a hydraulic or pneumatic unit, give make and size of packing or diaphrams.
Bearing Data: Indicate type of bearing in unit, such as ball bearings, roller bearings, bronze bushings. Make and catalog number should be indicated when available.
Lubrication: Indicate the type of lubricants used on the equipment; describe all lubricants if more than one type is used and indicate frequency for lubrication.
Drive Specifications: Indicate data on chains, sprockets, gears, belts, etc., in sufficient detail to permit reorder of spare or replacement parts.
Auxiliary Equipment: Indicate company inventory numbers and names of all auxiliary equipment.
This Machine Is an Auxiliary of No. —— Indicate the company inventory number and name of the equipment that this unit is a part of.
Frequency of PM Inspection: Insert frequency as designated in manual for the type of equipment.
Items for PM checking: List points requiring special attention at periodic intervals (other than points listed on inspection sheet).
Additional Data: Use this space for details and information for which no heading has been provided or for which insufficient space was allowed.

7. Secure complete inventory and data on all types of equipment in each location at one time working progressively through the plant. For example, when inventorying packing floor equipment secure inventory and data on auxiliary equipment as well, such as conveyors, motors, and starters, at the same time you take the respective packaging machines. This will eliminate backtracking and hasten completion of the inventory as a whole and the field sheets with regard to auxiliary-equipment data.
8. Upon completing a reasonable number of field inventory sheets they should be turned over to the office for typing of the equipment record. If possible, complete the spare-parts list, using the reverse side of the field sheet, so that this information can be typed on the form in one operation with the statistical data. *Caution:* Where you have a number of like pieces of equipment, spare-parts list should be shown on one field sheet and form only. The other sheets will show, in the spare-parts list section, reference to this sheet for spare-parts listing.
9. After the information on the field sheets has been transferred to the forms, the field sheets should be set aside and retained for possible necessary reference until such time as full installation of this program has been effected and these sheets no longer serve any purpose.
10. It is suggested that you arrange your schedules to secure a complete inventory of all equipment within a definite compact period, as piecemeal basis will complicate and retard the succeeding functions of setting up your storeroom, spare-parts lists, and inspection schedules. This is most important!

size and type.   The inspection-frequency schedule on the equipment record form provides a master control record.

After the equipment is cataloged, the sheets can be filed in loose-leaf binders indexed by departments, buildings, work centers, or type of equipment, for ready

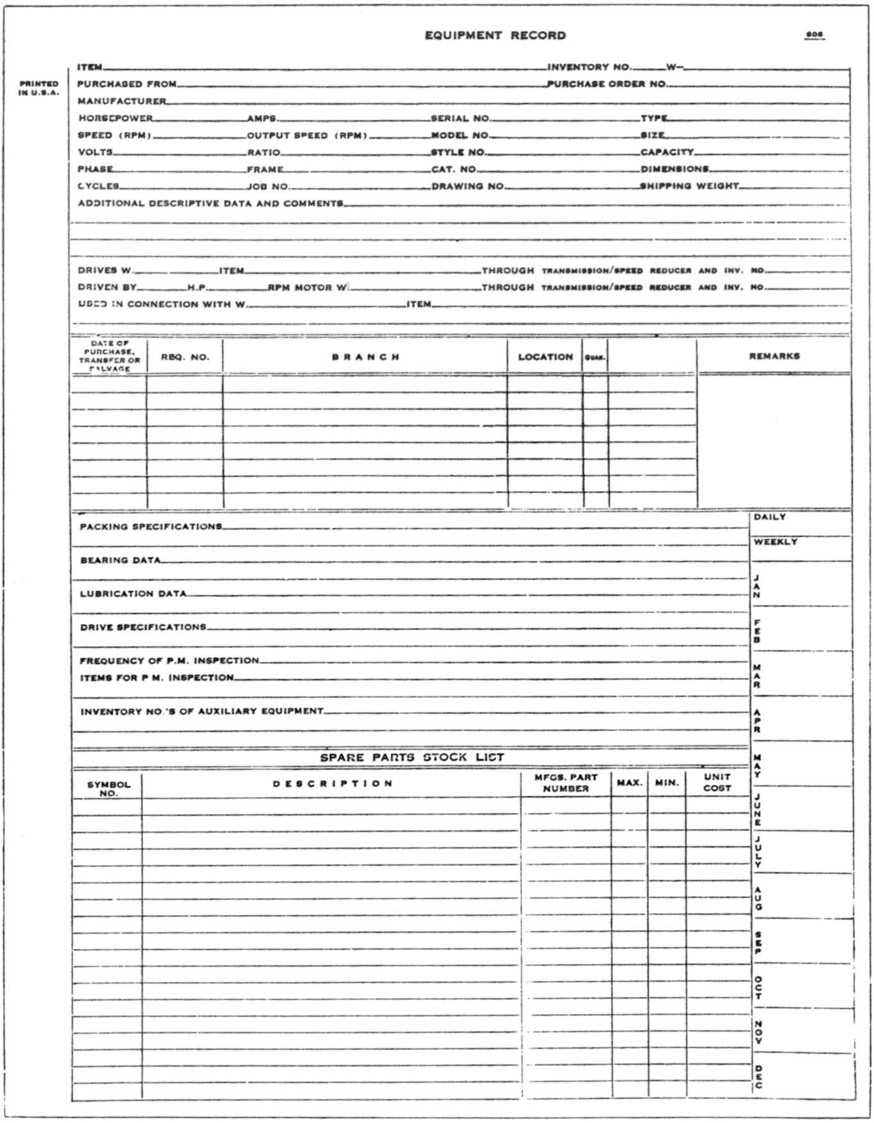

Fig. 5-2. Permanent equipment record on which data and history are recorded.

reference.   Sometimes it is found desirable to use a prefix letter or letters before the inventory number to facilitate reference to specific types of equipment.

The physical history on the reverse of the equipment record will indicate the following:

1. Normal or excessive maintenance cost.
2. Need for redesign (indicated by too frequent maintenance).
3. Replacement need to secure proper size.
4. Replacement need to secure correct equipment.
5. Replacement need because of inefficiency.

It will also provide cost data for management reports, show how to save production time on machines that give constant trouble, and help to improve maintenance department morale by indicating major sources of trouble.

FORM 608-A
PRTD. IN U.S.A.

PLANT ____________________

INVENTORY NO. ____________________

EQUIPMENT RECORD
SPARE PARTS STOCK LIST

LOCATION ____________________

SYMBOL NO.	DESCRIPTION	MFGS. PART NO.	MAX.	MIN.	UNIT COST

FIG. 5-3. Spare-parts stock list, to be made when number of parts is great, and to be attached to permanent equipment record.

There is no need to feel that there is only one good equipment record form to fit all industries. The type of equipment or the kind of industry may require variation. Another type of form, giving flexibility in a multiple-card record system, is shown in Fig. 5-4. This system consists of two cards. The master card carries all the information about the piece of equipment and sets up a schedule of inspection. Usually the schedule is set up on the basis of the manufacturer's recommendation, in cooperation with lubrication and mechanical engineers. The master card signals the dates when inspection must be made.

The second card is the inspector's work card. When, by scanning, it is determined that a particular machine is to be inspected, the work card is removed and routed to the maintenance department. At the same time a detailed work-order sheet is withdrawn from a loose-leaf file and sent with the work card. It sets out in detail the work to be performed according to the manufacturer's specifications.

When the inspection has been performed, the work card, the work-order sheet, and all time and material tickets are returned to the master file where the information is posted to the master record. Then the work card is returned to its position behind the master card. At the same time the next inspection period is determined and the signals on the master card are moved to their new position.

Equipment-card record forms are available from several manufacturers and are used by many companies. Electric-motor and control manufacturers have developed equipment record cards for their types of equipment for distribution to their customers to assist them in their electrical maintenance programs.

Work Orders. Work orders are written requests for services to be rendered by the maintenance department. They establish for both maintenance and management the information that work is to be done. They provide a record of the cost of these services. They provide the data on which material requisitions are prepared, individual work instructions are issued, and assignments of tasks to personnel and equipment are made. When the work has been completed and all entries have been made, they comprise records that serve the maintenance department in its control activities and the cost department in expense allocation.

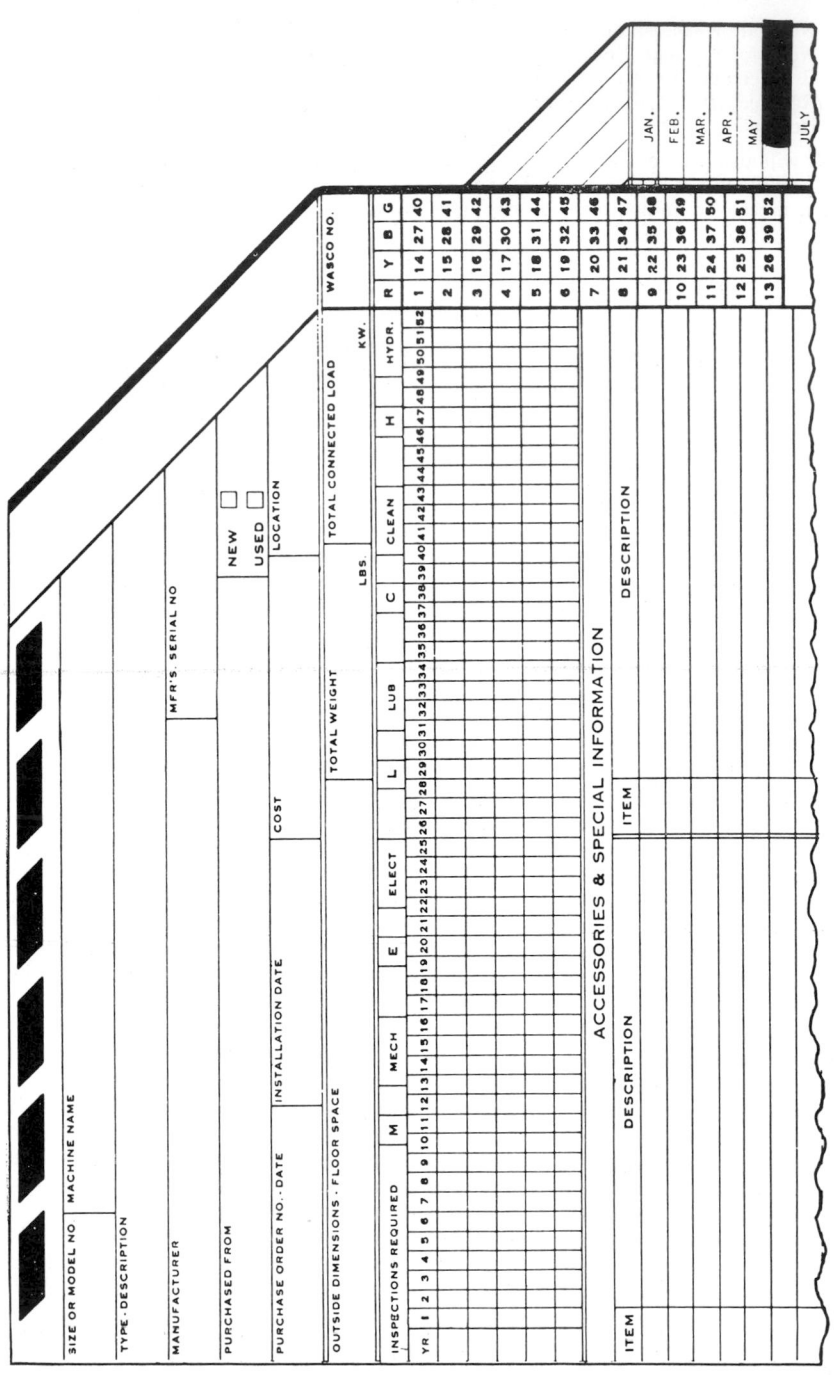

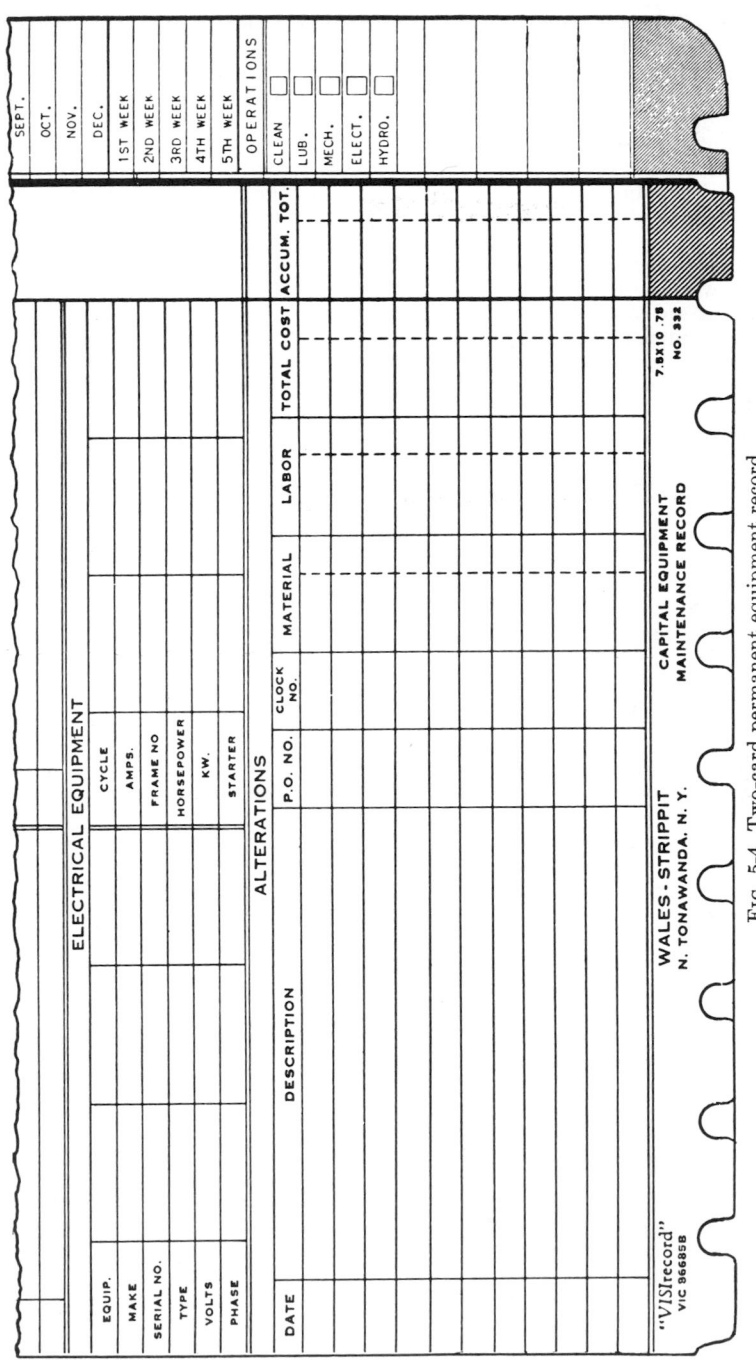

FIG. 5-4. Two-card permanent equipment record.

Because all maintenance work except routine operations should be scheduled, it is desirable to put all orders in writing regardless of job size.   This will permit proper planning and scheduling and serve to determine the maintenance backlog.   Verbal orders for jobs should never be given except in case of emergency; however, even then the work order should be made out later so that all the labor and material charges are accounted for.

Numerous types of work orders are used.   Some are small, with only a few lines for a brief description of the work to be done.   Others are large, with spaces for description of work, location, priority, time assigned, time completed, estimated and actual labor and material charges, and so on.

The data requested on the work-order form should be specific and should be of value for work assignment, establishing priority, and accumulating all labor charges. Forms that are too elaborate will only discourage the personnel who fill them out and the maintenance employees who must read them.   A work-order form that is neither too brief nor too elaborate is shown in Fig. 5-5.   A production supervisor, in originating the order, may specify, under "Item and Work Wanted," what he thinks is required.   The mechanic making the repairs indicates under "Mechanic's Report on Work Done," the changes or repairs made.   The two may differ radically. Space is provided to indicate whether the job is routine, urgent, or can be done only during a scheduled shutdown.   Craft required is indicated.

The time spent on the job by the men assigned is recorded on the reverse side and the summarized labor cost is posted on the bottom of the front side.   When a job is completed the work order takes on new importance because of the historical data it provides.

Closed-out work orders should be reviewed every 6 months to analyze repetitive repairs and frequency of breakdowns, and to obtain data for job-cost comparisons. Some companies keep on file all closed-out work orders for a year.

The sample work order described is ideal in plants that do not have a planning and scheduling department in which man-hours and job cost are estimated.   These items can be added to the work-order form.

Work orders are made out in triplicate.   The first and second copies are transmitted to the maintenance department.   The third copy is retained by the production department supervisor who originated the order.   The maintenance clerk stamps a work-order number on both copies.   The original is retained in the maintenance office for follow-up and control; the second copy is assigned to the maintenance personnel.

Work-order numbers are started at the beginning of each year and run consecutively until Dec. 31.

When work orders have been approved by the plant engineer or his deputy, they are ready for planning and scheduling.   In case of a breakdown or emergency, mechanics are assigned immediately to the job and the formal work order usually is made out by the maintenance supervisor after the work is completed or by the maintenance clerk at the time of assignment.

A separate work order is made out for each job.   If two or more trade groups are required on one job, separate maintenance work orders can be issued; however, the work-order number is the same.

The mechanic assigned the work order lists his clock number and the number of hours worked, and describes the type of work done.

When material is required for a specific job, the mechanic submits an approved storeroom withdrawal slip to the maintenance clerk or storeroom clerk.

It is fairly common practice that all work, with the exception of mechanical adjustments and minor repairs requiring less than $\frac{1}{2}$ hr of labor, must originate with a maintenance order.   All maintenance labor of less than $\frac{1}{2}$ hr per job is charged to standing work-order numbers.

All work orders on completed jobs should be turned in to the maintenance clerk who should screen the data, check on the satisfactory completion of the job, and pass the work orders on to the proper maintenance executive for his approval and closing out of the job.   The clerk summarizes the labor and material costs of the job and posts these charges on the equipment record sheet.

(FRONT)

| FORM NO. 808 |
| PRTD. IN U.S.A. |

WORK ORDER   DATE_____   JOB NO._____

REQUESTED BY:_____   LOCATION_____   INVENTORY NO._____

ITEM AND WORK WANTED _____

CHECK ONE

ROUTINE

URGENT

SHUTDOWN

| APPROVED BY | APPROVED BY | DATE WORK |
| PROD. DEPT. HEAD | MECH. SUPT. | SCHEDULED |

MECHANIC'S REPORT ON WORK DONE _____

| DATE | MECH. | APPROVED BY |
| COMPLETED | SIGNATURE | PROD. DEPT. HEAD |

REGULAR HOURS:	PAYROLL	CLASSIFICA-TION AVG. RATE	TOTAL LABOR COSTS	CHECK ONE
	HOURS:			MACH.
OVERTIME HOURS:		X	$	ELECT.
				CARPENTER
				PAINTER
				PIPEFITTER

| WORK | BY |
| APPROVED—DATE | MECH. SUPT. |

(BACK)

TIME RECORD

Record Time to the nearest Quarter-Hour

DATE WORKED	CLOCK NO.		CLOCK NO.		CLOCK NO.		CLOCK NO.		CLOCK NO.	
	HOURS		HOURS		HOURS		HOURS		HOURS	
	REGULAR	OVERTIME	REGULAR	OVERTIME	REGULAR	OVERTIME	REGULAR	OVERTIME	REGULAR	OVERTIME

FIG. 5-5. Work-order form suitable for almost any plant.

For maintenance organizations with planning and scheduling crews that estimate all jobs prior to assignment, an ideal work order is shown in Fig. 5-6. It has space for estimated and actual costs of labor and material, and the account number the job is to be charged to; and it can be issued to one craftsman or several in different trade groups.

Repair jobs or alterations involving a total cost over a certain limit, usually fixed somewhere between $100 and $500, should be formally estimated by a responsible engineer and should require approval on a higher managerial plane than the maintenance supervisor. Reasons for this are obvious: Detailed planning on scope, method, types of material and equipment, and perhaps planning on departmental shutdown should enter into the decision.

WORK ORDER

ORDERED BY	CHARGE	PROPERTY ITEM	DATE

OPER.	BLDG.	MECH	ELEC	RMH	SHIPPING	RESEARCH	MISC.	CLASSIFICATION

IS SHUTDOWN REQUIRED	DATE AVAILABLE	DATE WANTED BY	ASSIGNED TO

MAN HOURS	NUMBER OF MEN	CRAFTS	ACTUAL HOURS
		PIPE FITTER	
		WELDER	
		MACHINIST	
		MILLWRIGHT	
		CARPENTER	
		BRICKLAYER	
		INSULATOR	
		RIGGER	
		PAINTER	
		LABORER	
		ELECTRICIAN	
		INSTRUMENT	
	← TOTALS →		

WORK REQUIRED.

DRAWINGS:

MATERIALS REQUIRED:

COST SUMMARY — MAJOR JOBS	ESTIMATE	ACTUAL	APPROVED BY	DATE
LABOR				
MATERIAL				
TOTAL				

DATE STARTED

DATE COMPLETED

MAINTENANCE FOREMAN

ORIGINATOR - COMPLETE AS ORDERED

FIG. 5-6. Work-order form ideal for use when all jobs are estimated prior to assignment.

Standing Work Orders. Standing work orders are assigned permanent work-order numbers. They apply to a group of routine or repetitive operations such as inspections, machine adjustments, and jobs like replacement of light bulbs and fuses, packing pumps, lubricating, and cleaning equipment. Items of this nature are listed in Table 5-2. Many plants reserve numbers 1 to 50 for standing work orders.

The same standing-work-order numbers should be used without change each year if possible; this will enable each of the mechanics to memorize the numbers and directly associate them with the types of work they represent. Coded account numbers or letters can be used to cover the standing-work-order list. The time cards of employees assigned to routine maintenance indicate the coded accounts. The cost or accounting department records and summarizes standing-work-order charges.

Cost data can be transferred to punched cards to simplify the summarization of job costs by equipment, operations, or departments.

Time Cards. All maintenance employees are subject to time checking whether by time clocks or timekeepers. The method to be used depends on the type of plant, area of operations, or local conditions. Regardless of method used, it is desirable to have each employee make out a time card (Fig. 5-7) to cover each day's assignments. If work is performed without a work order, the employee can indicate the department in the first column. Hours worked (to the nearest quarter-hour) and comments on the nature of the work should be inserted by the mechanic after completion of each assignment.

Table 5-2. List of Standing Work-order Numbers

Work Order No.	*Description of Work*
1	Routine maintenance, Dept. A
2	Routine maintenance, Dept. B
3	Routine maintenance, Dept. C
4	Routine maintenance, power plant
5	Routine maintenance, warehouse
6	Routine maintenance, general office
7	Routine maintenance, grounds and lawns
8	Preventive-maintenance inspections
9	General lighting
10	General heating
11	Lubrication, Dept. A
12	Lubrication, Dept. B
13	Lubrication, Dept. C
14	Lubrication, power plant
15	Scale inspection and adjustments
16	Equipment cleaning
17	Sprinkler system, fire protection
18	Pump packing
19	Electric-power inspections, fuses
20	Elevator, adjustments
21	Ventilation and air conditioning
22	Conveyors
23	Drinking fountains

FORM 609-T
PRTD. IN U.S.A.

TIME CARD DATE______

NAME______ CLOCK NO.______

WORK ORD. NO. OR DEPT.	HOURS		NATURE OF WORK
	REGULAR	OVERTIME	
TOTAL HRS.			

FIG. 5-7. Employee time card.

Another type of time card (Fig. 5-8) has advantages where job-cost data are collected for each job assignment. It has five detachable sections which can be separated and filed with work orders, thus eliminating the clerical work that would be involved in taking information from the time cards.

Maintenance Storeroom and Controls. Operation and control of the maintenance storeroom can affect maintenance work schedules. Primary requirements are a central location, ample shelving and bins, proper lighting, a good system of perpetual inventory, correct withdrawal procedures, and capable supervision. All items carried in the mechanical storeroom should have part-number identification to simplify inventory, costing, and paper work.

Figure 5-9, a storeroom withdrawal order, shows an ideal form for withdrawals of

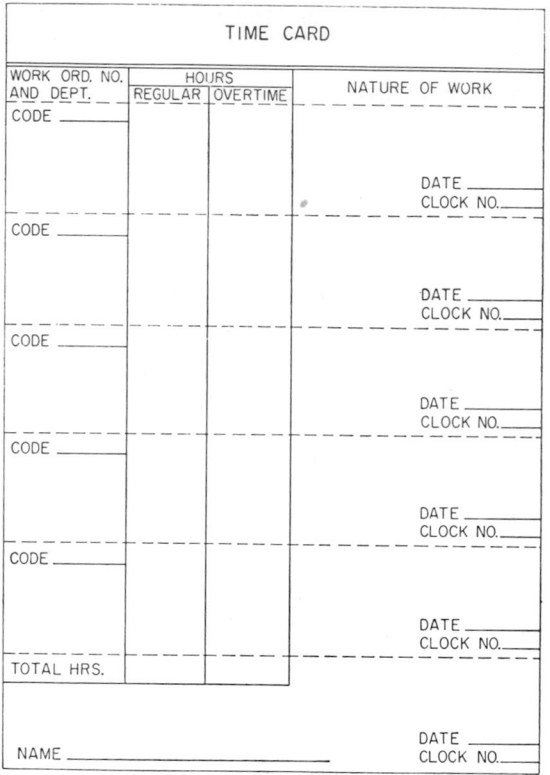

FIG. 5-8. Sections of this time card can be detached and filed with the work orders.

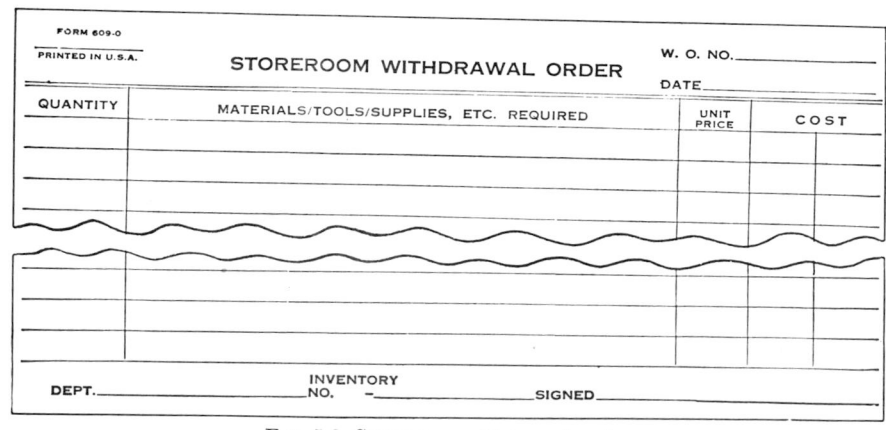

FIG. 5-9. Storeroom withdrawal order.

parts, supplies, and materials.   Mechanics fill out the form.   The foreman's approval is required by many companies.   The person making the withdrawal signs the form. Data such as work-order number, date, equipment inventory number, and department can be indicated.   Nuts, bolts, washers, nails, screws, etc., where the cost of paper work is greater than the cost of the item, may be obtained without withdrawal orders.

Some concerns set minimums of value for items requiring storeroom withdrawal orders.   The amounts range from 25 cents to $1, depending on the type of plant and kinds of materials.   Each company should set its own limits.   Of course the rule of common sense must prevail; for example, a hundred parts at 50 cents each is a charge that should be recorded on the unit equipment record.

The storeroom parts are priced on the withdrawal order.   The price data are contained on the perpetual-inventory form, known as "In-and-Out Stock Record" (Fig. 5-10).   The withdrawal order is then passed on to the maintenance clerk who attaches it to the work order for which the material is drawn.   Upon completion of the work order, all storeroom withdrawal orders charged to the specific work order are summarized.

The perpetual-inventory form is a positive means for controlling incoming supplies and withdrawals.   All invoices for spare parts and supplies should be routed through the storeroom so that quantities and items received can be verified, and unit prices recorded.   Items too large or bulky for the storeroom can be stored elsewhere but should be recorded on the perpetual inventory.   It is recommended that the estimates of stores requirements be reviewed annually, and adjustments made to ensure sufficient parts and materials on hand to carry on all scheduled production operations without having too much money tied up in maintenance inventory.

In plants that cover large areas it is common procedure to carry spare parts and supplies for special equipment in the area maintenance shop, to avoid having mechanics or messengers travel to the general storeroom.   Nevertheless, storeroom withdrawal orders should be used.

In some of the smaller plants the maintenance stockroom is also used to dispense large hand tools, electric drills, extension cords, etc., upon the presentation of a storeroom withdrawal order signed by the mechanic.   When they are returned, the withdrawal order is given back to the mechanic or destroyed by the attendant.   Other small plants substitute brass checks for the withdrawal orders.

Preventive-maintenance Inspection Forms.   Preventive-maintenance inspection records comprise a group of forms, specially designed for the purpose of recording and reporting the findings of the maintenance inspectors.   Each record should cover a specific class of equipment and contain a list of points to be checked.   The information to be gained by the inspection can be compiled from equipment records.   To be carefully considered are the location of the equipment, its value in maintaining production continuity, frequency of inspection, and maintenance work load.   The number of inspection record forms should be kept to a minimum; too frequent inspection of unimportant equipment can decrease interest in and reduce the benefits of preventive maintenance.

Preventive-maintenance inspection record forms are illustrated by Figs. 5-11 and 5-12.   The tickler-date spaces are used to indicate the scheduled date of inspection. This is a reference guide for the maintenance clerk who notes the next inspection period and files the form so that it is brought to his attention at the right time.

Running Inspection.   The term "running inspection" implies that the unit was operating during the inspection, or that the inspection was not a thorough over-all examination.   Running inspection can locate loose parts, vibration, misalignment, wear, lack of cleanliness, lack of lubrication, and so on.

Shutdown Inspection.   Shutdown inspections are made on equipment that is idle. All working parts that can be checked without dismantling the equipment are thoroughly examined.   Examples are bearings, gears, collars, setscrews, pins, belt tension, belting, and lubrication.   General condition and age of equipment have a great deal of bearing on the kind of inspection and frequency.   At least every third inspection should be of the shutdown variety.

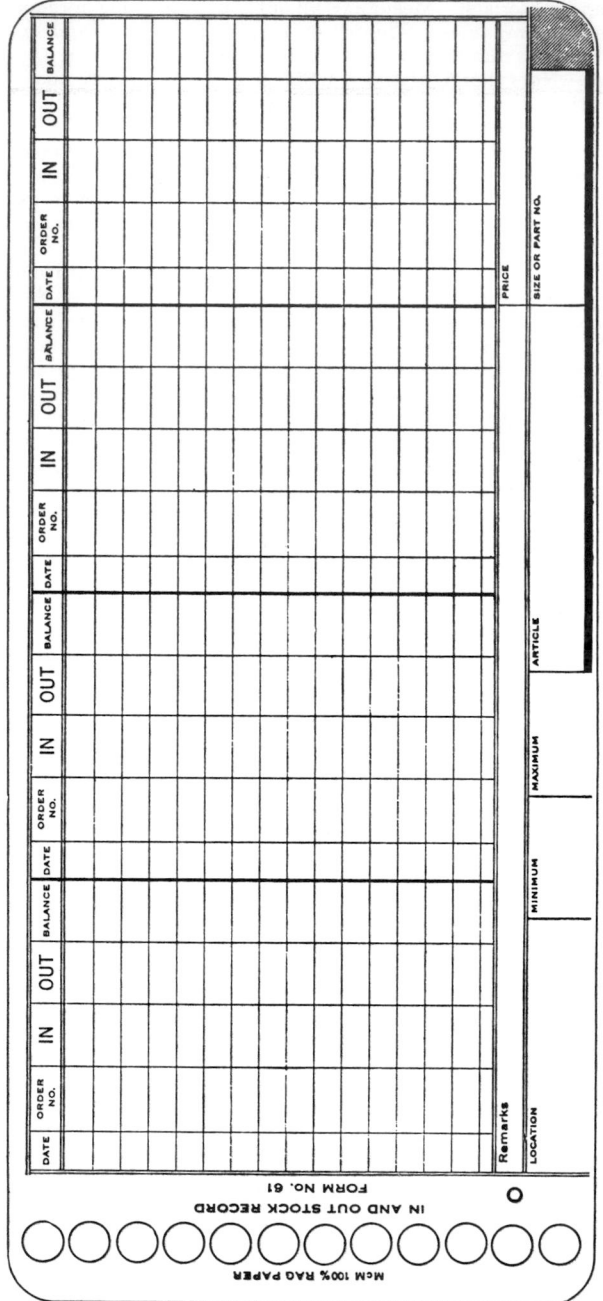

FIG. 5-10. Perpetual-stores inventory form.

The inspection routine should include making machine adjustments and minor repairs, provided the time required is not more than 15 min per unit.

All mechanical equipment inspections should be made by assigned mechanics; in many plants, area or night-shift mechanics do the work. As a check on the inspection work, and to ensure complete coverage, the same mechanic should not be assigned to make any two consecutive inspections on the same equipment.

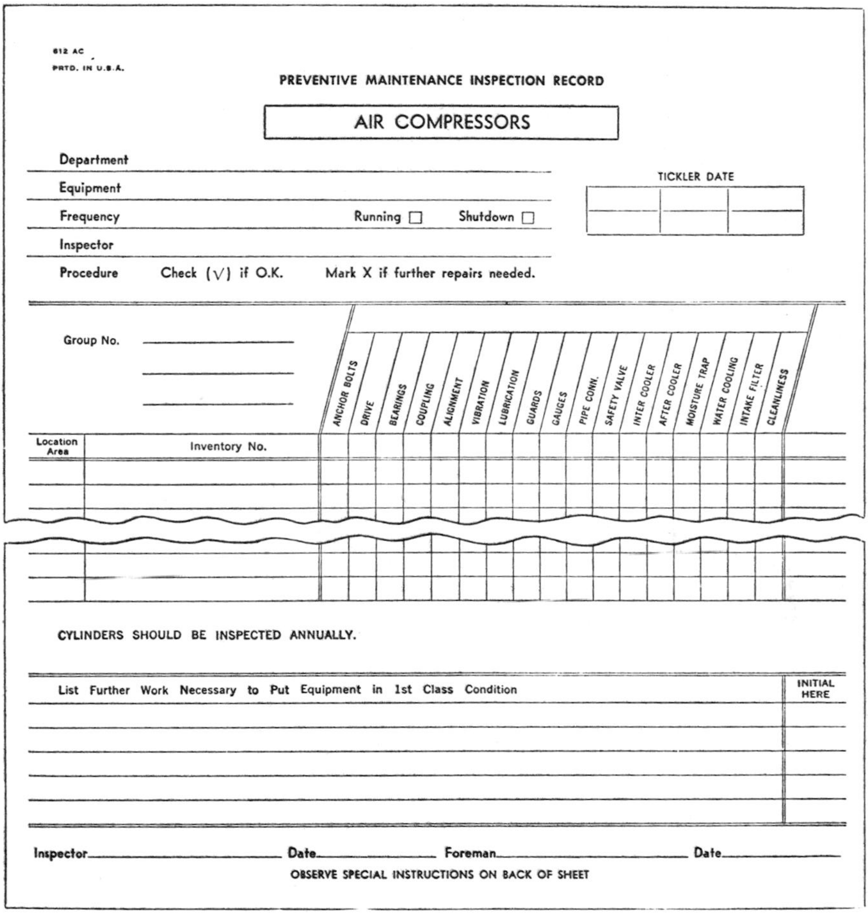

612 AC
PRTD. IN U.S.A.

PREVENTIVE MAINTENANCE INSPECTION RECORD

AIR COMPRESSORS

Department
Equipment
Frequency Running ☐ Shutdown ☐
Inspector
Procedure Check (√) if O.K. Mark X if further repairs needed.

TICKLER DATE

Group No.

Location Area	Inventory No.	ANCHOR BOLTS	DRIVE	BEARINGS	COUPLING	ALIGNMENT	VIBRATION	LUBRICATION	GUARDS	GAUGES	PIPE CONN.	SAFETY VALVE	INTER COOLER	AFTER COOLER	MOISTURE TRAP	WATER COOLING	INTAKE FILTER	CLEANLINESS	

CYLINDERS SHOULD BE INSPECTED ANNUALLY.

List Further Work Necessary to Put Equipment in 1st Class Condition	INITIAL HERE

Inspector________ Date________ Foreman________ Date________

OBSERVE SPECIAL INSTRUCTIONS ON BACK OF SHEET

FIG. 5-11. Typical form on which to record reports of inspections.

It is not desirable to select only one mechanic for making general inspections on all types of equipment, no matter how capable he is. Preventive-maintenance inspections can be used to advantage for building up the knowledge and ability of all.

Electrical-equipment inspections should be made only by assigned, capable electricians.

Preventive-maintenance Inspection Schedules. Inspection frequencies depend on many factors such as age of equipment, condition, hours of operation per day, and the importance of the equipment to the production line. Some plants list inspection frequency for production, mechanical, and electrical equipment, established by conferences among production, engineering, and maintenance personnel. An example is given in Table 5-3. Frequencies can be judged and revised after observing results

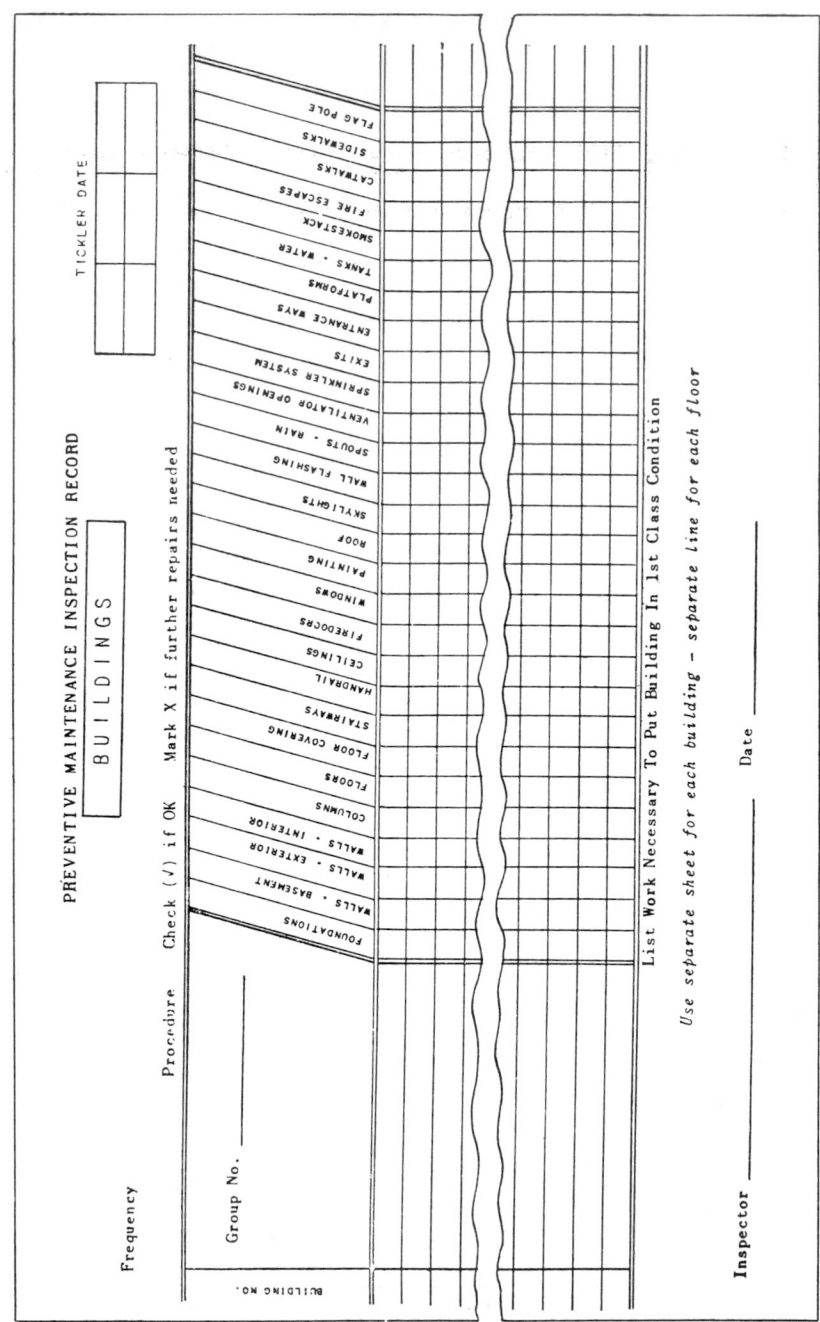

Fig. 5-12. A variation of the form shown in Fig. 5-11, to adapt it to the inspection of buildings.

Table 5-3. Inspection Frequency

Item	*Inspection Frequency*
Air compressor	Semimonthly
Air-conditioning equipment	Weekly and monthly
Automatic transporter	Weekly, monthly, quarterly
Automatic skylifts	Weekly, monthly, quarterly
Boiler, steam	Daily, weekly, monthly
Blowers	Monthly
Blenders	Monthly
Belts	Semimonthly
Buildings	Semimonthly
Battery-charging panels	Quarterly
Combustion control	Daily, weekly
Conveyors, belt	Monthly
Conveyors, pneumatic	Monthly
Conveyors, screw	Monthly
Chain falls	Quarterly
Electric trucks	Weekly, monthly, quarterly
Electric control equipment	Semimonthly
Elevators	Monthly
Fans, duct type	Monthly
Fans, electric	Annually
Fire-protection equipment	Semiannually and recharge annually
Grinders, electric	Quarterly
Gravity water-storage tanks (blinker lights, supports, heading equipment)	Semiannually except where local agreements or insurance company require more frequent inspections
Heat exchangers	Semiannually
Hot-water heaters	Quarterly
Hydraulic trucks	Monthly
Hoists, electric	Quarterly
Heating	Semiannually
Instrumentation	Semimonthly
Lighting	Quarterly
Monorails	Quarterly
Motors, electric	Semimonthly
Power-plant equipment	Daily, weekly, monthly
Pumps	Semimonthly
Photoelectric units	Weekly
Plumbing	Semiannually
Power-feed wiring	Semiannually
Refrigeration	Daily, weekly
Roofing	Semiannually
Scales, all types	Weekly
Starters and switches	Semimonthly
Switchgear	Annually
Trucks	Monthly at lubrication
Transformers	Quarterly
Ventilating equipment	Semimonthly
Water softener	Monthly
Work trucks	Monthly at lubrication
Welding machines	Quarterly

from the preventive-maintenance inspection reports made under specific operating conditions and requirements. Inspections that discover many critical conditions indicate they should be made more often; inspections showing no critical conditions found during two consecutive inspection periods indicate too frequent inspections.

The measure of the effectiveness of an inspection schedule does not lie solely in reduced maintenance costs. It may be measured also in the reduction of delays and the increase in equipment life.

Mechanical-downtime Reports. Many plants record production downtime as well as mechanical downtime, and it is desirable to tell the mechanics how mechanical downtime differs from production downtime.

Mechanical downtime is the period of time, usually recorded in minutes, that a scheduled production unit is shut down for repairs or replacements by maintenance personnel. It is recorded also for units other than production machinery where a shutdown of such units affects the production output. One of the best measures of the effectiveness of a sound preventive-maintenance program is the reduction of mechanical downtime.

Mechanical-downtime reports were developed to give maintenance mechanics a uniform way in which to report machine and equipment downtime. The data to be listed are indicated in Fig. 5-13. Each mechanic should carry a few mechanical-downtime report forms and make one out when there is a shutdown because of mechanical failure during a scheduled production period. He indicates the duration of shutdown for each production unit affected.

MECHANICAL DOWN TIME REPORT

DATE_____ SHIFT_____ DEPARTMENT_____

MACHINE	TIME LOST DUE TO BREAKDOWN	CAUSE OF BREAKDOWN	ACTION TAKEN

MECHANIC_____

FIG. 5-13. Mechanical-downtime report.

The data entered on the report are reviewed daily to determine whether the cause of breakdown was poor workmanship, faulty material, or something else, and an effort is made to avoid a repetition of the failure. The data also provide subject matter for review at the weekly maintenance meeting.

As mechanical-downtime records are accumulated, it may become evident that a production unit is constantly in need of repairs and adjustments. If the causes for these requirements can be eliminated by overhauling the unit, arrangements should be made for a scheduled shutdown. When difficulties arise in determining whether the shutdown was mechanical or production, it is usual to have the plant manager decide.

Mechanical-downtime records should be accumulated and summarized daily, weekly, and monthly, preferably by departments. It is advantageous to determine the cost per minute in each production department and convert the list of break-downs to dollars, taking into consideration such factors as idle labor, spoilage, rework, overhead, and overtime repair work.

Planning and Scheduling. Only through proper planning and control can the maximum benefits of a preventive-maintenance program be realized. In plants that have a good preventive-maintenance program, approximately 90 per cent of all maintenance work can be planned and scheduled. Data for effective planning and scheduling can be accumulated from equipment records, periodic inspection reports, departmental records, time studies, job analyses, and other sources. To indicate how much of the work can be planned and scheduled, maintenance may be broken down into types of jobs:

1. Routine work, such as lubrication, work done by area mechanics, cleaning, lamp replacements.
2. Preventive-maintenance inspections.
3. Routine assigned maintenance work.
4. Periodic equipment overhaul.
5. Long-range capital improvements.
6. Emergency breakdowns and repairs.

Routine Work. This can be readily planned and scheduled. Standing work orders are used and standard procedures established. Area mechanics can be used to cover many of the items.

Routine Assigned Maintenance Work. Should be done on submitted work orders. Should be planned and scheduled on an assigned priority basis. Schedules should be prepared on a daily, weekly, monthly, and for some process plants like chemical and oil refining, an annual basis. Week-end work should be planned and scheduled several days in advance to ensure the selection of proper personnel and the assembly of necessary materials to complete the work in the shortest time and at the lowest cost.

Periodic Equipment Overhaul. Schedules should be determined from the preventive-maintenance reports, and the overhauls planned 6 months to 1 year in advance to fit in with production schedules and sales planning. When sufficient manpower is not available, motors, pumps, compressors, even large-production machinery units, can be overhauled by outside contractors.

Long-range Capital Improvements. In large companies, especially those with multiplant operations, long-range planning for capital improvements usually is done by their centralized engineering departments and then fitted into maintenance schedules for the respective plants. In companies with small maintenance organizations and limited maintenance personnel, major capital improvements usually are handled by outside contractors.

Emergency Breakdowns and Repairs. Although this type of work cannot be planned, every attempt should be made to give it top priority. When a breakdown occurs, craftsmen should be assigned to make the repairs immediately, but work orders should be prepared as quickly as possible, and the regular work schedule should be adjusted to take account of the emergency. Excess maintenance manpower can be assigned to overhaul equipment. With such an arrangement a crew of craftsmen always is available for emergencies. An added advantage is that the peaks and valleys of the work schedule are evened out.

Planning is using a systematic, organized method of analyzing the work and laying it out in such a way that men and materials are used to greatest advantage.

Scheduling is determining when each part of the planned job should be done, taking into account production schedules, receipt of materials, and available manpower.

Planning and scheduling, when carried on in accordance with these definitions, make it possible to do the work with the least amount of interference with production, to handle the jobs in the proper sequence, and to keep the craftsmen working with a minimum of delay between jobs. The general objective should be to get the work done in the shortest time possible with existing manpower.

The number and type of personnel required for the planning and scheduling operation depend on the size of the plant, the area of operations, the daily work load, and the number of craftsmen available. But in any case enough people should be assigned to the job to handle all operations around the clock.

In the very small plant where the installation of a planning and scheduling department is not feasible, the work can be handled by the maintenance superintendent or the master mechanic on a daily and weekly basis, using a minimum of paper work.

In the medium-sized plant, having less than 100 maintenance men, planning and scheduling can be shared by the maintenance superintendent and the craft foreman. A maintenance clerk usually looks after much of the work; he may screen orders, passing the urgent ones to the superintendent for approval and assignment, and retaining the less urgent for scheduling and backlog. The maintenance clerk also frequently acts as a dispatcher, taking telephone requests for service. He often compiles records of maintenance jobs, and job costs, and schedules materials for planned jobs.

Planning and control boards frequently are used in small and medium plants but are recommended only if they save time. Where craftsmen are assigned routine maintenance work, letting them know their job assignments a full day in advance may save time and money by enabling them to go directly to the next assignment when one job is completed.

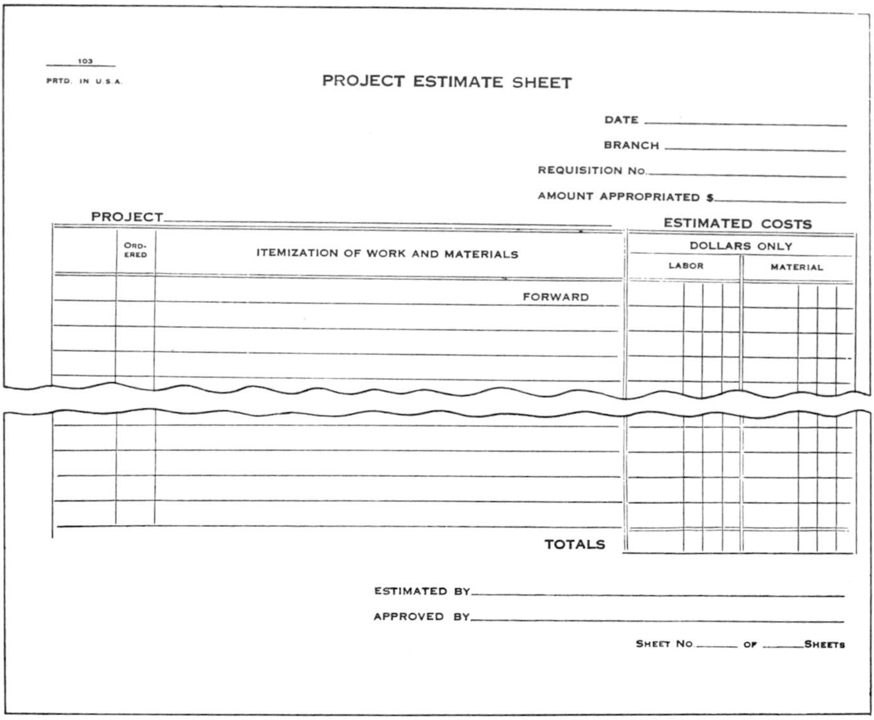

PROJECT ESTIMATE SHEET

DATE _____

BRANCH _____

REQUISITION No. _____

AMOUNT APPROPRIATED $ _____

PROJECT _____

ESTIMATED COSTS

ORD-ERED	ITEMIZATION OF WORK AND MATERIALS	DOLLARS ONLY	
		LABOR	MATERIAL
	FORWARD		

TOTALS

ESTIMATED BY _____

APPROVED BY _____

SHEET No _____ OF _____ SHEETS

FIG. 5-14. Form to facilitate estimating on large jobs.

In the plant with a hundred or more craftsmen, the function of planning and scheduling maintenance work is much more complex. The plant engineer, who usually has the responsibility for supervision of the maintenance operations, should divorce himself from the routine, detailed procedures, delegating them to specialists.

The planning and scheduling function will require about 1 person for every 100 craftsmen, though the ratio may vary somewhat, depending on the number of work orders issued. Personnel assigned to the function receive all the work orders, determine priorities, prepare job estimates, plan the work alone or with the assistance of craft foremen, line up the necessary materials for each job, schedule the work, follow up job progress, collect the time, and prepare reports and records. Planning and scheduling personnel, because they are familiar with the job requirements, the work done by crafts, and the efficiency of the maintenance crews, should work with the industrial engineering department on time studies, methods, methods-time-measurement data, and estimating.

Each job must be estimated in advance, with an analysis of man-hours by crafts for each operation, and materials required. These estimates can be prepared on specially developed forms appropriate to operations and craftsmen. The estimated labor summary should be posted on the work order for the specific job and later compared with the actual job cost.

When the job is large, it is desirable to estimate the project on a form which can serve as a job record. See "project estimate sheet," Fig. 5-14. This form is especially useful when a project is estimated for submission to top management for an appropriation.

Upon completion of a large job or project, a maintenance-cost data sheet (Fig. 5-15) can be prepared and used for comparison of actual with estimated job cost. Also, it can serve as a job-cost record.

C D 2 - 10M

MAINTENANCE
COST DATA
SHEET

WORK ORDER NO.________

ACCOUNT________

LABOR				MATERIAL		
EMP. NO.	HOURS	DATE	COST	DESCRIPTION	DATE	COST
TOTAL PAGE #1				TOTAL PAGE #1		
TOTAL PAGE #2				TOTAL PAGE #2		
TOTAL LABOR COST $				TOTAL MATERIAL COST $		

COMPLETED DATE................ TOTAL JOB COST $..............................

FIG. 5-15. Cost-data sheet used in comparing actual with estimated costs.

For large projects some companies use an estimating guide list of work to be considered (Table 5-4) which serves as a check list to assure the estimator that all items are covered.

Some plants with operations covering large areas, such as oil refineries, pulp and paper plants, and chemical works, handle projects that require drafting, engineering, and field surveys before they develop into actual work for maintenance crews. For record keeping on projects of this type it is well to maintain a project-cost-distribution record (Fig. 5-16). This form is particularly suited for new construction projects.

Estimating job costs is one of the most difficult phases of the planning and scheduling function, but by thinking out the logical steps of each job in their proper sequence, along with the material requirements, before the job is started, the procedure is simplified. Each craft foreman can do the estimating for the craftsmen under his supervision. Estimating goes hand in hand with planning. While thinking out the job the foreman can easily record the operations and material requirements on the work order.

Good estimating is the key to maintenance planning. The listing of job elements by the foreman forms the basis for preparing day-to-day plans. It also helps develop better work methods and provides more accurate information on craft loads.

It is difficult to find planning and scheduling personnel who have extensive practical knowledge covering mechanical and electrical equipment and building construction. Some companies have selected junior engineers who had been used previously in minor phases of maintenance supervision. Because of their knowledge of the plant areas, maintenance procedures, and craft duties and responsibilities, such men develop rapidly.

Table 5-4. Memorandum of Work to Be Considered When Estimating

1. Demolishing and moving equipment	16. Wiring motor drive
2. Equipment purchased	17. Wiring for power
3. Material purchased	18. Wiring for light
4. Patterns	19. Pipe fitting
5. Castings	20. Plumbing work
6. Excavating and filling	21. Pipe covering
7. Concrete and mason work	22. Insulation
8. Pipe trenches, ducts, etc.	23. Painting
9. Carpenter work	24. Freight and trucking
10. Blacksmith work	25. Watchmen
11. Machine-shop work	26. Safety devices
12. Millwright and erecting	27. Testing and inspection
13. Rigging	28. Experimental and operating adjustment
14. Sheet-metal work	29. Development work
15. Welding	30. Contingencies, unforeseen

PLANT _____ PROJECT COST DISTRIBUTION RECORD

W. O. NO.	DATE	PROJECT NO. & TITLE	DFT'G & ENGRG. HRS.	COST	MATERIAL EQUIP.	MISC.	LABOR COST	TOTAL COST	COST DISTRIB. EXPENSE	CAPITAL	% ENGR. COST

FIG. 5-16. Another aid in showing where the maintenance money goes.

Important in the planning and scheduling operation is the maintenance planning chart (Fig. 5-17). On receipt of the work order, each job is estimated and a start date is established. Then the job elements, as taken from the estimates, are laid out graphically on the planning chart to relate the operations to time. The chart shows the work to be done, the time that will be required, and the crafts concerned. This chart is made up for the following day, planned for all crews. When the wanted dates indicated on work orders obviously cannot be met, the orders are renegotiated.

In some cases operations are planned and scheduled as weekday jobs, urgent; weekday jobs, routine; and week-end jobs, shutdown. A planning and scheduling chart (Fig. 5-18), developed for their requirement, answers for this arrangement. For planning and scheduling on a daily basis, use is made, at times, of one labor-distribution and work plan each day (see Fig. 5-19).

After the schedule is established, the maintenance foreman should be given a work-in-progress or master schedule (Fig. 5-20). The date is obtained from the master planning and scheduling chart. The form is made out in duplicate, one copy being retained by the planning and scheduling department. It shows what work each crew will undertake the following day, approximate starting time, description, and location. Each foreman gets his work-in-progress sheets the afternoon before

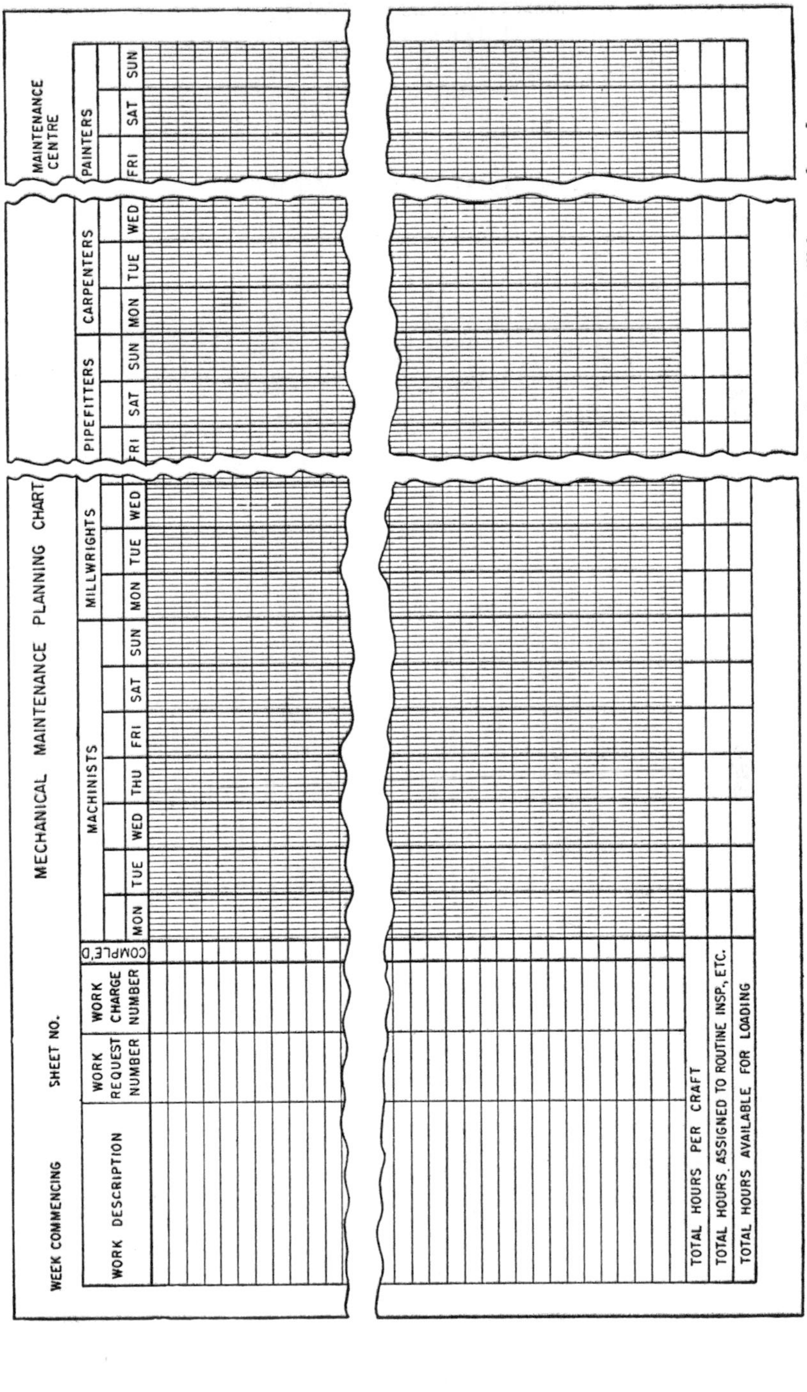

FIG. 5-17. Form of graphical presentation of work to be done, time required, and crafts that will be employed.

MAINTENANCE DEPARTMENT
WORK SCHEDULE FOR WEEK ENDING _____

WEEKDAY JOBS – URGENT				WEEKDAY JOBS – ROUTINE				WEEK END JOBS – SHUT DOWN			
WORK ORDER NO.	MACHINE	J O B		ASSIGNED TO	WORK ORDER NO.	MACHINE	J O B	ASSIGNED TO	WORK ORDER NO.	MACHINE	J O B	ASSIGNED TO

FIG. 5-18. A planning and scheduling chart devised to be used for three kinds of maintenance work.

the work is to be done, to allow time for drawing parts, tools, and materials from the storeroom before actual work is to start.

A daily report of available and demand hours for all crafts should be made to maintenance supervision. It should show total available, in process, not scheduled, and

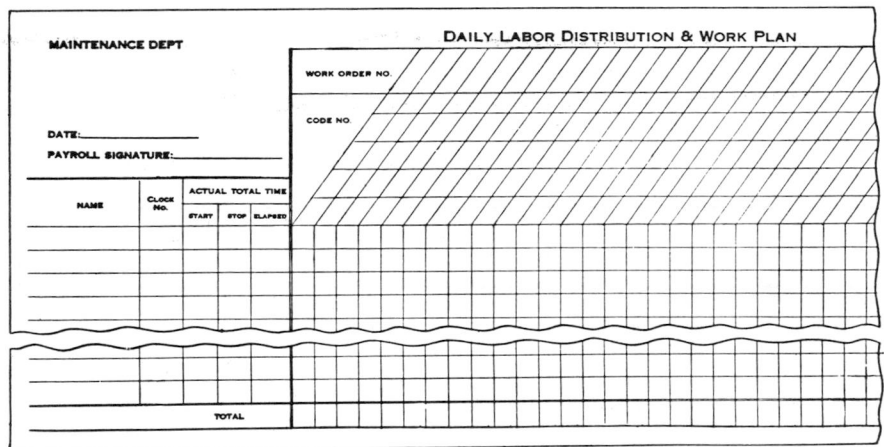

FIG. 5-19. Form for planning and scheduling on a daily basis.

FIG. 5-20. This form is used by foremen as "work-in-progress" schedule.

FIG. 5-21. Form for recording maintenance man-hour backlog.

total demand hours for all trades assigned to maintenance operations.   A maintenance man-hour backlog record (Fig. 5-21) should be kept to indicate the number of man-hours of work backlog for each trade group.

Where a dispatcher is used to record jobs and work assignments by telephone, a mechanical-dispatcher record form is used (see Fig. 5-22).

When planned and scheduled work orders have been completed they should be

Form 71066

MECHANICAL DISPATCHER RECORD

SHEET NO.		DEPT. NO.		SHIFT			DATE

Description	Time Reported	Reported By	Maint. Man	Man On Job. At.	Time Completed	M. O. No.	Nature of Trouble

FIG. 5-22. Form used by dispatcher who makes assignments by telephone.

R & M WORK ORDER SUMMARY

Work Order Number	Description of Work	Type Work	Date Received	Material Cost	Date Completed	Estimated Hours	Actual Hours

Labor Code No. _ _ _ _ _ _ _ _ _ _ _ _ _

FIG. 5-23. Form for summarizing repair and maintenance work orders.

72076

OVERTIME REQUIREMENT Date

Date Needed	Unit or Name	Hours	Explanation or Reason

Requested by _____   Agreed to by _____

Retain 1 Copy and Give 1 Copy to Union Representative Who Signs.   (For Scheduled Overtime, 3 Copies Should Be Sent To Personnel Dept.)

FIG. 5-24. Form used as an aid in controlling overtime.

WEEK END WORK SHEET

Machine Shop_____ Electric Shop_____ Pipe Shop_____ Date_____

JOB NO.	DEPT.	DESCRIPTION	MEN	HRS.

Job Sheet must be submitted not later than Friday morning in duplicate.
Explain extra jobs not planned on reverse side of sheet.

Total Number of Men

Foreman_____ Plant Eng._____ Chief Eng._____

FIG. 5-25. Form used in recording and analyzing week-end work.

PLANT _____

DATE ISSUED _____

REQUEST FOR ENGINEERING

PROJECT NO. _____

DATE REC'D. _____

DESCRIPTION OF WORK (BE COMPLETE, ATTACH ANY QUOTATIONS, SKETCHES, ETC)

REASON FOR JOB AND SAVINGS

THIS REQUEST IS FOR (CHECK WHICH APPLIES)
STUDY & REPORT ( ) ENGINEERING ( ) COST ESTIMATE ( ) PROCUREMENT ( ) CONSTRUCTION ( )

FOR FURTHER INFO. SEE	REQUESTED BY	PLANT ENGINEER	BRANCH MANAGER	DATE WANTED

SPECIAL INSTRUCTIONS

SPACE BELOW THIS LINE FOR ENGINEERING DEPT. USE ONLY

ASSIGNED TO _____

ASSIGNED TO _____

CHIEF ENGINEER   DATE

BY   DATE

	ESTIMATED ENGINEER DAYS	ESTIMATED DATES		ACTUAL DATES	
		START	COMPLETE	START	COMPLETE
PRELIMINARY STUDY					
DESIGN & LAYOUT					
DETAIL DRAFTING (B-AS'SY NO._____)					
ELECTRICAL DESIGN					
COST ESTIMATE					
AUTHORIZATION (JOPA NO._____)					
PROCUREMENT					
CONSTRUCTION					
INSTALLATION					

FIG. 5-26. Request for engineering is a form usable in many ways.

3-121

MONTHLY REPORT OF PREVENTIVE MAINTENANCE INSPECTIONS BAKERY MONTH	INSPECTIONS SCHEDULED	INSPECTIONS COMPLETED	*INSPECTIONS INCOMPLETE	CRITICAL POINTS FOUND	JOBS RESULTING	JOBS COMPLETED
PRINTED IN U.S.A.						
WAREHOUSE & MIXING						
1. Tanks, Bins, Hoppers						
2. Sifters & Blenders						
3. Electric Motors & Starters						
4. Scales						
5. Mixers						
6. Pumps						
7. Instrumentation						
8. Refrigeration						
9. Conveyors						
BAKING						
1. Ovens						
2. Baking Equipment						
3. Electric Motors & Starters						
4. Conveyors						
5. Instrumentation						
PACKING						
1. Packaging Machines						
2. Conveyors						
3. Electric Motors & Starters						
4. Instrumentation						
5. Scales						
ICING						
1. Icing Equipment						
2. Mixers						
3. Tanks, Bins, Hoppers						
4. Conveyors						
5. Pumps						
6. Electric Motors & Starters						
7. Instrumentation						
GENERAL						
1. Air Conditioning & Ventilation						
2. Refrigeration						
3. Air Compressors						
4. Power Plant						
5. Pumps						
6. Water Coolers						
7. Electric Motors & Starters						
8. Heating						
9. Lighting						
10. Buildings						
11. Instrumentation						
12. Elec. Trucks, Skylifts, etc.						
13. Storage Batteries & Chargers						
14. A C Control Equipment						
15. Misc. Elec. Equipment						
16. Elevators						
TOTALS						

*Explain on reverse side. Mail 2nd Working Day each month. Original to Engineering Dept. Copy to Plant Manager.

Fig. 5-27. The monthly report of preventive-maintenance inspections is another form useful as an aid to control.

posted on a repairs and work-order summary (Fig. 5-23) for record purposes and as a job-progress report to management.

Following is a list of suggestions to improve the administration of job scheduling:

1. Check all incoming work orders immediately for conformity to proper charge accounts and route them to the appropriate maintenance foreman for estimating.
2. Submit such recurring reports as pertain to job scheduling to the plant engineer each week.

3. Audit planning and scheduling charts once each week to ensure that they are being maintained current.
4. Supply to maintenance clerks information necessary to jobs that have been estimated, and work stoppage.
5. Prepare, publish, and maintain current the general maintenance department work schedule through daily counsel with maintenance foremen and submit to the plant engineer each day.
6. Screen active trade file once each week to ensure proper filing of work orders.
7. Disseminate nonscheduled priority jobs reported by the plant engineer or production superintendent to appropriate foremen.
8. Ensure that maintenance foremen receive copies of all scheduled jobs and drawings pertaining to them.

Close relations must be maintained with production personnel to schedule downtime to have the least effect on production. Often interested production men can be invited to participate in establishing the maintenance schedule and to attend all the meetings on this subject. This practice will serve to keep production posted on maintenance activities as well as assist in establishing good relationship.

Overtime Reports. The control of overtime assignments is important because they are maintenance work at premium rates and frequently nullify savings made during normal operations. An "overtime requirement" form (Fig. 5-24) is ideal for recording and controlling overtime. An effective way to curb overtime is to limit week-end work assignments. The "week-end work sheet" (Fig. 5-25) is a valuable record that should be prepared for all week-end assignments. Reports are reviewed every Monday morning by the plant engineer and staff responsible for planning and scheduling.

Requests for Engineering Services. For companies where the engineering department is not located at the scene of maintenance operations, frequently it is necessary to submit a request for engineering services. The form "request for engineering" (Fig. 5-26) covers this requirement. It can also be used for assignment of projects, studies and reports, cost estimates, procurement, or construction services. On the back of this form an "estimate of engineering time" is made.

Monthly Report of Preventive-maintenance Inspections. Any program, to be effective, must be checked periodically. This is especially true of multiplant preventive-maintenance operations that are administered from a central office. A "monthly report of preventive-maintenance inspections" form (Fig. 5-27) was developed to meet this requirement. It serves as a check list and is prepared monthly. The summary of inspections scheduled, inspections completed, inspections incomplete, critical points found, jobs resulting, and jobs completed is compared month by month. If the preventive-maintenance program is functioning properly, it will be evidenced by a gradual decrease in jobs resulting from the scheduled inspections.

Chapter 6

HOW TO ESTIMATE REPAIR AND MAINTENANCE COSTS

By Harold F. Allard
Maintenance Staff Consultant
Albert Ramond and Associates, Inc.
Chicago, Ill.

Estimating in maintenance is defined as a process of predicting costs before work is done. On this premise, estimating is the basis for most of the management tools used for effectively directing the maintenance function. Even when the term "estimating" is not used or the process recognized as part of the normal procedure, there is always at least an opinion or guess as to how long a job will take. The effectiveness of the operation may depend on how well this opinion is confirmed by the actual facts.

Control of labor costs, for example, may be accomplished by working toward target cost levels, or by scheduling work to limit overtime, regulate crew size, and provide a full work load—all based on estimated costs. Make-or-buy decisions, methods improvements, and over-all cost controls are necessarily built around cost estimates. Projects which do not require estimates for their development or execution still must depend on estimates for justification and approval. Thus the estimate is the foundation for managing maintenance work.

BASIC APPROACH

A maintenance cost estimate is based on two major factors:

1. What is known about the job, i.e., the requirements, work content, conditions, and urgency of the job.
2. How the estimate will be used.

These two factors determine *how* the estimate should be made, *which* of a wide variety of estimating *techniques* should be applied, and the *amount of detail* required. A study of how to estimate, therefore, includes the following general topics:

Classifying the job.
How the estimates will be used.
Who prepares the estimate.
Estimating techniques.
Selecting an estimating method.

CLASSIFYING THE JOB

What the estimator knows about the job is determined by the degree to which the job is or can be planned before the work is started.   Where there is more information, there are better planning, better estimates, and, usually, better costs.   In many cases an important benefit derived from having thorough estimating procedures is more effective management once the work is carried out because the work *had* to be clearly defined and planned to be accurately estimated.

Maintenance supervisors often feel that all of their work is emergency work and consequently both planning and estimating are impractical.   In order to avoid the obvious limitations which result from this position, it is important to have a realistic appraisal of the classifications of work in each individual plant.   This means that the real emergencies must be separated from the work which can be planned.   Careful consideration of each of the following general classifications will show that at least some of the maintenance work in every plant can be considered as "planned or repetitive."   These items *can* be planned and estimated as accurately as the end use of the estimate requires.

Planned and Repetitive Maintenance.

Repetitive repair or replacement of specific items, such as belts, bearings, motors, filters, and screens.
Scheduled routine work, such as oiling, cleaning, housekeeping, and inspection.
Spare-parts production and overhaul.
Planned equipment overhaul.
Building and facility repairs.
Assigned area service.
Planned nonrepetitive replacements and repairs.
Relocations.
Modifications.
Equipment improvements.
Repairs on noncritical or lightly loaded equipment that can be economically shut down pending scheduled repair.

Emergency Service.   While different techniques may be required, estimating procedures may be applied profitably to many emergency service situations also. Generally the key to accurate estimates here is having repetition of the same or similar problems.   In classifying these jobs it is first necessary to identify the highly repetitive items and then the high-cost items which may be expected to repeat after long intervals.   The latter includes the following general categories:

Trouble-shooting diagnostic calls.
Equipment breakdown.
Safety emergencies.

HOW THE ESTIMATES WILL BE USED

The extent of estimating detail and consequent estimating expense which is justified for a particular situation depends primarily on the end use of the estimate.   An easy method for determining relative accuracy requirements is provided by comparisons from a guide list of bench-mark uses.

The following list is arranged in approximate order of increasing demand for accuracy.   It should always be considered along with other criteria for selecting an estimating method.

1. Determination of extent of approvals required.   (Example: over or under $500?)
2. Evaluation of work-order backlog.
3. Long-range forecasting.
4. Evaluation of equipment purchase recommendations.

5. Evaluation of method proposals.
6. Make-or-buy decisions—limited annual dollar volume.
7. Critical path scheduling.
8. Monthly schedules and work-load forecasts.
9. Plant-wide cost-control reports of work performance.
10. Weekly schedules and manpower assignments.
11. Departmental cost-control reports.
12. Plant-wide group incentive.
13. Individual cost-control reports.
14. Daily manpower assignments and work schedules.
15. Make-or-buy decisions—high annual volume.
16. Departmental group weekly incentives.
17. Small-group daily incentive.
18. Individual weekly incentive.
19. Individual daily incentive.

Deferred Maintenance.   An important application of estimating procedures which does not fit into the pattern described above is the determination or prediction of the cost of deferring maintenance or repairs.   Frequently, there is more real value as a management tool in knowing how much it will cost if work is *not* done than in estimating the cost of actually doing the work.   Such estimates usually involve evaluation of the cost of replacing lost production as well as the cost of possible damage to equipment and material.   This information directly affects important management decisions such as those relating to production shutdowns, overtime authorization, and maintenance-crew size.   Frequently the application of industrial engineering viewpoints to typical situations will expose costly fallacies in reasoning.   For example, should a maintenance crew of four be called in at double-time rate to repair a machine on Sunday when it could have been repaired on Friday at a cost of two idle operators for 4 hr each?   The answer to such questions is not always apparent without careful consideration.   However, pinpoint accuracy is not as important as consideration of all major factors.

WHO PREPARES THE ESTIMATE

Estimates may be properly performed by any of four general groups: foremen, engineers, planners, or rate setters.   The question of who should do the estimating is really answered when the most appropriate estimating method is established to fit existing circumstances.   Each group is better qualified for, or can more conveniently carry out, a particular kind of estimating procedure.

Foreman Estimates.   Estimates by the maintenance foreman are generally the quickest and easiest to obtain, can be based on limited advance information, and may be made without formal requests or other controls.   In some situations it may be necessary to accept this approach as the only practical answer.   Where the end use of the estimate is served as well by an approximation as by a detailed plan or where it appears to be impractical to secure accurate advance information about the job, a foreman estimate may be the best.   Furthermore, the foreman must be familiar with the job in order to assign and supervise his men, and for someone else to plan and estimate requires some duplication of effort.   Why, then, consider having planners or estimators in addition to the foreman?   Why not have the foreman do all the estimating?

The answer here is one of practical economics.   Few maintenance jobs are so well supervised that they could not be improved to the extent of 5 or 10 per cent, or more, by better supervision.   If, for example, each of four foremen in four 20-man departments concentrated on direct supervision for 2 hr a day instead of spending that time on estimating and a cost reduction of 5 per cent was accomplished, the savings would be nearly *four times* the cost of a full-time estimator to do the 8 hr of estimating work.

Estimating by the foreman should be limited to situations where it does not interfere with needed supervision and where more detailed procedures are not practical.

Engineering Estimates.   Again, the source and availability of advance information and the purpose of the estimate indicate the estimating procedure to be used.   The procedure determines who should do it.

The design of major construction projects and the selection or design of equipment may require estimates of installation labor costs as well as purchase prices and contractors' quotations.   While maintenance foremen or planners may be called in for consultation, the design procedures involved usually require that engineering develop these estimates.

Should engineering estimate ordinary repair projects?   Yes, if the required estimating procedure is primarily one of obtaining equipment prices and contractors' quotations and particularly if the estimating information vitally affects design decisions. No, if the required estimating procedure can be done more effectively by the maintenance planner or foreman because the work to be done by maintenance personnel is the significant part of the job.

Planner Estimates.   Few production foremen still carry out the wide variety of activities they were expected to handle 30 years ago.   Procedures for scheduling, time keeping, wage administration, and methods improvement—these functions are generally developed and carried out by staff people, leaving the foreman free to supervise his people.

The "maintenance-planning" concept is now generally recognized as one of several important steps toward giving the maintenance foreman some of the staff support we have come to expect in production.   While the scope of this staff support may vary considerably from plant to plant, it will almost always include estimating.   The kind of estimating done by the planner may also vary widely.   In fact, flexibility to use various means of estimating to fit different situations is one of the prime advantages of having planners do the estimating.   Engineering and foreman estimates can be used ideally for only a limited range of estimating problems; planner procedures can be fitted to almost any requirement.

In most cases, obtaining information about the job is a basic responsibility of the planner.   Because he knows the purpose of the estimate, he is in an ideal position to decide what estimating procedure is most appropriate.   It is important to assure maximum utilization of this inherent flexibility of method, within a basic framework of company policy.   This requires thoughtful supervision of the planning activity.

Rate-setter Estimates.   Where detailed standards are applied to maintenance operations for performance measurement or incentives, some jobs may be "rated" or "applicated" from basic data during the progress of the work or after it is completed. While these standards cannot be termed estimates by our definition, the people who apply these rates are particularly well-qualified to make estimates, using a wide range of estimating procedures.   Recommendations regarding flexibility of methods for planners apply in general to this group also.

ESTIMATING TECHNIQUES

Analysis.   "Analysis" literally means to resolve into elements or constituent parts. This is the most important tool the estimator can use.   The most complex major project becomes merely a series of typical jobs when it is divided into its component parts.   Without proper analysis, most estimating procedures would be useless.

Analysis is the most important estimating tool, not only because we depend on it for results, but also because of the time it requires.   In a typical application of detailed estimating of machine-shop repair work, breaking the job down into operations required 90 per cent of the estimator's time, whereas actually estimating time values required only 10 per cent.   Therefore it is essential that the degree of analysis for a particular job be in accord with other phases of the estimating method for that job, particularly the end use of the estimate and the scope of available information.   As an extreme example to illustrate this point, one would not break down a job into micro-elements like predetermined time values if the time values were to be determined by personal judgment.

Judgment. In many cases, judgment based on personal experience achieves accuracy entirely adequate for a particular situation, with minimum cost for estimating. Clear definition of the scope of the job and analysis in line with the estimators' experience are essential for good results.

The principal objections to estimates based on personal judgment are fundamentally lack of *proof* of consistency. With clear-cut job definition, careful analysis, and experienced estimators, the resulting estimates may be well within the accuracy tolerance required and yet fail to stimulate confidence because their accuracy cannot be proved, even on a relative basis.

This problem may be intensified by a tendency to issue exact figure estimates where a round figure would be more appropriate (e.g., 267½ instead of 300 hr), with the inevitable result that if the same job is estimated twice, it will have two different estimates.

Slotting. Both of the prime objections to estimates based on pure judgment may be partially met by use of another tool called "slotting," in which the job is classified within a cost or time bracket. Classification is usually based on judgment, but judgment may be guided by comparison with "bench marks," typical common jobs for which actual cost is known to fit within the bracket. Issuing the estimate in terms of a slot or cost bracket tends to discourage quibbling about insignificant differences between jobs or between estimates.

The slotting technique is also used to express and apply "standards" for repetitive jobs based on the accumulation of average actual cost data. The recorded average cost may be used for scheduling or may be adjusted by an average productivity figure. In either case, all the jobs for which the average cost falls within the limits of a certain cost bracket or slot will be covered by one figure representing that bracket.

PERT Statistical Approach. In the application of the PERT program of computer-calculated scheduling, the elapsed time to reach each milestone or event is estimated on three bases: pessimistic, expected, and optimistic. The three figures are then used in the program to compute most-probable finish dates. This technique has its greatest value in planning projects which have indefinite scope and which are very difficult to estimate on a sound basis, such as research and development projects. Most maintenance jobs are more tangible and can be more readily estimated by other means.

Estimating the Cost of Deferring Maintenance. The cost of lost production and possible damage to equipment or product because of deferring maintenance generally can be estimated by judgment based on basic guide figures. Out-of-pocket costs will be most realistic and useful, and detailed accuracy is not necessary. It is important to consider carefully any overhead figures used. Common accounting practice of using operating hours on key machines for distribution of costs can produce misleading figures if these rates per hour are applied for evaluation of machine downtime. For example, the production lost during a 2-hr breakdown might be replaced by running 2 hr overtime, with little excess cost except the direct labor hours and overtime premium paid.

Practical and useful approximation of material or product losses can be made by utilizing average ratios of labor to material costs. For example, if direct labor for a product line averages half the material cost and ten units are produced per day by four people at $3 per hr, the approximate labor cost is $10 per unit and the material cost is $20.

Standards per Unit. The estimating methods for nonrepetitive jobs described above have one important limitation in common: there is no assurance of consistent application where judgment is the basis for the estimate. For this reason, comparison of the performance results of one department with another or of current results with past performance is meaningless. Improved productivity as measured by judgment estimates may mean only that the estimators are becoming more generous. Unfortunately, this assumption that estimates are generous may be made whenever performance figures based on judgment show improvement, even when the improvement is quite realistic.

The broad category of Standards per Unit includes a wide variety of estimating procedures, ranging from the builder's estimate of the total cost of construction per square foot of floor space to the application of predetermined elemental time standards to specific craft operations. All have the advantage of being based on fixed values per unit which can be reapplied consistently. It must be admitted, however, that this does not guarantee absolute accuracy of the final estimate, since the standards necessarily are based on some degree of averaging of conditions and requirements. Fundamentally, the probable accuracy of the result is a function of the degree of analysis, or "breaking down," of standards application. Estimating standards may be classified on this basis in five basic groups:

1. *Plant-wide or Industry-wide Averages or Ratios.* This includes such data as total maintenance costs per ton of product, per operating hour of primary equipment, or per mile of mobile equipment; basic construction figures per square foot or per cubic foot; and many others. While the limitations of estimates based on these figures are quite obvious, their value for preliminary planning and auditing should not be overlooked. Building construction data in particular are easily available in handbook form and should be considered as one of the tools of the maintenance estimator. For example, "The Vest Pocket Estimator" by Frank R. Walker includes more than 80 topics, from architectural concrete to weather strips, and covers material and labor costs.

2. *Comparative Job Standards.* This is one of the most effective ways to achieve reasonably good estimating accuracy with minimum cost. Repair jobs on similar equipment covering a large range of total costs per job may be related to one or two simple determinants by comparing standards which are based on detailed analysis. For example, standards for rewinding various sizes of large d-c motors were established by detailed application over a 2-year period and then compared graphically on the basis of horsepower only. The resulting formula provides estimates entirely adequate for that particular application and requires only the horsepower of the motor to determine the standard. Similar comparisons may be made for projects such as furnace rebuilding by relating the number of bricks to be replaced to the standards for the typical job. For other specific applications, the measure of the relative size of the job may be the number of rolls, tubes, or sections, or the size of the area.

   Comparisons based on detailed basic data standards are ideal for this purpose. Where good records of actual time spent on each job are maintained, these records may be used in the same manner, but with some reservations about the level of accuracy to be attained.

3. *Specific Job Standards.* Work sampling or time study can provide a measure of the work accomplished per day on a specific assignment such as electrical trouble shooting or assigned area maintenance in a production machine area. Relating the measure of work to determinants, such as the number of trouble calls per day or the operating hours of key equipment per day, results in an estimating figure which can be quite accurate as long as general conditions do not change substantially. Such standards should be periodically audited to provide a measure based on current conditions. Standards for repetitive repair jobs also come under this category, whether established by time study, application of basic data, or adjusted accumulation of actual time.

4. *Operational Basic Data.* Many maintenance operations are repetitive, although they occur as part of a complete job which may never repeat. For example, in electrical work, installing a complete junction box or mounting a panel box could not be properly called an "element," but the estimating standard for this operation can be added into a job estimate more easily than adding in each element of the operation. A series of these operation standards can provide a relatively quick way of building a complete job standard. Special applications of this technique usually are developed to fit individual plant practices as experience with elemental basic data grows.

5. *Elemental Basic Data.* The ultimate in estimating repair and maintenance work can be obtained through the application of elemental basic data. The accuracy

Table 6-1. Selecting an Estimating Method

Use	Job information and planning					
	Definite: none; Indefinite: end result, work, methods; Emergencies such as fires, new equipment run-in, repairs without planning	Definite: end result; Indefinite: work, methods; Trouble shooting, breakdowns, construction without planning	Definite: end result, some work, some methods; Indefinite: some work, some methods; Overhauls, relocations, modifications, building repairs with drawings, repeat jobs without specific instructions	Definite: end result, work; Indefinite: methods; Planned building modification, construction, spare parts, partially planned repairs	Definite: end result, work, methods (planned); Fully planned repairs and maintenance	Definite: end result, work, methods (repetitive); Routine, repetitive PM and changeovers
Approval, backlog, forecasts, equipment	Judgment	Judgment	Judgment, slotting	Judgment, slotting	Sampling by elemental data or slotting	Sampling by elemental data or slotting
Methods, CPM, limited make-or-buy, monthly schedule	Judgment, past records	Judgment, past-record ratios, construction data	Judgment, industry data, slotting	Judgment, construction data, slotting	Simple elemental data, comparative based on data	Simple elemental data, comparative based on data
Plant-wide controls, weekly schedules, departmental controls, group incentive	Past records modified by work sampling, simple ratios	Time-study analysis or ratios based on work sampling, construction data	Judgment based on detailed analysis, simple elemental data	Judgment based on detailed analysis, simple elemental data	Elemental data	Simple elemental data, comparative, time study
Individual controls, daily schedules, volume make-or-buy	....	Elemental data (verify work and methods)	Elemental data (verify work and methods)	Elemental data	Elemental data	Elemental data, comparative, time study
Departmental group weekly incentives	....	Elemental data (apply after completion)	Elemental data (apply after completion)	Elemental data (verify methods)	Elemental data	Elemental data, time study
Small-group daily incentive, individual weekly incentive, daily incentive	....	Elemental data (apply after completion)	Elemental data (apply after completion)	Elemental data (verify methods)	Detailed elemental data (verify details)	Detailed elemental data, time study

and consistency attained by this method can fill the most exacting requirements of the end use of the estimate.   Where the job information is adequate, the accuracy of job standards set by this method is as good as that normally found in production incentive standards.

Anyone familiar with the process for building up basic standard data for production operations may correctly visualize a tremendous industrial engineering project if the same approach is used to cover the wide variety of maintenance operations. But this has been done over a period of years, and data are now available for most of the common operations in any industry.   Several management consultants have developed elemental basic data for repair and maintenance work.   Published versions are also available, including a detailed set developed for the United States Navy.   Generally, it is far more practical to use existing data than to start from the beginning and develop your own.

When the elemental data are available, there is generally a question about the cost of application.   It would be reasonable to assume that this cost would be in proportion to the degree of detail and accuracy involved.   Actually, this is not quite the case.   Selection of the proper elemental values, factors, and multipliers can be reduced to a simple process by good systems study.   The extensions and summarizations are strictly clerical functions, which can be done by a clerk or by data processing.   The only really expensive part of the application is defining and describing the job in sufficient detail.   If good job information is easily available, there is usually little question about the practical value of estimating by applying basic elemental data.   If such information must be obtained specifically for the purpose of the estimate, then the end use of the estimate must justify the cost of obtaining the detailed job information as well as the minor cost of actually applying the data.   In evaluating this approach, the value of consistency in the application should be carefully considered.   This is especially important where wage incentives are involved and may be equally valuable where estimated values are used directly for control purposes.

To be effective, the application of basic data must recognize the significant variations in conditions.   Consider the relatively simple operation of painting a wall.   The standard time per square foot will be determined by the method (roller or brush), the type of paint, and the absorbency, regularity, and smoothness of the surface.   In addition, job height, interference and obstructions, extreme heat or cold, humidity, fumes, and unusual factors may have a significant effect. The most practical way to cover these factors is the use of prepared tables relating job conditions and standard allowances, such as those used by consultants experienced in this field.

SELECTING AN ESTIMATING METHOD

The foregoing discussions indicate that estimating methods for maintenance cover a very wide range of techniques, uses, and application costs.   The most important consideration in establishing an estimating program is the selection of the most appropriate method for each particular situation.

The following guide chart summarizes the criteria for selecting the best method. Based on, first, what is known about the job (what is definite and what is indefinite) and second, what use will be made of the estimate, the method to be used is indicated in the table.   For detailed explanations of these highlights, refer to the specific sections—Classifying the Job, How the Estimates Will Be Used, Who Prepares the Estimate, or Estimating Techniques.

The references to incentives are made to provide a full range of comparisons among the various estimating methods.

Chapter 7

MAINTENANCE MANUALS

By FREDERICK E. LENNOX
CDR, CEC, USN
Director, Maintenance Division
Bureau of Yards and Docks
U.S. Navy, Washington, D.C.

This chapter describes the maintenance manual, the need for it, and its contents, advantages, disadvantages, preparation, and format.

GENERAL

The increased use of manuals in industry and government has been accelerated by rapid technological changes in material and equipment and rapid growth in the size and scope of organizations. A manual is an effective medium for communication of accepted procedures or the "best way" of accomplishing a task. It is a basic device that is used in training or retraining personnel in the use of equipment or techniques. A manual is technically a small book, such as may be carried in the hand or conveniently handled: a handbook. Manuals can cover a myriad of subjects, from Boy Scouts to marriage.

Types of Manuals. The types of manuals that are in general use today can be categorized as:

Instructional Manual. Outlines a specific task, concerning what to do, when to do it, how to do it, and why to do it. Basically, it is used in training and retraining personnel. It is similar to the technical manuals used in the Armed Forces.

Procedural Manual. Describes, generally in detail, the methods by which specific tasks are accomplished. Usually it will contain paper flow charts, illustrate standard organization forms and formats, and explain what, when, where, and how they are used. It provides a basis for determining and following routine administrative procedures.

Policy Manual. Presents the policy of the company or enterprise to ensure uniform compliance with rules and regulations.

Technical Manuals. As used by the Armed Forces, they are publications and other forms of documentation containing a description of equipment, weapons, or weapons systems, with instruction for effective use. They include one or more of the following sections as required: instructions covering initial preparation for use; operation, maintenance, and overhaul instructions; related technical information or description of procedures except those of an administrative nature; and a parts list or parts breakdown.

Organization Manual. Sets forth the duties of individuals or positions within an organization and outlines their authority and responsibility. The responsibility

3–132

of the individual or position is related to other individuals and positions in the organization to avoid conflict and duplication of effort and to reduce omissions.

A maintenance manual may incorporate one or all of the categories of manuals described.

What Is a Maintenance Manual?　A maintenance manual outlines the policies, organization, and procedures as applied by an enterprise in performing the maintenance function.　It may also include standard methods for accomplishing maintenance and/or repair of plant facilities and equipment.　It is the organization's so-called bible for performing maintenance.　It outlines the organization's maintenance management concepts and their importance in supporting the organization's objectives.

What the Maintenance Manual Does.　The maintenance manual elevates maintenance from a "fix-it" to a businesslike basis.　The management of maintenance becomes an integral part of the enterprise and contributes to its objectives.

In the present market place, competition necessitates the reduction of product cost without loss of quality.　The use of a manual in implementing a sound maintenance management program can be effective in cost reduction.　With the escalation of labor, material, and equipment cost, the reduction of maintenance cost becomes a necessity for the economic well-being of an enterprise.　The maintenance manual, however, is not a panacea; it does not replace competent managers and a skilled maintenance force.

Need for a Maintenance Manual.　The increase in the number of industries, the growth of existing companies, and the rapid changes in material, equipment, and process technology have compounded the problem of maintenance of plant facilities and equipment.　The cost of maintenance is of such magnitude that the "handy man" approach is no longer generally economical.　Methods must be found to perform it on an effective and businesslike basis.　This can be accomplished by establishing effective management procedures and methods for maintenance and means of communicating them throughout the organization.　A maintenance manual is an excellent way of doing this.

The size of the organization is not necessarily the criterion for determining whether a manual is required or not.　Even in a small organization where routine maintenance procedures are well established, there still is a need for outlining procedures for major repair and replacement of facilities and equipment.　The size of the organization will have an effect on the size and contents of a manual but not on its need as a method of communicating.

One of the most significant problems that exists today in all endeavors, whether commercial or governmental, is effective communications, whether written or oral. The worker cannot be expected to perform a task properly if it is not adequately explained to him or understood by him.　Executives and supervisors often wonder why their policies and orders are not carried out to their satisfaction.　They often complain about the lack of completed staff work.　Their first reaction is to question the capability of their subordinates and not their own failure to properly communicate. Effective written communications can be obtained through the use of a manual. When it is properly organized, prepared, and written, it will outline what is considered the best method of accomplishing a task.　The manual also can be used as a means for clearly outlining policy.

A manual can also provide a standard basis for training and indoctrinating new personnel or retraining existing personnel.　Therefore, the type of information passed on to the trainee is not determined by the supervisor.　As a result, the age of the "indispensable man" is gradually eliminated.　Because procedures and methods are documented in a manual, the training time for an individual can be reduced and a ready reference is made available which can be consulted for guidance whenever necessary.

The personnel performing and managing maintenance generally do so in a set routine procedure that was established by their predecessors.　Any action taken that will change the "set routine procedure" is looked upon as a threat and is resisted. This is true when consideration is being given to the establishment of a maintenance manual. The attitudes of the maintenance personnel are reflected in such statements as: "Our organization and procedures are unique"; "Standard procedures stifle improvement and innovation, and reduce flexibility of operations"; "You are adding to the overhead costs and establishing a bureaucratic system with lots of red tape." These statements are typical and reflect the attitude of being satisfied and content with the *status quo*. This to a degree is indicative of a feeling of job insecurity and concern about having to "turn to" and perhaps having to work harder. This attitude can be overcome only if top management fully supports the development of a maintenance manual and carefully explains its objectives to all within the organization.

The decision by management to evaluate the need for a maintenance manual will in the process of the evaluation uncover many areas of poor management of maintenance. The methods and procedures for performing maintenance in many organizations are based on past practices that have been accepted over the years without question and for the most part have never been formalized in writing. In the review of existing maintenance management procedures, it is probable that the following will be found:

1. Duplication of effort exists.
2. Areas of responsibility are not clearly defined, nor are there clear lines of authority.
3. There are missing links in procedures.
4. Effort is being expended in areas where it is no longer required.
5. Excessive paper work and red tape exist.
6. Obsolete methods, equipment, and materials are being used.
7. Maintenance revolves about one key individual, or so-called indispensable man.

Contents of Manual

The contents of a maintenance manual will depend upon whether it will be a management- or technical-type of manual, or a combination of both. The major factor to be considered is the separation of the management aspects from the technical aspects. This is accomplished by dividing the manual into two parts, management and technical, within the same volume or by having a separate volume covering management aspects and one or more volumes covering technical aspects.

No attempt will be made to outline in detail the contents of various technical manuals because of the large number of variables and different requirements of a given company. The technical or instructional manual can cover such items as inspection, painting, lighting, and equipment maintenance and repair. The subject matter determines to a major extent the contents of the manual.

The Table of Contents of the Department of the Navy, Bureau of Yards and Docks, Washington, D.C., technical manual on "Building Maintenance—Painting," Nav-Docks MO-110, illustrates this point as follows:

CHAPTER 1. PAINTING

CHAPTER 2. ENVIRONMENTAL EFFECTS

CHAPTER 3. COATING SYSTEMS

The contents of a maintenance manual that is devoted to the management viewpoint of maintenance can have general application to most organizations and enterprises whether private or governmental.   This is true because there are fundamental maintenance management concepts that can be applied universally for effective and efficient management of the functions.

A maintenance management manual should contain the following:

Title.   Select an appropriate title that readily indicates the subject matter to be covered.

Letter of Transmittal.   The letter or a similar statement establishes the authority for issuing the manual.   Its wording should clearly show the support of top management for the organization's maintenance program.   The letter establishes a basis for insuring compliance with the procedures established by the manual and is customarily signed by the head of the organization.

Foreword.   The foreword usually is used by someone other than the author to commend the contents of the document to the reader.   In the maintenance manual it can be used by the president or head of the organization to show his support for the manual and the policies and procedures that are set forth.

Preface. The preface outlines why the manual was written and what the user of the manual will gain by using it.

Table of Contents. Outlines the contents of the manual. The breakdown of the index will generally follow the major headings that were used in the manual outline. The table of contents and the index should be revised when revisions are made in the manual.

Body of Manual. Refers to the subject matter that should be included in the manual as reflected by the table of contents. A discussion of this is covered under Maintenance Manual Topics.

Appendix. Provides a place for including reference material, such as forms, paper flow process charts, organization charts, etc.

Index. Is an alphabetical guide to the subject matter included in the manual. It should cover only significant items that require ready identification or location to assist the reader.

Maintenance Manual Topics. The following topics are typical of the kind that should be included in the manual:

Objectives. A clear statement of the objectives of the organization's maintenance program must be made. This is fundamental to the administration of any function. The statement may be brief, such as "to insure that plant facilities and equipment can continually meet or perform their designed characteristics within the economical expenditure of resources." Or it may be lengthy and refer to a systematic approach to:

1. Plant facilities and equipment.
   a. Items that are more economical on a breakdown basis than on a preventive-maintenance program.
   b. Items maintained and repaired on a planned and scheduled basis, not on a breakdown basis.
   c. Items maintained and repaired at minimum cost to meet operational and functional requirements.
   d. Items maintained and repaired to reduce major repair and replacement.
   e. Expenditure of funds and manpower to be based on effective estimating techniques.
2. Maintenance manpower.
   a. To be controlled through an appropriate system.
   b. Adequate and well-qualified supervisors to be provided.
   c. The work force to be in balance with the work load.
   d. Every effort to be made to reduce lost time.
3. Maintenance costs.
   a. Cost comparison between the estimated cost and the actual costs, followed by mandatory corrective action on variances.
   b. A management reporting system required to evaluate the performance of managing maintenance.
   c. Record keeping to be kept at a minimum consistent with the management reporting system.

The reasons for publishing the manual should be discussed under the objectives section and may be summarized in the preface. These reasons may be but should not be limited to:

1. Providing status and recognition for maintenance.
2. Reducing the cost of the maintenance function by simplifying, eliminating, and avoiding duplication of effort.
3. Providing a uniform system so that the function can be properly evaluated.
4. Reducing paper work and red tape.
5. Increasing the responsiveness of the maintenance work force.
6. Increasing production through more effective maintenance management.

Scope.   Define the extent of the function.

Responsibilities and Organization.   Define what departments and individuals are responsible for the maintenance of plant facilities and equipment.   In addition, the authority necessary to carry out the responsibilities should be clearly stated.   This section should also show the responsibility of the maintenance function in relation to the whole organization.   It should present appropriate organization charts and assign organizational elements specific tasks.   It should briefly outline the relationship of the contract work force to the in-house maintenance work force.

Definitions.   A list of definitions of words and terminology used in maintenance is most helpful in achieving effective communication between the maintenance force and these elements that it supports.   The definitions may be included in the text or in the appendix.

Maintenance Management Concepts.   This section should deal with the concepts, procedures, and techniques that are used in the maintenance and repair of plant facilities and equipment.   Consideration should be given to the following:

1. Inventory of plant facilities and equipment and its importance to effective maintenance management.   Inventory tells us what the plant is, where it is, its size, cost, type of facilities and equipment, type of construction, and, perhaps, replacement value.   The inventory of plant facilities and equipment may be included in the appendix or other publications.   The use of a separate inventory publication is recommended.

2. Inspection system including inspection by the operator, preventive maintenance inspection, and periodic inspection of plant facilities and equipment.   An adequate inspection system is mandatory in efficiently performing maintenance.   Inspection should generate most of the work for the maintenance force and indicate the condition of the plant as shown in the inventory.   However, certain items should be on a breakdown basis, when this is more economical than inspection.

3. Requests from other departments.   Outline the procedure whereby the service of the maintenance force can be requested by other units of the organization.   The system may be informal or formal depending on the type and size of the organization.   Where telephone requests are authorized, include appropriate telephone numbers.   Include the designation of a single point for receipt of requests, a list of who is authorized to request, a system of review, and a method for including the requests in work planning, estimating, and scheduling.   If a special printed form is used, include it in the discussion or in the appendix.

4. Planning and estimating.   Briefly discuss the need in planning for reviewing the scope of the job, justification of the job, requester's approval, specification requirements, manpower availability, and deadline for performing the job.   Outline briefly the method of estimating and who will do it.   Estimates generally should not be made by the work force.   Where feasible, estimates should be based on standards.   The importance of estimating should be stressed.   It is only through the use of sound estimates that comparisons between actual and estimated costs become meaningful and the performance of the maintenance force can be evaluated.

5. Work authorization.   The organization's job-order or work-order system should be briefly described concerning its use and importance.   The classification of the types of work that are under a work-order system should be described.   The job-order or work-order form should be discussed or referenced in the appendix. The procedures for processing the job order or work order should be clearly stated. The use of a work authorization system is essential in determining costs and for effective management of maintenance.

6. Scheduling.   Its importance in balancing shop capacity with shop work load should be outlined.   The types of scheduling used by the maintenance department should be discussed.   This is helpful to those served by the maintenance work force.

7. Shop performance.   The methods, procedures, and performance of the maintenance work force should be outlined.   This provides information on time keeping, material requisitioning, and the everyday routine operations of the work force.

Discuss or include in the appendix the labor time cards and material requisition forms that may be used.

8. Management reports. Outline briefly the reports that are used and their importance in evaluating work performance. Examples of the reports may be included in the appendix. Include in this section or separately the financial reporting system that the organization uses to collect cost data. The reporting of data on the performance of labor is necessary for evaluation of the maintenance force.

Telephone Directory. Include, as appropriate, telephone numbers of key individuals and organizations that are important to the maintenance of plant facilities and equipment. Examples are the plant engineer, doctor, local fire department and police force, the local utility companies, etc. A convenient method of handling this directory is to include it in the appendix.

Emergency or Disaster Plan. The organization plan for handling emergencies or disasters involving company property may be included in the discussion, in the appendix, or in a separate document with a reference in the discussion.

Cost Reduction Program. The company's program for cost reduction should be outlined briefly as it relates to maintenance. A detailed discussion of the program may be included in the appendix or other documents with appropriate reference in the text.

Safety. This can be covered by referring to the organization's safety manual if in existence. When such a manual is not in existence, a detailed discussion should be made in the text of the manual or in a separate appendix.

Training. Outline, if appropriate, the organization's training program for maintenance shop forces and supervision.

Work Simplification. Describe the techniques that are used in work simplification or work improvement and can be applied to increasing the effectiveness of maintenance and reducing its cost.

Advantages of Maintenance Manuals. The decision by management to establish a maintenance manual will result in both direct and indirect advantages. The direct advantages will include but not be limited to:

1. Elimination of duplication of effort.
2. Elimination of overlapping organizational responsibilities.
3. Reduction of paper work, forms, and red tape.
4. Establishment of a control mechanism for management.
5. Increased response to maintenance requirements with decreased cost.
6. Decreased cost of training and retraining personnel.

The indirect advantages that will accrue are:

1. Increased status and prestige of maintenance.
2. Provision of a basis for appraising and evaluating maintenance.
3. Provision of a ready reference for the guidance of management and personnel in the area of maintenance.
4. Provision of a basis for a better understanding between the maintenance worker and management, resulting in increased job satisfaction.

Disadvantage of Maintenance Manuals. The use of maintenance manuals has some disadvantages. The major ones are:

1. Rigid adherence to procedures tends to stifle workers' initiative for innovations and improvements.
2. Continual revision and updating is mandatory for the manual to be effective.

Preparation of Manual. Assigning the preparation of a manual to an individual cannot be done on the basis of a part-time job in addition to his normal responsibilities. The task of manual preparation is exacting. The assigned writer must have the full support of management.   This will assist in obtaining cooperation from all organizational levels.

Prior to the actual writing phase, consideration should be given to:

1. The requirement of flexibility due to potential changes in company policies, organization, or objectives.
2. The requirement for training personnel due to rapid turnover, anticipated plant expansion, or changes in technology.
3. The requirement and needs of decentralized organizations.
4. The necessity for uniformity and consistency of procedures.
5. The size and number of levels within the organization.
6. The purpose of the manual in terms of why it is being written and what it will accomplish.
7. Selection of an identifying title.
8. The educational level of the user.

These considerations will be helpful in determining the type and availability of existing information and source material.

In obtaining information for the manual, review existing procedures, organizations, and policy.   Procedures are more readily analyzed by means of flow charts which indicate the path of paper work as it moves from one group to another.   These charts highlight excessive paper work and unnecessary use of forms.   Personal interviews with people involved in maintenance are mandatory in obtaining information on current maintenance procedures.

Outline.   It is important to develop a detailed outline of the manual and have it approved by the individual who authorized the preparation of the manual.   This approval will save many hours of rewriting and reduce the potential for conflicts of opinion.   An outline for a management-type maintenance manual would resemble the following:

SUGGESTED OUTLINE FOR MAINTENANCE MANUAL

Chapter I—Introduction to Maintenance Management
    Section 1.   General
        1.1.1   Objectives and Scope
        1.1.1.1   Objectives
        1.1.1.2   Scope
        1.1.1.3   Related Publications
        1.1.1.4   Adoption
        1.1.2   Authorization
        1.1.3   Definitions
    Section 2.   Responsibilities for Maintenance Management
        1.2.1   General Responsibilities
        1.2.2   Plant Engineering Department
        1.2.2.1   General
        1.2.2.2   Maintenance Planning and Scheduling Division
        1.2.2.3   Administrative Division
        1.2.2.4   Engineering Division
        1.2.2.5   Material Division
        1.2.2.6   Mechanical Division
        1.2.2.7   Electrical Division
        1.2.2.8   Buildings and Grounds Division
        1.2.3   Relationship to Other Departments
        1.2.3.1   Production
        1.2.3.2   Quality Control
        1.2.3.3   Production Control
        1.2.3.4   Industrial Engineering
        1.2.4   Organization Charts
        1.2.4.1   Plant Engineering Department
        1.2.4.2   Staff Divisions
        1.2.4.3   Operating Divisions

An outline for an instructional or technical manual covering the maintenance and repair of plant facilities and equipment is dependent on the subject matter. A manual on maintenance of pavements and a manual on maintaining specific types of production equipment would have different outlines.

A further consideration in preparing a manual is to establish a financial budget and a time schedule. This is essential to ensure staying within funding limitations and meeting publication commitments.

Sources of Information.   In conducting research for useful and pertinent information, existing published manuals should be reviewed.   Apply your own experience and background to the subject matter.   Consult with others who have prepared manuals or have greater experience in maintenance.

Excellent sources on information to be included in maintenance manuals are readily obtainable from equipment and material manufacturers and suppliers.   Various associations, such as the National Association of Building Owners and Managers, the National Sanitary Supply Association, the American Management Association, the National Academy of Science, and the Associated General Contractors of America, Inc., are valuable sources in the preparation of maintenance manuals.

The Armed Forces of the United States prepare manuals on a multitude of subjects, including maintenance of plant facilities and equipment.   Examples of the instructional- or technical-type maintenance manuals published by the Bureau of Yards and Docks, U.S. Navy, are "Maintenance of Grounds," "Maintenance of Pavements," "Maintenance of Trackage," "Maintenance of Waterfront Facilities," "Building Maintenance—Painting," "Building Maintenance—Structures," "Building Maintenance—Roofing," and "Building Maintenance—Electrical."

These manuals and others can be purchased from the Office of Technical Service, Commerce Department, Washington, D.C.

Similar types of manuals are published by the United States Army, the United States Air Force, and other federal government agencies and are generally available for purchase from the Commerce Department.

In addition to the technical maintenance manuals, management-type manuals can be purchased.   Examples of these published by the Bureau of Yards and Docks are "Maintenance Management of Public Works and Public Utilities," NavDocks P-321, and "Inspection for Maintenance of Public Works and Public Utilities," NavDocks P-322.

The use of these manuals and others can make the job of preparing your own maintenance manual an easier and less costly task.

Periodicals covering the maintenance function also are important sources of information.   *Factory,* published by McGraw-Hill Publications, and *Plant Engineering,* published by Technical Publishing Company, are examples of periodicals in the maintenance field.   Extensive research on, and review of, available maintenance-type manuals can be a very useful aid in writing a maintenance manual.

Writing the Manual.   In writing the maintenance manual, adhere to the agreed-to outline and keep in mind the purpose of the manual and the reading level of the potential user.   The manual should be written in a precise, exact, and clear style.   The words used should be commonly understood and not highly technical or sophisticated. The sentences and the paragraphs should be short.   Each thought should have a separate paragraph.   Divide the text material by major headings and subheadings as contained in the outline.

The effective use of photographs and illustrations is important to the success of a manual.   The illustrations and photographs should be integrated into the text and clearly identified in the text material.   In many cases, line drawings can be used in lieu of photographs as an economy measure.   A paper flow chart used as an illustration will save many pages of text material and will more clearly explain the flow of paper and forms than words.

Having considered the importance of illustrations, word selection, sentence structure, and paragraphing, the writer must write the first draft of the manual following the approved outline.   The first draft is rarely the final draft.   It must be polished and evaluated in light of whether the manual has accomplished its objective.   It must be checked for accuracy, completeness, and readability.   This can be accomplished best by having the draft reviewed by personnel familiar with the subject matter.   If the draft passes the review, it can be polished and put into final form.   If not, the material should be revised and reworked according to the comments and advice of the reviewing personnel.   Detailed writing guidance can be obtained from the books listed in the bibliography at the conclusion of this chapter.

Format of Manual. The format of a maintenance manual is an important element and can greatly affect the usefulness of the manual. Like other publications, the manual should have a title page and a table of contents. A list of illustrations and tables is used when there are three or more. Additional considerations may be a fore-word, a preface, and a letter of transmittal or authorization. These were discussed under Contents of Manual. A primary requisite in the format is to provide an effective means for making revisions. Therefore, the most adaptable form is a loose-leaf manual. This may be the normal three-hole punch or the multiring. For a loose-leaf manual the selection of the proper cover is important. The use of a vinyl plastic cover of an appropriate color produces an attractive manual. A 1-in. binder of this type can be obtained at a nominal cost for use with 8- by 10-in. or 8½- by 11-in. standard paper. The title of the manual and the company name should be printed in a color that complements the color of the cover. The selection of the size of the cover is important if the manual is to be used. It should fit in an attaché case, desk drawer, or average library shelf; otherwise, it will be hidden away in some obscure place.

Format Considerations. In developing the format of the manual, consideration must be given to readability, ready reference, and a simple procedure for making revisions.

Readability. Readability can be achieved by writing to the reading level of the potential user. This is done by writing for clarity, conciseness, and accuracy. Select commonly understood terms and expressions. In all cases, use short sentences and paragraphs. In providing instruction on how to do something, give specific instructions and avoid direct references to other procedures or documentations that are not readily available to the reader. When explaining a detailed procedure or concept, make use of appropriate illustrations or flow charts.

Readability is enhanced by proper spacing of material and the effective use of headings, subheadings, and indentations. Headings should be emphasized by the use of type different from the text type or by underlining and should complement the numbering format used. Consideration should be given to the selection of the method that will be used in printing. The type should be clearly readable under normal working conditions. The cost of the paper is relatively small. Therefore, provide space for ample margins and spacing of the text material and illustrations. However, consideration should be given to the weight of paper that will be used to prevent bleeding through and to withstand the conditions under which the manual will be used.

Ready Reference. Ready reference is attained by the organization of the material in a logical manner. A numbering format or identification system for the chapters, sections, pages, etc., and the use of a table of contents and an index are necessary for ready reference of text material. Organization of the material in a logical manner is dependent upon the effectiveness and detail of the outline used in its preparation. The numbering format provides a quick method for identifying all elements. A recommended format is the use of a modified Dewey decimal system as follows:

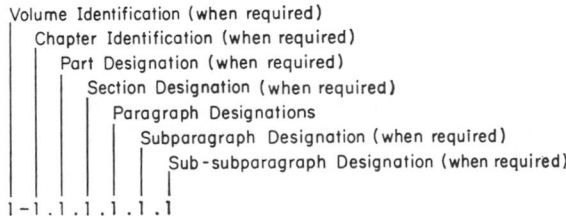

This type of numbering system relates all items clearly. A paragraph is readily identified and can be revised without changes in other paragraphs. This system limits one heading to a maximum of nine topics plus a general topic, providing for a logical breakdown of the information to be presented.

Revisions.   Corrections, additions, and deletions can more readily be accomplished by use of a loose-leaf cover.   The modified Dewey decimal system provides a ready means for making adjustments.   When a whole page is replaced an asterisk can be used to identify the changed paragraph.   When the page is not reprinted, pen-and-ink changes can easily be made when the decimal system for identification is used.

Illustrations of Manuals.   The following excerpts from maintenance manuals, published by the Department of the Navy, Bureau of Yards and Docks, Washington, D.C., illustrate the recommended format:

MANAGEMENT-TYPE MANUAL
"MAINTENANCE MANAGEMENT OF PUBLIC
WORKS AND PUBLIC UTILITIES"
NAVDOCKS P-321

Section 6.   Work Input Control
  3.6.1   GENERAL
    3.6.1.1   Methods of Work Generation.   There are various methods by which work may be generated under Controlled Maintenance.   The principal method consists of planned continuous inspection.   These inspections are planned, scheduled, and systematically performed by technically qualified inspectors and operators of the Public Works Department.   Outside specialists, such as boiler or elevator inspectors, may be brought in to supplement the work of this group.   Other methods comprise the expressed observations or desires of personnel who are not part of the prescribed group of public works inspectors and operators.
    3.6.1.2   Personnel.   Continuous inspection is performed by those who are familiar with the facilities and equipment to be maintained, who know and have reference to accepted maintenance standards and guides, and who function according to an integrated plan of operation.   This plan is calculated to provide complete inspection coverage of public works and public utilities at the activity.   Controlled Maintenance, however, does not preclude work generation by other methods.   Special needs most likely to be known only to personnel closely involved with specific situations must also be permitted equal entry into the maintenance stream.   These will take the form of work requests or requests for estimates. The full benefits of Controlled Maintenance are realized when the maximum amount of work results from continuous inspection.
    3.6.1.3   Application of Control Factors.   The control factors in work generation relate to procedures and criteria for both continuous inspection and other methods.   When these procedures and criteria are followed, unnecessary requests for estimates or for maintenance work will be eliminated or reduced to a minimum.
  3.6.2   CONTINUOUS INSPECTION.   Administration of planned continuous inspection is the responsibility of the Manager of the Inspection Branch under the Director, Maintenance Control Division.   Reference shall be made to Inspection for Maintenance of Public Works and Public Utilities, NavDocks P-322, for complete information on continuous inspection.
    3.6.2.1   Purpose.   The purpose of continuous inspection is to identify deficiencies in public works and public utilities and to initiate corrective action that will bring these facilities up to an established level of maintenance.   Properly administered and supported, these inspections should detect deficiencies in the early stages of development, reduce the number of breakdowns and cost of repairs, provide for a more constant flow of work to the Maintenance Division, and permit better planning for utilization of labor and material through predetermination of forthcoming work.
    3.6.2.2   Scope.   Continuous inspection deals only with existing facilities.   Inspection is not concerned with requirements for new construction, alterations, or improvements that may be considered desirable or necessary as a result of changes in the mission of the activity or changes in operational or maintenance procedures.
    3.6.2.3   Categories of Continuous Inspection.
    3.6.2.3.1   Operator Inspections.   Operator inspection consists of examination, lubrication and minor adjustments of equipment and systems for which the Public Works Officer is responsible and to which a specific operator is assigned.   Frequency and details of the inspections should be contained in standard operating procedures made accessible to the operator.   Deficiencies beyond the capacity and authority of the operator to correct should be reported to the supervisor; breakdowns of equipment should be reported immediately to the cognizant supervisor or to the Work Reception and Control Unit.

3.6.2.3.2   Preventive Maintenance Inspection.   Preventive Maintenance Inspection/ Service consists of examination, lubrication, minor adjustment, and minor repair of equipment and systems for which a specific operator is not assigned.   Preventive Maintenance Inspection is concerned primarily with items that, if disabled, would (a) interfere with an essential operation of the naval activity, (b) endanger life and/or property, or, (c) involve high cost or long lead time for replacement.   Generally, Preventive Maintenance Inspection should be performed by shop personnel under shop supervision.   It is the basic responsibility of the Inspection Branch to determine what is to be inspected and how often. Such determinations would normally be made with the advice and assistance of the shops involved.   Breakdowns should be reported immediately to the cognizant supervisor or to the Work Reception and Control Unit.   Deficiencies found are reported to the Manager of the Inspection Branch through the inspector's supervisor.   The Inspection Branch reviews reported deficiencies, initiates further action if required, and evaluates, at the time of Control Inspection, the effectiveness of Preventive Maintenance Inspection.

3.6.2.3.3   Control Inspection.   Control Inspection is a scheduled examination and/or test of public works and public utilities to determine the physical condition with respect to the maintenance standard.   The objectives of Control Inspection are: (a) to provide for examination of all items of public works and public utilities not covered by Operator or Preventive Maintenance Inspection, (b) to assure adequacy of Operator Inspection and Preventive Maintenance Inspection, (c) to obtain a reduction in the number of breakdowns and cost of repairs, (d) to provide a more constant flow of work to the Operating Divisions, (e) to allow improved planning for utilization of labor and determination of material requirements, and (f) to detect and reduce overmaintenance.

Control inspection is performed by personnel assigned to the Inspection Branch or made by others at the request of the Inspection Branch.   Control inspectors do not make adjustments on equipment but do report deficiencies to the Manager of the Inspection Branch. Breakdowns must be reported immediately to the cognizant supervisor or to the Work Reception and Control Branch.

3.6.3   OTHER METHODS

3.6.3.1   Customer Requests.   Work generated by this method includes work requests or requests for estimates made by personnel other than designated operators or inspectors. For emergency or breakdown situations, it includes the report made to the Work Reception and Control Branch by anyone who has become aware of the apparent need for immediate maintenance work.   Written requests involving emergencies and breakdowns need no controls other than those prescribed in Procedure Chart No. __.   Verbal and telephone reporting procedures, and the publicizing thereof, can approximate those established at the naval activity for fires.   The following controls are applicable to generating work, other than emergencies or breakdowns.

3.6.3.1.1   Forms and Procedures.   The use of forms and adherence to procedures provides a measure of control.   Requesters are to furnish certain Information that must precede review and action by the Public Works Department.   (See Procedure Chart No. __ and Exhibit No. __.)   Processing a work request requires considerable preliminary action by the requester, and so rules out the likelihood of haphazard or spur-of-the-moment requests.

3.6.3.1.2   Maintenance Representatives.   The designation and use of maintenance representatives is most important.   These are personnel of departments, divisions, or other component units within the naval activity or other activities, through whom requests for maintenance work are channeled for review and verification.   Availability of funds, duplicating requests, necessity for the work (unless apparent), requested completion dates, compliance with forms and procedures and so forth, are matters that should be looked into and properly checked within the requesting unit before an official request is made.

3.6.3.1.3   Customer Relations.   Good management requires that the best of relations be maintained with all customers.   A key to the establishment of good customer relations is through judicious processing of the Work Request.   There are two important steps that can be taken to establish and maintain proper relations with customers:

(1)   The customer should be notified of the date that a reply to a request for estimate may be received when more than one week will be required to prepare the estimate.

(2)   It is only natural for a customer to be interested in when the work may be performed.   Since the exact starting and completion dates of some jobs cannot be firmly established until all material is on hand and the job has been scheduled, it may be difficult to predict realistic completion dates.   This is particularly so when only an estimate is requested, as the Public Works Department does not know when the authorization will be forthcoming.   However, the Maintenance Control Division can obtain information from the Master Scheduler regarding the average leadtime required for obtaining material and the current status of the backlog of all work centers, and can fairly accurately predict the estimated starting date of requested work.   Item 15 of NavDocks 2351 has been provided

for this purpose. For the processing of a Work Request, from its inception until it is converted to a work authorization, refer to Procedure Chart No. __ and Exhibit No. __.

3.6.3.1.4 Activity Planning Board. The use of an Activity Planning Board to control all expenditures for work of an alteration or improvement nature is encouraged. A fixed dollar limitation for alteration and improvement work should be established for the fiscal year or quarter and all requests screened by the Board. The Planning and Estimating Branch can provide preliminary estimates for the Board's guidance.

3.6.3.2 Military Inspection. Military inspections, which are standard practice at most naval activities, fulfill an important function as a command audit of the physical plant. The maintenance work that could be generated by them might, under Controlled Maintenance, parallel work that has been or would shortly be generated by continuous inspection. It is vital that Commanding Officer recognize that planned continuous inspection is an integral part of the orderly processes of Controlled Maintenance. This recognition by command establishes continuous inspection as the officially designated first line of attack against substandard conditions in public works and public utilities and will provide substantial support to maintenance management. Command support may be demonstrated in a practical way by the exercise of restraint in requiring priority follow-up action to correct conditions reported by military inspections.

3.6.3.3 Other Programs. Maintenance work may be generated through established channels as a result of various programs at the naval activity, such as safety, utilities conservation, fire prevention, security, transportation (Shop Repair Orders), etc. Shop repair orders prepared by the Transportation Division for performance of work by the Maintenance Division should be submitted to the Maintenance Control Division and treated as work requests. Based upon the size and nature of the work to be performed, they should be issued to the Maintenance Division as Emergency/Service Authorizations, Minor Work Authorizations, or Specific Job Orders and the appropriate Labor Class Code applied.

3.6.3.4 Repetitive Requirements. Maintenance and operation service may be generated by action of the Public Works Department to meet certain highly repetitive needs, such as garbage disposal, trash removal, watch standing, and so forth. Because these needs are continuing or repetitive, they can be planned and authorized in advance.

3.6.3.5 Observations of Personnel Other Than Inspectors. Personnel at the naval activity, other than inspectors performing continuous inspection, should be encouraged to report observed deficiencies via established channels. These personnel may or may not know whether these deficiencies are below standard, but the existence of the deficiencies should be reported without delay. Public Works Department personnel, particularly journeymen, supervisors, and staff members, should be especially alert to observe and report conditions that require corrective action.

INSTRUCTIONAL- OR TECHNICAL-TYPE MANUAL
"BUILDING MAINTENANCE—PAINTING"
NAVDOCKS MO-110

CHAPTER 5—PAINT MIXING AND CONDITIONING

Section 1. Mixing

5.1.1 MIXING TECHNIQUE. When possible, mix paint materials in the paint shop or mixing room, using a mechanical agitator or a strong, smooth, clean wood or metal paddle. When a paddle is used, work pigment up from the bottom of the container and continue stirring until the pigment is completely blended with the vehicle. Be sure to scrape the bottom and sides of the container with the paddle to insure mixture of all pigment. If the pigment has settled in a hard cake, pour the vehicle into another clean container and break up the pigment with a paddle. While agitating until the mixture is homogeneous, pour the liquid back, a small amount at a time. Then box it by pouring the paint back and forth from one container to another until the pigment and liquid form a smooth mixture of uniform consistency and color. When it is necessary to store a partially-filled can of paint overnight or for a few days, cover the top of the paint with a layer of volatile paint thinner approximately $\frac{1}{16}$-inch deep. The paint thinner must be compatible with the paint to be stored. The thinner recommended for thinning the paint should be used. Do not add mineral spirits to the water-type paints or lacquer. Place a cover as tightly as possible on the partially filled can. This will prevent skinning of the paint during short-time storage. For re-use the slight amount of thinner remaining may be stirred into the paint without any adverse effect. Another method, suitable for longer storage, is to cut a circle of fairly heavy paper to the same diameter as the interior of the paint container, press the paper over the surface of the paint remaining in the container, and cover the container tightly. For subsequent use, cut the paper loose from the sides of the container with a spatula and lift the paper with its adhering paint skins from the paint. Remove all loose skins and stir the paint until it is uniform.

5.1.2 MIXING REQUIREMENTS. Mixing requirements vary with different types of paints. Varnish and shellac should not be stirred. Water-type or latex paints should be stirred gently to avoid getting air bubbles in them. When possible, purchase paints in the desired shade to minimize on-the-job tinting. Ready-mixed paints should be used. When paints meet the specification requirements, a minimum amount of adjustment or preparation will be necessary. Stir paints frequently during use to maintain uniform consistency.

5.1.3 READY-MIXED PAINT. To prepare or reduce ready-mixed paint other than enamel or emulsion paints, place unopened cans in a shaking-type mixer for a period of three to ten minutes. Paint in large containers should be stirred with a propeller-type mixer. Make any required additions of oil, thinner, or color after the paint has been mechanically mixed and continue mixing until added material is thoroughly dispersed.

5.1.4 ENAMEL OR EMULSION PAINTS. When mixing enamel, use small mechanical agitators of the propeller type or hand-stir with a paddle. Shaking-type mixers whip air into the enamel or emulsion paint, thereby causing it to bubble or froth. A settling period of six to eight hours then is required before the enamel or paint is satisfactory for use.

Section 2. Tinting

5.2.1 TINTING PAINTS. Before color is added, paints to be tinted should be of ready-to-use consistency. Colors dispersed in oil are used for tinting oil paints and enamels. These are concentrated color pigments made from natural earth or chemical compounds and are mixed with oil to form a smooth paste or semi-paste. The color-in-oil should be thinned to a liquid consistency with mineral spirits before it is added to the paint to be tinted. The paint should be thoroughly agitated while the color is being added and should be checked frequently against the color standard until the desired color is obtained. The tinted paint then should be strained to prevent streaking. Colors-in-oil should never be added to white paints intended for use as such; they should be used only in tinting base-whites that are made with an oil base. Latex paints, and lacquers should not be tinted with colors-in-oil, but rather with special color concentrates. White paints are used as a tinting base for light-colored paint.

Section 3. Straining Paint

5.3.1 USE SIEVE. To remove lumps, skins, or foreign material, strain paint through a fine wire mesh, silk, or cheesecloth sieve. Although desirable, it is not always necessary to strain paint that is to be applied by brush or roller; all paint, however, must be thoroughly strained before it is used in a spray gun.

"BUILDING MAINTENANCE—ROOFING"
NAVDOCKS MO-113

2.6.2 ROOF DECKS FOR ASBESTOS-CEMENT ROOFS

2.6.2.1 Asbestos-Cement Shingles. Wood decks for asbestos-cement shingle roofs should be made of well-seasoned sheathing lumber, not less than 1 inch in thickness, not more than 6 inches wide, and preferably tongued and grooved. Sheathing boards should be fastened to each rafter with two nails to provide a smooth, even surface. The roof deck should be kept dry at all times.

The deck should be covered with 15-pound asphalt-saturated felt prior to laying the shingles. This underlayer is necessary to guard against the infiltration of wind and rain. In addition, it provides a cushion for the asbestos-cement shingles.

2.6.2.2 Corrugated Asbestos-Cement Sheets. Corrugated asbestos-cement sheets are normally laid over open wood or steel framing.

2.6.3 STORAGE AND HANDLING OF ASBESTOS-CEMENT ROOFING

2.6.3.1 Asbestos-Cement Shingles. Asbestos-cement shingles should be kept dry at all times. Exposure to moisture during transportation or storage may cause discoloration of the shingles. They should be stacked on edge, preferably on planks at least 4 inches from the ground, when stored outdoors. Piles of shingles should be not more than 4 feet high. Asbestos-cement shingles should be handled carefully to avoid breakage. If bundles are wired together, they should not be lifted by the wires.

2.6.3.2 Corrugated Asbestos-Cement Sheets. Asbestos-cement corrugated sheets should be stored and handled with the same care as asbestos-cement shingles. They should always be kept dry. Crated sheets should not be uncrated until needed. When uncrated they should be placed on firm, level supports, preferably on pieces 2 inches by 4 inches spaced 12 to 18 inches apart and laid at right angles to the corrugations. Sheets should not be stacked more than 4 feet high. (Some manufacturers recommend 2 feet.)

2.6.4   TREATMENT FOR ASBESTOS-CEMENT ROOFS.   Investigation has shown that failure of fasteners and the mechanical damage that results from hail, traffic, contact with tree limbs, and the warping of roof decks are the principal reasons why maintenance and repair work are necessary on asbestos-cement roofs.

A rigid frame is required for this type roofing because of its tendency to crack at the fasteners when small movements occur.   A double overlap of the joints, and careful sealing during installation are required to reduce moisture penetration during wind-blown rains. Roofs should have a pitch of not less than 4 inches per foot.

When only a few shingles or corrugated sheets are broken, they should be removed and new ones applied.   When a large percentage (25 percent or more) is broken, they should all be removed and a new roof applied.   The age and condition of undamaged units should determine whether those salvaged from the old roof should be reused with new units.

When an asbestos-cement roof fails because of deterioration of the fasteners, the failure is usually a general one and piecemeal repair is futile.   When such failure occurs, normally on a very old roof, it is best to remove the entire roof.   Whether the old roofing should be reapplied must be determined by its age and condition.   Normally, if the roofing can be removed without damage, it may be reapplied safely.

2.6.5   MAINTENANCE AND REPAIR METHODS FOR ASBESTOS-CEMENT ROOFINGS.   No sharp distinction can be made between maintenance and repair work on asbestos-cement roofings.   Both are, therefore, treated under one heading.

2.6.5.1   Asbestos-Cement Shingles.

2.6.5.1.1   Shingles Applied by the American Method.   To replace a broken shingle that has been applied by the American method, follow the procedure described in paragraph 2.8.5.   This method is illustrated in Figure __.   The same procedure can be followed with multiple-unit shingles.

2.6.5.1.2   Shingles Applied by the Hexagonal Method.   To replace a broken shingle that has been applied by the hexagonal method, straighten the anchors, shatter the shingle, and remove the broken pieces.   Use the nail ripper to cut or draw the nail.   Punch a hole in a small piece of copper, galvanized iron, or painted tin, place over bottom anchor and nail firmly to the roof deck.   Notch a new shingle to pass side anchors.   Slide the new shingle into place over the bottom anchor and bend down anchors to hold it in place.

2.6.5.1.3   Shingles Applied by the Dutch-Lap Method.   To replace a broken shingle that has been applied by the Dutch-lap method, remove the metal anchor and nails, then remove the broken pieces of shingle and insert a new shingle with a new anchor.   If the nails cannot be withdrawn, notch the new shingle to avoid them.

2.6.5.2   Asbestos-Cement Corrugated Sheets.   Broken asbestos-cement corrugated sheets should be replaced with new ones fastened in the same manner as the original sheets. When this is not practicable, toggle bolts with lead or plastic washers may be used.   These bolts pass through holes somewhat larger than the bolt, and when drawn tight, the washer forms a waterproof seal.

2.6.6   REROOFING WITH ASBESTOS-CEMENT ROOFING.

2.6.6.1   Asbestos-Cement Shingles.

2.6.6.1.1   Preparing Deck for Reroofing.   To prepare the deck for reroofing with asbestos-cement shingles when (a) the existing roofing is removed or (b) the shingles are to be applied over an existing asphalt-shingle, roll-roofing, or wood-shingle roof, proceed in the manner described in paragraph 2.4.6.   However, a 15-pound asphalt-saturated felt should be applied over the wood-shingle deck.   Although it is entirely possible to apply asbestos-cement shingles over the roofings mentioned, the long service that is normally expected of asbestos-cement shingles indicates that the better practice is to remove the existing roofing, make repairs to the deck to bring it to as nearly "new" condition as practicable, and cover the deck with a 15-pound asphalt-saturated felt, laid horizontally, with a 4-inch head lap. End laps should be a minimum of 6 inches except at hips, ridges, and valleys, where 12-inch laps are recommended.   Nail the felt with sufficient large-headed roofing nails to hold it in place during application of shingles.

2.6.6.1.2   Applying Asbestos-Cement Shingle Roof.   Space limitations do not permit inclusion of instructions for applying all types of asbestos-cement shingles.   Step-by-step directions for installing multiple-unit shingles are given below.   Essentially, this same method is used for American-method shingles.   Detailed instructions for applying other types can be obtained from their manufacturers.

(1) Starter Course.   Lift up the edge of the underlayer at the eaves and lay a full-sized starter shingle.   Let it overhang the eaves and gable approximately 1 inch and secure it with four galvanized nails.   Apply succeeding starters, spaced $\frac{1}{16}$-inch apart, in the same manner until the entire course is laid.

(2) First and Succeeding Courses.   The first course of the main roof is laid directly

over the starter course beginning with a half shingle with the vertical edge projecting 1 inch beyond the gable and the butt edge projecting 1 inch beyond the eaves. Fasten each shingle with four galvanized nails. Do not drive nails "home" as in laying wood shingles. Lay the second course with a full-sized shingle so that the shoulder coincides with the point of the underlaying course. A 6-inch exposure is automatically obtained. Start the succeeding course with a half-sized shingle, then a full-sized shingle, alternating with each course.

(3) Hip and Ridge Finish. Lay roof shingles so that they butt closely against furring strips placed at hips and ridges. Cover furring strips with asbestos felt and apply hip and ridge shingles. Start laying the ridge shingles on main roof at the end of the ridge farthest away from prevailing storms. When covering hips, start at the lower end. Fasten each shingle with two nails and point up with slaters' cement.

(4) Nails. Large-head, galvanized, needlepoint roofing nails should be used. For new roofs, $1\frac{1}{4}$ inch nails are adequate; for application over existing roofs, 2 inch nails should be used.

2.6.6.2 Asbestos-Cement Corrugated Sheets. Asbestos-cement corrugated sheets should be applied in accordance with current specifications for new construction. Manufacturers of asbestos-cement corrugated sheets maintain engineering and estimating services to assist users in determining the quantities of materials required for particular jobs. At least two manufacturers should be consulted.

Revisions to Manual. The adoption of a maintenance manual by an organization necessitates the development of a procedure for accomplishing revisions. The instant the manual is published and maintenance policies and procedures are documented, events are taking place that will result in changes. The effectiveness of the manual is dependent upon keeping it current because an organization is dynamic and is undergoing continuing change. The use of the loose-leaf binder facilitates making changes. The word revision applies to any change. This can cover corrections, additions, and deletions. The procedure that is used to effect revisions, regardless of type, must be kept simple. If the procedure is complex, the user of the manual will not make the required changes. When revisions by complex procedure are frequent, it is best to cancel the manual in its entirety.

Corrections. Corrections to existing material, if of a minor nature, can be made as pen-and-ink changes. This is readily accomplished if material is logically organized and can be identified as to volume, chapter, section, page, and paragraph. Major corrections should be handled similarly to additions except that the existing numbering, or identification system, or the text material should be used.

Additions. The method used in handling additions or new material is the assignment of a section number or other identification number that will place the data in proper order in the existing material.

Deletions. When material is deleted, the identification number should be left vacant. To use the same number for new material would lead to confusion.

The ease in making corrections, additions, and deletions is dependent upon the identification system that is used in outlining the manual. The Dewey decimal system for numbering and identification that was previously described provides an effective basis for facilitating revisions.

Procedure. The procedure for making revisions should take into consideration that changes should be made only when they are significant. Relatively minor changes should be collected in a pending change file and issued periodically when warranted. When a major correction, deletion, or addition is to be made, incorporate into the revision all pending minor changes. Prior to the issuance of a revision, also check for typographical changes. When revisions are issued, make appropriate changes in the table of contents and the index.

Revisions should be issued under an appropriate letter of transmittal or a revision notice. This method establishes the authority for the change. The revision notice should be in a numerical sequence so that the user can be assured that he has received all the changes that have been made. The revision notice should be dated and show the effective date of the change. The changes to be made by the notice must be clearly indicated and they must specifically indicate where the revision is to be made.

When an existing page is to be reprinted, show the date of the revision in addition to the page number.

As was previously stated, the major disadvantage of a manual is the need to keep it current.   This can be overcome only by adopting a simple and effective method for effecting revisions.

Distribution of Manual.   The maintenance manual to be effective must be distributed to the potential users and to the organizational elements that are supported by the maintenance organization.   The specific distribution is dependent upon the organization of the company.   In certain companies, distribution is made to the top-level executives, selected department heads, maintenance shop forces, and contractors working in the company plants.   In large organizations, distribution should be made to decentralized plants; this provides a basis for uniform maintenance management procedures on a company-wide basis.   Some companies distribute their manuals on a numbered copy basis, necessitating the establishment of a record of holders.   Others distribute on a basis of so many copies per organizational element and maintain no record of the individual holders.   The method used is not too important.   The main objective should be to see that those needing the manual receive copies and revisions.

CONCLUSION

The use of a maintenance manual provides an effective medium for communicating an organization's policy and procedures for maintenance of plant facilities and equipment.   Effectively used, it can reduce maintenance cost, increase morale of the work force, and bring recognition to maintenance management in its support of the organization's basic objectives.

BIBLIOGRAPHY

1. "Maintenance Management of Public Works and Public Utilities," Department of the Navy, Bureau of Yards and Docks NavDocks P-321, 1961.
2. "Building Maintenance—Painting," Department of the Navy, Bureau of Yards and Docks NavDocks MO-110, 1963.
3. "Building Maintenance—Roofing," Department of the Navy, Bureau of Yards and Docks NavDocks MO-113, 1963.
4. Hicks, Tyler G., "Successful Technical Writing," McGraw-Hill Book Company, New York, 1959.
5. Jones, Manley H.. "Executive Decision Making," Richard D. Irwin, Inc., Homewood, Ill., 1957.
6. Brown, Alvin, "Organization," Hibbert Printing Company, New York, 1945.
7. Alford, L. P., and R. H. Beatty, "Principles of Industrial Management," The Ronald Press Company, New York, 1951.
8. Newman, William H., "Administration Action," Prentice-Hall, Inc., Englewood Cliffs, N.J., 1951.
9 Terry, George R., "Principles of Management," Richard D. Irwin, Inc., Homewood, Ill., 1953.
10. Moore, Franklin G., "Production Control," 2d ed., McGraw-Hill Book Company, New York, 1959.
11. Cooper, Joseph, D., "Procedural Coordination," Federal Security Agency, 1950.
12. Reisman, S. J., "A Style Manual for Technical Writers and Editors," The Macmillan Company, New York, 1962.
13. Malmgren, F. R., Why Not a Maintenance Manual?, *Factory*, January, 1956.
14. Graveley, O. W., Manual Drives Home the Maintenance Message, *Factory*, July, 1960.

Chapter 8

WORK SIMPLIFICATION IN MAINTENANCE

By RAYMOND I. REUL
Coordinator of Industrial Engineering
Chemical Divisions Management
FMC Corporation
New York, N.Y.

Work simplification can probably be best described as the intelligent employment of well-established human behavioral patterns to encourage and expedite the finding and implementation of more efficient work methods. Allan H. Mogensen was certainly the first to bring the many facets of this new approach together into a single, organized program. Prof. Erwin Schell, of the Massachusetts Institute of Technology, is credited with coining the name. In addition, Mr. Mogensen's famous annual training conferences held at Lake Placid, N.Y., and Sea Island, Ga., have been a potent and continuing force in teaching the essential know-how of work simplification and in gaining and holding world-wide acceptance of the workability of the philosophy involved. Much of the material in this article is from the training material used in these conferences. Many others have made major contributions to the basic concepts. Those made by Dr. Lillian Gilbreth, Prof. David B. Porter, Prof. Herbert Goodwin, and Prof. Leo Moore have been particularly outstanding.

Over the last twenty years, the work-simplification approach has earned a rapidly expanding popularity. Many industrial firms have sponsored formal work-simplification programs. Most of these have been phenomenally successful in delivering a multitude of cost-reducing and profit-increasing innovations. Many college engineering curricula now include courses in work simplification.

As originally conceived, the applicatoin of this approach tended to be concentrated in the area of production methods. But as more experience was gained, its universal applicability became more widely recognized. Work-simplification concepts are now utilized to improve performance in many other activities, including clerical functions, supervisory techniques, research, and *maintenance*. In fact, the term "work simplification" has actually become almost a synonym for "an organized grass-roots methods-improvement technique."

It is an approach that is particularly well-adapted to the study and improvement of maintenance performance. Applications in this area have been exceptionally productive. More frequent and broader applications appear likely to be equally successful.

Theory. The traditional approach to methods improvement has been to employ highly trained specialists in industrial engineering techniques to spend full time on this activity. These "experts" are assigned the task of studying one activity after another throughout the entire organization. They are expected to locate opportunities for improved performance, develop ways for these improvements to be achieved, evaluate their desirability, sell their acceptance, and assist in their implementation.   A great deal of progress has been achieved in this manner.   But the effectiveness of this "experting" approach is diluted in two ways:

1. Much time and effort must be expended by the "expert" to become familiar with each new activity studied, in order to be sure that all pertinent aspects and interactions with related activities are uncovered and properly evaluated.
2. The improvements developed and proposed by these "experts" are usually strongly resented by the prospective users.   Their implementation is often resisted, even occasionally deliberately sabotaged.

The work-simplification approach is designed to minimize these difficulties.   Each employee is assisted to become his own "expert" and is encouraged to study and recommend ways to improve the performance of his own job.   Motivation is developed by demonstrating the value to both workers and management of the results they can achieve by working together as a team.

Training in the use of a collection of simple but ingenious techniques provides each employee with know-how adequate to make the required methods-improvement studies.

The work-simplification approach is based upon the recognition of two basic truths:

1. The personnel at all levels of an industrial organization can be an excellent source of workable ideas for methods improvement.
2. The effective tapping of this fertile source requires:
    a. Cultivation of receptive attitudes to encourage participation.
    b. Development of an awareness and understanding of human motivation and behavioral patterns.
    c. Training in elementary analytical study techniques.

Practice.   Work simplification appears to be most productive when there is widespread participation by many individuals from all organizational levels in an "organized" program.   Carefully planned indoctrination sessions must be provided to develop effective motivation.   All participants should receive training in basic methods-improvement tools and techniques.   A means of handling ideas, such as a suggestion system, should be developed (or an existing one adapted) to make a method of communication readily available, to provide a way for obtaining prompt management review of improvement proposals, to facilitate recognition for contributions, and to provide adequate rewards for achievements.

THE LAW OF INTELLIGENT ACTION

William J. Reilly, in his book bearing the above title, states that: "When confronted with a problem, the intelligence of an individual's actions is dependent upon his

1. *Desire* to solve the problem
2. *Ability* to perform the tasks required
3. *Capacity* to handle the human relations involved."

Desire.   Motivations for the actions of human beings can be divided into two basic categories:

1. *To gain.*   (What's in it for me?)
2. *To avoid loss.*   (That's mine.   Hands off!)

Thus the employee seeks employment as a means of gaining:

1. Security (reasonable control over his own future).
2. Material reward (money to buy things).
3. Opportunity to improve his position (economic and/or social).
4. A sense of participation (belonging to a group and having a say in activities).

Employment is also a means of avoiding the loss of whatever he possesses of these same things.

It can be expected that the attitude of the individual toward an opportunity for personal gain will be almost entirely selfish. His controlling interest will be, "What's in it for me?" But his decisions and actions will tend to be rational, logical, and based upon fact. A direct appeal toward actions which will result in benefit to him and others can be expected to receive objective analysis. As Allan Mogensen expresses it, "intelligent selfishness" will provide effective motivation. Dwight Eisenhower referred to this as appealing to "enlightened self-interest."

However, the attitude of the individual toward the possible loss of something he already possesses can be expected to be entirely different. Decisions will tend to be based upon emotion rather than fact. Actions taken in connection with a possibility of losing existing possessions may often be devious and will sometimes appear completely illogical.

This difference in attitudes is of great significance when the acceptance of methods improvement is being sought. To an individual not directly involved, the introduction of a cost-saving proposal involving the use of a new piece of equipment or a new method can have the appeal of "intelligent selfishness." But to a person directly involved, *a change from the existing implies the loss of his own know-how applicable to the old procedure or equipment.* The fear generated by the prospect of such a loss can completely cancel out any appeal of mutual benefit. Therefore, to be successful, a work-simplification program must have identified with it specific management policies and practices which will assure the individual that he can gain and will not personally lose as the result of the implementation of work-simplification proposals.

A suggestion system can provide recognition and financial rewards, but an additional guarantee by management that participants will not suffer personal loss through downgrading or layoff is essential. An agreement to achieve force reductions via attrition or transfer of displaced individuals to other expanding activities is often a mutually acceptable approach. With careful planning, this method is usually adequate to absorb force reductions made possible by work-simplification proposals. Reductions via layoffs can eliminate any possibility of a successful program. After all, the cooperation of the individual just cannot be expected if he can see that this cooperation will result in direct losses to himself, his friends, or his associates.

Ability. Until the introduction of participative work-simplification programs, which provided both the receptive climate and the necessary training of the participants, the idea that the average employee could successfully conceive, develop, and implement worthwhile methods improvements was only a hypothesis. Management possessed little evidence and even less faith that such efforts were likely to be really productive of meaningful results. Today, however, the impressive results of many successful industrial work-simplification programs amply document the validity of this hypothesis. It has been unquestionably proved that the latent ability to develop methods improvements exists in the majority of individuals and can be effectively utilized if proper motivation and training are provided. It has been shown that with only minimal training in a few of the simple basic industrial engineering tools, the average individual can develop an amazing ability to recognize opportunities for improvement and to implement workable solutions.

Capacity. The basic pattern of human nature has been fairly well established and demonstrated to be essentially unchangeable. Human behavior, however, can be modified and to a certain extent controlled. In fact, human behavior is relatively predictable and can be measurably influenced by anyone with a thorough understanding of the basic mechanics of human nature plus a willingness to take the prerequisite actions. In respect to influencing attitudes toward prospective methods-improvement installations, it is usually sufficient to learn to recognize and deal with two of the most basic traits of human nature:

1. Resistance to change or to the new.
2. Resentment of criticism.

The fundamental idea of searching for a better way to perform a task has the built-in assumption that, when it is found, the new way will be substituted for the old. Thus, improvement implies change. From the point of view of the user of the old way, change tends to disrupt complacency and create a fear of possible unfavorable consequences. The firm feeling of "all's well" is replaced with a queezy feeling that perhaps he, the current user, may also become obsolete and have to be retrained, perform a harder task, or perhaps even be replaced. The user can see nothing in the change for him and an excellent chance of insecurity. Naturally, he resists change. It is almost a conditioned reflex. Everyone tends to be critical of, and resistant to, change.

A successful work-simplification program must make provision to assist participants to become familiar with this universal reaction and to learn how to minimize its hampering effect. Participants must learn:

1. To avoid confusing fact and opinion.
   Practice results in habits and can lead to the development of biased opinions that cannot be properly extrapolated.
   Experience increases knowledge of facts which provide a sounder basis for extrapolation.
2. To avoid misunderstandings.
   Failure to ascertain all the facts may result in incorrect conclusions.
   Reliance upon the results of a single nonrepresentative example may lead to erroneous decisions.
3. To avoid snap judgments.
   Time is required for mature judgment.
   Lack of experience must be taken into consideration in making evaluations.

The late Charles F. Kettering, of General Motors, said, "A man's mental age can be accurately measured by the degree of pain he feels when he comes in contact with a new idea." Participants must learn to think young, to be receptive to the fair evaluation of new ideas. It can be truthfully said that, "like a parachute, the mind functions only when it is open."

Allan Mogensen suggests that the desirability of maintaining an open mind can be dramatized by using the traffic light to symbolize the attitude adopted:

The *green* light symbolizes the open mind that is willing to explore facts and has an urge to seek ways to make new ideas feasible rather than reasons to explain why they won't work.

The *red* light symbolizes the closed mind that is perfectly satisfied with existing conditions, is unwilling to consider alternative approaches, and is sure that new ways are impractical and will not work.

This is actually a very effective psychological stunt with an excellent record of results. A continuing appeal to "avoid turning the red light on the consideration of new ideas" lampoons the uncooperative and can be both fun and amazingly productive of attitudes more receptive to new ideas.

A change for the better implies criticism of the old method and, what is even worse, criticism of the user of the old method. Direct or implied, constructive or destructive, the immediate reaction is fast and always the same. No one likes criticism. It is always taken as a personal affront. It is resented.

To develop a successful work-simplification program, participants must learn to expect this reaction in others and in themselves. They must learn to minimize offending others, to keep criticism from improperly affecting their own judgment, and to help others keep it from confusing their decisions.

However, by far the biggest assist in minimizing both resistance to change and resentment of criticism is the basic premise of the work-simplification approach which substitutes the "participative" development of new methods for the "experting" approach.   The participant is most unlikely to develop resistance to, or resentment of, what he believes are largely his own ideas.

THE SCIENTIFIC METHOD

Frederick W. Taylor, the alleged founder of scientific management once said, ". . . the art of management is knowing exactly what you want done and then seeing that it is done in the best and cheapest manner." Arthur D. Little, the famous research chemist, claimed that there were four facets of the scientific approach:

1. The simplicity to wonder.
2. The ability to question.
3. The power to generalize.
4. The capacity to apply.

The work-simplification approach applies each of these in a very literal fashion:

Maintaining an Open Mind.   (The simplicity to wonder.)   The participant with the *green* light on wonders about everything.   He is willing to explore all alternatives. He is not restricted by past practice, precedent, traditions, habits, customs, or fear of the consequences of change.

Observing the Present Way.   (The ability to question.)   Few people know how to do an adequate job of questioning.   Most of them stop asking too soon.   Sometimes this is merely to avoid embarrassing the person questioned.   To succeed in work simplification, one must "why" the devil out of everything.   Work simplification provides an organized plan for questioning.   It is called the questioning pattern and is a definite sequence of questions:

What is done?		is it done at all?
Where is it done?		is it done here?
When is it done?	*Why*	is it done then?
Who does it?		does this person do it?
How is it done?		is it done this way?

This is a training pattern which is to be followed literally at first but which soon becomes simply an organized way of thinking.

Exploring Opportunities for Improvement.   (The power to generalize.)   From the answers, tentative conclusions (generalizations) can be developed.   Possibilities for improvement are investigated:

What?		eliminate?
Where?		change place?
When?	*Why*	change sequence? combine?
Who?		change person?
How?		improve method?

Remember:

You are searching for possible solutions, not firm conclusions.
If it has never been done before, it may be a better way.
Don't admit it can't be done or you are licked before you start.
Try to find ways to make new ideas work, not to prove them unworkable.
Don't neglect suggestions by others.   Use them, but give credit to the source.

Implementing the New Method.   (The capacity to apply.)   It is not enough to wonder; ask why and develop a workable improvement.   An idea has no value until it is put to use.   The capacity to apply implies two things:

1. The ability to see the application of a general rule to a specific problem.
2. The ability to convert an understanding of human nature into an approach to the new method which will gain the cooperation of the people involved.

The Five Steps in Methods Improvement

Exact information requires measurement. "If you can measure that of which you speak and can express it as a number, you know something of your subject. But if you cannot measure it, your knowledge is meager and unsatisfactory."—Lord Kelvin. A definite and permanent advance is seldom made until use is made of measurement. This is particularly true where human factors are involved. Human performance tends to vary so much that unless some form of measurement is provided and used as a basis for decisions, there is little possibility of repeating a process accurately or predicting or controlling future conditions sufficiently to allow introduction of improvements.

Mere observation, done objectively, is a form of measurement. It can be used to classify, label, and compare. An interesting demonstration is to pick a task with which you are familiar but not directly involved. Now, subject the performance of this task to your concentrated and undivided attention. Chances are that you will find that you were completely unaware of many important aspects. It can be truthfully said that "the commonest article of commerce is misinformation about fundamental things."

An organized pattern of observation is of great assistance. Work simplification suggests a step-by-step program for studying tasks:

Select the task to be studied.
Observe the present way.
Challenge everything done.
Explore opportunities for improvement and determine the best.
Implement the best new way.

1. *Select* the task to be studied. Be careful that only one task is studied at a time. Failure to observe this caution can lead to confusing results or to ineffective efforts.

Because time is valuable, the best possible use of it must be made by doing first things first. Pick the job that needs improvement most. But remember the "human problem." Do not rush in too fast. Start by improving your own job or jobs in your department. Remember, if you work on someone else's problems, they will probably resent your help as implied criticism. Clean up your own back yard first. You need the practice. Look for:

a. *Bottlenecks.* Leave the smooth-flowing jobs alone until you crack troublesome ones.
b. *Time-consuming Operations.* Lengthy jobs usually offer the greatest opportunity for improvement.
c. *Chasing Around.* Activities of this type are almost always unproductive and often can be eliminated or drastically reduced.
d. *Waste.* We become so accustomed to some forms of wasted materials, time, or energy that we have difficulty in recognizing it as such. Increases go unnoticed. Look carefully.

2. *Observe* the present way in which the task is performed. Get all the facts. Be sure to include all the requirements for the performance of the task.

Don't forget to determine interactions with related tasks. Make a process or activity chart. Use it to record all details.

3. *Challenge* everything. Question what is done. Challenge the validity of the reasons given for doing these things. Use the questioning pattern:

a. Challenge the whole job being investigated. Why is it done? Is it necessary? Can it be done another way or at another time or place?

b. Next, challenge each "do" operation.   This is because if you eliminate the "do," you automatically eliminate the make-ready and put-away that go with it.

c. Then apply the check list of questions to every detail:

What?   What is done?   What is the purpose of doing it?   Why should it be done?   Does it do what it is supposed to do?

Where?   Where is the detail being done?   Why should it be done there?   Could it be done somewhere else?

When?   When is the detail done?   Why is it done then?   Could it be done at some other time?

Who?   Who does the detail?   Why does this person do the detail?   Could someone else do it?

How?   How is the detail performed?   Why is it done that way?   Is there any other way to do it?

These questions are listed in a definite order and should be asked in that order. The formalized approach helps, as a check list, to make our challenging orderly and comprehensive.   Every question to which a satisfactory answer is not received is a possible clue to a better method.

This questioning attitude helps develop a point of view that considers the good of the whole operation rather than that of any one department or individual.   It will often bring to light possibilities for eliminating useless or unnecessary work which adds no real value to products.   It tends to bring out the type of operation or equipment needed to perform the required work most economically.

It is here that the value of the open mind becomes apparent.   It is not easy to take a job, process, or procedure, especially if you are familiar with it or are working at it, and ask *why?*   Remember: *It is almost impossible for one to take a stand and say that a thing cannot be done and then try to do it.*   If you expect to get results from your analyses, you must take the attitude that *there are other ways* and *they may be better.   Try to find ways to make the other methods work, not ways to prove that they will not.*

Do not overlook the possibility of obtaining ideas from other people working on the same operation.   And do not forget that when you ask for these ideas you have a "human problem."   You will get the ideas only if they want to give them to you. They must be convinced that improving performance will help them.

4. *Explore* opportunities for improvement.   Consider all possibilities.   Examine each in detail.   Evaluate, compare, and select the best alternative.

Use the flow process chart or multiple-activity chart to pretest and demonstrate the feasibility of new methods.

a. Can operations be eliminated?   What is done?   Why is it done?   Is it necessary? In far too many instances a good deal of time is spent studying major operations for possibilities of improvement without asking the question, "Why is this operation performed?"

If it is found that an operation has been in the plant in the same way for a year or longer, it should be questioned.   A better way is probably available.   If operations cannot be eliminated, perhaps there are unnecessary *transportations* and *storages.*   Question every handling.   Then, if handling is absolutely necessary, look for:

(1) Back tracking of work.
(2) Heavy lifting or carrying.
(3) Trucking.
(4) Bottlenecks.
(5) Skilled operators doing handling work.

b. Can activities be combined?   Can sequence, place, or person be changed?   This is an important opportunity for improvements.   Whenever two or more operations can be *combined,* they are often performed at a cost approaching or even equal to the cost of one.   Likewise, transportations and storages between the operations may be eliminated.   If operations cannot be combined, find out if it is possible to combine a transportation and an operation.   The automobile companies have achieved much success in this way.   Your investigation should include examining every possible combination.

If the parts of the job cannot be combined, they may often be done more advantageously in a different order or *sequence.*   Here is where the flow diagram or templet layout of the department or plant often helps.   By changing the sequence of an operation, **one** may eliminate backtracking and duplication of work.   The order in which operations are performed may have been derived from the original nature of the process.   The process or product design may have been changed since then.   But has the order of operations been restudied and changed to regain optimum efficiency?

Sometimes, just changing the place where the work is done or by whom it is done will help.   Better lighting, better ventilation, better tools may be available elsewhere.   Perhaps another operator is better equipped to do the operation.

c. *Can the "do" operation be improved?*   How is it done?   Why is it done that way?   Is better equipment available?   Are other materials available?   Can new techniques be applied?

Unfortunately, it is here that a great deal of work simplification started in the past.   We must learn to consider this step the last resort.   Major savings can usually be found, but the price of the new equipment, materials, training, etc. is also usually high, sometimes beyond our reach.   Often relatively small rearrangements, method changes, and layout revisions will accomplish almost as much with negligible cost.   This does not mean that we should ignore the possibilities of new equipment, etc., but that we should explore all other possibilities first.

5. *Implement* the new method.   See that all people involved understand the objective of the task and desirability of the new method.

Take care that each person involved knows and understands his or her part in the new method.   Be sure that none involved will lose financially or socially as a result of the change.   And, even more important, be sure that they know it!

CHARTING TECHNIQUES

There are many charting techniques which have been designed to assist in the development of improved methods.   These include:

Flow process chart.
Multiple-activity process chart.
Gantt chart.
Critical path network.
PERT.

All these charting techniques are similar in principle.   They are a means of recording and studying activities required to perform a task.   This list is in order of increasing complexity.

The flow process chart is used to record a single sequence of activities.   The multiple-activity chart is used when several sequences of activities occur at the same time and their relationships with respect to time are significant.   The Gantt chart is used when the number of simultaneously occurring sequences of activities becomes large. The use of the critical path network is desirable when some of the sequences of activities are time related and some are not.   This approach can become quite complicated, and then computer programs must be used in conjunction with it.   PERT (programmed evaluation research technique) is a variation of the critical path technique into which another variable, probability, has been introduced.

THE FLOW PROCESS CHART

The flow process chart (see Fig. 8-1) was originally developed by Frank B. Gilbreth of "Cheaper by the Dozen" fame.   It is a detailed and graphic representation of the sequence of events in a process or procedure and includes measurements considered desirable for analysis, such as distances traveled, time required, delays, etc., together with reasons for these measurements.   It is a widely accepted tool of definitely proven worth.

Two of the most important values of the flow process chart are that the information is presented in condensed form and that, despite this brevity, all the desirable detail is shown.   Many a manager, supervisor, foreman, or clerk has been irritated and baffled by an inability to find out or visualize the whole process or procedure under his or her care.   Because of this, decisions are often made upon the basis of incomplete knowledge.   These may be little more than guesses and have occasionally proved disastrous.

How to Make a Flow Process Chart

1. *State the activity being studied.*   Be sure you are naming the activity you have chosen to study.
2. *Choose the subject to follow.*   Pick a person, material or paper form which goes through the entire process or procedure you wish to analyze.   Remember you will follow this subject and only this subject through every detail.
3. *Pick a starting and ending point.*   This assures you that you will cover all the ground you want to cover but no more.
4. *Write a brief description of each detail.*   Step by step, no matter how short or temporary, every operation, every move, every storage, and every inspection must be described.   To avoid missing details, make the chart on the job as you see it done.
5. *Apply the symbols.*   The description of the detail determines the symbol.   Draw connecting lines between the proper symbols.
   Operation: When something is done to an object or a person, when something is created, changed, or destroyed, use a circle to show that an "operation" is taking place.   (Typing a letter, filling out a form, driving a nail, picking up an object.)
   Transportation: When an object, a paper form, or a person is moved or moves from one place to another, use an arrow to show "transportation."   (A box moved by truck, a letter to another desk, a workman from shop to office.)
   Delay: When an object, a paper form, or a person is interrupted or held up in a process or procedure, use a letter *D*.   (A carton awaiting transportation, a letter in an outgoing mailbox, an operator waiting for a machine to complete a cycle.)
   Storage: When an object or form is kept and protected against unauthorized removal, use an inverted triangle.   (Goods in stock room, material in bin, letters in a file.)
   Inspection: When something is checked or verified, but not changed, use a square to denote an "inspection."   (Checking a requisition, gaging for size.)
6. *Black-in the "do" operations.*   Every job is made up of three parts:
   a. Make ready.
   b. Do.
   c. Put away.
   Make ready is the effort and time expended in setting up equipment or getting materials with which to work.
   Do is the actual work done or required.   It usually adds value to the product.
   Put away is the cleanup following the "do."

How To Make a

FLOW PROCESS CHART

1. STATE THE JOB TO BE STUDIED
Be sure you are really breaking down the job you intend to study. State clearly what that job is. Then stick to that job as you make the breakdown.

2. CHOOSE THE SUBJECT TO BE FOLLOWED
A person—an article or piece of equipment—a paper form. Follow the same subject all the way through. Don't switch! Each detail must be on that subject.

3. PICK A STARTING AND ENDING POINT
Decide how much ground you want to cover; then stick to your decision.

4. WRITE A BRIEF DESCRIPTION OF EACH DETAIL
Step by step, no matter how short, simple or incidental, list every detail. Make the chart on the job as you see it done.

5. APPLY THE SYMBOLS
The description determines the symbol. Draw a connecting line between the proper symbols. Use:

○ to indicate an OPERATION when something is being created, added to, or worked on—usually by a machine or the hands.

⇧ to indicate a TRANSPORTATION whenever the person or material being followed moves more than one step.

☐ to indicate an INSPECTION when something is checked or verified. When no work is done.

◠ to show a DELAY, interruption or interference in the completion of the job.

▽ to indicate a STORAGE when a material is deliberately kept or protected against unauthorized removal.

FMC CORPORATION
CHEMICAL DIVISIONS

FLOW PROCESS CHART

JOB: Cutting Filter Cloth

MAN ☐ MATERIAL ☒

CHART BEGINS: In Main Storeroom
CHART ENDS: Place Cloth in Storage
CHARTED BY: O. E. Stein   DATE: 6-5-52

NO. 1
PAGE 1 OF 1

ANALYSIS	QUESTION EACH DETAIL

SUMMARY

	PRESENT		PROPOSED		DIFFERENCE	
	NO.	TIME	NO.	TIME	NO.	TIME
○ OPERATIONS	8	5.4				
⇧ TRANSPORTATIONS	6	4.2				
☐ INSPECTIONS	0					
◠ DELAYS	1	2.0				
▽ STORAGES	1					
DISTANCE TRAVELED	1606 FT			FT		FT

	DETAILS OF (PRESENT / PROPOSED) METHOD	DIST. IN FT.	QUAN.	TIME IN MINS.		PROPOSED ACTION	NOTES
1	In main storeroom				○⇧☐◠▽		
2	Walk to #8 shed	90		.2	○⇧☐◠▽		
3	Unlock Door + Open			.1	○⇧☐◠▽		
4	Walk to pile	10		.1	○⇧☐◠▽		
5	Remove Roll from pile			.2	○⇧☐◠▽		
6	Take Roll to Cutting table	20		1.1	○⇧☐◠▽		
7	Remove Wrapping From Roll			.15	○⇧☐◠▽		
8	Pick up Pipe insert			.1	○⇧☐◠▽		
9	Insert into center opening of Roll			.9	○⇧☐◠▽		To Get Help in Lifting Heavy Roll
10	Walk to main storeroom	90		1.5	○⇧☐◠▽		
11	Walk Back to #8 shed	90		.2	○⇧☐◠▽		
12	Wait For Assistance			2.0	○⇧☐◠▽		
13	Place roll on rack			.2	○⇧☐◠▽		
14	Cut Fold and pile cloth	516		5.5	○⇧☐◠▽	✓	44-33" pieces
15	Carry Cut Cloth to storeroom	690		6.0	○⇧☐◠▽		Strips
16	Place Cloth in Storage	20		2.0	○⇧☐◠▽		
17					○⇧☐◠▽		
18					○⇧☐◠▽		
19					○⇧☐◠▽		
20					○⇧☐◠▽		
21					○⇧☐◠▽		
22					○⇧☐◠▽		
23					○⇧☐◠▽		
24					○⇧☐◠▽		

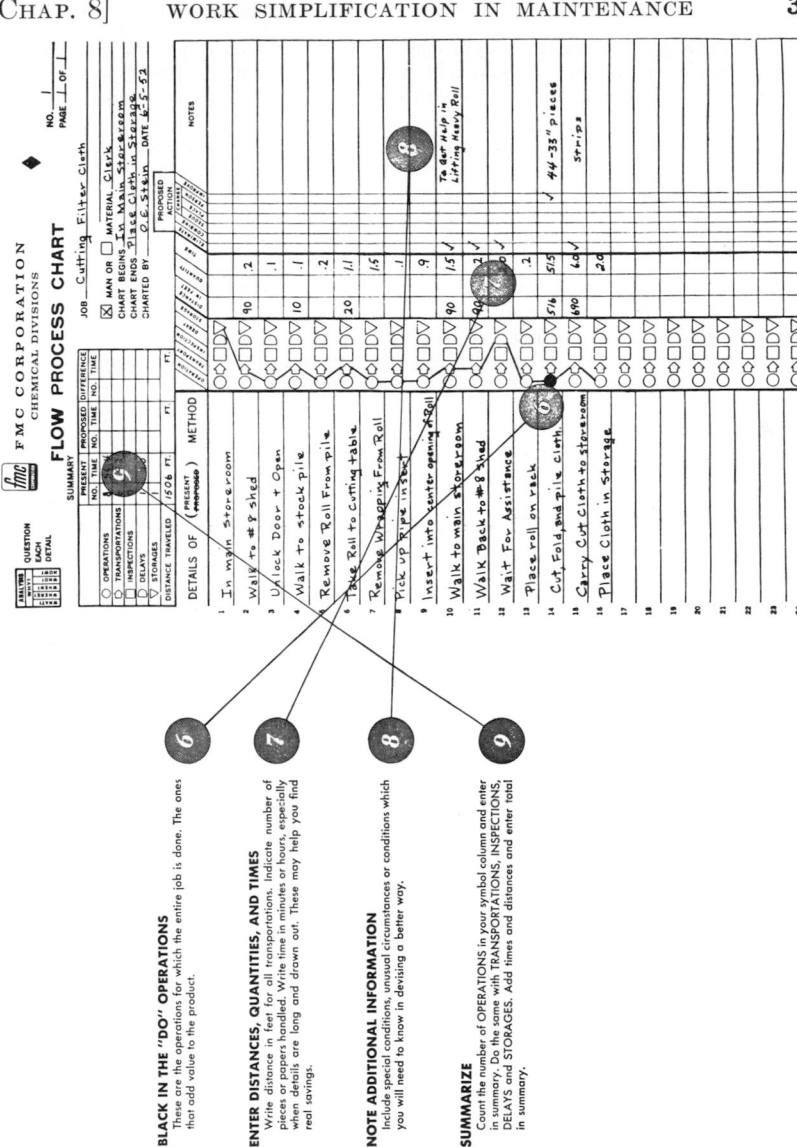

FIG. 8-1. Flow process chart.

6. **BLACK IN THE "DO" OPERATIONS**
   These are the operations for which the entire job is done. The ones that add value to the product.

7. **ENTER DISTANCES, QUANTITIES, AND TIMES**
   Write distance in feet for all transportations. Indicate number of pieces or papers handled. Write time in minutes or hours, especially when details are long and drawn out. These may help you find real savings.

8. **NOTE ADDITIONAL INFORMATION**
   Include special conditions, unusual circumstances or conditions which you will need to know in devising a better way.

9. **SUMMARIZE**
   Count the number of OPERATIONS in your symbol column and enter in summary. Do the same with TRANSPORTATIONS, INSPECTIONS, DELAYS and STORAGES. Add times and distances and enter total in summary.

Blacking-in the symbols for those operations which you decide are "do" operations will help later in challenging, as you will start, with the "do" operations.

7. *Enter distances.* Enter distances traveled every time there is a transportation.

8. *Add time if required.* Many process charts do not need time to develop a better method. However, if it will help, note the time required or elapsed.

9. *Summarize.* Add up all the facts and put them in a summary block. This summary should indicate the total number of operations, transportations, delays, storages, inspections, and feet traveled.

Be careful when making up a chart to follow either a product or a person. Stick to one or the other. Do not switch. This is perhaps one of the most common errors made in preparing a chart. If a man is carrying an object, puts it down, and goes to look for a truck and we are following the object, we record a delay. If we are following the man, we do not use the delay symbol but continue to follow the man. The object is delayed, but the man is not. Watch out for this difficulty.

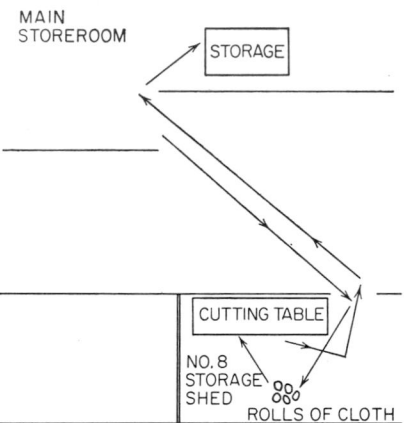

Fig. 8-2. Flow diagram.

Distinguish carefully between operations and inspections. Use the symbol for inspection only when you are sure no change occurs in the object involved. For instance, when a clerk is looking for a folder in a file, he or she is performing an operation. Looking at a check to see if it is signed is an inspection.

Pointers

1. Do not attempt to cover too much ground in one study.
2. You can make an accurate chart only by making it on the job, actually following the work as it is done.
3. Try not to omit any details.
4. Stick to the subject—one subject per chart.

A story is told of Frank Gilbreth taking a flow process chart in to a plant executive. When the chart, which stretched clear across the office, was unrolled for his inspection, the executive said, "See here, Gilbreth, roll that darned thing up and take it out of here. I don't even need to know what it is, to know that I am opposed to it."

"But," retorted Gilbreth, "this is not any proposal that I am making. It is only an exact representation of the process that already exists in your plant."

When a chart is being made, each detail is recorded in black and white, on the spot, exactly as it is done. No alteration can be made when the chart is scanned by many individuals. As a story varies in retelling, so, often, do orders vary as they are

handed down the line or conditions as they are reported up the line.   Charts are a record of facts.   They do not change.   *This is a key point.*
    To summarize, the flow process chart is a valuable tool because:

1. As a still picture it separates the job being studied from a background which may distract attention.
2. It breaks the job down into simple, individual, and reliable details so that one detail can be studied at a time.
3. Its condensed form enables us to visualize the process easily in its entirety.
4. By itemizing, it allows us to express the process or procedure in numerical fashion.
5. The make-ready, "do," and put-away are clearly indicated.
6. Through the mere act of making the close observation necessary to prepare the chart, we often observe ways of improving the process.

Flow Diagram.   It is sometimes helpful to supplement your flow process chart with a flow diagram (Fig. 8-2).   A flow diagram is simply a layout of the area involved in the job being studied over which you indicate by a line the path of the object or person followed in the chart.   It is often desirable to indicate the action taking place by using the same symbols as those used on the chart.   They may, if desired, be keyed to each other by item numbers.

THE MULTIPLE-ACTIVITY PROCESS CHART

    There are many situations, however, where two or more interrelated tasks must be studied at the same time.   The objective is to reduce the total time, the number of people, or the number of machines required to complete the entire series of tasks. The flow process chart is not adequate for this assignment.   A new tool, the multiple-activity process chart, is required.
    This tool may be described as a graphic method of measuring and demonstrating the time relationships between two or more interrelated operations or procedures. This can be the relationship between a machine and its operator, two or more machines working together on the same job and dependent upon each other, or two or more men working on the same job where each man does part of the work.   To illustrate:

Man-machine. . . . . Lathe and operator
Multiple machine. . . . . Power shovel and trucks
Multiple man. . . . . Mechanic and helper

How to Make a Multiple-activity Process Chart

1. The first step is to prepare a separate flow process chart on each participant in the operation or process being studied.   The time required for each detail must be measured and recorded.   An ordinary wrist watch is usually satisfactory for timing.   In some cases, merely estimating the time will be sufficient.
2. The second step is to choose a time scale large enough to allow plotting of each detail of one complete cycle but not so large as to result in an awkwardly large chart.
3. Then the details of each participant's activities are plotted in separate columns against the single time scale chosen.   Be sure that events which occur simultaneously are shown at the same place on the time scale.
4. Next, the activities of each participant are classified into one of the following three categories:
    a. Operating: doing work, producing.
    b. Stand-by: waiting, not producing but presence essential.
    c. Idle: neither producing nor standing by.
5. Sometimes it is desirable to break operating time down still further into:
    a. Make ready.
    b. Do.
    c. Put away.

6. The last step is to prepare the summary. This is especially important because data on per cent operating time, per cent idle time, and per cent waiting time usually give pretty good clues as to where to look for possible improvements.

The maximum possibilities of interrelated operations are easy to evaluate with this tool. Idle time and the reasons for it are dramatically demonstrated. Existing inefficiencies become less difficult to spot, improvements become easier to develop and demonstrate.

How to Use the Multiple-activity Process Chart

Whenever machines or equipment are used, there are three possible ways to lose time:

1. *Idle operator time.*
2. *Idle machine time.*
3. *A combination of Nos. 1 and 2.*

Idle operator time is time that is paid for but wasted. Often this idle time is not the operator's fault but inherent in the prescribed method of operation. The multiple-activity chart will assist in finding such conditions, measuring their significance, and

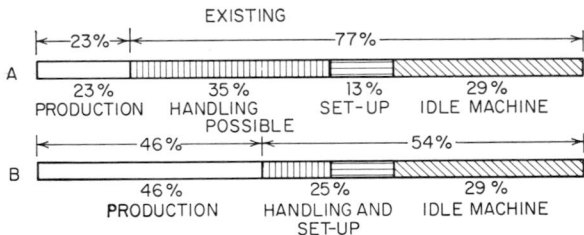

FIG. 8-3. As many plants do things now. (*From Work Simplification Master Notes—©️ by A. H. Mogensen. Available only to students at his training course.*)

assisting the analysts in exploring ways to eliminate or minimize them. The higher wages go, the more important efforts in this direction become.

Idle machine time can also be critical. As machines become more complex, the cost of having them stand idle part of the time may spell the difference between profit and loss. Often these idle times are individually small and hence not very noticeable, but they may occur so frequently in the cycle of operations that their total effect is considerable. In addition, there often is a tendency to consider the purchase of new facilities without a thorough study of how much the performance of already existing facilities could be improved without major expenditures. This can lead to the purchase of elaborate new facilities which are really not justified. The multiple-activity process chart is an excellent tool for problems in both of these areas.

The bar charts shown in Fig. 8-3 represent typical experience in many plants. Looking at bar chart A, it can be seen that idle machine time is 29 per cent and most people would say that the equipment in question is (by subtracting) working 71 per cent of the time. But is it productive 71 per cent of the time? Obviously it is not. Actual productive time ("do" time) is only 23 per cent, and the true nonproductive time is 77 instead of 29 per cent. The difference is handling time (35 per cent) and set-up time (13 per cent) which occupy machine time but are not productive. If the time required for these activities could be cut in half, the productivity of the equipment could be doubled as is illustrated in bar chart B.

It must be remembered that just because the wheels are turning continuously, the motors humming, or the operators perspiring, it cannot be assumed that maximum possible output is being achieved. A machine is being utilized only when it is actually performing the "do" function for which it was designed.

Sometimes, however, just the opposite situation may exist. When pay rates are high and machines or tools simple and cheap, it may be advisable to reverse our objective and purchase and put into use sufficient machines to obtain maximum effectiveness of labor. We can use the multiple-activity process chart to analyze our problem in either case. We merely change our objective.

Solution of a Typical Problem

Problem. Suppose we have a machine and an operator working together to produce a certain product. It takes the operator 2 min to set up the job in the machine. Then the machine runs for 4 min. The operator completes the job by doing the put-away in 2 min.

A multiple-activity process chart of these two interrelated activities would appear as in Fig. 8-4. Operator activity is shown in the left-hand column, machine activity

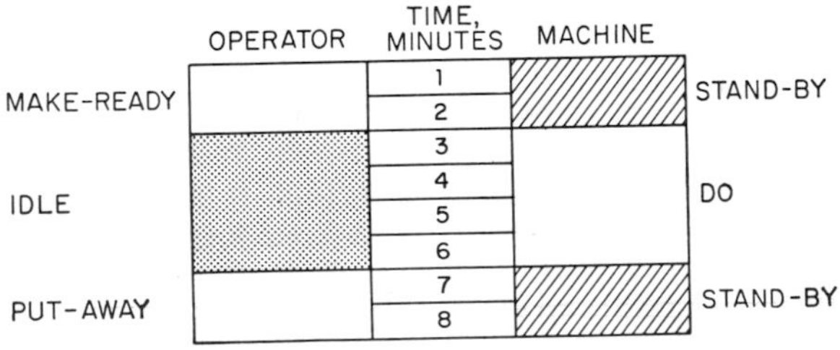

FIG. 8-4. Multiple-activity process chart. (*From Work Simplification Master Notes*—Ⓒ *by A. H. Mogensen.*)

in the right-hand column. The center is used for the time scale. The summary for our example is:

```
Total cycle time........  8 min
Total man time.........  4 min
Total machine time.....  4 min
Machine utilization.....  50 per cent (machine time divided by cycle time)
Operator effectiveness...  50 per cent (man time divided by cycle time)
```

One solution to this problem is to add another operator. When we do this, our chart would look like Fig. 8-5. Our summary would now appear as follows:

```
Total cycle time........  6 min
Total man time.........  2 min
Total helper time........  2 min
Machine time...........  4 min
Machine utilization.....  66 per cent
Operator effectiveness...  33 per cent
Helper effectiveness.....  33 per cent
```

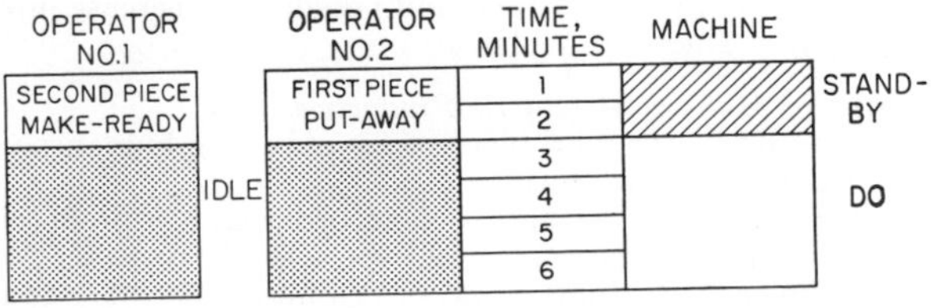

FIG. 8-5. With an operator added. (*From Work Simplification Master Notes*—Ⓒ *A. H. Mogensen.*)

We have increased the machine utilization and output at the expense of operator effectiveness.

Now, if we can devise some method so that the make-ready and put-away can be performed while the machine is performing the "do" by the use of some fixture, both

OPERATOR	TIME,MINUTES	MACHINE
FIRST PIECE	1	
PUT-AWAY	2	DO
SECOND PIECE	3	
MAKE-READY	4	

FIG. 8-6. The new method.   (*From Work Simplification Master Notes*—ⓒ *A. H. Mogensen.*)

machine utilization and operator effectiveness can be improved.   The need for the helper can be eliminated.   A chart of the new method would look like Fig. 8-6.   The summary would be:

Total cycle time......... 4 min
Total man time.......... 4 min
Machine time............ 4 min
Machine utilization...... 100 per cent
Operator effectiveness.... 100 per cent

This is, of course, a hypothetical and oversimplified situation.   In actual practice we would seldom find a problem which has so few factors and in which we can visualize the situation so easily without charting.   The 100 per cent utilization we have shown is also theoretical since there would obviously be downtime for lubrication and adjustment of equipment and rest periods for personnel.

We can use a man-and-machine chart (Fig. 8-7) to increase productivity.   In doing so, let us remember that we are not trying to find ways to work harder.   We want to work smarter, to do the work with less effort and in a shorter time, by eliminating unnecessary delays and wasted time.   Let us not forget the difference between effective (skilled) and hurried (speeded-up) work.   *Work done effectively will be good work because it is accomplished by eliminating the unnecessary parts of the job.   Work done in a hurry will be poor work because it is a speeding up of all parts of the job, both necessary and unnecessary.*

THE FOUR BASIC PRINCIPLES OF MOTION ECONOMY

The best use of the human body to yield a given result has received a great deal of study.   The results of these investigations may be summed up as the "principles of motion economy."   When thoroughly understood and intelligently applied, these principles can have a very favorable effect upon productivity without an increase in work effort.

Skills are frequently complex, but the basic principles upon which they are based are relatively simple.   They recognize the limitations of the human body and muscles and capitalize upon the strong human tendency to form habits.   If the fundamentals of motion economy are taken into consideration in the study of job procedures and workplace design, it will nearly always be found possible to decrease input effort while increasing work output.   These principles are:

1. *Physical Activities or Motions Should Be Productive.*
    a. Devise methods and design workplaces to avoid using human hands as holding devices.   Put both hands to work.
    b. Keep the workplaces, supplies, and tools in order and in predetermined places. This minimizes searching and fumbling.
    c. Design the workplace to fit human physical limitations.   Try to keep activities within normal work areas.   Avoid requiring movements outside of the maximum work area.

MAN AND MACHINE CHART

OPERATION Facing Bosses (Old Method) SHEET 1 OF 2

MACHINE TYPE Milling Machine DEPT. NO. 1

CHARTED BY John Doe DATE

MAN		TIME		MACHINE
Walk to Tote Box return to machine. Burr edge of hole. Blow off machine. Pick up and replace spud clamp. Start Machine.	27	10, 20	27	IDLE
IDLE	9	30	9	Milling.
Stop machine, remove part. Knock out spud.	15	40, 50	15	IDLE
TOTAL	51		51	
		120		

SUMMARY	CYCLE TIME			WORK			IDLE			UTILIZATION	
	Pres.	Prop.	Saving	Pres.	Prop.	Saving	Pres.	Prop.	Saving	Pres.	Prop.
MAN	51			42			9			82%	
MACHINE	51			9			42			18%	

A.H. MOGENSEN–WORK SIMPLIFICATION PROGRAMS

MAN AND MACHINE CHART

OPERATION Facing Bosses (New Method) SHEET 2 OF 2

MACHINE TYPE Milling Machine DEPT. NO. 1

CHARTED BY John Doe DATE

MAN		TIME		MACHINE
Start machine-turn to tote box and dispose of finished pc. Get next piece-burr hole.	9	10	9	Milling.
Remove finished part. Knock out spud.				
Blow off machine. Pick up and place spud in fixture. Place part on spud and clamp.	5	20	14	IDLE
	9	30		
TOTAL	23	40	23	
		120		

SUMMARY	CYCLE TIME			WORK			IDLE			UTILIZATION	
	Pres.	Prop.	Saving	Pres.	Prop.	Saving	Pres.	Prop.	Saving	Pres.	Prop.
MAN	51	23	28	42	23	19	9	0	9	82%	100%
MACHINE	51	23	28	9	9	0	42	14	28	18%	60%

A.H. MOGENSEN–WORK SIMPLIFICATION PROGRAMS

FIG. 8-7. Man and machine chart.

Human beings can work better in areas bounded by arcs of circles. This limitation should be considered in laying out workplaces. Note that there are two areas in each plane (Fig. 8-8).

The normal work area for each hand is determined by an arc drawn with a sweep of the hand across the work area with the elbow the pivot point. This is the area within which work can be done with a minimum of fatigue. The zone where the swings of the right and left hand overlap is the area where two-handed work can be performed with minimum effort.

The maximum work area for each hand is determined by an arc drawn with a sweep of the hand and arm across the work area with the shoulder as the pivot

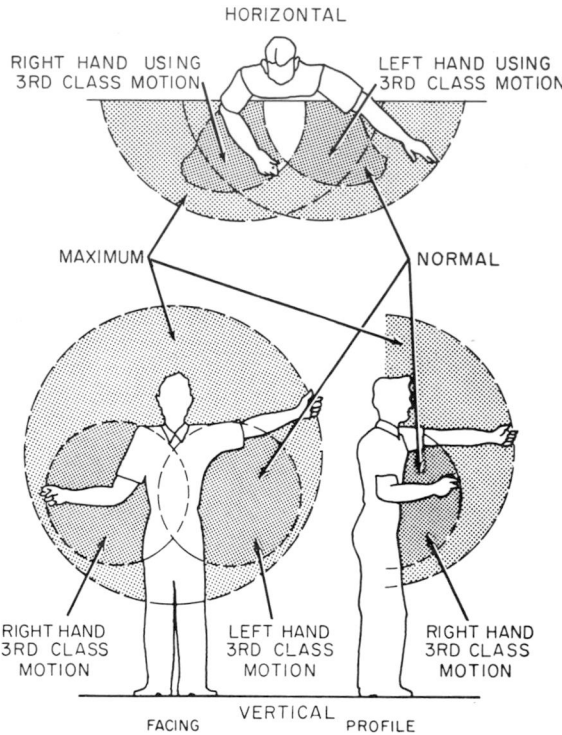

Fig. 8.8. Normal and maximum working areas for hand motions. (*A. H. Mogensen,* "*Work Simplification Programs.*" *No printed programs available.*)

point. This is the area within which work can be performed without experiencing excessive fatigue. The overlap zone limits the area for two-handed work with a reasonable amount of fatigue.

2. *The Path of All Motions Involved Should Be Rhythmic and Smooth.*
   a. When both hands are used, the motions should be rhythmic, equal, and in opposite directions. Motions made simultaneously and in opposite directions are natural and contribute to smooth flow or rhythm. When it is possible for the two hands to move at the same time in opposite directions, by arranging similar work on each side of the work place, the operator can produce more with considerably less mental and physical effort. Idleness of either hand is not productive. Use both hands for productive work.
   b. Motions should follow curved paths, be continuous, and not require sudden stops. Continuous curved motions give better rhythm than straight-line

motions.   Sudden stops or changes in direction interrupt smooth flow and spoil rhythm.   Motions which use the momentum of the motion itself to aid in performing the work are more effective and more rhythmic than controlled motions.   Devices which provide a stop against which momentum may be expended eliminate the need for muscular control of the stop.   An example of such a device is the carriage return stop on a typewriter.

   c. Workplace gimmicks, such as pre-positioning of tools, magazine-type supply methods, drop discharge of finished work, and the use of foot-operated holding or tripping devices, can do much to keep hand motions rhythmic and smooth. Micromotion studies have amply demonstrated the value of these procedures. More important than time saved in transporting the material or tool to its destination is the freeing of both hands so that they may proceed simultaneously in unbroken *rhythm—a prime requisite of skill.*

3. *Motions Should Be as Simple as Possible and Yet Be Consistent with Previous Principles.*
There are five classes of motions:

Class I........	Fingers only
Class II.......	Fingers and wrist
Class III......	Fingers, wrist, and forearm
Class IV......	Fingers, wrist, forearm, and shoulder
Class V.......	Entire body

In general, the amount of fatigue resulting from body movements increases with the increasing class number.   This relationship is not always strictly true, but it is usually sufficiently accurate to permit meaningful comparison of alternative methods on a numerical basis.

4. *The Worker Should Be at Ease.*
   a. Bench or desk tops should be at a height to permit work with minimum fatigue.
   b. Lighting and ventilation should be adequate to minimize discomfort.
   c. Tools and materials should be clearly identified.
   d. Provision should be made for alternate standing and sitting while work is being performed.

A MOTION ECONOMY CHECK LIST

1. Do motions stay within normal working areas?   Could they?
2. Are motions outside maximum working areas required?   Could they be avoided?
3. Are hand motions of lowest possible classification?
4. Is the workplace at the right height?
5. Is the workplace the best possible shape or design?
6. Is the workplace orderly?
7. Could tools be pre-positioned?
8. Are tools easy to recognize?
9. Could materials or supplies be pre-positioned?
10. Are tools and materials arranged in best sequence?
11. Can foot pedals relieve hands?
12. Can hand holding be avoided?
13. Does each cycle begin simultaneously with both hands?
14. Does each cycle end simultaneously with both hands?
15. Are arm and hand motions symmetrical and in opposite directions?
16. Can the work be pre-positioned for the next operation?
17. Is the workplace designed for sitting/standing operation?   Can it be?
18. Can sharp changes in the direction of hand motions be avoided?
19. Are small objects slid rather than picked up and moved?
20. Can your pre-positioned tools be grasped quickly and in the position used?

Check each job you study against this list.   See if you can make any changes to reduce fatigue and improve the method.

The greatest value of motion economy is the development of the ability to visualize operations in the terms of motions, to recognize good and bad motion practice, and to think in terms of motions as compared with operations. This might be called "motion-mindedness."

APPLICATIONS OF WORK SIMPLIFICATION TO MAINTENANCE

The expanding use of automation is steadily reducing the size of work forces employed in the production area. Electronic data processing continues to whittle at clerical staffs. But these same trends are increasing both the amount and complexity of maintenance requirements. Both opportunities and needs for improving maintenance performance are growing at a rapid pace. Maintenance activities are now and appear likely to continue to be in real need of work-simplification effort.

Maintenance work is different from production work in two basic ways:

1. Most maintenance work input is assigned and controlled on a job-by-job basis rather than unit-of-time or product-output. For this reason, work content is usually nonrepetitive in nature.
2. Direct correlation between work output and product or service output is seldom feasible. This tends to make verification of savings difficult.

These differences do not limit the usefulness of the work-simplification approach. But they do change the emphasis somewhat.

Improving Management Efficiency. The problems encountered in applying intelligent management to maintenance are very complex. Effective management usually requires a great deal of data. A huge volume of paper work and records are often generated. Work simplification can give a big assist to the streamlining of these activities. For instance:

1. *Work Control Procedures.* Efficient assignment and control of work on a job-by-job basis requires much planning and a large volume of paper work. This work is very repetitive in nature and an excellent subject for work simplification. One word of caution: simple elimination of paper work or arbitrary reduction in the number of work orders is not the answer if it results in loss of control. Much can be done, however, to reduce the complexity of these documents and decrease the effort and time required to process them without destroying their effectiveness.
2. *History Records.* The development of maintenance history records is absolutely essential to carrying on a productive preventive-maintenance program. But these records are often quite voluminous and time consuming, both in preparation and use. The methods used for the assembly and retrieval of information from these records represent an excellent area for work simplification.

Improving Technical Decisions. As equipment grows more and more complex, the following are areas of effort which can greatly benefit from the use of the work-simplification approach:

1. *Predetection of Incipient Failures.* Effective preventive maintenance will require improved techniques for predicting when, where, and how failures are likely to be incurred. This will probably involve the development of better inspection techniques, the introduction of the use of more diagnostic instruments, and perhaps the introduction of continuous monitoring techniques.
2. *Postfailure Remedial-action Decisions.* The determination of the exact nature and extent of equipment malfunctions and remedial action indicated is becoming increasingly difficult as the variety and complexity of facilities increase. The predevelopment of standard diagnostic routines offers an excellent opportunity for the development of better methods.
3. *Repetitive-job Standardization.* Use of standardized, preselected procedures for the same or similar jobs will increase the volume of work upon which detailed methods-improvement studies can be justified.

Improving Manpower and Machine Utilization. The multiple-activity process charting technique provides an excellent vehicle for exploring ways to:

1. *Reduce Crew Sizes.* Use of preplanned, shop make-ready, prefabrication or pre-assembly, special-handling equipment or tools, etc. can frequently reduce the amount of work done by field crews.
2. *Reduce Out-of-service Time.* Careful prescheduling can often appreciably reduce the total time required to complete jobs. The multiple-activity process chart is a good tool for this purpose. When the jobs are large and complicated, it is usually necessary to resort to the more complex critical path technique.

The Most Important Contribution. Perhaps the greatest potential for gain in maintenance performance through work simplification, however, is through the improvement of morale. With a successfully functioning work-simplification program, a maintenance department can become a spirited, dedicated team of people who are working together to improve total performance in every way they can—because they realize it is to the personal advantage of each of them to do so.

Chapter 9

DATA PROCESSING BY MANUAL OPERATION

By EDWARD W. SUTTON
Maintenance Superintendent
FMC Corporation, Inorganic Chemicals Division
South Charleston, W.Va.

In the management of the maintenance function, "data processing" has existed for a long time. In recent years the word has been used more and more frequently. This follows the current trend toward improved control and cost reduction. Management continues to require more facts in hand when making decisions. Control data gives this information.

Data processing plays an important part in all cost improvement programs. It is a procedure and can be defined as follows: *Data processing is the collection and processing of useful financial and historical information to publish certain reports and maintain records.*

In a manual system all functions are performed by hand by clerical or other personnel. Sometimes the steps are directly required, and at other times they are a by-product of some other function. Normally a certain minimum of paper work is required of supervision for effective control. With care, functions can be designed to provide supervisory control and at the same time contribute to the data processing system.

OBJECTIVES OF THE SYSTEM

In establishing a data processing system, it is important that objectives, or the final information desired, be spelled out and that a clear idea of what will be done with this information be established. It is equally important to keep these basic objectives continuously in mind and to resist the temptation to add additional bits or new information as the system is being developed. Once the basic system is functioning and doing its job, improvements in, and additions to, the system can be considered.

The system is measured by its final cost-saving results. Efforts should be directed to achieve this end with a minimum of procedures and paper-work systems.

ESTABLISHING A SYSTEM

In setting the objectives of and establishing a basic data processing system for maintenance, all costs will center around the labor and materials to perform the work. With this in mind, objectives can be established to collect and report the following information:

1. Individual-job costs for both labor and material charges.
2. Total monthly charges of both labor and material costs for each department.

3. The recording of historical repair costs on specific predetermined pieces of equipment.

This information is useful for establishing operating budgets and identifying high-cost areas that cause large budget variances. Items of high repair costs, or repeated repairs, can be singled out for engineered cost improvements.

In addition to this financial information, craft backlogs to establish manpower trends and overtime data to insure that control is being maintained can be established.

PROCEDURES REQUIRED

A work-order system is required to establish the data processing system. Figure 9-1 illustrates a work-order form that is used in a typical maintenance cost collecting system.

The originator states his maintenance need and gives the form to the maintenance foreman, who will plan the job and estimate its cost. The foreman then gives the costed work order to the maintenance clerk, who routes the form for the necessary approvals.

When approved, the work order is returned to the clerk to receive a work-order number. This is an important step in the operation because any error at this point will be very difficult to detect and correct later on. The work-order number is made up from an eight-digit code. The code is used later to compile data and identify costs. The work-order number is established as follows:

Digits	Pertain to
1–2–3	Operating cost center or overhead account
4	Year work order was opened
5–6–7	Serial number within cost center
8	Type of job such as routine, PM, capital

The clerk retains the approved copy of the work order in his file and sends a coded, or numbered, copy to each of the following:

1. To the maintenance foreman in charge of the job to alert him that the job is approved and ready for scheduling.
2. To the accounting department for the collection of labor and material costs.
3. To the originator to keep him informed.
4. To the maintenance engineer to inform and alert him to the activities in his area.

After receiving the coded work order, the foreman performs the work. Any special materials not in the storeroom are ordered by the foreman or the maintenance engineer. The work-order number is used on the purchase request so that the accounting department can apply these costs to the respective job.

Storeroom material is withdrawn by the mechanic on the job. There is a place at the bottom of the storeroom requisition (Fig. 9-2) for him to insert the work-order number. The stores clerk obtains the stock code number from the bin or his stores catalog and puts it on the requisition, also. This permits the accounting department to figure the material costs to be applied to the work order when it is closed out.

Every day each foreman turns in his daily work schedule sheet, listing the jobs on which he worked and the man-hours charged to each job. The maintenance clerk checks this sheet and forwards it to the accounting department. Overtime and week-end man-hours are collected from a night and weekend log sheet. All of this information is transmitted to the accounting department to accumulate the man-hours charged to each work order.

When the job is finished, the maintenance foreman returns his work-order copy to the maintenance clerk, who, in turn, notifies the accounting department. Total job

ORIGINATOR		CHARGE		PROPERTY ITEM		WORK ORDER NUMBER					
						C.C.	YR.	SER. NO.	TP.	F.C.	CLASS
SHUTDOWN?	AVAILABLE	DEADLINE		ASSIGN TO							

43 DIGIT ABBREVIATION ▶

JOB DESCRIPTION:

MATERIAL REQUIRED:

MAN HOURS	NUMBER OF MEN	CRAFTS	OCC. CODE							
		PIPEFITTER	1							
		WELDER	2							
		CARPENTER	3							
		INSTRUMENT (Mech & Fitter)	4							
		ELECTRICIANS	5							
		MACHINIST- MILLWRIGHT	6							
		BOILER REPAIR	7							
		PAINTER-INSULATOR -BRICKLAYER	8	W.O. DISP. INITIAL		ROUTE LIST			APPROVAL SIGNATURE	DATE
		RIGGERS - CRANE OPERATOR	9	DATE WRITTEN						
		MISCELLANEOUS	0							
	◀ TOTAL MAN HOURS			DATE OPENED						

ESTIMATE IN DOLLARS

DATE CLOSED

	LABOR		
	MATERIAL		
	TOTAL		W.O. DISPATCHER - MAINT. OFFICE

FIG. 9–1. Typical work order form.

costs are then assembled by the accounting department.   Each month they issue a list of completed work orders for each cost center or account.   This list gives:

1. A brief description of the work order.
2. The work-order number.
3. The labor cost.
4. The material cost.
5. The original job estimated cost.
6. The final total job cost.

Each month all production costs are compiled as a cost of producing each item.   All costs, including maintenance, which vary greatly from the budget must be explained. The monthly work-order report is useful in examining high-cost areas.   At the same time, maintenance supervision examines jobs which vary greatly from estimated

STOREROOM REQUISITION		Charge Req. - White		
		Credit Req. - Pink		
CHLOR-ALKALI DIVISION		Form 1510		
FMC CORPORATION				

DATE_____

QUANTITY	UNIT OF MEASURE	STOCK CODE NO.	DESCRIPTION	AMOUNT

Write in charge below (carefully)					REQUISITIONER	
	WORK ORDER				FOREMAN	
HOME	CC/JOB	YR	SER. NO.	TY		
CC					STOREKEEPER	

Fig. 9-2. Storeroom requisition.

costs to determine the reason for variance and improve job planning or craft performance.   It is essential in all this that maintenance and operating personnel work closely together.

As mentioned previously, historical maintenance repair costs are kept on all important pieces of equipment.   When the maintenance clerk codes the work order on such an item, he also puts the "property item" or PI number on the work order.   When the monthly completed work-order list is received, another clerk notes the job costs which apply to the selected list of property numbers.   He then hand-posts the costs to each piece of equipment on the item's equipment history card (Fig. 9-3).   These cards are set up in visible index-type panels.   In addition to serving as an equipment history record, they are used as a descriptive catalog of all important operating units. They also are the tickler system for preventive-maintenance inspections and are cross-referenced to the engineering equipment files.

By working closely with maintenance supervision and operating personnel, the maintenance engineer becomes closely associated with the equipment in his area. He develops a "feel" for these items.   With this background, he uses the equipment history file to identify items of high repair costs.   It is his responsibility to develop maintenance programs to reduce these costs.   It is not infrequent to find many items of high maintenance cost that would go undetected without good records and a systematic evaluation.   Once identified, it does not take too much engineering imagination to effect significant cost savings.

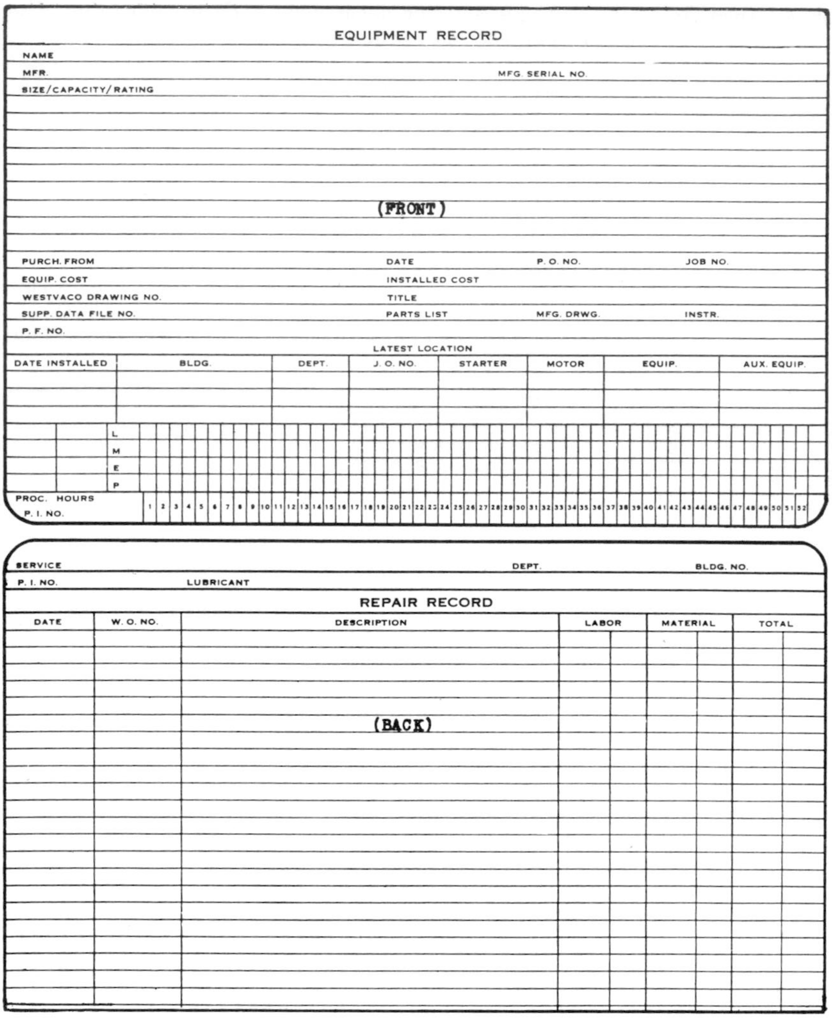

EQUIPMENT RECORD

NAME

MFR.   MFG. SERIAL NO.

SIZE/CAPACITY/RATING

(FRONT)

PURCH. FROM		DATE	P. O. NO.		JOB NO.
EQUIP. COST		INSTALLED COST			
WESTVACO DRAWING NO.		TITLE			
SUPP. DATA FILE NO.		PARTS LIST	MFG. DRWG.		INSTR.
P. F. NO.					

LATEST LOCATION

DATE INSTALLED	BLDG.	DEPT.	J. O. NO.	STARTER	MOTOR	EQUIP.	AUX. EQUIP.
	L						
	M						
	E						
	P						

PROC. HOURS
P. I. NO.   1 2 3 4 5 6 7 8 9 10 11 12 13 14 15 16 17 18 19 20 21 22 23 24 25 26 27 28 29 30 31 32 33 34 35 36 37 38 39 40 41 42 43 44 45 46 47 48 49 50 51 52

SERVICE   DEPT.   BLDG. NO.

P. I. NO.   LUBRICANT

REPAIR RECORD

DATE	W. O. NO.	DESCRIPTION	LABOR	MATERIAL	TOTAL
		(BACK)			

FIG. 9-3. Equipment history card.

ADVANTAGES AND DISADVANTAGES

The system described is a hand method. It has three major disadvantages:

1. It is costly in clerical time. Any effort to obtain more data requires additional clerks. This adds to the cost and must be justified.
2. It is slow. Monthly repair costs are received several days after the fact, and sometimes invoices take one or two months before they are finally closed out. People working with such cold data are not too interested in it, particularly with their energies concentrated on current problems.
3. Being a manual system, it is very subject to human error.

There are some advantages to a manual system such as this. Most significant is the personal feeling the various clerks get for the maintenance function. When certain things get out of line, the clerks are able to point this out to the maintenance engineers.   In addition, the system is very flexible within its limitations.   When immediate costs or other information items are required on a daily basis, the clerks can obtain them.   The quantity of such information, however, is limited.   Finally, a hand system is easily converted to machine accounting programs.   Once the procedures are established and operating manually, they can be readily transferred to machine methods.   This can be done in part, or all at once.

Any system such as this is only as accurate as the original data fed into it.   It is well, from time to time, to check the source data to insure that the individuals concerned have not been making changes or errors that others are unaware of.

Chapter 10

DATA PROCESSING BY MACHINE

By WILLIAM J. SMITH
Project Engineer, Plant Facilities
General Electric Company
Computer Department
Phoenix, Ariz.

The increased complexity of the plant engineering and maintenance function requires utilization of the latest technical advances to increase service and measure efficiency. Development of high-priced automatic production equipment makes it necessary to minimize downtime because a small decrease in downtime will cause an appreciable increase in production output. Data processing of maintenance records provides one method of reducing downtime by insuring preventive maintenance on production equipment.

Data processing also provides a historical record of repairs made to plant facilities, reduces the high clerical cost of posting from individual job tickets, and provides complete records on all plant equipment and buildings.

How to Establish the Procedure. To activate the procedure, it is necessary that suitable code numbers, as shown in Tables 10-1 to 10-3, be assigned to fully describe the maintenance function. The complete code number is composed of the following individual components:

1. Machine or building number.
2. Description of machine or building component.
3. Description of work done.

The first step requires that all buildings, machines, tanks, vehicles, in fact every item of the physical plant, be assigned a number. For most plants, this is no problem because this equipment is now numbered.

The second step requires that numbers be arbitrarily assigned to describe the classes of equipment or building components. For example, number 7 might be assigned to the interior partitions of a building and number 209 to a grinder. Thus, the component of a building or a specific machine can be described by the above two sets of numbers.

Table 10-1. Building and Machine Numbers

Description	Number
Building 19	19
Building 42	42
Machine No. 416	416
Vehicle No. 635	635
Lift truck No. 1947	1,947

Table 10-2. Building Component or Equipment Classification

Description	Number
Interior building partitions	7
Floors	8
Roof	10
Water piping	14
Lighting	21
Lathes	149
Grinders	209
Mills	210

The third step requires that all maintenance operations be coded to indicate work done on the machine or building. Numbers are arbitrarily assigned to the various maintenance operations to indicate the work done. For example, number 129 might be assigned to power sweeping and number 169 to repair of the hydraulic system.

The typical numbers in the tables are partial listings only; the complete list for a typical plant would probably have over 300 numbers in each category. The complete code numbers can be readily developed by maintenance supervisors on the basis of experience.

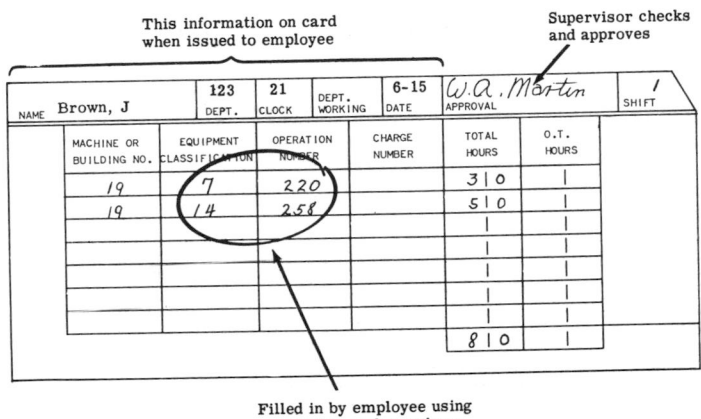

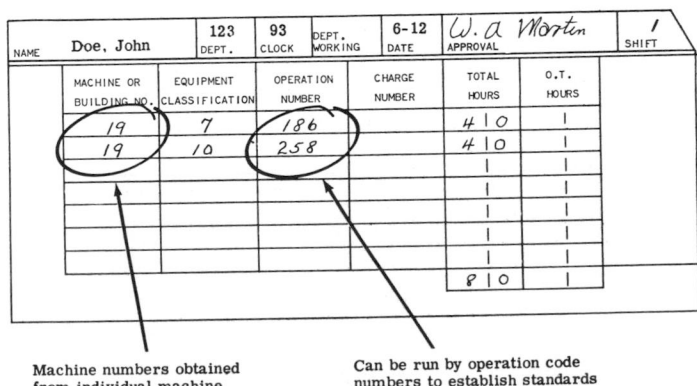

Fig. 10-1. Employee time cards, showing use of code numbers by employees (see Tables 10-1 to 10-3).

MACHINE OR BUILDING NUMBER	DESCRIPTION OF MACHINE OR BUILDING COMPONENT	DESCRIPTION OF WORK DONE	EMPLOYEE NUMBER	DATE	HOURS
19	7	186	93	6-12	4.0
19	10	258	93	6-12	4.0
19	8	129	46	6-12	3.2
19	10	258	17	6-13	5.0
19	14	258	36	6-14	2.0
19	21	49	93	6-14	3.6
19	8	129	46	6-15	6.0
19	7	220	21	6-15	3.0
19	14	258	21	6-15	5.0

FIG. 10-2. Format of monthly report showing tabulation of work from cards of employees in Fig. 10-1.

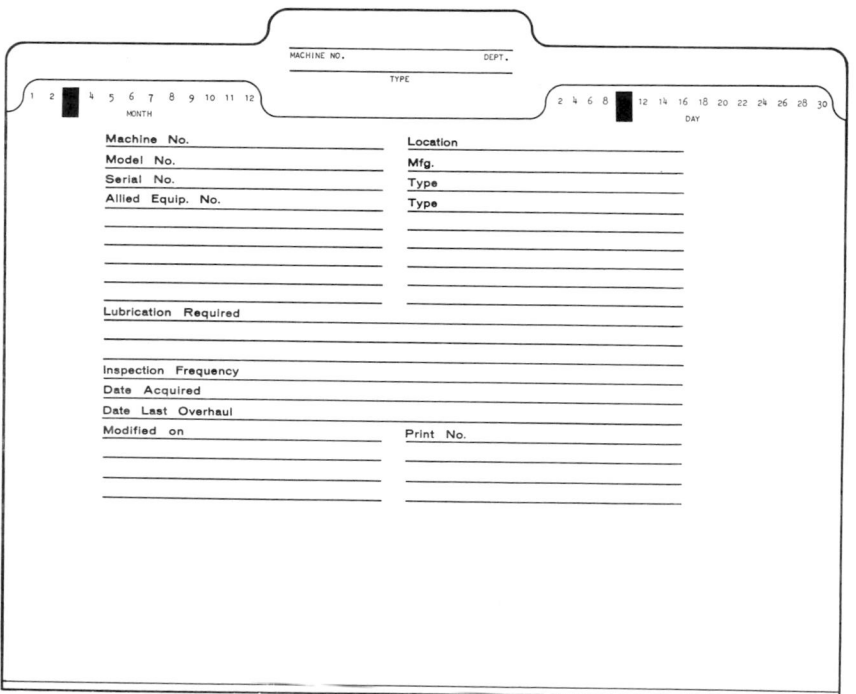

FIG. 10-3. Equipment folder showing information normally required on equipment items. Moveable colored tabs indicate next lubrication and inspection date.

Table 10-3. Maintenance Operation Number

Description	Number
Replace lamps	49
Power sweeping	129
Repair hydraulic system	169
Construct	186
Move	220
Repair	258

Numerical Description of Maintenance Work. With a combination of all of the above numbers, any operation of the maintenance department can be numerically coded. As the work is done, the employee writes the appropriate code number and the time spent on the operation on his daily time card. For example, repairing the roof of Building 19 would be coded 19-10-258. If we assume an employee worked four hours on the job, he would enter this in the time worked column of his card. Figure 10-1 shows typical time cards for maintenance employees. At the end of the day, the time cards, prepunched with the date, employee number, and department, are forwarded to accounting, where key-punch operators punch in the code numbers and hours worked.

Reporting of Maintenance Work. At the end of the month the cards are machine-sorted and a report is issued. This report lists each building or item of equipment by number, indicates the work done, hours required, employee doing the work, and date the work was done. Figure 10-2 shows items from a typical monthly report. The reports, after review by engineering and maintenance supervision, are filed in a folder for that particular machine or building. This folder (Fig. 10-3) should have complete information about the machine and tabs to indicate next lubrication and inspection date. The folders, filed in maintenance, provide a complete historical record of any building or piece of equipment.

Advantages of Machine Data Processing of Maintenance Operations.

1. *Lower Cost for Maintenance Records.* Normal recording of maintenance operations involves high clerical cost plus the possibility of error in transcription of records, because the job tickets must be posted to the permanent machine records. The use of data processing equipment eliminates the clerical cost and provides fewer chances for error because the clerical work is limited to filing the report, by machine number, at periodic intervals.

2. *Complete Maintenance Records.* This procedure will provide complete maintenance cost of repair or modification of buildings and equipment which is not available under the manual posting system. For example, cost of roof repair by individual building or cost of maintaining the water lines in a particular building can readily be ascertained.

3. *Control of Preventive-maintenance Programs.* Control of a preventive-maintenance program is achieved with little effort. The individual machine folders indicate the date of the next inspection and lubrication, and the reports indicate the results and date of previous inspections and the time consumed on them. Reference to past inspections and repairs will provide a historical basis for establishing economical inspection periods. If the records indicate no repairs during the past year, it is obviously not economical to inspect the machine weekly or monthly.

High-maintenance-cost items are readily apparent with the information supplied from data processing equipment because the monthly report will provide the time spent on any particular machine. This time, multiplied by the labor rate plus the cost of parts, will give total maintenance cost. The trend of this cost, compared with the cost of overhaul or replacement, will provide an irrefutable economic basis for decision as to replacement or overhaul. In the case of buildings, past records will indicate whatever replacement of a major part of the structure is warranted. Excessive costs of roof repair for a building will indicate that the projected costs of future repairs must be compared with the cost of a new roof.

4. *Costs for Routine Operations Available.* Certain routine maintenance duties, because of their repetitive nature, often are ignored in so far as costs are concerned; however, with data processing, the cost of these operations is readily available. Examples include the cost of sweeping a building or department, handling trash, repairing a time clock, or replacing light bulbs. This information provides a basis for analysis and possible reduction of these routine costs.

Standard Time on Maintenance Operations. The code numbers indicating the individual maintenance operation provide a ready means of determining standard times for some maintenance operations. Use of data processing equipment for a period of three to six months will show a definite pattern of times for any given operation: the time required to sweep a building, for example, should be a reasonably consistent figure. This, then, provides a standard against which work of individual employees can be measured. Any deviation from this historically established standard indicates that corrective action may be necessary. In certain operations of a repetitive nature, a learning curve may be applied to the standard and a continual improvement in efficiency and a lowering of times should be noted.

Standards can't be set on all maintenance operations; however, large, time-consuming jobs often can be broken down into components for which standards can be established. When time standards are established, it is possible to measure maintenance efficiency and justify manpower requirements.

Maintenance supervisors and managers have a yardstick to measure maintenance efficiency, because the time spent on routine jobs, reported under the operation number, can be plotted against the established standard for a graphic presentation of over-all maintenance efficiency or individual craft efficiency. As a general rule, unless a graphic presentation is desired, it is a simple operation to visually compare the time spent on an operation with the known standard for that operation. This comparison can be simplified by saving the key punched cards and rerunning them through the data processing equipment to provide a second report listing all work by operation number. In this way, all operation numbers are grouped together, providing an immediate basis for comparison with standards.

Established maintenance standards provide a basis for manpower requirements, and when expansion is contemplated, future manpower forecasts can be developed.

The key punched detail cards can be stored and rerun annually to combine a year's maintenance for each item of equipment on one sheet. This eliminates excessive storage requirements.

Detailed Costs on Productive Equipment. The procedure provides a means whereby a production department can obtain a detailed breakdown of costs incurred during an accounting period. Cards can be sorted to establish the time charged to a particular department; then a report can be run listing the machines in the department and the maintenance time charged to each machine. Thus, the production supervisor has available a tool that will help reduce production downtime because it enables him to identify problem machines or operators.

Analysis of Results. The information available as a result of data processing of maintenance records, with proper analysis, can improve maintenance efficiency and lower costs. For example, the report provides information that permits the evaluation of outside services for a specific portion of the maintenance work load. As mentioned previously, it is possible to obtain the cost of sweeping the floor in any particular building; similarly the cost of any other janitorial function or group of functions can be determined. With this information, potential savings from subcontracting part of the maintenance function can be ascertained. It should be remembered that the report will provide the time required in hours for any particular job; therefore, the labor rate used for comparison with a subcontractor's quotation should be determined with care. Not all items of overhead should be included in your direct labor rate; some will continue to be items of cost even if the work is subcontracted.

Precautions to Be Observed. Incorporation of the system requires the complete cooperation and understanding of maintenance supervision. Without a complete understanding of operation of this procedure and the advantages to be gained, you will not have the support of maintenance supervision or, obviously, of maintenance workers. Because the supervisors will teach the workers the use of the code system, it is necessary that the supervisors be thoroughly familiar with the procedures. Typically, the maintenance supervisors should code all the cards for two weeks to a month. This has the dual advantage of instructing supervision in the system and working out minor details of operation. Experience indicates that workers of low skill have trouble in determining the proper code number for the work done; therefore, keep the code numbers for unskilled workers simple and to a minimum.

At the very least, data processing will provide better maintenance records at a lower cost; properly used, data processing will provide a method of evaluating maintenance operations and a possible justification for new plant equipment.

Chapter 11

CRITICAL PATH METHOD

By VICTOR K. MOORE
General Foreman, Mechanical Division
American Oil Company
Whiting, Ind.

Critical path method is a management tool whereby the many aspects of a project can be made immediately apparent. It is a road map from which a person can see many items such as material or engineering bottlenecks, field problems, completion dates of various job phases, and over-all completion time.

DIAGRAM DRAWING AND IDENTIFICATION

Basic CPM requires only the ability to think, add, and subtract. Different terminology may be used to identify the various components of CPM, but the fundamental concepts are generally the same. The basis for CPM is a network representation of the project, known as an arrow diagram. Each job or part of a job is represented by an arrow. These are not vectors, and their length, whether they are straight ——→ , curved ⤳ , or kinked ⟋⟍ , is immaterial. CP diagrams proceed from left to right and are developed by locating the arrows in accordance with the following three criteria:

1. What jobs come before?
2. What jobs come after?
3. What jobs can be done concurrently?

For example:

A ——→ B ——→

Job B follows job A and cannot start until job A is finished. Conversely, job A comes before job B.

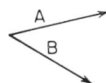

In the above example, jobs A and B can be done concurrently and are independent. In drawing arrow diagrams, it is helpful to remember that you are planning the next job and not trying to represent the way the job has always been done in the past. To get the best results, have people with different viewpoints contribute to the planning.   The man or men who will be responsible for implementation of the plan should be part of the planning team.

One often is concerned with the level of detail to be incorporated in an arrow diagram.   It is better to start with a simple diagram and expand.   On succeeding diagrams detail is added where it improves the plan.   The gross logic of most projects can be shown by 6 to 10 jobs.   One man can readily comprehend a diagram with 30 to 50 jobs represented and work from this to a more detailed layout of perhaps 300 to 400 jobs.   The use of more detail requires a team approach, the use of subchains, and the acceptance of another level of planning.   A diagram with more than 1,500 or 2,000 jobs is a problem difficult to comprehend, from the standpoint of both physical size and inherent complexity.   After the original plan has been developed and analyzed, detail may then be added to reduce project completion time or to improve project control.   This approach has the merit of tailoring your planning to a profitable effort.   The objective is *not* to see how much detail you can incorporate on one sheet of paper.

Since the number of arrows in a diagram for a job of any kind can be hundreds or even thousands, further identification is required. A, B, etc., or any other

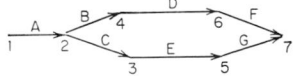

FIG. 11-1. Number at tail of first arrow is 1; progressively higher numbers are used at the heads of ensuing arrows.

FIG. 11-2. Diagram in Fig. 11-1 could have been numbered as shown here.

nomenclature the diagrammer desires, can be used to identify the arrows.   Further identification is provided by a number at the tail and the head of each arrow, the latter always being higher than the former.   In early use of CPM, the number at the tail of the first arrow was 1, and progressively higher numbers were used at the head of each arrow.   (See Fig. 11-1.)   As long as the number at the tail was lower than that at the head, it made no difference.   The above diagram could also have been numbered as in Fig. 11-2.

Arrows cannot have the same numbers at both the head and the tail.   For example, if two jobs start and stop at the same time, they cannot be diagramed as follows:

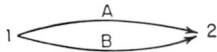

Instead, dummy arrows are used to avoid this situation.

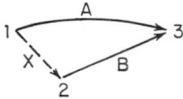

Dummy arrows are also used to indicate dependence and independence.   In the following example, B depends on the completion of A while D depends on the completion of A and C. B and D are independent.   If the arrow head on the dummy were reversed, B would depend on A and C, and D would depend only on C.

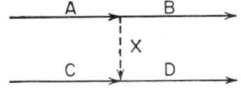

CALCULATIONS

Elapsed times are the units used in CPM, and each arrow in a diagram including the dummies has an elapsed time value.   The unit selected depends on the magnitude of the job and the amount of refinement that the person drawing the diagram desires. For example, the unit selected for a 1-year construction project might be days or weeks while the most desirable unit for a 4-hr maintenance job is probably minutes. The dummies have an elapsed time of zero.

Assume that the arrows in the foregoing diagrams (Figs. 11-1 and 11-2) have elapsed times in hours as follows:

$$
\begin{array}{ll}
A \quad 1 & E \quad 4 \\
B \quad 7 & F \quad 6 \\
C \quad 2 & G \quad 3 \\
D \quad 5 &
\end{array}
$$

These times are marked on the diagrams shown in Fig. 11-3.

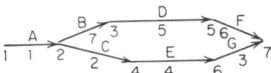

Fig. 11-3. Figures showing elapsed times in hours have been added to the diagram shown in Fig. 11-2.

It is immediately obvious that A, B, D, F is the longest route through the diagram and takes 19 hr while A, C, E, G takes 10 hr. Thus, route A, B, D, F governs the time of the over-all job and is the critical path while there is 9 hr slack or float time by the other route. On more complicated diagrams, the critical path is not readily obvious and it is necessary to resort to manual or computer calculations. To calculate the above diagram manually, a tabulation is prepared with the arrows listed in ascending order from their tails to their heads:

$$
\begin{array}{lll}
A \quad 1 \quad 2 & E \quad 4 \quad 6 \\
B \quad 2 \quad 3 & F \quad 5 \quad 7 \\
C \quad 2 \quad 4 & G \quad 6 \quad 7 \\
D \quad 3 \quad 5 &
\end{array}
$$

It is important to count the number of arrows in the diagram and the items tabulated so that none is overlooked. A matrix triangle is then constructed on cross section paper (see Fig. 11-4). The numbers at the heads of the arrows are listed horizontally, the numbers at the tails are listed vertically, and a heavy line is drawn diagonally. The elapsed times, including the zeros for dummies, of which there are none in this case, are inserted in the triangle in their proper locations. For example, arrow D with 3 at the tail and 5 at the head has an elapsed time of 5 hours and so 5 is inserted in the square at the intersection of 3 and 5. All numbers in the triangle must be above the diagonal, and there must be a number in every vertical column and every horizontal row or a mistake has been made. The zeros for dummies are considered as numbers when making this test.

The triangle is then used to calculate the earliest start and latest finish for each arrow. The calculation begins at earliest start zero as shown for number 1. For number 2, follow up Column 2 in which the only number is 1 and add this to the zero directly opposite it. The earliest start for 2 is 1. For number 5, follow up Column 5; the only number in the column is 5, which is added to the 8 directly opposite it. The earliest start for 5 is 13. When there is a multiple choice, such as in column 7, where the possibilities are 6 plus 13 and 7 plus 3, the earliest start is the one which results in the largest total or, in this case, 19. Following up the last column to the right also gives the total time the job will take, which is 19 hr as was previously determined by inspection of the diagram.

The number 19 is then inserted under 7, which is the number at the two arrow heads at the end of the project. To obtain the latest finish for number 6, follow horizontally across Row 6 in which the only number is 3 and subtract it from the 19 directly under it, which results in 16. For number 5, follow horizontally across Row 5 in which the only number is 6 and subtract it from the number 19 directly under it, which gives 13.

Where there is a multiple choice such as for number 2 $(12 - 2 = 10$, or $8 - 7 = 1)$, the lowest result is the one selected.   The matrix should result in zero for number 1 or a mistake has been made.

The previous tabulation is then expanded as follows:

Arrow	Tail	Head	Elapsed time	Earliest start	Earliest finish	Latest start	Latest finish	Total float	Free float
A	1	2	1	0	1	0	1	0	*
B	2	3	7	1	8	1	8	0	*
C	2	4	2	1	3	10	12	9	0
D	3	5	5	8	13	8	13	0	*
E	4	6	4	3	7	12	16	9	0
F	5	7	6	13	19	13	19	0	*
G	6	7	3	7	10	16	19	9	0

The earliest starts are listed in the tabulation for the numbers at the arrow tails from the matrix.   When a tail number such as 2 appears more than once, the earliest start is listed as many times as the number appears.

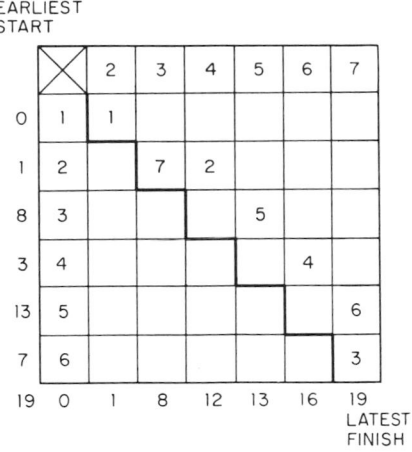

Fig. 11-4. Matrix triangle.   It is used to calculate earliest starts and latest finishes and the total project time.

To obtain the next column to the right, which is the earliest finish, it is merely necessary to add the elapsed time and the earliest start.

The latest finishes are listed in the tabulation for the numbers at the arrow heads from the matrix.   When a head number such as 7 appears more than once, the latest finish is listed as many times as the number appears.   The latest start column is calculated by subtracting the elapsed time from the latest finish.

Total float is the amount of time that the job can be delayed without affecting the critical path or over-all completion time.   It is calculated by subtracting the earliest finish from the latest finish.   Any job with a total float of zero will be in the critical path which is an unbroken chain.   Thus, the critical path is A, B, D, F.

Free float is the amount of time a job can be delayed without affecting another job. First, put asterisks in the free-float column for those jobs on the critical path since they cannot have any free float.   Then, examine the head numbers of the remaining jobs. The first is C with a head number of 4. Follow down the tail number column until the number 4 is reached at E. Subtract the earliest finish of C (3) from the earliest start of E (3), and the free float of C is zero. The next is E with a head number of 6. Following down the tail column, the number 6 is at G. Subtracting the earliest finish of E (7) from the earliest start of G (7) gives 0 free float for E. The last is G with a head number of 7 and hasn't any free float since there is no job following it.

This completes the computation table for the arrow diagram. The calculations are not complicated and can be done manually for jobs with any number of arrows. However, on big jobs involving hundreds or thousands of arrows, the calculations become extremely tedious and the matrix triangles cover large areas. For this reason, computer programs have been developed and the computers will make all the calculations. It is then only necessary to draw the diagram and estimate the elapsed time. Programs are refined to report starts and finishes keyed to calendar dates or the shifts of a day, to list the critical path items, and to report upcoming jobs. Updating procedures involve only a few cards with revised estimates that are run through the computer to yield another schedule in minutes. A manpower leveling program also has been developed. This computer program considers the crafts involved and levels demanded by shifting those jobs with float time. The intent is to develop a schedule with the most practical allocation of crafts by desired time increments, such as shifts, days, weeks, etc., throughout the entire project. Reports are compiled showing the total manpower by crafts and the manpower on critical and near critical jobs for each time increment. A report is then developed which is based on the leveling and shows the recommended start and finish for each job. If the manpower leveling reports show more time from any craft than is available, the arrow-diagram plan is revised and the calculations run again.

MAINTENANCE

CPM has been used with considerable success in maintenance, construction, research, engineering, training, operating, missiles, finance, and other fields. In

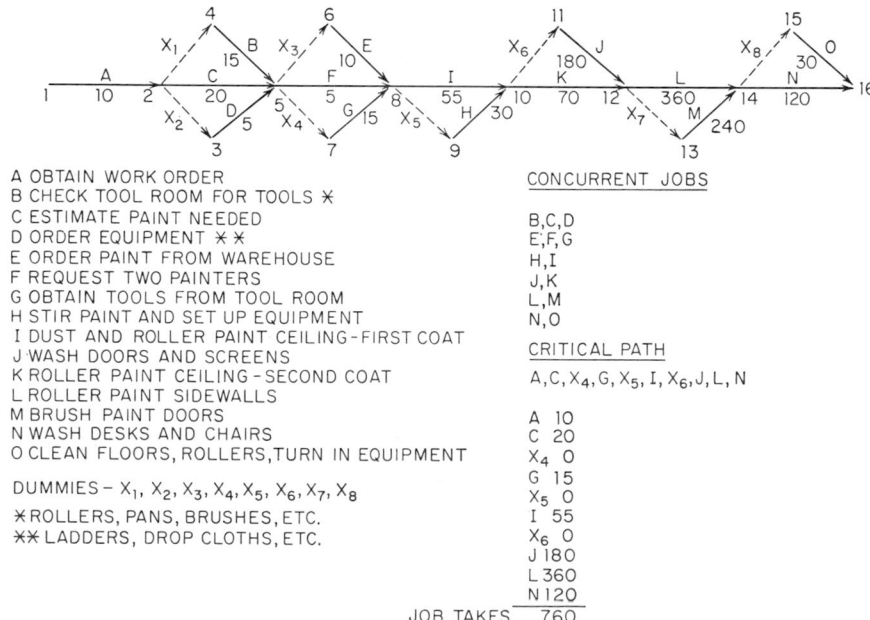

A OBTAIN WORK ORDER
B CHECK TOOL ROOM FOR TOOLS ✶
C ESTIMATE PAINT NEEDED
D ORDER EQUIPMENT ✶ ✶
E ORDER PAINT FROM WAREHOUSE
F REQUEST TWO PAINTERS
G OBTAIN TOOLS FROM TOOL ROOM
H STIR PAINT AND SET UP EQUIPMENT
I DUST AND ROLLER PAINT CEILING-FIRST COAT
J WASH DOORS AND SCREENS
K ROLLER PAINT CEILING-SECOND COAT
L ROLLER PAINT SIDEWALLS
M BRUSH PAINT DOORS
N WASH DESKS AND CHAIRS
O CLEAN FLOORS, ROLLERS, TURN IN EQUIPMENT

DUMMIES – $X_1, X_2, X_3, X_4, X_5, X_6, X_7, X_8$

✶ ROLLERS, PANS, BRUSHES, ETC.
✶✶ LADDERS, DROP CLOTHS, ETC.

CONCURRENT JOBS

B,C,D
E,F,G
H,I
J,K
L,M
N,O

CRITICAL PATH

$A, C, X_4, G, X_5, I, X_6, J, L, N$

A 10
C 20
X_4 0
G 15
X_5 0
I 55
X_6 0
J 180
L 360
N 120
JOB TAKES   760

FIG. 11-5. Diagram for painting office 14 ft × 20 ft × 12 ft. Elapsed times are in minutes.

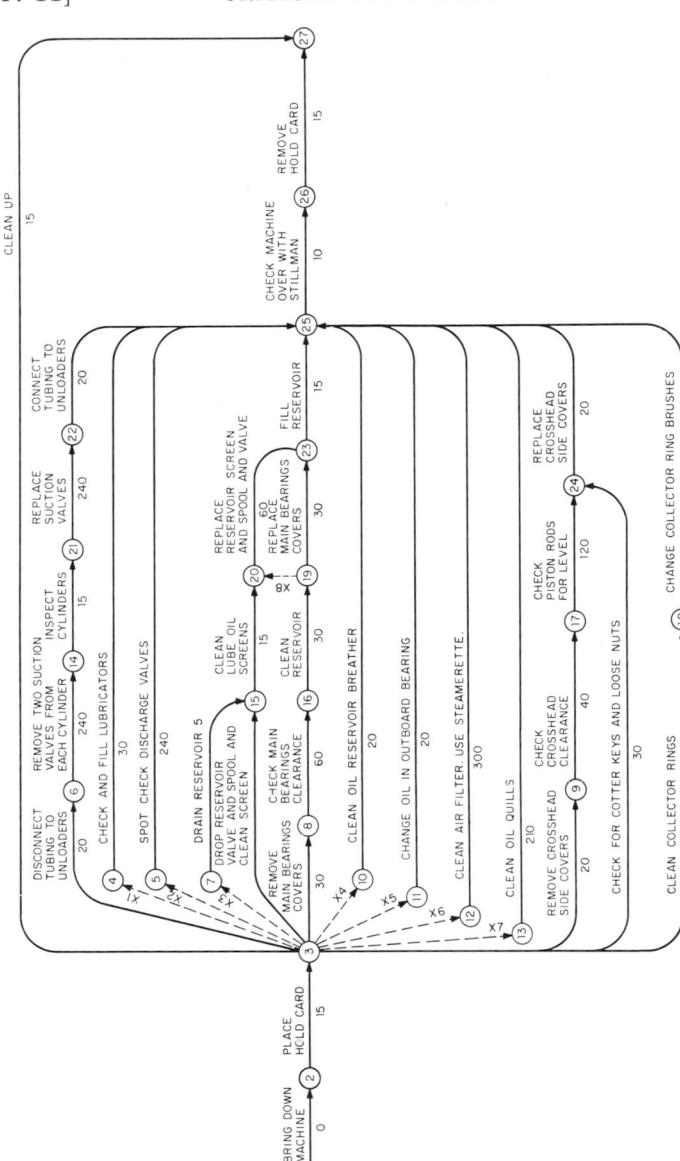

FIG. 11-6. Diagram for keying up a compressor. Elapsed times are in minutes.   The critical path consists of those arrows with a total float of zero: 1-2, 2-3, 3-6, 6-14, 14-21, 21-22, 22-25, 25-26, and 26-27.

BRANCH	I	J	Y	EARLIEST START	EARLIEST FINISH	LATEST START	LATEST FINISH	TOTAL FLOAT	FREE FLOAT
BRING DOWN MACHINE	1	2	0	0	0	0	0	0	0
PLACE HOLDING CARD	2	3	15	0	15	0	15	0	0
X1	3	4	0	15	15	520	520	505	505
X2	3	5	0	15	15	310	310	295	295
DISCONNECT TUBING TO UNLOADR	3	6	20	15	35	15	35	0	0
X3	3	7	0	15	15	455	455	440	440
REMOVE MAIN BEARING COVERS	3	8	30	15	45	355	385	340	340
REMOVE CROSS HEAD SIDE COVER	3	9	20	15	35	350	370	335	335
X4	3	10	0	15	15	530	530	515	515
X5	3	11	0	15	15	530	530	515	515
X6	3	12	0	15	15	250	250	235	235
X7	3	13	0	15	15	340	340	325	325
DROP RESERVOIR+SPOOL+CLEAN	3	15	60	15	75	400	460	385	0
CLEAN COLLECTOR RINGS	3	18	210	15	225	160	370	145	0
CHECK FOR COTTR LOOSE NUTS	3	24	30	15	45	500	530	485	150
CLEAN UP	3	27	15	15	30	560	575	545	545
CHECK +FILL LUBRICATORS	4	25	30	15	45	520	550	505	505
SPOT CHECK DISHARGE VALVES	5	25	240	15	255	310	550	295	295
REMOVE TWO SUCT VAL FR CYLN	6	14	240	35	275	35	275	0	0
DRAIN RESERVOIR	7	15	5	15	20	455	460	440	55
CHECK MAIN BEARINGS CLEAR	8	16	60	45	105	385	445	340	0
CHECK CROSS HEAD CLEARANCE	9	17	40	35	75	370	410	335	0
CLEAN OIL RESERVOIR BREATHER	10	25	20	15	35	530	550	515	515
CHANGE OIL IN OUTBOARD REAR	11	25	20	15	35	530	550	515	515
CLEAN AIR FILTER USE STEMERT	12	25	300	15	315	250	550	235	235
CLEAN OIL QUILLS	13	25	210	15	225	340	550	325	325
INSPECT CYLINDERS	14	21	15	275	290	275	290	0	0
CLN LUBE OIL SCREENS	15	20	15	75	90	460	475	385	45
CLEAN RESERVOIR	16	19	30	105	135	445	475	340	0
CHECK PISTON RODS FOR LEVEL	17	24	120	75	195	410	530	335	0
CHANGE COLLECTOR RING BRUSHS	18	25	180	225	405	370	550	145	145
X8	19	20	0	135	135	475	475	340	0
RPL MAIN BEARING COVERS	19	23	30	135	165	505	535	370	30
RPL RESERVOIR SREEN SPL VALV	20	23	135	135	195	475	535	340	0
RPL SUCTION VALVES	21	22	240	290	530	290	530	0	0
CONNECT TUBING TO UNLOADERS	22	25	20	530	550	530	550	0	0
FILL RESERVOIR	23	25	20	195	210	535	550	340	340
REPLACE CROSS HEAD SIDE COVR	24	25	20	195	215	530	550	335	335
CHECK MACH COVER STILLMAN	25	26	10	550	560	550	560	0	0
REMOVE HOLD CARD	26	27	15	560	575	560	575	0	0

FIG. 11-7. Computer output for the diagram shown by Fig. 11-6. The I column gives the numbers at the arrow tails, the J column gives the numbers at the arrow heads, and the Y column gives elapsed times.

maintenance, innumerable jobs are worth arrow-diagraming. Those for which the method is particularly desirable are major overhauls and turnarounds where production loss may be a factor. The arrow diagram and manpower leveling provide a program for the efficient utilization of available time and men. The diagram should be developed by running as many jobs concurrently as possible, provided it is logical to do so, since this will result in the maximum floats.

On a big job, the total number of arrows may be numerous but the critical path is generally only a few, perhaps 15 or 20. The calculations will show the jobs on the critical path and when the overhaul or turnaround will be done. The critical path jobs can then be examined, and strategies to shorten the critical path, such as overtime, contracting, etc., can be evaluated. In shortening, take care to insure that another route doesn't become the critical path.

In addition to the mechanical work, other factors which can affect the time of the job must be incorporated into the diagram to obtain a realistic picture. Such factors could be engineering, material deliveries, and the work of shutting down the facility and starting it up again after the mechanical work is done. All of these can be represented by arrows and elapsed times. The diagram will also serve to pinpoint the responsibilities of the various departments and personnel involved. Diagrams are often color-coded to show job progress, marked to reflect responsibilities, and identified to facilitate control of performance.

If the overhaul or turnaround is repetitive, the work of developing subsequent diagrams is much less than the work of developing the first. The estimated elapsed times should also improve with regard to accuracy after each successive job.

Many smaller maintenance jobs are profitable to arrow diagram. A few examples are compressor key-ups, maintenance of transportation equipment, reconditioning valves and pumps, repairing roads, fence maintenance, boiler turnarounds, exchanger retubing, furnace repairs and cleaning, tank cleaning and painting, etc. In general, jobs of a very short elapsed time, an hour or two, are not worthwhile diagraming unless they are extremely repetitive. The diagram of a small maintenance job is shown in Fig. 11-5 and that of a more complicated one in Fig. 11-6. The computer output for the latter is given in Fig. 11-7.

It is important to note that a number of persons may individually diagram the same job, even a small one and the diagrams may differ. This merely means that some diagrams are better than others, just as some persons think better than others.

The extent and complexity to which diagrams can be carried is strikingly illustrated in the development of the Polaris missile. This program involved approximately 11,000 contractors and a large degree of uncertainty about when research on the crucial components of the system would be completed. PERT (program evaluation review technique) was used for Polaris and is similar to CPM except that three elapsed times (optimistic, expected, and pessimistic) are used instead of one. The PERT program has been given major credit for reducing the Polaris missile program by 2 years.

SAVINGS

It is unusual when the savings from CPM can be measured exactly in dollars and cents. However, the following advantages illustrate some of the ways that savings are realized from the system:

1. The arrow diagram and manpower leveling drastically curtail overmanning jobs and make it possible for men to be used in a more efficient manner by taking advantage of the floats.
2. Job control is improved since planners can record progress in color on the diagram every step of the way and use the updating procedure for unforeseen circumstances and bottlenecks.
3. Communications are better since the diagram provides a clear picture of the job that can be easily read and understood. Supervisors can be changed after a job has

started and the replacement can see what has been done and what he has to do with a minimum of lost motion.

4. Data accumulated from past repetitive jobs is available for study and future improvement.
5. Alternate schedules can be evaluated to determine the optimum one.
6. Arrow diagrams are extremely useful for training new supervisors and craftsmen more quickly and easily.
7. Continued and extensive use of CPM is almost certain to improve a person's logical thinking and hence upgrade organizations.

Section 4

PROJECT CONTROL

Chapter 1

THE WHAT AND HOW OF PROJECT CONTROL

By Oswald Stewart II[1]
Superintendent, Maintenance and Construction Department
Dewey & Almy Chemical Company Division
W. R. Grace & Co.
Cambridge, Mass.

DEFINITION

The term "project control" as used in this section of the handbook means the organizing, budgeting, putting into operation, and controlling of certain industrial construction work which will embrace a variety of crafts and equipment.

An illustration of what is meant by project control is given by this typical example: Plant management,[2] engaged in the manufacture of a given commodity, wishes to make a change in the manufacturing technique in order to do one or more of the following: Make a better product, a less expensive product, or a different product, or increase the production rate of the given product. From the very beginning of the discussions, it is apparent to all concerned that a major change in production facilities is inevitable if the plans are to be carried out, whether it be by adding to the existing production equipment or by substituting more appropriate equipment for part or all of the existing equipment.

In order to give plant management the cost data upon which the proper decisions will be based, some one individual or group must prepare a study which gives equipment and installation costs, delivery and installation times, the manpower picture, and such other data as are required by the particular situation and company. Usually this report would be prepared by the plant engineering department. The degree of detail put unto the report would depend upon the importance of the work, the time available, and the customary requirements of plant management.

After receipt of the report, plant management reaches a decision based upon the accepted economic factors of costs, timing, sales picture, and financial position. If approval is given, then the task of translating the project into action comes under the heading of "project control." The person or group to which the project is delegated must:

1. Update the project specifications, taking into consideration the inevitable changes which occur during the discussion interval.
2. Prepare complete work estimates.

---

[1] Author is now Communications Coordinator, Sales Engineering Division, Bethlehem Steel Company, Bethlehem, Pa.

[2] *Author's Note:* The term "plant management" has been utilized in this text as a standardized term to replace various terms, such as top management and upper management. Even though in many instances "plant management" reports to a management group farther up the line, the term as used here indicates the particular management group which approves the expenditure of funds for typical projects.

3. Proceed with appropriate drafting, design, calculation, and test work.
4. Proceed with placing equipment-purchase orders.
5. Administer the scheduling, cost control, and supervisory work of the project.
6. Keep plant management informed as to progress by suitable reports.
7. Get the job done fastest and "bestest"!

The two chapters of this section discuss project control in further detail. The author wishes to point out at this time that the ideas presented here are not claimed to represent the total picture of project control, nor do the ideas fall into a sequence which is universally best for all applications. Instead, the author's ideas should serve as a kind of check list or guide from which the reader can choose certain appropriate items, and rearrange these items where necessary, to fit his own application.

The text has been divided into two chapters in order to treat general ideas and detailed ideas separately. With that rough division in mind, it is apparent that there will be a certain amount of unavoidable duplication of material. A second frame of reference can be taken concerning the division of material: The first chapter discusses a project in its formative stages where a quick over-all picture is required for purposes of making a decision. Perhaps the resultant answer will be "no" or "not at this time." Whether "yes" or "no," the *general* approach to the problem at hand requires a minimum of detail at this stage of progress toward a solution. The second chapter treats the problem at hand as if approval were certain of being given, and goes into some of the *detailed* steps required for optimum performance of the project.

ORIGIN OF PROJECTS

Projects can originate from any one of several sources. Because a manufacturing concern is in business primarily to manufacture and sell a group of products, its own sales division will constantly endeavor to keep ahead of its competition by creating a market for a new or better product, and thus will create the requirement for changes in or additions to plant equipment.

The expansion of existing markets can also furnish the requirements for adding to plant equipment, either in an existing plant location or in a new location selected with the component economic factors in mind such as raw-material supply, availability of labor, and marketing elements.

A second source of ideas which will result in additions to plant equipment is in the research or development group of a manufacturing concern. This source may develop a project requirement directly from the recommendation of a sales division or, as is often the case, may be ahead of the sales division in anticipating the opportunity for a new or better product.

A third source of project ideas is found within the manufacturing organization itself. Someone in this group may develop an original idea independently of sales or research because of his familiarity with manufacturing techniques plus his possession of an imagination adept enough to visualize some desirable new product which can be economically manufactured with certain modifications to existing plant equipment.

A fourth source of material for projects is found in plant engineering and maintenance departments. This source of course is close to the hearts of people who are most likely to be studying this handbook. With our own imagination and foresight, nothing need limit us from developing new ideas also. In addition, our specialized training should constantly prompt us to study existing equipment and recommend improvements based upon maintenance cost history. We can also update performance based upon new developments in the equipment field, such as utilizing automation techniques. A host of similar opportunities exists for plant engineers, maintenance engineers, or whatever our title may be, to suggest and put into practice projects which result in strengthening the competitive position of one's company.[1] Since it is beyond the scope of this section to develop this particular theme, the reader should refer to other chapters of this handbook.

A fifth source of ideas which can result in the initiation of projects should not be

[1] B. F. Coggan, Convair Goes Hollywood to Up Its Efficiency (use of motion-picture studies to improve plant layouts), *Plant Eng.*, March, 1953, p. 128.

overlooked: the very top men who head our concerns are constantly on the alert for better methods of improving our competitive standing.   Even though at an engineering or maintenance level we are prone to be preoccupied with our own short- and long-range work, let us not forget that the men upstairs have a deep responsibility toward the concern and are just as likely to toss ideas our way as men in sales or research.

SCOPE OF PROJECTS

The scope of projects can range from small ones to very large ones.   At the small end of the scale, just at what stage one defines it as a "project" depends upon the particular situation.   A small job that can be handled by verbal instructions and needs but little follow-up to ensure satisfactory completion could hardly be called a "project."   To bother with extensive records, schedule charts, and progress reports would not be worthwhile on this small job.   As the magnitude of a particular job grows, however, or as jobs multiply even though they may be individually small, there comes a point beyond which mere personal control is no longer efficient.   At this stage it becomes wise to establish project control on the bigger and more important jobs in order to keep the over-all program running smoothly.

At the upper end of the scale, there is no limit.   If a brand-new plant were being constructed, for example, all work must be carried out on an over-all project basis, and the probability exists that subprojects would be established under the direction of separate individuals reporting to one head.   In this fashion the details for components can be delegated to subordinate project leaders, and the project chief can devote himself to exercising general control over the entire project.

CLASSIFICATION OF PROJECTS: NEW WORK VS. ALTERATIONS

For an organization that is handling a considerable amount of new work and alteration work at any time, it may be convenient to classify projects into two general categories.   "Alterations," as the name implies, consists of construction work, repairs, modifications, or alterations accomplished on existing equipment or buildings. The financial policy of most companies dictates that this type of work be expensed. A certain amount of new accessory equipment could be installed as part of a project to improve performance or capacity of existing basic equipment, yet if the principal equipment remains substantially unchanged in value, the project would be classified as an alteration and would be carried on the books as an expense item.   As the magnitude of a particular job

"New work" properly refers to a project where everything is new from the ground up, including buildings, equipment, utilities, and so on.   Costs of such new project would be capitalized and depreciation procedures would be set up according to the company's financial policy regarding current tax regulations.

It has been brought out by conferees at the several plant maintenance and engineering conferences that various companies differ widely in their practices toward expensing or capitalizing various types of projects.   The author does not attempt to expand on this variation, other than to observe that the project engineer must familiarize himself with his company's current policy, and act accordingly.

PRELIMINARY PLANNING

Preliminary planning is a necessary step in the orderly development of a project. Based upon data gathered at this stage, management will decide whether to advance into detailed planning and estimating in view of probable project approval, or to cancel or postpone further work.   The extent of preliminary planning that one must accomplish depends as usual on the existing circumstances, and that old favorite, "the engineering compromise," should govern.   For a project that seems certain of approval by virtue of impressions gained from an enthusiastic plant management, a minimum of preliminary work may be all that is required in order to get approval for detailed planning.   If a project seems to borderline in nature, a greater amount of preliminary work might be required on which to base a sound decision for proceeding or canceling or deferring. Obviously as much preliminary planning must be accomplished as is necessary to present an accurate preliminary recommendation without wasting time that should have been used elsewhere if the project were dropped. On the other hand, the preliminary planning should not be carried out in such detail that presentation of recommendations will be delayed; if approved, one would much rather have that time available for concentrating on specific phases of a project.

Some typical factors follow that generally are considered in preliminary planning. As an example, assume that modifications are proposed for an existing product line, where several machines of greater capacity are to replace certain existing components.

1. Purchase costs and delivery of new items.
2. Dismantling costs and time requirements, including building repairs or reinforcing.
3. Additional utility requirements, with cost and installation times.
4. Installation times and costs of new items.
5. Downtime estimates of production losses during change-over.
6. Increased capacity estimates.
7. Such preliminary drafting or sketching as may be necessary to study the above factors in sufficient detail.
8. Listing of other advantages which are expected to accrue from the proposed project, such as improvements in working conditions, safety, morale, and quality.

BUDGETING

During the interval between discussions and preliminary planning, and prior to submitting plans to plant management for their consideration, an appropriate amount of budgeting or estimating is required. That requirement will be discussed in greater detail in Chap. 2, but for general presentation of plans, some order-of-magnitude cost figures are necessary, particularly where alternate ideas exist and the best idea must be selected. Generally, an economic study should then be carried out in order to reach the correct solution. In the following list of some of the factors that would be considered in making an economic study, it will be seen that budget figures prepared for equipment installations play an important part in the picture:

1. Expected capacity of proposed equipment.
2. Labor cost of operating the equipment.
3. Raw-materials costs of the product.
4. Cost of packaging materials.
5. Nonlabor operating costs, such as electricity, power, steam, and water.
6. Initial installed price of proposed equipment.
7. Probable maintenance costs of the equipment.
8. Depreciation.
9. Profit margin of the product manufactured by the equipment.

In preparing the equipment cost figures for this economic survey, and particularly if two or more alternate proposals are being considered, it will be seen that order-of-magnitude costs are generally all that are required in order to help determine which proposal should be singled out for detailed estimating. Also, this order-of-magnitude figure can be sent to plant management right away for budget purposes. For either purpose, a covering and approximate figure will suffice. No single component of the total picture need be estimated in detail, for the resultant close accuracy of one component will be lost among the rough figures of the remainder of the components.

To derive order-of-magnitude figures, the first step is to list all known components of the project, such as have been discussed under Preliminary Planning. Then examine each component separately. Put down a reasonable figure for each component. Use as much accuracy as your own skill and experience will afford, and call upon others if necessary, but do not be too careful about details of lesser importance or about the extreme accuracy of the component costs that you will be deriving. If time does permit, you can reexamine some of the more important elements, but do this reexamination work only if you feel that the total result will change significantly and that the conclusions of other people might thereby be affected.

To illustrate what is meant by order-of-magnitude estimating for budget purposes, here is an imaginary situation. You have been asked to help prepare an economic study on the advisability of installing an addition to an existing chemical-manufacturing building. Within the building extension is to be located a chemical-process vessel, two raw-materials storage tanks, a finished-goods storage tank, and appropriate accessory pumps, piping, and instrumentation. You have done your preliminary planning work and are satisfied that you have thought out all the major items of equipment and work components. Then one by one, you will set down cost figures opposite each component.

Here is the mythical conversation that you have with yourself or with your assistant as you put down your ideas on paper:

"For a building that size, better figure $8 per square foot. That's about what we built Building 10 for last year. Say $15,000.

"Let's add $2,000 for concrete footings under the big tanks. The yard crew ought to be able to do that in a week.

"Call up Tom Johnson of the ABC Manufacturing Company to get the current price and delivery on one of their 3,000-gallon stainless-steel agitator vessels. $12,500? All right, but don't forget to add $500 for freight.

"Let's see, we bought three of those raw-materials storage tanks 2 years ago. These are about the same size. I ought to add about 10 per cent for price increases. That'll make about $4,500 total for two, delivered.

"Finished-goods storage tank? It's larger than the two bulk storage tanks, and contains an agitator. It will come to at least $6,000.

"Rigging and mechanical installation? Our fellows can probably clear that work up in about 3 weeks' time. Call it $2,000. Let me add $500 for renting a crane, however. These tanks are too big for our yard crew to handle safely.

"Process piping? Six men from Mac's crew can easily handle that in a month's time. Say $3,000, and double it for materials.

"We can tap into the power line of the old building but there isn't enough steam capacity for heating the new vessel. We can pick it up one building back toward the boiler house. Remember, we put in a larger steam line to that point about 6 months ago. Better put down $5,000 for that remaining tie-in, plus another $1,000 for weatherproof insulation. That'll include the steam-return line, too.

"Sprinklers and lighting to tie in to the old building? Let's figure about $3,000 and also make a note right now to clear the sprinkler piping size with Mr. Smith over at the local office of the fire insurance company in case this project comes through.

"For instrumentation, I'd better put down $1,500. No, let's use $2,000. Sure as shooting, that development gang will come up with an improved gadget just about the time we're ordering the stuff that they now think we need.

"Painting? Our own men will be all tied up on the summer maintenance work just about the time this might come through. Better use a higher figure to cover work by an outside subcontractor. $4,000 should do it. Then, I can still have our own men do it if possible.

"Miscellaneous for small items; clean-up, testing, and running in the equipment? That'll come to another thousand.

"Contingency? I'd better use 30 per cent on labor and materials both. No telling what refinements will come up by the time this project gets OK'd.

"$84,500 is your budget figure, Joe, but I want to round it out to $85,000. Hope the project comes through. We could use that work with our crew in a few months."

See Table 1-1 for a summary of these cost figures.

Now that "Joe" has his construction figure of $85,000 to incorporate into his economic survey, he can send it along to plant management for their budgetary use. They know and you know that, if the project is approved for detailed estimating, your final figures will probably be within a few thousand dollars of that figure, provided that the specifications do not change radically in the meantime.

The use of significant figures should be noted. In the foregoing imaginary example,

Table 1-1. Example of Order-of-magnitude Cost Figures for Budget Purposes

Building structure	$15,000
Concrete footings for storage tanks	2,000
Chemical-process vessel, including freight	13,000
Two bulk storage tanks	4,500
One finished-goods storage tank	6,000
Rigging and mechanical installation	2,500
Process piping and pumps	6,000
Steam-supply piping, insulated	6,000
Sprinklers and lighting	3,000
Instrumentation	2,000
Painting	4,000
Miscellaneous	1,000
	$65,000
30% contingency	19,500
Total	$84,500
Rounded-out budget figure	$85,000

$500 was as close as the estimator tried to get. Therefore, it would not be worthwhile to take time to derive more accurate figures out to hundreds or tens for any of the component costs.

TENTATIVE APPROVAL

When general thought has been applied to a proposed project as outlined in this chapter, certain conclusions will have been reached that should be acted upon. The logical step to take at this point is to present the conclusions and recommendations to plant management for their decision.

The local situation will determine the method of presentation and by whom. It goes without saying that the need for project still exists and that the preliminary studies have borne out this conclusion. The recommendations to proceed with detailed planning and estimating may be presented in conference form or in a fairly complete written form. In any event, at this point plant management makes a decision to go ahead with detailed plans, thereby giving tentative approval to the project.

Chapter 2

PROJECT PROCEDURES FROM ORIGIN TO COMPLETION

By OSWALD STEWART II[1]
Superintendent, Maintenance and Construction Department
Dewey & Almy Chemical Company Division
W. R. Grace & Co.
Cambridge, Mass.

The purpose of this chapter is to set forth in approximate chronological order the major steps which should be taken in organizing a project such as that described in the preceding chapter.

PROJECT DESIGN

It is axiomatic for engineers of any specialized field of activity that in order to prepare accurate written material on a project one must get down to fundamentals by describing as accurately and as completely as time permits all the known elements that will comprise the final project. The first element is "the product to be manufactured," and the second is "how shall it be manufactured?" The first element generally has already been answered by management's approval of the given project. It is the second element of "how" that requires the greatest amount of creative work to be done, and afterward all successive elements can pretty much fall into a logical pattern of activity.

To illustrate the second element of "project design" the author has selected a chemical operation. Even though nomenclature is particularly appropriate to chemical-plant operations, the ordered steps taken in the example do have parallels in the manufacture of any product, and the reader can translate the steps into his own situation. (Trade journals and technical magazines, for instance, frequently carry stories on large and small projects that various companies are accomplishing.)

The premise of this particular project-design example is that research laboratory work has already been accomplished to prove the practicability of manufacturing a certain chemical product; that pilot laboratory work has borne out the conclusions of the research group and has also scaled up the process requirements; that marketing and sales people have vouched for the desirability of manufacturing the given chemical product; and that plant management has approved the initial budget figures for the project. Thereupon, "project-design" work can proceed by first establishing in written form and in chart form the flow diagram of the product.

The preparation of the flow diagram can be made the responsibility of one or more of a selection of departments, depending upon one's particular organizational arrange-

[1] Author is now Communications Coordinator, Sales Engineering Division, Bethlehem Steel Company, Bethlehem, Pa.

ment. Engineering, or research and development departments, for example, are logical selections.

The flow diagram must incorporate all known components of the manufacturing process. It should be established in some convenient graphic form, with an accompanying written report for background. All major pieces of equipment should be specified as carefully as the target time permits, and likewise all the important accessory components. In contrast, minor components, such as steam traps, mechanical drives, or electrical switches, should not clutter up the flow diagram at this stage of the project unless their specifications have a prime effect on the manufacturing process. In general, the specifying of minor accessory equipment should be delegated to the appropriate construction department in order to leave the flow-diagram engineers free for the key items.

Continuing with the example of a chemical process, a typical flow diagram and report would include some of the following items:

1. Raw-materials storage requirements: bulk storage tanks, drum, palletized supplies, etc.
2. Raw-materials handling: transfer piping and pumps, mechanical materials-handling equipment, etc.
3. Process vessels: measuring and mixing equipment, chemical reactors, condensers, coolers, etc.
4. Semifinished- and finished-goods storage requirements, bulk storage, packaging, warehousing, etc.

Each of the foregoing items should be amplified by appropriate technical data such as:

1. Materials of construction.
2. Capacity of vessels.
3. Pipe and pump sizes.
4. Ranges of flow rates.
5. Cycle times and production rates.
6. Utilities and power requirements.
7. Instrumentation requirements.
8. Waste- or scrap-disposal requirements.
9. Optimum maintenance objectives.

Once the flow diagram has been initially designed, approval of it by all parties concerned should be handled by an accepted means of communication, as by circulation of written copies or by conference. The production, engineering, construction, and development departments will have the most to say in the way of comments, but research and sales should also keep informed as to progress at this point, or else keep quiet in the future.

Following acceptance of the flow diagram, detailed planning work should start immediately. Some or all of the following components must be considered:

1. Incorporate standard equipment wherever practicable.
2. Design special equipment where necessary.
3. Prepare equipment layouts.
4. Prepare construction drawings.
5. Consolidate all components into a comprehensive "project-specification report."

At some point along the line, responsibility for carrying out the project must be assigned to one individual as project engineer. In a small company with a small project, this engineer may be in the picture practically from the beginning. In a large company, the practice might be to designate a project engineer only after the flow diagram (or equivalent) has been established and accepted. In general, however, the earlier a project engineer is assigned to the job the better. Whatever the local arrangement is, this chapter is based upon the assumption that a project engineer has been designated at this stage of the project, and the text from now on will read as through the eyes of that engineer.

PREPARE DETAILED COST ESTIMATES

The most important task of the project engineer following the completion of the comprehensive project-specification report is to obtain cost data for each of the written components.   For the purposes of this paragraph, the assumption is made that cost estimates are to be prepared as a necessary step in the submitting of a project request for final approval by plant management.   (A streamlined variation can be kept in mind of the case where "project approval" or a green light has already been given by plant management, based upon preliminary budget estimates.   In that event it may not be required that cost estimates be prepared in formalized detail, but they can be listed simultaneously with the placing of equipment orders and the giving of installation instructions.   These less formalized estimates should then be used by the project engineer as his own management tool to see that he is remaining within the budget or that he can take appropriate steps in case he finds that he is likely to exceed the budget.)

The actual preparation of cost-estimate components should be delegated to the individuals responsible for the particular components.   Duplicated copies of the project-specification report with copies of appropriate drawings attached should be given to each construction supervisor, whether he be known as craft foreman, area engineer, or construction superintendent, for example.

All craft installation costs are to be compiled, such as for carpenters, electricians, pipe fitters, millwrights, mechanics, laborers, painters, lead burners, and masons. If the scope of any construction component is beyond the efficient use of existing craftsmen, and therefore outside contractors are to be utilized, the project engineer must gather this cost-estimate component himself.

In addition, the engineer must obtain costs of all principal equipment items that are not otherwise covered by craft supervisors.   For example, he would be the person responsible for arranging for quotations from manufacturers bidding upon each major piece of new equipment.

Certain other aspects of the project which will affect the cost picture must be considered at this time by the project engineer.   Depending upon whether the size of his company is such that staff people are regularly assigned to these aspects on a part or full-time basis, the project engineer will go to these experts or must search for the recommendations himself, as the case may be.   Some of these other aspects of the project are as follows:

1. Utility requirements, including electric power, steam, air, gas, fuel, and water.
2. Building requirements.
3. Safety considerations.
4. Fire and explosive hazards.
5. Clearance with insurance company on suitability of buildings, equipment, and protective measures.
6. Clearance with local authorities regarding construction-code requirements.
7. Transportation considerations, including road or spur-track construction, shipping and receiving facilities, etc.

Figure 2-1 illustrates an example of an estimate sheet used for the accumulation of labor and materials costs of all aspects of a project.

Component craft costs are figured by multiplying estimated hours by the accepted labor rate.   The quantity of hours should be estimated only approximately, to the nearest practicable unit, such as man-days, man-weeks, crew-weeks, etc.   In this text, the phrase "accepted labor rate" means a labor rate which has been determined by company policy.   Some companies use a rate which consists solely of a man's wage plus specific benefits.   Other companies add to that combination certain overhead costs of the man's own department.   A third case is found in the example of certain companies which add a burden figure that includes all directly related overhead plus an arbitrary percentage of general overhead. (It is not within the scope of this chapter to discuss the derivation of a burden figure, although one basic reason for the range of figures is found in the variation of company policies concerning the extent of capitalization of new projects.)

While calculating craft costs, care must be taken to differentiate between straight-time rates and premium rates. Examples of the latter include the requirement to work certain crafts during shutdown periods (nights, week ends, or holidays) for minimizing interruptions to regular production equipment or personnel; or the requirement to work certain crafts on an overtime basis in order to ensure completion of one construction phase by a specified target date in a tightly controlled schedule.

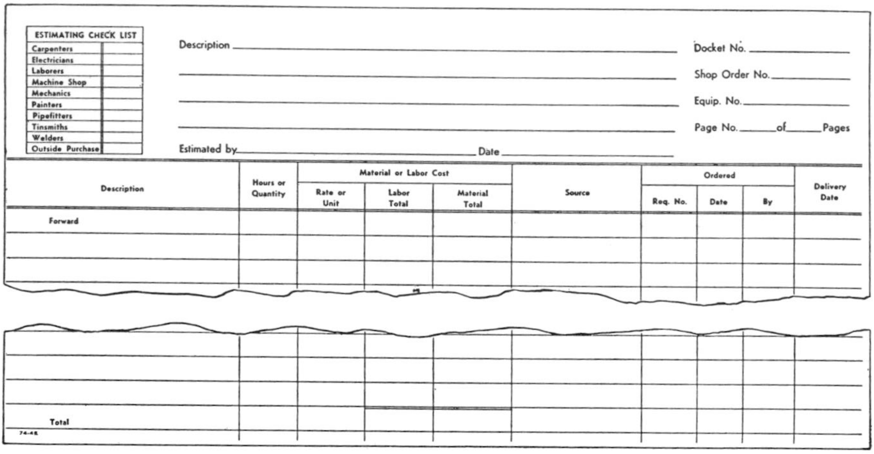
ESTIMATING CHECK LIST
Carpenters
Electricians
Laborers
Machine Shop
Mechanics
Painters
Pipefitters
Tinsmiths
Welders
Outside Purchase

Description ______

Docket No. ______
Shop Order No. ______
Equip. No. ______
Page No. ____ of ____ Pages
Estimated by ______ Date ______

Description	Hours or Quantity	Material or Labor Cost			Source	Ordered			Delivery Date
		Rate or Unit	Labor Total	Material Total		Req. No.	Date	By	
Forward									
Total									

74-48

FIG. 2-1. Estimate sheet used for the accumulation of labor and materials costs.

When all known labor and equipment items are finally set down, the question of how to handle contingency items should be considered. Again, the practice of one's own company will probably dictate the method. The author's own feeling is that contingencies should be handled in a straightforward manner, by adding a certain percentage to the estimated costs and labeling it as such. The size of the percentage would depend upon several factors such as:

1. Degree of detailed planning accomplished prior to making the estimate.
2. Type of project being handled.
3. Quality and quantity of experience of the estimators.
4. Ratio between firm quotation items and nonfirm items.
5. Ratio between material and labor.

Regarding the first statement, a project might be so carefully planned ahead of time that little or no contingency percentage need be added. In contrast, a project might be required to be presented and commenced with such accelerated timing as to preclude thorough estimating. In that event, the project engineer ought to add whatever percentage he feels necessary (say 20 or 30 per cent).

The type of project being handled has a definite relationship to the appropriate amount of contingency that should be considered. In the extreme, a project might be in the category where all people concerned know ahead of time that a degree of risk is present which dictates the adding of a substantial contingency factor despite the most careful preliminary planning.

The third item, experience, is one that should be considered particularly by the project engineer when completing his estimates. If he himself, and his craft estimators, have had good results in the past on similar work, then little or no contingency may be required, save a customary allowance such as plus 10 per cent.   In contrast, if the type of project is new to all, or if one or more estimators have submitted figures in the past which were consistently under the final results, then an allowance should be applied.

The fourth item takes into account the proportion of components of the project which are fixed in cost.   If the majority of the purchased items are based on firm quotations, no contingency need be necessary.   Conversely, if most of the equipment is entered on a guesstimate basis, an appropriate contingency value should be included in the total.   During periods of rapidly rising costs, escalator clauses often are contained in quotations.   These should not be overlooked in determining the contingency.

The last item, the ratio between material and labor, incorporates the thought that in projects where most of the cost represents work done by craft crews and relatively minor amounts of materials are required, a higher contingency would be desirable than if the percentage of labor is at a minimum.

In general, contingency items should be carefully added at the end of the project estimate, and labeled as such, so that all who review the estimate can know how it was derived.   If not done in this fashion, the temptation exists for the craft estimators to hide a larger-than-normal contingency in their figures.   Then the project engineer will be very likely to bounce the subtotals up once more.   By the time the next higher level of management adds their figure when presenting the project, the total has been compounded to an absurd level.   Somewhere along the line, the cost estimate for the project ought to be returned for closer figuring.

To conclude this subsection on cost estimating, mention should be made of an item which includes costs of start-up and running in the equipment prior to turning it over to the production department.   In some instances this could be handled as a contingency item.   In other cases, particularly if extensive tests are a prerequisite for acceptance of the equipment, a substantial amount of money might be necessary to fulfill this obligation, and accordingly it should be provided for in preparing the project estimate (ref. 9).

PREPARE THE APPROPRIATION REQUEST

The purpose of this subsection is to call attention to the fact that careful project-planning work warrants careful presentation of the conclusions and recommendations to plant management.   The foregoing subsections of this chapter have dealt with project design and project-cost estimates.   This subsection will deal briefly with the preparation of the request for funds which, if approved, will signal the green light for the project to start moving.

The fundamental point to keep in mind is that the project engineer by this time has in mind and on file a voluminous amount of data pertinent to the project but that he must sort out, condense, and finalize sufficient facts to form a brief and concise story on which a busy plant management will make its decision.

More likely than not, the technique for actual presentation of the request has been formalized in one's company through use of standard forms such as shop-order or work-order requests.   Figure 2-2 illustrates a typical shop-order request form.   Space exists for such entries as title, serial number, account number, fiscal appropriation, estimated cost, description, and routing.   Depending upon the policy within the company, one shop order might be written for all phases of the project, or several might be issued for major components of the job, or the project might be divided into capital and expense shop orders.   For good cost-control purposes, the project engineer will generally find it useful to have shop-order numbers for each category of work that he wishes to control.   The accounting department will doubtless take the opposite view that a minimum quantity of shop-order numbers is easier for them to keep track of.   Discussion between parties concerned should be arranged to see which viewpoint or compromise point will prevail.

The number of shop orders covering the project will largely determine the wording of the short descriptive title on each one.   Regarding presentation of the paper work

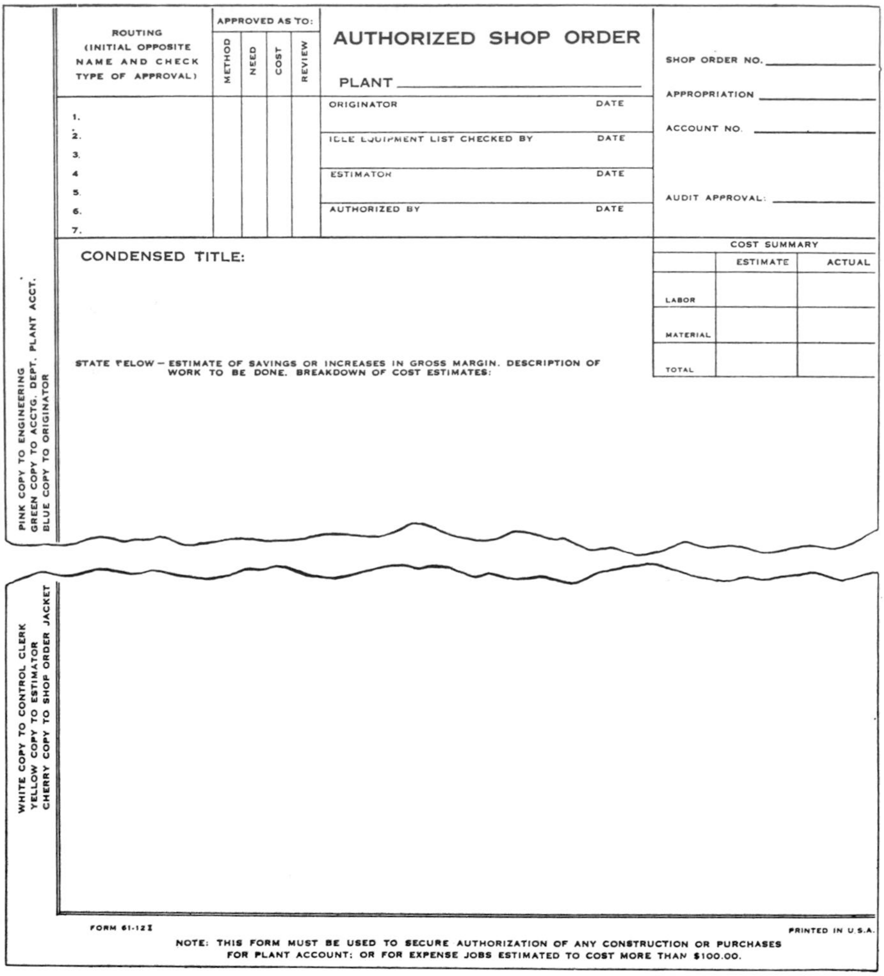

ROUTING (INITIAL OPPOSITE NAME AND CHECK TYPE OF APPROVAL)

APPROVED AS TO: METHOD | NEED | COST | REVIEW

1.
2.
3.
4
5.
6.
7.

AUTHORIZED SHOP ORDER

PLANT ______

ORIGINATOR DATE

IDLE EQUIPMENT LIST CHECKED BY DATE

ESTIMATOR DATE

AUTHORIZED BY DATE

SHOP ORDER NO. ______

APPROPRIATION ______

ACCOUNT NO. ______

AUDIT APPROVAL: ______

CONDENSED TITLE:

COST SUMMARY		
	ESTIMATE	ACTUAL
LABOR		
MATERIAL		
TOTAL		

STATE BELOW – ESTIMATE OF SAVINGS OR INCREASES IN GROSS MARGIN. DESCRIPTION OF WORK TO BE DONE. BREAKDOWN OF COST ESTIMATES:

PINK COPY TO ENGINEERING
GREEN COPY TO ACCTG. DEPT. PLANT ACCT.
BLUE COPY TO ORIGINATOR

WHITE COPY TO CONTROL CLERK
YELLOW COPY TO ESTIMATOR
CHERRY COPY TO SHOP ORDER JACKET

FORM 61-12 I PRINTED IN U.S.A.

NOTE: THIS FORM MUST BE USED TO SECURE AUTHORIZATION OF ANY CONSTRUCTION OR PURCHASES FOR PLANT ACCOUNT; OR FOR EXPENSE JOBS ESTIMATED TO COST MORE THAN $100.00.

Fig. 2-2. Typical shop-order request form.

in the case of multiple shop orders, a covering report should suffice to give the story, unless the practice is to require that each shop order be complete in itself. Assuming that a covering report for the project is acceptable, it should contain at least the following information:

1. Brief title.
2. Cost estimate.
3. Target date.
4. Purpose or aim.
5. Justification.

Whatever supporting facts are necessary for the approving parties to make, their personal evaluations should accompany the report. For example, some of the following would be a part of the preparation of an extensive and expensive project:

1. Project-specification report.
2. Flow diagram.

3. Selected assembly drawings.
4. Equipment-layout drawings.
5. Scale models.

Presentation of the request will vary from routine handling of paper work for small projects up to extensive conference discussions for those projects which greatly affect a company's future activities.

PROJECT ORGANIZATIONAL WORK

Equally important as cost estimating are several phases of organizational planning. These phases include, for example, the following items, and will be treated at this time:

1. Establish labor requirements.
2. Set target dates.
3. Prepare master schedule.
4. Establish running check lists.
5. Organize records system.
6. Organize reporting system.
7. Determine supervisory and staff requirements.
8. Organize the actual project.
9. Complete the project.

1. Establish Labor Requirements. The degree of detail required here can range from a simple summary by craft foremen that "we have enough men to do the job in the required time" in the case of small clear-cut projects, up to complicated long-duration projects that require considerable attention to detail in order that enough men are provided and at the right time. Basically, the detailed cost estimate will provide the correct facts for establishing labor requirements, because in that record will be found the estimated hours of work deemed necessary to do the particular craft job.

When calculating labor requirements from previously prepared cost estimates, and if certain of the hours are known to be figured on an overtime basis for reasons stated earlier, be sure to make allowance for those overtime hours. A simplified case will furnish an example: It is planned to use one welder for a straight-time week fabricating a steel frame for some components of a special machine. It is planned to use the same man during a Saturday-Sunday period to make welding alterations to a building where the presence of solvent vapors of a chemical process prohibit the use of welding or burning equipment during periods of factory operation. Planning in advance for these known limitations, the cost estimator would put down the cost for that amount of welding work as 40 hr at the straight-time rate and 16 additional hr at the appropriate premium rate, or a total of 56 hr of required welding time. Too hasty a look at this total when figuring labor requirements later on in the project might yield the incorrect conclusion that that portion of the project would need part of a second welder.

For calculating and tabulating labor requirements, a form can be devised to suit one's own requirements. An example of such a form is shown in Fig. 2-3. The purpose of this form is to gather data by crafts of all remaining work on existing shop orders plus new work on shop orders which are approved but not yet started. At the bottom of the form data have been entered for estimates of work of docket nature, that is to say work which has been estimated and submitted and approval for which is reasonably certain. In the author's own company, possessing a maintenance and construction department of less than 100 men, it has been found sufficient to update this particular form on a monthly basis. If a particular situation were more fluid or more complex, it might be helpful to gather these data more often than once a month, and to list them in more detail.

Utilizing the collected data is obviously the next step to take. Figure 2-4 shows a summary form which was developed for the needs of a department which combines the requirements for daily maintenance as well as new construction and alteration work. Most of the various entries are self-explanatory, with the purpose in mind of setting down in black and white the multitudinous commitments for the various craftsmen in order to learn how many men are readily available for project work.

In Fig. 2-4 note that potential work is tabulated in three categories: approved shop orders, unapproved shop orders or dockets, and expense job orders (by definition in the author's company, expense job orders cover work which is under $100 in magnitude). These three elements are added up for each craft, and the total is divided by 40 to give man-weeks of work ahead for each craft. Next, to find the number of men available to accomplish that work, enter the number of men in the existing crew,

APPROVED SHOP ORDER	REMAINING WORK BY HOURS AND CRAFTS	CARP.	ELEC.	LAB.	MECH.	PAINT	PIPE	TIN	WELD
	DATE OF REPORT: *APRIL 20*								
5268	DISMANTLE OBSOLETE MIXER, BLDG.35		40	160	80		8		
5269	FLOOR STRENGTHENING WORK, BLDG.35	320		480					40
5270	PURCHASE & INSTALL NEW MIXER, BLDG.35	80	160	240	320	80	80	40	40
5429	OVERHAUL WORN PROD. EQUIP., BLDG.28	60	100	200					
	------- ETC. -------								
	TOTALS	1120	960	1480	2440	640	1890	440	360

DOCKETS AND UNAPPROVED SHOP ORDERS		CARP.	ELEC.	LAB.	MECH.	PAINT	PIPE	TIN	WELD
—	CAPITAL PORTION OF BLDG.12 FUTURE IMPROVEMENT PROJECT	200	400	400	800	240	300	160	160
—	EXPENSED PORTION OF BLDG.12 FUTURE IMPROVEMENT PROJECT	400	160	600	300		120		80
6523	RELOCATE MACHINE #3 FROM BLDG.3 TO BLDG.11	40	120	160	100	40	40	20	
6538	INSTALL THREE 10,000-GAL.TANKS IN TANK FARM		200	300	120	300	240	40	80
6642	FABRICATE AND INSTALL NEW TRANSFER LINE FROM TANK FARM TO BLDG.28			100	100		900		300
	------- ETC. -------								
	TOTALS	1200	1080	2040	1680	920	2420	310	840

FIG. 2-3. Example of work-load form for tabulating labor requirements.

and deduct all who are unable to be utilized for the work load, such as preventive-maintenance men, night-shift men, vacation and sickness absentees. This net-available figure, when divided into the figure representing man-weeks of work for each craft, gives a ratio of man-weeks of work per each available man. This ratio can serve as a management tool in helping to determine proper craft-crew sizes. Experience will show what the best minimum and maximum limits should be, and when it is best to take action to augment or to deplete a given craft crew.

Like all management tools, an impersonal figure by itself does not give a complete answer, and thus the ratio must be adequately interpreted. It is the trend of the various elements making up the ratio which must be observed, also. For instance, even if the ratio is low, an educated guess should be made concerning the likelihood of future work being approved before trained men were placed on layoff.

Figure 2-5 illustrates the charting of the work load of a typical craft, showing four elements of data (approved shop orders, unapproved shop orders, expense job orders, and ratio of work ahead compared with available men).   If faithfully kept up to date, and if properly interpreted, this running-work-load chart can aid in making proper decisions concerning sizes of craft crews.

	DATE OF REPORT: *APRIL 15*							
		CARP.	ELEC.	LAB.	MECH.	PAINT	PIPE	TIN	WELD
1	SHOP ORDER LOAD, HOURS	1120	960	1480	2440	640	1890	440	360
2	DOCKET AND UNAPPROVED SHOP ORDER LOAD, HOURS	1200	1080	2040	1680	920	2420	310	840
3	EXPENSE JOB ORDER BACKLOG, HOURS	530	480	920	1040	230	1490	120	210
4	TOTAL HOURS OF CURRENT WORKLOAD	2850	2520	4440	5160	1790	5800	870	1410
5	TOTAL WEEKS OF CURRENT WORKLOAD	71.3	63.0	111.0	129.0	44.8	145.0	21.8	35.3
6	PRESENT CREW	11	16	13	28	7	22	6	5
7	DEDUCT FOR: NIGHT SHIFT COVERAGE		2		1		2		
8	PM	1	3		2		4		
9	BLDG. 4 AREA MAINTENANCE		1		4		3		
10	VACATION OR LEAVE OF ABSENCE	1		2	3			1	1
11	SICK			1		1	2		
12	NET AVAILABLE	9	10	10	18	6	11	5	4
13	RATIO OF LINE 5/LINE 12	7.9	6.3	11.1	7.2	7.5	13.4	4.4	8.8

REMARKS (WHEN INTERPRETED ALONG WITH WORK LOAD CHART)

1- LABORER AND PIPEFITTING GROUPS ARE SHOWING TOO MUCH BACKLOG OF WORK. IF UPWARD TREND CONTINUES NEXT MONTH, WILL HIRE NEW MEN.

2- TINSMITHING LOAD IS DOWN, BUT NOT ADVISABLE TO CONSIDER LAYOFFS AT THIS TIME, SINCE SUMMER VACATIONS WILL THIN DOWN CREW.

Fig. 2-4. Example of work-load summary sheet.

2. Set Target Dates.   Target dates, or expected dates for completion of phases of a project, should be determined after taking into consideration such factors as shipping dates, in-transit times of all key items of purchased equipment, expected period of construction, and pertinent completion dates imposed by market conditions of the product which is to be manufactured.

If market conditions are such that they are predominant in determining a target date, then the materials and labor components must take a back seat and must be adjusted to fit into the preset target date.   Adjusting the labor crew to fit the date may require a considerable effort in planning and scheduling.   First, for a given craft, and for a given phase of a project, as many men as practical must be placed on the job.   A point of diminishing return will be reached, beyond which men would just get in each other's way.   If the target date still cannot be met, one of two steps can next be taken: to accelerate by means of overtime, or by adding additional shifts.

Careful cost figuring should be accomplished as part of the study to accelerate target dates, in order to ensure that the additional administrative expense involved does not defeat the original purpose of accelerating a target date ahead of what would normally be expected of straight-time work.

Two other principal alternatives exist for speeding up certain phases of project work. Such phases are those wherein certain component parts of the work can be fabricated away from the job, even at the expense of additional supervision, drafting, handling, and the like, and if more people are available than can efficiently work on the job at the job location then these subassemblies can perhaps be fabricated back in the department shops.   If men are not available even if subassemblies can be fabricated away from the job, then the possibility should be explored of subcontracting the work to outside shops.   Particularly in the latter case, costs should be watched.

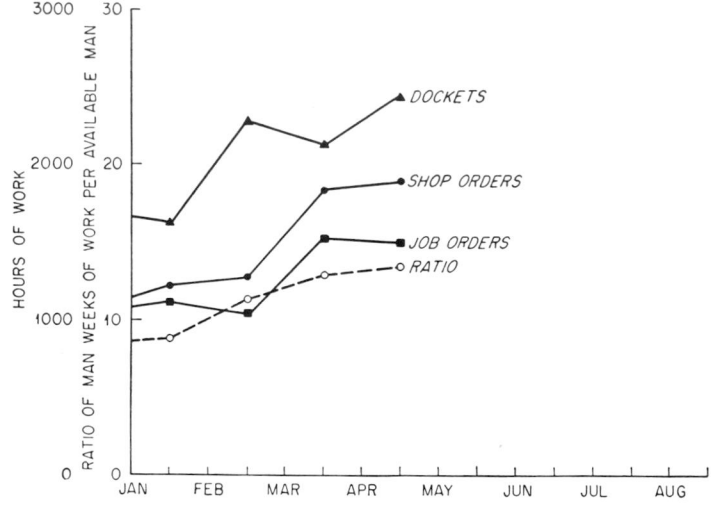

FIG. 2-5. Typical work-load chart for pipe-fitting craft.

Concerning the effect of delivery times upon an accelerated target date, the project engineer must here prove his worth.   This is the area over which he has least control, yet these dates basically determine the schedule of the project.   It goes without saying that, if identical or comparable items are available from more than one source, and if receipt of the particular item is important to the successful scheduling of an important project, then delivery dates as well as quoted costs from competitive suppliers must be vigorously explored.

The use of expediters to assist the project engineer is worthwhile if deliveries of critical items are known to be likely to affect a tight schedule.   Such men should keep track of all important items and take suitable action if certain items are anticipated to be falling behind schedule.

It is in the field of special equipment manufactured by one concern that the scheduling problem may become critical.   Perhaps nothing can be done, and the cherished target date will just have to wait.   Sometimes, however, certain assets such as persuasion, personal visits, mutual friends in upper management, and so on, can work wonders.   A determination to meet the date by hook or by crook usually works, with vigorous action and follow-up to be sure no loose ends unravel to spoil the result. (In this text no mention is made of delivery priorities which are set as part of planning for governmental work.)

3. Prepare Master Schedule.   After all data which govern the setting of a schedule have been gathered, including delivery times of major components, and if these delivery dates are now compatible with the desired target date, a master schedule should be prepared which will then become an operating timetable for the project. This master schedule will serve as one of the most important management tools available to the project engineer.

The fundamental purpose of preparing a schedule is to follow progress of construction and to see how the whole project is blending together toward accomplishment. If carefully operated, a good schedule will signal any delays of components that would affect progress of the project. It will call attention to areas where additional personal supervision or expediting should be placed, either to compensate for delays or to take advantage of improvements in the program.

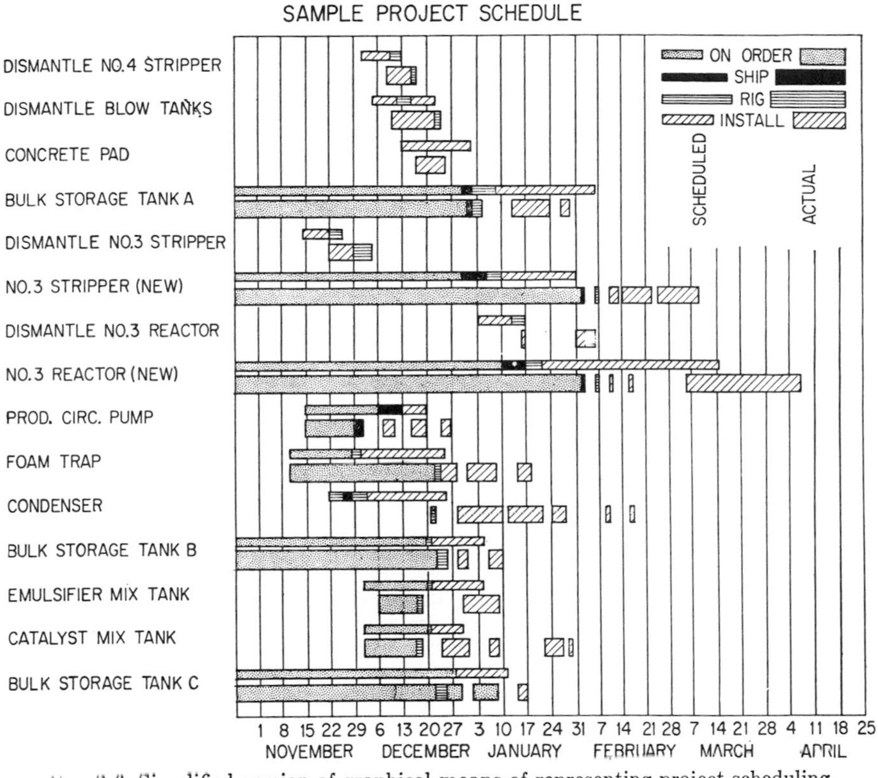

Fig. 2-6. Simplified version of graphical means of representing project scheduling.

A master schedule for a project can be established in any of several ways. Figure 2-6 represents a simplified version of a graphical means of representing project scheduling. In this example, pressure-sensitive tapes of varying characteristics are used to indicate desired data. The purpose in mind when this particular chart was being developed was to be able to make a weekly report of progress by utilizing black-and-white photographs of a large wall chart, and therefore black-and-white tape designs were used. Colored tapes would be equally satisfactory if no photographic report were required or if color photography were suitable, bearing in mind the additional cost and longer processing time for color work.

Once set up on a chart, the use of tapes enables the project engineer to keep track of progress easily. As indicated in Fig. 2-6 the legend gives the meaning of each design. In this case, provision has been made for four elements of data: items on order, shipping times, rigging times, and installation by craft crews. The arbitrarily selected design for each element of data which makes up the prospective target schedule is set down in narrow tapes at the beginning of the project. The same designs in a wider tape indicate actual progress, and the chart can be updated on a daily, weekly, or other periodic basis.

In this example of Fig. 2-6 the pressure-sensitive tapes are placed upon a plastic sheet having preprinted grid lines, and the titles are block-lettered upon labels cut from pressure-sensitive adhesive paper. This technique renders easily readable charts, and the basic grid sheet can be used over and over again.

A simpler version of portraying time-element data is to utilize colored pencils or ink, on paper or cardboard. In any event the user's imagination is the limit as far as how many data can be incorporated into a given master schedule or project-progress chart. For example, the single rendition of installation time in Fig. 2-6 can be further detailed by different designs or colors for each important craft. If one craft must finish work before the next craft can commence, the one line on the chart can be used. If crafts are overlapping, then additional lines must be used.

In addition to schedule charts or progress charts which can be "home-designed" for one's particular need, there are several manufacturers of ready-made equipment within the United States. On the market are many varieties of metal, wood, plastic, and cardboard assemblies which conveniently serve the purpose of presenting data such as items and dates. Most of this equipment is multipurpose in design, with built-in flexibility aimed at many uses such as production, loading control, inventory control, and order-scheduling control. Typical equipment is constructed with slides, pegs, tapes, strings, or other devices designed to portray target dates and actual dates of various components of the particular item being controlled. Not all these commercially available control assemblies are valuable to the project engineer for his special-purpose requirements, but he may find just the right one to meet his needs.

Before leaving this topic of commercially available equipment, a reminder is in order that articles frequently appear in technical magazines illustrating the use that some particular plant is making of a purchased control chart (ref. 10).

Regardless of how the master schedule is set up, the project engineer must keep it up to date and must watch it carefully to obtain maximum use from it. He and his construction supervisors and his equipment expediters are the ones who will derive maximum use from the schedule. A glance will tell whether action need be taken on any particular component. For example, if a heavy piece of equipment is expected, the schedule will give the key as to when the proper materials-handling equipment must be organized, such as crane or truck. For another example, the respective construction supervisors will learn from the schedule when they must have their crews available for the next job component, and when they must gather the construction materials which are too small to be charted separately.

Reverting to the first paragraph of this subsection on preparing a master schedule, it should be noted that the actual setting down of expected time components of each of the phases of the project will do much to bring the entire project into focus. Assuming that a tight and accelerated schedule is under consideration, then all time components must be carefully listed. Concerning key pieces of equipment, several components of the final delivery time must be considered, such as paper work for the ordering, discussion and acceptance of manufacturers' blueprints, fabrication time if a nonstock item is involved, and time required for shipment. Concerning installation by craft crews, close cross reference should be made to the cost and labor estimates described in earlier paragraphs.

Working backward from the expected receipt of principal equipment items, it will be quickly seen how certain prior items fit into the schedule picture. When these so-called "prior items" are pretty well fixed into position on the schedule by virtue of having to meet terminal dates of allied items, then the time available for installation will become apparent. As a corollary, knowing the time available for installing a given item, each construction supervisor can anticipate how large a crew will be necessary to accomplish the work, whether overtime or additional shift coverage will be necessary, and whether any other appropriate special treatment will be necessary. Conversely, proper interpretation of the master schedule will provide information as to what installation items could be safely deferred if it becomes necessary to concentrate crews upon a key item that is falling behind schedule.

The preparation and continuance of a master schedule have additional advantages to the project engineer.   One advantage is in its value to demonstrate physical and theoretical or target progress to the interested parties, such as the future occupants of the new equipment area, sales personnel, and inspecting groups from plant management.   A second value is in the aid it will provide in preparing progress reports. This feature will be amplified in subsection 6.

4. Establish Running Check Lists.   Correlative to the "project-specification report" which was listed early in this chapter, a series of check lists should be organized by practically all supervisors and other salaried people who have responsibility for any portion of the project.   The project-specification report is intended to contain as many appropriate technical specification data as were permitted by the available project-design time, yet countless other questions will come up, and answers must be forthcoming at the proper time if the project is to continue smoothly.   If the project is of practically any size whatsoever, more questions will arise than can safely be carried in one's head.   Therefore, some easy system of written notes or check lists should be adopted.   These check lists will tend to promote orderly thinking and action, so that, when the time comes for a certain detail to be handled, any questions will have already been thought out.   Consequently, time will not be wasted by construction crews awaiting decisions.   An important by-product is that there is less likelihood that a piece of equipment will be installed improperly.   Make it right the first time; don't get into the position of having to do a job twice over!

There are at least two varieties of check lists.   One is the personal-notebook list which should be adopted by each responsible person of the project.   This list should be added to continually as the individual goes about his work, supervising the jobs at hand and thinking ahead to the future related work.   "Be sure that electricians install temporary light by Thursday PM," and "Have lube man check oil level of new gearbox" are two likely examples of a personal check list.   When carefully reviewed during each day, and checked off when completed, personal check lists will help make the details of the project flow smoothly.

A second variety of check lists is the more formal list which is prepared by the project engineer for the guidance of his construction supervisor.   A common-sense balance must be achieved here, and it will be a mark of the leadership ability of the project engineer as to how well he strikes the right balance.   His function is to delegate certain responsibilities, and therefore he must not permit himself to do all the thinking for his supervisors or to attend to too many details.   On the other hand, in his frequent travels around the area of the project, an alert project engineer is bound to visualize certain aspects of the work that might have escaped the attention of men who are occupied with affairs of the moment.   His own personal check list should be utilized to jot down these ideas.   Then, back at the office, he should formalize his thoughts in some convenient form of instructions so that the matters are properly handled.

5. Organize Record System.   The keeping of proper records is of such a nature that much literature is available on the subject.   It is not the purpose of this subsection to explore fully all aspects of the problem.   Furthermore, records handling and records requirements vary widely from company to company, and each company is presumably more or less satisfied with what it has, else it would be seeking improvements.   Excluded from the discussion also are such basic records as payroll data, purchase orders, and the like.   With that premise, some comments on records keeping are nevertheless appropriate from the point of view of the project engineer.

It is undoubtedly a truism to state that with regard to records systems (as in all fields of activities) the project engineer must seek an engineering compromise in determining the extent of his administrative paper-work requirements.   If the scope is too broad, the system is likely to be cumbersome and expensive and will duplicate existing procedures handled by the main office.   If the scope is too narrow, then the project engineer may not be availing himself of certain vital data which are desirable for the control of his project.   Somewhere in between these two extremes is the proper course to be selected.

The engineering approach to the problem is to survey the existing data available, keeping in mind the frequency and rapidity of receiving such data.   If one or more elements of data are not being received quickly enough, consultation should be made with the appropriate staff group to determine whether an improvement can be arranged, at least temporarily, to fit the local requirements of the project. It may develop that no gain can be made here, because of local reasons apparent to both the engineer and the staff group with whom he has been consulting. The project engineer must then decide how important it is to collect this missing or slow component of data, and then act according to his conclusions.

The following list is intended to illustrate typical components of data useful to the control of a project. The list can serve only as a guide and is not claimed to be complete.

1. Hours worked by crafts.
2. Labor costs charged to project, including overhead.
3. Materials charged to project.
4. Overtime hours and costs charged to project.
5. Remaining hours and dollars on project.
6. Record of principal equipment items not yet received or not yet billed to the project.
7. Permanent data: equipment cards, manufacturers' prints, and instruction books.

It will be seen that certain items of the foregoing list can help to serve as a composite yardstick to measure physical and fiscal progress of the project. Bearing in mind the important instruction from plant management that the project engineer is held accountable for the proper administration of the project, the engineer should select those components of data which will aid him in his task of control.

For any of the foregoing components of control data which are not to be reported by the accounting department, it is reasonably easy for the project engineer to set up a simple duplicated form and to cause the proper entries to be kept. If desired, the data can be kept elaborately to fulfill some special purpose. For instance, a running record of hours remaining on a project, by crafts, can serve as an excellent stimulus to craft supervisors to make sure that their work is progressing on schedule.

Item 3 above can well be amplified to incorporate a great many important data on critical materials into one central location which is constantly available to the project engineer for immediate reference. The use of a duplicated form here is recommended for the orderly recording of certain data. Such data include the following:

1. Item on order.
2. Name of supplier.
3. Supplier's quotation number, if applicable.
4. Manufacturer's certified prints to be received, if applicable.
5. Date ordered, and by whom.
6. Date of expected shipment.
7. Requisition and/or purchase-order number.
8. Quoted cost, if available, or order-of-magnitude cost.
9. Other pertinent date if available or when available that might prove helpful later to an expediter such as date of written acknowledgment of order by supplier, revised shipment date, method of transportation, or bill of lading.
10. Instructions to receiving department for temporary storage of items as received, until ready for installation (copies of these instructions should go to receiving department and also to appropriate craft foremen and expediters.)

Figure 2-7 illustrates a log sheet for recording certain data concerning critical materials.

One's own local situation will determine the extent of data that should be recorded on the suggested form or log sheet shown in Fig. 2-7. If copies of purchase orders are quickly received from the purchasing department, a cross reference to a purchase-order copy on file will simplify matters greatly. On the other hand, if it takes several days to process and receive purchase orders, then an up-to-date log which is kept in the project engineer's office will provide answers to questions that arise in the interim.

The author knows of one manufacturing concern where the technique has worked well of posting daily "remaining hours" onto a large board near the time clock of the maintenance and construction department. In this particular company, the work load had proved to be constant enough through the years and a sufficient backlog of work always existed so that no psychological slowdown appeared as a given project neared completion. Instead, each craft group took pride in watching the daily posting and in comparing it with progress which they knew they were making on the job. If one craft group, for example, had progressed more slowly than the trained estimator had calculated when originally setting up the job, then the "remaining hours" posting would reveal the difficulty. Specifically, assume an example of a job that was figured to require 100 hr of welding time. If 75 hr had been spent on the job, 25 hr would show as remaining hours on the control board. If it were obvious to all concerned that the amount of welding were less than 75 per cent complete, then part of the job could be anticipated to run over the estimate. In the particular manufacturing concern referred to by the author, the craft crews had enough experience with the accuracy of the estimators that any discrepancies like the illustration served to jack up their performance in order that they might not end up with an unfavorable showing.

S.O. *5270*   TITLE: *PURCHASE AND INSTALL NEW MIXER, BLDG 35*

ITEM	SUPPLIER	ORDERED BY / DATE	REQ. # / P.O. #	SHIP WHEN ? / ACT. SHIP	HOW TO BE SHIPPED	SUPPLIER'S QUOTE #
MIXER, MODEL 3A	*BROWN CO.*	O.S. / 4/12	D-3248 / 18,386	6/15	*TRUCK, ABC TRANSP.*	A-1532, 2/10
VARISPEED DRIVE, 25 H.P.	*SMITH, INC.*	O.S. / 4/14	D-3250 / 18,433	5/20	*TRUCK, XYZ LINES*	283-B, 1/15
MOTOR, 25 H.P., 900 RPM	*SPECIFIC ELECTRIC*	J.F.K. / 4/20	D-4320 / 18,861	6/20	*EXPRESS*	NONE

FIG. 2-7. Example of log sheet for recording key information on critical items as orders are being placed.

Not all companies may be in the fortunate position of being able to use the "remaining hours" technique with such direct success as in the foregoing example. However, it is apparent that the technique does have control advantages for the project engineer and craft supervisors. Two main conclusions can be continually derived: First, a given craft component of the project is or is not on schedule, and appropriate action can be taken. Second, when translated into "dollars remaining," the engineer can have a daily insight into how he stands budgetwise. This information may be very important to him, particularly if the expenditure reports from accounting are received several days or more behind time. Armed with up-to-date information, the project engineer can at least ask for additional funds before rather than after the fact, if he finds himself in that situation.

6. Organize Reporting System. Correlative to the records discussed in subsection 5, another important responsibility of the project engineer is to initiate procedures whereby all interested personnel can be kept informed as to progress. Again, the degree of detail depends upon the situation. The magnitude and scope of the project and the complexity of the company will determine the extent of reporting. The range of reports might vary from informal periodic conversations up to detailed written reports of all phases of progress, including costs, physical progress, problems encountered, photographic enclosures, and so on.

Assuming that the project engineer himself has some say in the matter, a common-sense rule that ought to be followed in organizing a reporting system is that sufficient data should be included to enable one's superiors to exercise general control and yet not so many lesser important details should be included as to detract from the conciseness of the report. For discussion purposes, it is assumed that daily specific cost reports are a function of the accounting department rather than of the project engineer's staff.   General summaries of the cost picture, however, should be reported whenever significant.

It should be remembered that the preparation of reports has an important unpublicized value in addition to the obvious purpose of telling others what is going on. The actual preparation of a report forces the originator to focus his attention on what is happening in his own bailiwick.   As long as he is not required to prepare *burdensome* reports, the good project engineer will benefit from having to think out the good and bad points of his project, and to report on them accordingly.   Mentioning unfavorable items is a powerful stimulus to taking corrective action if it is at all within human capacity.

The following are suggested as typical items of information that could be presented in periodic progress reports:

1. Highlights of progress during the reporting period.
2. Photographic record of progress (refs. 11 and 12).
3. Major unforeseen obstacles encountered and overcome.
4. Major unforeseen obstacles encountered still to be overcome.
5. Significant changes to equipment from the original project specification report.
6. Approximate percentage of completion of major components.
7. Changes in target date, if any, brought about by pressures from sales department, or delays due to circumstances beyond control.
8. General cost picture.
9. Commendations for good work performed by individuals or groups.

When incorporated into an appropriate report, distribution of copies to all interested people gives one additional management tool to the project engineer.   By prior arrangement or by past practice within the company, acceptance of a written report by those on the distribution list should constitute approval if no contrary comments are forthcoming.   This arrangement will permit the project engineer to proceed rapidly on all but the most important questions, in which case he still may deem it wise to get into personal touch with those people directly concerned.   In addition, this arrangement places responsibility directly upon those individuals concerned to contact the engineer and to inspect the project location quickly enough to satisfy themselves that correct decisions are being made.   One important purpose of this stipulation is that it serves to protect the project engineer from the dilatory individual who otherwise might want to come down 2 weeks later to demand a costly change.

7. Determine Supervisory and Staff Requirements.   The author does not intend to devote much space to this phase of project organization.   Although vitally important to the project, the determination of proper supervisory and staff requirements is something that can be answered better by one's judgment and experience rather than by many pages of printed matter.   More often than not, supervisory requirements will be determined basically by what men are already available in the maintenance and construction department.   Both quality and quantity of the existing force will serve as a yardstick if the force is to be augmented.   To enlarge on this thought, assume that a sizable construction project is to be undertaken and that the decision has been made to augment the existing craft groups by increased hirings for all but certain specialty phases of the job.   For the latter, it is planned to obtain subcontractors.   The further assumption is made that the decision to increase the permanent force was based upon a long-range view of sufficient continuing work to support the larger force for a substantial period of time.   Obviously, the quantity of men to hire for hourly jobs has been determined largely through use of work-load calculations.

In determining the craft supervisory requirements for the combined force of present and new men, it follows that local conditions plus judgment of past performance will govern.

There is no arbitrary rule which flatly states how many workmen a supervisor is expected to manage.   Responses to questions put to group after group at the National Plant Maintenance and Engineering Conferences show that ratios in different plants vary from 1 to 5 to 1 to 40, or even more.   Some of the factors which go into the final result of supervisory ratios are as follows:

1. Existing practice of the locality for like or similar crafts.
2. Existing practice of the plant for like or similar crafts.
3. Degree of skill of the craft under question.
4. Technical considerations of the craft.
5. Competence, experience, and personality of the supervisor.
6. Craft efficiency expected.
7. Physical or geographical coverage expected of the supervisor.

At the risk of being redundant and nonconclusive, about all that can be stated in the foregoing hypothetical case of augmenting an existing work force is that the project engineer must carefully weigh all pertinent factors and come up with the right answer as to how many additional supervisors he will need in order to handle the large amount of workmen!

The question of establishing staff requirements is also one that cannot be arbitrarily answered.   However, since work measurement (as a general expression) often is easier to apply to staff people in lower echelons than to straight supervisory people, the problem is generally not difficult to solve.

For the purposes of this subsection, the category of "staff people" includes all nonsupervisory people who report directly or indirectly to the project engineer.   Such people, for example, are the following:

1. Assistant project engineer.
2. Expediters.
3. Order clerks.
4. Time clerks.
5. Secretaries.
6. Stenographers.

Quantity and quality requirements for staff people for the project are determined by the same sort of reasoning that is applied to the problem of establishing supervisory requirements.

8. Organize the Actual Project.   The foregoing subsections discuss various steppingstones which are necessary for the proper administration and organization of a project; this subsection deals briefly with more intangible matters that are the personal responsibility of no one other than the project engineer himself.   Much can be delegated, yet the qualities of good leadership demand that the alert project engineer reserve to himself and exercise certain top functions of control.   Nothing takes the place of coordinated direct supervision.   This theme of leadership is, of course, treated fully in the countless number of books on management and related topics. However, several specific functions can be listed which may prove helpful to a project engineer in his task of organizing, administering, and successfully completing the project which has been given to him by top management for executing:

1. Tread the fine line between too much and too little supervision of all personnel connected with the project.
2. Expect and receive prompt and accurate data on appropriate phases of the project.
3. Perform sufficient inspections of the project that he can satisfy himself as to progress and can ensure that the company is getting a fair return on all dollars spent for both labor and material.
4. Detect and act swiftly to smooth out any frictions that might spring up among project personnel.
5. Seek opportunities to commend project personnel for work well done.
6. Not attempt to shoulder all morale aspects alone.   Even though he represents upper management to the majority of project personnel, he should see to it that frequent visits are made by top people of the company so that even the men at the bottom of the totem pole know that their contribution to the project is appreciated all the way up the ladder.
7. Expect and receive technical competence from staff and supervisory personnel of the project.

9. Complete the Project. From heartfelt experience, the author knows that one of the most difficult parts of a project is how to conclude it successfully and properly. Psychologically, the finishing touches of a project are difficult to apply, frequently because a new assignment is already claiming one's attention. Perhaps the day will never come when a busy project engineer can leave a project with the honest satisfaction that he has done all that should be done. However, with that ultimate goal in mind, some conclusions are in order.

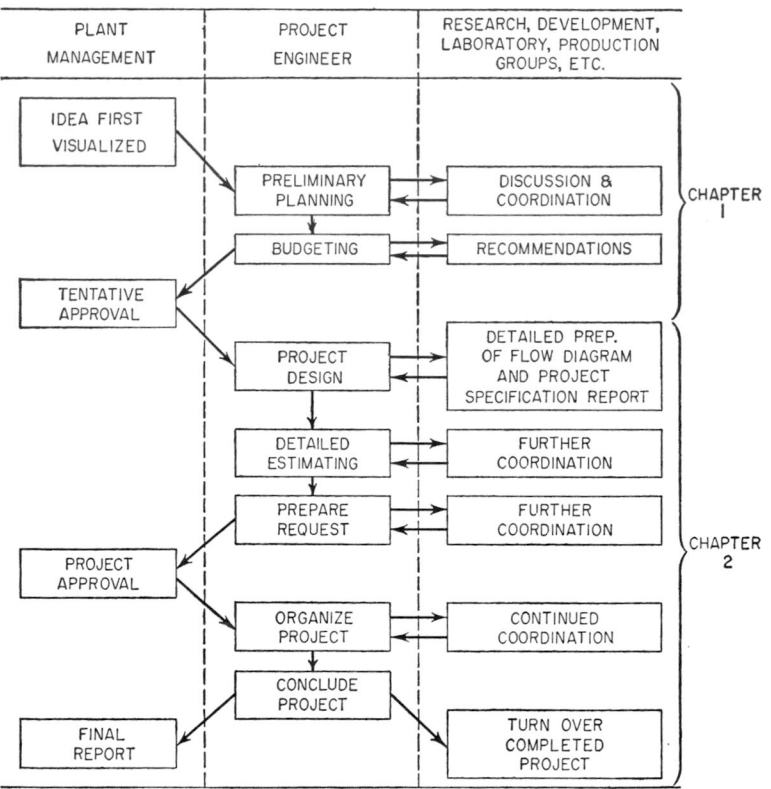

FIG. 2-8. Flow diagram of a project.

The following is a check list of concluding steps of a project. Doubtless other steps will occur to the reader for a given situation, and some steps will be unnecessary in certain situations.

1. Inspect physical completion of all components.
2. Test all components to ensure that project theoretical specifications have been met.
3. Test all components for proper operating characteristics, including mechanical, electrical, piping, and safety standards.
4. Coordinate test work with development personnel.
5. Prepare operating instructions or manual.
6. Instruct operating personnel in proper use of all equipment.
7. Prepare final report for engineering files, giving the original project specification report, with all changes thereto, and tabulate all manufacturers' specification data. Include copies of photographic records of project, if such a photographic story was made.

8. For maintenance department use, consolidate all appropriate data into equipment records.
9. Make recommendations for spare-parts procurement.
10. Supervise the organizing of preventive-maintenance programs for all project equipment.
11. Close out all appropriation requests, notifying plant management of final costs, with explanations of underruns or overruns if outside a prescribed plus or minus limit.
12. Prepare make-good report for plant management after a prescribed interval of time, indicating whether the performance of the newly installed equipment is living up to expectations.
13. Turn final responsibility for the equipment over to the user.
14. Notify insurance companies that the new equipment can be given a final inspection by them.

CONCLUSION

To summarize the principal components of project control, Fig. 2-8 has been prepared. It is in the form of an organization chart and could be termed a "flow diagram" of a basic idea as it is transformed into a finished project via the engineering mechanism of project control.

Each reader can alter the contents and location of some of the boxes of the diagram to fit his own situation, yet the general pattern will remain of an orderly approach to the task of organizing a project efficiently and rapidly in order to carry out a given assignment from plant management.

BIBLIOGRAPHY

1. Baird, D. R.: Machinery Moved Without Losing Time on Production, *Mill and Factory*, April, 1954, pp. 129–131.
2. Beard, C. S.: What an Instrument Department Might Do in Your Plant, *Plant Eng.*, September, 1954, pp. 96–98; October, 1954, pp. 114–115.
3. Muther, Richard: "Practical Plant Layout," McGraw-Hill Book Company, Inc., New York, 1955.
4. Turner, George: Scale Models Helped Plan Plant and Processes, *Factory Management and Maintenance*, October, 1954, pp. 110–112.
5. Plant Layout Made Easy Saves Dollars (story on American Airlines Maintenance and Supply Depot at Tulsa), *Factory Management and Maintenance*, February, 1955, p. 103.
6. A New Twist to the Use of Scale Models: Layout to Blueprint—No Draftsmen (Story on Kaiser-Frazer's Willow Run Plant), *Factory Management and Maintenance*, June, 1951, pp. 88–89.
7. Sleeter, Frank, R. F. McCaw, and P. R. Yeager: R.C.A.'s Cherry Hill Project—A Manual of Methods, *Plant Eng.*, December, 1954, pp. 65–80.
8. Forkos, J. F.: General Foods Compares All Costs Before Selecting Plant Equipment, *Plant Eng.*, April, 1952, pp. 83–85.
9. Sauerman, D. M.: How To Estimate Job Costs on the Nose, *Factory Management and Maintenance*, December, 1954, pp. 110–113.
10. Lincoln, H. T.: Maintenance Schedule Board Needs Only One Form for Tight Control, *Factory Management and Maintenance*, April, 1955, pp. 90–92.
11. Camera at Work, *Plant Eng.*, March and April, 1952.
12. Burns, H. A., and W. R. Sutton: Camera Short Cuts for Plant Changes, *Plant Eng.*, August, 1955, pp. 88–89.
13. Diary of Plant Construction: How Minneapolis-Honeywell Insures Fast, Accurate Buildings, *Plant Eng.*, February, 1955, pp. 79–80.
14. Oakhill, Frederic: For Best Results—Use Standard Procedures, *Plant Eng.*, April, 1952, pp. 92–93.

Section 5

COSTS AND BUDGETS FOR MAINTENANCE OPERATIONS

Chapter 1

RECORDING, SUMMARIZING, AND DISTRIBUTING COST DATA

By Charles E. Knight
General Superintendent of Engineering and Manufacturing Services
Monsanto Company
Plastics Division
Springfield, Mass.

There are two general goals of any cost system. One is to provide an accounting activity with information required for proper bookkeeping; the other is to provide the operating department with information required for its internal control and performance evaluation. Basically, this chapter explores the ways and means of recording and summarizing data, applying appropriate methods of distribution, and arriving at a complete cost picture which will satisfy those objectives.

The first step consists of a presentation of definitions and a discussion of terms. The next step is a discussion, under the heading, Accumulation and Distribution of Indirect Charges, of problems involved in an equitable distribution of the indirect type of costs which are difficult to segregate into units chargeable to a specific job or department. The basic steps of recording, summarizing, and distributing then are covered in the order of their normal occurrence.

DEFINITIONS

There are five general categories of maintenance department expense:

1. Additions to capital, which include:
   a. New equipment.
   b. Improvements.
   c. Replacements.
2. Repair and maintenance expense, including:
   a. Breakdown repair.
   b. Routine inspections and preventive maintenance.
   c. Upkeep, such as painting.
   d. Replacement from wear.
   e. Building repair.
3. Dismantling expense.
4. The cost of producing and distributing utilities, including electricity, steam, water, and compressed air.
5. Miscellaneous expense to include items such as:
   a. Experimental work that is written off.

  b. Equipment cleaning.
  c. Janitorial service.
  d. Trash removal.
  e. Other services included in maintenance department activity which are not in any of the above categories.

Additions to Capital.   This implies the total cost of work performed by the maintenance department on an addition to the capital assets of the company.   Naturally, the criterion for classifying this type of cost should be the interpretation placed on it by the Department of Internal Revenue for taxation purposes.   However, each company has considerable latitude to interpret Federal regulations within its own accounting procedures and policy.

  A complete new piece of equipment is easily defined as a capital addition whether it is purchased or built, and becomes a clear example of capital expense.   As such it must be given life for depreciation, and amortization charges are added to plant overhead in proportion to its cost.   Some organizations consider small items of new equipment as expendable and, therefore, do not define them as capital additions. This group may include such things as desk fans, fractional-horsepower motors, and office equipment, where life expectancy is short.   The monetary limit on such items may vary.   Capital equipment may be defined as a new and separate unit of property or a distinct extension of an existing unit of property.

  Improvements and betterments may be defined as alterations, modernizations, or structural changes to a building or unit of equipment which result in a better piece of property from the standpoint of increased durability, productivity, or efficiency. In general, an improvement should prolong the useful life of an existing facility. Frequently this necessitates substitution of a substantially new component for an outdated portion of the equipment.

  A replacement is defined as a substitution in kind of a unit or major part which results in a longer useful life of the unit of property.   A replacement may have a greater or smaller value than its predecessor.   However, since as a result of this replacement, either the entire original unit or a major portion thereof ceases to exist and its place is taken by a completely different unit with a life expectancy far in excess of that remaining in the original piece of equipment, it should be considered a capital expenditure with revised depreciation charges.

  Repair and Maintenance Expense.   This category includes all expense which accrues from maintaining the plant and its equipment in satisfactory operating condition.   Strictly speaking, no expense resulting in an improvement to existing facilities should be so classified.   In practice, however, it is extremely difficult for a maintenance department to perform its normal functions without improving the condition of the equipment.   Preventive maintenance in whatever form, whether it be routine inspections or a repair in anticipation of breakdown, must be included as part of the repair expense.   In many companies lubrication is considered part of the preventive-maintenance program.

  Breakdown repair, as the term indicates, includes that expense incurred in "fixing things when they break."   This category of expense has been traditionally considered the primary mission of maintenance, and the major cost-reduction efforts are in this area.   Where a preventive-maintenance program exists, it is frequently necessary to decide whether a planned shutdown for maintenance is part of preventive-maintenance expense or more properly classified as expense of the breakdown repair which it allegedly avoided.   This question is obviously academic so far as the plant at large is concerned, since the charges are all part of the maintenance bill and the differentiation, if necessary, should be at the discretion of the company involved.

  Upkeep maintenance is sometimes segregated from other categories since it usually involves routine operations which can be planned and budgeted in advance.   It is also an expense which usually can be geared at higher or lower levels, depending on the philosophy of the company at any particular time and the business situation.   These expenses can also be manipulated within rather broad limits without permanent loss of value or interference with plant productivity.   Such expenses are those resulting from painting, road repair, and building maintenance, except where such work is required to maintain standards of plant safety.

The above three groups, i.e., breakdown maintenance, preventive maintenance, and upkeep maintenance, must become a part of manufacturing expense and as such make up the true maintenance bill. It is important to separate them in the cost system to provide a more consistent means of comparison and to avoid distortion from expense of nonmaintenance activities.

Dismantling Expense.   This classification includes the cost of removal of obsolete or abandoned equipment. It should be incurred only when an entire unit or major portion is removed and such cost is over that capitalized in a new installation. Usually this is a minor item, but where major changes are in progress and the expense cannot be treated as new capital, the inclusion of it in maintenance expense can adversely affect the true cost of maintenance.

Cost of Producing and Distributing Utilities.   This category should include the cost of fuel, the cost of all purchased utilities such as steam, electricity, or water, and the cost of labor to produce and/or distribute them. Repair costs involved in maintaining utilities systems are a true maintenance expense and as such should be included as part of this cost picture. Utilities generally include steam, electric power, water, compressed air, centralized hydraulic systems, and illuminating gas which is handled through a plant-wide distribution system. In some cases plant-wide systems for oxygen, inert gas, etc., are included. Sewers are often considered a utility. The cost of all these items that are the responsibility of the maintenance department but are distributed plant-wide as a service to producing areas should be segregated from other maintenance expense.

Miscellaneous Expenses.   The category of miscellaneous expenses tends to be a catch-all for activities included with the maintenance department. These activities vary with different companies and are often the bases for difficulties in comparing maintenance performance between plants of essentially the same type. Many can be defended as being true maintenance, depending on the philosophy of the plant or company involved. In general, this category includes those services which vary considerably with occupancy or the standard of housekeeping while not materially affecting the direct output of the production unit; or it is work performed by the maintenance department by reason of expediency rather than its appropriateness to maintenance work. In the former category are such items of expense as janitorial service, trash disposal, snow removal, grounds keeping, and window washing. In the second group may be included work of an experimental nature.

Elements of Cost.   Most accounting departments use six major categories to define the elements of the cost classifications discussed above. These are: equipment, supplies, labor, outside services, maintenance department overhead, and plant overhead.

Equipment is normally considered to be those items purchased as units or manufactured in the plant shop as a complete assembly. This can range from a reducing valve to major units such as a loom or a rolling mill. There is a gray area in differentiation between equipment and supplies for smaller items but, in general, it can be resolved by classifying those things as supplies which would normally be stocked either in maintenance stores or mill supply house. A small general-purpose reducing valve may be considered a supply; while a large special-application valve may be considered a piece of equipment.

Supplies are those items normally carried in a maintenance department or in plant stores. They include such items as nuts, bolts, pipe and pipe fittings, spare parts, sheet metal, and other commodities normally purchased in bulk. It is true that many of these become a part of shop-fabricated equipment, in which case they lose their status as a supply. As such their cost should be differentiated from the cost of their use in repair work performed by the maintenance department.

Labor, of course, is the craft time charged against a specific job. This is normally considered to be only that time spent by a craftsman or a laborer in the actual performance of the work requested.

Outside services are generally in the form of labor and know-how purchased through a contractor or supplier where both the overhead and profit of the supplier are included in the bill. This classification may also include equipment rental or engineering service.

Maintenance department overhead covers all the expenses of maintenance department operation that cannot be directly charged to specific work units. In the area of supervision and engineering service there is considerable divergence in actual practice. Sometimes this entire expense is accumulated as a single item and becomes part of maintenance overhead, while in other plants it is charged entirely against specific jobs. The net difference in over-all maintenance cost is negligible, but the effect on comparison of costs for specific equipment types or departments can be considerably affected by differences in the methods of distributing supervisory and engineering overhead. Maintenance and depreciation of machine tools; cost of expense supplies such as drills, files, and gloves; insurance; vacation credit; and the like are also considered part of maintenance department overhead, as well as building rent, heating steam, and other utilities that are distributed to the maintenance department.

Plant overhead includes those plant administrative expenses that must be shared by all departments, including maintenance. Top-management salaries; the cost of personnel, purchasing, and other similar service organizations; as well as any other expense that is a necessary part of the company operation but which cannot be conveniently allocated to a specific department or activity go to make up the plant-overhead portion of the total cost of maintenance service.

Accumulation and Distribution of Indirect Charges. Distribution of maintenance department expenses can be directed more easily if these costs are divided into four major categories of work, i.e., work done on:

1. Process or production equipment.
2. Buildings.
3. Services.
4. Utilities.

Two types of charges must be accumulated in each of these categories. The first of these is the so-called direct charges which are essentially all those in cost elements 1 through 4 above which can be identified completely with one of these classifications. In some instances maintenance overhead, particularly supervisory coverage, also can be allocated directly and considered a direct charge. This could well be true of a major construction project. In general, all other costs allocated to these four classifications are the overhead or indirect costs and must be distributed on some equitable basis among them.

There are many bases for this distribution, some of which are:

1. Dollars spent.
2. Man-hours used.
3. People served.
4. Floor space.
5. Power consumed.
6. Dollar value of equipment maintained.

Distribution by Dollars Spent. The handling of most storeroom charges is an excellent example of this type of distribution. The overhead expense for operation of the stores activity is usually distributed to each item as a percentage of its cost in the same way the overhead cost of utility distribution is frequently redistributed in proportion to the amount of the utility used which, in turn, amounts to distribution based on dollars of cost.

Distribution by Man-hours Used. Supervisory overhead, as well as the operating cost of a maintenance shop and its equipment, is generally distributed on the basis of man-hours expended. This seems a simple and equitable method of getting these charges in the proper categories. The same basis can be used effectively for distributing the cost of expendable tools and supplies used by the maintenance department.

Distribution by People Served. Distribution of expenses such as maintenance of locker rooms and washrooms, cafeteria service, and medical personnel is generally done on the basis of people served since these costs are influenced directly by the number of people eligible for the service.   This may vary considerably among different plants, depending upon accounting procedure, but they are of concern to the maintenance department only when its scope includes such functions.

Distribution by Floor Space.   This method is helpful for building-expense items, including building maintenance, depreciation, taxes, heating, and lighting.

Distribution by Power Consumed.   Power consumed is not used widely as a basis for distribution of indirect charges.   Some attempts have been made to distribute otherwise unclassifiable costs in this manner, but this method is generally unsound because of the varying types of power consumption even within buildings and departments. If this method is used, careful account must be taken of the type of power consumption, as well as other local factors contributing disproportionately to the cost of the service performed.

Distribution by Dollar Value of Equipment Maintained.   Most companies distribute indirect charges resulting from taxes and depreciation on the basis of equipment value in the same way the cost of lubrication may be distributed by the maintenance department on the basis of the value of the equipment serviced.   Sometimes maintenance engineering overhead is distributed in the same way.

In this connection it should be stated that there is considerable variation in charging of engineering overhead in various companies.   Some consider this expense a part of maintenance department supervisory overhead and distribute it directly on the basis of hourly man-hours charged.   Others attempt to break down the engineering cost to specific jobs or departments or distribute it according to the value of the equipment maintained.

Accumulation of Charges.   In general, direct repair charges for all maintenance work are accumulated either by specific job or by department served.   Sometimes a combination of these is used which lumps small jobs together and the total is charged out to departments on some basis with larger jobs accumulated separately and charged to a specific department.   The extent to which a work-order system is in use influences the method of accumulating charges.   If complete listing of all charges is possible and can be justified, the better control is attained if charges are assigned to a specific job as they accrue.   Where such comprehensive record keeping and accounting cannot be justified, departmental segregation is appropriate.

The degree to which a plant is separated into departments in itself depends upon the amount of control needed.   In a small plant producing one product it is usually impossible to justify too small a breakdown of maintenance charges.   As the plant grows and more products are introduced, management generally needs a more nearly accurate determination of the cost to produce them including the cost of maintenance as a portion of the total.   Its accumulation by departments or products is then warranted.

Charges other than direct repair costs are accumulated variously, and it is the intention to discuss only those which are under the jurisdiction of the average maintenance engineering department.   Those indirect costs resulting from maintenance department activity are best accumulated in cost centers or service departments. These may be service departments with fixed operating budgets or operating departments with standards, depending upon the level of activity.   Janitorial service, fire protection, and watchman service can be handled in this way with the entire operating cost of the service accumulated against a cost center and the total redistributed to the plant on some equitable basis.   This charge accumulation, of course, includes the necessary maintenance work for the service itself as well as the labor, supplies, utilities, depreciation, and other cost elements.   The size of the plant and its accounting procedure dictate many modifications to this approach.   In a small plant there is little to be gained by separating the cost of these services from the total operating cost, while in a large plant more definition is necessary in order to arrive at a true manufacturing cost.

PROCESSING OF COSTS

It is now intended to discuss processing of costs from the initial steps of recording and summary, through distribution, concluding with the reporting of costs in a form suitable for interpretation by management and control within the maintenance department.

Many procedures are employed by various organizations to handle cost information originating in the maintenance department. The exact form selected is considerably influenced by the accounting procedures of the plant involved. In some cases the accounting department dictates all the steps down to and including the initial recording of basic information. In others the accounting department accepts summarized information, leaving the initial processing to the discretion of the maintenance department.

The actual responsibility for processing cost information varies from plant to plant. In some, accounting personnel or special clerical cost groups are responsible for this work, while in others the responsibility rests entirely within the maintenance organization. Because of the relationship between cost-data accumulation and processing and plant accounting procedures, a detailed discussion of this subject is more appropriately included in a discussion of plant accounting. For this reason the following remarks will be of a general nature aimed at assisting a maintenance organization in establishment of a cost-collecting, summary, and reporting system which can be adapted to the accounting requirements of its parent company.

Throughout this discussion of recording, summary, and reporting of cost, they will be considered in terms of basic elements mentioned earlier in this chapter, i.e., those of equipment, supplies, labor, outside services, and maintenance department and plant overhead.

Recording of Basic Information. *Equipment.* The cost of equipment is normally obtained from two sources—the invoice received from the supplier at the time of purchase or the summary of the job record which covers the manufacture of a piece of equipment within the plant. The normal flow of invoices for purchased equipment is through a purchasing department, some form of receiving or checking organization, through an accounts-payable section of accounting and, finally, to the point of summary for maintenance costs. With the possible exception of the checking-in step, the maintenance organization is not particularly concerned with processing the cost of purchased equipment, although information concerning these charges must be available to a maintenance organization. Of course, there are plants where, because the purchasing department is not organized for equipment purchases or because policy dictates such purchases to be handled directly by maintenance engineering, processing of these invoices and recording of costs is a function of maintenance.

In the case of equipment manufactured within the plant cost information is picked up in the usual maintenance department record system, accumulated against a job number until completion of the work and close-out of the job, and the total cost after close-out can be handled like an invoice with no need for processing through an accounts-payable group.

Supplies. The cost of supplies is handled by many different methods. If there is a general storeroom which services both maintenance and other plant activities or a mechanical stores unit, it is probably the policy of the company to route all supplies to the storeroom for subsequent distribution. Here the usual procedure for recording costs is some form of storeroom requisition or stores-disbursement report. Book value of supplies is recorded on these requisitions at the time of withdrawal, together with the necessary information for proper distribution of charges. This includes the designation of the job for which the supply was drawn or department number, a description of the item, and its cost. Sometimes the name of the individual authorizing the withdrawal is also recorded. This, of course, is more to provide some degree of accountability than as a step in the cost-recording system. These storeroom requisitions or disbursement reports then furnish the basis for further processing of the cost of supplies.

With plants which do not have a formal storeroom organization recording of supplies costs may be handled in several ways. In some instances the purchase of supplies is immediately expensed and becomes part of the maintenance department overhead. Here the recording of cost is handled in a manner similar to that for equipment except that the value of invoices covering supplies is accumulated in an overhead-cost center.

A modification of this method consists of the establishment of several cost centers based on production units or maintenance functions or crafts. Many plants use a combination of these two methods, with some supplies processed through a storeroom and others charged directly to a department or job number. Sometimes the maintenance department may attempt better control by using a semiformal inventory-control system for supplies charged immediately as an expense to a department. In this way information is processed independent of the plant accounting procedure with less formality and more latitude possible in record keeping. As an example, a departmental crib or supply center is established by the maintenance department, and for accounting purposes all material delivered at this crib is immediately charged as an expense and requires no further treatment accountingwise. The foreman in charge of this center may log supplies in and out for better control and appraisal of performance within the maintenance department.

An important factor in arriving at the scope of a storeroom is the cost of processing material through such a centralized unit. Storerooms gather labor and rental charges which must later be absorbed by the supplies that move through it. Superficially it would appear more desirable for supplies to flow directly to point of use and avoid this additional overhead cost. From the maintenance engineer's point of view, lower job costs would result.

However, there are certain fallacies in this reasoning. If a storeroom is maintained at all and its operating cost is not increased as the result of additions to its inventory, no real reduction in plant cost is accomplished by bypassing the stores activity. Further, the more economical purchasing which may result from stocking larger quantities, or reduction of inventory for some spare parts, may more than nullify the increased cost at the storeroom, if any, at the plant level.

Labor. The basic record for labor cost is, of course, the time card. There are, however, considerable differences in the use of this record which are influenced by the size of the plant, degree of accuracy that can be justified, and methods used in other parts of the plant. In some cases labor costs in maintenance are posted by time clerks located in operating areas who record actual time spent by craftsmen on various jobs either from observation of the clerk or from the craftsmen's reporting in and out with the clerk for each assignment. This type of service is usually too costly to justify and may be modified to the extent of having a foreman distribute the total time of his men at the end of each week.

Many plants provide each craftsman with some form of time sheet on which he records the distribution of his time. This may be augmented by time clocks which are punched between jobs, or the man may write in the time he spends on each job or in each department. In some shops the time card is used to record only the total hours that a man works, and the distribution of this time is obtained from job tickets covering specific work. In either instance there is a record made in hours by individuals for all work performed. The job tickets are often considered to provide more nearly accurate information than time cards since they are less likely to absorb idle time resulting from poor work planning. On the other hand, idle time must be paid for, and the difference between the total shown on job tickets and the over-all labor cost must be absorbed in maintenance overhead with the same eventual result.

Along with the actual time spent on a job, the cost per unit of time must also be recorded. This may be handled as a direct rate application (dollars per hour received by the individual) or as an average rate for a particular craft.

Outside Services. The cost of outside services can be handled in much the same way as the cost of equipment, with the invoice for the service forming the basic information for accumulating and summarizing maintenance cost. Usually no effort is made to break down cost of such services into the various components of equipment, labor, supplies, etc. Some plants, in order to complete the picture of cost distribution among these major elements, do require detailing of these components on invoices for outside services. In this way contractor overhead, profit, and other indirect factors can be separated from the true, direct cost of maintenance. Contractor overhead and profit may then be classified as maintenance overhead, and major fluctuations in the amount of outside services required will not distort the true maintenance overhead percentage. This is particularly important where a major part of the service is labor, and much of the engineering and other indirect costs are borne by the plant maintenance group.

Maintenance Overhead. In most plants maintenance overhead can be divided into two general categories—operating and "rental" cost. The operating classification requires recording of the cost of supplies, labor, and equipment necessary to operate the maintenance department, regardless of the level of service rendered to production. This would include cost of tool-crib attendants, janitorial service, shop-equipment repairs, etc., and would be handled in the same way as other items of this type except that the charge number is the budget center or department number used for accumulation of these data.

The second category termed "rental" cost would include building overhead, utilities, depreciation, taxes, etc., not recorded by the maintenance department but by a central accounting group and derived from total cost and distributions established on a plant-wide basis.

Plant Overhead. Normally the maintenance department has very little to say or do about plant overhead. This is simply one of those expenses that the maintenance department shares by virtue of its being part of the company organization, and normally no internal records are required in the maintenance department for this cost item.

SUMMARIZING COST DATA

There are two general approaches to the summary of maintenance cost data. Some organizations provide an accounting service to the maintenance department for complete processing of all cost data, and others delegate this job exclusively to the maintenance department. Although the methods used may be essentially the same in both cases, the extent of maintenance department participation and the problems involved are considerably different.

There are arguments for either approach. Some maintenance engineers, for example, feel that an accounting department does not have the best interests of the maintenance department in mind and may summarize cost data in a manner which places their department in an unfavorable or unrealistic light. Other maintenance departments feel that the accounting department is too slow and that, since maintenance cost data are of secondary interest to accounting's primary function, they do not receive the necessary priority. Still others may argue that a second party should not be involved until the information has been accumulated and summarized since many of the internal adjustments should be made by the maintenance department itself. One major area of disagreement is that of capitalization vs. expensing. Most accounting departments impose a rather strict interpretation here, whereas the maintenance engineering department may find it preferable to use considerable latitude, depending upon the current situation.

Maintenance departments, on the other hand, may not have a proper perspective of the over-all company needs. There is also the problem of accountability to top management and responsibility for the legal aspects of record keeping which, although at times appearing trivial to a maintenance department, must be considered. If the proper relationship exists between accounting and the maintenance department, the optimum division of duties is that which results in both departments participating in cost-data processing with delineation in those areas which best satisfy the needs of both groups.

The goal of summary of maintenance cost data is that of arriving at an over-all cost of maintenance work in terms of some unit—(job, department, or type of service) in such form that it can be charged where it belongs and form a basis for performance reporting by the maintenance department or plant management. This requires the use of some form of summary sheet on which all the various cost elements for such a unit of work are accumulated and totaled. Costs originating with invoices are normally recorded directly on this summary. Storeroom invoices, after application of overhead, are posted here, as well as distributed charges from other cost centers, and the value of labor.

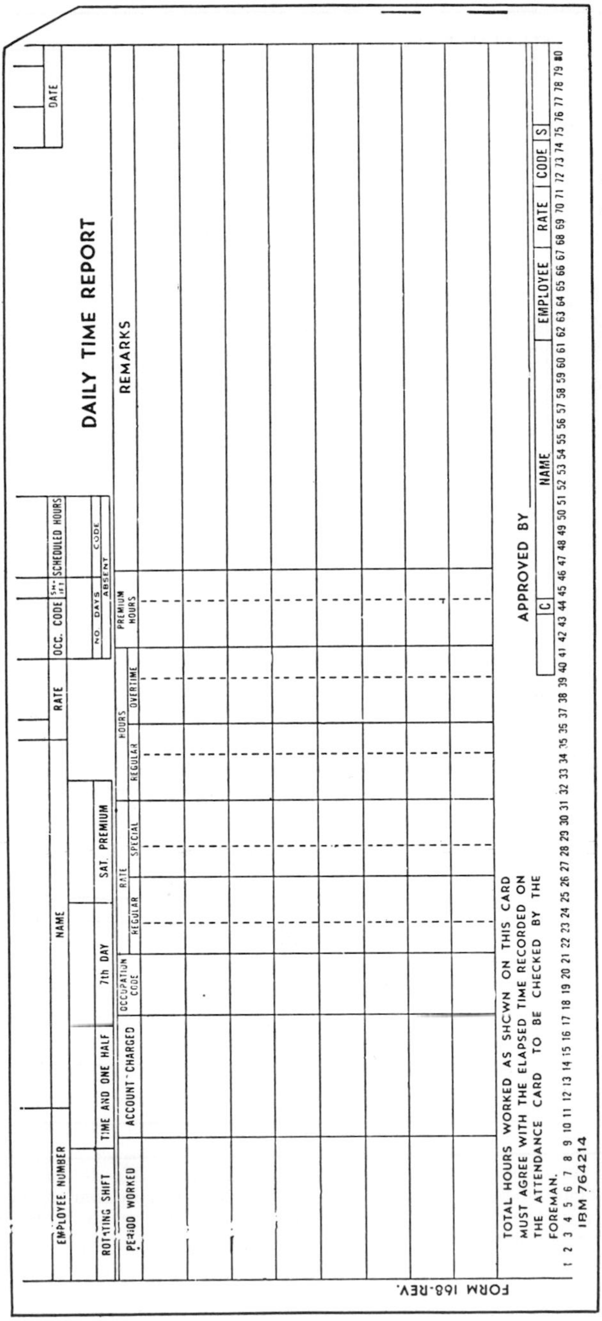

FIG. 1-1. Typical maintenance department time-distribution card that can be filled out by the men or the foremen. (The box heading in the top line which can't be read is "SHIFT.")

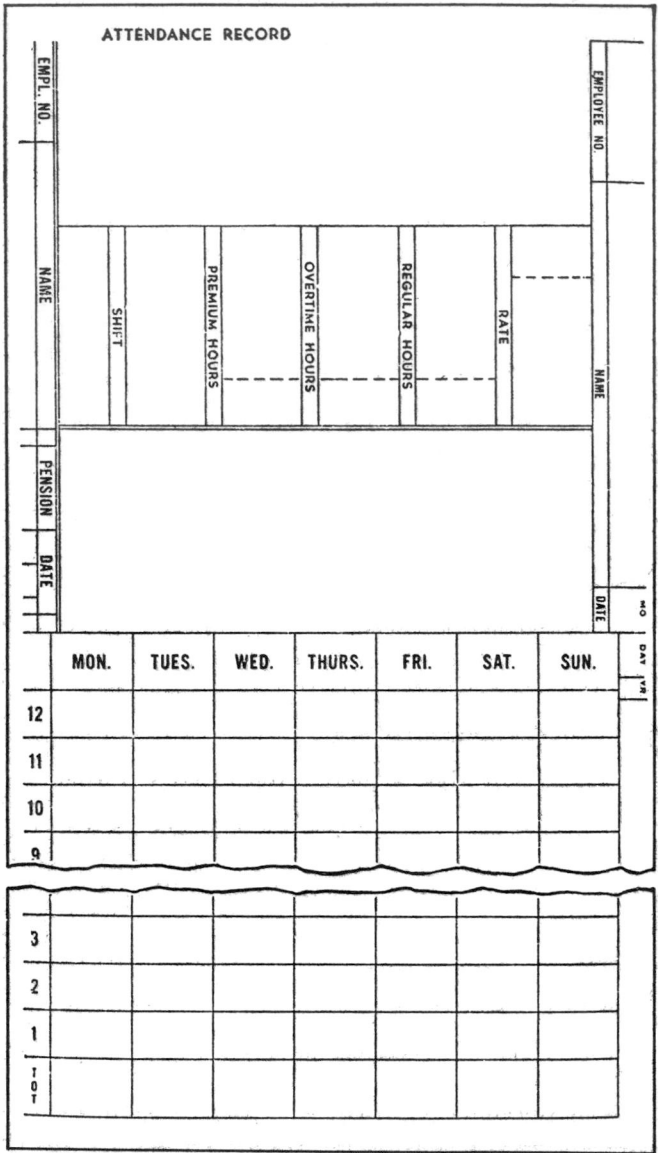

FIG. 1-2. Normal time card. This form and the one shown as Fig. 1-1 are used in plants having tabulating equipment. This form is not primarily for maintenance, but it indicates the additional step that must be taken in the time-distribution card to reconcile it with the basis for the man's payment.

STOREROOM REQUISITION

REQUIRED FOR_____

DATE	QUANTITY	DESCRIPTION	PRICE	AMOUNT
DEPT. NO.				
REPAIR NO.				
JOB NO.				
EXPENSE CLASS				
		TOTAL		
TOTAL EXPENSE				

SIGNED_____

FIG. 1-3. Typical storeroom requisition. The information necessary for properly distributing these costs is covered.

ROTATING										RATE	WEEK ENDING		EMPLOYEE'S SUMMARY CARD		
SHIFT	CLERK NO._____ NAME _____ FORM 13 AHB 8772														

	DEPT. ACCT.NO	OCC. CODE	DAILY TIME							RATE	HOURS		PRE-COMPUTED EARNINGS		
			MON.	TUES.	WED.	THURS.	FRI.	SAT.	SUN.		REG.	EXTRA	REGULAR	EXTRA	GROSS
STR.															
OT. H															
PR. H															
STR.															
OT. H															
PR. H															
STR.															
OT. H															
PR. H															
STR.															
OT. H															
PR. H															
STR.															
OT. H															
PR. H															
TOTALS										AVERAGE					

FIG. 1-4. Form typical of those used in summarizing labor distribution, by either jobs or departments.

If automatic tabulating equipment is available, basic information can be fed into it and total cost by job or department obtained very quickly. Since this equipment can usually be justified only in larger plants, processing of labor-cost data is frequently a manual operation necessitating considerable clerical work in transferring information from a multitude of time cards, application of the proper rate, and totaling of these amounts to arrive at the cost of labor on the summary sheet. Job tickets, when used, eliminate the need for posting incremental time units. Job

MECHANICAL JOB LABOR RECORD
MAINTENANCE DEPARTMENT

DEPT.			DEPT.			DEPT.			DEPT			DEPT.		
EST.			EST.			EST.			EST.			EST.			
OPER. NO.	DATE	HOURS	OPER. NO	DATE	HOURS	OPER. NO	DATE	HOURS	OPER. NO.	DATE	HOURS	OPER. NO.	DATE	HOURS
TOTAL			TOTAL			TOTAL			TOTAL			TOTAL		

JOB No.

Fig. 1-5. Form similar to that shown in Fig. 1-4, and used for same purpose.

WORK ORDER

DATE_____ DEPT. _____ WORK ORDER No. _____

DESCRIPTION AND REASON FOR EXPENDITURE

ESTIMATED COST _____
BUDGET No. _____
AUTHORIZED BY _____ AUTHORITY No. _____
                     ENGINEER IN CHARGE   ESTIMATE ITEM No. _____
CHARGE TO _____

PLANT _____   DATE CLOSED _____

EQUIP'T VALUES	OUTSIDE CONTRACT WORK	MATERIAL AND SUPPLIES	STORE EXPENSE	MISC L LABOR	SHOP EXPENSE	SALARIES AND TRUCK EXPENSE	TOTAL	DATE

Fig. 1-6. Form typical of those used to accumulate all maintenance charges and also may be used for either specific jobs or departments.

JOB TIME CARD

DATE	DEPT. & SEC. NAME	NO.	CLASS	CRAFT	JOB NO.

EMPLOYEE		CLOCK NO.

JOB TITLE

JOB DESCRIPTION	ELAPSED	F
		S
		F
		S
DISPATCHER	COST $	RATE $		OVERTIME PREMIUM
				TOTAL HOURS

Fig. 1-7. Typical job ticket used in a system that posts a man's time directly against a specific job.

REQUISITION FOR MECHANICAL STORES ITEMS

(To be used only for material charged to Capsule Engineering or Mechanical jobs)

Date   /   /19

DEPARTMENT	SECTION	DEPT. & SECT. NO.	JOB CLASS	JOB NO.

ITEM NO	DESCRIPTION	QUANTITY	UNIT COST	PER	TOTAL COST
			$		$

Form 200.1 Printed in U.S.A. (Jan. 54) (U 42)

SIGNED_____

SUPERVISOR

Fig. 1-8. Typical storeroom requisition.   Cost-distribution information is covered.

tickets also require, however, a summary which must be reconciled with the total cost of labor on some basis.

Storeroom and maintenance overhead are sometimes applied prior to posting the cost on the summary sheets and sometimes done on the summary sheets.   The exact point at which this occurs is unimportant, and it should be done with least clerical cost and greatest accuracy.   Many companies post raw costs on the summary sheets and then apply the proper overhead to the various items.   Others post only the costs after the application of overhead, i.e., total costs.   Following completion of a specific job or at the end of a predetermined period of time, usually a month, these summary sheets are totaled and plant overhead is applied either as a single unit or as the various elements that go to make up plant overhead. The summary sheets are then used for any further summarizing; for instance, in the case of jobs that must be divided between manufacturing cost centers and for reporting of maintenance costs.

ENGINEERING JOB RECORD					YEAR	SERIAL	PHASE
				ESTIMATE ENGINEER	APPROPRIATION		

Job Description _____

REFERENCE	PURCHASES	FREIGHT	STORES	LABOR	TOTALS	
					ADDITIONS	TO DATE
	$	$	$	$	$	$

FIG. 1-9. Form typical of those used to accumulate maintenance charges. Usable for jobs or departments.

There are many preferences in forms used for recording accumulation, processing, and summary of costs. These vary in detail depending on the extent or the aspect of cost which interests the individual company. This leads to internal forms and procedures tailored to the needs of the individual company. Probably a great deal could be done in standardizing maintenance cost reporting and in the use of standard procedures and forms, but it is not the intention to recommend any particular structure as being the best. It is recommended, however, that each maintenance organization study its own needs, and in conjunction with the accounting department establish a system that satisfies these requirements with a minimum of clerical work.

Figures 1-1 to 1-9, inclusive, are examples of forms currently being used by several companies for recording maintenance labor and supply costs as well as several summary sheets.

REPORTING OF COSTS

As has been mentioned, the primary purpose for the cost system is twofold: equitable distribution of the costs; and provision of a method for control and performance evaluation of the maintenance department. Therefore, the cost reporting and distribution of cost information should be in the form best suited to meet these requirements. Sometimes these two objectives do not appear compatible. Duplicate reporting often is necessary. Information required for accounting purposes and cost distribution often is not accumulated and reported in a form suitable for internal control of the maintenance department. There is considerably more detail necessary in final reporting of cost information to be used for cost control by operating departments than is necessary for strictly accounting purposes. Normally operating departments need a more rapid flow of information than the periodic close-outs of the accounting department provide, normally a month apart. Satisfaction of the two objectives often results in necessary duplication and requires careful study, leading to optimum results with minimum duplication of effort. Mutual understanding of each others' problems by maintenance and accounting departments will go a long way toward solving this problem and should be accomplished and maintained.

In general terms, the best system is that which uses a summarizing procedure that makes it possible to withdraw up-to-date information needed by the maintenance department at any time but which moves toward the ultimate needs of the accounting department at the end of its accounting period. Cost information for maintenance engineering control is reported in many ways. Summaries by job, by equipment type, by production departments, or by type of work are used. Sometimes maintenance costs are totaled by product type as one element in the total manufacturing cost. It is suggested that the reporting of maintenance costs for control purposes be in a form that serves the following specific requirements:

1. Craft supervision needs a measure of the effectiveness of its performance with respect to manpower and material utilization.
2. Maintenance management needs some indication of over-all trends in maintenance cost and in sufficient detail for detection of areas which require increased attention.
3. Maintenance engineering requires information which will highlight equipment or applications of equipment causing abnormal maintenance cost and subsequent need for engineering attention.
4. Production supervision must be in a position to know their maintenance costs by product and, occasionally, by equipment type.

The availability of these different types of information depends considerably upon the detail in the cost-processing routine. Individual job costs can be summarized to provide any of this information and, if summarized by equipment types and departments, will provide both engineering and production with important facts. If summarized and reported plant-wide by departments, it will provide maintenance administration with the over-all picture of maintenance-cost trends. Crafts supervision, on the other hand, needs labor-cost summaries by crafts in judging the general effectiveness of its work force. However, where individual job-cost summaries are available, there is usually a sufficient number of jobs that can be isolated to one craft to provide supervision with a good performance index. In maintenance-cost systems that do not provide for individual job costing, separation of the cost of specific pieces of equipment, or equipment types, as an intermediate step in cost accumulation will provide much of the necessary information.

Unfortunately, most methods of reporting maintenance costs are either so detailed that subsequent summaries are necessary or of such general nature as to be useless for performance evaluation, and they do not readily permit maintenance supervision to direct its effort toward trouble spots or those in which the greatest improvement can be effected.

Although top management is usually furnished with sufficient information to evaluate the over-all trend of maintenance costs, which run from 3 to 15 per cent of total manufacturing cost, it tends to regard this cost as subordinate to many other elements of plant performance. Consequently, the cost of maintenance is frequently regarded as a necessary evil with little appreciation for efforts made by maintenance administration to improve its performance and reduce this out-of-pocket cost component. Maintenance administration should provide top management with complete, concise reporting of maintenance-cost trends and their relation to external factors which influence the cost picture. It must be remembered that management is primarily concerned in the total cost of maintenance and reliability of equipment rather than man efficiencies, reduction in the cost of supplies, overhead, and other factors which go to make up the maintenance cost. The cost interpretation to top management should, therefore, be of such nature as to present the total cost of maintenance as a function of the total cost of manufacturing or of the conversion cost; the total cost of maintenance related to the value of equipment maintained; or in terms of the number of units produced, whether pounds, automobiles, or baby carriages.

Maintenance administration should also provide some report that will permit management to judge its performance as a plant service. This may be a report of equipment downtime due to maintenance activity; deviation from production schedules necessitated by such activity; or the improvement in equipment performance for the same reason.

All this information should be not only reported but also compared with some standard of performance. Unfortunately, it is difficult to set arbitrary limits which are acceptable for maintenance performance, and while there may be certain commonly accepted limits, most managements will accept trends as being more indicative of performance than absolute value at any one time. Superficially it may seem that all cost trends should be downward, but there are many factors affecting operations that can justify an upward trend, accompanied, nevertheless, by increased efficiency. The use of more complex equipment, the advance of automation, and the greater degree of utilization which must be realized with higher equipment costs, all act to increase relative maintenance expense. Maintenance administration should be aware of these trends and devise some means of evaluating their effect on service. Cost reporting by maintenance administration to top management should interpret the effect of these factors in order to permit sound evaluation of actual maintenance performance.

Chapter 2

SETTING UP BUDGETS FOR MAINTENANCE

By CHARLES E. KNIGHT
General Superintendent of Engineering and Manufacturing Services
Monsanto Company
Plastics Division
Springfield, Mass.

As it will be discussed in this chapter, a budget is understood to be a cost goal or an estimate of the cost of performing work covered by the budget for some future period. There are many types of budgets and many periods of time covered by them, as well as many methods used in their construction. Whatever the form or method of construction, however, it should be remembered that a budget is not primarily historical but should be considered always as a forecast of expenditures. Subsequent discussion will explore various types of budgets and methods of preparation and will include some discussion of the relationships between reliability and length of forecast and of the manner in which budgets are used.

TYPES OF BUDGETS

The two budget categories to be examined are those normally used by maintenance engineering departments, i.e., those which forecast the cost of maintaining equipment in satisfactory operating condition; and those which forecast the cost of operating certain service departments that are normally the responsibility of the maintenance group. Frequently there is a third type of budget, which is primarily an operating budget similar to manufacturing operating budgets. It is employed to forecast the cost of products subsequently used by production departments. Typical of this group are budgets for steam, electricity, and other utilities.

Repair Budgets. The primary purpose of the repair budget is to provide the information required by the production departments via accounting procedures in arriving at an anticipated cost to manufacture a given product or product type. The repair budget, or cost forecast, becomes one item in the over-all budget of an operating department, along with others such as raw materials, labor, and overhead.

Generally speaking, repair budgets can be classified into three types:

1. Those set at a fixed total cost per unit of time.
2. Those which are established at a unit cost per unit of production.
3. A modification of cases 1 and 2 which partially compensates for a change in the level of production activity, employing "bracket standards" which subsequently may be expressed in terms of total cost per unit of time or per unit of product.

The repair budget established as a fixed cost per time unit is by far the simplest budget to set up and use. In plants manufacturing few products at a relatively stable production level, this sort of budget provides sufficient accuracy. A utilities company, for example, might find this type of budget entirely adequate. Although repair costs may vary from week to week or month to month, the average cost over an extended period probably remains essentially constant. The selling price of the product fluctuates very little and may be fixed for considerable periods of time. Under these circumstances a fixed repair standard per month is adequate. Refinements are of little value except to focus attention on areas where increased control is necessary.

In plants manufacturing a large variety of products at a constant rate, or in any plant where the rate of manufacture of different products may not be relatively constant (from full production to idle plant), a repair budget expressed in cost per production unit is appropriate. In these plants the repair budget's primary purpose is to assist in fixing the relative manufacturing cost of various products. This, in turn, requires that the cost information be available by product. Repair budgets established on this basis, although of great value from an administrative standpoint, require additional information concerning the effect of varying production levels, if they are to be used as criteria of performance of the maintenance department.

The third type of budget, which may be expressed in terms of cost per unit of time or unit of production, is frequently used in a multiproduct plant where individual production rates vary appreciably over wide ranges. In this situation the use of a variable budget, the basis for which changes with the level of activity of the area under consideration, provides a more nearly accurate forecast of maintenance costs and a more realistic goal for maintenance department performance. Such a budget consists of both fixed and variable items and, therefore, does not result in straight-line variation with plant activity. Use of such a budget requires more interpretation by the accounting department in establishing selling cost based on total manufacturing cost. Their time can be justified, however, since this nonlinear cost variation in plants with varying production levels is true not only of maintenance but of many other manufacturing services and overhead costs. Through use of this variable type of budget employing "bracket standards" management can draw a much more realistic picture of actual costs at varying levels of plant activity.

Variable budgets employing "bracket standards" are most frequently prepared by establishing three or more activity levels and interpolating among these levels in arriving at the budget or standard cost of performance for any cost period. These points are usually selected at the minimum production level at which a department would operate, its normal or expected production level, and its peak level, assuming 100 per cent utilization. In such a budget many maintenance cost factors are essentially constant regardless of the level of activity, i.e., bracket. Others vary in direct proportion to the level of activity, This is true, of course, with many other cost elements in a production department. It may be possible to total the fixed-cost elements and consider this as a minimum expense for zero operations or idle plant. Generally, however, the brackets are established independently based on past performance at those conditions or on detailed prediction of the effects on maintenance costs of operation at these levels. A straight line or curve connecting these points can then be considered the budget standard for maintenance expense.

PERIOD OF TIME COVERED BY BUDGETS

The length of time covered by a maintenance budget, or cost forecast, is another subject to be considered in our discussion. Traditionally, many budgets are established on an annual-time base. Most fiscal periods are of 12 months' duration, and accounting procedures are generally geared to a 1-year period for financial control. Certainly the degree of stability in company operations influences the length of time for which costs can be forecast with any degree of accuracy. In a dynamic, changing industry there are two opposing influences to be considered in determining the budget period. First, rapid evolution of equipment types and equipment use increases the limits of estimating accuracy for repair costs over an extended period. Second, evolution and addition to the product lines accompanied by large capital investments requires long-range forecasting of operating costs to permit more nearly accurate evaluation of potential profit margin, as well as short-range budget preparation for control purposes. Increased complexity of production equipment and the accelerated trend toward automation are making maintenance costs an increasingly important part of total manufacturing costs, and long-range maintenance-cost forecasts are becoming more important than ever.

Obviously, the shorter the budget period, the easier is the prediction and subsequent control. Many organizations establish maintenance budgets 1 year in advance but permit periodic adjustments to be made semiannually, quarterly, or in some cases, monthly. At such times compensation is made for conditions that have changed since the original budget preparation. Such revisions should be done carefully to avoid using them as an opportunity to correct for poor control or poor cost forecasting which has led to an out-of-control situation rather than logical modification to include factors essentially beyond the control of the maintenance department. Usually the time intervals for these "reopenings" for budget adjustments are not controlled by the maintenance department and are accepted by it as an accounting department policy. Where uncontrollable variations do occur within these periods, some maintenance departments establish an internal budget for short-term control to ensure meeting the official annual budget at the end of its period.

Most of the above discussion applies primarily to repair budgets. Budgets for service centers or for service-producing areas such as utilities can usually be established with considerable accuracy on an annual basis. As with repairs, however, considerable variation from standard may result from month to month because of seasonal changes or other factors, and some maintenance departments will superimpose monthly goals for utilities which forecast a variation from the annual budget in order to ensure adherence to the annual budget at the end of its period.

WHO PREPARES REPAIR BUDGETS?

This subject can be divided into two parts—the first covering repair budgets, i.e., forecast of those cost elements which are a direct part of manufacturing cost; and the second covering budgets for the cost of services or producing departments entirely within the jurisdiction of the maintenance group.

There are usually three major plant groups involved in the preparation of repair budgets, which in most organizations can be called the maintenance engineering department, the production department, and the accounting department, all of whom must be involved. The relative degree of responsibility and participation, however, varies considerably among these groups from plant to plant. Understandably, the maintenance department usually has a bigger hand in this than the other two. Participation by accounting is considerably influenced by accounting procedures in effect and the availability of adequate information to that activity. Usually the contribution of accounting to preparation of maintenance budgets, as well as other operating budgets, is primarily one of consolidation and correlation of data plus a certain police function rather than responsibility for initiating the budget. Between maintenance and production the participation may vary widely, and in fact, some repair budgets are set exclusively by one department or the other. This choice obviously should be the department which management holds responsible for operating within the budget once it has been prepared.

If this responsibility rests with the maintenance department, it should prepare the budget. It is true that much information concerning anticipated production levels and equipment requirements must be secured from production, and the need for new types of expenditures can best be determined in joint discussion with production and other participating groups. The final cost, however, should be estimated by maintenance engineering. If, on the other hand, responsibility for operating within a fixed allowance rests entirely with production, the maintenance engineering department functions as a source of information regarding past performance and anticipated repair needs with the operating department interpreting this information in terms of a repair budget. The best solution would appear to be joint preparation of the repair budget by maintenance and production with equally shared responsibility for its execution. This can be difficult to handle from an administrative point of view, however.

Sometimes the repair budget is determined by the accounting department alone. This situation might be found in small plants with an informal organization in which the accounting department has the knowledge to prepare budgets or in companies that have a number of plants limited to the same products where standardization on manufacturing cost is advisable.

Budget preparation for service centers or departments within the jurisdiction of the maintenance department is usually the responsibility of the maintenance group. Often, however, the influence of top management or the accounting department is felt in this area because of the ease with which some of these services can be adjusted up or down, depending on the business situation or short-term philosophy. For example, in building maintenance actual expenditures are frequently a function of the company's economic position rather than the annual forecast in the budget. Over and above that minimum expense required to avoid deterioration, the level of building maintenance can be adjusted within rather broad limits, depending on management feeling with respect to appearance, modernization, convenience, etc. This effect may be manifested by management's arbitrary allocation of larger or smaller sums of money as a percentage of the investment or in lump sums, based on recommendations of the maintenance department, which, in turn, is responsible for operating within the new figure or for executing the aims underwritten by the increased amounts. In other service cost centers, where the anticipated expense may vary appreciably with the level of plant activity, information concerning this variation must originate outside the maintenance department. Final determination of budgets to be used in forecasting the cost of such services should be that of the maintenance department.

HOW ARE BUDGETS ESTABLISHED?

Obviously, a cost forecast for any operation that cannot be completely controlled must be based on human judgment and appraisal of the effect of uncontrollable variables. This is particularly true of the normal repair budget. Although they include many cost factors which can be forecast with reasonable accuracy, there are many others which can be predicted only within broad limits. As with any prediction, the more information gathering and correlation that can be done, the more nearly accurate will be the forecast of cost.

In approaching this problem it should be remembered that in any total cost forecast consisting of many individual factors the degree of accuracy of the total forecast or budget may be considerably influenced by the reliability of the least predictable variable. Consequently, the thoroughness of evaluation of all elements making up the budget should be geared to that which is practical for those least predictable elements, if these are potentially large. For example, in a department where the cost of materials to be used can be predicted down to the last nut or bolt, but where the cost of labor to perform repairs may vary over a wide range, considerable judgment should be exercised in the amount of time and detail expended on the nut-and-bolt portion of the forecast.

An important source of basic information in preparing repair budgets is cost experience. Past performance is of great value in predicting future costs if its use is tempered by consideration of variables whose effect is changing or new variables that can be foreseen. Among these factors are the level of activity, the age of equipment, and trends in the cost of labor and maintenance supplies. If a repair budget is to be based entirely on past performance, equipment and labor cost indexes must be applied to approach a realistic forecast. Correlation should be drawn between cost history and concurrent production levels. Accuracy of the budget will be increased with the amount of detail in examination of historical facts. For instance, the repair expense for pumps can be adjusted for variation in amount of usage, age of the pump, etc., in arriving at an anticipated cost for pump maintenance.   A summation of such cost elements for major equipment categories of a department will result in a more nearly accurate budget than one evolved from across-the-board adjustments to last year's performance.   Another differentiation which is useful is one between labor and supplies.

There are many modifications to extrapolation of past performance as a basis for budget preparation.   The extent to which they are employed depends both on the amount of historical information available and on the degree of accuracy justified in the final budget.

Another approach starts with a comprehensive study of a planned program of repair. In this type those cost elements which are reasonably uniform, such as lubrication and inspection and replacement of equipment with fixed life, are segregated.   The remaining repair-cost items are then studied individually, usually by equipment type.   By considering all variables that may affect this cost, such as age, expected utilization, and repair history, a detailed forecast for maintenance cost can be determined.   This approach requires the availability of many historical data on performance of equipment and help from the production department in anticipating variation from past use of this equipment.   This rather comprehensive undertaking would be particularly useful in a plant reorganization or in starting from scratch when the system in use seemed to require complete overhaul.

The amount of detail and study put into preparation of a budget should be controlled by the expected improvement in forecasting accuracy and the real value of such an increase to the company and to the maintenance department.   Our discussion has omitted reference to the application of overhead and redistributed costs to the maintenance budget.   Although such adjustments need not be considered in the preliminary phase of budget preparation, they obviously must be included before the budget becomes final.   If budget preparation is the result of a detailed study of its components, then the overhead factors are usually added after the preparation of the direct-cost portion.   Where the whole budget is based on past performance, however, the overhead portion would automatically be included in the new forecast and no correction is required.

While detailed procedures for preparation of budgets are too numerous and lengthy to be included here, the general philosophy can be summarized as follows: the accuracy and detail entering into budget preparation should be limited by the anticipated ability to perform within it.

Service department budgets, on the other hand, are susceptible to a somewhat different approach.   Usually the cost of their operation can be predicted with greater accuracy than is the case with repair budgets.   This is because in general service department unit costs are not so greatly affected by major fluctuations in production levels, and there are not so many major unpredictable expense items to consider. In a small plant where total cost of all service departments is small, little expense can be justified in preparing their budgets.   In this situation past performance adjusted for known changes in basic cost elements will produce acceptable results.   In larger plants, where the magnitude of service department cost justifies a more detailed study, it is appropriate to analyze the elements going into service expense, forecasting anticipated changes in the same way as for repair budgets, including the application of overhead.

For example, a building maintenance budget can be prepared by classifying all building repairs into categories such as roofing, painting, glazing, masonry, window washing, heating and ventilating, lighting, and elevators.   Each building in the plant can then be surveyed and its anticipated repairs forecast for the next budget period. Many of these classifications lend themselves to a planned schedule, while the amount to be spent for others can be allocated arbitrarily.   A very small percentage of the total anticipated expenditure would be of an unpredictable nature.   Detailing of these expenses by buildings and conversion to a total cost for the entire plant will result in a budget that can be easily substantiated and which will facilitate accuracy in control subsequent to its approval.   This same approach can be used for other service department budgets or for those of cost centers not included in maintenance budgets of the operating departments for one reason or another.

RESPONSIBILITY FOR PERFORMANCE UNDER MAINTENANCE BUDGETS

Although it may appear superficially that responsibility for performance within a repair budget should rest with the maintenance engineering department, such delegation of responsibility does not result in optimum performance. If the whole responsibility rests with maintenance, the authority to control maintenance expenditures should also be delegated here. If we assume that the primary reason for production equipment repairs is to ensure its optimum productivity, and that production departments are held responsible for their production costs and rates, then the production departments should have responsibility for the condition of the equipment in their department, i.e., the amount of money spent on its repair.

It is difficult, therefore, to place definitely the responsibility for performance within a maintenance budget or the authority for justifying major variations from this budget. In practice some companies do delegate this responsibility entirely to the production departments. Others consider it to be the responsibility of the maintenance engineering department, but most organizations divide the burden between production and maintenance. In general, production departments are held responsible for the amount of repair work needed, with maintenance being responsible for its cost. This can be complicated, however, by the fact that the amount of repair work needed can be considerably affected by the maintenance department's ability to anticipate and reduce repairs with a sound preventive-maintenance program and intensive preventive engineering to prolong equipment life.

All this discussion simply emphasizes the fact that maintenance and production must operate with a single purpose in the maintenance of production equipment and that the responsibility for its performance is a joint one. Although this statement may seem to conflict with an axiom of good organization, i.e., clear definition of responsibility and authority, any other course will not result in optimum plant performance in achieving the company's financial goals.

Responsibility for performance within other service department budgets, however, is more easily established. With these the responsibility of the maintenance department is simply to provide the necessary service (such as utilities) at a cost indicated in the approved budget or to justify major departures from it.

REPORTING OF PERFORMANCE VS. BUDGET

Since budgets are primarily established to assist a company in planning the cost of its operations to produce a profit and since a company's financial progress is charted by the accounting department, in most organizations information on performance relative to budget is issued by the accounting department. Although the form of this reporting differs considerably from one company to another, it generally consists of a presentation of actual cost, either as total dollars or as total cost per unit, compared with forecast cost indicated in the budget plus deviations of actual cost from budget figures. Some accounting activities include a cumulative total from some prescribed starting point, generally from the first of the fiscal year. In all such cost reports the detailing of the information follows the format used in establishing the original budget.

In plants where the budget for production-equipment repairs is determined on the basis of a unit of time or unit of production, whether the relationship be straight-line or one that includes adjustments for fluctuating production levels, the reporting of repair-cost performance is a single element in operating department cost sheets, and the comparison is made with a standard cost for the report period. This information is sometimes converted into total dollars compared with total standard dollars and summarized by departments for the entire plant.

In order to assist the maintenance department's cost control even further, accounting departments frequently provide a breakdown of cost performance by the various budget elements such as labor, materials, and overhead. This information, together with that discussed in the preceding chapter covering Costs, provides the maintenance department with the necessary tools for explaining deviations from budget and initiating formal modifications to it when necessary.

Variance Reports. Company managements are usually interested in the reasons for significant deviations from anticipated costs and require some form of analysis of these deviations at the end of each accounting period. Such an analysis is often termed a "variance report."

Although the maintenance department may feel that the variance report in use is superficial and misleading compared with other cost-control indices which may indicate a different performance trend, as members of the management team, maintenance personnel must realize that the variance report is of great importance in detecting and understanding major variations from the anticipated financial performance of a production unit. Philosophy regarding the classification of deviations as significant differs considerably. Some companies are interested only in the amount by which actual expenditures exceed anticipated ones. Others feel that such expenditures or loss variances should be explained each month. Still others are interested only in truly significant loss variances or cumulative trends in cost deviations rather than month-to-month fluctuations. Since company management cannot possibly be familiar with the details that may cause a normal fluctuation, the maintenance department should accept the responsibility for augmenting the unadorned numbers which indicate the variance with information to differentiate between normal and abnormal fluctuations. Often the requirement for variance reports in great detail, including minor fluctuations, is the result of failure to make this differentiation between fluctuations that can be expected in the normal course of operations and those which are really out of line.

Realistic explanations of cost deviations from the budget can be valuable to both company management and the maintenance department. Both plus and minus deviations should be scrutinized, and most important, the effect of such deviations on future trends should be estimated. Too frequently a perfunctory explanation singling out one major item which will in itself account for the total variance is used, while the real reason for the variance may lie with a completely different set of facts. Maintenance management realizes that there is considerable normal fluctuation in the cost of repairs and that exact adherence to forecast expenditures each month is impossible, save by gross manipulation. Company management often recognizes this by setting limits, say plus or minus 5 or 10 per cent, as being reasonable. However, a variation of this magnitude over a long period of time can result in a cumulative variation of considerable proportions. For this reason the cumulative variance should receive as much attention as the short-term totals. The practice of adding actual and budget cost for several departments may produce a more uniform performance for the group but tends to reduce highlighting of major problem areas.

Statistical control provides an excellent device for interpretation of deviations from the established budget. If demonstrated and proved to top management, application of statistical methods for explanation of cost variance can appreciably reduce the time spent on variance reports without a loss of control. This approach is particularly applicable to cost centers where it is frequently necessary to defer expenditures or to incur abnormal expense during a particular reporting period. If 3-sigma or 2-sigma limits are accepted, and if reported variances fall between these limits, indicating that expenditures are within the accepted control limits, further investigation and explanation are eliminated. A variance outside the established control limits, however, can be observed immediately and indicates the need for further investigation. For more complete interpretation of the performance of the cost center, a control chart covering year-to-date performance, as well as one for the individual variances, is of considerable value. The use of such a chart to interpret the performance of several such cost centers is illustrated in Fig. 2-1.

This explanation of cost variation from budgeted standards is an important tool for management of a maintenance department. It should not be considered as a necessary evil or a policing action by accounting and plant management but rather as a means of reviewing the performance of the department as it bears on the accomplishment of the company's financial goals. Serious deviation from these cost goals,

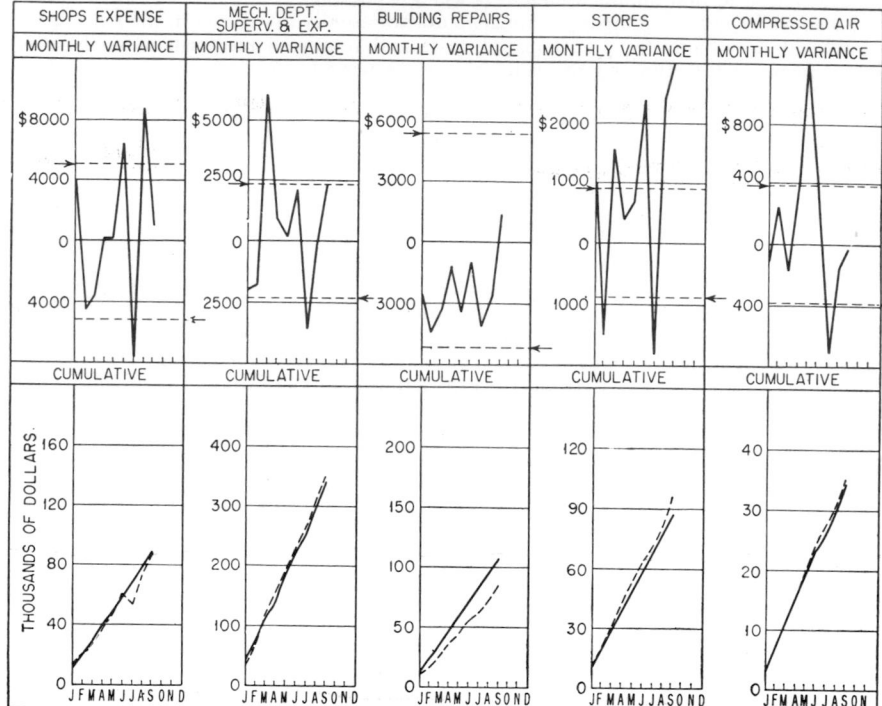

BUDGET CONTROL CHARTS
TWO SIGMA LIMITS 95% PROBABILITY

→ UPPER CONTROL LIMIT   ← LOWER CONTROL LIMIT   — BUDGET AMT.   --- ACTUAL AMOUNT

FIG. 2-1. Interpreting the performance of cost centers.

regardless of the maintenance department performance in terms of its other indexes, should be cause for concern whether it indicates need for budget adjustment or an improvement in the department performance.

SUMMARY

A budget, or cost forecast, is necessary to ensure the successful operation of a company. Cost accrued in performance of maintenance work is an important element in the over-all financial picture. Maintenance budgets, both for repair costs and for operation of service departments, should be prepared with as much accuracy as can be justified for the amount of money involved. Responsibility for performance within the approved budgets must be accepted in large part by the maintenance department. This department should assume full responsibility for detection and interpretation of major variations from the forecast expenditure and should provide the accounting department and plant management with the information necessary to project the effect of these variations to the company's total financial picture.

Chapter 3

ORGANIZING COST AND BUDGET PERSONNEL

By CHARLES E. KNIGHT
General Superintendent of Engineering and Manufacturing Services
Monsanto Company
Plastics Division
Springfield, Mass.

Functions. The functions of a budgeting and cost-control group can be divided into three general categories: information gathering; information processing; and interpretation and comparison of data from the first two steps for control, forecasting, and performance evaluation. The emphasis placed on each of these functions will have a profound influence on both the number and organizational position of personnel handling cost and budget information.

Information Gathering. Information gathering, or the recording of time distribution of workers and the cost of materials, may be performed entirely by the men working on the job. This practice minimizes the need for time clerks or job time-keepers located in the shop area. In other instances this basic recording is handled by a clerical staff for reasons of greater security and accuracy, necessitating a clerical organization in close proximity to the shop areas. In this case the recording of information for cost control may frequently be combined with its use for pay purposes, which suggests consideration of this clerical group as part of the payroll activity with its cost-control effort of secondary consideration. Between these two cases there is considerable latitude, and information gathering may frequently consist of combinations of (1) keeping records by the men performing the work and (2) checking and summarizing by a clerical group. Line supervision may be called on to perform the checking step.

When extreme accuracy is required for an incentive-wage system or for any other purpose, an independent clerical group becomes essential to proper information gathering. Its size can be determined only by consideration of the conditions existing at a specific plant. This may range from 1 clerk for every 10 men to 1 clerk for 30 or 40 men. In a large plant using an incentive system, this clerical organization may parallel the supervisory organization in structure—employing clerks, senior clerks, and clerical supervision.

In an average-sized plant not using incentives, where the degree of accuracy required is only that which permits reasonable control, this clerical staff may be considerably smaller and frequently is adjunct to the supervisory organization with its density as low as 1 clerk for each 50 to 75 men. If line supervision is employed in record keeping, or at least in reconciliation and checking of records kept by workers or clerks, this clerical group may be still further reduced, resulting in a density of purely clerical data-recording personnel of as low as 1 clerk to 100 or more men.

Information Processing and Cost Control. Data processing and cost control for budget purposes may sometimes be carried on by a separate functional group within the maintenance organization. Or it may be handled entirely outside the maintenance department, by the accounting department, or by a separate plant clerical group. One of the major considerations in determining the need for an information-processing group within the maintenance engineering department is the extent to which the data summary for control purposes parallels that required for the accounting department's reporting system. Ideally, these two needs would be satisfied by the same processing step, and where this situation exists, there is little need for more than one processing group whether it be in the maintenance department or not. Usually, it is found more expedient to do some preliminary processing of maintenance information with a maintenance department clerical group, because the need for exercising judgment exists, and judgment must be based on familiarity with the work involved. The final processing is handled by a central accounting or clerical group.

Interpretation of Data. Although considerable interpretation is done by the accounting department, its version is of necessity slanted at the top-management level for use in evaluating the company's financial performance. The particular interpretation required for short-range cost control and performance evaluation usually is best accomplished by a group operating within the maintenance department. This group may also be employed to augment the accounting department's presentation with data which will reflect trends and comparisons for management's benefit in evaluating the performance of the maintenance department. The maintenance engineering department cannot afford to lose sight of the importance of cost trends and the true implication of significant deviations, as well as the month-to-month cost variation as shown in strictly accounting reports.

Interpretation, analysis, and presentation of cost information are frequently handled by maintenance supervisory personnel. In a relatively small plant, no additional help can be justified. Caution should be exercised, however, to avoid dilution of supervisors' efforts with this type of work at the expense of their primary responsibility, i.e., performing the maintenance function. Exclusive use of supervisory personnel for this purpose may lead to time spent on devising excuses for poor cost performance while neglecting operations, or ignoring cost performance altogether because of the pressure of day-to-day operating activity. In general, it is preferable to have an individual or a group charged with the responsibility for scrutinizing, analyzing, and interpreting cost information. A group of this kind, functioning as an integral part of the maintenance department, can render an invaluable service to its management.

In all this it should be remembered that the primary function of the maintenance department is to perform mechanical work and that work of a strictly clerical nature should be minimized. Wherever possible, this type of work should be performed by other clerical groups which have the requisite personnel and equipment. Too frequently, in an effort to be self-sufficient, or because of some problem in establishing the proper relationship with the accounting department, a maintenance department will become more and more involved in record keeping. All such activity should be closely scrutinized before its undertaking, and every effort should be made to screen out that which is not absolutely necessary to maintenance operations or control. It is not intended to imply that the maintenance group does not require a clerical organization, but rather that great care should be used in defining the scope of its clerical activities in an effort to get optimum return from this overhead expense and avoid duplication of data processing which is performed elsewhere in the plant.

Organization of Cost-control Personnel. Since the cost-control function is department-wide and is essentially a policing job, the organization handling this activity should report to the individual in charge of the maintenance engineering department. The person in charge of the group should perform those analytical and interpreting functions mentioned earlier, and should, either through functional control or through his own clerical organization, control all steps in data gathering and processing within the maintenance department. He should also function as liaison between the maintenance department and other plant clerical groups involved with maintenance-cost data. In some plants other clerical functions, such as the keeping of equipment and property accounting records, may be delegated to him.

In practice, there seems to be no general format for organization of a group of this nature. In charge there may be an office manager, an administrative assistant, a chief clerk, or a coordinator. His organization may include supervisors, chief clerks, and timekeepers, or he may function as a staff specialist with clerical assistance only. These variations depend upon the methods used for gathering and processing information. If other duties mentioned above are included with the responsibilities of this group, additional personnel may be necessary.

A comprehensive study of the organization charts of 60 companies reveals no uniform pattern for a control organization. Usually there is some individual primarily concerned with this activity, as either a staff assistant or a maintenance clerical group leader. Often, control below this level is functional. In general, it appears that smaller companies do not require a particularly formal clerical organization, but as the company size increases, the maintenance clerical staff increases also, even to the point which justifies the use of mechanical data-processing equipment. When such equipment does become available, its ultimate effect will be a reduction in the size of the maintenance clerical organization to those people necessary for the data gathering and analysis steps plus such interdepartmental liaison as is required.

The number of clerks and other data-processing personnel which should be retained by a maintenance department depends on the degree of cooperation between the maintenance department and other plant areas. Often the problem of priority assignment for data-processing equipment is a factor. Such priority decisions must be made arbitrarily or defined in a general way and resolved over short periods of time by the relative importance of individual data-processing problems.

The major objective of the budgeting and cost-control group of the maintenance department should be to provide the information required of it with minimum clerical activity and least duplication of effort within and without the department.

Factors That Influence the Quantity of Work. Plant size, plant location, and the type of service rendered by the plant accounting department are, of course, the basic factors affecting the size of the maintenance department cost and budget group. Others which should be taken into consideration are the availability of tabulating equipment to the maintenance department and the extent to which cost and budget activities are detailed as dictated by company policy or considerations of internal control of the department.

The initial cost of mechanical data-processing equipment and the cost of its maintenance limit its use to the larger plants. In some cases the use of such equipment can be procured on a rental basis from a supplier or other outside interest. Major advantages resulting from mechanical data processing are the reduction in the amount of manual paper work and personnel to do it, as well as increased speed of processing and presentation of summarized data. Obviously, the data-processing installation will affect the amount of clerical effort required to the extent that it is used in the cost and budget work. Since tabulating equipment is high in cost and requires special skills for its operation, the installation usually can be justified only on the basis of processing information for all plant operations. That portion of its time devoted to maintenance-cost processing may be small and limited to that presentation which is required directly by the accounting department. Participation of clerical personnel of the maintenance department to develop basic information and interpret the results for control purposes may be more or less, varying with the availability of the machine data-processing unit.

The more detail required in the cost-control system for maintenance, the more need there is for both the manual operations of posting and transferring information and the steps of analysis and summary. Probably the most detail is required in a maintenance department using job standards and paying incentive wages. In this situation the cost-control functions are intimately associated with those of industrial engineering, job planning, standard-time determination, and wage-payment policies.

Chapter 4

COST CONTROL FOR EFFECTIVE OPERATION

By George E. Meyers
Management Consultant–Maintenance Specialist
Waban, Mass.

An organizational unit charged with the responsibility for maintenance-cost control should exist within the maintenance group. The technical aspects alone of everyday maintenance requirements, coupled with supervisory needs, not only take the entire time of all supervision but also often require many hours over and above normal working time. Supervisors simply do not have the time necessary for the mass of fact finding which is so imperative to outstanding maintenance performance. When one considers that management spends for maintenance labor, burden, and materials an average of from $10,000 is $14,000 annually per maintenance employee,[1] the real importance of a fact-finding, cost-controlling department becomes apparent. It is by the route of recorded costs and demonstrated economies to come that maintenance can secure the confidence of management in its plans and procedures.

OBJECTIVES AND ORGANIZATION FOR COST CONTROL

The major activity of this unit is to develop and carry out a simple but effective cost-control program which will:

1. Indicate where beneficial changes may be made in the supervisory structure.
2. Provide the basis for a sound preventive-maintenance program.
3. Provide the means for planning and scheduling all maintenance work.
4. Furnish data to aid in the improvement of the efficiency of productive equipment.
5. Determine costs for all maintenance jobs.
6. Substantially reduce total maintenance costs.

The supervisor of maintenance cost control, a title I shall use for the head of the fact-finding, cost-controlling unit, should be carefully selected, and the position should be given importance and prestige commensurate with the expected results. Companies which have inaugurated such a department have selected this individual from either the industrial engineering department or from supervision within the maintenance organization. It is a position which should be placed on the organization chart somewhere between top maintenance supervision and craft foreman. It could be considered as a staff job responsible to the plant engineer or superintendent of maintenance. There is also the possibility of responsibility for the cost aspects of the job being under the direction of the controller or the plant accountant. The specific placement of the responsibility should not be detrimental to the effectiveness of the unit.

[1] These figures are based on wage rates of from $1.75 to $2.50 per hour, fixed cost equal to the wage rate, and a materials cost of from 45 to 55 per cent of this total of labor and burden cost.

The personnel necessary to carry out the functions of the cost-control group will depend almost entirely on the size of the over-all maintenance organization. In companies of less than 75 maintenance employees, the assistance of a clerk or perhaps a part-time clerk will suffice, while for larger maintenance groups one additional man for each 50 to 60 maintenance employees would be required.[1]

When the organization goes beyond about 125 workers, then in addition to clerical assistance, there is need for an estimator. An individual to be qualified for such duties should be one who has had a good background of technical and practical maintenance work. Companies which have adopted programs similar to the one outlined here have had good results in choosing this man from the supervisory ranks of maintenance, more often from the machine shop or the millwright group.

The assigning of space to the maintenance cost-control personnel is important, and there are advantages to be gained by a location within the offices of the maintenance department.

THE DETERMINATION OF HISTORICAL COSTS OF MAINTENANCE

So as to have something tangible to pursue, a complete outline of procedures is furnished here by which maintenance can provide information for management which will indicate whether or not all phases of maintenance activities are well controlled. A simple and yet complete cost-control plan should provide for the determination of historical cost data and at the same time utilize procedures which accomplish the following:

1. Establish a preventive-maintenance program.
2. Provide for improved planning and scheduling.
3. Establish historical man-hour cost standards for all maintenance jobs.
4. Furnish complete information for the preparation of weekly reports clearly indicating the effectiveness, by crafts, of the maintenance organization.

In order to accomplish the above through the method of analyzing historical man-hour costs, it is first necessary to establish procedures to determine these costs. The first step in the program is to design and put into use a complete job-order-writing system in conjunction with a timekeeping system which will provide a means for workers to charge each maintenance job with the hours spent thereon.

A Job-order-writing Procedure. In designing an order form, it is well to have two types: one to be used for regular maintenance repair-work costing, say, up to $1,000, and a second for use where major repairs or capital-expenditure items are involved. The latter cases usually require preliminary estimates of costs so that they may be reviewed prior to authorization of the expenditure.

The regular repair order can be prepared in quadruplicate, or with as many copies as may be required. Space on the order form is provided for pertinent information and data, as shown in Fig. 4-1.

The form to be used for major-repair and large-expenditure items, usually called a work order, should have practically the same outline of printed matter thereon as the repair-order form with the following differences:

1. Provision of space to record the estimates.
2. Additional space to write a more detailed description of the work to be done.
3. Space to enter the actual cost of the job.

When starting the job-order-writing procedure, it should be decided whether the orders are to be written by the requesters of the work or are to be written at a central order-writing desk in the maintenance cost-control unit as a result of requests by authorized personnel. The advantages of central-order writing are as follows:

[1] Experience indicates that the volume of cost-control work required varies almost directly with the maintenance work load and therefore the number of maintenance employees.

1. Orders will always be in order-number sequence.
2. The two important aspects of order writing, namely, the stating of quantities needed and a good description of the work requested, can be better controlled.
3. Legibility may be greatly improved.

If four copies of the order are prepared by the requester, he retains one for his files and forwards three copies to the cost-control unit.   When the order is written at a

JOB ORDER					JOB ORDER NUMBER 1551		
DEPARTMENT Roll Shop					CHARGE ACCOUNT 108		
EQUIPMENT Windows					DATE 3/8/		
REQUESTOR Wolf		DATE WANTED 3/10/			APPROVED BY /s/ Wolf		
WHERE LOCATED Roll Shop Main Office					DELIVER TO Same		
SHOPS	Copies	CODE	HOURS Avg.	Act.	QUANTITY	DESCRIPTION OF WORK TO BE DONE	
Requestor	√				3	In order to help keep out sun rays please paint tinted panes in 3 windows on East end of office.	
Sup't Charged Ludwig	√						
Mech. Sup't	x						
4 S.P. Mach. Shop							
4 B.F. Mach. Shop							
6 Riggers							
6 Car Building							
7 Weld Shop							
8 Pipe Shop							
8-A Carpenter Shop							
8-A Painters-Carp.	x						
8-A Painters-Steel							
8-B Blacksmiths							
5 Millwrights						SHOP REMARKS	
Electr. Sup't							
9-E Instr. Shop							
9-B Elect. Shop							
9-C Elect. Constr.							
9-CA A. C. & Heat'g							
9-D Roundhouse							
DATE WANTED			DATE COMPLETED		SIGNED		
HOURS							MATERIALS

FIG. 4-1. Regular repair-order form (to be prepared in quadruplicate).

central-order-writing desk, one copy is sent to the requester so that he has a written record of his verbal request.   In either case, three copies are available for distribution by cost control.   One of these copies is retained and filed in a "work ahead" file in numerical sequence to be used later as the medium for accumulating the man-hour cost of each job or order.   The remaining two copies are sent to the foreman of the craft involved in the job.   In the event more than one craft is involved, three additional copies for each additional craft are prepared by the cost-control unit so that they may retain a copy for each craft involved for their files and send two copies to all crafts which may be required on the job.   All orders for each job should bear the same order number.

The two copies sent to each craft foreman can be used by him to plan and schedule the work under his jurisdiction and also indicate the volume of backlog for his men. At the time a job is started he can give the worker one copy indicating the work to be done. When the job is completed, this copy is returned to the foreman who enters the completed data on the copy in his file and then sends this copy to the cost-control unit, thus notifying them that the work of his craft has been finished. The worker's copy of the order can be retained in the foreman's office or destroyed. This completes

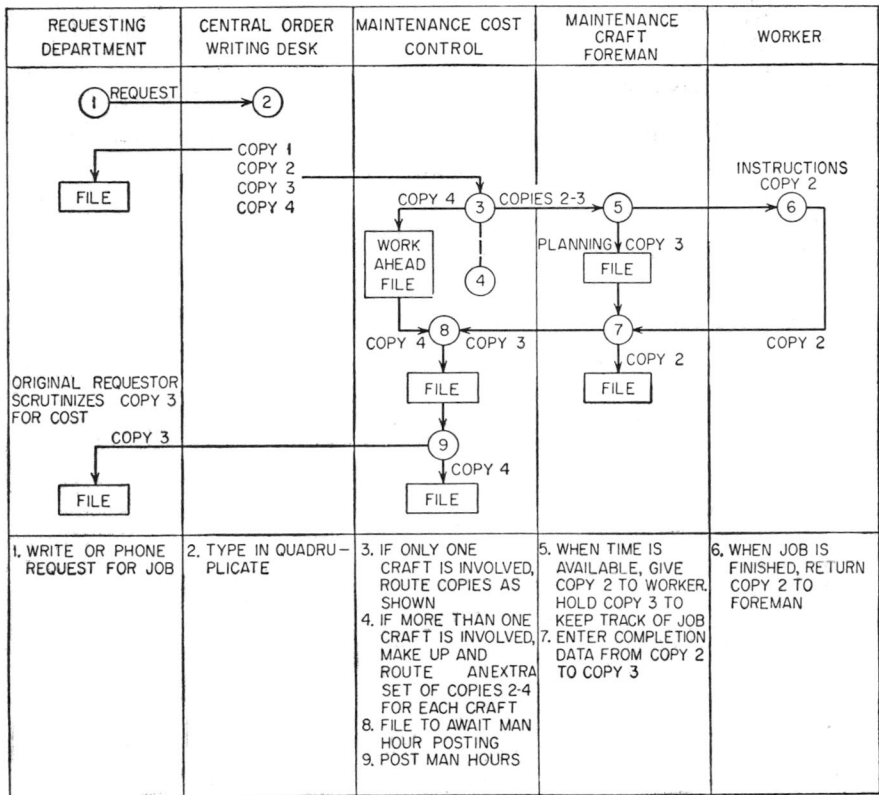

FIG. 4-2. Flow chart of order-writing procedure.

the repair-order cycle from the original request until the work is completed and a file copy returned to the cost-control unit. The handling and flow, after approval, of the order form for major repairs or capital expenditures follows the same routine. The file copies are then available for posting and accumulation of man-hour costs by the cost-control unit.

There is one major exception to this order-writing procedure, and that is the accounting for man-hour costs of routine jobs. A routine job is one which is done periodically and usually by the same worker or workers. Such jobs as lubrication, inspections, and changing of light bulbs or tubes are in this category. Permanent-routine account numbers can be assigned each of these jobs so that workers can report time against them and the cost-control clerk can accumulate the hours spent each week on such work. A flow chart of the entire order-writing procedure is shown in Fig. 4-2.

Timekeeping Procedures. We now proceed to the task of setting up timekeeping procedures, which is the second important step in determining historical costs. There are a number of ways by which time spent on jobs can be accounted for by the worker, and the following are the principal methods listed in order of preference:

1. Central timekeeping, whereby the workers report to a central desk the order number and the starting and stopping time for each job on which they work. At the time of the worker's call the central timekeeper records on the worker's daily time card the order or routine account number and through the means of an electric time clock records the start and stop time.
2. The worker carries his own daily time card and enters the order or routine number for the job on which he is working and punches the start and stop time on electric time clocks located at convenient places throughout the plant.
3. The worker enters on his daily time card the order or routine number for the job on which he is working and also enters in pencil the start and stop time and elapsed hours for each job. Sometimes he may enter only the time he spent on the job without listing the start and stop time.

At the close of the day either the timekeeper or clerk checks to see if the total of elapsed hours as shown on each maintenance worker's daily time ticket agrees with the total hours shown on the worker's over-all time card usually used for payroll purposes. In this manner there is assurance that all hours worked are charged to an order or routine job number.

Accumulating Time Data. The next step is to provide a procedure whereby all hours worked are posted to the various copies of orders on file in the cost-control unit and that hours worked on routine jobs are entered against an account for each routine job. This can best be accomplished by one of two methods, the preferable one being the use of tabulating equipment where cards are punched from the worker's daily time cards, indicating the following:

1. Craft code.
2. Order or routine number.
3. Hours worked on each order or routine number.

From these daily punched tabulating cards, a printed summary by pay periods can be prepared by the tabulating department showing in order-number sequence and in routine-number sequence the hours charged against each job by each craft. The total hours on this tabulating report should balance with the hours worked by maintenance employees for each pay period. Postings to copies of all orders and routine account numbers can be made from this report by a clerk in the cost-control unit.

The second manner of posting man-hours to orders is the method by which a clerk posts directly from the worker's daily time ticket. This procedure accomplishes the same result as posting from a tabulating report but is considerably more laborious for several reasons, as follows:

1. Loss in legibility.
2. Order numbers are not in sequence.
3. Volume of work is increased because of daily postings instead of weekly postings on those jobs which are worked on for more than 1 day.

Let us assume that man-hour costs by crafts have been posted to each and every job order and to routine account numbers (the form to record man-hour costs of routine jobs will be described later). During the course of this posting, those orders covering jobs which have been completed are put aside while those orders covering jobs not complete are refiled in numerical sequence in the same files from which they have been removed for posting. The copy of the order which had been returned by each respective craft foreman, when his part of the job was completed, still remains with the cost-control unit's copy, both in cases where completed orders (by all crafts) have been put aside and where those not completed are refiled.

The incomplete orders which are refiled at this point are awaiting the further posting of man-hours until the jobs covered are completed by all crafts involved. At this time the hours of all crafts on completed jobs as shown on the cost-control unit's copies which have been put aside are then posted to the copy or copies returned by craft foremen.   These copies are then sent to the original requester of the work to advise that the work has been done and to point out the man-hour cost by craft.

Analysis of Man-hour Costs.   Attention is now given to the cost-control unit's copies of completed orders which are to be analyzed and then posted to an account form which becomes a historical man-hour cost record of all repair jobs.   Maintenance repair work other than routine jobs usually falls into two categories—repetitive and nonrepetitive work.   Normally about 90 per cent of the orders written for maintenance work will cover the usual *everyday* repairs while the remaining orders will call for major repairs or work to be capitalized.   It is with the analysis and man-hour cost of the usual repair jobs, say up to $500 in total labor cost, that we are concerned here.

The first analysis of copies of orders for completed jobs is for the purpose of determining those jobs which are repetitive.   This means the scrutiny of the description of each job to find out if any jobs repeat as often as once a month or at least six to ten times a year, having determined such a figure as the minimum necessary to classify it as a repetitive job.

In addition to this method of setting up repetitive jobs, meetings can be held by the supervisor of cost control with the craft foremen and the supervisors of production departments to review maintenance work and, from knowledge of the various jobs done in the past, prepare a list of repetitive jobs.   When all jobs of a repetitive nature are established, an account should be opened for each job and for each craft which may be involved so that man-hour costs by crafts may be posted to this account each time a repetitive job occurs.   These postings are made from the cost-control copy of the order which has been previously posted from the tabulating report or from the worker's daily time card, as shown in Fig. 4-3.

When man-hour costs of repetitive job orders have been posted and these orders removed from the group of completed orders for each pay period, there remain the copies of orders for jobs of a nonrepetitive nature.   These orders are now sorted into craft classifications and then into the following five groupings regardless of the description of the work that has been done:

Jobs taking from   0.1 to   8.0 hr.
Jobs taking from   8.1 to 16.0 hr.
Jobs taking from 16.1 to 32.0 hr.
Jobs taking from 32.1 to 48.0 hr.
Jobs taking from 48.1 to 96.0 hr.

The number of orders and the total hours in each grouping should be determined and these totals posted to an account which is opened for each craft and each classification.   This posting should consist of the date of the pay period represented by the tabulating report, the total number of jobs, and the total hours.   In the case where tabulating reports are not available and postings are made to orders from daily time cards, the completed nonrepetitive jobs can be accumulated for a pay period before they are totaled and posted to their respective accounts.

The man-hour costs by crafts of routine repetitive and nonrepetitive jobs have now been posted to their respective accounts, and these postings should continue for a base period of 6 months.   This base period is of adequate elapsed time to establish the average historical man-hour costs for all maintenance jobs excepting those of a major nature which exceed, say, an average of over 96 man-hours per craft to complete.   Such jobs should be considered in the future as jobs for which the man-hours, by crafts, are to be estimated in detail and the estimates used as standards for control purposes in the same manner as the historical costs are used for the ordinary repair jobs.

The following cost classifications should result from the above analysis:

1. *Routine Job Costs.*   Inasmuch as man-hour costs have been recorded each week over a 6-month period for each routine job by crafts, there can now be established a

weekly average cost for each and every routine job. These average costs now become historical cost standards which are used to indicate the trend of future maintenance man-hour costs for routine work. For example, if the average cost of lubrication during the base period was 74 man-hours per pay period, then any changes from this

| DATE 1954 | Quantity | Pay PERIOD HOURS | | % | 8 PERIOD TOTAL HOURS | | PERIOD AVERAGE HOURS | | % |
		STANDARD	ACTUAL		STANDARD	ACTUAL	STANDARD	ACTUAL	
7- 2	3	4.5	4.0						
9	1	1.5	1.7						
16	5	7.5	7.0						
23	2	3.0	2.4						
30	3	4.5	3.6						
8- 6	4	6.0	6.9						
13	-		--						
20	-		--		27.0	25.6	3.4	3.2	107
27	7	10.5	9.8		33.0	31.4	4.1	3.9	105
9- 3	2	3.0	2.6		34.5	32.3	4.3	4.0	107
10	3	4.5	4.0		31.5	29.3	3.9	3.7	105
17	1	1.5	1.5		30.0	28.4	3.8	3.6	106
24	4	6.0	7.0		31.5	31.8	4.1	4.0	103
10-1	-	-	--		25.5	24.9	3.2	3.1	103
8	6	9.0	9.6		34.5	34.5	4.3	4.3	100
15	5	7.5	7.5		42.0	42.0	5.2	5.2	100
22	3	4.5	5.0		36.0	37.2	4.5	4.7	96
29	-	-	--		33.0	34.6	4.1	4.3	95
11-5	8	12.0	13.0		40.5	43.0	5.1	5.4	94
12	-	-	--		39.0	41.5	4.8	5.2	92
19	4	6.0	6.0		39.0	40.5	4.8	5.1	94
26	3	4.5	5.0		43.5	45.5	5.4	5.7	95
12-3	9	13.5	14.4		48.0	50.3	6.0	6.3	95
10	8	12.0	11.3		52.5	54.1	6.6	6.8	97
17	3	4.5	4.5		52.5	53.6	6.6	6.7	99
24	6	6.0	8.2		61.5	61.8	7.7	7.7	100
	90		135.0						
	135 Hours ÷ 90 items = 1.5 Hours per glass								

OPERATION __REPLACE WINDOW GLASS__   PLANT ____ CODE ____
STANDARD HOURS __1.5 Hours Per Glass__   SHOP __CARPENTER__

FIG. 4-3. Job cost developed from records of repetitive operation.

average cost in the future for lubricating similar equipment will be indicated by deviations from this figure.

2. *Repetitive Job Costs.* As a result of posting the man-hour costs by crafts to an account for each repetitive job for a 6-month period, there has developed an average cost for each of these jobs. As an example, the replacement of window glass might show an average cost of 1.5 hr per glass as a result of the account for this repetitive job showing 90 window glasses replaced during the base period with a total of 135 man-hours charged against the various orders issued for this work (see Fig. 4-3).

3. *Nonrepetitive Job Costs.*   The manner of posting man-hour costs for nonrepetitive jobs as outlined previously will permit, at the end of the 6-month base period, the determination of the average time per job spent by maintenance workers for each of the groupings shown.   For example, in the machine shop the following averages may result:

Groupings, hr	No. of jobs	Total hr	Avg time, hr
0.1–8.0	200	700.0	3.5
8.1–16.0	75	855.0	11.4
16.1–32.0	15	348.0	23.2
32.1–48.0	6	233.0	38.8
48.1–96.0	2	137.0	68.5

It is shown that, for all nonrepetitive jobs in the machine shop which have taken 8 hr or less to complete, the average time is 3.5 hr.   All averages for these groupings for each craft are computed.   These averages can be used as cost standards for indicating trends in future costs for nonrepetitive work.   The application of the nonrepetitive cost standards to all orders for nonrepetitive jobs in the future differs considerably from the application of cost standards for routine and repetitive jobs. In the latter two cases the jobs to be done in the future are known as to job description and job content and permanent historical cost standards can be applied to such jobs as they occur.

However, in the case of nonrepetitive jobs, each and every one may be of a different nature and content.   Therefore, as a part of the cost-control procedure, these jobs must be classified by qualified personnel within the unit in logical groups.   This classification or rough estimating means that before a nonrepetitive job is started the classifier must determine from the description of the work requested the grouping into which it should be placed.   The average base-period cost hours for the group in which the job has been placed becomes the cost standard.   It is understood, of course, that a separate set of groupings is developed for each craft, as brought out earlier.

USE OF HISTORICAL COSTS FOR MAINTENANCE COST CONTROL

Reference to the various accounts for routine repetitive and nonrepetitive jobs will prove interesting and informative.   These accounts clearly and accurately reveal the costs expressed in man-hours of all the various types of jobs completed during the base period except major-repair and capital-expenditure jobs.   A careful scrutiny of these costs will point out many high-cost situations for investigation and study. Such instances should be selected in sequence of importance so as to gain the greatest cost benefits as quickly as possible, which will serve the very important function of proving to management and maintenance supervision one of the major values of this type of cost-control plan.   These man-hour cost accounts will also reflect the extent of cost improvement by comparison of the new costs with those experienced during the 6-month base period.

The most important use by far of the average cost standards is in preparing for each pay period a cost-control report which will reflect, by craft, the trends in future costs of maintenance work as compared with base-period costs.   In addition, this report will show two important and necessary facts as follows:

1. It will determine the future effectiveness of maintenance personnel as compared with the base period.
2. It will indicate in man-hours the volume of maintenance work completed each pay period.

As you can see, this control report is the climax to the cost-control program and the barometer by which the effectiveness and benefits of the plan are pointed out to management and maintenance supervision.

The preparation of the afore-mentioned report is not difficult and is illustrated in Fig. 4-4.   Shown thereon in one column are the average cost hours, listed by crafts, for all routine, repetitive and nonrepetitive jobs completed during each respective pay period and the actual hours expended on these jobs.   This gives a comparison of average cost hours and actual hours, and by dividing the former by the actual hours,

WEEKLY STANDARD HOUR CONTROL REPORT

MAINTENANCE DIVISION

Period Ended _____

	Current Period			8 Period Average		
	Average Hours	Actual Hours	Perf. Ratio	Average Hours	Actual Hours	Perf. Ratio
Machine Shop	3590	3408	106	3710	3648	102
Sheet Metal Shop	663	682	103	645	632	102
Forge Shop	529	557	95	570	596	96
Structural Shop	5242	5379	97	5262	5328	99
Carpenter Shop	1995	2040	98	2008	2080	97
Pipe Shop	1864	1777	105	1926	1874	103
Welding Shop	1604	1520	106	1584	1540	103
Paint Shop	1197	1260	95	1215	1162	105
Pattern Shop	280	264	107	272	258	105
Diesel and Truck Repair Shop	1825	1755	104	1853	1892	98
Mechanical Department Total	18789	18642	101	19045	19010	100
Electrical Repair Shop	555	535	104	584	614	95
Electrical Construction	402	410	98	376	358	105
Electrical Department Total	957	945	101	960	972	99
Brick Mason Department	7909	7753	102	7745	7603	102
Coke Plant Mechanical	10227	10419	98	9865	9988	102
Coke Plant - Assigned	965	1012	96	940	912	103
Blast Furnace "	3042	2958	103	2978	3026	98
Open Hearth "	6080	6189	98	6118	5938	103
Rolling Mills "	4654	4575	102	4754	4702	101
Rod and Wire Mill "	2901	2802	104	2848	2905	98
Assigned Maintenance Total	17642	17536	101	17638	17483	101
GRAND TOTAL	55524	55295	100	55253	55056	100

FIG. 4-4. Cost-control report effective for comparisons.

a ratio will develop.   Any deviation from base-period average costs as compared with current actual-pay-period costs will be indicated by the ratio being above or below 100, which is the base ratio.   Inasmuch as the historical costs were based on averages over a 6-month period, this same report should, in addition to showing the current-pay-period figures, reflect average cost hours, actual hours, and ratios, using an 8-week moving average.   This can be accomplished by including on the report additional columns which will contain the average cost hours and the actual hours for all jobs completed during each 8-week period which includes the current pay and the seven pay periods preceding.   As each new pay period ends, it is included and the oldest week of the previous report dropped.

In this way moving totals or averages for 8-week periods are maintained and shown on the report.   An 8-week period is long enough to give results in terms of time required for a job which are stable and will result in significant cost comparisons.   A 10-week period could be used if the advantage of easier computation was felt to offset the slight loss in sensitivity which would occur.   A period shorter than 8 weeks is very likely to show wider fluctuations in time than are warranted by the situation.

MAJOR-REPAIR AND CAPITAL-EXPENDITURE ITEMS

Reference is now made to those jobs covering major repairs or capital-expenditure items not included thus far in the outline of the cost-control program.   These jobs, of course, must be controlled with at least the attention given to other maintenance work.   A separate report by pay periods showing comparisons by crafts of estimated and actual costs should be prepared for these jobs.   So that comparisons and ratios are indicative of performance, the estimates for this class of work should be reasonably accurate.   Time and effort are usually well spent in preparing careful estimates of man-hours, by crafts, for all these jobs.   Original estimates may be somewhat inaccurate for two major reasons.   First, the entire scope of the work may not be known at the time of estimating, or conditions or contingencies may arise after the start of the work which were not anticipated and which could have real effect on the estimate.

It has been mentioned elsewhere in this outline that all maintenance hours should be accounted for and that hours spent on major-repair jobs and capital-expenditure items should be posted, by craft, to an account covering such jobs.   It is a responsibility of the cost-control unit to scrutinize constantly the man-hours spent on each of these accounts which shows not only actual hours worked each pay period, but a record of the estimated hours.

It is a good policy for the cost-control unit to notify supervisors in charge of the different crafts on these jobs whenever actual hours amount to, say, one-half or two-thirds of the estimated hours.   When receiving this notification, supervisors should advise the cost-control unit as to the status of the job and further advise whether or not the job can be completed in line with the estimate.   If not, then investigation and a resultant revision of the estimate should be made so that, when a job is about two-thirds complete, the estimate will more truly represent the scope of the job and the conditions encountered in undertaking it.   If such a procedure is followed, the pay-period reports reflecting the comparisons of actual hours and estimated hours and the resultant ratios will be more realistic.

CONTROL OF MAINTENANCE MATERIALS AND SUPPLIES

It is best if important maintenance materials and supplies are kept in a central storeroom under proper supervision.   Items of an inexpensive nature and only in amounts constituting reserve stocks should be stored in the various maintenance shops.   Well-controlled inventories dictate that all withdrawals be on written requisition so that proper charges to routine and repair order numbers can be made.   In addition, the account number for accounting distribution should be shown on the requisition.   Therefore, the cost of all materials and supplies can be determined for each and every maintenance job and these costs can be posted on copies of the orders along with the man-hour costs.

BENEFITS TO BE DERIVED FROM MAINTENANCE COST CONTROL

The organization and operation of a cost-control program according to the procedures just given should result in the accomplishment of the objectives presented at the beginning of this section.

1. The Development of a Sound Maintenance Organization. During the entire base period when job costs are being developed it is usually found that many jobs are excessive in cost. One of the duties and responsibilities of the supervisor of cost control is not only to determine and disclose job costs which are excessive, but also to hold conferences with maintenance supervision to acquaint them with the facts in each case and assist in developing measures which will remedy such high costs. The possibility of better planning, the use of fewer men on the job, or the need for studies by the industrial engineering department, aspecially where costly routine or repetitive jobs are concerned, are some examples.

Valuable information will be forthcoming from the cost-finding aspects of the control plan indicating that many items which are being made in the various maintenance shops can be purchased from outside sources for a lesser cost. Again the cost-control unit plays an important part in bringing such matters to the attention of maintenance executives for decisive and proper action. Another source of excessive costs is the undertaking of jobs during overtime-pay periods which could have been done during regular working hours.

Report and analysis of the three types of excessive-cost jobs just mentioned becomes one of the major duties of the cost-control unit. The resulting discussions with maintenance supervision soon reveal the interest, conscientiousness, and qualifications of the supervisors in coping with excessive-cost operations. Such meetings bring out much information as to the everyday duties of supervisors, how they spent their time, and whether or not they are burdened with clerical or extraneous work. It is somewhat common to find that supervisors are extremely busy and work long hours, but you will note that they do many things which clerks or other assistants could do just as well. In reality, they have very little time to supervise properly, to plan and schedule work, or to devote to the economical operation of their respective activities.

These discussions reveal the relationships between supervisors and workers as well as indicate the ability of foremen to organize and direct their forces. All this aids in judging the quality of the maintenance organization as well as adequacy of supervisory personnel.

2. A Planned Preventive-maintenance Program. The next advantage of the plan is the fact that it establishes the basis and provides information for the formulation of a preventive-maintenance program. As far as routine jobs are concerned, such as lubrication and inspections, average man-hour costs will have been determined. Then charts and schedules can be prepared for two purposes: first, to get a much better idea of the man-hours which should be spent on such routine jobs; and, second, to ensure that all equipment is lubricated and inspected at regularly scheduled times. Further, assurance is given that proper oils and greases are used and, in the case of inspections, that the necessary tools and instruments are available.

In addition to routine work, the preventive-maintenance plan should include a record of all repair work on all machine-tool facilities and buildings. This can be done simply and informatively by preparing a master card for each piece of equipment or area of equipment where very large machines are in use. Such cards can also be set up for areas of buildings such as roofs, floors, inside walls, and inside and outside piping. After the master cards are prepared, the mere filing of a copy of the repair order behind the respective master card will tell the date and type of repair, the frequency, and the man-hour and material cost thereof. The copy of the order which was used in preparing the pay-period cost-control report will suffice for this filing. It can be seen that the simple filing procedure eliminates any additional writing or posting in order to effect a workable preventive-maintenance program. The cost and frequency of all repairs to equipment and buildings are known and can be readily analyzed so that sound decisions can be reached as to renewals or replacements of parts, machines, or buildings. Management will be periodically informed of the major benefits resulting from such a program such as greater machine life, more operating and productive hours of equipment, and less frequent and less costly repairs to both equipment and buildings. The accumulation and reporting of such data is a responsibility of the cost-control unit.

3. Effective Planning and Scheduling of All Maintenance Work. Another major accomplishment of the control plan will be its effect on planning and scheduling of maintenance repair work. One copy of the repair job order can be used for this purpose by each craft foreman or by the planner and scheduler in his department where the size of the maintenance organization warrants such personnel. Both production and maintenance supervision should be encouraged to request maintenance repair work when they think of the job to be done rather than when they want it done. Before effective planning and scheduling can be undertaken, a backlog of written orders must be accumulated. This backlog should reflect orders covering a volume of 6 to 8 weeks' work load. Certain jobs can be scheduled only a day or two in advance while others may be planned a week or several weeks ahead. Inasmuch as average man-hour costs or time standards have been developed for repetitive and nonrepetitive jobs, they can be posted to the copy of the order used for planning and scheduling. Thus the backlog can be computed in man-hours for each craft at regular intervals, say once each month. The benefits of good planning and scheduling are many, some of them being:

1. Efficient use of manpower.
2. Minimized downtime of productive equipment while making repairs.
3. Reduction in overtime penalty costs by accomplishing more work in regular hours.
4. Purchasing items at lower cost which, without planning, may become emergency work in maintenance shops.

Planning and scheduling again give an insight into the capabilities of the maintenance organization to carry out such a program so necessary to its effective and economical operation.

Chapter 5

RELIABILITY INDEXES AND EQUIPMENT REPLACEMENT OR REBUILDING

By JAMES H. SARGENT
Manager, Product and Service Planning
Utility and Marine Industries
General Electric Company
Service Shops Department
Schenectady, N.Y.

The high-speed, continuous-production systems of today demand great reliability of the critical pieces of equipment found in all modern automated and semiautomated manufacturing and service industries. These critical items may be individual pieces of equipment or combinations of pieces that form a process system. The single pieces usually will be the larger, higher-cost equipment in the operation. The process system may include one or more of the former but will nearly always include several smaller or less costly devices, some of which may be just as critical to the operation of the system as the large equipment.

In recent years, management's concern for the reliability of process equipment has been expressed through emphasis on maintenance—preventive, programmed, productive, engineered, etc. Because of the modernization or upgrading of plants through equipment replacement or rebuilding and retrofitting, plant engineering and plant maintenance often are combined under one head or are of equal stature in the organization. Both divisions are an important influence on the selection of new or replacement equipment. They know not only what the equipment does, but how it performs, what routine attention it requires, and what its serviceability and records' of reliability and maintenance cost are.

THE RELIABILITY INDEX

In preparing a recommendation to management regarding the rebuilding or replacement of capital equipment, the plant engineer evaluates the reliability of the equipment. He may express it as high, average, or low reliability or as high or low probability of failure. In a large plant or an organization having many plants, it is desirable to have a numerical value established to facilitate comparisons of similar equipment and assist in the planning and budgeting of equipment maintenance, improvements, or replacements.

The Reliability Index Number. This is a relative number arrived at to represent the reliability of a particular piece of equipment and to relate it to other similar pieces. This index number must be determined for each piece of critical equipment in a process system.   It also is possible to combine these pieces and express an aggregate Reliability Index number for the system.   There would be little value in doing so, however, unless there were other like systems to be compared with it.

Because it is a relative number, we must be consistent in determining the index number for each type of equipment used in the operation.   Some ground rules must be established to guide each craftsman or specialist in judging the factors involved. The optimum condition would be to have one individual in a plant responsible for determining the Reliability Index number for one type or class of equipment.   The next best condition is to have one person responsible for determining the Reliability Index number for a class of equipment and provide time for personal communication of the guide rules to those making the inspection of that equipment.

The base, or maximum numerical value, of the Reliability Index number does not have to be 100.   In fact, as will become evident, it may be preferable that it does not equal 100.   The resultant index number will then be expressed, for example, as $^{72}/_{124}$ or $^{65}/_{124}$, etc., with the divisor being the base and the dividend being the rating established for that piece of equipment.   The index numbers for other types or classes of equipment might be expressed as $^{92}/_{145}$, $^{86}/_{138}$, etc.

In the use of card systems or computer run-outs, we can use the different base numbers to collect like types or classes of equipment and make comparisons within each group.   Now we can establish priorities and budget for planned maintenance, major rebuilding and upgrading, and/or replacement of equipment that most requires attention.   To help in determining which type or class of equipment will receive attention, we should have productivity ratings established for each piece of critical apparatus or process system in the plant.   These should be in broad categories such as A, B, C, D.   (The fewer the better.)   Also we can convert our Reliability Index numbers from fractions into percentages and use them to help decide how much maintenance and equipment replacement can be done within our budget.   Management can also see the expected level of equipment reliability that will result.

For those who believe that perfect should always be 100 per cent, our Reliability Index can always have a maximum value of 100.   Because of the inherent differences in designs, to use a base of 100 may require the use of guide rules (rulers) having varying graduations.   Nevertheless, this may be the simplest index to apply, providing we can rely upon the use of good judgment by qualified personnel.

DETERMINING THE RELIABILITY INDEX NUMBER

There are five basic factors that must be considered in determining the reliability of any piece of equipment.   A perfect Reliability Index number of 100 would be made up of:

Visual inspection	40
Tests and measurements	30
Age	10
Environment	10
Duty cycle	10
Total	100

Visual Inspection.   When it is made by a qualified technician, visual inspection is the most important factor in determining the reliability of critical equipment.   The technician must know what to look for and how to evaluate what he sees.   Critical equipment seldom fails during normal operation without giving some warning.   We attempt to detect and interpret this warning before a failure occurs.   The frequency of thorough visual inspections must be based upon operating experience, the recommendations of equipment manufacturers, and some consideration of the age factor. The technician should have two opportunities to view the equipment: first, in operation under load; second, when partially or completely dismantled.   Also, he should have the report of the last visual inspection.   A suitable check list and report form must be used as this enables us to determine what attention is required and to prepare a cost estimate.

Guide rules must be set up for use by the technician in evaluating the best estimate of condition versus the maximum weighted value allotted (40 in our example). If these are to be kept as simple as possible, they must be made quite broad, such as:

$$
\begin{aligned}
&\text{Power input path} \dots \dots \dots \dots \dots \dots \quad 10\\
&\text{Power conversion path} \dots \dots \dots \dots \quad 10\\
&\text{Power transmission path} \dots \dots \dots \dots \quad 10\\
&\text{Frame, housings, and base} \dots \dots \dots \dots \quad 5\\
&\text{Sensing, indicating, and control} \dots \dots \dots \quad \underline{5}\\
&\qquad \text{Total (max)} \dots \dots \dots \dots \dots \dots \dots \quad 40
\end{aligned}
$$

The above guide rules facilitate the use of the over-all Reliability Index of 100 but require the inspector to be more flexible in applying his judgment. See Fig. 5-1, as

Using Check List Below, Rate Each Item as Follows:

2 = Acceptable
1 = Keep under Observation
0 = Requires Immediate Attention

If Any Item Does Not Apply, Rate That Item 2.

Stator

a. _____ Insulation condition
b. _____ Winding tightness
c. _____ Cleanliness
d. _____ Lamination condition
e. _____ Condition of leads
f. _____ Air gap
g. _____ Winding temperature

Rotor

h. _____ Insulation condition
i. _____ Winding tightness
j. _____ Cleanliness
k. _____ Laminations/poles
l. _____ Leads
m. _____ Slip rings
n. _____ Brushes
o. _____ Brush holder system
p. _____ Commutator
q. _____ Bearings
r. _____ Shaft-spider-coupling
s. _____ Vibration
t. _____ Lubrication

Comments (Describe Condition of All Items Rated 0):_____

_____

_____

_____

Rating = Sum of Items [   ]   (40 Max)

Fig. 5-1. Visual-inspection guide rules, motors and generators.

applied to a motor or generator, for an example of a more detailed rule. Regardless of the pattern of the guide rules used, we must always apply the same guide rules to similar equipment if our data is to have real significance. Note in Fig. 5-1 that we apply these to all large a-c and d-c electric motors and allow the maximum value to any item that does not apply to the motor under consideration. Even so, we must recognize the difference between the Reliability Index factors established by this method for a simple a-c squirrel-cage induction motor and for a more complex d-c motor or a wound-rotor a-c motor. For example, a number 30 applying to a squirrel-cage induction motor might not indicate any greater reliability than a number 25 applying to a d-c or wound-rotor induction motor because the latter has at least two insulated windings, bush rigging, and a commutator or collector, any one of which can cause the motor to fail.

For the maximum number to be most meaningful, it would be desirable to have a separate check list for each of the three basic types of motors and generators. See Fig. 5-2 for a suggested list for a squirrel-cage induction motor and Fig. 5-1 for d-c and wound-rotor a-c motors. Note that the values per item remain the same, but

Using Check List Below, Rate Each Item as Follows:

2 = Acceptable
1 = Keep under Observation
0 = Requires Immediate Attention

If Any Item Does Not Apply, Rate That Item 2.

Stator

a. _____ Insulation condition
b. _____ Winding tightness
c. _____ Cleanliness
d. _____ Lamination condition
e. _____ Condition of leads
f. _____ Air gap
g. _____ Winding temperature

Rotor

h. _____ Winding tightness
i. _____ Cleanliness
j. _____ Laminations/poles
k. _____ Bearings
l. _____ Shaft-spider-coupling
m. _____ Vibration
n. _____ Lubrication

Comments (Describe Condition of All Items Rated 0.):_____

_____

_____

Rating = Sum of Items [_____]   (28 Max)

FIG. 5-2. Visual inspection, a-c squirrel-cage motors.

that the totals for the visual inspection factor vary. This, of course, causes the over-all divisor (maximum base number) to be different in each case. As stated earlier, this can be beneficial. (The same reasoning applies to the next factor, tests and measurements.)

Tests and Measurements. These are next in importance in establishing reliability. Some may question the weighted value of visual inspection versus that of tests and measurements. If you can't make good visual inspections of equipment or if you don't have qualified personnel to make them, change the values. However, if you do lower the value of visual inspection for either of these reasons, the over-all accuracy of your reliability estimates will be lowered. It might be better to hire such qualified personnel from equipment manufacturers or service contractors on a contract basis and strive for accuracy in your ratings.

Again, we must establish guide rules to help achieve uniformity in the rating of similar equipment. In doing so, make the ratings to be applied to each subfactor as simple as possible, such as Good = 3, Fair = 2, Poor = 1, Requires Immediate

Attention = 0.   See Fig. 5-3 for ground rules that have been used for large electric motors and generators typically found in large industrial plants.

It must be pointed out that in very large motors or generators of high-voltage ratings, it is often desirable to add the a-c high-potential test, even though it is a go or no-go test.   However, this should be applied only after one or two of the other tests listed have been applied or when it is necessary to establish the suitability for service of the insulation system.   Likewise, a turbine-driven generator should be given other tests or measurements such as oil pressure (lubricating), bearing loading, vibration, alignment, clearance of bearings, clearance of wheels, etc.   Such large

Electrical Tests
(Record Data on SS-3 Form.)

A. Insulation Resistance—Megger

	Stator		*Rotor*
Megohm reading (1.0 minute)	_____	megohm	_____
Rated machine (kv + 1)	_____	(kv + 1)	_____
Megohms (kv + 1)	_____		_____

Megohms (kv + 1)	*Stator rating*	*Rotor rating*
Over 10	5	5
2–10	4	4
1–2	3	3
1.0	2	2
Less than 1.0	0–1	0–1

A. Rating = _____(Stator) + _____(Rotor) = _____(10 Max)

B. Polarization Index − Megohm Rating $\left(\dfrac{10\ \text{Min}}{1\ \text{Min}}\right)$ = PI

PI	*Stator rating*	*Rotor rating*
5 and over	5	5
2–5	3	3
1–2	1–2	1–2
Less than 10	0–1	0–1

B. Rating = _____(Stator) + _____(Rotor) = _____(10 Max)

C. High-Voltage D-C
Refer to Graph on Attached SS-3 Form
If No Discharge or Rapid Rise Exists, Rate 10; Otherwise, Rate 0–5.
C. Rating = _____ (Max)

Total Rating [   ] (30 Max)

FIG. 5-3. Tests and measurements as applied to large motors and generators.

apparatus usually is considered individually and no attempt is made to include it in this chapter.   These tests or measurements are mentioned only as examples to suggest guide rules or subfactors that might be applicable to some types of equipment. Obviously, many of our tests and measurements can be made during, or at the same time as, the visual inspection.

Age of Equipment.   Age has a definite bearing on equipment reliability, and not just because it may be very old.   Most equipment has a statistical life-expectancy curve (see Fig. 5-4).   When equipment is new, it has a higher likelihood of trouble than will be the case after it has operated for one or two years.   This is caused by manufacturing defects, design inadequacies, shipping damage, or application unknowns.   As it becomes old and worn, it requires closer attention to maintenance, unless major rebuilding or upgrading has been performed, which may tend to reestab-

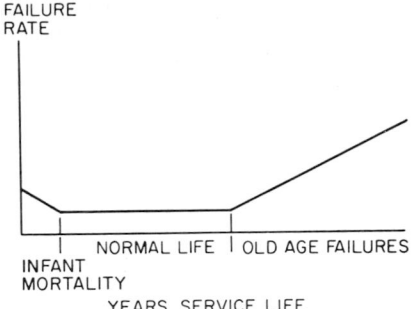

FIG. 5-4. Life expectancy of large rotating electrical equipment.

Age of Insulation

Stator _____   Rotor _____
(Record Age of Insulation.)

Age, years	Rating
0– 2	6
2–12	10
13–15	6
16–20	4
Over 20	0–3

Note: If Stator Age Differs from Rotor Age, Rate Older Component.

Rating [   ] (10 Max)

FIG. 5-5. Age guide rules, motors and generators.

Environment
Describe _____

Environment	*Open or DP	TE
a. Warm, dry	10	10
b. Hot (above 40°C)	7	8
c. Corrosive gas/vapor	5	8
d. Moisture	0–4	3–7
e. Abrasive dust	3–5	8
f. Conductive dust	2–4	7

*Add 3 Points to c, d, e, f for Sealed Insulation Systems.

Rating [   ] (10 Max)

FIG. 5-6. Environment guide rules, motors and generators.

lish the curve. For our use, let's pick a component of the equipment that may be most affected by age, such as the insulation system of a motor or generator, and apply a simple rating formula such as shown in Fig. 5-5.

Environment and Duty Cycle. These are important factors, but we rate them at only 10 points each (see Figs. 5-6 and 5-7 for applications to motors and generators), as contrasted to the much higher values for visual inspection and tests and measurements. This is because the undesirable effects of the difficult environment and duty cycles are more important than the causes per se and these effects are considered under visual inspection and tests and measurements.

Notice that under environment (Fig. 5-6) we allow for built-in features of the motor or generator that enable it to cope more effectively with the problem.

Again, under duty cycle (Fig. 5-7) we have favored the short-time rated motor, which may never reach name-plate maximum operating temperature, and the motor which is not plugged or reversed. However, we have penalized the motor that is plugged or reversed, or that is started and stopped frequently.

Duty Cycle

Select one condition from each of the five below:

Condition	Rate
a. Load	
Smooth	1–2
Uneven	0–1
b. Load	
100 % NP	1–2
>100 % NP	0–1
c. Duty	
Short-time	1–2
Continuous	1
d. Duty	
Nonreverse	2
Plug or reverse	0–1
e. Starts	
Few (<1/hr)	1–2
Frequent (>1/hr)	0–1

Rating [   ] (10 Max)

FIG. 5-7. Duty-cycle guide rules, motors and generators.

It should be obvious that the last three factors of age, environment, and duty cycle can be rated with a minimum of effort.

When all five factors have been evaluated and totaled, a single Reliability Index number results. The reliability rating report form used to establish the rating would consist of the five factors shown in Figs. 5-1 to 5-3 and 5-5 to 5-7. These can be incorporated upon a single page with appropriate headings for equipment nomenclature, location, productivity rating, and maximum Reliability Index value. An example is shown in Fig. 5-8. The Reliability Index number is not a magic number, above which all similar equipment will not fail in service and below which it will fail. One such number will have but little value; when compared with other numbers established by the same method for similar equipment, however, it can be very valuable.

Please note that our examples state that 0 = Requires Immediate Attention. If our Reliability Index report on a piece of equipment contains one or more 0 items, we must examine these before proceeding further. If they indicate that minor, or even routine, maintenance is required, it may be best to accomplish it right away and then correct the ratings accordingly. The resulting Reliability Index numbers will be more accurate and of more value to us in planning and budgeting for equipment maintenance, rebuilding, or replacement.

SELECTIVE MAINTENANCE RELIABILITY EVALUATION   TRANSFORMERS

CUSTOMER _____   LOCATION _____

NAMEPLATE RATING	RELIABILITY FACTORS	CODE NO.
SN_____ Wt. (lb)_____ Mfr_____ °C Rise_____ % Imp_____ Ph/Cycles_____ Class_____ Type_____ Voltage Rating_____ KVA Rating_____	I. AGE ____ of 20 II. ENVIRONMENT ____ of 10 III. DUTY ____ of 10 IV. VISUAL INSPECTION ____ of 30 V. OIL TESTS ____ of 30 RELIABILITY INDEX of 100	PRODUCTIVITY RATING RELIABILITY INDEX DATE INDEX RECORDED

I. AGE

Transformer Age_____

Age		Rating
0- 2	Years	10
2- 5	"	20
5-10	"	15
10-20	"	10
Over 20	"	0-10

Rating [____]   (Max. 20)

II. ENVIRONMENT

Describe_____

Environment	Rating
a. Clean, Dry	10
b. Excessive Dirt, Dust	6
c. Corrosive Gas/Vapor	4
d. Moisture	2-6
e. Hot (Above 55°C)	0-5

Note: Deduct 3 points for
       Outdoor Transformers

Rating [____]   (Max. 10)

III. DUTY

Describe_____

Duty	Rating
a. Within Rated Temperature and Load	10
b. Load or Temperature Up to 10% Above Rated Values	5

Other Factors Affecting Rating Are:
 1. Lightning or Switching Disturbances
 2. Long Periods of Inactivity
 3. History of Physical Damages

Rating [____]   (Max. 10)

IV. VISUAL INSPECTION

Using Checklist Below, Rate Each Item As Follows:

    2 - Acceptable Condition
    1 - Keep Under Observation
    0 - Requires Immediate Attention

If Any Item Does Not Apply, Rate That Item 2

a. ___ Rust, Corrosion, Surface Defects, Paint
b. ___ High Voltage Bushings and Terminals
c. ___ Low Voltage Bushings and Terminals
d. ___ Pressure Relief Diaphragm
e. ___ Oil Leaks - Bushings
f. ___ Oil Leaks - Gauges
g. ___ Oil Leaks - Valves
h. ___ Oil Leaks - Tank or Cover
i. ___ Oil Leaks - Cooling Radiators
j. ___ Oil Temperature Indicators
k. ___ Control and Tap Changing Mechanism
l. ___ Lightning Arrestor
m. ___ Pressure and Liquid Level Gauges
n. ___ Temperature Control (Fans/Alarm)
o. ___ Electrical Measurement Instruments

Comments (Describe All Items Rated 0)_____
_____
_____

Rating = Sum of Items = [____]   (Max. 30)

V. OIL TESTS

A. Oil Dielectric

KV Strength	Rating
30 KV and Over	10
22-29 KV	4-9
Below 22 KV	0

Rating _____   (Max. 10)

B. Oil Acidity

Neutralization No.
(Mg of KOH/gm Oil)

	Rating
Below 0.1	10
0.1 - 0.49	9-3
0.5 and above	0

Rating _____   (Max. 10)

C. Visual Analysis

Appearance	Rating
Clear, No free particles	10
Dark orange or reddish color, presence of free particles	0-8

Rating _____   (Max. 10)

Rating = A + B + C = [____] (Max. 30)

FIG. 5-8. Selective maintenance reliability evaluation, transformers.

EQUIPMENT REPLACEMENT OR REBUILDING

Our Reliability Index numbers will be significant when compared with similar equipment within the same productivity rating or classification. From this comparison, we can establish and assign priorities for equipment maintenance, rebuilding and upgrading, or replacement. We can expend our maintenance effort where it is most needed. By referring to the reliability rating report forms, we can determine the action that is required to *maintain operation at the normal level.* An estimate of the cost of such maintenance can be established, based upon our past experience or quotations from equipment builders or maintenance contractors.

If we have used the variable base Reliability Index numbers, we can convert them into percentages to be used as a guide in evaluating priority ratings to be assigned to different kinds of equipment within productivity ratings or classifications. An over-all average Reliability Index number can also be established for a process or an operation.

If we calculate the anticipated Reliability Index numbers that will result from the indicated maintenance actions, we can advise management of the *existing level* and the *anticipated level* that the execution of our maintenance budget will accomplish. This can be done by individual pieces of equipment, productivity ratings, or processes. If our budgeted maintenance costs must be curtailed, we can drop back on our priorities and the anticipated lower over-all level of the Reliability Index numbers will be readily apparent to all concerned.

Equipment Replacement. The decision to replace equipment will usually involve the following questions, other economic factors, and the Reliability Index number applying to the existing equipment:

1. Will the application of new equipment result in lower annual maintenance costs?
2. Will new equipment contain automated features that reduce the cost per unit of production?
3. Do long-range plans indicate the need for additional output that cannot be obtained by rebuilding and upgrading of existing equipment?

Equipment Rebuilding and Upgrading. If major investment is required to simply maintain old equipment, we should definitely investigate the possibilities of incorporating new and desirable features. It may be quite easy to change ratings or capacities of, or even to apply automation features to, equipment that is undergoing major rebuilding. We should contact the equipment manufacturer or rebuilder to determine the possibilities and estimate the costs of applying them.

In evaluating equipment replacement or major rebuilding and upgrading, we must remember that such action not only results in a higher Reliability Index number, but usually will add to the potential output of the process or reduce the cost of production.

Section 6

MAINTENANCE OF BUILDINGS

Chapter 1

CLEANING OF INDUSTRIAL PLANT OFFICES

By Gorman Sterzinger
Grounds and Services Manager
Caterpillar Tractor Company
Peoria Plant
Peoria, Ill.

If all members of a household, and their guests, are to consider that home is a pleasant place in which to live, an effective cleaning program must exist and each member of the family must contribute toward keeping the house clean. The same conditions prevail if industrial plant occupants, and their visitors, are to consider the company a good place to work. The objective of a good program of cleaning is to create an environment that will impress employees and visitors with quality of workmanship and quality of product. In addition to the cooperation of the occupants, the basic requirements of a successful industrial plant office-cleaning program include (1) general organization; (2) a competent supervisory staff; (3) adequate manpower; (4) proper equipment, tools, and supplies; (5) comprehensive work schedules; and (6) necessary assistance from other service groups.

1. **General Organization.** In the broadest sense, this includes the planning and direction required to elevate the cleaning program from a necessary evil to a service that is both necessary and desirable because of its contribution to the over-all company effort. More specifically, it prescribes the desired level of housekeeping at the lowest possible cost.

The desired level of over-all office cleanliness is an intangible factor most difficult to identify. It can be defined as that degree of cleanliness basically established by the judgment of the cleaning department supervision and modified by the stated opinions of others so that the end result remains practical. This usually will provide satisfaction for most office occupants. It must be recognized that each individual has a personal opinion about "how clean is clean," and each possesses a different degree of compulsion to voice that opinion. Since comments, usually involving requests for additional services, are frequently forthcoming from the executive level, the supervisory group, and the clerical staff, it is incumbent upon the cleaning department supervision to evaluate each request and determine whether adjustments are in order. It would be just as unrealistic to gear the cleaning program to satisfy the opinion of the most meticulous office occupant as it would be to reduce services to the point where those occupants who usually are oblivious to the cleanliness of their surroundings would be prompted to complain. In any event, it must be recognized that the comments of others play a significant role in the determination of the proper level of cleanliness. Such comments should be not only welcomed but solicited.

Industrial plant office facilities can be expected to vary within the same plant from executive offices with carpeted floors, paneled walls, and leather chairs to shop offices with concrete floors, masonry walls, and wood or metal furniture. The design of general office areas will fall between the extremes mentioned and normally will include the use of asphalt, vinyl, or rubber floor tile; painted walls; acoustical ceiling tile; and wood or metal furniture. Adjacent facilities such as entrance lobbies, rest rooms, and cafeterias also will vary in design, and it therefore becomes obvious that an extremely wide variety of individual cleaning chores must be performed. Adjustments in housekeeping levels are accomplished for the most part by increasing or decreasing the frequency of performing the necessary individual jobs. It is of utmost importance that an effective procedure be established for each chore and a never-ending attack be instituted to improve each by alteration, modification, or complete change if necessary.

Arrangements should be made for the calculation, interpretation, and retention of operating-cost data. At the very least, supervisory expenses, labor hours, and material, equipment, and labor dollars should be recorded on a weekly or monthly basis. When these items are applied against a relater, such as square feet of office area serviced, a unit factor is obtained which can be used for comparison. These records can be used to evaluate past and present effectiveness, as well as to determine realistic improvement goals and predict future costs.

2. **Supervisory Staff.** Too much emphasis cannot be placed on the selection of an employee who is to become an office cleaning foreman. Above all, he must already have demonstrated the degree of incentive and curiosity which repeatedly prompts the question "Is there a better way of doing it?" since his new assignment will require that he stimulate that philosophy in his employees. He must have the ability to deal with people, because he will be required to train, develop, and generate enthusiasm in each of his subordinates in such manner that he earns their respect and is accepted by them as their leader. He must be able to communicate with others, solicit their cooperation, and assign work. He must continuously inspect to determine that his work schedules are proper, quality work is being produced, and the best-known job procedures are in use. He must be thoroughly convinced that the cleaning work in his area of responsibility must be performed promptly, efficiently, and safely, and he must realize that he is held responsible for obtaining full value from each labor, material, and equipment dollar expended.

3. **Manpower.** Many plants use the janitor classification as a station for which new employees are hired and from which they are moved as vacancies occur elsewhere. This practice presents three situations. First, in most cases the new person will be on his first job and therefore requires considerable orientation. Second, an attitude problem can exist with those employees who feel that they are capable of more challenging work and become impatient while waiting for promotion. Third, disturbance is caused by rapid turnover of personnel.

Because of the generally lower physical and intelligence requirements of the janitor classification, it is possible to effectively employ a considerable number of physically limited employees in the cleaning program. Employees who would prove unsatisfactory in other job classifications because of lack of experience or formal education or because of age, health, or injuries can, in many cases, be given janitor work assignments on which the effects of their handicaps are minimized or negated. It should be realized, though, that such employees can be expected to have a higher rate of absenteeism, and departmental flexibility suffers because of the special work assignments that become necessary.

4. **Equipment, Tools, and Supplies.** These items must be of adequate quality and in ample supply and available as near the point of use as possible. Of utmost importance is the provision of strategically located supply rooms with periodic inventory and delivery to the supply rooms so that each janitor will be fully supplied at all times and with the least total time expended.

Considerable evaluation must be employed in the selection of equipment and products used in cleaning functions. The cheapest product may well become the most expensive when consumption figures and time required for use are compared. Advertising literature and recommendations from suppliers' representatives should be combined with actual demonstration and/or trial on the job before selections are made.

5. **Comprehensive Work Schedules.** The first step in the development of work schedules is the preparation of a complete listing of all cleaning operations to be performed in each area. An estimated or standard time allowance should be established for each item, and a performance frequency rate should be assigned. After this is done it will be possible to determine the individual employee's work burden and the number of employees required. Typical frequencies, as shown in the following listings, can be used as a base, and observation will determine whether the work must be performed more or less often than listed to provide the desired level of office cleanliness.

Typical Executive Office Cleaning Schedule

Carpeted floors, paneled walls, wood furniture, leather chairs

Once each day

1. Empty wastebaskets.
2. Empty and wash ash trays and smoking stands.
3. Spot-clean doors, walls, partition glass.
4. Wash desk glass.
5. Dust furniture, ledges, window sills, pictures.
6. Repair scratches on furniture.
7. Vacuum carpet and remove spots.

Once each week

8. Wash interior glass.
9. Vacuum registers, ventilators, venetian blinds.

Once each 3 months

10. Wash and polish wood furniture.
11. Wash and polish leather furniture.
12. Vacuum drapes.

Once each 6 months

13. Wash light fixtures.
14. Wash exterior glass.

Once each year

15. Wash walls and ceilings.

As required

16. Machine-shampoo carpeting.

Typical General Office Cleaning Schedule

In use one shift, men's and women's rest rooms included; asphalt
tile floor, painted walls, wood and metal furniture

As required when occupied

1. Replenish soap, towel, and tissue dispensers.
2. Clean washbasins
3. Clean up moisture tracked in during inclement weather.
4. Clean up after accidental ink, soft drink, or other spillage.
5. Other emergency janitorial functions.

Once each day

6. Sweep office floors.
7. Empty wastepaper baskets.
8. Empty and wipe ash trays and smoking stands.
9. Dust tops of desks, tables, file cabinets.
10. Empty pencil sharpeners.
11. Clean chalkboards and erasers.
12. Clean drinking fountains.
13. Spot-clean doors, partition glass, walls.
14. Sweep and wet-mop rest room floors.
15. Replenish soap, towel, tissue, and napkin dispensers.
16. Clean washbasins.
17. Clean toilet bowls.
18. Clean urinals.
19. Clean plumbing supply lines, drainpipes.
20. Clean mirrors.
21. Clean supply closet.
22. Empty napkin disposal receptacles.

Once each week

23. Machine-scrub and buff rest room floors and high traffic office aisles.
24. Dust all furniture.
25. Dust window sills, ledges, picture frames.
26. Wash interior glass, display cases, shelves, and doors.
27. Wash ash trays and smoking stands.
28. Vacuum air vents.
29. Wash toilet booth partitions.
30. Acid-clean toilet bowls and urinals.
31. Paraffin-treat toilet seats.
32. Spray rest rooms for insect control.

Once each month

33. Wash rest room walls.
34. Machine-scrub and refinish rest room floors and high-traffic office aisles.

Once each 3 months

35. Wash all desks, tables, chairs, file cabinets.

Once each 6 months

36. Wash light fixtures.
37. Vacuum and/or wash venetian blinds.
38. Wash wastepaper baskets.
39. Machine-scrub and refinish office floors.
40. Wash exterior glass.

Once each year

41. Wash all walls and ceilings.

Typical Shop Office Cleaning Schedule

Adjacent to machine-shop area, in use three shifts, men's and women's rest rooms and conference room included; asphalt tile floor, painted walls, metal furniture

Once each shift

1. Replenish soap, towel, and tissue dispensers.
2. Sweep rest room floors.
3. Clean washrooms.

Once each day

4. Sweep office floors.
5. Empty wastepaper baskets.
6. Empty and wipe ash trays and smoking stands.
7. Dust tops of desks, tables, and file cabinets.
8. Empty pencil sharpeners.
9. Clean chalkboards and erasers.
10. Clean drinking fountains.
11. Spot-clean doors, partition glass, walls.
12. Wet-mop rest room floors.
13. Clean toilet bowls.
14. Clean urinals.
15. Clean plumbing supply lines, drainpipes.
16. Clean mirrors.
17. Clean supply closet.
18. Replenish napkin dispenser.
19. Empty napkin disposal receptacles.

Once each week

20. Wet-mop and machine-buff office floors (alternate with No. 21).
21. Machine-scrub and buff office floors.
22. Machine-scrub and buff rest room floors.
23. Dust furniture.
24. Dust window sills, ledges.
25. Wash interior glass, display cases, shelves, doors.
26. Wash ash trays and smoking stands.
27. Vacuum air vents.
28. Wash toilet booth partitions.
29. Acid-clean toilet bowls and urinals.
30. Paraffin-treat toilet seats.
31. Spray rest rooms for insect control.

Once each month

32. Wash rest room walls.
33. Machine-scrub and refinish rest room and office floors.

Once each 3 months

34. Wash desks, tables, chairs, file cabinets.

Once each 6 months

35. Wash light fixtures.
36. Wash wastepaper baskets.
37. Wash exterior glass.

Once each year

38. Wash walls and ceilings.

It is obvious that many of the cleaning functions listed can be performed by one employee, while others must be performed by a team or crew. It is advantageous to assign as many of the one-man chores as possible in a particular area to a single employee, since this arrangement not only pinpoints the responsibility of general cleanliness in that area but also permits the employee assigned to become more closely identified with the end results of his efforts in "his" area. The janitor's attitude in this respect is all-important, especially in regard to finishing touches such as spot-cleaning and dusting.

The cleaning functions not assigned to the area janitor are best performed by employees who are assigned to spend full time on a specific function such as washing walls, ceilings, light fixtures, and furniture and machine-scrubbing operations.   This arrangement permits the employees assigned to become more proficient, reduces the amount of equipment necessary, and provides the greatest opportunity to utilize the handicapped effectively.

6. **Assistance from Other Service Groups.**   The assistance and cooperation of other departments will materially affect the efforts required of the cleaning department as well as the end result of those efforts.   Included are the purchasing department, which may be responsible for a steady flow of supplies to the plant, and the maintenance department, which provides building and plumbing repairs, light bulb replacement, repainting schedules, etc.   Other services that facilitate cleaning functions are prompt repair of tools and equipment, transportation of men and materials, and replacement of employees when vacancies occur.

The existence of an effective office-cleaning program is necessary to provide and maintain adequate health and safety factors.   In addition, it improves appearance, helps prevent costly repairs, and provides an atmosphere which tends to exhilarate occupants and give visitors a good impression.   If one were to select the factor which contributes most toward acquiring and maintaining an effective program, it undoubtedly would be the stipulation that each member of the organization be convinced that his job is important and that there *always* is a better way to do it.

Chapter 2

MAINTENANCE OF BUILT-UP ROOFS

By Edward T. Schreiber, Harold E. P. Smith,
William D. Wright, *and* William H. Kennedy
Construction Consultants, Inc.
Detroit, Mich.

Roof maintenance procedures usually are determined by the surface conditions of the membrane, flashing, and accessories. Before any maintenance systems can be implemented, a determination must be made about the roofing system and the materials involved.

Components. Every roof system is composed of these basic components:

I. The structural substrate (slab or deck)
  A. Nailable-type deck
  B. Nonnailable-type deck
II. The insulation system
  A. Insulation (optional)
    1. Physical properties
      a. Thermal conductance
      b. Organic
      c. Inorganic
    2. Types of insulation
      a. Boards
        (1) Fiber
        (2) Mineral
        (3) Glass
        (4) Plastic
      b. Monolithic-poured
  B. Vapor seal (optional)
    1. Fire retardant
    2. Bitumen and felt
III. The roofing (waterproofing) system
  A. Felt
    1. Rag felt
      a. Asphalt saturated
      b. Coal-tar-pitch saturated
    2. Asbestos felt
      a. Asphalt saturated
      b. Coal-tar-pitch saturated
    3. Fiberglass felt
    4. Mineral-surfaced felt

> *a.* 60-lb selvage edge
> *b.* 90-lb cap sheet
> *B.* Bitumen
>> 1. Asphalt (petroleum base)
>> 2. Coal-tar pitch (coal-tar base)
> *C.* Surfacing
>> 1. Bituminous coating
>> 2. Bitumen and aggregate
>> 3. Factory-prepared sheet

Materials. Two basic materials comprise the waterproofing and perform the following functions:

> I. Felt
>> *A.* Allows for the build-up of succeeding layers of the waterproofing (bitumen)
>> *B.* Acts as a plane of support for the bitumen
>> *C.* Distributes the stresses
> II. The bitumen
>> *A.* Is the waterproofing element
>> *B.* Acts as an adhesive
>> *C.* Provides a protective coat

Roof (Waterproofing) Systems. There are two basic roof systems over the insulation or structural substrate.

> I. Smooth-surfaced roofs
>> *A.* Asphalt and rag felts
>> *B.* Asphalt and asbestos felts
>> *C.* Asphalt and fiberglass felts
> II. Aggregate-surfaced roofs
>> *A.* Asphalt and aggregate
>>> 1. Rag felts
>>> 2. Asbestos felts
>>> 3. Fiberglass felts
>> *B.* Coal-tar pitch and aggregate
>>> 1. Rag felts
>>> 2. Asbestos felts

SURVEY

When a determination of the nature of the components and materials of a roofing system has been completed, a survey of the whole building and its usage is made. Check the following items for defects:

1. *Walls*—cracks and any indication of building movement.
2. *Interior bearing partitions*—cracks and any indication of movement.
3. *Lintels across doors and windows*—cracks or openings.
4. *Interior and exterior drains*—dampness.
5. *Underside of the roof deck*—dampness or deterioration.
6. *Copings*—cracks or joint deterioration.
7. *Sheet-metal accessories*—attachment security and material deterioration.
8. *Composition flashing*—breaks, damage, punctures, and surface deterioration.
9. *Composition edging*—breaks, damage, and surface deterioration.
10. *Main body of the roof*—debris to be removed; material or equipment to be stored elsewhere; broken or plugged drainage sumps; physical damage (holes, cuts, slits, tears, surface abrasion and scuffing); surface deterioration (exposed laps or felts, alligatored bitumen, dried felts, blisters, ridges, insufficient or nonexistent aggregate), sponginess (an unfirm membrane usually indicates moisture-filled insulation. If there is doubt, cut through the roof to the deck and remove a sample.)

Survey results will indicate the proper methods of required maintenance.

The general term "maintenance" is divided into two categories: preventive main-tenance and corrective maintenance. Preventive maintenance occurs before defects or damage develops in the roof, while corrective maintenance attempts to correct defects or damages after they have developed.

Preventive maintenance requires a knowledge of roofing specifications, materials, applicational procedures, and the process of deterioration. It involves temporary repairs which attempt to stave off the drastic repairs of corrective maintenance.

Corrective maintenance involves the complete replacement of physically damaged or deteriorated sections and requires much of the knowledge entailed in new con-struction, design, and specifications.

PREVENTIVE MAINTENANCE

Preventive maintenance is divided into three major types: (1) spot repair, (2) recoating, and (3) recovering.

Spot Repair

Patching is recommended for localized physical damage or deterioration to the roof and flashings. The materials used for the repair must be compatible with the original specifications and have the same standards. If the original roof coating appears to be in good condition, with no exposed felts, patching should suffice for this repair period. If, however, damage is general, it means that a major repair is needed. A leak in a roof which has been watertight for years is a warning that deterioration has begun to set in and that patching would be just an added expense.

Recoating

Usually roof coating will help preserve the roof if the felts themselves are in good condition. However, roof coating, like paint, is only a protection. The practice of recoating a roof at regular intervals is not recommended, as it is expensive and merely succeeds in building up layer upon layer of brittle bitumen. If the present roof coating appears to be in good condition but thinning in spots, the roof surface might be recoated. However, it must not show excessive surface wear or deterio-ration and must not extend completely through the waterproofing system.

If the felts are exposed and dried out or rotted, coating cannot put new life into them because complete destruction of the fibers has occurred, not merely a drying out of the bitumen binder. Therefore, this imbalance caused by failure of the strength element cannot be overcome by adding more of the waterproofing element, the bitumen. Such an addition results only in further imbalance, sometimes causing the entire roof to split through to the deck.

Types of Coating Materials. *Hot Asphalt Coating.* Asphalt films have limited structural strength; therefore when roofs are maintained with hot asphalt over dried-out roofing, alligatoring or checking usually results. This is caused by the build-up of thick layers of the material and also by the differences in expansion and contraction between the old roofing and the coating. Hot coating gives only limited protection and leaves a surface which makes additional maintenance difficult.

Cutback Cold Coating. Cutback-type coatings are usually composed of mineral and asbestos fibers suspended in an asphaltic petroleum solvent. These fibers make the coating much less susceptible to alligatoring and checking than hot asphalt.

As a general rule, cutback-type cold coatings are subject to the same wear and tear as hot asphalt, but since the recommended thickness is about half that of the normal hot asphalt film, they give better performance than asphalt, though costing more per pound than asphalt.

The quality of cutback cold coatings, usually covering a wide range, is hard to determine. The prices charged for these materials are a poor gage of their quality because high prices usually reflect the high cost of the sales effort put behind these materials.

National manufacturers of full line roofing products make no absolute claims concerning the longevity of their coatings for the obvious reason that so much depends on the condition of the roofs to which they are applied. However, some other manufacturers make broad general claims and issue ambiguous guarantees which seem to cover all contingencies but in reality promise very little.

Asphalt Emulsion Cold Coating. Asphalt emulsion-type coatings offer far better weathering surface than any of the other asphalts. The limitations are that they do not bond well with dusty or dirty surfaces and that their drying pattern makes them extremely vulnerable to wash-off during the drying period.

All surface defects, such as alligatoring, blistering, and cracking, are a hindrance to effective cleaning of the roof surface in preparation for recoating. Therefore, remaining pockets of dirt or soil under such coatings will be the nuclei for loss of adhesion and blistering.

Recovering

Recovering is the practice of leaving the old roof system in place and covering the surface with a new system, usually because deterioration has extended completely through the waterproofing system to the deck or insulation in many areas, leaving no alternative but to recover.

The proper application of recovering should be applied to suit the present condition of the roof structure and incline. Owing to the large variety of materials available, the proper selection is important.

Place reliance on the recommendations of the major roofing manufacturers. The application should be a complete roofing system and not the common but not recommended practice of mopping one or two additional plies of felt to the top surface of the roof. In general, deck inclines that level to a slope of $\frac{1}{2}$ in. in 1 ft require a coal tar pitch and aggregate specification; slopes between $\frac{1}{2}$ and 3 in. in 1 ft require an asphalt and aggregate specification, and slopes over 3 in. to 1 ft require steep asphalt and asbestos felts with an asphalt and emulsion surface coating. Rag felts are not recommended for this steep a slope.

All old roofs, regardless of their initial condition, must be considered as having a high moisture content, which may eventually cause a recovering to blister. Therefore it is always advisable to separate the old roof system from the new system with a layer of insulation or a coated base sheet. Venting the insulation can help relieve pressures that may build up due to moisture in the old roof system.

CORRECTIVE MAINTENANCE

Most problems in roofs stem from their being either poorly designed or poorly installed originally. A properly designed and installed roof requires little maintenance and should last almost the life of the building. If major maintenance is required, it is usually wise and much less expensive in the long run to completely remove the old system and replace it with a new system rather than continue costly maintenance.

Reroofing, then, is the complete removal of the old roof system and replacement with a new system. The five illustrations show typical examples of correct construction.

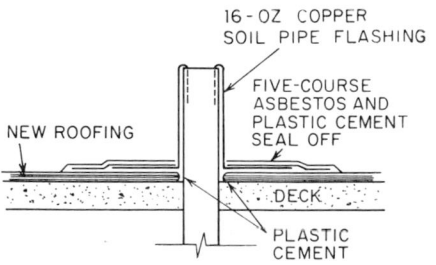

FIG. 2-1. Soil pipe flashing.

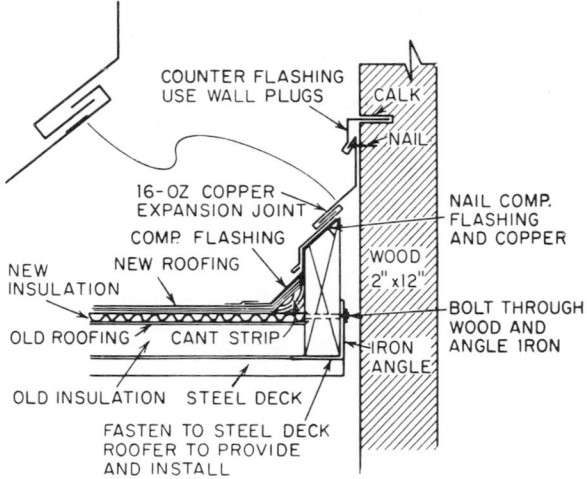

FIG. 2-2. Wall expansion joint.

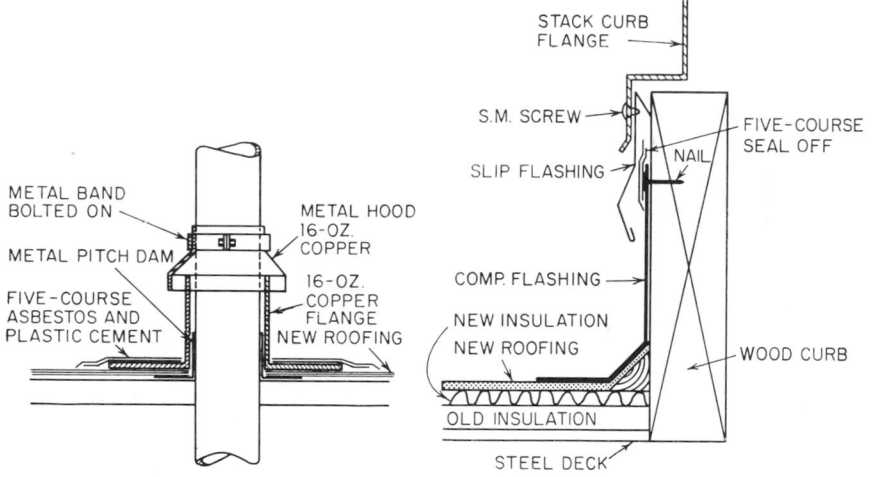

FIG. 2-3. Flange and umbrella.   FIG. 2-4. Slip flashing at existing curb.

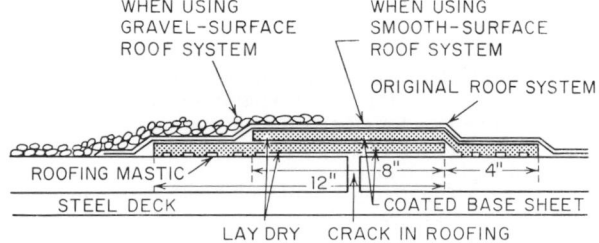

FIG. 2-5. Repairs for cracks in roof system.

If the old felts have been recoated, spot repaired, and patched for many years and have begun to decay and rot, the safe and economical thing to do is to replace them with a new system. Replacing the old roof with a new one is as sound an investment as insurance, as it insures against leak damage. The additional cost of complete removal is of small concern when compared with the possible damage resulting from leaving the old roof in place.

Minute cracks and blisters, prevalent in the surface of the old roofing, are depositories for moisture absorption. So, to ensure the best results, the old roofing should be completely removed. This removes any moisture trapped in the old roofing and also permits an examination of the deck.

After removing the old roofing, check the deck for defects. Check wood decks for dry rot, loose boards, and concave or convex boards. Look for broken welds and rust on steel decks. Check for open joints or bearing movement on precast concrete slabs. Also, before application of new roofing over the precast slabs, make sure all the joints are properly stripped and follow the manufacturer's directions for mopping over the slabs. Look for spalling, bad cracks, and ponding on poured concrete or mineralized decking. All decking should be free from moisture and completely dry before the application of new roofing. Care must be used when removing old roofing on an insulated deck so that the insulation is not scuffed or otherwise damaged during the process. If the insulation is damaged, or bad in places, it should be replaced to match the existing insulation. Sections of insulation should be removed by the roofer to inspect the deck.

For general safety, no more old roofing should be removed than can be completely roofed in and made watertight at the end of each workday.

Drainage.   Before applying the new roof, check the roof for low areas where water accumulates and then build these areas up to the proper level for an even flow of water to outlets.

Parapet Walls.   Check all brickwork for loose and spalled bricks and open cracks.

Coping.   Remove and reset loose coping in fresh mortar and remortar all cracked joints. Replace badly cracked coping with new coping.

Fire Walls.   Check all fire walls and repair as per parapet walls.

Penthouses.   Check all penthouse brickwork for cracked or spalled bricks. On stucco or smooth cement finished walls, look for minute cracks and check the inside lath for rust.

Tuck Pointing.   All brickwork, poured concrete, stucco, and outside cement plaster should be thoroughly inspected and repaired as necessary by a tuck pointing contractor.

Edging.   Check all edging for open end joints, loose sections, and roof strip flashing.

Composition Flashing.   Check all composition flashing for improper nailing, open joints, and slippage.

Sumps.   Check sump cages for broken or cracked sections and for attachment to the base.

Metal Flashing.   Repair or replace metal counterflashing, through-wall flashing, curb, corner, and vertical flashings.

Cant Strip.   Replace rotted cant strip or reset loose cant strip at the intersection of all vertical surfaces with the roof.

Expansion Joints.   Check all horizontal and vertical expansion joints and replace or repair where crushed or loose.

Valleys.   Replace all roof valleys when applying new roofing.

Gutters and Conductors.   Clean, scrape, and repaint all rusted galvanized iron. Reanchor loose elbows and check for rust. Repair and replace all copper gutters and conductors where crushed or missing.

Reglets.   Check all wall flashing reglets.

Pipes, Stacks, and Vents.   The roofer should contact plant engineering to determine which vents and stacks are to be removed. Install new decking over old holes.

Cutting Holes through Roof. If holes are over 8 in. in diameter, construct a header and stretcher beam system to prevent roof sag.

Signs. Check the bases on the roof and the guy wires.

Pitch Pans. Check for drainage of bitumen from pitch pans and refill as necessary.

Skylights. Replace all badly cracked glass and recalk. Clean and paint all skylight guards.

Condensation Gutters. Clean, replace, or reanchor all skylight and A-frame condensation gutters.

Scuttle Covers. Check the base and waterproof the covering and hardware.

Chimney Caps. If the caps are loose, have them reset by a mason. Tuck point corbel brickwork.

Conductor Heads. Replace if badly rusted, otherwise reanchor and solder.

Scuppers. Check and repair all through-wall scuppers.

A Frames and Butterflies. Repair all metal, glass, and hardware.

Fascias. Reanchor or replace all metal fascias where loose.

Gravel Stops. Check for bitumen drippage and felt movement.

Stub Columns. Repair or replace caps and flashings as needed.

Stacks. Repair or replace all collars, umbrellas, flashings, and guy anchors.

Painting. Make an annual check of all painted surfaces on the roof to prevent rusting or rot.

Roof Traffic. All unnecessary roof traffic by the company or outside contractors should be avoided.

WORKMANSHIP STANDARDS

1. There shall be no overheating of materials. Visible thermometer must be provided on kettles.
2. All materials must be clearly labeled and maintained in protected dry storage.
3. Roofing system shall be complete including the top surfacing up to the point of termination at the end of the day.
4. Base flashing system shall be compatible and as recommended by the approved manufacturer providing the roofing system.
5. All materials must be furnished by the same manufacturer approved for use in the roofing system.

Chapter 3

MAINTENANCE OF WALLS, RAMPS, STAIRWAYS, PLATFORMS, RAILINGS, SKYLIGHTS

By R. S. AUSTIN
Maintenance Consultant
Formerly Head, Mechanical Department, American Cyanamid Company
Warner's Plant
Linden, N.J.

WALLS

Walls for plant buildings are made of wood, brick, concrete, corrugated transite, wire lath and stucco, tile, concrete block, aluminum, glass block, and metal.

Wood. With the present price of lumber and the inherent fire hazard, the tendency is against the use of wood. The main advantages in using it are that repairs are simple; there need be no worry about corrosion except for the nails, and even they can be of monel or copper; and paint will keep up the appearance in spite of age.

Brick buildings are excellent for many reasons. If the proper lime-cement mortar is used, there is little to fear about moisture absorption. Repairs can be made without spoiling the appearance of the building. Passageway for machinery too big for existing entrances can be made by tearing out a section of the wall. Rebricking, if properly done, will not spoil the appearance of the wall. Many brick buildings in industrial New Jersey are still in excellent condition after 75 years.

Concrete buildings do not lend themselves so readily as some other types to low-cost repairs. Alterations should be kept to a minimum, to reduce the likelihood of unsightly repairs. Concrete provides excellent fire resistance and stands up well where there are acid fumes. However, acid spills can play havoc with it.

Cement-block buildings are easily and cheaply erected. Of the various types of blocks—slag, cinder, or concrete—the last-named is most to be preferred but is slightly more expensive. It is denser and the exterior can be waterproofed more easily, a procedure followed to prevent penetration of moisture to the finished inside surface.

Tile walls are quite satisfactory if the exterior is protected from the weather. Tile has some porosity, and when water penetrates in winter, a bad spalling can ruin a wall.

Robinson Protected Metal is a sheet metal covered with a tar or asphalt coating. It possesses some fire hazard and the metal can be attacked by heavy acid fumes.

Corrugated transite is a wall material made of asbestos and cement. Erection is quick and easy. The sheets should be fastened to the steelwork or wood framework by the use of zinc or stainless-steel bolts if the atmosphere is acid- or alkaline-corrosive. The use of an electric stud welder has greatly simplified erection, particularly on

6–16

high walls where scaffolding is expensive. It is fire resistant, and if careful attention is paid to the joints, the building is not too hard to heat. In summer, the light color of the transite acts to prevent ready absorption of the heat from the sun.

Wire lath and stucco walls must be erected carefully. Unless the exterior is tight, rust can deteriorate the lath and thereby weaken the wall. There is a tendency for the walls to crack unless the lath are securely fastened. The stucco must be thoroughly embedded in the mesh of the lath.

Aluminum walls can be made in flat panel construction or in corrugated sheets. Aluminum has the advantage of low weight. Buildings with aluminum walls are relatively cool in the summer, but insulation must be installed for winter use.

Glass-block walls give good lighting. Little trouble has been experienced. For best results the surface should be kept clean.

Partitions. Partitions seldom are an item of large maintenance cost except as changes in personnel make new office layouts necessary. The older materials, such as tile and wood, do not lend themselves to inexpensive and quick changes. The metal panel partitions with glass windows, or better still plastic, afford relatively low-cost construction. The metal panels come in standard sizes and it is an easy job to replace a damaged section or purchase new ones to suit the new layout. The plastic windows for plant use are gaining favor, for they give privacy to the offices and withstand temperature changes and even severe blows without breaking. The cost now is as low as or possibly lower than that of glass.

Windows. One of the larger items in building maintenance is the yearly cost in materials and man-hours of replacing broken window lights. In one of the larger chemical plants all glass, as it is broken, is replaced by plastic. The personnel rather like the subdued light, and the heat and fumes from the chemical processes have practically no effect on the plastic.

RAMPS

Ramps for foot traffic and walkways should be of sufficient strength to carry a live load of at least 100 lb per sq ft. Those for vehicular traffic and for aisle service should be constructed to carry whatever loads are required by the movement of equipment, materials, and products.

Ramps should not have a pitch of more than 1 ft in 10 ft. Curbs about 6 ft high and 4 in. wide should be installed if a ramp is to be used for trucking. The width should be the width of the truck plus 3 ft, and for a two-way ramp twice the width of the truck plus 3 ft.

The surface of the ramp must provide safe footing and proper traction. Minimum headroom for walkways and ramps should be 84 in. preferred, with a minimum of 80 in.

STAIRWAYS AND PLATFORMS

Stairways should be designed to carry a live load of at least 100 lb per sq ft and have a preferred width of 30 in. between the inside faces of the stringers.

Wood stringers should be of sound material at least 2 by 10 in. with the treads recessed in the stringers to a depth of $\frac{1}{2}$ in. Metal stringers—8- or 10-in. channels—fulfill the requirement regarding load capacity of 100 lb per sq ft.

The most popular riser and tread dimensions are $7\frac{1}{2}$ and 10 in., providing an angle with the horizontal of approximately 37°. The minimum angle should be $32\frac{1}{2}$°, maximum 45°. No tread should be less than 8 in., exclusive of the nosing, which should project from $\frac{5}{8}$ to 1 in. beyond the front of the riser. The product of the riser height and the tread width should be not less than 64 in. or more than 77 in. Riser heights and tread widths should be uniform within a given building.

Wood treads should be at least 2 in. in thickness with $\frac{3}{4}$-in radius at the nosing. At each fifth tread a $\frac{1}{2}$-in. bolt rod should be installed through the stringers and should bear against the tread.

Metal treads should not have a smooth or slippery surface, on either the tread proper or the surface of the nosing.

Concrete treads should have a wood-float finish for secure footing and abrasive materials should be included in the wearing surfaces of the treads. A good practice is to use Carborundum No. 12-30, or equivalent, at the rate of 1 lb per 44-in. tread. Prepared compounds are available.

The maximum vertical rise in a single flight of stairs, unbroken by landings or intermediate platforms, should be 12 ft.

Stairway platforms or flights should be at least 36 in. long measured between the topmost riser of the lower flight and the bottom riser of the upper flight and designed for a live load of 100 lb per sq ft.

STAIRWAY RAILINGS

Railings should be provided on open sides of all stairways and on exposed sides of platforms. They should be 42 in. in height on platforms and 32 in. above the nosing of the tread on the stairways. An intermediate railing should be installed. A 6-in. toeboard should be installed on all platforms above 6 ft high and above the stringers on stairways more than 6 ft high.

The preferred headroom in stairways is 84 in., with a minimum of 80 in.

A handrail should be provided on each side. When the stairway is more than 88 in. in width, there should be a handrail in the center. Handrails should be capable of supporting or withstanding a load of 200 lb applied at any point in any direction. There should be a clearance of 1½ in. between the railing and any obstruction.

SKYLIGHTS

Skylights are far from desirable, if of the flat type, because they can become so dirty as to limit their usefulness and can be troublesome because of leaks. The angular or vertical types, the latter as used in sawtooth roofs, are preferable. Wire glass usually is used and it is a good idea to buy the type that is tinted with blue or green. The calking compound should be nonhardening, to facilitate replacement and minimize the chances of damage or injury due to flying glass.

INSPECTION

In general, walls, ramps, stairways, platforms, railings, and skylights should be given a thorough inspection once a year. The walls must be watched carefully, both exterior and interior, for evidences of cracks, particularly under windows and at the corners of the building. These cracks could be caused by settlement and there is little to be done unless settlement continues, except to patch up the cracks to prevent water from getting into the walls with the likelihood of freezing and thus making repairs more serious.

The metal fasteners on transite and aluminum panels and sheets should be checked every 2 or 3 years for tightness. A high wind could tear off loose units.

The steel of stairs and ramps should be kept clean and well painted. Some concerns, paint the out-of-way corners white to keep workers from throwing things into them.

The stairs and ramp should be checked for oil spills and slipperiness to prevent accidents. The frequency of inspection will depend upon the nature of the work done in the plant, and the safety-consciousness of executives, both maintenance and production.

Chapter 4

LABOR COSTS FOR TYPICAL OPERATIONS IN BUILDING MAINTENANCE

By FRANK O. PIERSON[1]
Chief Manufacturing Industrial Engineer
and HENRY C. MOSSOR
General Zone Foreman
The Atlantic Refining Company
Philadelphia, Pa.

Building maintenance can be an expensive business, primarily because conventional controls must be adjusted in order to control building maintenance expense.

Controls should be provided to make sure that building renovations which provide convenience, or improvement in appearance—but which add nothing to the production value of the buildings—are justified and worth the cost.

Controls should prevent deferment of building maintenance beyond a reasonable tolerance provided by the maintenance schedule. Such controls would prevent retaining maintenance personnel on other projects to the neglect of the needed but less obvious building maintenance work. An example is roof repairs. Even a slight delay in making them may result in extensive damage to ceilings, walls, floors, and equipment.

An important part of the control should consist of the maintenance schedule, which can be set up on the preventive basis, and in connection with which tolerances (from days to weeks) can be provided. The preventive program should be based on periodic inspection and accurate records of deterioration. Provision should be made to alter schedules as experience indicates the desirability of either more or less attention. The building inspection report (Fig. 4-1) will provide the basis for scheduling, developing records of deterioration, and preventive activity.

The best system of building maintenance cost control does not provide for evaluation of building obsolescence. Management generally does a good job in evaluating the obsolescence of productive machinery and equipment. We apparently have little experience in evaluating the cost of using obsolete buildings. We may wait until maintenance expense alone justifies rebuilding. We are undoubtedly using, and maintaining, buildings which have for many years outlived their useful life as a *productive unit*.

The building maintenance supervisor should from time to time consider the building as a productive unit. He should compute the probable cost of its shortcomings and review such factors as adaptability for relocation of productive machinery, mechanization of materials handling, and capacity for intermediate storage. The product flow may be too long, because of building design, floor-load capacity, or other factors.

[1] Mr. Pierson is now Consultant and Engineer, Cherry Hill, N.J.

BUILDING INSPECTION REPORT

Name or Bldg. No. _____ Dept. _____

Location _____ Usage _____ Date of this inspection _____

If new or in an entirely satisfactory condition put a (✓) in the Satisfactory column. If not, rate "A", "B", "C", or "D" to describe the condition as defined below in an applicable column.

Date of last inspection _____

A = Passable, but maintenance should be anticipated.
B = Requires correction as soon as convenient.
C = Bad condition, requiring prompt treatment.
D = Hazardous condition, requiring immediate action.

	A
	B
	C
	D

All inspection items marked "B", "C", or "D" require a description of conditions to be listed on the back of this form.

#	Item
	STRUCTURE (EXTERIOR):
1	Foundations
2	Walls
3	Lintels & Sills
4	Windows
5	Doors
6	Beams
7	Columns
8	Platforms
9	Stairways
10	Ladders
11	Handrails
12	Other Structural Items:
13	
14	
15	
16	
17	Roofing
18	Flashing
19	Parapets
20	Canopies
21	Water Overflows
22	Rain Conductors
23	Skylights
24	Louvres
25	Chimneys
26	Stacks & Vents
27	Signs
28	Other Roof Items:
29	
30	
	STRUCTURE (INTERIOR):
31	Foundations
32	Walls
33	Lintels & Sills
34	Windows
35	Doors
36	Ceilings
37	Beams
38	Columns
39	Floors
40	Ramps
41	Platforms
42	Stairways
43	Ladders
44	Handrails
45	Other Structural Items:
46	
47	
48	
49	
50	Skylights
51	Louvres
52	Vents
53	Chimneys
54	Signs
55	Other Items:
56	
57	
	UTILITIES:
58	Piping Water
59	Piping Steam
60	Piping Sanitary Drainage
61	Piping Other Drainage
62	Piping Gas
63	Piping Air
64	Piping Insulation

#	Item
65	Sanitary Fixtures
66	Sinks & Showers
67	Drinking Fountains
68	
69	Electric Lighting
70	Electric Fixtures
71	Electric Receptacles
72	Electric Distribution Sys.
73	
74	Heating System
75	
76	Ventilating System
77	
78	Air Conditioning System
79	
80	Tanks - Water
81	Tanks - Heating Oil
82	Tanks - Other
83	
84	
	SAFETY & FIRE PROTECTION EQUIPMENT:
85	Fire Mains and Outlets
86	Sprinkling System
87	Extinguishers
88	Alarms
89	Fire Hose
90	Fire Blankets
91	First Aid Kits
92	Emergency Exits
93	Other:
94	
95	
96	
97	
98	
99	
	OUTSIDE AREAS:
100	Walkways
101	Driveways
102	Parking Areas
103	Fences & Gates
104	Signs
105	General Appearance
106	
107	
108	
109	
110	
	GENERAL OBSERVATION ITEMS:
111	Hot Water Heaters
112	Heating Boilers
113	Hot Air Heaters
114	Fans, Ducts & Blowers
115	Air Conditioning Machinery
116	Lunchroom & Kitchen Equip.
117	Locker Facilities
118	Pumps & Compressors
119	Hoists & Cranes
120	Elevators
121	
122	
123	
124	
125	
126	
127	

FIG. 4-1. This report provides the basis for scheduling, developing records of deterioration, and preventive activity.

Productive efficiency may be impaired because of poor lighting, uneven heating, or improper air conditioning. There may be hidden costs in unsafe aisles or stairs or in danger from crippling fires. It may be far more expensive to neglect these items than to neglect the controls of maintenance job costs, preventive maintenance, or proper priority selection.

However, in order to keep repair costs down, select the best method of repair, and know when to do the work with your own people and when to contract the job to outsiders. To do this, you need estimates of job costs and should compare your actual costs with these estimates whenever you do the work with your own staff.

Before you, or a contractor, can estimate a building maintenance job, it is necessary to develop a listing of *what* work is to be done. Except for surface jobs such as painting, up-to-date blueprints and specifications are necessary. Without them, costly exploration or mismatched repair work will result. When repairs have to be made using materials different from those originally installed, the prints should be revised to show where the old and new are joined. Specifications for the new materials should be included for future needs.

The next step in estimating a job is to determine *how* this work is to be done. Many suppliers of building materials provide their customers with standard-practice instructions for the use of their materials. These may be used as published, or revised to fit the needs of any individual user. In addition to these suppliers of building materials, periodicals and handbooks give specific data on building maintenance methods. Some trade associations publish methods manuals and some trade unions provide work-methods manuals. When no such guide is available, it would be wise to develop a standard practice for any type of work that is done frequently. Manuals should specify materials as well as methods so that a contractor will bid on the same basis as you estimate your costs.

Unfortunately there are few reliable published manuals on labor-cost expectancies in building maintenance. The following tables will give some reasonable figures from which labor-cost expectancies can be computed. These labor-cost data have been given in terms of time for one mechanic working alone, except when the physical work load or working relationship *requires* more men. Experience has shown that a team of mechanic and helper, working on a job that can be done by the mechanic alone, do about one and one-half times as much work per unit of time. As a helper's rate often is approximately equal to that of the mechanic, the unit labor cost of a mechanic and helper could be as much as 40 per cent higher than that of the mechanic alone. If, however, one helper can be assigned to two (or more) mechanics, this team may do work at a cost approximately equal to that of the mechanic alone.

To obtain labor dollars, convert the hours shown to total hours in order to reflect working relationships and any extra allowances such as rest periods or travel allowances. This figure can be changed to dollars by multiplying by the average labor rate with or without overhead, depending upon what type of cost data is desired.

One company, having many plants and warehouses throughout this country, has found that building maintenance costs divide as follows:

	Per Cent
Painting	20
Windows and sash	15
Roofs	15
Concrete and terrazo	10
Brick and plaster	$7\frac{1}{2}$
Wood floors and walls	$7\frac{1}{2}$
Doors and partitions	$7\frac{1}{2}$
Elevators	5 (excluding electrical)
Miscellaneous	$12\frac{1}{2}$

Cost data are given here for some of the major items listed above. They illustrate the approach that can be taken; it would be wise for each building maintenance superintendent to develop his own data, as needed. A plan of approach may be valuable for a long time; the actual data may soon be obsolete because of technological change.

Time Values for Painting. Painting time varies according to the method of applying paint (spray, roller, brush), surface painted (wood, steel, plaster, concrete, cinder block, shingle or clapboard, brick), and the type of paint applied (outside paint, enamel, varnish, emulsion paints). In addition, speed of painting is affected by continuity of surface and location and body position of the workman. The effect of some of these factors can be indicated only approximately; considerable judgment must be used in combining the factors. The net result should be reasonable.

In general, 1 hr per day should be set aside for preparation and clean-up. Thus these time values can be applied to 7 hr if the normal workday is 8, 6 hr if the normal workday is 7.

Brush Painting. Ideal *paints* (from the viewpoint of application *time*) are thin clear varnishes or shellac.

Ideal *surfaces* are flat wood, metal, smooth concrete, or plaster.

Ideal *conditions* are smooth, unobstructed, continuous flat surfaces at normal standing height.

Increments for Paints Other Than Ideal. Heavier-flowing paints such as rubber-base paints and gloss enamels take about 30 per cent more time to apply.

Still heavier-flowing paints, or paints requiring more brushing out, such as semigloss enamels and outside white or metal primers, take about 70 per cent more time to apply than the ideal paints.

Increments for Surface Variations. If the surface is rougher, such as cement or cinder blocks, about 30 per cent more time is required to apply the paint. If the surface is rougher than the above or uneven (such as shingles, clapboards, or brick) about 70 per cent more time is required.

Increments for Conditions. Conditions of application have still greater effect on brush-painting time. If the surface is reasonably smooth, but made up of many small areas, such as structural-steel work and window frames, any painting-time values should be increased by 50 per cent.

If the surface is rough, irregular, or pitted, so as to require short jabbing strokes, or when painting a ceiling, time should be increased by 150 per cent.

If in addition there is poor accessibility or many obstructions exist, or if continuous stooping is necessary, additional time up to 300 per cent of the base value may be required.

All the above increments are multipliers; that is, the final time is the base time *multiplied* by a product of *all* appropriate factors.

Base Time. Base time for painting 1 sq ft of ideal surface, under ideal conditions, using ideal materials is 0.10 min (6 sec). Actual time for a job is built up from the basic data noted above, and tabulated below.

	% Increment to Base Time
Paint Materials:	
Clear varnish or shellac...	Ideal, no increment
Heavier-flowing paints; rubber-base, gloss enamels, etc...............	30
Heavy flowing or paints requiring more brushing out—semigloss enamels, outside white, metal primers, etc...............................	70
Surfaces:	
Ideal, flat wood, metal, smooth concrete, or plaster..................	No increment
Rougher, such as cement or cinder blocks...........................	30
Quite rough or irregular, such as shingles, clapboards, brick...........	70
Conditions:	
Smooth, continuous, and normal height.............................	No increment
Many small areas, such as structural steel and window frames.........	50
Rough, irregular, or pitted, so as to require jabbing or using the brush like a stencil brush..	150
Lack of accessibility, or obstructions, continuous stooping, overhead (ceiling), etc..	300

In addition, allowances are *added* for auxiliary equipment such as drop cloths, short or stepladder, tall ladder, or ladders and extension planks.   These values are *added* to total times obtained from above multiplying factors.

	Time Added per Sq Ft
Drop cloths.....................................	0.02 min
Short ladder...................................	0.01 min
Stepladder.....................................	0.01 min
Tall ladder....................................	0.02 min
Ladder and extension planks....................	0.03 min
Strike a line (junction of 2 colors, etc.)...........	0.50 min per lin ft

Example.   Painting a room 30 by 40 by 10 ft height.
Material.   Plaster, walls and ceiling; cement, floor.
Paint.   6-in. baseboard—black semigloss enamel.   Baseboard to 8-ft dado—office green semigloss enamel.   8-ft dado to ceiling—cream semigloss enamel.   Ceiling—white gloss enamel.   Floor—gray rubber-base paint.

	% Increment to Base Time
Factors to Apply	
Baseboard:	
Semigloss paint......................................	70
Surface	
Conditions, continuous stooping........................	300
Walls:	
Semigloss paint......................................	70
Surface	
Conditions 6″– 2′ Cont. Stooping.......................	300
2′ – 6′ Ideal	
6′ –10′ Step ladder	Add 0.01
Ceiling:	
Gloss enamel..	30
Surface	
Conditions—Ceiling....................................	300
—Ladders and Extension..................................	Add 0.03
Floor:	
Rubber base...	30
Surface	
Conditions (use man helper)	
Others:	
Strike a line:	
Floor and baseboard..	0.50 per ft
Baseboard and wall...	0.50 per ft
Dado..	0.50 per ft
Wall and ceiling..	0.50 per ft
Dimensions:	
Circumference of room.................................	140 ft
Area floor or ceiling..................................	1,200 sq ft
Area baseboard..	½ by 140 ft = 70 sq ft
Area baseboard to 2 ft.................................	1½ by 140 ft = 210 sq ft
Area baseboard 2 to 6 ft...............................	4 by 140 ft = 560 sq ft
Area baseboard 6 to 10 ft..............................	4 by 140 ft = 560 sq ft

Computations:

	Base Time	Paint	Condition		Area	
Baseboard..............	0.10	× 170%	× 400%	×	70 sq ft =	48 min
	Strike a line 140 ft × 0.50				=	70 min
6 in. to 2 ft on wall.....	0.10	× 170%	× 100%	×	210 sq ft =	144 min
2- to 6-ft dado.........	0.10	× 170%	× 100%	×	560 sq ft =	95 min
6 to 10-ft ceiling........	0.10	× 170%	× 100% + 0.01			101 min
			(stepladder)		560 sq ft =	
	Strike a line, dado 140 ft × 0.50				=	70 min
	Strike a line, ceiling 140 ft × 0.50				=	70 min
Ceiling...............	0.10	× 130%	× 400% × 0.03			660 min
			(ladder and extension)	× 1,200 sq ft =		
Floor..................	0.10	× 130%	× 100%	×	1,200 sq ft =	156 min
Total work time..						1,414 min
Total work time..						23.6 hr

Allowing 1 hr per day for obtaining gear and other preparation, this job should take almost 3½ man-days.

The above example does not allow for windows, doors, or obstructions such as radiators and pipes. Painting window sash can best be determined by observation or estimate in any individual circumstance.

Spray Painting. Spray painting of interior flat and continuous surfaces requires about 0.15 min per sq ft. Add for drop cloths, ladders, etc., as for brush painting.

Structural steel requires about 0.25 min per sq ft.

Roller Painting. In general, roller painting (7-in. roller) takes about 50 per cent more time than spray painting. This is limited to common-type rollers on reasonably flat surfaces. Use 0.25 min per sq ft for average application. This does not cover the use of special-type rollers.

Special painting applications, painting pipe:

	Spray	*Brush*
½ to 1 in.............	0.20 min per lin ft	0.70 min per lin ft
1½ to 2 in............	0.25 min per lin ft	0.75 min per lin ft
3 in. and over........	0.25 min per sq ft	0.80 min per sq ft

Surface preparation:

Hand wire brush.................	0.30 min per sq ft
Power wire brush................	0.10 min per sq ft
Wash surface, water.............	0.20 min per sq ft
Wash surface, solvent............	0.40 min per sq ft
Brush surface, dry brush.........	0.01 min per sq ft

Add allowances for ladders, drop cloths, etc., as for painting.

Cyclone Fence (Special Case). This time allowance is based on the use of long-nap rollers and a three-man crew. One man with a long-nap roller on each side of the fence followed by a third man with a brush who touches up the barbed wire and metal parts. A good time value for this operation is 0.35 min per sq ft, both sides. A three-man crew can paint about 85 lin ft of 6-ft cyclone fence per hour.

Staging. For outside painting it may be necessary to erect scaffolds or use staging of some type. For light work, the tubular aluminum scaffolds are adequate. These data are reasonable for normal painting work.

Erect or dismantle 3-ring, 1-section tubular aluminum scaffold......... 0.5 man-hours

	Man-hours per occurrence, height, ft		
	Up to 25	26–50	51–75
Hang or remove painter's scaffold[1]..................	4.8	5.8	6.8
Shift—counterbalance shift—S hook or rope—per scaffold.	0.9	0.9	0.9
Shift—trolley swing carriage........................	0.3	0.3	0.3
Raise or lower scaffold per drop.....................	0.1	0.2	0.3

[1] Times include reeve and hang blocks as required, attach falls to stage, attach tag line, remove and unreeve coil rope, all preparation and clean-ups. Does not apply where blocks are already reeved.

The preceding data are illustrative of the type of data that can be developed and how they can be used by a qualified planner. The following data further illustrate a format that can be used for posting such data. By having time data collected in reasonably large units, the clerical cost of preparing the plan and control time value is minimized. Starting with the data given on the following pages, a planning group can develop its own time data, through the technique of analytical estimating, which will be explained later.

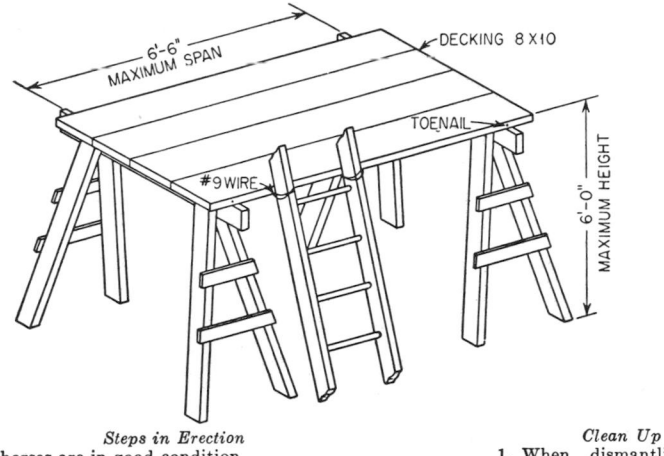

Steps in Erection

1. Make sure horses are in good condition.
2. All four legs must have good level foundation.
3. Horses must not exceed 6' 6'' center to center.
4. Use 8 by 10-in. scaffold lumber (fir or spruce).
5. Use only four planks on a pair of horses.
6. Planks must be toenailed to horses (one 10d nail in each end).
7. Install ladder on scaffold over 48 in. high.
8. Secure ladder with No. 9 wire nailed to underside of plank.
9. No horse scaffold to exceed 6' 0'' in height.

Clean Up

1. When dismantling scaffold remove all nails and return lumber and horses to storage lot.
2. Notify ladder center to pick up the ladder.
3. Used nails and wire should not be left lying around.

FIG. 4-2. Directions for using horse scaffolds.

Repairs to Concrete Work, Cement Finishing:

Man-hours

Manually mix and place grout, per cu ft................................... 0.6
  (Time includes transport and place grout; smooth surface; preparation and clean-up)
Finish concrete surface after removing forms, per sq ft...................... 0.04
  (Time includes cut wires, trim high spots; patch holes, smooth surface, preparation and clean-up)
Wood float finish concrete surface:
  Up to 150 sq ft surface area, per sq ft................................... 0.08
  Over 150 sq ft surface area, per sq ft................................... 0.06
  Level board, prepare and spread dry mix, site travel, preparation and clean-up

The following tables of time values include allowances for miscellaneous operations, such as:

1. Erect and dismantle horse scaffolds and pipe scaffolds (including moves) (see Fig. 4-2).
2. Install and remove ropes, blocks, ladders, scaffold planks, and workbenches (including moves).
3. Place and remove tarpaulins.
4. Remove old calking compound as required.
5. Fill and clean calking guns.
6. Position of calking (flat, overhead, or vertical).
7. Lay out, drill, and plug holes.
8. Lay out and cut decking to fit around pipes, brackets, etc.
9. Lay out and cut lumber, or other material, to fit around pipes, brackets, etc.
10. All necessary material handling at job site.

Siding and Roofing

Operation	Unit of measurement	Man-hours per unit
Corrugated sheet iron (nailed):		
Remove corrugated sheet iron	10 sq ft	0.6
Install corrugated sheet iron	10 sq ft	0.9
Remove and install corrugated sheet iron	10 sq ft	1.5
Corrugated transite (bolted or nailed):		
Install corrugated transite	10 sq ft	1.2
Install ridge or corner roll	lin ft	0.3
Tar paper (nailed):		
Remove old tar paper and wood strips	10 sq ft	0.10
Remove old tar paper (only)	10 sq ft	0.12
Install tar paper and wood strips	10 sq ft	0.3
Install tar paper (only)	10 sq ft	0.16
Roofing felt (nailed and cemented):		
Remove roofing felt	10 sq ft	0.1
Install roofing felt	10 sq ft	0.25
Remove and install roofing felt	10 sq ft	0.35

Note. Use over-all square feet of area; do not make deductions for doors, windows, etc.

Calking

Operation	Unit of measurement	Man-hours per unit
Calk door up to 3 by 7 ft, inclusive	Door	0.8
Calk door over 3 by 7 ft	Door	1.0
Calk window up to 3 by 5 ft, inclusive	Window	0.7
Calk window over 3 by 5 ft	Window	1.0
Calk miscellaneous	10 lin ft	0.7

Doors and Windows

Operation	Unit of measurement	Man-hours per unit	
		Remove	Install
Frames:			
Wood door frame and trim	Door frame	1.5	2.0
Wood window frame and trim	Window frame	1.5	3.0
Metal door frame	Door frame	1.5	2.0
Doors:			
Wood doors—cooling tower, hose box, meter box, etc. (max 3 by 4 ft)	Door	0.75	1.5
Wood doors—batten and inside up to 3 by 7 ft, inclusive	Door	1.0	2.5
Wood doors—inside over 3 by 7 ft, outside up to 3 by 7 ft inclusive	Door	1.5	3.5
Metal doors—up to 3 by 7 ft, inclusive	Door	2.0	4.5
Metal or wood monorail doors—up to 4 by 8 ft, inclusive	Door	...	12.5
Metal or wood monorail doors—over 4 by 8 ft, inclusive	Door	...	22.0
Wood overhead doors	Door	...	40.0
Windows:			
Wood 1—sash (hinge, pullman, or weights)	One sash	1.0	1.5
Wood 2—sash (pullman or weights)	Two sash	2.0	3.0
Metal sash	Sash	...	2.0
Special hardware:			
Any type door check, extra lock, etc	Per item	1.0	2.0

Seasonal Handling of Screen Doors and Window Screens

Operation	Unit of measurement	Man-hours per unit
Screen doors:		
Remove door for storage.................	Door	1.0
Install door from storage.................	Door	1.2
Install door from shop (new)..............	Door	2.5
Window screens:		
Remove screen for storage................	Screen	0.6
Install screen from storage................	Screen	0.8
Install screen from shop (new)............	Screen	1.2
Special hardware:		
Remove special hardware.................	Per item	1.0
Install special hardware..................	Per item	2.0

Repairs to Doors and Windows
(See Figs. 4–3 to 4–6)

Operation	Unit of measurement	Man-hours per unit	
		Minor	Major
Frames (wood):			
Door or window frame (including trim)...	See Figs. 4-3, 4-4, 4-5, 4-6	1.5	3.0
Doors:			
Wood door—batten or inside, up to 3 by 7 ft, inclusive.......................	See Fig. 4-3	1.5	3.0
Wood door—inside over 3 by 7 ft, outside up to 3 by 7 ft, inclusive..............	See Fig. 4-3	2.0	4.0
Metal door—up to 3 by 7 ft, inclusive.....	See Fig. 4-3	2.5	5.0
Windows:			
Wood 1—sash (hinge type)..............	See Fig. 4-6	1.0	2.0
Wood 2—sash (pullman or weights)......	See Figs. 4-4 and 4-5	2.0	4.0
Screens:			
Door—wood frame....................	See Fig. 4-6	1.2	2.4
Window—wood frame.................	See Fig. 4-6	0.6	1.2
Special hardware:			
Any type door check, extra lock, etc......	Per item	1.0	*

* Major repairs not permitted in the field—replace with new.

Miscellaneous
Horse Scaffolds

Horse scaffold (max 6 ft high)	Man-hours per scaffold		
	Erect	Dismantle	Total
Handrail and toeboard:			
Without...........	0.7	0.5	1.2
With..............	1.5	0.9	2.4

The above times include the following operations: Erect and dismantle mudrails, horses, decking toeboards, ladders, ladder clamps, midrails, and handrails.

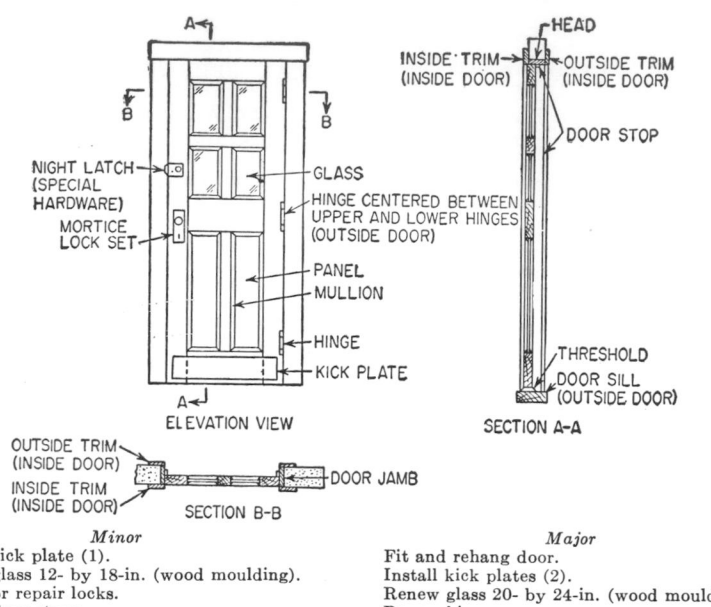

Minor	Major
Install kick plate (1).	Fit and rehang door.
Renew glass 12- by 18-in. (wood moulding).	Install kick plates (2).
Renew or repair locks.	Renew glass 20- by 24-in. (wood moulding).
Repair door stops.	Renew hinges.
Repair inside trim.	Repair door sill or threshold.
Repair mullion (1).	Repair head or door jamb.
Repair outside trim.	Repair mullions (2).
Reset frame by renailing.	Repair panel.

Fig. 4-3. Repairs to inside and outside doors.

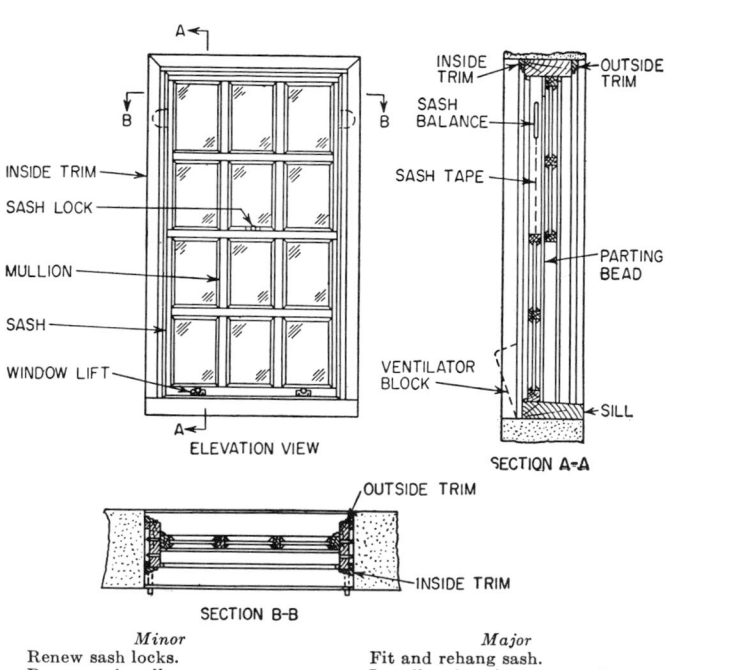

Minor	Major
Renew sash locks.	Fit and rehang sash.
Renew sash pulleys.	Install sash weight-type pulleys.
Renew window lifts.	Renew pulley jamb.
Repair mullion (1).	Renew sash (1).
Repair parting bead.	Renew sash cords.
Repair trim (inside or outside).	Renew sill.
Repair ventilator blocks.	

Fig. 4-4. Repairs to double-hung window, sash-weight type.

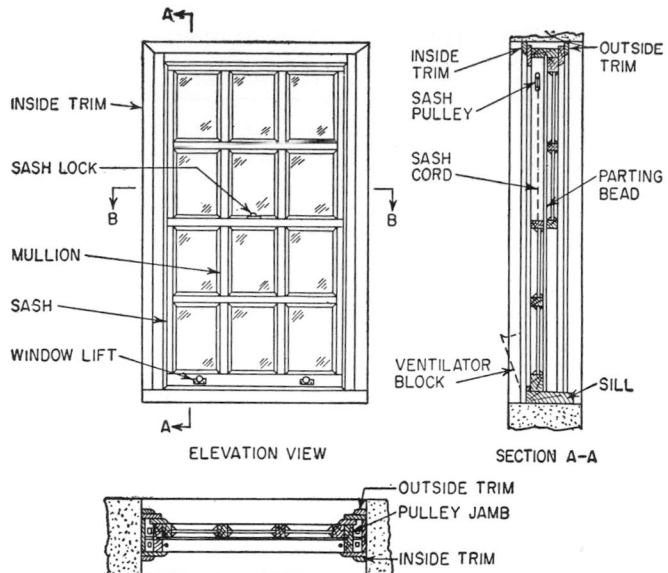

ELEVATION VIEW   SECTION A-A

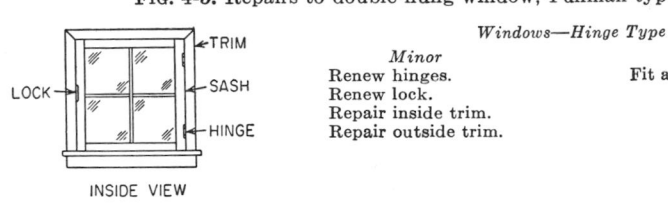

SECTION B-B

Minor	Major
Renew sash locks.	Fit and rehang sash.
Renew window lifts.	Install Pullman-type pulleys.
Repair mullion (1).	Renew sash (1).
Repair parting bead.	Renew sill.
Repair trim (inside or outside).	Renew sash balance and tapes.
Repair ventilator blocks.	

Fig. 4-5. Repairs to double-hung window, Pullman type.

Windows—Hinge Type

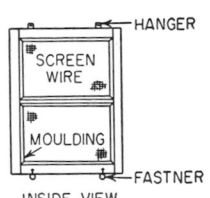

INSIDE VIEW

Minor	Major
Renew hinges.	Fit and rehang sash.
Renew lock.	
Repair inside trim.	
Repair outside trim.	

Screens

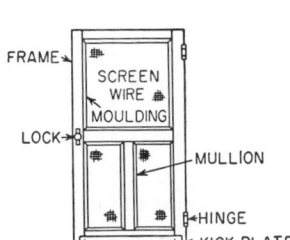

INSIDE VIEW

Minor	Major
Patch screen wire.	Renew screen wire.
Renew or repair fasteners.	
Renew or repair hangers.	
Repair moulding.	

Screen Doors

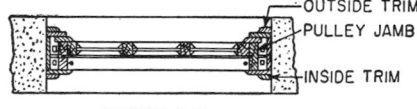

INSIDE VIEW

Minor	Major
Install kick plate (1).	Fit and rehang door.
Patch screen wire.	Install kickplates (2).
Renew hinges.	Renew screen wire.
Renew or repair locks.	Repair frame.
Repair mullion (1 or 2).	
Repair screen door stops.	
Repair to moulding.	

Fig. 4-6. Repairs to windows (hinge type), screens, screen doors.

Horse Scaffolds—Material List

Platform size	Trestles (48 in. wide)		Decking 2 by 10 ft, 8 ft No. of	Stanchions–handrail braces and toeboards 1¼ by 6 in.		Ladder	
	Height, ft	No. of		4 ft No. of	8 ft No. of	6 ft No. of	9 ft No. of
3 by 8 ft (4 plank)	2	2	4	4	4		
	3	2	4	4	4		
	4	2	4	4	4	1	
	5	2	4	4	4	. . .	1
	6	2	4	4	4	. . .	1

Assemble Lumber

Operation	Unit of measurement	Fbm per job	Man-hours per unit
Assemble lumber		0–10	0.8
		11–20	1.5
Boxes		21–30	2.3
Buildings		31–40	3.0
Eaves and show rafters		41–50	3.5
Flooring (sub and rough)	Total fbm	51–60	4.0
Framing	installed per	61–70	4.5
Furring	job	71–80	5.0
Partitions (studs)		81–90	5.5
Skylights and louvers		91–100	6.0
Stairs		101–110	6.6
Wood siding (rough 1 by 10)		111–120	7.2
		121–130	7.8
		131–140	8.4
		Above 140	0.6 per additional 10 fbm

Install and Dismantle Lumber
Unit of measurement total board feet per job

Operation	Fbm per job	Man-hours per job		
		Install	Dismantle	Total
Temporary:	1–10	0.5	0.3	0.8
	11–20	1.0	0.5	1.5
Barricades	21–30	1.5	0.8	2.3
Bins	31–40	2.0	1.0	3.0
Chutes	41–50	2.3	1.2	3.5
Guards on machinery	51–60	2.6	1.3	3.9
Platforms	61–70	2.9	1.5	4.4
Ramps	71–80	3.3	1.7	5.0
Runways	81–90	3.6	1.8	5.4
	Above 90	0.4 per additional 10 fbm	0.2 per additional 10 fbm	0.6 per additional 10 fbm

Interior Wall Materials

Operation	Unit of measurement	Man-hours per unit
Acoustic board:		
Install acoustic board (nailed to ceiling)................	10 sq ft	0.5
Install acoustic board (cemented to ceiling).............	10 sq ft	0.7
Fiberboard, flexboard, gypsum board, masonite, and plywood:		
Install fiberboard, flexboard, gypsum board, masonite and plywood on ceilings, partitions, and walls using 4 by 8 ft, 4 by 10 ft, or 4 by 12 ft sheets......................	10 sq ft	0.6
Molding or trim:		
Install molding or trim to cover joints between ceilings and walls, between floors and walls, etc....................	10 lin ft	0.6

The above tables of data illustrate the form of data collection that can be used to set up a job-estimating procedure for building maintenance. Necessary data can be originally prepared from past experience or analytical estimating. These data can be checked by job observation, and the data refined. The following description of analytical estimating may be helpful in setting up the necessary procedure for this control:

The Technique of Analytical Estimating. Analytical estimating is used to determine the work content of nonrepetitive jobs which do not justify calculation by the techniques of time study.

In analytical estimating, time values for any particular job are compiled by a trained estimator. The estimator breaks the job down into component elements. Generally these elements will be of longer duration than those taken from time studies. He then establishes the work content of as many elements as possible from known or verifiable elemental data. The work content of each of the remaining elements he establishes by direct estimation. The fundamental assumption is that a skilled craftsman, properly trained in these techniques, can make a reasonable estimate of the time required to perform the elements of work with which he is familiar. The breaking down of the job into elements makes the results of estimation more accurate than if the estimation were to be for a job as a whole.

The Procedure for Analytical Estimating. Before an estimate can be made, it is essential to decide upon the proper method by which the work should be carried out. Only after this has been done is it possible to divide the work into satisfactory elements. The process of analyzing the job into elements will often suggest possible improvements to existing methods. In other words, the job must be subjected to method study before the work content can be estimated.

The estimator will break down the job into elements, which will be of longer duration than those characteristic of time-study elements. Practice has shown that the smaller the elements into which the work is divided, the more reliable are the results obtained, since errors tend to cancel each other out. There is, however, a limit to the extent of detail economically justified. The estimator will then examine the work content of each element and determine a time to be allowed for performing that element. All times determined are based on normal work pace.

As pointed out above, as many of the elemental times as possible should be derived from time-study data or proved data so that the number of elemental times which have to be estimated can be kept as low as possible. One should aim at reducing the percentage of times estimated to nil, since times derived from time-study data are more accurate than those which are estimated.

When times for all the elements have been derived, they are added together to give the total time for the job at normal work pace. The total time must then be "normalized" in order to establish the time to be allowed for the job.

As in normal work-measurement procedure, a rest allowance has to be added. It is not assessed on each element of the job as in time study but is added to the job as a whole. Therefore, it is given in the form of a "blanket" allowance. This is a pre-determined fixed allowance covering a group of similar jobs, which is added to the total "estimated" time for the whole job. Unless the work is physically heavy, 10 per cent is adequate for this purpose.

After adding the rest allowances to the total time, all additional allowances are then added. These will include policy allowances (e.g., washing, putting away tools, etc.), and team allowances. Team allowances are given where more than one crafts-man is required on a job, and where there is an absence of labor balance, resulting in periods of *enforced* waiting time. The team allowance is normally based on the assumption that the nonskilled "mate" to the craftsman is essential for the effective performance of the job.

The Use of Analytical Estimating. *Improved Planning.* As a result of analytical estimating, it is possible to improve the manning for and planning of work, since facts about jobs can take the place of opinion. On maintenance work, analytical estimating provides an excellent and practical basis for preparing a schedule for preventive plant maintenance to a degree of accuracy otherwise unobtainable.

Estimators. It will be seen from the foregoing description of analytical estimating that the key to the whole technique lies in the *character* and *ability* of the estimators themselves. It is apparent that the selection of estimators is therefore an important managerial problem. Generally speaking, an estimator should have been a skilled craftsman in the type of work which he is employed to estimate, in order that he can be fully conversant with the work. The knowledge of the job is vitally necessary to his success. He must have a firm conception of what is a normal performance.

Chapter 5

PAINTING

By Arthur R. Cannon
President
Oliver B. Cannon and Son, Inc.
Philadelphia, Pa.

PAINTS

Paints have but two uses—protection and decoration. Whether they are used for one or a combination of these purposes, the composition of the coating is, to varying degrees, basically the same.

Paint is made of two broad components, pigments or solid powders and vehicles (carriers) that transfer the pigment onto the surface.

Miracle paints, or coating materials, do not, and probably never will, exist. All combinations have some drawbacks even though they are tailor-made, that is, composed of carefully selected ingredients to fulfill definite requirements.

Results are still compromises, and the experienced contractor and his chemists are aware of it. Their constant aim is to keep the compromises to a minimum. That assures a quality job.

The industrial contractor and his chemists start out with the two basic components—pigments and vehicles—then endeavor to select the best combinations for a specific job. Proportions are decided upon and the amounts and kinds of thinners and driers chosen. The formula is then submitted to a paint manufacturer. The resulting blend is "specification paint," a product conceived to give maximum results under given conditions.

In a broad sense, vehicles are any materials that will form a film when dry. They may be oils, varnishes, alkyd resins, ester gums, cellulose compounds, or chlorinated rubber.

Oils are linseed, castor, tung, soybean, cottonseed, and some derived from wood. In addition to the vegetable oils, there are the proteins, chiefly fish oil, which has a high rust-preventive value.

Varnishes are prepared from natural gums, boiled and processed to a clear liquid.

Alkyd resins are made from synthetics.

Cellulose compounds are commonly made from processed cotton or wood oils.

Chlorinated rubber is rubber combined with chlorine.

Pigments fall into four general classifications: white, colored, black, and metallic.

Whites may be zinc oxide, white lead carbonate, lithopone, titanium dioxide, magnesium silicate, and calcium and barium carbonates.

Colors are strictly in the field of organic chemistry with the exception of iron oxides, red lead, and chromates.

Blacks are made from carbon, bone char, asphalt, graphite, and other natural minerals.

Metallics are stainless steel, aluminum, and zinc.

White pigments are active or inert. Active, they have hiding power. Inert, this hiding property is lacking when dispersed in a vehicle.

Active pigments, such as carbonate of white lead, leaded zinc, zinc oxide, and titanium dioxide, possess hiding power.

Magnesium silicate, barium carbonate, barium sulfate, and calcium carbonate are inerts and have no hiding power, but they do contribute to the paint's durability and should not be considered either as adulterants or to occupy volume.

While the twin basic components—vehicles and pigments—make paint, other ingredients must be added to make the product usable. These are thinners and driers and, to a lesser degree, solvents, especially the aromatics. The last makes paint easier to apply yet evaporates when exposed to the air, leaving solids and vehicles behind to form an even paint film. Some aromatics are BTX solvents, namely, benzene, toluene, and mixed xylenes.

Thinners reduce viscosity so that paint may be brushed or sprayed. Turpentine is still among the best, and some others are turpentine substitutes, usually made from light petroleum or coal-tar hydrocarbons.

Driers are used to catalyze the vehicle. This is a chemical process involving condensation, oxidation, and polymerization.

The last—polymerization—is a chemical action within the paint compound that takes place without the aid of oxygen. Since oxygen is not needed in the process, polymerized films have higher molecular weights than the original compositions and do not break down readily from oxidation or normal exposure to air.

By contrast, oxidation is the drying of a paint film through vehicle oils combining with oxygen in the air.

Although the primary mission of thinners is to make paint appliable, they also help control the degree of penetration and make possible efficient function of driers in the proper sequence—evaporation, oxidation, and polymerization.

The sequence, necessary to produce the desired type of paint film, is vitally important. Therefore, in no case should a thinner be substituted for the one recommended by the paint manufacturer. Nor should it be used in greater or lesser quantities than the manufacturer's or industrial painting chemist's specifications. Too much or too little thinner makes it impossible for the desirable drying action to take place.

Driers are many but best represented by three, lead, cobalt, and manganese, which may be in the form of salts, acids, or oxides.

Lead, in oil vehicles, causes the film to dry, in varying degrees, from the bottom up. Cobalt dries from the top down. Manganese gives an over-all dry.

Type and amount of drier must be carefully calculated to result in the proper catalyzation; that is, acceleration of the reaction which ends in a paint film. Excess drier causes brittleness, loss of durability, and in the case of cobalt, which is a top drier, wrinkling.

In addition to pigment, vehicle, thinner, and drier, chemical-resisting paints and enamels contain another ingredient consisting of plastics, or synthetic materials, which must be blended in properly to satisfy a definite need for their use.

Obviously, the definition of paint, as given here, is sketchy but it should be apparent that each component contributes different properties and these must be combined to give the best compromise that comes closest to fulfilling a definite set of conditions.

Paints commonly used in plant maintenance fall within the following broad generalities.

Interior wall and ceiling finishes are usually titanium-base pigmentation in synthetic-resin vehicles, in whatever combination and refinement necessary to produce flat, semigloss, or gloss finish, as may be desired.

Flat finishes have less glare than materials having a gloss, while semigloss and gloss finishes, generally speaking, have a higher degree of washability.

One-coat, self-priming, flat finishes are in common use today for general clean-up work. "Clean-up work," as pertains to painting, means a one-coat job to "freshen things up." After a plant, shop, or even office has had a general housecleaning and all excess unused materials, etc., have been removed, the job just doesn't seem complete without a coat of paint. These materials are usually titanium-base pigments in specially processed vegetable oils.

Where color is no object, aluminum pigments are finding acceptance in some heavy manufacturing industries.

Paints for interior metalwork, trim, doors, windows, and dadoes are usually combinations of various pigments (determined by color requirements and possibly rust-preventive qualities) in a harder-drying synthetic-resin vehicle.

Lead, zinc, or titanium pigment in a linseed-oil vehicle is the accepted combination of material for exterior woodwork, particularly in white and tints of white.

Dark colors, such as chrome greens, browns, blacks, etc., are preferred in alkyd-resin vehicles. The better grades of exterior paints for metal are also desirable in an alkyd-resin vehicle, the pigmentation being governed by color requirements and rust-preventive qualities.

Alkyd coatings are probably the most widely used for general maintenance purposes. But, like every type of paint ingredient, the alkyd has plus and minus qualities.

On the plus side, it has exterior durability; is the most economical in cost per square foot per year under average conditions; has good film thickness and density; and, with oil, can be made to give good flexibility. It has good drying characteristics and the best color retention for home enamels and industrial uses.

On the negative side, it has low chemical, caustic, acid, and moisture resistance. Therefore, alkyd is most useful when not exposed to those elements.

Phenolic coatings answer the above problems. Phenolic resin itself is hard and brittle, flakes very easily, and has poor film qualities. But, when cooked with linseed, tung, or dehydrated castor oil, it forms a good film that dries well, is hard, and has high chemical and salt-spray resistance. But it too, like the alkyds, has its faults.

At one time, it was the most widely used chemical- and moisture-resistant coating in use, but its faults led to extensive research for a substitute. Phenolic coatings chalk on exterior exposure and become brittle as they age. They are also unsuited for white and pastel colors because of yellowing with exposure. These drawbacks limit the efficient use of phenolics to brush applications exposed to mild chemical attack and in areas with a high degree of dampness.

Otherwise, the improved qualities sought were found in vinyl coatings. These are probably the most chemical-resistant available today. They have good durability and good resistance to solvents such as grease, alcohol, turpentine, painter's naphtha, gasoline, and light hydrocarbons in general. They swell in the aromatics but return to original shape and form. They dry rapidly for recoat and have water resistance that, mil for mil film thickness, is unexcelled.

Note the "mil for mil film thickness" qualification. Like the other coatings discussed, vinyls are not perfect. Their film-thickness qualities are quite poor and their brushing qualities questionable. Continuous and extremely rigid inspection is necessary to ensure proper application.

Also, vinyls are not satisfactory over conventional primers. When used over linseed oil–red lead, the primer wrinkles, or "alligators." Vinyl coatings also have poor heat resistance.

Chlorinated rubber, as a vehicle, has good durability and good film thickness, provided it is plasticized correctly. Chlorinated rubber itself is a hard, dry, brittle powder and, without a plasticizer, is worthless as a coating vehicle. If properly treated with chemical-resistant plasticizers, which contribute flexibility, an excellent coating results. It has a fast dry for recoat and, because of the type of solvents used, has good nonlifting properties. Heat resistance is better than vinyl and moisture resistance is very good. Chemical resistance is about the same as vinyl types. And, whereas vinyl will average about 1 mil per coat, chlorinated rubber will run from $1\frac{1}{2}$ to $1\frac{3}{4}$.

Again, there is a negative side. Chlorinated rubber-base paints are not always compounded correctly. If plasticized with a poor chemical-resistant agent, they will fail because of the plasticizer, even though excellent properties otherwise may have been imparted to the coating.

Aromatic solvents such as toluol or xylol are used with rubber-base paints and, accordingly, any chemicals containing solvents of a like nature will attack the coating. These types of chlorinated rubber-base paints have poor solvent resistance and especially so if in contact with solvent solutions of vegetable oils such as castor and linseed. Finally, chlorinated rubber-base paints have an extremely short life in hydrochloric acid atmosphere.

From this brief discussion of paint, it can readily be seen that there are no universal paints. There are good compositions for certain conditions, but even they are compromises. It is the weighing and correct assaying of the compromises that results in the best paint job for the least money. The latter must be calculated on the length of time between repaintings and not on the original expense. Obviously, a job that costs $9,000 but breaks down in 3 years is more expensive than one at $12,000 which lasts 5 years. The first costs $3,000 per year, the second $2,400. That is reflected in overhead, since maintenance is part of a plant's fixed charges.

To arrive at the lowest yearly cost, the painting must be tailored to prevailing conditions. Some of these may be obvious, i.e., cold in the north, heat in the south, salt air along the coast, humid atmosphere, and direction of exposure (north, south, east, west, etc.).

Others, just as important, may not be so evident. For instance, direction of the prevailing winds may be known, but what do they carry? Whose smoke and exhaust stacks do they pass and what comes out of those stacks? Do the winds pass over open-pit mines and, if so, what comes out of the ground at those points?

PRIMERS

Like paint, primers will do only certain things well and, if they must be used to satisfy a definite need, may well dictate the type of paint components that go over them.

Essentially, a primer should do one or all of the following: prevent rusting; provide a good surface for paint; help provide film thickness to the finished job; make a good moisture barrier; and, when used over deep oxidation (deterioration such as rusting), have good wetting powers for complete penetration as in the case of rusting.

Red lead is a pigment and not a paint. When combined with vegetable oils, it is basically alkaline. As the linseed or other vegetable oils oxidize, forming acids, the basic alkalinity of red lead prevents an acid condition on the metal's surface. In addition, red-lead primer affords good adhesion and good water resistance, remains flexible, and contributes to film thickness. Negatively, when red lead is combined with vegetable oil, the dry is slow.

Zinc chromate primer, when applied, has on its plus side the ability to passivate metal—that is, there is no reaction. Like red lead, it is basic in nature, and acids, produced during the drying and oxidation period of the vehicle, are neutralized to a certain extent.

However, the salts formed are in many cases water-soluble, causing a porous-film result where the coating is exposed to moisture. When zinc chromate contains zinc dichromate, which is very soluble in water, the salts may leach from the primer film, making it very porous unless protected by a dense water-resistant top coating. This is an important negative item and should not be overlooked.

Zinc chromate primer, when covered with alkyd paint, will not stand up when faced with rusting because of the porosity of the alkyd film.

This brings in "wash primers." Using one of them, such as the vinyl butyral wash primer, under the same alkyd coating as above would permit little if any rusting and likely would show little creepage from the edges because of the density and thickness of the film over sharp corners.

Vinyl butyral wash primers give maximum rust protection, even with less dense top coating, when properly applied over sandblasted surfaces. Unfortunately, many shop primers are made from iron oxide, which has no rust-inhibitive characteristics and is generally mixed with cheap resin-modified varnish. This combination is of so little value that plant engineers should be on guard against its use.

It can be said in general that, once a surface has been properly prepared for painting, the next step is to select a primer that will answer the following questions in the affirmative:

1. Will the coating to be applied over the primer be compatible in every respect?
2. Will the primer give a good bond to surface?
3. If the coating is to be chemically resistant, is the primer coat also chemically resistant (alkalies, acids, organic solvents, etc.)?
4. Does the primer when dry provide a dense coating impervious to moisture, etc.?
5. Does the primer permit a good "solvent-type" action bond with finish coat?
6. Does the primer tend to give a uniform coating thickness regardless of the shape of object being prime-coated?

From a practical standpoint, it is almost impossible to have all the desired characteristics in a good primer, but it is so important that as much care should be exercised in selecting the proper primer as in selecting the finish coat.

FREQUENCY

Like paint itself, "when" to paint is a variable. A precise time element eludes definition, except from a minimum schedule, based strictly on the life of any given paint coating for an individual plant.

The minimum schedule ignores entirely the valuable benefits of improved lighting and worker efficiency and better public relations that accrue from a more frequently painted plant. The minimum merely avoids deterioration by repainting when the protective coating is worn off a surface. The concern that adheres to a minimum policy must exercise great care, or the adage "it costs more not to paint" may overtake them.

The truth of that statement can be seen in any of the older industrial centers. There will be scores of abandoned plants, yet nearby others will be under construction at today's high costs. The reason, of course, is that it's cheaper to build than to try to fix up the older plants that deteriorated, beyond the economical deadline, for lack of proper maintenance.

Frequently, the trouble started when a needed painting was skipped. When this defense against deterioration collapsed, deterioration began its insidious attack. Destroying the invader is far more costly than maintaining a protective film. Only thorough periodic inspection will disclose the danger signals of attack because each plant, and all its parts, differs from all others. Some of the more obvious symptoms and causes are given in Table 5-1.

As previously stated, no hard-and-fast rules can be laid down for durability. Only averages can be given, based on a specific part of the country. For example, in the Philadelphia-Baltimore area, exterior-painted sash surfaces have a life span of about 5 to 7 years. In Buffalo, ice and snow cut a full year off those figures. In New Orleans, with greater average heat and ultraviolet rays, the figures fall to 3 years instead of 5 as in Philadelphia. Near the coast, salt spray and ocean winds cut the life expectancy of the same paint job to about 2 years.

A good paint inspector will keep these things in mind and will also maintain a check list—his own, not somebody else's.

Some of the items on the list and the average lasting time in the Philadelphia-Baltimore area include:

Steel Sash. Under the best conditions, paint life is about 6 years. Corrosive conditions in the atmosphere or plant processes can cut that in half, to a third, or even to a quarter.

Wood Sash. About 5 years. Less on the weather side that is exposed to summer sun and winter alternate thaws and freezes.

Doors. Metal or wood; about the same as sash, but take into consideration the traffic in addition to the other factors. Paint on a little-used door may last 5 years, on one with heavy traffic, 6 months.

Wood Siding. About the same as wood sash, but watch the critical points such as joints. Siding needs to be resurfaced when the gloss has disappeared. That signifies the oil is dead and all that remains between wood and weather is a thin coat of pigment.

Exterior Masonry Surfaces. About 4 to 5 years. As with wood siding, refinishing should be done when the gloss disappears.

On unpainted surfaces, watch carefully for hairline cracks, the first sign of deterioration. Unless properly painted at once, with correct primer and finish coat, expensive surface repairs will be needed.

Metal Roofs. This is a tough one because too much paint is as bad as too little. Heavy layers crack and peel, water gets underneath, and rust sets in without being noticed until it has made damaging progress.

A properly painted metal roof is one from which all rust spots have been removed. Then a good anticorrosive primer should be applied, followed by application of a metallic oxide paint. The metallic oxide paint is slow to dust and wash away and, when worn, leaves the surface in good condition for repainting. This one-coat repainting should be done about every 3 years with a two-coat application (prime and finish) about the fourth or fifth repainting.

Roof Drainage (metal cornices, downspouts, and gutters). About 3 years. These are easy marks for corrosion. Telling signs are rust spots and rust streaks.

Caution. When replacing be sure all portions that will be inaccessible after erection are first painted. This relatively inexpensive protective step will add many years to the life of metal drainage items.

Fire Escapes. About 5 years. Repaint at the very first indication of rusting. Don't ever paint hinge and key points. That will cause them to bind and the fire escape won't work when needed. Protect the critical points regularly with penetrating oil and a light grease.

Storage Tanks. Interiors, when used for water, 2 to 3 years, provided that they were properly painted at the start; otherwise, 18 months. Exteriors, about 5 years, but watch carefully the grillage and other points not easily reached. These are critical and can lead to an expense out of all proportion to proper maintenance costs.

Because of impurities in water, some tanks must be completely repainted on the interior every 18 months. Also metal that is constantly subjected to the rise and fall of water will corrode faster. In the average tank, it's good practice to drop the level about one-third and paint the exposed interior once every 18 months.

Tanks that are out of service and left empty for an extended period corrode rapidly. This can be prevented by a thorough interior painting and then filling with oil, clean water, with or without an anticorrode additive (e.g., nitrite), or some other neutral liquid. The contents then protect the surface from free oxygen, and where there is no oxygen, there is no rusting.

Pipelines. Highly critical because of the difficult-to-see area where the pipe rests on supports. Corrosion makes headway there while the easy-to-see surfaces appear well coated and unrusted.

Steel-mesh Fences. Two extremes here and an untidy mid-course. Unpainted mesh will last about 15 years. Complete painting every 4 years gives a tidy appearance but the costs are out of proportion to replacing the mesh at the end of its life span. The economical untidy middle course is to paint the expensive posts before installation and regularly thereafter.

If set in concrete, the line where steel and concrete meet must be carefully watched. It will pay to paint the bottom 6 in., including 1 in. of the masonry, even when it does not appear to need it.

Cranes and Craneways. Very vulnerable to rust because of numerous hidden angles and joints. These must be carefully watched and kept flooded with paint. Watch the exposed surfaces for minute speckles of rust. Repaint at once.

Building Interior. This painting can be for protection, good housekeeping, or a combination of both. The dual role is in vogue with progressive management.

The importance of color, in relation to employee morale, efficiency, and favorable visitor reaction is discussed under the heading Color.

Unclean surfaces and those which flake, powder, sweat, engender mildew and mold, or harbor undesirable odors can have unfavorable reactions on plant products. This is explained under Product Contamination.

It was once widely believed that plant interiors required little, if anything, in the way of protective coatings. The opposite is a proved fact. Interior surfaces are highly vulnerable to deterioration and must be safeguarded if management is to avoid expensive repairs and replacements.

Frequency of interior painting can be cut through washing and scrubbing of soiled surfaces. This serves two purposes. The utmost is obtained out of the existing paint surface, and money is saved in surface preparation when repainting is needed.

Unweathered interiors gather dirt film that must be at least partially broken down before repainting. Otherwise, surfaces build up to thicknesses that result in crazing and alligatoring. Then the expensive job of removing all the layers must be done to obtain a good painting result.

Interior symptoms of failure, or need of repainting, are the same as for exteriors but not usually so grossly apparent. Interior dirt and grime often hide the inroads of damaging deterioration. Carefully inspect all points.

Structural Steel. The right paint, properly applied, should be good under nonacid conditions for 10 to 12 years. During the first 5, inspection for rust can be casual. After that, inspection should be regular. Again, the danger spots are angles, flanges, and corners where moisture can gather and lead to rusting. The rule here is: the harder the spot is to inspect, the more carefully it must be scrutinized.

Interior Sash. About the same life as other interiors. Watch out for putty failure. It may have dried and shrunk, allowing moisture to build a film of rust, in the case of steel, or the start of rot in wood.

SURFACE PREPARATION

A surface is not "painted" unless there is a bond between it and the coating material. When that union is lacking, the surface is merely "covered," affording little protection at excessive cost.

A painted surface will provide maximum protection against deterioration and will wear; that is, while the paint film may gradually become thinner, it remains fixed to the surface. This gives maximum return for the money (labor, materials, shutdowns, etc.) invested. There is also an added dividend. If repainting is done before the film is too far gone, surface-preparation costs are held to a minimum.

A surface that is only *covered* with paint gives minimum and frequently no protection against deterioration. The film does not wear but parts from the surface, and much of the invested money (labor, materials, shutdowns, etc.) is wasted. Then, should a first-class job be attempted, surface-preparation costs skyrocket.

Although surfaces receptive to paint are fundamental to a good job, the point is ignored so frequently that paint manufacturers annually market a great deal more of their product than is actually needed for efficient industrial maintenance. The difference is wasted.

Good industrial painting contractors are fully aware that proper surface preparation is important. At times, 70 per cent of their bid on a job may be for "cleaning." Where paint failure or corrosion exists, 45 to 60 per cent of the total cost is justified on a single-coat job. Dirt and dust removal, in the average plant, will constitute from 5 to 10 per cent and preparing structural steel may go to 40 per cent. These are only a few examples to serve as guides and to counteract the tendency to underestimate the importance of surface preparation.

Ordinary dirt, dust, and a microscopic grease film are the most prevalent obstacles to paint adhesion. Of these, "grease" is the worst villain. Its treacherous ways are not limited to the processing of petroleum but extend to all places within walls. Grease film also travels freely with air currents, settling on exteriors.

Traces of grease must be scrubbed and washed off. If extremely light, it can be ignored on a two-coat job, provided that the first covering contains a solvent which will dissolve the "grease" or cause it to be completely dispersed throughout the paint film as the surface is being painted. Of course, this procedure can be tolerated only when a well-brushed job is in order.

This is often an important factor in a priming coat, provided that the ingredients are properly blended and the solvent is present in the correct amount. Such solvents are turpentine, turpentine substitutes, light hydrocarbon solvents (painter's naphthas), and vehicle oils in general.

Where a detectable amount of grease is present, steam cleaning will remove the film and dirt. In production areas, the need for complete removal of dirt before painting is obvious. Compressed-air and vacuum cleaning will take care of the dust but will not remove a thin greasy film.

Straight solvent cleaning lies between the above two methods. It involves washing the surface with turpentine, or stoddard solvent, to remove grease and dirt, provided that the former is not too thick.

A variation of this method employs the use of a strong alkali cleaner. In cutting grease, this is likely to destroy the old paint film, but when rinsed off, it leaves a fair surface for repainting. It is used where other processes might cause machinery damage or interfere with production.

Sandblasting is necessary when heavy accumulations of rust, chemical scale, old coatings, grease, or other deleterious matter are on the surface. Where sandblasting is not feasible, or the adverse film does not demand its use, the power-driven wire brush and pneumatic or electric hammers do good jobs.

Hand wire brushing is used where the surface does not evidence a heavy scale or rust build-up. This procedure will take care of light rusting and plain dirt. Scrapers are satisfactory when only lightly adhering scale, or dirt and mud, may be caked in spots on the surface.

There is also flame cleaning, done by applying a torch to the surface. In the case of metal bases, they expand more rapidly than iron, steel, oxide rusts, mill scale, etc., and these pop off. On other bases, the surface expands faster, with the same result. A propane generator, to supply the gas, is better and faster than the gasoline torch. It permits doing the same job in about half to one-fourth the time. Flame cleaning removes old paint and destroys grease and oil films but is not popular because of obvious fire hazards.

The same risks are also inherent to the previously mentioned power cleaning implements. Electrically powered tools should never be used where a spark could ignite combustible gases or materials. Those conditions call for pneumatic power, provided that the tools themselves, such as wire brushes, cannot cause trouble by sparking.

For the same reasons—fire hazards—combustible solvents should not be used in confined places where flame or sparks could ignite them.

Outside, new metal, exposed to the weather, should not be red-leaded or painted until all mill scale is removed. The most economical way is to permit the scale to rust off. It requires 1 to 2 years. If a coating is put over new metal, the mill scale will peel off in time anyway and take the paint, prime, or red lead with it.

There are other surface-preparation situations that call for specialized approaches. These entail areas of tobacco, textile, brewing, food plants, and those employing acids or caustics such as paper and petroleum industries.

Wherever acid or caustics are used, maintenance must be perfect if management isn't to be burdened with excessive costs. There are good acid-resistant paints, but once acid has penetrated the coating to the base, there is no use repainting while acid conditions persist. The only remedy is complete shutdown, because no cleaning method will permit the application of paint before more acid has collected on the base substance.

In industries where high humidity prevails, such as tobacco, textile, brewing, and food, mold and mildew are common in at least portions of the plants. In these areas, surface preparation is of primary importance.

The first step, as with other jobs, is complete removal of all dust and dirt, from not only the surfaces but also the entire section that is to be painted. Following that, the surfaces to be painted must be thoroughly washed down with a strong solution of formaldehyde.

Proper coating protection can be found among the vinylite, resin, or rubber-base compositions. Then, to keep mold and mildew from forming, the surfaces should be washed down periodically with a mild solution of formaldehyde. The time interval for this varies greatly with plants. In some, the job may need to be done every few days and, in others, perhaps only once in 6 months.

As in the case of acids and caustics, maintenance engineers and management should note that surfaces subject to high humidity must absolutely be repainted *before they lose their good film protection.*

Should the repainting be delayed too long, management's only alternative is a long shutdown that may run up to 5 or 6 months. If that isn't done, management is faced with rapid and expensive plant deterioration and, eventually, plant abandonment.

It is important for maintenance engineers to remember that, once the film protection is lost, no satisfactory repainting can be done while the humid conditions prevail; hence the shutdown requirement.

Interior moisture is not always that hard to beat. There's an interesting case along those lines in the files of the Cannon organization in Philadelphia. One of our representatives contacted a rayon-manufacturing plant in Virginia that needed repainting sorely because of a mildew condition. It appeared a shutdown was needed, but since that would be expensive to management, further studies were conducted to see if another approach was possible.

It was found that the condensation which nurtured the mildew was present only when temperatures outside the plant were markedly lower than inside. The Cannon experts then suggested painting be attempted in the spring when exterior and interior temperatures were close to equalization and the condensation factor was at a minimum. The idea proved successful.

There are more frequent occasions when interior-surface preparations start from the outside. There is no use painting over surfaces, no matter how clean, if there is exterior water seepage. This builds up pressure under a paint film and it bulges or flakes off.

Vulnerable points are cracked masonry, areas around sash, places where pipes pass through walls, and similar situations. They must be waterproofed from outside before inside surfaces are ready for paint. The interior portions must also be permitted to dry thoroughly before a coating is applied.

On the outside, critical areas are the joints between frames and the walls and the putty that should act as a sealer for the glass. If calking around frames has broken down, or there are cracks where frames and wall join, they must be filled. Otherwise, hidden deterioration, under paint covering, will show one day in the form of expensive repairs.

Another insidious point is the junction between glass and the sash. Regardless of the base material, or whether the painting is interior or exterior, both sides of the glass must be checked.

When the edge of a penknife can be forced between glass and sash, putty or glazing compound is dead and must be replaced or subsequent painting is valueless. A good paint film may be present, but if the entire bed isn't impervious to water, moisture works behind it and can't evaporate quickly. This slow drying leads to rusting of steel sash and rotting of wood under the paint covering.

To assume that putty, calking, or glazing compounds are in good shape, without testing them, can turn out to be very costly. Paint will protect against such losses, but it must be given a chance.

APPLYING PAINT

To brush or spray is the leading question in paint application. One is usually more efficient. Seldom do the choices have equal merits.

Potentially, spraying has the edge where risks of product contamination, damage to equipment, and air carries are at a minimum. The method is also to be considered in vinyl applications and when fast driers, like aluminum, are to be used. Rough surfaces such as concrete, cinder and concrete block, brickwork, masonry, places inaccessible to the man with a brush, or surfaces where brushing would be difficult are generally suited to spraying.   So are clusters of beams or intricate mazes of piping, even though extra costs for protection of nearby areas are involved.

In all these situations the basic concepts of quality painting, which is another way of saying the most economical approach, should not be ignored.   Surfaces must be thoroughly cleaned.   If they are not, spraying, which normally results in thinner coatings, is likely to prove unsatisfactory when lasting qualities are considered, resulting in higher costs than anticipated.

The amount of additional time, if any, required to move protective cloths must also be weighed.   This consideration can sometimes favor the brush.   Preparing and shifting protective means can be expensive, and the amount of it necessary for spraying vs. brushing must be taken into account when costing.

Air currents, even mild ones, can play peculiar tricks with atomized spray particles. The mist can whisk through corridors, swirl up elevator shafts, leaving no trace of passage, and then bathe with paint machinery, products, or walls several floors or many feet away.

Until one of these remote spottings is actually experienced, it is hard to believe the damage or trouble that can ensue.   But it is these quirks that make it imperative that all spray-work sections be completely sealed off.

Outside wind carries are just as eccentric.   They may skip an automobile within 100 yards and mottle another a mile away.   Then trouble arises.   When it comes up, the industrial contractor pays off quickly.

Maintenance engineers should keep that in mind because the owner of a spray-dotted automobile or house can make a loud squawk that will fall on sympathetic ears.   Accusing fingers will point toward those doing the painting, which is bad from a public-relations standpoint.   And the public-relations angle is not to be lightly treated in these days of tight competition for good will and subsequent sales— direct or indirect.

Aside from drift, there are other factors to be considered when spraying is contemplated.   In general, the spray gun does not apply as much paint as brushing. Nor, except in the case of quick driers, where lapping is avoided, does the gun contribute toward an even coating layer.

The operator must also be well versed in spraying's limitations.   To cite one, the nozzle must be as close as possible to right angles with the surface to do a good job. If it isn't, the coating will vary in thickness, requiring maintenance and repainting that might have been avoided.

Moreover, a spray man may not check surfaces for cleanliness as carefully as the brush man.   The latter is keenly aware of the surface to be coated with the next stroke and is likely to stop and remove matter that will interfere with a good bond between coating and surface.

The gun man is tempted to keep moving and is likely to open the air trigger and blow the surface down.   Too often that does not remove the cause of future trouble, grease and other undesirable substances.

It should also be kept in mind that, in cases where spraying appears indicated, as when quick driers are used, the coating is reasonably sure to be thinner than brush applications.   Management then gets a nicer-looking job but less protective coating. In the case of warehouse interiors that would not matter.   The large unbroken surfaces can be quickly gone over with a minimum of protection against drifts, and the surfaces do not usually need to be highly resistant against deteriorating agents.

Unless spraying clearly meets conditions, as outlined, it is well to pause and think out the situation before reaching a decision.   Like any composition of paint, the gun is not a universal answer to coating applications.

When any doubt exists as to the method, use the brush.   It is basically sound, and no other medium has yet supplanted bristles as transfer agents for conveying paint to a surface.

COLOR

Color, in the right places and in the right combinations, has become an important phase of industrial painting.   Management may become disturbed by the suggestion that main offices be done in pink, rose, and yellow; at the idea of mocha ceilings or walls and ceilings a flat maroon; but experience has proved the worth of such combinations under the proper circumstances.

The hard-headed, practical business approach was once: "Paint it any color that will last and won't show dirt." The modern, hard-headed, practical business approach is: "Paint it in the proper color harmony that will result in maximum benefits."

Color harmony is an answer to some of management's headaches. In brief, a good industrial painting contractor, who is fully aware of color values, can redo a drab interior and exterior (provided that deterioration hasn't advanced to the point where paint itself is valueless) and accomplish one or more of the following:

Reduce labor turnover.
Cut absenteeism.
Increase worker efficiency.
Boost accuracy or the percentage of finished work that meets inspection standards.
Reduce worker dissatisfaction.

The medical profession recognizes the value of color harmony in relation to human emotions and reactions. Modern hospitals are outstanding examples of that concept. Today's version makes maximum utilization of color to create pleasant surroundings in contrast with the starkness of hospitals of 20 years ago.

In the industrial field, some actual examples will demonstrate the value of proper color harmony.

A cracker manufacturer in Detroit was troubled by rapid worker turnover among the office girls. Our representative learned of the difficulty while making a routine call. Color harmony was suggested as a possible answer.

Management went for the idea of doing over the cafeteria in fancy effects bordering on night-club trimmings. But management balked when pink, rose, and yellow were suggested for the main office instead of the conventional greens. If management hadn't been so desperate over labor troubles, they might never have given in, but finally they agreed.

Within a week after the painters moved out, girls who had been reporting to their desks wearing middy blouses, sweaters, and bobby sox were coming to work dressed up. The plant's troubles in securing and retaining girl employees dropped sharply.

Color can also make for better housekeeping. When dirt is easily visible, the inclination is to cause less of it or clean what is present. A color job on the equipment in a machine shop made the mechanics almost pettish in protecting the equipment from handmarks and smudges that had to be wiped off or else look unsightly.

Sometimes color can cut down on artificial lighting. This was demonstrated in painting two large work areas, each about 300 by 1,200 ft and well windowed, in an airplane plant on the Eastern seaboard.

Neither room had a partition in it. Each rose to 20 ft where hung the maze of beams, girders, pipes, and everything else that goes into an industrial plant. The ceiling and its maze were painted a soft light green, walls ivory. The resultant diffusion gave much more light at working levels and reduced the need for artificial lighting.

Sometimes there can be too much light. That was the case in the executive office of a well-known cigar manufacturer in Philadelphia. After considerable study, it was proposed that ceilings be painted a dark soft green, two walls in light green and two in ivory. Management was aghast. No—absolutely no—was their stand. After much persuasion, they finally agreed to a trial. They were so pleased that, when the offices were repainted, the same color scheme was used.

The ceiling tone caused pipes, ducts, and beams to recede and, simultaneously, killed glare from highlighting on the broken surfaces. The ivory was for the window wall, always the darkest in the room, and for the wall behind the desks. The light green was used on the wall facing the desks and the wall on the right.

Painting walls and ceilings a flat maroon may appear to be a radical step, but it worked in the case of a laundry marking room. For accuracy and speed, it was essential that all outside glare be eliminated and the machine lamps be used as the sole source of illumination. Within a week after the paint job was completed, production increased as much as 10 per cent.

Mocha was used on high ceilings to lower them and then pale green to raise others in the same building so that both appeared the same height when, in fact, there was 3 ft difference.

These are only a few of hundreds of examples where color harmony had definite beneficial results. It is unfortunate that no ready guide for the use of colors can be given, because each plant, office, and business has its own particular problems.

However, the need for color can be determined if these principles are kept in mind:

1. Color can reduce eyestraining glare in favor of light diffusion.
2. It can be used to focus worker attention on operating parts of machines and, in the right combinations, give the workers' eyes rest areas for eye relaxation.
3. Color can be used to give high visibility to danger areas; it can create pleasant surroundings for workers in lieu of drabness accompanied by lowered efficiency.
4. Color can make low ceilings appear higher and do away with that "bearing-down" feeling often created by overhanging beams, girders, pipes, etc.
5. Dark areas can be lightened and those overly bright dimmed; unsightly obstructions can be made to blend in with surroundings and machinery can be toned into a harmonious whole instead of appearing as a series of unsightly shapes.
6. If recreation or eating areas are provided for workers, they should not appear to be part of the plant but should encourage relaxation so that employees go back to their duties refreshed.
7. Color can be used to create an air of cleanliness which, in turn, will encourage cleanliness.
8. Cool color combinations can engender among workers a feeling of lower temperatures in work areas where heat must of necessity be high.

Finally, good color harmony is impressive to visitors. They might not be aware of the reason for the effect, but if it's favorable, they tend to react accordingly.

Along with management's greater cognizance of values inherent to harmonious interiors has come the realization that outside appearances are worth attention where feasible. The nature of some plants makes all but utilitarian painting impractical, but many others can be made pleasing to the eye.

In some instances, these steps may be forced on management, even to the extent of landscaping the grounds. That has been caused by the trend of industry to move to the outskirts of large cities where zoning laws may be in force.

Sometimes industry has been rebuffed when it tried to move into the fringe of residential districts. In other cases changes in zoning were made only when industry submitted to review boards detailed information, including landscaping, pertaining to the outward appearance of the plants and full assurances they would not be an eyesore.

Where management, of its own initiative, has made exteriors as pleasing in appearance as practical two benefits have accrued.

One is better employee morale. Workers, entering a drab plant, tend to experience a letdown, an oh, well—same old thing again today feeling. By contrast a neat, pleasant-looking plant fosters a feeling of pride among workers and they are not so grim over thoughts of the day's toil.

The second dividend pertains to public relations. There can be no question that the trim-looking plant creates a better public impression than a less sightly one. If management depends upon public acceptance of its products for business, that's an important consideration in these days when travel is almost a fetish with people. Now thousands may pass a plant in a given period where only a few years ago the count might only be in hundreds or less. That makes a good-looking industrial layout a first-rate advertising medium. Good looks foster good will.

PRODUCT CONTAMINATION

In plants where materials capable of absorbing odors are processed, painting becomes highly specialized. Examples are food, dairy, baking, cigar, and similar establishments.

Even paint film that has dried can be troublesome if the original compound was not the proper one for conditions. Minute flaking can cause product contamination, as one large rubber company learned.

When painting and production must proceed simultaneously, paint fumes may also prove undesirable. Many persons, especially women and girls, are made uncomfortable and even ill.

These problems can be resolved but only by those well versed in paint composition, application, and suitability for given conditions. The answer lies in odor-masking agents or deodorants. These are varied and their use must be rigidly controlled and properly blended in with other paint ingredients if the finished job is to be satisfactory.

A fraction of an ounce to the gallon of paint is all that is needed in most instances. The amount used must be held to a minimum because odor-masking agents tend to linger and sour, defeating the original purpose for their use. They can also mess up the paint formula.

The right agents, properly used, permit painting under circumstances formerly prohibitive because of product contamination or illness among female workers.

However, odor-masking ingredients remain in the field of industrial painting contractors and their chemists, since each job must be individually treated. In fact, before the main painting starts, usually several test areas are coated to determine the effectiveness of the composition.

Finally, in no circumstances should the spray gun be employed on any areas that cannot be absolutely sealed off from absorbent materials used in the plant's manufacturing processes. The most effective of odor-masking agents will not prevent contamination where even the slighest air current can carry atomized particles of paint.

PAINTING VS. PRODUCTION

Keeping surfaces adequately protected with coatings must frequently be reconciled with plant work schedules. If production can be modified or temporarily halted, normal painting routine can be followed.

When it is the other way about, and painting procedures must be adapted to production, the ensuing problems are invariably complex. They can be resolved, except in rare instances, but it takes careful planning.

Progressive management is aware that it derives maximum returns from paint that is applied at the proper time. But too often management is not aware of what can be accomplished without undue hindrance to production. Then protective coatings may be permitted to weaken beyond the economical point before preventive steps are taken.

The alternative, and correct, approach lies in cooperation between management, production supervisors, and those responsible for the painting. Jointly, they can work out a feasible plan.

Prime responsibility for advance thinking rests with management. It misses an opportunity to save money when aware that department(s) or plant shutdowns, other maintenance work, equipment installations, or relay outs are imminent and the need for painting in the affected areas is not checked in advance. Obviously, painting can be done at such times more economically than when production is underway.

When shutdowns are not contemplated, management, production supervisors, and those responsible for the painting can arrive at the next most economical conclusions by friendly discussions of problems in their respective fields.

The painting representative should tell management the period when application of coatings would be most desirable from the standpoint of existing physical conditions that might otherwise balk a good job. Management must then decide when, in that period, production interference would be at a minimum.

It is then up to the painting representative and production supervisors to work out a harmonious plan. If they are conscientious in their efforts, it is amazing what can be accomplished. Experienced painters will come up with a precise schedule that takes into consideration production's difficulties.

Just what can be done is best illustrated by an actual example from our case book.

A large rubber plant was in need of repainting. Shutdowns were out of the question. Worse, production had to be maintained at a peak. Industrial paint technicians first surveyed the entire plant. They found some areas that needed attention immediately. Others needed it but not so urgently. Finally, there was a third category that almost needed painting but it could be deferred.

A resurvey was made and each area, in the order of need, was calculated in terms of man-hours necessary to do the job. Then the various departments were checked. Some worked 24 hr a day, 6 days a week, and were accessible to painters only on Sundays. Others worked two shifts a day, 6 days a week. Next were those which worked one shift, 6 days a week. Finally, there were the warehouse and shipping areas where it didn't matter how many hours they were in operation because painting could be done at any time without interference.

When all the basic information was gathered, the painting representatives went to work on plans. Their problem was to paint the plant and keep painters busy a full day without slowing plant production. The answer was startling.

The painting schedule called for a 3-year job, based on keeping a fixed number of painters working at the plant.

At times they were to be split up, painting only in such places as would not interfere with production, while covering those areas most in need of painting. During short shutdown periods—some instances 1 hr in 24—the entire crew would work in a given area. On Sundays, a large force was brought in to finish up areas that could be only partially covered without a shutdown.

The key point, in the over-all plant, was the provision for a given number of painters, the maximum that could be kept constantly busy, on hand. Then, when the opportunity to do a spot task came up, they were available. Lost time was thus held to a minimum.

Admittedly, the example represents an extreme case but it should be noted management received a first-class job at minimum costs under highly adverse conditions. At the same time, the job was done in harmonious colors—sage green and ivory. Over-all results were so satisfactory that we were called in when repainting became necessary.

The basic principle of keeping a key crew working, without production interference, is also sound prior to the time management knows a shutdown for vacations or other reasons is impending.

If the advance men can be kept busy without production interference, preliminaries will be out of the way when the full crew reports, reducing to a minimum the lost-time factor inherent at the beginning of a job.

In brief, "planned painting" costs less and makes possible the third "P"—"production"—eliminating the "versus" between it and painting.

SPECIAL PAINTING

Experience has proved each industrial plant is an individual painting problem, and no two can be done in exactly the same manner for best results. In addition, there are special situations, and basic guides have been given for some of them, under Frequency of Painting.

There are, of course, many others and a few can be pin-pointed. For instance, there is no good heat-resistant paint in green or blue. Therefore, they should not be considered in the painting of ducts and stacks that get hot, boilers, adjacent piping, boiler doors, buck stays, and other places where heat is a consideration.

In lieu of expert recommendations, aluminum paint is a good choice. Its varnish vehicle rates on a par with enamels. Another good selection is often a light pearl gray in a semialkyd oil-base paint with semigloss finish. Those portions of the same system which are not subject to heat should be painted a contrasting enamel of dark grey or green.

There are special coatings for stacks that will withstand high temperatures, but when aluminum or other light color is used, a broad band of black should encircle the top to camouflage smoke and fume discoloration.

Cranes and similar pieces of mobile equipment, stairways, and other places where danger lurks are usually best painted high-visibility yellow.

There should be no reluctance about colors on metal railings. The top rail can easily be black so that soiling from hands won't show. The middle can be safety yellow and the remainder gray.

Fire lines should be red or red bands should be put on them for ready identification.

Generally, aluminum and light-colored lead and oil paint give good protection and excellent heat reflection on tanks.

Whitewash is one of the best heat reflectors among paints and some oil companies use it on top of their tanks. The metal is given a rust-preventive painting first; then the tops are whitewashed several times a year. However, whitewash looks messy when it begins to break loose.

Under Frequency of Painting, there are examples of special painting tasks such as those requiring maintenance before the main body of paint is redone. There are others in this classification.

The sunny side of a building is one. Southeast exposures receive considerably more sun during the day. That usually means the bottoms of sash, sills, and frames, for 3 in. up, be they wood or metal, may have to be done over every 2 or 3 years, although the main body of paint will last double that time.

The cause is winter snow and ice. They lie on the frames and thaw during warm sunny days. The water then runs down to the sills and recakes when caught by the chill of late afternoon or nighttime cold.

These alternate thaws and freezes split paint surfaces; water seeps into wood or lies against the metal, and the result is more damaging than if there were no paint at all.

Moisture exposed to air will dry, but once underneath the paint, it cannot dry. It remains to cause rot or rust.

A large baking concern discovered attention to these special conditions cannot be ignored. Now the sills on the sunny side of the plant are done every third year. The rest of the frames are painted every fifth year. But, on the shady side of the building, painted sash are good for an average of 7 years when the whole exterior is repainted.

Metal that expands or contracts rapidly, because of heat and cold, must also be watched carefully for splits and curls in the paint film.

Also to be checked for the need of special painting are all places inside and out where metal comes in contact with concrete or masonry. Outside, where the two join and meet weather, there is a chemical reaction. Inside this is abetted by condensation. Such portions of metal may have to be repainted two or three times more frequently than the remainder.

"Special painting" is not only excellent maintenance but pays dividends in the form of lowered overhead. Essentially it is protecting the chain by fortifying the weakest links.

INSPECTIONS

There are several references under Frequency of Painting, concerning the value of inspections. What follows here could have been added to those observations except that the subject is so important it deserves separate treatment. Periodic inspection of all surfaces is the surest and best method of determining the need for painting. The key phrase is *periodic inspection of all surfaces*.

To be of value, such inspections cannot be made casually or by an amateur. A good paint inspector must have these qualities:

1. Practical (not necessarily technical) knowledge of the effects of time, wear, and corrosion on paint film and surfaces. Preferably, the man should come from the engineering department. He should know the cause of all defects that are found so that he can assist in prescribing the cure through proper surface preparation and choice of coatings. In this last respect, consultation with a technical expert is frequently advisable.

2. An inquisitive mind, never satisfied with superficial appearance, that readily absorbs detail and is imbued with a passion for thoroughness.
3. Physical ability to crawl around in places not easily accessible. These include beams, roof structures, tank grillage, mazes of pipes, and all other places difficult to examine. He must not be afraid of getting dirty. Like a mouse, the good inspector must run around the foundations and up to the rafters, poking into remote corners and hidden places.
4. He must have authority, at least on the junior-executive level, and, above all, the confidence of management to the point that, when he says painting is needed, management is willing to accept the diagnosis.

A man with these qualifications needs few tools. Four will do:

1. A sharp penknife for checking putty, calking, and paint blisters and to probe wood to determine if life is still present.
2. A putty knife for scraping or pushing aside dirt and dust to examine the surface for paint failure.
3. A lightweight tack hammer for inspecting pipes, vessels, tanks, roofs, and the like. Under a gentle tapping, many a surface which looks good turns out to be paper thin. A heavy hand should not be used—ruptured surfaces and dangerous leaks may result.
4. Work sheets or other provisions for making notes as the inspection progresses. Notations should be precise and no details left to memory.

Add to these items the equipment needed to reach heights and ensure safety and the inspector is ready for his task.

A good inspector must be reconciled to paper work. His running notes must be transferred to records that clearly show the status of every surface in the plant. These would fall into three categories and possibly a fourth:

1. Bad areas that need painting at once.
2. Areas that show signs of trouble but not to the point that would justify immediate painting.
3. Areas in good shape.

All three classifications are important, especially the last one, although it is frequently not made a matter of record. However, without the information, the over-all picture is incomplete and continues to leave much to guesswork or memory, thus depreciating the value of inspections.

Information under item 2 should be transferred to a card-index file which then serves as a supplementary tickler to the regular inspection schedule. That assures close checks on doubtful areas.

Possibly a fourth item might be added to the basic three. It would comprise painted places that should have been left unpainted and protected with penetrating oil, light grease film, or both. They would include sprinkler heads, fire-escape joints and hinges, valve stems, etc., also paint on floor columns that are constantly being bumped by mobile equipment and the paint film broken. That's waste.

The columns should be encased in concrete throughout the length of collision points.

Signs of paint failure are given in Table 5-1. To them must be added two other critical conditions that inspectors should not ignore.

When small hairline cracks appear in unpainted exterior masonry surfaces, squalling will take place unless the situation is corrected. The cure is proper painting with masonry primer and a finish coat. Later, when the gloss goes dead, the surface should be repainted before excessive powdering takes place.

Another critical condition often overlooked until too late is interior rusting of metal under layers of dirt or product dust. Since rain cannot cause streaking, it is up to the inspector to ferret out the trouble. If scraping discloses the telltale signs of rusting, painting is imperative.

To be of maximum value, inspections should be made at regular time intervals.

Table 5-1. Symptoms and Causes of Deterioration

Symptom	How to recognize it	Cause
Alligatoring........	Looks like an alligator hide (cracks may or may not reach down to base surface)	Covering a relatively soft coat with a relatively hard one
Blistering..........	Unsightly blisters that usually break open and fall off	Water seeping from base surface pushes off the paint film. Sometimes skin drying of the paint is too rapid
Bubbling..........	Bubbles on the surface (usually wood)	Moisture or sap in unseasoned wood rises to surface and collects in bubbles
Chalking..........	Premature dull chalky appearance (all paint chalks mildly with age)	Paint may have been poorly formulated, or paint was applied over a badly weathered and porous base surface which absorbed oil out of new paint
Checking..........	Paint film is cracked open in spots	Shrinkage of film and breaking at weaker portions. This is due to uneven coating and poor bonding qualities (between coats or finish coating and primer); also due to improper compounding where certain ingredients did not dry in proper sequence, sometimes brought about by too much solvent or not enough, etc.
Chipping (also known as flaking)	Paint film completely broken away	Paint film lacks adhesion. Usually base surface expands or shrinks at a different rate than film and film pulls free. Sudden changes in temperature may cause it. If paint is properly made, only reason for chipping is preparation of surface, provided it is applied at proper temperature, degree of humidity, etc.
Crazing...........	Interlacing "checking" in a gridlike pattern	Same cause as checking
Discoloration.......	Off-shade or dark spots	Many reasons, some involving impurities under paint film, such as rust, too much active lime in plaster or cement, or resin or sap in woodwork. Or exterior attack from fumes or gas
Spalling..........	Areas of brick or concrete crack, split, and break off	Moisture seeps into fine hair cracks and expands when it freezes
Wrinkling.........	Looks like a grained leather surface	Improper drying of paint; coat was too thick or failed to dry properly because weather changed or job was done in unseasonable weather
Hidden rusting.....	Streaked surfaces	Failure to clean properly and flood with paint hard-to-reach corners, angles, trusses, especially those with angles back to back, and narrow intervening spaces between steel members
Peeling............	Paint film peels off cleanly. Chipping of large pieces	Moisture getting behind paint film through exposed ends, condensation in wall space or break of putty in sash; failure of calking compound or cracks in the sash-frame-wall joints

These vary so that each inspector must determine a schedule that meets conditions at his plant.

Best way to tackle the problem is set up an inspection routine based on the worst prevailing conditions. Then, by working backward to surfaces with greatest durability, the complete plant-inspection interval can be ascertained. Meanwhile critical areas are kept under surveillance. At the same time, a schedule is being developed for surfaces that fail most quickly.

When assembling data for an inspecting schedule, several things should be kept in mind.

Interior inspections can be made at any time of the year but should not be attempted in hot weather. Heat makes the task so disagreeable that even the conscientious inspector will skip the tough spots.

Exterior inspections should be made only in good weather and for the same reason. Excessive heat or cold discourages thoroughness. Springtime is best if it works in with the correct time interval.

And finally, most plants don't realize the value of a follow-up inspection after a painting job. Postpainting inspections forestall false reliance on inadequate surface protection from poor or careless painting jobs. Again, those hard-to-get-at spots should receive the most careful scrutiny on checkup inspections.

PROTECTION OF PRODUCTS AND EQUIPMENT

The potentials of masking agents or deodorants, where products may absorb odors during or after painting, are explained under Product Contamination.

The improper paint for conditions, or paint films permitted to age where powdering or flaking takes place can also cause product contamination.

Aside from odor, both absorbent and nonabsorbent products and equipment must be protected against contamination and damage by paint, or dirt, throughout the painting process. The drop cloth is still the standard in this respect.

Where delicate machinery is involved, it should be wrapped with paper before it is covered with a drop sheet. Perhaps additional support for the covering may be necessary, since drop sheets are heavy and grow more so during a job. They also become dirtier and therefore must be placed in such a manner that dirt will not drift under the edges.

When machinery and the like cannot be directly covered because production is underway, the drop sheets must be suspended or arranged in such a way as to form a protective barrier that will stop paint and dirt from doing harm. For brush painting, the sheets may overlap. That is not true when the spray gun is used. Single sheets that can be drawn up or otherwise placed to form draftless painting areas must be employed.

If the use of drop sheets is carefully planned, costs are held down. One placement to take care of both cleaning and the subsequent painting is obviously more economical in labor charges than two placements.

Throughout both operations—cleaning and painting—drops should be so arranged that dirt or paint cannot fall below. Aside from damage to plant equipment and products, there is the possibility of damage to humans. That's especially true of eyes.

And now a word of caution. Never stack or fold drop sheets unless the paint on them is absolutely dry. To do otherwise is an open invitation for spontaneous combustion to take place.

SAFETY

The plant that uses its own personnel or hires for wages outside men for painting needs supervisors that are definitely safety-conscious. If a large force is contemplated, an insurance safety engineer should be called in before work starts. Afterward may be too late.

On painting jobs, insurance statistics show the common ladder leads to more injuries than any other type of equipment.   It is debatable whether this is due to frequency of use or carelessness because of a ladder's uncomplicated construction.

Unless someone is around to stop them, men will persist in mounting ladders that are not held by another man or anchored or tied in at the base.   To reach greater heights, they will place ladders too straight.   To cover an extra few inches, they will lean out to the side.   And no man should ever stand on any of the top three rungs of a ladder regardless of its type.

No repaired ladder should ever be used.   The same applies to those showing signs of deterioration such as minute cracks and splits.

Ladders used or stored in the presence of intense heat or excessive dampness or where chemical or acid fumes can make contact should be examined very carefully.

Any ladder that is stored for awhile should be checked by experienced personnel. In the case of wood, a good carpenter should be able to detect signs of weakness or possible failure.

Rigging and use of scaffolding are not for novices.   Experts should be obtained. Most industrial painting contractors keep several such men on their permanent payroll to protect painters and persons below.

Again, repairs are to be suspected and all wooden components should be carefully examined by an experienced man or a good carpenter.

Rope that has been used around acid, caustic, or chemical fumes should be discarded.   Rope should never be stored where rats can get to the strands and should be kept where air can circulate freely around it.   Rope that has seen service should be scrapped after 1 year regardless of its condition.

There are times and places when safety nets should be strung to protect workmen above, personnel below, and materials.   Only nets more than adequate for the job should be used.

Swing falls, blocks, and all metal used to support painters should be carefully watched for weaknesses, and metal should be periodically tested for fatigue.

Sufficient warning and danger signs should be placed when men are working overhead.

Men wearing respirators or goggles in a spraying operation—and they should be wearing them—should have life lines or safety lines strung.   A painter with fogged goggles and no guide rope can easily step off into space.

Men painting from a plank should never be allowed to reach beyond its edge. And the planks should be kept clean.   Accumulated paint should be burned or scraped off.   Clean planks and scaffolds are safer if otherwise in good shape.

Danger also lurks in spots that are not so obvious.   In a plant where floor temperatures may be 70 to 80, it might be 100 to 110 close under a 50-ft ceiling.   Then ceiling ventilation must be provided.   Heat and paint fumes, when mixed, create a toxic condition that puts not only painters but also persons below in jeopardy.

At times, ventilating fans aren't sufficient and gas masks and goggles must be worn. That is especially true of some paints with the newer vehicles and thinners in them. In confined areas, the fumes are lung searing, and no matter how many fans were turned on the men, they would not be protected.   Under such conditions, masks that will filter out the harmful fumes are a must.

Where scale and rust that have been exposed to acid or caustics are to be chipped, goggles must be worn for eye protection.

Dust and certain fumes can be dangerous agents for flash fires and explosions. Wherever there is a high concentration of dust, in conjunction with dry conditions, danger exists.

Thick accumulations of dust atop ducts and pipes high in the ceiling require care from sparking that would set off a flash.   In those places, wood-handled dust brooms should be used for cleaning.

Greater danger lurks where sulfur or tobacco dust is present.   In the air, unless highly concentrated, there is not much danger, but when spread in the thin film on a dry surface, they command respect.   Then nonsparking tools, scrapers, hammers, and wire brushes are required.   These are made of monel metal or beryllium copper and are nonsparking, nonmagnetic, and noncorrosive.

The same tools should always be used in a chemical plant or where there might be illuminating- or natural-gas leakage, gasoline fumes, or similar hazards. In addition, the men must not have steel in their shoes. Sewed rubber or leather soles should be required.

Compressors and other motor equipment must be continuously serviced to make sure they are not becoming fire risks.

Soiled paint rags can easily cause spontaneous combustion. They should be put outside of buildings and in sealed containers at the close of every working period. For the same reason, drop sheets should not be folded or stacked unless the paint on them is thoroughly dry or all loose dirt is removed.

Thinners and paints should be kept in sealed containers and never exposed near flames or where fumes can drift toward open fire.

THE PAINTERS

Best returns to management from industrial painting are derived when proper ingredients are applied by skilled workmen under competent administration and supervision.

Giving a man a can of paint and brush doesn't make him a good painter, and if he isn't, management loses.

No large plant should be without its skilled maintenance crew. There are always retouch, clean-up, and emergency jobs to be done. That is good maintenance and of value to management.

It is the major periodic jobs that raise a question as to who is to do them. Basically, there are three answers—all with gimmicks. There is the choice of (1) keeping a large force of painters steadily on the payroll, (2) augmenting a small regular painting crew temporarily, and (3) calling in an outside contractor.

To keep a large force busy, management frequently, and in fact with few exceptions, must create work, thereby increasing maintenance costs.

To augment a small key crew temporarily, management must assume considerable in the way of responsibility. It must provide the technical and proficient supervisory personnel; handle labor relations, including the unions; plan safety precautions and insurance; secure, maintain, and store extra equipment; make all purchases; and, finally, assume all responsibility for the quality of the finished job.

If outside contractors are decided upon, management must still tread circumspectly. Going into the competitive market and obtaining a "firm" bid may appear a sure way of knowing the cost. But, and it is a big "but," straight competitive bidding is likely to put management into the hands of a contractor willing to skimp to show a profit.

By adequate inspection throughout the job, management, of course, can insist that proper standards be met. Sooner or later that means wrangling and more corner cutting that may be easily detected.

On a cost-plus form of contract, there is no incentive for the contractor to get the job done as economically as possible without sacrificing quality. The more it costs, the more he makes. Again management must depend on the integrity of the contractor.

A third approach lies between these two. It is the guaranteed-cost contract. Here the contractor tells management the job will not exceed a certain figure. If the contractor makes a mistake and goes over that amount, he takes the licking. If under, management gains. Since no contractor likes to bid himself out of reasonably profitable business, he keeps the guaranteed-cost figure competitive, at the same time making provisions for a quality job. That means the contractor must be highly experienced. His organization must include technical experts and top supervisory personnel. Otherwise, his guaranteed cost bid would be out of line, one way or the other.

Still, management is in the hands of the contractor but not to the same extent as the other two bid approaches. He knows the maximum figure to be paid. That's a settled issue. Next, the quality of the work can be checked, and if it is subpar, he can insist on corrections without encountering the same resistance as on the low-bid contract.

If management has selected the right contractor, inspections will be satisfactory and relations amicable. If things go exceptionally well with the contractor, management will receive a quality job at less cost than anticipated. If unforeseen difficulties arise, management still gains because the experienced, reliable contractor will endeavor to do a quality job at less cost than anticipated. If unforeseen difficulties arise, management still gains because the experienced, reliable contractor will endeavor to do a quality job at less, or no profit, to gain the customers' good will.

In essence, when management is dealing with industrial painting contractors, it is well to weigh how long a concern has been in business, how varied its experience, and the volume of business they do. A high score on all three counts can be achieved only through work that gives management the best returns on money expended.

Chapter 6

FLOORS OTHER THAN CONCRETE[1]

By CARL G. WYDER[2]
Senior Maintenance Editor
Factory
New York, N.Y.

Floors to be covered in this chapter include wood block, hardwood (maple, birch, beech, oak), metal-armored, mastic, oxychloride (magnesite), brick and quarry tile, resilient (linoleum, asphalt tile, vinyl tile, rubber tile, cork tile). Details on each will be given under the section headings Characteristics, Selection, Installation, and Maintenance.

CHARACTERISTICS

Wood Block. Short lengths of wood are set on end (i.e., end grain is exposed). Blocks usually are treated with creosote, set in mastic. Joints are sealed with cold asphalt. This type of floor is rugged. It will take heavy trucking and heavy impact blows in stride. While blocks may work loose or crack, they are easily replaced. The unusual advantage is that, if electrical duct or other service line must be run from one point to another, a row of blocks may be removed to provide a raceway that can be covered with a steel plate. At least until grease- or oil-coated, these floors are slip-resistant and offer good traction. And deep sanding or scarifying will give the floor a new start whenever necessary. Maintenance costs, by and large, are low.

Limitations? Yes. Unless properly sealed, blocks may swell. Dirt, grease, or water may work between joints and loosen the floor. Unless the joints between the blocks are tight, the edges of the blocks will wear first—resulting in a tough-to-truck-over cobblestone surface.

Hardwood. Maple, oak, birch, and beech are commonly used. They come in either strip form or squares, usually with a tongue-and-groove joint to speed installation and guarantee tight joints. These dense, rugged woods provide a wear-resistant surface; and their high strength-to-weight ratio often helps solve a remodeling problem where dead load has to be watched. With various new finishes (including urethanes) available, hardwoods are capable of taking far more of a beating than a few years ago; and with a sturdy and rigid subfloor, they will carry heavy-handling equipment with no trouble. If appearance is a factor, add a few points for hardwood.

Cost is the number one limitation for most factory installations where heavy-duty design is a must. While installation cost is relatively high, maintenance cost after original finishing is comparatively low. With modern coatings now available,

[1] For much of the information in this chapter indebtedness is acknowledged to Asphalt Institute, New York; Asphalt Tile Institute, New York; Maple Flooring Manufacturers Association, Chicago; National Bureau of Standards, Washington; Tile Manufacturers Association, New York.
[2] The author is now retired.

exposure to water (once a serious problem) today causes fewer difficulties. Wood should not be used, however, in wet areas.

Metal-armored. Some form of metal matting, plates, or interlocked bars is laid either in or on a subfloor. Suitable subfloors are mastic, concrete, and wood. Available in a wide variety of shapes and metals.

Big advantage: ruggedness. Most manufacturers will defy you to destroy their floor—and they're relatively safe in doing so. If metal is allowed to project above the surface, slip resistance and traction are good. Resistance to oil, grease, acids, and temperature is as good as the metal used. The armor itself can be used as a grating.

Disadvantages: Unless exclusively rubber-tired handling equipment is used, it will be noisy. Some types of armor are rough enough to slow handling. And first cost—since a base or subfloor is needed—will probably be high.

Mastic. A black monolithic floor made up of asphalt, silica fiber, silica sand and pebbles, and carbon. Normally a poured type of floor, the material is also available in blocks, planks, and sheets.

If a good installation job is done, there should be no trouble with deterioration. Any repairs should be easy. Can be used over less-than-ideal base. Skid resistance is good. Tends to collect and show dirt, making it less easy to clean.

Cold mastic—a type that is installed cold—is subject to acid attack, and the combination of too much water and heavy trucking may cause trouble. Hot mastic loses its excellent acid-resistant properties when it gets too hot, and may soften to an undesirable extent. If oil and grease are a problem, be sure to get a mastic that has good resistance.

Oxychloride (Magnesite). Wood or silica floor fillers and hard aggregates are bound together by a magnesium oxychloride cement. Result: a flooring that is easy to maintain, does not dust, has a high strength-to-weight ratio. Available in forms for heavy duty, high slip resistance, nonsparking qualities. Installation is comparatively easy; can be ready for use in 48 hr, does not require damp curing.

Where wet conditions are combined with heavy traffic, this floor is not a good bet. Stains are difficult to remove. Cost is higher than concrete. And, if high humidity is common, the floor has a tendency to become "slimy."

Brick and Quarry Tile. Consists of specially baked clay—in tile or brick form—laid in mastic with mortared joints. Is probably the number one choice for high resistance to acids or alkalies, other corrosives, oils, greases, or water—though to be top-notch it must be carefully installed. Steam cleaning and other harsh cleaning treatments are taken in stride.

In return for this special advantage, expect a high first cost. And the maintenance force must watch for cracks that will allow corrosives to seep through to the mastic base. Some types are slippery when wet; others will crack if given too hard treatment by handling equipment or impact loads.

Resilient Materials. These floors include the well-known linoleum, asphalt tile, vinyl tile, rubber tile, and cork tile. All have their specific advantages and disadvantages. All can be had in a wide variety of attractive forms and are resilient and noise-deadening. None is recommended for heavy trucking, and all dent under sharp or heavy loads.

Linoleum is probably the cheapest, but its protective finish won't stand up under strong cleaners. Moisture seeping through joints may destroy adhesive. Resistance to corrosive agents is not good.

Asphalt tile can be put down over concrete that is subject to dampness. And, like any tile floor, replacement of individual tiles is easy and inexpensive. Resistance to corrosive materials is not good, and it will deteriorate in extreme sunlight.

Vinyl tile, vinyl-asbestos, and closely allied materials have significantly improved resistance to abrasion. Easy to keep clean. Most types have good resistance to heat; fair resistance to corrosive materials. Cost is a little more than for other resilient tiles.

Rubber tile is resistant to many acids. But solvents, oils, and greases must be cleaned up immediately if deterioration is to be avoided. Where underfloor moisture is a problem, this is not a good choice.

HOW TO SELECT THE RIGHT FLOOR

Selecting the right floor is a tough job—one of the toughest in planning any new plant or modernization of an existing plant. A mistake in selecting the floor is one of the most costly that can be made. Here are a few suggestions that may help:

Don't assume that the floor throughout the shop has to be all the same type. Traffic conditions, heat conditions, and corrosive conditions vary. There is no reason why the floor shouldn't. Next step, therefore, is to . . .

Make a survey of the floor requirements. One way to do this is to break the shop into areas—machining, heat-treat, plating, assembly, shipping and receiving docks, aisles, corridors, office, cafeteria, employee facilities, and the like.

For each area, list the floor-service requirements. Be specific—"Floor in plating area is subject to such-and-such a concentration of such-and-such a chemical at a temperature of X degrees. Temperature in area is X degrees in summer. All parts delivered by conveyor, so heavy trucking not a factor." Another example: "Aisles in machining area subject to heavy fork-truck traffic—maximum total weight 8,000 pounds. Some steel-wheeled tractors still in use. Traffic must move at top speed, so smooth surface necessary. Heavy-duty cranes in use, floor must be able to stand considerable impact of rough forgings being set down." List everything that would affect floor service. Here is a list to start with:

1. Size of area involved.
2. Type and frequency of traffic. Continuous or infrequent; fast or slow; type of handling equipment—including weight under maximum load, type of wheels.
3. Floor loading. To include standing loads such as machine tools, conveyors, furnaces, and other process equipment—and moving loads. Don't forget loads on conveyors. And be specific—give weight, area of bearing surfaces, and type of load—standing, rolling impact, sliding, other.
4. Exposure to water, chemicals, weather.
5. Appearance required.
6. Cleaning requirements—if the floor must be cleaned with harsh cleaners daily to meet sanitary or safety requirements, you want to know.
7. Any unusual hazards—does the floor in one area have to be sparkproof?
8. Temperature extremes.
9. Grade location—floors under grade are subject to moisture.
10. *Future* use. Don't overlook the possibility that today's light-machining area may be tomorrow's punch-press department. Or that heavy-duty aisles may run through what is now a light-traffic area. Layout changes should be anticipated whenever possible.

Ask for plenty of help in surveying flooring needs. And no one knows the answer to this kind of question better than the plant people. Get details from them. Making sure you get a good floor is everybody's problem. But production men should remember that a poor floor is likely to cause delays, if not damage, in materials handling. The quality-control man should remember that parts bounced over a rough floor will be damaged. And the personnel man will have to answer beefs about slippery surface and fire hazards.

Then match floor to requirements. Here—unless you're an expert—you'll need and should get help. You may want to get all the information you can in the form of literature from manufacturers and associations. They're easy to find. At least you'll know the language.

Then, call in expert help. There are many sources: flooring salesmen, flooring consultants, architects, engineers, and builders. All of them have probably handled similar installations, are likely to find selection relatively easy. But they must know what your problems are. You should talk over, in detail, all the service requirements you checked earlier. They can't be held responsible for mistakes caused by your failure to explain every detail of your service exposure.

Rely on them—but not blindly. Though no salesman from a reputable company will sell you a floor that he knows will fail in service, he can make mistakes.   An engineer may have a "bug" on a certain kind of floor.   If you have the slightest doubt about your expert's advice, be careful.   Ask to see similar floors in plants with similar service conditions.   Or make your own comparison tests—you can probably arrange for several companies with competing products to lay down small test areas in your shop.

Finally, be sure that the person advising you makes clear the maintenance problem involved.   Some floors are easier to maintain than others.   Be sure you know just what kind of maintenance will be involved before you give the go-ahead signal.   Often, an attempt to save money on first cost will result in costly maintenance.

Unreassuring conclusion to these statements on selection: It would be hard to find a shop problem where it will cost you more—in money and headaches—to make a bad mistake.

INSTALLATION

Poor installation is probably the biggest cause of floor-maintenance headaches. The best materials in the world, poorly installed, will result in constant problems. Installation is a job for skilled labor and supervision.   Whether your own maintenance people are doing the job, or you've called in an outside contractor, there are general rules to be followed for installing any floor.

1. Spend enough money to get a good subfloor.   It should be rigid, flat, properly treated to receive the wearing surface.
2. Make specifications rigid.   Most floor manufacturers and flooring associations have detailed specifications available for their floors.   Many architects will insist on their own specifications.   If you feel it's necessary, you can insist on follow-up testing, with penalties up to and including a new floor if the one installed fails to meet specifications.
3. Enforce the specifications.   If your flooring contractor doesn't or won't supply full-time supervision, it's wise for you to hire someone who will.   Often the architect insists that this be part of his job.
4. If finishes are required, be sure they are applied before the floor is put into use. A guide to finishing floors is given in this chapter.
5. Make sure your floor contractor is qualified to install industrial floors.   Ask for references from other plants where he has done similar work.

With those general rules in mind, here is specific information on each of the types of floors covered in this chapter.

Wood Block.   Should be installed on smooth-finished level base.   Don't forget to allow for the depth of the blocks when planning the subfloor (i.e., if 4-in. blocks are to be used, subfloor must be 4 in. below desired finished-floor level).   It's worth the time it takes to remove all ridges or projections in the subfloor.   Give the smooth surface a good cleaning, prime it, and coat with pitch.   If this floor is on or below ground level (which it usually will be) waterproof the subfloor to eliminate as much ground moisture as possible.   If wood-block floors get wet, swelling will result.

The building in which the floor is to be installed should be heated before, during and after installation—to give stabilized temperature conditions.   And the blocks should be stored in the building for as long as possible prior to the installation—so they will stabilize.   They should be stacked in such a way that air can reach all of them—not in a neatly piled tight stack.

In laying the floor, blocks should be laid up tight, though expansion joints should be provided around columns and walls.   A concrete or metal curb should be used to end sections of wood-block flooring.

As with any wood-block floor, finishing is of prime importance.   The floor should be machine-sanded.   It may be finished with a penetrating seal, followed by hot coal-tar pitch to fill joints.   For a clear finish the sanded blocks may be coated with a urethane or epoxy material.   Colored coatings also are available.

Hardwood.   Again, a smooth solid foundation is vital.   Where supported on joists, joist spacing should not exceed about 16 in.

A hardwood-floor installation should be the last building-construction operation—to avoid scratching or marring. The flooring should be stored in the area in which it is to be installed, and that area should be heated. To allow for expansion, don't lay the floor too close to walls and columns—use temporary spacers until the new floor has "stabilized." Use the proper size and type of nails, and plenty of them. The finished floor should be laid down either at right angles or diagonally to the direction of subfloor boards.

Finishing is of top importance. Unless the floor is to be finished immediately, it should be protected with building paper. Sealing is a major problem in itself. Among new materials for finishing hardwood floors in heavy-traffic areas are the urethanes and epoxies. These are surface finishes. They have excellent durability and high gloss and are easy to clean. The Maple Flooring Manufacturers Association (35 East Wacker Drive, Chicago) has a list of approved sealers that is revised every 3 years.

Metal-armored. Again, a smooth level base is needed. And as with wood block, don't forget the thickness of the armor to be used when planning finished height of the floor. If the subfloor is wood, nail it tight and fill in all holes to provide a solid-as-possible bearing surface.

Each manufacturer will have specific instructions for fastening the armoring to the subfloor. Be sure to keep armoring sections level with each other, and fit them together as tightly as possible. No finishing is normally required.

Mastic. To avoid the common problems—cracks, softness, or ruts—make sure that the subfloor is dry at the time of application and that it is free from debris. Of course the subfloor should be structurally sound. If of wood, it should be of double-layer construction.

The installation itself is a job for experienced men—unless you have experience, it's a good idea to call in an outside expert for this type of floor. Make sure that your installer uses carefully graded aggregate of proper size, that the proper proportion of bituminous material to aggregate is used. The surface should be floated to the required smoothness and consistency. And proper slope should be provided to ensure drainage.

Finishing is normally not required, though the surface can be smoothed by rubbing sand or silica dust over it.

Oxychloride (Magnesite). Subfloor preparation is important. If the subfloor is absorbent, it should be wetted down with chloride solution just prior to the installation. If the subfloor is on a grade, the floor should be dampproofed. Oxychloride Cement Association (1832 M St. N.W., Washington 6) will recommend the right one. If this type of floor is to be installed over wood, all loose boards must be replaced, all knots or nail holes must be filled in to provide a solid "leakproof" base, and the floor should be covered with paper and wire mesh.

Number one rule in installing this type of floor: Don't use excessive magnesium chloride solution to make the mix easier to work. This is the cause of the "sweating" or "slimy feeling" sometimes encountered with this type of floor. It needn't happen if proper specifications are used—and you can get them from the Oxychloride Cement Association. The floor should get two hard trowelings; the second should not be done until the surface is fairly well set. Air temperature and circulation should be controlled, and floor should not be poured if temperature is—or is liable to be before floor is set—below 40°F. If oxychloride material has been stored for 60 days or more, ask your supplier to test its quality.

Finishing? Important. All but the conductive type should be coated with low-viscosity penetrating seal. Then a protective cover of water-vapor-permeable material should be put over the newly installed floor. The floor should not be used for at least 48 hr.

Brick and Quarry Tile. Installing this type of floor is no job for an amateur. The subfloor must be smooth, flat, and solid and should be cleaned thoroughly and all cracks filled. If the subfloor is wood, all boards should be nailed down tightly to provide a solid bearing surface.

Since this type of floor is normally used in an area where liquids—water, oils, and greases—are involved, don't forget to slope the floor to drain. If the floor is to be wet continuously or subject to standing water, install a waterproofing membrane. Joints between tiles should be tight.   If corrosive liquids will come in contact with floor, use correct nonshrinking and corrosion-resistant mortar.

Usually no finishing is required.

Resilient Materials.   If linoleum or resilient tiles are to be installed over concrete, the concrete must be thoroughly dry before application.   Waterproof any subfloor that is below grade or subject to water or dampness.

Uneven wood subfloors must be machine-sanded and planed before an attempt is made to lay resilient materials.   If the floor is in really bad shape, you may have to lay a new subfloor.   Plywood is ideal.   Another method is to use an underlay that is troweled on to fill valleys and cracks.   Ask the supplier for advice.

To apply tile over a surface where paint has been used, remove the surface coatings. The adhesives used in laying a tile or linoleum floor must penetrate into the wood.

If the floor is to be applied over concrete, the surface must be carefully cleaned and must be dry before installation.

In making the installation, use the adhesive suggested by the tile or linoleum manufacturer.   If some tiles don't seem to stick, don't worry too much.   Bonding often takes a day or so.   Fit tiles or sheets tightly together.

Waxing (or a resin-emulsion coating) is required for any of these types of floors. Be sure, though, bonding is complete before waxing or coating.

These suggestions are necessarily general.   The manufacturer of whatever floor is selected will have detailed specifications and installation instructions.   Follow them.

UPKEEP

There are three keys to floor care: Don't abuse them; use sound preventive-maintenance techniques; repair any damage immediately.

Floors, properly selected and installed, are a mighty tough article.   Even so, it pays big dividends to minimize, wherever possible, the tough service a floor has to take.   For example:

1. Steel-wheeled trucks just don't make sense floor-wise if loads being transported are heavy and wheels are small.   (The smaller the wheel, the smaller the wearing surface and the greater the load per square inch the floor must carry.)   Only the toughest concrete floors can take tough treatment of this kind without rutting or cracking.   None of the floors discussed in this chapter should get that kind of treatment, especially when the remedy—compared with the cost of serious floor damage—is so small.   At the very least, steel wheels or casters can be equipped with solid rubber or plastic tires.   Pneumatic tires are better.
2. Other concentrated loads should be avoided.   It is easy to increase the bearing surface of standing loads by installing mounting pads, or even just plain plates under the points of contact.   Use of this kind of support will prevent floors from denting or cracking.
3. Projection against impact loads should be provided.   Even sturdy wood-block floors will splinter and crack under repeated impact.   In spots where impact loads are common—under a crane-unload point, for example—provide resilient mats.
4. Water should be avoided.   Particularly in these days of one-story plants, where the major portion of any floor is ground level, every effort should be made to keep water from attacking the floor.   Water pressure beneath the floor can force an immense amount of moisture up through the subfloor attacking and loosening the floor itself.   Adhesives on a resilient floor give up fast under this treatment. Even a heavy-duty wood-block or mastic floor will be damaged.   Solution?   Get at the causes.   Provide adequate drainage away from outside walls.   Use waterproofing compounds liberally on all below-grade masonry walls.

Even a floor that resists damage from corrosive materials shouldn't be given an endurance test in everyday use.   Make every attempt to control spillage, and when it occurs, clean it up as soon as possible.

Fig. 6-1. Floor-scrubbing machine, also used for shampooing rugs and carpets. Tank on handle carries 3 gal of soap and water. Shown here in combined operation with heavy-duty portable vacuum. (*Courtesy of Hild Floor Machine Co., Chicago.*)

Preventive maintenance, when it comes to floors, is largely a matter of proper cleaning. What is proper cleaning? Depends on the type of floor. By all means follow the suggestions of the manufacturer. Irreparable damage can result from using the wrong cleaning methods. And once the correct cleaning method for each type of floor has been determined get it down in writing. If a new cleaning product or method interests you, give it a try—but in a small test area, not on the whole shop floor.

In planning any "preventive-cleaning" program, don't forget the excellent and effective floor-cleaning equipment that is available (see Figs. 6-1 to 6-5, inclusive). *Industrial floor machine* is a term so broad that it can apply to an 8- or 16-in. machine for waxing and polishing asphalt tile, or to a 21-in. machine for dry-buffing hardwood areas; and it is equally applicable to the powerful, heavy-duty scarifying-type machines for shaving heavy built-up grease accumulations from factory floors.

Floor scrubber usually implies a wet operation. In this case a liquid detergent is applied to loosen the soilage. Some scrubbers have rotary brushes and scrub the floor surface without picking up the soilage—which is done in a separate operation. An *automatic scrubber* applies the detergent (as a rule), scrubs the floor, and vacuum-sucks the dirty scrub water up, leaving a clean surface. Automatic scrubbers are battery-, electric-, or gasoline-

Fig. 6-2. Automatic floor scrubber, electrically operated, self-propelled. It feeds solution in controlled amounts, scrubs, rinses, squeegees, withdraws used solution, travels at selected speeds, floodlights dark areas. (*Courtesy of American Floor Surfacing Machine Co., Toledo.*)

FIG. 6-3. New type 3-in-1 sweeper has attachments for rapid change (15 to 20 min) from vacuumized sweeping to automatic scrubbing, or to snow removal. The sweeper's dirt hopper (right) is replaced by the scrubber attachment. Quick-connect couplings link 550/375 rpm dual scrubber brushes to sweeper's main hydraulic power system. (*Courtesy of G. H. Tennant Co., Minneapolis.*)

FIG. 6-4. Converted from sweeping to scrubbing, this machine automatically applies cleaning solution, scrubs with dual opposed-rotating cylindrical brushes (plus sidebrush), and picks up. It cleans a 50-in. path at speeds up to $2\frac{1}{2}$ mph and covers about 30,000 sq ft per hour. The unit has two 20-gal solution tanks and one 40-gal recovery tank. (*Courtesy of G. H. Tennant Co., Minneapolis.*)

powered. Some power sweepers have quick-change hook-on attachments for automatic scrubbing.

Floor scarifier is a term sometimes used to describe a type of heavy-duty industrial floor machine (9 to 35 hp) which pulverizes thick grease-caked dirt and picks it up in one operation, leaving a smooth clean floor surface. Cleaning action is provided by a rotating cylindrical brush, or by a cylinder equipped with steel cutters. Scarifiers clean paths from 16 to 36 in. wide in one pass. The operation usually is done dry, and clean pickup is aided by a built-in vacuum system.

Scarifiers are used on wood-block or steel-plate floors, as well as concrete, where the build-up is too heavy, impacted, or greasy for sweeping. They now do the work formerly done by crews of men with steel hoelike scrapers.

Scrubbers are used on concrete, asphalt tile, ceramic tile, and similar floors where use of water is not objectionable and where safety factors are not of prime importance during the operation. Scrubbers are oc-

FIG. 6-5. Self-propelled, walk-behind type of power sweeper efficiently sweeps congested aisles, also parking lots, docks, walks. (*Courtesy of Wayne Manufacturing Co., Pomona, Calif.*)

casionally used on wood floors in emergencies provided water pickup can be made immediately. As a rule, water should not be used to excess on any floor.

Why the big emphasis on repairing floors promptly? Floors are a little like the fabled one-hoss shay. Though failure is a slow process—you could miss the fact that your floor is deteriorating until much too late—once it starts to go, it goes fast. And the smart time to take action is *before* the floor gets in such bad shape that it cries for attention.

Floor inspection is the best guarantee that damage will be found in time. Impress on department foremen that they should report any minor floor damage—such as cracks or chipping. Then don't depend on them. Make floor inspection a part of the plant's standard preventive-maintenance procedure. Sometimes a team of inspectors—made up of production supervisors, materials-handling supervisors (few plant people have a bigger stake in good smooth floors than they), and maintenance people—would be a good bet.

And when you come across a floor fault—don't just fix it. Try to determine the cause. If it's something that can be corrected—like acid spillage, too-rough crane unloading—take action. And keep a record of floor failures and repairs. Sometimes a pattern of failure will be revealed by such records that will help you take major corrective action, be useful in future floor selection.

Below are a few hints on cleaning and maintenance of each of the types of floors covered in this chapter. While good general rules, they won't cover every contingency. Ask the supplier for detailed maintenance instructions.

Wood Block. Scraping off the hard grease and dirt accumulations that these floors collect—since they normally are used in heavy-duty service—is a job for a power scarifier. It can be done manually with a wire brush, but you wouldn't like the job and neither will the cleaning people. Power sweeping or automatic scrubbing can be used to remove ordinary dirt, but be sure to clean water up fast to avoid swelling trouble.

It is a good idea, to prevent the floor from buckling, to mop cold seal into the wood block every year or two. This treatment will also help prevent blocks from working loose. If they do loosen (caused by dirt working into cracks and breaking the bond between the block and the mastic adhesive), the only treatment is to remove the loosened blocks, scrape away the dirt, and relay. An occasional problem with this kind of floor is the edge-wearing "cobblestone" effect. One remedy, other than replacement: Level off the floor slightly with a drum-type scarifying floor machine; then sand with coarse paper and reseal.

Pigmented (or clear) urethanes or epoxies may now also be used effectively on clean, properly sanded wood-block surfaces.

Hardwood. Modern surface finishes, including urethanes or epoxies, have reduced wood-floor maintenance to sweeping—plus occasional damp mopping for oily, sticky soilage. Power sweepers are widely used. Abrasive cylindrical rolls on floor machines are used in some industries to remove stains. Automatic scrubbers (or scrubbing attachments on sweepers) allow rapid, one-pass cleaning with immediate pickup of detergent from the floor.

Waxes or other dressings are *not* recommended on industrial hardwood floors. When refinishing is needed, be sure to remove all traces of oil or soilage (by scrubbing); then buff the old finish with steel wool to provide a "tooth" for the new finish.

If resanding is necessary, as when replacing an old penetrating seal with a urethane-finish system, be sure to countersink all nails first. Remember, too, that modern, clear finishes magnify mistakes in sanding—so try for a perfect job.

If the entire floor wears thin, you can resurface with plastic-resin coatings that are available. They should be applied in several thin ($\frac{1}{8}$-in.) coats. If a heavier coat is desired, there are several types of mastic compounds that can be troweled on up to $\frac{1}{2}$-in. thickness. With this treatment, obviously, you no longer have a wooden floor.

Removing floor finishes is a ticklish job. Better consult the supplier for details.

Metal-armored. Cleaning is a heavy-duty operation. Again, a power scarifier usually is the ticket. Deep types of armor may require special cleaning procedures—your supplier will be able to advise you. Major maintenance problem is watching for loosening of the armor from the subfloor, and evidences of loose sections. They should be anchored promptly to prevent adjacent sections from loosening also.

Mastic.   Cold-mastic floors should not get too much water.   This can be prevented by cleaning small areas at a time, rinsing and drying each promptly.   Even hot mastic—the acid-resistant kind—should be dried promptly after cleaning with hot water and solvent-type cleaners.

Key to good maintenance is filling in any ruts or cracks with mastic patching compounds.   Any cracks left unrepaired will allow water and dirt to seep down to the subfloor and cause enlargement of the damaged area.   As mentioned under Characteristics, this type of floor should not be subjected to heavy standing loads or to small-wheel materials-handling equipment.

Oxychloride (Magnesite).   Water is poison to this type of floor.   So "avoid any long exposure to water" is the number one rule in both cleaning and preventive maintenance.   In cleaning, dry up any water promptly.   And as soon as the floor is absolutely dry, apply penetrating waxes.   Don't use harsh cleaners—mild alkaline detergents or neutral synthetic cleaners are OK.

Maintenance rules?   Keep floor surface protected from stains—they're hard to remove.   If sealed, wax floor regularly.   If not, apply penetrating dressings or waxes. Concrete hardeners can be used to boost durability.

Brick and Quarry Tile.   Cleaning is a cinch.   Use warm water with any good detergent.   Then rinse, and dry promptly to avoid slipperiness.

Weak spot, maintenancewise, is the pointing between tiles.   Watch for signs of cracks or other breakdown in the mortar, and repoint promptly.   This will prevent water or other liquids from reaching the subfloor, causing further deterioration. Either portland-cement mortar or acid-resisting mortar can be used, depending on conditions in the area.   Repointing with either is a job for experts.   No maintenance of the tiles themselves is needed—except common-sense handling to avoid cracking.

Resilient Materials.   Small, section-at-a-time cleaning is advisable to avoid overlong exposure to water.   Mild cleaners are recommended by the manufacturers. And keep floors protected with a good resin-emulsion finish.   These coatings often last three or four times as long as wax coatings under traffic, have a satisfactory gloss, and are easy to maintain.   Wax may be used in areas requiring maximum gloss for appearance, but it is not recommended for vinyl floors.

Any loose tiles should be taken up and reinstalled with adhesive.

Conclusion.   Your plant floor is, in effect, a piece of materials-handling equipment. And, like any other piece of handling equipment, it should be selected carefully, put into use carefully, and maintained carefully.   Only difference is: Your floor is without doubt the biggest and the most expensive piece of such equipment in your shop.   So select, install, and treat it accordingly.

Chapter 7

REPAIR AND TREATMENT
OF CONCRETE FLOORS

Courtesy of PORTLAND CEMENT ASSOCIATION
Chicago, Ill.

Failure to observe some fundamental requirement in construction may result in certain defects which often can be corrected by proper treatment or repairs.

Dusting. Floor finishes that dust under service may usually be improved by one of the hardener treatments discussed in later paragraphs of this chapter. Whether the hardener treatment will entirely stop dusting will depend on the construction methods used and the resulting condition of the surface.

Where there is a thin layer of soft, chalky materials at the surface, this may often be removed with pads of steel wool attached to a scrubbing machine. After removal of this material, the surface should be thoroughly cleaned, then allowed to dry and one of the hardener treatments applied. In other cases, it is necessary to grind the surface before treatment.

Cracking. Cracks in concrete floors may be classified as (1) structural cracks originating in the base and extending through the finish, and (2) cracks confined to the wearing course. The latter may extend through the wearing course or may be of a superficial nature, ordinarily called hair cracks or crazing.

Structural cracks may be caused by shrinking, temperature changes, or settlement. If there is recurrent movement, there is little that can be done other than to keep them filled with a mastic material. Crazing cracks may be removed by grinding if they are not too deep. The only other method of removing them is to remove the affected area and replace it with new material.

In many cases cracks may be filled with varnish or resin. Although they will remain visible, accumulations of dirt and leakage will be prevented. Artificial resins such as Cumar (available through paint and varnish manufacturers) may be used. This should be powdered and dissolved in a suitable solvent such as xylol, in the approximate proportions of 6 lb of resin per gallon of solvent. A varnishlike material is produced which can be run into the cracks. Cement may be added to make a thicker solution for wider cracks.

In patching concrete floors, the old wearing surface should be chipped off to a depth of at least 1 in., and the roughened surface should be thoroughly cleaned of loose particles and should be saturated with water for several hours before new concrete is placed. The area surrounding the patch should be wetted also. Figures 7-1 and 7-2 show correct and incorrect methods of patching; Figs. 7-3 and 7-4 show correct and incorrect screeding; Fig. 7-5 shows protection of patches.

Roughened Floors. Floors that have been improperly constructed may become roughened under service, or pitting may occur because of heavy impacts. Often such floors may be put into satisfactory condition by grinding off the roughened sur-

FIG. 7-1. Incorrectly installed patch. Patches installed with feathered edges will soon break down under trucking.

FIG. 7-2. Correctly installed floor patch. The chipped-out area should be at least 1 in. in depth with the edges perpendicular.

face and will give good service for many years. On the other hand, if the concrete is of such poor quality that the surface will soon become roughened or pitted again, it would be more economical to resurface it with the proper quality of concrete.

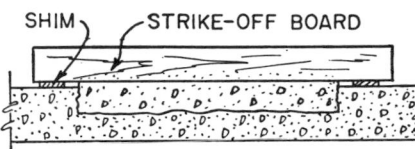

FIG. 7-3. Results of incorrect screeding of patch. When a patch is originally struck off to the level of the floor, the concrete will sag in the center because the straight-edge has a tendency to cut off slightly below its lower edge and the concrete shrinks during hardening. Additional concrete placed in the concave area will soon chip out under traffic.

Attaching Equipment to Floors. Machinery and other equipment may be rigidly fastened to concrete floors with expansion bolts. For satisfactory results the concrete must be of such quality that it will resist the stresses developed by the equipment to be attached. If large bolts extending into the base course are used, the base course should be well proportioned with not over 6 gal of water per sack of cement to provide a good grade of

concrete. The usual procedure is to mark the location of the bolts on the floor after it has hardened and cured, then drill the holes to the proper depth for insertion of the expansion shells.

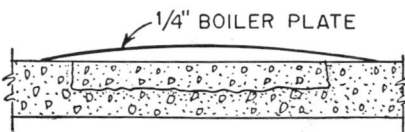

FIG. 7-4. Correct method of screeding patch. The strike-off board is held slightly above the level of the floor by strips or shims laid the length of the patch on two sides. For large patches the thickness of these strips will be greater than for small patches. The concrete is allowed to rest for 1 to 2 hr. This allows the concrete to attain some of its initial shrinkage before being troweled to its final plane and will result in a uniformly level surface, plane with the rest of the floor.

FIG. 7-5. Protection of patches. Patches should be kept continuously wet and protected from traffic during the curing period. An economical method of protection consists in using a piece of $\frac{1}{4}$-in. steel sheeting bent as shown and placed over the patch to take traffic during the curing and hardening period.

Maintaining and Cleaning Floors. Properly constructed concrete floors will require little maintenance other than cleaning. Periodic cleaning is essential to durability, as grit and dirt on floors subjected to considerable traffic will be ground into the finish and accelerate the rate of wear.

Floors subjected to spilled milk, sirups, fruit juices, brines, fats, oils, and many other industrial products should be thoroughly scrubbed frequently. In many plants it is necessary to scrub the floors at least once a day. Warm soapy water and stiff brushes should be used, after which the floor should be mopped clean. Electric scrubbing machines are widely used for cleaning large floor areas.

Surfaces subjected to heavy trucking should not be allowed to accumulate a crust of dirt, as sometimes happens in molasses, sugar, and oil warehouses. Trucks ride unevenly over these obstructions, imposing undue impact stresses on the floor finish and increasing the tractive effort of the trucks.

Garage and powerhouse floors frequently become soiled with oil. Usually the oil has no detrimental effect if the concrete is properly made, but its presence detracts from the appearance and makes the surface dangerously slippery. Such floors may be cleaned by scraping off thickened oil crusts, then scrubbing with gasoline, taking due precaution against fire. The floor should then be thoroughly scrubbed with warm soapy water and mopped. The treatment will not remove stains but will remove the objectionable coating of oil and grease. Special solvents are also available for removal of oil and grease.

Decorative floors should be cleaned with warm soapy water prior to use and at subsequent intervals depending on the severity of service. Only mild soaps should be used on terrazzo and other types of decorative floors. Soap should be removed by rinsing thoroughly to prevent the surface from becoming slippery. Terrazzo floors acquire a beautiful natural sheen when they are washed often for the first 2 or 3 months. After this period less work will be required in their upkeep.

Surface Treatments. The durability of concrete floors depends primarily upon observance of the fundamental rules in making, placing, curing, and finishing the concrete. Dusting of the floor surface may occur if these rules are violated.

Many of these floors may be improved by applying some material to assist in hardening and binding the surface. These treatments are not cure-alls for poor materials or careless workmanship and will not make a perfect wearing surface of a poorly built floor. Magnesium fluosilicate, zinc fluosilicate, aluminum sulfate, zinc sulfate, chinawood and linseed oils, and various gums, resins, and paraffins are substances used for this purpose. Sometimes paints are applied after these treatments as further protection.

It is essential that the floor be clean and free from plaster, oil, paint, or other foreign substances before giving any other treatment. It should also be fairly dry to assist penetration. When paint of any kind is to be used, it is important that the concrete be thoroughly dry.

Fluosilicate Treatment. The fluosilicates of zinc and magnesium dissolved in water have been used with good success. Either of the fluosilicates may be used separately, but a mixture of 20 per cent zinc and 80 per cent magnesium appears to give the best results. In making up the solutions, $\frac{1}{2}$ lb of the fluosilicate should be dissolved in 1 gal of water for the first application and 2 lb to each gallon for subsequent applications. The solution may be mopped on or applied with a sprinkling can and then spread evenly with mops. Two or more applications should be given, allowing the surfaces to dry between applications. About 3 or 4 hr are generally required for absorption, reaction, and drying. Care should be taken to mop the floor with water shortly after the first application has dried to remove encrusted salts; otherwise white stains may be formed.

Sodium Silicate Treatment. Commercial sodium silicate is about a 40 per cent solution. It is viscous and requires thinning with water before it will penetrate concrete. A good solution consists of 3 gal of water to each gallon of silicate. Two or three coats should be used, allowing each coat to dry thoroughly before the next one is applied. Scrubbing each coat with stiff fiber brushes or scrubbing machines and water will assist penetration of the succeeding application.

Aluminum Sulfate Treatment. This treatment consists of one or more applications of solutions of aluminum sulfate. The solution is made in a wooden barrel or stoneware vessel and the water should be acidulated with not more than 1 teaspoonful of commercial sulfuric acid for each gallon of water. The sulfate does not readily dissolve and requires occasional stirring for a few days until the solution is complete. About $2\frac{1}{2}$ lb of the powdered sulfate will be required for each gallon of water. For the first treatment the solution may be diluted with twice its volume of water. Twenty-four hours after this application the stronger solution may be used, and 24 hr should elapse between subsequent applications.

Zinc Sulfate Treatment. This treatment consists of the application of a solution containing $1\frac{1}{2}$ lb of zinc sulfate and a teaspoonful of commercial sulfuric acid to each gallon of water. The mixture is applied in two coats, the second coat applied 4 hr after the first. The surface should be scrubbed with hot water and mopped dry just before the application of the second coat.   This treatment gives the floor a darker appearance.

Oil Treatment.   Chinawood, linseed, or soybean oil may be diluted with gasoline, naphtha, or turpentine and applied with mops or large brushes.   About equal parts of oil and thinner give a good mixture for this purpose and often a single application is sufficient.   In some cases the oil treatment may be repeated to advantage at semi-annual intervals.

Coverage.   The amounts of the above solutions required to treat floors will vary considerably with the porosity of the concrete.   Generally a gallon of any one of the solutions will be required for each application on 150 to 200 sq ft of floor surface.

Chapter 8

DESIGN OF CONCRETE INDUSTRIAL FLOOR SURFACES

By R. F. YTTERBERG
Vice President
Kalman Floor Company
New York. N.Y.

From the standpoint of use, floor surfaces are the most important part of modern industrial buildings. Materials handling and plant cleanliness, in particular, are inescapably tied in with the serviceability of the floor surface.

Fortunately, floor surfaces do not have to be troublesome, although in far too many instances they are a source of continuous dissatisfaction. There is nothing inherent in industrial operations or in the materials used for industrial surfaces which makes troubles mandatory. In this chapter we shall set down in outline the techniques which have consistently produced good floor surfaces.

Why, then, in view of their importance, are so many industrial floors troublesome? Generally, it appears to me that two factors are responsible.

First, the vital roles that skilled workmanship and supervision play in the proper installation of industrial floors is not generally recognized. Consider for a moment that these floor surfaces are installed under an ever-changing variety of weather and job conditions that exist during the construction of the building. Installation of concrete floors must be a production operation to be economically feasible. Further, consider the fact that there are no mechanical or electrical quality-control devices which manufacturing industries consider as essential to the production of their products. Considered in this light, isn't it obvious why workmanship and supervision are important? Without them, where is the quality control to come from?

Second, while the principle which governs the strength and durability of concrete is widely known and respected, far too often during the installation of concrete floor surfaces its precepts are ignored. Knowledge of this principle was developed in 1917 by Prof. Duff A. Abrams, then with the Lewis Institute in Chicago. It is called the water-cement ratio law. Simply stated, it is: "The strength of a concrete mixture depends on the quantity of mixing water used in the batch, expressed as a ratio to the volume of cement, *so long as the concrete is workable and the aggregates are clean and structurally sound*. The strength of the concrete decreases as the water-ratio increases." (From: Quantities of Materials for Concrete, Structural Materials Research Laboratory, Lewis Institute, Bulletin 9, Chicago.) Some people misread this statement and conclude that a low water-cement ratio, of itself, makes for a high-strength concrete. But it should be noted that three things are involved in the law: (1) workability, (2) a water-cement ratio approaching that which is theoretically correct, and (3) a good aggregate.

Despite this knowledge, from its start the concrete industry has been beset by the idea that anyone with a wheelbarrow and a shovel can install concrete floors. The great number of troublesome concrete floors is mute testimony that such is not the case. Instead, all possible knowledge and ability must be used in the installation of concrete, especially for wearing surfaces.

CONCRETE WEARING SURFACES

There are two basic methods of finishing concrete floor surfaces. One is called monolithic finishing, the other deferred topping finishing. Essentially, the difference between the two is that the monolithic floor, because it is composed entirely of ready-mix concrete, has far too much water in it to permit the cement paste to reach its maximum strength. Whereas in the deferred topping, because it is applied to the base slab after the ready-mix concrete has set, it is possible to control the water-cement ratio to the point where the cement paste can achieve its maximum strength. There are other important differences between the two, but the one stated above is the heart of the matter.

MONOLITHIC FINISHING OF CONCRETE FLOORS

It was noted above that monolithically finished concrete floor surfaces have the inherent weakness of a high water-cement ratio. A ready-mix concrete surface, without anything added to the surface, must be weak and porous. With anything but the lightest use, inevitably the surface will become rough and dirty. To strengthen such floors it is necessary to densify the surface as much as possible and then to make certain the surface is smooth and tight.

The best way we have found to achieve this is to incorporate into the surface of the freshly screeded concrete a large amount of hard, tough aggregate (thoroughly mixed with cement with a minimum water-cement ratio)—approximately $1\frac{1}{2}$ to 2 lb per sq ft. When this volume of aggregate is embedded into the concrete, the topmost area of the slab is densified in precise relation to the volume of material so embedded. Then, by extended troweling, the concrete can be made to have an exceedingly durable surface. Properly installed, this type of surface can be good for moderate to heavy-duty use. But the slump of the base slab concrete must be in the order of 2 to 3 in. Otherwise, the material may sink below the surface where it will be useless. Also, if the water content is too high, the cement paste will be weakened as indicated by the water-cement ratio.

Other types of stone or mineral aggregate can be used for this operation. Sometimes these materials are referred to as "floor hardeners." However, the materials of themselves have no inherent hardening quality. They must be incorporated into the surface properly and in sufficient quantity.

A number of liquid floor hardeners also are often used in the hope that the dusting due to disintegration common in the average concrete floor will be allayed. These are essentially of two types. "Chemical" hardeners react with the free lime in cement, thus "hardening" the surface. Certain chemical hardeners also accelerate the natural process of hardening in concrete. Other materials seal the surface and hold down the dust due to disintegration by binding together the loose particles. Waxes, oils, varnishes, and some sweeping compounds all have this effect. All such treatments depend upon penetration for their effectiveness and have limited life. In other words, their value is greatest in soft, porous floors.

DEFERRED CONCRETE FLOOR TOPPING

The application of a topping to a slab that has already set produces a wearing surface that is much stronger than any that can be installed monolithically. The water-cement ratio can be controlled effectively in a deferred topping, and greater quantities of fine and coarse aggregates can be used.

Before describing this preferred installation procedure, it may be well to review some of the principles governing cement strength. This will show the reader one measure of the difference which exists between the two types of surfaces.

To achieve full hydration, a sack of cement needs only about 2.8 gal of water. If however, a water-cement ratio as low as this were used in the initial mix, it would be unworkable and impossible to place, screed, and compact. Because of the loss of workability, the benefits of the low water-cement ratio could not be realized, for the void content of the finished topping would be so large as to reduce compressive strength and increase permeability. On the other hand, if a sufficiently large quantity of water is used to obtain workability and if that water is left in the mix, some strength must be lost.

The procedure outlined in the following paragraphs and illustrated by Figs. 8-1 to 8-11 gets around this dilemma by using an initial water content of about 5 gal per sack of cement, including the water content of the aggregate, and then removing this water needed for workability and achieving a water ratio of only about 3.5 gal per sack, i.e., within 0.7 gal of the theoretically correct amount. By comparison, the average ready-mix concrete contains about 6 to 8 gal of water per sack of cement.

Fig. 8-1. The base slab is cleaned of laitance and scum by mechanical wire brushes.

This large excess of water in the typical ready-mix concrete may or may not eventually evaporate into the air, but the volume it occupies in the concrete can be considered to be voids or weak spots in the concrete.

Preparation of Concrete Subsurface. In new construction the base slab should be brought to ¾ in. below the finished grade. When it is partially hardened, the surface of the slab should be subjected to steel wire brushing to remove all laitance and scum, leaving the surface clean and rough with the coarse aggregate exposed. A second brooming is carried out later when the laitance clinging to the coarse aggregate will brush off and show clean stone. If this second brooming does not reveal clean stone, then a third brooming is required. The slab must have a rough texture, but partially exposed aggregate must not be loose. Since the topping may be installed up to several months after the slab has been poured, this brooming is necessary, for when the topping is installed, it must be bonded to the base slab. When the time comes to install the topping, the area must be thoroughly cleaned of all mortar, concrete, paint, oil, grease, mud, clay, or other foreign material from construction. The day before the topping is to be applied, the slab must be saturated to prevent the slab from drawing too much water from the topping while it is curing. A scrub-in coat of cement grout is then applied. Grout is the adhesive agent that bonds the topping to the base slab. The grout mixture must have a creamy consistency and must be worked into the slab with wire brooms.

Batching of the Mix. Stone aggregate is the strongest part of any concrete mixture. It has the most abrasion and shock resistance of any of the other elements which go into a concrete surface. Therefore, the ideal floor surface will have as much aggregate in it as possible. So, each cubic yard of topping mix should contain a full cubic yard of coarse aggregate. This volume of stone will have a void content of approximately 40 to 50 per cent. Practically all of these voids should be filled by

Fig. 8-2. The cleaned slab is kept saturated overnight. Water is brushed off before start of operations.

Fig. 8-3. Grout coat of pure cement is worked in.

Fig. 8-4. Mix is placed and screeded to true level.

fine aggregate, and the remaining voids will be filled by the cement-water paste. The precise batching will depend on the sieve analysis for sand and stone.

The aggregate used is a basaltic or granitic rock that has been tested for hardness, toughness, and soundness. [As a minimum, aggregate must conform to ASTM (American Society for Testing Materials) specification C33, with coarse aggregate meeting the No. 8 grading limits of ASTM D448.]

About 5 gal of water per sack of cement is used with about 12 sacks of cement per cubic yard.

Water Removal. After this mix is screeded, there is no longer any need for workability. Therefore, the water needed for this purpose must now be removed. This is accomplished by placing a burlap blanket on top of the freshly screeded topping mix and then spreading on the blanket a drier material which will remove by capillary

Fig. 8-5. Absorption blankets are put down on screeded floor.

action sufficient water to permit the topping mix to support the weight of a man without indentation. When this occurs, the drier material is removed.

Floating. Floating levels out the floor surface so that it can be worked by smoother tools (trowels).

Machine Troweling. Machine troweling is the final step in mechanical densification. It is not started until whatever moisture film was brought up by floating has evaporated. Several passes, at proper time intervals, are required.

Hand Troweling. This is the final step in densification. It is not enough merely to pull the blade across the floor. Downward pressure at the proper blade angle is required. The value of extensive and

Fig. 8-6. Drying mixture is spread on top of absorption blankets.

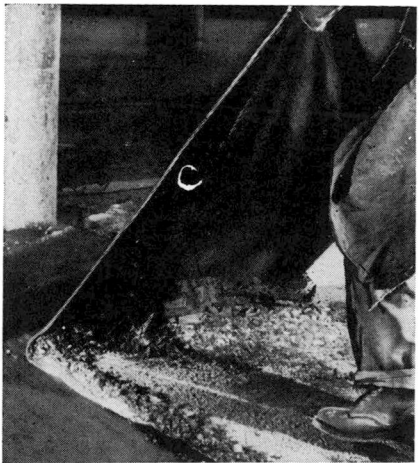

Fig. 8-7. Blankets are removed when correct water-cement balance is achieved.

proper troweling cannot be overemphasized. But neither can precise instructions be given about when and how often the troweling should be done. The troweling must proceed when the concrete surface is ready. Troweling tightens up the surface which is disrupted by water evaporation. The evaporation rate varies according to specific job conditions. The troweling rate must vary also. A number of trowelings are required, and as this may have to be done at overtime rates, the contractor must have the will to spend the money to get a hard, dense finish.

Curing. Proper treatment of the floor after it has been troweled is too frequently neglected. The concrete should be kept moist so that the cement will continue to combine chemically with the water. The curing process should be begun as soon as possible. Delay will cause rapid evaporation in the early stages, with resultant cracking, crazing, or dusting of the surface. Where floors are laid exposed to the

FIG. 8-8. Finishing operations with heavy compactors are begun.

FIG. 8-9. Several runs are made with mechanical trowels.

FIG. 8-10. Hand finishers follow the mechanical troweling.

FIG. 8-11. Floor is cured for 10 to 14 days, is kept wet down and covered with waterproof paper to contain moisture.

sun, it is frequently necessary to start curing the same evening with a moisture spray or vapor. The longer the concrete can be kept wet, the stronger, more impervious, and more wear-resistant the floors will be. The floors should not be used at all for at least 5 days and thereafter only lightly for an additional 10-day period.

If properly installed, this deferred topping should never need to be sealed.

CORROSION-RESISTANT SURFACES

Some floors are rough and permanently dirty because they have been attacked by substances inherently harmful to portland cement. Floors in areas subjected to this type of attack should have a corrosion-resistant floor surface to protect the subslab and to keep the surface itself smooth and sound.

A corrosion-resistant floor topping ⅛ to ¼ in. thick can be made, utilizing a mixture of aggregate together with a thermosetting plastic such as epoxy or polyester.

Corrosion-resistant floor toppings are ideally suited to provide trouble-free surfaces in such areas. They are smooth, virtually joint-free, and impervious. They are easy to clean, can be tinted in a range of colors, have remarkable abrasion and impact resistance, and will withstand substantial corrosive attack.

Epoxy or polyester floor toppings are not, of course, corrosion-proof materials. No material is. But it is difficult to draw generalizations about the limitations of this floor surface in actual use. Each design problem should be examined separately, for chemical resistance is a function of type of corrosive agent, its concentration and temperature, and length of time that the corrosive material is in contact with the floor surface. Floor design and drainage conditions, in addition to housekeeping and types of production activity, will substantially affect the floor's serviceability.

The entire field of epoxy and other thermosetting plastic coatings is, at this writing, relatively new and therefore in a constant stage of change as new developments occur. Thus it is not practical to set down in detail precise methods of how these materials should be installed. But it should be noted that the words "epoxy" and "polyester" are generic terms standing for a whole range of materials. This is to say that not all epoxy or polyester formulations are necessarily the same. Moreover, while epoxies achieved one of their initial successes for their marvelous adhesive powers, adequate attention must be paid to subslab preparation and bonding procedures.

STRUCTURAL FACTORS

Certain structural considerations have great bearing on the floor wearing surface, for if the slab beneath the surface is faulty, its faults will undoubtedly come through to the surface.

Earth Subgrade. When concrete floors are laid directly on the earth subgrade, that subgrade should be uniformly stable. Frequently, the earth is of such composition that changes must be made even in the undisturbed earth cuts to take care of problems such as expandable material and water-bearing soils. In such situations, the services of soil experts are indicated and justified.

The subgrade should generally be compacted to at least 95 per cent optimum, in accordance with ASTM specifications. It is particularly important to secure such compaction in all newly placed fills, in previously opened trenches, and at walls and columns.

Concrete Base Slabs on Ground. The primary function of the base slab is to support whatever loads—both static and dynamic—are placed on it. The lowest water-cement ratio consistent with workability will prove the ideal, not only for strength of concrete but for reducing shrinkage to a minimum and obtaining uniformity of the wearing surface. Most concrete floor slabs on ground can be placed with a slump of 2 to 3 in. Overvibration must be avoided to eliminate segregation and the raising of fine aggregate to the surface.

To minimize indiscriminate cracking of the floor slabs due to shrinkage, the slabs should be separated into panels, approximately square, and no larger than 40 by 40 ft. The most advantageous way of achieving this is to saw in the necessary jointing the day after a pour has been made. Weather conditions may necessitate making the saw cut sooner.

Generally, it is recommended that floor slabs have a minimum thickness of 6 in. and that all construction joints be doweled to hold the two abutting concrete pours in the same plane and to provide a sure way to transfer the weight of moving loads. Generally, where the surface is to be a deferred topping, a 2,500-lb 5-sack mix concrete is sufficient for the base slab. Where the surface is to be finished monolithically, a 3,000-lb strength minimum mix (5½-sack mix) is desirable. The design of each mix must be individually determined according to the availability of fine and coarse aggregates. But the tendency to oversand the mix in order to achieve easy workability and finishing should be avoided, since unnecessary shrinkage can result from oversanding.

JOINTS FOR CONCRETE SLABS ON EARTH

Concrete shrinks as it sets.   Approximately 90 per cent of the ultimate drying shrinkage will take place in a comparatively short period and will build up tension in the slab until the joint between two panels opens; or, if the tension exceeds the tensile strength of concrete, a crack appears.   Normally, every effort should be made to prevent such cracks from developing.   Control of the water content of the mix is, of course, the starting point in preventing such cracks.

Stress Relieving Joints.   One method of achieving control over shrinkage cracks is by the alternate-panel method.   Here the floor is laid out in rectangular panels, usually bounded by column centers, and the concrete is placed in alternate panels, with a 24-hr period between the placing of adjacent slabs.   Thus setting shrinkage is confined to the individual pours.   Generally, panels about 40 by 40 ft have been found acceptable in that few or no shrinkage cracks appear.

This procedure obviously involves the movement of men and materials from bay to bay and therefore has the inherent disadvantage of being somewhat more costly than the next method mentioned below.   It also suffers from an excess number of bulkheaded construction joints, at which curling of the slab can occur unless dowels are used.

In the weakened-plane method, the floor is installed in as large a block as can be handled in a day's work.   As soon as the concrete has set sufficiently—usually the day after the concrete has been placed—a vertical weakened plane is cut to approximately 20 to 25 per cent of the depth of the slab with a concrete saw.   This achieves the same segmentation as in the alternate-panel method but without the interruption of the work flow.   The concrete cracks irregularly below the saw cut and thus provides shear transfer across the saw cut joints.

Joints in the deferred topping should follow any joints in the slab below.

CONSTRUCTION JOINTS

Bulkheads should be straight, rigid, and vertical.   Some means of transferring loads from one panel to the next must be provided.   This may be done by forming a key in the bulkheads and/or by using steel dowels through the joint, fixed on one side and free to move horizontally on the other.   Steel dowels are the preferred method, as they provide more positive weight transfer across the joint.   Also, they tend to resist curling of the slab edges.   Keys, on the other hand, are rarely in contact, one side with the other, after shrinkage occurs.   Thus, they do not provide a positive means of weight transfer, allowing free movement of the slab edge under traffic, which may result in severe cracking behind the joint.   Because stripping the bulkhead away from a keyed joint is difficult, sometimes the upper lip of the key is broken.

The exposed edges of joints should be square.   They should not normally be tooled, as this will leave a depression in the surface.   The pounding of forklift trucks against such edges will result in rapid deterioration.   Joints should be filled with mastic, lead, epoxy, or silicone to protect the edges and also for appearance and sanitary reasons.

Chapter 9

CONCRETE FLOOR MAINTENANCE

By J. J. Skala
Manager, Chemical Research
G. H. Tennant Company
Minneapolis, Minn.

Longer wear-life of concrete floors under heavy traffic is a recent outgrowth of chemical advances—notably in developing improved types of floor finishes. As a result, concrete floor care—while still exacting and frequently complex—is now more systematic, practical, and economical than before.

Typical advantages of concrete floors include: (1) vastly improved *durability* of floors under traffic; (2) increased *dirt resistance*, with easier removal of soilage (3) more attractive *appearance;* (4) improved *chemical resistance;* and (5) *lower maintenance costs*—through longer floor life, reduced cleaning man-hours, and reduced expense for refinishing or recoating.

ROUTINE MAINTENANCE

Sweeping. Sweeping on a regular basis with a vacuum-equipped power sweeper is of prime importance. It is the most effective routine cleaning method for concrete—for removing dust, sand, loose dirt, dry chemicals, glass, metal chips, and food ingredients.

Power sweeping is not only 3 to 12 times faster than hand sweeping but also helps keep dust and dirt particles out of the pores and crevices in the floor. Used regularly in traffic and spillage areas it helps prevent the build-up of soilage under truck wheels, reduces stain problems, and protects the concrete surfaces from needless abrasion of grit and dirt particles. It also helps keep down air-borne dust, an indirect aid to personnel and critical factory operations.

Scrubbing. Scrubbing with correct detergent solutions or water, while less frequently needed, removes sticky, adherent soilage (such as sirups, oils, greases, and spray residues). Scrubbing also allows fast pickup of liquids and similar agents which might stain.

While manual cleaning is suited to spot work, *automatic scrubbing* is recommended for most floor areas. Automatic scrubbing machines (including some power sweepers with scrubbing attachments) work rapidly. They apply the cleaning solution, scrub vigorously, squeegee, and vacuum dirty water from the floor. Either disk or cylindrical scrubbers will do, but the latter work faster and can apply heavier brush pressure (per square inch of bristle contact with the floor).

Scarifying. Scarifying may occasionally be needed for removal of hard, compacted soilage resistant to other methods. But it should be used infrequently. Powered scarifiers are aggressive machines equipped with wire brushes. Some models shear off and pick up soilage at the same time.   When possible it is preferable to use wet-cleaning with an automatic scrubber for difficult soilage.   Wire scrubbing brushes, semilubricated by the water solution, can be used with little danger of staining the concrete.

PROTECTIVE MAINTENANCE

Despite progress in concrete formulations and application, most concrete floors are vulnerable, to a degree, to heavy traffic, chemical spillage, stains, dirt adherence, and surface degradation.   Even adjacent slabs, poured within minutes of each other, may show marked differences in density, compressive strength, and other characteristics.   Unvented salamander heaters, used during winter placement of factory floors, have been known to weaken the top $\frac{1}{8}$ in. of new concrete—merely through excess carbon dioxide neutralizing the exposed surface of moist concrete.

Special wearing courses and surface hardeners are often specified to improve the durability of the floor.   These are most effective when planned as a part of the original floor installation.   However, protective maintenance for existing floors usually involves concrete floor *sealers* and concrete floor *finishes*.   These are products which provide a durable layer or coating *in* the floor surface (sealer) or *on top* of it (as a *finish* or topping).

Successful use of these new materials in protecting concrete depends entirely on: (1) *soundness* of the concrete (2) *correct preparation* of the surface (3) *quality* of the seal or finish used and (4) painstakingly *correct application* methods.

Unless the basic construction of the concrete is good, no sealer or finish will work well—regardless of its quality or the skill used in applying it.   It is like dentistry: you need a sound tooth structure underneath, or the filling or inlay will fall out.

Floor Sealers.   Unlike finishes, floor sealers are designed to penetrate the concrete surface and fill the pores.   Applied by brush, spray, or lamb's wool applicator, the sealer coats, reinforces, and locks in the brittle, weak cement particles, which can cause recurrent dusting.

A well-designed and well-applied sealer normally fills voids and porous areas, reducing the tendency of these surfaces to seize and hold dirt particles.   The result is a concrete surface which allows faster, more effective sweeping.   Sticky soilage is likewise easier to remove.

To the eye, a concrete sealer appears to wear away slowly.   This is because the material is about on a level with the floor surface, sharing traffic abuse on a fifty-fifty basis with the concrete.   Several coats of sealer may be required to give desired protection.

For good lasting ability any concrete sealer should have resistance to extended attack by mild alkali solutions (such as 1 per cent sodium hydroxide).   Coatings offering this resistance include many types of organic compositions: rubber base types such as butadiene styrene (Pliolite); chlorinated rubber (Parlon); phenolic resins (Bakelite); tung oil compositions; epoxy ester products; epoxy two-package products; low-viscosity, oil-modified polyurethanes, or low-viscosity one- or two-package oil-free urethanes.   The most effective of these sealers are the two-package epoxies and the one- or two-package oil-free urethanes.   Both *have twice the durability of the other types of sealers* mentioned.

Concrete Floor Finishes.   These include organic coatings which leave a thin surface film (1 to 3 mils thick) on top of the floor.   Glossy or semiglossy in appearance, they fill concrete pores in two or three coats.   Application is with a brush, lamb's wool applicator (or roller), or spray, depending on the manufacturer's recommendation. Opaque pigmented coatings in various colors are available.   They can mask discolored concrete and improve plant appearance, as shown in Fig. 9-1.

Finishes, while chemically similar to sealers, are more viscous products.   Their higher solids content thus provides a "build-up" with fewer coats.   Like sealers, these coatings should have long-term resistance to mild alkali solutions.

Finishes, unlike sealers, are designed to provide a tough, on-top surface barrier which takes the entire brunt of abrasive traffic.   The concrete floor proper is thus isolated and protected from any direct contact with truck wheels, skidding traffic, scuffing, and other erosive abuse. Dusting, a common bugaboo of concrete, often caused by surface exposure and breakdown, is eliminated—as long as the protective concrete finish remains as an intact film.

FIG. 9-1. Pigmented, opaque finishes in various colors can mask discolored concrete and improve plant appearance.

Finishes also provide a far smoother surface than fine-troweled concrete, or even-sealed concrete. Since soilage cannot readily stick, sweeping and sanitizing are easier, faster, and more economical operations.

Chemical resistance of finishes has improved in recent years. Table 9-1 gives examples of the chemical resistance of typical coatings. While the oil-free urethanes are somewhat less resistant than some epoxies, they rate high in comparison with other floor coatings (though they are not recommended for the ultimate in chemical resistance).

Table 9-1. Clear Epoxy Resin Film
Resistance to Solvents and Chemicals

	Exposure time	Curing agents			
		Diamine	Triamine	Tetramine	Polamide
Aviation gasoline	7 days	H	H	H	S
	30 days	H	H	H	S
Ethanol (50 %)	7 days	S	S	H	S
Gasoline (premium)	7 days	H	H	H	H
	30 days	H	H	H	Sl S
Acetic acid (20 %)	7 days	—	—	H	H
	30 days	H	H	H	H
Sulfuric acid (50 %)	7 days	H	H	H	H
	30 days	H	H	H	H
Sodium hydroxide (20 %)	7 days	H	H	H	H
	30 days	H	H	H	H
Boiling water	30 min (0 recovery time)	S	H	—	S
Boiling water	30 min (1 hr recovery time)	Blush	Blush	—	Blush

H = Hard, S = Soft, Sl = Slight
Notes: Typical 900 MW Epoxy resin used. Curing agents used in optimum ratios. Film 1.5 mils, air-dried.

Abrasion resistance of certain finishes—primarily the oil-free urethanes—has won increased acceptance of these materials for severe traffic areas.   Their wear resistance and retention of a good glossy appearance is superior to that of other coatings. Figure 9-2 shows relative abrasion resistance values (wear-life) of different types of finishes.   In addition to durability, the urethanes, if properly designed, provide ample adhesion to concrete and have exceptional ability to resist dirt and sticky spillage.

Epoxy two-package solvent-system coatings have been used on concrete for many years.   Some types of catalyst-resin compositions harden much faster than others.

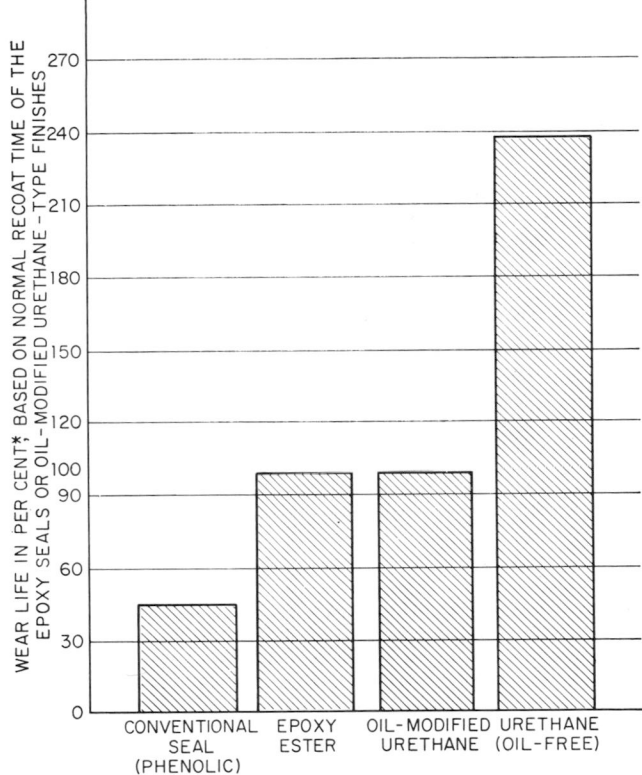

FIG. 9-2. Comparative wear resistance of floor finishes.

Still others perform better on damp floors.   On properly prepared, clean concrete floors the adhesion of these coatings is generally outstanding.

Correct Floor Preparation Needed.   The life of all concrete finishes is heavily dependent on sound concrete of good strength, plus correct, effective precleaning just prior to coating.

Oils, greases, waxes, and other residues must be completely removed to assure maximum coating life.   No trace of such material dare be left.   When properly done, this rigorous first coat cleaning and application should not have to be repeated.

This stress on preparation and cleanliness is a general rule—applying to all current high-durability concrete floor finishes.   The rewards for this extra effort are substantially increased wear-life, better gloss retention (Fig. 9-3), and simplified sanitation and maintenance.   Correct cleaning is essential to success.

In most cases it is advantageous to acid-etch the concrete surface as part of the preparation cycle.   This removes laitance (soft cement crust about $\frac{1}{20}$ in. thick).

Thorough rinsing, repeated several times if necessary, is most important in obtaining good adhesion.   Some detergents (including TSP) have effective cleaning action but often leave a residue which is hard to rinse off.   Easy rinse-off is essential in a good cleaner.   Many finishes fail because they anchor themselves to an "innercoat" of soilage residue and degraded cement particles rather than to the sound concrete underneath.

Considering the exotic nature of the more durable finish coatings, it is not surprising that their handling must be both disciplined and precise.   Basically "unforgiving," many of the top-quality finishes will not tolerate casual pour-it-out-of-a-can application methods.

Recoating Problems Finish Life.   Even with the best finishes, when used in heavy traffic lanes, it may be necessary to recoat the surface in 1 to 5 years.   Material costs for this are usually less than the cost of labor.

Fig. 9-3. Traffic aisle coated with oil-free urethane finish.   (*Courtesy of G. H. Tennant Company, Minneapolis, Minn.*)

Repeated studies show the importance of recoating a finish *before it is worn through*. This is a cost-saving move because any fracture or scratch in the finish may expose the concrete underneath.   Once a stain reaches the abraded porous concrete, it starts to sink in, causing discoloration.   To remove such stains (oils, contaminants, etc.) from the raw concrete is costly and time-consuming.   Recoating avoids this expense—when it's done in time.

Use Proper Equipment and Methods.   Good mechanical equipment, such as powered scarifiers for removing compacted dirt before initial floor cleaning, saves time and labor costs.   Portable rotary chipping machines are useful in corners, along walls, and next to machinery.   Factory-type tank vacuum units (with wet and dry pickup) have value on most cleaning, finishing, and recoating jobs.   In some cases, special equipment can be rented economically.

Correct techniques are even more important.   Responsible manufacturers of high-grade maintenance equipment and finishes have specialists in concrete cleaning and protection.   Their recommendations, based on long experience, help assure maximum value from the coatings used.   In some cases, test applications may be advisable in key plant areas before general refinishing.

In rare cases, traffic may be so cuttingly abrasive and concentrated (or the concrete so weak) that no finish will hold up.   An example of this is in bakeries where steel bread racks, guided in a constant identical track, gouge furrows in the floor.   No known finish will hold up under these conditions.

The best solution to such problems, other than floor replacement, is to apply a chemical hardener to the concrete.   Materials such as fluosilicates or zinc sulfates do the best job here.   They should be reapplied as often as necessary to provide some degree of wear resistance.   Repeated 1 to 1 dilutions may be helpful in giving added depth to the hardening process, thus avoiding superficial skin hardening.

SPECIAL PROTECTIVE COATINGS

For use in selected areas subject to abnormal chemical spillage, load stresses, abrasion, etc., thick protective toppings are available.

Usually applied in one coat, possibly using a special primer, these materials leave a layer $\frac{1}{16}$ in. or more thick.   Most toppings are specially compounded using epoxy, urethane, or other elastomer materials.

Epoxy Toppings.   Epoxy toppings are increasingly used in wet spillage areas in food plants where constant wetness from food acids readily attacks concrete.   They are likewise used where impervious concrete surfaces are required by sanitary and public health requirements.

Some terrazzo-type compositions are now used in offices, corridors, and reception areas where easy cleaning is desired.   The elastomers here offer speedier installation and less construction tie-up—since they harden faster than ordinary cement or magnesite terrazzo.

Topping materials with high ratios of aggregate of suitable size are useful even for wet conditions, because of their highly antislip properties.   Other variations in blends provide patching compounds for cracks, ramps, decks, etc.   Where crack movement is anticipated, it may be advisable to use open mesh fiberglass as a reinforcing agent for the topping.

Surface coatings are frequently of two or three components (such as resin, hardener, sand), depending on the need for strengthening aggregates.   A typical epoxy coating of 1 gal mixed with 50 lb sand provides enough mix to cover 50 sq ft with a $\frac{1}{8}$-in. layer.   The cost of materials per square foot is approximately 30 cents.

Urethane and Allied Elastomers.   These are increasingly used as toppings.   Some of the urethane formulations are more tough and abrasion resistant than epoxies, yet also more flexible.

These materials are best applied by contractors experienced in their selection and use.   Ingredient types vary and should be selected for specific conditions such as subsurface wetness, nature of chemical spillage, impact and shock factors, abrasive traffic, etc.   Dry, sound concrete is a must for an application of this type.   Tests are available for determining concrete strength, alkalinity, and objectionable hydrostatic water pressure.

Complete removal of oil, dirt, and surface contaminants is important.   For effective adhesion the surface should be acid-etched, sandblasted, or scarified.

Chapter 10

MAINTENANCE AND CLEANING
OF CLAY MASONRY STRUCTURES

Source: STRUCTURAL CLAY PRODUCTS INSTITUTE
Washington, D.C.

Completely filled mortar joints, characteristic of good workmanship, and the use of brick and tile, whose physical properties can meet those required for the proper grade, will help prevent structural cracks and leaky walls.

Care in workmanship will prevent mortar and paint stains. The use of drips under projecting sills, belt courses, copings, etc., will prevent water-washed dirt stains. Proper design to prevent rust or other metallic stains from streaking the wall will also reduce future maintenance costs.

The omission of flashing, the use of an improper type, or good flashing improperly placed often is responsible for the most serious maintenance problems. Unflashed brick or stone sills, projecting courses and, particularly, copings generally result in leakage or, at least, disfigured walls caused by efflorescence.

REPAIRING LEAKY WALLS

While properly constructed clay masonry walls are remarkably free of costly repair and maintenance, the repair of a wall that has developed leaks because of poor initial workmanship or design often is difficult and expensive. Care in the selection and use of mortar, and adequate flashing and tooling of joints will probably add only a small amount to the initial cost, but will ensure a low maintenance overhead throughout the life of the property.

Tuck-pointing. Where the mortar joints have softened or disintegrated, or cracked open, tuck-pointing is usually necessary. It is accomplished by cutting away defective mortar to a depth of at least ½ in. and then replacing with proper mortar. When a wall leaks, point all joints in affected areas, since it is usually impossible to determine defective joints by visual inspection. If some joints are noticeably deteriorated, it is likely that others soon will be. Generally, it is more economical to tuck-point a given area at one time, rather than at several times, because of the costs of transporting men and materials, setting up scaffolding, etc. If no leaking occurs, and tuck-pointing is done as normal preventive maintenance, pointing only visibly deteriorated or defective joints may be more economical.

Through the years, satisfactory tuck-pointing procedures have evolved. Follow these procedures for optimum results: Remove mortar to a depth of at least ½ in. with hand or power tools. When cutting is completed, remove all loose material with a brush or, preferably, with a hose stream.

Carefully select and proportion mortars. Because high-cement mortars may shrink excessively while hardening, avoid using mortar with higher portland-cement content than the original. Excessive shrinkage will reduce mortar bond, lowering resistance to water penetration.

Prehydrate all tuck-pointing mortars. To prehydrate mortar, thoroughly mix all ingredients dry. Then mix again, adding only enough water to produce a damp, unworkable mix which will retain its form when pressed into a ball. After keeping mortar in this dampened condition for 1–2 hr, add sufficient water to bring it to the proper consistency, i. e., somewhat drier than conventional masonry mortar.

For best results, duplicate the original mortar proportions. When in doubt, use prehydrated Type N mortar, e.g., 1 part portland cement, 1 part Type S hydrated lime, and 6 parts sand, proportioned by volume.

To ensure good bond, wet the mortar joints thoroughly before applying fresh mortar. Because the joints should not be visibly wet with free-standing water, allow water to soak into the wall. Pack mortar tightly in thin layers until joint is filled, then tool to a smooth, concave surface.

Joint Waterproofing. If openings and cracks in joints are sufficiently small, a grout coating will effectively seal them, significantly reducing water penetration. A typical recommended grout coating consists of $\frac{3}{4}$ part portland cement, 1 part sand that passes a No. 30 sieve, and $\frac{1}{4}$ part limestone flour, powdered flint, or fine hydrated lime. Shortly before using, mix all ingredients with water to obtain a fluid consistency. Wet joints thoroughly, but permit masonry to absorb surface water before applying grout. Brush the grout into joints vigorously with a stiff fiber brush. If a neat appearance is desired, use a templet to keep masonry units clean while applying grout. Two coats are usually required.

Painting. Although some masonry walls require protective coatings to impart color and help in resisting rain penetration, clay masonry requires no painting. Brick and tile generally are selected because, among other characteristics, they have integral and durable color and, when properly constructed, are resistant to rain. Most paint authorities agree that, once painted, exterior masonry will require repainting every three to five years.

Clay masonry walls may be painted to increase light reflection or for decorative purposes. However, painting will not protect under-burned units, frequently found in used brick, from disintegration. Some masonry paints also serve as waterproofers.

Unfortunately, many people assume that painting will protect masonry walls. For this reason, they give less attention to the freezing and thawing resistance of masonry units when painting is planned. In reality, if brick and tile masonry are to be painted, they should be more resistant to freezing and thawing than unpainted masonry.

If a changed wall appearance is not objectionable, cement-based paints can be used to reduce water penetration. Brush a single coat of cement grout onto all joints. Follow this with two coats of cement-based paint applied uniformly to the entire wall surface. National Bureau of Standards tests show that cement-based paints are durable and highly resistant to water penetration when properly mixed and applied. Water-thinned emulsion paints may also prove satisfactory where cracks are very small. However, once a wall has been painted it will require costly periodic repainting.

Paints *per se* are not necessarily good waterproofing agents. Furthermore, non-porous paints, i.e., oil paints and most other solvent-thinned paints, should not be used on exterior brick or tile masonry.

Silicones. Although they are often called *waterproofers*, silicones are really *damp-proofers*. Without actually sealing openings, silicones retard water absorption by changing the contact angle between water and the walls of capillary pores. This creates a *negative capillarity* which repels rather than absorbs water. However, because silicones are not 100 per cent effective, treated masonry will still absorb some water.

Masonry silicones are available from many sources. The two major classifications are water-based and solvent-based silicones, each of which can be applied by spraying or brushing. In general, solvent-based silicones penetrate better, because of their smaller molecular structures. Water-based silicones are usually less expensive.

Transparent Waterproofers. Beside silicones, a number of other transparent waterproofers are available, usually containing waxes and oils. The National Bureau of Standards published data from tests conducted to determine the effectiveness of many waterproofers, including several transparent types. In general, these test data indicate that those colorless waterproofers tested are ineffective when applied to walls that leak badly. Where leakage is through very fine cracks, some colorless waterproofers are effective, but this effectiveness noticeably diminishes with time, usually within two years. Undoubtedly, there are transparent waterproofers with fine performance records; but, since there is the possibility of obtaining an ineffective waterproofer, the performance of a particular material should be investigated before use.

Flashing. When the maintenance problem involves the replacement of defective flashing or the installation of flashing which should have been installed when the building was originally constructed, the only proper solution is an expensive repair job which requires removing the masonry units and placing suitable flashing around and under them. When continuous flashing is required in existing walls at spandrels or other locations, it can be placed by removing alternate masonry sections in widths up to 2 or 3 ft. After the flashing is placed and the masonry is aged properly, the intermediate sections can be removed and the flashing completed. This is a time-consuming and expensive procedure, but quite often the expense is justified if the work is properly done in order to assure a sound and maintenance-free structure in the future.

Calking. Improper calking often is responsible for the most serious water leakage around door and window frames, and quite often becomes a considerable maintenance expense. If the calking was omitted, this can be corrected easily by filling all cracks with good elastic calking compound placed with a pressure gun. On the other hand, if the original calking has cracked, peeled, or separated, it should be removed and replaced with new compound. Unless proper pressure is used, only a thin film of calking compound will be placed. Even with good material this will soon become ineffective. Thin films of calking should be removed and properly replaced before serious damage is caused.

CLEANING

Minute quantities of certain minerals found in some burned clay masonry units will react with some cleaning agents, particularly acids, and cause staining. Since the reactions cannot be predicted, it is recommended that, before applying any cleaning agent to a masonry wall, it be applied to a sample wall section of 10 to 20 sq ft and its effectiveness judged from an inspection of the sample after a period of not less than one week after application.

Cleaning New Masonry

In the construction of masonry walls, a skilled mason will generally keep the surface remarkably free from mortar particles and stains. However, in modern construction, where speed in erection is important, even the most skilled mason will find it difficult, if not impossible, to keep his work entirely free from stains. For this reason, most specifications require a final washing down of all masonry work.

Acid Solution. In the past, a solution of hydrochloric acid has been used most extensively as the cleaning agent for new masonry. The following procedures utilizing an acid or base solution are reproduced from the publication *Brick Cleaning* by J. L. Clark, published by the Robinson Brick and Tile Company, Denver, Colo., and are recommended as good practice.

Cleaning Dark Brick (red, red-flash, brown, and black). Dark-colored brick is most apt to show a light-gray mortar scum from failure to rinse off all dissolved mortar and dirt. Brown and yellow discolorations will show.

PROCEDURE A.   Requires no acid.   (Acid should be used only in difficult cases or areas.)

1. Make the cleaning operation one of the last phases of the job.   Don't start before mortar is thoroughly set and cured.
2. *Dry clean.*   Remove large particles of mortar with wood paddles and scrapers before wetting the wall.   In some instances it may be necessary to use a chisel or wire brush.
3. *Presoak wall.*   Saturate the masonry with clean water and flush off all loose mortar and dirt.
4. *Scrub.*   Scrub down walls with a solution of ½ cup of trisodium phosphate (Calgon) and ½ cup of household detergent (All) dissolved in 1 gal of clean water.   Scrub with stiff fiber brush only.
5. *Rinse.*   Thoroughly wash off all cleaning solution, dirt, and mortar crumbs, using clean, pressurized water.

PROCEDURE B.   When acid cleaning proves necessary, in certain areas, the following method is suggested.

1. Make the cleaning operation one of the last phases of the job.   Don't start before mortar is thoroughly set and cured.
2. *Dry clean.*   A good dry cleaning saves time and acid.   Remove large particles of mortar with wood paddles and scrapers before wetting the wall.   In some instances it may be necessary to use a chisel or wire brush.
3. *Presoak wall.*   Flush off all loose mortar and dirt.   Soak the area to be cleaned with plenty of clean water just before applying the acid.   As long as the masonry is saturated, the acid and dissolved mortar will not be drawn into the face of the brick.
4. *Acid.*   Use a clean, stain-free commercial grade of hydrochloric acid (muriatic). Mix, not more than, 1 *part of acid to 9 parts of clean water in a nonmetallic container*.   Apply and scrub with a long-handled fiber brush.   Pour acid into water, not water into acid.   Use only clean water.   *Note:* Screen wire scrapers, under no condition, should be dipped or placed in the container of acid solution.
5. *Look out below.*   Be aware of the area below the cleaning operation.   Keep all brickwork below the area being cleaned soaked with water and flushed free of acid and dissolved mortar.   This acid scum, if permitted to dry, may be impossible to remove when the area is cleaned.
6. *Scrub.*   Scrub the brick, not the mortar joints.   Use stiff fiber brushes, and wood panels when possible, and never allow metal tools to come into contact with the container of acid solution.   *Note:* Metal marks on brickwork will be oxidized (rusted) by the acid solution, so be sure to wash off these oxidized areas before they dry and stain the brick.
7. *Time and weather.*   Clean only a small area at a time, preferably not more than 10 to 20 sq ft.   It may be necessary to clean even smaller areas when heat, direct sunlight, warm masonry, or warm, dry winds increase the reaction rate of the acid and accelerate drying.   This is a precaution against the brick drying and sucking the dissolved mortar, dirt, and acid into the pores of the brick.
8. *Rinse.*   Wash the wall thoroughly with plenty of *clean* water after scrubbing with acid, but before it dries.   The acid solution in contact with mortar usually loses its strength after 5 to 10 min, and should be washed off.   Dissolved mortar and unreacted acid must be removed to give a bright, trouble-free wall.

Cleaning Light-Colored Brick (buff, gray, specks, and pink).   Light-colored brick is more susceptible to acid burn and stains than darker brick.   Iron impurities in the acid, and the reaction of acid with metal tools and metal marks produce yellow and brown colors on this type of brickwork.   They can be streaked and the color dulled by failing to wash off the cleaning scum.

PROCEDURE A.   Same as for dark-colored brick.   *Acid should not be used* on light-colored brick *except in extreme cases.*

PROCEDURE B. Same as for dark-colored brick, except as follows:

1. *Acid*. Use the highest grade acid (chemically pure) available. Clean, stain-free acid as a general rule will be free from any yellow or brown discoloration.
2. *Acid*. Use not more than 1 *part high-grade acid to* 15 *parts clean water*. When used, the acid wash should be neutralized as recommended below in section on Removing Vanadium Stain.
3. *Scrub*. Scrub with stiff fiber brushes and wood scrapers only. Avoid contact with all metals.

Textured Brick. A texture or lack of texture will not conceal faulty cleaning. No texture can prevent dirt, mortar stains, or acid stains from dulling the natural color and beauty of the brick.

SMOOTH TEXTURES. Mortar stains and smears are generally easier to remove from smooth brick. As there is less surface area exposed, it is usually easier to presoak and rinse this type of brick. The unbroken surface is more likely to show poor rinsing, acid staining, and poor removal of mortar smears.

ROUGH TEXTURES. Most rough textures permit mortar in laying and mortar dirt in cleaning to penetrate deep down into the textures. In addition, the rougher textures present additional area for water and acid absorption. It is absolutely essential to use pressurized water in rinsing to remove all dirt and dissolved mortar from the texture marks.

Cleaning Glazed Brick and Tile. Glazed brick and tile should be carefully wiped clean with a soft cloth, within a few minutes after laying. A final cleaning with a soft sponge or brush and ample water will usually do the job. The following procedures are necessary only in more difficult cases.

PROCEDURE A. Same as Procedure A for dark-colored brick, except as follows:

1. Use no metal cleaning tools, brushes, or abrasive powders.

PROCEDURE B. Same as Procedure B for light-colored brick, except as follows:

1. Use no metal cleaning tools, brushes, or abrasive powders.
2. Use no more than 1 *part high-grade acid (CP) to* 25 *parts of clean water*.
3. Acid should never be used in cleaning salt-glazed or metallic-glazed masonry units.

Sandblasting. A sandblasting technique for cleaning new masonry has been developed which is used extensively in some areas. It is reported to cost approximately the same as acid cleaning and, with an experienced operator, "there is virtually no change in texture of hard brick, except that caution must be used on brick with sand finish." This method obviously eliminates the dangers of mortar smear, acid burn, and efflorescence inherent in acid cleaning.

A prominent masonry contractor from Texas states:

We are gradually switching to sandblasting completely, because we do not have the problem of chemical reaction with vanadium salts and other foreign matter which is unavoidable in some types of clay with a liquid cleaner.

He describes his sandblasting operation as follows:

We use a very-low-pressure (from 60 to 120 lb) sandblasting technique. Although we try to keep the pressure as low as possible, the secret of cleaning the brick and not damaging the mortar joints lies in the type of nozzle and the distance the cleaner stands from the wall and the manner in which he directs the blast to the brick.

In other words, he must concentrate on cleaning and hitting the brick with the sand rather than the mortar joints and he must stand far enough away from the wall that he merely cleans the brick and does not etch it or deface it.

At present we are using a standard commercial size pot and hose with a quarter-inch sandblast nozzle, catalog number SC-4. We use white urn sand to blast these brick because this sand is round in nature instead of sharp and jagged. We find that the round, fine, urn sand is far better for cleaning purposes and does not cut nearly as deep as a sharp sand does.

I recommend that the person using the sandblast technique employ a very-high-caliber tuck-pointer-sandblaster, and experiment a little bit, as to how far away from the wall to obtain maximum cleaning results without defacing the brick or damaging the mortar joints.

Removing Efflorescence

The sources and methods of preventing efflorescence are discussed in *Brick and Tile Engineering*, 1962 edition.* As indicated, the term efflorescence generally refers to a white, powdery substance sometimes seen on masonry wall surfaces. It is composed of one or more water-soluble salts originally present in the masonry materials that have been brought to the surface by water and deposited by evaporation. It can frequently be removed by water applied with a stiff scrubbing brush. In those cases where this procedure does not remove all the efflorescence, the surface should be scrubbed with a solution of hydrochloric (muriatic) acid not stronger than 1 part of the commercial acid to 9 parts water by volume, as recommended for cleaning new masonry. It is highly important that the recommendation regarding water-soaking and rinsing of the wall, before and after washing, be followed.

Removing Vanadium Stain

It is generally agreed that "green staining" is caused by salts of vanadium. While the stain is usually green, sometimes it is a brownish green and, more rarely, a brown. The amount of vanadium in the brick is very small—of the order of 0.01 per cent. It is not known in what form the vanadium is present—not in the raw material, nor in the fired brick, nor in the stained brick surface. If these identifications could be made, the problem of eliminating vanadium staining would be simplified; research is presently directed toward the identification of the compounds involved.

There are three facts about vanadium chemistry that must be emphasized if an intelligent approach is to be made to the problem of washing vanadium-stained brick.

1. Vanadium salts may be divided into two classes (*a*) colorless salts which crystallize in alkaline or neutral solutions and (*b*) colored salts which are obtained from more or less acid solutions. The colorless salts are quite soluble in water, while the colored salts are only slightly soluble.
2. While the reactions of the colorless salts are practically instantaneous, the colored salts change slowly.
3. The vanadium salts react much more rapidly with acid than with alkali.

The fact that colored salts are obtained from the acid solutions explains something that is observed frequently: green-staining brick will often show no sign of staining until they are acid-washed, at which time the vanadium salts go into the acid solution and are precipitated, on drying, as colored salts.

Since it is impossible to predict whether or not clay masonry units contain sufficient vanadium to cause staining and, if so in what form the vanadium is present, it is important that the effect of any acid wash on the masonry units be determined by applying it to a sample wall area before it is applied to the entire project.

If, following the acid wash, green staining appears on the sample, the following procedure, which provides for neutralization of the acid, should be followed:

1. Immediately following the acid wash, as recommended for cleaning new construction, wash the wall with water.
2. Wash or spray the wall with a solution of potassium or sodium hydroxide, consisting of $\frac{1}{2}$ lb hydroxide to 1 qt water (2 lb per gal). Allow this to remain on the wall for two or three days, in order to neutralize the acid which causes green staining.
3. The white salt left on the wall by the hydroxide may be hosed off after two or three days, or it will be removed by the first heavy rain.

*By Harry C. Plummer, published by Structural Clay Products Institute.

To date, research has not developed any single method for removing green stain that can be recommended as best for all conditions.   The following recommendations of the Structural Clay Products Research Foundation, a Division of the Structural Clay Products Institute is based on information currently available: For the removal of only green stain, the first effort should be with sodium hydroxide.   A successful practice has been to apply it with a paint brush (scrubbing probably is wasted effort);

Table 10-1. Proprietary Cleaning Compounds

No.	Product	Manufacturer
	Dry powder form	
1	Saf-T-Klenz	Berman Chemical Company 1916 N. 12th St. Toledo 2, Ohio
2	Etch	Unknown
3	Devil Powder	Unknown
	Inorganic acid form (hydrochloric)	
4	Sure Kleen 101	Process Solvent Company 1040 Chelsea Trafficway Kansas City 2, Kan.
5	Sure Kleen 600	Same
6	Quick Masonry Cleaner— Brick Cleaner No. 22	Delta Plastics, Inc. P.O. Box 93 Anderson, S.C.
7	Deox	National Chemsearch Corporation P.O. Box 10087 Dallas 7, Tex.
	DC-6—same compound as Deox[1]	Hallmark Chemical Corporation P.O. Box 1207 Irving, Tex.
	Organic acid form	
8	Brick Klenz	Klenzade Products Beloit, Wis.
	Flash Klenz—same com- pound as Brick Klenz[1]	Klenzade of the Southwest _____Tex.
9	Calmal 22 Foam Masonry (also contains hydrochloric acid)	American Calmal Corporation 2540 West 6th Lane Hialeah, Fla.
	Emulsifying agents	
10	Big Red	Texas Refinery Corporation P.O. Box 711 Fort Worth 1, Tex.
11	ND-150	National Chemsearch Corporation
	WE-880—same compound as ND-150[1]	Hallmark Chemical Corporation
12	Clix	National Chemsearch Corporation
	GR-707—same compound as Clix[1]	Hallmark Chemical Corporation

[1] Manufactured by originator, but packaged and sold under another name by distributor listed.

simply put a liberal application on and give it plenty of time to work.   Pass no judgment on it for at least three days.

A convenient way to use sodium hydroxide is in the form of Drano.   The mixture that has been used successfully in field trials is one 12-oz can per qt of water.   A white salt will be left on the wall, which can be washed off with a hose after three days.

Various proprietary cleaning compounds have proved successful in some instances.   Their effectiveness on a particular project can best be determined by trial.

Removing Manganese Stain

This form of stain usually occurs on the mortar joints between manganese gray or brown brick.   Also, in some cases, it appears on the brick.   It has a brown, oily appearance and seems to run down from the brick-mortar interface.

This stain has been traced to the manganese used to color the brick.   Some of the manganese which is added to the clay is converted during firing to a form which is soluble in a mildly acidic solution.   Rain water acidified by carbon dioxide or sulfur in the air is sufficiently strong to dissolve some of these salts.   When the solution reaches the mortar joints, it is neutralized by the basic nature of the cement or lime in the mortar and the salts are deposited there.

Manganese stain is difficult to remove, since it is not particularly soluble in hydrochloric acid.   Theoretically, it is soluble in sulfuric acid, but such a strong solution is needed that the mortar joints would be eaten away, to say nothing about the danger of white efflorescence forming later.

The quickest, easiest method of removing the stain so far discovered is to use a solution of 1 part, by volume, of acetic acid (80 per cent or stronger), 1 part of hydrogen peroxide (30–35 per cent), and 6 parts of water.   This solution, when sprayed on the wall, removes the stain very rapidly.   The chief difficulty is that the stain often returns within a few days.

A proprietary cleaning compound, No. 8, Table 10-1, investigated on several jobs, appears to be effective in keeping the stain from reappearing, although it is not always as rapid in removing the manganese stain initially as the acetic acid-peroxide solution. The best method found to date for the long-term removal of the stain is:

1. After wetting the wall, brush or spray it with the acetic acid-hydrogen peroxide solution described above.
2. After the reaction is complete, rinse the wall again with water.   Brush or spray the wall with a solution of 1 part by volume of Brick Klenz to 3 parts of water. This solution is allowed to remain on the wall and is *not* flushed off.

Removal of Externally Caused Stains

These are stains caused by something being spilled on and absorbed by the brick. Each is an individual case and must be treated as such.

A large number of such stains can be removed by scrubbing with a good kitchen cleanser.   Others can frequently be removed by bleaching with a household bleach. A combination, such as found in some of the new kitchen cleansers, may prove most effective.   Table 10-2 lists sources, other than chemical supply firms, of some of the materials recommended below.

Poultice.   A poultice, as included in some of the following recommendations, is a paste made with a solvent or reagent and some inert material.   The inert material may be talc, whiting, fuller's earth, bentonite, or some other clay.   The solution or solvent used depends upon the stain to be removed.   Enough of the solution or solvent is added to a small quantity of the inert material to make a smooth paste.   The paste is smeared onto the stained area with a trowel or spatula and allowed to dry. When dried, the remaining powder is scraped off.

A poultice cleans by much the same type of action as takes place when efflorescence occurs.   The solvent in the poultice dissolves the offending stain on the brick.   The resulting solution then migrates to the surface of the poultice where the solvent evaporates.   The stain is left on the loose, powdery residue and can be removed along with it.   Repeated applications may be necessary since all of the stain may not dissolve the first time.   The chief advantages of poultices are that they tend to prevent the stain from spreading during treatment and they tend to "pull" the stain out of the pores of the brick.

If the solvent used in preparing a poultice is an acid, do not use whiting as the inert material.   Whiting is a carbonate which reacts with acids to give off carbon dioxide. While this is not dangerous, it does make a foamy mess and destroys the power of the acid.

Paint Stains. For fresh paint, apply a commercial paint remover, or a solution of trisodium phosphate in water—2 lb of trisodium phosphate to 1 gal of water. Allow to stand and remove paint with scraper and wire brush. Wash with clear water. For very old, dried paint, organic solvents similar to the above may not be effective, in which case the paint must be removed by sandblasting or scrubbing with steel wool.

Iron Stains. Iron stains are quite common, and in some cases have covered entire walls. These stains are easily removed by spraying or brushing with a strong solution (1 lb per gal) of oxalic acid in water. Ammonium bifluoride added to the solution ($\frac{1}{2}$ lb per gal) will speed up the reaction. The ammonium bifluoride generates hydrofluoric acid which etches the brick. This will be evident on very smooth brick and, therefore, should be used with caution.

Table 10-2. Sources of Cleaning Agents

Cleaning Agents	*Source of Supply*
Aluminum chloride	Available from your pharmacist.
Ammonia water	Household ammonia water available at the supermarket.
Ammonium chloride	Salt-like substance available from a pharmacist.
Ammonium sulfamate	Not now readily available. Was used as base in weed killers. Now substitute any weed killer solution as marketed by nursery and garden supply stores; use according to directions on the package.
Caustic soda	A material capable of destroying or eating away by chemical action. Use any of several brand-name substances, such as "Drano," available at the supermarket.
Kieselguhr	Diatomaceous earth; not easily available.
Lime-free glycerine	A liquid available on the counters at drug stores; usually used as a base for hand lotions.
Powdered pumice	Available at hardware stores for use as a sanding or polishing material.
Sodium citrate	Looks like enlarged salt granules; purchase from a pharmacist.
Sodium hydrosulphite	A white salt available from a pharmacist, or it is the "hypo" of photographic fixing agents.
Talc	An inert powder available on drug store counters as "purified talc"; or substitute bathroom talcum powder.
Trichloroethylene	A highly refined solvent. Purchase dry-cleaning solvent from service station or supermarket.
Trisodium phosphate	A strong base-type powdered cleaning material sold under brand names by all paint stores and some hardware stores.
Whiting	A powdered chalk used as a pigment in putty and cold-water paints. Available at paint manufacturers, or possibly some large paint departments. If purchase is too difficult, probably kitchen flour would suffice.

ALTERNATE METHOD. Mix 7 parts lime-free glycerine with a solution of 1 part sodium citrate in 6 parts lukewarm water, and mix with whiting or kieselguhr to make a thick paste. Apply paste to stain with trowel, and scrape off when dried out. Repeat until stain has disappeared and wash thoroughly with clear water. A poultice made from a solution of sodium hydrosulphite and an inert powder (such as talc) has also been used for the removal of iron rust stains.

Copper or Bronze Stains. Mix together in the dry form 1 part ammonium chloride (sal ammoniac) and 4 parts powdered talc. Add ammonia water and stir until a thick paste is obtained. Place this over the stain and leave until dry. When working on glazed tile, use a wood paddle to scrape off the paste. An old stain of this kind may require several applications. Sometimes aluminum chloride is used in the above procedure instead of the sal ammoniac.

Welding Splatter. A problem related to iron staining is welding "splatter." When metal is welded too close to a wall or pile of brick, some of the molten metal may splash onto the brick and actually melt into the surface. The oxalic acid–ammonium bifluoride mixture, recommended for iron stains, is particularly effective in removing welding splatters.   As much of the metal as possible is scraped from the brick.   The solution is then applied in a poultice.   When the poultice is dried, it is removed and, if the stain has not disappeared, sandpaper is used to remove as much as possible and a fresh poultice applied.   For stubborn stains, several applications may be necessary.

Smoke Stains.   Smoke is another stain difficult to remove.   A thorough scrubbing with scouring powder (particularly one containing bleach) and a stiff bristle brush, works surprisingly well.   Some of the alkali detergents and commercial emulsifying agents, such as Nos. 10 and 11, Table 10-1 brushed or sprayed on and given sufficient time to work, also do a good job.   These have the added advantage that they can be used in steam cleaners.   For the more stubborn stains, a poultice using trichloroethylene will pull the stain from the pores.   Precaution should be taken to ventilate a closed space in which trichloroethylene is used, as the fumes are harmful.

Oil and Tar Stains.   Oil and tar stains are also effectively removed by the commercial emulsifying agents Nos. 10, 11, and 12, Table 10-1.   For heavy tar stains they can first be mixed with kerosene to remove the tar and then with water to remove the kerosene.   After application, they can be hosed off the wall.   When used in a steam cleaning apparatus, Nos. 10 and 11, Table 10-1 have been known to remove tar without the use of kerosene.

Where the area to be cleaned is small, or in a place where a mess cannot be tolerated, a poultice using benzene, naphtha, or trichloroethylene is most effective in removing oil stains.

Dirt.   Dirt is sometimes difficult to remove, particularly from a textured brick. Scouring powder or Nos. 10 and 11, Table 10-1, and a stiff bristle brush are effective if the texture is not too rough.   Scrubbing with the oxalic acid–ammonium bifluoride solution recommended for iron stains has proved effective on some moderately rough textures.   For very rough textures, high-pressure steam cleaning appears to be the most effective method.

Straw and Paper Stains.   Straw and paper stains sometimes result when the materials used to pack brick for shipment become wet.   Not all packing materials will stain brick, but those that do may produce a very stubborn stain.   This stain can be removed by applying household bleach and allowing it to dry.   However, several applications may be required.   The solution of oxalic acid–ammonium bifluoride recommended for iron stain cleans the stain much more rapidly.

Plant Growth.   Occasionally an exterior masonry surface which is not exposed to sunlight and remains in a constantly damp condition will exhibit signs of plant growth, such as moss.   Application of ammonium sulfamate (marketed under the manufacturer's brand name and available in gardening supply stores) according to directions furnished with the compound has been used successfully in the removal of such growths.

Stains of Unknown Origin.   Stains of unknown origin can be a real challenge at times.   Appearance may be the first real clue.   Rust-colored stains may actually be rust.   Such stains are quite common and have been known to come from mortar ingredients, welding splatter on the back of the brick, or something being laid on the pile of brick before they were laid on the wall.

Green stains may be grass, moss, or vanadium efflorescence.   Brown stains, also, may be vanadium efflorescence, or possibly manganese staining.   Black stains can be almost anything.

One test, useful in narrowing down the list of possible causes of a stain, involves a substance which ordinarily should not be put on a wall.   When concentrated sulfuric acid comes into contact with an organic material, the organic material turns black. This is a quick and easy way to identify stains originating from such a material. Organic stains can usually be removed with household bleach or oxalic acid.

Cleansing Existing Masonry

In the paper, "Exterior Building Cleaning," by Rockwell Newman, President of the Rockwell Newman Company, Orange, N.J., which was published in the May–

June, 1957 issue of *Catholic Building and Maintenance*, Mr. Newman lists five methods of cleaning exterior masonry walls "in the order of their popularity." They are: high-pressure steam, sandblasting, hand washing, high-pressure cold-water blast, and chemical and steam. The following descriptions of various cleaning methods are summarized from his paper.

High-pressure Steam. Probably more buildings are cleaned by steam than in any other way, because this method lends itself more readily and more satisfactorily to the various types of masonry than any other. Buildings erected with a smooth, hard type of unit, or a material with a glazed or vitreous surface, should always be cleaned by the steam method. The group would include terra cotta, polished granite or marble, smooth vitreous brick, tile, or any unit which might be pocked or etched by sandblasting. Naturally, the more impervious a masonry unit, the easier it should clean, and this is generally the case.

In most cases, buildings can be cleaned satisfactorily with high-pressure steam only; but where stains have developed, it is sometimes necessary to use a solution of detergent.

Sandblasting. The most commonly used method of sandblasting is the dry one, which is simply a combination of sand from a tank forced through a hose and nozzle by compressed air at various pressures, depending upon the surface to be cleaned and the type of unit involved. This method should be employed only when the units will not be damaged and/or when certain types cannot be successfully cleaned with high-pressure steam. This sometimes is the case with respect to more porous material, such as limestone, sandstone, and certain types of brick; but regardless of the type of unit in the building to be sandblasted, a sample of substantial size should be done by the contractor before proceeding with the entire job.

Hand Washing. Many buildings of smaller size have been cleaned successfully by hand washing. It is a bit slower and does not give the added advantage of the heat in high-pressure steam. Usually this work is done by using some sort of soap or detergent with cold water. The method is more costly because it is slower, does not lend itself to a job of any size, and must be done more often.

High-pressure Cold-Water. Reasonably new in the field, high-pressure cold-water blast is being used a great deal in the Midwest and Pacific Coast regions but not much in the East or large eastern cities. It does a very satisfactory job; however, getting rid of the large volume of water used is sometimes a problem. Another requisite of this method is an ample water supply.

Chemicals and Steam. Mr. Newman points out that chemicals and high-pressure steam are used primarily to remove applied coatings to masonry, such as paint. This is a highly specialized field and frequently the proper cleaning agent can be determined only after analysis of the various factors involved in a particular project.

The following cleaning methods are described in literature of the Western Waterproofing Company, Inc., St. Louis, Mo.

Wet-sand Cleaning. This method is used on unpolished granite, hard brick, rock face, or rough-finished limestone. This type of cleaning depends on a water-cushioned abrasive action for its effectiveness. It is recommended for removal of paint or other surface coatings, or in other situations where abrasion of the surface is permissible. Wet-sand cleaning employs water in the cleaning action to eliminate dust.

Wet-aggregate Cleaning. This is a special process developed by the Western Waterproofing Company for use on limestone, soft brick, or sandstone, particularly effective on surfaces with flutings, carvings, and other ornamentation. It is a gentle but thorough process, employing a mixture of water and a friable aggregate free from silica, delivered at low pressure through a special nozzle with a "scouring" action which cleans effectively without damage to the surface.

PROPRIETARY CLEANING COMPOUNDS

During recent years the Structural Clay Products Research Foundation, a Division of the Structural Clay Products Institute, has investigated the effectiveness of some of the proprietary cleaning compounds now on the market, both for cleaning new masonry and for removing other stains.   Table 10-1 lists the compounds investigated. The absence of any commercial product from this list indicates only that it has not been evaluated by the SCPRF-SCPI Research Division.   The classification (form) is based on the manufacturer's description and classification of his products.   SCPRF-SCPI did not chemically analyze any of these proprietary materials.   The following references to compounds listed in the table are from the SCPRF-SCPI research report, *Cleaning Clay Masonry*.   However, since the manufacturers of the products do not disclose their chemical formulas and are at liberty to change them at any time, the results reported are obviously applicable only to those products whose formulas have remained unchanged.

Dry Powder Form.   Compounds 1, 2, and 3 are sold in the form of a dry powder that is dissolved in water at the job site and used in the same manner as hydrochloric acid.   The chief advantage of such compounds is their dryness.   There is also less likelihood of spillage and the weight of water used to make the solution does not add to the shipping costs.   Another advantage is the relatively low acidity.   While this makes contact with the skin somewhat less dangerous, it makes the resulting solution slower than hydrochloric acid in removing mortar stains.

The chief drawback of these dry powders stems from their chemical composition. Their primary ingredient is sodium bisulphate.   This chemical forms weak sulfuric acid in water.   Applying a solution of this to a wall may impart sulphates to the wall and thus may increase the possibility of efflorescence.

Inorganic Acid Form.   Among the liquid cleaning compounds are those composed primarily of hydrochloric acid, such as No. 4, to which have been added wetting agents to improve their action and buffering agents to inhibit their deterioration of the mortar joints.   The chief advantages claimed for these compounds are that they are safer to handle and there is less likelihood of "burning" the mortar joints.   These, when used according to manufacturers' directions, were found to be no more effective in removing mortar than conventional hydrochloric acid solutions of the same acid strength.

Some of these compounds have been further modified by the addition of oxidizing and chelating agents.   These agents are added to tie up and remove such metallic ions as those of vanadium.   Such action is desirable on brick which tend to green stain.   The compounds of this type investigated (Nos. 5, 6, and 7) appear to be as effective as hydrochloric acid in removing mortar.

Since most such compounds are no *more* effective in removing mortar than 10 per cent hydrochloric acid, and are usually much more expensive, it is advisable for the cleaner to evaluate each one for himself.

Organic Acid Form.   A new type of compound which has appeared recently contains a blend of organic acids (Nos. 8 and 9).   These are generally offshoots of the compounding of chemicals for some other industry and have unique properties of their own.   No. 8 proved effective in removing certain stains, but not very effective in removing mortar.   No. 9, when diluted with three parts of water by volume, was as effective as 10 per cent hydrochloric acid in removing mortar.

REFERENCES

The many *Technical Notes* of Structural Clay Products Institute, 1520 Eighteenth St., N.W., Washington, D.C. 20036.

Section 7

MAINTENANCE OF ELECTRICAL EQUIPMENT

Chapter 1

ELECTRICAL CALCULATIONS

By J. F. McPartland
Associate Editor
Electrical Construction and Maintenance
New York, N.Y.

This chapter sets forth basic information—including formulas, tables, charts, and proven procedures—on minimum requirements for safety in the installation, operation, and utilization of electrical wiring and equipment. It is not intended as a textbook on the theory and practice of electrical power distribution.

All tabulated data presented here are taken from the 1964 National Electrical Code (actually the 1962 edition of the Code). It is important to recognize that the NE Code is only a basic minimum safety standard. Compliance with the Code can effectively minimize fire and accident hazards. But safety is not automatically made a characteristic of a system by simply observing codes. Safety must be designed into a system.

The NE Code is recognized as a legal criterion of safe electrical design and installation. It is used in court litigation and by insurance companies as a basis for insuring buildings. In addition to the NE Code, other standards and recommended practices for electrical work are made available in pamphlet form by the National Fire Protection Association, 60 Batterymarch St., Boston.

In addition to safety, four other major characteristics must be considered in relation to any electrical construction:

1. *Capacity.* Every electrical system should have enough current capacity to serve the loads for which it is designed, plus a carefully determined amount of spare capacity to meet anticipated growth in the load on the system. Allowance for load growth is probably the most neglected consideration in electrical work today.
2. *Flexibility.* Depending upon the activities pursued within a given building, the electrical system must be designed to provide some flexibility in distribution and circuiting. Depending upon the nature of the building—commercial, industrial, or institutional—layout and type of equipment should accommodate changes in locations of lighting, motors, and other loads.
3. *Accessibility.* In its final form, every electrical system should provide ready access to equipment for maintenance and repairs and for any possible extensions or modifications in the system.
4. *Reliability.* Again depending upon the nature of activities in a building, continuity of electrical supply and over-all reliability of the wiring system can be a most important consideration. In such buildings as hospitals, many industrial process plants, and buildings with essential equipment, stand-by power plants or multiple services must be used for absolute reliability of supply.

Table 1-1 (NE Code Table 310-2). Application and Construction

(a) **Conductor Application.** Conductor insulations as specified in the following Table 310-2(a) may be installed for any of the wiring methods recognized in this chapter, except as otherwise provided for in the table or in Sec. 310-3 or as otherwise specified in this Code. They are suitable for 600 volts unless otherwise specified.

(b) **Conductor Construction.** Insulated conductors for use at 600 volts or less shall conform to the provisions of Table 310-2(b).

Table 310-2(a). Conductor Application

Trade name	Type letter	Max. operating temp.	Application provisions
Rubber-covered fixture wire	RF-1*	60°C 140°F	Fixture wiring. Limited to 300 volts
Solid or 7-strand	RF-2*	60°C 140°F	Fixture wiring, and as permitted in Sec. 310-8.
Rubber-covered fixture wire	FF-1*	60°C 140°F	Fixture wiring. Limited to 300 volts.
Flexible stranding	FF-2*	60°C 140°F	Fixture wiring and as permitted in Sec. 310-8.
Heat-resistant rubber-covered fixture wire	RFH-1*	75°C 167°F	Fixture wiring. Limited to 300 volts.
Solid or 7-strand	RFH-2*	75°C 167°F	Fixture wiring and as permitted in Sec. 310-8.
Heat-resistant rubber-covered fixture wire	FFH-1*	75°C 167°F	Fixture wiring. Limited to 300 volts.
Flexible stranding	FFH-2*	75°C 167°F	Fixture wiring and as permitted in Sec. 310-8.
Thermoplastic-covered fixture wire, solid or stranded	TF*	60°C 140°F	Fixture wiring and as permitted in Sec. 310-8.
Thermoplastic-covered fixture wire, flexible stranding	TFF*	60°C 140°F	Fixture wiring.
Cotton-covered heat-resistant fixture wire	CF*	90°C 194°F	Fixture wiring. Limited to 300 volts.
Asbestos-covered heat-resistant fixture wire	AF*	150°C 302°F	Fixture wiring. Limited to 300 volts and indoor dry location.
Silicone-rubber-insulated fixture wire	SF-1*	200°C 392°F	Fixture wiring. Limited to 300 volts.
Solid or 7-strand	SF-2*	200°C 392°F	Fixture wiring and as permitted in Sec. 310-8.
Silicone-rubber-insulated fixture wire	SFF-1*	150°C 302°F	Fixture wiring. Limited to 300 volts.
Flexible stranding	SFF-2*	150°C 302°F	Fixture wiring and as permitted in Sec. 310-8.

* Fixture wires are not intended for installation as branch circuit conductors nor for the connection of portable or stationary appliances.

Table 1-1 (NE Code Table 310-2). Application and Construction (*Continued*)

Trade name	Type letter	Max. operating temp.	Application provisions
Code rubber	R	60°C 140°F	Dry locations.
Heat-resistant rubber	RH	75°C 167°F	Dry locations.
Heat-resistant rubber	RHH	90°C 194°F	Dry locations.
Moisture-resistant rubber	RW	60°C 140°F	Dry and wet locations. For over 2,000 volts insulation shall be ozone-resistant.
Moisture- and heat-resistant rubber	RH-RW	60°C 140°F / 75°C 167°F	Dry and wet locations. For over 2,000 volts insulation shall be ozone-resistant. Dry locations. For over 2,000 volts insulation shall be ozone-resistant.
Moisture- and heat-resistant rubber	RHW	75°C 167°F	Dry and wet locations. For over 2,000 volts insulation shall be ozone-resistant.
Latex rubber	RU	60°C 140°F	Dry locations.
Heat-resistant latex rubber	RUH	75°C 167°F	Dry locations.
Moisture-resistant latex rubber	RUW	60°C 140°F	Dry and wet locations.
Thermoplastic	T	60°C 140°F	Dry locations.
Moisture-resistant thermoplastic	TW	60°C 140°F	Dry and wet locations.
Moisture- and heat-resistant thermoplastic	THW	75°C 167°F	Dry and wet locations.
Moisture- and heat-resistant thermoplastic	THWN	75°C 167°F	Dry and wet locations.
Thermoplastic and asbestos	TA	90°C 194°F	Switchboard wiring only.
Thermoplastic and fibrous outer braid	TBS	90°C 194°F	Switchboard wiring only.
Mineral insulation (metal-sheathed)	MI	85°C 185°F	Dry and wet locations with Type-O termination fittings. Maximum operating temperature for special applications 250°C.

Table 1-1 (NE Code Table 310-2). Application and Construction (*Continued*)

Trade name	Type letter	Max. operating temp.	Application provisions
Silicone-asbestos	SA	90°C 194°F	Dry locations—max. operating temperature for special application 125°C, 194°F.
Varnished cambric	V	85°C 185°F	Dry locations only. Smaller than No. 6 by special permission.
Asbestos and varnished cambric	AVA	110°C 230°F	Dry locations only.
Asbestos and varnished cambric	AVL	110°C 230°F	Dry and wet locations.
Asbestos and varnished cambric	AVB	90°C 194°F	Dry locations only.
Asbestos	A	200°C 392°F	Dry locations only. In raceways, only for leads to or within apparatus. Limited to 300 volts.
Asbestos	AA	200°C 392°F	Dry locations only. Open wiring. In raceways, only for leads to or within apparatus. Limited to 300 volts.
Asbestos	AI	125°C 257°F	Dry locations only. In raceways, only for leads to or within apparatus. Limited to 300 volts.
Asbestos	AIA	125°C 257°F	Dry locations only. Open wiring. In raceways, only for leads to or within apparatus.
Paper		85°C 185°F	For underground service conductors, or by special permission.

ELECTRICAL CALCULATIONS

A logical approach to electrical-system design starts with designing the branch circuits to supply the loads, then providing the panelboards to derive and protect branch circuits where they are energized by feeders, then laying out the feeder distribution circuits to carry blocks of power as needed, and finally, providing main-switchboard and service equipment.   The same sequence is involved in the various calculations that must be made.

CIRCUIT CONDUCTORS

Selection of suitable conductors for any circuit depends upon the voltage of the circuit, the required ampere capacity demanded by the load, and the type of insulation required by the conditions of use.   Table 1-1 [NE Code Table 310-2 (a)] presents data on the use of conductors of various insulations, for use up to 600 volts.   Particular reference to manufacturers' data must be made in the case of high-voltage (over 600 volts) conductors.

Table 1-2 (NE Code Table 8 of Chap. 9). Properties of Conductors

The values given in the table are those given in *Nat. Bur. Std. Circ.* 31, except that those shown in the eighth column are those given in American Society for Testing Materials Specification B33.

The resistance values given in the last three columns are applicable only to direct current. When conductors larger than No. 4/0 are used with alternating current, the multiplying factors in NE Code Table 9, Chap. 9, should be used to compensate for skin effect.

| Size AWG | Area, cir mils | Concentric lay stranded conductors | | Bare conductors | | D-C resistance, ohms/M ft at 25°C, 77°F | | |
| | | | | | | Copper | | Aluminum |
		No. wires	Diam. each wire, in.	Diam., in.	Area,* sq. in.	Bare cond.	Tin'd. cond.	
18	1,624	Solid	0.0403	0.0403	0.0013	6.510	6.77	10.9
16	2,583	Solid	0.0508	0.0508	0.0020	4.094	4.25	6.85
14	4,107	Solid	0.0641	0.0641	0.0032	2.575	2.68	4.31
12	6,530	Solid	0.0808	0.0808	0.0051	1.619	1.69	2.71
10	10,380	Solid	0.1019	0.1019	0.0081	1.018	1.06	1.70
8	16,510	Solid	0.1285	0.1285	0.0130	0.641	0.660	1.07
6	26,250	7	0.0612	0.184	0.027	0.410	0.426	0.674
4	41,740	7	0.0772	0.232	0.042	0.259	0.269	0.423
3	52,640	7	0.0867	0.260	0.053	0.205	0.213	0.336
2	66,370	7	0.0974	0.292	0.067	0.162	0.169	0.266
1	83,690	19	0.0664	0.332	0.087	0.129	0.134	0.211
0	105,500	19	0.0745	0.373	0.109	0.102	0.106	0.168
00	133,100	19	0.0837	0.418	0.137	0.0811	0.0844	0.134
000	167,800	19	0.0940	0.470	0.173	0.0642	0.0668	0.105
0000	211,600	19	0.1055	0.528	0.219	0.0509	0.0524	0.0837
	250,000	37	0.0822	0.575	0.260	0.0431	0.0444	0.0708
	300,000	37	0.0900	0.630	0.312	0.0360	0.0371	0.0590
	350,000	37	0.0973	0.681	0.364	0.0308	0.0318	0.0506
	400,000	37	0.1040	0.728	0.416	0.0270	0.0278	0.0443
	500,000	37	0.1162	0.814	0.520	0.0216	0.0225	0.0354
	600,000	61	0.0992	0.893	0.626	0.0180	0.0185	0.0295
	700,000	61	0.1071	0.964	0.730	0.0154	0.0159	0.0253
	750,000	61	0.1109	0.998	0.782	0.0144	0.0148	0.0236
	800,000	61	0.1145	1.031	0.835	0.0135	0.0139	0.0221
	900,000	61	0.1215	1.093	0.938	0.0120	0.0124	0.0197
	1,000,000	61	0.1280	1.152	1.042	0.0108	0.0111	0.0176
	1,250,000	91	0.1172	1.289	1.305	0.00864	0.00890	0.0142
	1,500,000	91	0.1284	1.412	1.566	0.00719	0.00740	0.0118
	1,750,000	127	0.1174	1.526	1.829	0.00617	0.00636	0.0101
	2,000,000	127	0.1255	1.631	2.089	0.00539	0.00555	0.00884

* Area given is that of a circle having a diameter equal to the over-all diameter of a stranded conductor.

Tables 1-2 and 1-3 (Tables 8 and 9 from chap. 9 of the NE Code) present data on the properties of conductors for a-c and d-c circuits.

For any 2-wire circuit, if the ampere load to be supplied is known and the length of the circuit is known, the cross-section area of the conductor required to serve the load can be determined from the following formula:

$$\text{Area in cir mils} = \frac{2K \times I \times L}{V \text{ (in volts)}}$$

where I = load, amp

L = one-way length of circuit

K = resistivity of copper 11.5

V = permissible voltage drop (1 per cent for lighting, 3 per cent for power)

Table 1-3 (NE Code Table 9 of Chap. 9). Multiplying Factors for Converting Resistance to 60-cycle A-C Resistance

Size	Multiplying factor			
	For nonmetallic-sheathed cables in air or nonmetallic conduit		For metallic-sheathed cables or all cables in metallic raceways	
	Copper	Aluminum	Copper	Aluminum
Up to 3 AWG	1	1	1	1
2	1	1	1.01	1.00
1	1	1	1.01	1.00
0	1.001	1.000	1.02	1.00
00	1.001	1.001	1.03	1.00
000	1.002	1.001	1.04	1.01
0000	1.004	1.002	1.05	1.01
250,000 CM	1.005	1.002	1.06	1.02
300,000 CM	1.006	1.003	1.07	1.02
350,000 CM	1.009	1.004	1.08	1.03
400,000 CM	1.011	1.005	1.10	1.04
500,000 CM	1.018	1.007	1.13	1.06
600,000 CM	1.025	1.010	1.16	1.08
700,000 CM	1.034	1.013	1.19	1.11
750,000 CM	1.039	1.015	1.21	1.12
800,000 CM	1.044	1.017	1.22	1.14
1,000,000 MCM	1.067	1.026	1.30	1.19
1,250,000 MCM	1.102	1.040	1.41	1.27
1,500,000 MCM	1.142	1.058	1.53	1.36
1,750,000 MCM	1.185	1.079	1.67	1.46
2,000,000 MCM	1.233	1.100	1.82	1.56

Tables 1-4 to 1-7 (NE Code Tables 310-12 to 310-15) give the maximum allowable current-carrying capacities of various types of insulated conductors under the indicated conditions of use. These tables establish the maximum current ratings on the basis of the ability of the given insulated conductor to withstand the heat produced by current flow. For use in any circuit, voltage drop in the circuit must be considered, frequently requiring conductors larger than they would have to be merely on a temperature basis.

Table 1-4 (NE Code Table 310-12). Allowable Current-carrying Capacities of Insulated Copper Conductors, in Amperes
Not More than Three Conductors in Raceway or Cable or Direct Burial
(Based on Room Temperature of 30°C, 86°F)

Size AWG or MCM	Rubber Type R, Type RW, Type RU, Type RUW (14-2), Type RH-RW See Note 9, Thermoplastic Type T, Type TW	Rubber Type RH, RUH (14-2), Type RH-RW See Note 9, Type RHW, Thermoplastic Type THW, THWN	Paper / Thermoplastic asbestos Type TA, Thermoplastic Type TBS, Silicone Type SA, Var-Cam Type V, Asbestos Var-Cam Type AVB, MI cable, RHH*	Asbestos Var-Cam Type AVA, Type AVL	Impregnated asbestos Type AI (14-8), Type AIA	Asbestos Type A (14-8), Type AA
14	15	15	25	30	30	30
12	20	20	30	35	40	40
10	30	30	40	45	50	55
8	40	45	50	60	65	70
6	55	65	70	80	85	95
4	70	85	90	105	115	120
3	80	100	105	120	130	145
2	95	115	120	135	145	165
1	110	130	140	160	170	190
0	125	150	155	190	200	225
00	145	175	185	215	230	250
000	165	200	210	245	265	285
0000	195	230	235	275	310	340
250	215	255	270	315	335	
300	240	285	300	345	380	
350	260	310	325	390	420	
400	280	335	360	420	450	
500	320	380	405	470	500	
600	355	420	455	525	545	
700	385	460	490	560	600	
750	400	475	500	580	620	
800	410	490	515	600	640	
900	435	520	555			
1,000	455	545	585	680	730	
1,250	495	590	645			
1,500	520	625	700	785		
1,750	545	650	735			
2,000	560	665	775	840		

Correction factors, room temps. over 30°C, 86°F

°C	°F						
40	104	0.82	0.88	0.90	0.94	0.95	
45	113	0.71	0.82	0.85	0.90	0.92	
50	122	0.58	0.75	0.80	0.87	0.89	
55	131	0.41	0.67	0.74	0.83	0.86	
60	140	....	0.58	0.67	0.79	0.83	0.91
70	158	....	0.35	0.52	0.71	0.76	0.87
75	167	....	....	0.43	0.66	0.72	0.86
80	176	....	....	0.30	0.61	0.69	0.84
90	194	....	....	....	0.50	0.61	0.80
100	212	....	....	....	....	0.51	0.77
120	248	....	....	....	....	....	0.69
140	284	....	....	....	....	....	0.59

* The current-carrying capacities for Type RHH conductors for sizes AWG 14, 12, and 10 shall be the same as designated for Type RH conductors in this table.

Table 1-5 (NE Code Table 310-13). Allowable Current-carrying Capacities of Insulated Copper Conductors, in Amperes
Single Conductor in Free Air (Based on Room Temperature of 30°C, 86°F)

Size AWG or MCM	Rubber Type R Type RW — Type RU Type RUW (14-2) — Type RH-RW See Note 9 — Thermoplastic Type T Type TW	Rubber Type RH — RUH (14-2) — Type RH-RW See Note 9 — Type RHW Thermoplastic Type THW — THWN	Paper — Thermoplastic asbestos Type TA — Thermoplastic Type TBS — Silicone Type SA — Var-Cam Type V — Asbestos Var-Cam Type AVB — MI cable — RHH*	Asbestos Var-Cam Type AVA Type AVL	Impregnated asbestos Type AI (14-8) Type AIA	Asbestos Type A (14-8) Type AA	Bare and covered conductors
14	20	20	30	40	40	45	30
12	25	25	40	50	50	55	40
10	40	40	55	65	70	75	55
8	55	65	70	85	90	100	70
6	80	95	100	120	125	135	100
4	105	125	135	160	170	180	130
3	120	145	155	180	195	210	150
2	140	170	180	210	225	240	175
1	165	195	210	245	265	280	205
0	195	230	245	285	305	325	235
00	225	265	285	330	355	370	275
000	260	310	330	385	410	430	320
0000	300	360	385	445	475	510	370
250	340	405	425	495	530	....	410
300	375	445	480	555	590	....	460
350	420	505	530	610	655	....	510
400	455	545	575	665	710	....	555
500	515	620	660	765	815	....	630
600	575	690	740	855	910	....	710
700	630	755	815	940	1,005	....	780
750	655	785	845	980	1,045	....	810
800	680	815	880	1,020	1,085	....	845
900	730	870	940	.....	.....	....	905
1,000	780	935	1,000	1,165	1,240	....	965
1,250	890	1,065	1,130				
1,500	980	1,175	1,260	1,450	.....	....	1,215
1,750	1,070	1,280	1,370				
2,000	1,155	1,385	1,470	1,715	.....	....	1,405

Correction factors, room temps. over 30°C, 86°F

°C	°F							
40	104	0.82	0.88	0.90	0.94	0.95		
45	113	0.71	0.82	0.85	0.90	0.92		
50	122	0.58	0.75	0.80	0.87	0.89		
55	131	0.41	0.67	0.74	0.83	0.86		
60	140	....	0.58	0.67	0.79	0.83	0.91	
70	158	....	0.35	0.52	0.71	0.76	0.87	
75	167	....	....	0.43	0.66	0.72	0.86	
80	176	....	....	0.30	0.61	0.69	0.84	
90	194	....	....	....	0.50	0.61	0.80	
100	212	....	....	....	....	0.51	0.77	
120	248	....	....	....	....	....	0.69	
140	284	....	....	....	....	....	0.59	

* The current-carrying capacities for Type RHH conductors for sizes AWG 14, 12, and 10 shall be the same as designated for Type RH conductors in this table.

Table 1-6 (NE Code Table 310-14). Allowable Current-carrying Capacities of Insulated Aluminum Conductors, in Amperes

Not More than Three Conductors in Raceway or Cable or Direct Burial
(Based on Room Temperature of 30°C, 86°F)

Size AWG or MCM	Rubber Type R, RW, RU, RUW (12-2) / Type RH-RW Note 9 / Thermoplastic Type T / TW	Rubber Type RH / RUH (14-2) / Type RH-RW Note 9 / Type RHW Thermoplastic Type THW / THWN	Paper / Thermoplastic asbestos Type TA / Thermoplastic Type TBS / Silicone Type SA / Var-Cam Type V / Asbestos Var-Cam Type AVB / MI cable / RHH*	Asbestos Var-Cam Type AVA Type AVL	Impregnated asbestos Type AI (14-8) Type AIA	Asbestos Type A (14-8) Type AA
12	15	15	25	25	30	30
10	25	25	30	35	40	45
8	30	40	40	45	50	55
6	40	50	55	60	65	75
4	55	65	70	80	90	95
3	65	75	80	95	100	115
2†	75	90	95	105	115	130
1†	85	100	110	125	135	150
0†	100	120	125	150	160	180
00†	115	135	145	170	180	200
000†	130	155	165	195	210	225
0000†	155	180	185	215	245	270
250	170	205	215	250	270	
300	190	230	240	275	305	
350	210	250	260	310	335	
400	225	270	290	335	360	
500	260	310	330	380	405	
600	285	340	370	425	440	
700	310	375	395	455	485	
750	320	385	405	470	500	
800	330	395	415	485	520	
900	355	425	455			
1,000	375	445	480	560	600	
1,250	405	485	530			
1,500	435	520	580	650		
1,750	455	545	615			
2,000	470	560	650	705		

Correction factors, room temps. over 30°C, 86°F

°C °F						
40 104	0.82	0.88	0.90	0.94	0.95	
45 113	0.71	0.82	0.85	0.90	0.92	
50 122	0.58	0.75	0.80	0.87	0.89	
55 131	0.41	0.67	0.74	0.83	0.86	
60 140	....	0.58	0.67	0.79	0.83	
70 158	....	0.35	0.52	0.71	0.76	
75 167	....	....	0.43	0.66	0.72	0.91
80 176	....	....	0.30	0.61	0.69	0.87
90 194	....	....	....	0.50	0.61	0.86
100 212	....	....	....	....	0.51	0.84
120 248	....	....	....	....	....	0.80
140 284	....	....	....	....	....	0.77
						0.69
						0.59

* The current-carrying capacities for Type RHH conductors for sizes AWG 12, 10, and 8 shall be the same as designated for Type RH conductors in this table.
† For 3-wire, single-phase service and subservice circuits, the allowable current-carrying capacity of RH, RH-RW, RHH, RHW, and THW aluminum conductors shall be for sizes No. 2-100 amp, No. 1-110 amp, No. 1/0-125 amp, No. 2/0-150 amp, No. 3/0-170 amp, and No. 4/0-200 amp.

Table 1-7 (NE Code Table 310-15). Allowable Current-carrying Capacities
of Insulated Aluminum Conductors, in Amperes
Single Conductor in Free Air (Based on Room Temperature of 30°C, 86°F)

Size AWG or MCM	Rubber Type R, RW, RU, RUW (12-2) / Type RH-RW Note 9 / Thermoplastic Type T, TW	Rubber Type RH / RUH (14-2) / Type RH-RW Note 9 / Type RHW / Thermoplastic Type THW / THWN	Paper / Thermoplastic asbestos Type TA / Thermoplastic Type TBS / Silicone Type SA / Var-Cam Type V / Asbestos Var-Cam Type AVB / MI cable / RHH*	Asbestos Var-Cam Type AVA Type AVL	Impregnated asbestos Type AI (14-8) Type AIA	Asbestos Type A (14-8) Type AA	Bare and covered conductors
12	20	20	30	40	40	45	30
10	30	30	45	50	55	60	45
8	45	55	55	65	70	80	55
6	60	75	80	95	100	105	80
4	80	100	105	125	135	140	100
3	95	115	120	140	150	165	115
2	110	135	140	165	175	185	135
1	130	155	165	190	205	220	160
0	150	180	190	220	240	255	185
00	175	210	220	255	275	290	215
000	200	240	255	300	320	335	250
0000	230	280	300	345	370	400	290
250	265	315	330	385	415	....	320
300	290	350	375	435	460	....	360
350	330	395	415	475	510	....	400
400	355	425	450	520	555	....	435
500	405	485	515	595	635	....	490
600	455	545	585	675	720	....	560
700	500	595	645	745	795	....	615
750	515	620	670	775	825	....	640
800	535	645	695	805	855	....	670
900	580	700	750	....	....	....	725
1,000	625	750	800	930	990	....	770
1,250	710	855	905				
1,500	795	950	1,020	1,175	....	....	985
1,750	875	1,050	1,125				
2,000	960	1,150	1,220	1,425	....	....	1,165
Correction factors, room temps. over 30°C, 86°F							
°C °F							
40 104	0.82	0.88	0.90	0.94	0.95		
45 113	0.71	0.82	0.85	0.90	0.92		
50 122	0.58	0.75	0.80	0.87	0.89		
55 131	0.41	0.67	0.74	0.83	0.86		
60 140	....	0.58	0.67	0.79	0.83	0.91	
70 158	....	0.35	0.52	0.71	0.76	0.87	
75 167	....	.....	0.43	0.66	0.72	0.86	
80 176	....	.....	0.30	0.61	0.69	0.84	
90 194	....	.....	.....	0.50	0.61	0.80	
100 212	....	.....	.....	.....	0.51	0.77	
120 248	....	.....	.....	.....	....	0.69	
140 284	....	.....	.....	.....	....	0.59	

* The current-carrying capacities for Type RHH conductors for sizes AWG 12, 10, and 8 shall be the same as designated for Type RH conductors in this table.

NOTES TO TABLES 1-4 TO 1-7 (NE CODE TABLES 310-12 TO 310-15)

Current-carrying Capacity. The maximum, continuous, current-carrying capacities of copper conductors are given in Tables 310-12 and 310-13.   The current-carrying capacities of aluminum conductors are given in Tables 310-14 and 310-15.

1. Explanation of Tables. For explanation of type letters and for recognized size of conductors for the various conductor insulations, see Secs. 310-2 and 310-3.   For installation requirements, see Sec. 310-1 to 310-7 and the various articles of this Code.   For flexible cords see Tables 400-9 and 400-11.

2. Application of Tables. For open wiring on insulators and for concealed knob-and-tube work, the allowable current-carrying capacities of Tables 310-13 and 310-15 shall be used. For all other recognized wiring methods, the allowable current-carrying capacities of Tables 310-12 and 310-14 shall be used, unless otherwise provided in this Code.

3. Aluminum Conductors. For aluminum conductors, the allowable current-carrying capacities shall be in accordance with Tables 310-14 and 310-15.

4. Bare Conductors. Where bare conductors are used with insulated conductors, their allowable current-carrying capacity shall be limited to that permitted for the insulated conductors of the same size.

5. Type MI Cable. The temperature limitation on which the current-carrying capacities of Type MI cable are based is determined by the insulating materials used in the end seal. Termination fittings incorporating unimpregnated organic insulating materials are limited to 85°C operation.

6. Ultimate Insulation Temperature. In no case shall conductors be associated together in such a way with respect to the kind of circuit, the wiring method employed, or the number of conductors that the limiting temperature of the conductors will be exceeded.

7. Use of Conductors with Higher Operating Temperatures. Where the room temperature is within 10°C of the maximum allowable operating temperature of the insulation, it is desirable to use an insulation with a higher maximum allowable operating temperature; although insulation can be used in a room temperature approaching its maximum allowable operating-temperature limit if the current is reduced in accordance with the correction factors for different room temperatures.

8. More Than Three Conductors in a Raceway or Cable. Tables 310-12 and 310-14 give the allowable current-carrying capacities for not more than three conductors in a raceway or cable.   Where the number of conductors in a raceway or cable exceeds three, the allowable current-carrying capacity of each conductor shall be reduced as shown in the following table:

Number of Conductors	Per Cent of Values in Tables 310-12 and 310-14
4 to 6	80
7 to 24	70
25 to 42	60
43 and above	50

Exception: When conductors of different systems, as provided in Sec. 300-3, are installed in a common raceway, the derating factors shown above apply to the number of power and lighting (Articles 210, 215, 220, and 230) conductors only.

Where the number of conductors in a raceway or cable exceeds three, or where single conductors or multiconductor cables are stacked or bundled without maintaining spacing as required in Art. 318 and are not installed in raceways, the individual current-carrying capacity of each conductor shall be reduced as shown in the above table.

9. Where Type RH-RW rubber insulated wire is used in wet locations, the allowable current-carrying capacities shall be that of Column 2 in Tables 310-12 to 310-15.   Where used in dry locations, the allowable current-carrying capacities shall be that of Column 3 in Tables 310-12 to 310-15.

10. Overcurrent Protection. Where the standard ratings and settings of overcurrent devices do not correspond with the ratings and settings allowed for conductors, the next-higher standard rating and setting may be used.

Except as limited in Sec. 240-5.

11. Neutral Conductor. A neutral conductor which carries only the unbalanced current from other conductors, as in the case of normally balanced circuits of three or more conductors, shall not be counted in determining current-carrying capacities as provided for in Note 8.

In a 3-wire circuit consisting of two phase wires and the neutral of a 4-wire, 3-phase Y-connected system, a common conductor carries approximately the same current as the other conductors and is not therefore considered as a neutral conductor.

12. Voltage Drop.   The allowable current-carrying capacities in Tables 310-12 to 310-15 are based on temperature alone and do not take voltage drop into consideration.

13. Deterioration of Insulation.   It should be noted that even the best grades of rubber insulation will deteriorate in time, and eventually will need to be replaced.

14. Aluminum-sheathed Cable.   The current-carrying capacities of Type ALS cable are determined by the temperature limitation of the insulated conductors incorporated within the cable.   Hence the current-carrying capacities of aluminum sheathed cable may be determined from the columns in Tables 310-12 and 310-14 applicable to the type of insulated conductors employed within the cable.   See Note 9.

LIGHTING AND APPLIANCE CIRCUITS

An individual branch circuit, that is, a branch circuit to one outlet or to a direct connection to a single-load device, may have any ampere rating.   Branch circuits which supply two or more outlets, such as circuits for general lighting and for receptacle outlets, must be rated at 15, 20, 30, 40, or 50 amp.   This rating of the branch circuit is based on the setting or rating of the overcurrent device protecting the circuit.   Any multioutlet branch circuit must have one of those ratings, with the conductors and other parts of the circuit rated in accordance with NE Code rules.   The following is a table of branch-circuit requirements from the NE Code:

Type R, RW, RU, RUW, RH-RW, SA, T, TW, RH, RUH, RHW, RHH, THW
and THWN Conductors in Raceway or Cable

Circuit rating.	15 amp	20 amp	30 amp	50 amp
Conductors, (min. size):				
Circuit wires.	14	12	10	6
Taps.	14	14	14	12
Fixture wires and cords.	Refer to Sec. 240-5, Exception no. 3			
Overcurrent protection.	15 amp	20 amp	30 amp	50 amp
Outlet devices:				
Lamp holders permitted.	Any type 15 max. amp	Any type 15 or 20 amp	Heavy-duty 30 amp	Heavy-duty 50 amp
Receptacle rating.				
Maximum load.	15 amp	20 amp	30 amp	50 amp
Permissible load	Refer to Sec. 210-24(a)	Refer to Sec. 210-24(a)	Refer to Sec. 210-24(b)	Refer to Sec. 210-24(c)

Calculation of the required current rating of branch-circuit conductors is based on the following formulas.

Branch Circuits—Lighting and Appliance.   Two-wire circuits at any power factor:

$$\text{Line current} = \frac{\text{volt-amperes of connected load (or watts at unity pf)}}{\text{line voltage}}$$

Three-wire circuits at any power factor:

Single-phase: Apply same formula as for 2-wire branch circuit, considering each line to neutral separately.   Use line-to-neutral voltage; result gives current in line conductors.

Three-phase:

$$\text{Line current} = \frac{\text{volt-amperes of balanced 3-phase load}}{\text{line voltage} \times 1.732}$$

MOTOR BRANCH CIRCUITS

Conductors for a motor branch circuit must have current-carrying capacity equal to at least 125 per cent of the full-load running current of the motor, with the running current determined from Tables 1-8 to 1-11 (NE Code Tables 430-147 to 430-150). Tabulated data on motor branch circuits, including conductors, running overload protection, and short-circuit protection for the branch circuit, are presented in Table 1-12 (Code Table 430-146).

Table 1-8 (NE Code Table 430-147). Full-load Currents, in Amperes, D-c Motors
The following values of full-load currents are for motors running at base speed.

HP	120 volts	240 volts
1/4	2.9	1.5
1/3	3.6	1.8
1/2	5.2	2.6
3/4	7.4	3.7
1	9.4	4.7
1 1/2	13.2	6.6
2	17	8.5
3	25	12.2
5	40	20
7 1/2	58	29
10	76	38
15	....	55
20	....	72
25	....	89
30	....	106
40	....	140
50	....	173
60	....	206
75	....	255
100	....	341
125	....	425
150	....	506
200	....	675

PANELBOARDS

Basic calculation of the mains ratings of panelboards required to serve branch circuits for lighting and appliance loads is made as follows:

Two-wire D-C or Single-phase. Total connected load (amperes) = sum of branch loads. At least 10 amp should be allowed for each spare or appliance circuit.

Two-wire D-C or Single-phase. The same calculations apply as for the 2-wire panel, applied separately to each side of the panel.

Four-wire, Three-phase. The load on any bus, except the neutral, is computed the same as for a 2-wire panel. The load on each of the phase buses is taken as that of the most heavily loaded bus.

NOTE: Section 384-13 of the code requires that a panelboard must have a rating (amperes capacity of its bus bars) not less than the minimum feeder capacity required for the total load. A panelboard may have a higher rating than the current rating of a feeder required for the load, but not a lower rating.

Table 1-9 (NE Code Table 430-148). Full-load Currents, in Amperes, Single-phase A-C Motors

The following values of full-load currents are for motors running at usual speeds and motors with normal torque characteristics. Motors built for especially low speeds or high torques may have higher full-load currents, in which case the name-plate current ratings should be used.

To obtain full-load currents of 208- and 200-volt motors, increase corresponding 230-volt-motor full-load currents by 10 and 15 per cent, respectively.

The voltages listed are rated motor voltages. Corresponding nominal system voltages are 110 to 120, 220 to 240, 440 to 480.

HP	115 volts	230 volts	440 volts
$\frac{1}{6}$	4.4	2.2	
$\frac{1}{4}$	5.8	2.9	
$\frac{1}{3}$	7.2	3.6	
$\frac{1}{2}$	9.8	4.9	
$\frac{3}{4}$	13.8	6.9	
1	16	8	
$1\frac{1}{2}$	20	10	
2	24	12	
3	34	17	
5	56	28	
$7\frac{1}{2}$	80	40	21
10	100	50	26

Calculating Current Which Feeder Conductors Must Be Rated to Carry

$$I = \frac{\text{load watts}}{K \times E \times \text{pf}} = \frac{\text{load volt-amperes}}{K \times E}$$

where K = 1 for 2-wire d-c or single-phase a-c
    = 1.73 for 3-wire, 3-phase a-c
    = 2 for 3-wire d-c or single-phase a-c
    = 3 for 4-wire, 3-phase a-c
E = voltage between outside wire and neutral or, if no neutral exists, between any two line wires, volts
I = current in any line wire except neutral, amp, which feeder must be rated to carry (check tables of conductor current ratings)

Calculating Power Loss in Circuit Conductors

Assuming resistivity of conductor metal to be as follows:
where K = 12 for circuits loaded to more than 50 per cent (copper)
    = 11 for circuits loaded to less than 50 per cent (copper)
    = 18 for aluminum conductors

Two-wire Circuit (D-C or Single-Phase)

$$P = \frac{2 \times K \times L \times I^2}{\text{cm}}$$

Three-wire, Three-phase Circuit (Assuming Balanced Load)

$$P = \frac{3 \times K \times L \times I^2}{\text{cm}}$$

where P = power lost in circuit, watts
 K = resistivity of conductor metal, cir mil-ohms/ft
 I = current in each wire of circuit, amp
 L = one-way length of circuit, ft
 cm = cross-section area of each wire, cir mils
When the resistance of conductors is determined from a table, the power loss is calculated from the relation

$$P = I^2R$$

Table 1-10 (NE Code Table 430-149). Full-load-current
Two-phase A-C Motors (4-wire)

The following values of full-load current are for motors running at speeds usual for belted motors and motors with normal torque characteristics. Motors built for especially low speeds or high torques may require more running current, in which case the name-plate current rating should be used. Current in common conductor of 2-phase, 3-wire system will be 1.41 times value given.

The voltages listed are rated motor voltages. Corresponding nominal system voltages are 110 to 120, 220 to 240, 440 to 480, and 550 to 600.

HP	Induction-type, squirrel-cage and wound-rotor, amp					Synchronous-type, unity power factor,* amp			
	110 volts	220 volts	440 volts	550 volts	2,300 volts	220 volts	440 volts	550 volts	2,300 volts
½	4	2	1	.8					
¾	4.8	2.4	1.2	1.0					
1	6.4	3.2	1.6	1.3					
1½	8.8	4.4	2.2	1.8					
2	11.2	5.6	2.8	2.2					
3	....	8	4	3.2					
5	....	13	7	6					
7½	....	19	9	8					
10	....	24	12	10					
15	....	34	17	14					
20	....	45	23	18					
25	....	55	28	22	6	47	24	19	4.7
30	....	67	34	27	7.5	56	29	23	5.7
40	....	88	44	35	9	75	37	31	7
50	....	108	54	43	11	94	47	38	9
60	....	129	65	52	13	111	56	44	11
75	....	158	79	63	16	140	70	57	13
100	....	212	106	85	21	182	93	74	17
125	....	268	134	108	26	228	114	93	22
150	....	311	155	124	31	...	137	110	26
200	....	415	208	166	41	...	182	145	35

* For 90 and 80 per cent pf the figures should be multiplied by 1.1 and 1.25, respectively.

MOTOR FEEDERS

Although the NEC allows sizing of motor feeders (and mains supplying combination power and lighting loads) on the basis of maximum-demand running current, calculated as follows:

$$\text{Running current} = (1.25 \times I_F) + (\text{df} \times I_T)$$

where I_F = full-load current of largest motor
   df = demand factors
   I_T = sum of full-load currents of all motors except largest
modern design dictates use of the maximum-demand starting current in sizing conductors for improved voltage stability on the feeder. This current is calculated as follows:

$$\text{Starting current} = I_s + (\text{df} \times I_T)$$

where I_s = average starting current of largest motor (from Table 430-152 or 430-153)

Table 1-11 (NE Code Table 430-150). Full-load-current
Three-phase A-C Motors

For full-load currents of 208- and 200-volt motors, increase the corresponding 220-volt motor full-load current by 6 and 10 per cent, respectively.

These values of full-load current are for motors running at speeds usual for belted motors and motors with normal torque characteristics. Motors built for especially low speeds or high torques may require more running current, in which case the name-plate current rating should be used.

The voltages listed are rated motor voltages. Corresponding nominal system voltages are 110 to 120, 220 to 240, 440 to 480, and 550 to 600.

HP	Induction-type, squirrel-cage and wound-rotor, amp					Synchronous-type, unity power factor,* amp			
	110 volts	220 volts	440 volts	550 volts	2,300 volts	220 volts	440 volts	550 volts	2,300 volts
½	4	2	1	0.8					
¾	5.6	2.8	1.4	1.1					
1	7	3.5	1.8	1.4					
1½	10	5	2.5	2.0					
2	13	6.5	3.3	2.6					
3	....	9	4.5	4					
5	....	15	7.5	6					
7½	....	22	11	9					
10	....	27	14	11					
15	....	40	20	16					
20	....	52	26	21					
25	....	64	32	26	7	54	27	22	5.4
30	....	78	39	31	8.5	65	33	26	6.5
40	....	104	52	41	10.5	86	43	35	8
50	....	125	63	50	13	108	54	44	10
60	....	150	75	60	16	128	64	51	12
75	....	185	93	74	19	161	81	65	15
100	....	246	123	98	25	211	106	85	20
125	....	310	155	124	31	264	132	106	25
150	....	360	180	144	37	...	158	127	30
200	....	480	240	192	48	...	210	168	40

* For 90 and 80 per cent pf the figures should be multiplied by 1.1 and 1.25, respectively.

Basic Calculations for Voltage Drop

Two-wire, Single-phase Circuits (Inductance Negligible)

$$V = \frac{2k \times L \times I}{d^2} = 2R \times L \times I \qquad d^2 = \frac{2k \times I \times L}{V}$$

where V = drop in circuit voltage, volts
     R = resistance per foot of conductor, ohms/ft
     I = current in conductor, amp

Three-wire, Single-phase Circuits (Inductance Negligible)

$$V = \frac{2k \times L \times I}{d^2}$$

where V = drop between outside conductors, volts
     I = current in more heavily loaded outside conductor, amp

Three-wire, Three-phase Circuits (Inductance Negligible)

$$V = \frac{2k \times I \times L}{d^2} \times 0.866$$

where V = voltage drop of 3-phase circuit
   Four-wire, Three-phase Balanced Circuits (Inductance Negligible). For lighting loads: Voltage drop between one outside conductor and neutral equals one-half of drop calculated by formula for 2-wire circuits.
   For motor loads: Voltage drop between any two outside conductors equals 0.866 times drop determined by formula for 2-wire circuits.
   In above formulas:
   L = one-way length of circuit, ft
   d^2 = cross-section area of conductor, cir mils
   k = resistivity of conductor metal, cir mil-ohms/ft ($k = 12$ for circuits loaded to more than 50 per cent of allowable carrying capacity; $k = 11$ for circuits loaded less than 50 per cent; $k = 18$ for aluminum conductor)

Voltage-drop Calculations, Including Conductor Reactance

When current flows in a conductor in which the reactance due to self-induction is negligible, the voltage drop is equal to the product of the current in amperes and the total resistance of the conductor in ohms. But when the reactance of the conductor is not negligible, the voltage drop is equal to the product of the current in amperes and the total *impedance* of the conductor, which is determined from the formula

$$Z = \sqrt{R^2 + X^2}$$

where Z = total impedance, ohms
     R = total a-c resistance of conductor, ohms
     X = reactance of conductor, ohms
The voltage drop in such a conductor is

$$V = IZ$$

where V = voltage drop, volts
     I = current flowing in conductor, amp
     Z = total impedance of conductor, ohms (see manufacturers' bulletins and catalogs for conductor impedance values in ohms per 1,000 ft)
Resistance and reactance data on wires and cables are given in literature made available by the manufacturers. Tables and graphs for quickly and easily computing voltage drop in large heavily loaded feeders operating at less than unity power factor and with considerable conductor reactance are also available.

Table 1-12 (NE Code Table 430-146). Overcurrent Protection for Motors
(See Code Tables 430-152 and 430-153)

These values are in accordance with Secs. 430-6, 430-22, 430-32, 430-34, 430-52, and 430-59, except as follows. The current values in Column 1 are to be taken from Tables 430-147 to 430-150, including footnotes, but the values shown for running protection in Columns 2 and 3 must be modified if name-plate full-load current values are different, as provided in Sec. 430-6. The current values shown in Columns 2 and 3 must be reduced by 8 per cent for all motors other than open-type motors marked to have a temperature rise of not over 40°C as required by Sec. 430-32. For certain exceptions to the values in Columns 4, 5, 6, and 7, see Secs. 430-52, and 430-59. See Sec. 430-53 for values to be used for several motors on one branch circuit. For running protection of motors, see Sec. 430-32. For setting of motor-branch-circuit protective devices, see tables in Secs. 430-152 and 430-153. For grouping of small motors under the protection of a single set of fuses, see Sec. 430-53.

(1)	(2)	(3)	(4)		(5)		(6)		(7)	
	For running protection of motors		Maximum allowable rating or setting of branch circuit protective devices							
Full-load current rating of motor, amp	Maximum rating of nonadjustable protective devices, amp	Maximum setting of adjustable protective devices, amp	With Code Letters — Single phase, squirrel-cage and synchronous. Full voltage, resistor or reactor start, Code letters F to V / Without Code Letters — Same as above		With Code Letters — Single phase, squirrel-cage and synchronous. Full voltage, resistor or reactor start, Code letters B to E. Auto-transformer start, Code letters F to V / Without Code Letters (Not more than 30 amp) Squirrel-cage and synchronous, auto-transformer start, high-reactance squirrel-cage*		With Code Letters — Squirrel-cage and synchronous autotransformer start, Code letters B to E / Without Code Letters (More than 30 amp) Squirrel-cage and synchronous autotransformer start, high-reactance squirrel cage*		With Code Letters — All motors code letter A / Without Code Letters — D-C and wound-rotor motors	
			Fuses	Circuit breakers (nonadjustable overload trip)	Fuses	Circuit breakers (nonadjustable overload trip)	Fuses	Circuit breakers (nonadjustable overload trip)	Fuses	Circuit breakers (nonadjustable overload trip)
1	2	1.25	15	15	15	15	15	15	15	15
2	3	2.50	15	15	15	15	15	15	15	15
3	4	3.75	15	15	15	15	15	15	15	15
4	6	5.0	15	15	15	15	15	15	15	15
5	8	6.25	15	15	15	15	15	15	15	15
6	8	7.50	20	15	20	15	15	15	15	15
7	10	8.75	25	20	20	15	15	15	15	15

(1)	(2)	(3)	(4)	(5)	(6)	(7)	(8)	(9)	(10)	(11)
8	10	10.0	25	20	20	20	20	20	15	15
9	12	11.25	30	30	25	20	20	20	15	15
10	15	12.50	30	30	25	20	20	20	15	15
11	15	13.75	35	30	30	30	25	30	20	20
12	15	15.00	40	40	30	30	25	30	20	20
13	20	16.25	40	40	35	30	30	30	20	20
14	20	17.50	45	40	35	30	30	30	25	30
15	20	18.75	45	40	40	40	30	30	25	30
16	25	20.00	50	50	40	40	35	40	25	30
17	25	21.25	60	50	45	40	35	40	30	30
18	25	22.50	60	50	45	40	40	40	30	30
19	25	23.75	60	50	50	40	40	40	30	30
20	30	25.00	70	70	50	50	40	50	30	40
22	30	27.50	70	70	60	50	50	50	35	40
24	35	30.00	80	70	60	70	50	70	40	40
26	35	32.50	80	70	60	70	60	70	40	50
28	40	35.00	90	100	70	70	60	70	45	50
30	45	37.50	90	100	70	70	70	70	45	50
32	45	40.00	100	100	80	100	70	70	50	70
34	50	42.50	110	100	80	100	80	100	60	70
36	50	45.00	110	125	90	100	80	100	60	70
38	50	47.50	125	125	100	100	80	100	60	70
40	60	50.00	125	125	110	100	90	100	70	70
42	60	52.50	125	150	110	125	90	100	70	100
44	60	55.00	150	150	125	125	100	125	80	100
46	70	57.50	150	175	125	125	100	125	80	100
48	70	60.00	175	175	150	125	110	125	80	100
50	70	62.50	175	175	150	150	110	125	90	100
52	80	65.00	200	200	150	150	125	150	90	125
54	80	67.50	200	200	175	150	125	150	90	125
56	80	70.00	225	225	175	175	150	150	100	125
58	90	72.50	225	225	200	200	150	150	110	125
60	90	75.00	225	225	200	200	150	175	110	125
62	90	77.50	—	—	—	—	—	—	—	—

Table 1-12 (NE Code Table 430-146). Overcurrent Protection for Motors (Continued)

(1)	(2)	(3)	(4)		(5)		(6)		(7)	
	For running protection of motors		Maximum allowable rating or setting of branch circuit protective devices							
			With Code Letters Single phase, squirrel-cage and synchronous. Full voltage, resistor or reactor start, Code letters F to V / Without Code Letters Same as above		With Code Letters Single phase, squirrel-cage and synchronous. Full voltage, resistor or reactor start, Code letters B to E. Auto-transformer start, Code letters F to V / Without Code Letters (Not more than 30 amp) Squirrel-cage and synchronous, auto-transformer start, high-reactance squirrel-cage*		With Code Letters Squirrel-cage and synchronous autotrans-former start, Code letters B to E / Without Code Letters (More than 30 amp) Squirrel-cage and synchronous autotransformer start, high-reactance squirrel cage*		With Code Letters All motors code letter A / Without Code Letters D-C and wound-rotor motors	
Full-load current rating of motor, amp	Maximum rating of nonadjustable protective devices, amp	Maximum setting of adjustable protective devices, amp	Fuses	Circuit breakers (nonadjustable overload trip)	Fuses	Circuit breakers (nonadjustable overload trip)	Fuses	Circuit breakers (nonadjustable overload trip)	Fuses	Circuit breakers (nonadjustable overload trip)
76	100	95.00	250	200	200	175	175	175	125	125
78	100	97.50	250	200	200	175	175	175	125	125
80	100	100.00	250	200	200	175	175	175	125	125
82	110	102.50	250	225	225	175	175	175	125	125
84	110	105.00	250	225	225	175	175	175	150	125
86	110	107.50	300	225	225	175	175	175	150	150
88	110	110.00	300	225	225	200	200	200	150	150

90	110	112.50	300	225	225	200	200	150	150
92	125	115.00	300	250	250	200	200	150	150
94	125	117.50	300	250	250	200	200	150	150
96	125	120.00	300	250	250	200	200	150	150
98	125	122.50	300	250	250	200	200	150	150
100	125	125.00	300	250	250	200	200	150	150
105	150	131.50	350	300	300	225	225	175	175
110	150	137.50	350	300	300	225	225	175	175
115	150	144.00	350	300	300	250	250	175	175
120	150	150.00	400	300	350	250	250	200	200
125	175	156.50	400	350	350	250	250	200	200
130	175	162.50	450	350	350	300	300	225	225
135	175	169.00	450	350	350	300	300	225	225
140	175	175.00	450	400	400	300	300	225	225
145	200	181.50	450	400	400	300	300	225	225
150	200	187.50	500	400	400	350	350	250	250
155	200	194.00	500	500	500	350	350	250	250
160	200	200.00	500	500	500	350	350	250	250
165	225	206.00	500	500	500	350	350	250	250
170	225	213.00	600	500	500	350	350	300	300
175	225	219.00	600	500	500	400	400	300	300
180	225	225.00	600	500	500	400	400	300	300
185	250	231.00	600	600	600	400	400	300	300
190	250	238.00	600	600	600	400	400	300	300
195	250	244.00	600	600	600	400	400	300	300
200	250	250.00	800	600	600	500	500	350	350
210	250	263.00	800	600	600	500	500	350	350
220	300	275.00	800	700	800	500	500	400	400
230	300	288.00	800	700	800	500	500	400	400
240	300	300.00	800	700	800	500	500	500	500
250	300	313.00	1,000	800	800	600	600	500	500
260	350	325.00	1,000	800	800	600	600	500	500
270	350	338.00	1,000	800	800	600	600	500	500
280	350	350.00	1,000	800	800	600	600	500	500
290	350	363.00	1,200	800	800	700	700	600	600
300	400	375.00	1,200	800	800	700	700	600	600
320	400	400.00	1,200	800	1,000	800	800		
340	450	425.00		…	1,000	800	800		
360	450	450.00		…	1,000	800	800		
380	500	475.00		…		800	800		

* See note at end of table.

Table 1-12 (NE Code Table 430-146). Overcurrent Protection for Motors (Continued)

(1)	(2)	(3)	(4)		(5)		(6)		(7)	
Full-load current rating of motor, amp	For running protection of motors		Maximum allowable rating or setting of branch circuit protective devices							
	Maximum rating of nonadjustable protective devices, amp	Maximum setting of adjustable protective devices, amp	With Code Letters Single phase, squirrel-cage and synchronous. Full voltage, resistor or reactor start, Code letters F to V. / Without Code Letters Same as above.		With Code Letters Single phase, squirrel-cage and synchronous. Full voltage, resistor or reactor start, Code letters B to E. Auto-transformer start, Code letters F to V. / Without Code Letters (Not more than 30 amp) Squirrel-cage and synchronous, auto-transformer start, high-reactance squirrel-cage.*		With Code Letters Squirrel-cage and synchronous autotransformer start, Code letters B to E. / Without Code Letters (More than 30 amp) Squirrel-cage and synchronous autotransformer start, high-reactance squirrel cage.*		With Code Letters All motors code letter A. / Without Code Letters D-C and wound-rotor motors.	
			Fuses	Circuit breakers (nonadjustable overload trip)	Fuses	Circuit breakers (nonadjustable overload trip)	Fuses	Circuit breakers (nonadjustable overload trip)	Fuses	Circuit breakers (nonadjustable overload trip)
400	500	500.00	1,200	...	1,000	800	800	800	600	600
420	600	525.00	1,600	...	1,200	...	1,000	...	800	700
440	600	550.00	1,600	...	1,200	...	1,000	...	800	700
460	600	575.00	1,600	...	1,200	...	1,000	...	800	700
480	600	600.00	1,600	...	1,200	...	1,000	...	800	800
500	...	625.00	1,600	...	1,600	...	1,000	...	800	800

* High-reactance squirrel-cage motors are those designed to limit the starting current by means of deep-slot secondaries or double-wound secondaries and are generally started on full voltage.

Table 1-13 (NE Code Table 1 of Chap. 9). Maximum Number of Conductors in Trade Sizes of Conduit or Tubing

For derating factors for more than three conductors in raceways, see Tables 310-12 to 310-15, Note 8.
Types RF-2, RFH-2, R, RH, RW, RH-RW, RHW, RHH, RU, RUH, RUW, SF, and SFF
Types TF, T, TW, THW, and THWN
(See Secs. 300-17, 300-18, 346-6, and 348-6)

Size AWG or MCM	Maximum number of conductors in conduit or tubing (based upon % conductor fill, Table 3, Chap. 9, for new work)											
	½ in.	¾ in.	1 in.	1¼ in.	1½ in.	2 in.	2½ in.	3 in.	3½ in.	4 in.	5 in.	6 in.
18	7	12	20	35	49	80	115	176				
16	6	10	17	30	41	68	98	150				
14	4	6	10	18	25	41	58	90	121	155		
12	3	5	8	15	21	34	50	76	103	132	208	
10	1	4	7	13	17	29	41	64	86	110	173	
8	1	3	4	7	10	17	25	38	52	67	105	152
6	1	1	3	4	6	10	15	23	32	41	64	93
4	1	1	1	3*	5	8	12	18	24	31	49	72
3	...	1	1	3	4	7	10	16	21	28	44	63
2	...	1	1	3	3	6	9	14	19	24	38	55
1	...	1	1	1	3	4	7	10	14	18	29	42
0	...	...	1	1	2	4	6	9	12	16	25	37
00	...	...	1	1	1	3	5	8	11	14	22	32
000	...	...	1	1	1	3	4	7	9	12	19	27
0000	...	...	...	1	1	2	3	6	8	10	16	23
250	...	...	...	1	1	1	3	5	6	8	13	19
300	...	...	...	1	1	1	3	4	5	7	11	16
350	...	...	...	1	1	1	1	3	5	6	10	15
400	...	...	...	...	1	1	1	3	4	6	9	13
500	...	...	...	...	1	1	1	3	4	5	8	11
600	...	...	...	...	...	1	1	1	3	4	6	9
700	...	...	...	...	...	1	1	1	3	3	6	8
750	...	...	...	...	...	1	1	1	3	3	5	8
800	...	...	...	...	...	1	1	1	2	3	5	7
900	...	...	...	...	...	1	1	1	1	3	4	7
1,000	...	...	...	...	...	1	1	1	1	3	4	6
1,250	...	...	...	...	...	...	1	1	1	1	3	5
1,500	...	...	...	...	...	...	...	1	1	1	3	4
1,750	...	...	...	...	...	...	...	1	1	1	2	4
2,000	...	...	...	...	...	...	...	1	1	1	1	3

* Where an existing service run of conduit or electrical metallic tubing does not exceed 50 ft in length and does not contain more than the equivalent of two quarter bends from end to end, two No. 4 insulated and one No. 4 bare conductors may be installed in 1-in. conduit or tubing.

NOTES:

1. Reactance in conductors carrying a-c power depends upon the size of the conductor, spacing between it and other conductors carrying current, the position of the conductor with respect to conductors close to it, the frequency of the alternating current, and the presence of magnetic materials close to the conductor. In an a-c circuit, the reactance of the conductors may be reduced by placing the conductors close together and/or by placing them in nonmagnetic raceway instead of steel conduit or raceway. In many large-size or long a-c circuits, the voltage drop due to impedance is often far greater than the drop due simply to resistance of the conductors.

2. Alternating-current flow in conductors is subject to "skin effect," which is an apparent increase in resistance over the resistance value that would obtain for d-c flow. This is due to a reduction in effective conductor cross section because alternating current tends to flow close to the surface (or "skin") of the conductor. Generally, this increase in resistance to alternating current is of little consequence in conductors smaller than 500 MCM.

CONDUCTORS IN RACEWAY

Table 1-13 (Table 1 of Chap. 9 of the NE Code) gives the maximum number of conductors permitted in each size of conduit or tubing, based on all conductors of the same size being used in any application. If a number of conductors of different sizes are to be used in the conduit, Tables 1-14 to 1-16 (NE Code Tables 3 to 5 from Chap. 9) provide for determining the allowable cross-section occupancy of the conduit for new work or rewiring; the total cross-section area occupied by the given group of conductors; and the relation of the conductors to the raceway size.

The general data for calculations of Table 1-17 will be found useful.

Table 1-14 (NE Code Table 3 of Chap. 9). Combination of Conductors
(See Secs. 346-6 and 348-6)

For groups or combinations of conductors not included in Table 1, Chap. 9, it is recommended that the conduit or tubing be of such size that the sum of the cross-section areas of the individual conductors will not be more than the percentage of the interior cross-section area of the conduit or tubing shown in the following table.

Per Cent Area of Conduit or Tubing

	Number of conductors				
	1	2	3	4	Over 4
Conductors (not lead-covered)..............	53	31	43	40	40
Lead-covered conductors....................	55	30	40	38	35
For rewiring existing raceways for increased load where it is impracticable to increase the size of the raceway due to structural conditions....................................	60	40	50	50	50

See Note to Table 5, Chap. 9, for size of conduit or tubing for combinations of conductors not shown in Table 1.

For carrying capacity of more than three conductors in a conduit or tubing, see Tables 310-12 to 310-15, Note 8.

See Tables 4 to 7, Chap. 9, for dimensions of conductors, conduit, and tubing.

Table 1-15 (NE Code Table 4 of Chap. 9). Dimensions and Per Cent
Area of Conduit and of Tubing—"New Work"
Areas of Conduit or Tubing for the Combinations of Wires Permitted in Table 3, Chap. 9

Area, sq in.

Trade size	Internal diameter, in.	Total 100%	Not lead-covered				Lead-covered				
			1 cond., 53%	2 cond., 31%	3 cond., 43%	4 cond., and over, 40%	1 cond., 55%	2 cond., 30%	3 cond., 40%	4 cond., 38%	Over 4 cond., 35%
½	0.622	0.30	0.16	0.09	0.13	0.12	0.17	0.09	0.12	0.11	0.11
¾	0.824	0.53	0.28	0.16	0.23	0.21	0.29	0.16	0.21	0.20	0.19
1	1.049	0.86	0.46	0.27	0.37	0.34	0.47	0.26	0.34	0.33	0.30
1¼	1.380	1.50	0.80	0.47	0.65	0.60	0.83	0.45	0.60	0.57	0.53
1½	1.610	2.04	1.08	0.63	0.88	0.82	1.12	0.61	0.82	0.78	0.71
2	2.067	3.36	1.78	1.04	1.44	1.34	1.85	1.01	1.34	1.28	1.18
2½	2.469	4.79	2.54	1.48	2.06	1.92	2.63	1.44	1.92	1.82	1.68
3	3.068	7.38	3.91	2.29	3.17	2.95	4.06	2.21	2.95	2.80	2.58
3½	3.548	9.90	5.25	3.07	4.26	3.96	5.44	2.97	3.96	3.76	3.47
4	4.026	12.72	6.74	3.94	5.47	5.09	7.00	3.82	5.09	4.83	4.45
5	5.047	20.00	10.60	6.20	8.60	8.00	11.00	6.00	8.00	7.60	7.00
6	6.065	28.89	15.31	8.96	12.42	11.56	15.89	8.67	11.56	10.98	10.11

Tables 4 to 7, Chap. 9 give the nominal size of conductors and conduit or tubing recommended for use in computing size of conduit or tubing for various combinations of conductors. The dimensions represent average conditions only, and although variations will be found in dimensions of conductors and conduits of different manufacture, these variations will not affect the computation.

Table 1-16 (NE Code Table 5 of Chap. 9). Dimensions of Rubber-covered and Thermoplastic-covered Conductors

Size AWG or MCM	Types RF-2, RFH-2, R, RH, RHH, RHW, RH-RW, RW		Types TF, T, THW*, TW, RU†, RUH†, RUW		Type THWN	
	Approx. diam., in.	Approx. area, sq in.	Approx. diam., in.	Approx. area, sq in.	Approx. diam., in.	Approx. area, sq in.
(1)	(2)	(3)	(4)	(5)	(6)	(7)
18	0.146	0.0167	0.106	0.0088		
16	0.158	0.0196	0.118	0.0109		
14	$\frac{2}{64}$ in. 0.171	0.0230	0.131	0.0135	0.105	0.0087
14	$\frac{3}{64}$ in. 0.204‡	0.0327‡				
14	....	......	0.162*	0.0206*		
12	$\frac{2}{64}$ in. 0.188	0.0278	0.148	0.0172	0.122	0.0117
12	$\frac{3}{64}$ in. 0.221‡	0.0384‡				
12	....	......	0.179*	0.0251*		
10	...... 0.242	0.0460	0.168	0.0224	0.153	0.0184
10	....	......	0.199*	0.0311*		
8	...... 0.311	0.0760	0.228	0.0408	0.201	0.0317
8	....	......	0.259*	0.0526*		
6	0.397	0.1238	0.323	0.0819	0.257	0.0519
4	0.452	0.1605	0.372	0.1087	0.328	0.0845
3	0.481	0.1817	0.401	0.1263	0.356	0.0995
2	0.513	0.2067	0.433	0.1473	0.388	0.1182
1	0.588	0.2715	0.508	0.2027	0.450	0.1590
0	0.629	0.3107	0.549	0.2367	0.491	0.1893
00	0.675	0.3578	0.595	0.2781	0.537	0.2265
000	0.727	0.4151	0.647	0.3288	0.588	0.2715
0000	0.785	0.4840	0.705	0.3904	0.646	0.3278
250	0.868	0.5917	0.788	0.4877	0.716	0.4026
300	0.933	0.6837	0.843	0.5581	0.771	0.4669
350	0.985	0.7620	0.895	0.6291	0.822	0.5307
400	1.032	0.8365	0.942	0.6969	0.869	0.5931
500	1.119	0.9834	1.029	0.8316	0.955	0.7163
600	1.233	1.1940	1.143	1.0261		
700	1.304	1.3355	1.214	1.1575		
750	1.339	1.4082	1.249	1.2252		
800	1.372	1.4784	1.282	1.2908		
900	1.435	1.6173	1.345	1.4208		
1,000	1.494	1.7531	1.404	1.5482		
1,250	1.676	2.2062	1.577	1.9532		
1,500	1.801	2.5475	1.702	2.2748		
1,750	1.916	2.8895	1.817	2.5930		
2,000	2.021	3.2079	1.922	2.9013		

* Dimensions of THW wire in sizes 14 to 8. No. 6 THW wire and larger are the same dimension as T wire.

No. 18 to No. 8, solid; No. 6 and larger, stranded.

The dimensions of rubber-covered conductors in Column 3 of this table are to be used in computing the size of conduit or tubing for new work for combinations not shown in Table 1, Chap. 9. For rewiring existing raceways, the areas in Column 5 or 7 are to be used.

† No. 14 to No. 2.

‡ The dimensions of Types RW and RHH wire. Also, these dimensions are to be used for new work in computing size of conduit or tubing for combinations of wires not shown in Table 1, Chap. 9.

Table 1-17. General Data for Calculations

D-C-circuit Characteristics

Ohm's law:

$$E = IR \qquad I = \frac{E}{R} \qquad R = \frac{E}{I}$$

where E = voltage impressed on circuit, volts
     I = current flowing in circuit, amp
     R = circuit resistance, ohms
In d-c circuits, electrical power is equal to the product of the voltage and current:

$$P = EI = I^2R = \frac{E^2}{R}$$

where P = power, watts
     E = voltage, volts
     I = current, amp
     R = resistance, ohms

A-C-circuit Characteristics

The instantaneous values of an alternating current or voltage vary from zero to a maximum value each half cycle. In the practical formulas which follow, the "effective value" of current and voltage is used, defined as follows:
Effective value = $0.707 \times$ max. instantaneous value
Impedance: Impedance is the total opposition to the flow of alternating current. It is a function of resistance, capacitive reactance, and inductive reactance. The following formulas relate these circuit properties:

$$X_L = 2\pi fL \qquad X_C = \frac{1}{2\pi fC} \qquad Z = \sqrt{R^2 + (X_L - X_C)^2}$$

where X_L = inductive reactance, ohms
     X_C = capacitive reactance, ohms
     Z = impedance, ohms
     f = frequency, cps
     C = capacitance, farads
     L = inductance, henrys
     R = resistance, ohms
     π = 3.14
Ohm's law for a-c circuits:

$$E = I \times Z \qquad I = \frac{E}{Z} \qquad Z = \frac{E}{I}$$

Power Factor

Power factor of a circuit or system is the ratio of actual power (watts) to apparent power (volt-amperes) and is equal to the cosine of the phase angle of the circuit:

$$\text{pf} = \frac{\text{actual power}}{\text{apparent power}} = \frac{\text{watts}}{\text{volts} \times \text{amperes}} = \frac{\text{kw}}{\text{kva}} = \frac{R}{Z}$$

where kw = kilowatts
     kva = kilovolt-amperes = volt-amperes $\times$ 1,000
     pf = power factor (expressed as decimal)

Single-phase Circuits

$$\text{kva} = \frac{EI}{1,000} = \frac{\text{kw}}{\text{pf}} \qquad \text{kw} = \text{kva} \times \text{pf}$$

$$I = \frac{P}{E \times \text{pf}} \qquad E = \frac{P}{I \times \text{pf}} \qquad \text{pf} = \frac{P}{E \times I}$$

where $P = E \times I \times \text{pf}$
     P = power, watts

Table 1-17. General Data for Calculations (*Continued*)

Three-phase Circuits, Balanced Star or Y

$$I_N = 0 \qquad I = I_p \qquad E = \sqrt{3}\,E_p = 1.73\,E_p$$

$$E_p = \frac{E}{\sqrt{3}} = \frac{E}{1.73} = 0.577E$$

where I_N = current in neutral, amp
  I = line current per phase, amp
  I_p = current in each phase winding, amp
  E = voltage, phase to phase, volts
  E_p = voltage, phase to neutral, volts

Three-phase Circuits, Balanced Delta

$$I = 1.732 \times I_p \qquad I_p = \frac{I}{\sqrt{3}} = 0.577 \times I$$

where $E = E_p$

Power: Balanced Three-wire, Three-phase Circuit, Delta or Y

For unity power factor (pf = 1.0):

$$P = 1.732 \times E \times I$$

$$I = \frac{P}{\sqrt{3}\,E} = \frac{0.577P}{E} \qquad E = \frac{P}{\sqrt{3} \times I} = \frac{0.577P}{I}$$

where P = total power, watts
  For any load:

$$P = 1.732 \times E \times I \times \text{pf} \qquad \text{va} = 1.732 \times E \times I$$

$$E = \frac{P}{\text{pf} \times 1.73 \times I} = \frac{0.577 \times P}{\text{pf} \times I}$$

$$I = \frac{P}{\text{pf} \times 1.73 \times E} = \frac{0.577 \times P}{\text{pf} \times E}$$

$$\text{pf} = \frac{P}{1.73 \times I \times E} = \frac{0.577 \times P}{I \times E}$$

where va = apparent power, volt-amperes
  P = actual power, watts
  E = line voltage, volts, phase to phase
  I = line current, amp

Power Loss: Any a-c or d-c Circuit

$$P = I^2 R \qquad I = \sqrt{\frac{P}{R}} \qquad R = \frac{P}{I^2}$$

where P = power heat loss in circuit, watts
  I = effective current in conductor, amp
  R = conductor resistance, ohms

Chapter 2

ELECTRICAL GROUNDING

By J. E. BARKLE
Chief Electrical Engineer
Bechtel Corporation
San Francisco, Calif.

Proper grounding of an industrial-plant distribution system is a most important factor in safety to personnel and electrical equipment in the plant. Rules for the proper grounding of systems and equipment are now well established, and once the decision to ground is made, the rules should be followed closely to assure adequate grounding.

From the standpoint of safety to the industrial plant and personnel, the electrical system and all equipment associated with it should be grounded. However, from the standpoint of the industrial process involved, the demands of continuity of the electrical service in carrying on production can dictate that the electrical system itself remain ungrounded.

By presenting the basic reasons for grounding or not grounding and by developing equipment- and system-grounding practices and methods, this section will serve as a guide to the maintenance engineer in determining and accomplishing adequate grounding for his system.

SYSTEM GROUNDING

Definitions. "Ungrounded" denotes no intentional connection to ground except through potential measuring or indicating devices.

As applied to an electrical system, this definition means that there is no intentional connection between the neutral conductor or any of the phase conductors and ground. The potential existing between any conductor and ground is determined by the distributed capacitance of the conductors to ground. In a three-phase system with reasonably balanced loads on all three phases, the system neutral normally is close to ground potential while the three phase conductors have approximately equal potentials to ground.

"Grounded" denotes an intentional connection to ground other than connections through potential measuring or indicating devices.

A grounded electrical system is one that has at least one of the conductors or a point in the system intentionally connected to ground either solidly or through some current-limiting device. In a three-phase system the grounded point may be one of the phase conductors, the neutral of a generator or transformer, or the neutral point of some device installed for the sole purpose of establishing a neutral grounding point, such as a grounding transformer. In single-phase systems, and in some three-phase situations, the grounding point is usually a middle wire or the mid-point of a transformer winding.

The degree of grounding is an important consideration in determining the characteristics of the grounded system. The term "solidly grounded" has little significance other than denoting that the ground connection is a solid connection with no intervening current-limiting device, such as a resistor, reactor, or transformer. "Effective grounding" is a term that has been introduced to define a system that is adequately grounded and meets certain specific conditions with respect to voltages and currents under abnormal conditions. Effective grounding is defined as follows:

ASA Standard C 42.35, 1957: An a-c system or portion thereof may be said to be effectively grounded when for all points on the system or specified portion thereof the ratio of zero-sequence reactance to positive-sequence reactance is not greater than three and the ratio of zero-sequence resistance to positive-sequence reactance is not greater than one for any condition of operation and for any amount of connected generator capacity.

These requirements are generally satisfied if the single line-to-ground fault current is at least 60 per cent of the three-phase fault current under all system operating conditions.

The degree of grounding can be anything from effectively grounded to ungrounded, these being the limiting cases, depending on the method of grounding and the impedance of the ground connection with respect to the impedance of the remainder of the system. The magnitudes of currents and voltages to ground during abnormal ground-fault conditions are affected directly by the degree of grounding.

Ungrounded Systems. Historically, a large percentage of industrial-plant distribution systems have been installed as ungrounded systems. The primary reason is the fact that an accidental contact between one phase conductor and ground does not require that service be interrupted to clear the trouble. The only effect of such contact is to change the system voltages to ground from their normal values, and unless this change in voltage causes an insulation breakdown at some other point in the system, no particular immediate harm is done.

Where the factor of electrical service continuity is important to the industrial process, the ungrounded system offers a solution, although its limitations must be recognized.

Location of Faults. Some device normally is used on an ungrounded system to indicate the presence of a ground on one of the phase conductors. Such devices operate as a function of the line-to-ground voltage of the system. A ground on one phase causes the voltage to ground on that phase to decrease to zero. The voltage to ground of the two ungrounded phases is raised to equal line-to-line voltage, an increase of 58 per cent. Thus, three lamps or three voltmeters connected between the phase conductors and ground will indicate the presence of the ground by changing the brilliance of the lamps or altering the readings of the voltmeters. Electrostatic ground detectors also are available, which operate as a function of the electrostatic capacitance of the conductors to ground and indicate when one of the conductors is grounded.

While these devices indicate the presence of the ground, they do not indicate its location on the system. Therefore, before repairs can be made, it is necessary to isolate the circuit or piece of equipment that contains the ground.

If there is only one phase-to-ground fault on the system, it can be located by removing from service one feeder or circuit at a time. When the feeder that contains the fault is removed from service, the ground-detecting device will return to normal operation, indicating that the fault has been located. Pinpointing the location of the fault on the feeder itself may require breaking up the feeder into minute parts. Since the ground fault does not cause an interruption of service, the search for its location can be delayed until such time as the plant process permits removing feeders from service, but it should be recognized that the insulation of the ungrounded phases has higher than normal voltage applied to it during this interval.

If more than one ground fault exists on any one phase of the system, the search for the fault locations is complicated, particularly if the faults are on different feeders.

In this case, the fault can be located by first removing all feeders or circuits from service and reconnecting them one at a time. Each time a grounded feeder is connected, the ground-detecting device will operate.

It is also possible to have ground faults on different phases of the system either on the same feeder or on different feeders. This condition appears to system relaying or other protective devices as a fault between two phases and ground, and these devices normally operate to remove the faults from the system. Where ground faults on two separate feeders are involved, both feeders are removed from service.

An alternate means of locating grounds on an ungrounded system is the use of an interrupted direct current obtained from a source of low d-c voltage. The d-c voltage is applied between the grounded phase conductor and ground, and the direct current can be traced to the grounded feeder to locate the fault. Theoretically, this method can be used without disconnecting the feeders from service, and this has been done in a number of cases. The d-c potential should be low in order to limit the direct current to a small magnitude. Obviously, this method has a definite advantage, because it is not necessary to wait until the plant load can be interrupted and the fault can be located immediately after it occurs.

As stated previously, a ground on one phase of an ungrounded system raises the voltage to ground of the ungrounded phases above that which normally exists. Thus, the insulation of these ungrounded phases is stressed at a voltage above normal, and the longer the ground is permitted to exist, the more likely is a second ground fault on another phase. Should this occur, the advantage of the ungrounded system is largely overcome because the outage of at least one and probably two feeders is forced and extensive damage can occur at the two fault locations. For best operation, it is essential that the ungrounded system be properly maintained and adequate steps taken to locate ground faults at the earliest opportunity after they occur.

Grounded Systems. From the standpoint of safety to plant personnel and equipment, all electrical systems should be grounded. The only argument in favor of ungrounded operation is that of service continuity, and modern principles of system planning enable a grounded system to be designed with service reliability closely approaching that of the ungrounded system. An ungrounded system should be used only in extreme cases when all other means of achieving adequate service reliability have been exhausted.

Safety. The knowledge that a circuit is grounded causes workmen to exercise involuntary care when working on the circuit. Records tend to substantiate the fact that fewer accidents from electric shock occur on grounded circuits.

A grounded system is less of a fire hazard than an ungrounded system. This is largely because the grounded circuit is immediately deenergized when a ground fault occurs. With an ungrounded system, grounds at two different locations on different phases cause a ground current that may flow through combustible material. The current may be insufficient to trip the fault-protective devices but may be sufficient to start a fire.

Under these conditions, the ground current can also cause an appreciable difference in potential between adjacent parts of the plant, and a person bridging these parts is subject to severe shock.

Maximum safety is obtained by connecting the system neutral to earth by connections to water-supply piping, a ground grid, and driven grounds. All uninsulated conducting objects in the plant, such as electric conduits, other pipes, metal plates, and structural members, should be solidly connected to the same ground. Interconnection in this manner will provide a low-resistance ground path that will limit potential differences within the path to low and safe values.

The purpose of preventing potential differences in these paths is to prevent the hazard of electric shock and to eliminate the possibility of electric arcs. To avoid electric arcs, the potential between adjacent conducting parts must be limited to a maximum of 8 volts. All electric circuits must be totally enclosed and thoroughly protected with fast-operating circuit-opening devices. All electrically conducting objects must be well bonded together to approach zero difference in potential, and all static-generating sources must be made ineffective.

The safety of the grounded system is dependent on adequate attention to all these details; otherwise there may be a false sense of security.

Overvoltage Hazards. Because the grounded system limits the voltages to ground to specific values, it is less subject to failure from overvoltages than the ungrounded system. Furthermore, the ungrounded or lightly grounded system is subject to transient overvoltages from arcing ground faults that may reach magnitudes of five or six times normal voltage. These can be prevented by grounding in such a manner that the line-to-ground fault current is at least 25 per cent of the three-phase fault current.

Methods of Grounding. Most systems are grounded by grounding the system neutral point at one or more locations. Four basic methods are generally accepted in practice: solid grounding, resistance grounding, reactance grounding, and ground-fault neutralizer grounding.

Solid Grounding. As implied, solid grounding is the direct connection of the generator or transformer or other system neutral point to ground without any intervening impedance device in the ground connection. The impedance between the system and ground is only that of the transformer or generator whose neutral is being grounded, and the effectiveness of the grounding is measured by the capacity of the transformer or generator with respect to the rest of the system. The ground source should be large enough to cause a line-to-ground fault current at least 25 per cent of the three-phase fault current.

Care must be exercised in grounding the neutral of a generator that the single line-to-ground fault current does not exceed the three-phase fault current in the generator windings. To prevent damage to the generator windings, it is recommended that the neutral be grounded through a small impedance sufficient to limit the ground-fault current to the three-phase fault current magnitude or less.

Resistance Grounding. In resistance grounding, the neutral is connected to ground through resistors at one or more points in order to limit the fault current magnitude to a relatively small value and yet give sufficient current for the detection and removal of ground faults. The resistor size is usually chosen so that the ground-fault current is between 5 and 20 per cent of the three-phase fault current, but it is essential that the ground-fault current be large enough for relaying purposes.

The characteristics of resistance grounding are such that transient overvoltages do not occur and the ground-fault current is substantially of the same magnitude regardless of the fault location on the system. This latter fact greatly simplifies the system relaying problem when compared with solid grounding.

The reasons for limiting the ground current by resistance grounding are the following:

To reduce burning and melting effects in faulted electric equipment such as switchgear, cables, and rotating machines.

To reduce mechanical stresses in circuits and apparatus carrying fault currents.

To reduce electric-shock hazards to personnel caused by stray ground-fault currents in the ground return path.

To reduce the momentary line voltage dip occasioned by occurrence and clearing of a ground fault.

Reactance Grounding. In reactance grounding, a reactor is inserted between the system neutral and the ground. The magnitude of the reactance determines how solidly the system neutral is grounded, and again this should be of such magnitude that the ground-fault current is at least 25 per cent of the three-phase fault current.

Resistance grounding and reactance grounding each have specific fields of application, and they are not ordinarily alternative methods of grounding. Resistance grounding provides a ground current considerably smaller than reactance grounding, and a reactor to provide the same impedance would be much more expensive than the resistor. Thus, the method of grounding as far as these two methods are concerned is determined primarily by the magnitude of ground-fault current required.

Ground-fault Neutralizer Grounding. This is a method of grounding not frequently employed in industrial practice. In principle, a tunable reactor is inserted in the system neutral connection to ground, and the reactor is tuned so that its reactance equals the system capacitance to ground. This is a series tuned or series resonant circuit, and when a ground fault occurs, the capacitive and inductive currents substantially cancel each other, leaving only a very small resistance component of current to flow in the fault path. If the ground fault is a solid one, the ground current is very small, and if the fault is an arcing ground, the current is so small that the arc will not sustain itself and is extinguished.

The ground-fault neutralizer is provided with adjustable taps to change its reactance, and it must be kept reasonably in tune with the system for the operation to be completely successful. Also, some means must be provided to detect and clear a solid and permanent connection to ground, which is not cleared by the neutralizer. Its chief advantage is in eliminating arcing faults to ground.

Delta-system Grounding. In some cases, low-voltage systems of 600 volts and below have been grounded at a point other than the system neutral. A compromise method for delta-connected systems is to ground one corner of the delta. This method is not generally recommended because it increases the potential on the ungrounded phases and it requires positive identification of the grounded conductor throughout the system for safety.

Where the delta system is supplied by three single-phase transformers with midtaps in each phase, it is possible to ground one of the midtaps and obtain some of the advantages of grounding.

In general, the best procedure to follow is to apply a grounding transformer of the zigzag or Y-delta type in order to establish a system neutral point that can be grounded. The application of the grounding transformer must be engineered to provide the proper characteristics, but grounding can be made as effective as the grounding of a Y-connected system.

Suggested Grounding Methods. Experience has developed fairly definite grounding practices for industrial systems, based on the system voltage.

Low-voltage Systems. Systems with voltages up to 600 are ordinarily solidly grounded. This is an inexpensive method of grounding because no neutral devices are needed. The basic reason for solid grounding, however, lies in the fact that the fault protective devices used on these circuits are nearly always of the series-trip type and large fault currents are required to operate them. Solid grounding is necessary to provide the large currents. It is also necessary that the ground-current return paths be of low resistance.

Medium-voltage Systems. Medium-voltage systems in the range of 2.4 to 15 kv are usually resistance grounded, because in the usual industrial plant it is desirable to limit the ground-fault-current magnitude. However, small systems where the fault-current magnitude is small may use reactance grounding or solid grounding.

The neutral resistor size is chosen to give sufficient current for relaying purposes and yet to limit the magnitude of current so that damage at the point of fault is restricted.

High-voltage Systems. Systems above 15 kv are almost universally solidly grounded. Such systems are less costly and more effectively protected against lightning surges. Since these systems are not ordinarily carried inside buildings, their grounding is treated on a different basis from the grounding of lower voltage systems.

Table 2-1. Magnitude of Single Line-to-line Ground-fault Current in Per Cent of Three-phase Fault Current

System *effectively* grounded using either solid or reactance grounding........	60 per cent or greater
System *not effectively* grounded but solidly grounded or reactance grounded..	25 per cent or greater
System resistance grounded...	Normally 5–20 per cent

Summary. Table 2-1 indicates the approximate magnitude of single line-to-ground fault current as a function of three-phase fault current that should be associated with each method of grounding. Fault currents within the prescribed ranges will eliminate or reduce the possibility of excessive transient voltages and accomplish other purposes for which the grounding method is designed.

Where to Ground. In order to obtain the full advantage of neutral grounding, each voltage level should be grounded and the system should be grounded at each possible source of power. The generator, transformer, or grounding transformer neutral chosen to ground the system should be one that is always connected to the system, or several such points should be grounded to ensure that at least one is always connected. Also, where it is possible that the system might be split into several operating parts, each part should have its own individual ground point connected at all times.

Grounding at the source of power is preferred to grounding at the load. Even though several loads may be grounded, it is possible that they might be disconnected, leaving the system without a ground. If the source is grounded, the ground is always present when power is available. Grounding at the source is also preferable from the system relaying standpoint, because the ground-fault current flows in the same direction as phase-fault current.

National Electric Code Requirements. The National Electric Code has established definite rules for the safe grounding of electrical systems and equipment. These rules must be followed closely in order to achieve an effective and safe grounding arrangement. The more important of these rules are included in the following.

EQUIPMENT GROUNDING

Reasons for Grounding. The main objectives of equipment grounding are to afford safety to personnel, authorized or unauthorized, and to ensure that steel structures, machine frames, equipment enclosures, or any other metallic bodies enclosing or near an electrical circuit are maintained at ground potential at all times.

Contact between an ungrounded metal body and an electrical circuit causes the potential of the metal body to become equal to the potential of the electrical circuit to ground. If this body is a machine frame, switch enclosure, or structural member, it constitutes a serious hazard should any person come into contact with it. Also, because the metal body may not be completely insulated from ground, a small current can flow through it, constituting a serious fire hazard.

Intentional and solid grounding of the metal body allows considerable current to flow through the ground-detecting devices upon contact between the metal body and the electrical circuit. Circuit breakers and fuses are operated to isolate the hazard from the system. Grounding also tends to prevent elevation of the potential of the metal body above ground, and even though considerable current may be flowing through the body, it is not necessarily a shock hazard.

It is essential, therefore, that all such metallic bodies be permanently and effectively grounded through low-impedance connections of sufficient current-carrying capacity. In the event that high voltage accidentally touches a metallic body through direct contact, insulation failure, flashover, or lightning, the potential difference momentarily existing between the body and any point on the ground should not be high enough to be a shock hazard. The ground connection must be adequate for both normal and fault currents.

Low Resistance Necessary. The resistance of the connections between metallic bodies and the ground must be held to extremely low values for the grounding to be effective. The purpose is to hold the potential difference to as low a value as possible for the maximum flow of ground current. For large installations the ground resistance should not exceed 0.5 to 1.0 ohm, but for small installations a resistance of up to 5 ohms may be acceptable. The product of the resistance and the maximum ground current gives the potential to ground that will exist, and this should be checked to be sure that it is within safe limits.

Equipment to Be Grounded. A typical industrial plant may include the following types of equipment which should be grounded: structures, outdoor stations, large generator and motor rooms, conductor enclosures, miscellaneous motors, and portable equipment.

Indoor Ground Bus. For indoor installations, a ground bus should be formed within the building and should run around the periphery of the building. The conductor material should be soft-drawn or medium-hard-drawn copper wire or bar, and the grounding bus should be connected at two or more points to grounding electrodes, the building structure, and water mains. The resistance to earth of the grounding bus should be less than 1.0 ohm, and each floor of the building should have its own ground bus.

The ground bus should be 18 in. below finished grade, if possible, or under structural slab, and it should be embedded in concrete. All connections to the buried ground bus should be made by brazing, thermit welding, or similar process. The bus conductor should not be smaller than No. 2/0 AWG for mechanical reasons, but it is recommended that No 4/0 AWG be used for small stations and 500 or 750 MCM copper wire, copper bar, or the equivalent in large stations. The current-carrying capacity of the ground bus conductor should not be less than 25 per cent of the highest continuous current rating of any piece of equipment in the station or building.

Outdoor Ground Bus. For the purpose of grounding an outdoor station, a grounding bus can be established by surrounding the station area with a continuous stranded copper cable buried from 12 to 18 in. below the ground surface and connected to driven ground rods at approximately 10-ft intervals. The size of the ground bus depends on the magnitude of the available ground-fault current and the operating time of the protective equipment, but it should not be less than No 4/0 AWG for small stations or 500 MCM for medium and large stations.

A more effective ground can be established by using a grid-type conductor arrangement wherein the conductors are spaced 10 ft apart in both directions and the points where the conductors intersect are connected together and to driven ground rods. The conductor sizes should be as determined above for the surrounding ground bus. Whether the grounding bus or the grounding grid is used is determined primarily by what is necessary to provide an effective ground of low resistance.

The ground bus should be connected to any metallic water pipes in the station area with not less than No 1/0 AWG copper cable. The ground bus also should be connected to any water mains in the immediate area. Connection should be to at least two points on the pipe separated by at least 20 ft, and the connecting cable should be the same size as the ground bus conductor.

All underground connections between copper cable to copper cable, copperclad ground rods, or steel or wrought-iron pipe should be made by brazing or thermit welding.

Structure Grounding. All structural members should be grounded to a ground bus which may also serve for grounding other parts such as large motors and generators.

The steel framework of the buildings should be grounded at the base of every corner column and intermediate columns at distances not greater than 60 ft. Taps to the ground bus should not be less than No. 2/0 copper. All buried grounding connections should be made by brazing, thermit welding, or equivalent process, and connection to the structure should be made by one of these processes or by solderless connector. Soldered connections should not be allowed.

The metal structures and enclosures for switchgear, lightning arresters, disconnect switches, transformers, grillwork, and similar parts should be connected individually to the ground bus in a manner similar to the building framework. Disconnecting switch frames bolted directly to a structural steel part need no further grounding, except that operating pipes of all gang-operated disconnecting switches should be grounded by a 1/0 AWG extra-flexible copper cable or equivalent connected directly above the operating handle and run to the nearest part of the grounded supporting structure.

Outdoor Station Grounding. For general applications, the ground bus should be designed so that the maximum ground resistance does not exceed 2.0 ohms for small outdoor stations or 0.5 ohm for large installations. The station structure should be grounded in accordance with the structure-grounding rules above. In general, it is desirable to ground each vertical supporting column of a steel structure. Wood structures should have all metallic hardware bonded or connected together and connected to the ground bus by one or more downleads of at least No. 1/0 AWG copper cable or equivalent.

A metal fence surrounding an outdoor station should be grounded. If the fence is near the station and the ground bus resistance to earth is less than 1.0 ohm, the fence should be connected to the ground bus at approximately 25-ft intervals, using not smaller than No. 1/0 AWG cable. If the fence is remotely located or if the ground bus resistance to earth is greater than 1.0 ohm, the fence should not be connected to the station ground bus. Instead, a series of $\frac{3}{4}$-in. by 10-ft copper-clad steel ground rods should be installed along the fence and spaced not more than 25 ft apart. The top of each ground rod should be approximately 12 in. below the surface of the ground, and the fence should be connected to the rods, using at least No. 1/0 AWG cable.

Where a system neutral point is being grounded, such as the neutral of a transformer bank, the connection should be made using a conductor equal in size to the phase conductors but not smaller than No. 1/0 AWG cable. Connection to the ground bus should be made at two separate points.

All ground bus and connecting cables should be protected from mechanical injury, and cables run underground should have a reasonable amount of slack.

Generator and Motor Room Grounding. The generator or motor room should have a ground bus installed in accordance with the indoor-grounding bus rules, and the structural steel, water mains, etc., of the building should be connected to the ground bus as prescribed above.

The ground connections from generators, motors, transformers, and switchgear to the ground bus should be at least No. 1/0 AWG cable, but they must not be smaller in current-carrying capacity than 25 per cent of the highest continuous current rating of any piece of primary apparatus to which they are connected. Connections to the apparatus to be grounded can be welded, or suitable solderless connectors can be used.

Conductor Enclosure Grounding. All exposed conductive material enclosing electrical equipment or forming a part of such equipment must be grounded. Included are items such as cabinets, junction boxes, outlet boxes, controllers, service raceway, conduit, couplings, fittings, cable armor, lead sheath, and grillwork. In addition there are switchgear, transformers, switchboard frames, motors, generators, elevators, frames and tracks of cranes, and portable equipment.

In general, metal boxes, cabinets and fittings, or other non-current-carrying metal parts of fixed equipment are considered to be grounded if connected metallically to grounded cable armor or metal raceway. Where the metal enclosure of a wiring system is used as part of the protective grounding, the electrical continuity of the enclosure should be assured, with special attention to obtain secure fastenings and joints.

For conduit, armored cable, or metal raceways, the ground connection should be as near as practicable to the point where the conductors in the raceway system concerned receive their supply.

Lead sheaths for single-conductor cables carrying alternating currents should be grounded and insulated in accordance with the manufacturer's specifications in order to avoid circulating currents in the sheaths.

The size of the grounding conductor for conduit, cable sheath, or armor and other metal raceways or enclosures for conductors and for equipment should not be less than given in Table 2-2.

All grounding connections should be tight and clean, and all protective insulating coatings such as enamel, rust, scale, etc., should be removed from the points of connection. Normally an approved type of solderless connector or clamp should be used to make all connections. The use of soldered connections is to be avoided.

Miscellaneous Motor Grounding. All motor frames should be grounded with a grounding conductor equipped with a brazed copper terminal or with a suitable solderless connector fastened to the motor beneath the head of an end shield bolt or by a $\frac{5}{16}$-in. (minimum) bolt tapped into a suitable place on the motor frame. The other end of the grounding conductor should be fastened with suitable clamps or terminals to the rigid metallic conduit or to the nearest available ground. Taps from a ground bus to larger motors and generators may be connected directly to the bedplate.

The size of the grounding conductor should be in accordance with the above table under conductor enclosure grounding. For the largest machines a conductor of 500 or 750 MCM should be sufficient.

Portable-equipment Grounding. Portable electrical equipment is equipment that can be moved from place to place and is supplied through a flexible cable. The cable can be permanently connected at each end or can be connected through a suitable plug or disconnecting device.

Portable equipment operating at voltages above 600 should be supplied through cable permanently connected at both ends. The complete equipment including the housing or structure should be grounded through a grounding wire or wires in the supply cable equal in current-carrying capacity to the largest line conductor. It is

Table 2-2. Sizes of Grounding Conductors for Conduit, Cable Sheath, Armor, and Other Metal Raceways or Enclosures for Conductors and Equipment

Rating or setting of automatic overcurrent device in circuit ahead of equipment, conduit, etc., not exceeding (amp)	Size of grounding conductor			
	Copper wire No.	Conduit or pipe, in.	Electrical metallic tubing, in.	Aluminum* wire No.
20	8	1/2	1/2	6
30	8	1/2	1/2	6
40	8	1/2	1/2	6
60	8	1/2	1/2	6
100	8	1/2	1/2	6
200	6	1/2	1	4
400	4	3/4	1 1/4	2
600	2	3/4	1 1/4	1/0
800	1/0	1	2	3/0
1,000	2/0	1	2	4/0
1,200	3/0	1	2	250 MCM

* Aluminum grounding conductors should not be used in direct contact with masonry or the earth or where subject to corrosive conditions. When installed outside they should not be installed within 18 in. of the earth.

desirable that such equipment be operated from a Y-connected system with its neutral grounded through a resistor that limits the ground-fault current to 50 amp. Suitable ground-fault relaying should be provided.

Portable equipment operating at 600 volts or less should be grounded through a separate grounding wire or wires in the supply cable equal in current-carrying capacity to the largest line conductor. If the cable is not permanently connected at each end, grounding should be through separate grounding contacts in the power plug and receptacle. Note that portable lamps with nonconducting guards and sockets need not be grounded. Special consideration must be given to certain equipment, such as soldering irons, where grounding may constitute a hazard.

System neutral conductors, although grounded at the source, should never be used for equipment grounding. Equipment-grounding conductors should be identified with green color cord.

The grounding contact in a connection plug should be so designed that it can never be inserted so as to make contact with any of the line conductors in the receptacle. When the plug is inserted in the receptacle, the ground contact must engage before any of the line contacts make contact.

The grounding of portable electric equipment can be a hazard instead of a safeguard if not properly installed and maintained. Only the green conductor should be connected to the parts to be grounded. Portable tools should be checked for proper grounding-conductor connection each time they are passed to the operator, and portable cables and their associated plug equipment should be inspected regularly.

GROUNDING FOR STATIC AND LIGHTNING

Static Electricity. The accumulation of static electrical charges on equipment, on materials, and even on personnel constitutes a serious industrial hazard. A static discharge in the presence of flammable or explosive materials or atmospheres can cause a fire or explosion. Such accidents account for the loss of many lives and millions of dollars each year.

All installations should be examined carefully to determine if static charges are a potential hazard. Simple grounding of the equipment is not necessarily a solution to the problem. Each case should be studied, and since a comprehensive discussion is not possible in this handbook, more specific and detailed references should be consulted to determine the proper procedure for control of static.

Causes of Static. Basically, a static charge is caused by the difference in potential between two substances. When two dissimilar materials, one of which is an insulator, are brought together, a static charge is established, and upon separation of the materials a static discharge can take place. The circumstances affecting the magnitude of a static charge are the material characteristics, the speed of separation, the relative motion between substances, the area in contact, and the atmospheric conditions. Extremely high static voltages can be established, and a static discharge can contain sufficient energy to ignite flammable or explosive mixtures.

The methods of determining the existence of static electricity are rather simple. A complete reference on the subject should be consulted in any questionable case.

Static Control. Bonding and grounding of parts of equipment are a solution to many static problems. The National Fire Protection Association's bulletin "Static Electricity" describes in detail several methods of making bonding and grounding connections.

Where bonding and grounding do not eliminate the static hazard, it is necessary to resort to other means, some of which are the following:

1. Where the process or materials are not affected by high humidity, static caused by a dry atmosphere may be controlled by maintaining a relative humidity of at least 60 per cent.
2. Grounded metallic combs or bars of tinsel may be effective in draining the charge off certain types of material.
3. Certain neutralizers are now available which ionize the air near moving material. These are of a radioactive type or of a type that uses high voltage. Protection of personnel must be observed.
4. The coating or impregnation of certain materials, particularly belts, is an effective means of static control in many situations.
5. Other special types of controls designed for specific applications are available.

Static-control devices must have adequate maintenance to be effective. Periodic inspections should be made to determine that all bonding and grounding connections are secure. The resistance to ground should be maintained at 1 ohm or less and can be measured with an ordinary ohmmeter. Static neutralizers should be maintained in proper position and properly energized. Conducting coatings should be periodically inspected and replaced. Periodic instrument measurements should be made to be certain that the static-control method used is continuing in effectiveness.

Lightning. The flow of lightning currents through lightning-struck objects or buildings can cause considerable damage as a result of heat and mechanical forces. Lightning damage can be caused by direct strokes to buildings and equipment and by surges coming into the plant over exposed power lines. Damage to a structure from a direct stroke can be prevented only by completely enclosing the structure in a grounded metal sheath.

The lightning protection of structures is based on providing a low-resistance path for the discharge to enter or leave the earth. Structures of grounded metal or metallic frame are normally self-protecting. In other cases, lightning conductors in or around the structure nearly always provide suitable protection.

A lightning-conductor system consists of air terminals placed above the structure being protected and a system of interconnecting and grounding conductors. A multiplicity of earth connections of low resistance should be made at uniform intervals around the structure being protected. The number of earth connections is more important than obtaining a low resistance at each connection. The most suitable earth connections are made with driven ground rods located at least 2 ft away from and extending below building foundations.

Interior metal parts of buildings and structures should be grounded independently unless they are within 6 ft of metallic walls, roofs, or down conductors, in which case they should be solidly connected to these parts.

The protection of substations and transmission lines is a complex subject, and specific references should be consulted for guidance. The shielding of lines and structures and the proper application of lightning arresters are the usual methods of protection. Lightning arresters should be locally grounded through a short connection to a driven ground rod. The upper limit of resistance to earth is 5 ohms, and the ground conductor should be of adequate size.

Tanks and tank farms for the storage of flammable liquids and gases require special attention. Tanks made completely of steel at least $\frac{3}{16}$ in. thick are self-protecting. Those with nonmetallic roofs should be protected with air terminals, masts, and shield wires. In all cases, the tank and the shielding must be well grounded.

Bibliography

System Grounding

Armstrong, and Simpkin: Grounding Electrode Potential Gradient from Model Tests, *AIEE Trans.*, vol. 79, pt. III, pp. 618–623, 1960.

Bibliography on Ground Resistance and Potential Gradient Measurements, AIEE Committee Report, *AIEE Trans.*, vol. 79, pt. III, pp. 52–58, 1960.

Clark, R. T., and B. O. Watkins: Some Chemical Treatments to Reduce the Resistance of Ground Connections, *AIEE Trans.*, vol. 79, pt. III, pp. 1016–1023, December, 1960.

Guide for Safety in Alternating-current Substation Grounding, AIEE Standards 80, 1961.

Kinyon, A. L.: Earth Resistivity Measurements for Grounding Grids, *AIEE Trans.*, vol. 80, pt. III, pp. 795–800, December, 1961.

National Electric Safety Code, National Bureau of Standards Handbook 81, 6th ed., U.S. Dept. of Commerce, Nov. 1, 1961.

Stevens, R. F.: Optimum Diameter, Spacing and Burial Depth of Ground-grid Conductor, *AIEE Trans.*, vol. 80, pt. III, pp. 313–316, June, 1961.

Thapar, B., and E. T. B. Gross: Grounding Grids for High-voltage Stations, IV, Resistance of Grounding Grids in Non-uniform Soil, *IEEE Trans. Power Apparatus Systems*, 1963, pp. 782–788.

Trouard, S. E., and M. J. Maier: The Role of Grounding Cells and Similar Devices in the Effective Cathodic Protection of Lead-sheathed Power Cable of Substation Exit System, *AIEE Trans.*, vol. 80, pp. 642–647, October, 1961.

Ufer, H. G.: Investigation and Testing of Footing-type Grounding Electrodes for Electrical Installations, *IEEE Trans. Power Apparatus Systems*, October, 1964, pp. 1042–1048.

Equipment Grounding

Barkle, Sterrett, and Fountain: Detection of Grounds in Generator Field Windings, *AIEE Trans.*, pt. III, pp. 467–470, 1955.

Elmore, W. A., and J. L. Blackburn: Negative-sequence Directional Ground Relaying, *AIEE Trans.*, vol. 81, pp. 913–921, 1962.

Humphries, J. D.: Earth Electrode System for Larger Electric Stations, *Proc. IEE*, vol. 104, pt. A, pp. 383–399, 1957.

Kulman, F. E.: Grounding and Cathodic Protection of Pipes for Pipe-type Feeders, *AIEE Trans.*, pt. IIIA, pp. 184–192, 1959.

Landy and Howell: Trends in Ground Bed Design for Cathodic Protection of Underground Structures, *AIEE Trans.*, pt. II, pp. 456–461, 1959.

Lantz, M. J.: Fault Location Experience Using Current Ratio Method, *Proc. American Power Conf.*, Chicago, vol. 18, pp. 502–504, 1956.

Lee, A. C.: Ground-fault-location Indicator, *AIEE Trans.*, pt. III, pp. 1370–1372, 1958.

Martin and Lantz: New Methods for Locating Transmission Line Ground Faults, *AIEE Trans.*, pt. III, pp. 134–136, 1962.

Neff, W. F., S. H. Horowitz, and R. B. Squires: Relay Protection of Motors in Steam Power Stations with 4-kv Grounded Neutral Systems, *AIEE Trans.*, pt. III, pp. 573–577, 1956.

Smoot, A. W., and C. A. Bentel: Electric Shock Hazard of Underwater Swimming Pool Lighting Fixtures, *IEEE Trans. Power Apparatus Systems*, pp. 945–964, 1964.

Grounding for Static and Lightning

Beach, R.: Static Electricity in Industry, *Elec. Eng.*, vol. 64, pp. 184–194, 1945.

Beach, R.: Electrostatic Neutralizer Discharge and Safety Characteristics, *Mech. Eng.*, vol. 71, no. 4, pp. 329–334.

Beach, R.: Industrial Fires and Explosions from Electrostatic Origin, *Mech. Eng.*, April, 1953.

Code for Protection against Lightning, National Bureau of Standards Handbook 46.

Johnson, Price, and Schultz: Lightning-current Distribution in Towers and Ground Wires, *AIEE Trans.*, pt. III, pp. 1414–1417, 1958.

Lightning Protection for Electrical Equipment, Factory Mutual Loss Prevention Bulletin 15.60, Associated Factory Mutual Life Insurance Co., Boston, 1950.

Static Electricity Bulletin 77, National Fire Protection Association, Boston, 1955.

Static Electricity, Factory Mutual Loss Prevention Bulletin 12.21, Associated Factory Mutual Life Insurance Co., Boston, 1950.

Static Electricity, National Fire Protection Association Pamphlet 60, Boston.

Testing Lightning Rod and Arrester Grounds, Factory Mutual Loss Prevention Bulletin 15.66, Associated Factory Mutual Life Insurance Co., Boston, 1950.

Chapter 3

ELECTRIC MOTORS

By M. J. Wohlgemuth
Consultant
Swindell-Dressler Company
Pittsburgh, Pa.

GENERAL

Any piece of electrical equipment will operate better, last longer, and require less maintenance because of failures if it is kept clean and lubricated properly. This is particularly true of rotating equipment such as motors. While the control equipment for a motor is vital to its operation, a failure of a control component usually will not result in a long operating delay. This is ordinarily not true in the case of a motor, as the failure of a vital part such as an armature can mean a delay lasting from several hours to days.

PART I. ALTERNATING-CURRENT INDUCTION MOTORS

The induction motor is one of the oldest types of motors and in its commonest form, squirrel cage, the simplest. The first commercial installation was in 1889, and the induction motor with distributed primary and secondary windings was developed in 1892. Since the first commercial installation, many designs of polyphase induction motors have been developed and two types have become the recognized standard: (1) the squirrel-cage rotor and (2) the wound-rotor construction.

The characteristic features of the stationary primary element—distributed windings and comparatively small air gaps—are common to both types. The squirrel-cage motor has no external secondary or rotating connection, while the secondary or rotor windings of the wound-rotor motor usually are connected through slip rings and brushes to some form of adjustable resistance.

The modern induction motor, especially the squirrel-cage type, is undoubtedly the most rugged rotating electrical apparatus ever developed. The majority of maintenance requirements, outages, and repair costs would therefore depend to a large extent on the correctness of application. However, the cardinal principle of any electrical maintenance is *keep the apparatus clean and dry*. This immediately points to periodic inspections, which are a highly desirable check on operating conditions.

Before details dealing primarily with maintenance are discussed, a few of the fundamental characteristics of the induction motor which may aid in solving some of the maintenance problems are presented.

Slip. At no load an induction motor will run at practically synchronous speed, but when it is loaded, the speed at which the motor will run is below synchronous speed by an amount known as the slip. Thus, if the synchronous speed of a given motor is 1,800 rpm and the full-load speed is 1,750 rpm, the slip at full load is 50 rpm, or 50/1,800, or 2¾ per cent. The slip of any induction motor is a function of the voltage drop in the secondary circuit, i.e., of the resistance of the secondary times current squared. The higher the secondary resistance, the greater will be the starting torque with any given current; the higher the slip, the higher also are the losses and thus the lower the efficiency.

Torque. In analyzing some of the maintenance problems, a consideration of torque characteristics is sometimes important. There are two torque characteristics to consider: starting torque and pull-out torque. Motor torque, in the design stage, must be balanced against efficiency and power factor. High starting torque results in lower efficiency and power factor as well as poorer speed regulation. However, if the starting torque is too low, the motor may not be able to start the load. High pull-out or stalled torque also results in low power factor and high starting current. If the pull-out torque is too low, the motor may stall on ordinary overloads and can result in "roasted" insulation.

Voltage and Frequency. To obtain optimum results induction motors should be operated at their normal rated frequency and voltage. Of course, some variation can be tolerated, voltage limits being approximately plus or minus 10 per cent from name plate and frequency plus or minus 5 per cent. Both should never be varied at the same time to the extreme allowable limits; neither should they be varied at the same time in opposite direction. The following tabulation shows the effect of variation of voltage and frequency on performance.

	Power factor	Torque	Slip	Full-load efficiency
Voltage high..................	Decreased	Increased	Decreased	Approx. same
Voltage low...................	Increased	Decreased	Increased	Approx. same
Frequency high...............	Increased	Decreased	Same	Approx. same
Frequency low...............	Decreased	Increased	Same	Approx. same

A good rule to follow is that if normal frequency is changed, a corresponding change in voltage should be made proportional to the square root of the ratio of the frequencies. It is not desirable to operate at decreased frequency with less than normal voltage because of increase in current input and temperature.

Stator Windings. At first glance, the stator of an induction motor appears to be so rugged and simple that the necessity for maintenance is frequently overlooked. However, an inspection of any electrical repair shop certainly indicates that the stator of the induction motor is a vulnerable item.

Trouble with stators usually can be pinned to one of the following causes: overloading, single-phase operation, moisture, bearing trouble, insulation failure.

Main contributing factors to stator failures usually are dust and dirt. Some forms of dust or dirt are highly conductive and contribute to insulation breakdown. A good example of this is found in rubber-mill operations where a large amount of lampblack is used in processing the rubber. The type of lampblack used in processing synthetic rubber is more conductive than that used in processing natural rubber, so that failure rates increased when synthetic rubber came in. This is but one of many examples of conductive dirt and dust hazards. Certain steel-mill applications are others.

In addition to insulation failures due to conducting dust, restriction of ventilation can result from dust clogging ventilating ducts, thus causing overheating with possible resultant insulation failure due to excessive temperatures. Periodic cleaning with clean, dry compressed air usually will suffice to keep dust accumulations to a minimum. However, some types of dust or dirt have a tendency to stick to windings, and blowing with air does not give a completely satisfactory cleaning. Other methods of cleaning are covered later.

One of the natural enemies of insulation is moisture. Some types of modern insulation have reasonable resistance to moisture, but in general, all types of windings should be kept reasonably dry.　Many applications make it almost impossible to accomplish this unless special enclosures or other means to keep out moisture are employed.　Some success for motors operating in damp locations has been obtained by using special treatment of windings.　This will be discussed later.

The life of a winding depends on how well the original, or new, condition is maintained.　A new machine has the winding snug in the slots, the insulation is flexible and, having been treated with varnishes, is therefore able to resist to a great extent the harmful effects of moisture and dust.　This condition can best be maintained by periodic cleaning and re-treating, as discussed later.

Vibration frequently hastens winding failures.　Vibration during operation may cause coil movement which eventually breaks or wears through insulation.　As the motor becomes older, the insulation dries out and loses its flexibility.　The mechanical stresses resulting during starting, plugging, and reversing, as well as natural stresses occurring under normal operation, may precipitate short circuits in coils or failures to ground.　Periodic varnish and drying treatments properly performed tend to maintain a solid winding, thus minimizing coil movement.

Rotor Windings.　General comments on stator windings here and in subsequent discussion apply equally to windings of wound-rotor motors.　However, since the rotor is a moving part, additional maintenance problems are introduced.

Practically all wound rotors have three-phase windings and can, therefore, have trouble due to single-phase operation.　An open circuit in a rotor shows up in lack of torque and slowing down in speed.　It usually is accompanied by a grumbling noise and sometimes failure to start the load.　The most logical place to look for an open rotor circuit is in the secondary resistor or the circuit external to the rotor. An easy way to localize the trouble is to short-circuit the rotor at the slip rings and then to start the motor.　This will usually indicate whether the trouble is in the rotor itself or in the external circuit.　The stud connections to the slip rings should be checked also, as the open circuit may be found there.

On rotors of greater capacity, where the coils are made of copper strap, clips are used to connect the bottom and top halves of the coil.　These connectors should be checked for signs of heating, indicating a partial open.　Such end connections, if faulty or improperly made, are a common source of open rotor circuits.　Some manufacturers now braze these end connections instead of soldering, which minimizes faulty connections.

A ground in the rotor circuit will not affect the motor performance unless a second ground develops, which may cause the equivalent of a short circuit.　This unbalances the rotor electrically and causes reduced torque, excessive vibration, sparking at the collector ring or brushes, or uneven wear of collector ring brushes.

A reasonably successful method for checking for short circuits in rotor windings is to raise the brushes and energize the stator.　If the rotor is free of short circuits, there should be little or no tendency to rotate even when the motor is disconnected from the load.　If there is evidence of considerable torque, or if there is a tendency to come up to speed, the rotor should be removed and the winding opened to determine where the fault exists.

Another check which can be made with the rotor in place and with stator energized and brushes raised is to check the voltage across the rings to determine if they are balanced.　When this check is made, the rotor should be rotated to several positions and readings taken at each position to be sure that inequality in voltage readings is not due to the relative positions of stator and rotor phases.

Squirrel-cage rotors, which comprise the large majority in induction-motor applications, are considerably more rugged and require less maintenance in general than wound-rotor motors but also may give trouble because of open circuits or high resistance points between the rotor bars and the end rings.　The symptoms of such troubles are practically the same as for the wound-rotor motor, that is, reduced starting torque and tendency to slow down under load.　Evidence of heating at the end rings usually results from this condition and can be particularly detected when shutting down after operating under load.

Cracked rotor bars usually are found at the point of connection to the end ring or where the bar leaves the laminated core. Heating also is indicated by discoloration of the rotor bars.

Repairs to squirrel-cage rotors, such as replacing bars or brazing broken bars, should be attempted only by competent personnel. Considerable skill is required, and proper care should be exercised in such repairs.

As stated previously, a small air gap is a characteristic of an induction motor. The size of the air gap has a direct bearing on the power factor of the motor, and any alterations that affect the air gap, such as grinding the rotor body or the stator teeth, increase magnetizing current and lower the power factor.

Good maintenance includes a periodic check of motor air gap with gages to ensure against a worn bearing that would permit a rotor rub. Measurements should be taken on the coupling or driving end of the motor. Four measurements of air gap should be made approximately 90° apart, and one of the points should be on the load side, i.e., the point on the rotor corresponding to the load side of the bearing.

On larger motors, a record of air-gap measurements should be kept so that a comparison can be made with previous checks to determine the amount of bearing wear. A rub resulting from bearing wear can generate enough heat to cause insulation failure.

Overloading of motors because of increased demands on the driven machine increases the operating temperature, resulting in shortened life of insulation. Momentary overloads within reasonable values usually do no damage; consequently, a thermal overload device offers best protection. Since the best place to measure the thermal effect of overloads is on the motor, a thermal device can be applied directly to the motor winding. Most manufacturers can supply such a device, which provides effective protection against sustained overloads.

The polyphase induction motor is beyond doubt the simplest and most foolproof piece of rotating electrical apparatus. Experience indicates that the most frequent cause of winding failures is probably due to the rotor rubbing the stator iron, usually because of a worn bearing or complete failure of the bearing. Since bearings and lubrication of bearings are common to all types of motors, they will be treated in a separate section.

PART II.   THE DIRECT-CURRENT MOTOR

The d-c motor is more likely to be damaged in operation than the a-c motor because a number of current-carrying parts are exposed. This motor comprises two parts: the stationary part, or field, and the rotating part, or armature.

The field of a d-c motor consists of a frame and field poles which are fastened to the inner circumference of the frame. The poles are steel, usually laminated, and have mounted on them the field windings which furnish the excitation for the motor. Field windings, in general, are subject to the usual failings of electrical equipment. They can become dirty or oil soaked, which can interfere with heat being dissipated, causing eventual burnout. Excessive field current caused by malfunctioning of control will cause excessive heating and failure. Field heating can be caused by high voltage, too low speed, brushes being off neutral, overloads, a partial short in one field coil. An open circuit in a field coil can result in failure to start or excessive speeds at light loads and heavy sparking on the commutator.

The armature of a d-c motor consists of two main parts, the windings and the commutator. Cleanliness, while important on all electrical equipment, is particularly so on the d-c commutator and brush rigging. Oil, dust, grease, moisture, and corrosive gases should be kept away from commutators and brushes, as they cannot give good performance under adverse conditions such as these.

The armature is the heart, so to speak, of the d-c motor. The main line current flows through it, and if the machine is overloaded, the armature shows the first signs of distress. Reasonable attention from the standpoint of cleaning should result in little or no trouble with the armature under normal operating conditions. Repairs to armatures should be done only by competent personnel.   Care should be exercised in handling an armature, some of the more important items being

1. Never roll an armature on the floor; a coil may be injured or a band nicked.
2. Support or lift an armature only by its shaft, if possible; otherwise use a wide lifting belt under the core.
3. Never allow the weight of the armature to rest on the commutator or coils.

Windings should be preserved with periodic varnish treatment followed by baking where possible.   This will be treated later.

If necessary to renew the banding on an armature, duplicate the banding originally supplied by the manufacturer; in other words do not change material, diameter, width of band, or location.   Band width should not be increased, as to do so may cause restriction of ventilation and also cause heavy current in the bands sufficient to overheat and melt the band solder.

The commutator is probably the most vulnerable part of a d-c motor, as it is an exposed current-carrying part rotating at relatively high speeds.   The success or failure in operation of a d-c machine depends to a large extent on commutation. Regardless of any other excellent feature a d-c machine has, if the commutation is unsatisfactory, the machine has no commercial value.   It is not the intent at this time to go into the details of manufacture or assembly of commutators but to assume that the manufacturer has produced a device which, under proper conditions, will give trouble-free operation.

Assuming that the design of the machine is such that good commutation may be expected, then continued satisfactory operation depends on maintaining the commutator surface in good condition.   In general, this means that the surface should be smooth, concentric, and properly undercut.   The brush holders should work smoothly and be free of dust and dirt; the brushes should be of the proper grade and manufactured to correct size and tolerance.   While conditions under which d-c machines are operated vary widely, there are some basic conditions which must be maintained on all such machines to ensure satisfactory commutation, brush life, and a minimum of commutator wear.   These conditions and recommended maintenance methods are listed below.

1. The commutator must be concentric.   On high-speed machines with peripheral speeds of 9,000 fpm or above, the commutator should be concentric within 0.0005 in., which is the practical limit in grinding.   For peripheral speeds of between 5,000 and 9,000 fpm, the concentricity should be within 0.001 in.   On slow-speed, large-diameter commutators, this figure can be 0.003 in.

   There should be no abrupt change in surface from bar to bar.   Variations of as little as 0.001 in. are enough to cause bad commutator performance.   This bar-to-bar roughness can be detected by using a stick sharpened like a pencil and held on the revolving surface at a slightly inclined angle.   If the commutator has negligible bar-to-bar roughness, the stick, so used, will feel as if it is moving over a smooth glass surface.
2. To get a commutator concentric, a grinding rig should be used in all but a few special cases.   The grinding rig consists of an abrasive stone setup similar to a lathe tool in a carriage which can be moved back and forth along the commutator and equipped with a feed to advance the stone into the commutator surface (see Fig. 3-1).   The support must be rigged so that the grinding stone is subjected to a minimum of vibration.   On most d-c machines such a rig can be mounted on a brush arm by removing the brush holders.   In order to be sure of obtaining maximum rigidity, it may be desirable to brace the brush holder bracket arm during the grinding operation.   In some cases, it is possible to support the grinder on parallels fastened to the bedplate, in which case the entire brush rigging can be removed.   Grinding should be done, if possible, with the armature in its own bearings and, in the case of a constant-speed machine, at rated speed.   Low-speed grinding, if there is any evidence of unbalance, will cause the commutator to run

eccentrically at rated speed. Care should be exercised to prevent copper and stone dust getting into the windings. It is important to provide a vacuum cleaner on the grinding rig. In extreme cases where a cleaner is not available, the commutator necks and risers and the coil ends can be covered with paper or cloth to keep the grinding dust out of the machine.

In order to grind a commutator, the armature must be rotated. Each case must be treated separately as local conditions will govern. At times it is possible to run the motor with half the brushes out, grinding half the commutator and then repeating with the other half. A driving motor can be used, coupled or belted to the armature on which the work is being performed. On some types of equipment, it is difficult because of space or other considerations to grind the commutator in place. If the machine speed is relatively low, the work should be done

FIG. 3-1. Commutator grinding rig in position.

in a lathe by taking a very fine cut off the surface and then polishing with a stone. On high-speed machines, a special rig should be used equipped with a grinding device, a driving motor and adapter for bearings, so that the armature can be run in its own bearings. Grinding should be done at a speed as near to rated maximum speed as possible and still not have the grinding stone affected by vibration.

There are three grades of stones used in grinding commutators: coarse, medium, and fine. The coarse stone has a grit of approximately 80 mesh and takes off large amounts of copper. In general, the use of the coarse stone is not too desirable because if a great deal of copper has to be removed, it is better to use a lathe tool which can be set up in the grinding rig. The medium stone has a grit of approximately 120 mesh and is used for the bulk of grinding work, finishing up with the fine stone with a grit of approximately 200 mesh for the fine finish.

3. After grinding is completed, all commutator slots should be cleaned out thoroughly and the bar edges beveled. Beveling accomplishes two things: Burrs, caused by the stone dragging copper over the slots, are removed, and the sharp edge is eliminated at the entering side of the bar under the brush. This is accomplished with a special beveling tool which should have about $\frac{1}{32}$-in. chamfer at 45° for bars of medium thickness. For thinner or wider bars, the beveling can be changed accordingly.

4. Almost all modern d-c machines have undercut mica in the commutator slots. This undercutting should be kept at $\frac{1}{16}$ in. deep plus or minus $\frac{1}{64}$ in.   If, when a commutator is to be ground, sufficient copper will be removed so that the under-cutting will be shallow, then the commutator should be reundercut before grinding is started.   This is done by using a small, circular, high-speed saw about 0.003 in. thicker than the actual thickness of the mica.   Where the extent of undercutting is not great, a hacksaw blade mounted in a wooden handle is a popular tool.   It is sketched, along with another tool, in Fig. 3-2.   Otherwise, one of the undercutting tools put out by any one of a number of manufacturers can be used.   Care should be taken when undercutting that a thin sliver of mica is not left against one side

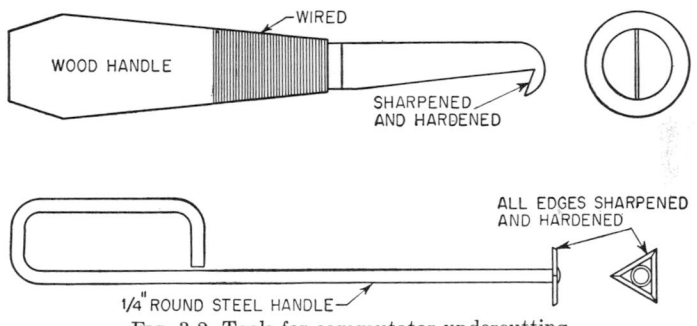

Fig. 3-2. Tools for commutator undercutting.

of the slot.   Slots should be checked, and if slivers are present, hand scraping will be necessary.   If these slivers are left, subsequent operation of the machine raises the mica above the edge of the bar and one of the worst conditions for good com-mutation develops.   As explained previously, the bars should be beveled after the undercutting is completed.

5. The bottom of the brush-holder box should be set at the correct angle and the cor-rect distance from the commutator surface.   The distance from the bottom of the brush box to the commutator surface on most machines is $\frac{1}{8}$ to $\frac{3}{16}$ in.   Failure to maintain the proper spacing results in brushes riding the commutator surface poorly and also has the affect of shifting neutral on machines using inclined brush holders.   This shift in neutral contributes to poor commutation.   To check this spacing and to ensure uniformity, a piece of hard fiber or similar material of the proper thickness should be used as a gage.

Spacing of brush holders around the commutator should be maintained evenly, and the spacings should not deviate more than plus or minus $\frac{1}{32}$ in.; also the holders should be aligned on the brush arm in a straight line parallel to the length of the commutator bars.   A popular method of checking brush-arm spacing is to stretch a piece of paper or adding-machine tape around the commutator under or near one brush path and mark the brush position on the paper with a pencil. The paper is then removed, and spacing checked for uniformity.   The brush arms can be shifted to obtain equal spacing.   The check should be taken several times to average out any errors.   After this work has been done, the brushes should be reinstalled or replaced with the brush holders staggered properly as per manufac-turer's recommendations.

Brush and Brush-holder Tolerances.   Brushes should slide freely in the brush boxes.   The standard tolerances for brush thickness are plus 0.000 minus 0.004 in. and for brush width are plus 0.000 minus 0.004 in. for brushes under $\frac{3}{4}$ in. wide and plus 0.000 minus 0.015 in. for brushes over $\frac{3}{4}$ in. wide.   The average industrial-type brush box maintains a tolerance of plus 0.003 to plus 0.006 in. on the thickness and plus 0.002 to plus 0.010 in. on the width.

With these close tolerances in the brush boxes and brushes, it can be readily seen that not much dust or dirt is required between brushes and boxes to cause sticking

brushes.   For this reason, a clean machine is essential to good commutator performance.   At times brushes will appear to be tight in the holder even after a thorough
cleaning.   The boxes should then be checked to determine if they have been warped.
This occurs at times if the machine has been run with excessive load which caused
heating or if the machine has had a severe flash which caused heating of the brush
holders.

Pressure.   Brush pressure springs should be set at the manufacturer's recommended values and should be adjusted to be as uniform as possible.   Uniform pressures prevent selective action whereby certain brushes tend to take more than their
proper share of the load.   Tension can be measured with a straight spring scale and
should be taken just as a new brush on being lowered touches the current collecting
surface.   The pull should be taken in the direction of normal brush motion to avoid
setting up friction values differing from those affecting the brush in operation.   Dividing the pull obtained with the scale by the cross-sectional area of the brush gives the
pressure in pounds per square inch.

Variables Affecting Commutation.   The maintenance suggestions outlined above
should result in satisfactory commutation, brush life, and commutator conditions.
However, there are a large number of variables which can upset the delicate balance
between brush and commutator.   The resulting unbalance is indicated in a number
of ways.   Following are listed several of the more common adverse conditions encountered and their remedies, together with what experience indicates as possible causes.
These should serve as a guide to the maintenance man in solving his commutation
problems but should not be taken as the final analysis on any particular trouble job.

Brush chatter is caused by high friction between the brush and the commutator or
by a poor commutator surface.   A very common cause of high friction between brush
and commutator is light load running.   On machines which operate for extended
periods with brush densities in the order of 25 amp per sq in. and below, the brushes
have a tendency to develop a highly polished glaze on the commutator which invariably causes brush chatter.   In order to correct this condition, the brushes in one or
more paths around the periphery should be lifted in order to raise the current density
in the remaining brushes to approximately 55 amp per sq in.   It is always better to
operate a brush overloaded for a short period than to operate it lightly loaded for an
extended period.   If it is not possible to raise the brushes as recommended above,
then a grade of brush with a slight amount of cleaning action should be used to prevent the formation of the high friction film, a grade of brush which has low-current
density should be installed, or a combination of both can be used.

High friction can also be caused when a commutator is run hot for an extended
period.   This condition usually does not develop unless the machine is run well
beyond rated capacity and cannot be corrected by any maintenance program.

Poor commutator surface and high mica also cause brush chatter, which, however,
can be distinguished from chatter caused by light load or overload conditions by its
lower frequency.   It can be corrected by grinding the commutator and beveling the
bars.

Brush chipping can result from brush chatter as described above.   It can also
result from extremely light or extremely heavy spring pressure, high mica, improper
fit of brushes in the holders, or severe shock or vibrations set up outside the machine.
Correction can be accomplished as described previously.

Threading or Streaking of Commutator Surface.   This is caused by the breakdown,
in the brush paths, of the film on the commutator surface.   The tendency then is for
the current to pass through the area where the film has been broken.   The surface
condition then is further aggravated, and finally threads or streaks are worn around
the periphery of the commutator.   This condition can also result from particles of
copper being embedded in the face of the brush.   These particles cut through the
commutator film, and since copper-to-copper contact drop is relatively low, these
areas carry more than their proper share of the current and threading results.   Brush
faces should be inspected periodically and corrected if necessary.

Selective action, the tendency for one brush or group of brushes to carry more than
its share of the load, is also a prime cause for threading or streaking.

Threading or streaking can be corrected or curtailed by using a brush with enough cleaning action to prevent formation of a film so heavy that current will not pass through it. The natural graphite brushes fill this function rather effectively. Some carbon-graphite and electrographitic brushes are suitable for this type of corrective action. In some cases, it is possible to use a brush which will put a film on the commutator surface. This film does not build up to a high resistance and consequently does not have to break down to permit current flow, a condition that results eventually in threading.

If selective action is causing the streaking or threading, it is necessary to check conditions which could cause unbalance in electrical paths. Electrical resistance in one path different from that in parallel paths causes selective action. Terminal connections, spring pressure, shunt to brush connections, brush size, brush-holder spacing, and brush material should be checked. Hardness of brushes ordinarily does not contribute to threading. However, the ash content of a brush can, especially if the ash particles are hard, as they can be if ash content is improperly controlled in manufacture.

Sparking. Practically every abnormal condition of the commutator, brush holders, brushes, fields, or armature results in sparking. If the maintenance practices, as outlined previously, have been followed and the machine was correct originally, we must then look for the cause of injurious sparking somewhere in the electrical or magnetic circuit of the machine or in the brush grade. The following are conditions to be looked for: bad connections between armature coils and commutator bars, particularly those which are bad only when the armature is rotating; short-circuited field coils; open-circuited armature coils; unequal air gaps due to worn bearings; brushes with too high contact drop; partial short in shunt field; neutral set-off. The following is a convenient check list on the most general causes of sparking:

Rough, eccentric, or dirty commutator.
Brushes sticking in holders.
Incorrect brush tension.
Poor brush fit.
Brushes not parallel with commutator bars.
Unequal brush-holder spacing.
Vibration.
Brushes off neutral.
Unequal spacing of main or commutating poles.
Reversed or short-circuited commutating pole coils.
Reversed compensating winding.
Open circuit in armature winding.
Short circuit in armature winding.
Unequal air gap.
Grounds.

Checking Neutral. When a machine is reassembled after it has been dismantled for cleaning or repairs, it is frequently necessary to check and set neutral on the machine. The following is an outline of the kick-neutral method.

This method is based on measurement of voltages induced in the armature coils as the current in the main field on the machine is interrupted. Voltages induced in the conductors located at equal distances to the right and left of the pole centers are equal in magnitude and opposite in direction. If the terminals of a low-range voltmeter are connected to commutator bars corresponding to conductors located midway between poles, no deflection will be caused by breaking the field current. When the brushes are set so that the center lines of their faces correspond with the center lines of the commutator bars between which there is no induced voltage, they are on neutral (see Fig. 3-3).

If the number of commutator bars is not evenly divisible by the number of poles, use the following method: With the machine at standstill, raise all brushes. Replace one of them on each arm by a special brush of the same thickness. This special brush should be beveled to a knife edge parallel with its longer side and in the center of its face.   Connect leads from adjacent brush arms to a d-c voltmeter, preferably one having 0.5-, 1.5-, and 15-volt scales.   Separately excite the shunt field from a d-c source through a quick-break switch.   Insert enough external resistance in the excitation circuit to keep the field current small at the beginning.   Use the smallest field current that gives a good deflection on the low scale of the voltmeter.   When "kick" voltage is read for the first time, begin with the 15-volt scale and change to lower scales only when it is certain that the voltage is within their respective ranges.   Before the switch is opened for each reading, wait long enough for the induced voltage caused by closing the circuit to decay.   Shift the rocker ring to the point at which the voltage is minimum when the field circuit is opened.   If the machine has double brush holders, the center of the brush holder is placed on the neutral mark instead of either of the double holder brushes.

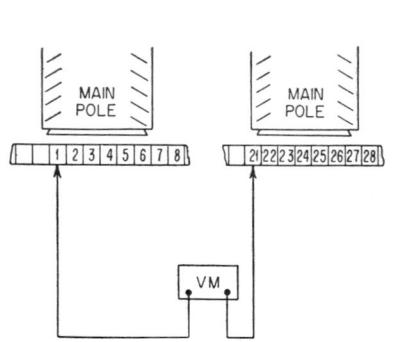

FIG. 3-3. Instrument connections for reading voltage induced in armature.

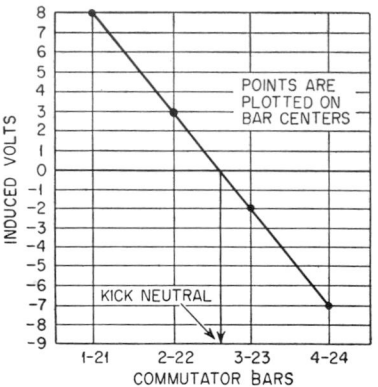

FIG. 3-4. Curve method of determining neutral.

If the number of bars between center lines of brushes on adjacent arms results in half a bar being included in the commutator pitch (such as $20\frac{1}{2}$ bars between center lines), this alternative method is used: Raise all brushes.   With the voltmeter points on bars 1 and 21 in the approximate neutral zone, open the field circuit as described in the paragraph above and read the deflection.   Move the voltmeter points to bars 1 and 22, and read the deflection as the field circuit is opened.   Rotate the armature slightly until the two readings are equal but opposite in polarity.   This indicates that the correct neutral is exactly on the center line of bar 1 and on the mica between bars 21 and 22.   The rocker ring is shifted until the center lines of the arc of the brush surfaces are exactly over these positions.   The same procedure applies here for double brush holders.

If the number of bars is evenly divisible by the number of poles, it is possible to be off neutral one-half bar with the method just described.   If the armature can be rotated, use this alternative method: Raise all brushes.   Determine the commutator pitch.   For example, if the machine has 20 bars per pole pitch, the throw for a multiple-wound armature would be bar 1 to bar 21.   With the voltmeter points on bars 1 and 21 in the approximate neutral zone, open the field circuit as described in the above paragraph and read the deflection.   Move the voltmeter points to bars 2 and 22, and read the deflection as the field is opened.   Rotate the armature in either direction, and repeat these operations until the two readings are equal but opposite.   This indicates that the correct neutral is exactly on the mica between bars 1 and 2 or between bars 21 and 22.   The rocker ring is shifted to these points as explained in the preceding paragraph.

If the armature cannot be rotated, the neutral is located by the use of a curve or a calculation (see Fig. 3-4).   If the number of bars is divisible by the number of poles, proceed as outlined in the above paragraph. Read the induced voltages on bars 1 and 21, 2 and 22, 3 and 23, etc., until a point is reached at which the polarity of the induced voltage reverses. Then record four readings, two on either side of the reversing point; plot the induced voltages as ordinates and the number of commutator bars as abscissas. Keep in mind that the number indicates the center line of the end of the bar. After the exact point of reversal has been determined from the curve, mark the relative position on the commutator. This is the correct neutral. Shift the rocker ring as described in one of the above paragraphs. It is possible to calculate the distance from the center line of a bar on either side of the point of reversal to the neutral without plotting a curve. Two readings only are necessary, one on either side of the point of reversal. Measure the distance between the center lines of two adjacent bars. The distance from the center line of one bar to neutral is found by dividing the reading on that bar by the sum of the two readings. This quotient is expressed in percentage of the total distance between center lines.

Effect of Setting Brushes off Neutral. At times it is advisable to shift brushes off neutral. This may be done to obtain results that are too expensive to get otherwise or to get better performance curves. When brushes are moved in a direction opposite rotation, the motor becomes undercompounded and compensation increases. Moving brushes in the direction of rotation overcompounds the machine and undercompensates it. Should there be a lack of compensation in a motor which is to run in one direction only and the additional amount of compensation needed is not too great, the machine may be made to commutate properly by moving the brushes slightly against rotation. If the machine is of a reversing type, this cannot be done because poor commutation would be obtained in one direction of rotation. Sometimes a motor-speed curve has a "hump" in it. Often this can be corrected by moving the brushes off neutral a slight amount as long as commutation is not affected. The limit of good commutation determines how far the brushes may be moved. If good commutation is not obtained by moving the brushes, then a change should be made in the commutating pole air gap.

Flashing. A question which has been argued pro and con for years is "Can the brush in itself be the cause for a machine to flash over?" A great deal of study and investigation has been devoted to this. A flash usually is the result of a suddenly changed condition in current or voltage or in the field strength of the machine. Disregarding control failures, the flashing results from a short circuit imposed by brush shunts breaking and touching on the opposite polarity, brushes breaking and causing shorting of commutator bars at the commutator surface, a piece of carbon from broken brushes becoming lodged between opposite polarities of the "wiring around frame" of the motor circuit, or bar-burning on flat spots on the commutator. The large factor of safety in today's standard of commutation is such that a given grade of brush is rarely the cause of flashing.

Commutator Films. The most satisfactory commutator film is evenly colored and is between a light brown or straw color to dark brown. The most important point is that it be a uniform color and not a highly glazed or extremely dull finish.

Undesirable films due to atmosphere conditions are usually quite dark, black or gray. These films can be detected by the fact that the discoloration of the copper is seen on the surface, not in the brush paths.

The amount of contamination in the air that can be injurious to a commutator surface by causing undesirable film is extremely low. Conditions which cannot be detected by smell often cause deleterious results. For example, it is known that 3 parts of sulfur in 1 million parts of air is sufficient to cause heavy formation of undesirable film. When such conditions are found, a cleaner brush should be used with enough cleaning action to prevent the formation of the heavy film or else a brush whose film-forming qualities may develop a satisfactory film of copper oxide on the commutator surface before the injurious film can be established.

Copper Pickup. This undesirable feature is the transfer of copper particles from the commutator surface to the brush faces where they become embedded. Once started, copper pickup is usually progressive to the point where commutation and current collection is impaired. When copper becomes embedded in a brush face, the contact drop is decreased to the point where commutation becomes impossible. The rubbing effect of the copper particles against the commutator surface causes threading and grooving. In order to remedy this condition, the proper bar edge beveling should be maintained, the machine must be kept clean by blowing out thoroughly after working on the commutator, and brush seating stones should be used sparingly. Also, the brush faces should be sanded to clean out the copper particles.

Brush Wear. This is one of the controversial subjects with operators of machines using brushes. All operators naturally desire longest possible brush life. However, increased commutator wear or poor commutation must not be resorted to in order to obtain long brush wear. Brushes wear away both electrically and mechanically, and these two have a complicated and strange relationship.

Brush life is at its best when the load on the brush is around 55 amp per sq in. Lightly loaded brushes set up friction and chatter conditions as explained previously.

A newly installed machine frequently has short brush life, caused usually by building and cement dust from the new construction. This condition gradually improves with time, although sometimes over a year may be required to overcome this trouble.

All the possible adverse conditions discussed above have an effect on brush life. Correction of the particular trouble also tends to correct short brush life.

PART III. INSULATION AND ITS CARE

The most important item in the maintenance of electric apparatus is taking care of the insulation. Commutators, collectors, and bearings require periodic attention; meters, regulators, etc., while requiring adjustments, can usually continue in service until a planned shutdown takes place. However, when insulation fails, you are extremely fortunate if only a temporary shutdown occurs. In order to be able to cope with insulation problems arising today, it is important to understand the qualities of insulating materials in order to discover incipient trouble before it becomes major. In other words, preventive attention is better than cure.

A motor insulated for damp applications might fail very soon if applied where ambient temperatures are high, and vice versa. The application of the motor should determine the class of insulation, and repairs should be made, using the best grade of materials to suit the application.

The American Standards Association publishes the various symbols used in classifying and identifying insulation materials, and these standards should be consulted. Standards have also been formulated and published on allowable temperatures that various insulations should be limited to in operation. For convenience, below are listed the limiting temperatures (sometimes called "hottest-spot" temperatures) to be used as a reference.

Material	*Temperature, °C*
Class O	90
Class A	105
Class B	130
Class C	No limit selected as yet
Class H	180

In actual practice, it is advisable to keep the operating temperature below the limit in order to prolong the life of the insulation. Practically all insulation on coils has a binder which is used to band the insulating material to the conductors. This binder keeps the insulation "alive" and pliable, and as long as the flexibility remains, the insulation will have long service life under normal operating conditions. Operation for extended periods at high temperatures or unfavorable atmospheric conditions affects this binder and shortens insulation life.

It is not the intention of this section to discuss the types of insulation, its manufacture, and application but to deal only with its care.

A check of the condition of insulation should be made periodically to indicate the presence of dirt, carbonized material, and moisture. Tests to indicate this that do not damage or "break down" the insulation are the most satisfactory for maintenance testing. The test most generally applied is that to determine the resistance of the insulation. Special conditions may justify other tests such as dielectric tests, over-potential tests, high-frequency tests, or power-factor tests. In some unusual cases chemical, physical, or laboratory tests may be needed in checking into insulation failure.

The resistance test gives a good indication of the condition of the insulation, particularly from the standpoint of moisture and dirt. The actual value of the resistance varies in different apparatus depending on type, size, voltage rating, etc. However, the importance of these values lies in the relative readings of insulation values taken under similar conditions at various times. They usually indicate how well the maintenance department has done its work.

High insulation resistance values, however, do not assure high dielectric strength, although low insulation resistance may indicate low dielectric strength. Coil insulation that is wrinkled or that has been damaged mechanically may have a high resistance but could fail at a relatively low value of dielectric test voltage. Insulation resistance varies inversely with the temperature, a rough check being that the insulation resistance will be halved for every 10° rise in temperature of the apparatus.

Insulation resistance can be measured by a self-contained instrument such as the familiar "Megger," either hand- or motor-operated; by the electronic type; with a resistance bridge; or with a milliameter, a voltmeter, and a d-c supply. Any of these instruments used in insulation testing must be well maintained to be sure that the readings taken will be factual.

Insulation resistance of apparatus in service should be checked periodically at approximately the same temperature and under similar conditions of humidity to determine possible insulation deterioration. If such measurements show wide variations, the cause should be determined and corrective measures taken to forestall an insulation failure.

No new equipment should be placed in service with insulation resistance less than 1 megohm. A good rule to follow on equipment in service is that the insulation resistance should be approximately 1 megohm for each 1,000 volts of operating voltage with a minimum value of 1 megohm.

Dielectric Tests. The purpose of dielectric tests is to determine if the insulation on the machine can withstand the voltage stresses set up during normal and possible abnormal conditions during operation.

The application of the a-c high voltage necessary to make a dielectric test presents hazards in that not only can the a-c voltage used puncture or break down the insulation but often severe burning of the machine laminations occurs, because the capacity needed to test larger machines is such that in case of breakdown, a large amount of power follows in the arc established. However, in many cases, the risk involved does not outweigh the possible long outage that might occur if the insulation failed while in an operation driving an important load.

The test voltage applied to new machines or to the winding of machines completely rewound with new coils and insulating material is specified by AIEE and ASA standards as twice rated voltage plus 1,000 volts held for 60 sec, with the exception of field windings of synchronous motors, which are given a test voltage of 10 times the exciter voltage but not less than 1,500 volts. For machines in commercial operation or for repaired machines, no standards have been set, but established practice is to use an a-c test voltage between 65 and 75 per cent of the test voltage for new windings. The lower value should be used for older windings.

Within recent years, high-voltage d-c testing has become more and more accepted. It has numerous advantages over a-c testing. The capacity used is small, and the test effect in searching out weak insulation is comparable to a-c testing. The unit used is considerably smaller physically than the test transformer, the equipment needed to test the largest machine being easily transported in a car, whereas the transformer requires a large truck. The device is electronic and consists essentially of a high-voltage rectification circuit. Instruments measure the current and voltage. Another advantage, which is of prime importance, is that in case of an insulation failure during test, no iron burning results because of the small amount of power used. The test equipment operates from the 60-cycle lighting circuit. Test values have been established whereby a d-c test voltage is applied 60 per cent greater than the a-c test voltage ordinarily used. Direct-current testing in time probably will be universally used. The cost of the d-c test outfit is considerably less, especially when compared with the cost of a test transformer with capacity to test the windings of large machines. The same d-c test outfit can be used to test the windings of machines, from the smallest to the largest.

A relatively new test has come into use to check turn-to-turn insulation in machine windings. The device is a surge comparison tester and is used to locate insulation faults and winding dissymmetries in all classes of equipment regardless of size. It is an electronic device and is portable, so that it can be used for maintenance work as well as shop work. High turn-to-turn voltages are applied without excessive winding to ground stresses, and the testing is nondestructive.

Cleaning and Drying Insulation. Operating instructions provided by machine manufacturers always emphasize the importance of keeping electrical apparatus clean and dry. Favorable locations, adequate ventilation, application of heaters to prevent condensation of moisture on the motor when the machine is out of service for any length of time, and suitable covers all help to reduce the number of outages and to lessen maintenance costs.

When a motor does get dirty, the insulation must be cleaned and restored to as near its original condition as possible. Various methods of cleaning are used, depending upon the type of dirt to be removed, if the machine is to go back in service immediately, etc. After cleaning, it is necessary to make sure the machine is dry. Experiences after floods have illustrated this. Also, after cleaning, the insulation should be tested as outlined above to determine if it has been properly reconditioned.

In order to keep accumulations of dirt out of the machine so that ventilating ducts remain open and low-resistance paths between line parts do not form, proper cleaning must be performed. Such cleaning may be by blowing with compressed air, by suction, or by wiping. If oil or grease is mixed with the dirt, it may be necessary to use a solvent, in which case a safety-type petroleum solvent should be used. Such solvents are less likely to attack insulating varnishes than stronger ones, such as chlorinated or coal-tar solvents

Most cleaning solvents used on electric machines are toxic, and care should be exercised in their use. Suitable gas masks should be used, especially in confined spaces such as tanks or hulls of ships. Some solvents are flammable, and extreme precautions are necessary if such solvents are used, but unless absolutely necessary, their use should be discouraged.

Methods for cleaning electrical insulation are, in general, as follows, the method selected depending on the type of apparatus, type of insulation, kind of dirt, and other conditions.

1. Wiping off with a clean dry cloth if the machine is small, the surfaces to be cleaned accessible, and dry dirt only is to be removed. Waste should never be used because lint adheres to insulation and increases the collection of dirt, moisture, and oil.

2. Blowing off the dirt with compressed air is effective, particularly if dirt is in places that cannot be reached by a cloth. Large motors, in general, can be cleaned more quickly with compressed air. However, if blowing moves dirt from one machine to another, little good is accomplished. Do not clean with compressed air unless it is certain that the air is dry; otherwise the water in the air will deposit in the machine where it can do no good. Air pressures above 50 psi should not be used, as high pressures may damage insulation and blow dirt under loosened tape. Do not direct the air stream in such a manner that the dirt is blown into a pocket in the machine from which it can be removed only with difficulty. It may clog ventilating ducts. *Caution:* When blowing with compressed air, goggles should be worn.

3. Vacuum. The well-known suction principle is very successful, especially if all parts of the machine are accessible. It is effective in removing dry, loose dirt, since it does not scatter it; therefore does not transfer it among machines.

4. Solvents. If the accumulated dirt contains grease or oil, wiping, blowing, or suction will not be effective and a solvent will probably be necessary. There are two types of solvents on the market: petroleum distillates; and other solvents, comprising chlorinated solvents, mixtures of chlorinated and petroleum solvents, and coal-tar solvents. For cleaning electrical apparatus with solvents, only petroleum distillates should be used. These are classed "safety-type solvents," have flash points about 100°F (38°C), and can be supplied by practically all oil companies under various trade names. Stoddart's Solution or Solvent, as described in the National Bureau of Standards Commercial Standard CS3-40, is a popular and good solvent of this type. However, all such sol-

vents are flammable, and the vapors form explosive mixtures with air if used at temperatures above their flash point. However, since their flash point is higher than that of other types of petroleum distillates, such as gasoline, the so-called safety type presents less of a fire hazard. Complete safety precautions should be taken in using commercial solvents. Under no conditions should carbon tetrachloride or any other chloride solvent, either alone or in mixture, be used, as it has a highly toxic effect. In some stubborn cases, where the petroleum solvent will not do a cleaning job and a stronger solvent is needed, a chlorinated solvent may be used providing all the precautions are observed. Coal-tar solvents alone or in mixture are good cleaners but are flammable and toxic, and their use should be avoided.

5. Water can be used to wash out motors that have been plugged with mud or other foreign matter by plant operations, dust storms, or floods. The motors should be washed with water from a hose and disassembled so that all parts can be thoroughly cleaned.

FIG. 3-5. Washing motors that are extremely dirty.

See Fig. 3-5. When water is applied to insulated parts, the pressure should not exceed 25 psi. Grease and oil may be removed by using a steam spray machine called a "steam jenny." Frequently a cleaning solution is used in the jenny.

After any cleaning operation where water is used, the surface moisture should be wiped off with a clean cloth and the insulation dried promptly to keep the penetration of water as low as possible.

Cleaning motors with high-temperature insulation of the "silicone" type represents a special case. Standard cleaning solvents ordinarily cannot be used, as they may attack the silicone varnish. It is recommended that the manufacturer of the equipment be consulted before cleaning such equipment. The generally recommended procedure for cleaning silicone insulation is to use water containing a detergent such as Dreft or equivalent. The cleaning should be done quickly, and the equipment dried out as rapidly as possible.

6. Dry Cleaning. Another method of cleaning motors which have oily or greasy dirt in them is to blow ground-up corncobs on them. The meal has a wonderful affinity for oil and grease and will clean a machine in excellent fashion. When this method is used, the machine should be covered and the dirty meal drawn off by vacuum. The cost is nominal compared with the results. The operator should use a dust mask or respirator.

Drying Electrical Insulation. After electrical apparatus has been cleaned, before it is placed in operation, the insulation must be dry. Drying is indicated if an insulation-resistance check shows the resistance to be below safe minimum value. New equipment may require drying out, especially if it has been exposed to high humidity before being placed in service. External or internal heat or sometimes a combination of both can be used.

Drying with External Heat. For plants with large numbers of motors, a permanent drying oven may be a good investment. Such an oven not only is convenient for

FIG. 3-6. Drying insulation by means of infrared lamps.

drying motors but can be used for small transformers, control apparatus, etc. However, temporary ovens can be constructed of asbestos board, sheet iron, bricks, or concrete blocks and lined with nonburning heat-insulating material.

Hot air can be used to dry insulation by blowing through the electrical apparatus. The air can be heated by electrical heaters, steam pipes, or a hot-air furnace. This is a quick way to drive off surface moisture but is rather costly and inefficient unless a blower and air duct are already installed for ventilation and a heater can be installed in the duct.

Drying with electric heaters distributed under the end windings is probably the best method. Space heaters are inexpensive and small and can be installed readily. When motors are dried by this or other methods, air circulation must be established to take away moisture-laden air and to prevent "hot-spot" temperatures from developing in the apparatus. A careful check should be kept on drying operations to prevent temperatures from becoming excessive or fires from starting.

Infrared lamps have become popular for drying insulation. A group of such lamps mounted on suitable frames around the apparatus to be dried is very effective (see Fig. 3-6). When these lamps are used, the same precautions should be taken as with other drying means.

Open fires should never be used except as an emergency measure when no other way is available. Fires are dangerous, and therefore, hazard is high. Smoke and soot from open fires are objectionable, and more harm can be done by products of combustion such as gases, ashes, or soot than from the original moisture.

Drying with Internal Heat. Insulation on coils of motors can be dried by the use of internal heat, generated by circulating current in the windings, but it is not generally to be recommended, as there are other better ways. It is mentioned here, however, as a possibility. Precautions should be taken, as the heat generated in the machine is not readily dissipated and may cause serious damage.

Commutators of d-c motors that are so wet that their insulation does not dry out when the winding is dried require special treatment. Usually such commutators will have water inside, in which case it is necessary to take out some of the V-ring bolts in order to drain out the entrapped water. On small machines, the commutator can be oven-dried, but on larger machines it will be necessary to force hot air inside the commutator or apply low-temperature electric heat to the commutator surface. Extreme care and close checking are needed when drying commutators.

After the drying is completed on insulation or commutators, the insulation resistance should be measured to be sure effective dryout has been accomplished. Practically all machines that have been wet or cleaned will respond to proper drying out if the insulation, before the wetting occurred or the cleaning was done, was in good condition. If proper drying does not bring the insulation to the proper level, then rewinding or repair is indicated.

PART IV. BEARINGS AND LUBRICATION

Proper care of bearings, which includes lubrication as a natural companion, is one of the most important maintenance items pertaining to motors. The rotating element of a motor which transfers the electric energy from the power supply into mechanical energy to drive the desired load of necessity must have bearings. The designer has a choice between sliding or sleeve bearings and rolling or "antifriction" bearings (ball or roller). All bearings present lubrication problems that must be solved to obtain proper operation.

An analysis of induction-motor failures over a long period shows that bearings are one of the principal sources. This also applies, in general, to all types of motors. Haphazard lubrication can result in deterioration of insulation due to oil leakage, as well as bearing failure and other mechanical troubles. Bearing failures can allow the rotor to rub against the stator, which brings additional troubles.

Until recent years, the most generally used bearing was of the sleeve type. Within the last 10 years or so, the trend has been to the "antifriction" type, either roller or ball, and for most applications this type has become a standard with all manufacturers. The sleeve bearings are still a "must," however, in certain specialized applications, particularly where large shaft diameters are involved and also for use in high speeds. Where a split bearing is required, such as for large heavy rotors, the sleeve bearing is still used.

When repairing sleeve bearings by rebabbitting, be sure to use materials from a reliable supplier, obtaining babbitt as recommended by the manufacturer of the motor. Do not make any changes in the composition of the babbitt. Two general types of babbitt are in popular use. Tin-base type contains 80 to 90 per cent tin with the remainder divided about equally between copper and antimony. Lead-base type contains about 75 to 85 per cent lead with 5 to 10 per cent tin and 10 to 5 per cent antimony. Either type is satisfactory for general-purpose use, but tin base babbitt is generally used in corrosive atmospheres. Reinstallation of a repaired bearing should be done carefully. Some manufacturers indicate diametrical clearance of 0.002 in. per inch of diameter of shaft except for small bearings, which will have larger clearance. Others use 0.001-in.-diametrical clearance for shafts 1 in. diameter or less, on larger shafts 0.001 plus 0.001 in. per inch of shaft diameter up to 0.006 in. A good rule for general use is the first one.

Since antifriction bearings operate on entirely different principles from sleeve bearings, it is misleading to make comparisons of the two types or to diagnose the troubles of one type by experiences with the other type.   The only true comparison is the service obtained over a period of time.

The antifriction bearing assembly is a self-contained unit made to very close limits and with a high degree of surface finish.   Therefore, it must be handled carefully, and dirt and corrosive conditions must be kept away.   Motor bearing housings using antifriction bearings must, therefore, be designed to exclude entry of dirt as much as possible.   Careful handling of the bearing during installation and protection from dirt during lubrication are extremely important to trouble-free operation.

In order to eliminate these hazards as much as possible, ball bearing manufacturers, in conjunction with motor manufacturers, developed prelubrication sealed bearings.   Experiments with such types began many years ago and have progressed to the point where prelubricated bearings are almost universally accepted.   In this country the bearing used generally has the width of the standard double-row bearing, but with a single row of balls, thus leaving space for an efficient seal.

Bear in mind that the standard ball bearing and the prelubricated do not differ fundamentally.   Both are made from the same material to the same specifications regarding tolerances and fits.   The prelubricated bearing is rated to carry the same load and have the same life as its open counterpart.   The textile industry gave the sealed bearing its impetus when bearing manufacturers were asked to develop a bearing to lick the tough problem of protecting grease fittings or oil cups from lint that settles in heavy layers on any surface wetted by oil.   Success in the textile field rapidly spread the use of prelubricated bearings to practically all industries.

Maintenance of antifriction bearings includes lubrication, removal, cleaning, and reinstalling.   These bearings, while requiring more care in handling than sleeve bearings, do not need to be handled like fragile china.   Since they are precision made, this precision must be maintained during their useful life.

Certain precautions should be taken before installing a new bearing.   First, be sure your hands are clean.   Wash your hands but not the bearing, as it has been pregreased by the manufacturer.   Press it in place on the shaft; *don't hammer it.*

When inspecting an old bearing, look for hardened areas.   Streaks or spots are an indication.   Look for cracked balls or rollers, etching from possible contact with acid, and discolored areas caused by overheating.   Any of these defects should cause rejection.

Removal of a bearing should be done with a bearing puller, which looks and works like a gear or pulley puller.   Always apply the pulling force on the inner ring or race which is on the shaft.   Never pull on the outer race.

Installation of a bearing usually calls for a press and a pipe sleeve.   After the bearing is lined up, select a pipe sleeve with the same diameter as the inner race. The sleeve should be placed between the press and the inner case, and even pressure applied.   The bearing will slide into place.   Some bearings are difficult to install. They may have to be heated in oil in order to expand the inner case so that it will slide on the shaft.   Heating to between 95 and 120°C (200 to 250°F) will give a good shrink fit on the shaft.   At times, it may be more convenient to use dry ice and shrink the shaft, which will allow the bearing to slide in easily.

Lubrication of bearings is one of the controversial items in the maintenance of motors.   It has become so important that most plants or companies now have a lubrication engineer whose training is such that he can make recommendations and advise on all problems regarding lubrication, not only of motors but of all equipment installed in the plants.   It is not the intent of this discussion to delve into the whys and wherefores and ramifications of lubricating oils and greases.   The plant lubricating engineer or representatives of oil companies should be consulted.   A few essential points, however, should be noted.

The manufacturer of the equipment recommends the type of lubricant to be used with his product to obtain what he feels to be the best results.   These recommendations should be followed unless conditions change.

Lubrication of sleeve bearings, in general, is accomplished by hand-oiling or greasing, dependent on the type required.   In some applications where a large number of motors are involved in an area, centralized lubrication is used.   This method is more efficient and less expensive than manual; it distributes the correct amount of lubricant at the proper time intervals.   Most motor bearings of the sleeve variety, where manual or individual lubrication is performed, have oil rings that carry the lubricant from a reservoir onto the shaft.   These rings should be checked at periodic intervals to determine that they are rotating and thus are carrying the lubricant to the journal and bearing.   Needless to say, oil added should be clean and the equipment used should be clean.   Dust and dirt are enemies of bearings of all kinds.

An antifriction bearing properly installed and properly lubricated according to the manufacturer's recommendations will give you the service you desire.   But if you slip up by neglecting your lubrication periods, using the wrong lubricant, or letting dirt get into the bearing, you let yourself in for trouble.   This type of bearing is more susceptible than a sleeve bearing to failures from dirt and incorrect lubrication.

Table 3-1. Good Maintenance Practices

Keep motor off line when not needed.	Saves unnecessary wear of brushes, commutator, and bearings; saves lubrication
Do not leave field circuit excited unless motor has been especially designed for this type duty	Check temperature of shunt fields with thermometer to see that temperature does not exceed 90°C. When field must be excited, caution maintenance men to be sure field circuit is opened before working on the motor
Keep motor clear of metal dust or cuttings that can be drawn into windings and pole pieces	Magnetic attraction will draw metal parts into the air gap and damage windings
Reassembling of motor	Be sure to retain proper air gaps in motor by checking bore of pole faces before dismantling. Reassemble, replacing poles and liners in original position
Note wearing parts and parts frequently replaced to determine anticipated repairs	Carry in proper store room stock of replacement parts. Make survey of standard repair parts to avoid duplication of parts to be carried

The main points to remember about bearings are to handle them carefully, remove and install them properly, and lubricate them with the proper lubricants.

To summarize maintenance procedure and provide a ready reference, Tables 3-1 to 3-4 are presented.

If the maintenance man or inspector is to do a satisfactory job, proper tools and instruments are necessary.   Also, he should have a good general knowledge of the electrical and mechanical characteristics of the equipment under his care, together with an understanding of the correct operation of the equipment.   The following should be made available:

1. Tools necessary to disassemble apparatus.
2. Extension cords, safety type.
3. Flashlights, rubber or molded cases.
4. Air-gage gages.
5. Micrometers, inside and outside.
6. Dial indicator with assortment of brackets.
7. "Megger," 500-volt.
8. Volt-amp-ohmmeter, tester such as Simpson, Triplett, or equivalent.
9. Thermometers and levels.
10. Portable instruments such as ammeters, voltmeters, and graphic meters.

Access to instruction books furnished by the manufacturer with equipment purchased should be a must.

Only by having suitably instructed personnel with adequate equipment can motors be given the attention they need for long, trouble-free operation.

Table 3-2. A-C, D-C Motor Check Chart

Trouble	Cause	What to do
Hot bearings—general	Bent or sprung shaft	Straighten or replace shaft
	Excessive belt pull	Decrease belt tension
	Pulley too far away	Move pulley closer to bearing
	Pulley diameter too small	Use larger pulleys
	Misalignment	Correct by realignment of drive
Hot bearings—sleeve	Oil grooving in bearing obstructed by dirt	Remove bracket or pedestal with bearing, and clean oil grooves and bearing housing; renew oil
	Bent or damaged oil rings	Repair or replace oil rings
	Oil too heavy	Use a recommended lighter oil
	Oil too light	Use a recommended heavier oil
	Insufficient oil	Fill reservoir to proper level in overflow plug with motor at rest
	Too much end thrust	Reduce thrust induced by driven machine or supply external means to carry thrust
	Badly worn bearing	Replace bearing
Hot bearings—ball	Insufficient grease	Maintain proper quantity of grease in bearing
	Deterioration of grease or lubricant contaminated	Remove old grease; wash bearings thoroughly in kerosene and replace with new grease
	Excess lubricant	Reduce quantity of grease. Bearing should not be more than $\frac{1}{2}$ filled
	Heat from hot motor or external source	Protect bearing by reducing motor temperature
	Overloaded bearing	Check alignment, side thrust and end thrust
	Broken ball or rough races	Replace bearing; first clean housing thoroughly
Oil leakage from overflow plugs	Stem of overflow plug not tight	Remove; recement threads; replace and tighten
	Cracked or broken overflow plug	Replace the plug
	Plug cover not tight	Requires cork gasket, or if screw type, may be tightened.
Motor dirty	Ventilation blocked, end windings filled with fine dust or lint	Clean motor will run 10 to 30°C cooler. Dust may be cement, sawdust, rock dust, grain dust, coal dust and the like. Dismantle entire motor and clean all windings and parts
	Rotor winding clogged	Clean, grind and undercut commutator. Clean and treat windings with good insulating varnish
	Bearing and brackets coated inside	Dust and wash with cleaning solvent
Motor wet	Subject to dripping	Wipe motor and dry by circulating heated air through motor. Install drip- or canopy-type covers over motor for protection
	Drenched condition	Motor should be covered to retain heat and the rotor position shifted frequently
	Submerged in flood waters	Dismantle and clean parts. Bake windings in oven at 105°C for 24 hr or until resistance to ground is sufficient. First make sure commutator bushing is drained of water

Table 3-3. D-C Motor Check Chart

Trouble	Cause	What to do
Fails to start	Circuit not complete Brushes not down on commutator Brushes stuck in holders Armature locked by frozen bearings in motor or main drive Power may be off	Switch open, leads broken Held up by brush springs; need replacement. Brushes worn out Remove and sand; clean up brush boxes Remove brakets and replace bearings or recondition old bearings if inspection makes possible Check line connections to starter with light. Check contacts in starter
Motor starts, then stops and reverses direction of rotation	Reverse polarity of generator that supplies power Shunt and series fields are bucking each other	Check generating unit for cause of changing polarity Reconnect either the shunt or series field so as to correct the polarity. Then connect armature leads for desired direction of rotation. The fields can be tried separately to determine the direction of rotation individually and connected so both give same rotation
Motor does not come up to rated speed	Overload Starting resistance not all out Voltage low Short circuit in armature windings or between bars Starting heavy load with very weak field Motor off neutral Motor cold	Check bearing to see if in first-class condition with correct lubrication. Check driven load for excessive load or friction Check starter to see if mechanically and electrically in correct condition Measure voltage with meter and check with motor name plate For shorted armature inspect commutator for blackened bars and burned adjacent bars. Inspect windings for burned coils or wedges Check full field relay and possibilities of full field setting of the field rheostat Check for factory setting of brush rigging or test motor for true neutral setting Increase load on motor so as to increase its temperature, or add field rheostat to set speed
Motor runs too fast	Voltage above rated Load too light Shunt field coil shorted Shunt field coil reversed Series coil reversed Series field coil shorted Neutral setting shifted off neutral Part of shunt field rheostat or unnecessary resistance in field circuit Motor ventilation restricted, causing hot shunt field	Correct voltage or get recommended change in air gap from manufacturer Increase load or install fixed resistance in armature circuit Install new coil Reconnect coil leads in reverse Reconnect coil leads in reverse Install new or repaired coil Reset neutral by checking factory setting mark or testing for neutral Measure voltage across field and check with name-plate rating Hot field is high in resistance; check causes for hot field, in order restore normal shunt field current

Table 3-3. D-C Motor Check Chart (*Continued*)

Trouble	Cause	What to do
Motor gaining speed steadily and increasing load does not slow it down	Unstable speed load regulation	Inspect motor to see it off neutral. Check series field to determine shorted turns. If series field has a shunt around the series circuit that can be removed
	Reversed field coil shunt or series	Test with compass and reconnect coil
	Too strong a commutating pole or commutating pole air gap too small	Check with factory for recommended change in coils or air gap
Motor runs too slow continuously	Voltage below rated	Measure voltage and try to correct to value on motor name plate
	Overload	Check bearings of motors and the drive to see if in first-class condition. Check for excessive friction in drive
	Motor operates cold	Motor may run 20 per cent slow due to light load. Install smaller motor, increase load or install partial covers to increase heating
	Neutral setting shifted	Check for factory setting of brush rigging or test for true neutral setting
	Armature has shorted coils or commutator bars	Remove armature to repair shop and put in first-class condition
Motor overheats or runs hot	Overloaded and draws 25 to 50 per cent more current than rated	Reduce load by reducing speed or gearing in the drive or loading in the drive
	Voltage above rated	Motor runs drive above rated speed requiring excessive horsepower. Reduce voltage to name-plate rating
	Inadequately ventilated	Location of motor should be changed, or restricted surroundings removed. Covers used for protection are too restricting of ventilating air and should be modified or removed. Open motors cannot be totally enclosed for continuous operation
	Draws excessive current due to shorted coil	Repair armature coils or install new coil. Locate grounds and repair or rewind with new set of coils
	Grounds in armature such as two grounds which constitute a short	
	Armature rubs pole faces due to off-center rotor causing friction and excessive current	Check brackets or pedestals to center rotor, and determine condition of bearing wear for bearing replacement
a. Hot armature	Core hot in one spot indicating shorted punchings and high iron loss	Sometimes full slot metal wedges have been used for balancing. These should be removed and other means of balancing be investigated
	Punchings uninsulated Punchings have been turned or band grooves machined in the core. Machined slots	No-load running of motor will indicate hot core and drawing high no-load armature current. Replace core and rewind armature. If necessary to add band grooves grind into core. Check temperature on core with thermometer not to exceed 90°C

Table 3-3. D-C Motor Check Chart (*Continued*)

Trouble	Cause	What to do
b. Hot commutator	Brush tension too high	Limit pressure to 2 to 2½ psi. Check brush density and limit to density recommended by the brush manufacturer
	Brushes off neutral	Reset neutral
	Brush grade too abrasive	Get recommendation from manufacturer
	Shorted bars	Investigate commutator mica and undercutting, and repair
	Hot core and coils that transmit heat to commutator	Check temperature of commutator with thermometer to see that total temperature does not exceed ambient plus 55°C rise, total not to exceed 105°C
	Inadequate ventilation	Check as for hot motor
c. Hot fields	Voltage too high	Check with meter and thermometer, and correct voltage to name-plate value
	Shorted turns or grounded turns	Repair, or replace with new coil
	Resistance of each coil not the same	Check each individual coil for equal resistance within 10 per cent, and if one coil is too low, replace coil
	Inadequate ventilation	Check as for hot motor
	Coil not large enough to radiate its loss wattage	New coils should replace all coils if room is available in motor
Motor vibrates and indicates unbalance	Armature out of balance	Remove and statically balance, or balance in dynamic balancing machine
	Misalignment	Realign
	Loose or eccentric pulley	Tighten pulley on shaft, or correct eccentric pulley
	Belt or chain whip	Adjust belt tension
	Mismating of gear and pinion	Recut, realign, or replace parts
	Unbalance in coupling	Rebalance coupling
	Bent shaft	Replace or straighten shaft
	Foundation inadequate	Stiffen mounting place members
	Motor loosely mounted	Tighten holding-down bolts
	Motor feet uneven	Add shims under foot pads to mount each foot tight
Motor sparks at brushes or does not commutate	Neutral setting not true neutral	Check and set on factory setting or test for true neutral
	Commutator rough	Grind and roll edge of each bar
	Commutator eccentric	Turn and grind commutator
	Mica high—hot undercut	Undercut mica
	Commutating pole strength too great causing overcompensation or strength too weak indicating undercompensation	Check with manufacturer for correct change in air gap or new coils for the commutating coils
	Shorted commutating pole turns	Repair coils or install new coils
	Shorted armature coils on commutator bars	Repair armature by putting into first class condition

Table 3-3. D-C Motor Check Chart (*Continued*)

Trouble	Cause	What to do
Motor sparks at brushes or does not commutate (*Cont.*)	Open-circuited coils	Same as above
	Poor soldered connection to commutator bars	Resolder with proper alloy of tin solder
	High bar or loose bar in commutator at high speeds	Inspect commutator nut or bolts and retighten and grind commutator face
	Brush grade wrong type. Brush pressure too light, current density excessive, brushes stuck in holders. Brush shunts loose	See Brushes
	Brushes chatter owing to dirty film on commutator	Resurface commutator face and check for change in brushes
	Vibration	Eliminate cause of vibration by checking mounting and balance of rotor
Brush wear excessive	Brushes too soft	Blow dust from motor, and replace brushes with a changed grade as recommended by manufacturer
	Commutator rough	Grind commutator face
	Abrasive dust in ventilating air	Reface brushes, and correct condition by protecting motor
	Off neutral setting	Recheck factory neutral or test for true neutral
	Bad commutation	See corrections for commutation
	High, low, or loose bar	Retighten commutator motor bolts, and resurface commutator
	Brush tension excessive	Adjust spring pressure not to exceed 2 to $2\frac{1}{2}$ psi
	Electrical wear due to loss of film on commutator face	Resurface brush faces and commutator face
	Threading and grooving	Same as above
	Oil or grease from atmosphere or bearings	Correct oil condition and surface brush faces and commutator
	Weak-acid- and moisture-laden atmosphere	Protect motor by changing ventilating air, or change to enclosed motor
Motor noisy	Brush singing	Check brush angle and commutator coating; resurface commutator
	Brush chatter	Resurface commutator and brush face
	Motor loosely mounted	Tighten foundation bolts
	Foundation hollow and acts as sounding board	Coat underside with soundproofing material
	Strained frame	Shim motor feet for equal mounting
	Armature punching loose	Replace core on armature
	Armature rubs pole faces	Recenter by replacing bearings or relocating brackets or pedestals
	Magnetic hum	Refer to manufacturer
	Belt slap or pounding	Check condition of belt and change belt tension
	Excessive current load	May not cause overheating, but check chart for correction of shorted or grounded coils
	Mechanical vibration	Check chart for causes of vibration
	Noisy bearings	Check alignment, loading of bearings, lubrication, and get recommendation of manufacturer

Table 3-4. A-C Motor Check Chart

Trouble	Cause	What to do
Motor stalls	Wrong application	Change type or size.　Consult manufacturer
	Overloaded motor	Reduce load
	Low motor voltage	See that name-plate voltage is maintained
	Open circuit	Fuses blown; check overload relay, starter, and push button
	Incorrect control resistance of wound rotor	Check control sequence.　Replace broken resistors.　Repair open circuits
Motor connected but does not start	One phase open.　Motor may be overloaded	See that no phase is open.　Reduce load
	Rotor defective	Look for broken bars or rings
	Poor stator coil connection	Remove end bells, locate with test lamp
Motor runs and then dies down	Power failure	Check for loose connections to line, to fuses, and to control
Motor does not come up to speed	Not applied properly	Consult supplier for proper type
	Voltage too low at motor terminals because of line drop	Use higher voltage on transformer terminals or reduce load
	If wound rotor, improper control operation of secondary resistance	Correct secondary control
	Starting load too high	Check load motor is supposed to carry at start
	Low pull-in torque of synchronous motor	Change rotor starting resistance or change rotor design
	Check that all brushes are riding on ring	Check secondary connections.　Leave no loads poorly connected
	Broken rotor bars	Look for cracks near the rings.　A new rotor may be required as repairs are usually temporary
	Open primary circuit	Locate fault with testing device and repair
Motor takes too long to accelerate	Excess loading	Reduce load
	Poor circuit	Check for high resistance
	Defective squirrel-cage rotor	Replace with new rotor
	Applied voltage too low	Get power company to increase voltage tap
Wrong rotation	Wrong sequence of phases	Reverse connections of motor or at switchboard
Motor overheats while running under load	Check for overload	Reduce load
	Wrong blowers or air shields, may be clogged with dirt and prevent proper ventilation of motor	Good ventilation is manifest when a continuous stream of air leaves the motor.　If not, check manufacturer
	Motor may have one phase open	Check to make sure that all leads are well connected
	Grounded coil	Locate and repair

Table 3-4. A-C Motor Check Chart (*Continued*)

Trouble	Cause	What to do
Motor overheats while running under load (*Cont.*)	Unbalanced terminal voltage	Check for faulty leads, connections, and transformers
	Shorted stator coil	Repair and then check wattmeter reading
	Faulty connection	Indicate by high resistance
	High voltage	Check terminals of motor with voltmeter
	Low voltage	
	Rotor rubs stator bore	If not poor machining, replace worn bearings
Motor vibrates after corrections have been made	Motor misaligned	Realign
	Weak foundations	Strengthen base
	Coupling out of balance	Balance coupling
	Driven equipment unbalanced	Rebalance drive equipment
	Defective ball bearing	Replace bearing
	Bearings not in line	Line up properly
	Balancing weights shifted	Rebalance rotor
	Wound rotor coils replaced	Rebalance rotor
	Polyphase motor running single phase	Check for open circuit
	Excessive end play	Adjust bearing or add washer
Unbalanced line current on polyphase motors during normal operation	Unequal terminal volts	Check leads and connections
	Single phase operation	Check for open contacts
	Poor rotor contacts in control wound rotor resistance	Check control devices
	Brushes not in proper position in wound rotor	See that brushes are properly seated and shunts in good condition
Scraping noise	Fan rubbing air shield	Remove interference
	Fan striking insulation	Clear fan
	Loose on bedplate	Tighten holding bolts
Magnetic noise	Air gap uniform	Check and correct bracket fits or bearing
	Loose bearings	Correct or renew
	Rotor unbalance	Rebalance

References

Acknowledgment is made to the following books, pamphlets, and articles:

1. "Productive Maintenance," General Electric Company.
2. "Maintenance Hints," Westinghouse Electric Corporation.
3. Various maintenance articles published in *Iron and Steel Engineer*.
4. Various maintenance articles published in *Power*.

Chapter 4

MAINTENANCE OF GENERAL-PURPOSE CONTROL

By Edward T. Shaw
Technical Service Section, Electric Service Division
Westinghouse Electric Corporation
Pittsburgh, Pa.

GENERAL MAINTENANCE REQUIREMENTS

The first requirement in a completely satisfactory maintenance program for all electrical apparatus is good apparatus, properly installed. No one can do a good maintenance job on equipment that is either inappropriate for the job or that has been installed haphazardly, with no regard for future maintenance requirements. If such conditions exist, it is preferable to bring them to the attention of the proper authority to be corrected, rather than try to establish a maintenance program.

A second requirement is properly trained, adequately equipped maintenance personnel. Persons who must maintain equipment should have a thorough knowledge of the equipment's operation and the ability to make thorough inspections and accomplish minor repairs. Of course, in our highly technological society, with the trend toward more complex apparatus, with sophisticated control or components, the maintenance man cannot be expected to completely overhaul and renew every piece of electrical equipment. This is a job for the specialist who knows that particular equipment. Frequently, the specialist is a representative of the manufacturer rather than an employee in the plant. Specialists are highly skilled technicians or engineers trained for the service requirements and equipped for the work. Frequently, special tools or instrumentation must be used to complete a repair and restore factory adjustments satisfactorily.

The third requirement is scheduling outages for preventive maintenance and periodic testing of electrical apparatus. This is a comprehensive aspect of maintenance which many plants are adopting in view of the importance placed on equipment reliability. Many plants cannot tolerate breakdown of their electrical apparatus. This is particularly true of those engaged in continuous processes. Chemical plants, laboratories, certain manufacturers, and those providing vital services (hospitals, institutions, airports, and communication centers) are examples. Others, including office buildings, apartment buildings, and department stores employing few if any skilled electrical-maintenance personnel, regularly turn to outside contractors for service. Several of the leading manufacturers of electrical equipment have recently entered this phase of service. Prompt, efficient response to customers' requests for service is accomplished by transporting the personnel and materials for the work in specially equipped vehicles. It is generally possible to service, repair, test, and return equipment to service using only the materials and equipment carried in these vehicles and customers' spare-parts stocks. Spare parts, in all instances, should be maintained at recommended levels with regard to expendable or vulnerable components.

Preventive Maintenance and Test. The term "preventive maintenance" has come to mean a system of routine inspections of equipment. These inspections, depending on the type and application of equipment, may also require proof testing of devices or complete apparatus test. More specifically, the term applies to systematic maintenance, designed to minimize or forestall future equipment-operating problems or failures by making minor or necessary repairs in advance of major operating difficulties. On electrical equipment specifically, a simple tightening of a screw or connection can prevent a serious short circuit or mechanical difficulty. The general condition of the apparatus is evaluated, and records are maintained for the purpose of recording this information for comparison at subsequent inspections. Actually, these records supplement the inspection and are designed to take the place of the maintenance man's memory. Records should be concise but complete as regards true apparatus condition. Records often are disregarded in small plants where one maintenance man services the majority or all of the electrical apparatus. But where a number of maintenance personnel are operating, records are vital to the proper operation of the maintenance inspection routine.

Inspection Records. Various maintenance record systems exist. IBM, Remington-Rand, Visi-Record, McBee, and others have systems adaptable to almost any type or size of plant. Each system has its merits and deficiencies with regard to universal application. All that is actually required of the record system is that it function easily with a minimum of effort on the part of the maintenance inspector and be available for ready reference. The system selected should contain five basic reference records; they may or may not be separate cards:

1. *The equipment record.* It lists the basic information on the equipment itself, e.g., manufacturer's identification, style, serial, size, location, etc. It frequently incorporates inventory-control data for spare parts.
2. *A repair cost record.* It permits a running record of repair and associated costs of maintenance for the device or apparatus. It is an essential diagnostic record for avoiding future difficulties if equipment is of poor quality or is marginal for the application.
3. *An inspection check list.* It contains the necessary and pertinent information on points to be checked on the designated apparatus and the establishment of the time when these checks should be made.
4. *The maintenance schedule record.* It differs from record 3 in that it is a complete listing of the day-to-day duties of the maintenance inspectors and the equipment to be inspected.
5. *Maintenance inspection and test records.* These are understandably necessary and vital documents. They should be completed in detail by the inspector or an assigned individual in the maintenance department. Maintenance personnel usually report their findings and corrective action on departmental forms developed for this purpose. When transcribed to permanent records, they are a useful guide to general apparatus condition, reliability, frequency of repairs, type of repair, and the need for complete rehabilitation or replacement at a convenient outage period.

Without these records, it would be very difficult for a preventive maintenance program to work and the knowledge gained from regular inspections would be quickly lost. This is particularly true if apparatus test results are incorporated. Unless records and data are maintained on the test and performance of equipment, the program is defeated. Unless records are up-dated at each succeeding test period, valuable information is lost which would materially assist a test engineer or specialist in his work. This is especially true if test results differ from manufacturers' recommended settings or actual factory test data. Significant changes in comparative test data can, in general, be related to apparatus condition and to the need of maintenance or failure to supply it.

The proper scheduling of equipment maintenance is based on the manufacturers' recommendations and the application of the equipment. Very often equipment is inspected on a shift basis or daily when its performance is vital to the functioning of a production line, a process, or the operation of an entire plant. Sometimes the equipment is not inspected at all and is allowed to perform until failure because the cost of such inspections and maintenance exceeds the cost of replacement. This applies generally to normally inaccessible, less costly devices of an expendable nature. In such cases, the maintenance department is responsible for maintaining an adequate stock of replacement equipment on hand.

Understanding Maintenance of Electrical Equipment. Because of the high diversity of electrical apparatus, many maintenance people have the mistaken attitude that electrical apparatus is different from production machinery and will operate under almost any conditions. It is a tribute to electrical-machinery manufacturers that this idea prevails, but the exact opposite is true. Electrical equipment can be damaged more readily by operating conditions than can almost any other kind.

Water, dust, heat, cold, humidity, lack of humidity, corrosive atmospheres, chemical residues, fumes, vibrations, and countless other conditions can affect performance and the life of electrical apparatus. These application hazards, combined with neglect and failure to maintain equipment, result in needless premature failure and, in some instances, complete destruction. Costly repairs can be avoided by observing the manufacturers' recommendations for maintenance and application. In most instances, instructions will include these cardinal rules to follow:

> Keep it clean.
> Keep it dry.
> Keep it tight and friction-free.

Whether the equipment consists principally of motors, starters, and contactors or includes more complete and elaborate electrical apparatus, the requirements mentioned are basic. For each type and classification of electrical equipment, other considerations necessarily will apply, but unless these basic requirements are observed, trouble with equipment can be expected and will normally follow.

Keep It Clean. Dirt is a principal cause of electrical failure. Whether the dirt is a day-to-day accumulation of normal atmospheric particles, lint, chemicals, or metallic particles from associated machinery or oil mists and vapors, these deposits, if allowed to accumulate, will contaminate electrical equipment and cause failures. Dirt on moving electrical parts can cause fouling, which can lead to sluggishness, arcing, and subsequent burning. Deposited in appreciable amount on coils, it can reduce creepage distances and obstruct normal air flow, increasing operating temperatures. Combined with oil or moisture, dirt can become a conductor and create flashover hazards when bare, normally insulated conducting parts are bridged by these contaminants. In almost every instance, dirt will affect resistance. Because of higher resistance, increased heating occurs, detrimental to apparatus life. It is understandable that certain applications are subject to heavy contamination. This is particularly true of steel mills, mines, foundries, smelters, quarries, cement plants, and other industrial applications. In such applications, special considerations are given to the design of electrical apparatus. Coils may be epoxy-encapsulated. Totally enclosed, self-cooled apparatus is commonly used, or a separate filtered-air supply is provided, with filters changed frequently. These precautions prolong apparatus life, and the device will usually operate satisfactorily under the severest conditions. But every schedule of maintenance should include a thorough systematic cleaning of the apparatus.

Keep It Dry. Electrical apparatus operates best in a dry atmosphere, for several reasons. One is that humidity can cause copper, aluminum, iron, or alloyed parts to oxidize. A build-up of oxides, particularly if caused by caustic fumes or acids, can destroy these metals and affect the resistance of electrical connections and contacts. Heavy accumulation should be removed, and severely corroded parts replaced. High humidity results in free moisture accumulating on the equipment, which can cause short circuiting and immediate failure. Another reason for controlling humidity, if possible, is that moisture can increase dirt build-up on electrical parts. This also leads to failure. Whenever there is doubt, the safest course is to use equipment that will operate properly under high-moisture conditions. This sometimes requires waterproof enclosures where conditions warrant.

Keep It Tight. Most electrical equipment operates with high-speed movement. This is particularly true of contactors and other types of control devices. It tends to cause wear of moving parts and some imbalance. Appreciable imbalance tends to create vibrations in equipment and loosen vital connecting parts. Imbalance is frequently increased by external vibrations set up by unrelated machinery; therefore continual vigilance should be maintained to detect wearing and loosening of apparatus parts or connections. Routine servicing of electrical equipment includes a check for tightness of mounting hardware and other bolted parts as a simple precautionary measure. The tightening of a screw or connection in a starter takes but a moment and can prevent hours of work searching for trouble, should it be intermittent. In rotating apparatus, motors especially, vibration not only can cause mechanical damage but, if allowed to become excessive, may create serious hazards and cause bearing failures, loosening of coils or supports, and general deterioration. Other electrical apparatus equipped with bearings is vulnerable in this respect.

Prevention of Friction. Electrical equipment that is operating properly does so with a minimum of friction. As indicated in the paragraph dealing with dirt, added friction and its effect on the freedom of movement of electrical devices can cause serious difficulties. A good electrical inspector or maintenance man will always check electrical equipment to see that it is operating properly and with an absolute minimum of friction; also, that it has a safe, smooth operating movement. Friction can result from numerous causes. When detected, there is a tendency on the part of maintenance personnel to lubricate the affected parts. This is dangerous practice and should never be resorted to unless there is a lubrication requirement specified by the manufacturer. Oil not only collects dust and abrasive materials; it also attacks insulation, particularly the older asphalt or rubber-covered types. Modern insulating materials are not so readily affected, but an oil film will spread, become unsightly, and may eventually oxidize into deposits difficult to remove. In general, frequently operated equipment will not develop friction unless parts become misaligned or excessively worn. If equipment is infrequently operated, friction and actual galling may develop as a result of rust or oxide deposits attacking the metal parts. It is good practice to mechanically check and electrically operate any device which is seldom if ever operated except in an emergency. Such devices are usually vital components in the electrical system, intended to protect other electrical apparatus or production equipment.

A high percentage of so-called electrical failures are actually of mechanical origin, having nothing to do with the electrical capabilities or qualifications of the apparatus. A bearing failure in a motor, if the air gap is small, can result in a locked rotor. If power is not rapidly removed, winding failure will result, with an added possibility of fire. Other conditions, such as a bent shaft, obstructions in a ventilating system, faulty alignment, a loose connection, dislodged hardware, or an unlubricated shaft or bearing, all can cause electrical failures, but are mechanical in nature. The significance of thorough mechanical inspection cannot be minimized, and personnel should be highly aware of the importance of this phase of maintenance.

Maintenance Responsibility. In a highly productive operation, too often the maintenance personnel overlook the fact that they alone are responsible for the continuous and successful operation of a plant. In modern automated plants, the maintenance of equipment may depend on production requirements and the losses associated with downtime. Certain continuous processes cannot be interrupted except at great expense or spoilage of the end product. In most plants, however, where the actual production responsibility rests on the shoulders of others, the maintenance man should diligently perform his duties and will not defer necessary maintenance at the insistance of production forces. Often equipment is allowed to remain in operation until it destroys itself or until serious hazards develop, forcing the maintenance department to act. A simple understanding, coupled with the necessary authority to act when equipment is in need of service, should be arranged berween maintenance and production forces. If a maintenance superintendent is faced with these situations, reasonable protests and discussion will usually correct them when brought to the attention of management.   It is recognized that these situations do exist and can be a serious impediment to good maintenance.

Proper maintenance entails preventive maintenance work and frequent inspections, which sometimes require apparatus shutdown.   Unless equipment can be regularly checked, the ultimate cost of production and more extensive repairs will be higher than with a regular preventive maintenance program.

Maintenance Testing.   This phase of the maintenance program is of growing importance to plants having a considerable investment in electrical apparatus; also where the type or characteristics of the equipment are such that performance is dependent on precise settings which must be maintained.   It was mentioned earlier that this portion of maintenance requires skills and instrumentation not common to small maintenance departments and, for this reason, is a service requirement usually performed by other than plant maintenance personnel.   It is important, however, that maintenance personnel be made aware of electrical test requirements, and if they are beyond the capability of these individuals or if the necessary test equipment is not available, the required tests should be conducted with prescribed regularity by experts.

Modern apparatus testing is a study in itself.   It is not practical in this discussion to review it at length or introduce it as a requirement of general maintenance for control equipment.   Today there are many types of sophisticated and elaborate control.   Some may be electronic.   Others use saturable core reactors, and more recently this type of equipment is being manufactured with solid-state semiconductor components and features silicon-controlled rectifiers and other complex components. As new discoveries are made, new applications are developed with regularity.   As a result, maintenance per se can no longer be performed by the semiskilled workman.

Companies with any amount of modern control, using these modern components and complex circuitry, frequently have their own test departments, staffed with technically trained personnel and qualified electrical engineers.   This is an impractical and uneconomical addition to a small plant unless most of its electrical equipment falls into this category.   Therefore, unless elaborate test requirements exist, testing of apparatus is generally limited to basic test functions associated with normal operation and prescribed by the manufacturer.   In the apparatus description that follows, certain test procedures will be suggested.   These functions are so general and widely accepted as to be endorsed practice by most manufacturers.   In every instance where tests are performed, it should be predetermined, by referring to manufacturer's literature, that the test will not harm the apparatus and that there are no restrictions against testing.   When in doubt, consult with the supplier or manufacturer on test procedures.

Recommended Safety Practices.   There are safety practices which every maintenance individual should observe when working with electrical apparatus.   They are important, particularly if electrical maintenance is not a regular function of the maintenance individual.   The purpose of electrical testing and of rechecking the electrical characteristics of apparatus and devices is to prove that the equipment will work as intended for the specific job to which it is applied.   The field testing of apparatus should, as much as possible, duplicate actual operating conditions.   In many instances this requires that the apparatus be in actual use.   It is always advisable to study the situation and evaluate the *safest and most efficient method* for conducting required tests under the prevailing conditions.   *The safety of the test personnel and others must be observed.*   Know the equipment you are working on.   Of equal importance is familiarity with the test equipment and test circuitry.

Where possible, testing of live apparatus must be avoided.

If certain circuits must be maintained, every precaution should be taken to avoid injury.   Bus runs and other sources of power should be shielded.   If at all possible, eliminate this hazard by disconnecting power on those circuits.

Equipment under test must be isolated from remote-control or feedback circuits to prevent its accidental energizing by others.   Preliminary checks must be made to insure that apparatus is deenergized, or if power must be maintained as part of the test, extreme caution should be exercised and the individual further protected from electrical shock by the required use of rubber floor mats, rubber gloves, goggles, and approved nonconducting safety hats and adequately insulated tools.

Bus runs that have been disconnected for test purposes should be grounded to prevent feedback of test voltages endangering other personnel working on the same or related apparatus connected to the bus. If it is not possible to ground these conductors effectively, the test area should be roped off and protected by warning signs or flashing lights.

Unauthorized personnel, and unnecessary personnel, should be excluded from the test area while the apparatus is being tested.

The test voltages and current can be deadly. Serious injury or death can result from contact with supposedly deenergized equipment. Sneak circuits that do not appear on drawings are sometimes found to exist.

Never proceed with tests without first reviewing the applicable and latest revision of the electrical drawings. This applies not only to the equipment being tested, but to control circuits and power connections to the apparatus. Changes and additions may have been made without being noted on the drawings.

Capacitive circuits and any device capable of storing electrical energy received from test voltages are significant hazards. They should be permanently grounded during the test, or if they are necessary and included in the test circuitry, they must be grounded after each application of test voltages, particularly if conducting parts or hardware are to be touched or adjusted as part of the test.

Do not rely on a third person to relay signals to personnel assisting with the test or leave test equipment energized and unattended. If it becomes necessary to leave the test equipment, even momentarily, to confer with others or to inspect the apparatus under test, *shut the test set off!*

Remove watches, rings, tie clasps, and other conducting articles from your person and clothing. If arcing conditions are expected from operation of contactors or other devices being tested under load, wear safety glasses. Arc interruption in air can result in melting and violent expulsion of contact material, particularly copper.

Test personnel should be trained in first aid, especially artificial respiration, in the event of injury to any member of the test crew. An industrial first-aid kit should be available, and approved fire extinguishers suitable for use on electrical fires must be available during the test.

Never work singly. Work only in pairs or under observation by others.

MODERN MOTOR STARTERS

Maintenance of a-c and d-c motor starters requires a systematic program of inspection. Although a specific schedule to a large extent depends upon the conditions of the application involved, the general statement can be made that inspections should be conducted frequently enough to prevent serious trouble. Experience will soon indicate any installations upon which the service is most severe, and such installations will require your most frequent inspection. As with all preventive maintenance, the personnel doing the inspection must be thoroughly trained and must be prepared to make quick repairs. An adequate system of recording inspection results and repairs is necessary.

There are a number of general points with which every inspector of electrical controllers should be thoroughly familiar to do a proper job. The first five points are of a general nature and can be applied to all good electrical maintenance work. The others apply specifically to good maintenance practices.

1. The Initial Installation Should Be Tested and Proved Satisfactory Before It Is Accepted. Before putting any equipment into actual operation, all installation work and wiring connections should be thoroughly checked to make certain that the workmanship is well done. All parts should have ample capacity. Tests should be made to prove the adequacy of the equipment and the installation before final acceptance is given by the user.

FIG. 4-1. Modern motor-control center.

FIG. 4-2. Modern design permits reduction in size without reduction in ability to handle power.   Shown are two size 1 starters.   The unit on the right is designed for application to motor-control centers where space is at a premium.

2. Apparatus Should Be Easily Accessible for Inspection and Repairs. For inspection and easy repair work, all parts should be as accessible as possible. It should be possible to renew contacts, coils, springs, and other important parts quickly and with few tools. Installations should be arranged so that all units are accessible for maintenance work.

3. Enclosures Should Be Chosen for the Operating Conditions. Most apparatus is mounted in some type of metal enclosure. This is done to protect personnel from live parts and to protect the device from mechanical damage, corrosive conditions, and unauthorized tampering. The most common is of sheet metal to enclose all live parts. It may be ventilated or nonventilated.

Dusty Atmospheres. For cement dust, coal dust, and locations where dirty atmospheric conditions exist, dust-tight enclosures will reduce the maintenance on parts. These enclosures require gaskets, and are so made that no dust or dirt can enter.

Wet Locations. Weather-resistant, drip-tight, watertight, and submersible-type enclosures are often necessary when there are corresponding service conditions.

Hazardous Locations. For hazardous locations such as mines, refineries, and cleaning plants or wherever explosive atmospheres are present, the enclosures are of heavy

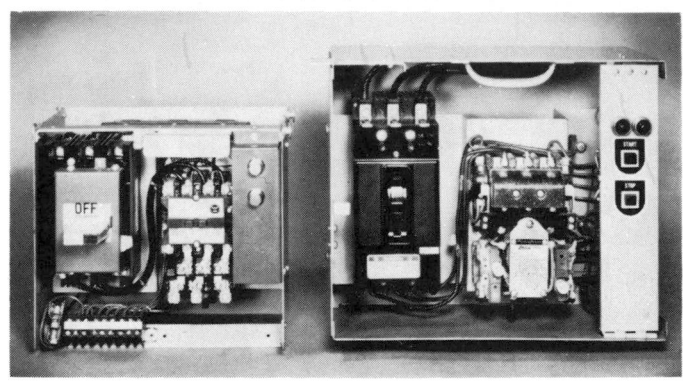

FIG. 4-3. Note reduction in size of cell modules made possible by redesign of components. Modular draw-out design permits rapid, easy servicing.

construction. They are designed to withstand explosions of the gases within the enclosure, without damage to it and without permitting any sparks or flames to emerge to cause general fires or explosions. Oil-immersed starters are used to prevent explosions in dangerous locations.

Corrosive Atmospheres. Where acid fumes or highly corrosive atmospheres exist, maintenance work will be minimized if the apparatus parts are immersed in oil and the enclosure is protected by a suitable resistant finish.

4. An Adequate Supply of Correct Renewal Parts Must Be Available. On most electrical apparatus, parts that need replacement during the life of the apparatus are generally inexpensive and easy to stock. Because of the high losses that will often occur when equipment is down for repairs, all manufacturers recommend that an adequate supply of correct renewal parts be on hand to prevent downtime. The parts should be obtained from the manufacturer of the original equipment to make certain they are correctly made of the proper materials. Substitutes have to be thoroughly checked for dimensional accuracy and correct materials.

5. Keep Control Centers Clean and Dry. Very few industrial motor starters operate in clean places. Oil and moisture often are present as liquids or as vapors. Dust, lint, and other materials are present as the natural result of operating conditions. These materials—dust, dirt, oil, and moisture—separately or in combination, create maintenance work.

Many hours of engineering effort have been expended in order to design trouble-free apparatus. Pole-face surfaces are accurately machined by the manufacturer to obtain "free releasing" when the magnet is deenergized.   An environmental condition such as described above occasionally causes a semiviscous smudge to form on the armature pole faces.   This retards "drop-out" and at times causes surface-tension-type sticking. These surfaces must be kept clean.

Accumulations of dust and dirt should be removed regularly by vacuum or by blowing with compressed air.   Excessive air pressures should be avoided because sharp, small particles may be driven into some insulating materials.   Special attention may be required to remove metallic dust with magnetic properties that readily collects and adheres to the magnetized parts.   Dirt, oil, and moisture usually are most readily removed by wiping the surfaces with cloths and suitable solvents.

Moisture due to condensation may collect within an enclosure.   Drainage holes rarely are acceptable to relieve this condition.   Heaters are most often used to prevent moisture by condensation.   The heaters are essential when the equipment is idle.

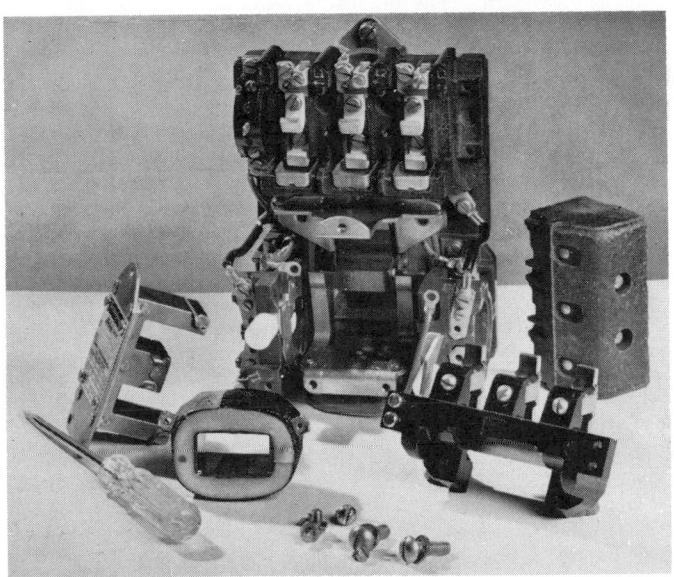

Fig. 4-4. Designs should permit rapid disassembly and reassembly with few tools.

When in operation, the coils and resistors within the enclosure usually will provide enough heat.

6. Replace Contacts That Are Worn Very Thin or Badly Eroded and Pitted. Replace contacts in pairs.   Maintain correct pressures.   Generally, every time contacts open or close they are subject to mechanical wear and electrical erosion.   The reason for this is that most contacts close with a rolling movement combined with a wiping action.   Although this insures good contact and confines the arcing, with resultant erosion, to the tips of the contacts, both conditions cause wearing of the contact materials.   Contact parts, therefore, are items that may require considerable maintenance, depending on the operating conditions.   The actual mechanical wear of contacts that operate frequently may be more serious than the electrical erosion caused by the arcing.

As contacts wear, the material in them gradually disappears because of both mechanical wear and electrical erosion.   During the wearing process the contact pressures decrease.   This affects the current-carrying ability of the contacts and, if allowed to go too low, will cause overheating of the contacts.   A small contact with suitable pressure may carry current with less heating than a large contact with little or no pressure.   Reasonable provisions are made for the wearing of the contacts, when the original designs are made, but replacements will be necessary eventually. Manufacturers will furnish information on correct contact pressures for their devices. The contact pressures may be reduced either because of worn contacts or damaged contact springs. If contact springs have been overheated, they may be unable to provide sufficient contact pressure because the material has been weakened by the overheating. Contact pressures should be checked and maintained within suitable limits.

Maintenance hint: With the contactor coil energized and the contactor sealed closed (observing normal safety precautions), the clearance of the moving contact from its stop (in deenergized position) should not be less than $\frac{1}{64}$ in. Renew contacts when this limit is reached.

Always replace both moving and stationary contacts.

Because contacts operate in pairs, replacement should be made in pairs. Because of the wearing of contact surfaces, the probability of a mixture of old and new parts operating badly is very high. The few extra cents and minutes spent in replacing both contacts will pay many times over in operating life.

7. Contacts Should Be Kept Clean. Do not change contact shape by rough filing or grinding.

Contacts fall into three general classifications:

a. *Copper contacts.* The application of copper as a contact material has been used for many years and, when properly designed into a device, works satisfactorily. Copper-contact surfaces are subject to oxidation and high resistance and, in most devices, incorporate proper wiping and cleaning action to maintain normal operating temperatures.

b. *Silver contacts.* Fine silver contacts, when properly applied, generally require lower contact force and are less subject to high contact resistance. Hence they require substantially no cleaning or servicing, since the normal oxides are easily broken down and are of low resistance. Substantially no wipe or roll is required in the low- to medium-current ranges.

c. *Fine silver compositions and/or sintered contacts.* In higher current ratings this type of material is used to obtain high conduction, low temperature, low erosion, and less tendency to stick or weld. Substantially no wipe is incorporated or contact maintenance required under normal service conditions.

Contacts should be kept clean. This is especially true of copper contacts. The discoloration that soon appears on clean copper is not a good electrical conductor. It increases the contact resistance and often is the cause of serious heating. When contacts are renewed it is important to clean the new contact and the surface against which it is mounted.

The slight rubbing action and erosion that occur during normal operation will generally keep the contact surfaces clean enough for service. Copper contacts that seldom open or close will readily accumulate the thin discolored film that may cause heating.

This is not true of silver contacts. The dense discoloration that soon appears on clean silver is actually not a good conductor, but the surface film breaks down easily. Experience has proved that it is not necessary to keep silver contacts clean except for the sake of appearance.

Eroded Contacts. Generally, every time contacts close and open they are subject to mechanical wear and electrical erosion, brought about by arcing and oxidation. On copper contacts it is more pronounced, because of the conditions mentioned above. On the other two contact materials, *b* and *c* above, it is primarily erosion, since substantially no contact wipe is required. As contacts wear, this material is eroded away.

It is not essential or even desirable to have contact surfaces entirely smooth. Slightly roughened surfaces that appear during normal good operation, if clean, may provide better contact area than smooth surfaces. Contacts with surfaces comparable with very coarse sandpaper may be considered in good condition.

Removal of contact irregularities from the contact face and barbs and other irregularities from around the periphery of the contacts must be carefully done.

Contacts such as illustrated in Fig. 4-6, and of this general classification operating several times per hour to several times per minute, will develop a surface appearance somewhat like that shown.   Its color may be a purplish dark gray to brown, which is normal, and the face should not be disturbed.   Clean only the periphery of the contact.   The contacts, for the most part, are self-cleaning, inherent in the design and application of the material.   When the contact force is on the low limit and the contact remains closed for long periods (which does not allow for the self-cleaning action inherent in the design), the contacts are more subject to overheating, and a reddish-brown hard copper oxide forms which is of high resistance.   This type of surface should be removed.   If and when such conditions arise, a fine file can be used, followed by medium sandpaper—*not emery cloth.*

Generally speaking, it is always desirable in starting a new operation to open and close the contacts under load twenty or thirty times at intervals of 10 sec or so to condition the contact faces.   This applies to the three classes of contact materials previously cited, classes *a* to *c*.   The condition occasioned by this operation tends to burn off films and deposits that act as deterrents to good conduction and low contact drop.   Miniature craters and projections will develop on the contact faces as the contactor continues to operate normally, exhibiting a surface similar to that shown in Fig. 4-6.   This contact-face condition is normal and should not be disturbed so long

FIG. 4-5. Excessive load current has caused contact to overheat.   Brazing alloy has melted and allowed contact tips to separate from contact finger.

FIG. 4-6. Contact has been severely eroded by interrupting high currents.   Sufficient alloy remains to permit salvage of contact if care is exercised.   Remove only the high spots; do not change contact shape by filing.

as normal contact-force and overtravel conditions prevail under reasonable environmental conditions.   In the event the contacts may be subjected to abnormal currents above load inrush currents, approaching short-circuit values, the contacts may be blown open; contact surface at times takes on a puddled bright-metal appearance. The contact's general contour needs only to be restored with a fine file, provided there is sufficient contact material remaining, and cleaned with medium sandpaper.

8. Keep Contacts and All Connections Tight.   Any loose electrical connection will eventually cause trouble.   An open circuit, or an unreliable one, may cause much lost time and production because it is often difficult to find.   And a loose connection can cause a poor contact of high resistance.   The higher resistance causes more heating, and the increased temperature causes more oxidation.   The effect is always cumulative, and the heating increases until the parts overheat, deteriorate, or burn. Other loose connections cause similar heating and, on thermally operated devices, such as a heater of a thermal overload relay, may cause the relay to trip and stop a motor when it is not overloaded.

The bolts or fastening devices that hold contacts in place should always be tight. Normal expansion and contraction of metals due to temperature changes or excessive vibration will cause bolts or nuts to become loose.   Frequent checking for loose contacts is advisable.

Welding of Contacts.   Very few high-speed contactors close without some bounce or rebound.   This is due to the reaction of the contact springs as they are compressed to provide the final contact pressure.   When the contacts bounce, they separate. At this time the contacts are carrying current, and even though the separation is very small, an arc is created.   This arc, if severe, may cause sharp projections of burned or roughened contact surfaces to overheat and may weld, or "freeze," the contact surfaces together.   Under such conditions, the contacts may not open when next expected to do so.   Other causes of contact welding are excessive currents when contacts close; insufficient contact pressure; sluggish operation when either

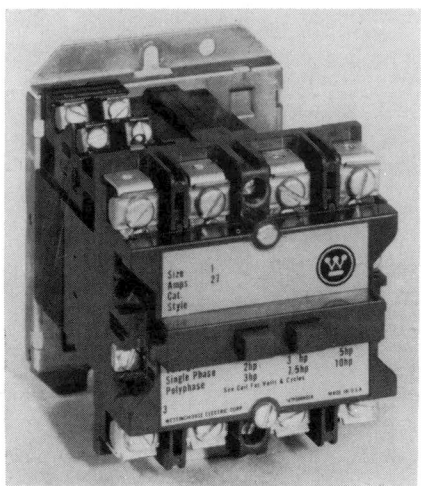

FIG. 4-7. This modern contactor has a minimum of moving parts.   Tight-fitting modular construction excludes dirt.   Lubrication is not necessary.

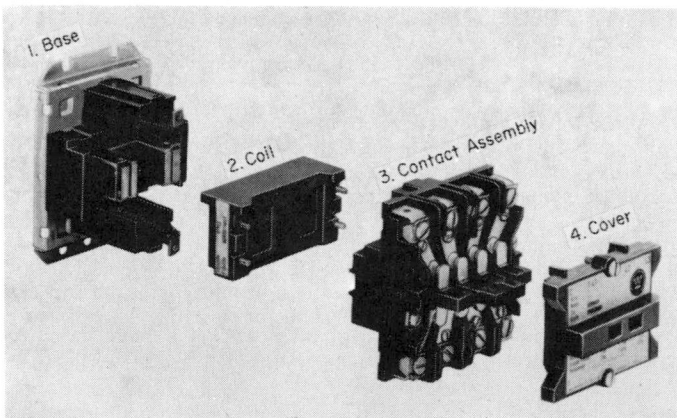

FIG. 4-7a. Exploded view of the contactor shown in Fig. 4-7.   The coil is totally encapsulated and plugs into connectors on the rear of the assembly.

closing or opening; and momentary closure of contacts without much or any pressure applied.

Silver contacts will weld more readily than copper ones.   Modern sintered contacts, properly applied, reduce this hazard to a minimum.

9. Do Not Oil Contactor or Relay Bearings Unless Lubrication Is a Manufacturer's Requirement.   Since the correct operation of the contactor depends primarily on the unit's being completely clean and free from foreign material, no oil or lubricant of any kind should be used on the bearings unless the manufacturer's literature specifies lubrication. In general, contactor and relay bearings are designed to require no lubrication. If lubricated, the accumulation of oil and dirt may cause sluggish mechanical action that will impair the arc-rupturing qualities of the device or cause welding of the contacts. Except for bearings of master switches, drum controllers, and similar units, no lubrication of controller parts is necessary. This, of course, does not apply to special controllers which are oil-immersed. Maintenance of oil-immersed controllers should be generally the same as for oil circuit breakers of a comparable voltage.

10. Operate Coils at Rated Voltage. Coils provide the electromagnetic pull that causes the contacts of relays and contactors to open or close. Series coils generally carry heavy currents and have relatively few turns of rather heavy copper. Shunt coils have many turns of insulated wire. They are usually impregnated in a vacuum or under pressure with insulating compounds and are covered with insulating tapes or materials. The impregnating compounds produce a firm resilient binding material that prevents cracks when temperature changes occur. The impregnation process eliminates air pockets within the winding, and it makes the coil a solid mass that is better able to radiate heat and is less subject to mechanical injury. More recent technology has brought about materials and manufacturing procedures which completely encase the shunt coil winding in a pressure-molded cell. This concept provides better protection, improved heat transfer, and lower operating temperatures than former types.

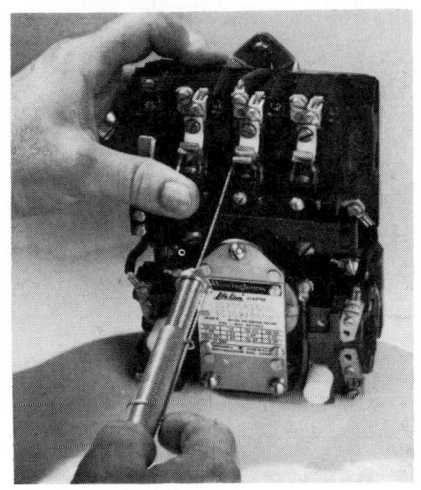

Fig. 4-8. Contact pressure is important. Spring pressure can be lost by overheating. Use a spring scale to measure spring pressure. Pull should be in a direction perpendicular to the contact surface.

Operating Voltages. Even at operating temperatures, shunt coils for a-c devices must close them at 85 per cent of the rated voltage. Coils for d-c devices will close them at 80 per cent of normal voltage. Any coil is expected to withstand 110 per cent rated voltage without damage. Measurement of operating voltages should be made at the coil terminals, and not at the source of the supply voltages.

Open-circuited Coils. A coil with an open circuit will not operate the contactor or relay. A questionable coil should be replaced immediately by one that is known to be satisfactory. The questionable coil can then be checked for open circuits.

Short-circuited Coils. If some turns of a d-c coil become short-circuited, the resistance of the coil will be reduced and more current will pass through. The increased current will cause higher operating temperatures, and frequently results in coil burnout. Short-circuited turns in an a-c coil result in a transformer action which permits a high current flow at the point of short circuit. Immediate burnout usually follows the short circuiting of an a-c coil, whereas a short-circuited d-c coil may continue to operate for an indefinite time, until total insulation failure results.

Overvoltage. Coils should be operated at the rated voltage. Overvoltage causes coils to operate at a higher temperature, which shortens coil life. Overvoltage also operates the contactor or relay with unnecessary force and causes more mechanical wear and bounce when closing.

Undervoltage. Undervoltage on coils causes contactors and relays to operate sluggishly. The contact tips may touch, but the coil may be unable to completely close the contacts against the contact spring pressure. In the case of a-c devices, if the voltage is at a level sufficiently low to move the armature to contact touch position, but not to seal it closed against the load of the contact spring, two things are likely to happen: (1) The device will "flutter" (or buzz), making and breaking the circuit, possibly causing the contacts to stick or weld.   (2) If the armature does not seal against the magnet face, the increased current will cause the coil to overheat or burn out.

Closing and Operating Currents. The impedance of a magnetic circuit having a large air gap is much lower than the impedance of the same magnetic circuit with little or no air gap. The current drawn by the coil of an a-c magnet is therefore much greater at "open gap" than at "closed gap." Since the closing time is relatively short, a-c coils are designed to withstand energizing under closed conditions. But an a-c coil will soon overheat if the magnet is blocked open or the voltage is too low to close it and the coil remains energized with a large air gap in the magnetic circuit. Direct-current coils are not subject to these conditions because the coil currents do not vary with the air gap. For certain applications, d-c coils are momentarily

Fig. 4-9. Coils should be readily accessible and easily replaced.

energized at much higher than rated currents. The high momentary energizing requirement at closing of electrical contactors or devices is not damaging unless the high current is maintained. For this reason, also, contactors should not be blocked open when testing since cutoff devices may be made inoperable.

11. Keep Arc-rupturing Parts in Good Condition and in Correct Operating Position. When contactors are expected to open circuits carrying currents that are difficult to interrupt, they are designed with arc-rupturing features. The arc-rupturing components generally surround the contacts and must be so made that they are easily moved out of position or removed entirely in order to inspect and replace both moving and stationary contacts. To be effective, the arc-rupturing parts must be in a definite position with respect to the contacts. Hence the interruptor should always be returned to the proper position if removed for any reason.

On d-c starters the arc-quenching structures generally include arc shields of molded ceramic or other heat-resistant material. These arc shields should always be down so the arc is broken within the field of the blowout coil; otherwise the shield will not give satisfactory results. Arc shields should be renewed before the molded material is burned away sufficiently to expose the metal parts to the arc.

One of the principal and interesting differences between the conventional d-c contactor with the magnetic blowout coil and the modern small a-c contactor is the arc quencher. On a-c applications, magnetic arc-splitting action confines, divides, and extinguishes the arc almost instantly as the circuit is broken. The usual flash and scattering of flame outside the arc box is done away with.

How this is accomplished is shown by Fig. 4-10. Deionizing action not only stretches the arc but confines and quenches it. As specially shaped contacts separate, a magnetic reaction occurs that forms and stretches the arc. It rises immediately into the metal grids, where it is sliced into a series of arcs. At the next zero point on the current cycle, the air adjacent to each grid is deionized instantly, the voltage per grid is insufficient to reestablish the current flow, and the arc is out.

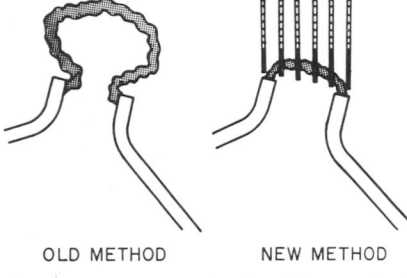

OLD METHOD   NEW METHOD

FIG. 4-10. Arc quenching by deion method.

The arc quencher is assembled over the contacts in much the same manner as the magnetic blowout coils and arc shields on the conventional d-c contactor and is easily removed for inspection of the contacts. Pitting and oxidation of contacts and arc box are greatly reduced and longer trouble-free life is provided with this system. The correct use of arc-quenching devices results in improved contact life.

12. Replace Frayed and Worn Shunts. The fine strands of flexible shunts sometimes break where the shunt bends. The unbroken strands must then carry the entire current. If many strands break, the unbroken ones become overloaded. They then overheat and eventually oxidize and fuse open. Frayed shunts should be replaced promptly by new ones.

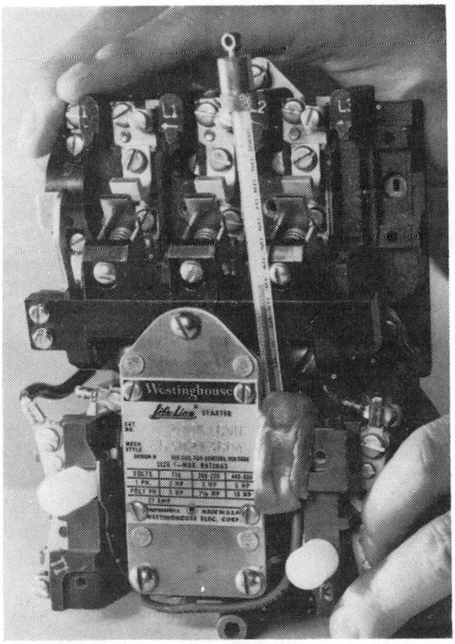

13. Keep All Dashpots Clean. Be sure oil dashpots have correct oil in them. Air or fluid dashpots are used to retard motions. They are machined to close clearances and must be kept clean and free to move. The proper amount and type of fluid should be kept in fluid dashpots. Since the viscosity of oil changes with temperature, substitute oils should not be used if the dashpot requires oil.

14. Correct Conditions That Cause Excessive Temperatures. Measure the temperature if in doubt about overheating. Overheated parts indicate trouble. However, it is often difficult to know when temperatures are excessive. Resistors are operated safely at 375°C rise above the ambient temperature, but organically insulated coils are generally restricted to 85°C above ambient. Most solid contacts are limited to a rise of 65°C, and copper bus work to 50°C rise. There is a growing use of high-temperature insulations capable of withstanding temperatures of 160°C rise. The laminated-iron core of an a-c contactor can have a temperature rise well over 125°C because of losses in the iron.

FIG. 4-11. When in doubt about coil temperatures, measure them. A thermometer should be held in contact with the coil until the temperature has risen to maximum value.

Barring the presence of gases, acids, or alkalis, discolored copper parts have been or are too hot. When in doubt, temperatures should be measured by thermometer or other means. It is not safe to rely on the touch of the hand because safe operating temperatures of many electrical parts are unbearable. It is best to know what the permissible temperatures are and then measure.

Motor starters equipped with thermally operated overload relays should be located in approximately the same ambient temperature as the motors they protect. If the relay is in a much higher ambient temperature, it will trip when the motor is not overloaded. If the relay is in a lower ambient temperature, it may not trip in time to protect the motor. If the ambient temperatures must be different, some compensation can be made by proper selection of the overload relay heaters or by providing a relay that compensates for temperature differences. Consult manufacturer's heating tables for this information.

15. Be Alert for Undesirable Grounds on All Circuits and Eliminate Them. Required grounds are useful and necessary. They are rather easily maintained because they require only good contact connections. An unexpected ground is a serious personnel hazard. Constant vigilance is required to prevent and eliminate undesirable grounds, which cause operating troubles with erratic and dangerous operating circuits. Because of them, motors may start unexpectedly; motors may

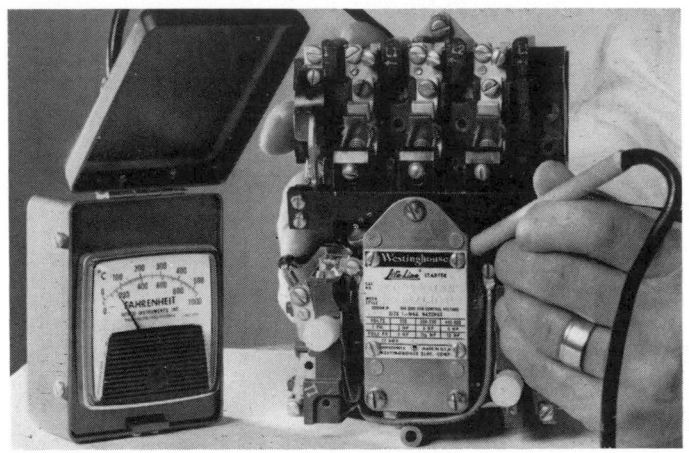

FIG. 4-12. Coil temperatures may also be measured by using an accurate contact pyrometer.

not stop when they should; overload and other protective features may be made ineffective.

Grounds often occur in push-button boxes or similar confined spaces where stray strands of wire may make contact at incorrect places. They occur when wires become chafed because of vibration on rough edges, such as conduit entrances. Conduits sometimes become wet from condensation or other causes, and the insulation on the wires becomes water-soaked and of low insulating value. Conduits should be installed so that moisture within them will always drain away. It may sometimes be necessary to remove the wires, clean the conduits, provide drain holes, and install new wiring. Clean and dry conditions always reduce maintenance.

Noisy A-C Contactors. Because the voltage on the coil of an a-c contactor or relay repeatedly passes through zero, the magnetic pull, or holding power, also passes through zero. The device has a tendency to open unless a shading coil is incorporated in its pole faces. The voltage, however, is soon effective in the opposite direction, and the device is again pulled closed. This operation causes a humming noise in any a-c-operated device and a decided chattering noise in a defective unit. The otherwise objectionable chattering is eliminated, and the device is kept closed by the use of a shading coil usually imbedded in the laminated circuit of the device in such a way that it encircles a major portion of the magnet face. It retards the cyclic flow of flux through that portion and provides sufficient holding power to keep the device closed during the short period when the flux in the unshaded portion is zero. Even with shading coils in use, the pole-face surfaces must be free from dirt and well fitted to avoid objectional noise. Broken shading coils are ineffective and of course cause noisy operation.

For quiet operation of a-c contactors it is necessary to provide well-fitted pole faces. Any dirt in this area introduces a greater air gap when the unit is closed, increases the duty imposed upon the shading coil, and results in more noisy operation. To prevent rusting of the fitted surfaces of the pole faces, devices are often shipped with a small amount of grease or oil on them. This lubrication, unless removed, may cause a "seal" that makes them sticky and sluggish in opening when first put into service. It should be wiped off.

Direct-current coils are not subject to a repeated zero-voltage condition. Hence d-c-operated devices are always quiet. For this reason a-c current-carrying contactors equipped with d-c operating coils will operate quietly.

Magnetic Sticking. When operating coils are deenergized, some residual magnetism remains in the magnetic circuit and is sometimes strong enough to hold the device closed after the coil is deenergized. This condition occurs most frequently on small devices on which contact spring pressures and moving parts are light. Magnetic sticking causes erratic, unsatisfactory, and sometimes dangerous operation. It is avoided by providing a permanent air gap or by adding a nonmagnetic shim in the magnetic circuit. It is very important to keep the permanent air gap free of magnetic particles, iron filings, etc. Should magnetic sticking occur, examine the device to see if the nonmagnetic shim is missing.

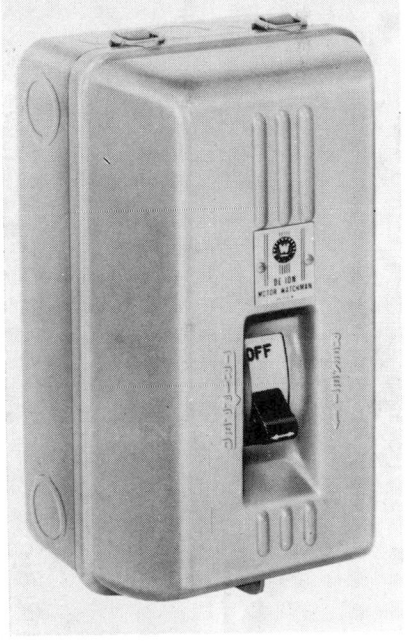

A-C SQUIRREL-CAGE INDUCTION-MOTOR STARTERS

The most commonly used motor starter is for the a-c squirrel-cage induction motor. We shall discuss in this section only the more common starting equipment for these motors. The NEMA classifications are:

1. Manual—across-the-line starters.
2. Magnetic—across-the-line starters.
3. Manual—reduced-voltage starters.
4. Magnetic—reduced-voltage starters.
   Autotransformer type.
   Primary-resistance type.
   Reactor type (uncommon).
5. Star-delta type.
6. Part-winding type.

FIG. 4-13. Typical manually operated small-motor starter features overload protection.

Manual Across-the-line Starters. Modern manual starters are available up to 7½ hp at 550 volts, three-phase. These starters are used to connect small motors directly to the line. The oil-immersed drum type was at one time used extensively wherever the air was charged with corrosive gases or highly flammable particles of dust or lint, such as encountered in textile mills, flour mills, and woodworking plants. The drum type was frequently made for reversing service and also for smaller multispeed squirrel-cage motors. Manual-type starters have largely been superseded by magnetic starters.

Magnetic Linestarters. Magnetic linestarters are suitable over a wide horsepower-voltage range. Linestarters are used where the design of the motor and the capacity of the circuit permit and where the advantages of simplicity and remote control are

FIG. 4-14. Magnetic reduced-voltage starter, autotransformer type.

desired. They may also be used as primary switches for wound-rotor motors in combination with suitable secondary controllers.

Reduced-voltage Starters. Reduced-voltage starters, both manual and automatic, have a broad range of application. Reduced-voltage starters of the autotransformer type find extensive application where the size or design of the motor or restrictions of the supply circuit require starting on reduced voltage. The auto transformer-type starter provides greater starting torque per ampere starting current drawn from the line than any other type of reduced-voltage motor starter.

The Resistance Type of Reduced-voltage Starters. Resistance-type starters belong in the general category of reduced-voltage starters. They are sometimes applied on network distribution systems where power-company regulations require that the circuit not be opened during the transition from reduced voltage to full voltage. They are particularly desirable to avoid sudden mechanical shock to the driven load, and they are normally applied where it is necessary to keep starting currents within permissive limits.

Multispeed A-C Motor Starting. Alternating-current motors, both squirrel-cage- and wound-rotor-inductive, and occasionally synchronous, may be arranged with windings that provide two or more speeds. Two-speed motors may have two separate windings or a single winding capable of rearrangement or pole changing. Four-speed motors

FIG. 4-15. Reduced-voltage starter, resistance type.

usually have two two-speed windings. In any case, the different speeds require different switching setups. Wound-rotor and synchronous motors require switching or pole changing in both primary and secondary (or field) windings. Multispeed motor starters may consist of manually operated drum switches or of magnetic contactors. Standards for connections and markings have changed over the years and have varied with different motor manufacturers. Therefore, when servicing multispeed controllers, connections and markings should be obtained from the wiring diagram or from the motor connection plate.

Maintenance Requirements of Each Type. In general, the maintenance points covered in the first part of this section apply to all squirrel-cage induction-motor starters. Specifically, these are the requirements for each particular type:

Maintainance of Manual Starters. On the types employing a toggle switch with a quick-make and quick-break, there is practically no maintenance except to check tightness of connections and be sure that heaters for overload relay are tight. Lubricate only if it is a manufacturer's requirement.

On the oil-immersed drum type the following precautions are recommended:

1. Check all connections.
2. Observe wear on removable contact tips and replace when two-thirds worn away or as directed by manufacturer's maintenance requirements.
3. Replace oil when it becomes dirty or badly carbonized.
4. See that all parts are clean and move freely.

Maintenance of Magnetic Linestarters

1. Do not lubricate contact tips or bearings.
2. Magnet sealing surfaces should occasionally be wiped with an oil-moistened cloth to prevent rust. Use transformer oil or similar type.
3. Check tightness of all connections, and particularly connections to overload heaters, since a loose connection here will cause local heating that will affect the calibration of the relay.

FIG. 4-16. Checking a magnetic linestarter for proper operation.

4. Make sure that shunts are not broken or touching other parts.
5. Contacts should be adjusted so that they will all meet at the same time.
6. In general, the contacts will not need attention during normal contact life. If they become excessively rough or burned in service, they should be dressed with a fine file. Remove only the high spots. Do not use emery cloth. Contact tips should be replaced when approximately two-thirds of their thickness is worn away or as directed by manufacturer's maintenance requirements. These are removable, and only simple tools are needed for the change.
7. Any excess deposits should be removed from the inside surfaces of the arc boxes adjacent to the contacts, and any broken arc boxes should be replaced.
8. See that all moving parts work freely.
9. Disconnect the motor, manually test the start button, the stop button, and the

overload relay, and reset. Overload relays should be checked for tripping at current values.

10. Most industrial linestarters are provided with overload relays whose action depends on the movement of a thermally sensitive element under heat. On very small motors the element actually carries the motor current, but on larger ones a separate heater carrying the motor current is placed close to the element. On still larger motors a current transformer reduces the motor current to a value that can be handled by the heater. Some manufacturers prefer to use a "solder-pot" type of overload element.

Overload Protection. Thermal relays have an inverse time-limit feature, which means the greater the overload the shorter the time of tripping. They provide excellent protection against overloads and momentary surges but do not protect against short-circuit currents. For protection against the latter, fuses not exceeding four times the motor full-load current, or time-limit circuit breakers set at no more than four times the motor full-load current, or instantaneous-trip circuit breakers should be installed ahead of the linestarter. Where fuses are used, it is good practice to use a disconnecting switch as well.

Heaters for thermal relays are made with different current ratings, so that, within its limits, any starter can be used with different-sized motors and still afford proper protection by selecting the size of heater that corresponds to the full-load current of the motor being used. Tables showing the ampere rating of heaters can be obtained from the manufacturer. In general, the ampere rating of the heater should be approximately 120 per cent of the motor full-load current.

FIG. 4-17. Overload protection is provided on this linestarter. A current-sensitive overload relay is built into the starter. The overloads are interchangeable to provide any range of protection.

A further adjustment is possible by means of a calibration lever on some types of relays. When set at 100 per cent, the current stamped on the heater will just trip the starter after several minutes. For tripping at a smaller current, move the lever toward 90 per cent; for a larger current, toward 120 per cent.

Maintenance of Reduced-voltage Starters. The maintenance requirements listed under linestarters apply also to manually operated reduced-voltage starters, commonly known as autostarters. In addition, the following points should be checked:

1. The moving parts of the low-voltage release mechanism should be carefully examined to see that they work freely.
2. Many of these starters previously used an overload relay of the magnetic type having a fluid dashpot to prevent tripping on momentary overloads. Care must be taken to see that the piston is not binding in the dashpot and that the dashpot is filled to cover the piston with the proper grade of dashpot fluid. If oil is used, it is specifically refined to have a flat viscosity-temperature curve.
3. The setting of the overload relay should be checked; it should be at not more than 125 per cent full-load motor current. The setting is usually marked on the dashpot and coincides with a line or pointer on the upper casting.
4. On some special starters the contacts are operated under oil. The pan should be

filled with oil to the oil-level mark.   If the oil becomes badly discolored or carbon-ized from service, it should be replaced with new oil after carefully cleaning the pan.

5. On automatic starters a definite time relay or other timing device is used to control the time on the starting tap.   If a type using an oil dashpot is employed, care must be taken to see that the pot is filled with oil.   This is a very light special oil. Substitutes should not be used.

6. Most starting transformers are provided with taps by which the starting volt-age can be varied.   The proper taps to use are those that will bring the motor up to speed without exceeding the capabilities of the starting transformer.   Periods longer than this may seriously overheat the transformer.   Use the manufacturer's recommended tap settings and check them against the speed settings given.

Maintenance of Resistance-type Starters. Many starters of the resistance type will use drum-type controllers in the smaller sizes and contactors in the larger.   The maintenance requirements have been covered by the preceding topics.   They are called resistance-type because resist-ance inserted in the primary circuit is cut off gradually by the starter as the motor comes up to speed.   They are usually designed to short-circuit the resistor in from 1 to 10 sec and for starting not more than once every 80 sec.

Specific information on the mainte-nance requirements of specific makes of motor starters is available for your use. Write to the manufacturer and state the name-plate information given on the starter.

MILL-DUTY CONTACTORS

For the purpose of this discussion, mill-duty contactors may be considered the big brothers of the various types of contactors and contact-making devices used with low-voltage motor starters.   Except for their application to circuits requiring the interruption of heavy-load currents, these contactors perform the same electrical

Fig. 4-18. A 300-amp a-c contactor.

functions as their smaller counterparts.   They are quite common in industry. Because they are subject to severe duty, and usually interrupt high-load currents and voltages, these devices are sturdily built and designed for long life.   Their application creates a wide range of maintenance requirements.   Industrial motors of large size may be started and stopped infrequently or may be required to start, stop, and reverse many times an hour.   This is true of the motors applied to rolling mills, traction duty, mine hoists, elevators, and many other duties.   Frequently, entire sections of control boards are devoted to an arrangement of contactors remotely located from the motors to which they are applied.   The operation of these contactors is accomplished by the manipulation of manual or automatic control devices such as drum controllers; speed regulators; reversing, jogging, and limit switches; and other control.   The motor control usually operates at a lower voltage than the main contactors because of safety requirements.   The heavy-duty contactors are needed to handle the higher utiliza-tion voltages and currents of the motors.

Since these main contactors interrupt the actual motor currents and voltages, the value of the currents can be quite high.   It is to be expected that more than routine maintenance attention must be given these components. The manufacturer of the device usually outlines the required maintenance and procedures to be followed to obtain maximum life from the equipment. Mill-duty contactors, depending on application, require special consideration when establishing a realistic program for effective preventive maintenance.

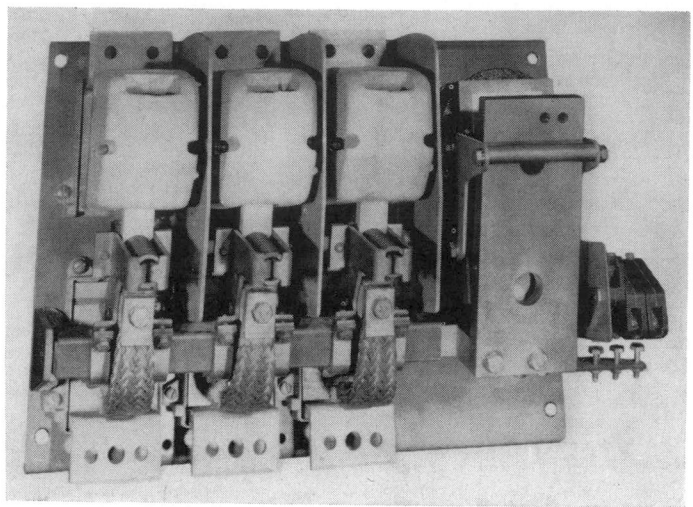

FIG. 4-19. A 600-amp a-c contactor.

FIG. 4-20. A 900-amp a-c contactor with d-c closing magnet.

Routine Contactor Inspection. A maintenance program should be established as soon as the contactor is put into service. After the contactor has been inspected a number of times at weekly or monthly intervals and the condition noted, the frequency of inspection can be increased or decreased to suit the conditions found, since this will depend upon the severity of the contactor duty. Power should be removed from the starter, and inspection should proceed as follows:

A. General inspection
  1. Check for loose, missing, broken, or corroded hardware, pivot pins, cotter pins, springs, and other mechanical parts. Do not oil moving parts since this will accelerate the collection of dust and dirt.
B. Arc boxes
  1. Check arc boxes for broken or eroded parts and grid plates and also for excessive collection of contact material or other foreign conducting material on the surface of insulating parts.
  2. Replace broken or badly eroded parts.
  3. Clean or replace parts having excessive build-up of conducting material.
C. Contacts
  1. Remove oxide or large beads of contact materials from the faces of contacts, using a fine file or sandpaper. (Emery cloth should not be used for cleaning contacts.)
  2. Do not file or sand silver or alloy contact faces unless considerable foreign matter has collected on the surface of the contacts.
  3. When replacing contacts or other current-carrying parts, clean surfaces which are to be bolted together.
  4. Realign contacts and set overtravel if necessary.
  5. Do not substitute contact material without factory approval.
D. Shunts
  1. Replace shunts having broken or frayed strands.
  2. Clean connection points if current-carrying parts are discolored.
E. Blowout coils
  1. Inspect blowout coils for discolored connections, shorted turns, and loose hardware.
F. Terminals, contact supports, bus bars, and connectors
  1. Discolored connections usually indicate that overheating has occurred, probably because of loose connections.
     Clean connection points which are discolored and tighten all hardware.
G. Insulators
  1. Remove dust and dirt from insulating parts.
  2. If carbonized tracks or cracked or broken insulators are found, replace the defective parts.
  3. As a last resort, carbonized tracks may be scraped clean and painted with insulating varnish.
  4. Before a repaired part is put into service give it an overvoltage test.
H. Magnet assembly
  1. Check magnet for dirty or corroded pole faces, pivot points, and other moving parts.
  2. Check for loose, broken, or missing shading coils, residual shims, and hardware.
  3. Inspect operating coil for evidence of electrical or mechanical damage.
  4. Operate armature by hand and check for mechanical interference and friction.
I. Electrical operation
  1. Operate the contactor electrically without load and observe magnet operation to be sure it opens and closes cleanly and that armature is fully sealed in the closed position.
     If an a-c magnet is used, check for abnormal magnet noise.
  2. Test a sample of oil used with oil-immersed contactors and fill oil tank to the proper level with good oil.
  3. Megger insulation between phases, to ground, and to the control circuit.
  4. Operate the contactor under load and check for abnormal report and arcing both on opening and closing. A loud report and arcing on closing is usually due to contact bounce. The magnitude of the report and arcing found on opening and closing will depend upon the type of contactor, operating load, and phase angle at which the contacts separate or touch. Since no absolute standard can be set for covering this detail, it will be necessary to judge performance on the basis of past experience with equipment when it was new or with other applications having similar equipment and operating conditions.

Table 4-1 will be of great help in trouble shooting.

Table 4-1. Contactor Trouble Shooting

	Magnet		
Defect	Cause	Remedy	See notes
Coil burned out.	Mechanical damage.	Replace.	
	Armature does not seal in.	See pages on starting, etc.	1 and 2
	Protective resistance or high-resistance winding is not inserted in series with d-c coil when armature seals in.	Adjust, repair, or replace interlock and series resistance so that continuous rating of coil is not exceeded when armature is sealed.	2
	Coil voltage is too high.	Correct coil voltage. Use higher-voltage coil.	
	Ambient temperature is too high.	Provide better ventilation. Relocate starter. Check factory for special coil.	
	Intermittent coil is energized too long.	Readjust operating cycle. Check factory for special coil.	
	Jogging duty is too severe.	Readjust operating cycle. Check factory for special coil.	1 and 2
	Abnormal atmosphere.	Relocate starter. Check factory for special coil.	
Does not pick up.	Defective coil.	Replace.	
	Low voltage.	Correct coil voltage. Use lower-voltage coil.	
	Mechanical interference or friction.	Check mechanical operation by hand and make necessary adjustments and/or repairs.	
	Magnetic lockout.	Use nonmagnetic-armature-stop details. Add nonmagnetic shim between armature and armature stop.	
Does not seal; hesitates at contact touch; drops open to contact touch. (This condition may exist only when operating coil is hot or line voltage is low.)	Mechanical interference or friction.	Check mechanical operation by hand and make necessary adjustments and/or repairs.	
	Contact force too high.	Replace springs. Remove friction from moving contact assembly. Adjust spring length if adjustment is provided.	
	Coil voltage too low.	Correct coil voltage. Use lower-voltage coil.	
	Series protective resistance or high-resistance coil winding is inserted too early, or series resistance is too high.	Adjust, repair, or replace interlock and/or series resistance.	2
	Coils of two-coil d-c magnet have bucking polarity.	Reverse polarity of one coil and check operation with load disconnected.	

Table 4-1. Contactor Trouble Shooting (*Continued*)

Magnet			
Defect	Cause	Remedy	See notes
Does not drop out, or drop-out is sluggish.	Welded contacts.	See pages on contactors	
	Dirt or grease on pole faces.	Clean.	
	Mechanical interference or friction.	Check mechanical operation by hand and make necessary adjustments and/or repairs.	
	Residual shim is pounded down or is missing. Residual air gap is pounded down.	Replace residual shim or magnet assembly.	
	Kickout spring is defective or missing.	Replace (kickout spring is not used on all contactors).	
	Control relay does not open d-c side of rectifier.	Add contact in control circuit. Repair or replace relay.	3
	Control relay has long arcing time.	Repair or replace relay.	
	Shorted coil turns.	Replace coil.	3
Magnet chatter or pumping.	Shading coil broken or out of place.	Replace.	1
	Series protective resistance or high-resistance coil winding is inserted too early, or series resistance is too high or is open.	Adjust, repair, or replace interlock and/or series resistance.	2
	Chattering contacts on control relay, control switch, pressure switch, temperature switch, etc.	Check overtravel and contact force on control device. Replace control device. Move control device to a location having less vibration, or insulate control device from shock and vibration.	
	Loose connections.	Tighten connections.	
Noisy a-c magnet.	Armature does not seal in tight.	Clean pole faces. Remove mechanical interference and/or friction.	
	Pole faces rough.	Replace magnet assembly. File pole faces as a last resort if new parts are not available.	
	Magnet misaligned.	Realign.	
	Shading coil broken or out of place.	Replace.	
	Coil voltage is low.	Correct coil voltage. Use lower-voltage coil.	

Notes:
1. Applies to a-c magnets.
2. Applies to d-c magnets having overvoltage during pickup.
3. Applies to all d-c magnets.

Table 4-1. Contactor Trouble Shooting (*Continued*)

Contacts

Defect	Cause	Remedy
Overheating.	Load current too high. Loose connections.	Reduce load. Use larger contactor. Clean discolored or dirty connections and retighten.
	Overtravel and/or contact force too low.	Adjust overtravel, replace contacts, and replace contact springs as required to correct defect.
	Collection of copper oxide or foreign matter on contact faces.	Clean with fine file or sandpaper. Use dust-tight enclosure for dusty atmosphere.
	Load is on in excess of 8 hr.	Change operating procedure. Check factory for more suitable contacts.
	Ambient temperature is too high.	Reduce load. Provide better ventilation. Relocate starter. Use larger contactor.
	Line and/or load cables are too small.	Apply cable in line with NEC Standards.
Welding of contacts.	Overtravel and/or contact force is too low.	Adjust overtravel, replace contacts, and replace contact springs as required to correct defect.
	Magnet stalls or hesitates at contact touch point.	See Magnet, this Table.
	Magnet drops open at contact touch due to voltage dip.	See Magnet, this Table.
	Magnet chatter.	See Magnet, this Table.
	Contact bounce on closing.	Correct coil overvoltage condition. Correct mechanical defects.
	Contacts rebound to contact touch when opening.	Correct mechanical defects in stop assembly. Correct mechanical defects in latch if one is used.
	Poor contact alignment.	Adjust contacts to touch simultaneously within $\frac{1}{32}$ in.
	Jogging duty is too severe.	Reduce jogging cycle. Check factory for more weld-resistant contact material. Use larger contactor.
	Excessive inrush current.	Readjust accelerating time or operating sequence. Use larger contactor. Check factory for more weld-resistant contact material.

Table 4-1. Contactor Trouble Shooting (*Continued*)

Contacts

Defect	Cause	Remedy
Short contact life.	Vibration in starter mounting.	Move starter to location having less shock and vibration. Insulate starter from shock and vibration. Provide more rigid support for starter.
	Low contact force.	Adjust overtravel, replace contacts, and replace contact springs as required to correct contact force.
	Contact bounce on opening or closing.	Correct coil overvoltage condition. Correct mechanical defects.
	Magnet chatters or pumps.	See Magnet, this Table.
	Abrasive dust on contacts.	Use dust-tight enclosure. Do not use emery cloth to dress contacts.
	Load current is too high.	Reduce load. Check factory for more durable contact material. Use larger contactor.
	Jogging cycle is too severe.	Reduce jogging cycle. Check factory for more durable contact material. Use larger contactor.
	Oil-immersed contactor is used where an air break contactor could be used.	Air break contactors may have 10 to 20 times longer contact life than oil-immersed contactors of equal rating.

Arc interruption

Defect	Cause	Remedy
Poor arc interruption.	Arc box not in place.	Install arc box in line with instruction-leaflet data.
	Arc box damaged.	Replace broken or eroded insulating parts, arc horns, and grid plates. Clean or replace insulating parts having a heavy coating of foreign conducting material.
	Dirt or paint on arc horns or steel grid plates.	Remove insulating materials which may have accumulated on arc horns and steel grid plates.
	Magnetic hardware substituted for nonmagnetic hardware in arc box and blowout assemblies.	Replace with correct hardware.
	Blowout coil reversed or short-circuited.	Replace coil. Correct defect.
	Oil level is low, or oil is worn out (in oil-immersed contactor).	Fill tank to proper level with good oil.
	Magnet opening is sluggish.	See Magnet, this Table.

STARTING AND SPEED-REGULATING RHEOSTATS FOR D-C MOTORS

General. Rheostats are used for starting and speed regulation of series, shunt, and compound-wound motors in nonreversing service. Specific examples are fans, blowers, pumps, machine tools, and similar d-c motor applications, ranging from ¼ to 150 hp.

To keep rheostats in good operating condition, periodic inspection, cleaning, and dressing of contacts with a file is usually all that is needed. However, some arcing and burning of the contact-making parts is unavoidable, and servicing of these parts will be necessary. Contacts should always be smooth. After each dressing with a file, polish with fine sandpaper. Contacting surfaces should then be thoroughly cleaned, including the areas between contacts. The contacts may be lightly greased with petroleum jelly or a comparable lubricant. Do not overgrease! Sometimes contact surfaces are damaged by burrs or sharp edges on the moving contacts. On occasion, abrasive particles in the air are responsible for this scoring action of the contacts. If this is the case, refrain from using any lubricant, or the condition will be worsened.

Servicing Rheostats. Many rheostats are designed to have reversible contacts. The movable and stationary contacts when worn can be turned over and used on the reverse side. This, in effect, gives the contacts a double life. Reversing of these contacts should be resorted to only when abnormal burning and subsequent dressing with a file has made the adjacent contact surfaces uneven. In operation, the moving contact should make the transition from one stationary contact to the next with a firm, even pressure if arcing is to be prevented. If this is not accomplished, irregular increments in speeds or voltages can result from poor regulation of resistance. On the larger types of rheostats, or those with movable contacts of the compensated type, a slight variation between contact surfaces will not impair operation. But it is generally advisable, when turning over one or more contact buttons, to turn over all others at the same time. Oxides will form on the unused copper surfaces of a rheostat. They should not be allowed to accumulate. Remove the oxide film at regular maintenance periods. Thoroughly clean and protect the unused contacts of the rheostat with petroleum jelly to prevent reoxidation. Should an application require "cutting in" previously unused portions of resistance, it is very important to measure this new resistance. A check should be made to insure that any additional travel of the moving contact is not restricted by the height of the previously unused contacts, and that contacts are properly connected to obtain the desired added resistance. Always clean the contact surfaces of a rheostat before placing it in service. A regulation check should be conducted, measuring the amount of variable resistance, preferably at the motor. This will take into consideration the resistance value of motor leads and should reveal any poorly made terminal connections and any irregularity or error in resistance stepping.

Contact-pressure Settings. The necessary pressure between moving and stationary contacts must be maintained by proper adjustment of spring tension to minimize pitting, heating, and oxidizing of contacts. These are abnormal conditions. Follow the manufacturer's recommendations on maintaining, setting, and adjusting contact pressures. The procedures to be followed are usually contained in the instruction books or literature shipped with the rheostat. The recommended moving-contact spring pressure is usually indicated in pounds or ounces per square inch and is generally checked with a hook spring balance. The force required to separate the contacts should be determined and compared with manufacturer's data. The general practice of manufacturers is to establish a pressure sufficient for good conductivity, yet not damaging to the surfaces of either the moving or stationary contacts. At the same time, care must be exercised not to create frictional forces that would prevent resetting of the arm on rheostats with low-voltage release and automatic-resetting characteristics. The turns of the pressure-setting spring should never touch; when they do, it indicates a weak or improperly applied spring, which must be replaced.

Magnet Coils and Low-voltage Release Devices. Practically all starting rheostats of a low horsepower rating have a magnetic holding coil as part of the low-voltage release mechanism. This coil is connected directly across the line. The release is adjusted to hold the operating handle in the last running position as long as the line voltage remains normal. This release may or may not be adjustable. If it is of the adjustable type, the manufacturer will have made provision for changing its holding characteristics over a prescribed range of undervoltage. Adjustments may be accomplished by following the manufacturer's instructions for changing the setting to a lower or higher value. If not adjustable, the device may be rendered inoperable by filing, bending, or shimming the mechanical parts. The operating arm should never be held in the running position by force. A starter that will not operate as intended should be thoroughly checked for mechanical defects and the possibility of misapplication. It is more economical to replace the starter or its mechanism than to risk harming the motor by excessive starting or running current. The control rheostat should not be used to stop the motor. A safety switch or circuit breaker should be provided for this purpose. The maintenance requirements indicated by the manufacturer should be observed when servicing, and regular inspections should be scheduled to insure proper maintenance.

FIG. 4-21. A typical frame of edge-wound resistors.

Resistor Replacement. Occasionally, abnormal starting or operating conditions may burn out a section of resistance. Plate resistors must be replaced with units of equal value. If the resistance is a wire-wound bobbin type, covered by a ceramic glaze, these units must be replaced by like components of equal or adjustable value. Others are of edge-wound resistance material supported on a ceramic core, lending themselves to temporary repair by welding or clamping the burned-out sections together until a new resistor can be obtained. As a general rule, heavy-duty resistors using cast grids and units using strip resistors cannot be repaired. Burned-out sections, like ceramic-coated units, must be replaced. To replace burned-out resistors, depending on rheostat design, partial or complete disassembly of the rheostat may be required. In most types of industrial rheostats, the field resistors are removable from the resistor mounting without disconnecting the wiring at the face plate or disassembly of the operating mechanism. Large-motor applications will frequently use separate frames of resistance, remotely located. This resistance is then connected to and varied by a rheostat face plate and mechanism.

Locating and Installing Rheostats and Resistor Blanks. Rheostats should always be mounted so that adequate ventilation can be provided. Ventilating hoods should be at the top. If resistors are stacked in racks, one on top of the other to conserve space, the accepted practice is to limit stacked height to four frames with ample separation distance between frames. Provide at least 1 ft of space between the floor and the first frame to permit unrestricted air flow through the units. Clearance between the ceiling and the top unit will be determined by the total height of the stacked arrangement, but should allow for adequate top ventilation. In most instances, manufacturers stipulate the necessary requirements for remote mounting of field resistors and the volume of cooling air to be provided, if forced-air ventilation is necessary. Resistance banks and rheostats, as stated for other electrical equipment,

must be kept clean and dry. Do not store combustible materials near or in the area of resistors. Cooling air should be free of oil mist, lint, and other contaminating particles which, if deposited on the hot grids or resistors, could cause fires. **Checking for Loose Connections.** When placing a rheostat or field resistance in service for the first time, it is important to check the resistance value before attempting operation. After placing it in service and during the initial observation period, the terminal connections and all interconnections should be checked at least twice to insure that they have not loosened as a result of heating. Loose connections can cause many annoying delays and create operating conditions that could be hazardous. They are difficult to find unless arcing or burning occurs. To guard against loose connections developing, resistor connections should be checked frequently.

Fig. 4-22. Check resistor connections frequently.

The effect of cyclic heating and cooling of resistors will have a tendency to create loose connections. It is good maintenance practice to occasionally check resistance values against manufacturer's data. Incremental values and composite values should be measured to guard against shorted resistors which affect total resistance value. One of the best devices for checking continuity and regulation of a rheostat is an ohmmeter. It is convenient, rugged, and small. Ohmic values are indicated on the dial and, depending on scale ranges of the ohmmeter, can be used for low- or high-resis

Fig. 4-23. Manually operated plate-type rheostat, one-, two-, and three-section units

tance circuitry. If extremely accurate readings are necessary, a Wheatstone bridge or similar accurate instrument should be used. When using a direct-reading ohmmeter to check resistance, any change between two points of resistance is readily determined by changes in the instrument pointer. From these fluctuations and their magnitude with reference to change, it will be obvious whether the circuit is normal or not. Burned-out or short-circuited resistance sections can be located rapidly in this manner. Unless they are required to be extremely accurate, most resistors are manufactured with a tolerance factor of ±10 per cent. For this reason, it is important to know resistance requirements when checking or replacing resistors. Unless there is some method of refining the accuracy by tapping or adjusting the fixed resistance values in the rheostat, change in motor performance may be noted when a considerable portion of a rheostat or resistance bank has been replaced for any reason. Always consult the motor and application data when replacing rheostats. The manufacturer's resistance data and resistor-connection drawings should be available when restacking or changing out resistors used in rheostats or banks of field resistance.

Arcing at the contacts or burning of contacts on the face plate of a rheostat is always an indication of trouble. There could be short circuiting or open resistance at these points in the resistance circuit. Also, the cause could be due to increased resistance at that step. Field rheostats must never be used if the current requirements exceed the name-plate value and rating of the rheostat.

Fig. 4-24. A typical motor-operated rheostat.

STARTING AND SPEED-REGULATING RHEOSTATS FOR A-C WOUND-ROTOR MOTORS

General. Rheostats of the face-plate type, with self-contained resistors, are commonly applied in conjunction with the manual or magnetic primary control for starting and for the speed regulation by secondary control of a-c wound-roto. motors ranging from ¼ to 25 hp. For reversing service and heavier-duty applications, drum or drum-contactor controllers are used with separately mounted resistors. Standard drum controllers are used on normal applications to motors of ½ to 100 hp. For heavier-duty applications, the drum-contactor type is used for the starting and control of motors up to 300 hp.

Special attention should be given to the maintenance of the secondary control of wound-rotor motors, particularly those used in speed-regulating service. In a large percentage of applications, it is possible for faults to develop though normal wear without causing either immediate shutdown or failure to start. A similar fault in the primary circuit would force immediate correction of the trouble.

Since the motor will continue to start and operate even though an actual open

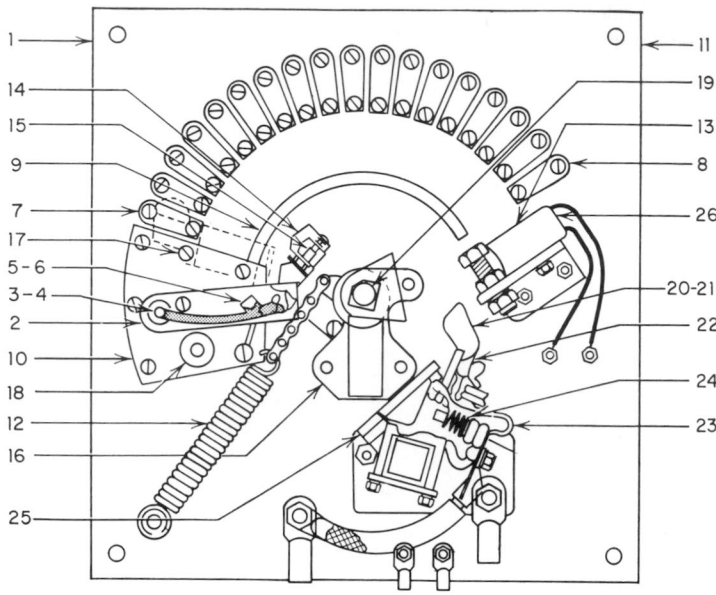

Ref. no.	Name of part	No. per rheostat
1	Face plate complete........................	1
2	Contact arm complete with contact..........	1
3	Contact with shunt—main...............	1
4	Contact spring—main....................	1
5	Contact without shunt—auxiliary.........	1
6	Contact spring—auxiliary................	1
7	Stationary contact........................	18
8	Stationary contact stud....................	18
9	Stationary contact segment.................	1
10	Rider..................................	1
11	Base...................................	1
12	Return spring...........................	1
13	Magnet core............................	1
14	Contact................................	1
15	Contact screw...........................	2
16	Bearing bracket..........................	1
17	Blowout coil............................	1
18	Rubber stop.............................	1
19	Shaft assembly..........................	1
20	Type A contact finger.....................	2
21	Finger tip...........................	2
22	Finger base..........................	2
23	Finger shunt.........................	40
24	Finger spring........................	2
25	Finger arc barrier....................	2
26	Magnet coil.............................	1

Fig. 4-25. Typical 25-hp starting rheostat.

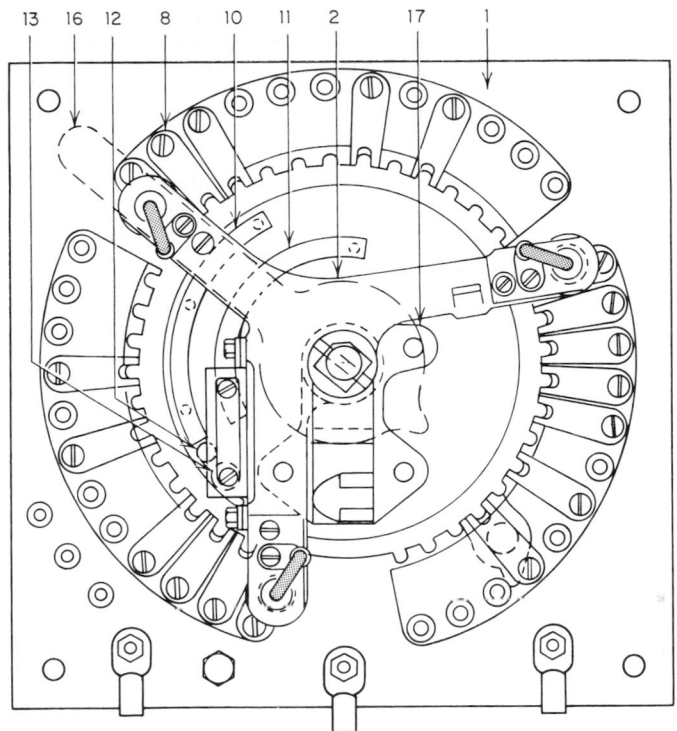

Ref. no.	Name of part	No. per unit
1	Face plate complete........................	1
2	Contact arm complete with contacts..........	1
3	Main contact with shunt..................	3
4	Auxiliary contact.......................	2
5	Main contact spring.....................	3
6	Auxiliary contact spring..................	2
7	Insulation channel for auxiliary contact.....	1
8	Stationary contact.........................	21
9	Stationary contact stud.....................	21
10	Contact segment—outer.....................	1
11	Contact segment—inner.....................	1
12	Stationary contact button...................	1
13	Stationary contact lava button..............	1
14	Shaft assembly............................	1
15	Base......................................	1
16	Handle....................................	1
17	Bearing...................................	1

Fig. 4-26. Typical face-plate controller for motors of ¼ to 25 hp.   See Fig. 4-27 for part numbers listed above but not shown in this drawing.

circuit or serious unbalance of resistance may exist in the secondary circuit at certain points on the controller, it is not always understood or appreciated that this condition may have serious consequences. Roasting out of the rotor windings, burning, and severe arcing at the brushes, damage to collector rings, and overheating or burnout of resistors can result. In addition, undue stress on the equipment may be produced when the smooth steps of acceleration provided by the control are lost by poor contact or no contact at certain points on the controller. Such conditions may develop without the operator either noting or reporting any difficulty or unusual operating conditions, until a serious breakdown occurs. Then it may be recalled that "they did have to notch the controller up a step" or that "it has jumped a bit on that point." A definite and regular inspection schedule is essential, not only for these reasons, but also because this class of apparatus is of such rugged design and construction that it normally requires minimum attention, for which reason alone it may be neglected.

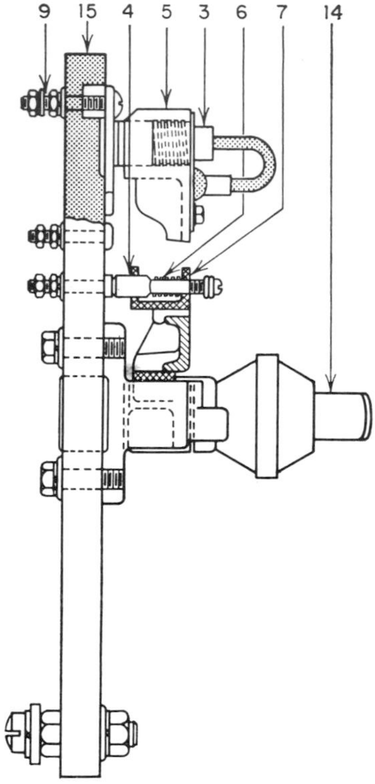

FIG. 4-27. Face-plate controller. See parts list, Fig. 4-26, for identification of numbers.

General Maintenance. To insure against service interruptions and keep all types of secondary control in good operating condition requires only regular inspection and the cleaning and maintenance of contacts. Some arcing and burning of contact-making parts is unavoidable. These should be kept smooth to prevent unnecessary burning and to insure a positive, low-resistance contact at all times. Occasional dressing with a file may be necessary. Some manufacturers recommend a conducting lubricant; however, lubricants should not be used unless endorsed or recommended by the manufacturer.

Rheostat maintenance has been adequately covered in the preceding text. The continuity of resistance related to the operation of controllers should be checked occasionally, using the ohmmeter method. The continuity check may be made across the contacts of the controller, but the general practice is to raise the collector-ring brushes, insert a test lamp, ohmmeter, or other suitable test instrument across the brush holders or outgoing leads, and move the secondary controller through its full sequence, step by step. If this check is repeated across each phase, it will not only verify the continuity of the resistors and tapped connections, it will indicate any open contacts in the controller as well.

In general, the values of secondary resistance are relatively low. The continuity check will determine only the continuity factor. Many plants lack the proper instrumentation to accurately measure or set low resistance values. In these instances, it is extremely important to make frequent visual inspections to locate and correct loose connections or low-pressure contacts. The tap connections on grid-type resistors, if found movable by hand, and resistor connections showing evidence of heating should be removed, and the connectors cleaned or replaced. All pressure-type connections should be checked; if loose or poorly conducting, the pressure should be increased by tightening the pressure nuts at the ends of the assembly. On ribbon or edge-wound resistors, the clamp-type connections should be tightened if they are not solid. On all new installations, at least two checks should be made after initial start-up and energizing of equipment to insure that resistance connections and all controller contacts remain tight.

Resistors, if properly applied and their connections maintained, require no further service, but they should be checked occasionally.   Investigate any excessive heating of the resistors to determine if heating is caused by open or unbalanced connections in the secondary circuit.

On new installations, the duty cycle should be checked against the resistor class to verify proper application, since all have definite limitations.   For example, NEMA Class 114 is for starting duty only, and on that basis the motor it serves should be started and brought up to speed in approximately 5 sec, with a minimum of 75 sec, between successive starts.

In variable-speed applications, the speed obtained is dependent on the load.   If the required speed reduction is not obtained, the motor is probably underloaded and the load must be increased or additional resistance inserted.

Fig. 4-28. Typical resistance bank using edge-wound resistors.

Resistor Connections.   All standard a-c wound-rotor motors, whether for two- or three-phase circuits, have their secondaries wound for three-phase.   The resistors used in each phase of the circuit are normally of equal value and differ only with respect to terminal marking or nomenclature.   Always refer to the manufacturer's instruction books and drawings for correct application data and connection scheme. The actual resistance will consist of three individual resistors, or multiples of resistors, necessary to obtain correct ohmic value.   Depending on application and requirements, the resistors may be plate, tube, grid, strip, or ribbon type.   (For special applications, other types of resistance may be used.   These are not considered general-purpose resistors.)

When multiple resistors have been supplied, or resistor banks must be assembled, consult assembly drawings and connection diagrams for proper identification of these components.   Check name plates to insure that all frames or resistors have been received.   When several resistor frames are required per phase, sort out the frames for each phase and connect in accordance with the terminal marking.

No standards have been adopted to date for the marking of resistor connections.

In general, the resistor for the first phase has its terminals marked R-1–R-2–R-3. The second-phase marking may be R-11–R-12–R-13, and the third-phase marking, R-21–R-22–R-23. Each manufacturer is permitted to use his own nomenclature. For consistency, the connection diagram will repeat these phase markings and show the points of resistance connection to the actual resistance load. When two or more frames are used in each phase, they are usually connected in series: A to A, B to B, C to C, etc. Particular care should be exercised to mate the proper resistors and to see that all connections are properly made.

Secondary resistors for a-c motors are designed for star connection. Resistors for most manual controllers may be connected with all three secondary phases closed, or with one secondary phase open on the first phase of the controller. Resistors for magnetic controllers are connected with all three phases closed in the secondary or on the first point.

The torque obtained with a resistor of a given class number varies with the connection used on the first point of the controller. The torques available on the first point with single-phase and three-phase starting can be determined from manufacturer's data or by reference to NEMA standards. Where it is possible to use both methods of connection, the control diagram will show one method of connection and usually explain the alternative method. The method appearing on the diagram is usually the preferred method, but if a change in starting torque is desirable, the alternative method may be used.

Since the capacity, and to a degree the life, of resistors depend largely on heat dissipation, never locate resistors in poorly ventilated areas. Undesirable variations in resistance may result, and may necessitate forced ventilation if overheating becomes a problem. Some resistors may operate at temperatures sufficiently high to cause them to glow. However, most applications are based on NEMA standard 375°C rise.

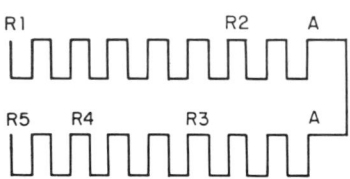

Fig. 4-29. A simple resistor connection.

CONTROLLERS

With the present trend toward automation, more and more operator-controlled functions are being automated. Many processes formerly controlled by hand are now fully automated. They require only that an operator be in attendance to oversee the equipment operation and perhaps make minor control adjustments to insure quality control.

There are, however, and will continue to be, many operations where the starting, stopping, and speed regulation of equipment and processes must be manually controlled. Therefore the manual controller can be expected to remain in the maintenance picture for the foreseeable future. Its application need not be explained, although a brief discussion of its mechanical features is desirable.

There are two common types, drum controllers and drum contactor controllers. Two types of drum assemblies are used.

Low current ratings have contact-supporting disks assembled on an insulated steel shaft between insulating collars, with the reversible contacts bolted directly to the supporting disks.

Larger ratings—150- to 300-amp sizes—have heavy, curved, copper segment plates supported by molded insulating supports bolted to a steel shaft. On these types, the upper and lower segments have the same shape to permit interchange and reversal. It is almost universal practice to manufacture these larger types with drum segments that are reversible. As these segments wear, they may be reversed, the old trailing edge becoming the leading edge when turned 180°. This not only provides double life, it offers material advantage in simplifying maintenance.

Contact fingers should be adjusted to drop no more than $\frac{1}{8}$ in. below the surface of the drum contacts. The controller bearings, star wheel, and pawl should be cleaned

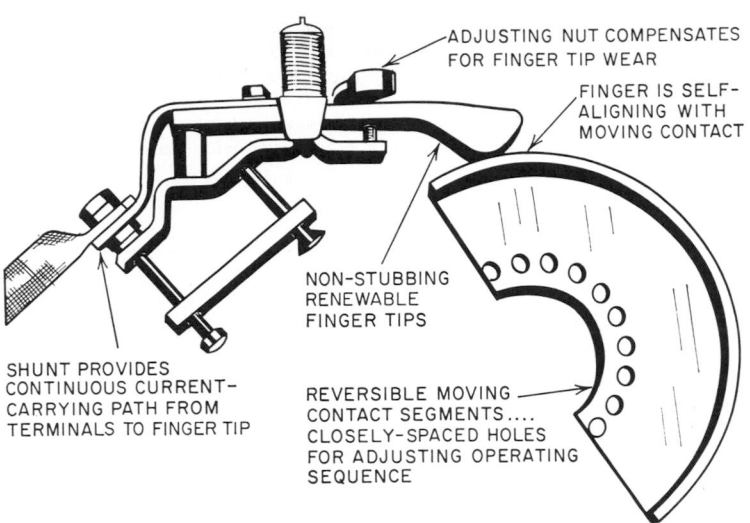

ADJUSTING NUT COMPENSATES
FOR FINGER TIP WEAR

FINGER IS SELF-
ALIGNING WITH
MOVING CONTACT

NON-STUBBING
RENEWABLE
FINGER TIPS

SHUNT PROVIDES
CONTINUOUS CURRENT-
CARRYING PATH FROM
TERMINALS TO FINGER TIP

REVERSIBLE MOVING
CONTACT SEGMENTS....
CLOSELY-SPACED HOLES
FOR ADJUSTING OPERATING
SEQUENCE

FIG. 4-30. Sectional arrangement of a controller-finger assembly of the type used in lower-rating drum-type controllers.

FIG. 4-31. Typical nonreversing drum controller.

FIG. 4-32. Reversing-type drum controller.

and lubricated regularly. Other points of wear should be routinely checked, and the proper maintenance accorded the controller. It is very important to keep all wiring connections tight and to check contact pressures and springs with the frequency called for by the manufacturer.

Drum Contactor Controllers. This type, which is designed for the most severe operating conditions, consists of a series of contactors which are closed by cams on the operating shaft and opened by positive spring pressure. The contacts are the

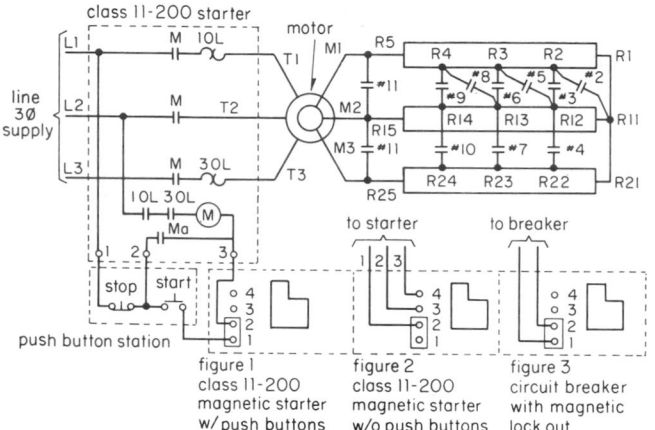

FIG. 4-33A. Typical nonreversing motor-control scheme.

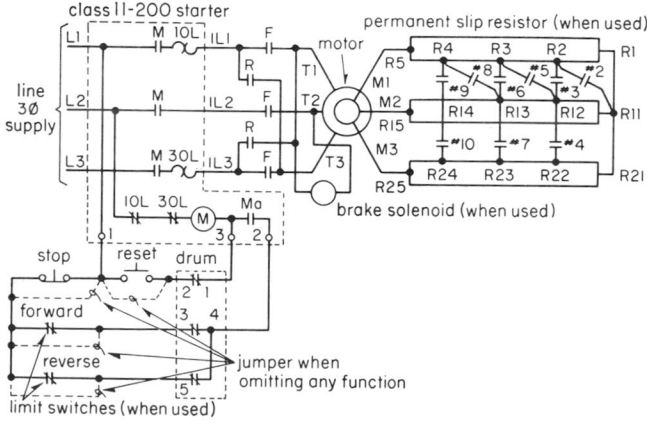

FIG. 4-33B. Typical reversing motor-control scheme.

same as those used in corresponding sizes of magnetic contactors and, in general, are of the rolling type. The rolling action limits all arcing and burning to the contact tips. This quick-make and quick-break action results in only momentary arcing due to current interruption by the contact tips and leaves the current-carrying contact surfaces in perfect condition. The contacts need replacement only when they are so burned that little, or no rolling action is left. When new contacts are installed, they should be adjusted so that proper rolling action is obtained.

Typical Drum Controllers. These are illustrated in Figs. 4-31 and 4-32. Both are heavy-duty types. The nonreversing type is used principally with wound-rotor induction motors on pumps, blowers, crushers, and kilns and for similar applications. They control the secondary circuitry of the motor only.   Suitable primary control must be added.   The reversing type is used for controlling wound-rotor induction motors on cranes, hoists, turntables, bridges, and similar equipment.   They control both the primary and secondary circuits of the motors.   Typical wiring diagrams are shown in Fig. 4-33A and B.

MOLDED-CASE BREAKERS

By strict definition, molded-case breakers should not be labeled a control device. They are so closely allied to the operation of motors, however, particularly motors of medium horsepower rating, that they are generally considered part of the motor control.

If the motor starter does not feature overload protection, it is common practice to install overload protection in the motor supply circuit.   Usually a low-cost thermal magnetic breaker of molded-case design is used.   The timing of these breakers is over a relatively wide band to prevent nuisance tripping and may also be ambient-compensated.   In 225-amp and larger frame sizes, the magnetic trip elements are adjustable.

Until recently, standard molded-case breakers were limited to moderate current applications in the 70- to 225-amp range.   The range of application has steadily increased because of improved design.   In many plants, 400-, 600-, and 800-amp units are common.   Today 1,600- and 2,000-amp molded-case circuit breakers are being applied as standard switchboard apparatus.   On many applications, they are now replacing the usually applied switchgear-type air circuit breakers.

By design, molded-case breakers are sealed units, reasonably tamper-proof.   For industrial application, molded-case breakers in ratings up to 100 amp are considered expendable from a replacement-vs.-maintenance viewpoint.   Unless factory seals are broken, no extensive maintenance is possible.   Breaking of the factory seal terminates warranty and could invite trouble with insurance underwriters.   However, when used in a circuit, certain maintenance practices should be followed.   If the proper test equipment is available, molded-case breakers should be electrically tested under load for calibrated and positive operation at least once a year.

Unless the breakers are operated occasionally, manually and electrically, they can become inoperable through disuse.   Experience has shown that if they are allowed to remain in service for an extended period without an electrical operation, the internal mechanism and linkage may become stiff and not permit the breaker to trip even if three or four times rated current is applied to the terminals.   Once operated, however, the breaker, in most instances, is found to be serviceable.   Therefore even an occasional manual opening and closing can materially reduce the possibility of its failing to operate under load.   But electrical testing under load conditions will require all its components, including magnetic or thermal trip mechanisms, to function.   Failure to trip indicates trouble of more serious nature that is preventing proper electrical operation.

A thermal or magnetic breaker that will not trip is nothing more than a switch in the circuit.   It must be manually operated to perform an electrical interruption. Finding and eliminating defective molded-case circuit breakers from important control circuits is the underlying purpose in submitting them to an electrical test.

The electrical testing of molded-case breakers can be accomplished by using a regulated power supply, provided a smooth, accurate regulation of test currents can be accomplished and meters of known accuracy are used, along with a means of timing the test.   Compact, portable test sets are commercially available for testing molded-case breakers at low voltage/high current.   One popular model has a range of 200 amp at 3 volts and features a built-in timer.   It operates from a standard 110/120-volt single-phase power source and has a rating of 0.6 kva.   It can be appreciated, however, that for higher current limits, more powerful test equipment must be employed. Load tests are generally made at 200 to 300 per cent of full-load breaker rating to expedite testing.   Instantaneous-trip-test current values will be from nine to eleven times the rated current value of the breaker.   We again point out that the perfor-mance testing of electrical apparatus is not a normal maintenance function.   It should be performed only by qualified, properly equipped personnel.   For this reason no further comment will be made concerning electrical testing of molded-case breakers.

Maintenance of Molded-case Breakers.   The breaker should be kept clean and dry, and the line and load connections should be checked occasionally for tightness. If located in a dirty or dusty atmosphere, it should be blown out frequently with clean, dry, low-pressure air.   Do not blow the dirt into the recesses of the unit.

Check for excessive heating.   Heating may be due to poor contact or actual over-load of the breaker.   If in doubt as to load factor, measure the current flowing in the

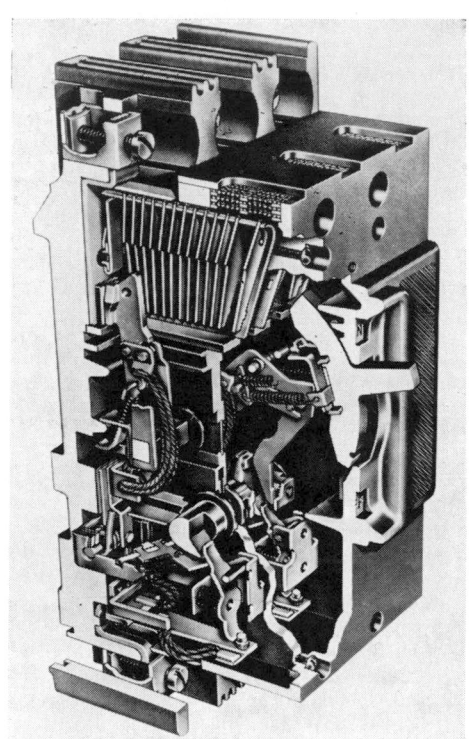

Fig. 4-34. Typical molded-case-breaker construction.

individual phases.   Failure to trip could also be due to a broken shunt, welded con-tacts, friction in the tripping mechanism, or poor contact of the heater element with the current-carrying parts.   Occasionally, misalignment of the trip unit, if the breaker has a removable trip, will prevent tripping under load.

Should heating be abnormal, as evidenced by discoloration of terminals, deteriora-tion of molded material, or possibly nuisance tripping, measurement of load current is advised.   If the current flowing in the individual poles is less than the rating of the breaker, all bolted connections and contacts should be examined.   Low contact pressure or dirty contacts may be a source of heating, as may loose bolted connections. If the currents measured are greater than 125 per cent of the breaker's rating and the breaker has not tripped, test the breaker mechanically by opening and closing the contacts.   This test should reveal any friction in the tripping mechanism or welded contacts, should either of these conditions be present.

If the breaker has a removable trip unit or is of the more modern Tri-Pac design, which incorporates fuses, the trip function can be readily checked.   On units with removable trip units, the loosening of the mounting hardware is usually sufficient to cause tripping.   Under no circumstances should a molded-case breaker remain closed and latched once the trip unit is physically removed.

The Tri-Pac units have an added feature that may be readily checked.   The fuses installed in these units have spring-loaded plungers which release when a fuse blows. The plunger in turn strikes a trip bar extension on the trip unit.   This action of the fuses causes the breaker to trip on any damaging fault current above the rating of the fuse.   A safety feature requires that the breaker be in the open position when checking or replacing the fuses.   If the breaker does not trip when the fuse cover is removed, the breaker is defective.   It should be returned to the manufacturer.

To determine if the mechanism is trip-free under a blown-fuse condition, remove one of the fuses and substitute a blown fuse for the good fuse and replace the cover.   It should be impossible to close and latch the breaker with a blown fuse in any of the fused legs of the breaker.   If the breaker will close and latch with a blown fuse in any of the phases, it is defective; replace the breaker with another unit.

Table 4-2. Underwriters' Specifications for Tripping Time on Molded-case Breakers

Breaker Rating, Amp	Trip Time at 200% Current, Min
0– 40	2
41– 50	4
51–100	6
101–225	8
226–400	10
401–600	12

If a molded-case breaker does not trip under abnormal load conditions or within the required underwriters' specified times as shown in Table 4-2, and mechanical factors are not the underlying cause, in all probability it is out of calibration.   Recalibration of molded-case breakers can be accomplished only under the controlled test conditions of the manufacturer.   It is unwise to attempt, or make, uninstrumented changes in the calibration of the breaker trip unit.   Any variable characteristics of the trip unit will be made accessible to the user by calibrated dials or levers adjustable from the outside of the complete breaker.

INDUSTRIAL ELECTRONIC APPARATUS

Most electronic equipment is designed to operate for long periods with little maintenance or attention.   Once installed, it should be regularly checked and inspected for proper function and output.   Periodic replacement of expendable tubes or components is considered routine maintenance.   Preventive maintenance consists primarily in taking the following precautions:

1. Keep the apparatus clean and dry.
2. Maintain the equipment in a manner and in such condition as to insure utmost reliability, highest efficiency, and maximum life.
3. Maintain cleanliness to avoid flashovers of high-voltage circuits.
4. Carry out inspection to determine the need for maintenance.   Equipment should be examined for overheating, cable or lead displacement, solder "run" or loose connections, and oxidation of conductors, tube caps, and pin conductors.   Check tightness of *all* bolted or mechanical power and control connections.   Look for leaking electrolyte if capacitors are bulged or corroded.
5. Limit adjustment to restoring proper output or performance.   Frequently, tube replacement will correct conditions without altering factory settings of fixed components.

6. Lubrication is generally unnecessary, except where bearings, motors, or shafts are involved. Certain parts are factory-lubricated and need no further attention. The use of oils or fluids with lubricating properties should be carefully controlled around electronic equipment.

7. In electronic equipment, relays may be used for the following functions: to interlock other circuits, to close power circuits, and to provide overload or under-voltage protection. Time-delay and telephone-type relays are frequently used to sequence circuits or provide warm-up periods for apparatus.

Relays should be regularly maintained, adjusted, and cleaned in accordance with good practice and to insure reliability. Particular attention should be given to contacts. Relatively small voltages and currents are usually handled by these relays, and positive contacting and low-contact resistivity is a requirement.

Hermetically sealed relays can be replaced only when operational condition or performance dictates.

8. Check switches for operation and positive contact. Replace worn or erratic operating switching devices and interlocks.

9. Rheostats and potentiometers can be either open-type or totally enclosed. Inspect the rheostat or potentiometer thoroughly. The arm should be keyed tight to the shaft, and the shaft should turn easily. Determine if the bushing is cracked or broken and that the contact arm has sufficient tension. If spring-loaded, establish that the spring is not weak or broken. Also check for looseness of the resistance winding, for burning, cracks, corrosion, and for chipped porcelain body of the resistance element. Tighten all screws and clean the resistance contact surface with Barton cloth or a soft cloth dipped in neutral mineral spirits. Brush or blow out all carbon or dirt; check continuity of the resistance winding. A light film of petrolatum may be used on contact surfaces of the resistance. A small amount of machine oil (one or two drops) may be used on shaft or bearings if they are unduly tight. After cleaning, an ohmmeter may be used to check continuity and regulation of resistance over the range of the potentiometer or rheostat.

10. The instruments used on electronic gear are normally miniature-type and relatively inexpensive to replace. Defective meters should be replaced or returned to the supplier for repair.

Normal checks for range and accuracy can be made on panel instruments by using portable standards for comparison while the device is in service.

Inspect meters that have broken cover glass carefully for damage and install new glass. Dust and dirt entering through broken cover glass will soon destroy meter accuracy.

11. Maintain all pilot lights and other visual operating devices, targets, glow lights, or ground detectors in operating condition.

Replace light bulbs and check associated wiring to the indicating device *before* assuming that the trouble is in the equipment.

Caution! Because of the high voltages normally used on power supplies of electronic devices and the possibility of stored energy charges in capacitors, extreme care should be exercised in servicing this type of apparatus. Make certain that all power to the device is off and that capacitors and condenser circuits have been discharged before servicing.

SEMICONDUCTOR APPARATUS

Power Supplies

There is no art or mystery involved in semiconductor apparatus, of which silicon power supplies are a simple type. The rules governing application, operation, and maintenance are known. If they are followed, satisfactory performance will result. The same holds true for servicing.

Silicon power supplies are sold on the basis of long life and reliability. Troubles, particularly cell failures, should not be treated casually.   Every possible step should be taken to determine the cause of trouble and to correct it.

The majority of troubles in silicon and controlled rectifier power supplies result in failure of the rectifier cells and blown fuses.   Silicon cells and controlled rectifier cells fail by short circuiting.   These devices are very sensitive to inverse voltages exceeding their peak rating; many troubles have been traced to this characteristic.   There have been isolated cases of silicon-cell failure by open circuiting, which would appear to be the result of defective cells.

Other than locating and correcting cell-failure problems, the servicing of rectifier apparatus follows the same pattern as for any apparatus containing transformers, contactors, breakers, etc.

FIG. 4-35. Floor- or wall-mounted rectified power supply.

Silicon-controlled rectifiers are comparable with the Thyratron electronic tube in that they can not only rectify by blocking current flow in one (reverse) direction, but they can also block current flow in the other (forward) direction until energized by a low-power "gating" impulse.   By use of phase-shift controls to adjust the point on the forward voltage wave at which the rectifier "gates," the output voltage can be adjusted.

The circuit used in any power supply will depend upon the range of adjustment required.   A rectifier bridge has controlled rectifiers in three legs and silicon cells in the other three.   The output-voltage wave will change with adjustment, and has a useful range of 2 to 1, including line-voltage variation.

There is no standard regulated power supply.   Regulated power supplies make use of those adjustable voltage systems in which the output voltage can be varied by electrical means.   This is frequently accomplished by means of SCR—saturable core reactors—self-saturating reactors, and of course silicon-controlled rectifiers.

A signal voltage proportional to the output voltage (or current) is compared with a reference voltage which represents the desired output.   In the SCR and self-saturating types, the difference between signal and reference is applied to a transistorized controller circuit which will reduce saturation if the output is high and increase saturation if the output is low.   For silicon-controlled rectifiers, the different voltage goes into a transistorized phase controller which will shift the phase or gating impulses to correct any deviation in output.   These functions are usually combined into one physical package, or panel, as the regulator.

If adjustable voltage or current is required, the reference voltage is applied with an adjustable factor and the regulator will correct for a deviation from any particular setting.

The regulator assembly can usually be disconnected and removed as a unit.   Unless the maintenance personnel has had considerable experience in trouble shooting and analyzing transistor circuits, it is recommended that complete new regulators be installed and the inoperative unit returned to the manufacturer for repair.   In emergencies which will not permit time for this, and in the absence of replacement regulators, the manufacturer should be contacted for field service.   Transistors can be damaged by improper procedures, and require elaborate test setups to check them for proper function.

Although power supplies can be manufactured to so-called standard ratings and characteristics, many are tailored to meet the needs of particular applications.   Any application capable of producing regenerative power must be carefully considered from an application standpoint, and provisions should be made to handle the regeneration without exceeding the inverse-voltage limits for the rectifier unit.   Adjustable-speed motors, crane magnets, crane motors, elevator application, inverters, and mine power supplies are good examples of high-regenerative-load applications.

Lifting magnets, because of their high inductance and energy storage, can be a source of damaging voltage surges unless properly controlled.   These surges do not occur when the current through the magnet is interrupted; they are generated when the polarity is reversed to bring the residual magnetism to zero to get a clean drop of the material.

The hoist motor of a crane can regenerate power when a heavy load is being lowered. This usually occurs on the intermediate control points.   However, this regeneration is self-limiting in that the controller resistance in series with the field (connected in shunt across the armature) will absorb the regenerated power, even if no external resistors and control are provided.

Omitting external regenerative control will result in increased voltage at the rectifier.   Depending on the manufacturer's design practices, if the regenerative voltage does not exceed 400 volts on a 250-volt system, it will not damage the power supply.

More significant on crane applications have been the troubles from surge voltages. Certain cases have been traced to poor contact of sliding shoes on power rails.   This resulted in severe arcing and surges.   In such cases, the surge suppressors should be carefully checked for defects, and the surge capacity increased if there is any question of adequacy.

It is not unusual to parallel two or three unregulated power supplies to handle a single load or bus.   When these units are identical in rating and components, start-up and satisfactory load division are not difficult to obtain.   The transformer taps should be adjusted to give equal no-load or light-load output voltages.   The load should then be increased until one unit is at rated output.   The other unit(s) should then be loaded within 15 per cent of rating.   This is considered satisfactory load division. Most installations will divide the load within 5 to 10 per cent on identical tap settings. If it is not possible to bring the load up gradually, arrangements should be made to hold the load to 200 per cent of the rating of one unit.   Most power supplies have an overload rating of 200 per cent for 10 sec.   Paralleling at this point can be checked by a quick measurement of the load-sharing capabilities.   Regulated and adjustable-voltage supplies are usually not paralleled.   If paralleling is necessary, special load-division circuits are required; they are specified when the application is being made.

When a single d-c motor is operated from a rectifier unit rated at or about the full-load requirements of the motor, care must be exercised to make sure that the starting currents do not exceed the short-time capacity of the power supply.   If the starting current will exceed 200 per cent of the rectifier unit rating, more cell and fuse capacity is needed.   For multiple-motor installations operating from a single power supply, it is often possible to take advantage of a diversity factor based on nonsimultaneous motor-starting loads.   This factor is based on the total load requirements under any given starting condition remaining within the 200 per cent overload rating of the power supply.

These general observations pertaining to application are made because the semiconductor junction, which actually does the rectifying, is a very thin filmlike barrier. It has extremely low capacity for heat, unlike selenium or copper oxide rectifiers, even though it can operate at higher temperatures than either of these.   Because of this factor, any appreciable overload or short circuit must be cleared very quickly. The only device in general use today that will clear a fault quickly enough is the current-limiting fuse.

Silicon cells almost always fail by short circuiting.   This creates an internal short circuit on the rectifier transformer through the remaining good cells.   Current-limiting fuses are used to protect these remaining good cells.   They also provide protection against load short circuits.   There are, at present, three classes of protective coordination available, each fulfilling different service requirements:

1. *The standard fused circuit.*   In the present design of unregulated constant-voltage power supplies, current-limiting fuses are provided in the secondary a-c line to the rectifier bridge.   These fuses are coordinated with the silicon cells so that they will protect the cells on both internal and external faults, as well as overloads.
2. *Coordinated fuse and breaker.*   Power supplies may be provided with both fuse and breaker coordination so that on external short circuits and overloads the breaker will trip before the current-limiting fuses and diodes are damaged.   Power supplies of this nature must have sufficient capacity beyond that needed for full-load output to provide the overload capacity required before the relatively slow acting breaker will trip.   This extra capacity is usually provided by paralleling silicon cells. Modifications of this type of protection can be provided which will allow the current-limiting fuses to handle short circuits, with the breaker protecting the fuses and diodes against overloads after about 0.1 sec.   This type of protection usually will not require as much extra rectifier capacity.
3. *Continuity of service applications.*   On applications where continuous power must be provided and an occasional shutdown cannot be tolerated, power supplies are available to maintain full-load output with one-cell failure in each leg of the rectifier.   In this type of circuit, the current-limiting fuses are usually located in series with each individual string of cells.   Because of the large number of silicon cells and fuses required on units of this design, the relatively slow acting circuit breaker can be coordinated to trip on external faults, thereby protecting the cells and fuses.

Fuse-failure Monitoring and Alarm Systems.   There are many variations of fuse-failure indicators, making a fuse failure easy to determine.   The simplest is connecting an indicating light (usually neon) across each fuse, with the open circuit voltage across the blown fuse supplying power for the indicating light.

If the open-circuit voltage is insufficient to operate a light, or if it is desired to operate an alarm, small auxiliary "trigger fuses" are connected in parallel with each main fuse.   These fuses have a spring-actuated plunger which is released when the fuse blows.   The plunger causes a microswitch to close the indicating and alarm circuits.   Much more complicated circuitry is necessary for continuity of service applications.   These require that a light or an alarm operate if one cell or string of cells in a bridge fails, and that the unit shut down if a *second* cell in the *same leg* fails. Each cell or string must be fused with its own trigger fuse.   Circuitry to count the first and second failures in each leg is necessary.

Fuses. The current-limiting fuse is the only device fast enough to protect silicon cells and controlled rectifiers. Available in different current and voltage ratings, current-limiting fuses are of special construction. Their elements will melt in approximately 0.01 sec at currents of 3.5 to 4 times the rating of the fuse. Under short-circuit conditions, these fuses will clear in about one-half cycle, limiting the current through the cell to less than the available system short-circuit current.

In cases where more than one fuse may feed short-circuit current to a single fuse, as in continuity of service power supplies, a minimum of three fuses in parallel is needed to insure that only the single fuse clears without damage to those feeding it; otherwise the fuses may partially melt and fail later. For these reasons, all three fuses in a standard unregulated power supply should be replaced when any one fails. It is very difficult to detect damaged or partially melted fuses. Total replacement is not necessary on multiple-fused circuits such as continuity of service, but fuses should be checked with an ohmmeter.

Instruments. Power supplies above 25 kw normally include a d-c voltmeter and ammeter. These are standard switchboard type instruments of 2 per cent accuracy. The ammeter is usually calibrated to indicate full load at one-half to three-quarters of full scale, but is not selected to indicate overloads, although overloads will not damage the instrument.

Silicon Cells and Bridge Assemblies. Medium- and high-power silicon cells are used in the manufacture of power supplies rated 1 to 170 kw. The current ratings of these cells will depend on the type of cooling and circuit configuration. The cells are hermetically sealed, usually nickel-plated, and mount in any position. They are either bolted or threaded into a heat sink. Good contact is important. It is general

Table 4-3. Torque Values for Commonly Used Silicon Cells

Thread size	Torque, lb-in.	Semiconductor			
		Thyristor	Diode	Zener	Transistor
0.190–32	10	. . .	. . .	x	
0.190–32	15	x	x		
$\frac{1}{4}$ –28	25	:.	x	x	
$\frac{5}{16}$ –24	35	x	x	. . .	x
$\frac{3}{8}$ –24	125	x	x		
$\frac{1}{2}$ –20	125	x	x		
$\frac{3}{4}$ –16	200	x	x		
1 –12	500	x	x		

Torque requirements have been tabulated as a function of thread size. When applying torque, the torque wrench should be used on the nut, the semiconductor being held firmly with another wrench.

practice to torque these cells as they are mounted to the heat sink in accordance with the manufacturer's specifications for assembly. A representative data sheet is shown in Table 4-3; it gives nominal torque values for commonly used silicon cells.

Various peak inverse-voltage ratings are selected, depending on the d-c output voltage and the expected inverse voltage. The type number of the cell is marked on its outer case, and a serial number is usually assigned to each high-power cell. Polarity is indicated by an arrow stamped on the case of the cell.

Bridge Assemblies. Various kinds and configurations of heat sinks are used to meet the requirements of different types of cells and cooling methods. Shown in Fig. 4-36 is an assembly of Type 439 cells in a 6-1-1 arrangement mounted on 7- by 7- by $\frac{1}{4}$-in. plates. For adaptation to panel type construction, it is generally necessary to resort to better cooling methods. Typical assemblies are shown in Figs. 4-37 and 4-38.

When two or more cells are connected in series in one leg of a bridge, or when the

FIG. 4-36. Three-phase bridge assembly (6-1-1 arrangement) using silicon diodes.

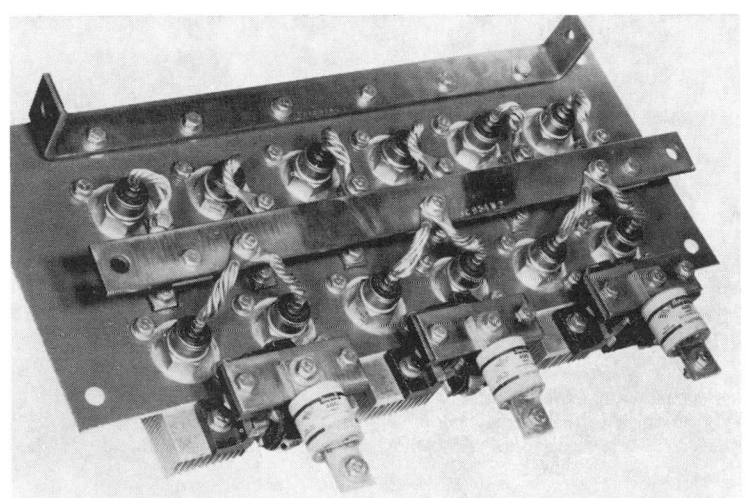

FIG. 4-37. Three-phase bridge assembly (6-1-2 arrangement) using silicon diodes.

FIG. 4-38. Three-phase bridge assembly (6-2-1 arrangement) using silicon diodes.

bridge is to be subjected to an inverse voltage from the load, voltage-dividing resistors are connected in parallel with each cell. This equalizes the distribution of inverse voltage. These resistors are visible in the illustration of a 6-2-1 three-phase bridge assembly (Fig. 4-38), and are mounted on the heat sink. For a more detailed description of silicon cells and their application, refer to publications of the manufacturers of semiconductors.

Servicing. If a rectifier unit has shut down because of blown fuses, each cell should be checked.

An ohmmeter or flashlight can be used to check open- or short-circuited cells. Forward and reverse readings are not indicative of the condition of a cell. Buzzer tests may damage the cell.

To test a cell properly, either it should be removed from the assembly or the d-c bus connections should be removed to eliminate all parallel paths which may give a false indication. If faulty cells are located, the voltage-balancing resistors shunting them should be checked.

When replacing cells, always make sure that the replacement cell is an exact duplicate in type and voltage rating. *Do not* exceed the recommended torque rating for assembly. The use of a torque wrench is recommended.

Make sure the surfaces of the heat sink are clean before installing new diodes. A thin coating of silicon grease is usually recommended, and should be applied to the bottom surface of the diode case.

If a fuse fails, all fuses in the assembly should be checked with an ohmmeter. Any fuse having a resistance value significantly higher than an unused good fuse is probably damaged, and should be replaced.

Repetitive fuse failure or failures of cells must be investigated for cause, and the condition corrected, or continual trouble may be expected. The greatest threat to operation is inverse peak voltages which have not been considered when designing or applying the silicon power supply.

Transient Voltages. Although it is of interest to know the source of inverse voltages, it is rarely practical to suppress or eliminate these voltages at their source. Surge suppressors on the power supply or regenerative controls should be adequate.

Transient surges are usually of short duration and random in magnitude and frequency of occurrence.

Switching in the a-c line feeding the rectifier transformer can result in surges from:

Energizing the transformer primary.
Deenergizing the transformer primary.
An inductive a-c load in parallel with the rectifier on the load side of the switch.

Load switching on the d-c side of the rectifier can produce surges from:

Alternating-current source and transformer leakage reactance.
Filter reactance in the LC filter. This may be a sustained voltage, depending on the filter shunt resistance for the duration.

In continuous-service power supplies, the failure of one cell produces short-circuit current until the fuse in series with the cell opens. The recovery voltage produced by the line and transformer may be sufficient to destroy cells in parallel unless properly suppressed.

Line transients from outside, such as those caused by lightning, may be encountered, especially in outdoor equipment. Lightning arrestors usually prevent damage; they are recommended protection and should be installed by the purchaser of this type of apparatus.

Surge Suppressors. Two methods of surge suppression are commonly used on power supplies of 1- to 170-kw rating. Some designs use only capacitor filters. Others feature, or combine, specially designed surge suppressors in the circuit to prevent damage from transient voltages.

Capacitor filters consist of 10- to 150-μf capacitors and series resistors to limit inrush. Bleeder resistors are used to discharge the capacitors after shutdown. The value of capacitance depends on the rating of the power supply.

A high-speed oscilloscope, preferably with a long persistence screen, is the most useful tool for detecting and measuring transients. To get significant results, the oscilloscope should have a transient response of at least 0.1 microsecond rise time and be capable of writing speeds in excess of 10 million inches per second.

Nonrecurrent transients are the most difficult to detect. The amplitude of these can best be observed by using only vertical deflection on the scope, so that the eyes can be focused on the exact part of the screen where the transient will appear. The oscilloscope should be connected across the d-c output, as close to the cells as possible.

Chapter 5

MAINTENANCE OF
INDUSTRIAL ELECTRONIC CONTROLS

By CARTER SINCLAIR
Development Engineer
Specialty Control Department
General Electric Company
Waynesboro, Va.

A three-point program is required to hold unscheduled downtime on electronic control to a minimum.

First, it is necessary to plan the installation to protect the control from its worst enemies—vibration, conductive dust, fumes, and excess dampness. While all reputable control manufacturers try to design their equipment to work under adverse conditions, these controls will require less maintenance if they are not subjected to such conditions.

The *second* requirement is periodic cleaning out and inspection for mechanical defects such as worn relays, frayed wires, loose connections, and cracked insulation. The frequency of these inspections will have to be based on operating experience in the particular plant. Obviously, a control operating in a location where it is subjected to excessive amounts of dirt and vibration will need attention much more often than one working under more favorable conditions. Once a month might be a good starting rate, with the frequency of inspections being reduced or increased as indicated by operating experience.

The *third* and probably most important part of good maintenance is being ready for trouble when it does develop. This means having at least one man in the plant thoroughly familiar with the operation of the control so that when trouble arises, he will know where to look and what to look for. Assigning a plant electrician to spend full time for several days studying a piece of equipment which is not giving trouble may sound rather expensive at the time. But it is far cheaper to give a maintenance man time to study the equipment at his regular rate of pay than to wait until trouble develops and have downtime costs piling up while the man is busy studying. If the equipment is big enough to require installation and adjustment by representatives of the manufacturer, make certain that the individual who will be responsible for its maintenance gets as much opportunity as possible to learn from them while they are in the plant. The control manufacturer recognizes that the chances of his getting future business from you depends in part on how well his equipment already in your plant serves you; therefore, his representatives usually are willing to take a little extra time to train one of your men to keep his permanent representative in your plant—his control—doing a good selling job for him.

PLANNING THE INSTALLATION

Planning of the installation often will find conflicting interests developing. Naturally, integrated equipment, with all controls mounted on the machine which they are to control, is the easiest and cheapest to install initially and also the cheapest to move if relocation within the plant becomes desirable. Unfortunately, this often subjects the control to the worst operating conditions and correspondingly increases maintenance costs. If the machine itself will produce serious vibration or shock, floor or wall mounting of the control separate from the machine, use of shock mounts, or both, if necessary, will greatly reduce the maintenance required. (*Example:* A mechanical life test was being operated by a three-tube panel. The panel was suffering about one tube failure per week until it was shock-mounted to protect it from the jar of two solenoids mounted on the same test rack. After the shock mounting, the test continued to its conclusion months later without any tube failures.)

Dust, particularly a conductive dust like metal grindings, carbon black, or one which will absorb moisture, is bad for electronic equipment. The complexity of electronic equipment dictates minimum distances, and the high resistances involved in many types of electronic circuits make them sensitive to leakage paths high enough in resistance that no actual breakdown occurs. With circuits values altered by dust leakage paths, a control may become erratic or fail altogether. Controls can be obtained with dusttight cases, but generally this requires forced ventilation through filters to get the heat out of the enclosing cases. As the filters clog, the cooling decreases until either the filter is changed in time or the equipment overheats and breaks down. The best answer to the problem of dust is to locate the control where free convection cooling will be permissible with occasional cleaning out of the equipment, even if this means locating the control at some point away from the machine. (A large steel mill put the controls and drive motors in a room separate from the main mill lines and keeps the dust out of that room by feeding in a supply of filtered air. The drive shafts of the motors extend through the walls of the room. Chances are very good that reduced maintenance and downtime will pay for the extra cost in a short time.)

Moisture is particularly harmful when the equipment does not generate enough heat to keep itself dry. This is true of electronic equipment when it is shut down. (A welder control, which worked perfectly at the manufacturer's plant, operated erratically at the customer's plant because it was wet, having absorbed moisture while waiting to be installed. The control manufacturer's representative was called in. While he searched for the trouble, the control dried itself out and resumed correct operation. No other trouble was found.) Many manufacturers expressly state that their equipment should be stored in a cool, dry place while awaiting installation. The same applies if it is to be left out of service for a period of several weeks in damp weather. The easiest way of protecting a control which is going to be idle for some time in damp weather is to burn a sufficient number of light bulbs inside the enclosure to keep the temperature up.

Corrosive fumes can do a lot of damage to a control, and the higher temperatures inside the enclosure make many types of fumes even more damaging by speeding up their action. This should be considered in picking location.

The cost of possible downtime should be figured in when selecting the most economical way of installing electronic control equipment. The method which will give the lowest first cost or the lowest material handling may run the cost of maintaining the equipment and the cost of the resulting downtime up to the point where they far overshadow the supposed gains.

PREVENTIVE MAINTENANCE

Preventive maintenance, consisting of periodic cleaning, checking for mechanical defects, and checking filament voltage to make sure that changes in plant conditions have not changed the line voltage, definitely pays. Going beyond this is of questionable value because, while it is easy to estimate the remaining life in a set of relay tips, it is very hard to estimate the remaining life in a tube, transformer, or any other electronic component.   A tube which has already given a thousand hours of reliable service is better than one fresh off the shelf put in the same socket.   Poor welds and other manufacturing defects which do not show up at first cause more tubes to fail during their first hundred hours of operation than during any comparable period later in the life of the surviving tube.   Some tubes are given a run of several hundred hours by the manufacturer to weed out the early-life failures.   Most, however, are not given this test.

The mechanical inspection should include cleaning out the dust, preferably with an air hose, and inspection of relay condition where relays are used.   Where ignitron tubes are used, the condition of their water connections should be observed.   A thorough examination for frayed wires, loose connections, etc., will help if it is not overdone.   The thing to guard against, both on the cleaning and inspection, is flexing the wires so often and so much that they finally break from too much maintenance rather than too little.   The average connection will last the life of the equipment if not disturbed too often.   The best answer is a lot of looking and a minimum of touching.

Checking filament voltage periodically is important where large thyratron tubes are included in the equipment.   These are designed to stand only plus or minus 5 per cent voltage.   The controls using these tubes generally provide some means of compensating for different line voltages in small steps, much as with a buck-boost winding on a supply transformer.   If the filament voltage is incorrect on the large thyratrons, this adjustment should be changed to correct it.   Too high filament voltage causes some of the cathode material to boil off, and too low voltage causes destruction of the cathode by ion bombardment.   Tube life falls off very rapidly when either situation takes place.

Some plants have had the idea that checking all tubes periodically with a tube checker and weeding out those which do not read in the satisfactory zone is a good idea.   Unfortunately, doing this usually will cause more trouble than it will prevent. In radio service, vacuum tubes usually are being worked continuously at a point near their rated load.   If the load is far below tube rating, a smaller tube is selected to reduce cost; therefore, tubes in radio service are rarely run far below rating.   In industrial service, it is common to select a tube deliberately which will be run at a fraction of its rating in order to get long life.   Tube cathodes have a way of adjusting their emission to match the load at which they are being run.   The tube does this itself over a period of time.   If a tube which has been run on a light industrial load is checked on an emission tester designed to test tubes which have been in radio service, the tube will read low, although it has just really started its useful life in the actual panel.   The only way a test of this sort would be truly useful in spotting tubes nearing the end of their useful life would be if a record of the reading given by each tube was kept and a sudden change in reading after several months of consistent readings was taken as an indication of approaching failure.

One very important point concerning tubes should be remembered at all times. Whenever the tubes are removed from a control which is operating correctly, the same tubes should be put back in the same sockets every time—not just the same type of tube but the same individual tube.   The tubes should be marked before being removed from their sockets to make sure they do not get mixed up.   It is possible to get a control in all sorts of trouble by mixing up tubes which have been used in different sockets.   With the cathode self-adjustment effect mentioned above, putting a tube which has been working in a lightly loaded circuit over in a circuit where it carries a much higher load could put the control out of operation completely.

Many controls have adjustments which have to be set to match tube characteristics.   As long as only one tube is changed at a time, recalibration is easy, but if all the adjustments are thrown off at one time by interchanging tubes at random, recalibration becomes a job for an expert because of the interactions between adjustments. This is why controls are shipped by the manufacturer with as many as possible of the tubes in their proper sockets.   These are the actual tubes with which the control was tested and adjusted.

PREPARING FOR TROUBLE

Electronic industrial control involves a whole new outlook on trouble shooting for a person familiar with purely relay equipment.   The very first problem is seeing what the circuit is doing.   With *magnetic* equipment it is possible to observe directly with the eyes what is happening in the circuit.   Relays pick up and drop out when they function.   Tips fall off and coils burn up when relays fail.   In *electronic* circuits there is very little to observe.   If there are thyratron tubes and output relays, a few clues may be obtained from their action, but most of what goes on is completely invisible to the human eye.   This usually calls for the use of a cathode-ray oscilloscope which will convert the invisible circuit activity into a corresponding light picture very much as a television set takes an invisible electric wave and makes a picture out of it.   A good cathode-ray oscilloscope for industrial use costs several hundred dollars, but the plant which hires a man to maintain its controls is wasting money on him if it does not provide him with the equipment he needs to do his job.

There are all kinds of cathode-ray oscilloscopes on the market, the largest number of them designed for television service.   The requirements for television service are so different from those for industrial service that the best television oscilloscope on the market, which might cost many times the price of a good industrial model, is still next to worthless in an industrial job.   A good industrial oscilloscope does not need very high gain in the vertical amplifier; quite often the problem is just the opposite.   The gain cannot be reduced low enough to make a 460-volt rms sine wave fit on the screen.   The amplifier must be able to amplify small d-c signals.   Many oscilloscopes will not read pure direct current and thus are of limited use for industrial work.

Another requirement for industrial work is low-frequency sweeps.   Many oscilloscopes offer sweep frequencies of many thousands of cycles per second, but very few will get down to 2 cps or less—almost necessary to examine welding current patterns.   Trouble shooting is rarely done with sweep speeds above 60 cps, although a few applications might require 1,000 cycles.   A triggered sweep, one which can be started by a random external signal rather than being strictly recurrent with time, is a big help, as very often the signal being observed is not recurrent, e.g., a photoelectric counter being actuated by packages moving past a phototube.

Unfortunately, nearly all triggered sweeps on the market today have one common connection with the signal input, but a good high-impedance isolating transformer can be used in most cases to take the synchronizing signal from a circuit at a different potential from the signal circuit.   Usually, the best place to get a synchronizing signal is across the anode load of a thyratron while the signal to be examined is from grid to cathode on another tube.   Here the transformer is a big help.   A long-persistence screen in the cathode-ray tube, combined with enough anode voltage on the tube to give plenty of intensity, is another great aid on intermittent signals.   This permits examination of the instantaneous action for several seconds after it took place.   Don't be misled into thinking that just because a long-persistence-screen tube will fit into an oscilloscope, the oscilloscope has voltage enough to drive it.   With these pointers in mind, make sure that the maintenance man has an oscilloscope immediately available and suitable to industrial use.

A second big difference between electronic and magnetic controls is that on a magnetic control all the parts which function together are physically located together and immediately recognizable as an operating unit or stage.   On an electronic control the parts of a single operating unit usually are not physically located together.   It is much as if a coil located in one corner of the panel operated a magnet in the opposite corner of the panel to close a set of tips on another panel.   When thinking in terms of contactors and relays, this sounds absurd, but in electronics, the equivalent of the relay—the electronic stage—may have its parts scattered all over the equipment for very good reasons.

In the case of a timing stage, the potentiometer which determines the time interval may be on the operator's control station for his convenience, the transformer which the tube energizes at the end of the time interval may be located on a stationary back panel because of its weight, and the tube itself may be located on a swinging front panel for easy access.   With several stages in the control, as, for example, a resistance welding control with four timing stages, it looks like one big complex piece of equipment when actually it is just four simple timers with the parts distributed around on one panel with little regard for which timer they are parts of.   Careful study of the elementary diagram and the description of operation as given in the instruction book for a particular control will result in breaking the control down into stages, so that the trouble can be first isolated to one stage and then located within that stage just as trouble in a magnetic panel is first located as to device or stage and then within the device.

Any attempt to cover in one chapter of a book the exact circuit details of the multitude of electronic industrial controls which have been built would be absolutely hopeless.   These details usually are given in the instruction books covering the specific equipment.   This almost infinite variety of equipment is composed of combinations of a much smaller variety of basic stages and variations on these basic stages, which are, in turn, composed of a very limited number of types of components such as resistors, capacitors, tubes, transformers, and other basic components.   Understanding of the explanations given in the instruction books for the particular equipments and interpretation of the pictures obtained with the cathode-ray oscilloscope are greatly aided by a thorough understanding of the basic components and stages.   The balance of this chapter will be devoted to a discussion of the various components involved and some of the basic stages into which they are combined, including certain trouble-shooting techniques.

Understanding the characteristics of components is helpful in analyzing the function of the various stages into which the components are combined, in identifying defective components, and in making emergency substitutions.   It is wise to keep the spare parts recommended by the control manufacturer on hand at all times, but in emergency breakdowns, knowledge of components will help in obtaining usable substitutes from the nearest source.

TUBES

All tubes have one factor in common—they conduct electricity in one direction only when they are working properly.   Electrons are liberated from the cathode and attracted to the anode.   Since the flow of electrons is from negative to positive, this means that a tube can conduct when the anode or plate is positive with respect to the cathode but should not conduct when the cathode is positive with respect to the anode.

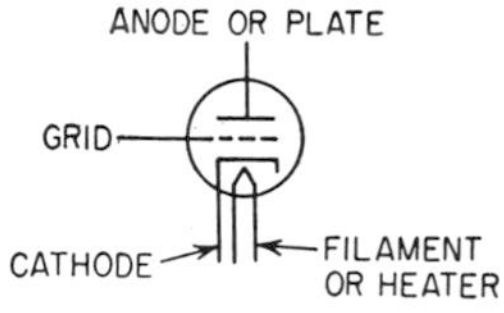

Fig. 5-1.   Typical tube symbol with elements identified.

In a tube having an anode and a cathode, conduction will always take place when the anode is positive with respect to the cathode providing the cathode is emitting electrons.   In tubes having grids in addition to anode and cathode, conduction will also depend upon what voltage is impressed on the grids (Fig. 5-1—Triode symbol).

Emission from the cathode is continuous in most tubes; the emission being produced by heating the cathode, by passing a current either directly through the cathode or through a heater close to the cathode.   The cathode is coated with a material which emits electrons freely when heated.   Examples of these hot-cathode tubes are the thyratron tubes like the 2050 and the 6011, amplifier tubes like the 6SN7, diodes like the 6H6, and power supply tubes like the 5R4.

Fig. 5-2.   Symbol for a phototube.

Not all tubes use heated cathodes; some use controlled emission from the cathode as a means of control.   The phototubes are in this class.   Light falling on the cathode of the phototube causes electrons to be emitted, and the amount of current the tube will conduct is a function of the amount of light falling on the cathode (Fig. 5-2).

Ignitron tubes use an initially unheated pool of mercury as a cathode.   When conduction of the tube is desired, a pulse of current up to 40 amp is applied for up to 1/10,000 sec to a third element called the ignitor.   This current initiates a momentary cathode spot on the surface of the mercury pool which emits electrons.   These electrons are quickly drawn to the anode, which establishes conduction between the cathode and the anode; this maintains the cathode spot to continue conduction (Fig. 5-3).

In tubes having grids, the grid is a structure between the cathode and the anode. It is a series of wires with space between them for the electrons to pass through on their way to the anode.   If a negative charge is placed on the grid, it will try to force the electrons back toward the cathode in opposition to the effect of the positive anode,

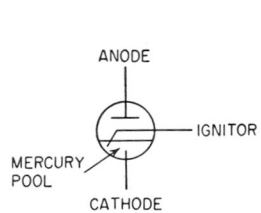

FIG. 5-3. Symbol for an ignitron tube.

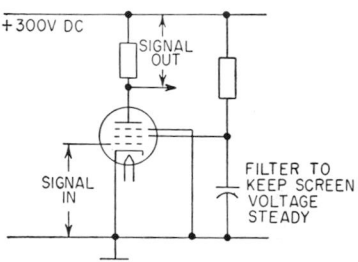

FIG. 5-4. Pentode tube connection.

which is trying to attract them.   Since the grid is closer to the cathode than the anode is, it has a stronger effect on the electrons than the anode has and a small charge on the grid can overcome a much higher voltage on the anode and keep the electrons from passing to the anode at all.   Additional power gain in grid control is obtained from the fact that the grid draws very little current in comparison with the current it controls.   Multiple grids in the tube can be used for additional control over the tube; for example, the circuit may feed two separate signals in on separate grids so that the

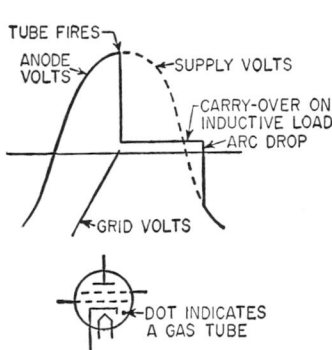

FIG. 5-5. Thyratron symbol and voltage waveforms with a-c anode voltage and inductive load.

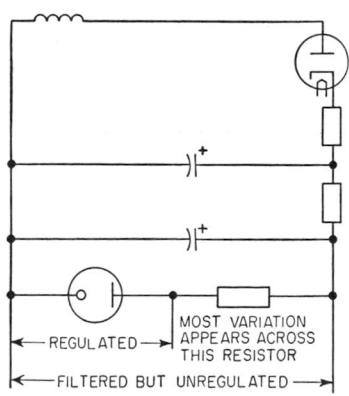

FIG. 5-6. Simple power supply showing use of regulator tube to establish a regulated bus.

tube current will become a function of the two signals combined.   In typical use of pentode tubes which have three grids (see Fig. 5-4), the signal is fed in on the grid nearest the cathode, the middle grid is held at a fixed positive potential, and the grid nearest the anode is held at cathode potential.   This makes the current almost entirely a function of the potential applied to the first grid and almost independent of the voltage of the anode.

An additional variable in tube design is the atmosphere inside the glass envelope.

If there is no gas inside which can be ionized, full control of the tube will normally be maintained at all times by the grid.   This is known as a vacuum tube and is generally used for amplifier stages.   The voltage across the tube is a function of the current flowing through the tube and the potentials applied to the grids.   If the tube is filled with a gas which can be ionized, such as in a thyratron, the action is different.   Negative voltage on its grids can be used to hold it off until the grid is driven positive at the desired time; but once it has fired, it keeps on firing until the anode current is reduced to zero by other means.   The voltage drop across the tube is entirely dependent upon the potential required to ionize the gas, not on the amount of current flowing.   The grid is unable to shut off a tube of this sort once it has become ionized.   If an a-c voltage is used as anode supply for a thyratron and a phase-shifted a-c voltage used to control the grid, the point at which the tube fires on each half cycle of positive anode voltage can be controlled by varying the point in the cycle where the grid is swung positive.   Thyratron tubes will deliver far higher current for the same anode voltage than will vacuum tubes of comparable size (Fig. 5-5).

Another type of gas tube frequently seen in electronic controls is the cold-cathode gas tube with only anode and cathode.   This is a voltage-regulator tube.   It is used as one element in a voltage divider circuit (see Fig. 5-6) consisting of a fixed resistor and a voltage-regulator tube in series across an unregulated d-c supply.   The voltage across the regulator tube will be determined by the gas used to fill it and will be practically independent of the current being drawn, while the differences between this voltage and the supply voltage will appear across the resistor in the divider.   If the supply voltage goes up, the current will go up, increasing the drop across the resistor but not across the tube.   The load to be supplied with regulated voltage is connected in parallel with the tube.

TRANSFORMERS

Components other than tubes are also vital in the operation of electronic control. Transformers are used to provide isolation of circuits while transmitting the a-c voltage, modified as desired, to the required point.   Certain characteristics of transformers not commonly encountered in power work are worth noting.   Since a transformer cannot transmit a d-c voltage when its primary winding is fed half-wave current as from a thyratron tube with a-c anode voltage (see Fig. 5-7), its secondary voltage will have a negative kick with gradual decay depending upon the other circuit constants.   This negative kick can be used as a control signal for a following stage requiring a signal after the first thyratron has stopped conducting.   The use of the signal can be as a negative signal, or by reversing the phasing of the secondary winding, it can be used as a positive signal, with the initial signal negative.   This is used in circuits where one tube is required reliably to trail a second tube firing on the opposite half cycle of an a-c wave.

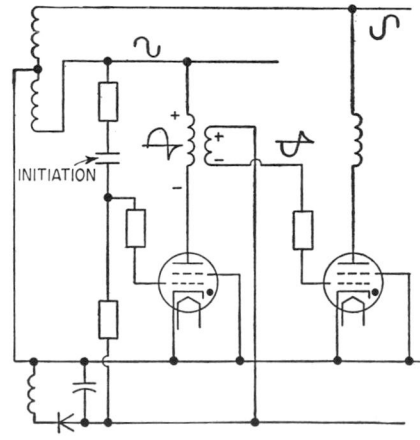

Fig. 5-7. Simple circuit showing use of transformer flux decay to fire a thyratron on opposite polarity.   Note waveforms.

Another unusual application of transformers seen in industrial control is in peaking transformers.   A low-voltage winding with a current-limiting resistor in series with it is put across a source of a-c voltage sufficient to saturate the iron of the transformer within a few electrical degrees after the voltage across the transformer changes polarity.   This results in an output voltage which consists of sharp peaks immediately following the voltage zeros of the driving voltage without the very high voltages which would be obtained later in the half cycle if the same transformer ratio were maintained over the remainder of the half cycle.

With the vast flexibility of design possible in transformers, it is most difficult to find any satisfactory substitute for an exact replacement obtained from the original control manufacturer. Even such seemingly minor details as type of material used for the laminations can make an apparently exact copy fail to operate properly.

Resistors and capacitors do not present quite the problem that transformers do, and in the event that the control manufacturer's recommended replacement part is not immediately available, a suitable replacement usually can be obtained locally. Because of a recent change-over in standard values throughout the industry, exact replacement of capacitors and resistors in controls built under the old standards will be difficult or impossible in the future. This is not a serious situation, as the new standards are close enough to the old standards to permit changing to the new values without disturbing the operation of the control. In nearly every case a 0.05-mfd capacitor can be replaced by a 0.047-mfd—the new standard. Where there is doubt as to which of the new standard values to use, the one higher or lower than the old value, both can be tried. One is practically sure to work, and in most cases either one can be used.

Resistors have only four main variables to compare in determining if they will make a satisfactory substitute. The first is nominal resistance, the second is tolerance, the third is wattage, and the fourth is maximum permissible voltage. Obviously the same nominal resistance should be used if possible. The tolerance is indicated by the last band in the color code, gold for 5 per cent, silver for 10 per cent, and no band for 20 per cent. Wherever possible, the 5 per cent resistors should be used. Use of 20 per cent resistors can throw a control much further off than changing from the old standard values to the new, for the 20 per cent resistors usually are the culls which did not fall within the closer limits. The replacement resistor should be of at least equal wattage to the previous one for obvious reasons. The last matter, that of maximum voltage, is the reason that it is sometimes necessary to use a resistor of higher wattage rating than the calculated power in the circuit indicates. A common 1-megohm 1-watt resistor should not be used across a 1,000-volt circuit, since its maximum voltage rating is 500.

Capacitors likewise have four variables: nominal capacity, tolerance, working voltage, and type. Nominal capacity and tolerance are pretty obvious, but the other two take some explaining. The working voltage listed is usually the d-c working voltage— what the capacitor will take on a pure d-c circuit. For use on a-c, the capacitor must be derated at least so the crest of the a-c wave does not exceed the d-c rating. In most cases the derating has to be greater than this owing to internal heating of the capacitor from the current flowing in and out of the foil layers and from dielectric heating of the insulating layer between. Assumption of an a-c 60-cycle rating (rms) of 50 per cent of the d-c rating usually will be safe providing there are not peaks in excess of the d-c rating.

Capacitors come in many types; care should be taken to see that the right type is used. The most common type is the rolled foil with wax or plastic covering. These are good capacitors at line frequency; some are also good at high frequency. This depends upon the construction of the capacitor. If connection to the foil is made with a single tab, they are not good for transient suppression, while if connection is made by extending the foil and crimping it around the lead, they will handle transients well. This is a detail of internal construction which is hard to determine and means that care should be taken in replacing grid-to-cathode capacitors of this type to make sure that they are good for the job.

The oil-filled capacitors in metal cans were formerly the best by a wide margin, but recent developments in the rolled-foil, plastic-covered capacitors make them equal to the oil-filled in some sizes. Above 1 mfd, the oil-filled are still the best.

Mica capacitors are still the ultimate in the low-capacity, very-high-frequency field, although, again, the rolled-foil type has greatly narrowed the former gap.

Electrolytic capacitors still give the greatest electrical capacity in the least volume and can give very satisfactory service. They do have one definite limitation: They must not be used in a circuit which subjects them to any reverse voltage; even an inductive decay sufficient to produce a definite reverse-voltage reversal across the capacitor will cause them to fail quickly. They also have high leakage currents.

Relays, while not truly an electronic component, often are used as a part of an electronic control. In earlier controls, relays developed a bad reputation as trouble-makers, so there was a gradual swing away from their use and toward all-electronic controls, even if it took two tubes and several transformers to replace one relay. A tremendous improvement has occurred in relays during the last several years. The result is that some of these vastly improved relays are finding their way into applications where one relay can replace one or more tubes, particularly in switching circuits for d-c. One four-pole, double-throw relay can switch four isolated d-c circuits and in so doing replace up to eight tubes. With modern environment-proof relays good for many millions of operations, electronic designers are beginning to turn back to relays for switching jobs as a means of giving the customer the most for his money and reserving the tubes for the jobs where their characteristics really count.

On open relays trouble develops more often than on the sealed relays, but often an open relay can be doctored to give additional service, at least until a replacement can be received. Dirty contacts are the most frequent cause of trouble on the open relay, particularly when equipment is started up after several days of being out of service and the relay is switching low-power circuits. Often a pole will fail to make contact the first time it is closed, but a few operations will break through the dirt and get it going again. Slipping a piece of paper between the contacts and pulling it back out with the contacts closed will cure stubborn cases.

Alternating current relays of the shaded pole type will sometimes get noisy after service, and an emergency repair is possible here also. This type of relay can be identified by a copper ring recessed into part of the pole face. The idea is that the flux through the copper ring sets up an out-of-phase current in the ring which holds the relay in during the time the coil current is passing through zero. The ratio of flux passing through the ring to the total flux must be about right if the relay is to be quiet. This is controlled by allowing the armature to come down flat on the laminations encircled by the copper ring and milling a small air gap between the armature and the laminations not encircled by the copper ring. The proper gap is very small, only a very few thousandths of an inch. If wear on the part of the pole face which the armature is hitting reduces this gap too much, the relay will become noisy, but careful work with a file to restore the gap will often get the relay back in service.

CHARACTERISTICS OF STAGES

Every stage will consist of one or more tubes—at least one of the tubes having a grid or other control element in it—and other associated components. These associated components will include the anode load, which may consist of a transformer, relay, reactor, resistor, or a combination of these loads, including the components to couple the tube to the grid circuit of following stage. There are additional components associated with the grid circuit of the stage. These serve to modify the output of the preceding stage to drive the tube properly. They may include transformers, resistors, and capacitors in various combinations. If the grid circuit includes a timing RC circuit, diodes may be included to change the capacitor. The cathode circuit may have components in it to provide self-bias. Sometimes the entire tube load is in the cathode circuit rather than in the anode circuit, in which case the anode is tied directly to the line. The screen grid may also have associated components for feeding in a signal or for merely limiting current. All these components together form a single stage in a complex control which may have several dozen stages. Effective trouble shooting consists of isolating the trouble to a single stage by checking performance stage by stage and then checking only the components associated with that stage to find the cause of the trouble.

The vast majority of controls consists of variations on a limited number of basic stages which will be described next.

The simplest stage for an ex-radio man to understand is the a-c amplifier (see Fig.

5-8). This is a triode or pentode tube with its grid connected through either a capacitor or transformer to the output of the preceding stage.   Bias may be either fixed or obtained by filtering the output of a resistor connected in the cathode circuit.   This filtering is necessary to prevent the variation in current through the tube swinging the cathode up and down with the grid and thus reducing the net signal applied between grid and cathode.

Unfortunately, in many industrial applications, the signal to be amplified is a d-c signal, which cannot be handled by the common a-c amplifier because its coupling capacitor or transformer cannot handle d-c signals.   In this case it is necessary to use a resistor network for coupling.   (See Fig. 5-9.)   Basically, this consists of two resistors acting as

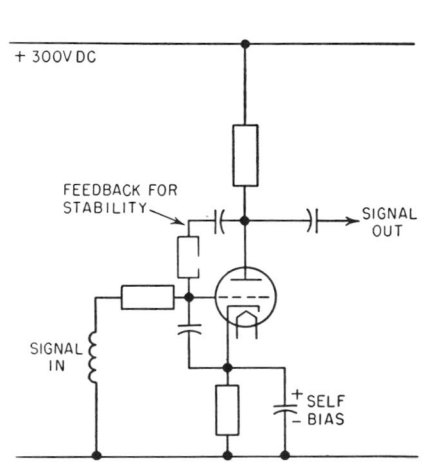

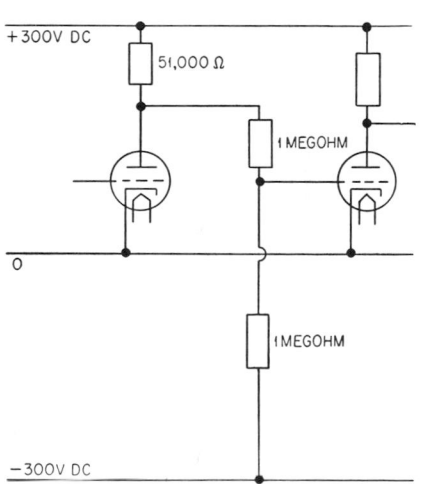

FIG. 5-8. One stage of an a-c amplifier having self-bias and a stability feedback to reduce amplification of high-frequency signals.

FIG. 5-9. Coupling between stages in a d-c amplifier.

a voltage divider with one end tied to a fixed negative voltage and the other end tied to the anode of the preceding stage.   The negative voltage cancels out the anode supply voltage of the preceding stage to put the grid in the right operating range, and the output signal of the preceding stage is attenuated by the voltage divider and applied to the grid of the tube.   This d-c amplifier loses part of the tube gain in the voltage divider; thus more stages are needed than would be necessary in an equivalent a-c amplifier, but for signals such as are found in industrial applications it is often needed.   Another common variation is the so-called long tailed pair (see Fig. 5-10), where two tubes are connected with a common cathode resistor having no filter capacitor across it.   The signal is fed in on the grid of one tube, while the grid of the other is held at a fixed potential.   As the grid of the first tube is driven positive, the cathodes are also driven positive, which effectively puts a signal of opposite polarity on the grid of the second tube and reduces its current.   The anodes of the two tubes then give opposite signals controlled from a single signal; the opposite signals are used to control other stages which are intended to work in opposition to each other.

Still another variation is the cathode follower (see Fig. 5-11).   This is primarily used to translate accurately a very low current signal into a much higher current signal of very slightly less voltage.   Here the load resistor is in the cathode and the output is taken from the cathode.   Cathode followers are used to lower the impedance level of signals so that they can be sent from one part of an equipment to another without picking up a lot of stray voltages on the wire or to feed a low-input-impedance stage from a high-impedance stage.   They have the advantage over other circuits in that differences in tube characteristics have very little effect on circuit performance.

In the preceding discussion it was assumed that the tube was being operated in its linear range so that the output was shaped like the input. This is not always true (see Fig. 5-12). These same stages can be used for wave-shaping, producing an output looking very different from the input merely by deliberately putting in a larger

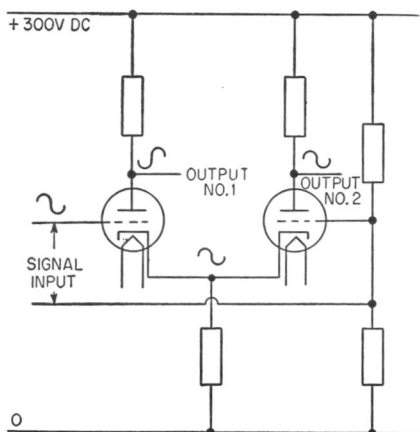

FIG. 5-10. The long-tailed-pair circuit.

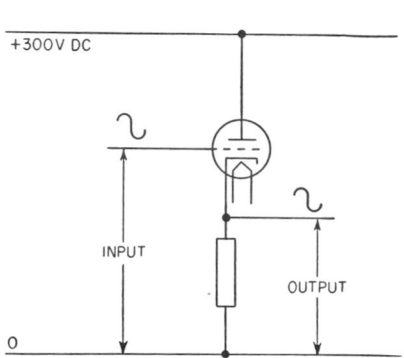

FIG. 5-11. The cathode follower circuit. Note that in this circuit the signal does not change polarity as in the circuits where the output is taken from the anode.

signal than the tube can handle or by other means. Suppose, for example, that a sharp positive peak was wanted coincident with the start of every line frequency cycle. This could be obtained from a dual triode tube by applying an oversize a-c wave to the first grid. The first anode will give out a square wave. If this is fed through an RC coupling net, designed for high-frequency coupling to the grid of the second section of the tube, only the steep wavefronts of the square wave will be transmitted. If the second half is run with no grid bias, it will ignore the spikes trying to turn it on farther, because it is already at saturation, but will cut off momentarily every time a spike of voltage drives its grid negative, so it will put out a positive spike every time the grid of the first tube swings positive.

You can't tell just by looking at a diagram if a stage is wave shaping or just amplifying, so it pays to find out its intended purpose while the equipment is working right.

Other common stages are timing stages. These can usually be spotted very easily on the elementary diagram because they will commonly have large capacitors in the grid circuit. They will utilize either a very-high-gain vacuum tube or a thyratron

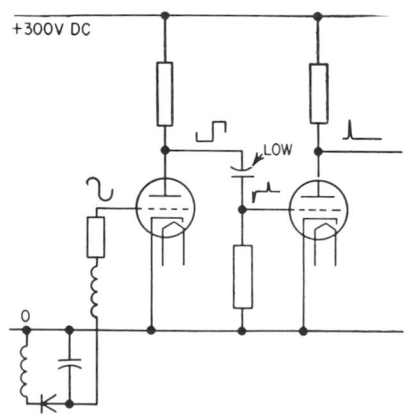

FIG. 5-12. Wave shaping by overdriving and deliberate use of a small coupling capacitor.

tube to switch from full off to full on with a small change in grid voltage. The large capacitor is charged up to a high d-c voltage, and its charge allowed to leak off through a resistor until the firing point of the tube is reached. The time for the charge on the capacitor to leak off to this point represents the time interval to be timed. There are so many varieties of timing circuits in existence that trying to cover them all is out of the question, but all have in addition to the tube the following features in one form or another:

1. Every timing circuit must have a rectifier circuit to change the timing capacitor. This may be a separate rectifier, or one of the grids of the timing tube may perform this function, even the grid which is being controlled. Since many timing circuits use a-c voltage on the anode of the timing tube, the grid may be driven positive during the half cycle that the anode is negative to charge the capacitor without firing the tube.
2. Every timing circuit must have some means of stopping the charging of the capacitor at the beginning of the timing interval.
3. Every timing circuit must have a reference against which to compare the remaining voltage on the capacitor. This may be a nice obvious d-c bus, but on the other hand it may not be so obvious. It may be the tube drop of another tube, the charge on another capacitor, or something like that.

When trying to understand a timing circuit, the first step is to hunt these three parts out. Then the basic operation of the circuit will become clearer.

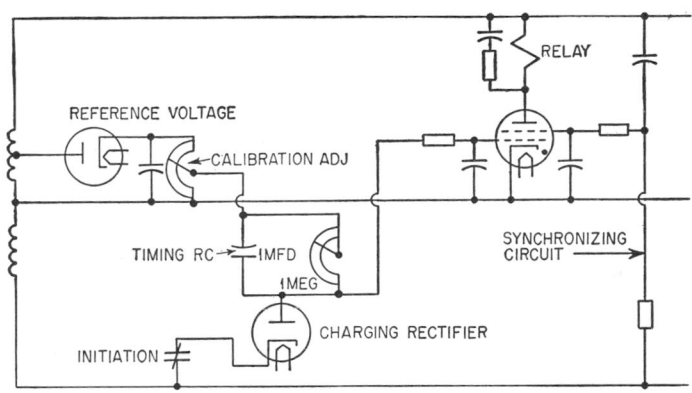

FIG. 5-13. A simple timing circuit to delay pickup of a relay. In this circuit all the functions are obvious. In most circuits they are less easily seen.

Precision timing circuits usually must have some calibrating adjustment. This can work in many ways, but it will all fall into one of three classes: It may alter the initial charge on the timing capacitor, it may alter the reference, or it may introduce a voltage which will alter the discharge characteristic of the capacitor and resistor combination.

Synchronizing circuits often are required on timers which must fire either at the beginning of a cycle or not at all. These usually consist of a sine wave almost, but not quite, out of phase with the anode voltage and injected some way into the grid-to-cathode voltage or on a separate grid. Since the almost-out-of-phase condition usually is obtained with a capacitor, a failure of the capacitor which causes the synchronization to shift exactly out of phase is an example of a really baffling trouble for someone who does not understand the operation of the circuit (see Fig. 5-13).

Another important class of stages is the switching stages. They come in all varieties, depending upon what is to be switched and how. A pair of ignitron tubes connected in opposite polarities between an a-c line and a welding transformer is one example of a switching stage for alternating current.

The take-over circuit is a switching circuit consisting of a diode and a resistor connected as a signal-mixing network. When the anode of the diode is negative with respect to its cathode, it acts as a very high resistance so that the signal coming through the resistor dominates the output. When the anode of the diode is positive with respect to its cathode, the diode acts like a very low resistance and the signal through the diode dominates. This can be used to limit the amplitude of a signal as in Fig. 5-14. The take-over circuit can also be used to give a positive signal only when two independent signals are simultaneously positive by feeding one through the resistor and the other through the diode.

Once the operation of each stage is understood, the next step is to understand how the various stages work together to perform the function of the control. On open-loop systems like welding controls or any other strictly on-off controls, the operation can be traced directly from stage to stage and checked at any point with suitable instruments during actual operation. Closed-loop systems, like motor controls or any other systems where the output must be regulated to hold a fixed relationship to some reference despite fluctuations in load, are more difficult to work with. They work by comparing a signal proportional to the output with the reference signal and using the difference between these two signals as an error signal to tell the control what to do. When something goes wrong anywhere in the system, the whole system acts up because the error signal is no longer able to reduce the error correctly.

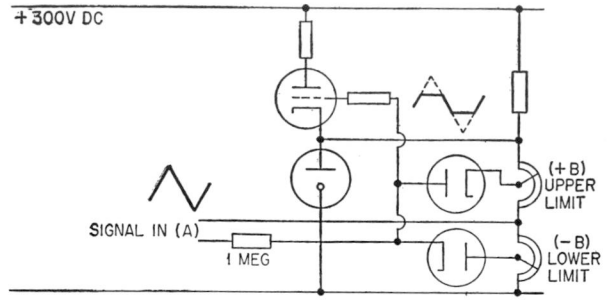

FIG. 5-14. Circuit illustrating use of diodes to switch to preset limits when incoming signal exceeds these limits.

The first step in a closed-loop system is to determine exactly what each loop is composed of and prepare a simple block diagram of it unless the control manufacturer already has done so on his diagram (see Fig. 5-15). This will include not only the stages which are physically part of the control but also those parts of the machine which are parts of the actual loop. Actual servo theory as used in the design of closed-loop systems is far beyond the scope of this text; let it be sufficient to point out that such characteristics as backlash in gearing, static friction of ways, and end play of lead screws enter into stability calculations just as much as design parameters of the amplifiers and other electronic circuits do. For this reason, instability can be produced just as easily by dirt in a bearing as by a bad tube in the control, and until something is done to separate machine performance from control performance, the symptoms may be identical.

The closed-loop performance of any regulating system is directly determined by its open-loop characteristics—its characteristics when the signal fed back from the output is replaced by a signal not influenced by the output. The open-loop characteristics in turn are the product of the characteristics of each stage in the loop. This means that the trouble can be isolated by comparing the open-loop characteristics of each stage in turn with its open-loop characteristics before the trouble developed, provided those have been recorded while the equipment was working properly. The exact duplicate of the normal working signal does not have to be used for these checks. In most cases, satisfactory test signals will be provided by a 6.3-volt filament transformer with a voltage divider across its output so small signals may be obtained and fed through a capacitor into the grid circuit of a tube. The gain through the loop probably will be too high to permit checking more than one or two stages beyond the point at which the signal is being fed in before the amplitude of the signal has been amplified to the point where it is overdriving the circuits. At this point it will be necessary to feed the signal in at a place nearer the point being checked.

Actual written records of system open-loop performance as obtained with a synthetic signal and as recorded with a cathode-ray oscilloscope as well as all knob settings of the oscilloscope forming a part of this record would be a lifesaver in case of serious trouble.   Waveforms should be carefully sketched for comparison with those obtained after trouble develops.   For a plant having much varied and complex equipment, a 35-mm oscilloscope camera which attaches to the cathode-ray oscilloscope can prove a very quick and accurate way of recording waveforms by photographing rather than sketching.

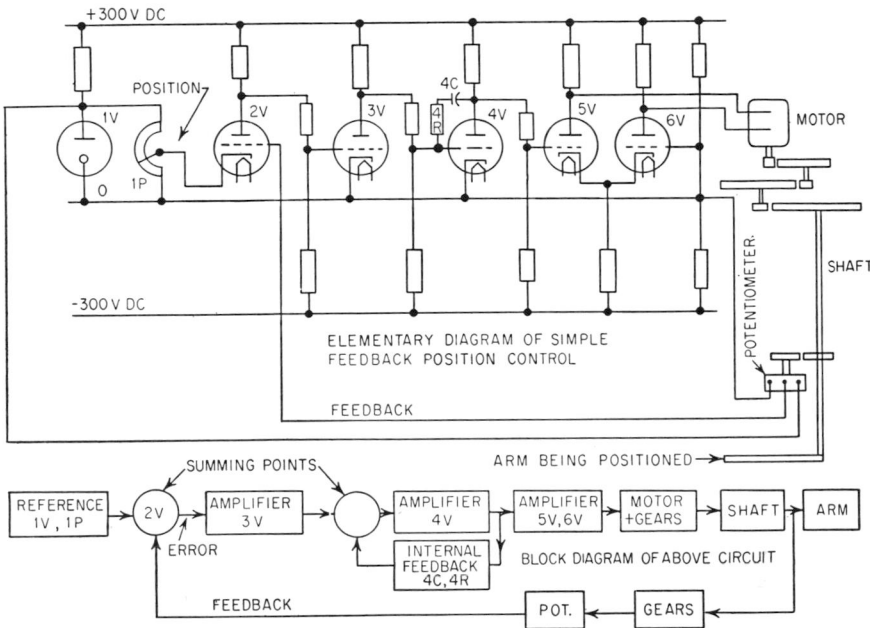

Fig. 5-15. Simple feedback position control showing block-diagram representation of circuit.

When dealing with d-c amplifiers, such as occur in the circuit of Fig. 5-15, it is necessary to be sure that the stage being checked is working in its range of control.   If tube 3V was removed from its socket and a filament transformer signal applied to the anode connection of socket 3V to check the performance of tube 4V and its associated components, no signal would be found at the grid of tube 5V because the 4V would be working out of its operating range.   A small rheostat with resistance about equal to that of the anode resistor should be connected from the anode to the cathode connections on the tube socket and adjusted to simulate tube 3V putting a normal operating load on the load resistor.   Then with the filament transformer signal fed to the anode of 3V, the rheostat can be adjusted until a signal appears on the grid of tube 5V and the gain of the 4V circuit determined.

Chapter 6

CUTTING DOWN ELECTRIC POWER BILLS

By Joseph W. St. Andre
Chief Electrical Engineer
Kaiser Aluminum & Chemical Corporation
Newark, Ohio

The amount of electric power that is used is only part of the story of the monthly power bill. The *rate* at which it is used also is a big factor in the size of the bill. Whether power bills are large or small, it is good business sense to study them carefully to see that all the power is being used efficiently and that penalties are kept to a minimum.

RATES

All power bills are based on rates set, in most cases, by the public utilities commissions of the states. Every power company has several rates to cover the various types of services that are obtainable. These rates are based on the voltages, amounts used, at what rate used, during what period of the day or night, and other conditions. Confusion exists because almost every power company has its own way of calculating power bills. One industrial power user, with 57 plants, has 40 power contracts, some with two or more rates.

The question of which rate is the best for the individual plant is one which has to be taken up with the power sales department of the power company supplying power to the plant. It will gladly advise the best rate for the manufacturing schedule that you are working to. One word of caution. The different rates are based on the usage of power under certain conditions. The rates are established for definite periods of time, from 12 months' to 3 or 5 years' duration. For example, suppose a plant worked a heavy day shift, a medium second shift, and a light third shift. The power company will have a rate that is most favorable to that kind of operation. Then business picks up, and the two lighter shifts become equal to the day shift. This means greater loading and more uniform loading of power lines. The power company may have a rate that is more favorable for that kind of usage.

CHARGES

Regardless of the many rates and different ways of calculation of the many power companies, all power bills follow the same pattern. There usually are four charges that make up these bills: power demand, energy, fuel adjustment (steam generation) power factor.

The demand charge is based on the cost of providing generating, transmission, and distribution facilities. It covers the carrying charges on the investment, including interest, taxes, return, etc.   The energy charge covers the cost of fuel, maintenance, and other operating expenses.   Usually the two charges are about equal.

Demand.   The demand charge is based on the highest amount of power used in the month during a certain period, usually of 15- or 30-minute duration.   It is recorded on a demand meter or may be a fixed percentage on small loads.   The charges vary from $1.50 to $2 per kw.   The demand may also affect the rate of energy as will be explained later.   So demand is usually the largest factor in which to get quick results.

Demand can be explained this way: Suppose a plant makes tin cans.   The output of each machine is 10,000 cans a day.   An order for 300,000 cans will require 30 machines to turn out this volume in one day.   But, if the order is spread over 10 days, the plant can get by with only 3 machines.   The cost of the investment in machines has to be included in the cost of the cans.   If the customer can be persuaded to wait for the cans, he can be offered a better price.   Reduce the overhead, and a better unit price can be obtained.

The same goes for power.   Only in this case the power company has no choice.   When a switch is turned on, power must be there to light the lights.   Pushing a button calls for power to start a motor, and that power must be there in the required amount.   Usually, not all the lights are burning all of the time.   The same is true for motors.   But all could be on if the customer so wished.

Therefore the power company has to have enough equipment on hand to take care of that load 24 hours a day.   But it is not dealing with one plant or ten plants.   It may have hundreds or thousands of plants.   It must have vast amounts of power available at all times.   The cost of these additional facilities standing by for maximum effort is passed on to the users in the form of a demand charge.   The more power used in any 15-minute period, the greater the demand charge.   The more the use of power can be spread out in a plant, the less the demand and the lower the total bill.

The rates are normally predicted on 15- or 30-minute periods rather than instantaneous demand.   Because generating and distributing equipment facilities are designed to withstand the sustained efforts of a particular load, they are able to supply instantaneous demands within reasonable limits without reinforcement.   However, in some cases, service facilities have to be reinforced to carry instantaneous demands, in which cases other means are used to determine demand charges.

This is true particularly where large amounts of power are used for testing.   An aircraft plant may employ a large wind tunnel.   The load may be on for one minute, and then for some reason the test must be shut down.   Total revenue to the power company might amount to $1.50.   Yet the power company has to tie up generating facilities of 20,000 kw to take care of this load.   It might even have to start up another generator at a cost of thousands of dollars.

Energy Charge.   Operating costs of the energy portion of the electric bill are based on the number of kilowatthours recorded over a certain period of time, normally one month.   In comparing bills, take this billing period into account.   The number of working days and the number of days covered by the bill will vary.

Power is measured either as primary power at the incoming voltages, in which case the transformer losses are included in the bill, or as secondary power, where the power company stands the losses.   In primary-power measurement, a discount is given by the power company or some other adjustment is arrived at to take care of the losses.   For large amounts of power or where power is taken in at high voltages, more favorable rates usually are offered.

Practically all rate schedules incorporate two or more steps in the energy charges.   The number of kilowatthours in each step may vary with the demand, or they may be fixed in a predetermined schedule rate.

Fuel Adjustment.   This charge is to compensate for changes in price of fuel and other raw materials over or under the basic cost of these items when the original rates were determined.   A fuel-adjustment clause is incorporated in the rate schedule because of the obvious impracticability of filing for new rates every time the price of coal fluctuates.

Power Factor.   The term power factor shows up in power bills, and its effect is felt in other ways throughout the electrical-power-distribution system in the plant.   Power factor is a ratio and is explained in the following way:

Power is the product of current in the circuit and the voltage in the circuit. It is amperes times volts. In a-c circuits, however, the current required by induction motors, transformers, fluorescent lights, induction heating furnaces, resistance welders, etc., is made up of two kinds of current: magnetizing current and power-producing current.

The power-producing current is that current which is converted by the equipment into useful work, such as turning motors, making a weld, or pumping water. The unit of measurement is the kilowatt (kw).

Magnetizing current (also known as wattless, reactive, or nonworking current) is that which is required to produce the magnetic flux necessary to the operation of induction devices such as listed above. Without magnetizing current, energy would not flow through the core of a transformer or across the air gap of an induction motor. The unit of measurement for this power is the kilovar (kvar).

Power factor may be expressed as the ratio of the power-producing current in a circuit to the total current in that circuit.

$$\text{Power factor} = \frac{\text{kw}}{\text{kva}}$$

or
$$\text{kw} = \text{kva} \times \text{pf}$$

Power bills are measured in kilowatts of demand and kilowatthours of energy.

From the formula it can be seen that in order to get a certain amount of power to a customer, the utility must transmit a larger amount of current to a system having a low power factor than to one having a higher power factor. The additional amount of current does not register on the kilowatthour meter measuring the incoming power to the customer and represents a loss to the power company. It also means larger cables, transformers, generators, and other devices whose ratings are based on their ability to carry current.

In order to compensate for the extra investment required to serve low-power-factor loads, utilities introduced the power-factor clauses in power bills. These clauses offer a reduction in power billing for high load power factor or impose penalties for low power factor. The net result is extra money on the power bill if the power factor is below 85 per cent in most cases. Some utilities base their rates on 100 per cent power factor.

Types of power-factor clauses. Power-factor clauses range all over the lot. They contain bonuses and penalties in various shapes and forms. Here are a few of the more popular types:

1. Billing demand dependent on the ratio of base to actual power factor.

> *Example:* 1,000 kw demand
> Actual power factor.................. 70 per cent
> Base power factor required............. 85 per cent
> Charge $1.50 per kw of demand.
> Billing demand 1,000 × $^{85}\!/_{70}$ = 1,213 kw
> Cost 1,213 × $1.50 per kw............. $1,819.50
> Improving to base power factor of 85 per cent
> Cost 1,000 × $1.50 per kw............. $1,500.00
> ———————
> $ 319.50

2. Same as 1 plus energy kilowatthour charge dependent upon billing demand.

> *Example:* Total energy used 550,000 kwhr
> Rates 1.2¢ per kwhr for first 100 kwhr × demand
> 0.9¢ per kwhr for next 200 kw-hr × demand
> 0.7¢ per kwhr balance of energy

Here is how the bill will work out for the power factor rating of 70 and 85 per cent required by the power company to avoid any penalties.

Cost at 70 per cent power factor:

$$100 \times 1{,}213 = 121{,}300 \text{ kwhr @ } 1.2¢ = \$1{,}455.60$$
$$200 \times 1{,}213 = 242{,}600 \text{ kwhr @ } 0.9¢ = 2{,}183.40$$
$$186{,}100 \text{ kwhr @ } 0.7¢ = 1{,}302.70$$

550,000 kwhr
Total cost of energy = \$4,941.70
Demand charge (from 1) = 1,819.50
Total charge = \$6,761.20

Cost at 85 per cent power factor:

$$100 \times 1{,}000 = 100{,}000 \text{ kwhr @ } 1.2¢ = \$1{,}200.00$$
$$200 \times 1{,}000 \times 200{,}000 \text{ kwhr @ } 0.9¢ = 1{,}800.00$$
$$250{,}000 \text{ kwhr @ } 0.7¢ = 1{,}750.00$$

550,000 kwhr
Total cost of energy = \$4,750.00
Demand charge (from 1) = 1,500.00
Total charge = \$6,250.00
Difference in bills = \$ 511.20

3. Billing demand based on actual kva with energy charges dependent or independent of billing demand. This means that the bill calculated on actual kva demand will include the nonworking current which produces no useful power in the plant. Penalties will be in direct proportion to the power factor all the way up to 100 per cent.
4. Flat percentage increase or decrease to the power bill depending upon the amount the average power factor is less than the base power factor.
5. A charge for the amount of kilovars (magnetizing current) is sometimes used for billing instead of a power-factor clause. The charge is usually 25 cents per kvar as measured on the demand meter.

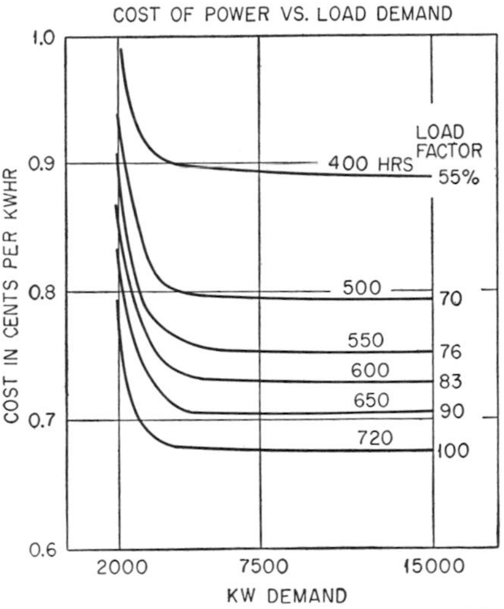

FIG. 6-1. How cost of power varies with load factor.

There are few power companies that don't have some sort of penalty attached to poor power factor. These penalties may not be identified with power factor as such, but they are incorporated somewhere in the bill. It is well to check the power company on this item. Methods of correcting power factor and other benefits beside direct monetary return will be discussed later.

Load Factor. This is the ratio of the average load to the peak demand. If the customer utilizes the full capacity, or maximum demand, for 24 hr a day, he is said to be operating at 100 per cent load, or load factor. This would provide the cheapest power rate per kilowatthour. However, as the extent of plant operation decreases, the demand charges are spread over fewer kilowatthours and therefore the demand charges get higher for each kilowatthour. The chart, Fig. 6-1, shows how the cost of power varies with the load factor. It is well to make up such a chart for your plant so that the proper allocation of charges for power can be based on the meter readings for departments.

Example: Using the chart, Fig. 6-2, if the plant demand is 4,000 kw and the utilization or load factor is 300 hr, the cost of power is 1.0 cent per kwhr. Increasing the load factor to 450 hr will drop the cost of power to 0.8 cent per kwhr. On the other hand, if the load factor is decreased to 250 hr, the cost of power goes up 1.1 cent per kwhr. These figures are especially useful when curtailing production during vacation periods or short days in winter when heavy lighting loads are picked up.

To make such a load chart, multiply the hours from 100 in steps of 50 up through 720 by whatever blocks of demand power you may want to use for your plant. In the chart shown, 500 kw was used, but it may be only 50 for your plant depending on your load. 720 hr × 500 kw = 360,000 kwhr. Using your power rates under your power contract, calculate the cost of power for that amount of power and demand. If a power-factor clause is in effect, assume a normal power factor and add in the surcharge. Divide the total amount of the bill by 360,000, and that will give you the cost

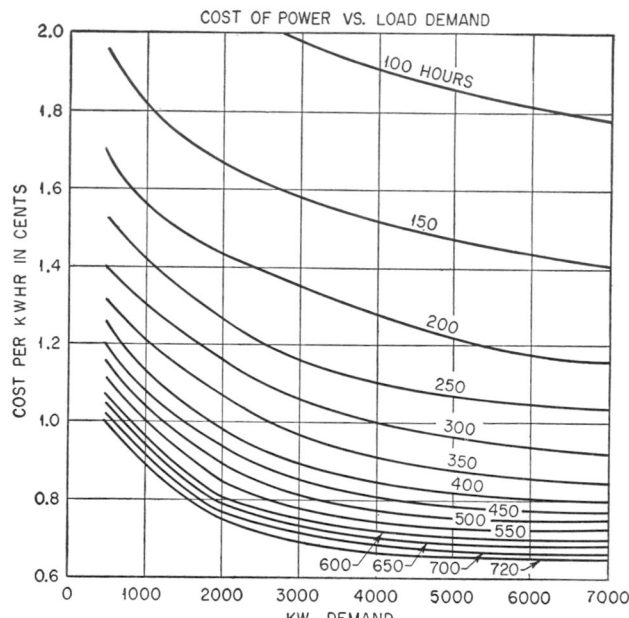

FIG. 6-2. Relation of load demand to cost of power.

per kilowatthour at that amount of power at 500-kw demand. Do the same for the different demand ratings, multiplying each by 720 to get the total kilowatthours. From the various points on the chart draw a curve. Do the same using the other hour ratings and get curves for those loadings in the same manner.

To use the chart, simply divide the total kilowatthours for the bill by the demand kilowatts, which will give the load factor in hours. When the curve for that particular load factor is used, the cost per kilowatthour can be easily located.

REDUCING THE BILL

Now that the bill is understood by everyone concerned, we are ready to start the process of looking at the means for reducing it. The first rule to observe is that no cost reduction can succeed without the full cooperation of the individuals who are responsible for the use of the power. The program must be sold to the production supervision, and they must be convinced of its merits if any benefits are to become permanent.

Demand Charges. The largest single component to work with in a power bill is the demand charge. The rates per kilowatt are high, and large savings can be made in this direction usually with no curtailment whatsoever in productive output. Here are some examples of how reductions were made in a cable plant.

The power bills in this plant averaged $26,000 a month. Top management issued an edict to "reduce that power bill or else." It was reduced all right, by over $8,000 *a month* inside of 2 months of investigation and recommendations to production. This is how it was done.

Analysis of power bills for the previous 6 months revealed that the period of maximum demand fell between the hours of 10 A.M. and noon. Therefore, the search for the causes of this high demand were confined to that time. In looking for loads to reduce in the demand bracket, the rule is to look for large power loads. Turning off lights here and there in the plant accomplishes very little along these lines. However, loads of 500-kw furnaces, 350-hp motors, and the like are the items to start with. In the case of this company, there were four 500-kw electric annealing ovens in one department. These ovens went on the line at 10 in the morning because the 2 hr loading operation started at 8. The ovens were unloaded by the third shift.

The operation was changed so that unloading was done by the first shift, starting at 8. This operation, plus loading, consumed 4 hr, and the ovens went on the line at noon instead of 10. But at noon the plant load was way down because of lunchtime and the 2,000-kw load was accommodated without exceeding normal demand.

Oven and furnace loads are 100 per cent loads during the time it takes to get up to heat. After that, they go on control heat, that is, on and off as heat is required to hold the desired temperatures. So the loads of these four ovens were not 2,000 kw but averaged only 1,000 kw. The afternoon peak, which was always lower than the morning peak, was not reached until 3, and by that time the ovens were on control heat. A reduction of 2,000 kw in the demand represented $3,000 a month, with no reduction in output.

Reducing Energy and Demand. The next step in the reduction was in the boilerhouse. There were four compressors, two driven by 350-hp motors, one by a 250-hp motor, and one by a 150-hp motor. Air pressure was 120 psi. The pressure was reduced to 90 lb, and no complaints were received. One of the compressors was shut down. Thus 250 hp was saved on the demand charge and also on the energy kilowatthours.

It was found that the output of the 150-hp compressor was required just to take care of leaks in the air piping. Eliminating leaks and repairing air valves resulted in shutting down the 150-hp compressor. Total saving in the boiler room amounted to 400 hp, or approximately 300 kw. This meant savings of $450 per month on demand and $1,250 a month on energy.

There was a rod mill in this plant with a motor load of 1,800 kw. It was a one-shift daytime operation. The operation was put on the second shift; the 40 men were paid 10 cents an hour more. The savings were $2,000 a month in the power bill.

Reducing Power Wastage. The second area for reduction in power bills is in the use of electrical energy itself. Lights that somebody forgot to turn off, large areas lit up to take care of two or three workers, machine-tool motors left running, blowers left on, all are signs of waste of power that shows up in the power bill.

In many cases panels are so located as to make it difficult to turn out the lights. Directories in the panels may not show which switch controls what lights. There is no reason why janitors must have 100 ft-c when cleaning offices. In one plant it was determined how much light was necessary, and the handles of the appropriate switches were painted white. All the janitors had to do was to turn the white-handled switches for their lighting needs, and again when they were through. The reward was a $250 reduction per month in the power bill.

Waste of water shows up on the power bill in plants that have their own wells or pump from streams or lakes. Every gallon represents horsepower through the power meter. Water for processing, such as cooling rolls in a steel mill, furnaces, air conditioning, plating tanks, must be pumped in large volume. In a plant that had 12 rubber mills, the work cycle was 20 min on and 30 min off, yet the flow of cooling water was never shut off. To save power, thermostatic controls were applied to the water lines in order to reduce the flow of water beyond the amount required. Other uses of water in this plant were investigated, and the whole water-conservation plan resulted in shutting down one 250-hp pump during the week and two more pumps during the week end.   The pumping bill had been running at the rate of $6 an hour, or $300 a week end.

Consider electric furnaces and ovens, which have to be preheated.   One plant had 6,000 kw of annealing ovens, which were started at 4 on Sunday afternoon to be ready at the beginning of the work week at midnight.   A new schedule called for starting work at 8 on Monday morning.   But nobody thought of changing the work schedule of the electric furnaces.   Furthermore, load charts showed that the ovens came up to heat in 3 hr, so that 5 hr had been wasted on the old schedule.   The waste power alone amounted to over $600 a week end, besides the overtime for the workmen.

Power Dispatchers.   The best way to curtail waste in power is to have load dispatchers.   It is the duty of these men to make sure that large power loads are not put

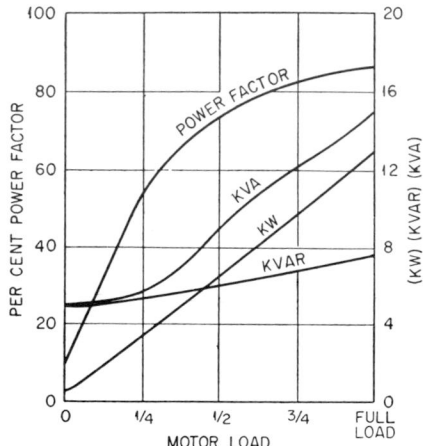

FIG. 6-3. Relation of power factor to load, induction motor of medium size and speed.

on the line at near-peak periods.   Also, they can patrol the plant and look for wastage of power in connection with air, water, ventilation, and other services.   Even part-time load dispatchers are likely to more than pay their way.

A plant had several electric furnaces in its experimental laboratory.   A demand meter costing $650 was installed.   By scheduling the demand of the laboratory furnaces to coincide with the low-demand periods of the plant, the peak demands were eliminated.   The power bill was reduced $1,000 the first month.

In a large plant, three load dispatchers were appointed to work around the clock. The first month they reduced the power bill $17,000 on a total of $75,000.   Close regulation of demand, shutting down motors and blowers, and shutting off water were responsible.

Week ends are the bad times.   Waste of power at this time means 60 hr of waste, and the kilowatthours pile up.   One plant pays two or three electricians 2 hr overtime every week, after the plant shuts down, to go around and "button up" the plant for the week end by shutting off lights and the other power wasters.

Power Factor.   The effects of power-factor charges on the power bills were discussed.   Improvement of power factor can be made by installing capacitors and overexciting synchronous motors.   Both of these methods cost money.   Why not get at the cause of low power factor?   The biggest cause is underloaded induction motors. The accompanying chart, Fig. 6-3, shows how bad this really is for an induction motor of medium size and speed.

In plants having large numbers of machine tools, the problem is acute.   Most machine tools are overmotored to take care of peak loads.   They do not operate on full load most of the time.   The result is poor power factor over the whole distribution system.

Pumps are another source of poor power factor.   One chemical plant carefully tests every pump brought in for repairs.   It has found 90 per cent of them overmotored, some by as much as 75 per cent.   With the installation of proper motors, power factor has been increased from 70 to 81 per cent.

Synchronous motors are widely used for power-factor improvement.   When over-excited, they supply their own kilovar requirements and in addition can supply kilo-vars for the system itself.   Synchronous motors should be considered for driving air compressors, pumps, blowers, and other equipment calling for considerable power.

When current flows through wire, it generates heat.   The lower the power factor, the greater the current that must flow over the wires in the plant and through the transformers, with consequent greater heat loss.   In large distribution systems these losses may be really significant.   It is estimated that power factor accounts for 15 per cent of these losses.   An indirect benefit of increased power factor is the reduction of heat losses.

Chapter 7

MAINTENANCE OF ELECTRIC BRAKES

By C. S. Brinker

Assistant Manager, Generator Service
Westinghouse Electric Corporation
Pittsburgh, Pa.

ELECTRIC BRAKE MAINTENANCE

It is necessary that we know on what basis brakes are applied in order to determine if the application is correct or if braking conditions have changed so as to make brake maintenance costly and impractical.

To select the correct size of brake for use with a motor for a particular application, there are three items that must be given consideration:

1. The retarding or holding torque required by the brake.
2. The heating cycle to which the brake coil or electrohydraulic motor will be subjected.
3. The amount of energy that must be dissipated by the brake wheel in stopping the motor and load. The energy that must be dissipated depends upon the stored energy of the motor and moving load, at the speed from which it is to be stopped, and upon the number of stops per minute.

To select a brake for a given application, the following method of determining the correct size can be followed:

1. Determine the torque of the motor by use of the following formula:

$$T = \frac{\text{hp} \times 5,250}{\text{rpm}}$$

   T = torque, lb-ft
   Hp = horsepower of driving motor
   Rpm = speed of the motor at full load or of the shaft to which the brake is supplied
2. Determine whether a continuous or intermittent rated brake is required. A *continuous* rated brake should be used with continuous rated motors or with intermittent rated motors where the brake is connected to the line for periods of more than 1 hr or in excess of 50 per cent of the time. An *intermittent* rated brake should be used with short-time rated motors where the duty is equivalent to one-half time on and one-half time off, with the continuous application of normal voltage not exceeding 1 hr.
3. Select a brake having a torque equal to or greater than the torque of the motor. For hoisting applications, the brake must be capable of holding the heaviest load that the motor will be called upon to lift.
4. Check the stored energy of the armature. With a-c motors dynamic braking is not available, and the friction brake must dissipate the entire stored energy of the motor and driven load.

On a d-c brake, if a shunt coil is used, the continuous or intermittent rating of the brake should be selected, depending upon the application.   Coils for shunt-wound brakes are usually wound for half voltage or lower, and a separately mounted resistor is furnished to be connected in series with the coil.   The resistor is provided with taps so that adjustments can be made depending upon requirements.   The low-voltage coil with a series resistor gives faster operation than if a full-voltage shunt coil were used.   If a series brake is used, the time rating of the brakes should be checked against the motor rating.   Since the brake coil is connected in series with the motor armature, it should be capable of handling the full range of load to which the motor may be subjected and should have the same overload capacity.

When rotating machinery must be stopped within a specified time limit, the stopping time may be determined by the following equation:

$$T = T_1 + \frac{WK^2N}{308B_C}$$

T = specified time limit, sec
T_1 = Interval between signal and when brake lining makes contact.   Usual 0.3 to 1.0 sec on d-c shunt brakes, 0.5 to 1.1 sec on electrohydraulic brakes, and 0.05 sec on series d-c brakes and a-c shunt brakes
W = weight of rotating mass, lb
K = radius of gyration of mass, ft
N = speed of brake wheel, rpm
B_C = rated brake capacity, ft-lb

For loads of high inertia or where electric motor braking is not provided at the motor shaft, the braking capacity required can be calculated as follows:

$$\text{HP sec per min} = \frac{\text{total } WR^2 \times (\text{max. motor rpm})^2 \times \text{No. operations per min}}{3,220,000}$$

From the results of these calculations, a suitable brake can be selected from the manufacturer's data on braking capacity in horsepower seconds per minute.

On any motor drive the cost of the brake is usually a small portion of the total cost, and where brake maintenance is excessive, replacement with a more suitable brake may be the most practical solution.

All brake manufacturers have published data concerning the torque ratings on their brakes, but as a guide the standard NEMA ratings are quoted here.

Direct-current-operated brakes				Alternating-current-operated brakes	
Torque of shunt brake lb-ft		Torque of series brake lb-ft		Torque ratings lb-ft	
Continuous*	1 hr*	1 hr*	½ hr*	Continuous*	1 or ½ hr*
3	. . . . .	. . . . .	. . . . .	1.5	
10	15	. . . . .	. . . . .	3	
25	35	. . . . .	. . . . .	10	15
50	75	. . . . .	. . . . .	25	35
70	90	60	90	50	75
150	200	135	200	125	160
400	525	350	525	325	400
675	900	600	900	600	800
1,350	1,800	1,200	1,800	1,200	1,600
2,700	3,600	2,400	3,600	2,400	3,200

* These refer to the continuous, 1- or ½-hr thermal ratings of the operators or coils.

The AISE brake committee in conjunction with the NEMA committee have also established the following rating for d-c brakes to be used with specific mill motors:

Motor number	Torque rating of series motor at full load, lb-ft		Torque rating, lb-ft of brake		
	0.5 hr	1 hr	0.5 series, 1 hr shunt	1 hr series	8 hr shunt
2	46	29	100	65	75
602	78	49	100	65	75
603	116	72	200	130	150
604	166	121	200	130	150
606	337	228	550	365	400
608	502	350	550	365	400
610	765	525	1,000	650	750
612	1,220	830	2,000	1,300	1,500
614	1,780	1,140	2,000	1,300	1,500
616	2,625	1,750	4,000	2,600	3,000
618	3,615	2,560	4,000	2,600	3,000

The NEMA standards specify the following range of operating voltage and current for electric brakes:

Direct-current brakes operated by series coils should release at 40 per cent or less of rated motor current and set at 10 per cent or less of rated motor current.

Direct-current brakes operated by shunt coils should release at 80 per cent or less of rated voltage and operate satisfactorily at 110 per cent voltage.

Alternating-current brakes operated by shunt coils should release at 85 per cent of rated voltage and operate satisfactorily at 110 per cent of rated voltage. A brake operated by a shunt coil shall operate successfully at minimum voltage when the temperature of the brake coil or operator is at the maximum temperature obtainable under its normal operating rating.

The above electrical characteristics are essential for maintenance in determining if the coil on a brake in difficulty is being supplied with the proper voltage or current and if normal operation may be expected.

All brakes are classified by the type of operator employed and the main characteristics of the various brake operators are as follows:

Alternating-current Solenoid Operator for Brakes. This operator may be identified by its laminated core construction and the fact that it is equipped with a shading coil to prevent hammering and noise during operation. The armature is usually ground to seat properly with the stationary core, and any foreign matter between the armature and core will cause excessive noise and coil burnouts. It is operated by a shunt coil from a single-phase source, and the air gap and torque setting must be carefully maintained so the plunger will pick up and seat properly to prevent overheating of the coils.

The coils on this type of brake may be readily changed, but care should be used in properly centering the coils to prevent friction. In general, this type of brake requires more careful and more regular maintenance than d-c brakes of the same type. The chief advantage is that it is very quick in setting and releasing and requires no special control contacts. The torque ratings on this type operator are limited because of the excessive maintenance required on higher torque ratings.

Direct-current Solenoid Operator for Brakes. Operators of this type may be equipped with either shunt or series coils. Because they have a solid steel plunger and magnet, they are considered very reliable and long lasting with minimum maintenance. Unlike an a-c operator of this type, they are not subject to coil burnouts in case the air gap or core travel becomes too great and the brake fails to open.

Faster operation on a d-c shunt brake can be obtained by using a reduced-voltage coil with a resistor in series. By use of proper control contacts, part of the resistor can be shorted out to obtain quicker pickup and resistance again inserted to obtain a low holding current and quick release.

A discharge resistor is used across the shunt coil to reduce the time required to release the brake and also to limit the voltage on the coil. The only disadvantage of a shunt brake is that control contacts are required to obtain quick operation and release and these contacts must be maintained properly or improper brake operation will result. A typical diagram of connections for the shunt brake operator is shown in Fig. 7-1.

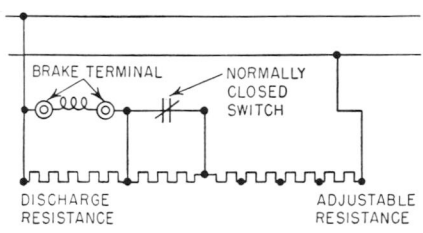

Fig. 7-1. Schematic diagram for d-c brakes with switch to reduce holding current.

The d-c shunt brake operator can be operated equally well from an a-c source through a suitable rectifier (see Fig. 7-2).

A series coil used on the solenoid-type operator has been popular for many years when used on series motor drives. The series coil is of low inductance, making rapid pickup and quick release possible.

No special control features are required to operate the series brake, and for this reason a minimum of maintenance is required on this type of operator when equipped with a series operating coil.

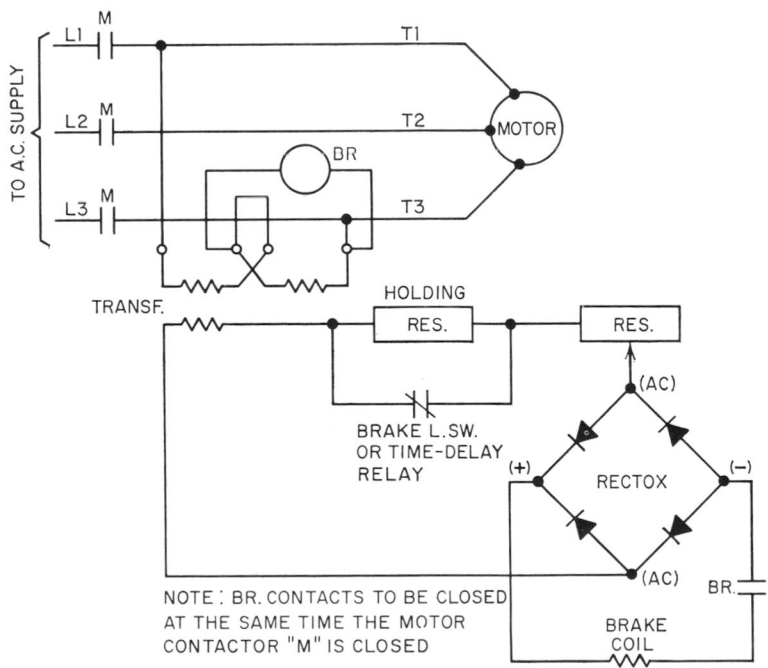

Fig. 7-2. Schematic diagram for d-c brake operated from a-c rectifier.

Alternating-current and Direct-current Brake Operator with Clapper-type Magnet. This type of operator is becoming more widely used by brake manufacturers on account of its simplicity and short stroke. Maintenance is considered to be lower than on the solenoid type because of the shorter stroke with less destructive hammering action.

Brake operators of this type, when equipped with an a-c shunt coil, have the same limitations as the solenoid type in that the air gap and torque adjustments must be maintained properly or the armature will fail to seat and the operating coil will burn out or overheat.

When d-c shunt coils are employed, the inductance of the coil is very high, so a reduced-voltage coil with resistor and special control contacts is necessary to obtain prompt release and quick setting the same as on a solenoid-type operator using a d-c shunt coil. Direct-current series coils can be used with fast operation and a minimum of maintenance.

Electrohydraulic Brake Operator. This type of operator consists of a motor, impeller, piston, push rods, and oil system. When the motor is energized, the oil pressure is built up, forcing the piston upward, operating the push rods, and releasing the brake shoes from the wheel. The speed of release and setting can be adjusted independently to suit the application, but in any case operation is slower than with other types. Usually operated by a three-phase induction motor, the operator may operate continuously without overheating. If this operator is subjected to many starts within a short period of time, the motor may overheat, and it may be well to consult the manufacturer if such duty is required by a change in operating conditions.

The oil level and oil purity should be checked occasionally, and the oil renewed if necessary. Contamination of the oil or improper oil level will not permit the operator to function properly. Likewise, the oil system should be checked for oil leaks, and new packing or seals installed when necessary. The seals should not be tightened excessively, or the brake will be sluggish and rapid wear of the brake lining will result. The proper grade and viscosity of oil should be used at all times, as a heavy oil will cause the operator motor to overheat. During the winter months, if the brake is subjected to temperatures below 20°F, the manufacturer should be consulted for the proper grade of oil to use.

A time-delay feature is usually supplied, providing up to 5 sec delay in setting time. This adjustment is independent of the releasing time.

The electrohydraulic operator can be tilted at an angle of not more than 45° either side of the vertical; a greater angle will cause oil leakage.

Disk-type Brake Operator. This type is usually supplied as a definite part of the motor on which it is applied, since a special motor end bracket is required for mounting. Shunt coils for either a-c or d-c supply are used. The operator is used to apply force between a rotating molded lining and the stationary rubbing plate. The moving and stationary parts of this type of brake move very close together, so the brake must be carefully maintained in order to obtain proper braking action and minimum wear.

BRAKE PARTS AND THEIR MAINTENANCE

Mounting the Shoe-type Brake. The vertical and horizontal center line of the brake shoes should be checked against the manufacturer's outline drawings to determine if the brake shoes are centered with respect to the brake wheel. If the brake shoes are not centered properly, the shoes may drag on one edge, causing excessive wear on the wheel and shoes.

Brake Wheels and Their Care. Brake wheels are usually made of annealed cast iron or alloy steel, as these materials will resist wear and are of high tensile strength with no surface cracking. They may be installed on a tapered shaft and held in place by a nut and lock washer or applied to a straight shaft and keyed in place with a light press fit on the shaft. The interference between the brake wheel and shaft is approximately $\frac{1}{4}$ mil per in. of shaft diameter on a straight shaft. When a new brake wheel is applied, it should be heated evenly in boiling water or in an oven before it is installed on the shaft.

All brake wheels are balanced, and if the wheel becomes badly scored or broken, it should be removed with a wheel puller and a new wheel installed. Care should be used in installing the new brake wheel so that the rubbing surface will not be damaged or the wheel cracked.

When a brake is installed or braking conditions have changed, the wheel should be observed for temperature.   A brake wheel should not operate above 200°C or 392°F, and if this temperature is exceeded, the adjustment of the brake should be checked to see whether the shoes are rubbing or the duty cycle of the brake has been exceeded.   By tests it has been proved that the brake lining will wear in proportion to the total temperature of the brake wheel from 160 to 390°F, assuming that a molded asbestos lining is used.   Since brake wheels are more expensive and difficult to replace than the brake lining, normal wear should be confined to the lining.

The brake wheel should never be operated beyond the safe speed as specified by the manufacturer because excessive brake wear will result or the wheel may fly apart owing to centrifugal force.   The brake wheel should be kept free of oil, water, and dirt if possible.   Water will cause the wheel to rust and the brake lining to swell, which will reduce the shoe clearance and increase wear.   Abrasive dirt will cause scoring of the brake wheel and increase the wear on the brake lining.   Oil will cause the brake to slip, and time of stopping will be increased.   Where brakes are subjected to foreign material such as water, dirt, or oil, it may be well to consider an enclosure which will eliminate the trouble encountered by its presence.

Brake Linings and Their Care.   Brake linings are made from an asbestos material of either the fabric or molded type.   The fabric-type lining is made from asbestos with brass wire woven in and may be treated with a rubber compound and vulcanized. The molded lining is made from an asbestos material treated with rubber and molded under heat and pressure.   This molded lining has more resistance to foreign materials, such as dirt, grease, and oil, so it is used on most modern brakes.

The lining may be riveted to the brake shoe or molded into the shoe.   It is considered good practice to use the original type of lining when replacement is made, as a different type will require readjustment of the brake to obtain the same braking. The brake-shoe lining should be replaced when the wear approaches the rivets holding the lining in place or if there is danger of the brake lining cracking and becoming mechanically weak.   To replace the lining, the brake shoes should be removed from the brake.   If rivets are used, the rivet heads should be drilled so that they can be driven out.   Brass rivets are generally used to hold the lining in place with the heads of the rivets countersunk to one-half the depth of the lining.   Tubular rivets are considered more satisfactory and easier to work than solid rivets.   If the lining is molded and formed into the shoe, it will be necessary to install new lined shoes or send the shoes to the factory for installing new lining.

After a brake has been relined, the brake should be released manually and the clearances on the shoes equalized.   A thickness gage may be inserted between the wheel and lining to determine if the clearances are the same on both sides of the wheel and if the brake lining is parallel to the face of the wheel.   A short period of operation is usually required to make the new lining fit the contour of the wheel uniformly, and for this reason, the lining will wear faster immediately after being replaced.

After new linings are installed, the plunger or magnet travel and also spring pressure should be checked to see that adjustments agree with original settings.

Bearings and Pins.   Bearings and pins are usually made of heat-treated steel or bronze.   When brakes are used in a corrosive atmosphere, such as marine service, bronze bushings and bronze pins are used.

Bearing wear will reduce the normal shoe clearance for the same amount of travel for the brake operator.   When bearing wear becomes excessive so that the brake is difficult to keep in proper adjustment, new pins and bushings should be installed.

Brakes require very little lubrication; however, pins and bearings should be lubricated with a small amount of oil or light grease.   Excessive lubrication may involve the brake wheel and reduce the braking action as well as cause dirt to accumulate on parts, with resultant abrasive action.

Manual Release Devices.   Manual release devices are provided with all types of brake and will permit manual release of the brake without disturbing the torque adjustment.   This device may be provided with a self-reset feature, manual-reset feature, and an electrically interlocked manual release.   In any case, when maintenance work is being performed on an electric brake, care should be taken that the motor or brake cannot be energized.   This can be accomplished by removing the fuses or opening the disconnect switch on the circuit serving the motor and brake.

Torque Adjustments.   In order to lift the brake shoes from the brake wheel, the spring on any shoe brake must be overcome by the force of the operator.   Thus the braking torque on a shoe brake is proportioned to the spring compression, but in no case should the spring be so adjusted that the brake operator cannot open the brake under all operating conditions.

The amount of spring compression for rated braking torque is usually found on the brake name plate or manufacturer's instruction.   When this adjustment is made, the compression nut is tightened until the weight of the parts balances the force of the spring with no movement of the shoes, then the adjusting nut is tightened the required distance in inches as specified by the manufacturer.

The speed of travel of the plunger on a magnetic brake depends on the retarding action of the spring.   For this reason spring compression should never be reduced to the extent that the speed of the plunger or armature becomes excessive and hits into the stationary magnet seat with such force that the plunger or magnet is damaged.   On electrohydraulic brakes, reduced spring tension will result in sluggish setting of the brake, causing the load to drift.

It is recommended that on all brakes the spring compression be not reduced more than approximately 50 per cent of the specified name-plate rating.   Special brake coils for the magnetic brakes and special lever ratios may be required when the spring is reduced to such values.

The necessity for reducing spring tension usually arises when an oversized brake has been applied for greater "braking capacity."   If the oversized brake was set for rated torque, the load would then be retarded too quickly.

Increasing spring compression to produce brake torque higher than the rated torque is not recommended.   This would result in rapid destruction to the brake lining and wheel.   Also the brake will fail to release if the spring compression is increased appreciably beyond the specified value.

How to Adjust Electric Brakes.   The air gap on a brake operator should be so adjusted that when it is energized electrically, sufficient clearance is obtained between the lining and wheel to prevent rubbing.   This fact holds true even with a slightly eccentric brake wheel or when the wheel has expanded at maximum operating temperatures.

On most solenoid- or magnet-operated brakes, one shoe usually releases ahead of the other, and in order to provide the same clearance at both shoes, an adjustment is provided.   On some brakes one shoe strikes an adjustable stop which can be so set that when the stop is reached, force is applied to the opposite shoe and it is released.   By adjustment of this stop, the same clearance can be obtained at both shoes.

On some magnet-type brakes, an adjustment of the magnet position and linkage is necessary to obtain clearance at both shoes.

Regardless of the type of operator, the brake may be released manually or electrically to determine if both shoes have the same clearance from the brake wheel, and where clearances are small, a thickness gage is a valuable tool in adjusting these clearances.

It is vitally important that the brake be readjusted before the plunger travel or air gap is allowed to exceed $1\frac{1}{2}$ times normal.   This is especially true of an operator having an a-c coil, as the coil will overheat if the magnet does not seat properly because of improper adjustment.

Alternating-current brake plungers and stationary magnets are constructed of laminated steel to reduce heating.   The laminations sometimes become burred owing to plunger operation, which results in excessive brake humming caused by normal magnetic reversals.   Should this occur, the plunger and stationary magnet faces should be filed in order to obtain a good seat.

To reduce magnetic humming on a-c solenoid brakes, a single turn of metal (shading coil) is pressed into the plunger or stationary magnet face.   Should the shading coil become loose or broken, excessive noise and heating will develop.   It will then be necessary to repair the shading coil or replace the plunger or magnet if the shading coil cannot be repaired.

Plungers and stationary magnets on d-c brakes are made of solid high-magnetic quality steel. The plunger travels in a brass bushing to protect the coil spool and to guide the plunger in normal operation. If bushing wear becomes excessive, the plunger may become cocked against the side of the magnet housing. This increased friction will result in failure of the plunger to pull in and release the brake. The bushing should be periodically checked, and a new bushing installed before failure occurs.

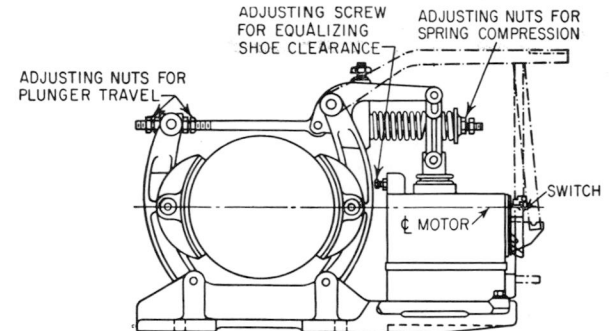

Fig. 7-3. Typical adjustments on brakes.

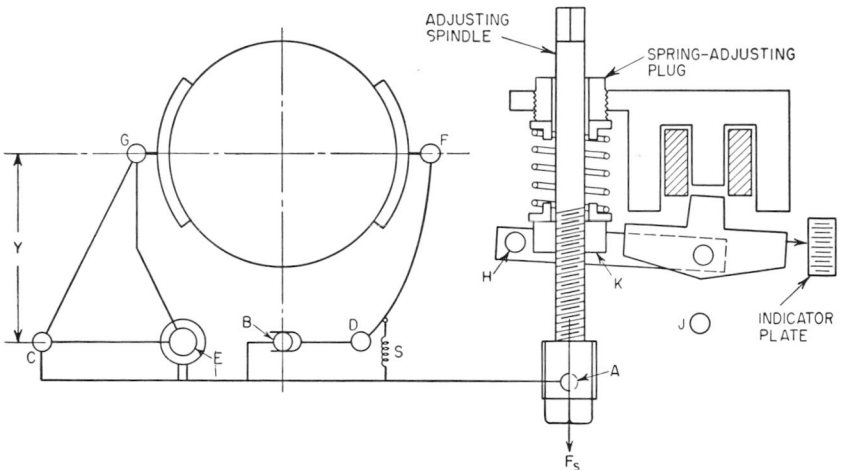

Fig. 7-4. A-c brake with single adjustment for lining wear and armature travel. The brake arms are pivoted on fixed pins D and E, while lever ABC is pivoted to solid arm GEC at point C and is connected to arm FBD at point B by a pin riding in a slot. Because of the geometry of the system, force F_s presses the shoes against the wheel with equal pressures.

Faulty alignment on all solenoid brakes will cause the plunger to ride against the stationary sides. This will produce excessive friction, resulting in failure of the brakes to pull in.

When a brake is initially placed in service or the brake shoes are relined, the brake adjustments should be checked more often than after the brake lining has worn so as to conform to the surface of the wheel. Brake lining when used for the first time has a number of high spots on which the initial wear is concentrated, and until these high spots wear down, the brake adjustments will change rapidly.

Spring or torque adjustments are usually made at the factory, and it is not necessary to disturb these adjustments. However, in case the spring adjustment is not considered correct, the adjusting nut may be loosened until the force of the spring just balances the weight of the parts. This is considered the point of no tension, and with this point established, the spring nut may then be tightened the required dimension in inches as specified on the name plate or by the manufacturer. This adjustment should provide rated braking torque.

The sketch, Fig. 7-3, shows the typical adjustments on a solenoid brake.

Alternating-current Brakes with One Single Adjustment. Most brakes have three adjustments—for magnet travel shoe clearance, and spring compression; however, in order to simplify maintenance an a-c brake with single adjustment (Fig. 7-4) has been manufactured for several years. This brake is equipped with a visible indicator plate which tells the maintenance man when to readjust for brake wear and how much adjustment is necessary.

The brake can be readjusted with practically no outage time. The torque rating can be changed by making adjustment to the spring adjusting plug, but once the proper torque adjustment is established for any application, no further adjustment is necessary. The brake linkage is so designed that it will take care of slight misalignment of the brake wheel from the vertical center line, but for best results, careful alignment is recommended when the brake is installed.

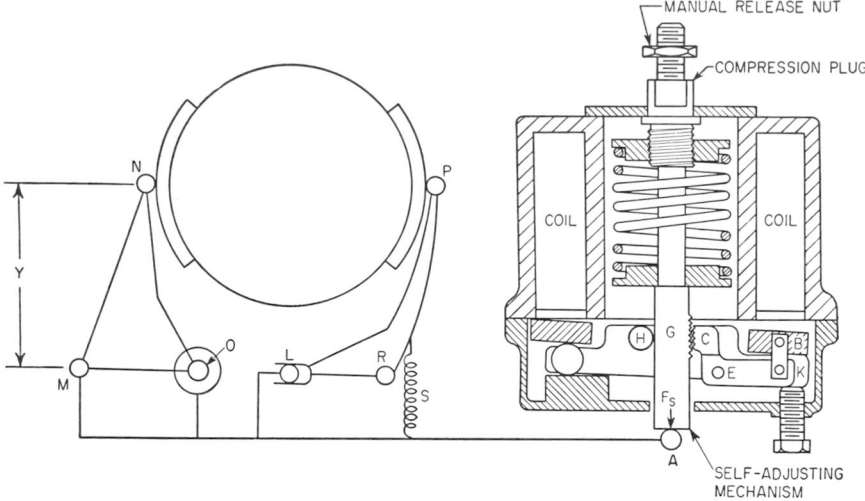

FIG. 7-5. D-c brake with self-adjusting feature to compensate for lining wear.

On large ratings this brake may be equipped with an electrohydraulic operator where breaking torques above 125 lb-ft are required.

Direct-current Brakes with Self-adjusting Feature. A d-c self-adjusting brake operator (Fig. 7-5) has been marketed for several years. It is so designed that no adjustment after installation is necessary until the brake shoes require relining. This operator is of the magnet type and will do away with the necessity for adjustments for change in magnet travel, spring compression, or unequal brake-shoe clearances.

The force of the compression spring is applied to the serrated block G which acts through lever ALM to hold the brake shoes against the wheel with the magnet deenergized. When the magnet is energized, the armature B lifts up, pivoting around point E, which causes clutch piece C to engage with block G backed up by roller H. With the clutch pieces engaged, any further movement of the armature will overcome the force on the spring and cause the brake shoes to release.

As the brake linings wear, the serrated block G drops slightly, causing the clutch piece to engage at a higher point on the serrations. The upward movement of the armature remains the same as determined by stop K; consequently, the shoe clearance remains the same when the magnet is energized.

The brake may be manually released by turning the manual-release nut down against the compression plug on top of the spring. Then the shoe bolts can be removed to permit dismantling so that new brake lining can be applied.

Brakes are often located in difficult places, such as on cranes, so the tendency is to overlook the necessity for adjustment, and with a brake of this type, little maintenance is required until the brake lining becomes worn.

Brake Enclosures. Brake enclosures should be used where conditions might allow water, oil, or dust to come in contact with the brake. Water or oil on the brake wheel will produce a certain amount of brake slippage that is undesirable; also water would

BRAKE SET (DE-ENERGIZED)   BRAKE RELEASED (ENERGIZED)

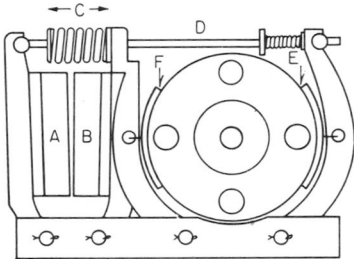
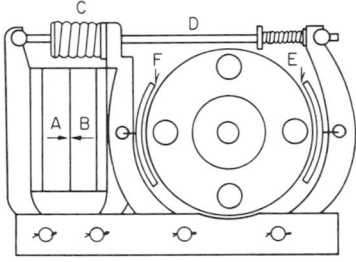

WHEN THE TWIN MAGNETS (A AND B) BECOME DE-ENERGIZED, SPRING C SIMULTANEOUSLY MOVES TIE ROD D TO THE LEFT AND MAGNET B TO THE RIGHT, FORCING BOTH BRAKE SHOES (E AND F) TO APPLY BRAKE TORQUE TO THE WHEEL AT THE SAME TIME

WHEN THE TWIN MAGNETS (A AND B) ARE ENERGIZED, THEY PULL TOGETHER COMPRESSING SPRING C. THIS ACTION SIMULTANEOUSLY MOVES TIE ROD D TO THE RIGHT FREEING SHOE E. AT THE SAME INSTANT, THE MOTION OF MAGNET B TO THE LEFT FREES SHOE F.

FIG. 7-6. Operation of twin-magnet, d-c, clapper-type brake.

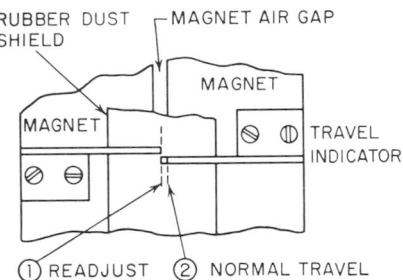

FIG. 7-7. Magnet travel indicator.

cause damage to the electrical parts. Where dust of an abrasive nature is present, rapid destruction of the brake wheel and linings will occur. "Weatherproof" enclosures are ventilated to protect the brake from dripping or splashing liquids. This includes indoor service where oil or water might come in contact with an unprotected brake or outdoor service to protect the brake from rain, snow, or ice. "Water- and dusttight" gasketed construction provides protection from great quantities of water or dust that would penetrate the ventilation openings of a weatherproof enclosure. When this type of enclosure is used, consideration must be given to the dissipation of heat generated by the wheel because of its completely enclosed construction. It is therefore necessary to check the duty cycle with the manufacturer when ordering. All watertight and dusttight enclosures are provided with drain plugs to allow for draining the enclosure of condensed moisture. These should be periodically checked. Frequency of draining will depend on operating conditions.

The latest addition to the brake family is a twin-magnet d-c clapper-type brake. A static-type rectifier may be used with this brake for operation on alternating current. The special features of this brake are its small over-all size and trouble-free magnet coils, which are encapsulated in epoxy resin for longer life. Easy maintenance is obtained by an over-the-wheel tie rod that is conveniently accessible and permits all adjustments from the top. Suspended loads may be held during coil replacement, and shoe replacements can be made in one step by removing the unitized tie rod and spring assembly. The operation of this brake is shown in Fig. 7-6.

An illustration of the magnet travel indicator with which this brake is equipped is shown in Fig. 7-7. When the magnet gap progresses to a point where the ends of the indicators line up, it is time to readjust for lining wear.

Chapter 8

LEAD-ACID STORAGE BATTERIES

By J. D. HUNTSBERGER
Manager Application Engineering
Gould-National Batteries, Inc.
Industrial Division
Trenton, N.J.

The purpose of this chapter is to assist the plant engineer in selecting the correct lead-acid storage battery for his industrial electric truck or other mobile equipment and, having selected it, properly use, maintain, and repair it. An industrial battery, properly selected and cared for, will take the beating of everyday in-plant use without a murmur. Skip over the small amount of care and attention it deserves, and you'll have a continuous maintenance headache. And you may well see a considerable investment go down the drain.

How to select a battery, to install it, and operate it; how to determine its condition; charging; maintenance; and repair will be covered. Only the basic points can be treated. It is therefore essential that every battery user have in his files—where he can find them—the installation, operating, and maintenance instructions supplied with the battery by the manufacturer. If you run into special problems, call on the manufacturer. He is anxious for his product to make a good showing and will give you fast and expert help.

BATTERY SELECTION

There is no excuse for guessing at the correct battery to buy. Determining exactly the capacity needed is a reasonably simple and straightforward matter. A little time spent with a pencil and paper before purchasing a battery is a wise move. Buy a unit with too little capacity, and it will run down before the end of the shift—always inconvenient, often costly in terms of lost production. Buy an overcapacity battery, and you are spending money that needn't be spent.

Sometimes the capacity of a storage battery is expressed in terms of watthours. In that case, all you need do is select a battery of the proper voltage (the voltage will be specified on the equipment to be powered) and a watthour capacity equal to or slightly greater than the watthours of work that you have calculated must be done each shift.

More often, however, the capacity of a battery is expressed in ampere-hours. Since, as mentioned above, the voltage is established by the motor in the truck, all you have to do is divide the watthours required by this fixed voltage to get the ampere-hours required to do the job. Select a battery with that or a slightly greater ampere-hour capacity.

Figure 8-1 shows the watthours per ton required to operate industrial lift trucks over level concrete. It is just one of the useful charts given in the "Handbook of Material

Handling," published by The Electric Industrial Truck Association in 1950.   Using it, together with other constants given in the handbook, we can arrive at a power-requirement figure that will cover not only level concrete hauls but travel up and down grades, empty and loaded, and lifting and tilting the load.

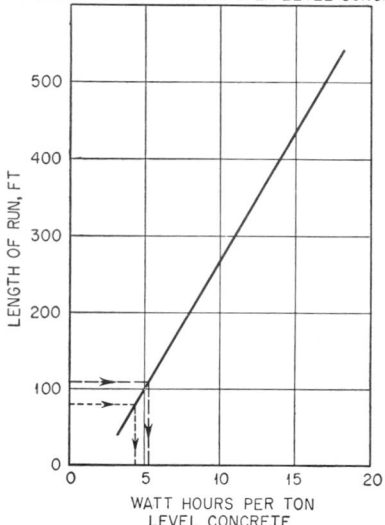

WATT HOURS PER TON REQUIRED TO OPERATE INDUSTRIAL LIFT TRUCKS OVER LEVEL CONCRETE

FIG. 8-1.   Data for use in figuring capacities.

Example: A lift truck is required to move a load of 1 ton over 80 ft of level concrete, then up a 10 per cent grade for 30 ft, lift the load an average of 3 ft for stacking, tilt, return to the starting point unloaded. The truck, with its battery and operator, weighs 1.825 tons.

Step 1. Determine the total distance to be traveled loaded.   Here it is 80 ft on the level plus 30 ft on the grade, or 110 ft.

Step 2. Determine the watthours required to move the truck loaded over that distance, assuming no grade is involved. From the chart (see dashed lines) we find that it takes 5.4 watthours to move 1 ton over 110 ft of level concrete.   Therefore to move 2.825 tons over 110 ft of level concrete takes $2.825 \times 5.4 = 15.25$ *watt-hr.*

Step 3. Determine the extra power to cover the 30 ft of 10 per cent upgrade. From the "Handbook of Material Handling" we find that extra power necessary for grade = weight in tons × length of grade × per cent of grade × 0.013 (a constant).   The extra power required in our case is, then,

$$2.825 \times 30 \times 10 \times 0.013 = 11.02 \ watt\text{-}hr$$

Step 4. Determine power to lift.   The handbook gives this formula:

Watthours per lift = load in tons × feet of lift × 2 (a constant)

In our case, then,

$$\text{Watthours per lift} = 1 \times 3 \times 2 = 6 \ watt\text{-}hr$$

Step 5. Determine power to tilt.   The handbook gives this formula:

Watthour per tilt = load in tons × 1 (a constant)

In our case, then,

$$\text{Watthours per tilt} = 1 \times 1 = 1 \ watt\text{-}hr$$

Step 6. Determine watthours for unloaded return trip.   Total distance is 110 ft. The 30-ft downgrade requires no power.   Therefore, all that needs to be figured is the watthours for traveling, unloaded, 80 ft on the level.   From Fig. 8-1 we find that it takes 4.4 watt-hr to move 1 ton over 80 ft of level concrete.   Therefore to move 1.825 tons (unloaded weight) over 80 ft takes

$$1.825 \times 4.4 = 8.03 \ watt\text{-}hr$$

Step 7. Add the watthours required for each step to get the total per round trip.   In this example the items are as follows: run level with load (Step 2), extra power for upgrade (Step 3), lifting (Step 4), tilting (Step 5), return empty (Step 6).   Total watt-hour requirements per trip equal, then,

$$15.25 + 11.02 + 6.00 + 1.00 + 8.03 = 41.30 \ watt\text{-}hr$$

Step 8. Determine watthours per shift.   Assume that the truck makes 250 trips per shift.   Requirements per shift are, then,

$$250 \times 41.30 = 10,325.0 \; watt\text{-}hr$$

Step 9. Determine ampere-hours required.   From the name plate of the truck determine what voltage its motor operates on.   Assume 32 volts, meaning that a 32-volt battery is required.   Ampere-hours required per shift is, then,

$$\text{Watthours} \div \text{volts} = \frac{10,325}{32} = 322.6 \; amp\text{-}hr \; per \; shift$$

Step 10. Determine battery needed.   We already know that the battery must be of the 32-volt type.   As to capacity, it should be rated at or slightly in excess of 323 amp-hr.   And naturally, it must be of the proper dimensions to fit physically the battery rack in the truck.

The above is a simple example.   Often trucks do not travel over a specified route with a specified load for an entire shift but instead do a variety of jobs.   In this case, you must use common sense in determining the average ampere-hour requirements per shift and allow a little extra for unforseen demands.

The example assumes, too, that the battery will be recharged each shift.   Naturally the time between rechargings can be shortened or lengthened, depending on operations. Bear in mind that the battery will deliver at rated capacity only for a specified length of time.   The ampere-hour capacity of a battery increases as the discharge rate decreases.   Conversely, if the discharge rate is increased, the ampere-hour capacity of the battery decreases.   (*Example:* A lead-acid battery described as "300 amp-hr capacity at the 6-hr rate of discharge" delivers 50 amp for 6 hr.   This same battery will deliver 192 amp for 1 hr—or 192 amp-hr "at the 1-hr rate of discharge."   It will deliver 21 amp for 20 hrs—or 420 amp-hr, "at the 20-hr rate of discharge.")   Therefore make sure, in calculating the capacity of the battery needed for an application, that it will deliver the ampere-hours required over the period of time you wish to elapse between rechargings.   Although lead motive power batteries are rated in ampere-hours at the 6-hr rate and normally the load is intermittent at 1½- to 4-hr rate, the battery voltage recuperates during the short idle periods of the intermittent discharge and the 6-hr. rated ampere-hour capacity can be obtained.

The foregoing calculations can be avoided by calling in a battery-company representative.   He will, undoubtedly, give you good advice on the type and capacity of battery needed.   But certainly you should understand the calculations involved both as a check on his conclusion and to make sure that he doesn't overlook any special problems inherent in your particular operation.   Merely purchasing another battery of the type already in the truck assumes that conditions under which the truck operates are still the same as they were (an unlikely condition in any plant these days) and, for that matter, that the existing battery was properly selected (not necessarily a good assumption).

INSTALLATION AND USE

Precautions should be taken before placing a battery in service.   When it is received, examine the outside of the packing case for signs of rough handling before accepting the battery from the carrier.   And look for wet spots on the packing case—they may indicate that battery jars were broken in shipment.   Leaking jars should be removed from the battery immediately (see Repairs, later in chapter).   If a replacement jar is not available, the elements of the damaged jar should be immersed in a glass, porcelain, or rubber container holding enough pure distilled water to cover them completely. When new jars are available, follow instructions given under the Repair section of this chapter to put the complete battery back in service.

Assuming, however, that there is no indication of damage, a new battery should be given a freshening charge for 3 to 6 hr or until the specific gravity indicates no further rise.   This charge should be given at the low or finishing rate (as indicated in the instructions accompanying the battery or the name plate fastened to the battery.   See next section on Charging.)

Under shop conditions, there is always a temptation to extend the working time of a battery.   This should not be done.   Extending the work means overdischarging the battery, which will greatly shorten its life.   In use, a battery should always be recharged immediately following a complete discharge.   It should never be allowed to remain in a discharged condition.   If service requirements demand only partial discharge, it is unnecessary to recharge after each partial discharge.   When a battery is from 75 to 100 per cent discharged, it should be recharged.

CHARGING THE BATTERY

Batteries used in powering industrial trucks (in fact, in most industrial situations outside stand-by emergency use) are used in what is called cycle operation.   That is, the battery is either being charged or being used (i.e., being discharged).   As a guess, most batteries are charged between 1,500 and 2,000 times during their lives.   Incorrect charging for a few cycles will do little harm, but incorrect charging day after day will shorten the life of the battery.

"Correct charging" means charging the battery sufficiently without overcharging, overheating, or excessive gassing.   To accomplish this, the charging of batteries usually is started at a high rate of ampere flow known as the "starting rate."   Later in the charge, this rate of ampere flow is reduced to the "finishing rate."   Manufacturers feel, as a rule of thumb, that the finishing rate should not exceed 5 amp per 100 amp-hr of rated battery capacity.   The starting rate may be 4 or $4\frac{1}{2}$ times the finishing rate.   Just how this is accomplished will be discussed below.

Power Sources.   The charging power for the cycle method of battery operation is provided by one of the following: a motor-generator set, a rectifier, or a d-c bus within the plant fed from the utility.   Motor generators and rectifiers, while their operation is quite different, do the same thing: change a-c power into d-c power.   Direct-current power is, of course, the only power that should be used to recharge a battery.

It is beyond the scope of this chapter to discuss these various sources of d-c power.   In most industrial plants, only one such source will be available, so that debates as to the most desirable have no point.

Charging Methods.   There are two systems of charging batteries that are in general use: the modified constant-voltage method and the two-rate method.   Most equipment in plants will be of one of these types.

The Modified Constant-voltage Method.   This method employs a constant-voltage source supplying power to the battery, which is connected in series with a resistance.   Figure 8-2 shows this schematically.

In the diagram, A is a source of constant voltage.   The diagram shows a generator, but a rectifier or d-c bus powered by the utility will serve as well if the voltage is stable and equal to 2.63 times the number of cells in series to be charged.   The voltage applied to the charge circuits C in diagram A must be 2.63 times the number of cells in the battery.

Notice that the batteries are connected in series with resistors K.   These are used only to adjust the charge rate.   Typically they are adjusted by the manufacturer of the charging equipment to give a complete recharge, in 8 hr, to a fully discharged battery.   If, in your case, batteries are not completely discharged during the normal duty cycle and you have 8 hr for recharging, it is advisable to increase the resistance by adjusting resistance K, thus reducing the charging rate slightly.   Within commonsense limits, you can decrease the recharging time by reducing the value of resistance K.

In charging a battery with this setup, there is a tapering off of the current flowing to the battery.   This is the result of the increasing countervoltage of the battery as it is recharged.   Thus the battery is charged rapidly at first ("starting rate"), but as the countervoltage builds up, the current to the battery decreases gradually to a lower and safer "finishing rate."

As indicated in Fig. 8-2, a number of batteries can be charged from the same motor-generator set by the modified-constant-voltage method, but it is essential that the batteries are all of the same number of cells.

(The "taper charge" is a variant on this basic charging method. It is obtained by connecting the battery to a specially designed generator having a dropping voltage characteristic. The charge duplicates the charge obtained by the modified constant-voltage method.)

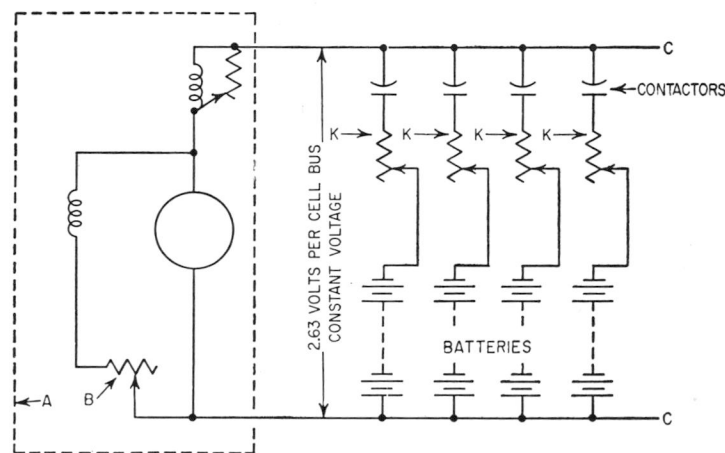

Fig. 8-2. Modified constant-voltage charge—schematic wiring diagram—four batteries being charged.

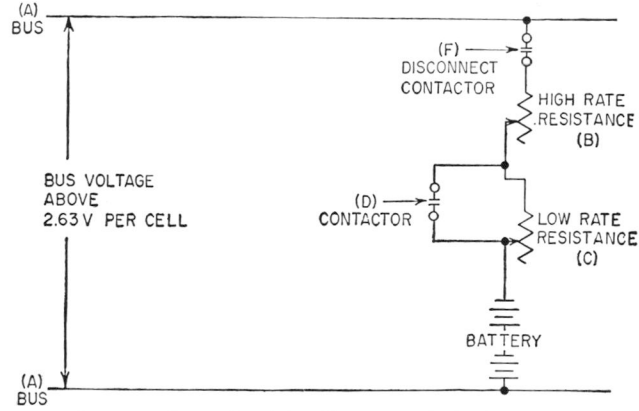

Fig. 8-3. Two-rate charge—schematic wiring diagram—single circuit from high-voltage bus.

The Two-rate Method. This is a method in which the charge rate is changed from a relatively high value during the first part of the charge to a lower, safer rate for the finish. The schematic wiring diagram, Fig. 8-3, shows how this is done.

A voltage of at least 2.63 per battery cell must be supplied between the busses *A* by generator, rectifier, or outside source. During the first rapid part of the charge, the "low-rate resistance" *C* is shorted out by contactor *D*. During the later slow part of the charge, the current through the battery is reduced to the "finishing rate" by opening contactor *D*, increasing the resistance in series with the battery. Notice that both the high-rate resistance *B* and the low-rate resistance *C* can be adjusted to regulate both the high and low charging rates. [The various makers of two-rate charging equipment actually provide different methods of accomplishing the change in rate from high (starting) to low (finishing) rate. With rectifier equipment, for example, some manufacturers call for a change in transformer taps while others have resistance inserted in series with the primary of the transformer to effect the change in rate. See the manufacturer's instructions for your particular equipment.]

Other Types of Charging. The two methods described are the ones commonly used for regular, routine charging. But sometimes supplementary charges are required. There are three types:

1. Boost charge. This is a charge given to the battery when it is not possible or practicable to give it a regular charge. The boost charge is usually a charge of high rate and short duration given to prevent overdischarge of the battery. It is given during a lull in the work cycle of the truck the battery is powering. The boost charge usually is in order when the truck is required to do more work during any shift than was contemplated when the battery was purchased. If boost charges are frequently needed because the battery capacity is insufficient to meet new and increased duty requirements, consider either purchasing a new battery with greater capacity or supplying one or more duplicate batteries so that the battery of the truck can be changed and charged at the normal rate instead of forcing it to take this fast charge.
2. Equalizing charge. This is a special charge that should be given periodically to ensure that the battery is at maximum capacity. The purpose of this type of charge is to restore all cells in the battery to their fully charged condition. To do this, continue the charge at the finishing rate—after the regular charge—until the specific gravity of all cells stops increasing for a period of 3 to 4 hr. An equalizing charge should be given monthly on a light-duty cycle (where the battery is charged only once every 2 or 3 days), every week on a heavy-duty cycle (where the battery is discharged daily or more often).
3. Emergency charge. In the case of an emergency requiring that the battery be recharged within as short a time as possible, a starting rate of twice the normal starting current may be used and continued until the cells begin to gas. Then reduce the rate to the normal starting rate, and continue as directed for a normal charge. (*Warning*: The emergency charge may not be used if, at any time, the temperature exceeds 110°F.)

CONTROL OF CHARGING

Daily overcharging of a battery is one of the surest ways of causing its life to be less than normal. Therefore it is necessary to protect against this possibility in charging operations. There are two common automatic methods of terminating a charge, the voltage-relay-timer method and the ampere-hour-meter method, and two common manual methods, specific gravity and volt-ampere, to guard against this hazard.

Automatic Control. *Voltage Relay Timer.* There are various kinds and variations of this type of automatic control, but the basic principle upon which they operate is this: As a battery approaches a charged condition, the battery voltage increases rapidly. The use of a voltage relay and timer may be coordinated in several ways. For example, when using modified constant-voltage charging, the operation of the voltage relay causes the timer to start and time the rest of the charge. When two-rate charging is used, the operation of the voltage relay not only starts the timer but also changes the charge rate from high to low. In another combination, the timer is used to time the entire charge and the voltage relay is used to change the charge rate from high to low. The exact operation of the unit in your plant will be described by the manufacturer's instructions. But, as with any automatic equipment, it is essential to make periodic checks in order to determine that it is operating correctly.

The Ampere-hour Meter. In this method you set the meter to cut off the charging circuit after the necessary ampere-hour input has been supplied to the battery. This input depends upon the number of plates per cell, the normal specific gravity of the electrolyte in the cells when fully charged, and the specific gravity of the electrolyte in the cells when the charge begins.   The necessary input is determined by reference to a chart supplied with all batteries by the manufacturer.   A section from one such chart appears as Fig. 8-4.

Manual Control.   *Specific-gravity Method.*   In the specific-gravity method of manual control, the specific gravity of a pilot cell (a test cell selected at random but changed perhaps monthly) is recorded hourly.   If the charge is being applied by the modified constant-voltage type of equipment, it is terminated when the specific gravity is 10 to 20 points below the last equalizing charge value.   If the charge is being applied by the two-rate method, the charge rate is *reduced* when the battery starts to gas or when the specific gravity reaches 1.200 to 1.220.   One or more reductions may be required.   Use the finish rate when the specific gravity is above 1.200, and stop charging when the specific gravity is 20 points below the last equalizing charge value.

Volt-ampere Method.   In this method the battery is put on charge and the charge rate and battery voltage are recorded hourly.   The charge is continued until the

AMPERE HOUR METER CHARGING CHART
STORAGE BATTERIES

Relation of Electrolyte Specific Gravity to Ampere Hour Input Required For A Complete Charge

Sp. Gr. of Electrolyte at start of charge. Temp. 77° F. (25° C.)	Use the following values for setting the ampere hour meter														
	NUMBER OF PLATES PER CELL														
	9	11	13	15	17	19	21	23	25	27	29	31	33	35	41
1.280	0	0	0	0	0	0	0	0	0	0	0	0	0	0	0
1.270	15	18	22	26	29	33	37	40	44	48	51	55	59	62	73
1.260	29	37	44	51	59	66	73	81	88	95	103	110	117	125	147
1.250	44	55	66	77	88	99	110	121	132	143	154	165	176	187	220
1.240	59	73	88	103	117	132	147	161	176	191	205	220	235	249	293
1.230	73	92	110	128	147	165	183	202	220	238	257	275	293	312	367
1.220	88	110	132	154	176	198	220	242	264	286	308	330	352	374	440
1.210	103	128	154	180	205	231	257	282	308	334	359	385	411	436	513
1.200	117	147	176	205	235	264	293	323	353	381	411	440	469	499	587
1.190	132	165	198	231	264	297	330	363	396	429	462	495	528	561	660
1.180	147	183	220	257	293	330	367	403	440	477	513	550	587	623	733
1.170	161	202	242	282	323	363	403	444	484	524	565	605	645	686	807
1.160	176	220	264	308	352	396	440	484	528	572	616	660	704	748	880
1.150	190	238	286	334	381	429	477	524	572	620	667	715	763	810	953
1.140	205	257	308	359	411	462	513	564	616	667	718	770	821	872	1026
1.130	220	275	330	385	440	495	550	605	660	715	770	825	880	935	1100

SETTINGS FOR BATTERY WITH FULLY CHARGED SPECIFIC GRAVITY OF 1.280

FIG. 8-4. Section from charging chart.

battery voltage at the switchboard reaches the equivalent of 2.30 volts per cell at the battery terminals.   Then the charging rate is reduced as required to keep the battery voltage from exceeding this value until the charge rate has been reduced to the finishing rate.   Charging should be stopped 1 hr after the battery voltage reaches 2.30 volts per cell and after the rate has been reduced to the finishing rate.

During the past ten years, rectifiers have been developed for motive-power battery charging that have an inherent characteristic of causing the charge rate to decrease as the charge progresses, similar to the decrease with a modified-constant-voltage charger.   No contacts are used in the control circuit to accomplish this.

One type of rectifier has what, when first observed, appears to be an unusual characteristic in that, when the battery is approximately 80 per cent charged, the charge rate oscillates from zero to about one-half the start charge rate of the battery. Oscillating of the charge rate is normal for this type of rectifier, and as the charge progresses, the rate tends to remain at approximately zero most of the time, with an occasional pulse to a higher rate, but dropping back immediately to the very low rate.   This is a normal characteristic for this charger, and no effort should be made to adjust the charger to remain on the higher charge rate all the time.

A static-type silicon-diode charger has been developed which employs no contacts in the control circuit, but does provide a taper charge. This charger has an inherent design characteristic of automatically compensating for a plus or minus 10 per cent voltage fluctuation in the a-c line without affecting the d-c output.

Before attempting to adjust any charger, it is well to study the manufacturer's instructions furnished with the charger.

When a battery is at the end of its recharge and is gassing, the charge rate should be down to finishing rate or lower. Whenever it is observed that the charge rate is in excess of the published finishing rate at the end of charge, and cell voltages are above 2.50 volts, an investigation should be made to determine the cause and correct it. Charge rates in excess of published finishing rates cause a reduction in the life of the battery.

UPKEEP

Routine Care. Once each week inspect the battery carefully, making sure that all connections are tight; remove any dust or dirt accumulation from the top of the battery. Keeping the battery clean by washing with water, neutralizing as required, is important. Any acid accumulation on the cover or case should be neutralized with ammonia or baking soda at least once a month. All terminals and other metal parts should be kept free of corrosion.

The height of the electrolyte should be checked daily. The level should never be allowed to drop below the top of the plates. Conversely, when electrolyte that has evaporated is replaced, cells should not be filled above the bottom of the vent tubes. Overfilling causes loss of acid, therefore reduced capacity.

Use only water approved for battery use. Usually, tap water is OK, but if in doubt, use distilled water. And be sure to add any necessary water before the battery is recharged; this will ensure that the water will be thoroughly mixed with the electrolyte. Keep records of the amount of water used and the date of each filling. Excessive water requirements (if, say, water is required more than once a week) are an indication of overcharging, and a check on your charging equipment is indicated.

Make sure that vent plugs are always kept tightly in place, and see that the small gas escape holes don't become clogged. If plugs need cleaning, let them stand in a bucket of clear water for 30 min or so.

How to Prevent Excessive Discharge. This is one of the most common causes of battery problems.

Past Experience. This is perhaps an overly obvious but common method. As outlined above, batteries should be rated according to the job for which they are being used. A fully charged battery is capable of doing a certain amount of work or lasting a certain length of time in a specific service. As long as the job is reasonably standardized (i.e., the equipment powered by the battery is not called on to do extra work during the time cycle), a schedule can be made for battery recharging with very few production failures.

Operators' Experience. A skilled operator can tell from the action of the equipment when the batteries are reaching the point at which they should be charged.

Discharge Indicator. An indicator of this type is mounted on the panel of the truck. It indicates the voltage of the battery. Usually, the scale is marked—instead of in volts—"Full—½—Empty." Such meters should be read when the truck is moving under battery power, not when the truck is standing. A variation of this type of indicator is also commonly used. In this type, the voltage of the battery activates a temperature-compensated relay that in turn operates a bulb that glows when the battery should be charged. The indicator light goes on and off during normal operation but stays on when the battery is close to failure.

Ampere-hour Meter. With this type of meter, the number of ampere-hours removed from the battery is recorded. (Some scales are calibrated in "ampere-hours remaining.") Thus the operator knows how much power is left in the battery.

How to Determine Battery Conditions. Three methods are in common use: (1) maintenance records, (2) test discharge, (3) internal inspection.

Records. The purpose of records is to provide a day-to-day case history so that any variations from normal can be detected quickly and acted upon. Daily records should include date, battery number, number of truck battery was taken from, specific gravity of battery when put on charge (pilot cell reading), temperature of pilot cell, time put on charge, time taken off charge, specific gravity when taken off charge, and truck number battery is assigned to. These are enough facts to keep a good case history on the battery.

If specific-gravity (corrected for temperature) and time-on-charge data are compared with the previous day's reading, any abnormal battery use or abuse will be indicated and can be acted upon.

As a long-run check, most manufacturers recommend that special specific-gravity and voltage readings be taken of each cell of the battery every 6 months—after an equalizing charge has been applied. Comparison of these readings with the readings of the last such test will show any long-term changes in battery condition as well as differences between cells.

Test Discharge. Such a test should be made any time there is a question as to whether or not the battery is delivering its rated capacity. The procedure is as follows:

The battery is given an equalizing charge, and the fully charged specific gravity of each cell is adjusted to normal. Starting time is noted, and the battery is discharged at the standard "6-hr rate" given in the operating data supplied with the battery by the manufacturer. Individual cell voltages and the over-all battery voltage should be recorded 15 min after the test is started, then hourly until the voltage of any one cell gets down to 1.80. Thereafter, voltage measurements should be made at 15-min intervals. Record the time when each cell voltage reaches 1.75. When the majority of the cells reach 1.75 volts, record the time and terminate the test. Measure the specific gravity of each cell immediately.

An examination of the specific-gravity readings will indicate whether the cells in the battery are uniform or one or more of them is low in capacity. If the cells are uniform and the battery delivered 80 per cent or more of rated capacity (took at least 4 hr and 48 min to get down to 1.75 volts), it may be returned to service.

Internal Inspection. If the test discharge indicates that the battery is not capable of delivering at least 80 per cent of rated capacity and all cells are uniform, an internal inspection of one of the cells is indicated. . Failure to meet capacity ratings may be caused by an internal shunt which can be repaired. The positive plates, which wear out first, should be examined. If they are falling apart or the grids (the lead framework that supports the lead peroxide) have many frame fractures, a new battery is needed. But if the positive plates are in good condition and the cells contain little sediment, the battery may be sulfated. The negative plates of a sulfated battery will have a slatelike feeling, being hard and gritty and having a sandy feeling when rubbed between the fingers. (A good negative plate, when fully charged, is spongy to the touch and gives a metallic sheen when stroked with the fingernail.) Sulfation is such a common condition that a special section on its causes and treatment is included below.

Causes and Treatment of Sulfation. A "sulfated" battery is one in which abnormal lead sulfate has formed on the plates. This affects the normal chemical reactions within the battery, causing loss of capacity. Most common causes of sulfation are undercharging, repeated partial charges, neglect of equalizing charge, standing in a partially or completely discharged condition, low electrolyte, specific gravity more than 0.015 above normal, and high temperature. The following steps often will restore a sulfated battery to operating condition:

1. Clean battery.
2. Bring electrolyte level to proper height by adding water.
3. Put battery on charge at the prescribed finishing rate until full ampere-hour capacity has been supplied the battery. If during this charge the temperature of the battery exceeds 110°F, reduce the charge rate. If any cell gives test voltage readings 0.20 volt below average cell voltage, pull and repair the cell before continuing the charge.

4. Continue the charge at the finishing rate until the specific gravity shows no charge for a 4-hr period.
5. Give the battery a test discharge (procedure outlined in previous section).
6. If the battery gives rated capacity, no further special treatment is needed, except that battery should be recharged again immediately. If the battery does not deliver at least 80 per cent of rated capacity, continue the discharge until one or more cells reach 1.0 volt.
7. Repeat steps 3, 4, and 5.
8. If the test does not show that the battery has delivered at least 80 per cent of capacity, repeat steps 2, 3, 4, and 5. If the battery does not now deliver at least 80 per cent of capacity, assume that it should be replaced.

Causes and Remedies of Common Battery Troubles. In the listing that follows it is impossible to consider all sources of battery trouble. The ones listed are common troubles and will serve as a starting point for investigating the cause of unsatisfactory performance. Eight symptoms are listed; after each are listed possible causes. Where the remedy for the cause is perfectly obvious, it is omitted. Where, however, there might be some doubt as to the correct remedy, it is indicated along with the cause, is marked with the symbol R, and is enclosed in parentheses.

Symptom: Battery will not take a charge.

Possible causes: (1) Direct-current charging circuit fuse blown or missing. (2) Circuit in charging receptacle or plug open, or connection of cable to stud loose. (3) Alternating-current line fuses blown or missing. (4) Alternating-current line switch open. (5) Circuit in control lead or circuit open, preventing contactor from pulling in. (6) Charging plug not pushed all the way into receptacle. (7) Charging rate too low. (R: Check ammeter for accuracy. See below, under Symptom: Battery takes too long to charge.) (8) No voltage output from generator. (R: Check field circuit; if open, correct. Check brush contact to armature; correct by replacing brushes or adjusting so they don't stick.) (9) Bus voltage too low, caused by incorrect tap setting in rectifier or too low voltage from generator. (10) With initial equipment, connections to charging receptacle reversed.

Symptom: Battery takes too long to charge.

Possible causes: (1) Connection poor in charging circuit. (R: Check lugs, bolted connections, charging leads, plugs, and receptacles for high resistance joints, and correct.) (2) Battery overdischarged. (3) With two-rate charging, charging equipment does not provide high starting rate. (R: Check for open in control circuit to provide high rate. Determine cause and correct.) (4) With two-rate rectifier charging equipment: (a) voltage relay connected for smaller number of cells than in battery; (b) applied a-c voltage too low under load conditions (R: Install greater capacity line to rectifier to reduce voltage drop, or relocate rectifier nearer to incoming a-c source); (c) primary transformer taps not set for voltage applied; (d) voltage relay operating below standard voltage (i.e., 2.37 volts per cell); (e) start of charging rate too low; (f) end of charging rate too low; (g) start of charging rate too high. (5) Where voltage relay is used in control circuit for two-rate charge, temperature of charging control equipment may be materially higher than battery operating temperature. (R: Provide better ventilation for charging equipment, or relocate it to an area where atmospheric temperature is the same as temperature in area where battery operates.) (6) With modified constant-voltage charging: (a) bus voltage too low; (b) bus voltage decreases as load decreases (R: Adjust generator for flat characteristic); (c) ballast resistance too great. (7) Charging leads reversed, or charging-equipment polarity reversed. (8) Battery not placed on proper charging circuit when installation has various battery sizes. (9) Charge not terminated when battery is fully charged.

Symptom: Battery will not work full shift.

Possible causes: (1) Cell voltages and specific gravity uneven. (R: Give an equalizing charge.) (2) Electrolyte level low. (3) Battery not charged before going into service. (4) Two or more cell leakers in steel tray. (R: Replace broken jars.) (5) One or more cells cut out of battery. (6) Battery with incorrect number of cells assigned to equipment. (7) Specific gravity below normal. (8) Impurities in electrolyte. (9) Operator riding brakes. (10) Operator using reverse instead of brakes. (11) Load too great. (12) Wheels, axles, and bearings need grease. (13) Tires underinflated. (14) Brakes dragging. (15) Wheels deeply grooved. (16) Ruts in roadbed deep. (17) Series field in motor shorted or grounded. (R: Clear grounds and insulate wiring.) (18) Armature needs repairs. (19) Grounds on equipment. (20) Excessive grades along route traveled. (21) Service required exceeds capacity of equipment. (22) When batteries are in two halves, discharged half has been paired with a charged half. (23) Uneven number of cells in two halves, where split batteries are used in parallel-start, series-run control circuits.

Symptom: Battery overheats on charge.
Possible causes: (1) Finish rate too high. (2) High-charge rate on too long. (R: Reduce voltage operating point of voltage relay.) (3) Timer not set correctly. (4) Ampere-hour meter not set correctly. (5) Per cent overcharge setting of ampere-hour meter set above correct level of 12 per cent. (6) Timer set for too many hours. (7) Two-rate charge did not change over to low rate. (R: Check operation of voltage relay. Check for open voltage-relay circuit. Check for open in change-rate control lead. See if voltage relay is connected for same number of cells as in battery.) (8) Bus voltage too high. (9) Charge rate too high. (10) Charge not stopped—automatic mechanism does not terminate charge. (R: See that voltage relay is connected for same number of cells as in battery. Check timing mechanism. Check for open in control leads. Check operation of voltage relay. Check ampere-hour meter for accuracy and operation at low rates; clean and calibrate it.) (11) Ventilation poor. (12) Separators worn through. (13) Sediment space filled. (14) Internal shunt. (15) Fully charged specific gravity is below normal, and attendant continues charge to increase specific gravity. (R: Adjust specific gravity with acid.)

Symptom: Battery overheats on discharge.
Possible causes: (1) Overdischarge (beyond allowable limit of 1.130). (2) Battery too small. (3) Ventilation poor. (4) Burn of connectors to cell terminals poor. (5) Load excessive. (6) Battery worn out. (7) Separators worn through. (8) Internal shunt. (9) Battery capacity temporarily reduced because of low fully charged specific gravity. (10) Battery not fully charged before being put in service, resulting in overdischarging. (11) Electrolyte level low. (12) Battery not heat-insulated from resistor in charging equipment. (13) Atmospheric temperature too high.

Symptom: Electrolyte level low.
Possible causes: (1) Jar broken or cracked. (2) Water additions neglected. (3) Cell overlooked when adding water. (4) Too much overcharging (R: If automatically controlled, check voltage relay, timer, change-rate relay. If manually controlled, terminate charge when specific gravity is 10 points below last equalizing charge value. Change from high rate to low rate when specific gravity reaches 1.200).

Symptoms: Cell voltages unequal.
Possible causes: (1) Overdischarge. (R: Give an equalizing charge.) (2) Equalizing charges lacking. (3) Internal shunt. (4) Top of battery very dirty. (5) Cells operated with low electrolyte level. (6) Fully charged specific gravity of cell low. (7) Sediment space filled. (R: Replace battery.) (8) Positive plates worn out. (R: Replace battery.) (9) Half tap on cells for lower voltage circuit. (R: Remove tap, and connect load to battery terminals through resistance.) (10) External source (such as charging resistance on locomotive) heating certain cells. (11) Contact poor in controller on split-circuit batteries (parallel and series on discharge, all series on charge). (12) Impurities in cell. (13) Charging rate varies. (14) See also symptom below.

Symptom: Unequal specific gravity between cells.
Possible causes: (1) All items under "Cell voltages unequal," above. (2) Overfilled with water. (3) Cell operated with cracked jar. (4) Acid not adjusted properly when jar was changed. (5) Battery operated with vent caps out of place. (6) Sealing compound leaks. (7) Battery operated with broken cover. (8) Neutralizing material in cell.

REPAIRS

Most of the repairs to storage batteries consist of removing a part of the battery and replacing it. In this section, we shall therefore outline the procedure for disassembling and reassembling a typical battery. The manufacturer's instructions that were received with the battery will undoubtedly outline any specific procedures in handling their units.

Drilling Intercell Connectors. In most batteries, the lead insert of the cover, the cell post, and the intercell connectors are all welded together. To remove a cell from the circuit of an element from a jar, it is therefore necessary to remove the connector or cut it in two.

There are two methods of removing a connector. One is to use a special drill, Fig. 8-5, that allows the cell post to remain but cuts the bond to the lead insert of the cover. The other method is to drill through the center of each post, using a $1\frac{5}{16}$ drill, to a depth of $\frac{3}{8}$ in. After the intercell connectors are drilled, they can be lifted off. On some batteries it is possible to saw a connector. It should be cut above the space where the two jars meet. Then the cell can be pulled out of the tray.

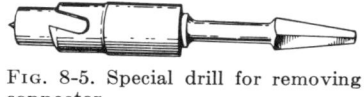

Fig. 8-5. Special drill for removing connector.

Removing a Cell from a Tray. After the connector is removed, use a warm compound knife and cut the compound from between the jar of the cell and the adjacent cells or tray. Penetrating oil or kerosene mixed with regular oil should be run into the space between cells to act as a lubricant. Work the cell back and forth to see that it is loose; then lift straight up. Small cells can be lifted manually. To lift heavy cells, attach a cell puller (a self-tapping nut with loop attached). Always attach the puller on the negative post. If the cell has two negative posts, use two pullers with a piece of wood through the loops. Lift slowly and carefully, vibrating the lifting rope after a strain is put on to loosen the cell.

Replacing a Jar. Have the new jar ready. Remove the jar to be replaced from the tray (as outlined above). If the cell is to remain out of the battery for a day or two, the space in the tray should be blocked to prevent jars in the tray from bowing out into the space from which the cell was removed.

Cut the compound from around the top of the jar with a warm compound knife, keeping it very close to the inside of the jar cell. Heat the outside of the jar on all four sides with a blowtorch. Place the jar hold-down clips and chains on the jar, and use the cell puller to lift the element halfway out of the jar. Allow the element to remain in this position a minute or so to drain. Then remove the element, lay it down on a wood board surface with the flat side of the negative plate down. The element should not be exposed to air any longer than necessary. (If the element starts to heat, sprinkle it with water and place in a jar.)

After warming the clean jar so that it is pliable, slide it over the bottom of the element carefully, using the compound knife as a guide. Then lift up the jar and lower the element into the jar slowly and carefully so that the separators are not broken or damaged. (If the jar is square, be sure that the element is placed in the jar so that the ribs of the jar are in the correct direction—at right angles to the plate.)

Clean, neutralize, and dry the surface of the jar, and cover. Reseal the cover with a sealing compound. (When pouring a seal, use a compound knife in one hand, hold the saucepan of compound in the other. The knife is used to cut off the pour and catch excess compound.) Remove any excess compound that may have run down the outside of the jar. Fill the cell with correct electrolyte (the same as in adjacent cells or higher) to the top of the splash plate. The cell should then receive an equalizing charge, and the acid should be adjusted.

Place the cell in the tray, being sure polarity is correct. The final step is to reburn the intercell connector. This is covered separately below. But first it is important to note that the post and connectors have been cleaned in preparation for burning, all vent caps must be removed from the surrounding cells and each cell blown to make sure that all gas is removed from each cell before starting to reburn the connectors. (The gas given off by surrounding cells while charging is highly explosive.)   Vent holes of adjacent cells should be covered with layers of damp cloth before burning begins.

Lead Burning.   Lead burning, or welding, may be done with an acetylene and oxygen torch or with a carbon burning outfit.   The following paragraphs describe how to use a carbon burner, but the same precautions and sequence of operations will apply when using a flame.

The carbon burner tool uses 6 volts or three cells for its power.   The burning tool may be connected directly to the battery being worked on.   The carbon rod is pointed like the writing end of a pencil with approximately a $\frac{1}{8}$-in. tip.   When possible, the carbon burner is connected to the battery so that the carbon is of negative polarity. This makes lead welding easier, as it tends to keep the joint and working surface clean.

The lead surfaces to be burned together must be clean.   A wire brush may be used for cleaning after the surfaces have been neutralized.   The inside hole of a connector may be cleaned with a knife.   Clean the tip of the carbon with a wire brush before starting the operation.

Dark glasses are recommended to protect the eyes.   Use about $1\frac{1}{2}$-in. carbon extension.

The secret of making a good joint is to have clean materials, use a hot carbon without too high a voltage (three cells of a partially charged battery is sufficient), and thoroughly heat the center of the part being worked on to a molten condition before adding lead.   Work rapidly to complete the operation before the entire part melts. Whenever possible, use a damp rag to surround the part being worked on.   This applies to building up posts, burning on connectors, and burning the button to the top of the connector.

After making a burn, allow the joint to cool undisturbed.   In cooling, the lead will shrink slightly.   Do not move or disturb the joint during cooling, as this may cause the lead to crystallize and result in a poor joint.   To determine if the joint was properly made, grip the part with pliers after the burn has cooled and endeavor to remove the part by pulling straight up.   If it is possible to pull the connectors, post, or terminal off, the burn was improperly made, and the weak point or cause of failure may be seen by examining the two surfaces that pulled apart.

Following is a detailed description of various jobs that can be done using a carbon burner.   In all cases, the lead surface must be clean, dry, and free of acid.

Building up Post.   If the post was damaged in removing the old connector, it is possible to build up the post, using a post mold, which can be purchased from the battery manufacturer.   Place the mold firmly over the post, extending down over the post about $\frac{3}{16}$ in.   The small-diameter hole of the mold should be at the top.   Place the tip of the carbon in the center of the post, and hold it there until it is cherry red. Then touch the new burning lead to the hot carbon.   The lead will melt and drop into the mold.   Move the point of the carbon around so that the new molten lead is mixed with the molten lead on the top of the post.   Add more lead, and gradually raise the carbon until the post mold is full.   Allow the lead to cool before disturbing or removing the mold.   (Do not let the carbon touch the side of the mold during the operation.)

Burning on a New Connector.   Clean the new connector, both posts.   Place the connector on the posts to be connected, and surround the post ends of the connector with a damp rag.   Place the tip of the carbon in the center of one post, and hold it there until it is white hot.   Then gently move the carbon around the top of the post with about $\frac{1}{16}$ in. of the tip of the carbon in molten lead until the carbon is out to the joint between the post and connector and molten lead from the post mixes with molten lead from the connector.   Only one trip around the post is required to burn the post to the connector.   Then return the carbon to the center of the post and add new lead until the post is built up to the level of the top of the connector.   Make another pass with the carbon tip around the outside of the post.   Remove the carbon, and allow the joint to cool.   Then place the button mold on the connector, follow the same operation of melting the top of the post, and add molten lead to fill to the top of the button mold.   Repeat this operation for the other post to be connected.

Reconnecting Sawed Connector.   As mentioned above, sometimes connectors are sawed through when a cell is removed.   The connector can be burned together by using a connector mold, which is simply a shallow trough that fits under the break. It is blocked into place with small wedges.   Place the tip of the carbon on the piece of the connector that is in the electrical circuit for the carbon burner, and hold the carbon there until it is white hot.   Add new lead, and move the tip of the carbon through the molten lead to ensure that the new lead is fused with the lead of each half of the connector.

Chapter 9

NICKEL-IRON-ALKALINE STORAGE BATTERIES

By A. E. CARY
Exide Industrial Division
The Electric Storage Battery Company
Philadelphia, Pa.

A storage battery, like any other kind of electrical equipment, always gives the best results when it is properly applied. Correct application is largely a matter of selecting the proper number and capacity of cells to provide the voltage and current required by the equipment with which it is to be used and the conditions under which the equipment operates.

Note: Cycle service is one in which the battery is discharged to or nearly to the equivalent of 1 volt per cell at normal rate at regular intervals, usually once a day, and is charged at the same intervals. *Examples:* Industrial trucks, mine locomotives and shuttle cars, and, in general, any electrical equipment for which the battery is the normal power supply.

Stand-by service is one in which the battery stands by ready to furnish power during interruptions in the normal power supply. *Examples:* Controls and signals of various kinds, railway passenger-train car-lighting and air-conditioning systems, and, in general, any electrical equipment which, for safety or other reasons, must be kept continuously operable.

A *trickle charge* is a continuous charge at a very low rate which compensates for standing losses and maintains a stand-by battery in a fully charged condition. The term also is applied to low rates of charge which compensate for small amounts of intermittent discharge in addition to standing losses.

The number of cells needed in the battery is determined by the voltage requirements of the equipment it is to operate in relation to the average voltage per cell. When discharging at their normal rates, all types and sizes of cells have an average discharge voltage of 1.2. This voltage, like that of a series-wound d-c generator, tends to increase at lower rates and decrease at higher rates, so that the rate of discharge is also a factor. In most cases, however, the number of cells is not far from the number needed, on the basis of 1.2 volts per cell, to add up to the voltage required. For example, an electrical industrial truck having 36-volt motors should be provided with a 30-cell battery.

The ampere-hour capacity of the cells needed in the battery is determined by the rate of current consumed by the equipment to be operated by the battery and the length of time it is to be operated on one charge of the battery. This time period, in the principal applications in which the battery is the normal power supply for the equipment (cycle service), is usually the regular daily working period—in the majority of cases, one 8-hr shift—while in stand-by applications it is usually the maximum expected outage of the normal power supply.

After the required ampere-hour capacity has been determined, cells are selected having a rated capacity not less than 25 per cent higher. This is a safety factor which allows for contingencies and ensures that the battery will be of ample capacity up to the end of its normal service life (see Table 9-1).

Table 9-1. Cell Data

| Type of cell | Capacity, amp-hr | Normal rate, amp | Electrolyte | |
			Recommended level above plates, in.	Renewal per cell, lb
A3	$112\frac{1}{2}$	$22\frac{1}{2}$	$\frac{1}{2}$	2.21
A3H	$112\frac{1}{2}$	$22\frac{1}{2}$	3	3.12
A3HW	$112\frac{1}{2}$	$22\frac{1}{2}$	3	6.72
A4	150	30	$\frac{1}{2}$	3.13
A4H	150	30	3	4.47
A4HW	150	30	3	8.09
A5	$187\frac{1}{2}$	$37\frac{1}{2}$	$\frac{1}{2}$	3.60
A5H	$187\frac{1}{2}$	$37\frac{1}{2}$	3	5.34
A5HW	$187\frac{1}{2}$	$37\frac{1}{2}$	3	9.15
A6	225	45	$\frac{1}{2}$	4.39
A6H	225	45	3	6.61
A6HW	225	45	3	10.11
A7	$262\frac{1}{2}$	$52\frac{1}{2}$	$\frac{1}{2}$	5.07
A7H	$262\frac{1}{2}$	$52\frac{1}{2}$	3	7.24
A7HW	$262\frac{1}{2}$	$52\frac{1}{2}$	3	13.26
A8	300	60	$\frac{1}{2}$	5.86
A8H	300	60	3	8.69
A8HW	300	60	3	13.22
A10	375	75	$\frac{1}{2}$	7.78
A10H	375	75	3	11.22
A10HW	375	75	3	15.31
A12	450	90	$\frac{1}{2}$	9.44
A12H	450	90	3	13.80
A12HW	450	90	3	17.14
A14	525	105	$\frac{1}{2}$	11.01
A14H	525	105	3	15.78
A14HW	525	105	3	19.43
A16	600	120	$\frac{1}{2}$	12.33
A16H	600	120	3	17.95
A18H	675	135	3	20.51
A20H	750	150	3	23.25
A24H	900	180	3	28.19
B1	$18\frac{3}{4}$	$3\frac{3}{4}$	$\frac{1}{2}$	1.33
B1H	$18\frac{3}{4}$	$3\frac{3}{4}$	$2\frac{1}{4}$	1.93*
B2	$37\frac{1}{2}$	$7\frac{1}{2}$	$\frac{1}{2}$	1.07
B2H	$37\frac{1}{2}$	$7\frac{1}{2}$	$2\frac{1}{4}$	1.61
B4	75	15	$\frac{1}{2}$	1.94
B4H	75	15	$2\frac{1}{4}$	3.03
B4HW	75	15	$2\frac{1}{4}$	4.88
B6	$112\frac{1}{2}$	$22\frac{1}{2}$	$\frac{1}{2}$	2.68
B6H	$112\frac{1}{2}$	$22\frac{1}{2}$	$2\frac{1}{4}$	4.34
B12H	225	45	$2\frac{1}{4}$	8.93
C3	169	$33\frac{3}{4}$	1	4.02
C4; C4A	225	45	1	4.86
C5; C5A	281	$56\frac{1}{4}$	1	5.51
C6; C6A	338	$67\frac{1}{2}$	1	6.74
C7; C7A	394	$78\frac{3}{4}$	1	7.63
C8	450	90	1	8.65
C10	563	$112\frac{1}{2}$	1	11.42
C12	675	135	1	13.72

* When ordering for B1H, specify as "B1H Renewal Solution."

Table 9-1. Cell Data (*Continued*)

Type of cell	Capacity, amp-hr	Normal rate, amp	Electrolyte	
			Recommended level above plates, in.	Renewal per cell, lb
MC4; 4A	285	57	$\frac{3}{4}$	5.53
MC5; 5A	355	71	$\frac{3}{4}$	6.51
MC6; 6A	425	85	$\frac{3}{4}$	7.63
MC7; 7A	495	99	$\frac{3}{4}$	8.78
MC8	570	114	$\frac{3}{4}$	10.24
MC9	640	128	$\frac{3}{4}$	13.40
MC10	710	142	$\frac{3}{4}$	13.80
D4; D4A	300	60	$1\frac{1}{4}$	6.45
D5; D5A	375	75	$1\frac{1}{4}$	7.56
D6; D6A	450	90	$1\frac{1}{4}$	8.96
D7	525	105	$1\frac{1}{4}$	10.20
D8	600	120	$1\frac{1}{4}$	11.48
D10	750	150	$1\frac{1}{4}$	15.15
D12	900	180	$1\frac{1}{4}$	18.59
F2B	10	2	$\frac{5}{8}$	0.21
N1	$5\frac{5}{8}$	$1\frac{1}{8}$	$\frac{1}{2}$	0.43
N2	$11\frac{1}{4}$	$2\frac{1}{4}$	$\frac{1}{2}$	0.31
E3; E3B	300	47	$\frac{3}{4}$	5.8
E4; E4B	400	63	$\frac{3}{4}$	7.7
E5; E5B	500	78	$\frac{3}{4}$	9.7
E6; E6B	600	94	$\frac{3}{4}$	11.2
E7; E7B	700	110	$\frac{3}{4}$	13.5
E8; E8B	800	125	$\frac{3}{4}$	15.5
E10; E10B	1,000	157	$\frac{3}{4}$	19.2
F4B	500	78	1	11.2
F5B	625	98	1	13.7
F6B	750	117	1	16.2
F7B	875	137	1	18.7
F8B	1,000	157	1	21.2
F10B	1,250	196	1	26.2

As an example of the selection of a battery for regular cycle service, assume that a battery is to be applied to an industrial truck which consumes 44 amp-hr per hr for one 8-hr shift per day.   The total required ampere-hour capacity would amount to 44 multiplied by 8, or 352 amp-hr, and the rated capacity of the cells to be selected would be 352 plus 25 per cent, or 440 amp-hr.

If the truck operates two 8-hr shifts, use two batteries, each of ample capacity for 8 hr of operation, and exchange them between shifts.   If the work extends over three shifts, use three batteries of the same capacity and exchange them at 8-hr intervals, or if the necessary space is available, it is good practice to use two batteries of sufficient capacity for 12 hr of operation and exchange them at 12-hr intervals.   In this way it is possible to provide the necessary battery capacity for any schedule of operation up to 24 hr a day and, at the same time, to avoid working any one battery more than one cycle a day.   This is an important rule of sound battery application.

A battery for stand-by service is selected in the same manner as for cycle service except that the calculation is based on the ampere-hours required for the maximum expected outage instead of an 8-hr shift.   Assume that a battery is needed to furnish stand-by power for caboose communication equipment during intervals when an axle-driven generator, the normal power source, is not in operation and that a total operating reserve of 20 hr is desired. The equipment draws 6 amp for 40 min per hr while receiving and 15 amp for 20 min per hr while transmitting. Under these conditions the amount of current required of the battery would amount to $\frac{40}{60}$ of 6 plus $\frac{20}{60}$ of 15, or 9 amp-hr per hr, and 180 amp-hr for 20 hr of stand-by operation. The rated capacity of the cells to be selected would be 180 plus 25 per cent, or 225 amp-hr.

In stand-by installations, it is important not only that the battery be of suitable voltage and capacity to carry the load satisfactorily during outages in the primary power supply but also that the power available for charging be ample to recharge the battery without undue delay following the intervals of discharge and maintain it in a satisfactorily charged condition. How much power will be required depends mainly upon how often, how long, and at what rates the battery will be on discharge.

If the discharge is infrequent, short, and at low rates, power sufficient only for continuous trickle charging would be enough. Emergency power-supply systems for call bells, signals, and other equipment having small and infrequent current demands are examples.

On the other hand, when the discharge is frequent or prolonged, especially if at relatively high rates, sufficient power may be needed to charge the battery at an average of its full normal rate if it is to be maintained at a satisfactorily high state of charge.

OPERATION

The required charging voltage varies according to the method of charging employed and ranges from approximately 1.50 to 1.55 volts per cell for trickle charging to 1.84 volts per cell or more for charging at normal and higher rates. The charge input is measured in ampere-hours and is the average ampere rate multiplied by the number of hours the battery is on charge. The ampere-hours required are the ampere-hours previously discharged plus an efficiency factor which averages approximately 25 per cent. Charging at an average of the normal rate of the battery usually gives the best over-all results and is generally recommended.

For rating purposes, a discharged battery is defined as one that has been discharged to the equivalent of 1 volt per cell at normal rate. This usually represents the lower limit of the range in voltage needed for fully satisfactory operation of the equipment for which the battery supplies power. It is not necessary, however, that the discharge be stopped at this or any other prescribed limit if further output at a lower voltage can be utilized. This will not harm the battery. Temperature rise is the principal limitation on charge rates. Any rate is safe as long as it does not result in raising the electrolyte temperature above 115°F.

Boosting, or supplementary charging at high rates during brief periods of idleness, is sometimes useful *as an emergency measure only* in order to obtain more than the usual day's work from a battery that is regularly cycled. Regular or frequent boosting is an indication that the battery is of inadequate capacity for the work, and is not recommended. It is not a substitute for a correctly applied battery. In case you consider it necessary to boost a battery, use the following as a guide:

5 times normal for 5 min
4 times normal for 15 min
3 times normal for 30 min
2 times normal for 60 min

Take thermometer readings of the electrolyte in the cells nearest the center or warmest part of the battery, and stop the charge if the temperature rises to 115°F. Any frothing at the filler openings is also an indication that boosting has gone too far and should be discontinued immediately. A battery that has been discharged need not be immediately recharged. No injurious reactions will take place if charging is delayed.

Charging Batteries That Are Cycled. Sources of d-c power for charging batteries that are cycled may be (1) d-c power lines, (2) motor generators which accept either d-c or a-c primary power, or (3) rectifiers which accept a-c primary power.

If a d-c power line is available at a potential of 1.84 to 1.85 volts per cell or higher, the principal equipment needed to use it for charging at an average of the normal rates of the batteries consists of a reverse-current relay and a control panel for each battery, together with suitable leads between the power line, the panels, and the batteries.   A 115-volt d-c power line can be utilized satisfactorily for charging batteries of 50 to 60 cells or for charging two or more batteries in series when the total cells add up to not more than 60 and the cells have the same normal rate.

Unless a number of batteries of the same normal rate are to be charged at one time, it is usually more convenient to charge from a power source of a voltage suitable for the purpose.   For this reason, motor generators and rectifiers are usually preferable.   They are commercially available in a range of voltages and capacities suitable for charging virtually all types and sizes of batteries in general use and are furnished complete with control equipment for automatic charging.

Since a battery does not always require the same input, it is desirable to employ some means of determining the amount needed each day so that the ampere-hour meter or time switch may be set accordingly.   For this purpose, the use of the Exide charge test fork is recommended.

To ensure maximum cooling, be sure the battery is exposed to free air circulation while it is standing and on charge.   If it is charged in an enclosure of any kind such as the battery box of an industrial truck or locomotive, open the cover.   If it is charged on a bench, use a bench having an open top so that air can circulate upward through the bottom of the battery.

Table 9-2. Recommended and Minimum Levels of Electrolyte

Type of cell	Recommended electrolyte level	Minimum electrolyte level
A	$\frac{1}{2}$ in. above plate tops	At plate tops
AH	3 in. above plate tops	$1\frac{1}{2}$ in. above plate tops
AHW	3 in. above plate tops	$1\frac{1}{2}$ in. above plate tops
B	$\frac{1}{2}$ in. above plate tops	At plate tops
BH	$2\frac{1}{4}$ in. above plate tops	1 in. above plate tops
BHW	$2\frac{1}{4}$ in. above plate tops	1 in. above plate tops
C	1 in. above plate tops	At plate tops
MC	$\frac{3}{4}$ in. above plate tops	At plate tops
D	$1\frac{1}{4}$ in. above plate tops	At plate tops
F	1 in. above plate tops	At plate tops
G	$\frac{1}{2}$ in. above plate tops	At plate tops
GH	3 in. above plate tops	$1\frac{1}{2}$ in. above plate tops
L	$\frac{1}{2}$ in. above plate tops	At plate tops
N	$\frac{1}{2}$ in. above plate tops	At plate tops

Charging Stand-by Batteries.   The rate at which charging current is forced through the battery will vary with the voltage at the battery terminals.   At normal temperatures, it usually ranges from 1.50 to 1.55 volts per cell for trickle charging up to 1.70 to 1.72 volts per cell for constant-potential charging at an average of approximately the normal rate.

But these values are not exact; they vary with the age of the battery, the specific gravity of the electrolyte, the temperature, and other conditions.   Therefore, when adjusting the voltage, do so on the basis of ammeter readings, not voltmeter readings. Voltmeter readings are useful, however, in determining when a battery is charged. Stabilization of the voltage at the battery terminals for a half-hour period while current is flowing through the battery at a constant rate is a trustworthy indication that the battery is fully charged.

When adjusting the voltage to produce the desired charge rate, connect the ammeter so that it will indicate the current actually going into the battery, not the current output of the rectifier, generator, or other charging source. A part of this output may be going into the circuit to the load.

For any given charge rate, the voltage necessary at the battery terminals varies with the electrolyte temperature. Therefore, if the battery is exposed to seasonal changes in the surrounding temperature, a higher setting will be needed during the winter than the summer.

Rates for trickle charging should result in overcharging rather than undercharging. In practice it is virtually impossible to arrive at a charge rate which will result in precisely the amount of input required, especially since the output usually tends to vary from day to day. In the interest of consistently high dependability of operation, the best practice is to use rates ample for the maximum rather than the average or minimum requirements, especially since any overcharging that may result at low trickle-charge rates is not harmful.

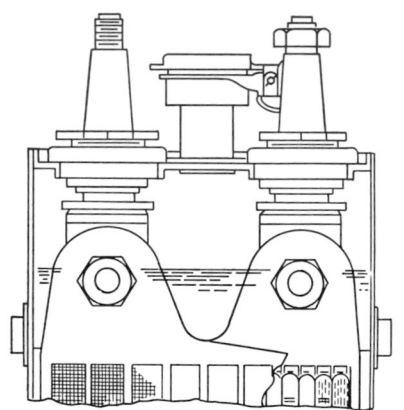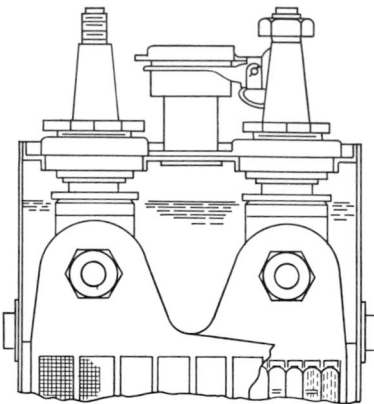

Fig. 9-1. Electrolyte at the recommended level (left) may rise to a higher level (right) toward the end of a charge as a result of gassing.

In case a battery on trickle charge should, as a result of a prolonged outage, discharge a substantial part of its capacity, set the voltage for a higher rate until the stabilization of the voltage for a half-hour period indicates that the battery is again fully charged.

For batteries furnishing larger amounts of power per day and requiring correspondingly more input, the best voltage setting is one that results in the highest average rate during the charging intervals consistent with rates that are not excessive after the battery is fully charged, that is, rates which will not result in raising the electrolyte temperature above 115°F or in dissipating so much water from the electrolyte that it falls below the minimum level. As long as these rates are not excessive, it is desirable to adopt settings which, on an average, will tend to result in a slight amount of overcharging rather than undercharging.

Watering. During the operation of the battery, water is dissipated from the electrolyte chiefly as a result of gassing during charge. This loss must be made up by adding distilled or approved water, using as a guide the recommended and minimum levels shown in Table 9-2 (see, also, Fig. 9-1). (*Caution:* Do not add electrolyte, as this will raise the specific gravity of the solution; if the specific gravity is allowed to exceed 1,230 in standard cells or 1,215 in high or high-wide cells, the battery may be damaged.)

Always keep the electrolyte as near the recommended level as practical. Never let it fall below the minimum level, as the plates would be exposed in standard cells or the solution would grow too concentrated in high and high-wide cells, either of which would be injurious. When adding water, raise the solution to the recommended level, but no higher; if raised to a higher level, the solution may be unnecessarily diluted and also may overflow as a result of gassing the next time the battery is charged or may slop out when the battery is moved.

The time to add water in batteries that are cycled is just before charging; then the gassing during charge will mix the solution.   Never add water during or immediately after charging.   This avoids the false solution level caused by gassing during and immediately after charging which makes it virtually impossible to add the correct amount of water.   It is also the safest procedure because the hydrogen and oxygen gasses form a mixture that is capable of being ignited.   Do not open the filler caps of the cells until you are ready to add water, and close them immediately after filling. An electric filler is recommended.

MAINTENANCE

Putting New Batteries into Service.   Always unpack and inspect batteries immediately on arrival so that in case of damage, claim may be filed promptly with the transportation company.

Test the height of the electrolyte in a few cells to see if any has been spilled.   Use a glass tube (included in the shipment).   Do not use a match or other open flame.   If the electrolyte is below the recommended level but is above the plate tops or can be seen with a flashlight, raise it to the recommended level with distilled water.   If it is so low that it cannot be seen, raise to the recommended level by adding refill solution.

Batteries are shipped in a charged condition unless otherwise ordered, so they may be put into service immediately on arrival.   In case a charged battery stands idle for a period from a week to a month, charge it at an average of its normal rate for 2 or 3 hr before putting it into service.   If you expect to hold a battery idle for more than a month, order it shipped discharged and store it in that condition.   Then when you are ready to put it into service, give it a 15-hr charge at its normal rate. A charged or partially charged battery left standing idle for more than a month is likely to become sluggish.   Before placing such a battery in service, charge it 15 hr at normal rate, then discharge it at normal rate to an average of 1 volt per cell.   If it does not deliver normal rate for at least 5 hr before 1 volt per cell is reached, it may need further cycling.

Batteries assembled in cradles or demountable boxes have their cell-to-cell connectors in place so that all that is necessary to complete the assembly is to apply the tray-to-tray jumpers (see Fig. 9-2).   If a battery is assembled in trays only and consists of more than one tray, first arrange the trays so as to ensure correct polarity. Then apply the jumpers.   The necessary jumpers and tools (pole-nut wrench and lug-disconnecting jack) are included with each shipment.

The lugs on the ends of the jumpers are provided with an inside taper that corresponds to the taper on the poles of the cells.   Be sure both of these contact surfaces are clean.   Remove any oil, grease, or dirt that may stick to them, using a clean cloth.   If an abrasive is necessary, use 00 sandpaper or 00 emery cloth; never use a file or other cutting tool that might score or abrade the contact surfaces.   Then slip the jumpers into place.   If the lugs do not fit exactly on the poles, bend the jumpers until they do; never hammer or force them on.   After the lugs are in place, grease the pole threads slightly.   Then apply the hexagonal pole nuts.

After completing the connections you can check their tightness by putting the battery on charge or discharge at its normal rate for 15 or 20 min.   Any loose or dirty connections will cause excessive heating of jumper lugs, which will be readily perceptible to the touch.   (*Caution:* Disconnect battery from charging circuit before touching jumper or connector lugs.)   Remove any such jumpers, clean the contact surfaces of the lugs and poles, and reapply.   Check the tightness of the connector lugs in the same manner.   Connectors are removed and applied in the same manner as jumpers.   By having all connections clean and tight, you will avoid unnecessary voltage drop in the battery circuit.

FIG. 9-2. Applying and removing jumpers.   To apply: (*A*) be sure jumper lugs fit the poles exactly; bend jumper if necessary until they do.   (*B*) put jumper into place.   (*C*) grease the pole threads slightly.   (*D*) tighten the pole nuts.   To remove: (*E*) use the special lug disconnecting jack.   These directions indicate the procedure to be followed in removing the connectors.

Cleaning. Keeping a battery clean is not merely a matter of good housekeeping but is also an assurance of good performance and life. By keeping the cell tops and connectors clean, you lessen the risk of getting impurities into the cells when you open the filler caps to add water. By keeping dirt from accumulating below or between the cells, you reduce the possibility of ground, especially if the battery is exposed to dampness.

Batteries assembled in cradles or demountable boxes are best cleaned when supported so that dirt can be blown out through the bottom. Use a wet steam jet followed by an air blast to blow off any accumulated moisture. Clean the cell tops and connectors first, then blow out any dirt that may become lodged between cells. Be sure all filler caps are closed so that no dirt can get into the cells. Wear goggles when using the steam jet and air blast.

Batteries assembled in trays only can be cleaned by wiping cell tops, connectors, and jumpers occasionally with a wet cloth. In this way you can avoid letting the dirt fall down into the spaces between the cells, but if you see dirt beginning to accumulate there, remove the trays to a floor drain or other suitable place and clean them by wet steam or warm water followed by an air blast as already described. Be sure cells and trays are dry before reassembling, also that the contact surfaces of the cell terminals and jumper lugs are clean and that all connectors are tight and of correct polarity.

Keep the cell tops coated with Esbaline, and after cleaning, touch up any bare spots. Follow directions on the label. This serves the double purpose of protecting the surface and making the tops easier to clean the next time. Do not use oil, as it will disintegrate the rubber insulation around the poles.

At the same time inspect the cells for any necessary attention. Make sure the filler caps, hinge bands, and lid springs are in proper alignment to ensure free operation and correct seating of the valves (see Fig. 9-3). To prevent contamination of the electrolyte, it is just as important to maintain the valves so that they seat properly as it is to keep the filler caps normally closed. Screw down the gland caps of any cells showing evidence of leakage around the stuffing-box assembly. Use

Fig. 9-3. Dealing with gland caps and hinge bands. (a) How to tighten the gland caps: In case any cells indicate leakage around the stuffing-box assembly, remove the connector or jumper lug and tighten the gland cap. A special wrench is available (F). (b) How to remove and replace hinge bands: The filler cap and the filler valve of the coil are held in position by means of a hinge band which is a force fit on the filler body. To facilitate repairs or replacements, special tools are available. They consist of a hinge-band-removing jack and block (G) and a hinge-band-replacing jack and block (H).

the special wrench available for the purpose, and be careful not to damage the gland caps.

Cycling. A battery that is not kept in regular use or is used only intermittently may become sluggish and deliver less than the capacity of which it is capable. This can be corrected by cycling the battery as follows:

1. Charge the battery if it is not already charged.
2. Discharge through a resistance that can be varied to keep the rate at normal until the potential of the battery falls to the equivalent of 0.5 volt per cell (15 volts for a 30-cell battery, etc.).
3. Short-circuit each tray, and let stand until the resulting heat is dissipated and the electrolyte cools to not more than 5°F above room temperature.
4. Water as necessary to bring the electrolyte to the recommended level, and charge at normal rate for 15 hr.
5. Discharge at normal rate, and keep a record of the time until the potential of the battery falls to the equivalent of 1 volt per cell.

Except while the battery is short-circuited, keep the electrolyte temperature below 115°F. Take the voltage readings only while current at normal rate is flowing. Usually one such cycle is sufficient although, if the battery still appears sluggish, another cycle or two may bring further improvement.

A discharge at normal rate for 5 hr before the equivalent of 1.00 volt per cell is reached indicates full rated capacity. If less capacity is indicated, continue the discharge as in step 1 and report steps 2, 3, and 4.

Laying up. In case a battery is to be laid up for a month or more, discharge and short-circuit as described in operations 1 and 2 under Cycling. Check height of electrolyte solution, and add water if necessary to raise to correct level. Then store in a clean, dry place. Batteries may be left standing idle in this condition indefinitely without injury. When the battery is to be returned to use, charge it at normal rate for 15 hr. If it was laid up for a year or more, follow this charge by a discharge at normal rate to an average rate of 1 volt per cell; then follow with operations (1), (2), (3), and (4) under Cycling. Also inspect the cells for any necessary attention as described under Cleaning.

Renewing Electrolyte. When a battery is new and fully charged, the electrolyte has a specific gravity of approximately 1,200 at 60°F if thoroughly mixed and at the recommended level. During use of the battery, the electrolyte tends to weaken gradually and must be renewed if its specific gravity falls to between 1,160 and 1,170. Do not operate a battery with an electrolyte of a gravity below 1,160. (*Caution:* Do not attempt to raise the specific gravity of weakened electrolyte by adding solution.)

To test the electrolyte for specific gravity, use an Exide hydrometer. Take readings only when the electrolyte has been thoroughly mixed by charging, and wait a half hour or more after the charge has been completed to allow for dissipation of gas. Using a thermometer and a test tube, check the temperature and the height, and correct for any variation from 60°F and the recommended level. To correct the hydrometer reading for temperature, add or subtract $\frac{1}{4}$ point for each degree above or below 60°F. To correct for height, add or subtract 20 points per in. for any distance above or below recommended level. *Example:* Hydrometer reads 1,180; temperature is 100°F, or 40°F above 60°F; height is $\frac{3}{8}$ in. below normal level. Reading corrected for temperature is $1,180 + (40 \times \frac{1}{4}) = 1,180 + 10 = 1,190$. Reading corrected for both temperature and height is

$$1,190 - (\tfrac{3}{8} \times 20) = 1,190 - 7\tfrac{1}{2} = 1,182\tfrac{1}{2}$$

To renew the solution, proceed as follows:

1. Discharge, short-circuit, and cool the battery as described in operations 2 and 3 under Cycling.
2. Pour out the old solution.
3. Fill immediately with standard renewal solution.
4. Charge at normal rate for 15 hr.

For ease in pouring out the old solution, disconnect the jumpers so you can do it one tray at a time. Avoid splashing. Do not shake or rinse; just tip the trays so that the old solution will run out. A floor drain is a good place to do it, provided the floor is cement or asphalt and the drain is equipped with iron or steel pipe fittings. The electrolyte is injurious to wood, brass, copper, lead, aluminum, and zinc. Short lengths of scrap 2 by 4's or similar timbers can be used to support the trays while they are tipped over.

Always keep in mind that the solution is injurious to the skin and clothing. Wear rubber gloves, goggles, and preferably also a rubber apron. If, in spite of these precautions, any solution should be splashed or spilled on the skin or clothing, wash it away immediately with plenty of water. As a further precaution, it may be well to keep available a supply of 4 per cent sterile boric acid solution and an eye cup for additional treatment of the skin and eyes. Meanwhile, arrange the containers of standard renewal solution so that you can refill immediately. Do not let the cells stand without solution. The containers may be elevated, and the solution poured into the cells through a hose, or for small cells and small containers, the solution may be poured in directly from the container through a funnel.

Replacing Spilled Electrolyte. An accident which overturns a battery rarely causes damage because of the steel cell construction but may spill electrolyte solution from the cells. To replace spillage use standard refill solution. Standard renewal solution may also be used in an emergency if diluted with pure distilled water to a gravity of 1,215 at 60°F; an easy way to do this is to mix 1 part of water by volume with 5 parts of renewal solution by volume.

If you have no electrolyte solution on hand, the best thing to do depends on how much solution was spilled. If the solution left in the cells is still above the plate tops or can be seen by a flashlight after the battery has been turned right side up, merely add water and continue the battery in service. If so little solution remains in the cells that it cannot be seen with a flashlight, take the battery out of service, make sure all filler caps are closed in order to keep out impurities, and wait until you can obtain a supply of refill solution.

Chapter 10

VENTED NICKEL-CADMIUM BATTERIES

By William W. Jakobi[1]
in consultation with F. C. Anderson
Research and Development Laboratory
Gould-National Batteries, Inc.
Minneapolis, Minn.

Nickel-cadmium batteries are alkaline batteries, using a solution of potassium hydroxide (KOH, or "caustic potash") as the electrolyte. They are very rugged physically, and will sometimes withstand more shock and vibration than will the equipment they are powering. They will take considerable electrical abuse (overcharging, standing in the discharged state, occasional overdischarging). They have low internal resistance, and consequently have good charge acceptance and perform well at high discharge rates. They have relatively low self-discharge. They will outperform any other common storage-battery type at low temperatures; many designs will deliver 80 per cent of their rated capacity at −40°F. They are not intended for cycle applications, being used rather in engine starting, railroad signaling, emergency lighting, communications, alarm, switchgear, marine, and stand-by applications.

Specific points of comparison that might be mentioned with the lead-acid storage battery, most commonly used, are as follows: Nickel-cadmium batteries have lower self-discharge, and can be left standing for long periods of time in the discharged condition without fear of deterioration. They release no corrosive fumes. Nickel-cadmium batteries with sintered plates (described below) can, if required, be recharged in one or two hours. They can be severely overcharged with little damage, provided that temperature is controlled. They are not damaged by freezing. Electrolyte volume can be held to the minimum necessary to provide conductivity, without fear of limiting capacity. Water loss is considerably less. Disadvantages are as follows: Nickel-cadmium cells have considerably lower voltage; the average discharge voltage is 1.2 to 1.25 volts at ordinary discharge rates. They are not capable of extended, deep-cycle service. With the pocket-plate types (discussed below), the ratio of energy per unit volume and unit weight is no greater—in some cases, less. The state of charge of nickel-cadmium batteries cannot easily be determined, as can be done with a hydrometer with lead-acid batteries. They are considerably more expensive; their cost ranges from two to four times that of lead-acid batteries of comparable capacity. In high-rate applications, the cost of a battery adequate to do a given job is more nearly equal, since nickel-cadimum batteries deliver a considerably greater percentage of their normal rated capacity at high rates.

The electrochemical mechanisms of the nickel-cadmium system are very similar

[1] Author is now with Medtronic, Inc., Minneapolis, Minn.

to those of the other alkaline batteries such as the silver-zinc, the silver-cadimum, and the nickel-iron, or "Edison," battery (discussed in Sec. 7, Chap. 9), but differ greatly from the reaction mechanisms of the lead-acid battery. In a discharging lead-acid battery, the sulfuric acid electrolyte reacts both with the lead dioxide positive plate and with the lead negative, forming lead sulfate in both cases. So acid is actually consumed in these reactions. It is for this reason that the acid becomes more dilute as the discharge proceeds, so that the state of charge can be determined by measuring the specific gravity of the electrolyte. This, also, is the reason why the capacity of a lead-acid battery is limited by the amount of acid available to the plates; why the battery is subject to freezing when it is discharged and the acid is very dilute; and why the internal resistance of the battery rises during discharge (as the electrolyte loses conductivity), so that the voltage declines steadily.

In all alkaline batteries, the electrolyte serves only as a carrier for electrons. The KOH is not consumed during discharge; it acts only to shuttle electrons back and forth between the positive and negative plates as the battery is discharging or being charged. For this reason the capacity of these batteries is not as limited by electrolyte availability, discharge voltage is more constant, and the batteries are not as vulnerable to freezing. The disadvantage follows, however, that there is no easy way to determine state of charge.

Other important effects follow from the chemical nature of alkaline batteries. KOH in solution concentrations ranging around 30 per cent, has very high electrical conductivity, so that these cells have low internal resistance. There is no sulfation problem; most alkaline batteries, including the nickel-cadmium, can be left standing in any state of charge for long periods without fear of permanent damage being done to the plates. KOH does not form corrosive fumes to damage adjacent equipment; it is actually a preservative of steel, so that cells can be built in strong steel cases, and plates can be made with steel grids.

The nickel-cadimum system is now built both in open- and in sealed-cell types. The sealed, rechargeable nickel-cadimum cell has appeared fairly recently on the American market, though experimentation with this cell type began in Germany before World War II. These are small cells; the readily available types have maximum capacities of 4 to 6 amp-hr, and the smallest are about 20 ma-hr. They are available in three basic configurations: cylindrical cells having the same configuration (and available in most of the same sizes) as ordinary flashlight cells; small disk-shaped "button" cells; and rectangular, or "prismatic," types, with capacities starting at 100 ma-hr. (In Europe, rectangular cells with capacities up to 23 amp-hr are built.) Being completely sealed, they can be operated in any position, give off no fumes whatever, can be stacked, and do not require that service access be provided. Because of these characteristics, they are attractive choices for a wide variety of consumer appliances, electronic units, industrial equipment, communications devices, and defense and space applications. These cells require no maintenance other than normal recharging according to the manufacturer's instructions. This chapter therefore concerns only open- (or "vented-") cell types.

PLATE PROCESSING AND BATTERY CONSTRUCTION

There are two basic types of open nickel-cadmium cells available, those with pocket plates and those with sintered plates. Pocket plates have the longer history; Thomas Edison worked with this plate type prior to the turn of the century. They are extremely rugged, and are used in applications requiring maximum life, great resistance to shock or vibration, and maximum cell size. Sintered plates yield much lower cell internal resistance, and are therefore used in applications requiring very high discharge rates, such as engine starting and switchgear applications.

A complete discussion of battery construction and electrical performance is beyond the scope of this chapter. The reader who desires more detailed information than is given below should consult a reference[1] or make inquiry of the battery manufacturer.

[1] For example, "Encyclopedia of Chemical Technology," *Batteries and Electric Cells, Secondary*, 2d ed., vol. 3, John Wiley & Sons, Inc., New York, 1964.

Pocket-plate Types. Production of pocket plates begins with strips of thin steel ribbon perforated with roughly two thousand holes per square inch, and then nickel-plated. The edges of this ribbon are turned up into a troughlike configuration. The active materials—nickel hydroxide plus graphite for the positive and cadmium hydroxide (or cadmium oxide) plus iron powder for the negative—are pressed into this trough. A second piece of perforated steel ribbon is applied over this, and the edges of the two ribbons are crimped together, forming a very long flat "pocket" of perforated steel containing the active material. The width of this pocket material is about $\frac{1}{2}$ in.; thickness ranges between $\frac{1}{16}$ and $\frac{1}{4}$ in. The material can be cut to pieces of any length to form plates of any desired width. These pockets are then laid horizontally into plate frames stamped from sheet steel; these frames have the length and width of the desired plate and are open in the center to receive the pockets. The pockets are crimped into this frame in such a way that the joints formed along the sides of the plate frame serve also to seal off the cut ends of the individual pockets.

Fig. 10-1. Pocket-plate nickel-cadmium battery in wooden tray.

The plates are then assembled into positive and negative "groups," bolted together to the proper terminal post by means of a threaded connector rod passing through the base of the post, or in some cases welded to comblike teeth extending from the terminal post. The positive and the negative groups are then interleaved. The separators—either plastic rods placed vertically between the plates or corrugated perforated plastic sheet—are inserted. The assembled "element" is then placed in the cell case, and the cover with its insulating and sealing washers and nuts is placed over the terminals and welded (or cemented) in place. The resulting assembly is indicated by Fig. 10-1.

Smaller pocket-plate cells (up to 200 amp-hr capacity) are available either in plastic or in steel cases. Plastic cell cases have many advantages: They are transparent or translucent. In applications involving large numbers of cells, this can mean a considerable saving of maintenance time; electrolyte levels can very easily be checked; and it is easy to fill to the proper level when watering. Since the cases are nonconductive, they can be touching, thus saving installation space. There is less likelihood of accidental grounding with these cells, and it is a little safer to work around them with metal tools. Plastic cases are resistant to electrolytic corrosion. For some applications requiring great physical ruggedness, they are assembled into steel battery trays. Smaller sizes may be assembled into plastic or wood battery cases.

Steel cell cases are formed of welded sheet steel, are nickel-plated, and can be produced in a variety of sizes without extreme tooling expense. Most important, they offer the advantage of great strength. It is for this reason that larger cells are built only in steel cases. The cost of steel cases is roughly the same as that of plastic cases of comparable size.

Cells in steel cases are usually painted with an alkali and corrosion-resistant paint and assembled into wooden battery trays. Smaller sizes are available in trays containing from 2 to 10 cells. With increasing cell size, the maximum number supplied per tray decreases. These trays are composed of side slats and end pieces, and may have open bottoms. The cells are suspended within the tray by means of projecting steel bosses welded to the cell walls; these bosses fit into recessed plastic or hard-rubber buttons, which in turn fit into holes in the tray slats. This construction, shown in Fig. 10-1, prevents shorts and grounds by holding the cells well apart from each other and off the ground.

Sintered-plate Types. Sintered plates involve first a sintered nickel plaque, which serves as the plate grid. This plaque is made by sintering fine nickel powder (made by the "carbonyl" process) to a piece of nickel screen or perforated nickel sheet. The resulting plaque material is a very porous, tough, flexible sheet of pure nickel, usually between 0.025 and 0.08 in. thick. Though this material appears solid to the eye, roughly 80 per cent of the volume of this sheet is open-pore space. The positive and the negative active materials are then deposited into these pores by any of several different types of impregnation processes. The resulting cells have very low internal resistance and consequently perform well at very high discharge rates; this is the prime advantage of the sintered-type nickel-cadmium cell.

Plate leads are welded to the corners of the plates. Alternating positives and negatives are then assembled, together with the separators. In most designs, the separators are sheets of nonwoven (felted) or woven synthetic fabric, sometimes with a layer of cellophane added. Each group of plate leads (positive and negative) is then gathered together and welded to the base of the appropriate cell terminal, the element is placed in the cell case, and the cover is seated. The resulting assembly is illustrated in Fig. 10-2. Most sintered cells are built in plastic cases, as shown here, though a few types have been built in steel cases. The cells are in turn assembled into steel or (for smaller sizes) plastic or wood battery cases. A steel-cased vehicle battery is shown in Fig. 10-3.

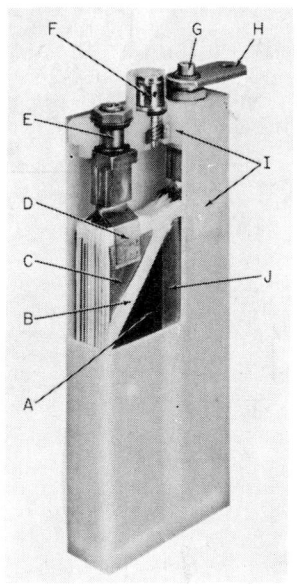

Fig. 10-2. Cutaway sintered-plate nickel-cadmium cell. (A) Positive plate (nickel hydroxide); (B) separator (synthetic fabric); (C) negative plate (cadmium); (D) plate leads (welded to plates and to terminal); (E) positive terminal; (F) vent plug (cut away to reveal rubber pressure-release sleeve); (G) negative terminal; (H) intercell connector; (I) plastic cell case and cover; (J) plastic banding (primarily for assembly purposes).

PERFORMANCE CHARACTERISTICS

A few special terms that the user will encounter in battery literature should be defined. Cell sizes are specified in terms of a "nominal," or "rated," capacity. This is the amount of energy, usually expressed in ampere-hours, that an average cell would be expected to deliver under normal conditions throughout most of its life. It is important to know the discharge rate under which the nominal capacity was established, since the capacity delivered does depend on discharge amperage. Ratings for most pocket cells will be based on the 8-hr discharge rate, and for most sintered types, on the 5-hr rate. "Hourly rates" are a convenient means of expressing the charge and discharge rates at which a cell is operated. Hourly rates are established by the manufacturer and reported in his technical literature. The hourly rate is that discharge amperage which will exhaust the cell in the stated number of hours. For example, when discharging a cell at the amperage given as the "3-hr rate," the cell would be approaching exhaustion and the voltage would start to decline rapidly, at the end of the third hour of discharge. When reading hourly-rate figures, it is important to note the "cutoff" voltage at which the hourly rate was established; the higher the required voltage at the end of discharge, the shorter the discharge period will be at a given rate. The cutoff voltage is that discharge voltage at which a discharge should be stopped; repeated discharging beyond this point may damage the cells. "Efficiency" is that percentage of charge input which can be withdrawn from the cell on the following discharge. "Energy density" is the power delivered per unit weight or per unit volume of the battery; it is expressed as watthours per pound or watthours per cubic inch.

Voltage. The open-circuit (or at-rest) voltage of nickel-cadmium cells is about 1.35 volts. The average discharge voltage, which can be used for calculating the number of cells needed for a given application, is generally given as 1.2 volts. At lower discharge rates (5 to 8 hr and lower), the average voltage would be about 1.25 volts; at these rates, the voltage would drop 0.15 to 0.2 volts from the beginning to the end of the discharge. Pocket cells can be discharged at the 1-hr rate, and sintered cells at two or three times the 1-hr rate, before average discharge voltage falls below 1.2 volts. Sintered cells will deliver 12 to 16 times the 1-hr discharge rate at voltages no less than 1.0 volt. Considering low-temperature operation, these voltage levels will not drop significantly until temperature gets down to −10 to −20°F.

For lower-voltage applications (i.e., 6 volts, 12 volts), the number of cells used is the exact (or the nearest) equivalent to the quotient obtained by dividing application

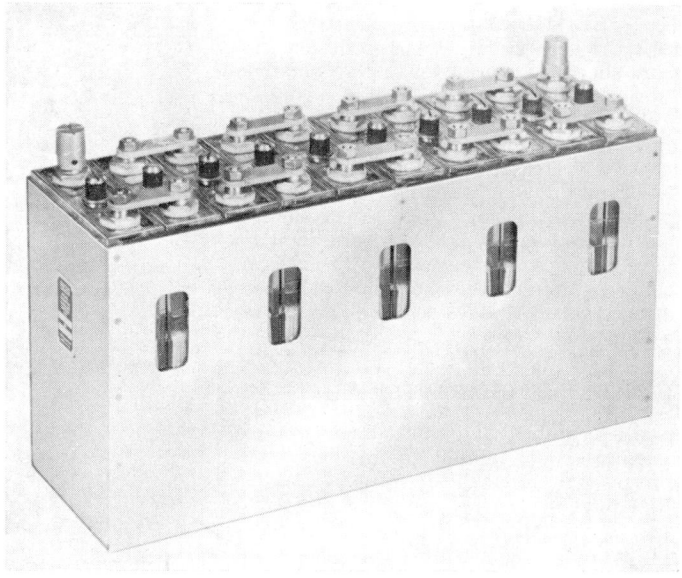

FIG. 10-3. Sintered-plate 12-volt nickel-cadmium battery.

voltage by 1.2; i.e., 5 cells are used for 6-volt applications, and 10 cells for 12-volt. With higher-voltage applications, this factor may not be strictly adhered to. As examples, 18 to 20 cells may be used for 24-volt circuit-breaker applications, and 92 to 95 cells for 125-volt control applications. The exact number of cells selected depends on discharge rate, line loss to be counteracted, float voltage available, and other factors. The manufacturer's service engineers should be consulted in selecting the proper number of cells and the electrical operating characteristics for such batteries.

Capacities, Discharge Rates, and Depths. Pocket-plate cells are available in capacities ranging from 10 to about 1,000 amp-hr or more, the larger sizes being typically available only on special request. Sintered types from 0.5 to over 200 amp-hr are made. Most pocket-plate designs will deliver their nominal capacity, though to a lower end voltage, when discharging at rates as high as the 1-hr. High-rate sintered-plate cells will deliver nominal capacity at discharge rates several times the 1-hr rate; at 16 times the 1-hr rate, they will deliver two-thirds of nominal. When discharging into loads which offer very low resistance (switchgear, engine-starting applications), sintered cells will deliver some 15 to 18 times the 1-hr rate for 10 sec. For some sintered types, 5- and 1-sec capacity ratings are published by the

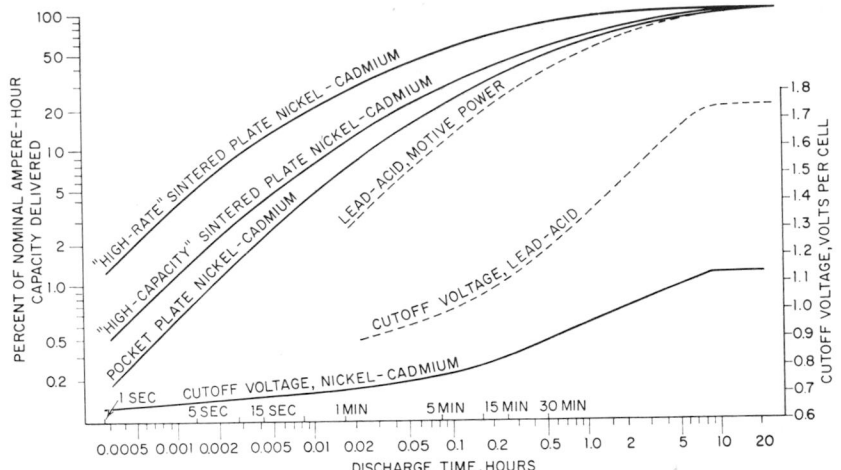

Fig. 10-4. Typical per cent of capacity delivered vs. discharge time.

This figure shows the effect of discharge rate on the capacity of typical nickel-cadmium designs. Data on the lead-acid system have also been included, for purposes of comparison. To avoid having to plot curves for specific cell sizes, discharge rate has been expressed as discharge time, and per cent capacity is reported for any battery of a general design type, discharged at that amperage which would bring the battery down to the cutoff voltage shown within a certain length of time. Logarithmic scales have been used to show clearly very short lengths of time and very low percentages, as well as much larger values.

As can be seen, for most battery types the per cent of nominal capacity delivered begins to decline very rapidly at discharge rates greater than the 1- or $\frac{1}{2}$-hr values. Hence the user generally plans to accommodate lower cutoff voltages in high-rate applications, to obtain the greatest ampere-hour output possible. The curves of cutoff voltages shown are somewhat arbitrary, and are simply an attempt to present values which are typical for a number of applications. If, for any given discharge time, a lower cutoff voltage can be tolerated, the ampere-hour output obtained will be increased accordingly. This capacity improvement will be more pronounced the higher the discharge rate (or the shorter the discharge time).

To determine the approximate maximum current, in amperes, that can be drawn from a particular cell type for a certain length of time, multiply the nominal ampere-hour capacity specified for the cell by the per cent capacity delivered, indicated on the appropriate curve for that time; then divide this by the time required (expressed in hours or fractions thereof); e.g., the maximum amperage that can be drawn from a 275-amp-hr pocket-plate cell for 5 min is

$$\text{Per cent of nominal delivered} = \text{approx. } 20\,\%$$
$$0.20 \times 275 = 55$$

$$\frac{55}{\frac{5}{60}} = \text{approx. } 660 \text{ amp}$$

With a cell of given design type, to determine the approximate cell capacity which will be required to deliver a certain amperage for a given length of time, find the approximate per cent capacity delivered on the appropriate curve for that time, and divide this percentage (expressed as hundredths) into the required current; then multiply this by the time required (expressed as hours or fractions thereof); e.g., considering high-rate nickel-cadmium cells, to provide 150 amp for 15 min, the cell capacity required will be

$$\text{Per cent of nominal delivered} = \text{approx. } 70\,\%$$

$$\frac{150}{0.70} = 214$$

$$214 \times \frac{15}{60} = \text{approx. } 53 \text{ amp-hr}$$

manufacturers. Most nickel-cadmium types will deliver about 80 per cent of nominal at 0°F at normal discharge rates. Figure 10-4 shows the percentage of nominal capacity available vs. discharge rate for several nickel-cadmium cell types.

When discharging at 3- to 4-hr rates or lower, nickel-cadmium batteries should not be repeatedly discharged below 1.0 to 1.1 volts. At very high rates, such as are involved in engine-starting applications, discharge may be carried down to 0.65 volt. Repeated discharging below these limits will lead to declining capacity. Sintered types can tolerate overdischarging somewhat better than can pocket types.

Efficiency and Energy Density. On an ampere-hour basis, most nickel-cadmium batteries are 70 to 80 per cent efficient. On a watthour basis (which involves voltage as well as amperage), their efficiency is 55 to 70 per cent, depending on the spread between the charge and the discharge voltage at the particular rates used. Pocket-plate cells discharging at moderate rates deliver from 6.5 to 9 watthours per pound and 0.2 to 0.4 watthour per cu in., the larger values being for bigger cells with thick plates. Sintered cells deliver from 8 to 14 watthours per lb and 0.35 to 1 watthour per cu in.

Life. The life expectancy provided by most pocket-plate types in float operation is about 15 years, depending on the severity of service conditions. Occasional stand-by applications have been reported in Europe in which 25-year life was attained. Sintered-plate batteries have somewhat shorter life; in severe service such as vehicle-starting applications, lives of 5 to 7 years are reported. Batteries in emergency lighting, alarm, and communications use can be expected to deliver 8 to 15 years. Some manufacturers produce types that are satisfactory for cycling under carefully controlled conditions and will deliver a maximum of 1,500 to 2,000 cycles.

SELECTION AND INSTALLATION

It is proper in a source of this type to give only the general principles of battery selection. The battery manufacturer should be contacted for guidance on the specific battery type needed for a given installation.

From the foregoing discussion of the advantages and disadvantages, construction, and performance characteristics of nickel-cadmium batteries, the reader should be able to judge whether there is a nickel-cadmium design type that merits consideration for his application. The general principles of battery selection outlined in the section on nickel-iron batteries (Sec. 7, Chap. 9) apply here. Bear in mind when reading this, however, that (1) nickel-cadmium batteries have lower internal resistance than nickel-iron (so that the voltage drop at a given discharge rate will be less), and (2) nickel-cadmium batteries are not generally used in cycle service.

Having determined the general battery design type that should be considered for your application, the approximate number of cells that will be needed, and the ampere-hours to be supplied between chargings, contact the firm of your choice manufacturing that cell type and supply them with the detailed information they will need to recommend the proper battery configuration for your application. This information should include the following:

Voltage required; the allowable maximum and minimum values; the degree of voltage regulation preferred.

Capacity and rate capability required; the currents that the battery will be expected to deliver, and the length of time over which these stated currents will flow. If the current is unknown, state as explicitly as possible the work that is to be done by the equipment which the battery will power, in terms of torque or horsepower delivered, transmitting and receiving power, etc.

Charging conditions: type of charge routine to be used—constant-current, constant-voltage, float, trickle (see the paragraphs on Charging, below, for a discussion of each of these methods); type of charge equipment you plan to use, rates and voltages it can deliver, degree of control it exercises; length of time allowable for each charge, frquency at which charging can be done.

Resistance to shock and vibration required; angular inclination to which the battery will be subjected.

Installation conditions: available space; ambient temperature; ventilation available; proximity of lead-acid batteries or other contaminating conditions.

Any special maintenance conditions: desire to minimize frequency of watering; need to avoid special tools; type of personnel that will care for the battery.

Installing the Battery. In this discussion we shall assume that the purchaser of a new battery has received detailed instructions from the manufacturer on installation. In general, it can be said that nickel-cadmium batteries are shipped charged and filled with electrolyte (except those for export, which are shipped dry and discharged).

Throughout the unpacking and installation procedure, these cells must be handled with the caution due a live battery. As an example, chains or metal hooks must not be used to hoist cells from the packing crates; rope slings, passed under the intercell connectors, may be used. After having checked for shipping damage, remove whatever shipping plugs have been put in the cell vents and replace with the vent plugs provided. Then check the electrolyte level in each cell. With most of the medium and larger cell sizes, electrolyte should be at least $\frac{1}{2}$ in. above the plates. The maximum level should be obtained from the manufacturer's literature; it will often be about half the distance from the tops of the plates to the underside of the cell cover. If electrolyte has been spilled and the level is below the tops of the plates, add "refill" electrolyte to bring the level up (see page 7-189 for a discussion of "refill" and "renewal" electrolyte). If refill electrolyte is not available and the cells are of the pocket type, add enough distilled water to cover the plates well, and hold the battery out of electrical service. Inform the battery manufacturer of the details of the accident; he will recommend the amount and the type of replacement electrolyte needed and the procedure to follow. With sintered-plate cells, do not add water; there is enough electrolyte absorbed in the plates and separators so that the cells can stand for the length of time necessary to acquire replacement electrolyte. When the electrolyte is received, simply add enough to bring the level up to the proper point (see page 7-188 for determination of proper level in sintered cells).

Cells in steel cases and wooden battery trays may now be permanently installed. Nickel-cadmium batteries do not release corrosive fumes; they may therefore be installed next to machinery or instruments, although machinery or instruments should not be subject to direct spray from the cells. Appropriate battery racks may be purchased from the manufacturer or, if convenient, may be built by the user to the manufacturer's specifications. A small amount of space (about $\frac{1}{8}$ in.) should be left between trays for circulation of air. Smaller batteries should be placed on shelves. Batteries in trays with special extended sides (providing extra clearance under the cells) may be set directly on the floor. Plastic-cased cells in plastic or steel battery trays require no special installation. Vehicular or marine batteries must be securely held down. In all cases, if the batteries are to be serviced from the side of the compartment, a minimum of 8 in.—preferably 12 in.—should be provided between the cell tops and the compartment roof. If servicing is to be done from above, 2 in. above the cell tops is adequate. Batteries should not be installed in areas where the temperature will frequently rise above 100°F.

After positioning the batteries and placing the intercell connectors, check the polarity of all cells, following the connectors from one battery terminal throughout the battery to the other terminal to make sure that the cells are correctly connected in series. Any cells connected into the circuit with reversed polarity will be damaged. Look for a plus sign marked on the cell terminal or on the cover next to the terminal, a red mark on the side of the vent wall toward the positive terminal, or (in some larger cell types) a red rubber insulating gland on the positive terminal. Then make sure that all terminal post nuts are tight. Check that the main battery cables to the battery are heavy enough to carry the maximum current that will be required without excessive voltage drop. Battery cables should be fitted with nickel-plated lugs; bare copper lugs are likely to corrode. All cables should be kept up off the cell tops. Wipe off any electrolyte that may have splashed out onto the cell tops during installation. With steel-cased cells, when the cell tops are perfectly clean and dry, completely cover them with a thin coating of petroleum jelly. This will prevent electrolyte spray from gradually building up a hard-to-remove crust on the cell tops.

If the battery is not to be placed in service within 90 days, it should either be put on continuous trickle charge as described on page 7-184 or given a freshening charge at the 5-hr rate for 3 hr when it is put back into service.

In order to minimize the frequency of watering and decrease the effort required to keep tops of pocket-type cells clean, a layer of mineral oil $\frac{1}{2}$ to $\frac{1}{4}$ in. thick can be poured over the surface of the electrolyte. Use only pure, acid-free mineral oil, acquired from the battery manufacturer or meeting his specifications. Oil is never used in sintered cells nor in motive-power batteries. It is used, however, in the majority of stationary applications containing pocket cells.   The oil is simply poured in through the vent opening.   When adding the oil to the first cell, pour repeated small quantities from a graduated container, and with an electrolyte level test tube (see page 7-188), repeatedly check the thickness of the oil layer.   When the thickness has reached $\frac{1}{8}$ to $\frac{1}{4}$ in., note the total amount that was added and add this same quantity to the remaining cells.

CHARGING

With nickel-cadmium batteries, it is important to establish a reliable, regular charge procedure and adhere to it, since it is not possible to check quickly the state of charge as can be done with lead-acid batteries.   It is possible, though, to determine whether or not the battery is in the fully charged state.   Place the battery on charge at the 5-hr rate.   (Hourly-rate values are used in the same manner with charge current as with discharge; the 5-hr rate is the amperage necessary to return 100 per cent of the battery's rated capacity in 5 hr.)   If after 5 min the battery voltage is holding at a point below 1.5 volts per cell, the battery is below 90 per cent of full charge.   When the battery is 90 per cent charged or above, the on-charge voltage will level off at a point between 1.6 and 1.7 volts.

If there is a strong need to determine the state of charge more precisely, it is possible in many applications to design a method of simultaneously reading voltage and current during a brief, high-rate discharge, or of reading the amount of current drawn when the battery is placed on a brief constant-voltage charge.   The manufacturer's service engineers should be contacted for help in establishing the most satisfactory method for the particular application.

Nickel-cadmium batteries tolerate overcharging quite well.   If in doubt, it is always better to overcharge than to undercharge.   Precautions against excessive overcharging are stated, not because of any direct effect on the plates, but rather so that maximum permissible temperature is not exceeded and so that electrolyte loss and build-up of conductive film on the cell tops is minimized.   On any charge routine, battery temperature should be held to a maximum of 115°F.   Occasional temperatures of 125°F can be tolerated if necessary, but repeated charging at these high temperatures is likely to result in reduced capacity and shortened life.   When checking temperature, always take it from cells in the middle of the battery; these are likely to be the warmest cells.

Nickel-cadmium batteries are recharged with either of the two basic types of charge routine used with any battery type: the constant-voltage (or "constant-potential") and the constant-current.   They are maintained in the fully charged state by trickle- or float-charge routines.   The "equalizing charge," also discussed below, is a variation of the constant-current routine.   Constant-voltage charging involves supplying charge energy at a fixed, regulated voltage; the voltage level is selected so that the current, high at first, tapers off to a very low level as the battery nears full charge and the countervoltage of the battery rises.   This is one of the two most commonly used methods.   It lends itself readily to automatic control, and can be performed rapidly.   The constant-current charge method offers the advantage of easy calculation of the ampere-hours of charge put into the battery.   However, if it is to be performed manually, it calls for frequent adjustment of the rate.   With the trickle-charge method, the battery is left permanently connected to a source delivering very small amounts of charge current; an example is the charger-battery combinations included in many emergency lighting or alarm units.   Trickle charging can be done either with constant current or constant voltage.   Float charging, the second very common charge method used for nickel-cadmium batteries, differs from trickle charging in that the battery is permanently connected in parallel across the line between the power source and the equipment to be powered.   The power source normally supplies both the equipment and the charge current to the battery; the battery is discharged in the event of failure or inactivity of the power source.   This is the typical stand-by application.

Constant-voltage (or "Constant-potential") Charge.   In most cases a modified rather than a true constant-voltage method is used so as to limit the high initial surge of current that would otherwise be taken by a discharged battery. With this scheme the voltage is automatically reduced below the preselected value until the current taken by the battery at that voltage drops to a value that can be supplied by the charger. This reduces the size, and hence the cost, of the charging equipment. This method has been found particularly suitable for sintered-plate batteries. By use of a setting of 1.55 volts per cell, the charge can be completed within 1 to 2 hr.

Generally, pocket-plate cells are charged at 1.6 volts per cell, sintered cells at 1.55 volts. In cold temperatures, these voltage settings should be about 0.05 volt higher. Charging at these voltages usually will be completed within 7 hr. At the end of the charge, the current drawn should have dropped to a few per cent of the nominal (or 5-hr) rate. With vehicle and aircraft applications in which lead-acid batteries may also have been used, the voltage regulator should be set at its maximum setting, which will usually provide 1.40 to 1.50 volts per cell (while the engine is running). Unless the engine is started frequently and is run for very short periods, this will be adequate to keep the battery charged. If the engine is run infrequently, or for short periods, place the battery on a trickle-charge routine.

Constant-current Charge. If it is necessary to fully charge a battery within 7 hr using the constant-current method, the charger must be capable of delivering the 5-hr rate, at a voltage of at least 1.8 to 1.85 volts per cell. In many installations smaller chargers are used, delivering lower rates (the 8- to 10-hr), thus requiring only 1.55 to 1.65 volts per cell; longer charge times are therefore necessary. Water consumption will be lower with these lower charge rates. A variable resistance must be placed in series with any battery to be charged at constant current; make sure that this variable resistor, and the ammeter and shunts used in the charging equipment, are capable of handling the currents involved. This resistance should be adjusted to hold the charge rate steady, at least every half hour. Batteries to be series-connected and charged on one charger must be of similar design type and in a similar state of charge; if the state of charge is unknown, charge each battery on a separate charger or at a separate time.

A charge-back factor of about 140 per cent is recommended for all nickel-cadmium batteries, that is, the battery is charged until 140 per cent of the ampere-hours taken out on the previous discharge is returned. If the amount of capacity withdrawn previously is unknown, simply start the charge at a convenient rate, preferably at or near the 5-hr value. Observe the on-charge battery voltage. Using approximately the 5-hr rate, the initial on-charge voltage of a fully discharged battery will range between 1.35 and 1.45 volts per cell. The voltage will increase very gradually to 1.47 volts per cell, at which point most of the nominal capacity value will have been returned; gassing will begin at this point. As the cell approaches full charge, the voltage will rise suddenly and will level off at 1.65 to 1.8 volts per cell (depending on cell design type and actual charge rate). Charging should be continued until the on-charge voltage has remained steady at this level for 60 min (as indicated by three identical readings, taken 30 min apart). When using this method, it is particularly important to watch this end-of-charge point. If the charge is not terminated, the battery will continue to accept current, which will go entirely into the formation of hydrogen and oxygen; water loss will therefore be very rapid, and battery temperature may rise above the maximum permissible level.

Because of the sharp voltage rise at the end of charge, charging can conveniently be terminated by a voltage-sensing relay or some similar device. In almost all cases, nickel-cadmium batteries can be automatically charged on modified constant-current charge equipment designed for use with lead-acid batteries of comparable size.

Trickle Charge. Trickle charging should be used only to keep a charged battery in the fully charged condition. It is not satisfactory to charge back a completely discharged battery by this method.

Pocket-plate batteries may be maintained on trickle-charge routine at voltages between 1.40 and 1.45 volts per cell; for sintered batteries, use 1.36 to 1.38 volts per cell. Follow the manufacturer's instructions as to exact values. Self-discharge losses will be replaced when operating at the lower end of the voltage range; operating at the higher voltage will ensure return of capacity taken out in partial discharge.

Stay below the gassing potential of 1.47 volts. If water consumption is observed to be excessive, decrease the on-charge voltage. If the battery is cold (32°F or colder), raise the voltage by about 0.05 volt per cell. These voltages are critical. If charge voltage fluctuates because of changes in line voltage, it may be necessary to monitor the voltage for an initial period of operation, then choose the average value for routine operation.

Trickle charging can also be done by the constant-current method. Set the charger to supply a few milliamperes of current for each ampere-hour rated capacity of the battery. The exact value that will provide a balance between minimizing water consumption and maintaining full charge can be determined through trial and error.

Batteries maintained on trickle charge should periodically be tested to make sure that they are being held at full charge. Place the battery on charge at the 5-hr rate; if the voltage does not level off at a point between 1.6 and 1.7 volts per cell within 5 min, the battery is not fully charged. Similarly, the voltage of each cell should be checked periodically while being trickle-charged; if observed cell voltage varies by more than ±0.05 volt, the cells are going "out of balance." In the case of either full charge not being maintained or of cells going out of balance, perform periodic equalizing charges, as described below.

Float Charge. Pocket-type batteries are maintained on float at 1.40 to 1.45 volts per cell; sintered types, at 1.36 to 1.38 volts. As with trickle charging, the lower values cited are adequate to replace self-discharge losses and will ensure minimum water loss, but will not replace any significant amount of discharge current withdrawn from the battery. Voltage must be held below 1.47 volts to avoid gassing and excessive water loss. Operating at these voltages, the battery will draw current at the 35- to 50-hr rate.

As described under Trickle Charge above, maintenance of charge and uniformity of cell voltages should be periodically checked in all batteries maintained on float. Perform equalizing charges as needed.

Equalizing Charge. Batteries operating on float- or trickle-charge routines should occasionally be given an equalizing charge to keep the cells "in balance." Cells are said to grow "out of balance" when, because of small unavoidable differences in chemical or physical condition, they begin to differ in their state of charge, in the degree to which they are discharged. When this happens, some of the cells in a battery will reach full charge before the others and will exhibit an early increase in cell voltage. In float operation, where the charge voltage is not too far above that voltage at which cells will accept no charge current, this early rise in the voltage of some cells will result in decreased current delivered to the battery as a whole, before the other cells have reached full charge. Moreover, the cells with higher voltage will continue to receive a disproportionate amount of the incoming power. Hence misbalance, once started, tends to be progressive.

Some commercially available chargers have two charge positions, one for normal charging and one for equalizing charging. In the "equalizing" position, these chargers usually deliver current equivalent to the 15 to 20-hr rate for the battery. This is barely adequate. To ensure complete equalization, charging should be done at the 5-hr to 10-hr rate if possible. Once a year, when the battery is observed to have lost capacity or to go out of balance, charge it at the equalizing rate until the voltage of each cell, measured individually, has reached a plateau (at about 1.65 volts per cell) and has ceased to rise.

Normally, equalizing charges are required only for batteries operated on trickle- or float-charge routines. In other applications, charging is done by constant-current or constant-potential methods, and the charge current delivered is sufficient to bring all cells up to full charge and keep them in balance.

MAINTENANCE

Once nickel-cadmium batteries are properly installed and are being operated correctly, the major maintenance effort involved is maintaining electrolyte level and gravity and keeping the battery exterior clean. The rough cost of maintaining these batteries may be estimated by calculating the cost of the labor necessary to check electrolyte and clean cells with the frequencies described below, then adding a small percentage of this value to cover the remaining inspection and upkeep discussed in this chapter.

Typical instruments and materials needed for maintaining and overhauling nickel-cadmium batteries are as follows:

Refill electrolyte (1.220 sp gr KOH).
Renewal electrolyte (1.240 sp gr).
Adjustment electrolyte (1.300 sp gr).
Petroleum jelly.
Pure mineral oil, acid-free, nonsaponifying.
Asphalt-base paint, caustic- and corrosion-resistant.
Hydrometer (reading 1.150 to 1.300 sp gr).
Spirit thermometer (reading 0 to 160°F). Special types with scale indicating gravity correction factors are available.
Electrolyte level test tube.
Filling squeeze bottle or bulb.
Equalizing bottle or bulb (see below).
Special post nut and vent tools (as recommended by the manufacturer).

The principles to be observed in maintaining nickel-cadmium batteries are as follows:

Follow carefully the prescribed charge procedures as described previously.

Maintain proper electrolyte level, gravity, and purity. Having ensured that the electrolyte level of new cells as received is correct (as discussed on page 7-183), set up a schedule for the regular checking of level, to be followed as long as the cells are in operation. Cells in stand-by applications, which may have to be recharged fairly frequently, should be checked once a month for the first 6 months; by this time the user will see the pattern of electrolyte loss and may find it possible to reduce the frequency of checking. In float- and trickle-charge applications, the electrolyte level should be checked every 3 to 6 months. In the infrequent cases where nickel-cadmium batteries may be used in cycle applications, the level should be checked every other cycle, until the pattern of electrolyte loss becomes clear. Cells in so-called H-type ("high-type") cases contain about $2\frac{1}{2}$ times the electrolyte above the plate tops as compared with ordinary cells of the same rating. All conditions being equal, these cells would serve about $2\frac{1}{2}$ times as long between waterings as ordinary cells. However, application conditions are usually not equal; these cells are acquired specifically for applications where, except for this extra electrolyte, frequency of watering would be excessive.

Water should be added to maintain solution levels in accordance with the manufacturer's instructions. Where these are not available, the following instructions will give satisfactory results: Electrolyte must never be allowed to fall below the plate tops; if the tops of the plates are exposed to the air, serious damage will usually result. The maximum level in most cells is one-half to two-thirds of the distance between the tops of the plates and the underside of the cell cover. If this maximum is exceeded, there is danger that during a heavy-charge routine, electrolyte will overflow, causing leakage currents and loss of KOH. In pocket-plate cells, maintaining the electrolyte level between these two points is fairly simple. In cells with sintered plates, maintaining proper level is a bit more involved, since in these cells the level varies more with the state of charge. This is so because there is less excess electrolyte per unit plate volume, and because a greater proportion of the cell's electrolyte is absorbed within the body of sintered plates than is the case with pocket plates. The electrolyte is always lowest when the cell is fully discharged. Therefore, if the level in sintered-plate cells is checked when they are discharged, add only enough water to cover the tops of the plates. Check the level again after the following charge and add water to bring the level to the line on the jar. If there is no line, adjust until the level is halfway between the tops of the plates and the cover.

Many manufacturers of cells with transparent plastic cases put two marks on the side of the cell case, the lower one corresponding to the plate tops (the minimum level), and the upper mark indicating the maximum level. In small sintered-plate cells there may be only one mark, indicating maximum level; this mark will be slightly above the tops of the plates. In cells with opaque plastic or metal cases, the electrolyte level may be checked with a level test tube, in the manner shown in Fig. 10-5. These tubes may be obtained from the battery manufacturer, but any clean, uncontaminated, clear plastic tube of convenient length (8 to 12 in.), having a bore of roughly $3/16$ in., will do. The tube is held vertically and placed into the cell until it comes to rest on the plate tops. The forefinger is then placed tightly over the end, and the tube is withdrawn, permitting one to view the height of the electrolyte above the plate tops. Of course, the electrolyte contained in the tube must be returned to the cell. Wash out the tube in water after each use.

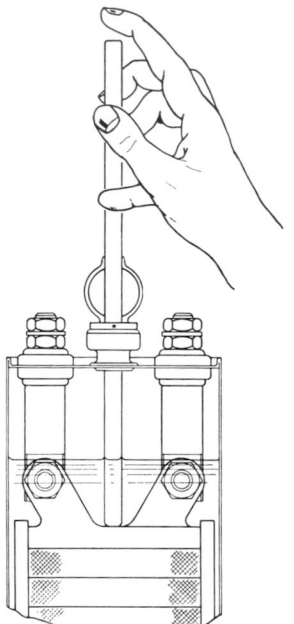

FIG. 10-5. Use of electrolyte level test tube.

Normal charging procedures do not cause any significant loss of KOH. Only water is lost, through the formation of hydrogen and oxygen that is characteristic of any storage cell being charged. Similarly, no KOH is lost through evaporation. Therefore water alone should be added to correct the level drop due to charging and evaporation; KOH electrolyte is added to a cell *only* in the case of spillage. As a general rule, use only distilled or deionized water. In some parts of the country tap water has the necessary purity, but this can be decided only by chemical analysis; some manufacturers will perform this service if requested.

If it seems that the frequency at which water must be added is excessive, or that spray is building up on the cell tops at an extraordinary rate, check the charging operation. It may be necessary to decrease the charge voltage, or to decrease current and use longer charge periods. If constant-current charging is being done, make sure also that the charge is being terminated at the proper point. Water consumption should be considerably reduced by maintaining a layer of oil on the electrolyte surface, as discussed on page 7-184.

Water may conveniently be added with a squeeze bottle or bulb, sometimes furnished with the battery. When watering cells of larger batteries, establish a regular orderly pattern of working through the cells, and use this pattern consistently. This will decrease the likelihood of missing a cell. Most plastic-cased cells have removable, screw-type vent plugs. When watering these batteries, it is good practice to remove the plugs and soak them in warm water for several minutes to remove crystallized deposits from the vent passages. When replacing these plugs, screw them in with only moderate force; otherwise undue pressure will be exerted on the O ring or washer generally used to provide seal between the plug and the cover.

If there are many cells to maintain, it may be convenient to provide a second "equalizing" bottle or bulb to withdraw excess electrolyte. This may be acquired from the manufacturer, or it may be prepared by the user. To prepare it, first determine the exact distance above the plate tops at which the maximum electrolyte level falls. Measuring this same distance from the end of the spout of a squeeze bottle or bulb, drill a small hole through the side of the spout. The end of this spout is then seated on the plate tops, and excess electrolyte is drawn into the bulb; the electrolyte level will fall until it reaches the proper height, at which point the hole in the spout will draw air. If there are a great number of cells and watering is fairly frequent, an automatic filler may be justified. This consists of a water reservoir, a spout with a manually operated valve, two electrical contacts at the end of the spout, and an electrically operated bell or buzzer. The spout has a stop, set so that when the spout is placed into the cell vent as far as the stop will allow, the end of the spout falls at the maximum electrolyte level. The valve is then opened, admitting water. When the electrolyte has risen to the end of the spout, it conducts current between the two exposed contacts on the end of the spout, completing a circuit and sounding the bell. The automatic filler should be acquired from the manufacturer of the cells. The cell type on which the filler is to be used must be specified, to enable the supplier to set the positioning stop properly.

The concentration (specific gravity) of the electrolyte is important. Most pocket-plate cells as manufactured are filled with electrolyte of 1.190 to 1.210 gravity; the exact value will be specified by the manufacturer for the particular cell design type. More concentrated electrolyte (1.280) may be used for cells intended for low-temperature operation; this concentration would damage cells operated at room temperature, however. Refill electrolyte also has a concentration of 1.190 to 1.210, and is used to replace electrolyte lost by spillage. Renewal electrolyte is generally about 1.240 sp gr, and is used to replace electrolyte in cells in which plates have been covered by distilled water after shipping or installation accidents, or to replace electrolyte which has become excessively contaminated or diluted through use.

When ordering or preparing refill or renewal electrolyte, gage the quantity needed by the rule of thumb that in most pocket-type cells 1 qt of electrolyte will be needed for each 70 to 90 amp-hr rated capacity. Considerably less electrolyte is needed for sintered cells. For more accurate values check with the battery manufacturer.

When filling cells in which plates have been covered with distilled water following accidental spillage, it may happen that the renewal electrolyte will be diluted by the water in the plates, so that the resulting concentration is below the recommended value. In this case it will be necessary to adjust the gravity, using 1.300 sp gr electrolyte. This adjustment must be done while the cell is being overcharged, so that the gassing will mix the electrolyte as readings are taken. When the battery has been charging at a steady voltage of 1.6 to 1.7 volts per cell for 30 min, check the specific gravity. Then estimate the total amount of electrolyte contained in the cell. For each quart of electrolyte, a difference of 20 gravity points (0.020) below the necessary value calls for the addition of roughly 60 ml (or 2 fl oz) of 1.300 electrolyte. Add this amount of 1.300 electrolyte, let the cell charge for another 30 min, and check the gravity again. Repeat this procedure until the gravity is correct. If gravity is too high, it may be corrected by withdrawing a portion of the electrolyte from the cell and replacing it with distilled water.

All gravity readings, taken in the course of any maintenance procedure, must be corrected for temperature. This is particularly important when adjusting electrolyte gravity, since the battery is on charge and is likely to be warm. For each 4° that electrolyte temperature is above 72°F, add 0.001 to the observed gravity reading; for each 4° below 72°F, subtract 0.001. Similarly, electrolyte must be at the proper level over the plates whenever gravity readings are taken. Always place the hydrometer all the way into the cell, so that its tip rests on the tops of the plates. This will prevent mineral oil from being drawn up into the hydrometer.

With pocket batteries operating on uninterrupted float routines, check the gravity once a year. When operating on any routine that involves recharging, gravity should be checked once each 6 months. The concentration of the electrolyte will decline slowly as small quantities of KOH are thrown out along with the gases and spray is released during the charging. When the gravity has dropped to the minimum value specified by the manufacturer (usually in the neighborhood of 1.160), the electrolyte must be renewed. Continued operation beyond this point will result in a fairly rapid decrease in cell life.

The procedure for renewing electrolyte is as follows: First prepare or acquire the necessary amount of renewal electrolyte. Then discharge the battery at the 7-hr rate to a voltage of 0.5 to 0.8 volt per cell. This will minimize the danger of shocks or damage through shorting. With cells maintained in wooden trays, disconnect the intercell connectors, incline the tray to one side, and remove the slats from one side. Take out and invert each cell individually, emptying out all electrolyte. Do not allow the cell to touch any conductive material, causing short-circuiting. Batteries assembled in steel or plastic trays are simply inverted so that all cells are emptied simultaneously. The electrolyte is injurious to aluminum, copper, zinc, or tin. Do not rinse cells with water or electrolyte. Do not allow any cell to stand empty for more than 30 min, or the plates will be damaged through exposure to air. Fill each cell as it is emptied with renewal electrolyte, to the maximun permissible level (halfway between plate tops and cell cover in most cell designs). Wash out the vent cap and replace it immediately. Add oil in stationary cells, as described on page 7-183.

Clean each cell, preferably by a blast of low-pressure steam followed by compressed air drying. It is good practice at this time to repaint the cell cases with corrosion-resistant paint. Reassemble the cells into the trays, coat the covers with petroleum jelly, make sure the intercell connectors are tightened securely, and charge the battery at the 7-hr rate for 14 hr. The battery is now ready to be returned to service.

With sintered cells, there is usually not enough free electrolyte in the cell to obtain a gravity reading. Judgment as to when to renew electrolyte is therefore based on electrical performance. If the cell has been cycled considerably or overcharged, or has been used for a period of a few years and is beginning to decline in capacity in spite of good maintenance and proper charging, the electrolyte probably needs renewing. Dump the electrolyte, following the same general procedure as described above. Replace the electrolyte with 1.300 sp gr solution. The cell will be discharged at this point. Therefore fill it only to the tops of the plates, and then charge it. Following the charge, the electrolyte level may be brought up the rest of the way to the maximum mark.

Potassium hydroxide reacts with the carbon dioxide in the air to form potassium carbonate, which will decrease capacity when its concentration in the electrolyte exceeds a few per cent. Formation of carbonate can be minimized by several means: (1) Open cell vents no more frequently, and for no longer, than is absolutely necessary. (2) Make sure that vent components and the glands or washers around the terminals make a good seal against the cell cover. (3) Maintain a layer of oil on the surface of the electrolyte. (4) Minimize overcharging, particularly overcharging at high rates. This condition causes agitation of the electrolyte and formation of crusts of carbonate on the underside of the cell cover, which then fall back into the electrolyte. (5) Control electrical operation and scheduling of maintenance so that frequency of adjustment of electrolyte level is minimized. (6) Store the electrolyte stock in tightly sealed containers only.

Carbonate concentration can be determined by chemical analysis. This is a service that most manufacturers will provide. This service is also available from many commercial testing laboratories. The decision as to when to have an analysis performed can be based on the performance of the battery. It should not be necessary to have this analysis done more frequently than every 2 years. If the battery is not yet approaching end of life but exhibits marginal performance in spite of proper charging and correct electrolyte level and concentration, carbonate contamination should be suspected, and an analysis should be done. On the other hand, if, at the end of a 2-year period, performance is good, an analysis can be deferred. When carbonate concentration in the electrolyte reaches 10 per cent by weight, the electrolyte should be renewed.

Electrolyte can be procured from most manufacturers either as dry crystals, to be mixed to the proper concentration by the user, or as solution mixed to a specified concentration. Using dry crystals can save considerable shipping cost and avoids having to order several different concentrations, but does involve handling and mixing. Solutions should be mixed in a large glass, porcelain, or plastic vessel that is perfectly clean and free from contaminants. Electrolyte crystals should be ordered from the battery manufacturer; the container will usually include mixing instructions. As a general rule, preparing 1.240 sp gr solution calls for about 2.56 lb of pure KOH per gallon of water—2.33 lb per gal will produce 1.220 solution. Some users may prefer to mix just one solution strength, the strongest needed, for storing, and then dilute this to the other strengths required as they are needed. Starting with 1.300 solution and mixing 7 parts of this with 2 parts water will produce 1.240 sp gr electrolyte; $8\frac{1}{2}$ parts of 1.300 and 4 parts water will yield 1.220 sp gr.   Also, 10 parts of 1.240 solution and 1 part water can be mixed to yield 1.200 sp gr.

When handling KOH in any of these procedures, it should be remembered that it is a corrosive chemical, injurious to skin and eyes.   The standard goggles, face mask, and rubber garments should be considered for use.   If electrolyte is spilled or splashed on skin or clothes, wash immediately with liberal quantities of water.   It is wise to have on hand a stock of boric acid solution to neutralize spilled electrolyte.   Diluted pharmaceutical-grade boric acid can be used to rinse the eyes.

Guard against stray currents and shorts, by the following means:

Under no circumstances allow metal cell cases to touch each other.   Even though both terminals are insulated from the steel cases and covers by rubber glands, current will be conducted by the electrolyte from the plates to the cases, and thence via touching cell cases to plates of the opposite polarity, thus shorting out the battery.

Keep the cases and the covers clean.   Films and paths of dirt, moisture, and electrolyte spray will not only conduct current between points of opposite polarity and self-discharge the battery, but also will lead to electrolytic corrosion of the steel cases and covers.   Wipe off moisture and carbonate that build up on the cover; keep the cover coated with petroleum jelly.   Prevent debris from building up between the cell cases, or under the cells so as to bridge to ground.   It is good practice to go over the entire battery periodically with a low-pressure blast of steam, followed by an air blast to thoroughly dry the cells.

Never stack cells or trays on top of one another.

Do not overfill cells with electrolyte and risk overflow during charging.

Dress all cables up and away from cell tops.   Never allow cables to lie on cell tops or on intercell connectors.

After installing or doing maintenance on the battery, make sure that no tools, screws, or other metal parts are left in the battery compartment.

Use only spirit thermometers.   Mercury is an electrical conductor.   If a mercury thermometer should break, allowing mercury to run down into the cell interior between the plates, serious shorting would be likely.

When taking battery voltage readings, check also for possible voltages between each of the battery terminals and ground.   Such a voltage is an indication of a ground somewhere in the system.

Instruments or devices which would cause a constant drain of current must not be left connected across the battery permanently.   As an example, if the user wants to have a voltmeter connected in readiness, it should be wired through a normally open push-button switch, so that it is connected to the battery only when the switch is depressed.

Make sure connections are tight and making good electrical contact and that post and vent seals are maintained.

Good electrical contact at terminal connections will prevent wasteful voltage drop. This can be checked by putting the battery on a high-rate or discharge for 15 to 20 min.   Defective connections will have resistance and will feel warm to the touch. Take these connections apart and clean the contact areas of the terminal posts, connectors, and nuts with solvent or cleanser and fine emery cloth or steel wool.

If the seal around posts and vents does not remain tight, air and impurities may be admitted to the cell interior, and there will be excessive buildup of carbonate and electrolyte film on the covers.   Leaks will be indicated by encrusted carbonate developing at the seal area.   In these cases, tighten the lower terminal post nut or the vent plug.   If the rubber sealing glands on the terminal posts or the seal components on the vents have become brittle or deformed, they should be replaced. If special tools are necessary to turn terminal or vent components, they will be available from the manufacturer.

Avoid introducing any sulfuric acid. Sulfuric acid will ruin nickel-cadmium batteries. Even trace amounts, working over the years, will corrode the steel cell cases and cause disintegration of the plates.

If a nickel-cadmium battery is to be installed in a compartment which formerly housed lead-acid batteries, the compartment must be thoroughly washed out, neutralized with ammonia or soda solution, dried, and then painted with asphalt varnish. Wood compartment liners cannot be washed free of all sulfate; they must be removed and replaced. Nickel-cadmium batteries should not be installed in the same room as lead-acid batteries unless there is ample ventilation to carry away the sulfuric acid fumes as they are formed. When watering batteries, do not use water from containers bearing a characteristic label reading "distilled water for storage batteries"; this water generally contains small amounts of sulfuric acid through having been stored in carboys which have also been used for electrolyte for lead-acid batteries.

Maintain strict separation between the tools and appliances used for servicing lead-acid batteries and those for nickel-cadmium batteries (or indeed any alkaline battery). Glass and plastic devices, such as level test tables and filling devices, which have been used for lead-acid batteries, may be used only after they have been thoroughly washed in hot water and neutralized in ammonia or soda solution. Rubber tubes and hydrometer bulbs, corks, and stoppers and other porous objects that have been used for lead-acid batteries should never be used for nickel-cadmium batteries.

Avoid high temperatures. See that the temperature of the installation does not regularly rise above 100°F. Hence, do not install batteries near a boiler or radiator.

Allow no open flame or sparks. The gases released by any battery on charge are hydrogen and oxygen—a very explosive mixture. Open flames must therefore be eliminated from the battery area. If heavy overcharging is done, ample ventilation must be provided to prevent hydrogen and oxygen from building up to an explosive concentration in the battery compartment or the exhaust flues.

Use only a flashlight to examine the battery; a plastic-cased flashlight is preferred, so as to minimize the chance of striking an arc. Make sure all battery connections are tight so that there is no arcing; guard against arcing in nearby electrical equipment.

With pocket cells, repaint the cell cases and trays as needed with alkali-resistant paint, available from the manufacturer. If the battery is exposed to the weather, this may have to be done every 2 to 3 years.

LAYING UP AND STORING

A fully charged nickel-cadmium battery in storage will lose between 20 and 40 per cent of nominal capacity in the first year and roughly half the first-year value in each succeeding year. The exact rate of self-discharge depends primarily on the impurity content and the general condition of the cells, the cleanliness of the cell covers, and the storage temperature. Ideal storage temperatures are 40 to 60°F. These cells will not be damaged by temperatures down to −20°F, or lower.

Cells may be placed in storage in any state of charge and left for years if necessary. The specific gravity and the electrolyte level should be checked as the cells go into storage to make sure they are within the ranges specified. Intertray connectors should be removed, and the covers recoated with petroleum jelly.

When the battery is removed from storage, it should be charged at the 5-hr rate for 12 to 15 hr. If storage has been prolonged, it may be necessary to cycle the battery a few times to restore full capacity.

Chapter 11

POWER DISTRIBUTION[1]

By FRANK W. MICHAL[2]
Associate Editor
Factory
New York, N.Y.

This is a book on maintenance. Nevertheless, in this chapter, there will be quite a few pages of general discussion preceding the pages containing the nuts and bolts of preventive maintenance. There are several reasons:

A new concept, "electricity is everybody's business," is gaining importance.

There are major trends with which everyone charged with the responsibility for maintaining the electrical backbone of a plant should be familiar.

Different types of distribution systems vary in cost, reliability, and flexibility. While the merits of these systems—radial, secondary selective, network, and the like— are normally argued on initial-cost and/or reliability grounds, the type of system that a plant has (or the type installed in a new plant) will have a marked effect on the daily operations of the man responsible for maintaining it.

ELECTRICITY IS EVERYBODY'S BUSINESS

Gone are the days when the electrical system could be installed and promptly forgotten by everyone but the maintenance man. Nowadays, the success of the whole operation is intimately tied to the adequacy of the distribution system. A system with inadequate capacity may block important changes in the production setup. I know a plant where the distribution system was the single limiting factor holding back a proposed expansion of the production capacity—and it took the plant engineer two years to make this point clear to the company's financial management.

A system that is not sufficiently reliable can cost money so fast it hurts. Frequent outages, even though short, can cause a lot of downtime and a lot of lost labor hours. Production men in a foundry who just once have watched helplessly while 7 tons of molten steel solidified in the furnace and the maintenance men worked frantically to get power back on the electrodes seldom overlook the matter of reliability in the future. The same reasoning, though perhaps less dramatic, applies to every plant.

On the other hand, as is the case in your personal life, you can insure yourself into the poorhouse. Not every plant needs or should pay for a tops-in-reliability network distribution system. But the plant-operating men *as a group*, not just the plant engineer or the electrical "hot shot," whatever his title, should decide what kind of system the plant should have. It is the job of everyone involved—the production men who know how much load they are going to put on the system and how much downtime

---

[1] In addition to the material specifically credited in this chapter, the author is indebted for much information made available by the General Electric Company, Schenectady, N.Y.

[2] The author is now Consulting Engineer, Maplewood, N.J.

they really can afford, the industrial engineers who have to sweat out the layout changes that are sure to come, and the plant engineer who probably will be responsible for the installation and its maintenance—to determine what the requirements are capacity-wise, reliability-wise, and flexibility-wise and then decide whether or not the present system can do the job and if it can't, what is to be done.

One more example: flexibility. The operating men in a plant that consists entirely of 15-ton presses resting on reinforced concrete foundations have a very different electrical-distribution problem from their opposite numbers in a screw-machine shop. There will have to be an awfully good reason before those big presses are moved, whereas, unless history stops repeating itself, the screw machines are going to be repositioned, and soon. If you were to find a grid network of bus duct in the press shop, you would know that the management had been charmed by a salesman. The degree of flexibility in layout that a grid of bus duct affords is just not necessary or worth the money. But managers of a shop full of movable equipment that *does not* have bus duct will pay for their oversight or penny pinching in headaches and frustration, because they can't set up their shop the way they want to. The neatest production layout in the world is no good if there is no economical way to power it.

To sum up, there is little excuse for any operating man's confessing, "I can't understand that electrical stuff." If you are one of those, you are confessing to a serious weakness. If you do have a firm grasp of matters electrical but are surrounded by plant-operating men who do not, point out their stake. As a plant engineer, you can't be expected to do the worrying about production layout and future production expansion. If you don't alert the others on the plant staff to their responsibilities in the matter of the distribution system, it is going to be "your" system when trouble comes. Don't be the goat. Electricity—these days—is everybody's business.

THE TRENDS IN ELECTRICAL DISTRIBUTION

It is a rare plant where power usage isn't increasing—and fast—thanks to increased mechanization, new equipment, or just more equipment. An often-quoted statistic: Power requirement of plants has been doubling every 10 years, and there is no indication of any slackening in this growth rate. Every time you make a change in or addition to your distribution system, you have an opportunity to take a step in the right direction. Here are ten commonly accepted such steps:

1. Better Power Planning. First things first would put at the top of the list adequate power. Assuming that your plant is growing, are you sure that your utility is in position to supply the power you will need 1, 2, 5, or 10 years from now? (Reword the question a bit if your plant generates its own power.) Again, as a plant operating group, it is your responsibility to keep your utility updated on your plans. Don't surprise it with the news that four new arc furnaces are on the way from the manufacturer. The utility, with the help of plant men on their feeders, have to plan ahead. too. The power company needs to know:

a. How much power you are going to be using and the rate at which you are going to use it so it can figure its demand load.

b. The number of shifts. If you plan to change to three shifts, the utility will have to know so it can make arrangements to do its maintenance work.

c. Whether you can use power during off-peak periods. Often you can shift some of your operations to take big chunks of power during the night, when most utilities have excess capacity. For example, if you have to test units with big motors from time to time and can schedule such tests at night, the utility may be able to offer attractive rates.

d. How much outage you can stand. If processes are such that power outages will cause major damage (as in the steel furnace example cited) or be excessively costly, you and the utility together should work out all possible guarantees against outage, such as dual incoming feeders, different main transformer, and the like.

e. Your growth anticipations. If you foresee major increases in electrical load within the next few years, talk it over with the power company, which may be able to save you real money by revising your service, tying you in to a higher-voltage feeder.

f. Your needs for any special services such as underground, underground transformer vault, and the like.

2. Higher Incoming Voltages. As the number of plants in a locality increases and they move farther from the utility's generators, higher voltages must be used to move the power to the plants with a minimum of line losses and with good voltage regulation. Few utilities will undertake to deliver power at voltages lower than 2,400 these days. They are distributing up to 230 kv, talking about going to 350 which, for plants as a whole, is all to the good, because rates for power bought at higher voltages are much lower. These savings and discounts normally repay the slightly higher installation cost for a master substation within several years.

Rule of thumb: Loads less than 300 kw, 2,400 to 4,160 volts incoming power. Loads from 300 to 8,000 kw, 12 to 33 kv incoming power. Loads of 8,000 kw and up, 66 kv and up. Incoming power at 132 kv is not uncommon.

3. Higher In-plant Voltages. For the same reason—to feed power over long distances throughout the plant without excessive line loss or loss of regulation—most plants are switching to higher in-plant voltages. The most popular utilization voltage in new plants today is 480, though 240 is still popular. The best over-all secondary utilization voltage is 480. Besides costing less, it provides lower line losses and less voltage drop. The only place where 240 volts makes real sense is where most equipment is rated 220 or where it doesn't pay to convert just to gain operating advantages. Actually, 600-volt systems are less expensive than 480-volt systems. But the 550-volt motors, controls, etc., needed for 600-volt systems are not so readily available as 440- or 220-volt equipment.

But almost all new plants have gone over to load center distribution (with unit substations close to the load) with primary distribution being made throughout the plant at 2,400, 4,160, or 13,800 volts. The best primary-distribution (between master substation and load center) voltage depends on the size of the load and the distance to be covered. In general, 4,160 volts is recommended for loads under 10,000 kva, 13.8 kv for loads over 20,000. For loads between 10,000 and 20,000 kva, it's rather a toss-up. Lean to 4,160 volts for compact plants, 13.8 kv for long, rambling layouts.

4. More Unit Substations. The economies of in-plant distribution at these higher voltages is one of the prime reasons behind more unit substations. Placing these load centers in the center of heavy concentrations of load has the following advantages over the older system of transforming power at one point and distributing it throughout the plant at the utilization voltage:

a. Less voltage drop and better voltage regulation.

b. Lower first cost.

c. Lower cost in the event of future expansion.

d. Reduced engineering and planning.

e. Much lower cable cost (it takes a lot more copper to distribute 480-volt power throughout a shop than it does to cover the same area with power of higher voltage).

f. Easier installation.

g. Greater system flexibility.

The most economical ranges for size of unit substations are 240 volts, 300 to 750 kva (500 kva lowest cost); 480 volts, 500 to 1,500 kva (750 kva lowest cost).

An interesting sidelight to the expanding use of unit substations is the change in normal location. When these load centers first came into the picture, they were usually plunked on the plant floor in the center of the load they were supplying. It didn't take long for smart plant men to realize that needless waste of production space was involved. Now virtually every new plant locates its substations on the roof, on mezzanines, in the basement, atop shop toilets, or over production offices. Not only has this the advantage of eliminating loss of production space, it keeps an at least semi-permanent installation out of the way of production layout changes, keeps production employees at a safe distance, gives maintenance men unobstructed and uncrowded room to wield their trade and tools.

5. More Flexible and Reliable Circuit Arrangements. About 75 per cent of plants have simple radial primary and secondary distribution. But there is undoubtedly a trend toward the greater flexibility and reliability of selective systems to prevent complete stoppage in the event of a fault. Details will be given later in this chapter.

6. Better Conductors. The business of repairing cable damage, making installations and changes, and hooking up electrical utilization equipment is becoming easier, thanks to the increasing use of:

a. Insulated cables. The old stand-by, lead-covered cable is fading. With it goes the troublesome problem of making up lead joints at splices.

b. Overhead cable. Few new plants are installing underground cable. There are people who worry about running 13.2-kv cable (in conduit, of course) out in the open, but few insurance carriers or code writers do any more.

c. Interlocked armored cable. This kind of cable can be pulled and bent easily and requires no conduit. It easily follows roof contours, takes 90° bends, and so on.

d. Bus duct, in both primary- and secondary-voltage applications. For carrying loads up to 5,000 amp, bus duct has a greater current-carrying capacity, pound for pound of copper, than most types of cable in general use. But out in the plant, for distributing low-voltage power to the loads, it offers maintenance the biggest boost. Hooking up relocated production equipment is made a simple problem by plug-in bus with openings on 1-ft centers.

e. Trolley bus. Though this type of enclosed busway was originally designed for powering mobile equipment such as cranes, the big move today is to use it as a combination mechanical support and electrical raceway for lighting and portable tools. With a network set up on reasonable centers, it is a simple matter to shift lighting fixtures around or to add new ones as lighting requirements in an area change.

7. Better Controls. The life of the maintenance man is simplified indeed the day motor controls are concentrated in a control center, because:

a. Controls can be located away from the dirt, fumes, chips, and coolant surrounding the equipment involved.

b. Interrupting capacities of devices are engineered into the control center. By keeping the control centers off to one side and safely locked, the maintenance man can be sure the machine operator doesn't make any "adjustments" or tamper with the control during idle moments.

c. All the internal wiring of the control can be done at the manufacturer's plant, easing the load on the maintenance force.

d. Everything is in one place, making for quicker repairs.

e. By keeping the control centers out of the middle of valuable production space, there is more space to operate in around the center than would be the case with individual units tucked "out of the way" at the machine location.

8. Combined Power and Lighting Circuits. In new plants, 50 ft-c is commonplace, 80 or more not uncommon. There are four basic ways to get the power needed for the lamps:

a. Use a separate substation for supplying 120-volt power for lights. This is expensive, because it requires long lengths of cable carrying power at low voltage, which means heavy cable losses.

b. Use small dry-type transformers (receiving primary-voltage power from the 480-volt distribution system) at the center of lighting loads to cut power to 120 volts. Cheaper than option 1.

c. Use 277-volt lighting. Get 277 volts direct from the 480-volt system, using four-wire grounded-neutral wiring. This works for fluorescent and mercury-vapor lighting only. Plants that use this system have a small number of dry-type transformers for any incandescent lighting that is required.

d. Use 480 volts direct. Fixtures to operate on 480 (465 volts is the actual rating) cost a little more than 277- or 120-volt fixtures, but the net cost usually is lowest of all with this system, thanks to the elimination of transformers and reduction in wire size. This system has not as yet gained widespread favor. My guess as to the most popular lighting system in plants being built: 277-volt fluorescent.

9. Design for Operating Economy. Correctly or incorrectly, it is the plant engineer to whom the purse-string holders in most plants look for an explanation of the power bill—and for its reduction. And so of all plant operating men, it behooves the plant engineer to be alert to the trends in electrical distribution that are cutting power bills for smart managements everywhere. There are several:

a. Instrumentation to control demand charge. One of the most common setups makes use of recording instruments that give a minute-by-minute record of power usage on each feeder. Not only will the resulting records warn against overloads and abnormal conditions, but they will indicate trends, time moments of high demand, and the like. Another setup uses indicating instruments for checking voltages and loads. With the help that instruments will give, you can often, by reducing loads or delaying the addition of new loads at peak load periods, save hundreds of dollars in demand charges. *Example:* A plant with several electric furnaces can save considerable on its power bill by scheduling their operation during periods when the rest of the plant load is at a low point. Once you establish a new high in demand, you must live with it—under the rate schedules of most utilities—for at least a month.

b. Automatic controls to reduce energy charge. For example, lighting circuits should be designed so that by operating a few switches you can cut off units that need not be operating. Lighting can be controlled by the module system—one switch for an entire group, or there can be push-button control in the superintendent's office.

c. Power-factor correction. Unless some sort of correction has been applied, the power factor of the average plant is quite low—between 70 and 80 per cent, probably. Cables are unnecessarily loaded, as are transformers; bad voltage conditions and reduced illumination from lighting (especially incandescent) result. Where low power factor hurts most (except in rare instances where the utility rate schedule applies no penalty for low power factor) is in the power bill.

The most common cause of low power factor is partially loaded induction motors. Frequently, the drives on production equipment are overmotored for everyday operation; that is, the drive is engineered for the heaviest load conditions, under which the equipment is rarely operated. Other causes are replacement of incandescent by fluorescent lamps, use of rectifiers instead of synchronous motor-generator sets to generate d-c power, increasing use of induction devices such as heaters and air-conditioning units. In general, as plants become more and more mechanized (and use more and more motors), the power factor tends to fall.

Correction is worth while because power costs will be cut, the effective capacity of the entire distribution system will be increased, voltage level will be raised, system losses will be reduced. There are two common methods of correction: installation of shunt capacitors and use of synchronous motors. At the time of the installation of an air compressor or other large motor-driven device, it makes sense to install a synchronous motor drive. Where no such installation is contemplated, installation of capacitors is the normal power-factor boosting technique. The maximum operating benefit of capacitors is obtained when the units are located at the load. Since capacitors come in standard sizes, try to "match up" an individual capacitor to each load on the load side of the motor control starter. Where that is not possible, capacitors are installed at one or several central locations (such as the panel switchboard) to cover many small loads and on the feeders to any single heavy load.

Standard cost comparisons can be made to determine how long it will take, with calculable reductions in the power bill, to pay off the cost of installation. The calculations required can be determined from most texts on electrical distribution.

d. Relaying. Although a proper system of relaying is not directly a means of reducing power bill, it will aid materially in reducing total production costs. The purpose of relaying is to set up or "time" circuit protective devices so a minimum of breakers opens to isolate any fault. For example, in the simple circuit, Fig. 11-1, suppose there is a fault as shown. Ideally, the 480-volt feeder breaker protecting that particular feeder would open first, isolating the fault. But unless the relays on the system are operating just right, there is a strong possibility that the 480-volt transformer breaker will open first, cutting off power not only to the faulted feeder but to all other feeders on the entire 480-volt bus fed by that transformer. With properly coordinated relays (either cascade or selective), only the interrupting device closest to the overload fault will open. Any devices nearer to the power source will operate only when the correct device, for one reason or another, fails to function properly.

In a cascaded system the transformer breaker as well as the low-voltage feeder breaker will trip should the fault current exceed 80 per cent of the interrupting rating of the feeder breaker. The advantage of this system (as opposed to the selective system) is cost, since it permits using a transformer breaker with lower interrupting capacity. Savings in breaker cost alone can amount to $5,000 for a 1,000-kva unit substation. Its disadvantage is some downtime of circuits fed from other feeder breakers in the same substation. The transformer breaker must be reclosed manually before the other feeder breakers put out of action can be reclosed.

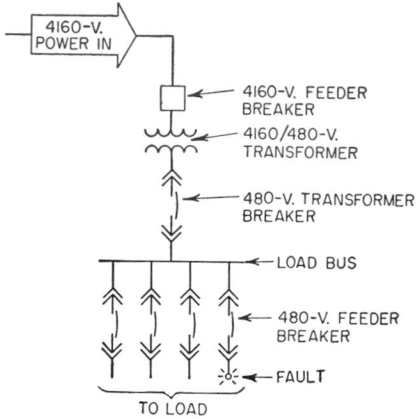

Fig. 11-1. Simple circuit illustrating need for coordinated relays.

Multiply the simple case cited many times. Take a perhaps overdramatic case like a short on a portable power tool causing the loss of power to a main assembly conveyor—and it could happen—and you see the importance of adequate relaying.

10. Better Protection against Short-circuit Currents. Higher power loads in plants and greater amounts of power on utility systems have multiplied the needs for adequate interrupting capacity throughout the distribution system of a plant   If you are in the dark about the interrupting capacity of your circuit breakers, now is a good time to do a little checking.

It is no longer enough to consider the load current in buying circuit breakers. Breakers have to be equipped to handle the amount of current that will flow in the event of short circuits on the system. This short-circuit current is independent of the load on the cable. It is dependent on the capacity of the power system that is supplying power to the cable. For example, a 440-volt 10-hp motor draws about 14 amp of current at full load. It will draw this amount whether the power is supplied by a 25- or a 2,500-kva transformer. So if only the load currents are considered in selecting the protective equipment for the feeder of this motor, a 15-amp circuit breaker would do the job. But if the motor is fed from a large transformer, currents of 25,000 amp could flow through the feeder in case of a short.

To sum up: For adequate short-circuit protection, circuit breakers must be able to handle the maximum fault current that can be introduced by the power system (including motor contribution). Figuring these short-circuit currents is not easy; if necessary, ask for help from manufacturer or consultant.

TYPES OF DISTRIBUTION SYSTEMS

There are many variations and types of distribution systems, and there is no widespread agreement on names. But it is generally agreed that there are three main types: simple radial, secondary selective, and secondary network.

Simple Radial System. This is the least expensive. The system diagramed in Fig. 11-2 might be called "simple radial with load centers." The simplest radial system, diagramed in Fig. 11-3, is commonly used only in small plants with loads below 1,000 kva, since with only one transformer, even if it is centrally located, there are of necessity long runs of cable carrying low-voltage power and losses are great.

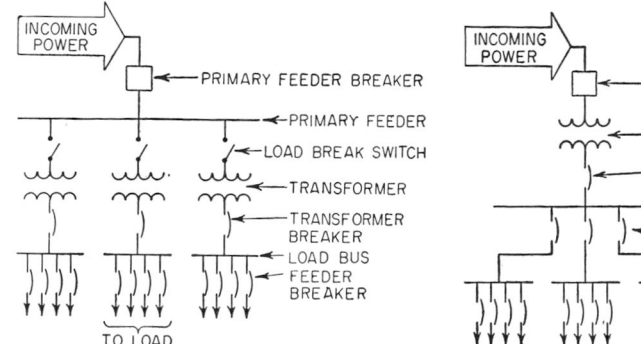

FIG. 11-2. Simple radial system with load centers.

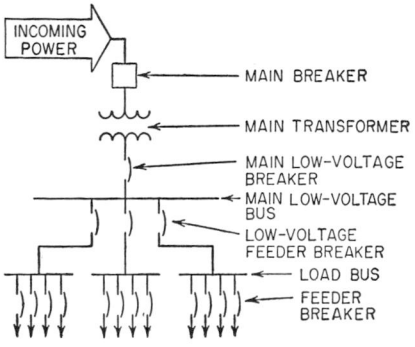

FIG. 11-3. Simple radial system.

The radial with load centers, Fig. 11-2, is the commonly used system in plants where at least fairly long cable runs are required and the peak load exceeds 1,000 kva.

The simple radial system with no load centers uses a single master substation where power is received at the supply voltage and stepped down to the utilization voltage. Low-voltage feeders are run from the substation to the various load centers in the plant. At the load center, power is distributed through switchgear over smaller load circuits, either direct or through panelboards. Under this system, obviously, the entire plant load is fed through a single substation and from a single low-voltage bus. This takes full advantage of the diversity among load centers. Thus, the minimum amount of transformer capacity is needed. On the other hand, since all power is distributed from a single point, voltage regulation and efficiency are poor. Cost of load feeders and their circuit breakers is excessive, except in very small plants. And a fault on the substation bus or transformer will interrupt service to all loads in the shop. A fault on the feeder from the substation to a load center causes an outage to all loads supplied by that load bus.

The simple radial with load centers, a more modern version of the simple radial, overcomes many of the objections just cited by distributing power to the various load centers at the higher distribution voltages (typically 4,160 or 13,800 volts) rather than the much lower utilization voltage (typically 480 or 240 volts). The distribution voltage is stepped down to the utilization voltage through relatively small load center transformers (unit substations). The unit substation transformer is normally connected to the primary-voltage feeder through a circuit breaker. Since, under this system, each of the several load center transformers is "on its own," it must have sufficient capacity to carry the peak load of its area. Hence more transformer capacity is needed. On the other hand, since power is distributed through the shop at a higher (i.e., the distribution) voltage, there is far less power loss in the cables, much less copper is needed, regulation is improved, and large, low-voltage feeder breakers are eliminated. For these reasons, this is by far the most popular system. Of the basic types, it is the cheapest.

For most plants it is sufficiently reliable. General Electric Company has estimated from its operating records that askarel transformers average about one failure in 2,500 transformer-years (to coin a unit). High-voltage cables average about one failure per mile per 100 years of service. Sounds pretty good. Two things to remember, however: Those are averages, and averages have a habit of overlooking *your* plant in the wrong direction; and maintenance of equipment or cables will necessitate a complete production shutdown in the area fed. For most plants this is not a problem, but if yours is a plant where downtime really costs money, you'll probably find it worth while to spend a little more for one of the systems described below.

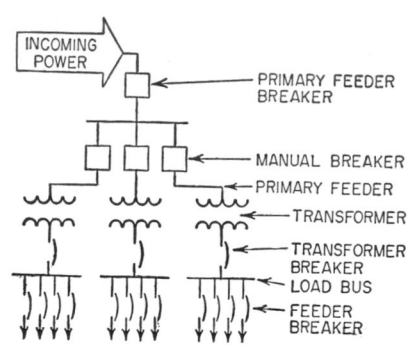

Fig. 11-4. Simple radial system with separate primary feeder.

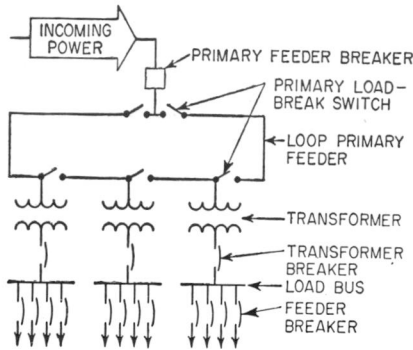

Fig. 11-5. Simple system with looped primary radial.

Before moving on to these systems, however, take just a glance at the two further variations of the simple radial system that enjoy some popularity. Both offer slightly better guarantee of service continuity at moderate increase in cost (see Figs. 11-4 and 11-5). This type of system puts more of a burden on the man responsible for maintenance than do the other two basic systems. When there is a fault anywhere on the system, more, if not all, of the system is down. With production men fuming, the heat will be on for fast repairs. On the other hand, there is—by the relatively simple nature of the system—less to maintain.

Secondary Selective System. This type of system, diagramed in Fig. 11-6, will normally cost between 10 and 30 per cent more than a simple radial system with load centers (i.e., Fig. 11-2) of comparable size. What do you get for your money? Quite a bit, from the point of view of both production and maintenance:

An individual feeder or transformer can be taken out of service at any time without dropping any important load. Suppose (see Fig. 11-6) that there is a fault in substation 1. By opening the 480-volt breaker between the load bus and the transformer, you isolate the load from the fault. Notice that there is a tie breaker between its load bus and the load bus of substation 2. By closing the normally open (N.O.) breakers at each end of the load bus, the load of substation 1 is connected with the load bus of substation 2. Open the breaker between the transformer and the high-voltage load bus, and the faulted transformer is completely isolated, ready for repair or replacement —under most conditions at the relative leisure of the maintenance force.

Can the transformer of substation 2 carry the combined load on load busses 1 and 2? As a practical matter, no. Assuming that both substations were equally loaded prior to the fault, substation 2 now has twice the load. Few distribution systems are designed with transformers that have 100 per cent extra capacity; common practice is to load unit substation transformers to somewhere in the neighborhood of 70 per cent. But by dropping nonessential loads (such as air-conditioning or ventilating equipment, production equipment of lesser importance, and the like) and by pushing the remaining transformer a bit, you can usually keep essential loads on both load busses in action. If you have no "nonessential" loads and choose this type of system, you should figure loads in advance and provide sufficient capacity in either transformer to carry the joint load that will result from a transformer fault.   Fans, incidentally, come in handy at moments like these.   A compromise elected by many companies is to keep in stock one stand-by transformer that fits all the substations ready for quick replacement of any faulted unit.   Under this setup substations normally are tied in pairs.

Advantages, maintenance-wise, of this system should be obvious.   While there will be a few frantic moments when nonessential loads are cut off the line and the tie breakers closed, you then will be under less pressure from production to get the faulted

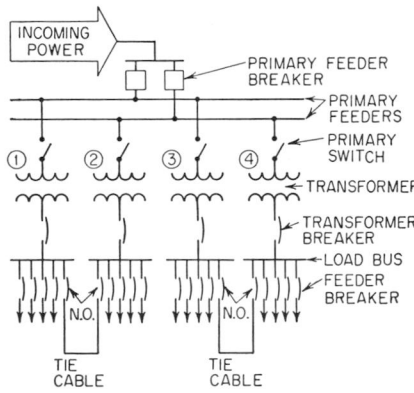

Fig. 11-6. Secondary selective system.

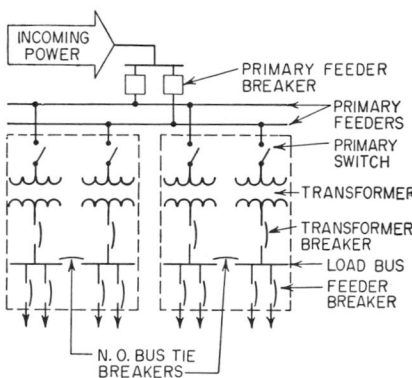

Fig. 11-7. Secondary selective (double-ended substation type).

unit repaired or replaced.   This does not mean, however, that prompt action is not essential—since you now have no more insurance.

There is another variation offering the same type of reliability.   Cost is slightly greater; reliability slightly better.   There are two transformers at each load center (called a double-ended substation), each capable of carrying the entire load of the load center and each fed by a different high-voltage feeder (see Fig. 11-7).

Network System.   This is the system for plants with processes such that downtime is out of the question.   Its cost is often about 40 per cent more than the cost of a simple radial system.   It is characterized by having all substations in the plant tied together by normally open tie lines between low-voltage load busses (all substations are tied into a loop, or network, hence the name).   The high-voltage feeders are the same as in the radial or secondary selective system.   This type of system is diagramed in Fig. 11-8.

Every load on the system is shared by all the transformers in the system collectively. For that reason, the load on every transformer is equal.   The system can take surges of load, such as are caused by the starting of a heavy motor, without the dimming of a light.   From the point of view of maintenance, as long as there is even a reasonable amount of excess capacity in the transformers, a single unit can be faulted with practically no effect on the system.   Of course, if only three transformers are on the network, any two of them must have sufficient capacity to carry the entire load—a capacity equal to 150 per cent of normal.   But if four, five, or six transformers are so looped, the excess transforming capacity required is small indeed.

Under this system, when a primary feeder or transformer fault occurs, the defective unit is automatically disconnected from the system by tripping the associated primary feeder breaker and network protectors.   The network protectors are special air circuit breakers controlled by network relays.   Since the network relays function to trip their breakers only when current flows *from* the secondary loop *to* the transformers, only the network protectors associated with the faulty transformer open.   Therefore the

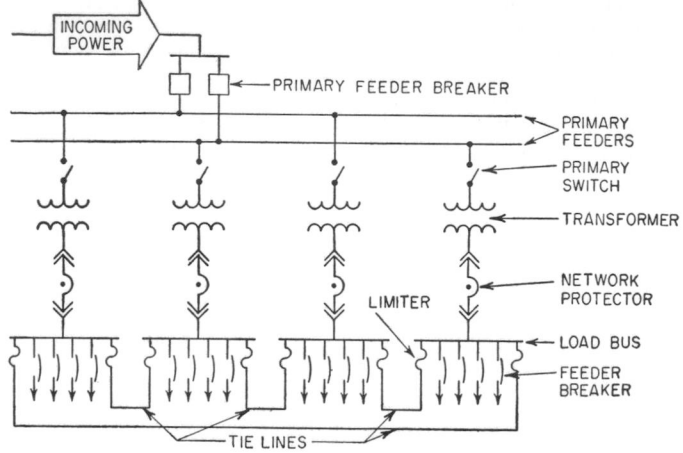

FIG. 11-8. Network system.

plant load continues to be supplied over the good feeders and their transformers.   A transformer fault on a network system will not cause even a momentary interruption to any load.

The system diagramed in Fig. 11-8 suffers from the weakness that while it will carry without trouble any fault on one of the transformers, the failure of one of the two primary feeders would put out of action half of the transformers.   Hence although there is good protection against transformer failure, there is not enough protection against primary feeder failure. That situation can be remedied by installing a *primary* selective system as well under which all transformers can be switched, either manually or automatically, to either feeder.   Normally, however, half of the transformers are fed by one, the other half by the other.   Obviously, either feeder must be capable of handling the load of all the transformers.

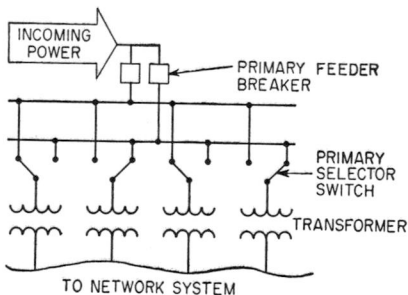

FIG. 11-9. Selective primary.

The primary feeders of such a system are diagramed in Fig. 11-9.   The system beyond the transformers would be the same as in Fig. 11-8.

"THERE'S NO SUCH THING AS 'ELECTRICAL' MAINTENANCE"

That statement is true, of course, in only a limited sense.   I make such a point of it for only one reason: So many people, including otherwise sophisticated plant operating men, think there is something highly mysterious about maintaining electrical-distribution equipment.   Think about it a moment, and you will realize that almost all electrical maintenance (not trouble shooting) is mechanical maintenance work. When you have trouble on the distribution system, it is usually caused by a *mechanical* failure of some sort—a switch or contact badly worn or pitted, loose connections, mechanical damage to cable, failure of some contact to operate because of mechanical blocking or faulty lubrication, just plain dirt in operating parts of switchgear, leaks in oil tanks, and the like.

Of course, you have to understand the electrical concepts behind your distribution system to maintain it effectively.   But as will be demonstrated in the maintenance suggestions that make up the remainder of this chapter, there is little maintenance work that would not logically come under the heading of *mechanical* work.

So what? I've used this much paper on what perhaps seems to some readers to be a flimsy concept to point out just one idea: Electrical maintenance doesn't consist of anything more than mechanical maintenance of the mechanical components of the distribution system—the switchgear, the transformers, the capacitors, the lightning arresters, the voltage regulators, the bushings, the cables.

Because of the wide variety of equipment available, the information given must be fairly general and does not pretend to cover all possible contingencies. Installation, operating, and maintenance instructions, always supplied by the manufacturer, should be used for detailed procedures. When you buy new equipment, make sure that these instructions are passed along to the man who actually has to use them and are not left to languish in the files of the purchasing agent. If you can't find such instructions for existing equipment, write the manufacturer for a new set. There will come a day when production is down for some fault and seven foremen and the production superintendent are screaming for action, when the plant engineer will wish he had the instruction book covering the offending piece of gear.

MAINTAINING SWITCHGEAR

Power Circuit Breakers. The frequency of inspection depends on the type of installation, operating duty, atmosphere in the area, and the like, but in any case twice-yearly checks are recommended, and a special check should be made after each interruption of a heavy short-circuit current. Furthermore, when for any reason a breaker must be kept in either the open or the closed position for long periods, it should be opened and closed several times at periodic intervals to insure that it operates properly.

A rule that will be repeated many times: *Before starting any inspection or making any adjustment to power circuit breakers, be sure that all lines leading to the circuit are dead and that the breaker is completely disconnected from the busses and lines. See that the grounding connection on the frame is intact and directly connected to a dependable ground* (breakers in metal-clad switchgear are inherently grounded, and it is necessary only to see that the switchgear ground is intact). Finally, *temporarily ground all breaker studs and current-carrying parts during the inspection.*

Of the following items, check the *oil every 6 months,* the other items *every 12 months:*

OIL. If oil shows signs of moisture, carbonization, or dirt, it should be filtered and tested. If its dielectric strength tests less than 22,000 volts, as measured by the standard test between 1-in. disks spaced 0.1 in. apart, it should be filtered. The dielectric strength of new oil should be not less than 25,000 volts. The oil level in the tanks must be maintained at the correct height. Don't depend on the oil-level gage; make sure it is indicating properly during this twice-yearly inspection. Check for oil leaks through all oil valves and gaskets. In addition to this inspection, oil should be tested similarly after each operation of the breaker at or near the rating of the breaker.

BUSHINGS. Clean the external surface (in atmospheres where accumulations of dirt, grease, or any other air-borne materials are likely to load the unit, cleanings more frequent than once in 12 months are necessary). Carbon tetrachloride may be used (*avoid breathing fumes*). If the glossy surface of the bushing becomes marred or pitted, or if there is any doubt of its condition, a power-factor test should be made. Make sure that vibrations caused by operation of the breaker have not moved the bushings, resulting in misalignment of the contacts. See that the oil level (of oil-filled bushings) is at the correct level.

INTERNAL INSULATING PARTS. After the oil is drained, the surface of bushings and other insulating and internal parts within the tank should be cleaned. On magneblast breakers, insulating parts should be kept clean and dry. Dust and other foreign material collected on insulating parts should be removed. If there is evidence of dampness, heaters should be installed in the breaker compartment. Scale on the inside of arc chutes should not be removed, but loose scale collected in the muffler should be.

Porcelain air-line insulators at the rear of the arc chutes should be wiped off and inspected for mechanical damage, removed, and cleaned with carbon tetrachloride.

CONTACTS. They should be checked for alignment and firm, uniform pressure. Badly pitted or burned contacts should be replaced, but those that are only roughened should be smoothed with a clean, fine-tooth file. (In cleaning or dressing any silver-surfaced contact, take care not to eat through the silver.)

All arcing contacts, whether of the butt or finger type, should be replaced before the main contacts are affected. All breaker instruction books show the correct relation of arcing contacts to main contacts, and if the dimension of the arcing contacts is less than it should be, burning is excessive and the contacts should be replaced.

Because of the wiping action of finger contacts, they require more dressing than butt contacts; roughness may cause stubbing, which will result in bent fingers and improper contact.

Contacts of interrupters used on oil-blast circuit breakers similarly require checks on contact and alignment. Butt-type contacts on high-voltage interrupters perform both the arcing and current-carrying functions. These are high-pressure contacts, and it is not necessary to smooth their surfaces. However, since the contacts are burned away by arcing, it will be necessary to adjust them to maintain contact pressure.

The cross-blast interrupters (used on 14.4- and 34.5-kv 1,200-amp breakers) have arcing contacts of the rod and segment type and main contacts of the finger type. The main contact requires little attention except for checks on alignment and smoothness. The arcing contacts should be replaced as soon as they are found to be badly pitted or worn (see Fig. 11-10).

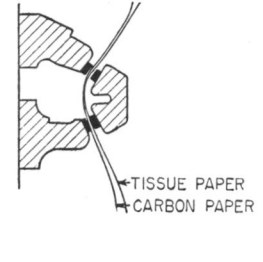

FIG. 11-10. How to check contact impression. (A) Impression shows at least 75 per cent contact, which is satisfactory. (B) Impression shows less than 75 per cent contact, which means adjustment is needed.

BREAKER MECHANISM. See that it operates smoothly and freely. All bearing surfaces should be lubricated with a suitable lubricant (see manufacturer's instructions). Be sure all cotter pins are open and that all snap rings, locking plates, nuts, and the like are tightened. Check the stop clearance against the dimension in the instruction book. Make sure all oil-filled dashpots are full. The length of the breaker stroke and its opening and closing speed should be checked and adjusted according to instructions. The operating rod for movable contacts should not bind against its guide.

OPERATING MECHANISM. See that it is properly lubricated and operates freely throughout the stroke. Parts which show excessive wear should be replaced, and adjustments should be within the tolerances listed in the instruction book. The voltage at the mechanism terminals should be checked with full operating current flowing to see that it is adequate for correct operation; this is especially important on solenoid-operated mechanisms. Check the air pressure of pneumatic mechanisms to see that it is adequate to ensure operation and that it is restored after each breaker operation. Check for air leaks. Check the closing relay to see that it is functioning properly, that its contacts are in good condition, and that all electrically operated valves of pneumatic mechanisms function properly. Make sure the tripping mechanism operates properly. Auxiliary-switch adjustments should be checked, and contacts examined, dressed, replaced if necessary. Check the opening and closing speeds, with an analyzer if possible, to detect any changes in adjustments or incorrect operation. Clean the air system by changing or cleaning compressor filter pads, blowing off water condensation, and cleaning air strainer, check valve, unloader, and other parts which have collected dirt. Replace the screen if it is punctured or is rusting. Check adjustments of all pressure switches and lockout devices. Finally, see that all bolts, nuts, pins, and cotter pins are in place, properly tightened.

To sum up, here are the things to look for in regular inspections of power circuit breakers: overheating, failure to trip, failure to close or to latch closed, insufficient oil, leaky gaskets, insulation failure. The preventive-maintenance schedule outlined should sharply reduce the incidence of any of these troubles.

Air Circuit Breakers. Inspections should be made after each operation under a severe short circuit, and frequent inspections should be made when the unit is located in a dirty, grassy atmosphere. When conditions are such that air circuit breakers must be kept in either the open or closed position for long periods, they should be opened and closed periodically to make sure that parts are in working order. Each of the items treated in the following paragraphs should be inspected *every 12 months:*

CONTACTS. Make sure they are clean, and check the amount of "wipe" in closing and opening. Check condition of the arcing contacts, and if badly pitted or burned, dress or replace. Do not attempt to repair laminated contacts that are badly burned or pitted; they should be replaced.

CONNECTIONS. Make sure that cable terminal connectors are not overheating and that connections are mechanically intact and in good condition.

MECHANISMS. See that all nuts and bolts are in place and tight, that no pins or cotter pins have worked out of place, and that all cotter pins have sufficient spread to hold them in place. All mechanism rods and moving parts should be checked for binding. Operate the breaker several times to check the functioning of all parts. Lubricate all bearing points lightly.

TRIPPING DEVICE AND TRIP LATCH. See that parts move freely and that the armature of each overcurrent trip device has sufficient travel to assure a positive blow that will release the breaker latch. Check the calibration setting to make sure that proper protection is obtainable without undue tripping. Where breakers are equipped with oil-film timers, the oil cups should be cleaned and refilled with oil specifically made for these devices.

LOAD CURRENT. Make sure that the load current does not exceed the ampere rating of the breaker and that current-carrying parts do not overheat.

VOLTAGE. With electrically operated breakers, make sure the operating voltage is adequate.

CONTROL SWITCH. Check the control switch and the closing relay to see that they are functioning properly, and replace burned-out indicating lamps.

BREAKER ENCLOSURE. This should be examined for mechanical condition. Make sure the operating handle is in good working condition and is not blocked in any way. See that ground connection of enclosure is mechanically intact.

ACCESSORIES. Check positive tripping of undervoltage devices. If they are provided with oil dashpot for delayed operation, make sure dashpot is clean.

To sum up: Troubles to watch for on air circuit breakers are overheating, failure to trip, unnecessary tripping, failure to close or to latch.

Switchgear Relays. Maintenance of relays is imperative, since their function is to protect. Their failure means the failure of the protective device. All relays should be checked *at least once a year*; precision and high-speed relays *at least every 6 months*. The *annual* check should include the following:

GENERAL. See that all covers are in place and that there are no broken glass parts, no loose or missing nuts, no dirt or other foreign matter.

CONTACTS. A flexible burnishing tool should be used for cleaning silver contacts. Do not use an ordinary file; it is too big and too coarse. Knives and abrasive paper or cloth will leave scratches that increase arcing, and small pieces of abrasive may be left in the contact, preventing closing.

MOVING PARTS. Check them for mechanical operation. If the movement appears to be sluggish or blocked, remove the bearing and inspect the jewel. A crack in a jewel can be detected by moving the point of a needle *lightly* (so as not to scratch a good jewel) over its surface. Defective jewels should be discarded and replaced. New steel pivots should be inserted at the same time. Usually, no lubrication is required except when a new jewel is installed, and then only a minute drop of the finest grade of watch oil should be used.

OPERATION INDICATORS.   When relays are provided with targets to indicate operation, they should be checked to see that they are functioning and that they have target coils of the proper current rating to operate positively on the minimum available tripping current.

CONNECTIONS.   Make sure that they are intact and tight.

INSULATION.   Inspect for evidence of deterioration.   If in doubt, make a dielectric-strength test.

TIME FEATURES.   Time settings should be checked by operating relay under simulated overcurrent conditions (or other type of fault against which the relay is designed to provide protection).   If leather or equivalent bellows are used, the leather must be examined and dressed to keep it pliable and in good condition.   If oil-film or oil-dashpot features are used, check to see that oil is clean, not gummed, and at proper height

CALIBRATION TEST.   Each relay element should be checked for current, potential, and power at pickup, dropout, and intermediate points.

TRIPPING TEST.   The relay should be operated electrically to see if the circuit breaker operated by the relay functions.   This tests operation of both relay and tripping circuit.

Switchgear Equipment.   *At least annually,* inspect the following:

SWITCHBOARD AND ENCLOSURE.   Metal enclosed switchgear should be opened and cleaned with a vacuum cleaner having an insulated nozzle.   All insulators should be cleaned.

METERS AND INSTRUMENTS.   These should be examined to see that they are in good condition, are registering properly, and have no broken or cracked glass or damaged cases.   If the plant maintenance force is not equipped to make repairs, call in a specialist.

CONTROL AND INSTRUMENT TRANSFER SWITCHES.   Operation of all infrequently used control and instrument transfer switches should be checked, and all switch contacts inspected.   When the equipment controlled by the switch is infrequently operated, the inspection should also include operation of the controlled device.

INDICATING LAMPS.   Burnouts should be replaced.

TEST BLOCKS.   See that contacts are in good condition, that there are no loose connections and no cracked bases or covers.

BUS BARS AND CONNECTION BARS.   Examine to make sure of good condition.   If any evidence of overheating, look for poor or loose connections.   If connections are OK, you will probably find that additional load has been added since the last inspection. The overheating should be corrected by either beefing up the bus or transferring part of the load to an underloaded bus.

INSTRUMENT TRANSFORMERS.   Make sure that primary and secondary connections, grounding (of both frame and secondary), and potential transformer fuses are intact.

POSITION-CHANGING MECHANISMS.   The elevating and lowering mechanisms of metal-clad switchgear and the drawout devices, if any, should be inspected and tested to check operation and should be lubricated.

SHUTTERS AND INTERLOCKS.   Safety shutters should be checked to make sure that the shutters close when the breakers are removed.   All interlocks should be inspected.

DIELECTRIC TEST.   This test is advisable after any abnormal occurrence such as fire or flood.   Where high-potential tests are not practical, the insulation of the high-voltage elements (as well as insulation of control connections) to ground should be measured with a megohm-meter.

Knife Switches, High-voltage Fuses, and Disconnect Switches.   *At least yearly,* and more often if conditions seem to indicate the need for it, inspect the following: (Here, again, *take extreme care not to come into contact with live parts.   After it is certain that the switch parts are dead, they should be solidly grounded before you touch them. Remember that no disconnecting switch should be opened or closed unless the circuit is open at some other point.*)

CONTACTS.   Can be checked with a 0.002-in. feeler gage.   It should not enter between the blade and the contact.   Most switches made recently have silver contacts.   These should be wiped clean.   Copper switches need frequent cleaning to remove oxide. This can be done by opening and closing the switch several times. Do not use abrasives, because they will cause poor contact. Check contact pressure (see Fig. 11-11 and Table 11-1).

ENCLOSED SWITCHES. This type of switch, particularly the "safety enclosed switch," requires special attention. In addition to the above checks, the enclosures should be examined. Make sure that the operating handle and mechanism are in good condition, that the full-load current is not above the switch and fuse rating, that the location is not blocked so that the switch is not quickly accessible, and that the ground connection of enclosure is tight.

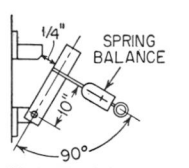

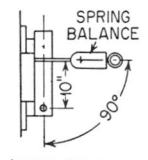

TO CHECK PULL NECESSARY TO OPEN BLADE AGAINST HINGE FRICTION ONLY   TO CHECK PULL NECESSARY TO OPEN BLADE FROM FULLY CLOSED POSITION

FIG. 11-11. How to test hinge contact adjustment, showing spring-balance test of switch contact adjustment. Adjustment for proper contact pressure is made by tightening or loosening the contact-adjusting nuts uniformly. See Table 11-1 for correct pounds pull required to operate switch. (*Courtesy of General Electric Co.*)

OUTDOOR HIGH-VOLTAGE FUSES. Contacts should be kept clean and bright. If the fuse does not operate over long periods, inspect regularly to guard against oxidation. Contact clips and ferrules can be covered with noncorrosive lubricant, though "cup" grease or other grease that hardens in air should not be used. If the finish on the fuse tube begins to deteriorate, it should be cleaned and given two coats of insulating varnish.

HIGH-VOLTAGE DISCONNECTING SWITCHES. Follow instructions for regular switches. Be sure that the surfaces of the insulators are clean. See that blade latches function properly and that they latch the blades securely when the switch is closed, yet operate freely to release the blade when the switch is to be opened.

Table 11-1. Pounds Pull Required to Open Switch*

Ampere rating	Hinge only, all voltage ratings	Complete switch, voltage rating, kv				
		5	7.5	15	23	34.5
200	2–3	9–11				
400	3–4	13–17	13–17	18–22	23–27	27–33
600	4–5	18–22	18–22	23–27	27–23	32–38
1,200	6–8	32–38	32–38	41–49	50–60	59–71
2,000	6–8	45–55	45–55	59–71	59–71	86–104
3,000	8–10	50–60	63–77	63–77	77–93	90–110
4,000	8–10	54–66	68–82	68–82	81–99	95–115
6,000	9–11	59–71	72–88	72–88	86–104	99–121

Pull given in above table is per blade for multiple-tongue switches.
* Courtesy of General Electric Co.

GROUP-OPERATED SWITCHES. Check the adjustment of the mechanism, operating rods, and interphase shafts to see that all poles of the switch operate simultaneously and that each blade enters the contacts squarely. Lubricate bearings, and oil or grease moving parts. If motor-operated, check motor and mechanisms.

MAINTAINING TRANSFORMERS

All transformers. *Every shift*, check:

LIQUID-LEVEL GAGE, AMBIENT TEMPERATURE, LIQUID AND WINDING TEMPERATURE INDICATORS. These readings should be checked to see if they are within limits and should be recorded by the attendant. Running records of this type will help anticipate trouble and give the best indication of operating performance.

LOAD. The load current on transformer banks should be checked. Kilowatt readings are not good enough, incidentally, since heating is determined by the load current and voltage, and not by the kilowatt output (and unless the power factor is 1.00—which it seldom is—these readings are different).

VOLTAGE. Make sure the proper tap connection is being used. *Every 3 months,* check:

RELAYS. For details, see preceding paragraphs on Maintaining Switchgear. *Every 6 months,* check:

OVERVOLTAGE PROTECTIVE EQUIPMENT. These devices are used to limit impulse voltages to design conditions, and unless they operate properly, damage to the transformer may result.

GROUND CONNECTIONS AND RESISTANCE TO GROUND. Low ground resistance is essential for proper lightning-arrester operation and for relaying.

Open-type Transformers. *Every 3 months,* check:

"BREATHING." This type of transformer depends upon the free passage of air through the ventilators. Make sure the ventilators are free of any restriction. If the unit is equipped with calcium chloride ventilators, make sure the chemical has not acquired moisture.

CONDITION OF OIL. A dielectric test of 25 kv or above is adequate. Filtering is needed when oil has dropped to 20 kv or when there is evidence of moisture.

Every 6 months, inspect:

UNDER THE COVER. Look for evidence of moisture under the main cover, manhole cover, and bushing supports. Monthly inspection is recommended during the first six months of operation. Check the bottom oil for accumulations of water. Most common causes of condensation are leaky gaskets, cracked or damaged bushing, restricted breathing.

Every 2 years, inspect:

ABOVE THE CORE. Look for oil-sludge deposits and moisture. If the oil is drained to the top of the core, inspection for sludge can be made easily. Water can be found by taking bottom-oil samples.

Every 5 years, inspect:

OVERALL. If there are any deposits of sludge, raise the interior of the transformer in the tank and wash it with new oil, applied through a small nozzle with about 80 psig pressure. After washing, drain oil from parts cleaned and remove from the tank. Refilter old oil. Before replacing in the tank, clean the tank thoroughly. Examine internal parts.

Askarel Transformers. *Every 3 months,* check:

RELIEF DIAPHRAM. Look for cracks. Replace any cracked unit; test askarel.

GAS ABSORBERS (if any). Look for damp or caked compound in the trays. If any is found, replace with fresh compound.

Every 6 to 12 months, check:

CONDITION OF ASKAREL. If it tests below 25 kv at room temperature, a filter press should be used to restore the dielectric strength to 30 kv or higher.

TANKS. Subject them to an internal pressure of 5 psi for 12 hr, using either dry compressed air or dry nitrogen. Leaks above the askarel level can be located by applying a soap-water solution to all joints, and if any are found, the askarel should be tested and the underside of the cover inspected for condensation. Check diaphragms for leaks when making the pressure test.

Every 5 years, check:

UNDER THE COVER. For condensation under main cover, manhole cover, and bushing supports.

Every 7 to 10 years, an over-all inspection should be given.

Dry-type Transformers. *Every shift,* check:

FANS. Check their operation.

Every 3 months, check:

CORE AND COILS. Check for dust accumulation on horizontal surfaces of windings and internal leads. If dust is found, deenergize the transformer and blow off with clean, dry compressed air at 50 psi. If corrosion is found on exposed metallic parts, eliminate the corrosive agent from the ventilating air.

TEMPERATURE ALARM. Move the temperature pointer manually above the alarm temperature to see if the alarm functions.

Every 12 months, check:

FAN LUBRICATION. Lubricate with recommended oil or grease.

Every 12 months or when taps are changed, check:

CONTACT SURFACES. Make sure terminal-board contact surfaces are clean. Operate ratio adjusters several times through the new position to "wipe-in" a good contact.

Oil-conservator, Gas-seal, Gas-oil-seal, and Sealed transformers. *Every shift,* check:

GLASS PRESSURE-RELIEF DIAPHRAGM (on conservator transformers). Cracked or accidentally broken diaphragms should be replaced immediately.

PRESSURE-VACUUM GAGE (gas-oil-seal and sealed units). If pressure does not change with changes in oil temperature, there are leaks above the oil.

Every 6 to 12 months, check:

INSULATING LIQUID. Check for moisture. In water-cooled transformers, more frequent tests are required. Oil that tests lower than 22 kv should be filtered.

OIL LEVEL ON IDLE OR SPARE TRANSFORMERS. Make sure oil contraction does not empty conservator and allow air to enter main tank.

Every 12 months, perform:

PRESSURE TEST (for gas-oil-seal and sealed transformers). Test for leaks above the oil level. Apply maximum operating pressure of dry nitrogen to gas-oil-seal transformers, a pressure of 5 psi to sealed units. Loss of gas pressure will indicate a leak.

Every 5 years, check:

ABOVE THE CORE. Drain off sufficient oil to permit inspection of general condition above the core.

Every 7 to 10 years, give over-all inspection.

Gas-seal Equipment. *Every shift,* check:

GAS PRESSURE. It will vary from a maximum of 3, 5, or $7\frac{1}{2}$ psi to a minimum of $\frac{1}{2}$ psi. Any drops in normal pressure will indicate leaks. See also that the gas regulator is adjusted properly to avoid high pressure at low temperature.

Every 6 months, check:

OXYGEN CONTENT. It should not exceed 5 per cent in the nitrogen. (More frequent tests are required during the first month of operation.)

Every month, check:

GAS CYLINDER. See that it is not depleted before a replacement is available.

Every 3 months, check:

PRESSURE-RELIEF VALVE. You can make sure it operates by closing the inlet and outlet valves in the gas piping to the main tank and opening the by-pass valve. Open the regulating valve slowly, and note the pressure when the relief valve begins to function (3, 5, 7 psi, depending on type).

MINIMUM-PRESSURE ALARM CIRCUIT. The mercury-pressure gage may include an electric alarm, or a separate alarm device can be provided to give warning if the pressure drops. Check operation as above.

GAS REGULATOR. See that it is functioning properly.

Oil-immersed Air-pressure-cooled Transformers. *Every shift,* check:

OIL TEMPERATURE. Note whether or not fans should be in operation. *Every month,* start fans to make sure they work. Also inspect automatic control of the motors, including fuses or circuit breakers in the fan circuit.

Water-cooled Transformers. *Weekly,* record ingoing and outgoing water temperatures as a future check on the efficiency of the cooling system. The cooling coil should be checked for leaks at frequent intervals, depending on such factors as age and water chemistry.

Every 6 months, check:

WATER PRESSURE AND FLOW. Any changes in flow, with the same pressure, indicate clogging.

Forced-oil-cooled Transformers. *Every shift,* check:

PUMP GLANDS AND OIL LEVEL. Glands can be "taken up" to prevent leakage of air or oil. Check the oil level to make sure there is no oil loose.

Every week, check:

INGOING AND OUTCOMING OIL TEMPERATURE.   This is a check on cooler efficiency.

COOLER SCREENS.   Remove any foreign material.

OIL STRAINER.   Any increase in pressure drop through the strainer indicates clogging.

Air-blast Transformers (indoor).   *Hourly,* check:

AIR TEMPERATURES.   The rise in temperature between outgoing air and incoming air should be recorded.   Make sure forced draft is on at all times when the transformer is in service.

Weekly, the transformer should be blown out with dry compressed air to remove dirt and dust.

Load-ratio-control Apparatus.   *Every shift,* check:

RELIEF DIAPHRAGM.   If cracked or broken, replace immediately.

Every month, check adjustments and operation of the voltage-regulating relay, auxiliary relays, fuses, or other overload protective devices.

Every 3 months, check the insulating liquid in compartments containing arcing ratio adjusters or contactors.   Replace if it is darkened or saturated with impurities. Filter if it tests below 20 kv.

Every 12 months, check:

FILTERING AND CLEANING.   Filter the oil in arcing-ratio-adjuster and contactor compartments.   Clean all insulating surfaces and the bottom of the compartment.

CONTACTORS.   See that they make good contact (Fig. 11-10).

ARCING RATIO ADJUSTERS.   On transformers of low kva rating, where arcing duty is relatively small, arcing takes place directly on the ratio-adjuster contacts.   Inspect contact tips for wear and alignment, and correct tip pressure.

STUFFING BOXES.   On rotating shafts they must be kept oiltight.   Glands must be checked and "taken up" if necessary to compensate for wear.   Avoid excessive tightening, which will cause shaft scoring.

MECHANISM.   Check limit switches and motor-reversing relay; make sure there is no accumulation of dirt and no evidence of corrosion, excessive heating, loose connections.   Operate the mechanism through the entire top range.   Lubricate where magnetic braking is used for stopping the mechanism accurately, brake shoes should be checked and adjusted.   If d-c commutators are used, keep the commutator clean, see that brushes ride free in holders.   See that shafts, gears, and levers are aligned and operate freely.

VENTILATORS.   Inspect to make sure that no obstruction hinders free passage of air and that conduit connections do not permit air to enter the housing of the mechanism where it would cause condensation.

INSULATING LIQUIDS.   The two insulating and cooling liquids normally used in transformers are mineral oil and askarel (a nonflammable synthetic liquid that is chemically stable and nonsludging).   The two should not be mixed.   Drums of either liquid should be stored indoors or otherwise protected from the weather.   They should be placed on the side with the bung tight and pointing downward at a 45° angle. Containers, pipes, and metal hose used for handling askarel should be free from oil, grease, or other foreign material.

How to Fill a Transformer.   Sample and test the liquid.   Make sure no dirt or oil enters and that the liquid is at least as warm as the surrounding air.   Open all air vents.   Fill the transformer through a filter press, using a metal hose.   To prevent aeration, fill the transformer through the bottom drain valve.   But when a new transformer is received partially filled, complete the filling from the top.   If no filter press is available and the liquid tests satisfactorily, pass the liquid into the transformer through two or more thicknesses of muslin that has been thoroughly washed to remove the sizing and dried.   Allow 12 hr for the liquid to permeate the apparatus; then inspect and adjust to the proper level.

How to Test Insulating Liquids.   Cleanliness of sampling and testing equipment is vital.   An absolutely clean sample bottle should be filled several times from the valve, then thoroughly drained before the sample is taken.   Seal the container tightly with a clean glass or cork stopper (never rubber or composition).   A dielectric test can be made from a 1-pt sample.   Adjust the 1-in.-diameter electrodes of the test cup to a

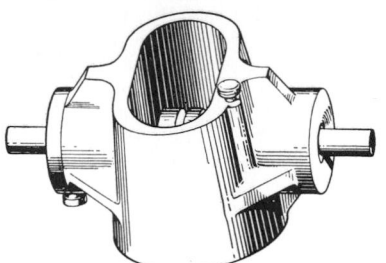

FIG. 11-12. Testing receptacle for portable oil tester.   (*Courtesy of General Electric Co.*)

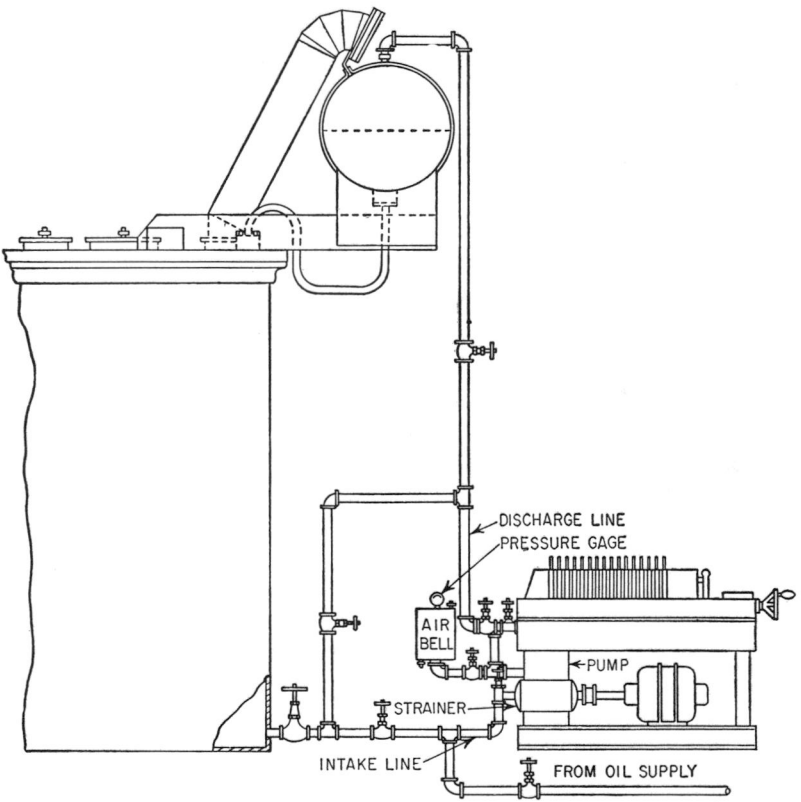

FIG. 11-13. Connections for filling transformers and filtering oil.   (*Courtesy of General Electric Co.*)

spacing of 0.1 in. (see Fig. 11-12).   Fill the sample cup with liquid to be tested, agitate the sample gently, and allow to stand 3 min to permit air bubbles to escape.   Then apply voltage uniformly at a rate of about 3 kv per sec.   Disregard occasional momentary discharges, which do not result in a permanent breakdown.   Take an average of at least three cup fillings.

When to Filter Insulating Liquids.   Oil testing lower than 22 kv should be filtered to raise its dielectric strength to at least 25 kv.   Askarel testing lower than 25 kv should be filtered to raise the dielectric strength to at least 30 kv.

How to Filter Oil.   Oil can be dried rapidly and thoroughly in a filter press if the filter paper is carefully dried, transferred to the press without reabsorbing moisture, and replaced when its effectiveness is exhausted.   The paper should be dried in an oven at 100° C for 6 to 12 hr, then transferred directly to the filter or to storage under dry oil in a sealed container.   When the frames and plates of the filter are assembled, three sheets of filter paper should be placed between each plate and the adjacent frame. The holes in the paper should correspond to the holes in the plates.   Then the filter is closed with the clamping screw.   Piping connections are shown in Fig. 11-13.

How to Filter Askarel.   Askarel seldom requires filtering, because askarel transformer tanks are sealed.   If it should be necessary to filter askarel to raise the dielectric strength, it can be done with an oil filter press provided it is thoroughly cleaned of oil.   However, most manufacturers make a slightly different piece of filtering equipment for askarel, which uses fuller's earth together with the filter paper.   Operation is similar to the filtering described in the paragraph on how to filter oil.

Chapter 12

ILLUMINATION[1]

By BERLON C. COOPER
Associate Editor
Electrical Construction and Maintenance
New York, N.Y.

Objectives of the maintenance of lighting systems are to keep light loss at a minimum and to provide the maximum amount of light as economically as possible. The work can be done haphazardly, or it can be done according to a carefully planned schedule.

Light loss is caused by dirt and dust accumulation, lamp aging, lamp outages, luminaire inefficiency, lamps operating below rated voltage, and low reflection factors of the ceiling, side walls, floor, and machine or furniture surfaces. These are some of the factors which must be considered by the maintenance engineer when he is planning a lighting maintenance program for an existing lighting installation or by the illuminating engineer when he is designing a new lighting system.

LIGHTING SYSTEMS MUST BE MAINTAINED

Once lighting systems have been selected, designed, and installed to provide specific lighting intensities throughout the various production and work areas, it may be assumed that the illumination levels chosen were selected carefully to provide the amount of light needed for the different seeing tasks as economically as possible. That being the case, those lighting levels should be maintained if maximum production, minimum rejects, and other benefits of good lighting are to be realized. Only through proper maintenance can the original lighting investment be protected. The light which is lost because of lack of maintenance continues to be paid for and at the same unit rate as when the system was delivering what it was designed for.

Experience has shown that lighting systems which are not maintained drop in performance until their total light output may be less than half that for which they were designed (see Fig. 12-1). Consider a typical installation in an industrial plant which had no scheduled plan for maintenance. A light-meter survey revealed an average intensity of 33 ft-c in unmaintained condition. Then six maintenance steps were taken, and a light-meter survey made after each step. The illumination increased a total of 128 per cent to 75 ft-c.

WHO SHOULD MAINTAIN THE LIGHTING?

In smaller plants lighting maintenance consists primarily of installing new lamps when the old ones burn out and sometimes, but not always, cleaning the luminaires

---

[1] In addition to the material specifically credited in this chapter, the author is indebted for much information made available by the Lamp Division of the General Electric Company, Cleveland, Ohio.

when new lamps are installed or periodically—maybe once a year. Electrical contractors are usually brought in for the larger and heavier plant electrical work; if ballasts burn out or other electrical trouble develops, they usually are employed to make the repair.

In larger plants, where the maintenance department includes an electrical crew (one or more employees), electrical repairs of all types, including the *cleaning* of lamps and luminaires, are made by the plant's own crew.

Since the introduction of mercury and fluorescent lamps with their complicated ballast and transformer circuits (as compared with relatively simple circuitry of incandescent lamps) and with their larger and more complicated luminaire designs, it has

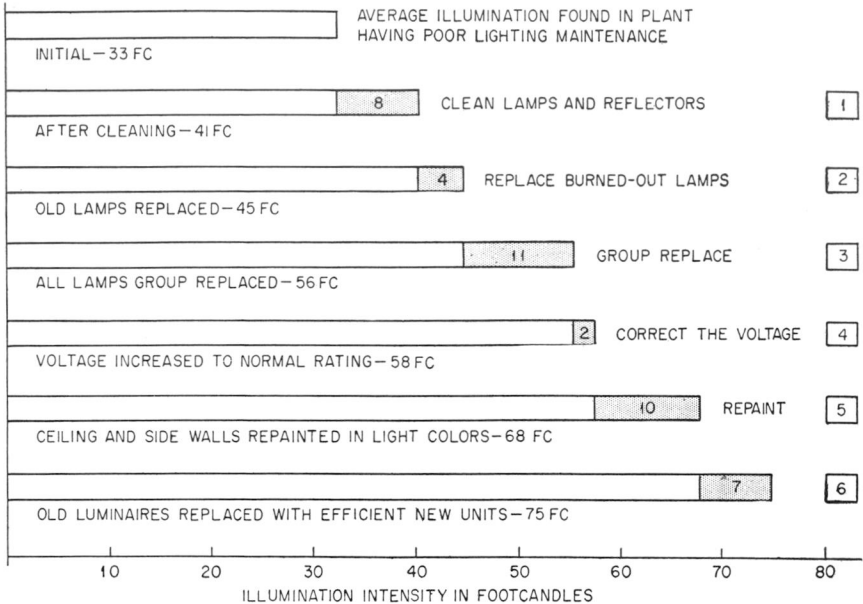

Fig. 12-1. Good lighting maintenance more than doubles illumination.

been found desirable and necessary to use trained lighting maintenance crews to do this work. Such crews reduce the time required for cleaning, relamping, diagnosing, and repairing faults in the lighting systems.

Many plants have developed their own trained crews to do this work, especially if they have sufficient lighting units and equipment to keep a team of two or more men occupied most of their time.

Because fluorescent lighting systems are too complicated to be maintained by a janitor or regular cleaning man, as had been done in earlier years with simple incandescent lighting systems, specialized lighting maintenance companies have been organized. These companies have developed trained crews, efficient maintenance techniques, and specialized equipment to provide complete maintenance economically. In general, they can maintain lighting systems more thoroughly and at lower costs than can the owners of the systems who do not have trained lighting maintenance crews. For this reason many of the larger plants, even those having their own general maintenance departments, are using these specialized lighting maintenance companies to do their lighting maintenance.

To make an accurate decision about calling in an outside maintenance company, it should first be decided just what work is to be done and how much it will cost with maintenance department personnel. To do this a specific lighting maintenance schedule should be set up. The plant manager can then prepare his cost estimate based on this schedule.   Doing so will involve the labor of his own personnel, clean-ing materials, repair parts, ladders, platforms, hoists, etc., and may require some checking for labor units involved.   For comparison he can obtain the estimate of an outside maintenance company for doing the same work, furnishing its own labor, lad-ders, repair parts, etc., all based on the same specific maintenance schedule.   Details for developing an estimate of this type are described more fully later in this chapter.

SOME FUNDAMENTALS OF LIGHTING DESIGN

To plan a lighting maintenance program intelligently it is necessary to know and understand the lighting fundamentals, including calculations and design.   Some are presented here.   For more detailed study, a good lighting design and layout handbook or reference manual should be consulted.

Table 12-1. Formulas for General Lighting Design
(Lumen method of calculation)

Average L reaching work plane

$$= \text{total initial } L \times CU \times MF \tag{1}$$

Average foot-candles

$$= \frac{\text{total initial } L \times CU \times MF}{\text{area of room, sq ft}} \tag{2}$$

$$= \frac{\text{initial } L \text{ per lamp} \times CU \times MF}{\text{area per lamp, sq ft}} \tag{3}$$

$$= \frac{\text{initial } L \text{ per luminaire} \times CU \times MF}{\text{area per luminaire, sq ft}} \tag{4}$$

$$= \text{total watts per sq ft} \times \text{over-all } L \text{ per watt} \times CU \times MF \tag{5}$$

Area per lamp, sq ft

$$= \frac{\text{initial } L \text{ per lamp} \times CU \times MF}{\text{foot-candle level desired}} \tag{6}$$

Area per luminaire, sq ft

$$= \frac{\text{initial } L \text{ per lamp} \times \text{no. of lamps per luminaire} \times CU \times MF}{\text{foot-candle level desired}} \tag{7}$$

Total watts per sq ft

$$= \frac{\text{foot-candle level desired}}{\text{over all } L \text{ per watt} \times CU \times MF} \tag{8}$$

$CU = $ coefficient of utilization
$L \ \ = $ lamp lumens
$MF = $ maintenance factor

Lighting Calculations.   There are two general methods in use for calculating the lighting intensity for an area: the *lumen* method and the *point-by-point* method.   The lumen method is used here because it is relatively simple, it has been widely adopted for calculating the general average of lighting intensities, and it is accurate to the extent that each factor in the formula, Table 12-1, is accurately evaluated.

Average "in-service" foot-candles of general illumination can be estimated for a room or area when lighted by various types of luminaires by inserting proper values in the formula.   The procedure is as follows:

1. Determine the "total initial lamp lumens" by multiplying the number of lamp lumens per lamp by the total number of lamps in the area (see Tables 12-2 and 12-3).
2. Determine the area of the room or bay in square feet, and look up the "room index" in any room index table (see any good lighting catalog).
3. Determine the coefficient of utilization (CU) for the type of luminaire installed (or under consideration).   (Most lighting equipment manufacturers will supply CU data for any type luminaire they produce.)

Table 12-2. Average Light Output and Operating Life for Typical Industrial Lighting Lamps

(Based on burnouts per billion lumen hours)

Incandescent lamps

Lamp designation	Rated life, hr	Initial output, lumens	Mean output, lumens	Burnouts per BLH‡
200-watt A25	750	3,700	3,500	380
300-watt PS35	1,000	5,650	5,100	196
500-watt PS40*	1,000	14,900	10,200	98
750-watt PS52*	1,000	17,100	15,800	63
1,000-watt PS52*	1,000	23,400	21,300	47
500-watt R52	2,000	7,500	6,900	72
750-watt R52	2,000	12,500	10,000	50

* Coiled-coil filament axially mounted.

Fluorescent lamps

Lamp designation	Rated life,* hr	Initial output, lumens	Mean output,† lumens	Burnouts per BLH‡
F40T12/CW	7,500	2,500	2,150	62
F40T12/D	7,500	2,300	2,000	67
F90T17/CW	7,500	5,150	4,250	31
F90T17/D	7,500	4,800	4,000	33
F48T12/CW/RS (800 ma)	7,500	3,100		
F72T12/CW/RS (800 ma)	7,500	4,800		
F96T12/CW/RS (80 ma)	7,500	7,250	6,150	22
F48R12/CW Slimline	7,500	2,300	2,000	67
F96T12/CW Slimline	7,500	5,050	4,500	30

* For 3 burning hours per start (see Table 12-5).
† Approximate mean output in lumens at 40 per cent life.

Mercury lamps

Lamp designation	Rated life,* hr	Initial output, lumens	Mean output, lumens	Burnouts per BLH‡
H250A5	6,000†	11,000	8,900	19
H400E1	6,000†	21,000	16,400	9.9
H400J1	6,000†	20,000	15,600	10.7
H400R1	6,000†	18,000	14,900	11.2
H400RC1	6,000†	20,500	17,000	9.8
H1000A15	6,000	54,000	35,100	4.7
H3000A9	6,000	132,000	103,000	1.6

* Life figures shown are averages from tests of lamps burning 5 hr per start in appropriate industrial-type luminaires.
† Designates economic life of the lamp under typical operating conditions.
‡ Average lamp burnouts per billion lumen hours (calculated).
Source: Lamp Department, General Electric Company.

4. Determine the maintenance factor (MF). This factor will depend upon the design of the luminaire, its light-distribution characteristics, the degree of dust and dirt accumulation in the area, and whether lighting maintenance will be good, medium, or poor. In general, MF values range from about 40 per cent for poor maintenance conditions to about 75 per cent for good conditions.

Table 12-3. Fluorescent Lamp Lumen Ouptut Ratios
(Standard cool white = 1.00)

Color of Lamp	Multiplying Factor
Deluxe cool white............	0.71
Deluxe warm white..........	0.71
Daylight...................	0.93
Soft white.................	0.68
Green.....................	1.20
Gold......................	0.60
Blue or pink...............	0.45
Red......................	0.06

Source: General Electric Co.

5. Apply the data obtained in formula (2), Table 12-1. The result will be the calculated "average foot-candles" which may be expected after the luminaires have been installed and in use long enough for dust, dirt, and lamp depreciation to become effective as estimated. If the MF value is left out of the formula, the resulting calculated intensity will be "initial" foot-candles.

	TYPE D	TYPE SD	TYPE G	TYPE SI	TYPE I
	0-10%	10-40%	40-60%	60-90%	90-100%
UP ↑ ↓ DOWN					
	90-100%	60-90%	40-60%	10-40%	0-10%
	DIRECT	SEMI-DIRECT	GENERAL DIFFUSE	SEMI-INDIRECT	INDIRECT

FIG. 12-2. Classifications of lighting systems.

Lighting Systems. Lighting systems are normally classified under five types, ranging from direct to indirect, according to the light-distribution characteristics of the luminaire (Fig. 12-2). These systems may be comprised of individual lighting units, such as recessed reflector incandescent downlights (direct), or may be structural elements, such as cove lighting (indirect). Recessed troffers, whether individual units or continuous-row equipment, are also classified as a direct-lighting system.

The lighting for a specific area may be entirely from one type of luminaire, such as mercury direct-lighting reflectors in a high-bay production area, or it may be from two or more types of units, such as recessed fluorescent troffers (direct) combined with suspended incandescent indirect luminaires in an office area or drafting room. In estimating illumination levels for areas lighted by more than one type of lighting system, the intensity is calculated for each system and the results are added.

Light Sources. There are three types of light sources in general use: incandescent, mercury, and fluorescent. All three are used extensively in industrial lighting, and each of the three has its own particular characteristics, advantages, and disadvantages. From a maintenance standpoint, burnouts per billion lumen hours, Table 12-2, or the number of lamp replacements required for a given output of light, is an important factor. However, this factor has to be modified with other factors, such as using enough lighting units or close enough spacings to provide a fairly uniform lighting intensity.

The color of the light produced by light sources varies greatly. The light from incandescent lamps is generally described as yellowish white, or of daylight white from blue daylight lamps. The light from mercury lamps is of two types. One is the characteristic blue-green white from the standard mercury lamps, and the other a cool white from the fluorescent-mercury color-corrected lamps.

Fluorescent lamps are made in several shades of "white" as well as in specific colors. The light output, or lumens per watt, varies with the colors (Table 12-3). These colors divide roughly between "warm" and "cool" white light, with warm types having more yellow and orange light and with cool having more blue or blue-green light. The warm colors include standard (3500°) white, soft white, warm white, and de luxe (color-corrected) warm white. Cool colors include cool (4500°) white, daylight (6500°) white, and deluxe (color-corrected) cool white.

All three types of light sources are made in a wide range of sizes and shapes to make possible maximum flexibility in lighting results. For industrial applications the larger sizes are more popular for most general lighting purposes.

Lighting Intensities. The trend in industrial lighting is to higher levels of illumination and to intensities of 100 to 200 ft-c of general illumination. These intensities are now practical and a sound investment for production areas where the seeing tasks are critical and difficult.

The recommended lighting levels for production (Fig. 12-3) vary according to the degree of severity of the visual tasks. They are divided arbitrarily into general classifications of rough, casual, average, above average, difficult, very difficult, and extremely difficult. These seven steps are further roughly divided so that any visual task that is twice as difficult as another represents the next degree of severity of the visual task, and twice the lighting intensity is recommended for equal seeing ease. The Illuminating Engineering Society's "American Recommended Practice on Industrial Lighting" lists a range of 5, 10, 30, 50, 100, and 200 ft-c, respectively, for the first six of the seven steps enumerated above and suggests special handling for extremely difficult seeing tasks. It is recommended that these lighting intensities be considered as minimum values only, especially for rough, casual, average, and above-average visual tasks, and that more practical values, on the order of double the IES recommended values, be used in the lighting of modern plants. Some of the more recent lighting installations have been with these higher foot-candle intensities.

Lighting Quality. The trend in industrial lighting is definitely to higher quality—lighting that is free from glare, with minimum variations in brightness, and much higher in intensity. The trend since about 1950, when luminaires were redesigned to provide an upward light component, has been to finish ceilings white or in very light colors and to install reflectors having top openings which permit enough upward lighting to illuminate the ceiling softly. Current practice is to use reflectors having an upward light component ranging from 5 to 40 per cent. Reflectors can be selected to conform with the various reflectances of the overhead ceiling or roof structures—more upward light for poor reflectances, less for good reflectances. Also, wall areas, floors, and machines and furniture are generally finished in light colors, and reflectors are shielded properly to eliminate direct glare.

Luminaire Designs. Industrial reflectors for incandescent and mercury-vapor lamps have undergone very few changes in recent years. They are available generally in aluminum, prismatic, and silver-mirrored glass and in porcelain enameled steel, in sizes and a range of light distributions to meet the demands for different mounting heights and spacings between units. Top ventilation keeps them from blackening and discoloring to the same extent and at the same rate as when nonventilated.

Industrial fluorescent luminaires are now available with open slots on top of the reflectors to provide upward light to illuminate the ceiling softly. The trend is to larger units and to the use of high-output (800 ma) fluorescent slimline lamps in order to provide the higher levels of illumination being demanded with as few luminaires as is practical. More and more good lighting and mechanical features are being incorporated (Table 12-4) in industrial fluorescent luminaires.

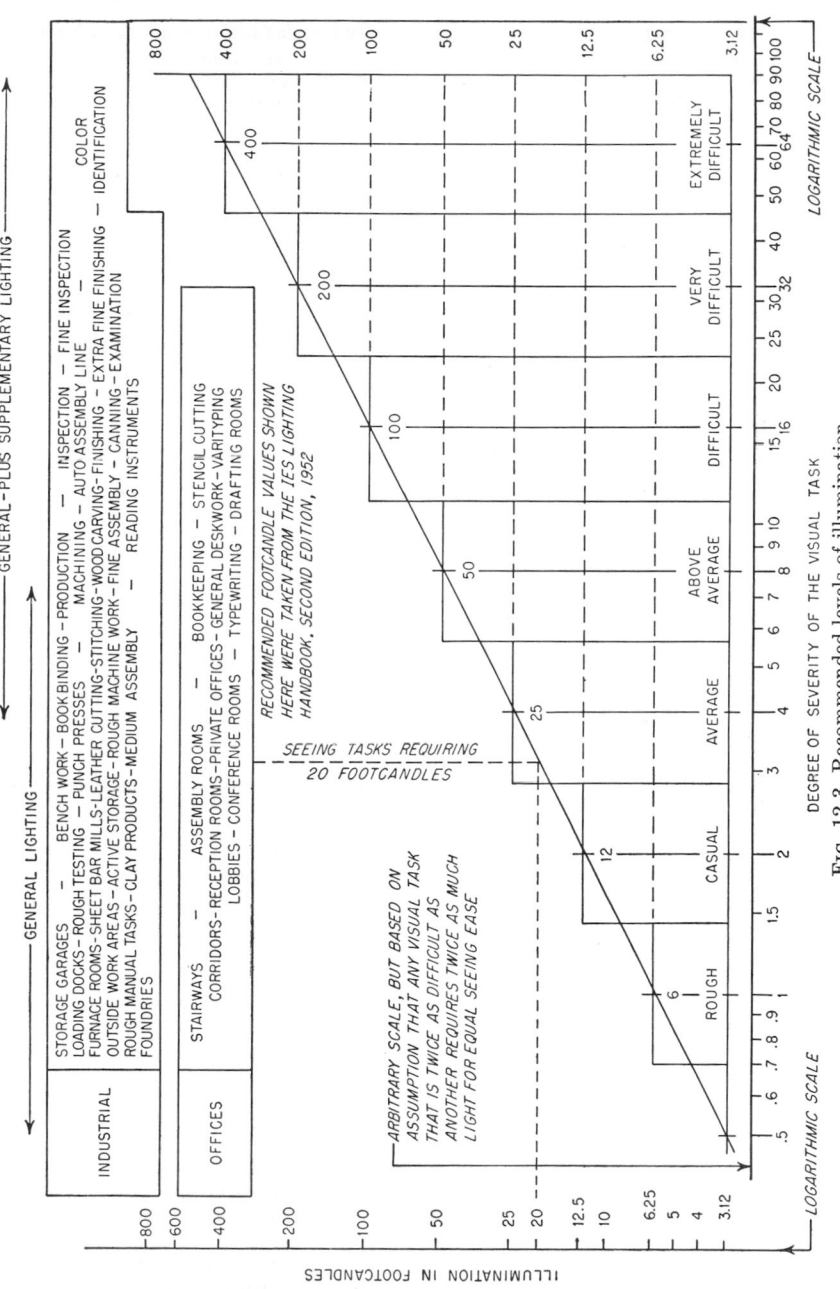

FIG. 12-3. Recommended levels of illumination.

Table 12-4. Essential Features of a Modern Industrial Fluorescent Luminaire

1. Basic two-lamp (or multiple) unit—for two-lamp ballast operation
2. Direct glare shielding—for 30 to 45° shielding both laterally and longitudinally
3. Semidirect light distribution—with 15 to 40 per cent upward light component
4. Efficient—70 to 78 per cent over-all light output
5. Light finished exterior—30 per cent or higher reflectance on all exterior surfaces or low-brightness luminous sides
6. Durable reflection surfaces—white porcelain, baked enamel, Alzak aluminum, etc.
7. Easily maintained—removable louvers, with easy access to lamps and accessories
8. Well-ventilated—to permit operation of lamps and ballasts at design temperatures and provide self-cleaning action

LIGHT-LOSS FACTORS

To decide upon the type of maintenance program needed for a specific lighting installation, the plant maintenance engineer must be able to determine accurately and evaluate critically the light loss which results from each light-loss factor. The six light-loss factors which are responsible for about 90 per cent or more of the light loss in any lighting system are discussed herewith.

Lamp Depreciation. The lumen output of light sources decreases with age, that is, with the number of hours they are kept burning. This decrease in light output is called lumen depreciation and is an inherent characteristic of all lamps (Fig. 12-4). Users can do nothing to improve the inherent characteristics of the lamps. They can, however, help to keep this lumen depreciation at a minimum by maintaining socket voltages fairly constant at the rated voltage of the lamps, which will prevent undue bulb blackening and fast deterioration of filaments, and they can reduce the effect of lumen depreciation by group-relamping the entire lighting system.

In incandescent lamps the filament "evaporates" gradually as the lamp is burned, and the tungsten evaporation is deposited on the lamp bulb, causing blackening. This action causes the filament to become thinner, hence to consume less power. Thus the light output decreases as the lamp is used because of lowering filament temperature and bulb blackening. The adoption of coiled-coil filaments

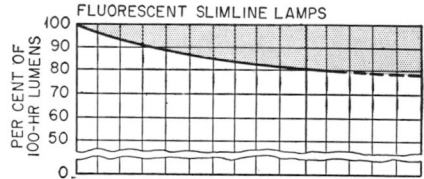

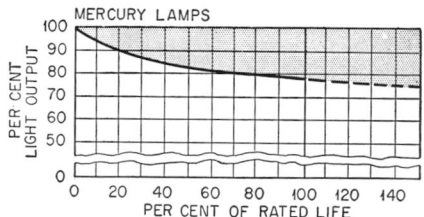

Fig. 12-4. Typical lumen depreciation of lamps. (*Source: General Electric Co.*)

mounted axially in the lamp bulbs, in 300- to 1,000-watt sizes, has helped to reduce the bulb blackening and results in some improvement in light output throughout the life of the lamps. (Results of this improvement were not available as of publication date for inclusion in Fig. 12-4.)

Fluorescent lamps have a rated average life, except for a certain few types, of 7,500 hr (Table 12-5) based on three burning hours per start. Rated life is influenced by burning hours per start because the active compounds on the small filament-type cathodes at each end of the lamps are gradually used up. Starting of fluorescent lamps uses up this cathode coating at a faster rate than normal in-use operation.

Fluorescent lamps blacken fairly uniformly throughout the length of the tube. This is usually not very noticeable but causes, more than any other factor, its depreciation of light output.   Light output decreases rather rapidly during the first 100 hr of operation and may amount to as much as 10 per cent.   It may depreciate 20 to 30 per cent by the end of rated life, depending upon operating conditions, but averages about 85 per cent of the 100-hr value under average conditions.

Mercury lamps have inherently long life (Table 12-2), and lamp life is related to burning hours per start as is the case with fluorescent lamps.   Starting the lamp boils off much more of the electron-emissive material from the electrodes than does normal operation, and the lamps fail when the electrodes are deactivated or completely deteriorated.   Life ratings are therefore based on burning hours per start.

Light output of mercury lamps throughout life compares favorably with that of filament lamps.   The mean lumens fall between 80 and 85 per cent of initial—the variable being the actual life obtained in service.

Table 12-5. Rated Average Life of Fluorescent Lamps

Type of lamps	Burning hours per start			
	3	6	12	Continuous*
Starter-operated (15-, 20-, 25-, 30-, 32-, 40-, 90-, and 100-watt)......	7,500			
Rapid start......................	7,500	Plus 25%	Plus 60%	Plus 250%
All T-12 Slimline................	7,500			
T-6 and T-8 Slimline.............	6,000			
Cold-cathode LP..................	15,000	Life not affected by number of starts		
Cold-cathode HP.................	25,000			

* Light output depreciates steadily as lamps are burned.   Where infrequent starting or continuous burning is involved, lamps should be replaced before they reach average life for greatest lighting value.

Dirt and Dust Depreciation.   Depreciation of lighting intensity because of dirt and dust accumulation, under average conditions, ranges up to about 30 per cent, depending upon the frequency of cleaning.   However, in extremely dirty locations and under severe atmospheric conditions, the depreciation can be much higher.   In air-conditioned and fairly clean areas the light loss will naturally be less.   Light loss due to dirt and dust can be determined for a specific lighting installation by making a few spot tests.   All that has to be done is to make some foot-candle readings in an area before and after cleaning the lamps and luminaires.   The time interval since the preceding cleaning will permit calculation of rate of depreciation.   A constant rate of depreciation may be assumed; while not exactly correct, that is close enough to be used as a rule of thumb.

In actual practice, it has been found that the average depreciation of the lighting intensity due to dirt and dust accumulation is about as follows: 1-month cleaning intervals, 10 per cent; 3-month cleaning intervals, 15 per cent; 6-month cleaning intervals, 20 per cent; and cleaning luminaires when lamps burn out, 30 per cent.

The results of tests conducted in various industrial areas over a period of 25 months, using closed-top fluorescent industrial luminaires, are summarized in Fig. 12-5.   These tests and data revealed several important facts: (1) If ventilated luminaires were used, maintenance would be generally better; (2) light loss due to dirt and dust depends upon the kind and amount of dirt and atmosphere in the area; (3) rate of accumulation is influenced by luminaire design, type of light source, and fixture finish.   (Notations on curves indicate lamp wattage and reflector finish; 40AT, 40-watt lamp in aluminum troffer; 40S, 40-watt lamp in synthetic enamel reflector; and 40P, 40-watt lamp in porcelain enamel reflector.)

Luminaires with openings or vents in the top collect dirt less rapidly than those with closed tops.   This requires careful luminaire design and placements of the openings.   Temperature differences between the lamp and surrounding air cause convection currents which aid in carrying dust and dirt past the lamp and reflector rather than allowing it to accumulate on the surfaces. Two high-bay reflectors were installed in an industrial area for the same period of time, one a nonventilated unit, the other with ventilating holes in the top near the neck. The decrease in efficiency of the nonventilated reflector was 46 per cent; for the ventilated reflector, 5 per cent. The month-to-month decrease in light output of the two reflectors is shown in Fig. 12-6.

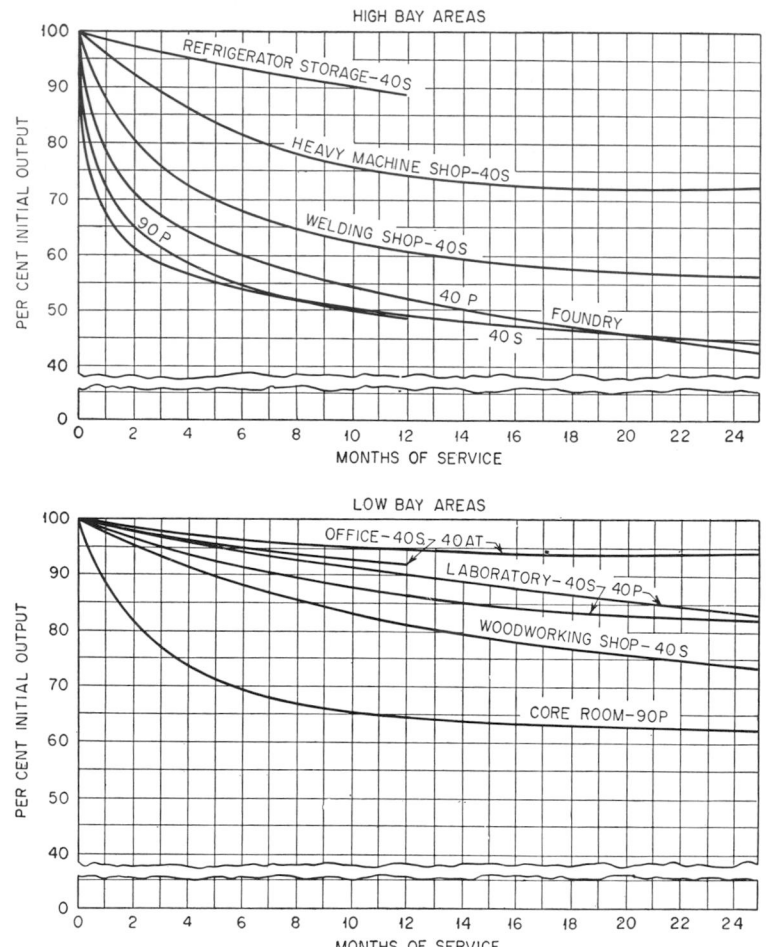

Fig. 12-5. Light output depreciation due to luminaire dirt only. (*Source: General Electric Co.*)

The case described relates to incandescent- or mercury-lamp reflectors. The same effect is inherent in fluorescent reflectors equipped with top openings, now adopted as standard practice to provide an upward light component. This type has the further advantage of maintaining a normal ambient temperature around the lamps at which they operate most efficiently (see Fig. 12-7).

Lamp Outages. Another light-loss factor which can and does become a problem in many lighting systems is caused by lamp outages. This factor causes decreases in lighting intensities of up to 10 per cent (Fig. 12-1), depending upon maintenance policy for relamping individual lamp burnouts.   In high-wattage mercury- or incandescent-lamp installations a burned-out lamp is likely to be replaced promptly, as in most cases it will provide most of the illumination over a fairly large area.   But in small-wattage reflector installations where reflectors are installed on close centers or in multiple-lamp fluorescent luminaire systems, the outage of individual lamps may not be noticed promptly.   Thus in many installations the lighting level may decrease slowly over a period of time before the burned-out lamps are noticed or replaced. Regular checks should be made for burned-out lamps, and replacements made promptly.   Group relamping can also help keep this light-loss factor at a minimum.

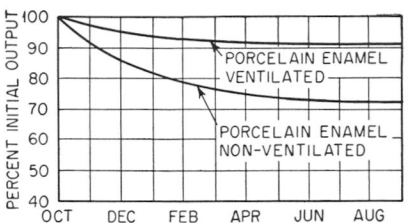

FIG. 12-6. Reflector maintenance study.
(*Source: General Electric Co.*)

Luminaire Inefficiency.   The most efficient luminaire absorbs some light and delivers something less than 100 per cent of the total lumens produced by the lamps in the luminaire.   This factor is of major importance in the design of a new lighting system.   Once an installation is completed, it may prove uneconomical to remove the existing units and install new ones.   But the maintenance engineer should be thoroughly familiar with the over-all efficiencies and light-distribution patterns of typical industrial luminaires (Fig. 12-8) and have this information on file for all luminaires installed in his plant and for other units which could be substituted if necessary or desirable to reduce luminaire light loss to

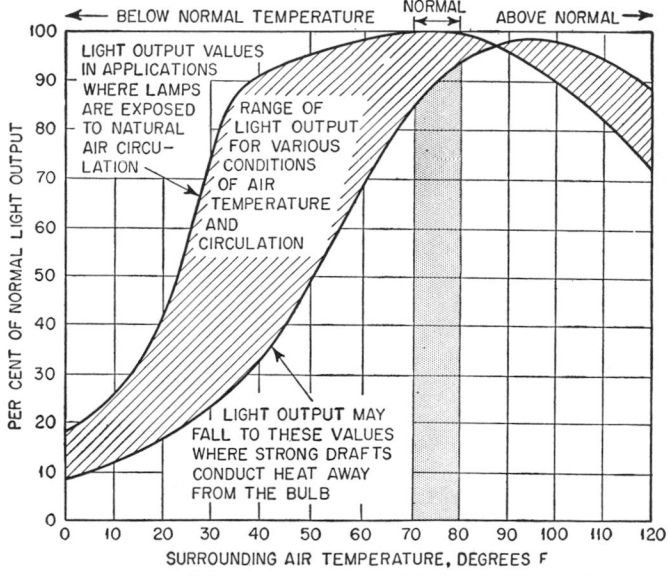

FIG. 12-7. Temperature affects fluorescent lamp efficiency.   (*Source: General Electric Co.*)

a minimum.   Many lighting-equipment manufacturers publish photometric and efficiency data in their catalogs, and most of them can furnish such information on request.

Low Voltage.   Any drop in voltage due to poor wiring, overloading of circuits, or poor voltage regulation causes a decrease in light output of the lamps (Fig. 12-9). This rate of decrease is different for the different light sources.   Incandescent lamps are more sensitive to voltage changes than the other light sources, and the light output drops about 3 per cent for each 1 per cent drop in rated line volts.   Fluorescent-lamp

CANDLEPOWER DISTRIBUTION
1955 Composite Curve of RLM Two-75-watt Open End
Semidirect Fluorescent Unit—Spec. SD-1
Rendered to RLM Subscribers

Reflectors from nine manufacturers.
Lamps: Two, 75 watts; 5,100 lumens; 96-in. T12 Standard Warm White Fluorescent.
Unit: White porcelain enamel reflector, reflection factor 0.85; specified mean 0.85, min. 0.83.
Test: Candlepower distribution in three vertical planes intersecting in the center of a plane through the lamps.
Per cent light output: 84.5; specified mean 77.0, min. 75.0; upward component 26.0; specified 20 min., 30 max.
Candlepower ratio: 0.633; specified min. 0.60.
Angle of cutoff: 33°; specified mean 27°, min. 25°.
Brightness at 25°: 1.3 c/sq in., specified less than 40 % of bare lamp (1.6 max.).
Maximum temperature rise: 46.5°C; specified 65°C max.

LUMINAIRE DISTRIBUTION DATA

Mean Vertical

Mid-zone angles	Candle-power at 40 ft	Zonal lumens	Mid-zone angles	Candle-power at 40 ft	Zonal lumens
180° zen.	1,330	...	90° hor.	9.1	49
175	1,310	124	85	44.6	256
165	1,150	325	75	242	516
155	925	428	65	520	978
145	680	427	55	1,090	1,293
135	457	354	45	1,670	1,269
125	308	276	35	2,020	1,056
115	194	193	25	2,280	713
105	98.5	104	15	2,520	250
95	18.2	20	5	2,630	
			0° nadir	2,640	

Light Flux Values

Zone	Lumens luminaire	Per cent	Zone	Lumens luminaire	Per cent
0-30°	2,019	20.0	0-90°	6,380	62.5
0-40	3,288	32.0	90-180	2,251	22.0
0-60	5,559	54.5	0-180	8,631	84.5

LIGHT LOSS = 15.5 %

FIG. 12-8. Luminaries absorb light.   (Source: RLM Institute and Electrical Testing Laboratories, Inc.)

light-output decrease is at an approximate 1 per cent drop in lumens for each 1 per cent drop in rated line volts.   Mercury-lamp decrease in light output is in between the other two light sources.

It is important that rated voltage be maintained on lighting systems for several reasons.   Overvoltage will shorten the life of the lamps, especially that of incandescent

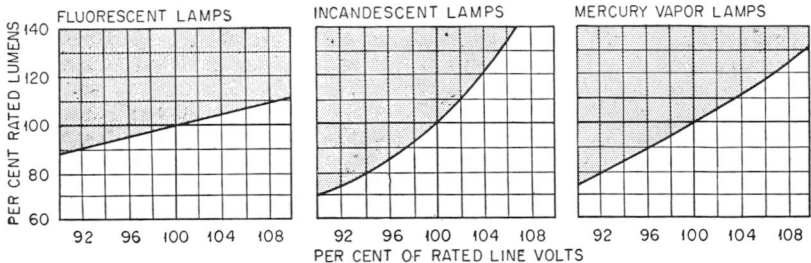

FIG. 12-9. Low voltage decreases light output.   (*Source: General Electric Co.*)

lamps, and will cause overheating of ballasts on fluorescent- or mercury-lamp systems. Undervoltage decreases the light output with all types of light sources and also causes unstable operation of fluorescent and mercury lamps.

Low-reflectance Surfaces.   All surfaces in a room, including the ceiling, walls, columns, floors, machinery, etc., absorb light (Table 12-6).   Thus, the reflectances of these surfaces affect the ultimate lighting result and over-all efficiency of the lighting

Table 12-6. Ceilings and Side Walls Absorb Light
(Coefficients of utilization decrease as light absorption increases)

Type of light distribution	Reflectances, ceiling, %			Ratio C/A
	75	50	30	
	Reflectances, side walls, %			
	50	30	10	
	Column			
	A	B	C	D
Direct (3)*	0.59	0.55	0.53	0.90
Semidirect (29)*	0.47	0.41	0.37	0.79
Direct-indirect (38)*	0.52	0.42	0.36	0.69
Semi-indirect (46)*	0.37	0.26	0.20	0.54
Indirect (53)*	0.36	0.22	0.12	0.33

* CU values taken from Sec. 9, IES "Lighting Handbook," 2d ed.   Numbers shown (3) refer to type luminaires in handbook.   Room index of D assumed for all CU values.

system.   If most of these surfaces are dark in color or dark because of the accumulation of dirt and dust or discoloration of once-light finishes, a high percentage of the light output of the luminaire will be absorbed.   Conversely, if all room surfaces are finished in light colors having high-reflection factors and maintained in this condition, most of the light striking these surfaces will be reflected and the light utilization of the area will be fairly high.

The type of light distribution produced by the luminaires installed in the area will also affect the coefficient of utilization of the system.   To illustrate this factor, the five basic lighting-system classifications (Fig. 12-2) have been used for the basis of comparison in Table 12-6, and the coefficient of utilization for a typical luminaire in each classification has been taken for three reflectance values for ceilings and side walls. It can be seen that the CU value decreases as the reflectance values decrease for all five lighting-system classifications.   Column D shows the ratio of CU values in column C to those in column A.   This ratio varies from 0.90 for a direct lighting system to 0.33 for a totally indirect lighting system, indicating that reflectances of ceilings and side walls influence lighting efficiency and final lighting result even for direct lighting and considerably more so as the light distribution changes from direct to indirect.

In any lighting installation where it appears that the illumination intensities are relatively low for the total energy consumed by it or are revealed by light-meter checks, it would be well to investigate what effect painting the entire area in lighter finishes would have on the intensity.   This may be done very easily by calculation.   Use the proper formula from Table 12-1; determine the room index from any standard room index table and the coefficient of illumination for the luminaires installed in the area. Calculate the intensity based on the existing reflectance values and at some higher reflectance value.   This difference in intensity is what may be expected by repainting in the lighter finish.   Elimination of dark finishes throughout an area also aids in providing a better brightness ratio and better seeing conditions.

TYPES OF MAINTENANCE EQUIPMENT

In order to maintain lighting systems efficiently it is necessary that the lighting equipment be easily accessible.   Lighting-equipment manufacturers have done much

Table 12-7. Types of Maintenance Equipment Used for Servicing Lighting

Equipment	Mounting height, ft			
	To 12	12–18	18–30	Over 30
Stepladder	X	..	..	..
Straight ladder	X	X	..	..
Scaffolding (portable)	X	X	..	..
Scaffolding (telescoping)	..	X	X	..
Lift truck	X	X	..	..
Disconnecting hanger	..	X	X	X
Lamp changer	X	X	..	..
Catwalk, crane, cage, etc	..	..	X	X
Relamping bridge	..	..	X	X
Vacuum cleaner or blower	X	X	..	..
Wash tank	X	X	X	X

in the design of their luminaires and equipment to make maintenance and cleaning easy.   The lighting engineer can plan for easy maintenance when designing a new lighting system by selecting equipment which has good maintenance features and by providing easy access to all units.   The maintenance engineer can further simplify the maintenance problem by equipping his department with the types of maintenance equipment (Table 12-7) needed to do the job efficiently and with a minimum of time and effort.

Time, labor, and expense of maintaining a lighting system can be greatly reduced by choosing the maintenance equipment with features most suitable to the requirements of each system.   Many kinds of maintenance devices are available to facilitate the cleaning job.   The choice of equipment will depend on several factors, such as mounting height, size of area, accessibility of luminaires, and obstacles in the area.

Ladders. Ladders are often used in lighting maintenance because of their light weight, simplicity, and low cost. Ladders can often be modified to make them more useful. For example, a combination of ladder and cart makes it easier to transport the ladder and necessary equipment to the job; attaching brackets to help hold the ladder in position against a girder or other structural member facilitates the work.

Scaffolding. Portable scaffolding generally has greater safety and mobility than a ladder. More equipment can be carried, and the operator has a firm platform upon which to work. Scaffolds should be mobile, light, sturdy, adjustable, easy to assemble and dismantle. Special requirements often dictate the type of scaffolding which can be used; it may have to be mounted on uneven surfaces as on a stairway, it may have to fit over obstacles such as tables or machines, or its dimensions may be limited by such things as aisle width and ceiling height, or elevator cabs.

Telescoping Scaffolds. More elaborate than the portable scaffold is the telescoping unit. It is a quick means of reaching lighting equipment at a variety of mounting heights. This equipment comes in various sizes with platforms that can be raised and lowered manually or by power. It finds greatest application in those areas where it can be easily rolled beneath the lighting equipment. Often, such scaffolds will fit into elevators or small trucks, which simplifies their transportation from one location to another.

Lift Trucks. Often the quickest and most efficient maintenance device is the lift truck. Although there are different types on the market, the method of operation of all is basically the same. An elevating platform is mounted on a mobile truck. The platform can be raised or lowered automatically, and in some types the truck can be driven from the platform. In this type, the operator does not have to leave the platform; all the equipment needed can be carried on it.

The speed, safety, and mobility of lift trucks greatly reduce lighting maintenance costs. While the initial investment for such equipment is higher than for many other types, this expense can often be justified, particularly when the equipment can be fully utilized.

Disconnecting Hangers. Disconnecting hangers lower the lighting units to a convenient work level, enabling the worker to maintain them with a minimum of equipment. They usually pay for themselves through their life by lower maintenance costs and elimination of more costly equipment. When the lighting units are raised into place, the hanger positions the fixture and makes the proper electrical circuit connection automatically. An additional safety feature of this type of device is that the electrical circuit is disconnected when the fixtures are lowered.

Lamp Changers. Lamp replacement can often be simplified by using lamp changers. By gripping the lamps either mechanically or by using air pressure as in the vacuum-type, lamp changers are effective up to 25-ft mounting heights, sometimes higher. The maximum height at which they can be used depends upon the skill and strength of the maintenance men. While incandescent-, mercury-, and fluorescent-lamp changers are available, the incandescent changers have had the greatest use.

Catwalks, Cranes, Cages. It is often good investment to put lighting maintenance provisions in as an integral part of the lighting system. Luminaires can be maintained from catwalks paralleling the rows of lighting units. In high-ceiling areas, cranes are often used for access to the lighting units. (Where this is done, it is often advisable to service the lighting after working hours; maintenance costs may be higher because of overtime pay.) Maintenance cages mounted on cableways are effective maintenance devices. A cable, with carriage suspended, is installed along each row of fixtures.

Relamping Bridge. In plants where cranes are in continuous operation or where there are monorails but no traveling cranes of the usual type which could be employed for reflector maintenance, the craneway or monorail can be utilized for relamping purposes. Relamping bridges are light structures that span the craneway and are towed to position under a row of reflectors. The bridge is left at this location until the reflectors have all been cleaned and relamped and is then moved to the next position. This type of equipment is well suited for group replacement of lamps.

Vacuum Cleaners and Blowers. A blower or vacuum cleaner is sometimes used to remove dust from the lighting units. Loose dirt can be removed in this way, but greasy and sticky dirt cannot.   The luminaires still have to be washed, but the use of a vacuum cleaner or blower can prolong the cleaning interval.

Fixture Wash Tanks.   It is desirable to have a wash tank for lighting maintenance. It should be designed to handle the specific types of luminaires and fittings used in the plant.   Both wash and rinse sections should be provided.   Electric heating elements can be installed in each section to keep the cleaning solution hot.   Fluorescent

Table 12-8. How to Clean Typical Luminaire Finishes

Use of proper cleaning compounds saves time, protects finishes, provides maximum lighting efficiency.   The following information will help to determine the ones best suited to any particular luminaire cleaning application.

ALUMINUM

Most soaps and mild cleaners are suitable for cleaning aluminum if it is thoroughly rinsed with clean water immediately after washing.   Strong alkaline cleaners should never be used.   Even mildly alkaline or acid solutions may cause discoloration or chalking of the oxide surfaces.   (The Aluminum Company of America recommends that the surfaces be wiped and polished with a liquid or paste wax—or a lacquer coating can be applied where more practical—after cleaning.)

PORCELAIN

Most automobile and glass cleaners do a good job under average industrial-plant dirt conditions.   Porcelain finish is not injured by nonabrasive cleaners.

SYNTHETIC ENAMELS

The usual normally available detergents are recommended, as they produce no harmful effects.   Alcohol or abrasive cleaners should not be used.   Some strong cleaners may injure the finish, particularly if the material is left to soak in the solution.

GLASS

Most nonabrasive cleaners can be used satisfactorily on glass, as on porcelain enamel. Dry cleaners are usually preferred on clear glass panels, but not on etched or sandblasted surfaces.   On these surfaces, as on prismatic glass reflectors and lenses, most detergents will work well under average dirt conditions.

PLASTIC

A major problem in cleaning plastic of the types used in lighting systems is that in most cases dust accumulation is due in large part to a static charge which develops on it.   Most of the common detergents do not provide a high degree of permanence in their antistatic protection.   However, it has been found that in most cases if the plastic is cleaned at least twice a year with a common detergent, the plastic will be kept clean and fairly satisfactory relief from static dirt collection is obtained.   When a detergent is used for cleaning, the plastic should not be wiped dry but should be left to drain dry after the application of a rinse solution.   Wiping creates a new static charge.

Some new types of "nonionic" cleaners have been made available, which are claimed by their manufacturers to have improved cleaning properties.   These and any other cleaning compounds designed for specific application should be tried out experimentally to determine their exact properties as they apply to specific types and shapes of plastic luminaire parts.

Source: General Electric Co.

luminaire louvers or reflectors can be set on a rack to drip dry after washing and rinsing while another unit is being cleaned.   Other features may include large locking casters, storage space, and long lengths of electrical cord to provide power for the heater strips.

Cleaning Materials.   There are no hard-and-fast rules regarding the types of soaps, detergents, powders, etc., which should be used for washing and cleaning lighting equipment.   But in general, no harsh abrasives should be used.   Ordinary detergents and mild cleaners are satisfactory for most types of equipment.   The maintenance engineer will develop through experience the solutions and techniques which are best suited to the types of finishes involved in the lighting equipment under his supervision. Some specific recommendations have been made in Table 12-8.   For cleaning units which have not been maintained for a long time, it may be necessary to use stronger detergents for the first cleaning and milder solutions for future more frequent cleanings.

Test Board. Fluorescent- and mercury-lamp circuits are complicated to the extent that in checking for faults on lamps which fail to burn, it is usually desirable to have test facilities available to speed up the checking of lamps, ballasts, starter switches, and similar circuit devices. A suggested wiring hookup for a fluorescent lamp and ballast test board is shown in Fig. 12-10. For large installations of fluorescent luminaires, such a test board will prove useful, convenient, and time-saving.

Instruments. A good lighting maintenance program involves periodic checking of lighting intensities, line voltages, brightnesses, and, in the analysis of certain work,

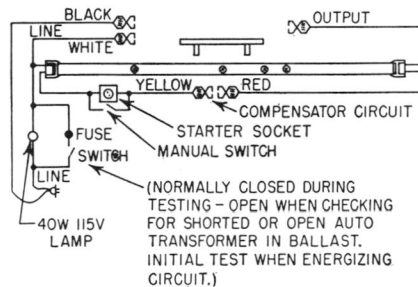

Ballast Connections

Two-lead ballasts—Connect to black and output.
Three-lead ballasts—Connect line leads to black and white as coded. Connect remaining lead to output.
Tulamp ballasts—Test in two parts, lag and lead. Test lag by connecting leads to black and white as coded.
Connect blue ballast lead to output.
Test lead circuit by connecting either red lead to output in place of blue. Connect yellow and red compensator leads to remaining ballast leads as coded. (Black and white remain connected to line.)
Note: Compensator circuit to be closed except for lead lamp test.

FIG. 12-10. Make your own fluorescent lamp test board. (*Source: General Electric Co.*)

the severity of the seeing tasks involved. Certain instruments are necessary in order to make these checks and to maintain full information required to analyze and appraise properly the lighting and the effects of various steps of maintenance.

Four types of instruments are available for lighting analysis. These are light meters, voltmeters, brightness meters, and visibility meters. The first two are indispensable to good lighting maintenance analysis, and the last two are at least highly desirable. All are made in portable types for on-the-spot or general field use.

Light meters are made in several sizes and types and measure lighting intensities directly on a foot-candle scale. Such instruments are also referred to variously as foot-candle meters and illuminometers. They use light-sensitive photoelectric cells. While the spectral response of these cells is not identical for different types of light sources, the meters can be obtained with filters which correct for color quality of the light and with cosine correction to eliminate error due to light striking the cell face at angles.

A good voltmeter with two scales, one to 150, the other to 300 volts, is needed. It is important to record impressed voltage at the lamp socket or ballast leads when making foot-candle intensity readings, since rapid change in light output results from any change in line voltage. Every lighting-survey record should show socket voltage as well as foot-candles for each light-intensity reading, and both readings should be made at one time.

With increased emphasis being placed on brightness values in visual environments, there is need to survey brightnesses—of luminaire surfaces or lamps exposed to view and of ceilings, walls, and the sky through open windows. Direct-reading brightness meters are now available for this purpose, as is the older Luckiesh-Moss brightness meter, which requires the operator to match the brightness of two fields to get a reading. Both types of meters indicate brightness values measured in foot-lamberts, which values may be converted into candles per square inch if required. There is also available a visibility meter (Luckiesh-Moss) which indicates the foot-candle intensity of illumination needed for a visual task.

TROUBLE SHOOTING

Lighting maintenance incorporates not only cleaning and lamp replacement but repairs to the lighting components. While the operation of fluorescent and mercury lamps is more complex than that of incandescent lamps, troubles can generally be diagnosed and repairs quickly made with simple test equipment, such as is usually found in a typical electrician's kit.   This should include a soldering iron, pliers, wire cutters, tape, and screwdrivers.   A voltmeter with necessary leads, as described above, can be used to advantage, especially to test the voltage and current available between lamp-holders of preheat fluorescent lamps.   An alternative is a 100-watt 230-volt filament lamp or two 50-watt 115-volt filament lamps connected in series.

HOW TO REPLACE LAMPS

Lamps in a lighting system can be replaced individually as they burn out, or the entire installation can be replaced before the lamps reach the end of their average life and while they are still in operable condition.   This problem has received much attention in recent years, with analysis indicating advantages for group replacement for many installations; yet very few firms do anything about it.

Individual replacement is usually called "spot replacement"; mass replacement is called "group relamping."   The labor costs saved by group relamping usually more than compensate for the value of the depreciated lamps that are thrown away before they burn out.   Other advantages always accompany group relamping, too: more light, fewer work interruptions, better appearance of the lighting system, and less maintenance of the auxiliary equipment.

Group relamping had its origin in the field of street lighting, where it is still widely practiced, to save money and reduce the number of unsafe dark areas.   Significant improvements during recent years in the length and uniformity of lamp life have helped make group relamping even more desirable, and many examples can now be cited where management has recognized the economic gains that result and have adopted group relamping as a policy.

Fluorescent and incandescent lamps are both well suited to group-relamping programs, one reason being that total cost of these lamps in relation to total costs for lighting is small, usually less than 10 per cent.   Group relamping of mercury lamps is less widely practiced; however, it is still economical to do so on many installations, especially where the lamps are in hard-to-reach locations making it necessary to reduce the number of maintenance trips.   The higher proportional cost of mercury lamps to total cost of lamp replacement has acted as the deterrent to group relamping.

There are five principal advantages that group relamping offers to the user.   The first three apply to all lighting systems, while the last two apply chiefly to fluorescent lamps.

Net Savings from Reduced Labor Costs.   Group relamping saves on labor costs and reduces travel time and setup time required to change lamps individually.   Labor cost per lamp with group relamping generally ranges from one-fifth to one-tenth of the spot-replacement labor cost; for fluorescent lamps the labor cost per lamp seldom exceeds 20 cents.   As labor cost of spot replacement increases (Fig. 12-11), group relamping becomes more attractive, because labor costs are a larger proportion of the total maintenance cost.   When lamps are group replaced after relatively few have failed, costs are usually reduced considerably.

More Light Delivered.   All lamps depreciate in light output (Fig. 12-4) continually as they burn.   The earlier they are replaced, the higher the maintained illumination will be—without adding to the cost of electric energy or the number of luminaires being used.   This means that employees will have the good seeing conditions that the system was designed to provide.   When the higher illumination levels are properly appraised in terms of work output or sales of product, shorter group-relamping intervals can be justified economically.

Fewer Work Interruptions.   Group relamping can be done at a convenient time—during vacation shutdowns or after working hours, for example—when there will be no interruption of operations.   The number of interruptions to report burnouts or to replace them will also be reduced.

Better Appearance for Fluorescent-lighting System.   Black ends, color variations, and differences in brightness between adjacent old and new fluorescent lamps are common when spot replacement is used.   With group relamping, all the lamps are the same age and appearance is far more uniform.   Since most of the lamps are replaced before they burn out, the distraction of blinking, flashing, or swirling lamps is minimized.

Less Maintenance of Fluorescent Auxiliaries. When fluorescent lamps are replaced before they reach the end of their rated life, auxiliary equipment lasts longer and

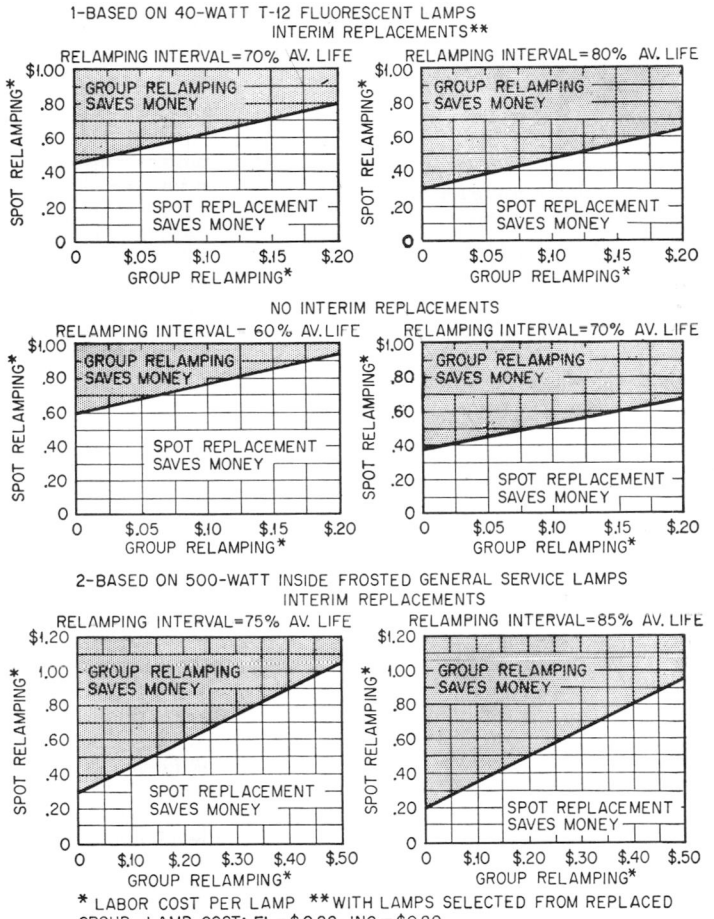

Fig. 12-11. Break-even point on lamps and replacement labor costs—spot vs. group relamping. (*Source: General Electric Co.*)

operates better. Abnormal operating conditions that may occur at the end of fluorescent lamp life can damage ballasts and starters.

These five benefits of group relamping mean more satisfaction with the lighting system, as well as cost savings.

SPOT REPLACEMENT OF LAMPS

Spot replacement consists of replacing burned-out lamps as they fail. This may be (usually is) a tedious process that uses up a considerable amount of productive time. With high production and labor costs, total costs for spot replacement become excessive. In many areas a modified spot-replacement program is used where appearance is not a factor: The maintenance crew checks over the lighting system periodically (weekly, for example) and replaces all burned-out lamps.   While more efficient than individual replacement, this modified system is still less economical than group relamping; also, there is an appearance problem caused by old and new lamps being adjacent.

GROUP RELAMPING

The time at which a lighting system is group relamped should be related to lamp life.   The "group-relamping interval" can be varied slightly to fit into convenient schedules when there will be less interruption of production work by the replacement process.

A practical way to determine when a lighting system should be group relamped is to use lamp burnouts as a guide.   This may be done because the number of failures in a group reliably indicates the portion of average life delivered by the group.   Typical lamp-mortality curves (Fig. 12-12) may be used for this purpose.   The mortality curve for fluorescent lamps shows that when these lamps have reached 70 per cent of their average life, 12 per cent of them will have burned out or that when they have reached 80 per cent of their average life, 21 per cent will have burned out.   After 80 per cent average life, the rate of failure increases rapidly.   A similar analysis may be made for incandescent lamps.

Ideally, the interval selected for group relamping would be the point that gives the lowest annual cost per foot-candle.   In many cases this interval is as short as 50 per cent of average lamp life.   Relatively long intervals (up to 80 per cent of life) tend to give lowest lamp and labor costs, while shorter intervals minimize work interruptions, improve appearance,

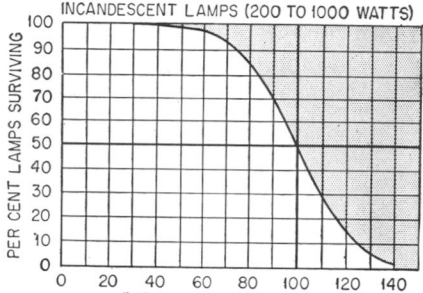

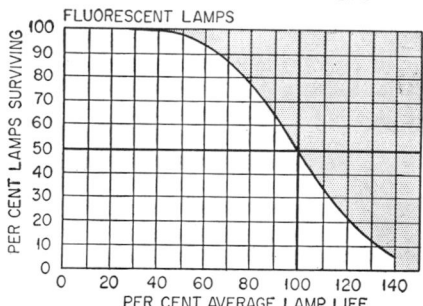

Fig. 12-12. Typical lamp-mortality curves. (*Source: General Electric Co.*)

and result in a higher maintained level of illumination.   In practice the interval selected is usually a balance between lowest cost per foot-candle and lowest maintenance costs.

The mortality curve to determine the group-relamping interval can be used in either of two group-relamping systems.   The simple system is chiefly suitable for large areas with fluorescent lamps where each work location receives light from several luminaires.   Individual burnouts are left in the sockets during the group-relamping interval until the number of burned-out lamps indicates that the group-relamping point has been reached.   Chief advantage of this system is that the only labor cost involved is the cost of group relamping; no individual replacements are made during the interim period between group relampings.

This system of making no interim replacements is limited to relamping intervals of not more than about 70 per cent of average lamp life because of the reduced illumination caused by the number of failed lamps in the system.   Also, it is not suitable for incandescent- or mercury-lamp installations where the failure of one lamp may greatly reduce the illumination in a specific work area.

The second group-relamping system, which uses the mortality curve to determine the group-relamping interval, is usually more desirable.   With it, lamp replacements between group relampings keep all the luminaires lighted, giving the user more light. With this system, when the installation is group relamped, at 80 per cent of average life, for example, 20 per cent of the best remaining lamps are set aside to use as individual replacements during the interim period before the next group relamping. These should be the lamps with the best appearance from the standpoint of brightness and clean ends. Then as lamps burn out, they are replaced from this stock of interim-replacement lamps. When the stock is used up, that is a signal that group relamping time has come again, and the cycle is repeated.

LAMP-REPLACEMENT COSTS

The cost of lamp replacement is made up of the cost of the lamp and the cost of the labor required to replace the lamp. When the sum of these costs is reduced, of course, the total annual operating cost of the lighting system is reduced and more foot-candles per dollar result. Economical lamp replacement also means better over-all lighting economics.

With spot replacement, the total replacement cost per lamp is equal to the cost per lamp plus the labor cost of replacement. Group-relamping cost, to compare with this, is equal to the lamp cost plus group-relamping labor cost plus the cost of any interim spot replacements divided by the group-relamping interval to put both systems on an equal time basis. This can be expressed in formulas as follows:

For spot replacement: $$C = L + S$$

For group relamping, using selected lamps as interim replacements:

$$C = \frac{L + G + (B \times S)}{I}$$

For group relamping, with no interim lamp replacements:

$$C = \frac{L + G}{I}$$

where C = total cost of lamp replacement per lamp
   L = lamp net price
   S = spot-replacement labor cost per lamp
   G = group-relamping labor cost per lamp
   B = per cent burnouts at end of group-relamping interval (Fig. 12-12)
   I = group-relamping interval in terms of average lamp life

Labor costs vary over a wide range. In many medium to large installations the labor cost of spot replacement may be as low as $0.40 per lamp or as high as $2 per lamp. Surveys indicate an average cost of about $1.40. These costs vary, depending on accessibility of the fixtures, labor rates, cost of overhead, and other factors. Most of the cost of spot replacement is in travel time to and from the burned-out lamp, not in actual lamp replacement. When travel and setup time are reduced to a minimum, as is done in group-relamping programs, labor costs are usually very materially lowered. In many cases group-relamping labor cost can be reduced to nearly zero by replacing lamps when the luminaires are cleaned. This is because the cost of removing a new lamp from a package is about the same as the cost of cleaning an old lamp.

It is relatively easy to determine whether or not group relamping will save money if the labor cost of group relamping can be estimated and the cost of spot replacement is known. The charts shown in Fig. 12-11 have been developed to indicate the break-even points on lamp and replacement labor costs. By inserting the known costs in these charts according to the existing conditions, it is an easy matter to determine whether the point falls in the group-relamping or spot-replacement area. These charts were developed for an equal time period for both group relamping and spot replacement.

LUMINAIRE CLEANING OPERATION

Fluorescent-lighting installations, with a lower light output per lamp, need more lamps to provide a given light output and therefore generally require much larger luminaires than do incandescent or mercury lamps to produce the same lighting intensity. Thus fluorescent luminaires require more time and labor for cleaning and usually more cleaning steps and operations. The job of cleaning fluorescent-lighting systems has therefore increased the scope of lighting maintenance per system, and the number of installations is increasing rapidly. The typical fluorescent-lighting system involves the following steps in cleaning, which will, of course, vary somewhat in sequence depending upon the type of luminaires, mounting height and spacing, and types of maintenance equipment provided or available. Also, a one-man cleaning operation differs from a two-man. The methods of performing each step can, however, be applied to most cleaning programs. Some of the methods used, based on a two-man operation, are described below.

Remove and Clean Louvers. The louvers are usually removed by the man on the ladder and handed to the floor man to clean while the luminaire is cleaned. A sponge can be used efficiently to clean cross louvers by moving it back and forth between the louvers. Ganged brushes can be moved up and down through the louvers to clean modular louvers. If they are cleaned often enough, louvers do not become very dirty and can usually be cleaned by shaking them in a cleaning solution.

Remove Lamps and Clean. Lamps are more easily washed on the floor but are sometimes washed at the luminaire if equipment and work space can be provided safely. One good lamp-cleaning technique makes use of two sponges—one for washing and the other for rinsing. A downward stroke with the wash sponge, which is held in one hand, is followed by the rinse sponge, held in the other hand. The wash sponge is then dropped, and the lamp held with a cloth to finish the rinse stroke.

Make Luminaire Shock-free. For safety, luminaires should be made shock-free. This can be done by turning off the electrical circuit, but such action usually results in too little illumination for the maintenance workers. Instead of the lighting being turned off, a suitable insulating tape can be used to cover the lamp sockets or dummy lamp bases can be inserted in the sockets.

Clean Top and Outside of Luminaire. Heavy deposits of dirt are often found on the top surfaces of luminaires. A large amount of this dirt can be removed by brushing. A blower may also be used if there is no objection to dirt being blown into the air. Then the rest of the dirt and film can be washed off. Often a special bucket of detergent solution is used for this cleaning operation.

Clean Inside of Luminaire. A paintbrush works well to clean the dust and dirt around the lamp sockets. The wash solution is brushed on first, followed by a rinse, which is allowed to drain dry. The reflector can be washed by using a wash sponge in one hand and a rinse sponge in the other or removed and washed in a wash tank if it is of the easily removable type.

Incandescent and mercury luminaires do not require so many cleaning steps as outlined above for fluorescent luminaires. However, for the steps above which are common to all lighting systems, the same cleaning methods can be used.

OPERATING A LIGHTING MAINTENANCE DEPARTMENT

Lighting maintenance should be performed by a separate division organized and operated as a part of the maintenance department. It should have its own personnel, stock room, workshop area, and general facilities so that it can operate as an independent unit subject only to departmental supervision. In large companies it usually operates as a branch unit of the electrical maintenance department, both of which in turn are a subdivision of the electrical department of the maintenance division. This setup puts lighting maintenance work under supervision of the nominal head of the electrical department and makes his services and advice generally available to the maintenance group. The size of individual companies will, of course, influence greatly the organizational setup of the maintenance group for lighting; the number of employees in this group; how they are housed, supervised, and operate; and other similar details.

It has been found that two-man crews are preferred for most lighting maintenance work. In this case, it is desirable for the crew foreman to be an electrical technician (or electrician) and for the helper to be a nontechnical employee. However, in some cases apprentice electricians work as helpers. The electrician is qualified to check electrical problems and to make repairs as they are encountered on the job during maintenance operations. Practices differ from one plant to another. In some groups nontechnical cleaning crews only wash and clean lamps and luminaires and merely report outages or electrical troubles to the electrical department as they are located.

HOW TO SET UP A LIGHTING MAINTENANCE PROGRAM

Before proceeding to set up a new or reorganized lighting maintenance program, it is important to analyze in detail the existing lighting system and its related factors and to record and put into report form all the details. This report should include information on data of installation of the lighting system, past maintenance and repair schedules and practices, first cost of the equipment, an accurate layout of the existing lighting and wiring systems, and full information as developed through a series of tests conducted as outlined in Table 12-9.

Before beginning the survey of existing lighting, it is well to outline the steps that are to be followed in considerable detail and to work up forms for recording all the necessary data and related information for each step. The key to a good maintenance program is *records*. Records are needed on each light-loss factor. Such records will provide factual data on each factor under actual operating conditions, removing the problem of estimating and guesswork, and will give the maintenance engineer a sound basis for his lighting-system analysis and for his recommendations for a new and improved maintenance program. Setting up a record file on each light-loss factor is, therefore, the maintenance engineer's first step, and one of the most important, in planning a new lighting maintenance program.

The existing lighting layout for each building, department, or area of the plant should be drawn up to scale for file and reference purposes. These plans should then be kept up to date as changes and additions are made. (Unless the plant is an old one, these plans are probably already on file in the company or will be available from the architect's office.) It is also desirable to have on file the electrical plans for all areas, showing the lighting branch circuits, spare circuit provisions in panels, and other pertinent data.

When the necessary forms are prepared and the lighting layouts have been recorded on drawings, the lighting survey can be begun. A voltmeter and good light meter will be required. The steps outlined in Table 12-9 should then be followed, and the results tabulated. In order to estimate maintenance costs fairly accurately, it will also be helpful to note the number and type of employees involved in making the tests and the length of time required for each operation. Unit costs for the different maintenance operations can then be developed from these records, based on prevailing wage rates, for use as may be required at any later date.

The next step is to prepare a report and recommendation for submittal to management. With the data developed from the survey and tests plus the information on initial lighting-system costs, it will be possible to estimate with fair accuracy the total cost of the lighting at the time the report is made, on a monthly or annual basis, and to relate this to specific average lighting intensities. This total cost can also be further broken down into "annual cost per foot-candle." Then the cost of maintaining the lighting in accordance with a proposed maintenance program and schedule can be estimated, added to the original estimated annual cost of the unmaintained (or poorly maintained, as the case may be) lighting systems, and the annual cost per foot-candle again determined. Since the average foot-candle intensity with a well-maintained system will be much higher than without maintenance and the added annual cost for

Table 12-9. How to Analyze Your Existing Lighting System to Determine Over-all Efficiency and Need for Maintenance

Maintenance factors	*Methods of checking factors and what to look for*
Initial lighting intensity	Make a survey to determine the "initial" horizontal lighting intensity. Do this for each different area or for each different type of lighting system. Where lighting intensities vary throughout an area, make the survey over the entire area. Use a portable photoelectric light meter, preferably, and one in which the photoelectric cells are equipped with filters and the meter is corrected for cosine error. Set up enough illumination measurement stations* to give an accurate "average" result. Be sure to record socket voltages, time of day, model and number of meter used, and any other pertinent facts of this nature.
Lamp outages	Count and record the number of lamps which are burned out or which are not burning for any other reason. If lamps are of different types and sizes, record details of outages fully and clearly (on a lighting layout plan if one is available).
Lamp depreciation	All light sources give off less light as they grow older. If it is not known how long the lamps in use have been installed and burning, inspect them carefully and estimate the approximate percentage of rated life the lamps have burned, based on the extent of the blackening. Record this percentage for future reference. If it is impossible to estimate approximately how long the lamps have been burned, a test may be conducted which will give accurate results. Take a typical area (a complete room or a large bay in an open area) and make a series of foot-candle readings at several designated measurement stations. Then replace all old lamps in the area with new lamps, and repeat the foot-candle readings at the same measurement stations. By comparing the "averages" of these readings and checking against a typical lumen depreciation curve (Fig. 12-9), the approximate percentage of total rated lamp life can be determined. Also, the exact foot-candle values of the lighting with the old lamps, which is more to the point, will be a matter of record as compared with the illumination values with new lamps.
Socket voltages	Check the voltage at lamp sockets or at ballast terminal leads for fluorescent and mercury-vapor lamps, and make a record of the readings. This should be done when initial lighting-intensity readings are made and again when final or adjusted lighting-intensity readings are made. All lighting units should be turned on when the voltages are checked. If voltages vary appreciably from rated voltage of lamps being used, actual light output at rated voltage should be determined from Fig. 12-9.
Luminaire inefficiency	The light-distribution characteristics and over-all lighting efficiency of the luminaires in use should be determined and placed on file as a permanent record. These can be obtained upon request from the manufacturer of the units. If the existing luminaires appear to be of the wrong type or inefficient (Figs. 12-2 and 12-8), obtain light-distribution curves and over-all efficiency ratings of other luminaires considered more appropriate and compare with the units now in use.

Table 12-9. How to Analyze Your Existing Lighting System to Determine Over-all Efficiency and Need for Maintenance (*Continued*)

Maintenance factors	*Methods of checking factors and what to look for*
Room-surface reflectances	Determine and record the reflection factors for the ceiling, side walls, floor, and furniture (machines) as they now exist. (Reflection factors can be calculated from light-meter measurements—see instructions furnished with these instruments—or can be determined with a reflection-factor scale supplied by most paint manufacturers.) By interpolation, existing reflectances can be appraised in comparison with other reflectances (Table 12-6), and the effect of lighter finishes on the final lighting result can be estimated. Use a coefficient of utilization table for the luminaires now installed for accurate results.
Dirt and dust	Take initial foot-candle readings in a typical room or large bay area, with lamps and luminaires dirty as found. Then wash and clean all luminaires, repeat the foot-candle readings at the same measurement stations, and record. If possible, estimate the time lapse since luminaires and lamps were last cleaned, and determine the rate of depreciation (per time interval) due to dirt and dust collection on lamps and luminaires.
Maintained lighting intensity	Determine the maintained or adjusted lighting intensity, either by calculation or by actual test. To do this, follow the seven steps outlined above. Use charts and tables in this chapter, or obtain specific data from lamp and lighting equipment manufacturers for the equipment now in use for calculated results. If it is desired to run an actual test for the final lighting-intensity result, use a typical closed room (preferably), or a large bay area. Then do these things: (1) Measure the existing lighting intensity as found in unmaintained condition; (2) adjust voltage at sockets or ballast leads to the rated voltage of the lamps (can be done usually by changing transformer taps when the voltage is off by several volts); (3) repaint the ceiling and side walls (or wash down where this is practical)—plans under consideration will guide— also clean floor and machines, and paint the machines if this is also to be considered as part of the modernization program; (4) clean all luminaires, reflectors, louvers, parts, etc., and install new lamp bulbs; (5) measure the lighting intensity provided by the newly maintained and newly lamped lighting system, using the same measurement stations as in step 1; (6) compare the final maintained or adjusted lighting intensity with the initial intensity existing before the system was maintained.

* See IES "Lighting Handbook," 2d ed., Sec. 4, pp. 4–8, for Interior Lighting Survey Procedure. Copies of the official IES foot-candle survey form (IS-10) may be ordered from IES headquarters. These forms are supplied with supplementary sheets which give standard IES-light-measurement procedures.

maintenance will probably be low, a good case for the proposed lighting maintenance program can be made.

Included in the report should be listed the many benefits and advantages accruing from a good lighting maintenance program. Many of these have already been mentioned but are listed again for emphasis: more light delivered; better appearance; **greater** accuracy of workmanship resulting from an improved quality of product with less spoilage and rework; increased production and decreased costs; better utilization of floor space; greater ease of seeing, especially among older employees, thus making them more efficient; improved cleanliness and neatness in the plant; less eyestrain among employees; better supervision of workers; improved morale among employees, resulting in decreased labor turnover; and greater safety.

Included in the report also should be an estimate of the cost of maintenance done under contract by an outside maintenance company. A quotation from the outside firm can be obtained for this purpose, based on the same scheduled maintenance program and features proposed for the new program.

If the estimates and facts indicate the need for and economy of a lighting maintenance department operating within the company, such a department should be proposed and the proposal submitted as a recommendation with the report. This proposal should include recommendations for space, personnel, equipment, repair parts and stocks, cleaning materials and other needs as may be required.

Chapter 13

SOLID-STATE ELECTRONICS

By Norman Peach
Associate Editor
Power
New York, N.Y.

Within the last ten years, and especially within the last five, a whole new category of electric devices has become established in industry. Today this family of devices has generally been called *solid state*, since all the activity takes place within a solid block of materials, without any moving parts, without even electrons moving through a gas or vacuum as they do in an electronic tube. In the broadest sense, transformers and capacitors are solid-state devices, but as the term has come to be used, it refers to *semiconductors*, devices such as the transistor and thyristor. (A thyristor is commonly called an SCR, the abbreviation for silicon controlled rectifier.)

Solid-state (semiconductor) devices have been rapidly increasing in power capacity and in the complexity of functions which they can perform. Solid-state devices have all but taken over some areas of the electric system (rectification) and are being used as components in new parts of familiar machines (brushless synchronous motors). A knowledge of their behavior and how to take care of them are essential today for the successful operation of an industrial electric system.

HOW SEMICONDUCTORS WORK

A semiconductor device is actually a composite substance; its activity takes place at the junction, or barrier, between two or more different substances. Selenium and copper oxide rectifiers are familiar semiconductor devices, but because of the limitations of these substances, they have not been developed to perform as complicated or as heavy-duty functions as have silicon and germanium.

For the sake of simplicity let us consider a hypothetical semiconductor with a crystalline structure resembling germanium (Fig. 13-1). The small spheres represent atoms, and the pairs of parallel lines represent covalent bonds—the forces binding the atoms together to form molecules (in this case a crystal lattice). Each atom produces eight covalent bonds (four pairs). To produce eight covalent bonds each atom must have *four* valence electrons. (A valence electron is one which shares in the bonds with other atoms.) Now, if an atom of another element with *five* valence electrons is inserted in place of a normal atom, there is an extra electron which cannot participate in any of the bonds. Such electrons are attached by relatively weak forces and tend to drift off among the atoms; an example is shown in a number of positions (1, 2, 3) in Fig. 13-1a. By controlling the number of atoms present with an extra electron (said to be adding donor impurities), the number of free electrons can be prescribed. Crystals with free electrons are called N crystals (negative).

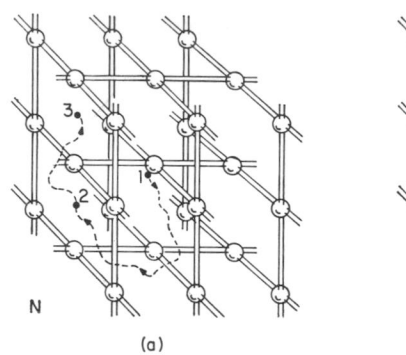
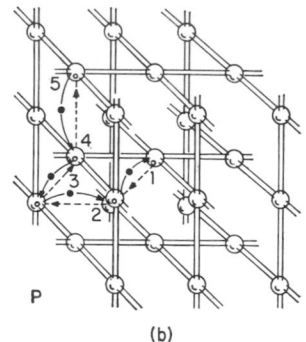

N   (a)   P   (b)

FIG. 13-1. Crystals of semiconductor material are of two kinds.   N-type crystal (a) has extra electrons; P-type crystal has deficit of electrons, or holes, shown at (b).

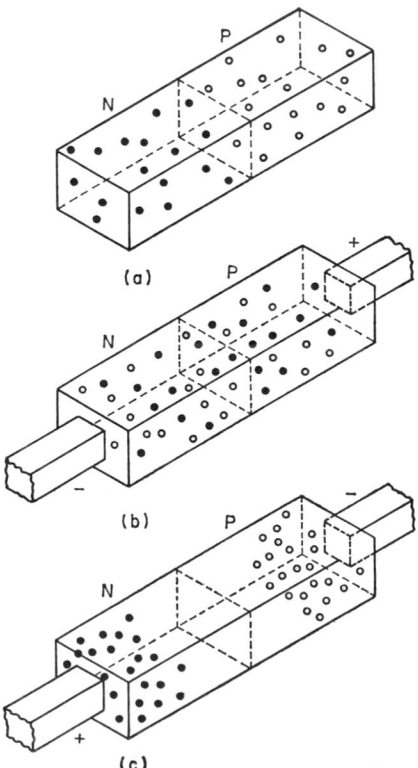

FIG. 13-2. Junction of N and P crystals forms a rectifier element. Unenergized crystal (a) is neutral.   With proper polarity applied, voltage makes electrons and holes migrate so current flows (b).   With polarity reversed (c) electrons and holes segregate so current does not flow.

Crystals of a P (positive) character can be made by adding to the originally pure structure atoms having *three* valence electrons, that is, one less than the four required to form a normal covalent bond. This lack of one electron in an atom, or "empty place," is called a *hole*.   An atom with a hole (1, in Fig. 13-1b) exerts a strong force to fill it and may cause an electron from an adjacent atom to jump over into the hole.   The hole is now transferred to atom 2 (Fig. 13-1b).   This process is repeated from time to time, and the hole is said to travel from 1 to 2, 3, 4, to 5, though actual movement is by separate electrons jumping from 2 to 1, 3 to 2, etc. By controlling the amount of impurities (atoms with three valence electrons) added to the crystal, the number of holes can be prescribed.   Thus P and N substances are produced.   These P and N substances are then combined to form solid-state devices.

Diodes.   Most solid-state rectifiers are composed of a few or a great many silicon diodes.   Diodes are made by joining a piece of N crystal to a piece of P crystal in one of several ways. Let us consider the example shown in Fig. 13-2.

Without applying voltage, a few electrons and holes will cross the barrier between the N and P crystals (Fig. 13-2a) but will cancel each other out.   Now if voltage is applied across the junction so that P is + and N is − (Fig. 13-2b), electrons will be attracted from N to P, and holes will be attracted from P to N. Holes will be filled with electrons arriving at the − terminal. Conduction therefore takes place through the junction and current flows in the circuit.

Blocking occurs when polarity of the applied voltage is reversed (Fig. 13-2c). Electrons are attracted away from the barrier toward the + terminal while holes are attracted to the − terminal. There is no exchange of electrons between N and P, and therefore the diode does not conduct.

Zener Diodes. When a certain value of voltage is applied across a diode in the blocking direction, electrons are forced through the barrier from the external circuit as in an ordinary conductor. If the current which flows is not too large, it will not damage the diode; and when the diode is again applied at its normal voltage, the diode will again function as a rectifier, blocking in one direction and conducting in the other.

This phenomenon—conducting in the blocking direction at a specific voltage (zener voltage)—is made use of in some circuits to limit voltage and to protect sensitive electronic devices. A diode designed for this purpose is called a zener diode, and it may be connected in parallel with the sensitive device. Normally the zener diode has such high resistance that it may be regarded as an open circuit; but if the circuit voltage rises to the zener voltage level, the diode conducts and acts like a short circuit across the sensitive device, removing voltage from it. Zener diodes also have other functions in complicated electronic circuits.

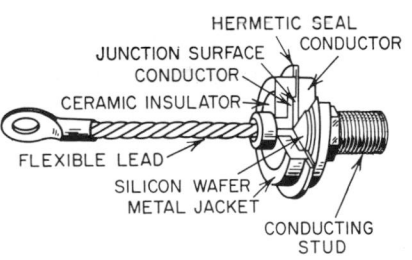

High-power Silicon Rectifier Diodes. Semiconductor diode elements, or *cells*, such as the typical unit shown in Fig. 13-3, consist of the semiconductor junction with terminals connected to the junction. Provision is made for removing heat, which is the purpose of using the heavy stud as one terminal. These components are then hermetically sealed in a "package" to give the cell mechanical strength and exclude

FIG. 13-3. Silicon cell consists of thin wafer of P-N junction between metal terminals. Cell is hermetically sealed to exclude contaminants, keep characteristics stable.

contaminants. For heavy-power applications today, silicon cells are used almost exclusively. (Selenium has some applications, but the selenium cell is quite different from the silicon cell and will be described later.) Junctions in silicon cells are thin wafers—up to about an inch in diameter and a few thousandths of an inch thick—soldered to metal terminals, usually copper or aluminum. One terminal is generally a stud connected to a heat sink. The other terminal normally includes a pigtail for ease of attachment. These cells are mechanically rugged; they can withstand vibration, can be operated in any position, and even rotated at high speeds in the excitation systems of synchronous motors and generators.

Thyristors (SCR's). The preferred name for a semiconductor device generally known as an SCR (silicon controlled rectifier) is *thyristor,* and we encourage its use even though SCR is more likely to be encountered on diagrams today. Their appearance (Fig. 13-4) is similar to that of the silicon diode except for a small third terminal called the *gate.* Internally, they are made up of four semiconductor layers in the order N-P-N-P. This arrangement is shown in Fig. 13-5, where the proportions of the parts are distorted for the sake of better illustrating the principles involved. The gate terminal is connected to the P layer nearer the cathode terminal. The load, with a voltage source, is connected in series with the thyristor through its anode and cathode.

With no signal on the gate, the thyristor blocks in both directions, and current cannot flow in the load circuit. But if the gate switch S_G is closed, the gate current I_G flows from N to P to the cathode. (In these descriptions of semiconductor devices, we will refer to the direction of actual electron flow rather than to conventional current flow, which is, of course, directly opposite.) The current through the thyris-

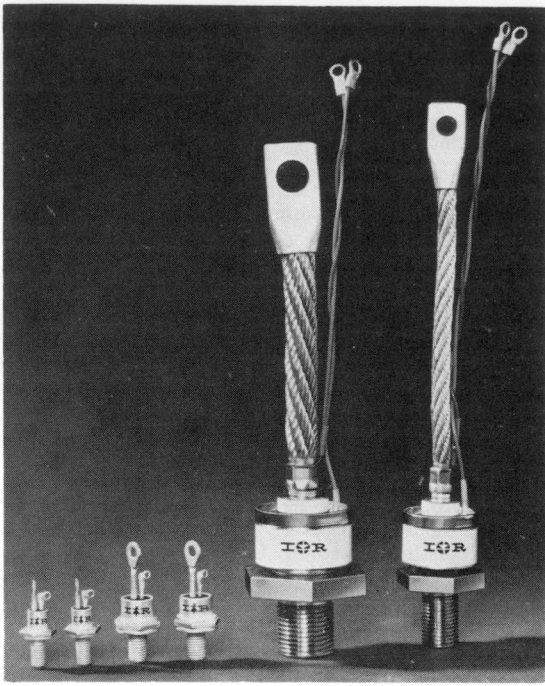

FIG. 13-4. Thyristors are available in a range of power ratings.   (*Courtesy of International Rectifier Corp.*)

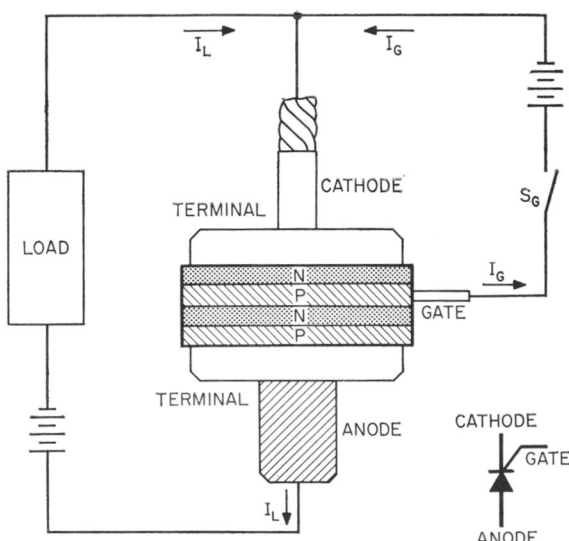

FIG. 13-5. Diagram of thyristor shows N-P-N-P junction with connection of gate.   Thyristor symbol is at lower right.

tor causes the whole N-P-N-P combination to conduct between the cathode and the anode, permitting load current I_L to flow. Now, if the gate current is shut off, the thyristor will continue to conduct the load current. To stop conduction, voltage across the device must be reduced to zero (or have its polarity reversed). If the voltage is an alternating sine wave, voltage is naturally brought to zero every half cycle. In a d-c circuit, however, provision must be made to drive the voltage to zero (or reverse it) whenever it is desired to shut off conduction.

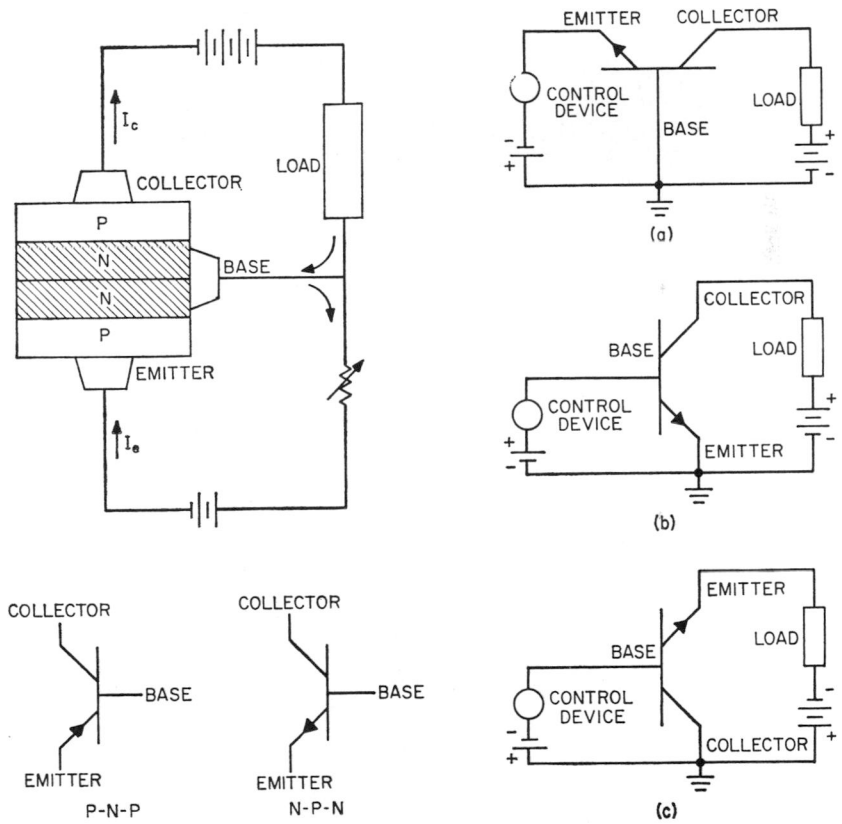

FIG. 13-6. Diagram shows connection of typical P-N-P transistor. Symbols for P-N-P and N-P-N transistor are shown below the main diagram.

FIG. 13-7. Typical transistor circuits: (a) common base, (b) common emitter, and (c) common collector.

Transistors. A more complicated device, though developed earlier, the transistor bears much the same relationship to the vacuum-tube triode as the thyristor does to the thyratron. The transistor is essentially a solid-state triode. This device is also made up of layers of P and N semiconductors, but they are arranged so that the device conducts only when the input signal (comparable to the gate signal of the thyristor) is applied. When the input circuit is opened, the transistor stops conducting. What is more, the ease with which a transistor conducts depends on the magnitude of the input-signal current. By controlling the low-power input signal, it is possible to control a much larger power in the load circuit. The transistor is thus a power amplifier, while the thyristor is a switch.

The arrangement of two P-N junctions to form a P-N-P transistor is shown in Fig.

13-6. The three regions of the transistor and their corresponding terminals are called *emitter, base,* and *collector*. (The emitter was so named because it "emits" electrons into the base region, while the collector "collects" electrons from the base region.) These regions may be connected into circuits in a number of ways; the connection shown in Fig. 13-6 is one of the simplest. With this arrangement the emitter-base circuit is the input or control circuit, while the collector-base circuit is the output or load circuit. It is possible to have other arrangements in which the emitter or collector instead of the base is the common terminal (Fig. 13-7). Also, there are N-P-N transistors as well as P-N-P types, and the difference may be indicated on schematic diagrams by the symbols shown at the bottom of Fig. 13-6. The relative merits of the different circuit arrangements are matters of decision for the electronic circuit designer; for our purposes it is sufficient to recognize how the transistor is being used when we encounter it in a piece of equipment.

POWER TRANSISTORS

FIG. 13-8. Typical power transistor has accessible mounting. (*Courtesy of Deltron, Inc.*)

Transistors used in industrial apparatus may be classified as *power transistors* and *small-signal transistors*. Power transistors are used to regulate current in electric machines, as, for example, in the field excitation current of d-c and synchronous motors. They are rated in watts, and higher ratings are being continually developed which can be economically applied. They are usually separately mounted with ample provision for dissipation of heat (Fig. 13-8). Small-signal transistors are used for control functions, usually to provide the input signals to power transistors or the

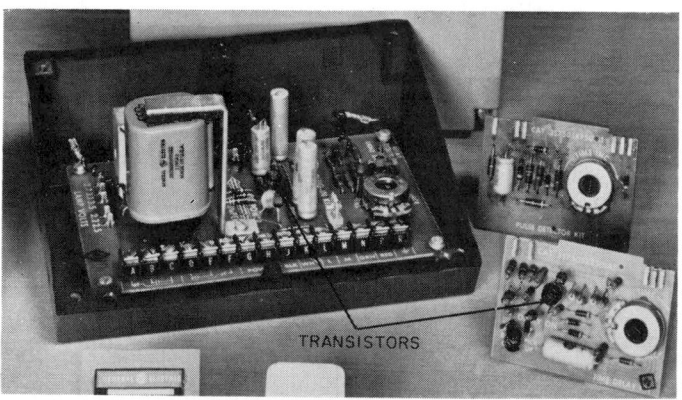

TRANSISTORS

FIG. 13-9. Small-signal transistors are mounted on cards along with other electronic components. (*Courtesy of General Electric Co.*)

gate signals for thyristors. At the heart of the "logic circuitry" of complex control systems, they may require only a few microwatts, and are usually mounted on cards along with resistors, capacitors, and other circuit components (Fig. 13-9).

Thermistors. Members of the semiconductor family, thermistors are resistors whose resistance varies substantially according to the temperature to which the ther-

mistor is subjected.   They are thus very useful as sensitive detectors and control
devices.   There are a great many different types of thermistors in use in electronic circuits.   The type which is probably of greatest interest in industrial equipment is the
positive temperature coefficient thermistor.
This type has a very high resistance until a
certain critical temperature is reached, at
which the resistance drops suddenly to a relatively low value.   If connected in a series
with a suitable relay, the thermistor can be
used to shut down a piece of machinery when
a dangerous temperature has been reached.
Thermistors of this type have been widely used
in recent years for the protection of electric-
motor windings; they are imbedded in the
windings themselves and respond to temperatures which would be harmful to the motor.
A typical thermistor used for motor protection
is shown in Fig. 13-10.

Selenium Devices.   Selenium rectifiers have
been used for more than 20 years for control
purposes and for power applications up to 50
kw or more.   While they have been displaced
for most rectifier applications today by silicon,
they still have advantages for certain jobs.
The semiconducting layer is applied to a relatively small area of a large metal fin or plate;

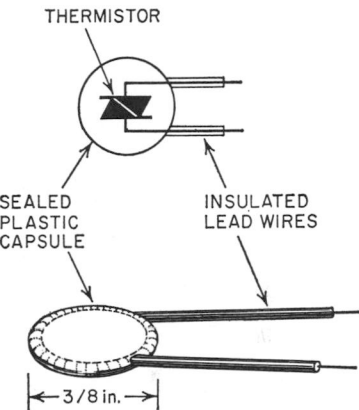

FIG. 13-10. Typical positive temperature coefficient thermistor is designed
for embedding in machinery windings.

the plates are then stacked on an insulated bolt (Fig. 13-11).   The fins serve to dissipate
heat, since selenium rectifiers are usually air-convection-cooled.   The actual physical
principle of the selenium rectifier does not lend itself to as clear an explanation as that
of the crystalline semiconductor like silicon, and it has not received as much theoretical

FIG. 13-11.   Heavy-duty selenium rectifiers have large cooling fins.   (*Courtesy of International Rectifier Corp.*)

attention.   Methods of making selenium rectifiers have been greatly improved in
recent years, however, so that their characteristics are much better than those of their
predecessors.

Selenium rectifiers are much more thermally rugged than silicon types, and where they may be subjected to overloads without adequate protection, they have a definite advantage. For many applications they are less expensive, though this is a factor of decreasing importance. Their chief disadvantage is a tendency to age—to increase their forward resistance with operating time. New designs are much improved in this respect, however.

A unique characteristic of selenium rectifiers (or selenium diodes, as the smallest sizes are sometimes called) is their ability to *heal* themselves. When a selenium cell is subjected to a voltage or power surge (up to a limiting value), a short circuit may occur between the plates. But if the surge is of short enough duration, the arc burns itself clear, leaving a still-effective selenium element. This characteristic has led to the use

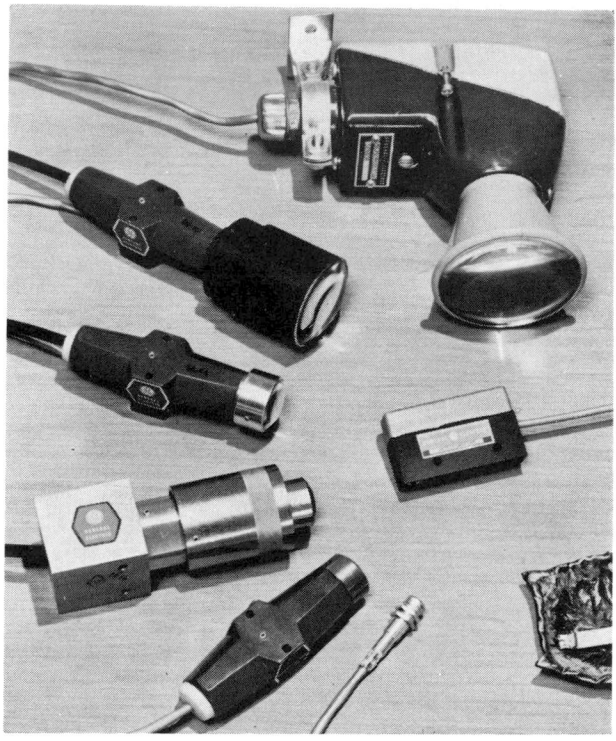

FIG. 13-12. Photocells are used for "electric eye" applications. (*Courtesy of General Electric Co.*)

of selenium elements not as rectifiers but as surge suppressors to protect other semiconductors, including silicon, which are susceptible to surges. Selenium surge suppressors and special-purpose rectifiers used in electronic circuits come in many different forms that bear no resemblance to the power unit of Fig. 13-11, although larger surge suppressors may be in this form.

Photocells. There are two basic types of semiconductor photocells: photoconductive and photovoltaic. The photoconductive cell is one which changes its conductivity when light impinges on the cell. A typical cell of this type is a P-N-P-N junction, which resembles a thyristor, but instead of being triggered by an electric signal applied to its gate, it is caused to conduct when light strikes its light-sensitive region. Before light strikes, the photoconductive cell has a high resistance, equivalent to an open-circuit or "off" condition. When light strikes the cell, the resistance falls to a low value, equivalent to a closed circuit or "on" condition. In this type of photoconductive cell, conduction continues until shut off by electric means, as in the case of the thyristor. Other types of photoconductive cells behave more like transistors, and the conductitivity is a function of the illumination on the cell.

Photoconductive cells have been making wide headway in replacing electron-tube photosensitive cells. They can be used to switch on devices such as street lamps, which are energized when a particular desired value of ambient illumination is reached. They can also be used to replace the familiar "electric eye" in many applications, and often have an advantage in their much smaller size. Photocells for such applications are packaged with their required auxiliary circuitry (Fig. 13-12).

The second type of photocell, the photovoltaic cell, has the property of generating a voltage (about ½ volt) when light impinges on its light-sensitive surfaces. By combining enough of these cells in series-parallel groupings, an effective voltage and power output can be obtained. Such solar batteries have been used to energize control equipment, to drive certain instruments, and to operate the shutters of cameras. Solar batteries involving great numbers of photovoltaic cells are used to power space satellites. An instrumentation type of photovoltaic cell is shown in Fig. 13-13.

FIG. 13-13. Instrument-type photocell or solar battery produces electric energy from light. (*Courtesy of International Rectifier Corp.*)

SOLID-STATE APPARATUS

Rectifiers. In their many forms rectifiers probably represent the most common use of solid-state power devices. Rectifiers and diodes are also widely used in control circuits. Solid-state power rectifiers can be broadly classed as those for constant-voltage applications and those requiring regulated d-c outputs. Let us consider the constant-voltage types first. The simplest of these are replacements for selenium rectifiers or small motor-generator sets for local d-c requirements such as modest plating operations, battery chargers, lifting magnets, and magnetic chucks.

For larger rectifier applications it is possible to obtain replacement units which match the characteristics of mercury-arc rectifier tubes such as ignitrons and excitrons (Fig. 13-14). In many cases silicon replacement assemblies are so tailored to the complete rectifier equipment that the mercury-arc unit need merely be disconnected and the silicon diode unit connected in its place. Silicon rectifiers are, in fact, proving so effective as replacements for mercury-arc types that some manufacturers foresee the day when the mercury units will be discontinued entirely.

Still larger applications requiring enormous quantities of direct current, such as chlorine production and aluminum pot lines, probably represent the most extensive use of silicon diode rectifiers. In recent years they have largely replaced mercury-arc rectifiers and rotary converters.

Rectifiers are made up of rectifier elements, such as silicon diodes, combined in suitable circuits. A single element in a circuit permits only the positive half cycles of the a-c sine wave to pass; that is, the diode conducts when voltage across it is + to −, as shown in Fig. 13-15. Such an arrangement is called a half-wave rectifier. During the negative half cycle, when the voltage across the diode is − to +, the diode does not conduct. The voltage which the element can withstand without breaking down in the nonconducting direction is called the *peak reverse voltage* and is an important characteristic of a rectifier element.   In the circuit of Fig. 13-15, the output voltage across the load is unidirectional, but it is not continuous, as shown by the graph.   With a resistive load, the current wave has the same form as the voltage wave.

Full-wave rectification can be obtained from a single-phase source if two rectifier elements are set up so that one conducts during the positive half cycle and the other

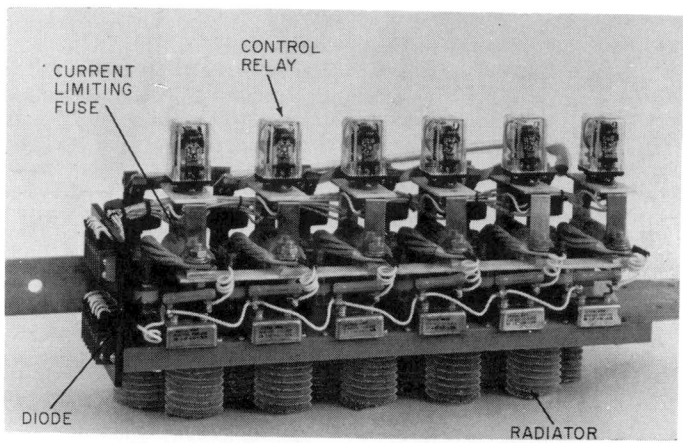

Fig. 13-14. Solid-state rectifier unit may be used as a direct replacement for a mercury-arc tube.   (*Courtesy of Rapid Electric Co., Inc.*)

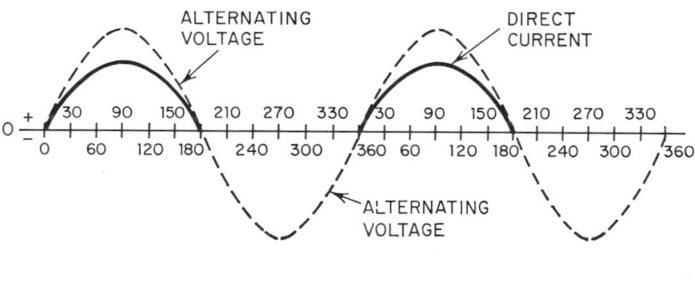

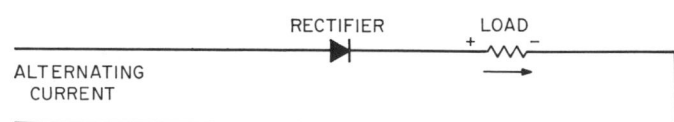

Fig. 13-15. Half-wave rectification is produced when a single rectifier element is connected in series with a single-phase circuit.   Negative half cycles give no output current.

conducts during the negative half cycle (Fig. 13-16).   The center tap circuit (Fig. 13-16a) has an input transformer with a tap at its mid-point P.   When the voltage induced in the secondary is from A to B, current will flow through half of the secondary from P to B, through the rectifier element (+ to −), through the load, and back to the point P.   When the voltage across the secondary reverses during the next input half-cycle, current will flow from P to A, through the other element (+ to −), through the load in same direction as before, and back to P.   This procedure is repeated for every cycle of the a-c supply.

   The bridge circuit (Fig. 13-16b) also produces full-wave rectification.   When the a-c voltage is $+$ at A and $-$ at B, current flows from A to D, through the load, then from C to B, passing through two elements.   When the supply voltage is $-$ at A and $+$ at B, current flow is B to D, load, and C to A.   Bridge circuits require four elements instead of two, but have some advantages.   An input transformer may not be needed if a-c and d-c voltages are satisfactory; but if an input transformer is needed, it is more efficient, since all the winding is operating at the same time.   Also, for the same output voltage, the bridge elements need block only half the reverse voltage that the elements of the center-tap circuit do, since the two are in series.

   Large power rectifiers are generally three-phase.   Simplest of these is the Y connection with a neutral tap (Fig. 13-17).   One element conducts at a time—the one with greatest positive voltage across it.   An obvious advantage of a three-phase rectifier

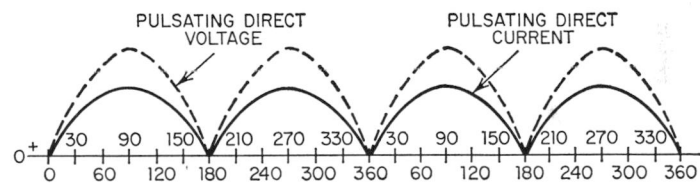

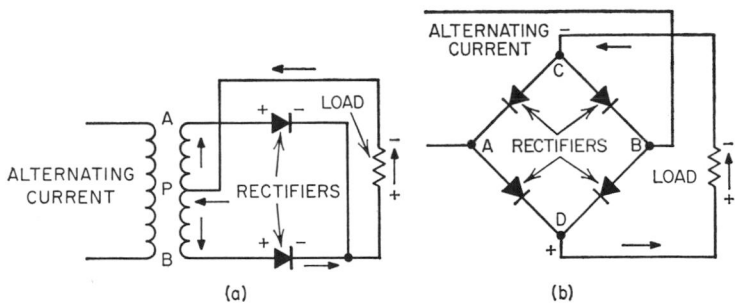

Fig. 13-16. Full-wave rectifier produces continuous, pulsating current.   Center-tap single-phase circuit (a) uses two rectifying elements.   Bridge circuit (b) uses four.

is that the output voltage never goes below a certain value, while the voltage of a single-phase rectifier pulsates between a peak value and zero.

   More complicated circuits for three-phase inputs (Fig. 13-18) have output waves closely approximating true direct current.   The variation of output voltage from a true constant d-c value is known as *ripple*.   Ripple may be thought of as an a-c component superimposed on a constant d-c component.   In some respects the a-c component behaves like real alternating current, producing inductive effects, for example.   For some applications the ripple can be virtually eliminated by *filter* circuits—combinations of resistors, capacitors, and inductors.   In applications the ripple can be tolerated.

   Adjustable-output rectifiers are made possible by using thyristors (SCR's) instead of diodes in the rectifier circuits.   As we have seen, the thyristor does not conduct until a firing signal is applied to its gate (page 7-241), and it stops conducting when the voltage across it is reversed.   This means that it is possible to control the portion of the sine-wave half cycle which is permitted to flow.   The output voltage is therefore a series of nodes and spikes whose peak (and rms value) can be controlled by applying

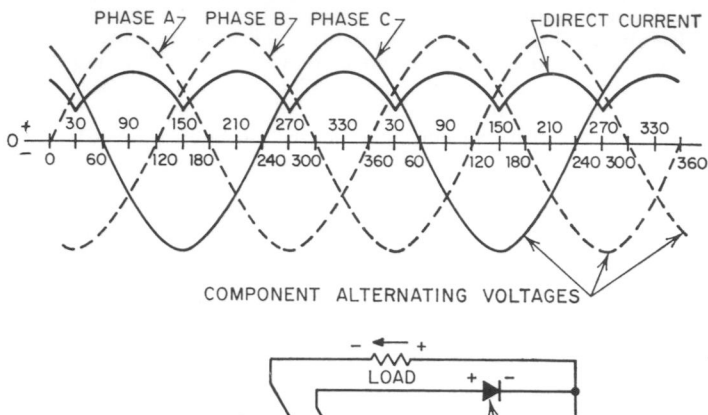

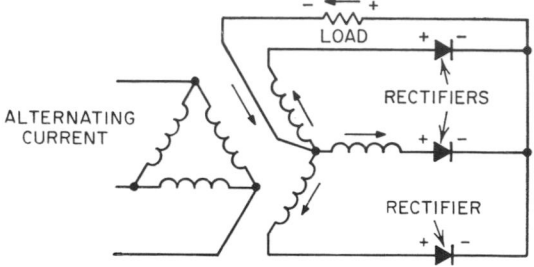

FIG. 13-17. Simplest three-phase rectifier uses three rectifier elements.   It produces continuous current that does not fall to zero.

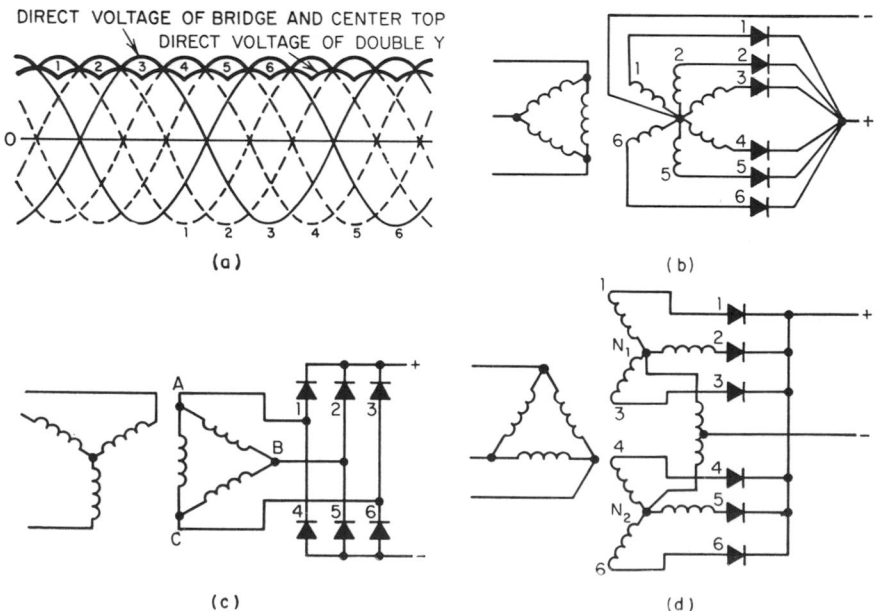

FIG. 13-18. Increasing number of phases reduces output ripple so that direct current is sufficiently flat for most purposes.   Center-tap circuit is shown at (b), three-phase bridge at (c), and double Y at (d).

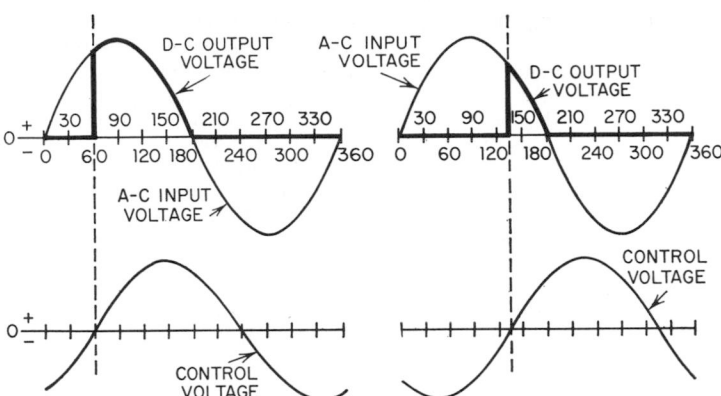

FIG. 13-19. Conduction of thyristor occurs when it is triggered by positive control voltage. The angle at which control voltage goes positive can be adjusted by shifting its phase.

the gate signal at a particular angle (Fig. 13-19). This firing method is commonly used and employs positive phase shift. The firing circuit is supplied from the same source as the rectifier, but a phase-shifting circuit displaces the control sine wave by the desired number of degrees. The control signal is continuously on the firing terminal of the rectifier, but nothing happens until the control voltage begins to increase in a positive direction. At this point conduction occurs and continues throughout the remainder of the positive half cycle of voltage.

Direct-current Adjustable-speed Drives. Direct-current motor drives have the advantages of stepless speed adjustment and close regulation at the speed selected. They have thus retained their popularity for driving many kinds of machinery in spite of the general disappearance of d-c distribution systems. Motor-generator sets, electronic tubes, and mercury-arc rectifiers have been used to supply the requisite direct current. Today, solid-state rectifiers in conjunction with solid-state regulators and controls are rapidly replacing the older conversion methods. Several d-c adjustable-speed drive systems are available. The simplest of these uses a single constant-voltage solid-state rectifier and a shunt motor; speed adjustment is obtained by field control using a rheostat, with the rectifier simply taking the place of a d-c bus. (See Chap. 3, Sec. 7 for the description of motors.)

A combination of armature voltage and field current control gives the most precise speed adjustment and maintains the speed selected with the least variation with load and temperature drift. A solid-state drive

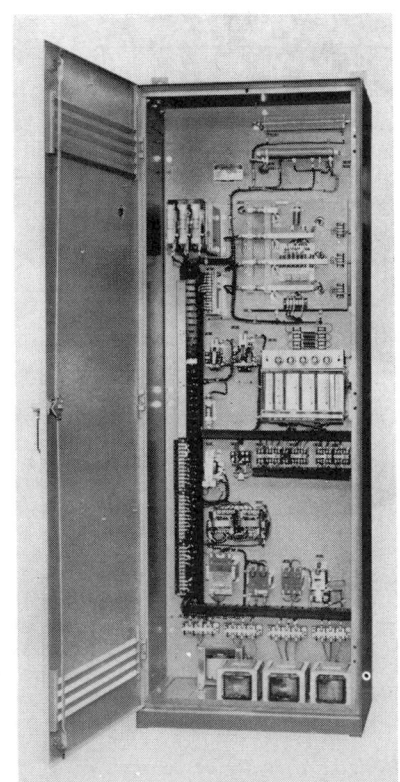

FIG. 13-20. This d-c adjustable-speed drive has thyristors in controlled rectifier unit. (*Courtesy of General Electric Co.*)

of this type is shown in Fig. 13-20 and the schematic diagram of the system in Fig. 13-21.   Such a drive consists of three main sections: (1) the converter or rectifier, shown with reactors and surge suppressors to protect the solid-state devices; (2) the regulator, which provides the gate signals for the thyristors; and (3) the d-c drive motor with field control.   (In the most complicated systems the field control may be tied in with the regulator.)   In this case direct current for the field is supplied by a simple single-phase bridge rectifier, which also supplies the input power to the regulator.

The main rectifier supplying the armature is of the adjustable-output type as described on page 7-247, and the armature voltage is determined by the point on the sine wave (R_1, R_2, R_3 in Fig. 13-21) at which the thyristor (SCR) is made to conduct.   Actually the armature receives a much smoother wave; first, because the the the rectifier is three-phase, and second, because inductive circuits tend to level the sharp peaks.   It is important to note, however, that the d-c motor chosen for such a drive should be specified by the engineers who designed the drive.   Replacing the motor without taking this into consideration may result in overheating or other undesirable effects.

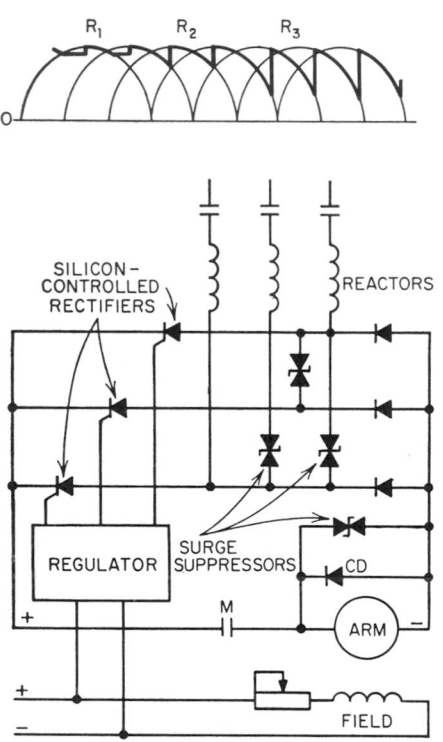

FIG. 13-21. Thyristor converter is bridge rectifier with thyristors to control output wave shape and consequently the average d-c voltage on the armature.

The regulator is the "brain" of the adjustable-speed drive.   It contains the electronic circuitry which interprets the input signals (such as speed feedback from a tachometer generator) and sends out the appropriate control signal to the rectifier section.   Solid-state regulators (Fig. 13-22) are usually made up of small subassemblies (or "cards") which can readily be removed for replacement or to change a control function.   As much as possible control functions are differentiated into separate cards so that a relatively simple drive may have a simple regulator whereas a very complicated drive may require several regulator cards.

Alternating-current, Adjustable-speed Drives.   The speed of a-c induction motors and synchronous motors depends on the frequency of the power supplied to them.   Thus a given induction motor can be made to run at different speeds if the frequency can be adjusted.   (It is also necessary to simultaneously adjust the voltage so that the volts per cycle stay approximately constant.)   For some applications it is necessary to have a number of motors running at exactly the same speed, or in definite proportions, and to have the speed adjustable.   Adjustable-frequency generators driving synchronous motors (of the reluctance type) have been used for this purpose.   In recent years solid-state units have been designed which supply the adjustable-frequency power for the motors.

Input power to these solid-state units comes from the regular three-phase, 60-cycle supply.   There are several different methods by which the 60-cycle alternating current can then be converted to adjustable-frequency alternating current.   One method is to first rectify the 60 cycles to direct current, then invert the direct current to adjustable frequency.   An incidental advantage of this system is that a standby

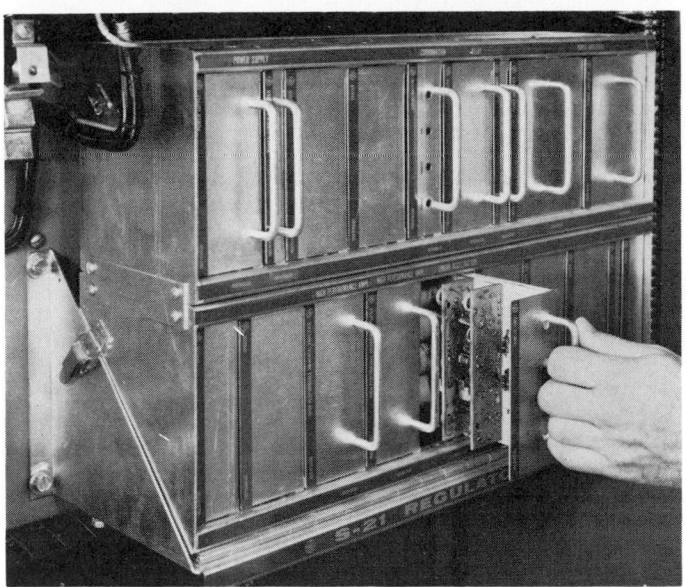

FIG. 13-22. Solid-state regulator for an adjustable d-c drive. (*Courtesy of General Electric Co.*)

battery can be connected to the d-c section to serve as an emergency source of power should the 60-cycle supply be interrupted. This is important, since this type of drive is most often used on a process which must not be interrupted even momentarily, such as the spinning of synthetic fibers.

Figure 13-23 is a block diagram of the rectifier-inverter system showing the major elements.

Internal circuitry involves many components, but it can be seen from the simplified inverter schematic (Fig. 13-24) that the principal elements consist of thyristors and diodes and "commutating networks," the main purpose of which is to shut off the thyristors at the proper time. (Unlike an a-c supply, a d-c input provides no natural zero or reversed voltage to stop the thyristors conducting.) The frequency is determined by the firing signals originating in a solid-state electronic oscillator and applied to the gates of the thyristor. The oscillator is a separate assembly or card with low-power components; frequency settings may be changed manually with a simple dial or by various automatic control devices providing the input to the oscillator.

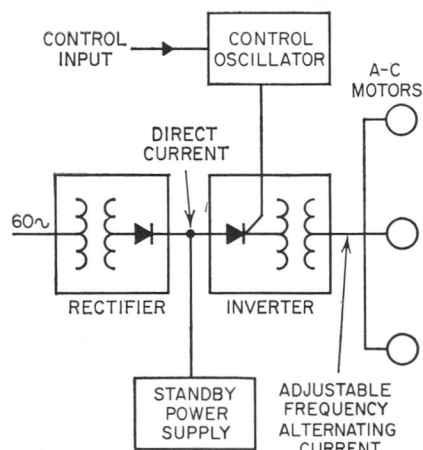

FIG. 13-23. Block diagram for an adjustable-frequency drive.

Output wave shapes are basically composed of combinations of d-c pulses, as can be seen in Fig. 13-25. The current wave shape comes fairly close to being a sine wave. By increasing the complexity of the circuitry, a true sine wave can be more closely approximated.

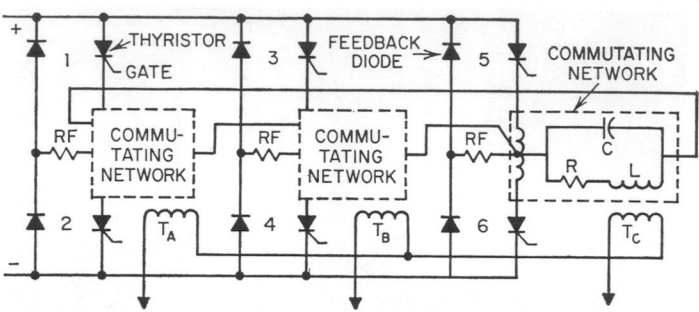

FIG. 13-24. Simplified circuit for adjustable-frequency a-c drive has three-stage inverter with a pair of thyristors for each stage. Commutating circuit shuts off the conducting thyristor when the opposite thyristor is turned on. Feedback diodes and resistors are used to dissipate or recover commutation energy.

Another approach to obtaining an adjustable frequency for driving a-c motors is the frequency converter, which omits the rectification stage and builds up the output wave out of portions of the 60-cycle input. The basic principle is adjusting the firing angles of a large number of thyristors to provide the component pulses of output (Fig. 13-26). It can be seen that the resulting wave is of frequency lower than 60 cycles. This type of converter is used for applications where an adjustable slow-speed drive is required.

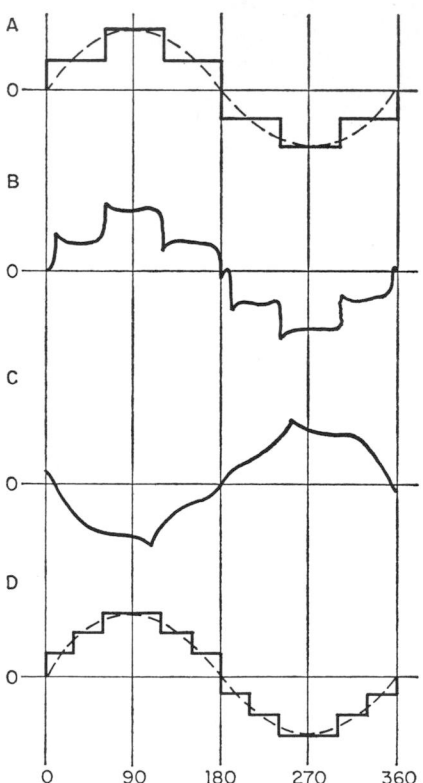

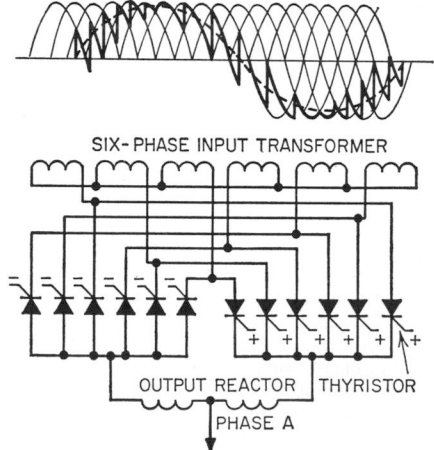

FIG. 13-25. Output wave shapes depend on circuitry. *A* shows theoretical six-stage voltage wave; *B* is actual voltage wave; *C* is a current wave. Increasing the number of stages to 12, as shown at *D*, more closely approximates a sine wave.

FIG. 13-26. Basic circuit of a-c frequency converter consists of an input transformer, positive and negative thyristor banks, and an output reactor. Wave shape shown is a 20-cycle converted wave built up of pulses cut from a 60-cycle 6-phase voltage wave by switching.

High-frequency Lighting. Higher efficiencies can be obtained from fluorescent lighting systems at frequencies above 60 cycles. Lamp efficiency is increased a few per cent, but probably more important, small capacitor ballasts can be used instead of heavier higher-loss inductive ballasts required with 60-cycle fluorescent lamps. Early high-frequency lighting systems used rotating converters with 420 and 840 cycles as standards. Today's solid-state converters produce frequencies as high as 3,000 cycles, and higher frequencies can be expected. The over-all economics of these systems have delayed their wider adoption, but this picture could change.

The high-frequency lighting converter is not unlike the rectifier-inverter system described for adjustable-speed drives except that, since a constant frequency is

FIG. 13-27. Converter changes 60 cycles to 300 cycles for banks of fluorescent lamps. (*Courtesy of the General Electric Co.*)

desired, a relatively simpler circuit can be used. A 60-to-3,000 cycle lighting converter is shown in Fig. 13-27.

Brushless Generators. Alternating-current generators use direct current to energize their fields. Traditionally this direct-current has come from an external source, or exciter. Direct-current generators, whether driven by the main generator shaft or a separate motor, were the original (and still used) source of excitation. Rotating generators have been giving way to solid-state rectifiers, however. In any case, the d-c excitation had to be fed to the generator field through brushes and collector rings on the generator shaft. With the development of silicon diodes to the point where they could withstand the stresses of rotating along with the generator shaft, it became possible to design an a-c generator with a self-contained excitation system (Fig. 13-28).

A small a-c generator is mounted on the shaft along with the rotating field of the main generator.   The d-c field of the exciter generator is stationary; it is supplied from a simple rectifier.   The a-c output of the exciter generator is fed to a bridge rectifier mounted on a rotating disk.   In turn, the d-c output of the rectifier is fed directly to the rotating fields of the main generator.   Adjustment of the main-generator field flux is ultimately accomplished by adjusting the stationary field of the exciter generator.   This is readily done either manually or automatically in this relatively low power circuit.   This system has been widely adopted for small generators and also for some very large ones.

Brushless Synchronous Motors.   The success of the brushless generator led to the development of the brushless synchronous motor.   Typical synchronous motors are very similar in construction to a-c generators; both had the necessity of supplying d-c excitation current to a rotating field.   The synchronous motor, however, had the additional problem of starting first as an induction motor and then having the d-c

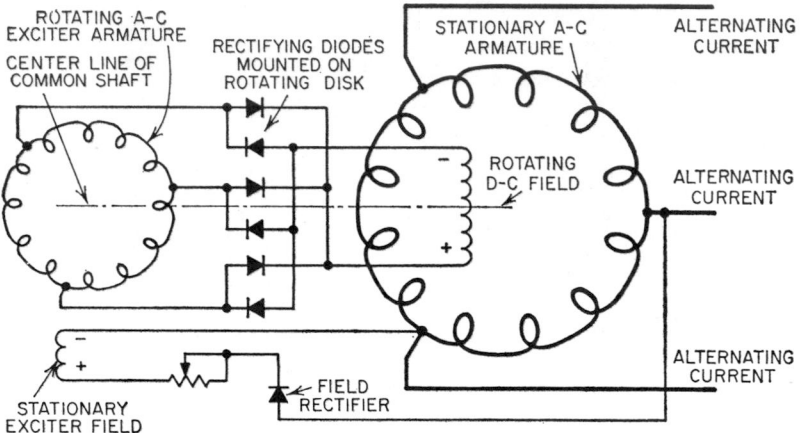

FIG. 13-28. Brushless generator has rectifying diodes mounted on a disk which rotates with main generator field and a-c exciter generator.   Field current is controlled by stationary exciter field.

excitation applied at a critical speed and position of the rotor so that the rotor would pull into synchronism.   These functions normally were accomplished with external relays.   What is more, a discharge resistor is required to absorb the energy stored in the d-c field when the field circiut is opened.   All these functions have now been built into the rotating member of the brushless synchronous motor.

One design of brushless synchronous motor is illustrated in Fig. 13-29.   It has an a-c generator and rotating rectifier essentially the same as that of the brushless generator.   In addition, there is a rotating discharge resistor and a relatively com-plicated solid-state control assembly.   Thyristors (SCR's) are used instead of con-tactors to apply and remove excitation.   These in turn are activated by the control circuit composed of transistors, zener diodes, etc.   The control circuit must provide the following functions: (1) ensure that the discharge path is closed during starting, but open this circuit when field excitation is applied; (2) apply field excitation at the proper rotor frequency and angle of the induced current, which is a measure of the rotor speed; (3) remove excitation immediately if the motor pulls out of synchronism for any reason.

Protective Relays and Trip Devices.   Circuit breakers for the protection of circuits above 600 volts are usually actuated by an auxiliary d-c tripping circuit on a signal derived from a protective relay.   Input to the protective relay comes from instrument transformers connected to the a-c circuit being protected.   Below 600 volts, the circuit breaker does not ordinarily have auxiliary tripping power but has a tripping device (series trip) through which all or a definite part of the a-c power-circuit current flows. Until recently, all these devices were of an electromechanical or thermal-element character.

Protective relays have been made with a great variety of modification to perform many functions. Several of these types are now available as solid-state devices. Inputs to the solid-state relays are always obtained from instrument transformers, so that the low voltage protective devices are essentially in the same form as the higher-voltage protective relays. A low-voltage protective relay is shown in Fig. 13-30. Adjustments are made by small dials. Internal components are totally enclosed and may be encapsulated in an insulating compound. Internal circuitry and principles of operation are entirely different from those of electromechanical or thermal devices.

Circuits consist of thyristors, transistors, diodes and resistors, capacitors, etc. Circuits must accurately measure the input quantities (current, voltage, etc.) and provide timing with respect to these quantities so that the protective relay will have a desirable and dependable time-vs.-current characteristic curve. One of the great advantages of solid-state relays is that they can be designed for almost any time-current characteristic desired. Characteristics of today's solid state relays are

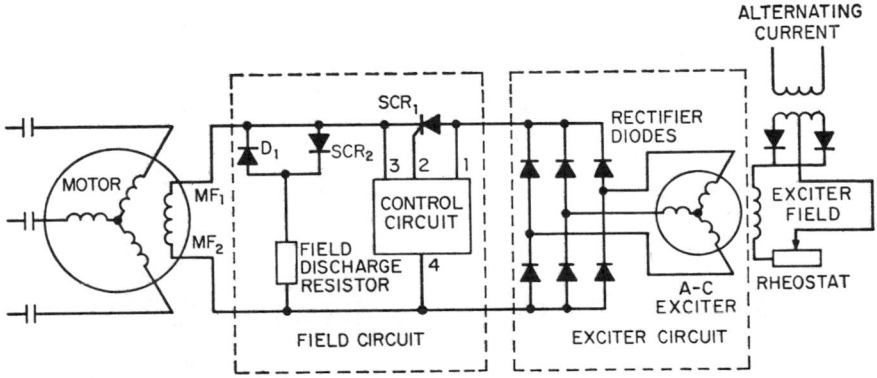

FIG. 13-29. Brushless synchronous motor uses an a-c generator with rectifier diodes to supply d-c excitation. Field discharge resistor and motor excitation control are also mounted on motor shaft.

usually a compromise which will permit them to coordinate best with existing protective relays and fuses.

Controls. Solid-state devices have largely taken over industrial controls except for contactors with requirements beyond the power capabilities of today's thyristors. (For special applications where the cost can be justified, solid-state contactors with capabilities of 40 kw or more are already available.) Solid-state controls appear in three areas: (1) in place of the more familiar electron-tube controls; (2) in place of electromechanical control devices; (3) as adaptations of computers.

As a replacement for vacuum tubes, usually the circuit is completely redesigned to fit the new components, although the electronic principles of the different circuits described in Chap. 5, Sec. 7 remain unchanged. In some cases, solid-state components or subcircuits may be directly substituted for electron tubes (Fig. 13-31). Reliability is one of the major reasons control manufacturers have been adopting solid-state devices instead of electronic tubes. Failures are fewer, and since solid-state devices do not wear out, neglect of routine maintenance is less likely to be reflected in failure. Size of solid-state devices is much smaller, and watt loss (with consequent heating) much less. A vacuum tube amplifier, for example, which dissipates about 65 watts of heat can be replaced with a solid-state amplifier which dissipates only about 8 watts of heat.

Solid-state relays have taken the place of electromechanical relays in many applications. Often a number of complicated relaying or switching operations can be built into a single small module. In industrial control today, solid-state devices may be used in conjunction with electromechanical control devices, depending on which best suits the particular function. It is well to be on the lookout for some solid-state components in apparatus that is not essentially solid-state in character.

Process control computers are taking over an increasing number of plant operations, and these have become largely solid-state. Following on this development, the transducers or sensing devices for the input variables, such as temperature, pressure, level, etc., are becoming solid-state devices. Typical of the latest transducers are those converting the measured quantities to a low-power d-c output suited for use with d-c switchboard instruments, null-balance indicators, and recorders. In similar fashion, electrical quantities such as frequency, a-c watts, power factor, and a-c voltage and current are transduced to direct current for use with indicating instruments and direct-acting recorders.

Fig. 13-30. Solid-state overcurrent trip device actuates low-voltage circuit breakers. (*Courtesy of Allis-Chalmers Manufacturing Co.*)

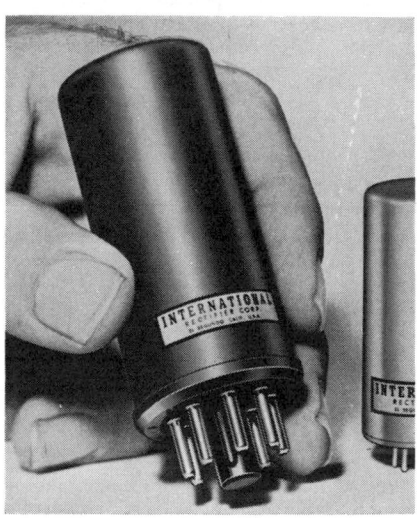

Fig. 13-31. Some solid-state control elements are mounted on bases which directly replace electron tubes. (*Courtesy of International Rectifier Corp.*)

MAINTENANCE OF SOLID-STATE APPARATUS

Inspection. Solid-state devices do not wear out in the same sense as mechanical parts or electron tubes. They have a small incidence of failure because of undisclosed defects; but if adequately protected, solid-state components have an extremely long life. Power equipment, however, requires some cooling means. Fans are used for air cooling in medium-power ranges, while water cooling of higher-rated equipment involves pumps. It is these conventional components which are subject to mechanical wear and need regular attention. A scheduled inspection of the equipment cooling system is required. A common recommendation by manufacturers is that filters on air-cooled units should be checked at least once a week and clogged filters replaced. Similarly, if the equipment is water-cooled, the system should be inspected weekly for leaks or signs of corrosion in cooling-system piping.

Solid-state power equipment should be shut down once a year for a careful inspection of components and cleaning if necessary. Dust and dirt, which may be conducting and cause short circuits, or which may thermally insulate heat sinks and cause overheating, should be carefully removed.   More frequent inspections may be indicated, or special precautions should be taken to prevent dust from entering the equipment.

Be on the lookout for signs of overheating at connections.   Fuses should be checked to make sure they are tight in their holders; if bolts are used to fasten the fuses in place, check the tightness of the bolts.   Indicator lights that are normally off, as well as protective devices such as air-flow relays, water-flow relays, and overtemperature relays, should be checked to make sure they will operate.

Control devices require only visual inspection to make sure that they are clean and have unobstructed ventilation and that the cards are properly secured in place by their plugs or connectors.

Electrical Protection.   While solid-state devices are mechanically rugged, they are sensitive to abnormal electric disturbances.   Having limited thermal capacity, they have very specific overload ratings which cannot be exceeded.   It is essential that solid-state equipment have adequate electrical protection.   Protective components are built into solid-state apparatus along with the diodes, thyristors, etc., to protect them against incoming power-line surges, switching transients, motor transient voltages, transformer inrush surges, etc.   Reactors, capacitors, and resistors are used to

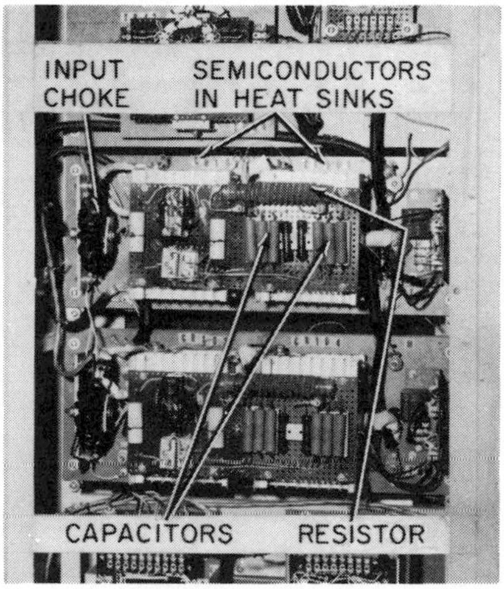

FIG. 13-32. Diodes and thyristors are used in combination with components intended to protect them from abnormal conditions. (*Courtesy of General Electric Co.*)

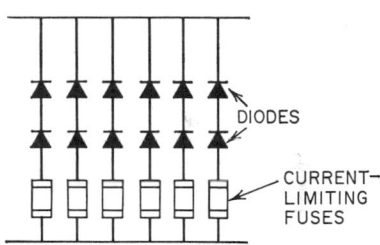

FIG. 13-33. Diodes are connected in series to get required voltage ratings of equipment, and in parallel to produce necessary current. A current-limiting fuse is included in every series group.

limit current and voltage surges (Fig. 13-32).   Surge suppressors, especially designed for the purpose and frequently employing selenium rectifiers because of their "healing" property (page 7-247) are also used.   The surge suppressor is designed not to conduct at normal voltages and does not affect the semiconductor with which it is connected in parallel; but when a higher voltage is applied, the surge suppressor conducts current with very little resistance to its flow.   Thus, if there is a voltage transient or surge that approaches or exceeds the limit of the silicon device, the suppressor will effectively clip or limit the surge and shunt it from the semiconductor device.

Overtemperature protection is incorporated to shut down the equipment or to sound an alarm should the cooling system fail.   Temperature-sensing or air-flow relays are used with air-cooled systems, while water-cooled units usually have water-pressure and water-temperature relays.

If they fail, silicon devices usually fail as a short circuit.   Since several cells are in parallel to get the required current capacity, the failed cell shorts out the others.   The parallel groups are likely to be in series with other groups, and the latter probably will be destroyed by the increased voltage placed across them (Fig. 13-33).

For these reasons it is essential that the failed cell be removed from the circuit as quickly as possible. Special current-limiting fuses, which open in a fraction of a cycle, are connected in series with each cell. When a cell fails, it blows the fuse, and this is registered by an indicating light. Much of today's solid-state power equipment is designed to operate continuously at reduced power capacity with one or two failed cells. If the reduced capacity is taken into consideration, the equipment can be kept running until repair parts are obtained or until a convenient shutdown can be scheduled.

Troubleshooting. Failure of semiconductors in power equipment is usually easy to locate by individual indicators; where a general alarm is used (or, rarely, none is provided), the condition of current-limiting fuses should be checked with an ohmmeter or a flashlight continuity tester. Diodes and thyristors may also be checked in this

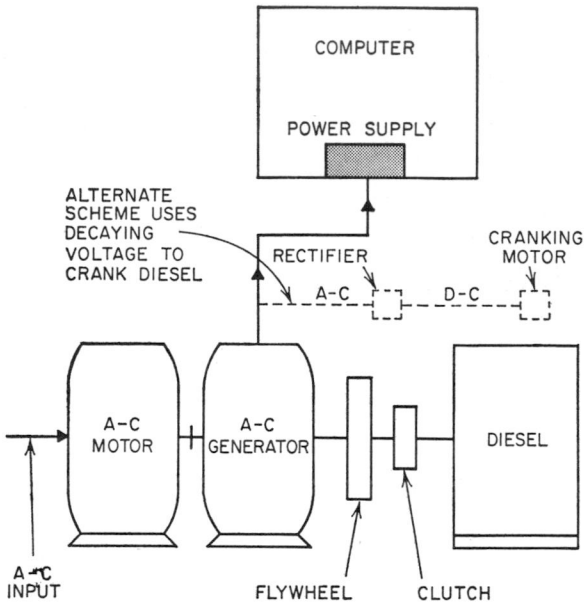

FIG. 13-34. This buffer set has flywheel to provide uninterrupted power to critical computer load.

manner to find out if they are shorted, but be careful not to include the gate or control lead, since even low voltages may damage a thyristor at this point. Special diode and thyristor testers are available; where a plant uses a large number of silicon devices such testers are a good investment.

New thyristors or diodes must be installed carefully, with special attention to their connection to the heat sink. Use of a silicone grease between the device base and the heat sink (but not on the threads) is often recommended. A torque wrench with a special socket to allow for the leads should be used to tighten the silicon devices in the heat sinks to the torque specified by the device manufacturer. Fuses should be replaced by the type specified by the manufacturer; otherwise, they may fail to protect the equipment even though they have the same nominal rating.

Troubleshooting of solid-state control elements is frequently simplified by indicating lights or the use of plug-in test units. In other cases, voltages and wave shapes may be measured at conveniently located test points. Defective cards or subassemblies may then be quickly replaced with good ones. Most manufacturers recommend sending the faulty cards back to the factory for repair or replacement rather than attempting to locate the individual component which is giving trouble. In some cases, a particularly vulnerable component may be located on the card in a position where you can easily test and replace it. If your plant has a skilled electronics technician in its employ, you may want to make repairs to cards and sub-assemblies. Such work should be performed on a test bench with specific test setups and should not be attempted at the equipment site.

Additional Protection. Transients and surges originate on utility systems, in your own and neighboring plants, which have not been recognized in the past because their low energy content did not affect existing equipment. Solid-state power equipment and the simpler kinds of controls are now usually adequately protected by the built-in devices we have discussed. Computers and some of the more elaborate control equipment may need additional protection from power-system transients. One important and relatively simple measure is to provide a separate shielded ground connection for sensitive equipment. It is also helpful to have such equipment fed off its own separate transformer.

Simple measures in a few difficult cases do not prove sufficient to exclude power-system transients. In such cases it is necessary to interpose motor-generator sets or batteries to isolate the sensitive equipment from the line. Isolating or "buffer" sets may combine a feature to give uninterrupted power should the normal power system fail. This is often a requirement where sensitive electronic controls are used, since the process is likely to be a critical one. Figure 13-34 shows a continuous-power set with an internal-combustion engine and a flywheel. The flywheel rotates continuously, its inertia storing mechanical energy. Should the power supply fail, the flywheel continues to drive the load and at the same time cranks the engine. The engine starts up quickly and carries the load before the energy of the flywheel is sufficiently reduced to cause a serious dip in the generator output.

Determining the nature of the troublesome transients is likely to be a difficult job; more often than not the trouble can be eliminated, or bypassed with a buffer set, without knowing the exact nature or cause of the transient. Instruments exist today which can analyze a great many power-system transients, but not all. Frequently the equipment manufacturer will investigate the problem and suggest a solution without charge. The remedy, such as modifying the electric distribution system or providing a buffer set, will then be at your expense.

Section 8

MAINTENANCE OF MECHANICAL EQUIPMENT

Chapter 1

PLAIN BEARINGS

By W. N. Goldenbogen
Manager, Material Quality
Cleveland Graphite Bronze
Division of Clevite Corporation
Cleveland, Ohio

DESIGN

Materials. Plain bearings, or sleeve bearings, are designed to support rotating or oscillating shafts and at the same time protect them from damage. The ideal bearing offers low friction, low journal wear, conformability, and embedability. During abnormal operating conditions the bearing metal should yield rather than damage or distort the shaft. Observation of this "yielding" should indicate to the operator or mechanic that unusual conditions exist. This should be a warning sign to investigate thoroughly and make minor repairs or adjustments before costly maintenance becomes necessary.

Designers, machinists, and metallurgists have combined their efforts to improve bearing performance. Refinements in materials, manufacturing methods, tolerances, and lubricants have increased the life and capacity of bearings.

Chief among design factors are materials, loads, size, tolerances, temperature, and lubrication. Except for load-carrying capacity, the well-known "white" metals, tin-base and lead-base babbitt, are still the best all-around bearing metals. Where size is no limitation and unit loads can be kept low (2,000 psi maximum), these metals have operated on shafts with hardnesses as low as 170 Brinell. With increased power ratings from smaller machines, the increased loading has demanded bearings with greater load capacity. Bronzes, copper-leads, cadmium-base, aluminum-base, and silver have been developed to meet this need. Some surface qualities have been sacrificed to boost the fatigue resistance (load capacity), and a corresponding increase in shaft hardness has been required. Plated overlays of lead- or tin-base material have been used in the range of 0.001 in. thick to improve the surface action of the bronzes and silver. The fatigue life of babbitt increases as the thickness drops below 0.008 in. (see Fig. 1-1). Automotive bearing thicknesses are 0.002 to 0.004 in. today. The use of these thin MICRO* layers is not practical where conditions of dirt or wear may expose the steel backing.

Loads. Modern bearing design demands that bearing loads be accurately determined. After due consideration to inertia, deflection, distortion, shaft whip, radial loads, and shaft speeds, it is possible to select a bearing material and a suitable bearing area that can be expected to perform satisfactorily. Figure 1-2 gives some idea of the relative load-carrying capacity of several typical bearing materials.

* Registered trade-mark of Clevite Corp.

Tolerances.   After selection of a suitable bearing material, attention is given to establishing dimensional tolerances.   Permissible variations in the automotive field are listed in Tables 1-1 through 1-5.

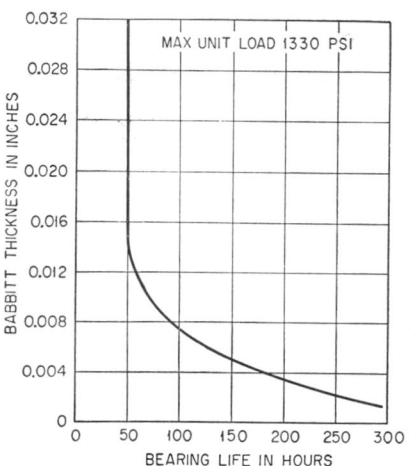

Fig. 1-1. Bearing life vs. babbitt thickness.

Lubrication.   To make any bearing perform with maximum life requires adequate lubrication.   Not only should the supply of oil be maintained, but also an oil of proper viscosity should be used.   A weight of oil that will provide a liquid film and consume the least amount of power is normally selected.   Usually the equipment manufacturer makes a recommendation for the grade of lubricant to be used.   The ideal design will provide for a large enough volume of oil to keep the bearing reasonably cool.   The volume of oil to be pumped is a function of the temperature rise and will determine the size of the grooves and clearances.   A temperature rise of 60°F is considered a safe figure for satisfactory operation.

Grooving.   Grooving design is important to the operation of plain bearings because it distributes the lubricant from the point of entry to the places where it is needed. The edges of the axial grooves must be well blended to avoid shearing of the oil film on the sharp corners.   Properly designed grooves prevent lubricant leakage from the ends of the bearing.   Introduction of the oil ahead of the highly loaded area is essential to

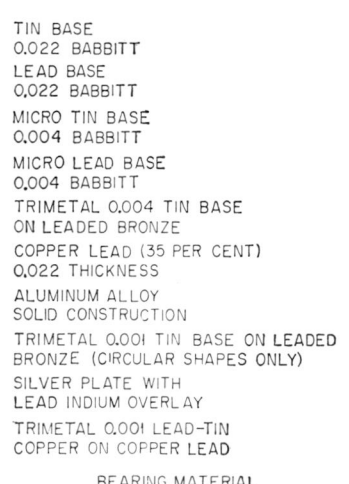

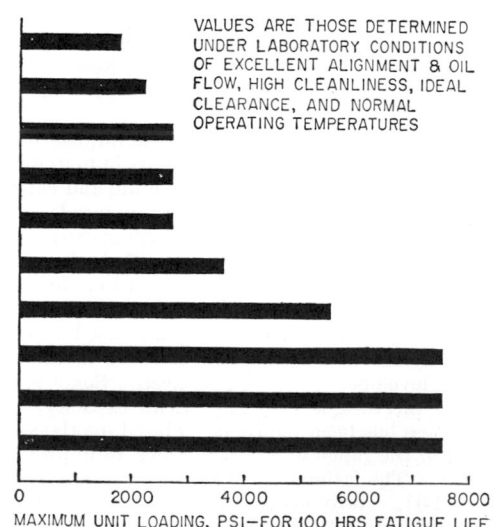

Fig. 1-2. Relative load-carrying capacity.

the development and maintenance of a hydraulic film to separate moving surfaces. Figures 1-3 through 1-7 show examples of grooving design.

CARE AND MAINTENANCE

Lubricant.   Selection of lubricants for modern complex machinery should not be done entirely on a dollars-and-cents basis.   The least expensive oils may eventually cost the most.   Nor will high-priced oils provide the greatest protection against break-down.   Usually the equipment manufacturer has decided which of the many additives are required for any particular condition.   For maintenace purposes it is necessary only to see that the recommended lubricants are properly applied.   By this we

Table 1-1. Case Tolerances

Bore tolerance:
    0.001 in. up to 10-in. bore
    0.002 in. over 10-in. bore
Taper tolerance:
    0.0002 in. up to 1-in. length
    0.0004 in. 1 to 2-in. length
    0.0005 in. over 2-in. length
Out-of-round tolerance:
    0.001 in. max. allowed if horizontal is larger than vertical
Alignment:
    Alignment bar with diameter 0.0005 to 0.00075 in. under low limit of case bore should turn freely with the use of small lever when cap bolts are properly torqued

mean that drain and replacement schedules are observed, filtration is provided if necessary, contamination is minimized, and operating temperatures are kept as low as possible.

The statement that a lubricant never wears out may be true.   However, in many cases, before the lubricant has a chance to wear out, it has been contaminated with

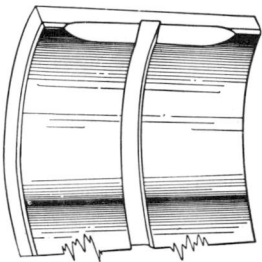

Fig. 1-3. Spreader groove and chamfer at parting line.

Fig. 1-4. Chamfer at parting line.

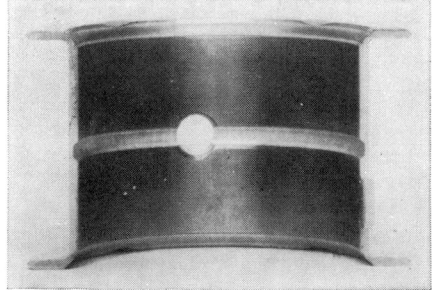

Fig. 1-5. Main bearing oil groove and hole.

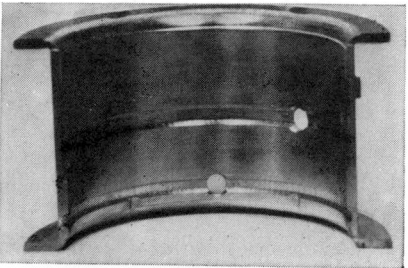

Fig. 1-6. Grooving in main bearing.

foreign material (water, metal chips, abrasive particles, or acidic organic compounds) which will cause wear or loss of bearing material.   Changing the lubricant becomes necessary to remove these potential sources of bearing wear and destruction.

Cleanliness.   The life of a lubricant can be extended by continuous removal of contaminants (filtration) and good housekeeping to exclude dirt and water.   Such items as air filters, clean lubricant containers or transfer equipment, and tightly fitting covers on oil reservoirs are important.

Temperature. In addition to the maintenance of the lubricant, there are at least two other precautions which can be observed in bearing operations. They are temperature and pressure. High temperatures rob bearing materials of their strength (Fig. 1-8). High temperatures (above 275°F) also promote rapid breakdown of lubricants to form sludges or corrosive compounds. Temperature control of bearings therefore becomes an important factor in their life. By suitable means, either a temperature gage at the bearing or in the oil or by feeling, the temperature of a bearing should be determined at frequent intervals. If an abnormally hot bearing is discovered, some means must be found to cool it immediately. If necessary, shut down the machinery.

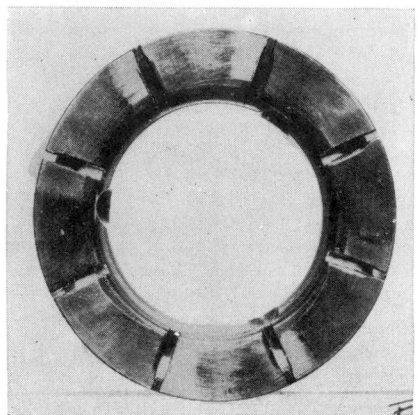

FIG. 1-7. Thrust face tapered lands.

Pressure. When pressurized lubrication systems are used, a normal operating pressure is established. A frequent look at the pressure gage will reveal any great variation from this normal value. Either an abnormally high or low pressure can be a danger signal. If a pump or line fails, lubrication of a part will be impaired and dangerous conditions may develop. On the other hand, the oil flow may be restricted. Although the gage reading may be high, the flow of lubricant may be

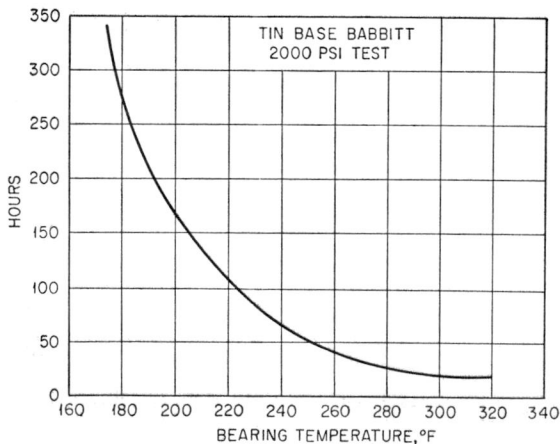

FIG. 1-8. Temperature vs. fatigue life.

inadequate to prevent trouble. Investigate these conditions, and take corrective measures immediately.

INSPECTION AND RECONDITIONING

When it becomes necessary to dismantle a bearing, certain precautions should be observed. It is extremely important to mark or identify each part so that when the machinery is reassembled, it can be installed in its original position. The matching of parts during the original (breakin) period makes them unfit for operation in other positions.

Journal. Examination of the parts of a bearing can be a valuable source of information for the immediate trouble and for averting possible future difficulty. If the journal surfaces are excessively worn, ridged, or scored, the shaft must be reground for further service. For minimum specifications of a shaft to continue in service see Table 1-2.

Table 1-2. Automotive Shaft Tolerances

Diameter tolerance:
  0.0005 in. up to $1\frac{1}{2}$-in. journal
  0.001 in. $1\frac{1}{2}$ up to 10-in. journal
  0.002 in. for over 10-in. journal
Taper tolerance:
  0.0002 in. up to 1 in. of length
  0.0004 in. 1 up to 2 in. of length
  0.0005 in. for over 2 in. of length
Hourglass or barrel shape:
  Same as taper tolerance
Out-of-round condition:
  0.0005 in. up to 5 in. diameter
  0.001 in. for over 5 in. diameter
Maximum misalignment:
  Main journals 0.0015 in.
  Crank pins—parallel with main journals within 0.001 in. in 6 in.
End clearances:

Shaft diameter:	Shaft end clearance:
2–$2\frac{3}{4}$ in.	0.004–0.006 in.
$2\frac{13}{16}$–$3\frac{1}{2}$ in.	0.006–0.008 in.
$3\frac{1}{2}$–5 in.	0.008–0.010 in.
Over 5 in.	0.009–0.013 in.

Shaft journal finish:
  20 microinch or better is desirable

Table 1-3. Connecting Rod Tolerances

Diameter:
  0.0005 in. up to $3\frac{1}{4}$ in. diameter
  0.001 in. $3\frac{1}{4}$–10 in. diameter
  0.002 in. over 10 in. diameter
Taper, hourglass, or barrel shape:
  0.0002 up to 1 in. length
  0.0004 in. 1–2 in. length
  0.0005 in. over 2 in. length
Out of round:
  0.001 in. max. if rod is larger horizontally than vertically
Parallelism and twist:
  0.001 in. max. in 6 in.

Out-of-roundness is checked by taking readings at 45° intervals around the journal diameter. A comparison of the readings will reveal the need for regrinding. Excessive journal taper, barrel or hourglass shape will be indicated by variable-diameter readings in a straight line along the length of the journal. Further, to inspect a shaft having several journals, set the shaft on V blocks and check the alignment with a dial indicator.

If the shaft is to be used without reconditioning, it should be thoroughly cleaned including oil passages. Also, carefully measure the diameters of the journals, because these values will be used to select the size of the replacement bearings that will provide the proper oil clearance.

Surface areas of a reground shaft are made up of a series of tiny, sharp ridges. These are created by the cutting action of the abrasive grains on the face of the grinding wheel. Although these ridges are scarcely detectable, they present an unsatisfactory surface which will cause excessive bearing wear unless the roughness is reduced by a finishing operation. For final polishing, set the shaft in V blocks and polish off the ridges with a fine emery cloth and light machine oil, using a reciprocating motion. Some prefer to place the shaft in a lathe and polish while the shaft rotates in the *same direction* as it would *in an engine.*

All fillets should be checked to ensure against interference with the ends of the bearings. The conditioned shaft should be thoroughly washed, and all oil passages cleaned.

Connecting Rods. If connecting rods are involved, two conditions require checking: parallelism and twist (see Table 1-3). The rod bore and piston pin should be

FIG. 1-9. Edge loading has caused fatigue at upper edge of bearing.

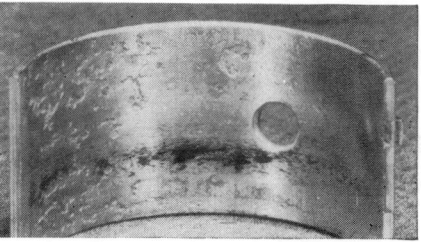

FIG. 1-10. Condition of bearing surface resulting from fatigue.

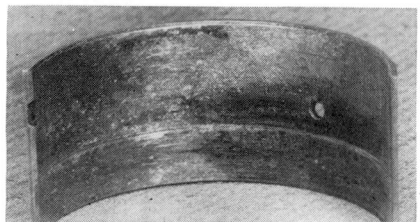

FIG. 1-11. Result of high temperatures caused by dirt.

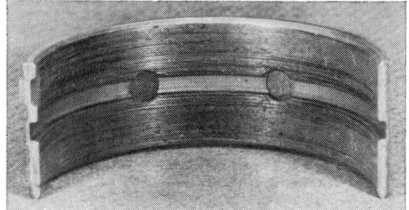

FIG. 1-12. Scoring caused by circulating hard particles.

parallel within 0.001 in. in 6 in. A bent rod will cause an uneven distribution of load on the bearing area, forcing the piston skirt out of parallel with the cylinder bore. This will result in uneven and excessive bearing wear, piston-ring wear, and out-of-round cylinder wear.

Twist in a rod should also be limited to 0.001 in. in 6 in. Out-of-roundness beyond 0.001 in. for rod and main bores causes variation in oil clearance. A maximum out-of-round rod should never be matched with a maximum out-of-round shaft. Bore finish must be smooth enough (80 microinches) to ensure proper bearing contact and heat transfer.

Bearing Replacement. The usual practice is to replace or renew the bearing surfaces at the time of overhaul. However, there may be times and conditions under which it is not necessary to do so. The condition of the bearings must be evaluated and compared with the cost of a subsequent overhaul. If the bearings are not worn, fatigued, or damaged in any way and all the applicable tolerances are within established limits (consult manufacturer's service manual), it is not necessary to replace the parts.

Many teardowns reveal the bearings to be ready for renewal or replacement. Such evidence as wear, edge loading (Fig. 1-9), fatigue (Fig. 1-10), embedment (Fig. 1-11), scoring (Fig. 1-12), lack of clearance (Fig. 1-13), hourglass journal damage (Fig. 1-14), without a doubt calls for replacement or renewal of the bearings. After the journals have been examined or repolished, the job of selecting or fitting the bearings to the

shaft is begun.   It is advisable to follow the manufacturer's original equipment specifications for bearing materials and running clearances.

FIG. 1-13. Wiping caused by insufficient clearance.

FIG. 1-14. Fatigue caused by hourglass journal.

REASSEMBLY

Crush.   It is of utmost importance that the bearing inserts have good contact with
the housing or seat.   To assure this, the diameter of the two inserts at right angles to
the parting line when placed together is slightly greater than the diameter across the
parting surface when the bearing is in place, thus requiring this amount to be compressed when the bearing is drawn up tight.   For example, each half shell is made
slightly in excess of an exact half circle.   The excess is called crush (see Fig. 1-15),

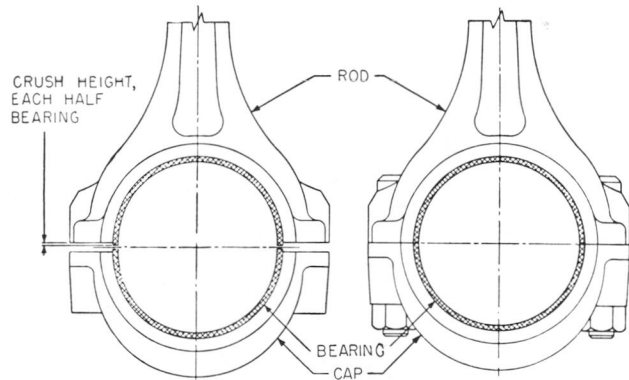

FIG. 1-15. Diagrammatic illustration of bearing crush.

and its purpose is to permit the shell to be firmly clamped in the bearing seat.   If the
bearing does not have the proper amount of crush, it will not be held securely and will
have a slight degree of movement during operation.
    Loose inserts also will allow oil to work in between the back of the bearing and the
housing.   This cuts down the heat conductivity and tends to raise the bearing temperature.   Also, a certain amount of flexing of the insert will take place, which adds
to the normal friction heat and under retarded rate of heat transfer will lead to a premature bearing failure due to overheating.
    Insufficient crush can be due either to filing of the parting surfaces of the shells or to
the presence of dirt and foreign matter between the parting faces of the bearings and
bearing cups.   The dirt will act as shims to prevent the faces from coming together
as they should.   Under no circumstances are the parting surfaces of the bearing insert,

the cap or shank, or the saddle to be filed. In assembling the bearing, be absolutely sure that no dirt, nicks, or burrs remain upon the parting faces of either the cap or saddle.

Do not attempt any operation on the bearing insert other than correcting the spread, and this only when necessary. The spread (see Table 1-4) is built into the bearings so

Table 1-4. Spread

Free spread (width across the open ends):
Main bearings—crankcase bore plus 0.005–0.020 in. depending on the thickness and structural stiffness of the bearing

Table 1-5. Recommended Oil Clearances

Bearing oil clearances:
The general rule for the size of the oil clearance for pressure lubricated bearings is to allow 0.001 in. for each inch of journal diameter, subject to modification according to the bearing metal alloy used

Bearing alloy	Shaft diameters	
	2–$2\frac{3}{4}$ in.	$2\frac{13}{16}$–$3\frac{1}{2}$ in.
Lead and tin base babbitts....	0.0015–0.0025 in.	0.0025–0.0035 in.
Cadmium.................	0.002 –0.003 in.	0.003 –0.004 in.
Copper-lead...............	0.0025–0.0035 in.	0.0035–0.0045 in.

that the inserts have to be lightly pressed into place. If the parts have excessive spread, they can be tapped gently on the end to cause close-in. If they are too loose, the insert can be opened by placing on a wooden block with convex side up and tapping with a mallet.

Bolt Torque. On all service installations it is an absolute necessity to use recommended bolt torque values and a torque wrench (Fig. 1-16) when tightening the bearing nuts or cap screws. Almost all the engine builders perform their boring operations with the bolts torqued to the same specifications as recommended in their service

Fig. 1-16. Torque wrench.

manuals. It is well to remember that any variation in bolt torque may seriously affect the crankcase or rod-bore sizes, bearing crush, clearances, and resulting bearing performance.

Oil Clearance. The various bearing metals have individual requirements for oil clearances. A general rule for the amount of oil clearance for pressure-lubricated bearings is to allow 0.001 in. for each inch of shaft-journal diameter. Table 1-5 lists recommended oil clearances for bearing alloys and shaft sizes.

Measure Oil Clearance. The inside diameter of the bearing, in assembly, can be measured with inside micrometers if dial indicator bore gages are not available. The journal diameter is best measured with micrometers that read in ten-thousandths of an inch.

There are various practical methods for determining oil clearance. A material which will deform can be squeezed between the journal and the bearing with the cap bolts properly torqued (see Fig. 1-17). After removal of the cap, the flattened material is compared with a prepared chart and the tolerance can be read in thousandths directly from the chart. Several commercial items of this nature are available from automotive-parts manufacturers.

Fig. 1-17. Gaging oil clearance by means of plastic material.

An alternative method is the use of lead or brass shims whose thickness ranges are standardized. A shim of suitable thickness, shorter than the bearing and about ¼-in. wide, should, when clamped between the shaft and bearing, allow the shaft to turn easily. A shim 0.001 in. heavier than the required clearance should lock the shaft from rotation. This check requires experience and care to avoid damaging the bearing inserts, and it is made with all bearing caps loose except for the position under consideration. It is necessary to apply the correct torque to the clamping bolts. Extreme care must be used to eliminate false readings that can be caused by housing bore or journal misalignment. If out-of-roundness is found to exist, use the largest journal diameter, because minimum clearance is the critical condition.

End Clearance. Table 1-2 lists the recommended values of end clearances for various sizes of shafts. Checking this dimension is absolutely necessary, since the lack of clearance can easily cause thrust bearing failure. End movement can be measured by forcing the shaft in each direction and checking either with shims at the thrust faces or with an indicator on the flywheel face.

Final Checking. In all final assembly operations and after finished surfaces have been prepared, use the utmost care to exclude dirt, chips, and all foreign matter from bearing surfaces. If included in the assembly, these particles will damage the bearing and the journal by scoring and wearing during the initial revolutions of the engine. Excessive conditions of dirt have been known to cause almost immediate failure through wear and high temperatures due to friction.

Preliminary Lubrication. Another precaution is to flood the unit whenever possible with clean oil just prior to initial startup after the final assembly. This will provide temporary lubrication until the normal supply of oil is available through the lubrication system.

Free Rotation. If there is any doubt about the clearance and contact area between journals and bearings, it can be checked by manual rotation of the unloaded shaft. It must rotate freely. Any indication of binding must be traced, and its cause removed. The best way to make this check is with the block mounted on a stand. Assemble the shaft with a light, uniform coating of bluing on the journals, and after rotating the shaft a couple of revolutions, turn the block over and rotate the shaft again. The transfer of blue to the bearing shells will indicate alignment condition and causes for binding. Lack of contact on a bearing also means trouble. It could be excessive clearance, or it could be shaft and/or case bore misalignment. A suitable blue pattern covering 45 to 90° at the center of all bearings will predict good bearing performance. This check is also a good place to pick up evidence of hourglass journals, taper, shaft burrs, and fillet ride.

RENEWING CAST-BABBITT LINERS

Rebabbitting large cast-in-place bearings may be not only desirable but practical in maintaining bearings used in heavy stationary machinery. During the teardown, one should look for the usual signs of misalignment, uneven wear, lack of lubrication, excessive shaft wear, excessive dirt, and high temperatures so that an attempt can be made to correct these conditions during reassembly or in the method of operation after overhaul.

Reclamation of Housing.   Removal of the old babbitt liner can be done by heating the inside surface with a "buffalo" torch.   Use as low a temperature as possible to avoid distortion of the steel back.   Wiping the molten surface with a dry cloth will effectively remove all but a thin layer of the babbitt.   If the removal of the old babbitt can be accomplished without severe oxidation, the residual layer will serve as the bonding layer for the new babbitt.   The surface should be light golden or straw colored; otherwise do not attempt to flux and rebabbitt without further preparation.   If the remaining metal is brown or black colored or if there appear to be cracks in the surface, a light machine cut should be taken to expose sound metal of the steel shell.

For proper tinning, the steel surface must be chemically clean and slightly etched. Dip the whole shell into a hot (180°F) alkaline metal cleaner until no water breaks appear, which will indicate a clean surface.   After rinsing in clean running water, pickle the shell in 1 part water and 1 part muriatic acid at 160°F for 2 to 4 min or until the surface has a gray matted finish.   Remove from the acid, and rinse in clean water. Immerse the shell in soldering flux (commercial brands available) kept above 150°F. After removal from the flux, dip the shell into molten pure tin at approximately 550°F. Use caution when dipping the wet shell in the molten tin to avoid spattering of hot metal because of steam generation.   Wear safety clothing to protect from possible burns.   Allow the shell to remain in the tin pot long enough to approach the temperature of the tin.   The length of time required for this will depend on the mass of metal present.

To pour the babbitt, remove the shell from the tin bath and attach the heated core and end plates.   Immediately pour the heated babbitt (700 to 800°F) into the annular space between the core and shell.   Pour sufficient metal at one time to fill the entire space.   This will prevent lamination and segregation.   If at all possible, it is desirable to cool the shell quickly by quenching with water applied on the bottom side.   As soon as the babbitt has set, the assembly can be thoroughly cooled and knocked apart.

Determine the dimensions to which the bearing is to be machined by checking the journal size and making sure that its condition is satisfactory or by reconditioning it. Apply the manufacturer's recommendations for tolerances and grooving.   Use sound machining, locating, and measuring techniques.   The final cut should be made in such a manner that the best possible surface finish is obtained.

Precautions in checking clearances, alignment, lubrication, and cleanliness as described earlier are recommended.

Chapter 2

BALL AND ROLLER BEARINGS

By FRANK W. WELLONS
Chief Engineer
SKF Industries, Inc.
King of Prussia, Pa.

A primary requirement for satisfactory bearing performance in any type of machinery is to follow closely the maintenance procedures recommended by the original equipment manufacturer.   Further assistance on specific bearing problems is available from the nearest office of the bearing manufacturer; replacement bearings and considerable on-the-spot technical service can be readily obtained from local bearing distributors. As with all other critical mechanical parts, ball and roller bearings should be handled with the greatest possible care to avoid mechanical abuse and corrosion damage. They should be constantly protected from all forms of dirt or foreign matter that might dent or wear the highly polished surfaces of the balls, rollers, and races.

DESIGN

Cutaway sketches of typical ball, straight roller, ball thrust, and needle roller bearings are given in Fig. 2-1.   They show proper nomenclature for the various surfaces and components.   The most common types of ball and roller bearings are pictured in Fig. 2-2.

The great majority of bearing sizes have been standardized by the manufacturers to permit dimensional and functional interchangeability.   However, there is not complete uniformity of the bearing numbers for such interchangeable sizes.   The more popular ball and roller bearings are furnished in three basic sizes: light, medium, and heavy, which are numerically designed by most manufacturers as the 200, 300, and 400 series.   Generally, the bearing manufacturer will prefix the series size with additional coding to identify particular design features and to differentiate among his own lines of dimensionally similar ball and roller bearings.   The last two digits of the 200, 300, or 400 series number can be multiplied by 5 to determine the bearing bore in millimeters. Example: The 210 size would be a basic 200, i.e., light series bearing with a 50 mm ID.

The manufacturer will show additional suffixes and prefixes to the basis number to describe refinements in dimensional accuracy, retainer design, external shields or seals, internal clearance, and numerous other design features that have been found necessary for a particular application.   These design variations, when indicated on the machine builder's bill of material, are extremely important and should not be deviated from without his express approval.   If information on conversion to other competitive bearing makes is not readily available from the machine builder, it can be obtained from the local bearing distributor or from the bearing manufacturer.   In most cases the identification stamped or marked on the bearing parts will merely define dimensions and bearing type. The full identification is marked on the bearing carton. Consequently, extreme care should be taken to maintain bearing stocks in the original cartons, preferably unopened.

Shaft and Housing Fits. A basic rule in mounting antifriction bearings is that the bearing ring which rotates relative to the load should be mounted with an interference fit. The other ring, which is fixed relative to the load, can be loosely mounted. With a conventionally geared shaft supported by two bearings, where the gear load is fixed in space and the shaft rotates, the inner rings would be mounted with an interference

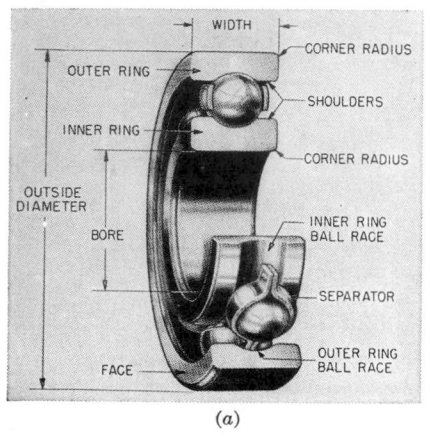

(a)

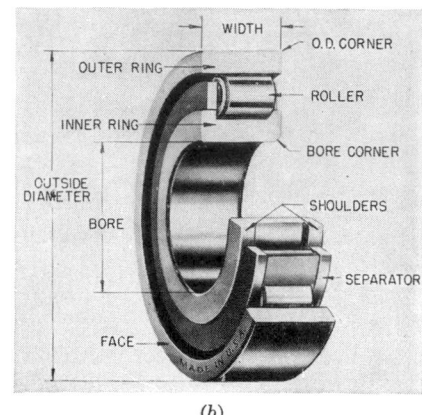

(b)

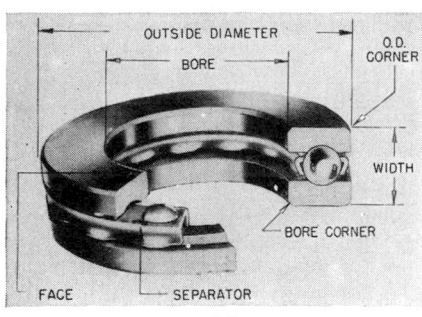

(c)

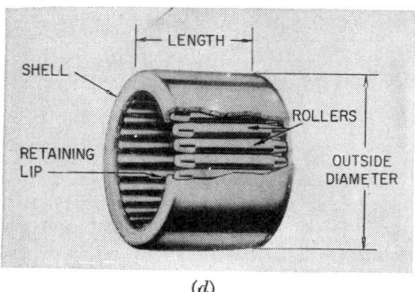

(d)

FIG. 2-1. Bearing parts and their names: (a) ball bearing, (b) straight roller bearing, (c) ball thrust bearing, (d) needle roller bearing.

fit on the shaft while the outers would be a slip fit in their housings. Conversely, with an automobile front wheel bearing, where the load is fixed relative to the ground and the inner ring is stationary on the axle, the rotating outer is pressed into the wheel hub and the inner is loose on the axle. The only means which can prevent creep of a bearing ring with a rotating load is to maintain an interference fit. Axial clamping of the ring will not prevent creep unless the clamping force is many times higher than the radial bearing load.

In some cases the operating conditions, in so far as direction of load and ring rotation is concerned, cannot be readily defined. In a machine with a high-speed rotor, the shaft bearings would support the rotor weight while a rotating force may develop owing to an unbalance of unknown magnitude. Depending on the relation between the rotating unbalance and the shaft weight, the resultant bearing loading may be either oscillating or rotating. To this resultant load an additional variable working load may sometimes be added to alter the operating conditions further. Thus, par-

BALL BEARINGS

*4. DUPLEX BEARINGS ARE SPECIALLY
   FACE GROUND FOR USE IN PAIRS

*5. SNAP RING BEARINGS ARE USED
   BOTH WITH AND WITHOUT SHIELDS

*6. SHIELDS MAY BE ON EITHER ONE
   OR BOTH SIDES

*7. SEALED BEARINGS MAY HAVE SEALS
   ON BOTH SIDES—ARE THEN WIDER

*9 & 10. MAGNETO AND FRONT WHEEL
   BEARINGS ARE SEPARABLE

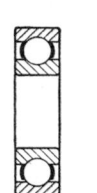 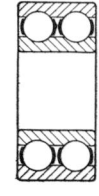 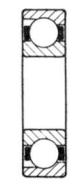 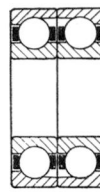

1. SINGLE ROW   2. DOUBLE ROW   3. RADIAL-THRUST   *4. DUPLEX

 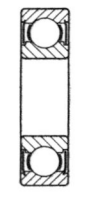 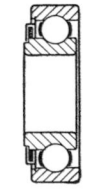 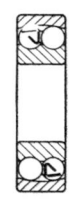 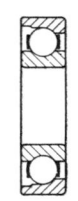 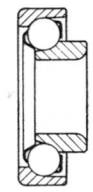 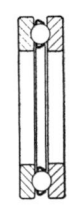

*5. SNAP RING   *6. SHIELDED   *7. SINGLE SEAL   8. SELF-ALIGNING   *9. MAGNETO   *10. FRONT WHEEL   11. BALL THRUST

ROLLER BEARINGS

*1, 2, 4, & 6. THESE BEARINGS ARE
   ALL SEPARABLE EITHER AS
   TO INNER OR OUTER RINGS

*8. IN SOME CASES NEEDLE BEAR-
   INGS MAY HAVE INNER RINGS
   WHICH ARE SEPARABLE

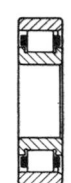 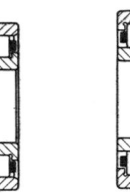 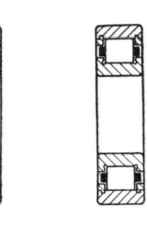 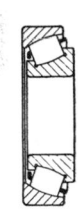

*1. STRAIGHT ROLLER SEPARABLE OUTER RING   *2. STRAIGHT ROLLER SEPARABLE INNER RING   3. STRAIGHT ROLLER NON-SEPARABLE   *4. BARREL ROLLER

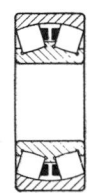 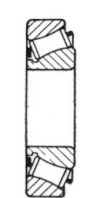 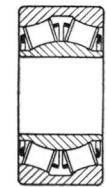 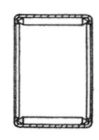

5. BARREL ROLLER DOUBLE ROW   *6. CONCAVE ROLLER   7. CONCAVE ROLLER DOUBLE ROW   *8. NEEDLE ROLLER

Fig. 2-2. Most common types of ball and roller bearings, except tapered roller.

ticularly in vertical machines where radial load due to the weight of the parts is eliminated, the direction of load may be difficult to determine. In choosing shaft and housing fits for such applications, it is customary to speak of the load direction as being indeterminate.

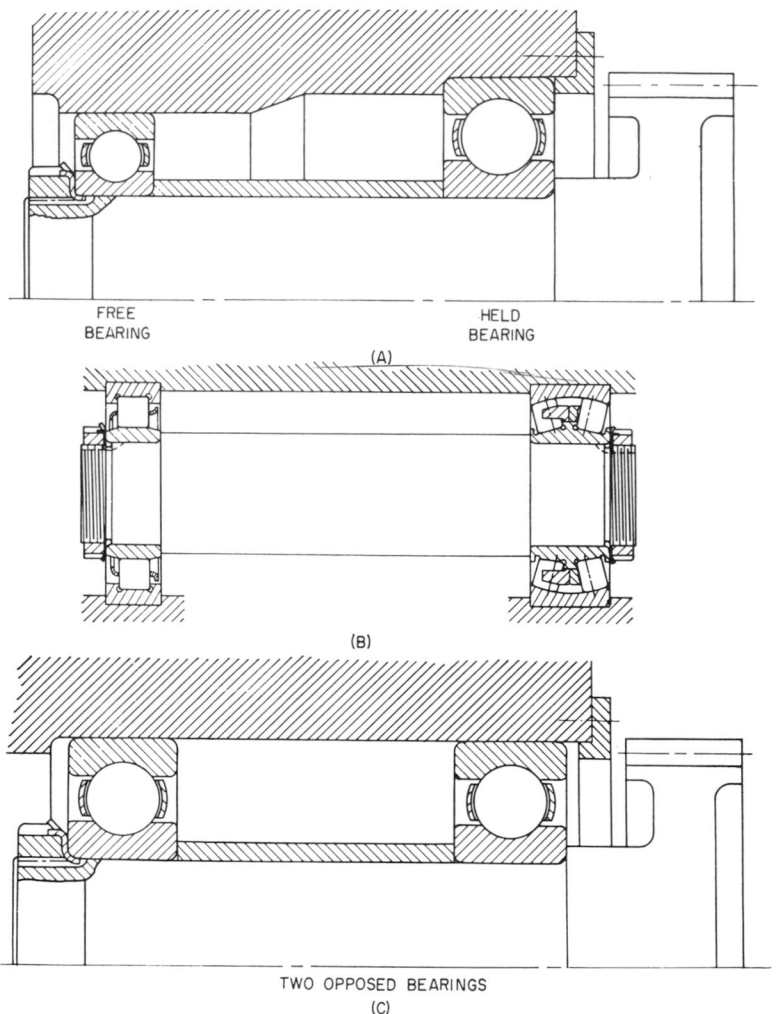

FIG. 2-3. Axial shaft locations: (*A*) one free and one held bearing, (*B*) roller bearing used for floating location; (*C*) opposed mounting of ball bearings.

When the load is indeterminate, creep of the bearing can be prevented only by interference fits both on the shaft and in the housing. For such cases, it is common practice to use a bearing with a greater than normal internal clearance. This is necessary because of the additional clearance loss due to both expansion of the inner and contraction of the outer. In other cases the manufacturer, through years of experience, has determined the optimum mounting practice and may mount one or both rings with a line-to-line fit, thus simplifying assembly and avoiding the necessity for bearings with special internal clearances. The equipment manufacturer's fitting practice should be carefully followed, and any evidence of smearing between the bearing and the shaft or housing should be immediately called to his attention.

When considering shaft and housing fits and their effect on bearing performance, the special case should be considered where a bearing is completely unloaded for certain intervals of operation.   Loose mounting fits should be avoided in such cases, even though the load while it is acting does not change direction in relation to one ring.   If the load on the ring is zero, the friction at the fit surface is also theoretically zero, and the ring can rotate owing to the higher friction moment within the bearing.   The tendency to slip might be further aggravated by lubricant drag, particularly at low temperature.

Axial Shaft Location.   When a shaft is mounted on ball or roller bearings, provision must be made for differential axial expansion of the shaft and housing due to temperature variation in service.   Furthermore, the shaft usually must be accurately positioned relative to its housing to maintain proper relation of the rotating parts.   The shaft can be located with one "held" and one "free" bearing, or the two bearings can

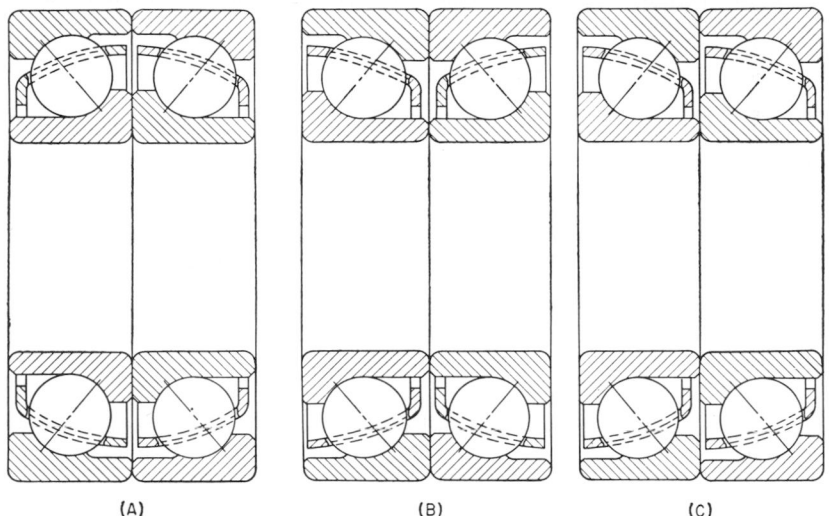

(A)   (B)   (C)

Fig. 2-4. Methods of mounting two flush-ground angular contact bearings: (A) face to face, (B) back to back, (C) tandem.

be mounted "opposed" (see Fig. 2-3).   In a held mounting, one bearing is axially locked on the shaft, generally between a shaft shoulder and a lock nut, and is located in its housing between closely fitted shoulders.   The opposite, or "free," bearing is locked on the shaft in the case of a rotating inner ring load, and its outer ring is loosely fitted in the housing without restraining shoulders.   Thus, the "free" bearing can slide axially in the housing to accommodate changes in length on the shaft.

As an outer ring fit sufficiently loose to assure slippage of the "free" bearing under all operating conditions might result in objectionable outer ring creep, a cylindrical roller bearing is often substituted for this location.   The outer ring of the roller bearing can be tightly fitted and axially held in its housing, and the necessary axial float obtained by using either an inner or outer ring that does not have restraining flanges (see Fig. 2-3B).

In an opposed mounting, Fig. 2-3C, both bearings are locked on the shaft and each loosely fitted outer ring is shouldered only on one side so that one bearing will carry the shaft thrust in one direction and the opposite bearing will carry the reverse thrust.

In an opposed application extreme care must be taken to maintain the proper relation between the housing shoulders and the shaft shoulders.   Generally the span between bearings is sufficiently close to eliminate any danger from extreme differential expansion.

Figure 2-4A shows a face-to-face "duplex" mounting of two flush-ground angular contact bearings.   These bearings are specially ground by the bearing manufacturer so that the corresponding faces of the inner and the outer rings will be flush with each other under a predetermined thrust load. In this case, the thrust load would be developed by clamping the two outer rings, which would create an opposing thrust load between the two bearings. Similar mountings can be developed with a back-to-back mounting, Fig. 2-4B, where the two bearings would be reversed and an internal preload created by clamping the inner rings together. For application purposes, a face-to-face or back-to-back preloaded pair can be considered a single bearing. Such bearings are used for very accurate axial shaft location, since the preloaded pair will have less axial and radial yield under load than a single bearing.

A third method of mounting angular contact bearings, Fig. 2-4C, is to stack two or more in tandem so that the face of one outer ring will be adjacent to the back of the next outer ring. Thus, all bearings in the stack will carry thrust in the same direction. Such mountings are used where a heavy thrust load must be carried in a limited space or where the speed is so high that a single bearing of adequate capacity would be operating at a dangerously high rpm.

OPERATING DIFFICULTIES

High Running Temperature. The most common cause for suspicion of bearing difficulty is a sudden or abnormal rise in the bearing temperature, which is generally detected by a rise in temperature of the housing parts immediately surrounding the bearing. A fairly well established rule of thumb is that the housing for a properly operating bearing will be warm to the touch, but not so hot as to be unbearable. This standard is not necessarily reliable for equipment of present-day manufacture, though a sudden rise or change in bearing temperature should be always considered an indication of possible bearing trouble. Modern machines are being developed with increasingly high bearing loads, with a corresponding increase in bearing speeds, and to operate with new lubricants of improved high-temperature properties. These application developments will permit a normal bearing running temperature upward of 200°F, though in cases of questionable bearing temperatures, the original equipment manufacturer should be immediately consulted.

Perhaps the most common reason for excessive bearing running temperatures is overlubrication. In the absence of more detailed guidance from the equipment manufacturer, the oil level in the bearing housing under nonrotating conditions should extend to the center of the lowest ball or roller. Similarly, with grease lubrication the bearing voids, plus one-quarter of the housing cavities, should be filled with lubricant.

Another important factor responsible for high running temperature is excessively tight shaft or housing fits, which tend to reduce the bearing internal clearance and preload the balls or rollers between the raceways. The shaft seat and housing bore should be accurately checked for diameter, taper, and roundness against the manufacturer's limits. In the case of overhauled machinery, care should be taken to use a replacement bearing of the same internal clearance as originally furnished with the equipment.

For a shaft supported by an opposed bearing mounting, abnormal bearing temperatures can develop from excessive preload caused by improper assembly or from insufficient housing shoulder clearance to accommodate unequal axial shaft and housing expansion (see Fig. 2-5).

When the shaft is supported by a "held" bearing and one or more "free" bearings, the mounting for the floating races should be checked to ensure that axial float is not restricted by too tight a fit or by surface pickup between the ring and shaft or housing.

In the case of preloaded angular-contact ball bearings as described in Fig. 2-4, which are flush-ground under a specified thrust load by the bearing manufacturer, the substitution of bearings with different preload, i.e., flush-ground under a different thrust load, can cause increased bearing running temperature.

A misalignment of the shaft or housing will cause the individual balls in a bearing to follow an uneven path in the inner and outer ring raceways. This skidding across the race groove and in the cage pocket will generate excessive friction heat, and, in addition to a temperature warning, will generally result in severe cage distress.

Inasmuch as the bearing running temperature is generally judged by the temperature of the surrounding housing, friction-type seals and any other rubbing surfaces adjacent to the bearing should be thoroughly examined before changes are made in bearing selection or mounting.

Noise, Vibration, or Rough Running. Any of the factors discussed above as possible causes for excessive bearing temperature might also become apparent as a noticeable change in noise level. Assembly damage can brinell the balls into the raceways sufficiently to create a rough running bearing, or the same effect can be created through overload when the shaft is not rotating. Very similar raceway denting, defined as "false brinelling," results from mechanical wear between the balls and the raceways due to minute vibration when the shaft is not rotating. A noisy bearing can result from the passage of foreign matter between the balls and grooves and quite often from

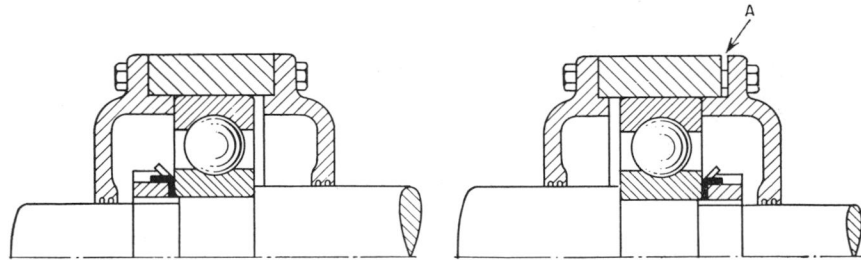

FIG. 2-5. Preload due to incorrect mounting (bearings pinched by improper shaft and housing shoulder distances as at *A*).

the entrapment of fragments created by the failure of a gear or another bearing located in the same area. High-speed starts with insufficient or congealed lubricant may cause local skidding at the ball or roller contacts which will become apparent as bearing noise and eventually as a premature fatigue failure of the running surfaces.

BEARING EXAMINATION

Fatigue Failure. An effectively protected and well-lubricated ball or roller bearing will operate indefinitely until repeated stresses initiate subsurface cracks which develop into spalling of the loaded surfaces. The first signs of spalling, which are generally detectable by noisy operation, denote the end of the useful life of the bearing. When a fatigue failure occurs, the bearing should be immediately replaced, as the flaking will progress rapidly, throwing metal fragments into the lubrication system and causing eventual shaft seizure.

Extensive laboratory endurance tests and years of service experience have shown an appreciable dispersion in the individual lives of a group of bearings operating under identical loads and speeds. Consequently, the lives of individual bearings in a battery of similar machines will show considerable variation, and the failure of one bearing is not cause for mass replacement of all other bearings of the same size and identical application. Normal design practice is to select a bearing size such that 90 per cent of all bearings installed in the identical application for a particular machine will still be in service at a life consistent with the expected performance for the other machine components. Premature fatigue failures can be caused by bearing overload resulting from alterations to the machine construction or from a more severe operating cycle than recommended by the machine builder. When such changes are contemplated, the affected bearings should be studied on the basis that the fatigue life in hours will vary inversely with the rpm and inversely with the third power of the load.

Lubrication Distress. A bearing operating with inadequate lubrication will show heat discoloration and metal smearing, particularly at the contact with the retainer pockets; this is generally associated with a hard carbonized deposit that is unaffected by normal cleaning solvents. Also, extended operation with limited or insufficient lubrication can cause surface distress at the race contacts, which rapidly progresses to open cracks and eventual spalling of the raceways. Such failures have an appearance very similar to a conventional fatigue failure.

Care should be taken in selecting a bearing lubricant to ensure that the oil or grease will have adequate physical characteristics to lubricate and to protect the bearing for the full range of operating temperature.

Wear. An antifriction bearing should not wear unless dirt or abrasive foreign matter gets into it. If allowed to get into a bearing, such foreign matter will mix with the grease or oil and form a lapping compound which will quickly wear down the rolling elements and distort the geometry of the inner and the outer raceways. For certain applications, bearings are furnished by the manufacturer with a looser than normal internal clearance; therefore, what may seem to be excessive internal freedom should not be the sole reason for condemning a service bearing. Where excessive wear has taken place, the balls and raceways will clearly show a frosted or worn appearance that is quite different from the ground surfaces of a new bearing.

Corrosion. Any used bearing will show some signs of contact on the raceways and usually some surface staining, particularly on the external areas. Such bearings can generally be reused, though considerable judgment should be exercised in screening questionable service bearings, as the cost of a replacement is generally insignificant in terms of downtime and labor costs for an operating failure. In general, corrosion staining can be ignored on all surfaces, while pits on the critical rolling surfaces that cannot be readily felt with a dull-pointed scriber (i.e., such as the ball of a ball-point pen in the case of small bearings for critical applications) should not be cause for rejection. More liberal standards can be developed with larger radii scribers for larger, less critical bearings.

If a new or service bearing is degreased or washed in a cold volatile solvent, moisture will precipitate on the cold surfaces. Moisture may not be noticeable, but if the bearing is then dipped in cold oil or covered with a cold slushing compound, the moisture cannot evaporate and will expend itself in corroding the steel surfaces. The preferred alternative is to immerse the bearing in hot oil or slushing compound of suitable temperature and allow the bearing parts to assume the temperature of the bath. All moisture will then be driven off, and there can be no opportunity for corrosion.

Other Types of Bearing Damage. The most common visible damage to a service bearing is smearing of the bearing bore or outside diameter due to improper fitting practice. The loosely fitted ring, generally the stationary outer, will very often rotate in service and show some contact lines on the outside diameter and possibly on the face if the ring is shouldered in the housing. This condition is normal and not serious unless the wear is enough to exceed the drawing limits or to have developed sufficient temperature to cause heat discoloration and possible rubbing cracks.

In lightly loaded ball thrust bearings operating at fairly high speed, the balls tend to climb out of the ball tracks because of their gyroscopic moment. Under such conditions, the raceways will show a series of tangential wear marks and corresponding abrasion of the ball complement. The situation can be readily corrected either by decreasing the spindle speed or by increasing the thrust load.

If, through accident or faulty design, electric current is shunted through a rotating bearing, the rolling surfaces will have a multitude of small pits or craters caused by localized melting of the bearing steel. Very often this condition will be apparent as a characteristic washboard pattern on either the inner or the outer ring. Electric pitting is dangerous because of the possibility of premature fatigue failure and also because of the rapid increase in bearing clearance as the melted race material forms a lapping compound with the bearing lubricant.

As previously mentioned, in a nonrotating bearing subjected to vibration, the contacts between the balls and raceways will develop minute pockets which appear quite similar to those caused by extreme static overload. Such damage might occur while a machine is in transit or with stand-by equipment subjected to the vibration of adjacent operating machinery. This phenomenon may be minimized by rigidly locking the shaft and housing to prevent vibration of the bearings or by slowly rotating the shaft on its bearings when the equipment is otherwise inoperative.

LUBRICATION

Fundamentally, lubricant is supplied to a rolling bearing to support the sliding contact which exists between the retainer and other bearing parts and to accommodate the sliding that is unavoidable in the contact area between the rolling element and raceways. In addition, the lubricant protects the highly finished surfaces of the bearing from corrosion, tends to exclude foreign matter and, in the case of high-speed bearings or those running in a hot ambient, to carry away excess bearing heat.

Oil Lubrication. As low friction torque and, consequently, minimum oil viscosity are generally secondary to dependable lubrication with higher oil flows, the Annular Bearing Engineers' Committee (ABEC) has, after extensive research, developed the oil-selection chart shown in Fig. 2-6. The operating speeds (rpm) are given on one coordinate of the diagram, and the bearing loads in pounds on the other, both to a logarithmic scale. The lines intersecting the coordinates indicate viscosity groups for oils that are preferred for these loads and speeds. When ambient temperatures are low, the

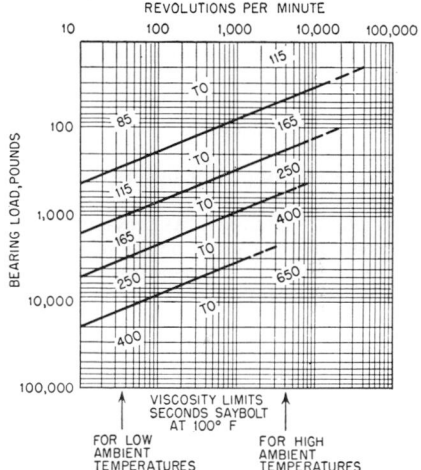

FIG. 2-6. Oil-selection chart (developed by Annular Bearing Engineers' Committee).

lower viscosity ranges should be used, and when the ambient temperature is high, a higher viscosity should be selected. For cases where the bearing load is not known, it is a good rule to select an oil that will have at least the following viscosities at the operating temperature:

For ball bearings and cylindrical roller bearings............ 70 sec Saybolt
For spherical roller bearings........................... 100 sec Saybolt
For spherical roller thrust bearings..................... 150 sec Saybolt

Oils of higher viscosity generally can be used without difficulty, though the stiffer lubricant will cause higher bearing friction, resulting in a hotter running application. In addition to the higher bearing temperature and increased power loss, a stiffer oil may congeal to such an extent as to cause skidding of the rolling elements during rapid starts or with low-temperature operation.

Grease Lubrication. Antifriction bearing greases usually are a mixture of lubricating oil and a soap base. The latter acts merely to keep the oil in suspension. When moving parts of a bearing come in contact with the grease, a small quantity of oil will adhere to the bearing surfaces. Oil is, therefore, removed from the grease near the rotating parts. The oil that is picked up by the bearing is gradually broken down by oxidation or lost by evaporation, centrifugal force, etc. Bleeding of the grease should, therefore, take place so as to continue to supply a small quantity of oil, which is usually sufficient for satisfactory operation. But needless to say, the bearing cannot function properly unless the supply of oil keeps up with the demand. Also, the process cannot go on indefinitely. In due course of time the grease will oxidize, so that the oil in the grease near the rotating parts may be depleted.

Greases to be used below 32°F should contain lithium soap as a jelling agent, as the soap used in greases for higher than 32°F operation, such as soda or soda-lime, begins to stiffen or harden at the lower temperature. To obtain the lowest possible running temperature and torque, an apparent channeling grease should be used for ball bearings. These usually are stiffer greases with an ASTM penetration of 190 to 210 and are mostly used in high-speed applications. Greases to be used in roller bearings should have an ASTM penetration above 300 and should not channel.   A suitable ball and roller bearing grease should show no evidence of deterioration following 18 months' storage in bearings packaged in individual sealed boxes.

Extensive tests have revealed that only the grease which is immediately adjacent to and in contact with the bearing takes part in the lubrication.   Excessive grease space is, therefore, of no value in so far as lubrication is concerned.   Generally speaking, it is objectionable to pack the space around the bearing full of grease because of possible churning, which could result in overheating and subsequent breakdown of the grease or loss of lubricant through the shaft seals.   There are, however, exceptions to this rule, as it may sometimes be desirable, where speed will permit, to fill the housing completely with grease to give better protection against the entrance of foreign matter and moisture.

No grease completely offsets the effect of time, even if left on the shelf- so that provision must be made for the systematic removal of old grease from a bearing on a predetermined schedule.   As previously pointed out, the quantity of grease packed in the bearing housing cannot be the measure of the relubrication cycle.   The type of grease and the operating temperature are important factors, and where conditions are favorable, the consumption of oil from the grease may be so low that the time intervals will depend on how long the grease will resist oxidation.

Because of the great variation in operating conditions an accurate prediction of grease life cannot be made.   In spite of this uncertainty, the relubrication chart on Fig. 2-7 has been prepared to give an approximate idea when a small amount of grease should be added.   The diagrams, which are given as a guide only, are based on accumulated experience with greases of reputable manufacturers, properly selected for the application and properly applied.   They do not represent the time the grease will last if the bearing is run to lubrication failure, as considerably longer life has been obtained in certain cases.   These charts should rather be understood to represent the time after which it is advisable to add a small amount of grease to safeguard the bearing.

In all cases of grease lubrication it is good practice to remove all the old grease about once a year regardless of whether or not new grease has been added in the meantime. When a small amount of grease must be added at certain intervals, it is, of course, important that the new grease reach the bearing internal surfaces where it is most needed.   If the new grease is forced in under the old grease along the side of the outer ring, the resistance of the old grease will tend to force the new grease into the bearing.

Protection against Moisture.   No antifriction bearing lubricant has yet been developed which will give complete protection against moisture, but ball and roller bearings are, however, often used with success where moisture is present, provided due consideration is given the housing design, the shaft seals, and the selection of the proper lubricant.   Compounded oils are more water repellent than straight mineral oils and, therefore, better able to keep moisture from the bearing surfaces.   If, however, the oil is permitted to oxidize, it will be more destructive to the bearing surface if moisture is present.

A sodium-base grease usually will form a noncorrosive emulsion when mixed with a limited quantity of water.   Agitation is necessary to form this emulsion, so that if water should enter the bearing housing while there is no rotation, the bearing surfaces may be rusted.   There is a limit to the amount of water which the grease can absorb and still offer protection to the bearing.   When moisture is present, it is necessary to replenish the grease more often to compensate for the limited grease solubility.

Nonemulsifying and water-repellent greases are necessary for those applications where the water flow is sufficient to wash away the lubricant, such as for roll neck bearing applications on rolling mills.   Since this type of grease will not emulsify with water, it is necessary that the bearing be completely covered by the grease, and attention should be given the seals and housing construction to deflect the water flow from the bearing.

Protection of Idle Machinery.   Equipment which is not in service should be set in motion periodically in order to spread the lubricant over all bearing surfaces.   Suitable intervals are 1 to 3 months, depending on atmospheric conditions.   If the equipment cannot be exercised on a fairly frequent schedule, all bearings should be cleaned and

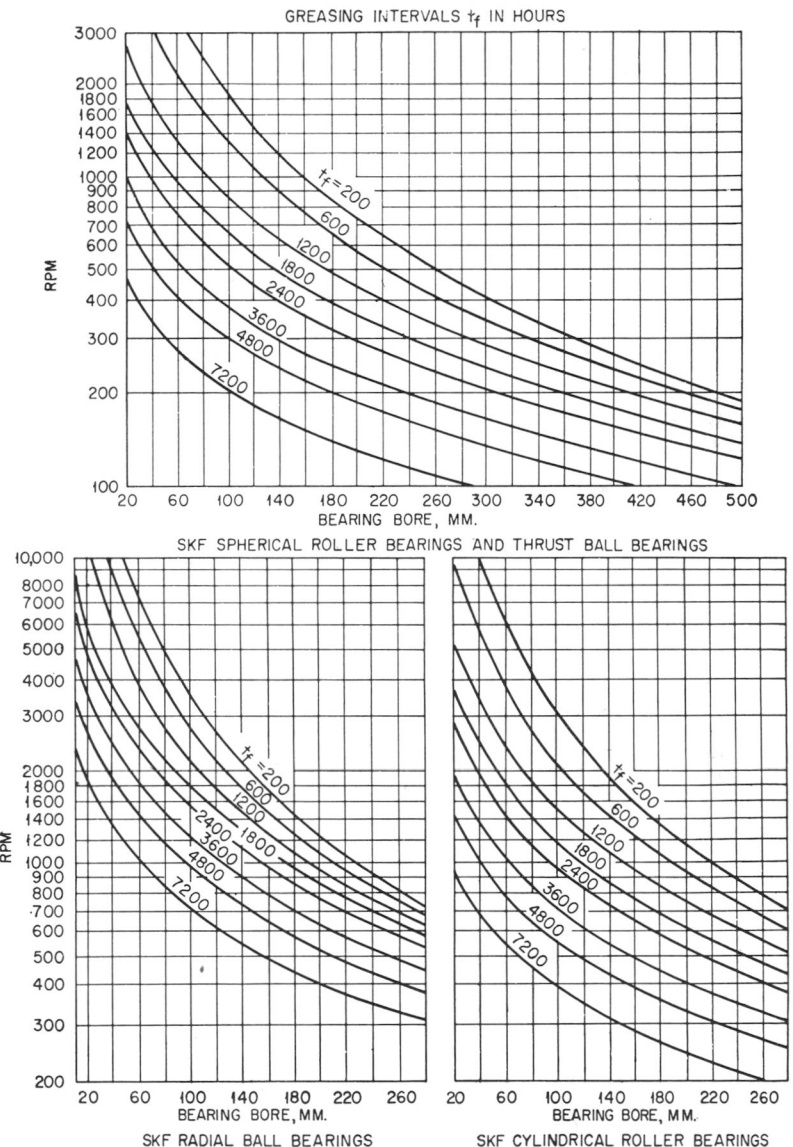

Fig. 2-7. Relubrication charts. The time, t_f operating hours, between successive addings of small amounts of grease, is a function of the rpm n and the bore diameter d mm. t_f 2,400 hr corresponds to 1-year service at 8 hr per day.

packed with petrolatum or other suitable antirust agents according to the advice of the equipment manufacturer or a reputable lubricant supplier.

Cleaning. The ABEC recommends that dismounted service bearings be placed in a suitable container with a clean, cold petroleum solvent or kerosene and allowed to soak for preferably 12 hr. In cases of badly oxidized grease, it may be expedient to soak the bearings in hot light oil (200 to 240°F), agitating the basket of bearings slowly through the oil from time to time.   In extreme cases boiling in emulsifiable cleaners diluted with water will usually soften the contaminating sludge.   If the hot emulsion solutions are used, the bearings should be drained and spun individually until the water is completely evaporated.   The bearings should be completely washed in a second container of clean petroleum solvent or kerosene, and each bearing should be individually cleaned by revolving by hand with the bearing partly submerged in this solvent.   The clean bearing should be immediately spun in light oil to remove the solvent completely and coated by hand with petrolatum if the bearing is not to be reassembled immediately.

Light transformer oils, spindle oils, and automotive flushing oils are suitable for cleaning bearings, but anything heavier than light motor oil (SAE 10) is not recommended.   An emulsifying solution made with grinding, cutting, or floor-cleaning compounds and hot water has been found effective.   Petroleum solvents must be used with the usual precautions associated with fire hazards.

The use of chlorinated solvents of any kind is not recommended in bearing-cleaning operations because of the rust hazard, nor is the use of compressed air found desirable in bearing-cleaning operations.

For cleaning bearings without dismounting, hot light oil at 180 to 200°F may be flushed through the housing while the shaft or spindle is slowly rotated.   In cases of badly oxidized grease and oil, hot aqueous emulsions may be run into the housings, preferably while rotating the bearings until the bearing is satisfactorily cleaned.   The solution must then be drained thoroughly, and the bearing and housing flushed with hot light oil and again drained before adding new lubricant. In some very difficult cases, an intermediate flushing with a mixture of alcohol and light mineral solvent, after the emulsion treatment, may be useful.

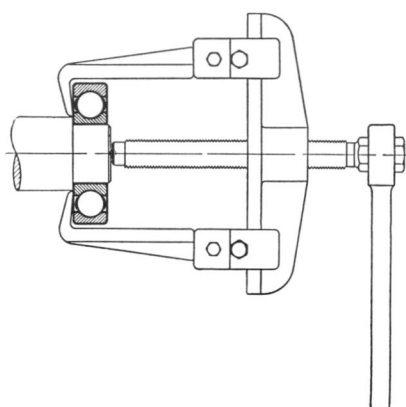

Fig. 2-8. Bearing puller.

If the bearing is to be relubricated with grease, some of the fresh grease may be forced through the bearing to purge any remaining contamination.   This practice is not recommended unless there are drain plugs which can be removed so that the old grease may be forced from the housing.   Also, newly lubricated bearings should then be operated for at least 20 min before the drain plugs are replaced, as excess grease will cause overheating of the bearing.

Bearing Removal and Assembly.   If force must be used to dismantle a mounted bearing, it should be applied to the ring which has the tighter fit.   If, in an emergency, the removal force must be applied to the opposite ring, the bearing should be turned during the process to avoid damage to the tracks or rolling elements, and extreme care must be taken to apply a steady, well-distributed pull to the bearing.   A steady pressure exerted by means of a press or puller, Fig. 2-8, is least likely to damage the bearing.

When assembling relatively small bearings, where the shaft can be easily handled, the most convenient method of forcing the inner ring on the shaft is to use a hand press. A piece of tubing or other convenient material is located against the inner ring of the bearing so that force can be applied directly against the tightly fitted ring.   If the bearing cannot be readily assembled with a hand press, a suitable piece of tubing can be placed against the bearing ring, Fig. 2-9, and the ring can be forced on its seat by hammer blows applied to a plate laid across the open end of the tubing.

When flush-ground angular contact bearings are mounted in pairs or in stacks, it is absolutely necessary that the inner and outer rings be properly aligned.   While the shaft locknut or end-cover bolts are being tightened, the bearings should be constantly rotated so that the outer rings, which are generally loosely fitted, will properly center themselves. The bearings should rotate freely after the locknut or cap bolts have been completely tightened. For a back-to-back mounting, which is generally a bench assembly with the bearings out of their normal housing, the outer rings can be accurately aligned by mounting them in a closely fitted dummy sleeve while the shaft nut is tightened.

For larger bearings it is sometimes necessary to pound directly against the inner ring, and in such cases a soft metal drift should be used and care should be taken to avoid cocking the ring on the shaft. Often larger bearings can be more conveniently

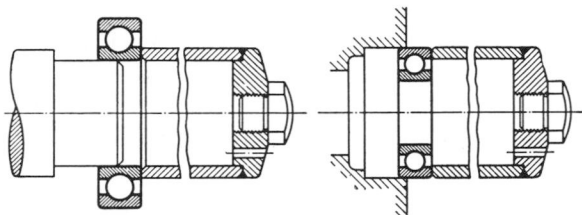

FIG. 2-9. Applying force against inner ring, in assembly, by means of tubing.

mounted by heating either the separable ring or the complete bearing in oil or in a solution of 10 per cent soluble oil in water. This noncorrosive solution boils at approximately 210°F, and this automatically prevents overheating the bearing.

Many large roller bearings are furnished with tapered inner ring bores for mounting on similarly tapered bearing seats or on tapered sleeves which mount between the cylindrical shaft outside diameter and bearing bore. The bearing is mounted by tightening a shaft locknut which moves the bearing in an axial direction, causing the inner ring to slide up the mating shaft taper, thus developing an interference between inner ring and shaft with a corresponding reduction in internal looseness. For such bearings the degree of shaft interference is determined by the difference in internal clearance as measured on the unmounted bearing and again after mounting on the tapered shaft. The amount of internal clearance reduction due to expansion on the tapered seat will depend on the particular application, and the equipment manufacturer's recommendation should be closely followed. It is important to note that the reduction in clearance is the dimension to be controlled rather than the final mounted clearance. If a bearing with a proper internal clearance is selected, the remaining clearance will automatically be adequate for the operating conditions.

Chapter 3

TAPERED ROLLER BEARINGS

By Elmer Anderson
Service Manager
The Timken Roller Bearing Company
Canton, Ohio

Fundamental Principles. The tapered roller bearing is so constructed that lines drawn coincident with the working surfaces of the rollers and races will meet at a common point on the axis of the bearing as shown in Fig. 3-1. True rolling motion is obtained, and the bearing will handle all loads—radial, thrust, or both—in any combination. The parts are an inner raceway, an outer raceway, the tapered rollers, and the cage or roller retainer. In the Timken bearing these are designated as the

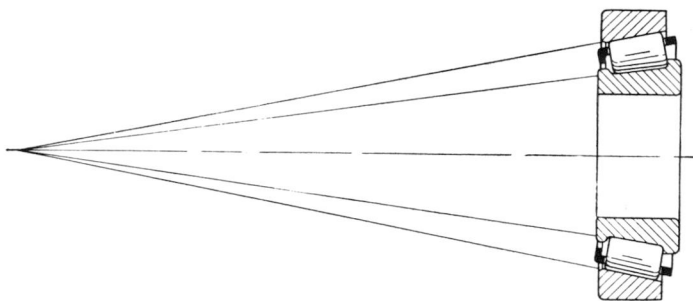

Fig. 3-1. Basic principle of the tapered roller bearing.

cone, which it resembles in its mechanical profile construction; the cup which fits over the cone and rollers; the rollers, which roll between the cone and cup; and the cage, which retains the rollers, properly spaced about the cone (see Fig. 3-2).

Each roller aligns itself between the tapered faces of the cup and cone without guidance by the cage. This is accomplished by so grinding the large end of the roller that it squares itself with the cone back face rib. As each roller revolves about the cone, wide-area contact is made between the large end of the roller and the cone rib, compelling each roller to maintain accurate alignment (see Fig. 3-3). The cage is relieved of all function except properly spacing the rollers about the periphery of the cone. Types of bearings are shown in Fig. 3-4; nomenclature is given in Fig. 3-5.

Identification. The part number is stamped on every Timken bearing cup and cone. The cup number is stamped on the outside diameter of the cup on the smaller sizes, but in most cases the number is on the face of the cup. The part number of the cone is stamped on the face of the cone (see Fig. 3-6).

8–26

Some large-bore bearings, such as used on roll necks of rolling mills, have a serial number in addition to the regular part number. Serial numbers consist of two parts which incorporate the year and number of the bearing in the sequence of manufacture. *Example:* Bearing 50-1 was made in 1950 and was the first one made that year of that particular number. All cups, cones, and spacers in one bearing are marked with the

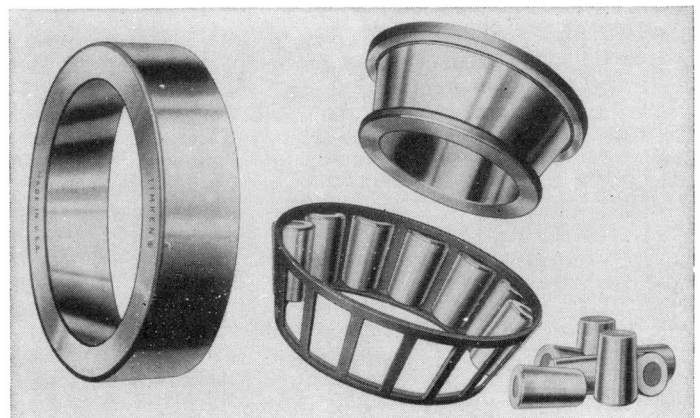

FIG. 3-2. The parts of a tapered roller bearing: cage, rollers, cone, and cup.

same serial number. All parts with the same serial number should be kept together. Single-row bearings should be assembled so that the cup and cone of the same serial number are together. Double-row bearings or four-row bearings with and without spacers should be assembled so that all cups and cones of the same serial, and spacers, where used, are in the same bearing assembly. On all multiple-row bearings that have serial numbers, there are letters etched along with the serial number. These are to assist in the assembly of the bearing. Corresponding faces are marked with corresponding letters. Classes of bearings and tolerances to which they are manufactured are shown in Fig. 3-7.

Bearing Removal. When and how often should bearings be inspected? In applications such as automotive wheels, which include passenger cars, trucks, and buses, and in similar applications, bearings should be inspected every 25,000 to 30,000 miles. In cases where mileage piles up slowly, the bearings should be inspected once a year. In steel-mill roll-neck applications, bearings should be inspected at least once a year and sometimes more frequently. These applications are such that the lubricant and the bearings themselves get contaminated

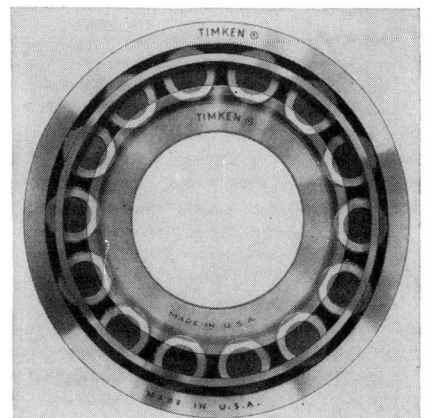

FIG. 3-3. Roller alignment is secured by contact between roll end and rib.

from water and dirt. It is difficult to incorporate seals that will completely hold out the water and dirt, so it is better to set up fairly frequent inspection periods and thoroughly clean the parts, removing lubricant at that time.

On units such as gear drives, machine tools, and applications that are well sealed or protected, it is necessary to inspect the bearings only when the units are down for regular overhaul, renewal, or repair. Usually the seals are such that the gear boxes are kept clean. They often have drains to permit oil removal and flushing. Clean

Timken Bearings, Single-row, Multiple-row, and Thrust

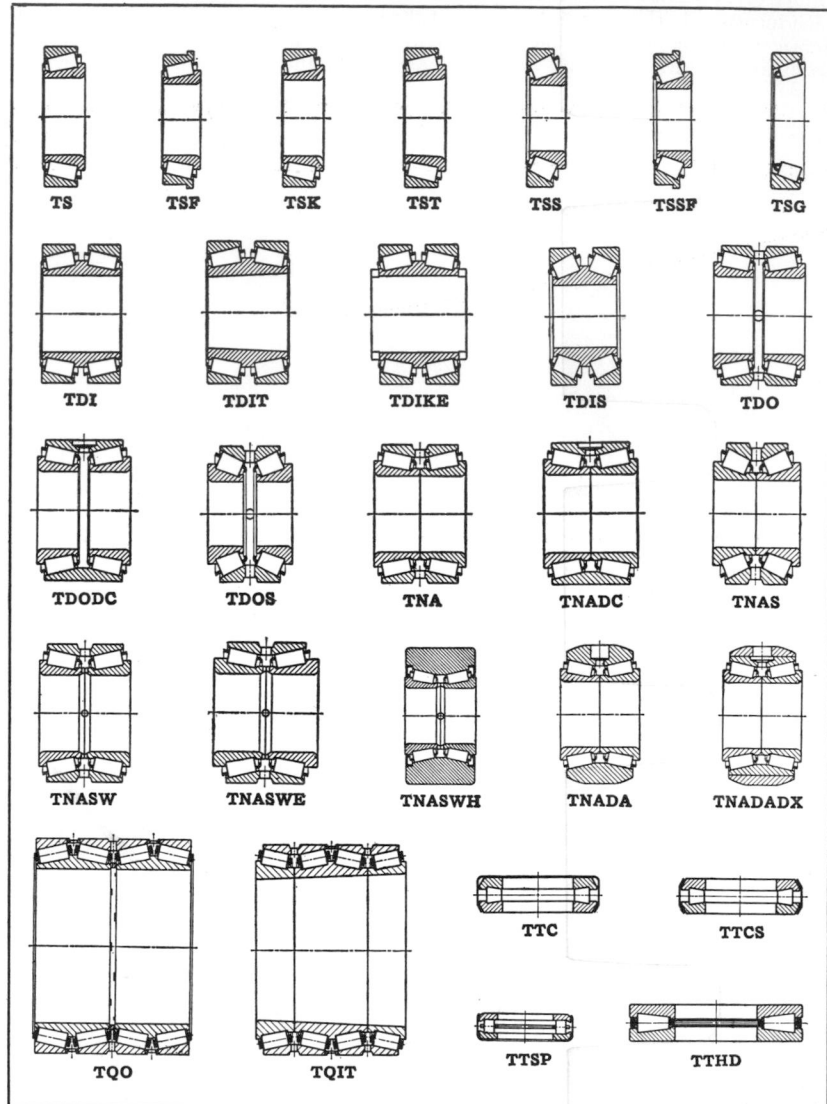

FIG. 3-4. Types of tapered roller bearings.

oil can be put in without tearing down the unit or taking out the bearings. In some cases these types of units run for many years before it is necessary to touch the bearings.

The first step in the proper maintenance of bearings is their removal. A regular gear or bearing puller should be used as shown in Fig. 3-8. The puller shown is operated hydraulically, but the same type of puller with many variations can be obtained for manual operation. With a puller, a direct, straight pull is obtained on the bearing and the bearing can be salvaged for further use if necessary. Sometimes it is impossible to get behind the bearing race with a standard-type puller, and then a special type of puller, as shown in Fig. 3-9, is recommended.

There are times when it is very difficult to remove the bearings even with a puller. In these cases, hot oil can be used along with the puller, or in the cases of hollow shafts, dry ice can be used to shrink the shaft. With the puller attached and pressure applied, hot oil can be poured into the housing, and when the heat has expanded the bearing but before it expands the shaft, the puller will start moving the race. Dry ice in a hollow shaft will tend to shrink the shaft and lessen the fit of the race so that the puller will be able to remove it readily. In an emergency, steam can be used

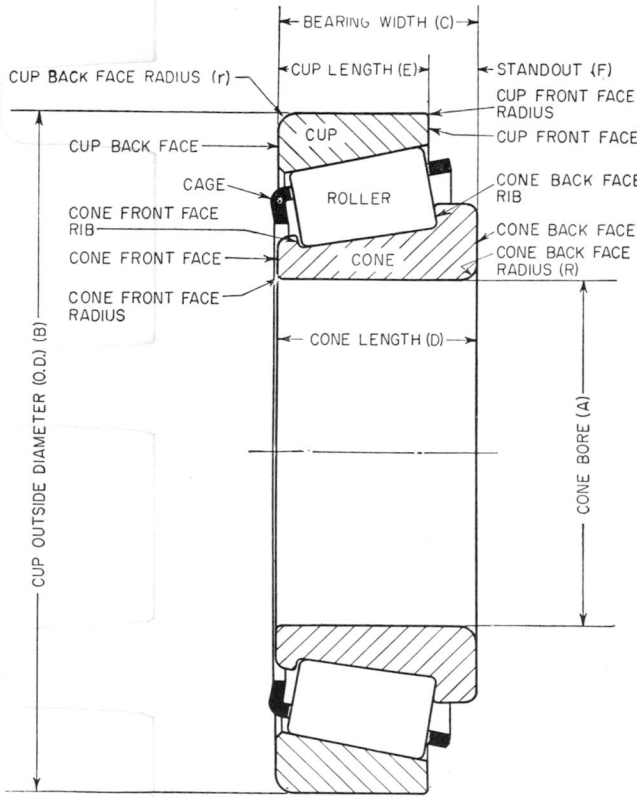

FIG. 3-5. Nomenclature of bearing parts.

instead of hot oil, but extreme care must be taken to clean and dry the bearing thoroughly immediately after the steam has been used so the bearing will not become rusted or etched from the moisture.

Another method of bearing removal that is becoming very popular, particularly in larger sized bearings and tapered bore bearings, is the hydraulic method. Figure 3-10 shows the oil holes and grooves in the bearing seat through which the oil is applied. The pressure of the oil against the race expands and loosens it. This hydraulic assistance can be of value in straight bore bearings when used along with a puller or press.

Sometimes it is necessary to resort to the use of a rod or bar and hammer to drive a bearing off, as shown in Fig. 3-11. This method is not recommended if a puller is available, but sometimes in the field all the desired equipment is not available. When this method is used, it is recommended that a mild steel bar be used and precaution taken against damaging any of the bearing parts or the bearing seats.

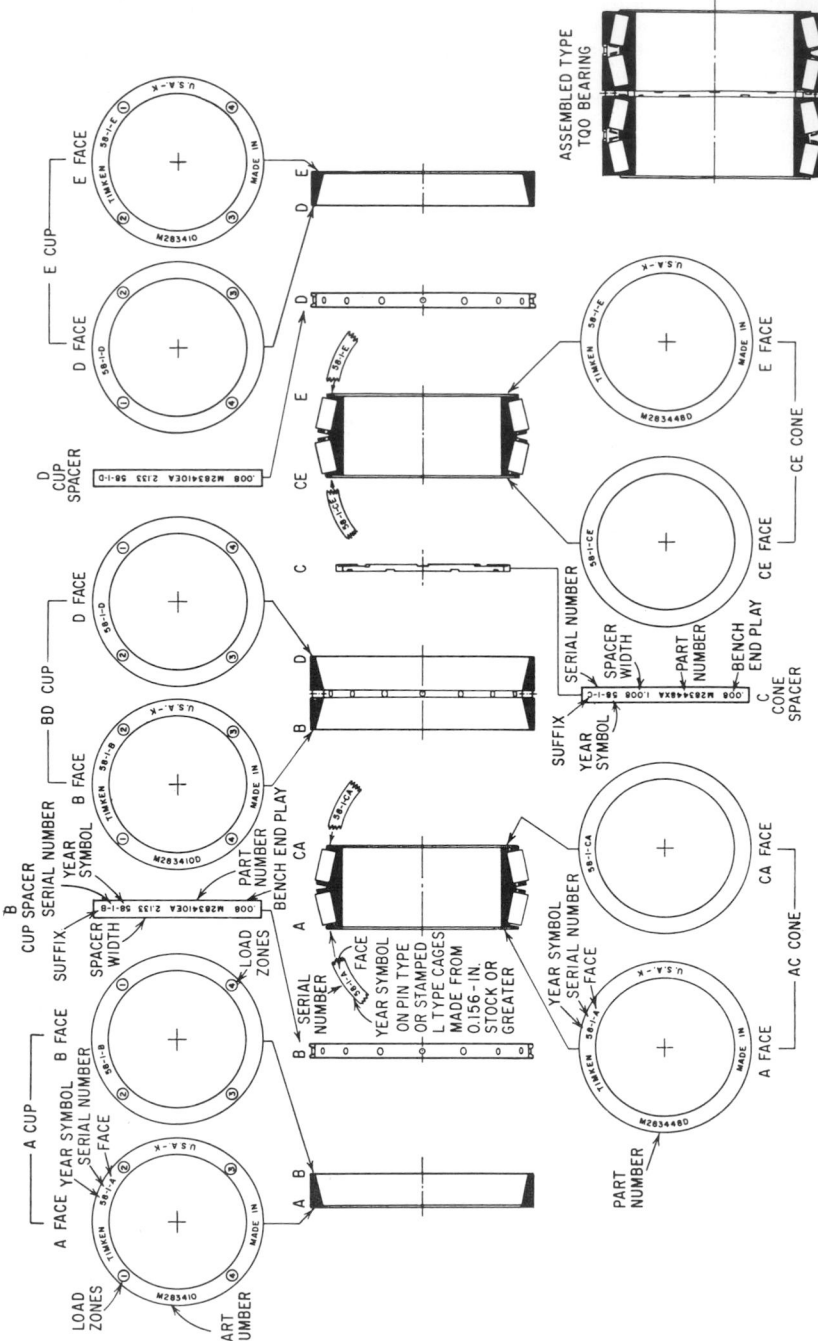

FIG. 3-6. How bearings are marked for identification.

Timken Bearing Tolerance Chart
Cone bore tolerance, in.

maximum dimension →	class 4 all sizes	class 2 24" max. cone bore	class 3 all sizes	class 0 12" max. cup o.d.	class 00 10½" max. cup o.d.
cone bore tolerance cone bore ▼					
up to 3" incl.	+.0005" −.0000" ▲	+.0005" −.0000"	+.0005" −.0000"	+.0005" −.0000"	+.0003" −.0000"
over 3" to 12" incl.	+.0010" −.0000"	+.0010" −.0000"	+.0005" −.0000"	+.0005" −.0000"	+.0003" −.0000"
over 12" to 24" incl.	+.0020" −.0000"	+.0020" −.0000"	+.0010" −.0000"	—	—
over 24" to 36" incl.	+.0030" −.0000"	—	+.0015" −.0000"	—	—
over 36" to 48" incl.	+.0040" −.0000"	—	+.0020" −.0000"	—	—
over 48"	+.0050" −.0000"	—	+.0030" −.0000"	—	—
cup o.d. tolerance cup o.d. ▼					
up to 12" incl.	+.0010" −.0000"	+.0010" −.0000"	+.0005" −.0000"	+.0005" −.0000"	+.0003" −.0000"
over 12" to 24" incl.	+.0020" −.0000"	+.0020" −.0000"	+.0010" −.0000"	—	—
over 24" to 36" incl.	+.0030" −.0000"	+.0030" −.0000"	+.0015" −.0000"	—	—
over 36" to 48" incl.	+.0040" −.0000"	—	+.0020" −.0000"	—	—
over 48"	+.0050" −.0000"	—	+.0030" −.0000"	—	—
overall bearing width tolerance bearing type ▼					
TS — up to 4" bore, incl.	+.008" −.000" ▲	+.008" −.000"	+.008" −.008"	+.008" −.008"	+.008" −.008"
TS — over 4" to 12" bore, incl.	+.014" −.010"	+.008" −.000"	+.008" −.008"	+.008" −.008"	+.008" −.008"
TS — over 12" bore - up to 20" cup o.d. incl.	+.015" −.015"	+.015" −.015"	+.008" −.008"	—	—
TS — over 12" bore - over 20" cup o.d.	+.015" −.015"	+.015" −.015"	+.015" −.015"	—	—
TNA — up to 5" bore, incl.	+.010" −.000"	+.010" −.000"	+.010" −.000"	—	—
TNA — over 5" bore	+.030" −.000"	+.030" −.000"	+.030" −.000"	—	—
TDI and TDO — up to 4" bore, incl.	+.016" −.000" ▲	+.016" −.000"	+.016" −.016"	+.016" −.016"	+.016" −.016"
TDI and TDO — over 4" to 12" bore, incl.	+.028" −.020"	+.016" −.008"	+.016" −.016"	+.016" −.016"	+.016" −.016"
TDI and TDO — over 12" bore - up to 20" cup o.d. incl.	+.030" −.030"	+.030" −.030"	+.016" −.016"	—	—
TDI and TDO — over 12" bore - over 20" cup o.d.	+.030" −.030"	+.030" −.030"	+.030" −.030"	—	—
TQO and TQIT | all sizes	+.060" −.060"	+.060" −.060"	+.060" −.060"	+.060" −.060"	
assembled bearing maximum runout bearing o.d. ▼					
up to 12" incl.	.0020"	.0015"	.0003"	.00015"	.000075"
over 12" to 24" incl.	.0020"	.0015"	.0007"	—	—
over 24" to 36" incl.	.0030"	.0020"	.0020"	—	—
over 36"	.0030"	—	.0030"	—	—

▲Tolerances for bearings in the LM11700, LM11900, M12600, L44600, LM48500 and LM67000 series are: Bore = +.0008", −.000"; Overall bearing width = +.014", −.000" for TS Type and +.022", −.000" for TDI and TDO types.

FIG. 3-7. Classes of bearings and tolerances to which manufactured.

FIG. 3-8. Bearing puller with hydraulic attachment.

Cleaning Bearings. After the bearings have been removed from the housings or shafts, the next step is to clean them thoroughly so they can be readily inspected or prepared for reinstalling.

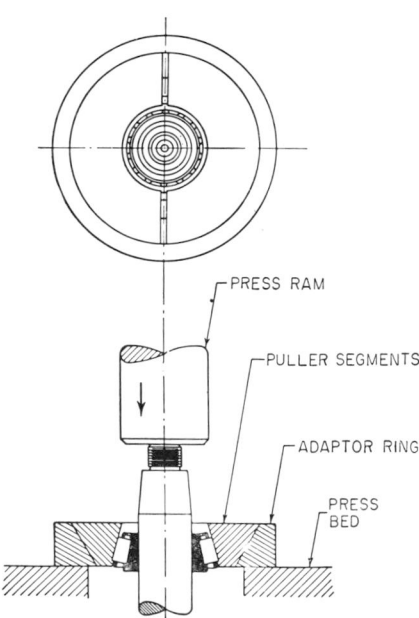

FIG. 3-9. Special bearing puller, used when standard puller cannot be inserted behind the race.

For smaller bearings and smaller quantities of bearings, kerosene or mineral spirits are recommended as the cleaning agent. They are much safer than the more volatile cleaning agents such as gasoline or naphtha. A small cleaning tank can be used to advantage. These tanks can be purchased and come complete with a small pump and filter so that clean fluid is available at all times for washing the parts. Where buckets or pans of kerosene are used, the supply should be renewed fairly frequently so that it is clean and does a thorough job of cleaning the bearings.

For large bearings such as the multiple-row bearings used in various types of mill equipment, a large washing tank using hot solution as indicated in Fig. 3-12 is recommended. In these heated tanks neutral oil which has a viscosity of 100 sec at 100°F heated to 300°F can be used. Other compounds that are excellent are known as alkali cleaners. Some of them are trisodium phosphate, soda ash, and metasilicate. Alkali cleaners should be used in solution with 2 or 3 oz of compound to the gallon of water, and the solution should be hot.

After the bearings have been washed by any of the methods mentioned, they must be thoroughly dried. Larger bearings washed in hot solutions dry rapidly from the heat soaked up during the washing. Smaller bearings, washed in kerosene or something similar, can be dried by blowing with clean dry compressed air. Never spin the bearing; a relatively dry bearing spun at high speed can be seriously injured.

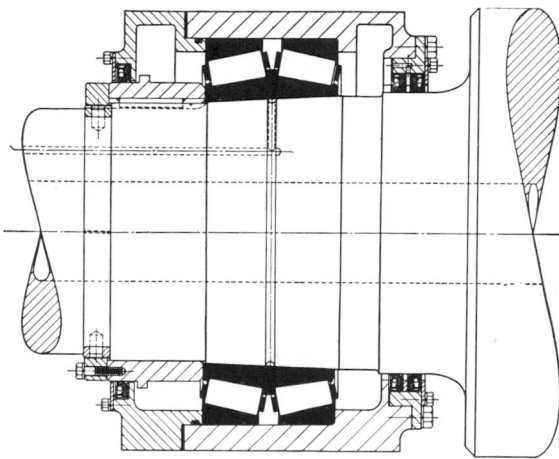

FIG. 3-10. Oil holes and grooves in bearing seat for hydraulic removal.

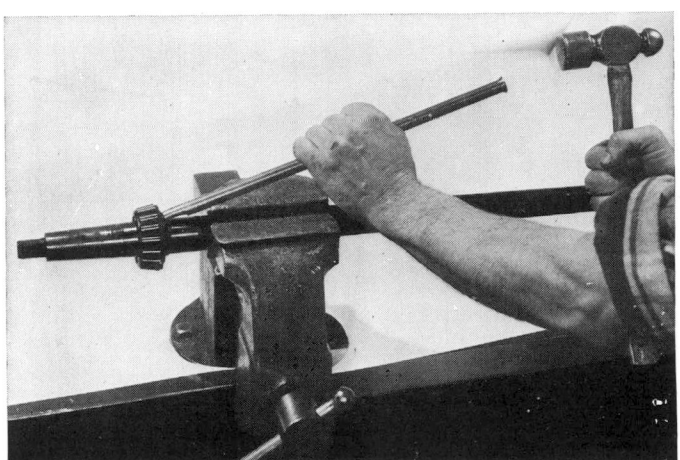

FIG. 3-11. Bearing removal with mild-steel bar and hammer.

After washing and drying, the bearings should be dipped in oil or preservative and wrapped in clean paper, preferably waxed or oiled. They should be stored in a clean, dry place. New bearings should be left in their original containers until they are to be used; they are shipped with a coating of pure petrolatum as a rust preventive. It is not necessary to remove this coating when installing the bearings. Petrolatum is of little value as a lubricant, but it is compatible with all types of lubricants and, therefore, will do no harm if it remains on the bearings.

Inspection of Bearings. After used bearings have been thoroughly cleaned, they are ready for inspection. If they are free from rust or damage and there is no flaking

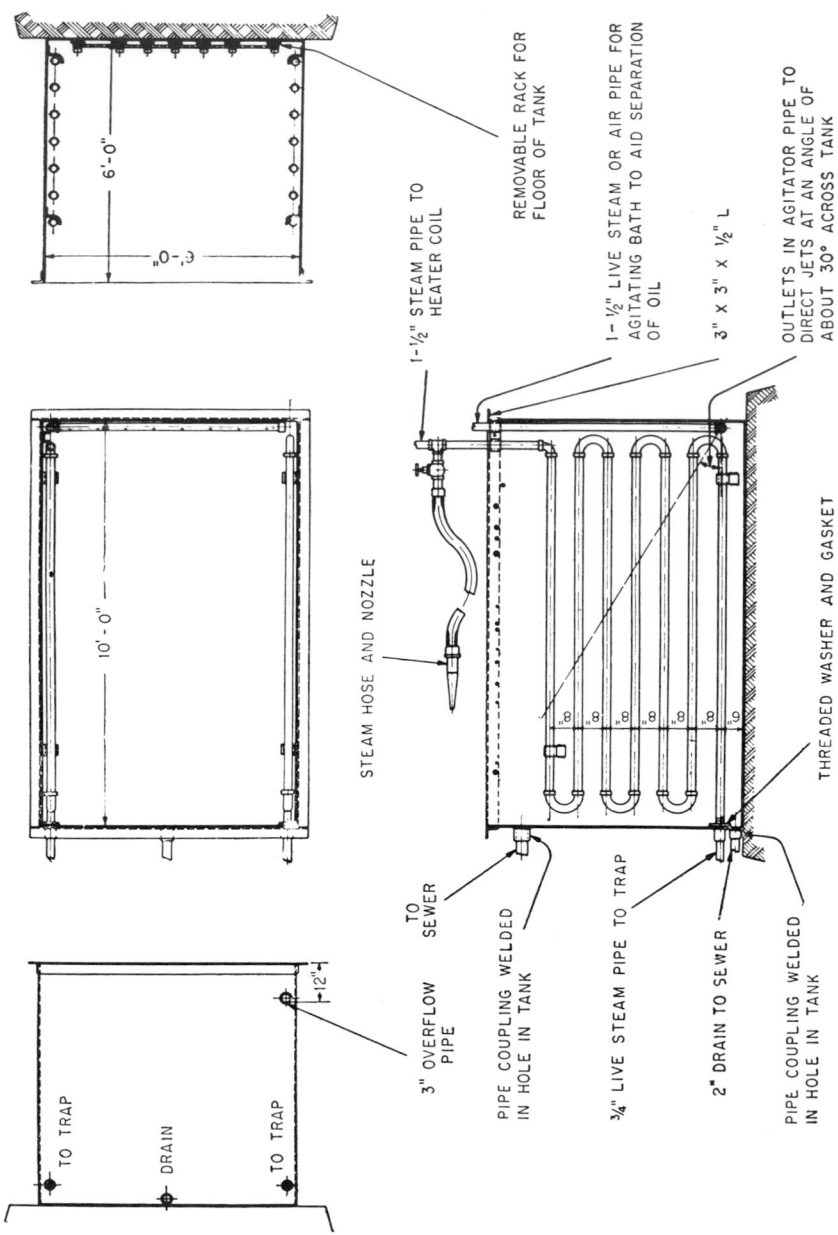

Fig. 3-12. Design of tank for cleaning bearings (½-in. steel plate, welded).

or spalling of the metal, they may be used again.   Generally, it is more economical to install new bearings than to take a chance on bearings that have been damaged, rusted, or etched to any extent.   The cost of tearing down a unit, removing the bearings and parts, and installing new is often much greater than the cost of the bearing.   Whether or not the bearing should be used again will actually depend on the individual case.   There are many factors to be considered in making the decision, so it is impossible to make a general rule.

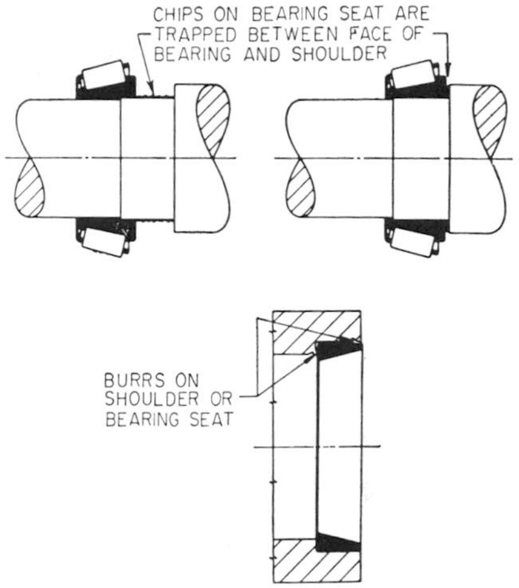

Along with the inspection of bearings, particularly the larger sizes, we find it is necessary to measure them.   This is true where spacers are used to make the bearing adjustment.   If the bearings have become lapped or worn because of foreign material getting into them, it is sometimes necessary to regrind the spacers to compensate for wear.   Detailed information regarding the methods of measuring the bearings should be obtained from the manufacturer.

FIG. 3-13.   Effect of burrs and dirt on shafts and in housings.

Inspection of Housings, Shafts, and Parts.   When the cleaning and the inspection of the bearings themselves have been completed, the next step is to inspect all the parts in a machine that affect the bearing assemblies.

Burrs and chips on the bearing seat are illustrated in Fig. 3-13.   Damage or high spots and dirt or burrs, as noted, will prevent the bearing from being properly seated or will tend to seat the parts improperly by throwing them off square, inducing misalignment in the bearings.   Dirt piling up behind the races prevents them from seating solidly against the shoulder.   During operation this dirt may loosen or wash out, and load on the bearing will cause the race to move until it is seated solidly against the shoulder.   Consequently, there may be considerable end play introduced by the backing movement of the race until it gets up against the shoulder.

When shafts or housings are found to be badly worn, they should be built up by one of several methods in order to provide the original recommended bearing fit.   Shafts and housings may be built up by welding or spray welding and then machining, or they may be built up by chrome plating.   This is particularly true in the case of shafts.   Another method is to machine the shaft or the housing quite a bit oversize or undersize and then install a bushing and machine the bushing to the proper size.

It is important that proper fits be used on the inner and outer races or the cups and cones of the bearings in order to get the maximum life or performance from the bearing.   A general rule to be followed is that the race that goes on or in the rotating element should have a press fit and the race that goes on or in the stationary element can usually be put on with a light or adjustable fit.   As an example, the outer race that goes in the wheel hub is in the rotating element and should be in with a fit of 0.001 to 0.003 in. tight.   The cone or inner race which goes on the stationary spindle or axle has a fit of 0.0002 to 0.0012 in. loose.   These fits may vary some, depending on the tolerances of the bearing and the shaft or housing.   Figures 3-14, 3-15, and 3-16 cover the recommended fits for automotive and industrial applications.

Aluminum and magnesium housings, because of their greater expansion rate, require heavier press fits when used as housings than do steel housings.   It is recommended that a press fit of 0.0010 to 0.0015 in. per inch of diameter be used for aluminum and a press fit of 0.0015 to 0.0020 in. per inch of diameter to be used for magnesium.

In machining or remachining bearing seats, it is recommended that the finishes as shown in Fig. 3-17 should be followed.   If the finishes are rougher than those shown,

Automotive Applications—Recommended Cone Fitting Practice

industry	type of application		cone bore					
			⅝" to 3" inclusive			over 3"		
			toler-ance	recom-mended fit	cone seat equals minimum cone bore	toler-ance	recom-mended fit	cone seat equals minimum cone bore
automotive (rotating shafts)	pinion	adj. cone (clamped)	+.0005 −.0000	.0005 tight .0005 loose	+.0005 max. +.0000 min.	+.0010 −.0000	.0015 tight .0005 loose	+.0015 max. +.0005 min.
		non-adj. cone	+.0005 −.0000	.0020 tight .0010 tight	+.0020 max. +.0015 min.	+.0010 −.0000	.0030 tight .0010 tight	+.0030 max. +.0020 min.
	transmission, cross shaft, transfer case	non-adj. cone	+.0005 −.0000	.0015 tight .0005 tight	+.0015 max. +.0010 min.	+.0010 −.0000	.0025 tight .0005 tight	+.0025 max. +.0015 min.
	rear axle shafts	non-adj. cone	+.0005 −.0000	.0020 tight .0010 tight	+.0020 max. +.0015 min.			
	differential	non-adj. cone	+.0005 −.0000	.0025 tight .0010 tight	+.0025 max. +.0015 min.	+.0010 −.0000	.0035 tight .0015 tight	+.0035 max. +.0025 min.
automotive (stationary shafts)	front wheels, full-floating rear wheels, trailer wheels	adj. cone	+.0005 −.0000	.0002 loose .0012 loose	−.0002 max. −.0007 min.	+.0010 −.0000	.0002 loose .0022 loose	−.0002 max. −.0012 min.
			+.0008 −.0000	.0002 loose .0015 loose	−.0002 max. −.0007 min.			

Automotive Applications—Recommended Cup Fitting Practice

industry	type of application		cup outside diameter								
			less than 3"			3" to 5" inclusive			over 5"		
			toler-ance	recom-mended fit	cup seat equals minimum cup o.d.	toler-ance	recom-mended fit	cup seat equals minimum cup o.d.	toler-ance	recom-mended fit	cup seat equals minimum cup o.d.
automotive	front wheels, full floating rear wheels, pinions, differentials	non-adj. cup	+.0010 −.0000	.0005 tight .0025 tight	−.0005 max. −.0015 min.	+.0010 −.0000	.0010 tight .0030 tight	−.0010 max. −.0020 min.	+.0010 −.0000	.0010 tight .0040 tight	−.0010 max. −.0030 min.
	differential	adj. cup	+.0010 −.0000	.0020 loose .0000 loose	+.0020 max. +.0010 min.	+.0010 −.0000	.0020 loose .0000 loose	+.0020 max. +.0010 min.	+.0010 −.0000	.0020 loose .0010 tight	+.0020 max. +.0000 min.
	transmissions, cross shafts, other applications	adj. cup	+.0010 −.0000	.0010 loose .0010 tight	+.0010 max. +.0000 min.	+.0010 −.0000	.0010 loose .0010 tight	+.0010 max. +.0000 min.	+.0010 −.0000	.0020 loose .0010 tight	+.0020 max. +.0000 min.
	semi-floating rear wheels	adj. cup	+.0010 −.0000	.0030 loose .0005 loose	+.0030 max. +.0015 min.	+.0010 −.0000	.0030 loose .0005 loose	+.0030 max. +.0015 min.			

FIG. 3-14. Recommended fits for automotive applications.

Industrial Equipment—Cone Fitting Practice

mounting conditions	shaft finish	service	line no.	up to 3" inclusive — cone bore equals A*	up to 3" — fit	up to 3" — cone seat equals A*	over 3" to 12" inclusive — cone bore equals A*	over 3" to 12" — fit	over 3" to 12" — cone seat equals A*	over 12" to 24" inclusive — cone bore equals A*	over 12" to 24" — fit	over 12" to 24" — cone seat equals A*	over 24" to 36" inclusive — cone bore equals A*	over 24" to 36" — fit	over 24" to 36" — cone seat equals A*
class: 4 and 2 product **													**class: 4 product only ****		
rotating cone	ground	steady loads with moderate shock	1	+.0005 / −.0000	.0005 tight / .0015 tight	+.0015 / +.0010	+.0010 / −.0000	.0005 tight / .0015 tight	+.0025 / +.0010	+.0020 / −.0000	.0010 tight / .0050 tight	+.0050 / +.0030	+.0030 / −.0000	.0015 tight / .0075 tight	+.0075 / +.0045
rotating or stationary cone	unground or ground	heavy loads or high speeds shock	2 †	−.0005 / −.0000	.0010 tight / .0025 tight	+.0025 / +.0015	+.0010 / −.0000	use heavy duty fitting practice (see p. C-27)	use heavy duty fitting practice (see p. C-27)	+.0020 / −.0000	use heavy duty fitting practice (see p. C-27)	use heavy duty fitting practice (see p. C-27)	+.0030 / −.0000	.0090 tight / .0150 tight	+.0150 / +.0120
ungground		moderate loads no shock	3	+.0005 / −.0000	.0005 loose / .0005 tight	+.0005 / +.0000	+.0010 / −.0000	.0010 loose / .0010 tight	+.0010 / +.0000	+.0020 / −.0000	.0020 loose / .0020 tight	+.0020 / +.0000	+.0030 / −.0000	.0030 loose / .0030 tight	+.0030 / +.0000
stationary cone	unground / ground	special sheaves, wheels, etc. / moderate loads no shock	4	+.0005 / −.0000	.0010 loose / .0000 loose	−.0000 / −.0005	+.0010 / −.0000	.0020 loose / .0000 loose	−.0000 / −.0010	+.0020 / −.0000	.0040 loose / .0000 loose	−.0000 / −.0020	+.0030 / −.0000	.0040 loose / .0000 loose	−.0000 / −.0030
	hardened and ground	wheel spindles	5	+.0005 / −.0000	.0012 loose / .0002 loose	−.0002 / −.0007	+.0010 / −.0000	.0022 loose / .0002 loose	−.0002 / −.0012						
class: 3 and 0 product **													**class: 3 product only ****		
rotating or stationary cone	ground	precision spindles	6	+.0005 / −.0000	.0002 tight / .0012 tight	+.0012 / +.0007	+.0005 / −.0000	.0002 tight / .0012 tight	+.0012 / +.0007	+.0010 / −.0000	.0005 tight / .0025 tight	+.0025 / +.0015	+.0015 / −.0000	.0010 tight / .0040 tight	+.0040 / +.0025
class: 00 product **															
rotating or stationary cone	ground	precision spindles	7	+.0003 / −.0000	.0002 tight / .0008 tight	+.0008 / +.0005	+.0003 / −.0000	.0002 tight / .0008 tight	+.0008 / +.0005						

class: mill product

mounting conditions	shaft finish	service	line no.		up to 3" inclusive	over 3" to 4" inclusive	over 4" to 5" inclusive	over 5" to 6" inclusive	over 6" to 8" inclusive	over 8" to 12" inclusive	over 12" to 24" inclusive	over 24" to 36" inclusive
rotating cone	ground	rolling mill main roll necks type TDI & TQO low & medium speeds	8	neck dia. equals A*	−.0020 / −.0030	−.0030 / −.0040	−.0040 / −.0050	−.0050 / −.0060	−.0060 / −.0070	−.0070 / −.0080	−.0080 / −.0100	−.0100 / −.0130
				fit	.0020 loose / .0040 loose	.0030 loose / .0050 loose	.0040 loose / .0060 loose	.0050 loose / .0070 loose	.0060 loose / .0080 loose	.0070 loose / .0090 loose	.0080 loose / .0120 loose	.0100 loose / .0160 loose

** = see bearing tolerance chart page A-9. A* = minimum cone bore. † cannot be used for TNASW and TNASWE type over 3.500" bore.

FIG. 3-15. Recommended fits for industrial equipment—cone fitting practice.

Industrial Equipment—Cup Fitting Practice

class: 4 and 2 product **

mounting conditions		line no.	cup outside diameter														
			up to 3" inclusive			over 3" to 5" inclusive			over 5" to 12" inclusive			over 12" to 24" inclusive			over 24" to 36" inclusive		
			cup o.d. equals B-k	fit	cup seat equals B-k	cup o.d. equals B-k	fit	cup seat equals B-k	cup o.d. equals B-k	fit	cup seat equals B-k	cup o.d. equals B-k	fit	cup seat equals B-k	cup o.d. equals B-k	fit	cup seat equals B-k
stationary cup	clamped or floating type TDO-TNA, etc.	1	+.0010 / −.0000	.0030 loose / .0010 loose	+.0020 / +.0030	+.0010 / −.0000	.0030 loose / .0010 loose	+.0020 / +.0030	+.0010 / −.0000	.0030 loose / .0010 loose	+.0020 / +.0030	+.0020 / −.0000	.0060 loose / .0020 loose	+.0040 / +.0030	+.0030 / −.0000	.0090 loose / .0030 loose	+.0060 / +.0090
	alternate clamped only TDO-TDOS, etc.	2	+.0010 / −.0000	.0020 loose / .0000 loose	+.0010 / +.0020	+.0010 / −.0000	.0020 loose / .0000 loose	+.0010 / +.0020	+.0010 / −.0000	.0020 loose / .0000 loose	+.0010 / +.0020	+.0020 / −.0000	.0040 loose / .0000 loose	+.0020 / +.0040	+.0030 / −.0000	.0060 loose / .0000 loose	+.0030 / +.0060
	adjustable	3	+.0010 / −.0000	.0010 loose / .0010 tight	+.0000 / +.0010	+.0010 / −.0000	.0010 loose / .0010 tight	+.0000 / +.0010	+.0010 / −.0000	.0020 loose / .0010 tight	+.0000 / +.0020	+.0020 / −.0000	.0030 loose / .0010 tight	+.0000 / +.0030	+.0030 / −.0000	.0050 loose / .0010 tight	+.0020 / +.0050
stationary or rotating cup	non-adjustable or non-moveable sheaves clamped TDO-TNASW TNASWE	4	+.0010 / −.0000	.0005 tight / .0025 tight	−.0015 / −.0005	+.0010 / −.0000	.0010 tight / .0030 tight	−.0020 / −.0010	+.0010 / −.0000	.0010 tight / .0030 tight	−.0020 / −.0010	+.0020 / −.0000	.0010 tight / .0050 tight	−.0030 / −.0010	+.0030 / −.0000	.0010 tight / .0070 tight	−.0040 / −.0010
rotating cup	sheaves unclamped type TDO-TNASW TNASWE	5	+.0010 / −.0000	.0020 tight / .0040 tight	−.0030 / −.0020	+.0010 / −.0000	.0020 tight / .0040 tight	−.0030 / −.0020	+.0010 / −.0000	.0020 tight / .0040 tight	−.0030 / −.0020	+.0020 / −.0000	.0020 tight / .0060 tight	−.0040 / −.0020			

class: 3 and 0 product **

(over 12" to 24" and over 24" to 36" columns are class: 3 product only **)

spindle mounting conditions		line no.	up to 6" inclusive			over 6" to 12" inclusive			over 12" to 24" inclusive			over 24" to 36" inclusive		
			cup o.d. equals B-k	fit	cup seat equals B-k	cup o.d. equals B-k	fit	cup seat equals B-k	cup o.d. equals B-k	fit	cup seat equals B-k	cup o.d. equals B-k	fit	cup seat equals B-k
stationary cup	floating type TDO-TNA, etc.	6	+.0005 / −.0000	.0015 loose / .0005 loose	+.0010 / +.0015	+.0005 / −.0000	.0015 loose / .0005 loose	+.0010 / +.0015	+.0010 / −.0000	.0025 loose / .0005 loose	+.0015 / +.0025	+.0015 / −.0000	.0035 loose / .0005 loose	+.0020 / +.0035
	clamped type TDO-TNA, etc. or two type TS or TSF, moveable	7	+.0005 / −.0000	.0010 loose / .0000 loose	+.0005 / +.0010	+.0005 / −.0000	.0010 loose / .0000 loose	+.0005 / +.0010	+.0010 / −.0000	.0020 loose / .0000 loose	+.0010 / +.0020	+.0015 / −.0000	.0030 loose / .0000 loose	+.0015 / +.0030
	adjustable	8	+.0005 / −.0000	.0005 loose / .0005 tight	+.0000 / +.0005	+.0005 / −.0000	.0005 loose / .0005 tight	+.0000 / +.0005	+.0010 / −.0000	.0010 loose / .0010 tight	+.0000 / +.0010	+.0015 / −.0000	.0015 loose / .0015 tight	+.0000 / +.0015
	non-adjustable or non-moveable	9	+.0005 / −.0000	.0000 loose / .0010 tight	−.0005 / −.0000	+.0005 / −.0000	.0000 loose / .0010 tight	−.0005 / −.0000	+.0010 / −.0000	.0000 loose / .0020 tight	−.0010 / −.0000	+.0015 / −.0000	.0000 loose / .0030 tight	−.0015 / −.0000
rotating cup	non-adjustable or non-moveable	10	+.0005 / −.0000	.0005 tight / .0015 tight	−.0010 / −.0005	+.0005 / −.0000	.0005 tight / .0015 tight	−.0010 / −.0005	+.0010 / −.0000	.0005 tight / .0025 tight	−.0015 / −.0005	+.0015 / −.0000	.0005 tight / .0035 tight	−.0020 / −.0005

class: 00 product **

stationary cup					
11	floating	+.0003 / –.0000	.0009 loose / .0003 loose	+.0006 / +.0009	
12	clamped moveable	+.0003 / –.0000	.0006 loose / .0000 loose	+.0003 / +.0006	up to 10½" cup o.d.
13	adjustable	+.0003 / –.0000	.0003 loose / .0003 tight	+.0000 / +.0003	
14	non-adjustable	+.0003 / –.0000	.0000 tight / .0006 tight	–.0003 / –.0000	

class: mill product

		size	up to 12" inclusive	over 12" to 24" inclusive	over 24" to 36" inclusive	over 36" to 48" inclusive	over 48" to 60" inclusive
stationary cup	15 rolling mill main rolls	chuck bore equals B*	+.0020 / +.0030	+.0040 / +.0060	+.0060 / +.0090	+.0080 / +.0120	+.0100 / +.0150
		fit	.0030 loose / .0010 loose	.0060 loose / .0020 loose	.0090 loose / .0030 loose	.0120 loose / .0040 loose	.0150 loose / .0050 loose

** see bearing tolerance chart page A-9.   *B = minimum cup outside diameter

FIG. 3-16. Recommended fits for industrial equipment—cup fitting practice.

★ Cone seats—ground 63 microinches max.
★ Cone seats—turned 125 microinches max.
★ Cup seats—turned 125 microinches max.

FIG. 3-17. Recommended finishes for bearing seats.

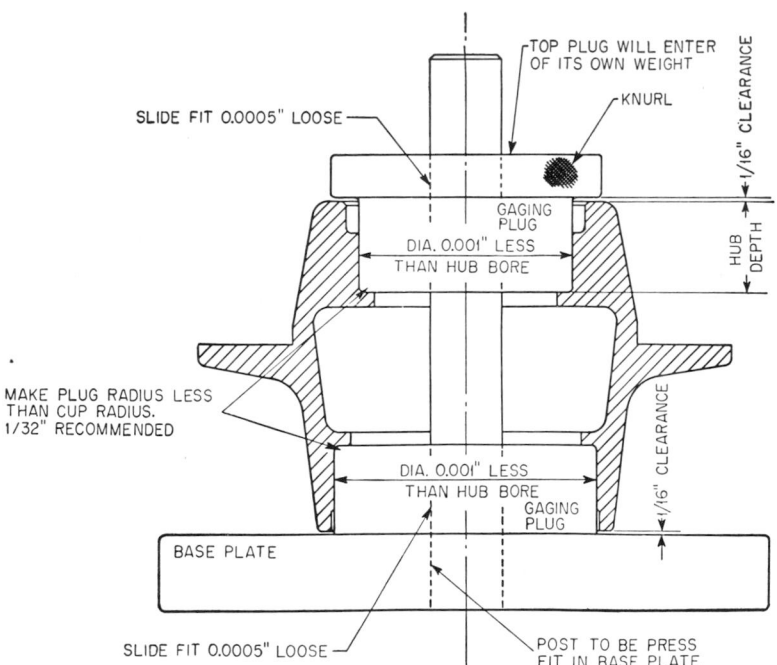

FIG. 3-18. Alignment plugs for checking cup seat or bore alignment.

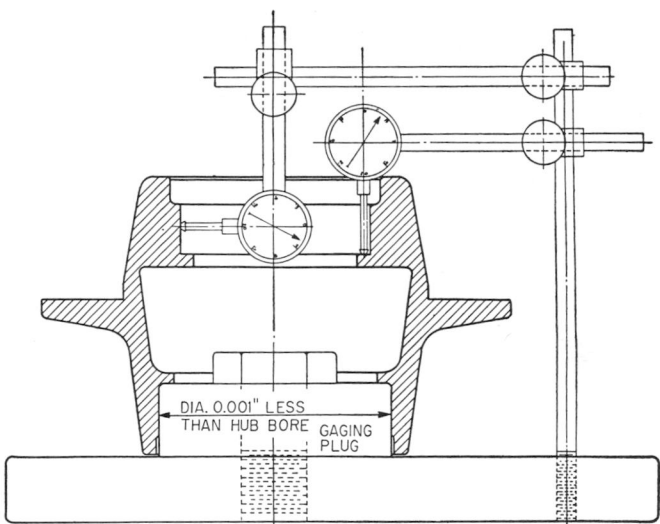

FIG. 3-19. Indicator fixture for checking bore alignment.

they will not hold the fit properly, as the surface will have a series of high spots which will be sheared off or only a small proportion of the surface will actually be in contact with the bearing race.

When parts such as built-up housings have to be remachined, extreme care must be taken to see that the bores are properly aligned. Figure 3-18 shows a go or no-go type of alignment-checking fixture. If the bore alignment is within limits, the plugs will enter. If it exceeds the limits, the plugs will not enter. Figures 3-19 and 3-20 show other alignment-checking fixtures. These use dial indicators for checking one bore against the other or for checking the sides of the housing against the bores, in the case of steel-mill chucks, and the indicators give the actual amount of runout or misalignment of one bore with respect to the other or the bore with respect to the side of the chuck.

Performance is greatly affected if the bearings are not kept properly aligned. The misalignment should not exceed 0.0005 in. eccentricity or 0.001-in. indicator runout per inch of bearing spread. As an example, if the bearing spread or the distance between bearing centers in a wheel hub is 6 in., the indicator runout of one bore with respect to the other should not exceed 0.006-in., as the runout is twice the actual eccentricity or misalignment.

Figure 3-21 illustrates the effect of misalignment. As will be noted, the rollers contact the races only at the extreme end

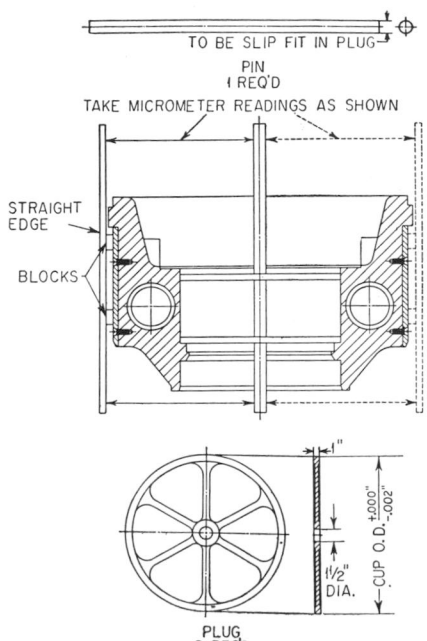

FIG. 3-20. Fixture for checking alignment of bores with sides of chuck.

or in a small area near the end of the roller instead of along the whole length. The cocked condition of the bearing causes this contact to be at the small end of the roller on the one side and the large end at 180°. If only a small length of the roller is used, only a small portion of the bearing is being utilized and the carrying capacity of the bearing as well as the full life expectancy are reduced.

Figures 3-22, 3-23 and 3-24 show some of the causes of misalignment in bearings. Figure 3-22 shows the center lines of the two bores being parallel but actually off center. Figure 3-23 shows the center lines being off parallel. Figure 3-24 shows shoulders and nut faces off square with the bore. Any of these conditions can cause cocking of the bearing or misalignment as shown in Fig. 3-21.

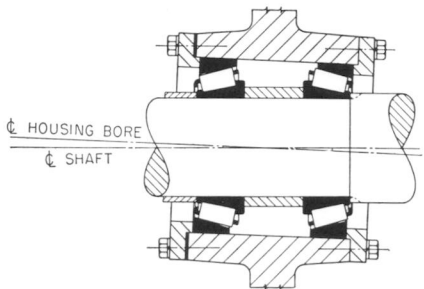

Other points to be watched in checking the shafts and housings are the radii in the shaft and housing shoulders and cage clearance on the bearing. The fillets in the

FIG. 3-21. Effect of misalignment.

housings and on the shafts should be smaller than the corresponding radius on the bearing race; otherwise the bearing will seat against the fillet rather than against the shoulder. When load is applied to the bearing, the race will tend to back up or climb the shaft or housing fillet until it gets good solid backing against the shoulder flat. If this happens, the bearing adjustment is changed by the movement of the

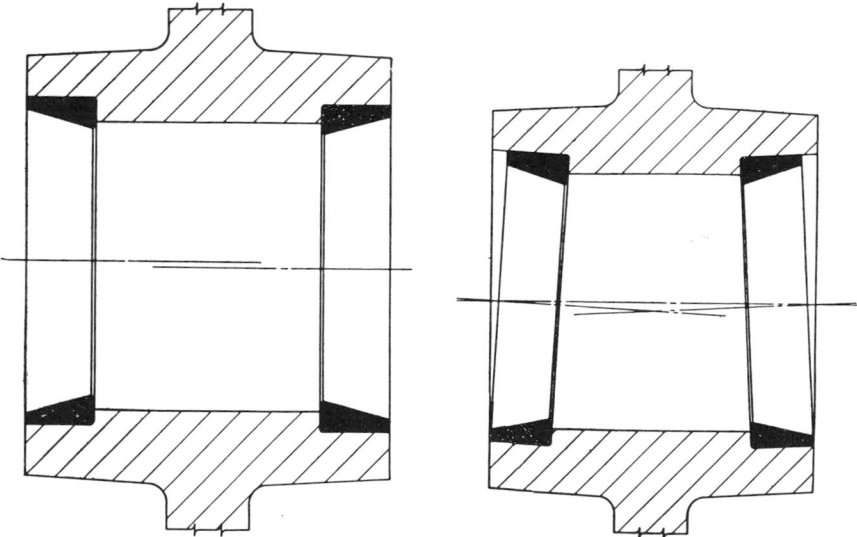

FIG. 3-22. Misalignment caused by bores out of line.

FIG. 3-23. Misalignment due to bores off parallel.

bearing, and it may result in premature failure of the bearing. Cage clearance of $\frac{1}{8}$ in. minimum is recommended. It can readily be seen that if the bearing cage rubs on the housing or any part of the shaft, it will tend to drag, causing the rollers to skew and probably damage or break the cage, resulting in complete bearing failure. This is illustrated in Fig. 3-25.

Figure 3-26 shows what may happen in the machining of split housings. When the tool hits the split at either side, it tends to jump and may leave a high spot which will throw the bearing race out of round. Housings should be checked, and if there is a high spot, it should be ground or filed, leaving a slight relief rather than a hump. This will ensure the perfectly round seat for the race.

In checking over the parts pertaining to bearings, it is important that seals as noted in Fig. 3-27 be carefully checked. Often it has been said that the bearings are no better than the seals or the surrounding parts. This is true, since if the seal is not retaining the lubricant and excluding dirt and water, the bearing will not function properly.

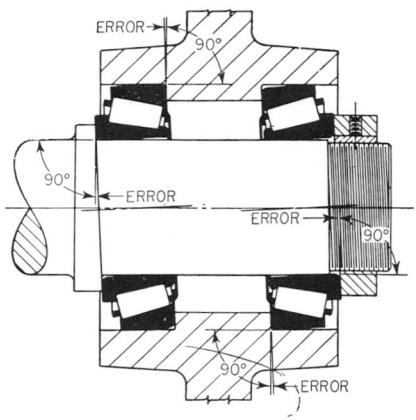

If the seals are at all worn or damaged, they should be replaced with new seals, as the cost of a new seal would ordinarily be very small in comparison with the expense of replacing worn or damaged bearings.

It is important that the housings and shafts be given a careful check to make sure they are thoroughly clean. Special care should be taken to see that any oil pockets or oil channels are cleaned out with a brush or air so there are no foreign particles from worn or failed parts that may have been removed previously. New bearings can be quickly damaged or ruined by pieces of metal that have been left in the housings when new parts were installed.

Fig. 3-24. Misalignment due to shoulders or nut faces off square.

Assembly of Bearings. With the cleaning, inspection, and repair of all parts including the bearings completed, the next step is the assembly of the bearings.

Care should be exerted in assembling bearings on the shafts or in the housings so that no damage is done. Bearing drivers are recommended wherever possible. When the bearings are pressed or driven on shafts or into the housings, drivers as shown in Fig. 3-28 are recommended. These drivers line up the bearing squarely with the bore or with the shaft, making the installation much easier. The drivers prevent nicking of the races or the rollers, and they prevent damage to the cages. Care must be taken

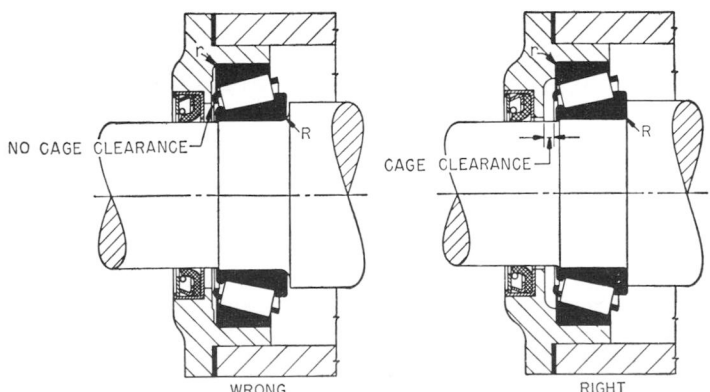

Fig. 3-25. Cage clearance and proper fillet on bearing seats must be provided.

to see that the driver, whether as shown in the illustration or a steel bar, does not contact the bearing cage. The cage, being of soft steel, will bend or distort easily. Any distortion of the cage will cause the rollers to skew or become misaligned, and an early failure of the bearing will be the result. Drivers similar to those shown can be purchased from several suppliers.

Heating the bearing cones to make assembly easier is recommended. By expanding the races, they will drop on the shaft quite readily.   One precaution must be taken, and that is to see that after the race has cooled, it has not pulled away from the shoulder as it may tend to do.   If it does pull away, it should be tapped back against the shoulder.   If this is done while the bearing is cooling, it will be easy to get the race back solidly against the shoulder.   Heating of the bearings can be done by means of an infrared lamp as shown in Fig. 3-29.   Other heating devices are electric ovens of

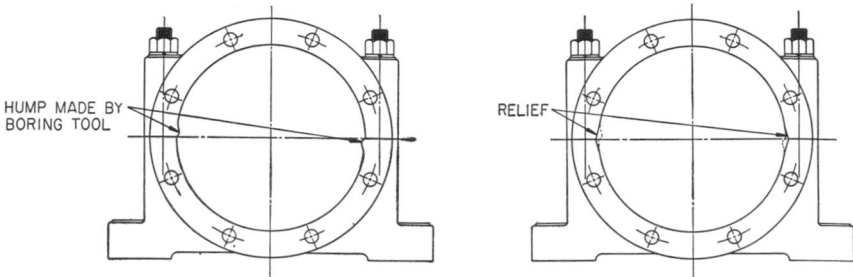

HUMP MADE BY
BORING TOOL

RELIEF

FIG. 3-26. Illustrating relief in bore to ensure against pinching of races.

various types or a hot oil bath.   With either hot oil or an oven-type heater, thermostatic control should be used.   It is important that the temperature of the bearings should never exceed 300°F.   Above 300°F the bearings will start to temper or draw.

To make assembly of the outer races easier, particularly with the very heavy press fit used in aluminum or magnesium housings, freezing of the cup or outer race is recommended.   This freezing or shrinking of the races can be accomplished in a deep-freeze unit as shown in Fig. 3-30 or in a dry ice and alcohol bath.   Sometimes with very heavy press fits, it may be necessary to heat the housings in addition to freezing the race in order to make assembly easy. When the parts are assembled in this manner, care must be taken to see that the races do not pull away from the shoulders as they reach normal temperature.   As the parts warm up, the races should be tapped to make sure they are kept solidly against the shoulder.

FIG. 3-27. Worn or damaged seals should be replaced.

In large, heavy-duty applications where it is difficult to make adjustments because of bulk and weight of the parts, spacers often are used to get the proper bearing adjustment.   Spacers generally are made at the factory and furnished with the bearing, or in other words, the adjustment is predetermined and set at the factory.   The adjustment built in at the factory is based on certain definite fits of the cups and cones, and therefore the recommended fits must be followed in order to hold the proper adjustment in the bearings when they are assembled.   The recommended procedure for assembling bearings with cup and cone spacers may be had from the manufacturer.

Adjustment of Bearings.   One of the big advantages of tapered roller bearings is that they are adjustable.   This allows more latitude in the tolerances on the shaft and in the housing, as variations in fits can be taken care of by adjustment of the bearings. Also, the fact that the bearings can be adjusted to a certain amount of end play, or some preload, allows the bearings to be set to the exact adjustment that is needed for the particular application.   In the case of bevel pinions or machine-tool spindles, the bearings can be preloaded so as to hold the shafts absolutely rigid.   In wheel bearings and other applications, the preferred setting is a free-running clearance of a few thousandths end play.   In general, the desired setting for any antifriction bearing is a slight amount of end play.   The bearings are preloaded or set tight only where some

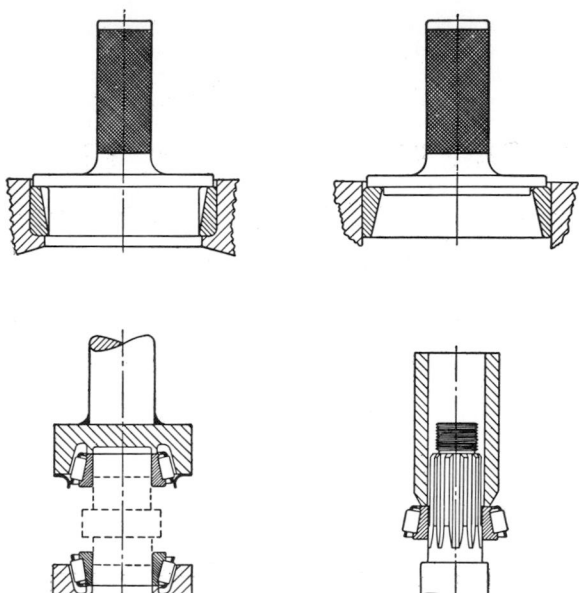

Fig. 3-28. Design of drivers for bearing cups and cones.

outside factor makes it necessary, such as the necessity of holding the hypoid or spiral bevel gear absolutely rigid to maintain perfect gear-tooth contacts.   Any preload on a bearing does use up some of the capacity of the bearing, and therefore the carrying capacity and the life of the bearing are reduced by the amount of load that is put on through this pre-loading.   It can be seen, then, that it is better to set the bearings with a free-running clearance and take full advantage of all the load-carrying capacity of the bearings and to preload only where absolutely necessary.

There are a number of basic adjusting devices used with tapered roller bearings, and a few of these are described in the following paragraphs:

The slotted nut as shown in Fig. 3-31 is probably the most common adjusting device for bearings.   It is used particularly on automotive front wheels and implement wheels.   In general, the adjustment is made by pulling up on the nut with a wrench until there is a slight bind or drag on the bearing, and the nut is then backed off approximately one castellation or slot which gives a free-running clearance in the bearing.

The double nut and tongued washer as shown in Fig. 3-32 is another adjusting device that is com-monly used on wheels, particularly on heavier truck and bus wheels.   The inner nut is pulled up until there is a slight bind on the bearing, and then it is backed off from one-sixth to one-fourth turn, and the outer or locked nut is then tightened and both nuts locked with the washer.   In this device, it is

Fig. 3-29. Heating races by means of infrared lamp.

important that allowances be made for clearance in the threads, as the jamming action against the inner nut will tend to reduce the running clearance in the bearing. It is necessary to back off the inner nut enough to allow for looseness in the threads.

Shims between the end plate and the end of the shaft as shown in Fig. 3-33 are another device commonly used. Here again the end plate can be drawn up without shims until there is a slight bind in the bearings. Then the gap between the plate and

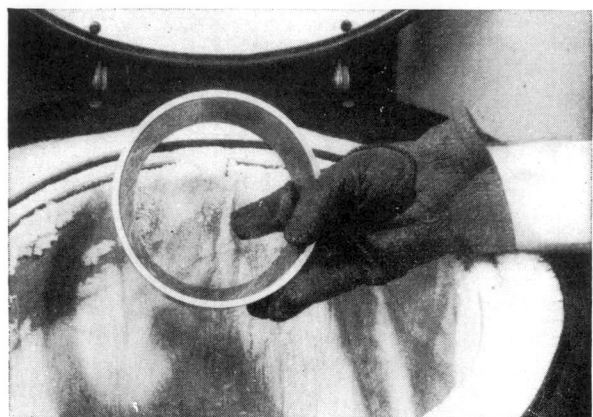

FIG. 3-30. Deep-freeze unit for shrinking races.

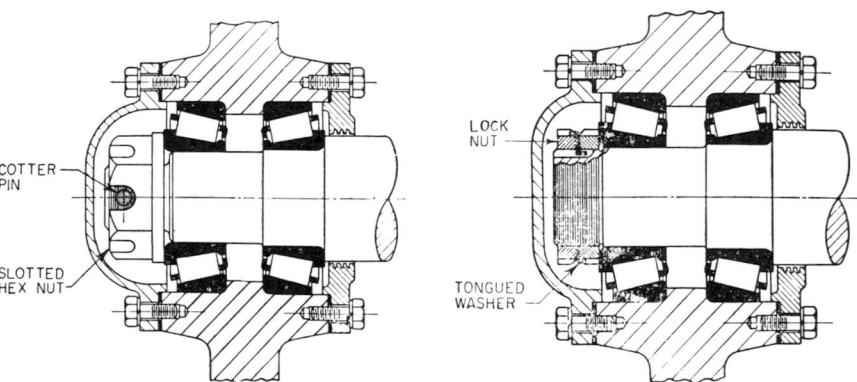

FIG. 3-31. Slotted-nut adjusting device.

FIG. 3-32. Double-nut and lock-washer adjusting device.

the end of the shaft is measured, and 0.003 or 0.005 in. added for running clearance; then a shim pack equal to this total is put in, and the plate and bearings clamped in position.

In Fig. 3-34 is shown the adjustment made by means of shims between the housing and the end cap. The shim pack is selected to give the desired end play or preload on the bearings.

Figure 3-35 shows the adjustment made by means of shims between the cup carrier flange and the housing. This is similar to the previous one except the bearing cups are mounted directly in the carrier instead of the housing.

Figure 3-36 shows the cup-adjusted mounting with the adjustment made by means of a threaded cup follower. Here the threaded cup follower is pulled up until the bearings bind, and then it is either backed off for end play or pulled up slightly to give preload as desired.

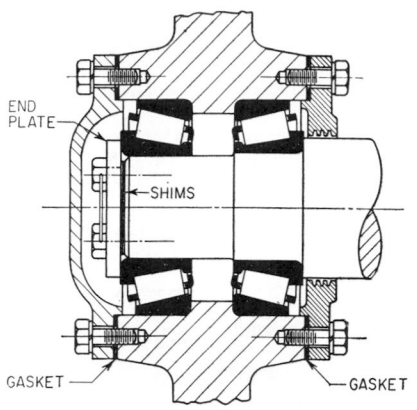

FIG. 3-33. End-plate and shims adjusting device.

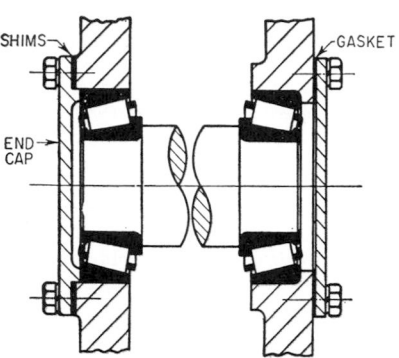

FIG. 3-34. End-cap and shims adjusting device.

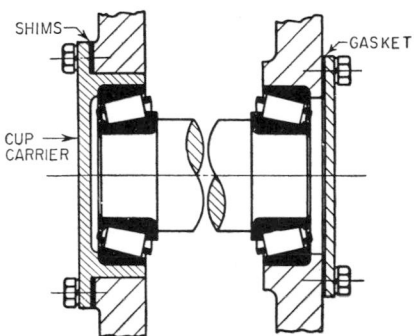

FIG. 3-35. Cup-carrier and shims adjusting device.

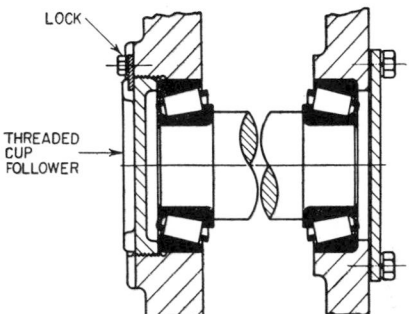

FIG. 3-36. Threaded cup-follower adjusting device.

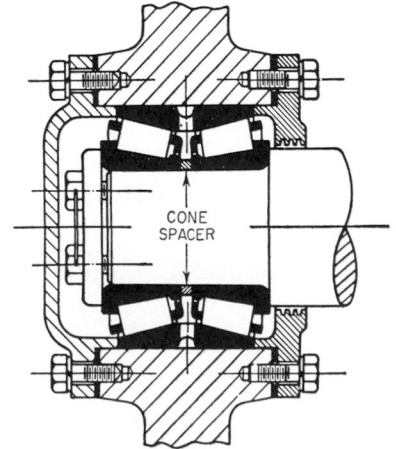

FIG. 3-37. Cone-spacer adjusting device.

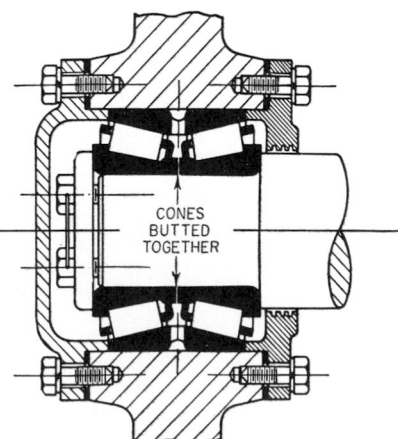

FIG. 3-38. Nonadjustable bearing.

Figure 3-37 shows the adjustment made by means of a spacer between the cones. Spacers are measured either at the factory or on the assembly bench to give the desired setting of the bearings.   After the bearing is clamped in place with the recommended fits on the races, the adjustment cannot be changed on these spacer-adjusted bearings except by using a new spacer or regrinding the one used.

Figure 3-38 shows the type TNA, or nonadjustable, bearings.   Adjustment is built into the bearing at the factory by grinding the ends of the races to give a definite setting of the bearings after they are installed.   It is necessary to follow the recommended fits, or the proper adjustment will not be maintained.

Figure 3-39 shows the cup spacer.   This is similar to the spacer adjustment shown in Fig. 3-37 except it is used between the cups instead of the cones.   The principle is the same, and again it is necessary to follow prescribed fits in order to hold the adjustment that was built in at the factory.

Lubrication of Bearings.   Proper lubrication is essential to all types of bearing applications, whether they be journal or antifriction type.   The kind of lubricant used is governed by the design and operating conditions.   As antifriction bearing applications are continually on the increase, it is only natural to encounter new lubrication problems, even though the same kinds of lubricants are used on all types of bearings.   The lubricant makers, however, have been quite progressive in that many syn-

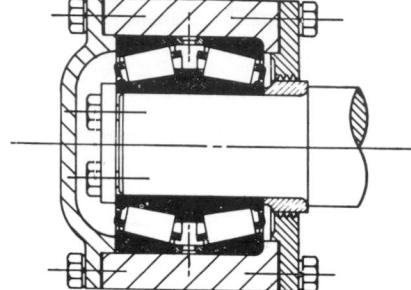

FIG. 3-39. Cup-spacer adjusting device.

thetic, more stable products have been developed for standard and special applications. New-type greases with special properties have been developed and are on the market. Lithium soap and barium soap greases are becoming common, although now used mainly for special applications where the unique properties of these products justify their higher cost.   Silicone fluids and silicone greases have been used, particularly for high-temperature applications.   The large volume of applications, however, is still taken care of by the standard, well-refined mineral oils and the standard lime-soap and sodium-soap greases.   Owing to the use of many new types of testing apparatus and scientific improvements in the production of oils and greases, the so-called regular lubricants are better in many respects than these products were as late as 1941. World War II gave rise to many advances in lubricants and their application.

The main functions of lubricants are:

1. Reduce friction.
2. Carry away heat.
3. Protect bearing surfaces from corrosion.
4. Aid the seals or act as seals in keeping foreign material out of the bearings.

Industrial Greases.   For normal roller bearing applications, greases meeting the following specifications are proving satisfactory:

Greases should be compounded from a high-grade soap and refined mineral oil free from acid, alkali, and any filler which could act as a lapping agent.   The consistency will vary with the temperature and operating conditions.

Corrosion: A bright copper or steel plate must show no marked discoloration after being submerged in the grease for 24 hr.

Moisture. . . . .   Maximum, 1 per cent
Ash. . . . .   Maximum, 2 per cent

Separation: Grease should show no bleeding or separation either in storage or in use.

For moisture conditions and low-temperature operations, use water-repellent greases. For high-temperature operations, use high-dropping-point greases (sodium or lithium soap base).

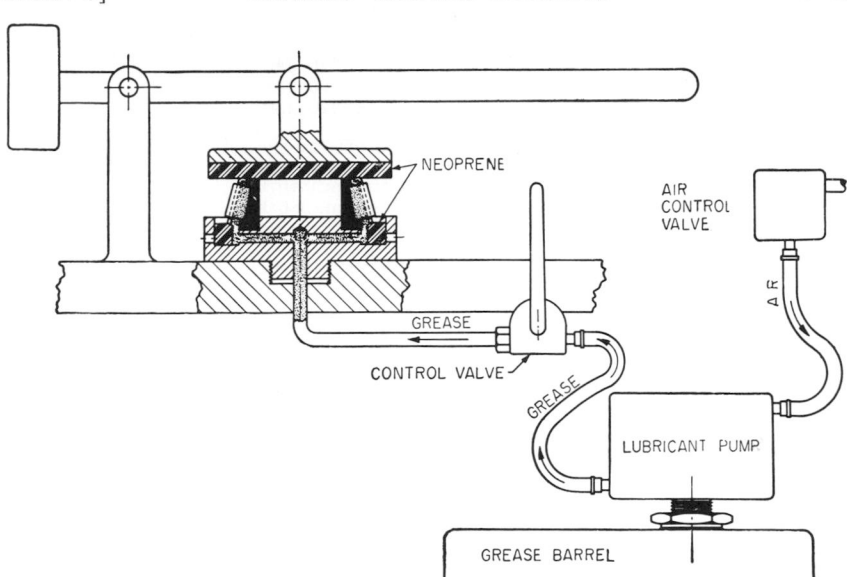

FIG. 3-40. Bearing grease packer.

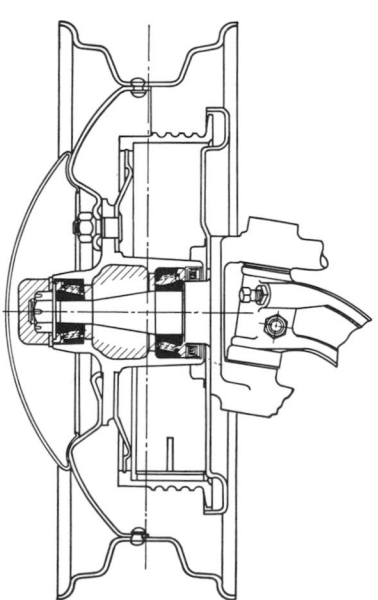

FIG. 3-41. Wheel bearing lubrication.

Penetration, ASTM at 77°F

                    No. 1 grease......... 310–340
                    No. 2 grease......... 265–295
                    No. 3 grease......... 220–250

Oil from which grease is compounded must conform to the following tests:

                    Flash.................... Minimum, 340°F
                    Fire..................... Minimum, 380°F
                    Viscosity at 100°F.......... Saybolt Universal, 200 sec min

Wheel-bearing Greases.   The recommended grease for wheel bearings is a No. 2 or 1 consistency soda-soap grease or possibly a lithium-base grease.   The soda-soap grease is more commonly used.   It is important that nothing heavier than a No. 2 consistency grease be used.   Experience has shown that No. 3 greases tend to channel in cooler weather, and channeling leaves the bearings dry, causing them to score.   Also when the bearings are dry, they are exposed to condensate or moisture and etch rapidly. The etching that occurs with channeled grease reduces life of the bearings greatly. Number 1 grease is softer and is preferred if the seals are in good condition and will hold it.

Grade	Vis. at 210°F, sec
0	44
1	54
2	70
3	90
4	110
5	130
6	150
7	200
8	400
9	500
10	900

In general, it is recommended that wheel bearings be packed with a bearing packer which is operated manually or by air pressure.   If a packer is not available, the bearings can be hand packed.   Packing the bearings with grease gets the grease in between the cage and rollers to the spots where it is needed.   If grease is not put into the bearings as shown in Fig. 3-40 but just put in the housing near the bearings, it may take some time for the grease to warm enough so that it will flow into the bearings, and by that time the bearings can be burned.   At the high speeds at which bearings operate, it is important that grease be at the spots where it is required when the unit starts operating.

FIG. 3-42. Grade and viscosity of lubricants.

Figure 3-41 shows the recommended amount of grease to put into the bearings and wheel hub.   Experience has taught that this is the best method to follow.   Grease in the hub itself merely fills up voids or space; it does, however, prevent the grease from getting out of the bearings.

Fluid Lubricants.   Fluid lubricants may be applied by oil-drip, oil-level, oil-mist, oil-splash, or oil-circulating systems.   Each use is dependent upon the operating conditions.

SAE viscosity No.	Viscosity range, Saybolt Universal, sec	Consistency must not channel in service at °F
80	100,000 at 0°F, max.	−20
90	800–1,500 at 100°F	0
140	120–200 at 210°F	+35
250	200 at 210°F, min.	

FIG. 3-43. Lubricants for severe service.

Oil-mist and oil-drip systems are used only at extremely high operating speeds.   Oil splash is usually combined with an oil level in the bearings.

The grade and viscosity of various fluid lubricants for general use are shown in Fig. 3-42.

Bearings exposed to extreme cold are best lubricated by an oil with a low viscosity and cold test.   A highly refined mineral oil with a viscosity of 75 to 500 sec, Saybolt

Type and Viscosity of Lubricants Recommended for Timken Bearings
(Speed up to 500 rpm)

operating temperature	bearing size	moisture present		no moisture	
		oil	grease	oil	grease
Below 32° F.	Up to 6" O.D.			Neutral Mineral; Viscosity 75 sec. to 500 sec. at 100° F. Saybolt Universal.	Calcium, Sodium or Lithium Base; Medium Consistency ASTM Penetration 265-295.
	6" O.D. and above			Neutral Mineral; Viscosity 75 sec. to 500 sec. at 100° F. Saybolt Universal.	Calcium, Sodium or Lithium Base; Medium Consistency ASTM Penetration 265-295.
32° F. to 125° F.	Up to 6" O.D.	Neutral Mineral; Viscosity 100 sec. to 700 sec. at 100° F. Saybolt Universal.	Calcium or Lithium Base; Medium Consistency ASTM Penetration 265-295.	Neutral Mineral; Viscosity 100 sec. to 700 sec. at 100° F. Saybolt Universal.	Calcium, Sodium or Lithium Base; Medium Consistency ASTM Penetration 265-295.
	6" O.D. and above	Neutral Mineral; Viscosity 100 sec. to 700 sec. at 100° F. Saybolt Universal.	Calcium or Lithium Base; Medium Consistency ASTM Penetration 265-295.	Neutral Mineral; Viscosity 100 sec. to 700 sec. at 100° F. Saybolt Universal.	Calcium, Sodium or Lithium Base; Medium Consistency ASTM Penetration 265-295.
125° F. to 180° F.	Up to 6" O.D.	Neutral Mineral; Viscosity 60 sec. to 100 sec. at 210° F. Saybolt Universal.	*Calcium or Lithium Base; Medium Consistency ASTM Penetration 265-295.	Neutral Mineral; Viscosity 60 sec. to 100 sec. at 210° F. Saybolt Universal.	Sodium or Lithium Base; Medium Consistency ASTM Penetration 265-295.
	6" O.D. and above	Neutral Mineral; Viscosity 60 sec. to 100 sec. at 210° F. Saybolt Universal.	*Calcium or Lithium Base; Medium Consistency ASTM Penetration 265-295.	Neutral Mineral; Viscosity 60 sec. to 100 sec. at 210° F. Saybolt Universal.	Sodium or Lithium Base; Medium Consistency ASTM Penetration 265-295.
Above 180° F.	Up to 6" O.D.	Neutral Mineral; Viscosity 100 sec. and up at 210° F. Saybolt Universal.	Consult the Timken Company Engineering Department.	Neutral Mineral; Viscosity 100 sec. and up at 210° F. Saybolt Universal.	Consult the Timken Company Engineering Department.
	6" O.D. and above	Neutral Mineral; Viscosity 100 sec. and up at 210° F. Saybolt Universal.	Consult the Timken Company Engineering Department.	Neutral Mineral; Viscosity 100 sec. and up at 210° F. Saybolt Universal.	Consult the Timken Company Engineering Department.

*Oil separation from the grease occurs at an increasing rate over 160°F.

FIG. 3-44. Lubricants for speeds up to 500 rpm.

Type and Viscosity of Lubricants Recommended for Timken Bearings
(Speed 500 to 1,000 rpm)

operating temperature	bearing size	moisture present		no moisture	
		oil	grease	oil	grease
Below 32° F.	Up to 6" O.D.			Neutral Mineral; Viscosity 75 sec. to 500 sec. at 100°F. Saybolt Universal.	Calcium, Sodium or Lithium Base; Medium Soft Consistency ASTM Penetration 310-340.
	6" O.D. and above			Neutral Mineral; Viscosity 75 sec. to 500 sec. at 100°F. Saybolt Universal.	Consult the Timken Company Engineering Department.
32° F. to 125° F.	Up to 6" O.D.	Neutral Mineral; Viscosity 100 sec. to 700 sec. at 100° F. Saybolt Universal.	Calcium or Lithium Base; Medium Consistency ASTM Penetration 265-295.	Neutral Mineral; Viscosity 100 sec. to 700 sec. at 100° F. Saybolt Universal.	Calcium, Sodium or Lithium Base; Medium Consistency ASTM Penetration 265-295.
	6" O.D. and above	Neutral Mineral; Viscosity 100 sec. to 700 sec. at 100° F. Saybolt Universal.	Consult the Timken Company Engineering Department.	Neutral Mineral; Viscosity 100 sec. to 700 sec. at 100° F. Saybolt Universal.	Consult the Timken Company Engineering Department.
125° F. to 180° F.	Up to 6" O.D.	Neutral Mineral; Viscosity 60 sec. to 100 sec. at 210° F. Saybolt Universal.	*Calcium or Lithium Base; Medium Consistency ASTM Penetration 265-295.	Neutral Mineral; Viscosity 60 sec. to 100 sec. at 210° F. Saybolt Universal.	Sodium or Lithium Base; Medium Consistency ASTM Penetration 265-295.
	6" O.D. and above	Neutral Mineral; Viscosity 60 sec. to 100 sec. at 210° F. Saybolt Universal.	Consult the Timken Company Engineering Department.	Neutral Mineral; Viscosity 60 sec. to 100 sec. at 210° F. Saybolt Universal.	Consult the Timken Company Engineering Department.
Above 180° F.	Up to 6" O.D.	Neutral Mineral; Viscosity 100 sec. and up at 210° F. Saybolt Universal.	Consult the Timken Company Engineering Department.	Neutral Mineral; Viscosity 100 sec. and up at 210° F. Saybolt Universal.	Consult the Timken Company Engineering Department.
	6" O.D. and above	Neutral Mineral; Viscosity 100 sec. and up at 210° F. Saybolt Universal.	Consult the Timken Company Engineering Department.	Neutral Mineral; Viscosity 100 sec. and up at 210° F. Saybolt Universal.	Consult the Timken Company Engineering Department.

FIG. 3-45. Lubricants for speeds from 500 to 1,000 rpm.

Type and Viscosity of Lubricants Recommended for Timken Bearings
(Speed over 1,000 rpm)

operating temperature	bearing size	moisture present		no moisture	
		oil	grease	oil	grease
Below 32° F.	Up to 6" O.D.			Neutral Mineral; Viscosity 75 sec. to 500 sec. at 100° F. Saybolt Universal.	Sodium or Lithium Base; Short Fibre Medium Soft Consistency ASTM Penetration 310-340.
	6" O.D. and above			Neutral Mineral; Viscosity 75 sec. to 500 sec. at 100° F. Saybolt Universal.	Consult the Timken Company Engineering Department.
32° F. to 125° F.	Up to 6" O.D.	Neutral Mineral; Viscosity 100 sec. to 700 sec. at 100° F. Saybolt Universal.	Calcium or Lithium Base; Medium Consistency ASTM Penetration 265-295.	Neutral Mineral; Viscosity 100 sec. to 700 sec. at 100° F. Saybolt Universal.	Sodium or Lithium Base; Medium Consistency ASTM Penetration 265-295.
	6" O.D. and above	Neutral Mineral; Viscosity 100 sec. to 700 sec. at 100° F. Saybolt Universal.	Consult the Timken Company Engineering Department.	Neutral Mineral; Viscosity 100 sec. to 700 sec. at 100° F. Saybolt Universal.	Consult the Timken Company Engineering Department.
125° F. to 180° F.	Up to 6" O.D.	Neutral Mineral; Viscosity 60 sec. to 100 sec. at 210° F. Saybolt Universal.	*Calcium or Lithium Base; Medium Consistency ASTM Penetration 265-295.	Neutral Mineral; Viscosity 60 sec. to 100 sec. at 210° F. Saybolt Universal.	Sodium or Lithium Base; Medium Consistency ASTM Penetration 265-295.
	6" O.D. and above	Neutral Mineral; Viscosity 60 sec. to 100 sec. at 210° F. Saybolt Universal.	Consult the Timken Company Engineering Department.	Neutral Mineral; Viscosity 60 sec. to 100 sec. at 210° F. Saybolt Universal.	Consult the Timken Company Engineering Department.
Above 180° F.	Up to 6" O.D.	Neutral Mineral; Viscosity 100 sec. and up at 210° F. Saybolt Universal.	Consult the Timken Company Engineering Department.	Neutral Mineral; Viscosity 100 sec. and up at 210° F. Saybolt Universal.	Consult the Timken Company Engineering Department.
	6" O.D. and above	Neutral Mineral; Viscosity 100 sec. and up at 210° F. Saybolt Universal.	Consult the Timken Company Engineering Department.	Neutral Mineral; Viscosity 100 sec. and up at 210° F. Saybolt Universal.	Consult the Timken Company Engineering Department.

*Oil separation from the grease occurs at an increasing rate over 160° F.

FIG. 3-46. Lubricants for speeds over 1,000 rpm.

Lubricants Recommended for Heavy Duty Applications

operating temperature	moisture present		no moisture	
	oil	grease	oil	grease
Below 32° F.			Extreme pressure oil viscosity 75 sec. to 100 sec. @ 210°F. Saybolt Universal. Load capacity minimum 35 lb. lever load. Timken Lubricant Tester.	Extreme pressure grease. ASTM Penetration 310-340. Load capacity minimum 35 lb. lever load. Timken Lubricant Tester.
32° F. to 125° F.	Extreme pressure oil viscosity 100 sec. to 175 sec. @ 210°F. Saybolt Universal. Load capacity minimum 35 lb. lever load. Timken Lubricant Tester.	Extreme pressure water resistant grease. ASTM Penetration 265-295. Load capacity minimum 35 lb. lever load. Timken Lubricant Tester.	Extreme pressure oil viscosity 100 sec. to 175 sec. @ 210°F. Saybolt Universal. Load capacity minimum 35 lb. lever load. Timken Lubricant Tester.	Extreme pressure grease. ASTM Penetration 265-295. Load capacity minimum 35 lb. lever load. Timken Lubricant Tester.
125° F. to 180° F.	Extreme pressure oil viscosity 100 sec. to 250 sec. @ 210°F. Saybolt Universal. Load capacity minimum 35 lb. lever load. Timken Lubricant Tester.	Extreme pressure water resistant grease. ASTM Penetration 265-295. Load capacity minimum 35 lb. lever load. Timken Lubricant Tester.	Extreme pressure oil viscosity 100 sec. to 250 sec. @ 210°F. Saybolt Universal. Load capacity minimum 35 lb. lever load. Timken Lubricant Tester.	Extreme pressure grease. ASTM Penetration 265-295. Load capacity minimum 35 lb. lever load. Timken Lubricant Tester.
Above 180° F.	Extreme pressure oil viscosity 175 sec. to 250 sec. @ 210°F. Saybolt Universal. Load capacity minimum 35 lb. lever load. Timken Lubricant Tester.	Consult the Timken Company Engineering Department.	Extreme pressure oil viscosity 175 sec. to 250 sec. @ 210°F. Saybolt Universal. Load capacity minimum 35 lb. lever load. Timken Lubricant Tester.	Consult the Timken Company Engineering Department.

FIG. 3-47. Lubricants for heavy-duty applications.

Universal, at 100°F is recommended, depending on the application; that is, the lighter-bodied oils are used at high speeds and light loads; the heavier-bodied oils at lower speeds and more heavily loaded units.

High-speed applications usually require a light oil and a drop-feed or wick-feed system. Adequate provision to drain away the surplus oil must be provided as any excess of lubricant will cause the bearings to heat because of churning. The drain should be so located that the lowest point of the bearing will not dip into the oil more than $\frac{1}{8}$ in. This condition may also be obtained through the use of constant-level oilers. In applications subjected to extreme heat, such as certain paper-mill units, or where it is impossible to keep out dirt or water, a circulating-oil system is recommended. When these units are installed, care must be exercised that the proper amount of oil is fed to the bearings. Whenever necessary, suitable filters and cooling units should be included in the system. Applications which have physical limitations preventing the use of suitable closures to hold oil are best lubricated with special greases.

Extreme-pressure Gear Lubricants. Extreme pressure lubricants are used extensively in mill-gear drives and roller bearings in these units. For gear drives, extreme-pressure gear oils are in common use with the Saybolt viscosity grades as shown in Fig. 3-42.

These gear oils usually have an extreme-pressure value between 33 and 68 lb when rated by the Timken Company lubricant tester.

For automotive hypoid gears, where both the gears and antifriction bearings used in the units require lubrication, two SAE grades, 90 and 140, are normally used. For extremely cold operating conditions (around −40 to −60°F), a lighter 80 grade is used, and for high-temperature or heavy-duty applications, the SAE 140 grade is used. For extremely heavy loads and high temperatures, the SAE 250 is recommended (see Fig. 3-43). These grades, meeting U.S. Ordnance Specification 2-105B, are in common use and are quite satisfactory. A number of large companies are using these gear oils for industrial gear oil applications with very good results.

Types and viscosities of lubricants recommended for Timken bearings at all speeds are given in Figs. 3-44 to 3-47.

For a glossary of lubrication terms see Sec. 12, Chap. 1, Lubricants.

Chapter 4

FRICTION CLUTCHES

By Alex T. Bodle[1]
Chief Engineer
Dodge Manufacturing Corporation
Mishawaka, Ind.

The proper installation, care, and maintenance of a friction clutch requires a knowledge of what a clutch is, what it does, how it operates, and its details of construction.

A friction clutch is a device by means of which one rotating element may impart rotation and transmit torque to another element by friction.

Friction clutches are used in almost all situations involving the necessity for connecting or disconnecting a power source and a driven machine with the power source in motion.

These situations fall in two general classes: first, those in which it is necessary to disconnect the driver from the load in order to permit starting the driver under no load. In these cases the clutch is then used to pick up the load after the power source is up to at least partial normal speed. The most common examples are internal-combustion engines with clutch power take-off. Heavy starting loads driven by electric motors may also be clutch driven in order to protect the motor from severe starting demand.

In the second general classification are those cases where the driven machine or load must be started or stopped without stopping the power source. This may be a multiple operation, as when several machines are independently driven from one common drive shaft, or it may be an individual operation, as, for example, the clutch driving a punch press, in which case the clutch may be engaged for each stroke of the press without stopping the motor.

The clutching arrangement may be either of two general forms: one in which two shafts are directly connected together by means of a clutch coupling, the other in which power is delivered to or from the clutch through a wheel which runs loose on the shaft when disengaged. The first is confined to those cases in which the driving and driven shafts are coaxial and run at the same speed. The clutch in this case is known as a friction clutch coupling. The second form is, in general, referred to as a *sleeve-type* clutch because one element of the clutch often is a sleeve on which the wheel is mounted. In this general type both the driving and driven elements of the clutch are mounted on the same shaft and power is transmitted to or from another parallel shaft by means of belts, chains, or gears. In this arrangement the driving and driven shafts need not run at the same speed.

Both the clutch coupling and the sleeve clutch may employ clutch designs of several types, and the operator should be familiar with the general characteristics of the type used in each of his particular installations.

Types of Friction Clutches. The operating principle of all friction clutches is the same in that in all cases torque is transmitted from one part to another by friction produced by pressure between the parts.

[1] The author is now retired.

The main part of the clutch which provides means for producing this pressure is commonly called the "mechanism" (see Figs. 4-1 and 4-2).   The mechanism may be either the driving or the driven part.   The other part may be a cutoff coupling hub, a sleeve on which a wheel is mounted, or it may be the wheel itself (see Figs. 4-3 to 4-5).

Both mechanism and its mating part carry friction surfaces which are pressed together when the clutch is engaged.

The friction surfaces employed may be of either flat or cylindrical form.   The former employs flat disks or rings which rotate about an axis perpendicular to the surface.   These are known as *disk-type* clutches.   They may employ one or more disks, the torque being proportional to the number of friction surfaces.

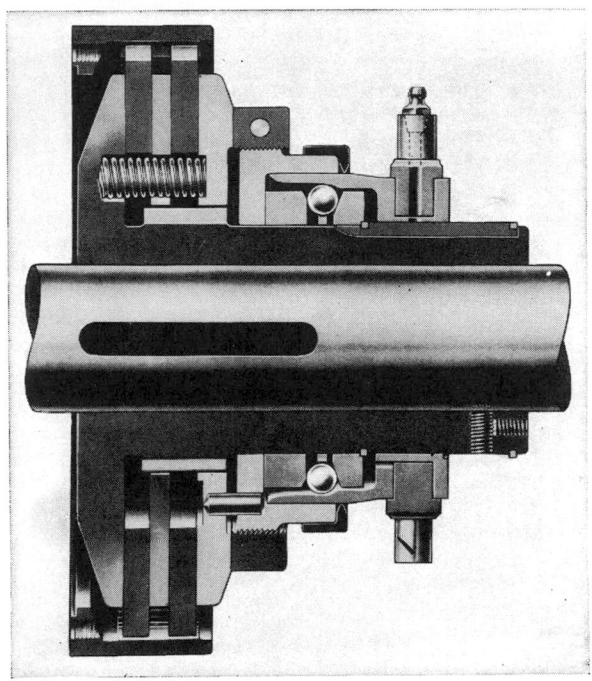

FIG. 4-1. Clutch mechanism, basic working part of the clutch.   It must be built into a pulley, sleeve, cutoff coupling hub, or flywheel before it can be used to transmit power.

In cylindrical types the axis of rotation is parallel to the friction surface.   Either the internal or the external or both internal and external surfaces may be employed. These types are generally known as *expanding-ring, band,* or *shoe-type* clutches. "Cone" clutches are a variation of the cylindrical type in which the wedging action of one cone inside another is utilized to magnify the pressure.

Nature of Friction Surfaces.   In all types one of the rubbing surfaces usually is of bare iron or steel.   The mating surface generally is lined with some sort of "friction" material which may be either nonmetallic or metallic.

Nonmetallic linings usually employ an asbestos filler bonded together with various resinous or other compounds designed for high friction quality and good heat and wear resistance.   The asbestos may be in the form of a woven fabric, in which case the product is known as a "woven" lining.   In other types the asbestos is in macerated form, and the product is known as a "molded" type.   In both instances a wire reinforcing, usually brass, is sometimes employed.

Another type of nonmetallic lining consists of a cork filler bound together with resinous, protein, or synthetic type of binder.   These linings are usually bonded to a metal backing plate by means of special thermosetting adhesives furnished by the manufacturer.

Metallic frictions may be solid plates of steel or bronze, or they may consist of sintered bronze material bonded to a steel backing.

These types have the advantage of being relatively thin, thus permitting compact designs, particularly in multiple-plate disk clutches. They also have good wear and heat resistance and permit rapid heat transmission. Allowable pressures are relatively high.

Coefficient of Friction. The coefficient of friction of the various types of linings varies over quite a wide range depending on their composition. Asbestos types usually range from 0.2 to 0.4 coefficient when used dry. A normal average is about 0.24 to 0.28.

Cork linings vary from 0.10 to 0.50 depending on pressure, speed, and design. Sintered types also vary quite widely according to their composition but are usually designed to give a coefficient of about 0.20 to 0.25 for smooth starting.

Most friction materials can be used in oil but with considerable loss in coefficient of friction, values ranging perhaps from 0.06 to 0.15.

Plates for oil operation require grooving to give a squeegee effect and to help prevent oil film formations. Care must be taken to see that these grooves do not become clogged.

Because of the great number of compositions of all types it is not possible here to give specific values; information regarding the exact characteristics for any specific material under any given conditions must be obtained from the manufacturer.

Types of Mechanisms. Clutch mechanisms may be actuated mechanically, by air pressure, or by magnetic force. In all cases the actuating force is used to produce the clutch engaging pressure while spring pressure is utilized to disengage the clutch when the actuating force is released.

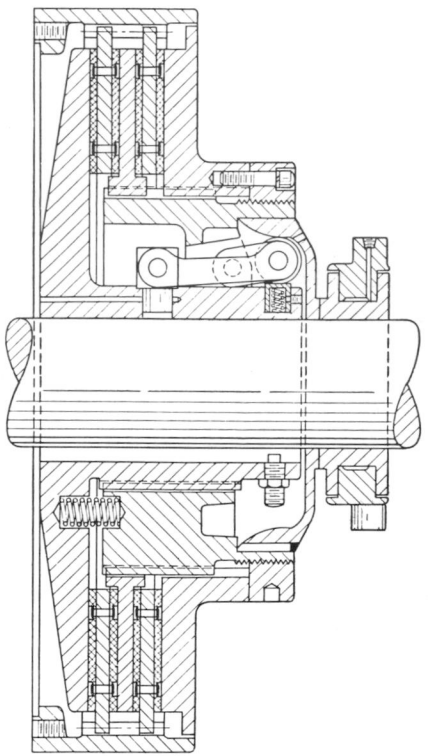

FIG. 4-2. Section of clutch mechanism.

Mechanical clutches, Fig. 4-6, usually employ a "toggle" system for multiplying the engaging force. This may be a system of levers or cams or a combination of both.

So-called "overcenter" clutches employ toggles or cams which lock in the engaged position, thus eliminating the necessity of maintaining constant pressure on the operating levers after the clutch has been engaged. For very rapid frequency of operation the "overcenter" feature often is omitted.

Mechanical clutches usually are manually operated but may be operated by air or hydraulic cylinders or by solenoids. Pressure is applied to the mechanism through a sliding cam or spool on which is mounted a nonrotating slip ring.

Pressure applied to the slip ring is in turn magnified by the mechanical advantage of the toggle system.

Mechanical clutches require means of adjustment to compensate for wear and to control the plate pressure. Tight adjustment increases the pressure and torque capacity but requires greater force on the operating lever. Since the pressure applied to the slip-ring operating lever is an external force, there is always a reaction tending

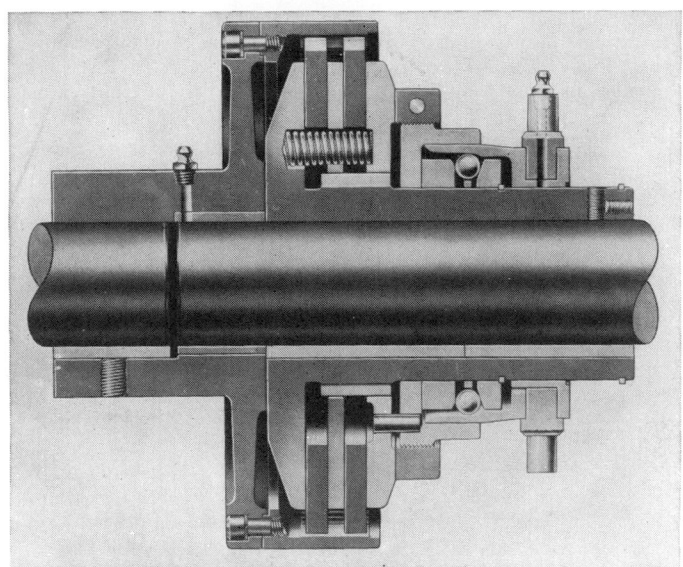

FIG. 4-3. Cutoff coupling.   It is mounted on one end of a shaft, and the cutoff coupling hub is on the end of the mating shaft.

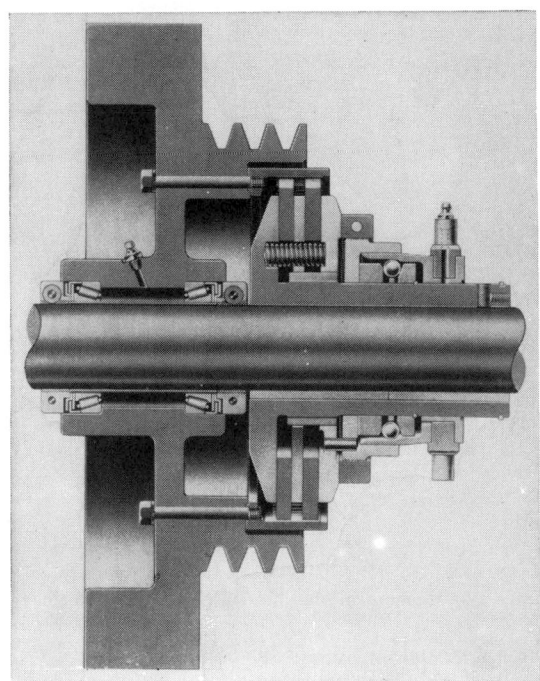

FIG. 4-4. Clutch flywheel, applied to standard mechanism.   Flywheels are designed to meet requirements of specific applications.

to move the mechanism on the shaft and to move the shaft itself. It is, therefore, necessary to provide positive means of preventing either of such movements.

Air clutches, Figs. 4-7 to 4-11, employ air pressure to actuate the friction surfaces. Disk types utilize, in effect, a built-in piston, which may be in reality a piston or may

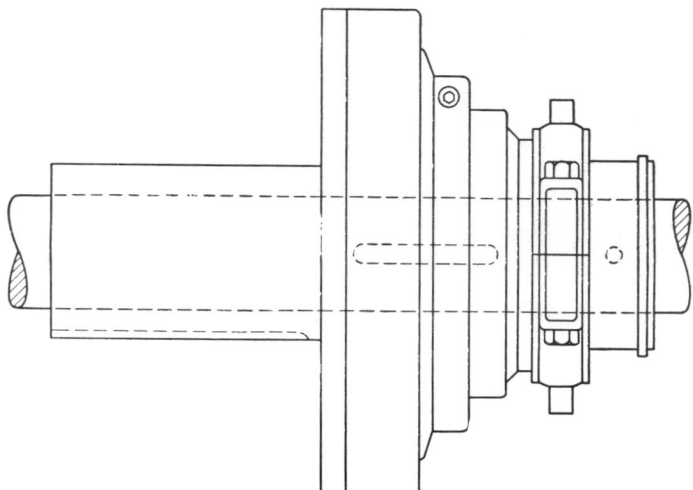

Fig. 4-5. Clutch with sleeve.

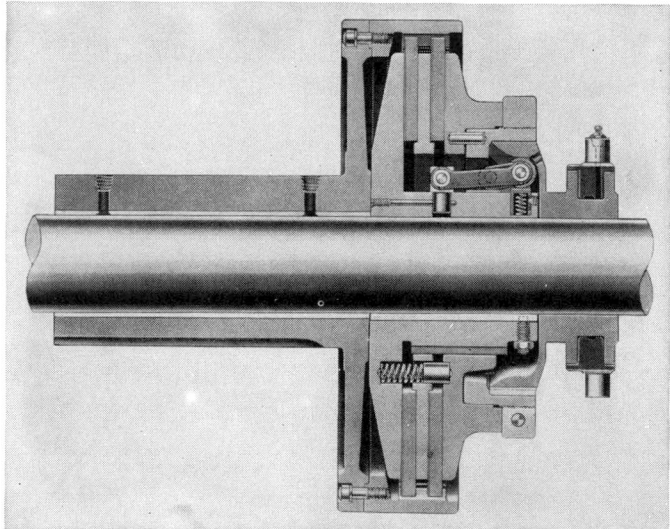

Fig. 4-6. Mechanical clutch with bronze bushed sleeve.

be a diaphragm or an expanding tube or bladder. Cylindrical types employ a tire-shaped tube so arranged and restricted that inflation causes pressure between the tube and the cylindrical friction surface. They may be either expanding or constricting type, the latter being generally used on high speeds to prevent engagement by centrifugal force.

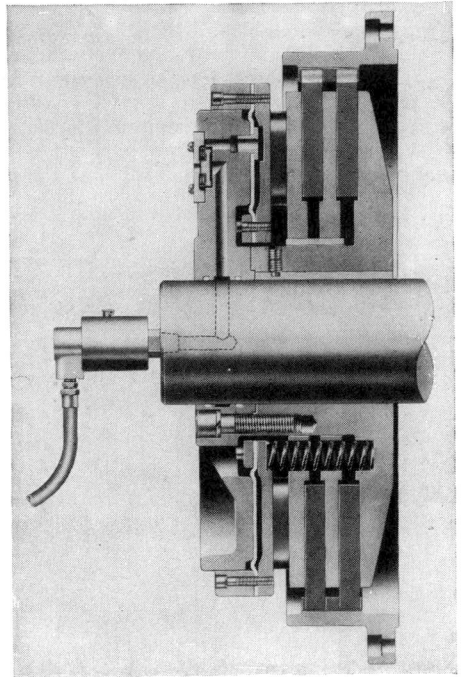

FIG. 4-7. Air clutch mechanism.

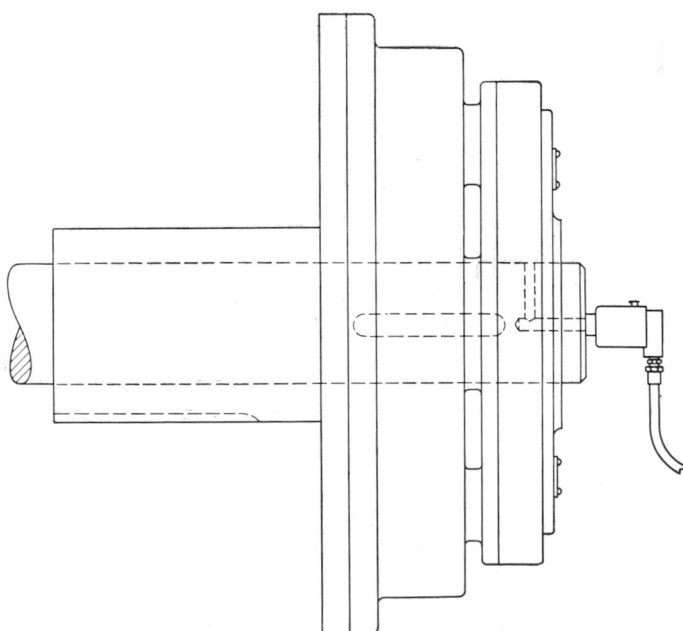

FIG. 4-8. Air clutch with sleeve.

The friction lining in band or segment form is attached to the air tube, which in turn is attached to one of the principal members of the clutch.

The torque capacity of air clutches may be varied over quite a wide range by varying the air pressure. Most manufacturers base the normal rating on 80 to 100 psi. Pressures as low as 20 psi may be used where slipping conditions require a clutch relatively large in comparison with torque requirements to permit sufficient heat dissipation.

When maximum torque is required, pressures as high as 150 psi may be used.

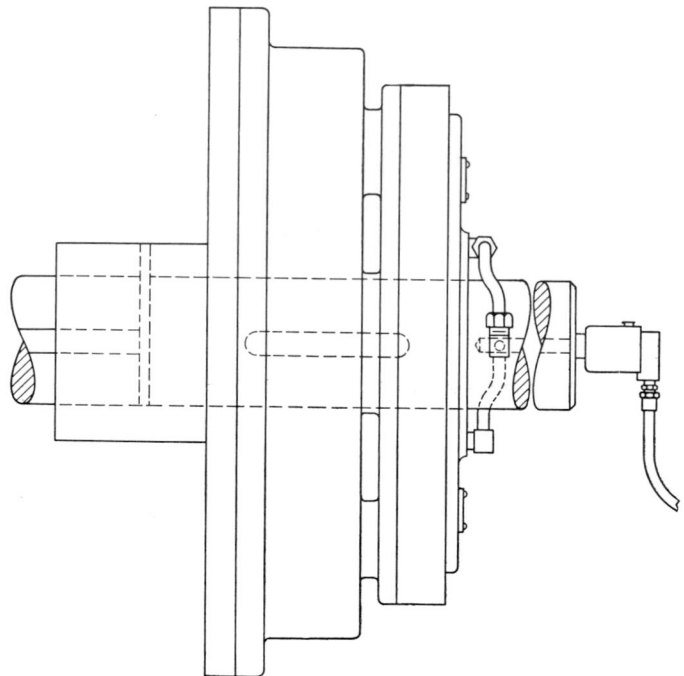

Fig. 4-9. Air clutch cutoff couplings.

When air supply is of constant pressure, the pressure applied to the clutch may be varied by means of a pressure-regulating control valve which permits use of any pressure up to the maximum available.

For sensitive control, particularly where "inching" is required, a variable-pressure control valve should be used which admits air under gradually increasing pressure, depending on the position of the control handle.

For continuous running after final engagement, a valve which locks in at final position should be used. For very rapid operation where the clutch must be under constant control by the operator, a valve which automatically returns to the "off" position when released should be used. These cases usually require a "quick-release" valve to afford instant disengagement. Such valves are available either as a built-in feature or as an accessory.

Air clutches require no mechanical adjustment, since the moving parts automatically take up any wear on the friction surfaces.

Air pressure must be maintained continuously while the clutch is engaged. This requires an ample supply of air. In many plants air is available from general-purpose air lines. When such supply is not available, or when available air is of insufficient pressure, then a special unit comprising a motor-driven air compressor and reservoir tank is required. The volume of available air supply required varies with the size of the clutch, the volume of the supply line between the control valve and the clutch, and the frequency of engagement.   The volumetric capacity of the clutch itself varies with the size and design and must be obtained from the manufacturer.

Air supply should be as free from moisture as possible.   A small amount of oil in the air is not objectionable, and for designs of the piston type a slight amount of oil is desirable as a lubricant.

Air clutches require the use of rotating air seals to permit entrance of air to the clutch.   These are fitted concentrically to the end of the shaft and air is usually conducted from the seal to the clutch through passages drilled in the shaft.   This requires

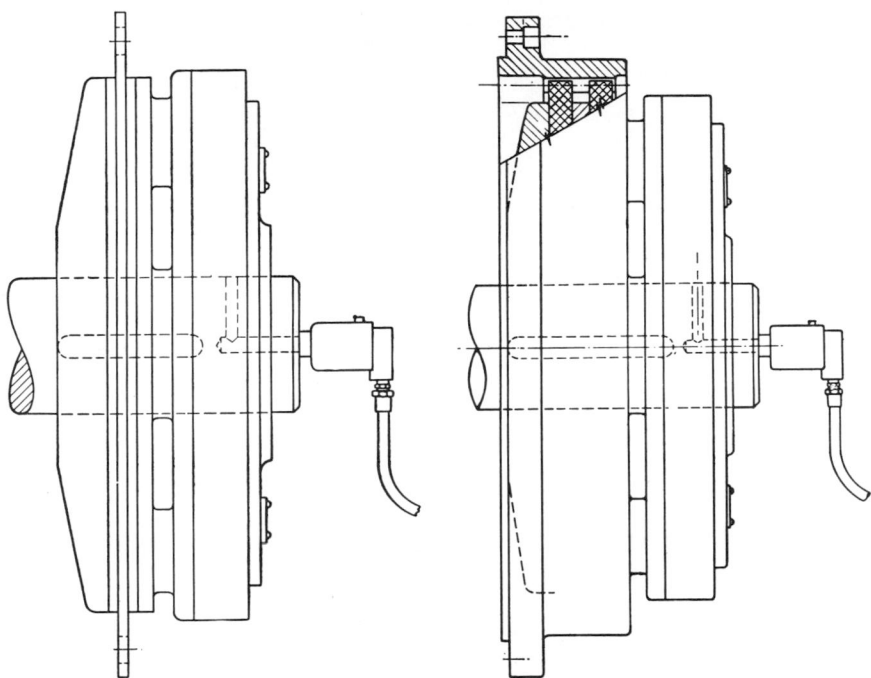

FIG. 4-10.   Air clutch bolted-plate mechanism.

FIG. 4-11.   Air clutch gear-tooth plate mechanism.

that clutch be located relatively close to a free end of the shaft and limits the length of shaft which can be directly coupled by an air clutch coupling.   However, it is possible in some cases to conduct the air a considerable distance along the shaft by means of tubing.   Rotating air-inlet seals for mounting anywhere along the shaft are possible but involve quite costly designs that are not generally available.

Duplex air-inlet seals for shaft end application are available.   Such seals permit the use of two clutches on the same shaft, with air inlet at the same end of the shaft.   Such clutches may be operated independently but require separate operating or control valves.   When it is desired to operate them alternately, they may be operated by one control valve but it must be of the "four-way" type having two independent outlets.

Air clutches are suitable for remote-control operation.   However, as the length of air line from control valve to clutch increases, the volume of air required increases and operation becomes less sensitive.   Solenoid-operated valves permit locating valves close to the clutch and allow operation at great distances.   However, this arrangement should be limited to cases where gradual engagement or great sensitivity for inching is not required.

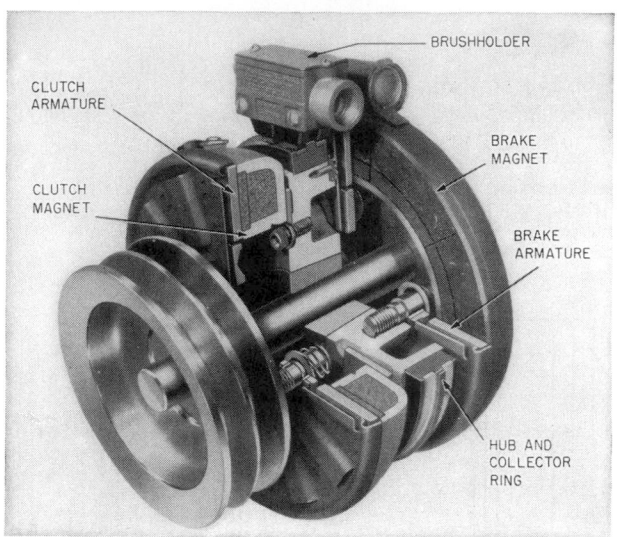

FIG. 4-12. PC-PB (primary clutch-primary brake) line clutch.   Primary refers to the fact that the electric coil and friction facing are embodied in the same shell.   (*Courtesy of Warner Electric Brake & Clutch Co., Beloit, Wis.*)

Magnetic clutches, Figs. 4-12 to 4-15, inclusive, as the name implies, are actuated by magnets energized by application of electric current.   Current must be direct, and in plants where alternating current only is available, a rectifier must be used.   Magnetic clutches are commonly designed for either 220- or 110-volt operation.

Current is applied to the energizing coils through annular bronze slip rings and carbon brushes.   These clutches may, therefore, be applied at any point along the length of a shaft and are especially suited to coupling applications.

Magnetic clutches are well adapted to remote control, but in cases requiring low starting torque for the protection of electric motors in starting, rather costly special controls are required.   This is usually accomplished by means of manually operated rheostats.   A variety of controls is available for push-button operation and for various starting devices.   Recommendations for proper controls should be obtained from the maker.

Continuous current flow is necessary to keep clutches in engagement comparable to the constant air pressure required for air clutches and in contrast to the overcenter mechanical clutch, which requires force only while being engaged or disengaged.

FIG. 4-13. Electric stationary-field line clutch, including pin-type armature and hub.   No collector rings or brushes. Field (1) embodies the coil and is mounted stationary to the machine.   Rotor (2), mounted to shaft, contains friction facing. Armature (3) is second friction member and usually is mounted to a pulley, sheave, sprocket, or other such device.   (*Courtesy of Warner Electric Brake & Clutch Co., Beloit, Wis.*)

To a limited extent magnetic clutches require no mechanical adjustment to compensate for friction surface wear.   However, most magnetic clutches are provided with such an adjustment for the purpose of maintaining a constant air gap and, therefore, constant magnetic pull and plate pressure.

In general the mechanical, air, and magnetic clutches discussed comprise the types usually found in common industrial use.   Other types such as magnetic induction clutches of the high-hysteresis and the eddy-current type as well as the magnetic fluid types are found principally only in special machine applications requiring low torque, variable speed, or other special characteristics and are not included in this discussion.   Figures 4-16 to 4-18 illustrate applications.

Selection, Installation, and Maintenance.   In many applications, friction clutches have acquired a rather undeserved reputation as troublemakers.   This is in part

Fig. 4-14.   Fig. 4-15.

Fig. 4-14. Magnetic clutch, type "DL," with plug-type lining carrier support, for applications where torsional vibration may be severe.   The magnet, consisting of both the field and armature members, is supported on a single hub generally mounted on the driving shaft.   The friction lining is supported between the field and armature rings by a splined lining carrier ring attached to the driven nut by a spring plate.   When deenergized, the magnet half of the clutch rotates independently of the lining carrier half.   When the magnet member is electrically energized, the armature is attracted toward the field, gripping the lining between the armature and field rings and producing the driving torque. (*Courtesy of Cutler-Hammer, Inc., Milwaukee, Wis.*)

Fig. 4-15. Magnetic clutch, type "DL," with pin-type lining carrier support, used for most general-purpose applications where torsional vibration is not severe.   See caption of Fig. 4-14 for description of operation.   (*Courtesy of Cutler-Hammer, Inc., Milwaukee, Wis.*)

because they have a very tough job.   By their very nature they are expected to slip at every start; otherwise a much cheaper positive-engagement clutch could be used.   In many cases this slippage is very severe, as in starting heavy inertia loads.   Other operations require inching or a very high frequency of engagements.   In doing this the friction clutch protects other machinery from shock and overload and in many instances permits the use of smaller power units.   These things it does by absorbing shock and limiting applied torque through its ability to slip.

But slip produces both heat and wear.   So the friction clutch becomes at once a benefactor and a martyr.   Nevertheless, clutches of proper design and size, properly installed and cared for, give a very good account of themselves.   It is a matter of record that many clutches are still in use after more than 30 years of service.   When a friction clutch does give trouble, it is usually due to improper selection, improper installation, or improper attention.

Selection of Friction Clutches.   In the selection of a friction clutch it is first necessary to choose the most suitable type and, when this is done, then to determine the proper size.

In the determination of the most suitable type, it is useful to consider the following summary of the obvious advantages and disadvantages of each as they are indicated by the foregoing description.

Mechanical clutches are relatively low in total over-all cost, since they need very little accessory equipment with which to operate them.   They do not require constant application of force on the operating mechanism to keep them engaged.   They may be

Fɪɢ. 4-16. Air clutch application in metalworking plant.

Fɪɢ. 4-17. Mechanical clutches on cutter cylinder drive in paper-board mill.

located anywhere on a shaft and may readily be used as cutoff couplings between shafts regardless of shaft lengths.   Torque capacity may be varied within certain limits by varying the adjustment.

Among their disadvantages are poor sensitivity, making inching difficult, physical effort required on the part of the operator particularly in the larger sizes and where frequent operation is required, lack of adaptability to remote control, difficulty in maintaining proper adjustment, and additional maintenance occasioned by the slip ring, particularly at high speeds.

Obviously these disadvantages do not apply in all cases, since inching may not be required, for occasional use physical effort may not be objectionable or may be overcome by use of power shifting devices, remote control may not be desired, infrequent engagement may minimize need for frequent adjustment, and slip ring wear is minimized when clutches idle a large part of the time with mechanism stationary.

Air clutches have the advantage of great range in torque capacity, not requiring adjustment, adaptability to inching or slipping service, and adaptability to reasonable remote control.

Disadvantages are need for constant air pressure and supply, necessity of location near a free shaft end, necessity of specially drilled shafts, and in some cases, need for costly auxilliary equipment.

Magnetic clutches have the advantage of being suitable for location anywhere along the length of a shaft or for cutoff couplings and of being readily remote controlled provided delicate sensitivity for inching or gradual starting is not required.

Their disadvantages include the necessity for constant d-c supply, the continuous use of current while engaged, and the necessity for rather elaborate control apparatus, particularly when variable torque is desired.

Fig. 4-18. Mechanical clutch on veneer-peeling machine.

It is obvious from the foregoing that the selection of the most desirable type of clutch for a particular job will involve a careful study of the features desired and their relative importance, followed by a check against the various features offered by the several clutch types. For example, an installation involving a cutoff coupling, infrequently engaged and not requiring remote control, would normally indicate the use of a mechanical clutch. However, if we require of the same job very frequent starts, a clutch of the air or magnetic type should be considered. It is not feasible here to cite all the possible combinations of features that might be involved. It is necessary, therefore, for the user to analyze his requirements and choose the type of clutch that most nearly meets them.

Determination of Clutch Size. The one good rule to follow in selecting the size clutch to use is to select one of ample capacity. An oversize clutch is subject to less wear and tear and to lower stresses and is capable of absorbing more heat. However, when heat due to frequent starting of heavy inertia loads is of prime importance, excess torque capacity alone is not necessarily the answer. In these cases, large-diameter clutches with a maximum of radiation surface are indicated, and in the case of disk clutches, a single-plate clutch would be preferable to a double- or multiple-plate clutch. Exact solution of clutch heat problems is very difficult because of indeterminate factors involved and variable conditions. Many clutch manufacturers offer derating factors depending on starting loads and frequency of engagements. Some merely recommend that for frequent engagements the clutch rating should be reduced by one-half. None of these methods is exact, but all tend to lessen the danger of overheating, since they result in the use of clutches with torque capacity in excess of that otherwise required. Whenever possible these problems should be referred to the manufacturer in order to gain the benefit of his experience.

Clutches must also be selected with due regard to peak torque conditions regardless of frequency of engagement. Rough power sources such as low-speed engines with one to three cylinders, also rough driven loads such as crushers, reciprocating compressors, and the like, produce torque peaks considerably above that corresponding to the normal average running horsepower. Whenever possible the clutch should be selected ample for the peak torque. When this value is unknown, allowance should be made by selecting a clutch with rating equal to or greater than the actual load increased by 50 to 150 per cent depending on the severity of the conditions.

In no case should a clutch be selected for a load greater than its catalog rating or for speeds higher than the maximum allowable listed.

Clutch Installation. After a clutch has been chosen, it must still be properly installed to ensure maximum satisfaction. This presupposes that the size of shafting upon which the clutch is to be mounted is of ample proportion, since the determination of proper shaft size is not within the scope of this discussion. However, it may be mentioned that it is of utmost importance that shafts be of such size as not only to carry safely the stresses induced by torque and by bending but also to have sufficient stiffness to prevent excessive deflections. To this end and to avoid unnecessarily large shafts, it is important that shaft bearings be located as close as possible to the clutch in order to reduce bending. Clutch couplings should in all cases have a bearing on each shaft located as close as possible to the coupling. Shaft deflection within the length of a long clutch sleeve is very detrimental to both plain-bushed and antifriction bearing sleeves.

It should also be remembered that the use of a high-tensile-strength steel does not increase the stiffness of a shaft but that the use of a larger shaft increases the stiffness very rapidly. For example, a $2\frac{1}{2}$-in.-diameter shaft is more than twice as stiff as a 2-in. shaft. Since so much can be gained in this respect by the use of a slightly larger shaft, it is frequently very false economy to be stingy with shaft size.

Before a clutch is installed on a shaft, the latter should be checked for straightness and for size. The bored parts of the clutch should also be checked. Clutch parts which are keyed to the shaft should be as tight as is practical for assembly. Commercial clutches with commercial shafting usually result in fits from a little loose to a little tight, which is generally satisfactory for normal conditions. For high speeds, shock or reversing loads, special shafts should be used to give from a line fit to a tight fit up to one-half-thousandth per inch of shaft diameter.

Shafts should be checked to be sure they are clean and free from burrs. Check location and size of keyways and fit of key before assembling the clutch on the shaft.

When it is evident that force will be required for assembly, a press should be used in preference to sledging. If no press is available, the clutch parts may be heated by a torch through the bore until the parts will slide readily on the shaft.

In the case of clutch couplings the mechanism will be fitted to one shaft and the coupling hub to the other. When shafts are installed in their bearings, extreme care must be taken to be sure the two shafts are concentric and parallel. Most clutch coupling hubs are fitted with a bronze bushing or a ball-bearing pilot. This serves to help center the shafts initially and to help maintain alignment, but the pilot bearing should not be expected to serve as a supporting bearing for one shaft. On high-speed installations, when both shafts are well supported and permanently aligned, the use of a pilot bearing is frequently omitted. This is because at high speed the pilot bearing becomes difficult to maintain and better results may be obtained by eliminating it entirely.

Sleeve clutches also involve a bearing, since, when idling, the sleeve runs loose on the shaft. Sleeve bearings are commonly bronze bushings for fairly light loads and low speeds. Bushings are usually grease lubricated and commonly have "figure-eight" grease-distribution grooves. Bronze bushed sleeves vary in length to suit the size of wheel to be mounted, the usual range being from two to five shaft diameters. Sleeves longer than three times the bore are not desirable unless the shaft is of relatively large size in proportion to the sleeve load. Long sleeves are often bushed at both ends with a grease chamber between. This minimizes danger of interference due to shaft deflection and provides a reservoir of grease.

Bronze sleeve bushings should have a running clearance on the average of about 2/1,000 in. per inch of shaft diameter. Their use should be limited to a maximum rubbing speed of about 750 fpm. The greater the rubbing speed, the less will be the allowable load on the bushing. At maximum speed the load should usually not exceed 10 psi. However, allowable loads and speeds depend largely on the per cent idling time, and no rigid rule can be given. A good rule of thumb is to limit the value

Pv^2 to 1,000, where P is the load in psi projected area and v is the shaft rubbing speed in feet per second.

In general, for loads and speed beyond this limit it is recommended that ball or roller bearings be used. The fitting and installation of these depend on the individual design. Some are mounted bearings that can readily be slipped on the shaft and secured there, while in others the bearings are fitted directly on the shaft. In this case shafts must be prepared with special tolerances and various other details and in both types instructions for mounting furnished by the manufacturer should be followed.

In both bronze-bushed and antifriction types it is often expedient to eliminate the sleeve and mount the bushing or bearings direct in the wheel hub. The wheel is then designed for attaching directly to the clutch.

It should be noted that in order to permit engaging and disengaging, one of the two mating friction surfaces must be free to move. Disk clutches are, therefore, usually designed with floating friction plates keyed to their respective members with keys, splines, or gear teeth. This permits axial movement of the plates without relative rotation. Such construction should always be used in clutch couplings, multiple-plate disk clutches, and in sleeve clutches using ball or tapered roller bearings. So called "bolted plate" clutches, (Fig. 4-11,) in which a single friction plate is rigidly connected to the sleeve member, may be used with plain bushed or straight roller bearing sleeves where the entire sleeve may float. Bolted plate and ball or tapered roller bearing sleeves do not require locating collars. Bronze-bushed and straight roller bearing sleeves when used with floating-plate (gear-tooth) types do require locating collars. Care must be taken that such collars are located with sufficient clearance to permit the necessary axial movement. Expanding or band-type clutches have inherent axial movement between the friction surfaces and may be used with either fixed or floating sleeves or couplings, but when they are used with floating sleeves, locating collars are required.

Belt, chain, or gear drives mounted on floating sleeves should be carefully aligned to avoid excessive tendency to cause endwise movement.

Mechanical clutches employing slip rings and mechanical yokes or levers should have the latter so located as to produce a minimum pressure on the slip ring due to the weight of these parts. Such pressure as is unavoidable should tend to disengage rather than to engage the clutch.

Long linkages connecting the operating lever to the clutch should be avoided as much as possible. In any case all levers, links, and bell cranks that may be required should be of ample size to prevent bending or buckling and all connections should have a minimum of looseness and lost motion. All fulcrum and pivot joints should have rigid support.

Rotating air seals for air clutches should employ a short length of flexible tubing between seal and air pipelines to prevent bind or excessive load on the seal bearings.

Final connection to the contact brushes of magnetic clutches should be made through flexible conduit to prevent bind.

Standard clutches are, in general, designed for use on horizontal shafts. However, most types may be successfully used on vertical shafts, but in some cases certain modifications are necessary. Such applications should not be undertaken without consultation with the manufacturer, who will supply recommendations and instructions.

Regardless of type of clutch, the instructions furnished by the maker should be carefully preserved and followed.

Clutch Care and Maintenance. As noted, clutches which have been properly selected and installed give trouble-free service if properly maintained.

Difficulty, if encountered, will usually manifest itself in excessive heating or excessive wear.

These conditions may be centered in either the running parts, such as coupling pilot bearings, sleeve bearings, or slip rings, or in the friction elements.

A first rule for prevention of bearing difficulty is the establishment of a suitable lubrication routine. Periodic lubrication is essential, but the length of such periods can be determined only by experience.

On new and untried installation, it is advisable to make daily checks for evidence of heat in each of the bearings and to add lubricant frequently even at the risk of over-lubrication. The length of time that the running parts may operate without relubrication will vary with the speed, the frequency, and the duration of running periods. Bearing loads are also a factor but are not so influential as speed and running time. In general, the higher the speed, the more frequent is the required attention, but even at high speed a clutch may require little attention to the pilot or sleeve bearing if the clutch is engaged most of the time. However, these conditions require more frequent attention to the slip-ring bearing. Conversely, a clutch which idles most of the time may require frequent attention even though the speed may be low.

Plain bushed sleeve bearings are more susceptible to the effect of heavy loads than are ball or roller bearings and require more frequent attention. This is also true of plain brass slip rings as compared with ball-bearing slip rings.

If heat persists in bearings even after lubrication, the clutch should be disassembled and bearings checked for adjustment, running clearance, and presence of dirt or broken-down lubricant. In any event, a complete washing and reassembly with fresh lubricant are good insurance. This may be desirable after only a few months or perhaps as seldom as one or two years, depending on general operating and surrounding conditions.

Care should be taken to use a high-grade lubricant of a type recommended by the clutch manufacturer.

Excessive heat originating in the friction surfaces is caused by excessive slip. What constitutes excessive heat is rather difficult to define. Temperature on the exterior surfaces too hot to bear on the hand might be allowable if it occurs only at starting and at relatively long intervals. On the other hand even a small amount of heating which occurs continuously would be objectionable because it would be accompanied by constant wear and loss of power.

Slip which occurs during engaged operation, of course, means insufficient torque capacity. This may be a result of improper selection or due to a change in the load requiring more power than originally required. The driven machinery should be checked to determine if an increased load exists and if so whether or not it is permanent and unavoidable. Some corrections here may eliminate the difficulty. If this is not possible, the clutch may have to be replaced with one of larger size.

On the other hand, operating slip may occur with a clutch of ample capacity which is not developing the torque that it should. Such a condition may result from improper adjustment in clutches requiring adjustment, and this point should be checked at once. In the case of air clutches the torque loss may be caused by loss of air pressure, and in magnetic clutches, by voltage drop, indicating the need for a prompt check of these conditions.

In any type of clutch a loss of capacity will occur if the friction surfaces become contaminated by oil or grease. If this condition is found, the clutch should be disassembled and the parts thoroughly cleaned with solvent. In extreme cases replacement of linings may be necessary.

Operating slip may occasionally result from failure of the clutch to engage fully. This may be a case of loose adjustment but may also result from parts being so worn as to prevent their free movement, from the presence of some foreign obstruction, or from corrosion of sliding parts. A thorough cleaning and lubrication of such parts are indicated. Extreme wear may necessitate some replacement.

Clutches sometimes develop heat when idling as a result of drag caused by failure of the clutch to disengage fully. This may result from the same causes mentioned above. To avoid, sliding parts must be kept clean and oiled. It is particularly necessary to keep the joints of toggle systems well lubricated to prevent sticking.

Release springs which may have broken or become weakened by heat will also cause drag and should be included in the check points when this condition exists.

The shifting mechanism employed with mechanical clutches should be checked for lost motion which may result in insufficient slip ring travel. Air lines and quick-release valves used on air clutches should be checked to be sure passages have not become clogged.

Another type of heat problem may be encountered in the case of clutches required to start heavy inertia loads, particularly if such starts are frequent. In those cases where starting load is predominately due to overcoming inertia, the heat which must be absorbed and dissipated by the clutch is equivalent to the final kinetic energy developed in the driven parts, plus a relatively small amount due to friction. This is true regardless of clutch size and length of time taken in bringing the inertia load up to speed. Consequently, in cases of this kind excessive heating can be prevented only by using a clutch with greater heat-radiation ability. When the difficulty is encountered, there is little that the maintenance man can do other than to decrease the frequency of engagement if possible or to increase the radiation rate by air cooling the clutch with fans. Increasing the clutch torque capacity will not help unless it is accompanied by an increase in radiation.

In installations involving starting loads consisting of both heavy inertia and considerable friction, the total heat per engagement may be reduced by shortening the slipping time, thus reducing the work done against friction. This may be accomplished by rapidly engaging the clutch provided it has and is adjusted for large torque capacity. However, care should be taken that engagement is not so sudden as to produce severe shock load on the equipment. In general, clutches should be engaged as gently as possible. For heavy starting, it is helpful to engage and disengage the clutch several times during the acceleration period. High-speed clutches of the floating-plate type should be disengaged for a few seconds after attaining full speed. This permits parts to become centered and tends to prevent vibration.

Both heat and wear caused by slip can best be minimized by the use of clutches having both ample heat and torque capacity. This permits the operator some atitude in regulating the torque and the handling technique to produce the most satisfactory operation.

Such clutches properly installed on well-supported shafts of ample size, given reasonable care and protected from abuse, will give the best possible service.

Chapter 5

FLEXIBLE COUPLINGS FOR
POWER TRANSMISSION

By G. C. WERNER
Manager of Engineering
Thomas Coupling Division
Rex Chainbelt, Inc.
Warren, Pa.

General. There are some 100 to 120 manufacturers of flexible couplings in the United States. A detailed account of each type would be impossible. For this reason, most of the information in this chapter will be confined to the generalities related to the types most frequently found in this field.

The fundamental purpose of a flexible coupling is to transmit the required torque from the driving to the driven shaft and at the same time compensate for angular or parallel misalignments or combinations of both. There are many supplementary functions such as providing for axial float and restricting axial float.

Normally the ratio of the value of a flexible coupling to the value of the connected equipment is approximately 1 to 100, although there are individual cases where the ratio may be as low as 1 to 20 or as high as 1 to 1,000. Often, in light of the above, all too little attention may be given to the selection, specification, purchasing, installation, and maintenance of this item. It is not uncommon to find applications where no expense is spared in procuring the best prime mover money can buy. In a like manner the driven equipment may cost hundreds of thousands of dollars. Yet the connecting coupling is purchased on the most meager information (usually horsepower, speed, and shaft size only), and the lowest priced coupling is obtained even though it may not be compatible to the job.

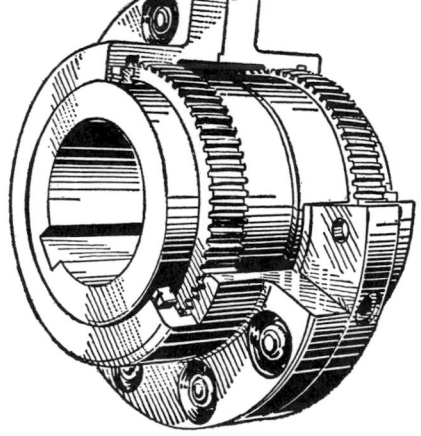

FIG. 5-1. Gear-tooth coupling. (*From* "*Plant Engineering Handbook.*")

Types of Couplings. Basically all flexible couplings are divided into two categories: (1) those which provide flexibility by elements which slide and (2) those which provide flexibility by elements which flex a material such as steel or rubber. Couplings have been broken down into these two categories because their basic method of compensating for misalignment is a key as to the amount and type of maintenance required.

Description of Types. *Gear-type couplings* (see Fig. 5-1) depend solely upon sliding surfaces to adjust to misalignment conditions. The torque is transmitted from the driving hub to the driven hub by means of gear teeth which engage the splines in the flanged sleeve. The teeth on the hubs are usually curved slightly to prevent binding when the coupling is misaligned.

To prevent wear it is important that the oil reservoir be properly filled with the type of lubricant recommended by the manufacturer. It is worth while to note that the type of lubricant may vary depending upon the operating conditions; i.e., one kind of lubricant may be recommended for high-temperature conditions, and another for cold applications. Some outdoor installations may require changes in the spring and fall.

Routine flushing and refilling are required. The time between changes is dependent upon the type of service, but every 6 months is a good average. Because the lubricant is subject to high centrifugal forces the filler plug must be tight and leakproof. Care

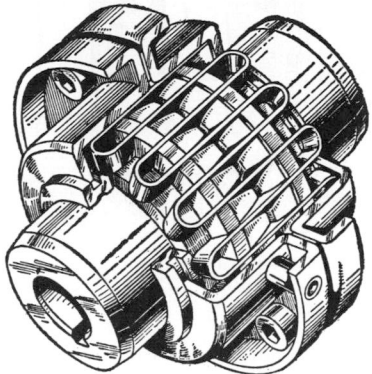

Fig. 5-2. Oldham, or block and jaw coupling. (*From "Plant Engineering Handbook."*)

Fig. 5-3. Grid-spring coupling. (*From "Plant Engineering Handbook."*)

should be exercised in assembling and dismantling the flanged sleeve so that the gasket and mating surfaces are not damaged.

A worn gear-type coupling is not repairable. The downtime for equipment during replacement may be considerable. The motor or turbine must be moved on its foundation a sufficient distance to pull the hubs. A new coupling must be procured, bored, keyseated, and mounted. The motor must then be replaced and realigned. To avoid this costly downtime, it behooves the maintenance personnel to do everything possible to minimize wear in the coupling. It is important to remember that:

1. The lubricant must be clean and adequate at all times.
2. The alignment must be maintained to reasonably close tolerances.

The Oldham-type coupling (see Fig. 5-2), also known as the block-and-jaw coupling, relies exclusively on the use of sliding surfaces to compensate for misalignment conditions. The torque is transmitted from the driving hub to the driven hub by means of jaws engaging a floating center block. By use of dissimilar materials impregnated with lubricant, the manufacturers have avoided the use of oil reservoirs. As a consequence the application of this coupling is limited to slow speeds and low horsepower. Some types are available which can be repaired.

The grid-type coupling (see Fig. 5-3) uses a combination of sliding surfaces and flexing springs to adapt itself to various conditions of misalignment. The driving and driven hubs are slotted axially. A bent flat-spring member, or grid, transmits the torque from driving to driven hub. Because there are sliding surfaces, it is mandatory to pack the oil reservoir with the proper lubricant in order to preclude wear. The oil plug and grease-retaining seals and gasket must be tight to prevent loss of the lubricant. The cover should be opened occasionally so that the old lubricant can be flushed away and new lubricant added. The grid members of this type of coupling are replaceable; if worn appreciably, they should be replaced. This is an in-line coupling and must be aligned to tolerances recommended by the manufacturer.

The Thomas flexible disk-ring coupling (see Figs. 5-4 to 5-6) relies entirely on the principle of flexing a laminated steel ring. There are no sliding parts, so no maintenance is required other than occasionally checking the tightness of the bolts and making sure the alignment is good. The parts are all metallic and under ordinary

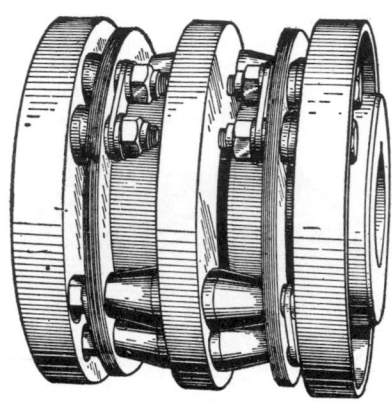

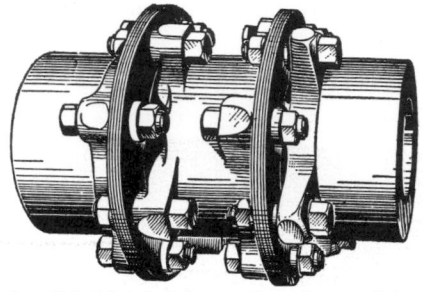

FIG. 5-4. Metal-disk coupling—heavy duty, high speed. (*From "Plant Engineering Handbook."*)

FIG. 5-5. Metal-disk coupling—heavy duty, medium speed. (*From "Plant Engineering Handbook."*)

conditions not subject to deterioration. Stainless steel or other noncorrosive materials are available for ambient conditions which are severe.

The coupling is completely repairable without disturbing the connected equipment. It offers the ultimate in preventive maintenance in that it can be visually inspected without disassembly. For those applications involving equipment, such as paper-making machines, where a "planned downtime" is paramount, the coupling can be minutely examined with a stroboscopic light.

Should examination reveal a laminated disk ring showing signs of deterioration, the

FIG. 5-6. Floating-shaft metal-disk coupling. (*From "Plant Engineering Handbook."*)

ring should be replaced. Alignment should be rechecked immediately inasmuch as the deterioration of the laminated rings is an indication of excessive flexing due to misalignment greater than the capacity of the coupling. All bolts must be pulled up tight to ensure proper functioning.

This is an in-line coupling, and the manufacturer recommends that initial misalignment be reduced to the smallest practical limits.

The rubber-biscuit coupling has no sliding parts and obtains its ability to compensate for misalignment by flexing and displacing the rubber insert. The routine maintenance involves occasional check of alignment, bolt tightness, and condition of the rubber insert. This coupling is encountered in the smaller range of sizes only.

General Causes of Coupling Failures. In general, coupling failures are divided into two categories:

1. Failures due to internal faults such as improper or poor machining. The most common problems have to do with concentricities, squareness of mating faces, and tolerances on the various diameters used as pilots or registers. Defective materials have contributed to many premature coupling failures. Another cause of failure due to internal faults is design. To provide lubrication at the exact point where it

is required is a formidable problem in that it is admittedly difficult to get the lubricant to the area of extreme pressure between the sliding contact faces of the coupling. This is particularly true where the transmitted load is smooth and steady. Under such conditions the pressure across the sliding surfaces never relaxes. If this pressure is sufficient, the film of lubrication is squeezed out and the surfaces are left without the benefit of lubrication. A coupling of this type, even when badly misaligned, does not have sufficient sliding movement to reestablish the film of lubricant.

Contrary to popular belief, centrifugal action does not force the lubricant between the contacting faces. For all practical purposes the pressures cancel out because they work with as well as against the forces caused by torque. The forces and pressures developed by torque transmission are many times the forces and pressures developed by centrifugal rotation even at extreme coupling speeds.

2. Failures due to external conditions beyond the capacity of the coupling. The most common are:

    a. Improper coupling selection.
    b. Excessive misalignment.

Consideration of each of these items is given in the following discussion.

Coupling Selection. At some time or other the maintenance supervisor will be faced with the problem of replacing worn-out couplings. He will be fortunate indeed if the coupling gives sufficient warning before failure to allow consideration for a proper replacement. Most of the larger manufacturers of couplings have representation in the larger cities throughout the nation. They are usually qualified to make recommendations and possibly obtain the required coupling from strategically placed warehouses. Counsel should be sought for even the smallest application.

The coupling should be conservatively rated for the application. If the speed is high, the coupling should be dynamically balanced. It should be borne in mind that some motor manufacturers demand modifications to the sliding-surface type of couplings for applications on motors with sleeve bearings. To avoid troubles, these modifications (which involve the restriction of the end float of the coupling) should be made.

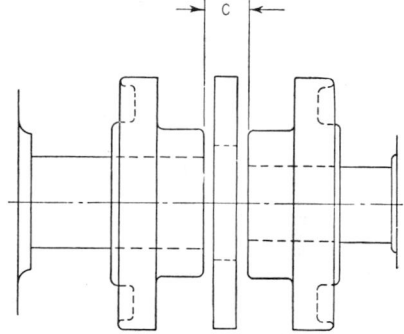

Fig. 5-7. Gap (*C*) of coupling must be right for successful operation.

Alignment of Flexible Couplings. In a state of perfect alignment, there is no movement—sliding or flexing—in a coupling. As such, there could be no wear or deterioration in the coupling and it would probably last forever. It is, however, the duty of the man who installs the coupling (and later on, the man who maintains it) to strive for perfection in coupling alignment so as to ensure the long life of which the coupling is capable. It is not unusual to find gear-type couplings which have operated for 20 to 30 years with only occasional lubrication. There are flexible-disk-type couplings which have operated the same length of time without any maintenance at all.

Either of the above types of couplings, when badly misaligned, could fail in less than a week or even in a day. The following portion of this chapter is devoted to fundamentals in coupling alignment.

The first (and most often overlooked) task is to space the driving and driven equipment properly so that the ends of the shafts are in the proper relation (see Fig. 5-7). This is necessary so that the coupling can operate in its normal position.

In any type of coupling it is important that the mating surfaces or flexing members be in their normal positions when the connected equipment is in its normal position. A sleeve-bearing motor may have $\frac{1}{2}$ in. of float. It should be assumed that this motor *is on* magnetic center when it is located midway between the limits.

If the exact normal gap of the coupling is not known, this can be obtained from catalog or certified print dimensions.   Many manufacturers send data sheets with every new coupling.   Copies can be had for the asking.   If the normal gap dimension is not available, it usually can be obtained by measuring the coupling and calculating the normal position.   Slight axial adjustments can be made after assembly.

The next problem is to square the driving and driven machines one with the other. This is more commonly known as eliminating angular misalignment.   For many years the accepted method of aligning couplings has been the use of a straightedge and scale. There is no question but what some mechanics became quite adept at the art.   However, with the arrival of smaller equipment doing a bigger job at higher speeds and stresses, the straightedge has given way to the indicator as a better means to good alignment.

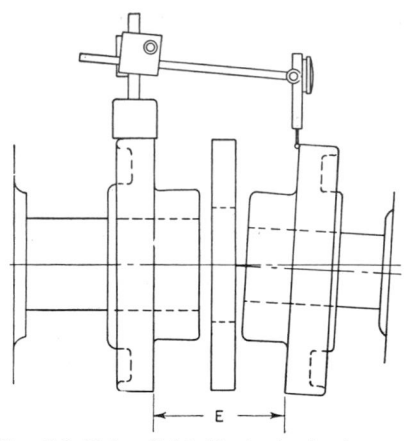
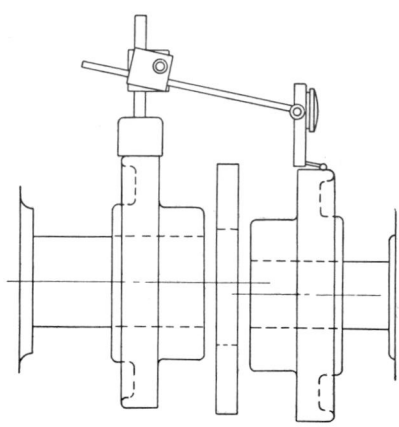

Fig. 5-8. Using dial indicator to check angular misalignment.

Fig. 5-9. Using indicator in correcting
parallel misalignment.

No specific rules or methods can be given for mounting an indicator for a specific aligning job.   This must be left to the ingenuity of the mechanic.   Magnetic bases have found much favor for this type of work.   It must be pointed out that regardless of how the indicator is mounted, the entire support as well as the extension rods must be rigid so as to preclude false readings.

In some cases alignment must be made with the coupling opened or partially dismantled.   If this is the case, it is necessary to rotate one piece of equipment so that the indicator stem "wipes" the surface of the stationary piece of equipment.   It is preferable to align the equipment with the coupling fully assembled.   The indicator then rotates with the equipment, and the stem remains stationary on the contacting surface.   In the following description it will be assumed that the coupling is fully assembled and the driving and driven members can be rotated together.

To check angular misalignment, the indicator is attached rigidly to one hub member and the stem is placed against the *face* of the opposite hub member (see Fig. 5-8).

The connected shafts are then *rotated together* several revolutions to allow them to take up their normal axial positions.   Rotation is then continued in the same direction until the indicator needle registers a maximum reading.   The indicator dial is then set to zero, and rotation again continued for one-half a turn.   At this point the indicator reading will show the total angular displacement in a distance equal to the diameter of the circle which the indicator has described.

As an example, assume that the indicator stem is 6 in. from the center of the shaft. The total indicator movement from maximum to minimum is 0.060 in., and the maximum gap occurred at 4:30 o'clock (135° clockwise), facing the motor from the shaft end.   The distance from the coupling to the outside end of the motor is roughly 3 ft.

In that the maximum gap occurred at 4:30 o'clock (not 3, 9, or 12), it is known that some shims must be added under the motor and it must also be moved sidewise to some extent.   How much?   The total is 0.060 for every 12 in. because the indicator registered 0.060 while describing a circle 12 in. in diameter.   If the motor is 3 ft long, it would be reasonable to move the outside end of the motor a distance of 0.060 × 3, or 0.180 in.   In that the whole correction cannot be made by sidewise adjustment or shims alone, it would be found that a movement of ⅛ in. up (or down) and ⅛ in. sidewise would correct the angular displacement.

The movement up or down and to the left or right would have to be made in such a way as to reduce the gap at 4:30 o'clock at the coupling.

After the motor has been moved, the indicator movement is again checked in the same way and further improvements made until the total indicated runout is reduced to not more than 0.002 in. for each inch of diameter described by the indicator.

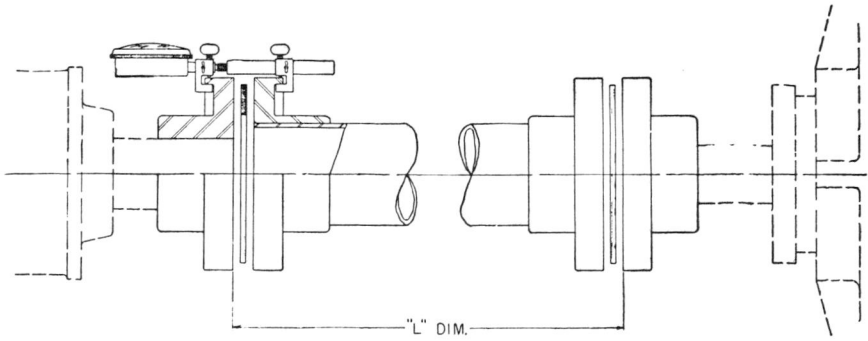

Fig. 5-10. Alignment method used with long span.

While the figure 0.002 in. is given as a value for ordinary applications, there are cases where alignment to 0.0005 or even 0.0002 in. per inch of diameter may be required for ultrahigh speed or extreme reliability.

Correcting Parallel Misalignment.   To correct parallel misalignment the indicator stem must be moved to such a position that it will contact a radial surface—usually the outside diameter of the flanged hub (see Fig. 5-9).

Again the equipment is rotated until a maximum reading is obtained and the dial set to zero.   Continued rotation for one-half turn will show the position and amount of parallel misalignment.

As an example assume that the indicator reading is 0.030 at 12:00 o'clock.   In that the indicator reads twice the axial displacement, it would be necessary to put 0.015 shims under all the feet of the motor.

At this point, extreme care must be exercised so that the two previously described corrections are not disturbed.   It must also be remembered that tightening down the anchor bolts invariably changes the alignment.   For this reason it is necessary to make a final recheck of all three steps.

No blanket rule can be applied to the permissible misalignment at installation.   For the average type of coupling and installation most often encountered the following amounts could be considered allowable:

Coupling Size, In.	Max. Misalignment
1–2	0.010 total indicator reading
2¼–4	0.015 total indicator reading
4–7	0.020 total indicator reading

Special Applications.   *Cooling Towers.*   The typical arrangement shown in Fig. 5-10 is particularly difficult to align.   In some instances the span L may be as high as 10 ft.   It is practically impossible to align equipment this far apart by using a straightedge on the relatively narrow aligning surfaces incorporated into the coupling.   For this reason the alignment method shown in Fig. 5-10 is highly recommended.   If the indicator is used clamped as shown, the flexing at each element can be reduced to 0.005 or 0.010.

Three Bearing Drives.   A single-engagement, flexible coupling of the laminated-disk type is frequently used to support a heavy radial load.   Typical applications

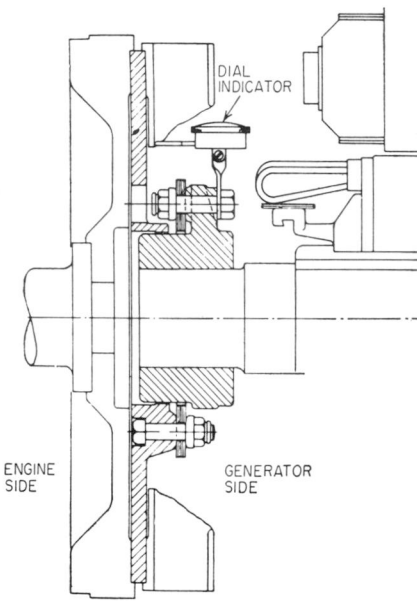

FIG. 5-11. Proper mounting of indicator when aligning flywheel adapter couplings.

are engine-driven, single-bearing generators; compressors driven by single-bearing motors; multiple V-belt drives; etc.   The coupling used for these applications is highly specialized and cannot be used for routine flexible coupling applications.   On these specialized applications the coupling is capable of compensating for angular misalignment only.   The same method of aligning is used as previously described under Correcting Angular Misalignment.   Figure 5-11 shows the proper method of mounting the indicator for aligning flywheel adapter couplings.

Chapter 6

BELTING, FASTENERS, PULLEYS, AND SHAFTING

By WILLIAM STANIAR
Formerly Mechanical Power Engineer
E. I. du Pont de Nemours & Company, Inc.
Wilmington, Del.

Since industry still depends to a large extent on flat belting and its accessories such as fasteners, pulleys, and shafting for the transmission of power mechanically, the factors of corrective and preventive maintenance play an important part in their efficiency, maintenance cost, and production effectiveness.

CORRECTIVE MAINTENANCE

Definition. To utilize information, techniques, proper belting materials, fastening devices, and pulleys and the latest engineering developments in the design of flat belt drives.

Purpose. To reduce both operating and maintenance costs and to provide a sound basis for corrective design before the drive goes into operation.

Results. Increased safety, better quality of product, greater productivity, improved operating efficiency, lower unit cost of product, and economical utilization of technical improvements.

PREVENTIVE MAINTENANCE

Definition. To utilize planned and coordinated inspections, adjustments, repairs, and replacements in maintaining a power belting installation.

Purpose. To make necessary and timely repairs and prevent unscheduled interruptions and undue deterioration of belting and its accessories.

Results. Minimum operating downtime, better over-all maintenance planning, emphasizes weakness in belting material and accessories, and reduces maintenance costs.

FLAT BELTING DRIVES

Corrective Maintenance

Design. The correct design of a flat belt drive is the real "corrective-maintenance" factor, since if this is initially accomplished, a drive of this character will operate for a long period with a minimum of maintenance, which will result in production efficiency.

The belt should be of the proper material and construction for the atmospheric and mechanical conditions involved. It should be of the proper width and thickness for

Table 6-1. Minimum Center Distances for Belt Drives Based on Power and Ratios

Horsepower to be transmitted	Ratio of driver to driven	Center distance, ft
1–4	2–1	4
	3–1	5
	4–1	7.5
	5–1	10
5–9	2–1	
	3–1	8
	4–1	16.5
	5–1	12
10–14	2–1	8
	3–1	10
	4–1	12
	5–1	14
15–24	2–1	9
	3–1	11
	4–1	13
	5–1	15
25–39	2–1	10
	3–1	12
	4–1	14
	5–1	16
40–49	2–1	12
	3–1	13
	4–1	15
	5–1	17
50–74	2–1	13
	3–1	14
	4–1	16
	5–1	18
75–99	2–1	18
	3–1	20
	4–1	22
	5–1	24
100–124	2–1	20
	3–1	22
	4–1	24
	5–1	26
125–149	2–1	22
	3–1	24
	4–1	26
	5–1	28
150–200	2–1	26
	3–1	28
	4–1	30
	5–1	32

Note: These center distances are based on actual experience. The figures should be employed on belted motor drives and all manner of belting installations where reasonable pulley diameters are used. Belt drives from engine flywheels and power above 300 hp by belting are now exceptional; therefore for such service operating conditions must be considered.

the horsepower, speeds, and pulley-diameter requirements. It should be rugged enough to withstand shock loads and the edge action of shifter forks and tough enough to hold lacing and metallic fasteners firmly.

The fastener, if metallic, should be of the proper type for the belt thickness and width, pulley diameter, and speed of the belt. If endless, the joint of whatever type belt being used should be made by one skilled in the art.

The pulley should be of the proper material and construction for the atmospheric conditions and load requirements and of the proper face width and crown for the belt and speed involved.

The shafting should be of the proper type of steel and of the proper diameter for the horsepower, speed, load, and bearing-supporting facilities.

The center distance between driving and driven pulleys should be suitable for the pulley diameters, speed, load requirements and direction of pull (see Table 6-1).

Preventive Maintenance

Regular inspection and anticipation of flaws and faults are the real "preventive maintenance" of flat belt drives, since they result in a minimum of breakdowns, a minimum of time lost by men waiting for repairs, and a minimum loss in production.

The Belt.   Inspect for dryness and brittleness, dirtiness or oil or grease saturation, glazed driving surface, condition of laps and plies, condition of joint, whether metallic

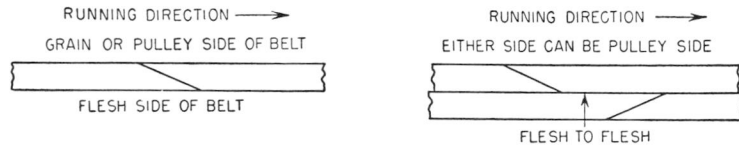

RUNNING DIRECTION ———→   RUNNING DIRECTION ———→

GRAIN OR PULLEY SIDE OF BELT   EITHER SIDE CAN BE PULLEY SIDE

FLESH SIDE OF BELT   FLESH TO FLESH

NOTE. ALL LEATHER BELTS SHOULD RUN SO THAT THE POINT OF THE LAP ON THE OUTSIDE DOES NOT RUN INTO THE WIND

Fig. 6-1. Belt laps for single- and double-ply leather belts.

or endless, slackness or tightness (tension), and alignment of shafting and pulleys. Systematic care and attention are given to the power source and production machines. Similar attention to power belting is necessary if efficiency of operation and maximum production are to be maintained.   The cost of repairs to a belt may be small, but the enforced idleness of men and the production losses due to such repairs are expensive. The value of a machine as a producer exceeds the wages of the men who operate it.   A slipping belt can cause heavy expense through loss of applied power.   A belt a trifle larger in width and thickness will more than repay in increased life and lessened maintenance expense the additional cost over a smaller overloaded belt.   Properly selected and installed belting requires little attention provided it is given regular and systematic care.   Neglect and abuse are generally responsible for belting troubles and failures.

Belting maintenance should be centralized so that one man is responsible.   This man should make periodic inspections of all belt drives so that breakages, slip, and other faults can be anticipated and therefore avoided.   Belting requires dressing or lubrication; therefore it is important that the dressings be of suitable type to accomplish the results desired.   Such dressings should be capable of relieving the internal friction of fiber on fiber, keeping pliability, and furnishing a cohesive but not sticky grip on the pulleys.   A sticky grip is destructive to belting.   When so maintained the belt will carry its load without high initial tension.   High belt tension has no value or purpose other than to prevent slip.

The Fastening Method.   If endless, inspect for looseness or curling of the lap joint, uneven surface at the joint due to an accumulation of excess cement, and whether or not the lap is running against the wind (see Fig. 6-1).   If metallic, inspect for atmospheric effects and determine if proper size and type of fastener is being used for belt width and thickness and pulley diameter, if the belt has been cut square, and if the belting material is tough enough to hold the fastener securely and there is no possibility of fastener bump or constructional interference as the belt passes around the pulley.

Belting joints should be carefully made.   The belt ends should be absolutely square so that the belt can run true and not stretch unevenly.   Heavy lacings, which result in "bunches" at the joints, and oversized metallic fasteners cause loss of pulley contact, breaking of the belt at the joint, and stiffness and thumping of the belt against the pulley face. A projecting fastener striking an obstruction or a badly adjusted shifter fork will cause rapid destruction of any type of belt.

The Pulley. If paper, inspect for atmospheric effects such as temperature, dampness, and other deleterious actions. If cast iron, inspect for balance, trueness of diameter, condition of face, and alignment. If fabricated steel, inspect for atmospheric effects, balance, trueness of diameter, and alignment. Pulleys should have a face width slightly wider than the belt they are to carry. This will prevent the belt from running over the face or rim and striking adjacent objects. The pulley should not have a sharp or too much crown. An overloaded belt will slide off a crowned-face pulley more easily than it will from a straight-face pulley.

The Shaft. Inspect for alignment, rigidity, and proper bearing support.

LEATHER BELTING

There are four distinct types of leather power belting, namely, (1) nonwaterproof oak tanned, (2) waterproof oak tanned, (3) waterproof mineral retanned, and (4) waterproof combination oak and mineral retanned. Each of these types is for a particular service and if properly selected, installed, and maintained will give long life and efficient power transmission.

Nonwaterproof Oak. *Manufacture.* It is made in single, double, and triple plies of any reasonable width and cemented with hot soluble glue.

Uses. It can be used for any normal drive where dampness, moisture, high temperatures, and corrosive conditions are not present, can be made endless, and will accommodate all types of metallic fasteners.

Atmospheric Effects. Dampness and moisture will separate the plies and laps, and ambient temperatures above 120°F will loosen the cementing medium and have a deteriorating effect upon the leather. The mists and vapors of the corrosive acids will rapidly destroy the leather.

Waterproof Oak. *Manufacture.* It is made in single, double, and triple plies of any reasonable width and cemented with a waterproof pyroxylin cement.

Uses. It can be used on any normal drive and in the presence of steam, dampness, moisture, and ambient temperatures to 130°F. It should not be used in an atmosphere charged with the mists or vapors of corrosive acids. It can be made endless and will accommodate all types of metallic fasteners.

Horsepower Formulas and Tables for Oak-leather Belting (Nonwaterproof and Waterproof)

SINGLES:

Light: ⅛ in. thick, 40 lb allowable effective tension per inch width
Medium: ⁵⁄₃₂ in. thick, 45 lb allowable effective tension per inch width
Heavy: ³⁄₁₆ in. thick, 50 lb allowable effective tension per inch width

FORMULA:

$$\text{Hp} = \frac{T \times W \times S}{33{,}000}$$

$$W = \frac{\text{hp} \times 33{,}000}{S \times T}$$

where T = allowable effective tension, lb per in. width
W = width of belt, in.
S = speed of belt, fpm

Waterproof Mineral Retanned. *Manufacture.* It is made in single, double, and triple plies in any reasonable width and cemented with a waterproof pyroxylin cement.

Uses. This type is extremely flexible and tough and possesses a high frictional coefficient; therefore it can be used with efficiency on small-diameter-pulley high-speed work such as direct motor drives and complicated machine-tool drives. It can be used in the presence of steam, dampness, moisture, and temperatures to 140°F.

Table 6-2. Horsepower Rating for Medium Single-oak Belting $\frac{5}{32}$ In. Thick, Based on 45 Lb Effective Tension

Width of belt, in.	Belt speed, fpm											
	750	1,000	1,250	1,500	1,800	2,000	2,500	3,000	3,500	4,000	4,500	5,000
1	1	1.36	1.71	2.03	2.43	2.7	3.4	4.1	4.8	5.4	6.1	6.9
2	2	2.72	3.42	4.06	4.86	5.4	6.8	8.2	9.6	10.8	12.2	13.8
3	3	4.1	5.1	6.1	7.3	8.2	10.2	12.3	14.4	16.2	18.3	20.7
4	4	5.4	6.8	8.12	9.72	10.8	13.6	16.4	19.2	21.6	24.4	27.6
5	5	6.8	8.5	10.1	12.1	13.5	17.0	20.5	24.0	27.0	30.5	34.5
6	6	8.1	10.2	12.18	14.5	16.2	20.4	24.6	28.8	32.4	36.6	41.4
7	7	9.5	12.0	14.21	16.91	18.9	23.8	28.7	33.6	37.8	42.7	48.3
8	8	10.8	13.6	16.2	19.4	21.6	27.2	32.8	38.4	43.2	48.8	55.2

These ratings are based on 165° arc of contact and are not corrected for the action of centrifugal force.
For light singles $\frac{1}{8}$ in. thick, figure 90 per cent of these ratings.
For heavy singles $\frac{3}{16}$ in. thick, figure 112 per cent of these ratings.

Doubles:
Light: $\frac{1}{4}$ in. thick, 60 lb allowable effective tension per inch width
Medium: $\frac{5}{16}$ in. thick, 65 lb allowable effective tension per inch width
Heavy: $\frac{3}{8}$ in. thick, 75 lb allowable effective tension per inch width

Table 6-3. Horsepower Rating for Medium Double-oak Belting $\frac{5}{16}$ In. Thick, Based on 65 Lb Effective Tension

Width of belt, in.	Belt speed, fpm												
	500	850	1,000	1,250	1,500	1,800	2,000	2,500	3,000	3,500	4,000	4,500	5,000
3	3	5	6	7.4	9	10.6	12	15	18	20	24	27	30
3½	3.42	5.8	6.9	8.6	10.3	12.3	14	17	20.8	24	28	31	35
4	4	6.7	8	10	12	14	16	20	24	27.5	31.5	35.5	39.5
5	5	8.5	10	12.3	14.7	17.5	20	24	30	35	40	44	49
6	6	10	12	15	18	21	24	30	35	41	47	53	59
8	8	13.5	15.5	20	23.5	28.5	31.5	40	47	55	63	71	79
10	10	17	20	25	30	35	40	49	59	69	79	89	99
12	12	20	23.5	30	35	42.5	47.5	60	71	83	95	107	118
14	14	23.5	28	34.5	41	50	55	69	83	97	110	124	138
16	16	26.5	31.5	39	47	57	63	79	94	110	125	142	157
18	18	30	35	44	53	64	71	90	107	123	142	160	177
20	20	33	40	49	59	71	78	98	118	139	158	177	200
24	24	40	47	59	71	85	95	118	142	166	190	212	236
30	30	50	59	74	89	106	118	147	177	206	236	266	300

These ratings are based on 165° arc of contact and are not corrected for the action of centrifugal force. For light doubles $\frac{1}{4}$ in. thick, figure 92 per cent of these ratings.   For heavy doubles $\frac{3}{8}$ in. thick, figure 114 per cent of these ratings.

Triples:
Medium: $\frac{1}{2}$ in. thick, 100 lb allowable effective tension per inch width
Heavy: $\frac{9}{16}$ in. thick, 110 lb allowable effective tension per inch width

Table 6-4. Horsepower Rating for Medium Triple-oak Belting ½ In. Thick, Based on 100 Lb Effective Tension

Width of belt, in.	Belt speed, fpm										
	200	400	600	800	1,000	1,500	2,000	2,500	3,000	3,500	4,000
12	7	14	21	28	35	55	70	91	110	127	140
14	8.5	17	25.5	34	42.5	64	85	106	128	148	170
16	9.5	19	28.5	38	47.5	73	95	121	146	169	190
20	12	24	36	48	60	91	120	151	182	212	240
24	14.5	29	43.5	58	72.5	110	145	182	220	254	290
28	17	34	51	68	85	127	170	212	254	300	340
30	18	36	54	72	90	136	180	228	272	320	360
36	22	44	66	88	110	164	220	274	328	380	440
44	27	54	81	108	135	200	270	334	400	465	540
48	29	58	87	116	145	218	290	362	436	510	580
60	36	72	108	144	180	272	360	450	544	635	720
72	44	88	132	176	220	326	440	550	652	820	880

These ratings are based on 165° arc of contact and are not corrected for the action of centrifugal force. For heavy triples, $\frac{9}{16}$ in. thick, figure 111 per cent of these ratings.

Table 6-5. Horsepower Rating of Medium Single Mineral-retanned Belting $\frac{5}{32}$ In. Thick, Based on 50 Lb. Effective Tension

Width of belt, in.	Belt speed, fpm										
	650	850	1,000	1,250	1,500	1,800	2,000	2,500	3,000	3,500	4,000
1	1.0	1.29	1.52	1.9	2.3	2.7	3.0	3.8	4.5	5.3	6.1
1¼	1.23	1.6	1.9	2.4	2.8	3.4	3.8	4.8	5.7	7.6	7.5
1½	1.48	1.92	2.3	2.8	3.4	4.1	4.5	5.6	6.8	8.0	9.1
2	2.0	2.6	3.0	3.8	4.5	5.4	6.0	7.5	9.1	10.6	12.0
2½	2.46	3.2	3.8	4.8	5.8	6.8	7.6	9.4	11.4	13.3	15.2
3	3.0	3.9	4.5	5.7	6.8	8.2	9.1	11.4	13.7	16.0	18.2
4	4.0	5.1	6.0	7.6	9.1	11.0	12.0	15.2	18.2	21.2	24.1

These ratings are based on 165 deg arc of contact and are not corrected for the action of centrifugal force. For light singles $\frac{1}{8}$ in. thick, figure 90 per cent of these ratings. For heavy singles $\frac{3}{16}$ in. figure 112 per cent of these ratings.

Doubles:
Light: ¼ in. thick, 65 lb allowable effective tension per inch width
Medium: $\frac{5}{16}$ in. thick, 70 lb allowable effective tension per inch width
Heavy: ⅜ in. thick, 80 lb allowable effective tension per inch width

It is not acidproof but will withstand the effects of corrosive acid mists and vapors longer than any other type of leather belting. It can be made endless and will accommodate any of the flexible types of metallic fasteners.

Combination Oak and Mineral Retanned. *Manufacture.* It is made only in double and triple plies of any reasonable width and cemented with a waterproof pyroxylin cement. In doubles one ply is oak and one mineral retanned; in triples the pulley ply is mineral retanned and the two outer plies are oak.

Uses. It can be used on slow-speed, hard-pull drives where a high frictional pulley grip is essential and where shifter forks are used. The mineral retanned ply should

Table 6-6. Horsepower Rating of Medium Double Mineral-retanned Belting $\frac{5}{16}$ In. Thick, Based on 70 Lb Effective Tension

Width of belt, in.	Belt speed, fpm												
	500	850	1,000	1,250	1,500	1,800	2,000	2,500	3,000	3,500	4,000	4,500	5,000
2	2.1	3.6	4.2	5.3	6.4	7.6	8.5	10.6	12.6	15.0	17.0	19.0	21.0
$2\frac{1}{2}$	2.7	4.5	5.3	6.6	8.0	9.5	10.6	13.2	16.0	18.5	21.0	24.0	26.5
3	3.2	5.4	6.4	8.0	9.6	11.5	12.8	16.0	19.0	22.0	25.0	29.0	32.0
$3\frac{1}{2}$	3.7	6.3	7.5	9.3	11.1	13.4	15.0	18.5	22.0	26.0	30.0	33.5	37.0
4	4.2	7.2	8.5	10.6	12.8	15.3	17.0	21.0	25.0	30.0	34.0	38.0	42.5
5	5.3	9.0	10.6	13.2	16.0	19.0	21.0	26.5	32.0	37.0	42.0	48.0	53.0
6	6.4	10.8	12.8	16.0	19.0	23.0	25.0	32.0	38.0	45.0	51.0	57.0	64.0
8	8.5	14.5	17.0	21.0	25.0	30.0	34.0	42.0	51.0	60.0	68.0	76.0	85.0
10	10.6	18.0	21.0	26.5	32.0	38.0	42.0	53.0	64.0	74.0	85.0	96.0	106.0
12	12.7	21.6	25.0	32.0	38.0	46.0	51.0	64.0	77.0	89.0	102.0	115.0	127.0
16	17.0	20.0	34.0	43.5	51.0	61.0	68.0	85.0	102.0	118.0	136.0	152.0	170.0
18	19.2	32.5	38.0	48.0	57.0	69.0	76.0	95.0	115.0	134.0	153.0	172.0	190.0
20	21.0	36.0	42.0	53.0	64.0	76.0	85.0	107.0	128.0	150.0	170.0	190.0	210.0
24	25.5	43.0	51.0	64.0	76.5	92.0	102.0	127.0	152.0	178.0	204.0	230.0	256.0

These ratings are based on 165° of contact and are not corrected for the action of centrifugal force. For light doubles $\frac{1}{4}$ in. thick, figure 92 per cent of these ratings.   For heavy doubles $\frac{3}{8}$ in. thick, figure 114 per cent of these ratings.

Triples:
Medium: $\frac{1}{2}$ in. thick, 110 lb allowable effective tension per inch width
Heavy: $\frac{9}{16}$ in. thick, 120 lb allowable effective tension per inch width

Table 6-7. Horsepower Rating of Medium Triple Mineral-retanned Belting $\frac{1}{2}$ In. Thick, Based on 110 Lb Effective Tension

Width of belt, in.	Belt speed, fpm									
	500	1,000	1,500	2,000	2,500	3,000	3,500	4,000	4,500	5,000
12	20	40	60	80	100	120	140	160	180	200
14	23	46	70	92	115	140	161	184	207	230
18	30	60	90	120	150	180	210	240	270	300
24	40	80	120	160	200	240	280	320	360	400
30	50	100	150	200	250	300	350	400	350	500
36	60	120	180	240	300	360	420	480	540	600
42	70	140	210	280	350	420	490	560	630	700
50	83	166	250	332	415	500	581	664	747	830
60	100	200	300	400	500	600	700	800	900	1,000
72	120	240	360	480	600	720	840	960	1,080	1,200

These ratings are based on 165° arc of contact and are not corrected for the action of centrifugal force. For heavy triple, $\frac{9}{16}$ in. thick, figure 108 per cent of these ratings.

Table 6-8. Horsepower Correction Factors for Leather Belting*

Correction factors for type of motor and starting method used		Correction factors for diameter of smaller pulley		Correction factors for special operating conditions	
Motor type and starting method	Correction factor, M	Diameter of small pulley, in.	Correction factor, P	Operating conditions	Correction factor, F
Squirrel cage, compensator starting....	1.5	4 and under	0.5	Oily, wet, or dusty atmosphere	1.35
		$4\frac{1}{2}$–8	0.6		
Squirrel cage, line starting...........	2.0	9–12	0.7	Vertical drives	1.2
		13–16	0.8	Jerky loads	1.2
Slip ring and high starting torque......	2.5	17–30	0.9	Shock and reversing loads	1.4
		Over 30	1.0		

* Courtesy of J. E. Rhoads and Sons.

Table 6-9. Horsepower Losses Due to Centrifugal Tension

Speed of Belt, Fpm	Percentage off Rated Horsepower
1,000	1
2,000	4
3,000	8
4,000	15
5,000	23
6,000	34
7,000	46
8,000	60
9,000	76
10,000	95

Note: These losses are applicable to belting running without automatic idler or pivoted motor base control.

Table 6-10. Minimum Pulley Diameters in Inches for Oak-tanned Leather Belting at Various Belt Speeds

Belt thickness, in.	Belt speed, fpm					
	1,000	2,000	3,000	4,000	5,000	6,000
Single ply:						
$\frac{8}{64}$	$1\frac{1}{2}$	2	$2\frac{1}{4}$	$2\frac{1}{2}$	3	$3\frac{1}{2}$
$\frac{10}{64}$	2	$2\frac{1}{2}$	3	$3\frac{1}{2}$	4	$4\frac{1}{2}$
$\frac{12}{64}$	$2\frac{3}{4}$	$3\frac{1}{2}$	4	$4\frac{1}{2}$	5	$5\frac{1}{2}$
$\frac{14}{64}$	$3\frac{1}{2}$	4	$4\frac{1}{2}$	$5\frac{1}{2}$	6	7
Double ply:						
$\frac{16}{64}$	5	6	7	8	9	10
$\frac{18}{64}$	6	8	9	10	12	13
$\frac{20}{64}$	8	9	11	12	14	16
$\frac{22}{64}$	9	11	13	15	17	19
$\frac{24}{64}$	11	14	16	18	20	22
Triple ply:						
$\frac{28}{64}$	18	21	24	28	31	35
$\frac{32}{64}$	20	24	28	32	36	40
$\frac{36}{64}$	22	27	32	36	40	45

run against the pulley face. It can be used in the presence of steam, dampness, moisture, and temperatures to 130°F but should not be operated in an atmosphere charged with the mists or vapors of corrosive acids. It can be made endless and will accommodate any type of metallic fastener.

Horsepower Formulas and Tables for Leather Belting.

Horsepower ratings: see Tables 6-2 to 6-7 inclusive.
Horsepower correction factors: see Table 6-8.
Horsepower losses due to centrifugal force: see Table 6-9.
Minimum pulley diameters for oak tanned leather belting at various belt speeds: see
    Table 6-10.

CORRECT WAY TO INSTALL LEATHER BELTING

Better leather belt performance is ensured by taking the time to check alignment, tension, and other details described below before starting up a leather or any other type of belt drive.

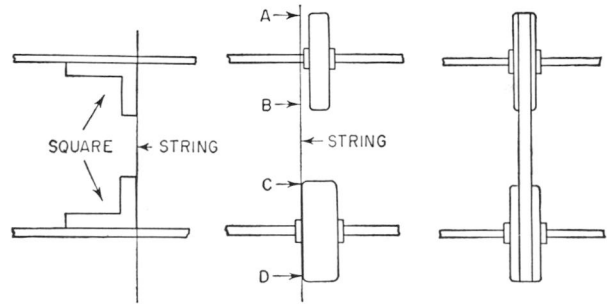

Fig. 6-2. Method of aligning shafting and pulleys.

Method of Aligning Shafting and Pulleys. An easy way to do this is shown by Fig. 6-2.

1. Check shafts with a level.
2. Determine if shafts are parallel by placing a taut string between the shafts and checking it with a large square.
3. Check alignment of pulleys using a string along their edges. If pulleys are the same width, the string should touch lightly at four points: *A, B, C,* and *D.* If pulleys are of different widths, the distance from string to pulley at points *A* and *B* should be the same. If possible give the pulley a half turn and recheck. When pulleys are installed one above the other, a string with plumb bob can be used to check alignment.

Belt Tension. For best results a leather or any type of belt should be run with the least tension needed to transmit the load without slipping. If a belt is too slack, it will slip causing its surface to glaze, then crack and peel. If the belt is too tight, it may put excessive loads on bearings. Wherever possible, leather or any type of belt should be operated with the slack side on top (see Fig. 6-3). This will provide a greater arc of contact between the belt and the faces of pulleys, permitting lower tension. On short center or vertical drives it is good practice to use an automatic motor base of either the gravity or reaction torque type. Maximum pulling power of a leather belt is obtained by running the grain or hair side of the belt next to the pulley faces.

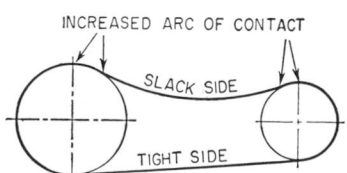

Fig. 6-3. Proper method of running belt.

Installing Endless Belts. Care should be exercised in forcing an endless belt over the pulleys to avoid putting a crook in it. Belts, particularly those 6 in. and wider, should be either made endless on the job by means of clamps and rods or slipped on after temporarily shortening the center distance between pulleys. This can be accomplished by moving the motor on slide rails, loosening hanger bolts, etc.

Running Direction. Care should be taken to have the outside feather edge of the lap faced away from the direction in which the belt runs, as shown in Fig. 6-1. This tends to protect the outside points of the lap if they should strike guards, guides, or shifters. It also protects the lap from being opened up by windage.

Quarter-turn Drives. To overcome the belt distortion encountered in quarter-turn drives and to distribute wear evenly on both of its sides, give one end of the belt a half turn (180°) before making the splice. In a single-ply belt made up in this way the grain side at the joint is adjacent to the flesh side. This half-turn method of construction is particularly adaptable to double-ply belts which have the grain exposed on both sides. The tension of the belt, side to side, also turns it edge to edge, with the result that not only is the wear distributed over the face of the belt but the tension is also kept equalized on the edges of the belt. When installing quarter-turn drives it is particularly advantageous to make the belts endless with clamps and rods right on the job. Better production, fewer shutdowns, and longer belt life will result.

LEATHER BELT MAINTENANCE

Inasmuch as belting is the connecting link between power and production, it pays to have a competent individual in definite charge of its installation and maintenance.

Regular Inspection. It is important to establish a system of inspection at regular intervals. The following are some of the points to check:

1. Is the belt too dry (see Cleaning and Dressing, item 1)?
2. Is the belt dirty or saturated with oil or grease (see Cleaning and Dressing, item 2)?
3. Is the belt too slack or too tight (see Belt Tension, item 3)?
4. Are shafting and pulleys in alignment (see Alignment of Shafting and Pulleys, item 4)?
5. What is the condition of laps, plies, lacing, and ends of laced belts (see Laps and Plies, item 5)?

1. Cleaning and Dressing. The term "dressing" as applied to leather belting signifies the lubrication of the fibers of the leather. It does not mean creating a sticky surface. Leather belting of all types requires periodic dressing or lubrication, since the heat generated by frictional contact with the pulleys tends to dry out the currying ingredients. This results in the leather becoming dry and hard. The leather should be dressed with a compound containing the currying ingredients so that penetration and a relubrication of the fibrous structure result.

Leather-belting manufacturers supply dressing compounds which contain the currying materials employed in the manufacture of oak-tanned nonwaterproof and waterproof leather belting. Mineral-retanned leather requires a compound different from that required by oak-tanned leather. Such compounds can also be obtained from the respective manufacturers.

When pulley faces begin to polish, it is a sign that dressing is needed on the belt. Under normal atmospheric and operating conditions, dress belts every 3 to 6 months.

The most effective results are obtained by applying the lubricant to the outer surface or ply. This permits the material to work its way through the leather and therefore prevents a slippery driving surface on the belt and an accumulation or gumming of the lubricant on the pulley face. If the pulley-contact surface of the belt is very dry, a small amount of the lubricant can be applied to this surface with safety.

Cheap and low-grade stick and semiliquid belt dressings which generally contain the ingredients shown in Table 6-11 should not be used on leather belting of any type.

Correct Dressings for Leather Belting. *Oak-tanned Nonwaterproof.* Preferably, compounds supplied by leather-belting manufacturers. Commercial castor oil and neat's-foot oil (3 parts castor to 1 part neat's-foot).

Oak-tanned Waterproof. Same as for oak-tanned nonwaterproof.

Mineral-retanned Waterproof. Compounds supplied by leather belting manufacturers only.

Combination Oak Tanned and Mineral Retanned. Compounds supplied by leather belting manufacturers only.

2. Keep belts as clean as possible at all times for best results. Oil or grease thrown from machine bearings will reduce belt life and pulling power. If oil or grease leak cannot be stopped at the source, the installation of deflectors or throwing disks will prove helpful. A small amount of oil or grease on a belt can sometimes be removed by ordinary wiping. If this does not do the job, give the belt a thorough scrubbing with a solution of carbon tetrachloride and naphtha, using a stiff jute brush and working in the direction of lap joints so as not to lift them. Another method is

Table 6-11. Unsatisfactory Belt Dressings

Stick type	Per cent	Semiliquid type	Per cent
Graphite............	22	Tar	36
Rosin...............	27	Rape seed or cotton oil	54
Vegetable oil........	44	Rosin	10
Paraffin.............	7		

to remove the belt and soak it for 5 or 6 hr in a degreasing solution consisting of 1 part carbon tetrachloride to 3 parts naphtha. If carbon tetrachloride is not available, the belt can be soaked in any of the cleaning fluids used by dry-cleaning establishments. Because of the fire hazard and toxic effect, the soaking and drying of the belt should be done in the open or where ventilation is good. After removing the belt from the bath, allow it to dry thoroughly. Always dress a belt after cleaning.

3. Belt Tension. It is important to keep the belt tight enough at all times to transmit power without slippage. A belt that is too slack will slip and burn, causing excessive wear. If the belt is too tight, it places undue strain on the shaft bearings.

4. Alignment of Shafting and Pulleys. Belting cannot give good service if the shafting and pulleys are out of alignment. Indications of misalignment are:

1. Belt running off the pulley at one side.
2. Belt rubbing or climbing on flanged or stepped cone pulleys.

A simple test to determine whether the fault is the alignment or a crooked belt is to turn the belt inside out or end for end. If it still runs to the same side of the pulley as before, the fault is in the alignment and not the belt. It is important to check drive alignment at least once a year. In multiple-story buildings, shifting of loads on the floor above the shafting may cause it to be distorted or thrown out of alignment. Some common faults in drive alignment are:

1. Shafting carrying driving and driven pulleys may not be parallel.
2. Shafting may be sprung out of line. (Hangers should always be located near the pulleys, the points of maximum load.)
3. Driving and driven pulleys may be offset.
4. Pulley may be eccentric with shafting (see Fig. 6-2 for easy method of aligning shafting and pulleys).

5. Laps and Plies. When cementing laps of a leather belt, if the first coat does not dry with a shine, a second coat should be applied and allowed to dry. If the sizing coat turns cloudy, apply a second coat and continue brushing until cloudiness dis-

Table 6-12. Transmission-belt Trouble-shooter Helps*
(Flat leather belts)

Trouble	Cause	Remedy
1. Belt slips and squeals	a. Belt too loose b. Insufficient belt capacity c. Pulley crown too high, causing increased wear of narrow center section of belt d. Leather surface too dry and shiny	a. Increase belt tension b. Use thicker or wider belt c. Decrease crown taper to $\frac{1}{8}$ in. per ft d. Apply suitable dressing
2. Excessive belt stretch	Belt capacity too low	Use thicker or wider belt
3. Belt runs crooked	a. Belt stretched on one side by forcing over pulley b. Belt ends not squared when joining c. Belt unevenly stretched by running on misaligned pulleys d. Loose belt unevenly stretched by running up on flanged or step-cone pulley	a, b, c, d. Repair damaged belt section or replace belt. Eliminate physical cause when installing
4. Belt runs off pulleys	a. Misalignment of pulleys or shafting (if belt continues to run off same side when belt is turned end for end) b. Crooked belt c. Pulley crown too high	a. Eliminate cause b. Repair belt c. Decrease crown taper to $\frac{1}{8}$ in. per ft
5. Belt runs to one side of driven pulley	a. Belt too slack b. Load too great c. Crooked belt (if it runs to opposite side when turned end for end) d. Misalignment of pulleys or shafting	a. Increase belt tension b. Use thicker or wider belt c. Repair belt d. Eliminate cause
6. Belt whips and flaps	a. Pulsating load at power source b. Shaft, motor, or machine not rigidly supported c. Lopsided pulley d. Bent shaft e. Too much or too little belt tension	a, b, c, d, e. Eliminate cause where possible. Try change of speed or addition of fly wheel to smooth out load.
7. Belt weaves back and forth across pulley	a. Wobbly pulley b. High spot on pulley c. Belt extremely crooked	a, b. Correct faulty condition c. Repair or replace belt
8. Cracked outside ply	a. Excessive belt tension b. Pulley diameter too small	a. Reduce tension b. Provide proper pulley for belt thickness
9. Cracked inside ply	Burning caused by excessive slip	See item 1
10. Peeling grain	a. Excessive slip b. Improper belt dressing c. Chemical fumes or oil	a. See item 1 b. Clean belt with commercial solvent, scrape off any loose grain, and use suitable dressing c. Provide guards if possible, and use type of belt best suited for condition

* Courtesy National Industrial Leather Assoc.

appears. If the sizing coat does not dry in 30 min, wipe it off and apply another coat. (This condition is generally caused by an excessive amount of oil in the belt.) If cemented laps show signs of opening, recement them immediately. If belt guard, shifters, guides, or pulley flanges rub against the edge of the belt, the lap and plies may open. This condition should be corrected immediately. A good belt shifter has broad and well-rounded surfaces so as to spread the thrust over a large belt-edge area.

Another cause of ply and lap separation is running too thick a belt on a small-diameter pulley (see Table 6-10).

6. Other Maintenance Pointers. On flanged or step-cone pulleys, belts frequently have a tendency to climb. Figure 6-4 shows a simple method of correcting this condition by machining or undercutting the fillet. Recrown fiber or paper pulleys when they wear. When belts run off the center of motor pulleys, it may be the result of a worn crown. If blisters occur on belt and an immediate shutdown for repair is not possible, puncture the blister with a knife or awl on the trailing end. Travel of the belt over the pulley will then flatten out the blister, and it

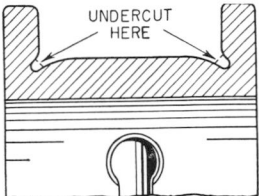

Fig. 6-4. Undercutting to prevent belt climb.

can be cemented when time permits. A guide showing possible leather belting troubles, their causes, and how to remedy them is given in Table 6-12.

RUBBER BELTING

Rubber flat power belting, generally known as "friction surface rubber," is a good transmitter of power when properly selected for the service requirements and for the atmospheric conditions involved. The belt is constructed of cotton-duck plies frictioned together with a rubber compound. The cotton duck is the element of tensile strength, and the "friction" or the grade of rubber compound employed governs the degree of adhesive tendency between the duck plies and also the frictional qualities of the belt.

The Cotton Duck. For the average rubber belting the duck weight varies from 28 to 32 oz, which, according to the United States Trade Standard, signifies that the actual scale weight of a piece of duck 36 by 42 in. when dry is 28 to 32 oz. The actual weight of the duck is not the sole strength factor, because quality, weave, and length of fiber have a decided effect. The average ultimate tensile strength of 32 oz duck 1 in. wide is 440 lb. In calculating the strength of rubber belting a factor of safety of 20 is employed. The tensile strength of the entire belt is approximately one-third less than the sum of the plies when taken separately.

The Rubber-compound Friction. The grade of the rubber compound employed is measured in pounds and is based on the quality of the rubber compound. Frictions used are 20, 22, 24, 26, and 28 lb. This pound friction is determined by the resistance of the rubber compound to the weight required. If a 28-lb friction is desired, a 28-lb weight or pull is applied to a peeled back ply of the belt 1 in. wide. It must not separate longitudinally more than 1 in. per min. The duck and the friction are the grading characteristics of rubber belting, as a 28-oz 28-lb friction belt.

Atmospheric Effects. An atmosphere charged with steam, dampness, moisture, or temperatures to 115°F has no bad effect. However, an atmosphere charged with the mists or vapors of the corrosive acids deteriorates and finally destroys the outer or surface cotton duck plies. When exposed to nitric acid or its fumes, the rubber compound becomes slimy and the duck disintegrates. Continuous exposure to mineral oil or grease causes deterioration of rubber compound but not of Neoprene compound. At temperatures above 120°F the rubber compound tends to dry out and crack; much higher temperatures are possible when Neoprene is used as a friction compound.

Maintenance, Installation, and Inspection. With the exception of dressing, practically all the information given under the heading of leather belting is applicable to rubber belting.

Proper number of plies, based upon pulley diameters and speeds, is given in Table 6-13, and minimum and maximum plies for various widths in Table 6-14.

Table 6-13. Proper Number of Plies for Regular 32-oz Duck Construction, Based on Pulley Diameter and Speed

Number of plies	Pulley diameters, in.		
	Under 2,000 fpm	2,000–4,000 fpm	4,000–4,500 fpm
3	2	3	5
4	4	6	8
5	10	14	18
6	16	20	24
7	22	26	30
8	28	32	38
9	34	38	44
10	40	44	50

Table 6-14. Minimum and Maximum Plies of Rubber Belting

Width of belt, in.	Minimum number of plies	Maximum number of plies	Width of belt, in.	Minimum number of plies	Maximum number of plies
2	3	4	16	5	8
3	3	4	18	5	8
4	3	5	20	5	8
5	4	5	22	5	8
6	4	6	24	5	8
8	4	6	26	6	8
10	4	6	30	6	10
12	4	6	36	6	10
14	5	8	42	6	10

Horsepower Capacity of Rubber Belting

Horsepower Formula for Rubber Belting (Standard-weight Duck Type).   The general expression for horsepower transmitted by a belt is as given for the various types of leather belting, but for belting made of plies of fabric, the effective tension or $(T_1 - T_2)$ is expressed in pounds per inch width per ply of thickness or "pounds per ply inch."   Therefore, the formula for duck-ply belting is expressed as follows:

$$\text{Hp} = \frac{WNS(T_1 - T_2)}{33,000}$$

where W = width of belt, in.
N = number of plies
S = belt speed, fpm
T_1 = tight-side tension, lb per ply inch
T_2 = slack-side tension, lb per ply inch
$(T_1 - T_2)$ = effective tension, lb per ply inch

Rubber-belt manufacturers have revised and simplified the formula for horsepower capacity in terms of maximum tension T_1.   The simplified formula is

$$\text{Hp} = \frac{WNS(T_1 - T_c)}{33,000} \left(1 - \frac{1}{R}\right)$$

where Hp = hp capacity of belt
   W = width, in.
   N = number of plies
   S = belt speed, fpm
   T_1 = tight-side tension, lb per in. width
   T_c = centrifugal tension per in. width
$[1 - (1/R)]$ = correction factor for arc of contact (see Table 6-15)

Thirty-two-ounce duck is generally used for good-quality rubber belting. Based on an average ultimate tensile strength for this weight of 440 lb, the allowable effective tension is 25 lb per in. width of duck or a factor of safety of $17\frac{1}{2}$. $(T_1 - T_c)$ can therefore be calculated as 25 lb for a 32-oz duck belt and 20 lb for a 28-oz duck belt.

Table 6-15. Correction Factor for Arc of Contact, Rubber Belting

Arc of contact, deg	$1 - (1/R)$	Arc of contact, deg	$1 - (1/R)$
90	0.29	190	0.51
100	0.32	200	0.53
110	0.35	210	0.55
120	0.37	220	0.57
130	0.39	230	0.58
140	0.41	240	0.60
150	0.44	250	0.61
160	0.46	260	0.63
170	0.48	270	0.64
180	0.50		

Initial Stretch of Ply-construction Rubber Belting. Friction-surface ply-constructed rubber belting will stretch initially; therefore under normal operating conditions it should be adjusted occasionally during the early periods. When applying this type of belting, it should be cut short of the actual length necessary as follows:

Three-, four-, and five-ply thickness, cut short $\frac{5}{32}$ in. per foot.
Six-, seven-, and eight-ply thickness, cut short $\frac{1}{8}$ in. per foot.
Nine-, ten-, and twelve-ply thickness, cut short $\frac{3}{32}$ in. per foot.

Dressings. A rubber belt of any grade or type cannot be penetrated by dressing compounds; therefore it is not possible to lubricate the internal fibers. All compounds applied remain on the surface of the belt; hence caution must be exercised in their use. Ply separation and loss of power-transmission ability are frequently the result of the use of sticky, resinous dressings, which cause the belt to stick to the pulley and an accumulation of lumps to be deposited on the pulley face.

Rubber belting of all types should be dressed periodically with vegetable, castor, or linseed oil. These will remove the rubber "bloom" from new belting and soften the surface of used belting. These oils furnish a nondangerous tackiness or adhesiveness between the belt and the pulley faces.

STITCHED COTTON-DUCK IMPREGNATED BELTING

This type is commonly known as "stitched canvas." It is composed of plies of impregnated cotton duck stitched or sewed together. The quality of the belt depends upon the grade and weight of the duck, the method of stitching, and the impregnating compound. It is generally made from 36- to $37\frac{1}{2}$-oz duck cut and folded to the required belt width and thickness and firmly stitched together. The structure is impregnated with suitable compounds to furnish durability, lubrication, and frictional value. Two types are available: the "round edge" and the "folded edge." The round-edge construction employs the "innerlocked" stitch, particularly above four ply, in addition to the straight-through stitch, while the folded-edge construction employs the straight-through stitch for all thicknesses. The round-edge type in view of the innerlocked stitch results in a securely bonded belt and therefore furnishes better resistance to ply separation and edge abrasion from shifter forks and possible structural interferences. This type of belt is a good transmitter of power if properly selected for the power and speed requirements and the atmospheric conditions involved.

Table 6-16. Horsepower Ratings of Good-grade, Stitched-Cotton-Duck, Impregnated Belting

Belt speed, fpm	Horsepower transmitted by a belt 1 in. wide				
	4 ply	5 ply	6 ply	8 ply	10 ply
200	0.36	0.45	0.54	0.63	0.72
400	0.72	0.90	1.08	1.26	1.44
600	1.08	1.35	1.62	1.89	2.16
800	1.44	1.80	2.16	2.52	2.88
1,000	1.80	2.25	2.70	3.15	3.60
1,200	2.16	2.70	3.24	3.78	4.32
1,400	2.52	3.15	3.78	4.41	5.04
1,600	2.88	3.60	4.32	5.04	5.76
1,800	3.24	4.05	4.86	5.67	6.48
2,000	3.60	4.50	5.40	6.30	7.20
2,200	3.94	4.93	5.92	6.89	7.88
2,400	4.26	5.32	6.38	7.46	8.52
2,600	4.56	5.70	6.84	7.98	9.12
2,800	4.86	6.08	7.29	8.50	9.72
3,000	5.15	6.44	7.73	9.02	10.30
3,200	5.42	6.78	8.12	9.50	10.84
3,400	5.67	7.08	8.50	9.92	11.34
3,600	5.90	7.38	8.86	10.33	11.80
3,800	6.11	7.64	9.16	10.68	12.22
4,000	6.29	7.86	9.43	11.00	12.58
4,200	6.46	8.07	9.69	11.30	12.92
4,400	6.60	8.26	9.91	11.55	13.20
4,600	6.73	8.42	10.10	11.77	13.46
4,800	6.83	8.54	10.25	11.95	13.66
5,000	6.92	8.65	10.38	12.11	13.84
5,200	7.00	8.75	10.50	12.24	14.00
5,400	7.06	8.83	10.59	12.35	14.12
5,600	7.11	8.89	10.66	12.44	14.22
5,800	7.14	8.92	10.71	12.49	14.28
6,000	7.15	8.94	10.73	12.51	14.30

This table, based on an arc of contact of 165°, is corrected for centrifugal force.

Maintenance, Installation, and Inspection. The information given under the heading of leather belting is applicable to this type of belting.

Characteristics. This belting is made in 3, 4, 5, 6, 8, 10, and 12 plies and in widths from 2 to 72 in. It possesses flexibility, elasticity, and resistance to ply separation. It will accommodate any type of metallic fastener and can be laced with rawhide or wire.

Atmospheric Effects. It will resist steam, dampness, moisture, slight amounts of mineral oil or grease, and temperature to 130°F. It should not be operated in an atmosphere charged with the mists or vapors of the corrosive acids or where any caustic is likely to come in contact with it, since caustic stiffens its entire structure. Temperatures above 140°F cause a drying out of the impregnating compound.

Dressings.   The impregnating compounds of the better grades of this belt serve as a lubricant to the cotton fibers during its life.   When the belt is used under the proper atmospheric conditions, a tacky frictional surface is evident.   Other forms of dressings are not required.   The pulley surface of the belt should be periodically brushed, particularly where abrasive substances are present.

Horsepower Ratings and Relation of Number of Plies to Pulley Diameters and Speeds: See Tables 6-16 and 6-17.

Table 6-17. Relation of Number of Plies to Pulley Diameters and Speeds

Belt speed, fpm	Pulley diameter, in.				
	4 ply	5 ply	6 ply	8 ply	10 ply
Up to 1,000	3	4	6	12	24
1,000–2,000	4	5	8	15	30
2,000–3,000	5	6	10	18	36
3,000–4,000	6	7	12	21	42
Over 4,000	7	8	14	24	48

Table 6-18. Horsepower Table for High-grade Solid-woven Cotton Belting, Based on an Allowable Effective Tension of 100 Lb

Speed, fpm	Width, in.																			
	1	2	3	4	5	6	7	8	9	10	11	12	13	14	15	16	17	18	19	20
500	1½	3	4½	6	7½	9	10½	12	13½	15	16½	18	19½	21	23	24	26	27	29	30
1,000	3	6	9	12	15	18	21	24	27	30	33	36	39	42	45	48	52	55	58	61
1,500	4½	9	13½	18	23	27	32	36	41	45	50	55	59	64	68	73	77	82	86	91
2,000	6	12	18	24	30	36	42	48	55	61	67	73	79	85	91	97	103	109	115	121
2,500	7½	15	23	30	38	45	53	61	68	76	83	91	98	106	114	121	129	136	144	152
3,000	9	18	27	36	45	55	64	73	82	91	100	109	118	127	136	145	155	164	173	182
3,500	10½	21	32	42	53	64	74	85	95	106	117	127	138	148	159	170	180	191	202	212
4,000	12	24	36	48	61	73	85	97	109	121	133	145	158	170	182	194	206	218	230	242
4,500	13½	27	41	55	68	82	95	109	123	136	150	164	177	191	205	218	232	245	259	273
5,000	15	30	45	61	76	91	106	121	136	152	167	182	197	212	227	242	258	273	288	303
5,500	16½	23	50	67	83	100	117	133	150	167	183	200	218	233	250	267	283	300	317	333
6,000	18	36	55	73	91	109	127	145	164	182	200	218	236	255	273	291	309	327	345	364
6,500	19½	39	59	79	98	118	138	158	177	197	217	236	256	276	295	315	335	355	374	394
7,000	21	42	64	85	106	127	148	170	191	212	233	255	276	297	318	339	361	382	403	424
7,500	23	45	68	91	114	136	159	182	205	227	250	273	295	318	341	364	386	409	432	455
8,000	24	48	73	97	121	145	170	194	218	242	267	291	314	339	364	388	412	436	461	485
8,500	26	52	77	103	129	155	180	206	232	258	283	309	335	361	386	412	438	464	489	515
9,000	27	55	82	109	136	164	191	218	245	273	300	327	355	382	409	436	464	491	518	545
9,500	29	58	86	115	144	173	202	230	259	288	317	345	374	403	432	461	489	518	547	576
10,000	30	61	91	121	152	182	212	242	273	303	333	364	394	424	455	485	515	545	576	606

Based on an arc of contact of 165° and not corrected for centrifugal force.   Horsepower capacities for the various allowable effective tensions can be proportioned to this tabulation.

SOLID WOVEN IMPREGNATED COTTON BELTING

This type is made from long-fiber, fine-quality domestic cotton woven solidly together to form various belting thicknesses. To protect the cotton from mechanical and atmospheric effects it is thoroughly impregnated with special compounds.

Maintenance, Installation, and Inspection. The information given under the heading of leather belting is applicable to this type of belting.

Characteristics. It is made in single, heavy single, double, and triple thicknesses and in widths from 1 to 36 in. It possesses the ability to absorb shock loads.

Table 6-19. Allowable Effective Tensions, Pound per Inch Width

Weight	Pounds
Single	40
Double, up to 8 in	80
Double, 8 in. and over	100
Triple	120

Table 6-20. Relation of Thickness to Pulley Diameters and Speeds

Thickness	Minimum pulley diameters, in.	
	Up to 2,000 fpm	2,000– 5,000 fpm
Single	4	6
Heavy single	6	8
Double	8	10
Triple	15	18

Atmospheric Effects. Alternate wet and dry conditions cause stretch and shrinkage. This belting is not affected by mineral oil or grease unless excessive. It is steam- and moistureproof and will operate satisfactorily in temperatures to 140°F. It should not be operated in an atmosphere charged with the mists or vapors of the corrosive acids. Nitric acid contact will destroy the belt.

Dressings. This belt is dressed by the impregnating compounds. They protect and lubricate the cotton fibers. It should be replaced periodically by special dressings furnished by the belt manufacturer. No other dressing should be used.

Horsepower Formula and Rating (see Table 6-18). Since this belting is a solid woven product, the horsepower capacities are based on definite allowable effective tensions per inch of width. The formula is similar to that used for leather belting. See Table 6-19 for allowable effective tensions. The relation of thickness to pulley diameters and speeds is given in Table 6-20.

BALATA BELTING

This type is constructed from 36- to 38-oz cotton-duck plies thoroughly impregnated and frictioned together with a balata gum which resembles gutta percha. The properties that distinguish it from other gums and make it especially valuable as a substance for power belting are its toughness and waterproof qualities. Balata gum will not bond with any foreign material; it will bond with balata only.

Maintenance, Installation, and Inspection. The information given under the heading of leather belting is applicable to this type of belting.

Characteristics. It is made in 3, 4, 5, 6, 7, 8, 9, and 10 plies and in widths from 1 to 72 in. It possesses low stretch. It will accommodate any type of metallic fastener and can be made endless by its manufacturer.

Table 6-21. Horsepower Rating for Balata Belting 1 In. Wide

Speed of belt, fpm	3 ply	4 ply	5 ply	6 ply	7 ply	8 ply	9 ply	10 ply
500	0.60	0.90	1.21	1.51	1.81	2.12	2.42	2.71
750	0.90	1.36	1.81	2.27	2.72	3.18	3.63	4.08
1,000	1.21	1.81	2.42	3.03	3.63	4.24	4.84	5.44
1,250	1.51	2.27	3.03	3.79	4.55	5.30	6.06	6.82
1,500	1.81	2.72	3.63	4.55	5.45	6.36	7.27	8.17
1,750	2.12	3.18	4.24	5.30	6.36	7.42	8.48	9.54
2,000	2.42	3.63	4.85	6.06	7.27	8.48	9.70	10.90
2,250	2.72	4.09	5.45	6.82	8.18	9.54	10.90	12.27
2,500	3.03	4.54	6.06	6.58	9.10	10.60	12.12	13.64
2,750	3.33	4.99	6.66	8.34	10.00	11.66	13.32	14.99
3,000	3.63	5.44	7.26	9.10	10.90	12.72	14.52	16.34
3,250	3.93	5.90	8.87	9.85	11.81	13.78	15.74	17.71
3,500	4.24	6.36	8.48	10.60	12.72	14.84	17.96	19.08
3,750	4.54	6.81	9.09	11.36	13.63	15.90	18.18	20.44
4,000	4.84	7.27	9.70	12.12	14.54	16.96	19.40	21.81
4,250	5.15	7.72	10.30	12.88	15.45	18.02	20.60	23.17
4,500	5.45	8.18	10.90	13.64	16.36	19.08	21.80	24.54
4,750	5.75	8.63	11.51	14.40	17.28	20.14	23.02	25.91
5,000	6.06	9.08	12.12	15.16	18.20	21.20	24.24	27.28

Based on an arc of contact of 165° and not corrected for centrifugal force.   Ratings based on 38-oz duck.   For 36-oz duck, figure 92 per cent of ratings given.

Table 6-22. Relation of Number of Plies to Pulley Diameters and Speeds

Number of plies	Minimum pulley diameters, in.		
	Up to 2,000 fpm	2,000– 4,000 fpm	4,000– 5,000 fpm
3	3	4	5
4	5	6	8
5	8	10	12
6	12	14	16
8	18	20	24
10	30	34	38

Atmospheric Effects.   It will resist steam and moisture and is dry heatproof to 105°F.   It cannot be used in temperatures over 115°F, since balata gum melts at 120°F.   It should not be used in an atmosphere charged with the mists or vapors of the corrosive acids.

Dressings.   This type cannot be penetrated by any dressing compound.   If the pulling surface becomes dry and hard, vegetable castor oil should be applied sparingly. This oil has a softening effect and produces a "tacky" nondangerous surface on the belt.

Horsepower Ratings and Relation of Number of Plies to Pulley Diameters and Speeds: See Tables 6-21 and 6-22.

SELECTION OF BELTING TYPE

Operating atmospheric conditions and surrounding ambient temperatures to a considerable extent control the life expectancy of any type of power belting. Actual plant testing by the author of belting materials and constructions under various atmospheric conditions and temperatures has furnished authoritative information on the subject (see Table 6-23).

Table 6-23. Selection of Belting to Meet Atmospheric Conditions

Type of belting	Actual acid contact	Acid mists and vapors	Abrasive dusts	Steam and moisture	Temp. to 115°F	Temp. to 130°F	Temp. to 140°F	Mineral oil and grease	Normal
Nonwaterproof oak leather............	No	No	Yes	No	Yes	No	No	Yes	Yes
Waterproof oak leather............	No	No	Yes	Yes	Yes	Yes	No	Yes	Yes
Mineral retanned leather............	No	Yes	Yes	Yes	Yes	Yes	Yes	Yes	Yes
Comb. oak and min. retan. leather......	No	No	Yes	Yes	Yes	Yes	No	Yes	Yes
Rubber—friction surface.............	No	No	Yes	Yes	Yes	No	No	No	Yes
Rubber—rubber covered...........	No	Yes	No	Yes	Yes	Yes	No	No	Yes
Stitched—cotton duck.............	No	No	Yes	Yes	Yes	Yes	No	Yes	Yes
Solid woven cotton....	No	No	Yes	Yes	Yes	Yes	Yes	Yes	Yes
Balata belting.......	No	No	Yes	Yes	Yes	Yes	No	Yes	Yes
Camel's hair—solid woven	Yes Slight	Yes	Yes	Yes	Yes	Yes	Over 140°F	Yes	Yes

BELT DRIVING

Driving Ratios. The relation of the diameter of the driving pulley to the diameter of the driven one controls the speed ratio and the arc of contact of the belt on the driving pulley or the smaller pulley of the two. Without the use of an idler pulley a ratio of 1 to 1 furnishes a maximum arc of contact of 180° on open drives and relatively more on a crossed-belt drive. For efficient service a ratio of 6 to 1 should not be exceeded.

Vertical Drives. A belt operating vertically without center adjustment or idler control is a source of high maintenance and power loss. The stretch of the belting substance causes the belt to drop away from the bottom pulley. If a vertical drive is necessary and take-up facilities are not possible, the center distance should be comparatively short, based on the least amount of accumulated stretch per foot. Adjustable centers should be used, or a controllable idler pulley placed against the loose side of the belt, or a vertical-type pivoted motor base used. An angle of 15° from the vertical will help to eliminate vertical-drive difficulties.

Crossed-belt Drives. Crossed belting is used to reverse the d rection of rotation and to increase the arc of contact. It is practicable, but the following factors must be considered:

1. The ratio of a crossed drive should not exceed 4 to 1.
2. The cross should occur as close to the center between the pulleys as possible.
3. The width of the belting should not exceed 8 in.
4. The fastener must not interfere at the point of crossing.
5. Extremely short center drives should not be crossed.

Quarter-turn Drives. A quarter-turn belt drive is employed to transmit power at right angles in a vertical, horizontal, or angular direction. It is a source of trouble and should not be used unless absolutely necessary. For best results a leather belt specially constructed for quarter-turn driving should be used. The quarter-turn drive should be installed correctly.

Rule for Installing Quarter-turn Drives. The center of the face of the loose side of the driver must line with the center of the face of the tight side of the driven.

Shifting of Belting. Frequent or periodic sliding of a belt on tight and loose pulleys subjects it to edge wear and considerable transverse stress and crumpling action. Such strains and crumpling are more pronounced in wide belting regardless of thickness. To avoid such action, single leather and four-ply or equal thickness fabric should not exceed 5 in. in width and double leather or six-ply or equal thickness fabric should not exceed a width of 8 in. when employed on shifting installations. Edge wear is primarily caused by wrongly adjusted and rough shifter forks. The fork should be smooth and straight and come in contact with the belt only when shifting. The roller-type shifter fork eliminates edge wear.

Pulley Diameters and Revolutions

Problem 1. Diameter and rpm of driver and diameter of driven known; to find rpm of driven.

$$Formula: \frac{\text{Diameter of driver} \times \text{rpm}}{\text{Diameter of driven}}$$

Problem 2. Diameter and rpm of driven and diameter of driver known; to find rpm of driver.

$$Formula: \frac{\text{Diameter of driven} \times \text{rpm}}{\text{Diameter of driver}}$$

Problem 3. Rpm of driver and diameter and rpm of driven known; to find diameter of driver.

$$Formula: \frac{\text{Diameter of driven} \times \text{rpm}}{\text{Rpm of driver}}$$

Problem 4. Rpm of driven and diameter and rpm of driver known; to find diameter of driven.

$$Formula: \frac{\text{Diameter of driver} \times \text{rpm}}{\text{Rpm of driven}}$$

FASTENING OF POWER BELTING

Joining a power-transmission belt in an improper and careless manner results in high belting-maintenance costs, short belting life, and production loss.

Belt-joining Fundamentals

1. The belt should not be strained at the joint.
2. The fastener should not cut or weaken the belt.
3. The fastener should conform to the curvature of the pulley.
4. The fastener should resist wear caused by pulley contact.
5. The correct size and type of fastener should be used for pulley diameters and speeds.
6. The fastener should not prevent the belt being square and close fitting at the joint.
7. If metallic, the minimum amount of metal should be at the joint.
8. The fastener should be quick of application.

General Methods of Belt Joining

1. Endless.
2. Laced.
3. Metallic.

The Endless Method

The endless method is the most efficient belt-joining method, since the joint is integral with the belt.   Initial stretch is evident in all types of belting; therefore center adjusting facilities should be provided when this method is employed.   The leather belt offers the greatest possibility for the endless method because it is a multiple of cemented joints.

Making the Leather Belt Endless.   *Regular Oak Nonwaterproof.*   Scarf or scrape the ends down to a thin edge, 3, 4, or 6 in. back, depending upon the width and thickness of the belt, and apply the hot glue to the two scarfed surfaces.   Place the glued surfaces together and subject to continuous pressure for at least $2\frac{1}{2}$ hrs.

Waterproof Oak, Mineral Retanned, and Combination Tannage. Scarf or scrape the ends down to a thin edge as described above and size the two scarfed surfaces first with a waterproof pyroxylin cement; allow this to dry.   Apply another coating of the cement to the sized surfaces, place them together, and subject them to continuous pressure for at least 6 hr.

Uses of the Endless Belt:

1. On motor drives when the motor is provided with slide rails.
2. On pivoted motor drives.
3. On motor drives, automatic-idler-pulley controlled.
4. On high-speed spindle operations of machine tools when idler pulley control or center adjustment is possible.
5. On adjustable mule-pulley drives.
6. On large-powered engine drives.

Directions for the Use of Regular Nonwaterproof Leather Belt Cement.   Place the can in hot water and heat it.   Thin to the consistency of thick syrup, and apply while hot in a thin coat, well rubbed in with a brush.   Put the surfaces together quickly before the cement chills, rub the outside of the joint with a block of wood, and tap lightly with a hammer.   *Have the cement hot, but do not allow it to boil.*

Directions for the Use of Waterproof Leather Belt Cement.   *Caution: Keep this cement away from flames or cigarettes, etc.*   Before applying cement, any grease or oil should be removed with gasoline or carbon tetrachloride and all the old cement must be cleaned off.   After preparing the splice, make sure that the laps are absolutely of even thickness in order to obtain a smoothly running belt.   Roughen the surface with card cloth if available.   Apply two coats of cement, using a brush, letting each dry 15 to 30 min before applying the next.   After applying the third coat, immediately clamp the splice between boards with C clamps and let it stay 6 hr.   Hammering the laps down instead of clamping is not acceptable.

The Laced Method

The laced method of joining belting employs rawhide or wire and is applicable to all types of belting.

Rawhide lacing is applied manually and results in an efficient and strong joint. The time required for application must be considered based on other equally efficient methods available.   Rawhide lacing should always be employed on hand-shifted belting.   It cannot injure the hands.

Wire lacing is applied either by machine or hand and results in an efficient, strong, and flexible joint.   There are two machine methods: One actually sews the ends of the belt together, while the other forms wire loops through which a pin of either rawhide or fiber is inserted.

Metallic Fasteners

Wire Hook with Rawhide or Fiber Pin.   See Table 6-24.

1. Easy to apply by either portable or stationary machine.
2. Results in an accurate and flexible joint.

3. Proper-size selection gives minimum amount of metal at joint.
4. Pressed into ends of belt so as to form a series of loops.
5. Loops are meshed together, and either rawhide or fiber pin is inserted.
6. Hooks are furnished on cards.
7. Hooks are of plain steel, stainless steel, bronze, or monel metal.

Table 6-24. Minimum Pulley Diameters and Belt Thicknesses for Wire Hooks*

Standard hook size	Belt type and thickness	Minimum pulley diameter, in.
2	2-ply fabric and light single leather	2–3
3	3-ply fabric and medium single leather	3–4
4	4-ply fabric, heavy single and light double leather	4–5
5	5-ply fabric, light and medium double leather	6–8
6	6-ply fabric and heavy double leather	8–12

* Courtesy of the Clipper Belt Lacer Co.

Pressed Steel, Hinged. See Table 6-25.

1. Manual application.
2. No special machine or tools required.
3. Applied with a hammer.
4. Results in a strong and accurate joint.
5. Furnished in strips with jaws open.
6. Grips belt from both sides without weakening the leather or fabric.
7. Two hinge pins employed, designed to furnish rolling action at joint.

Table 6-25. Minimum Pulley Diameters and Belt Thicknesses for the Pressed-steel Hinge-pin Fastener*

Manufac- turers' size	Belt type and thickness	Minimum pulley diameter, in.	Standard length of lacing, in.
20	3-ply fabric	3–5	12
L-27	4-ply fabric and heavy single-oak leather	6–7	12
M-35	5-ply fabric and light double-oak leather	8–11	8
U-45	6-ply fabric and medium and heavy double-oak leather	12–14	12
X-65	7- and 8-ply rubber, cotton, or balata	14–16	12

* Courtesy of the Flexible Steel Lacing Co.

Bolted-plate Fastener. See Table 6-26.

1. Manual application.
2. Punch, hammer, and wrench required.
3. Light canvas or leather between belt and plates recommended.
4. Specially designed bolts and nuts used for securing plates to belt.
5. Results in a strong and efficient joint.
6. Plates are designed to conform to curvature of pulley.
7. Pulley-surface washer designed to embed itself in belt.
8. When applied correctly, washer does not come in contact with pulley face.
9. Screw the bolt nuts tight.

Steel-prong Hook. *Characteristics*

1. Manual application.
2. No special machine or tools required.

3. Applied with hammer.
4. Results in strong and efficient joint.
5. Prongs bend flush with pulley side of belt.
6. Belt must be against hard surface when hook is driven through.
7. Is quick of application.

Table 6-26. Plate Size, Based on Belt Width

Size of plate	Belt width, in.	Diameter of bolt, in.
0	$1\frac{1}{2}$–2	$\frac{7}{32}$
1 small	$2\frac{1}{2}$–4	$\frac{1}{4}$
1 large	5–6	$\frac{9}{32}$
2 small	7	$\frac{5}{16}$
3 small	10–16	$\frac{3}{8}$
3 large	17–20	$1\frac{3}{32}$
4	21–24	$\frac{7}{16}$
5	Above 24	$\frac{1}{2}$

Riveted Steel-plate Fasteners.   See Table 6-27.

1. Manual application.
2. No special machine or tools required.
3. Plates secured to belt by specially designed rivets.
4. Easily applied by a hammer.
5. Results in a strong and efficient joint.
6. Combines strength with light weight.
7. Distributes power strain evenly across belt.
8. Rivets spread flush with pulley side of belt when driven through.
9. Belt can be joined without removal from pulley.
10. Prongs of rivets easily penetrate leather or fabric belting.
11. Plate is designed to conform to curvature of pulley.

Note: The plate fastener, owing to its construction, forms a nonflexible joint; therefore the plate used must conform to the curvature or circumference of the pulley.   If the plate does not conform, premature breakage of the belt will occur immediately back of the plate.

FLAT-BELT PULLEYS

For efficient and economical power transmission by belting, the proper type and design of pulley should be used for the operating mechanical and atmospheric conditions.

Pulley Types.   Six types of pulleys are available: paper, cast iron, fabricated steel, all wood, wood rim with cast-iron center, and metallic center with paper rim.   Each type is manufactured in a number of designs to suit industrial requirements.

Pulley Essentials.   The following factors should be considered when selecting type and design:

1. Frictional value of face surface.
2. Face must be smooth.
3. Ability to resist overload and shock.
4. Ability to conduct heat.
5. Solid or split design; split design facilitates installation and removal.
6. The pulley should be true in diameter.
7. Minimum air resistance.
8. Ability of material to resist steam, moisture, acid drip, and acid fumes.

9. Whether flywheel effect is required.
10. Should face be crowned or flat?
11. Do power and speed require a keyed or clamped pulley?
12. Interchangeability of bore.

Pulley Specifications. Pulley ordering will be facilitated by observance of the following:

1. *Service.* Specify character of service, horsepower requirements, and revolutions per minute.

2. *Description.* State whether solid, split, clamp hub or keyed, bushed or straight bored, tight or loose, flanged or special.

3. *Diameter.* Specify diameter in inches. This should be the first dimension given. If exact diameter is required, mention this and state whether measurements

Table 6-27. Plate Sizes and Number to Use for Transmission, Conveyor, and Elevator Belting*

Belt width, in.	Light high-speed work	Light work	General work		Heavy work	Extremely heavy work
	2-in. diameter of smaller pulley	3-in. diameter of smaller pulley	6-in. diameter of smaller pulley	9-in. diameter of smaller pulley	12-in. diameter of smaller pulley	24-in. diameter of smaller pulley
	High-speed plates	Short-grip plates	Medium-grip plates	Special-grip plates	Long-grip plates	Jumbo plates
1/2	One 20					Used also on conveyor and elevator belts on pulleys smaller than 24 in. where speed is not excessive
3/4	One 20	. . . .	. . . .	. . . .	. . . .	
1	One 40	One 25	. . . .	. . . .	. . . .	
1 1/2	One 44†	One 45	One 67	One 63	. . . .	
2	One 60	One 65	One 607	One 83	. . . .	
2 1/2	Two 44	One 85	One 87	One 83	. . . .	
3	Two 44	One 805 or two 45	Two 67 or one 107	One 103	. . . .	
3 1/2	. . . .	Two 45	One 127	One 123		
4	. . . .	Two 65	Two 607 or one 147	Two 63	One 189	
5	. . . .	. . . .	Two 87	Two 83	Two 109	
6	. . . .	. . . .	Four 67 or two 107	Two 103	Two 149	
7	. . . .	. . . .	Two 127	Two 123	Two 1,409	
8	. . . .	. . . .	Four 607 or two 147	Four 63	Two 189	Four 1,011
9	. . . .	. . . .	Three 107	Three 103	Three 149	Four 1,011
10	. . . .	. . . .	Four 87	Four 83	Four 109	Five 1,011
12	. . . .	. . . .	. . . .	Four 103	Four 149	Four 1,611
14	. . . .	. . . .	. . . .	Four 123	Four 1,409	Four 1,611
16	. . . .	For belt widths wider than 24 in., use sufficient plates of the same grip series to cover the width of the belt completely			Four 189	Four 2,211
18	. . . .				Six 149	Six 1,611
20	. . . .				Eight 109	Five 2,211
24	. . . .				Six 189	Six 2,211

* Courtesy of the Crescent Belt Fastener Co.
† Where smaller pulley is 4 1/2 in. diameter or larger, use No. 66; covers 1 1/2 in. of belt width.

shall be made at crown or edge of rim. Unless otherwise specified, the diameter of a pulley is the diameter at the top of the crown.

4. *Face.* Specify face in inches. This should be the second dimension given and should be in accordance with the width of the belt unless an exact width of face is desired. If exact face is required, the word "exact" must follow the face-width dimension.

5. *Bore.* Specify exact diameter of shaft in inches. This should be the third dimension given.

6. *Crown or Straight Face.* Specify whether crown or straight face. Crown face will be furnished if no specification is given. Drum pulleys for shifting belts have straight face. Tight and loose pairs have crowned faces.

7. *Key Seat or Setscrew.* Specify whether pulley is to be keyseated or setscrewed, or both.

Relation of Width of Pulley Face to Width of Belt. The face width of a pulley is determined by the required belt width. A pulley specification of 24 by 6 in. indicates a pulley having a crown-point diameter of 24 in. and sufficient face width to accommodate a 6-in.-wide belt. A 24- by 6-in. pulley will actually measure approximately $6\frac{1}{2}$ in. width of face. This is standard practice for the purpose of securing full face belt contact. Up to and including 10-in. belt width, $\frac{3}{8}$ to $\frac{1}{2}$ in. wider pulley face is provided. From 12-in. belt width up, the pulley face is approximately 1 to $1\frac{1}{2}$ in. wider than the belt.

Relative Speed Capacities of Pulley Types in Feet per Minute. *Cast-iron Type.* The cast-iron pulley is designed for rim speeds of 3,500 to 4,000 fpm. Rim speeds of 4,500 to 5,500 fpm are permissible and possible, but cast-iron pulleys to run at such speeds must be specially built and perfectly balanced. The cast-iron pulley can be employed for any practical power requirement.

Pressed-steel Type. Fabricated construction of the pressed-steel pulley permits with safety rim speeds of 4,000 to 5,000 fpm. This type, under test, has been operated at 14,000 fpm for 30-hr periods without failure. Such speeds, however, are not practicable for industrial driving. The pressed-steel pulley can be employed for any practical power requirements.

Wood Type. The all-wood pulley or the wood-rim pulley with cast-iron hubs and arms can be run with safety at rim speeds of 5,000 to 6,000 fpm. This type can be employed for any practical power requirement.

STEEL SHAFTING

Shafting is an important factor in mechanical power transmission. All methods employ shafting; therefore success or failure of the installation depends largely upon the proper selection of shaft size and the grade of steel employed.

Shafting for "group" power-transmission purposes, such as head-, line-, counter-, and jackshafting, is cold-finished, low-carbon steel of screwstock quality. Sizes up to about $2\frac{3}{4}$ in. are cold-drawn, while larger sizes are turned and polished. The physical properties of such steels vary and cannot be guaranteed; therefore the working stresses recommended are comparatively low. Shafting of large size or that requiring uniform physical properties is hot-rolled or forged and turned to finished size. The limits and methods vary by different manufacturers.

Shaft Failures. Transmission shafting usually fails from abnormal deflection, torsional fatigue, or progressive fracture. The usual term applied is "crystallization." This term is a misnomer because all steel is crystalline, and the structure is not changed by breakage. Breakages result in a crystalline appearance of a portion of the fracture, while other portions of the fracture have been smoothed or rubbed down by abrasion or wear of the parted contacting surfaces prior to complete rupture.

Shafting for Group Method. Cold-finished shafting is usually employed. Power requirements are comparatively low, and shaft speeds in rpm are such that high stresses are not involved. In view of this, empirical formulas by Thurston have been arranged for quickly solving shafting problems of this character.

Identification of "Group-method" Shafting.   Figure 6-5 indicates the name and location of the various shafts employed in the group system of driving by belting, chain, or a combination of these mediums.

Note: This arrangement is not necessarily standard for the group method, since in many cases the motor is directly belted or chain connected to the line shaft.   The line shaft is then known as the "head line shaft."   The jackshaft is used for ratio purposes and also to break up long center distances.   Frequently the use of a countershaft is unnecessary, the machines being direct belted or chain connected from the line shaft.

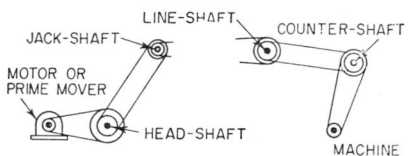

FIG. 6-5. Identification of shafting, group drive.

Head Shafts.   *Location.*   First shaft from motor or prime mover.

Service.   Reduces speed between motor and line or jackshaft and must have load capacity for entire installation.

Stresses.   Torsional and bending.

Supports.   Usually two bearings of the rigid type on adjustable base plates.   The shaft is short, based on the usual provision for one power-receiving pulley, sprocket, or sheave from the motor and one power-delivery pulley or sprocket from the head shaft. Three bearings may be used, but for the average head shaft this is the maximum.

Speeds.   Industrial range 25 to 550 rpm.

Formula:

$$\text{Hp} = \frac{D^3 R}{125}$$

$$D = \sqrt[3]{\frac{125 \times \text{hp}}{R}}$$

where Hp = horsepower
       D = shaft diameter
       R = rpm
     125 = constant for a combined torsional and bending safe-working stress of 2,800 psi

Note: Use constant of 125 only when head shaft is subjected to heavy strains, such as slow speeds and intermittent loads, or where clutches, shifters, or gearing are necessary. For the average head-shaft installation use 110 as the constant.

Line Shafts.   *Location.*   Can be first shaft from motor or first or second shaft from head shaft.

Service.   Acts as a power-distributing shaft to the various pieces of apparatus or machines of the group.

Stresses.   Torsional and bending.

Supports.   Usually three or more bearings, spacing depending upon power pulls by belt or chain and the dead load of pulleys, gears, sprockets, sheaves, clutches, and couplings.   Self-aligning adjustable bearings should be employed wherever possible. If the rigid type of bearing is necessary, provide adjustable base plates.

Speeds.   Industrial range 70 to 400 rpm.

Formula.   For line shafts 75 to 100 ft long, heavily loaded, and bearings spaced on 8-ft. centers

$$\text{Hp} = \frac{D^3 R}{100}$$

$$D = \sqrt[3]{\frac{100 \times \text{Hp}}{R}}$$

where Hp = horsepower
    D = shaft diameter
    R = rpm
    100 = constant for a combined torsional and bending safe-working stress of 3,200 psi

Note: For line shafts 50 to 75 ft long, medium loaded, with bearings spaced on 8-ft centers, use constant of 90.   For line shafts 20 to 50 ft long, lightly loaded, with bearings spaced on 6-ft centers, use constant of 75.

Table 6-28. Basic Numerals for Kinds of Steel

Steel	Basic Numeral
Carbon	1
Nickel	2
Nickel-chromium	3
Molybdenum	4
Chromium	5
Chromium-vanadium	6
Tungsten	7
Silicomanganese	9

Specification Numbers for SAE Steels.   A numeral index system is used for the specification of SAE steels, which facilitates the specifying of these steels on drawings and in the field.   Such numerals are partially descriptive of the quality of material covered by these numbers.   The first numeral of the number indicates the class to which the steel belongs; thus the numeral 1 indicates a carbon steel, 2 a nickel steel, and 3 a nickel-chromium steel.   In the case of the alloy steels the second numeral of the number generally indicates the approximate percentage of the predominant alloying element.   Usually the last two or three numerals of the number indicate the average carbon content in "points" or hundredths of 1 per cent.   Thus 2340 indicates a nickel steel of approximately 3 per cent nickel (3.25 to 3.75) and 0.40 per cent carbon (0.35 to 0.45), and 71360 indicates a tungsten steel of about 13 per cent tungsten (12 to 15) and 0.60 per cent carbon (0.50 to 0.70).   The basic numerals for the various qualities of steels specified are shown in Table 6-28.

Chapter 7

CHAINS FOR POWER TRANSMISSION

By JOHN V. MOYNES
Vice President and General Sales Manager
Morse Chain Company
Division of Borg-Warner Corporation
Ithaca, N.Y.

This section on precision chain drives places before the plant engineer general information and instructions for their installation, lubrication, and maintenance. It will aid him in advising his maintenance departments on how to obtain the best results from chain drives.

Chains have been used to transmit power for useful work since the days of antiquity. Over the past twenty-five years, chain drives have contributed greatly to industrial

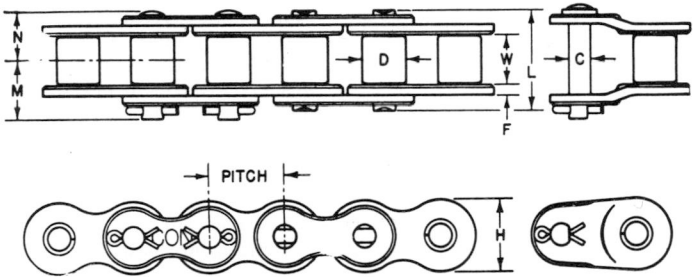

FIG. 7-1. Dimensions for roller chain identification.

advances and to the mechanization of modern industry. This industrial contribution was made possible through great progress in chain design and application, as well as the precision manufacturing and control processes developed by various chain manufacturers.

Chain drives consist of an endless series of chain links which mesh with toothed wheels, called sprockets. The sprockets are keyed to the shafts of the driving and driven mechanisms.

A roller chain has two kinds of links—roller links and pin links—alternately assembled throughout the chain length. A roller link consists of two sets of hollow rollers and bushings, the bushings being press-fitted into the apertures in the roller link plates, the rollers being free to rotate on the outside of the bushing. The pin link has two pins press-fitted into the apertures of the pin-link plates.

When the chain is assembled, the two pins of the pin links fit within the cylindrical bushings of the two adjacent roller links. The pins oscillate inside the bushings, while the rollers turn on the outside of the bushings. This latter action eliminates rubbing of the rollers on the sprocket teeth.

Roller chain is identified by three principal dimensions: pitch, width, and roller diameter (Fig. 7-1).

The term *silent chain* has been generally adopted to describe the inverted-tooth-link type of chain. This type of precision chain is a series of toothed links alternately

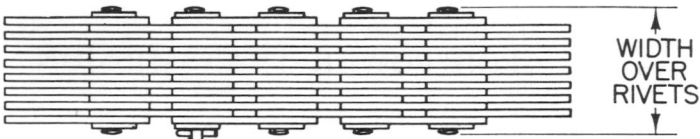

Fig. 7-2. Silent chain construction.

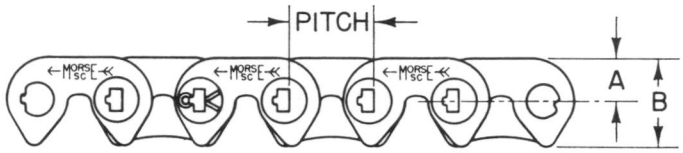

Fig. 7.3. Silent chain and sproket.

laced on pins or a combination of joint components in a manner permitting joint articulation between adjoining pitches (Fig. 7-2).

The ends of the toothed links engage the faces of alternate sprocket teeth. The center sections of the links are recessed to provide clearance so that the links straddle one tooth and engage the adjacent teeth (Fig. 7-3).

Fig. 7-4. Silent chain sprocket guide grooves.

The chain is retained on the sprockets by means of guide links (not recessed) assembled in the chain. The guide links track in a groove cut in the sprocket teeth (Fig. 7-4).

The use of precision chain drives has steadily increased during the past quarter century through their constantly expanding field of application. This is owing primarily to the following advantages:

1. *Drive efficiency:* This is normally in excess of 98 per cent.
2. *Uniform driven speed:* Roller and silent chain drives are positive; the principle of teeth, not tension, results in no loss in rotative speeds through slippage or creep.
3. *Low bearing loads:* Slack side tension is not required.
4. *Larger ratios:* Less wrap on driver sprocket is required, which permits a higher speed ratio in given area than can be obtained from belt drives.
5. *More power per inch of width:* Strength of steel permits greater loads for any given diameter and speed.
6. *Relatively unrestricted center distances:* Chain can be made endless to any length.
7. *Ease of installation:* Center distances and alignment are not subject to exacting limits.
8. *Standardization:* Industry standardization of chain and sprockets means that replacements are available from many sources.
9. *Repair on the job:* Repair links are available for quick replacement of worn or damaged links.
10. *Drive multiple shafts:* Chain is one of the most convenient methods of driving several shafts from one power source.
11. *Long drive life:* Wear is reduced through distribution of load over a number of sprocket teeth. Normal chain wear is slow process and, therefore, requires infrequent adjustment.
12. *No deterioration:* Chains do not deteriorate with age, nor are they affected by sun, oil, and grease.

No one type of chain is ideal for all kinds of service. Certain chain drives are most efficient at very low speeds, others at intermediate speeds, and still others are capable of fairly high-speed operation.

In the design of chain drives, the power to be transmitted and the rotative speeds of the driving and driven sprockets are known. Usually the approximate center distance between the shafts and their relative positions is also known.

Chain speed, quietness of operation, service life, freedom from maintenance, and the relative first cost will vary within limits according to the combination of chain and sprockets selected. Too much emphasis should not be placed on first cost. Low cost at the expense of other requirements is false economy. Usually it is a matter of compromise to arrive at the best possible combination of specifications to fulfill the requirements of any one drive. Therefore, it is well to evaluate the relative importance of various drive requirements.

All chain manufacturers' catalogs contain adequate design information on the method of selecting a chain drive. Manufacturers will offer design suggestions for particular applications providing they are furnished adequate information.

Basic data needed for the correct design of chain drives:

1. Revolutions per minute of shafts and whether exact or approximate.
2. Horsepower or torque to be transmitted.
3. Center distance and amount of adjustment to be provided.
4. Type of driver (electric motor, gasoline engine, diesel engine, torque convertor, jack shaft, etc.).
5. Type of driven unit (machine tool, hoist, conveyor, agricultural equipment, construction equipment, timing and motion control, lift hoist, tension member, etc.).
6. Service—continuous or intermittent—average number of hours per day.
7. Type of load—smooth and uniform, load reversals, moderate shock or heavy shock.
8. If speed is variable, the maximum, minimum, and usual speeds; the horsepower or torque to be transmitted at each speed; and the approximate percentage of operating time at each speed.
9. Shaft diameters and lengths, keyways and setscrew dimensions.
10. Available space dimensions.
11. Approximate position of the drive (horizontal, vertical, etc.) and the direction of rotation.
12. Operating conditions (wet, dusty, etc.).
13. Lubrication—whether drive will be encased or otherwise adequately lubricated.

Horsepower-rating tables appearing in chain maufacturers' catalogs are based on an average life expectancy of approximately 15,000 service hours under optimum drive conditions and a service factor of 1.

SERVICE FACTORS

Horsepower ratings for roller chains must be modified according to the service conditions. It is impossible to give fixed factors by which rated capacities must be multiplied to conform to each variable service condition or combinations of those conditions which affect the life of a chain drive. However, the most prevalent conditions and their accompanying factors are given in Table 7-1. Conditions which may require a

Table 7-1. Service Factors

Type of load	Int. comb. eng. hydraulic drive	Elect. motor or turbine	Int. comb. eng. mechanical drive
Smooth.............	1.0	1.0	1.2
Moderate shock.......	1.2	1.3	1.4
Heavy shock.........	1.4	1.5	1.7

modifying or service factor to be applied to the horsepower ratings are given in the following list.

Favorable service conditions which will contribute to chain life:

1. Drive for intermittent or for stand-by service.
2. Less than maximum service life required.
3. Slow speeds, smooth steady load.
4. Low ratios permitting larger number of teeth in the sprockets.
5. Unusually long centers.
6. Exceptionally good lubrication.

Service conditions which require extra chain capacity:

1. Small sprocket having fewer number of teeth than recommended by chain manufacturers.
2. Unusually large sprockets.
3. Impulse, load reversals or shock loading.
4. Three or more sprockets in the drive.
5. Poor lubrication.
6. Dirty or dusty conditions.

Impulse or shock loading should not be confused with high starting or momentary overloads. Because of the high factors of safety with respect to tensile strength, high starting loads or peak loads of short duration do not necessarily require an increase in horsepower rating.

Service factors as given in Table 7-1 should be used in connection with the horsepower ratings, the load being multiplied by the factor to obtain the required chain capacity.

Adherence to recommended principles and service factors in selecting drives from horsepower-rating tables will normally result in satisfactory service life. Deviations may result in unsatisfactory service from fatigue and abnormal joint wear, accelerated chain elongation, and resulting damage to sprockets.

Normal chain wear is caused by the flexing of the chain joints in both roller and silent chains. Wear in the chain joints is usually the limiting factor in the life of a chain. Such wear results in chain elongation, or in other words, the chain pitch is increased. This increase in pitch permits the chain to ride out on the sprocket teeth, which are usually designed to permit moderate pitch elongation. When excessive pitch elongation occurs, the chain must be replaced before it overrides the sprocket teeth.

HY-VO

Hy-Vo, the Morse version of an inverted-tooth chain designed expressly for high horsepower and high-speed application where service is severe, utilizes a new tooth form on the sprocket and a new chain-link profile, materially reducing the effect of chordal action and linear pulsation.

Chordal action is a serious limiting factor in roller-chain performance. It may be described as the vibratory motion caused by the rise and fall of the chain as it goes over a small sprocket. Figure 7-5 shows schematically a roller chain entering a sprocket (A); the line of approach is not tangent to the pitch circle. The chain makes contact below the tangency line, is then lifted to the top of the sprocket (B), then dropped again (C), as sprocket rotation continues. Because of its fixed-pitch length, the pitch line of the link cuts across the chord between two pitch points on the sprocket and remains in this position relative to the sprocket until the chain disengages. This chordal action seriously detracts from chain performance and life.

1. There is a very definite surge of force in the chain caused by the acceleration and deceleration of the chain as it makes this chordal rise and fall.
2. When the chain enters the sprocket, the tooth gap into which the joint is to fall is rising while the chain strand is falling. Therefore, at contact there is a definite impact. This impact is very much aggravated by any increase in velocity.

Chordal action, therefore, not only produces pulsations in the chain and generates noise and vibration but also, because of all these things, considerably curtails the power-transmitting capacity and speed range of a roller chain.

The Hy-Vo drive is designed to minimize chordal action. Smooth engagement with the sprocket minimizes shock loading and stresses in the links as well as noise, vibration, and heating. In Figure 7-5, *D* shows how the chain meets the sprocket. It enters approximately tangent to the pitch circle and maintains this position as it travels around the sprocket.   This is made possible by two design features: (1) pitch elongation produced by the compensating joint action and (2) mating contours of the sprocket's involute-tooth form and the chain links.

The compensating joint is so designed that as flexure takes place the pitch of the chain actually elongates.   The joint consists of a pin and rocker of identical cross

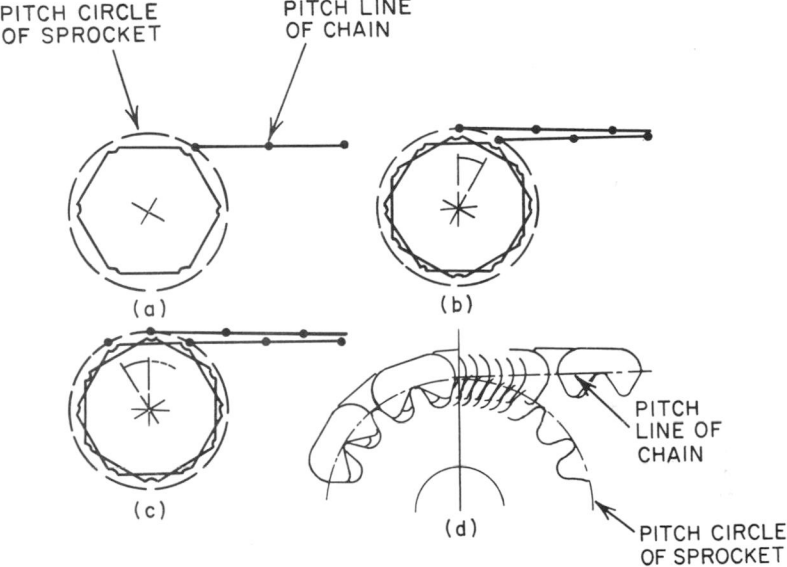

FIG. 7-5. Chordal action.

section—the curved surfaces in contact with each other being tilted in such a manner that the contact point is below the pitch line of the chain. As the joint articulates, the contact point moves upward and the pitch of the chain elongates; the amount of elongation is equal to that required for the chain to wrap the sprocket along the pitch circle.   This is known as "chordal compensation."   The combination of involute-tooth sprocket design and the compensating joint assures approximate tangential engagement of the chain into the sprocket for smooth and quiet operation.

INSTALLATION OF CHAIN DRIVES

A chain drive is essentially a flexible medium, and its installation is less difficult than many other forms of power transmission.   However, care during installation will more than repay the time involved.   Improper or careless installation will destroy the precision of any finely designed engineering system.

The shafts must be well supported by suitable and rigidly mounted bearings. Shafting, bearings, and foundations should be suitable to maintain the initial static alignment.   Shaft displacement will destroy alignment and so shorten chain life.   All shafts should be horizontal and parallel with each other.

Sprockets must be aligned axially on the shafts and secured against axial movement.

Proper chain tension is essential. Too tight a chain will cause excessive bearing loads. Too loose a chain will result in noisy operation and chain pulsations which will cause abnormal chain and sprocket wear. To assure proper chain tension some means of center adjustment is desirable.

Contact between the drive and surrounding objects must not be permitted. Ample clearance should be provided to allow for chain pulsations and for possible end float of the shafts. If loose material such as coal, dust, gravel, etc., is present, sufficient clearance is essential to prevent accumulation around the drive.

Installation Procedure. Align each shaft with a machinist's level applied directly to the shafts. (Shafting with silent chain or multiple-width roller chain sprockets may be aligned by applying the level across the sprocket teeth.) Check shafts for parallelism with a feeler bar (Fig. 7-6). After adjusting for parallelism, recheck the shaft levels. Repeat these adjustments until both level and alignment are satisfactory.

Mount sprockets on shafting, and align by checking with a straightedge along the finished sides of the sprockets (Fig. 7-7). A taut wire may be used if the center distance is too great for a straightedge. If a shaft is subject to end float, block it in its running position before aligning the sprockets. Secure the sprockets against axial movement by tightening setscrews.

Before installing the chain, recheck the preceding adjustments and correct any that may have been disturbed.

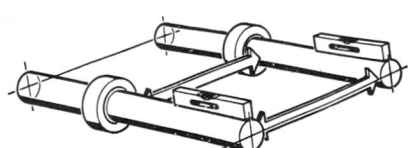

Fig. 7-6. Shaft alignment.

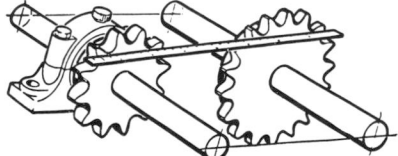

Fig. 7-7. Sprocket alignment.

Wrap the chain around the sprockets, bringing the free ends together on one sprocket. To accomplish this, shorten shaft centers sufficiently. Connect the free ends by use of the connecting link or pins provided.

Readjust shaft centers to check chain tension. Chains should be installed fairly tight with only a small amount of slack. An inclined drive should have less slack than a horizontal drive. In the case of vertical drives, the chain should be kept snug and provision for adjustment of chain is necessary.

New chains will loosen slightly owing to the seating of the joints as the chain is cycled over sprockets under load. After the first several weeks of operation, it is advisable to adjust the centers, if needed, particularly on long center drives. After this initial elongation, with proper care and lubrication, precision chain drives will give long service without undue elongation or wear.

LUBRICATION OF PRECISION CHAIN DRIVES

Since precision chains are actually a series of journal bearings, lubrication is essential for effectively minimizing metal-to-metal bearing contact of pin-bushing joints of the chain.

Figure 7-8 is a cross section through a roller chain with the clearances greatly exaggerated to show the required flow of lubricant. The flow of lubricant to silent chain joints is very similar.

Most important is the lubrication of pin-bushing surfaces which oscillate in relation to each other while the chain is under cycling load. Lubrication is also required between the rollers and bushings. To reach these surfaces the lubricant is applied to the upper edges of the link plates on the lower strand of the chain shortly before the chain engages a sprocket. As the chain travels around the sprocket, the lubricant is carried by centrifugal force into the clearances between the pins and bushings. Excess lubricant flows over to the interior and end surfaces of the rollers.

Characteristics of desirable lubricants are as follows:

1. Low viscosity to permit flow to internal surfaces.
2. Sufficient body to maintain lubricating film under the bearing pressures.
3. Freedom from corrosive ingredients.
4. Ability to maintain lubricating qualities under operating conditions of temperature, moisture, etc.

Normally, these specifications are met by a pure mineral oil. Heavy oils and greases are too viscous to reach the inner surfaces. Low-grade or impure oils should obviously be avoided. They may leave deposits in the chain joints which gradually

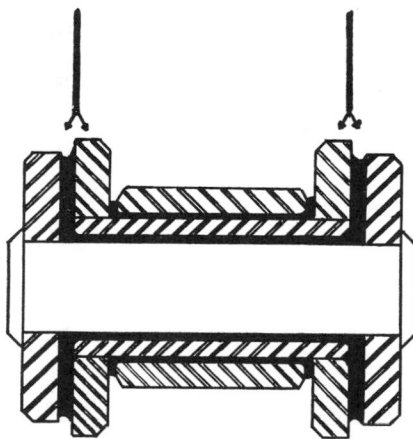

Fig. 7-8. Lubrication flow.

prevent effective lubrication. If oils are not acid-free, they will damage the chain beyond repair.

Table 7-2. Recommended Lubricants and Temperatures

Temperature Degrees F	Recommended Lubricant
20–40	SAE 20
40–100	SAE 30
100–120	SAE 40
120–140	SAE 50

There are four basic types of lubrication for chain drives. The recommended type shown in horsepower-rating tables is influenced by the chain speed and the amount of power transmitted. These are minimum lubrication requirements, and the use of a better type (for example, Type IV instead of Type III) is acceptable and may be beneficial. Chain life can vary appreciably, depending upon the way the drive is lubricated. The better the lubrication, the longer the chain life. For this reason, it is important that the lubrication recommendations be followed when using the ratings given in these tables.

Type I. Manual Lubrication Oil is applied periodically with a brush or spout can, preferably once every 8 hr of operation. Volume and frequency should be sufficient to prevent discoloration of the lubricant in the chain joints.

Type II. Drip Lubrication. Oil drops are directed between the link plate edges by a drip lubricator. Volume and frequency should be sufficient to prevent discoloration of the lubricant in the chain joints. Precaution must be taken against misdirection of the drops by windage.

Type III. Bath or Disk Lubrication. With bath lubrication the lower strand of the chain runs through a sump of oil in the drive housing. The oil level should reach the pitch line of the chain at its lowest point while operating. With disk lubrication, the chain operates above the oil level. The disk picks up oil from the sump and deposits it on the chain, usually by means of a trough. The diameter of the disk should be such as to produce rim speeds between 600 fpm minimum and 8,000 fpm maximum.

Type IV. Oil-stream Lubrication. The lubricant is usually supplied by a circulating pump capable of supplying each chain drive with a continuous stream of oil. The oil should be applied inside the chain loop and evenly across the chain width and directed at the lower strand.

Consult chain manufacturers when it appears desirable to use a type of lubricant other than that recommended.

Table 7-3. Maximum Chain Speeds, Fpm

Lubrication	Chain number									
	35	40	50	60	80	100	120	140	160	200
Type I Manual	370	300	250	200	170	150	130	115	100	85
Type II Drip	1,700	1,300	1,000	850	650	520	430	370	330	260
Type III Bath	2,800	2,300	2,000	1,800	1,500	1,300	1,200	1,100	1,000	900
Type IV Pumped	Suitable up to the maximum chain speed.									

MAINTENANCE OF PRECISION CHAIN DRIVES

As in the case of any precision-built mechanism, proper maintenance contributes toward long, satisfactory service life.

Before discussing maintenance procedure, it must be assumed that the drive components have been properly selected for the installation, the chain and sprockets have been properly installed, and adequate lubrication has been provided.

1. Every chain drive should be checked periodically for alignment. Misalignment is conclusively indicated when the sides of sprocket teeth or inside surfaces of the chain link plates show wear. Immediate steps should be taken to realign the drive when these defects are evident.
2. Chain should be checked for excessive slack. If the chain is running close to the tips of the teeth of the larger sprocket, the chain should be replaced. This can be checked visually while the drive is running or by lifting the chain away from the large sprocket, making sure the chain is in mesh with the sprocket teeth as indicated by arrows in the drawing, Fig. 7-9. Excess clearance is conclusive evidence that the chain has elongated in pitch, and no amount of tension adjustment will keep it properly meshed with the sprocket teeth. Continued operation will quickly destroy the sprocket teeth, which otherwise may be perfectly good.
3. Do not install a new chain on sprockets that are badly worn. Worn sprockets should be replaced to ensure proper chain fit on the sprockets, thus eliminating the possibility of premature wear of the replacement chain. The life of a worn sprocket may be extended by reversing it on the shaft to bring a new set of working tooth surfaces into use. If this is done, be careful to check alignment and make sure the sprocket runs true in its new position.
4. New drives should be frequently inspected for any possible interference with the chain. Naturally, if a chain is rubbing or striking against any obstruction, it will necessitate premature replacement.

5. Packing foreign material between the sprocket teeth will occasionally cause the chain to ride high on the sprocket teeth, exert undue stresses and accelerate wear in the chain, and cause abnormal wear of the sprocket teeth.

6. For all types of lubrication, check the quality and grade of the lubricant. For *manual* lubrication, make sure that the lubrication schedule is being followed, and that the oil is being properly applied.

   For *drip* lubrication, inspect the filling of the oiler cups and the rate of feed; check that the feed pipes are not clogged.

   For *bath* or *disk* systems, inspect the oil level and check that there is no sludge. Drain, flush, and refill the system at least once a year.

   For *force-feed* systems, inspect the oil level in the reservoir, check the pump drive and the delivery pressure; check that there is no clogging of the piping or nozzles. Drain, flush, and refill the reservoir at least once a year.

7. If roller chains have not been lubricated properly, the joints will have a brownish (rusty) color and the pins of the connecting link of the chain, when removed, will be discolored (light or dark brown).   Also, the pins will be roughened, grooved, or

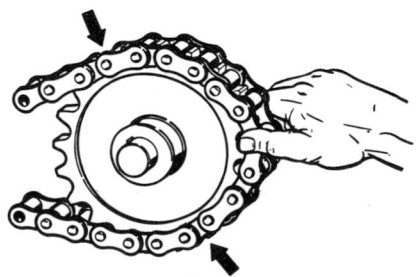

Fig. 7-9. Elongated chain.

galled.   Properly lubricated chains will not show the brownish color at the joints and the connecting link pins will be brightly polished with a very high luster.

8. Even under the best operating conditions, periodic cleaning of the chain is good economy.   Gummed lubricant and the products of normal wear cause abnormally rapid pin and bushing wear.   A chain exposed to dusty surroundings requires more frequent cleanings.

   Clean a chain as follows:

   a. Remove the chain from the sprockets.
   b. Wash the chain in kerosene.   If the chain is badly gummed, soak it for several hours in the cleaning fluid and then rewash it in fresh fluid.
   c. After draining off the cleaning fluid, soak the chain in oil to restore the internal lubrication.
   d. Hang the chain over a rod to drain off the excess lubricant.
   e. Inspect the chain for wear or corrosion.
      While the chain is off the sprockets, clean the sprockets with kerosene and inspect them for wear or corrosion.

9. Unless properly protected, the components of a chain drive will deteriorate during long periods of idleness.   If a chain is to be stored, remove it from the sprockets and coat it with a heavy oil or light grease.   Then wrap it in heavy, grease-resistant paper.   Store the chain where it will be protected from moisture and mechanical injury.

   The sprockets may be left in place on the shafts.   Cover each with grease, and protect them from mechanical injury.

   Before placing the drive in service again, thoroughly clean the chain and sprockets to remove the protective grease; then relubricate the chain.

Chapter 8

CRANES—OVERHEAD, MONORAIL, AND OTHER

By G. A. Mitchell[1]
Manning, Maxwell & Moore, Inc.
Crane & Hoist Division
Muskegon, Mich.

A crane, whether overhead, monorail, gantry, or other type, represents a major investment made to acquire the services and savings that only a crane can give. This investment can and should be protected, and it can be by a proper and carefully developed and regularly followed maintenance program.

Maintenance of cranes is divided into two parts: preventive and normal. The preventive phase occurs during the erection of the crane and should be completed prior to placing the crane in service. If the things listed below are done during the erection of the crane, much expense will be saved, accidents avoided, and less maintenance will be required after the crane has been placed in service.

1. Crane runway rails should be accurately aligned to the correct span the entire length of the runway.
2. It is of utmost importance that girders be square with the end trucks and the "fit" bolts furnished with the crane be used for making the connection between the girders and end trucks.
3. Under no circumstances should the erectors be permitted to "drift" holes to permit entry of connecting bolts.
4. Check all connecting bolts for tightness, and be sure lock washers have been used.
5. Check for and remove any loose articles, such as bolts, hammers, wrenches, or the like, that may have inadvertently been left on top of the trolley or girders or on the platform.
6. Check for any oil spillage that may have occurred during erection, and wipe all oil spots dry.
7. Thoroughly grease every bearing on the crane and check gear housings for oil.
8. Grease the hoisting cables.

Before a crane is placed in service, there are three very important things to be done. First, check the direction of each controller to effect movement of each of the motions of the crane. Next, check the operation of the hoist motor brake. Then set the upper limit stop so that current is shut off when the crane hook reaches its highest safe position. Slight adjustment at each of these points may be necessary. Instructions for these adjustments are contained in the instruction manual supplied with the crane.

Crane maintenance really starts with the crane operator, because the frequency and the amount of maintenance and maintenance attention required depends upon the way the crane man operates the crane. Upon him depends the life of the motors, con-

CRANE INSPECTION REPORT

Owner _____   Manufacturer's Serial No. _____ Shop Tool No. _____

Address _____   City _____   State _____

MECHANICAL PARTS

TROLLEY	Good	Fair	Should Replace	BRIDGE	Good	Fair	Should Replace
Trolley Wheels				Bridge Wheels			
" Wheel Axles				" Wheel Axles			
" " Axle Bearings				" " Axle Bearings			
" Driver Gear				" Drive Gears			
" " Pinion				" " Pinions			
" Motor Gear				Cross Shaft Bearings			
" " Pinion				" " Couplings			
" Gear Shaft Bearings				Bridge Motor Gear			
Trolley Current Collectors				" " Gear Shaft			
Insulated Trolley Pole				" " " " Bearings			
Trolley Pole Bracket				" " Pinion			
Hoist Motor Pinion MAIN/AUX.				Bridge Brake Band			
" " Gear MAIN/AUX.				" " Wheel			
" " Gear Shaft Bearings MAIN/AUX.				" " Linings			
Intermediate Gear MAIN/AUX.				" " Arms			
" Pinion MAIN/AUX.				" " Bushings			
" Gear Shaft Bearings MAIN/AUX.				Main Current Collectors			
Drum Gear MAIN/AUX.				Insulated Trolley Pole			
" " Pinion MAIN/AUX.				Trolley Pole Bracket			
" " Shaft Bearings MAIN/AUX.				Bumpers			
Mechanical Load Brake MAIN/AUX.				Rail Fastenings			
" " " Band MAIN/AUX.				" Chocks			
Upper Equalizer Sheaves MAIN/AUX.				" Sweeps			
" " Sheave Bearings MAIN/AUX.							
Lower Block Sheaves MAIN/AUX.							
" " Sheave Bearings MAIN/AUX.							
" " Thrust Bearing MAIN/AUX.							
Hoisting Cable MAIN/AUX.							
Motor Brake Wheel MAIN/AUX.							
" " Linings MAIN/AUX.							
" " Arms MAIN/AUX.							
" " Bushings MAIN/AUX.							

Note: Check in the proper column the condition of each part of the crane. This will give you a comprehensive picture of its actual condition today. It would be a good investment to order and replace those parts that should be replaced immediately. By doing this you would insure against a tie-up when you could least afford one. A careful inspection today may mean the prevention of an accident or tie-up tomorrow.

All new Shaw-Box Electric Traveling Cranes have Hydraulic Bridge Brakes, Taper Tread Truck Wheels, Heat Treated Pinions and many other improvements that contribute much to their superior performance, longer life, and low maintenance cost. Any, or all of the principal improvements may be applied to your crane, and the cost is no greater than that of the parts they would replace.

ELECTRICAL PARTS

PART	MAIN HOIST CONDITION			AUX. HOIST CONDITION			TROLLEY DRIVE CONDITION			BRIDGE DRIVE CONDITION		
	Good	Fair	Should Replace	Good	Fair	Should Replace	Good	Fair	Should Replace	Good	Fair	Should Replace
Motor												
Motor Shaft and Bearings												
" Coils												
" Brush Holders and Brushes												
" Commutator												
Controller												
" Contacts and Fingers												
" Brush Holders												
" Brushes												
" Return Spring												
Resistors												
Limit Switch												
" " Contactor												
Electric Brake Coil												
Switchboard												
Wiring												
Strain Insulators												
Cross Wires												

MANNING MAXWELL & MOORE, INC.
MUSKEGON MICHIGAN
SHAW-BOX CRANES

Date Inspected _____

Inspection Made By _____

Fig. 8-1. This inspection report is being employed by many users of cranes.

trols, and brakes and the frequency with which adjustments need be made. The measuring stick of the good operator is the smoothness of the movement of the crane.

The good operator starts all motions slowly and accelerates the speed step by step until the fastest speed is reached. He stops the crane by returning the control handle to the "off" position step by step also. This reduces the amount of maintenance necessary on controllers and motors and increases their life. He learns to judge the "drift" of each of the crane's motions after power is shut off to minimize the necessity for using the brakes. This increases the life of the brakes.

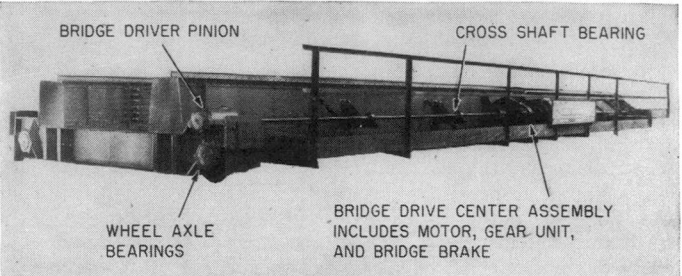

FIG. 8-2. Bridge, showing important parts requiring inspection.

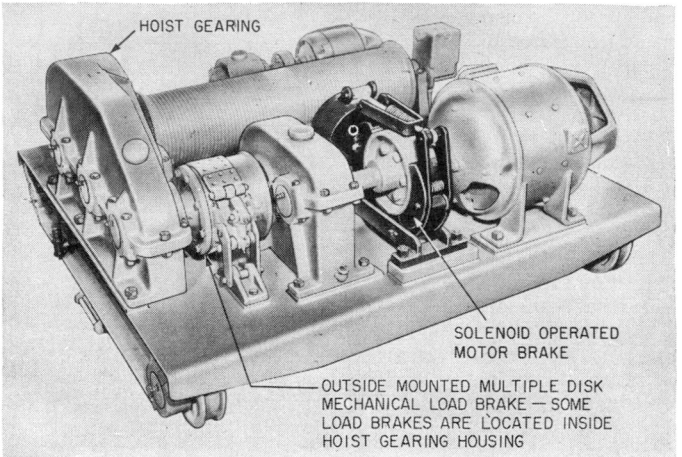

FIG. 8-3. Identifying parts of hoist mechanism.

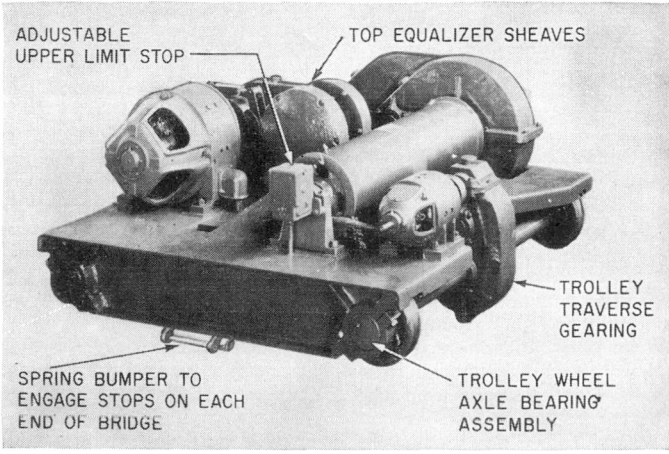

FIG. 8-4. Identifying parts of travel mechanism.

Jumpy and jerky operation, flying starts, quick reversals, and sudden stops are the trade-marks of the careless operator.   Cranes operated in this manner require more maintenance attention, life of their parts is less, and the maintenance cost is higher than need be.

Experience has shown that the majority of failures of any mechanical appliance are usually traceable to lack of lubrication, and cranes are no exception.   Therefore, it is of paramount importance that the cranes be regularly lubricated at all points, including the cables, directed by the crane manufacturer with the lubricants recommended. This is the first step in proper maintenance.   The second is regular, thorough inspection, and the third is that the adjustments the inspection shows should be made are made, the fastenings the inspection shows should be tightened are tightened, and the parts the inspection shows should be replaced are replaced—all as quickly as possible after the inspection.

The majority of crane tie-ups and failures are attributable to superficial instead of thorough crane inspections.   This situation may be avoided if it is set up with the maintenance department of the plant to schedule regular, thorough inspections and the responsibility for the inspections is delegated to a particular supervisor.   Thorough inspections can be ensured by using a form on which every part of the crane, mechanical and electrical, that should be inspected is listed.   Such a form is reproduced herewith as Fig. 8-1.   This form is being effectively used by many of the country's largest crane users.

Except for cranes operated continuously, it will be a considerable length of time before parts begin to show wear.   But when wear begins to show, then thorough inspections, regularly, are a necessity if excessive maintenance costs are to be avoided.

Starting immediately after the crane is installed, there are a few check points on the crane which should be examined weekly.   They are the connections between the girders and end trucks for loose fastenings; the commutators or slip rings, brushes, and brush holders of motors for proper contacts; the contacts and fingers of controllers for pitting and burning; each of the gear housings for proper oil levels and oil leakage; the upper limit stop for operation; the cables for broken strands; and the brakes for correct adjustment.   If the crane is operated by alternating current and the motor brakes are solenoid-actuated, it is of particular importance that the air gap of the solenoid be checked and the proper gap maintained at all times to prevent solenoids from burning out.

It is also important that the runway rails be maintained in proper alignment; otherwise bridge wheels will bind and wear excessively.   All switch points and contactors should be inspected for burning; otherwise crane will become inoperative.

After the crane has been thoroughly broken in, if it is for continuous duty, a thorough inspection of all parts should be made weekly.   If the crane is for average industrial duty, a monthly thorough inspection is satisfactory.

In making thorough crane inspections, the examination should include the following parts (see Figs. 8-2 to 8-4, inclusive).

Trolley:
  Trolley wheels.
  Trolley wheel axles.
  Trolley wheel axle bearings.
  Trolley driver gear.
  Trolley driver pinion.
  Trolley motor gear.
  Trolley motor pinion.
  Trolley gear shaft bearings.
  Trolley current collectors.
  Insulated trolley pole.
  Trolley pole bracket.
  Hoist motor pinion.
  Hoist motor gear.
  Hoist motor gear shaft bearings.

Intermediate gear.
Intermediate pinion.
Intermediate-gear shaft bearings.
Drum gear.
Drum-gear pinion.
Drum-gear shaft bearings.
Mechanical load brake.
Mechanical load brake band.
Upper equalizer sheaves.
Upper equalizer sheave bearings.
Lower block sheaves.
Lower block sheave bearings.
Lower block thrust bearing.
Hoisting cable.
Motor brake wheel.

Motor brake linings.
Motor brake arms.
Motor brake bushings.
Bridge:
    Bridge wheels.
    Bridge wheel axles.
    Bridge wheel axle bearings.
    Bridge drive gears.
    Bridge drive pinions.
    Cross shaft bearings.
    Cross shaft couplings.
    Bridge motor gear.
    Bridge motor gear shaft.
    Bridge motor gear shaft bearings.
    Bridge motor pinion.
    Bridge brake band.
    Bridge brake wheel.
    Bridge brake linings.
    Bridge brake arms.
    Bridge brake bushings.
    Main current collectors.
    insulated trolley pole.
    Trolley pole bracket.

Bumpers.
Rail fastenings.
Rail chocks.
Rail sweeps.
Electrical:
    Motor.
    Motor shaft and bearings.
    Motor coils or stator.
    Motor brush holders and brushes.
    Motor commutator or slip rings.
    Controller.
    Controller contacts and fingers.
    Controller brush holders.
    Controller brushes.
    Controller return spring.
    Resistors.
    Limit switch.
    Limit switch contactor.
    Electric brake coil.
    Switchboard.
    Wiring.
    Strain insulators.
    Cross wires.

Strange as it may seem, many crane tie-ups are caused by excessive lubrication.   In lubricating a crane, only sufficient oil should be poured into the gear housings to bring the oil up to the oil level indicated.   Only a small amount of grease should be supplied to ball and roller bearings; otherwise they cannot perform their function properly.

Where crane performance is a vital function in the production process and a crane out of service is a serious and expensive matter, it is advisable to have on hand, at all times, replacement parts for each crane.   A minimum supply should consist of:

1. Armatures or rotors for at least the hoist and bridge motions, also brushes for all motors.
2. A complete set of bridge wheels.
3. Current collectors—both main and for cross travel.
4. Solenoids or brake coils for the brakes.
5. Brake linings for each brake.
6. A complete set of pinions.
7. Cables.
8. Contacts and controller fingers.

When spares are carried in case of breakdown, the time out of service is reduced to hours instead of days.

Some cranes, most of them of heavy capacity, are installed for what is termed "stand-by" service, usually in power plants, in pumping stations, and for other similar service.   After they have been used to install the heavy equipment, they are required only in case of equipment breakdowns, so they should always be ready for use.   A good practice is to operate each of the motions of such cranes for a few minutes daily and make any adjustments that may be necessary so these cranes are always in top operating condition.

All the foregoing applies to overhead cranes, whatever their type, gantries, and other special-purpose equipment, because in their make-up, all the units employed are those used in overhead cranes.

(*Note:* For details concerning maintenance of gear drives, bearings, wire rope, clutches, flexible couplings, motor brakes, and electrical controls, see other chapters.)

Chapter 9

CRANE HOOKS AND SLINGS

By G. A. MITCHELL[1]
Manning, Maxwell & Moore, Inc.
Crane & Hoist Division
Muskegon, Mich.

Crane hooks and the chain slings used to attach loads to them should always be kept in first-class condition to prevent expensive accident and possible loss of life. Both are made from either wrought iron or alloy steel. Maintenance practices differ for each kind of material. For both, the maintenace required can be termed preventive maintenance.

Very seldom does a crane hook fail, because, in general, they are so liberally proportioned. But even the exceptional failure can be prevented by taking a few simple precautions. In general, crane hooks are forged from either wrought iron or alloy steel, though on some of the older cranes the hooks may be cast steel. Regardless of the material, it is necessary to do the following:

1. Always arrange slings so load is carried on the saddle, and not the tip of the hook.
2. Hooks should be examined frequently for gouges, nicks, and wear.
3. Because work hardness develops after considerable use, hooks require normalizing from time to time. If cranes are in continuous use, at yearly intervals is satisfactory. Unless hooks are heat-treated alloy steel, this can be readily done, but if they are, it is necessary to send them to the hook manufacturer to have this done.
4. If hooks appear to be opening, and this is usually because of loading on or near the tip of the hook, the hook should be replaced.

Today, there are two equally important items to be watched in the use of chain slings because they are made of wrought iron and heat-treated alloy steel. The capacities for the same size chain as well as the maintenance practices are different for each. First, it is of paramount importance that the proper size sling be used for the load to be handled and the proper maintenance practices for each type be employed.

It is well to recognize also that the safe working load for slings changes with the angle of pull on the chain. As an example, a load of 4,950 lb may safely be suspended on a single strand of ½-in. wrought-iron chain, but if a chain was attached to each end of a load weighing 4,950 lb and the ends centered over the load so the chains were each at a 30° angle with the load, then two ½-in wrought-iron chains would be required to suspend the load safely.

Fig. 9-1 shows how the safe working load for slings varies with the angle of pull on the chains.

SIZE OF CHAIN	SINGLE CHAIN 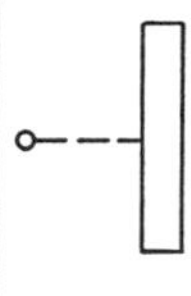		AT 60° ANGLE 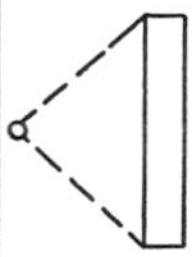		AT 45° ANGLE 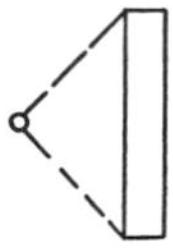		AT 30° ANGLE 		AT 10° ANGLE 	
	WROUGHT IRON	ALLOY STEEL	WROUGHT IRON	ALLOY STEEL	WROUGHT IRON	ALLOY STEEL	WROUGHT IRON	ALLOY STEEL	WROUGHT IRON	ALLOY STEEL
3/8"	2970	6600	5140	11425	4450	9325	2970	6600	1000	2275
1/2"	4950	11100	8560	19250	6275	15725	4950	11100	1500	3825
5/8"	7625	16500	13175	28500	10700	23300	7600	16500	2575	5700
3/4"	11150	23000	19300	39750	15725	32500	11150	23000	3750	7925
7/8"	15400	28750	26625	49750	21700	40625	15350	28750	5225	9900
1 "	20450	38750	35375	67100	28800	54750	20400	38750	6950	13350
1 1/4"	33750	57500	58475	99500	50700	81300	33750	57500	11475	19850
1 1/2"	47500	- -	82150	- -	71250	- -	47500	- -	16150	- -
2 "	73250	- -	126800	- -	103300	- -	73250	- -	24900	- -

FIG. 9–1. Average safe working loads in pounds for wrought-iron and alloy-steel chain slings.

It is important that the first part of the sling maintenance program consist of the following procedures:

1. Slings, when not in use, should be stored at one place at the plant—preferably on a rack.
2. There should be a sign over the rack giving the capacities of slings under different conditions of use; such signs usually are available from the sling manufacturer.
3. A record should be set up of each sling containing its complete history of maintenance from the day it is put into service.
4. The responsibility for all sling maintance should be delegated to one individual.

In many plants, chain slings made from wrought iron and also heat-treated alloy steel are in use.   Maintenance and reconditioning of wrought-iron slings can be done by the user, but slings made from heat-treated alloy steel must be sent to their manufacturer for reconditioning.

Chain slings should be carefully examined every time they are used and thoroughly inspected monthly, even if they appear to be in good condtion.   The things to look for in the thorough inspection are:

1. Opening of hooks or end rings.
2. Bent links.
3. Stiff sections.
4. Elongated links.
5. Gouges and nicks on links and hooks.
6. Links worn at bearing points.
7. Lengthening of the entire sling.

Some of these things can be discovered only by a link-by-link inspection.

Wrought-iron slings, even if they are in first-class condition, should be annealed semiannually if they are in continuous use or yearly if used intermittently.   In annealing, the sling should be heated to 1350 to 1375°F from 15 min to 2 hr, dependent upon the size of the material from which the chain is made, and air cooled.   Alloy chain should never be annealed, because annealing destroys its properties.

Stiff sections, elongated links, and links worn at bearing points and hooks and rings with gouged sections of wrought-iron slings discovered during the inspection should be replaced.   After this has been done, the entire assembly should be annealed.   In the case of alloy-steel slings, they should be sent to their manufacturer, who will recondition the sling, heat-treat it, test it, and return it certified to be in new condition.

Chapter 10

CHAIN HOISTS

By A. Cotesworth
Service Manager
Chisholm-Moore Hoist Division
Columbus McKinnon Chain Corporation
Tonawanda, N.Y.

GENERAL

Chain hoists, both hand- and electric-operated, are today the most widely used type of hoisting equipment. Their simplicity, dependability, and relatively small cost have made them standardized equipment in manufacturing plants, foundries, mills, repair shops, and garages and in practically every phase of the construction field.

This chapter describes the various types of chain hoists, explains their relative advantages and usual applications, and provides graphic information on preventive maintenance, inspection, and upkeep.

TYPES OF CHAIN HOISTS

Differential Hoists. In this type, Fig. 10-1, the mechanical advantage is gained by a differential in the diameters of the two pocketed grooves of the upper sheave. An endless-link chain is reeved continuously through the double upper and the single lower sheave. This is the simplest and least expensive type of chain hoist.

Screw-geared Hoists. This type, Fig. 10-2, gains its mechanical advantage through the worm and gear principle, and its efficiency is approximately twice that obtained in the differential hoist. Although it is somewhat slower than the differential, it is much smoother in operation. It is recommended for applications requiring vibrationless motion where speed of lift is not important.

Spur-geared Hoists. This type, Figs. 10-3 to 10-6, is much more efficient than the preceding two, although higher in initial cost. It operates on the principle of gear reduction and reduces friction to such an extent that some type of automatic brake is required to hold the load. The spur-geared hoist is the accepted standard for industrial applications, and this basic type is available in several model variations.

Spur-geared hoists are available also in lightweight models which duplicate performance characteristics but utilize more compact design, lightweight alloys, and more antifriction bearings to achieve greater portability through a weight reduction of about 50 per cent. Other standard model variations are as follows:

Twin-hook Hoists. Spur-geared hoists with twin hooks, Fig. 10-7, are available for applications requiring widely separated load chains for two-point suspension of long pieces.

Extended-hand-wheel Hoists. The extended-hand-wheel variation of the spur-geared hoist, Fig. 10-8, is designed for applications where it is desirable for hand chain and operator to be clear of the load being lifted. Standard extensions range from 3 to 10 ft.

Low-headroom Trolley Hoists. This type is a spur-geared hoist built integrally with a trolley for installation where minimum headroom is available. In the 1-ton model about 1 ft of headroom is saved by this design. In heavier capacities the headroom

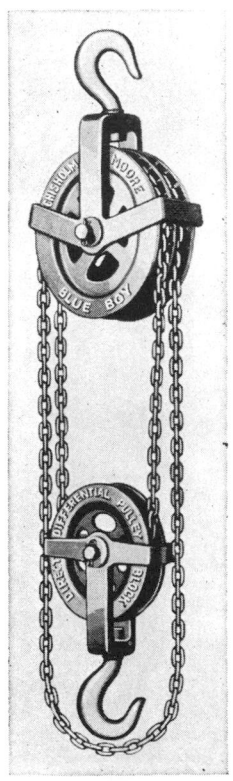

FIG. 10-1. Differential hoist.

FIG. 10-2. Screw-geared hoist.

saving is correspondingly greater. Figure 10-9 illustrates a low-headroom hoist with plain trolley. Geared trolleys are also available.

Pullers. A puller, Fig. 10-10, is a simple form of chain hoist operated by a ratchet lever instead of a hand wheel and is designed for lifting, pulling, dragging, or stretching vertically, horizontally, or at any angle. Pullers are available in both link and roller chain types in capacities from ¾ to 15 tons.

Electric Hoists. Electric hoists, Figs. 10-11 to 10-13, are motor-driven spur-geared hoists and have either push-button or pendant-rope controls. They are made in both link and roller chain types and usually are equipped with limit switches, as a safety precaution, to control both "up" and "down" extremes of travel.

While electric hoists are available for use with all types of current, many small-capacity models are equipped with single-phase 115-volt motors, which can be plugged into any lighting circuit. Some manufacturers offer three-phase dual-voltage hoists designed to operate on 60-cycle a-c 220/440-volt power.

Electric chain hoists in capacities from ⅛ to 2 tons are widely used throughout industry because of their portability, speed, safety, economy, and reduction of operator fatigue.

SELECTION OF CHAIN HOISTS

In selecting either hand-operated or electric hoists, certain considerations are basic and common to both types.   Figure 10-14 provides a graphic comparison of the three

FIG. 10-3. Spur-geared hoist.

FIG. 10-4. Conventional, spur-geared, single-reeved hoist with link chain.

types of hand hoists.   Figure 10-15 illustrates the important performance and physical characteristics of both hand and electric types which must be considered in selecting a hoist for a given use and specific installation.

Initial cost and upkeep, frequency of use, labor savings, safety, and portability are over-all factors having a bearing on selection.   Capacity, in terms of the heaviest load to be lifted, is of prime importance.   Unusual atmospheric conditions, whether inside or outdoors, may require weatherproof covers or special protective coatings on housings, chains, and other fittings.   Under normal inside atmospheric conditions, standard hoists are generally satisfactory.   Headroom, height of lift, drop of hand chain or location, and height of push-button or pendant controls; type of suspension; hoist and trolley clearances; etc., are factors affecting decisions on specific installations.   Figure 10-15 is an explanatory check diagram which will be found useful in selecting either hand or electric hoists.

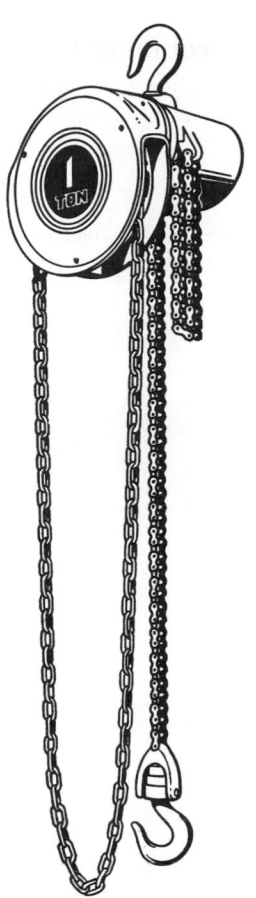

FIG. 10-5. Spur-geared, single-reeved hoist with roller chain.

FIG. 10-6. Multiple-reeved, spur-geared hoist with link chain.

FIG. 10-7. Twin-hook hoist with link chain.

FIG. 10-8. Extended-handwheel hoist with link chain.

FIG. 10-9. Low-headroom trolley hoist with link chain.

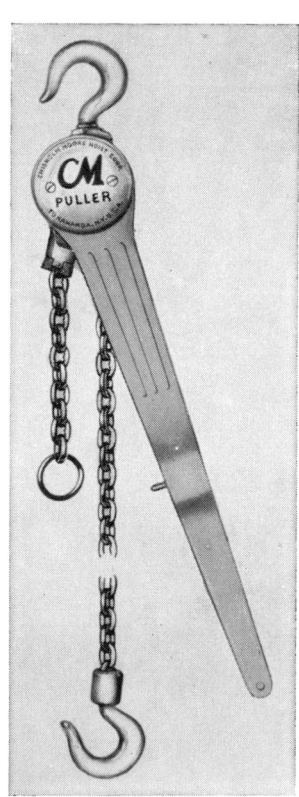

FIG. 10-10. Puller, or ratchet-lever hoist with link chain.

FIG. 10-11. Lightweight, electric chain hoist with push-button control and low-headroom trolley.

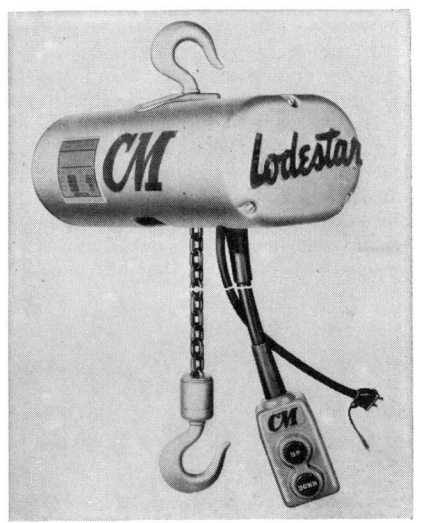

FIG. 10-12. Lightweight electric chain hoist with push-button control and hook suspension.

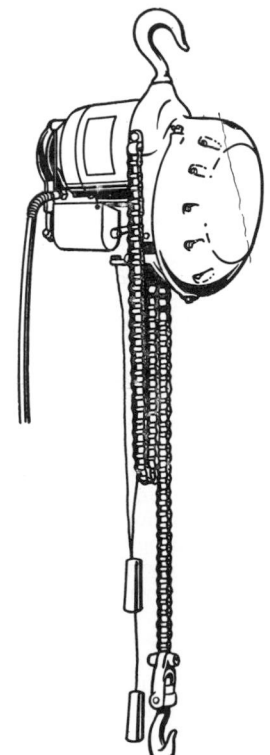

FIG. 10-13. Electric chain hoist with roller chain and pendant rope control.

PREVENTIVE MAINTENANCE

The design of modern hand and electric hoists is such that maintenance, particularly lubrication, has been reduced to a minimum.   Many older models still in active service, however, are to be considered in these general instructions.   In all cases it should be remembered that a hoist is an operating mechanism usually performing severe service and therefore is subject to normal wear.

Hoist hand chains and load chains are very carefully manufactured, and size of links and pitch of chains are held to close tolerances.   Pockets of lift wheels, idler sheaves, and handwheels similarly are accurately formed to ensure a close fit.   Any

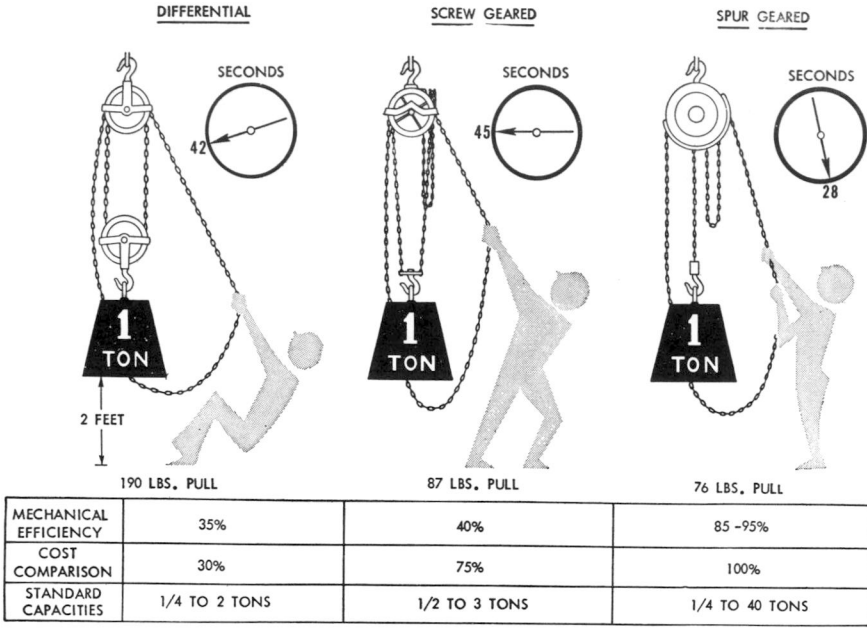

DIFFERENTIAL	SCREW GEARED	SPUR GEARED

	190 LBS. PULL	87 LBS. PULL	76 LBS. PULL
MECHANICAL EFFICIENCY	35%	40%	85 –95%
COST COMPARISON	30%	75%	100%
STANDARD CAPACITIES	1/4 TO 2 TONS	1/2 TO 3 TONS	1/4 TO 40 TONS

FIG. 10-14. Comparison of hand hoists.

accumulation of dirt or foreign matter on chains therefore restricts free operation of the hoist, imposes undue strain, and accelerates wear of parts.

Most hoist manufacturers will provide users with a table of dimensions of their various sizes of standard pitch chain and will supply information on permissible stretch and wear beyond which a chain is unsafe and should be repaired or replaced. It is then a simple matter to gage a specified number of links with an adjustable gage as illustrated in Fig. 10-16.   Lacking manufacturer's data, a fairly accurate check on stretch and wear can be made by comparing dimensions of a section of the "loose end" chain where it attaches to the hoist body with sections of the chain between load hook and lift wheel where greatest strain is concentrated.   Gaged chain must be clean, free of twist, and pulled taut.

The following instructions will serve as an inspection and maintenance guide and may be used in conjunction with Fig. 10-17, which identifies parts normally requiring maintenance services.   Time intervals (W = weekly, M = monthly, Y = yearly) indicate recommended frequency of services for hoists in continuous industrial use under normal indoor atmospheric conditions.   Intervals can be extended for hoists in occasional or intermittent service and shortened for hoists in more severe service and/or under abnormal conditions.

Inspection and Maintenance Schedule.   When a new hoist is put in service, it is well to establish a definite maintenance schedule in accordance with the manufacturer's instruction book and to keep adequate records.

Hoist (*M*).   Operate hoist without load, and check for free operation and smooth running of hand and load chains.   Service as necessary in the manner described below under the specific component heading.   Lubricate in accordance with manufacturer's instructions.

Load Chain (*M*).   Clean with solvent, and inspect for worn, bent, or stretched links.   Gage to manufacturer's specifications.   Replace or repair as necessary.   If

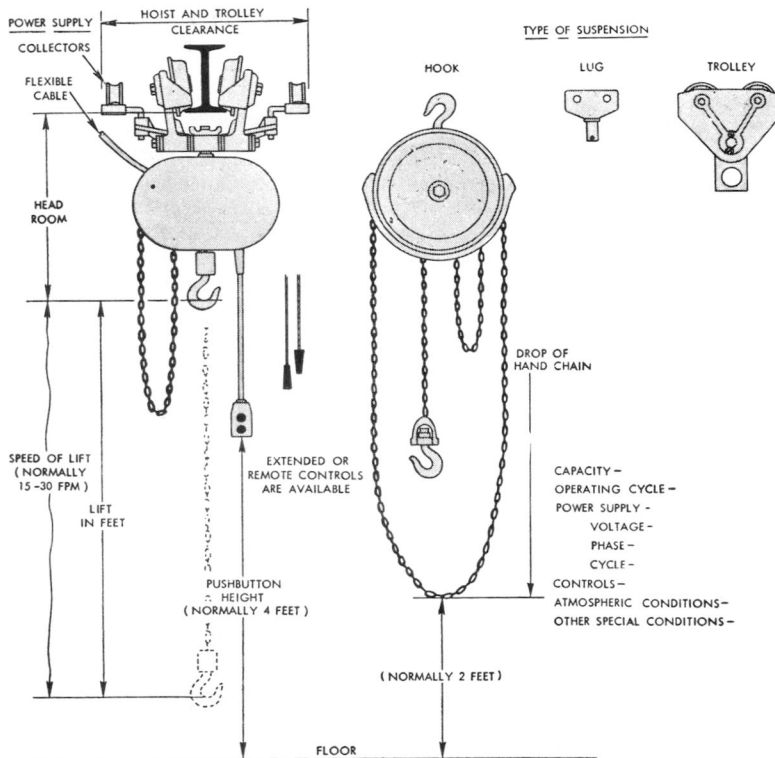

Fig. 10-15. Hoist installation check diagram.

wear is localized, it is sometimes practical to reverse the load chain, end for end, and allow a new section to take the wear.   Lubricate the chain by wiping down with penetrating oil and graphite.   Remove excess with rag or waste.

Hand Chain and Handwheel (*M*).   Clean chain and wheel pockets with solvent. Inspect chain for worn, bent, or stretched links.   Inspect pockets for excessive wear and/or hard encrustations of foreign matter.   Gage chain to manufacturer's specifications.   Replace or repair as necessary.   Never put new chain in a wheel with worn pockets or vice versa.

Upper Hook (*M*).   Inspect for stretch, wear, or damage and for free swiveling. See that bearings, nuts, collars, and pins are in good condition and securely in place. Repair or replace as necessary.   Lubricate if the design requires lubrication.

Lower Hook (*M*).   Inspect for stretch, wear, or damage and for free swiveling.   On double-reeved hoists, disassemble the hook block and examine the sheave pockets for wear.   See that bearings, nuts, collars, and pins are in good condition and securely in place.   Repair or replace as necessary.   Lubricate if the design requires lubrication.

Load Brake (*M*).   Hand-hoist brakes are friction brakes and are all similar in principle.   Maintenance instructions, however, vary with make and age of the hoist. Some earlier models use a combination of ratchet disk and pawl with leather and metal friction disks.   This type requires good lubrication, and special treatment of the leather disk is recommended when the brake is overhauled.   Most modern brakes utilize metal friction disks or disks of a woven or molded composition and are designed

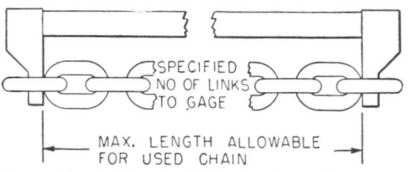

FIG. 10-16. Load chain gaging diagram.

to operate dry—without lubrication.   All brakes should be tested under load for free operation and holding power and serviced in accordance with manufacturer's instructions.

Load Brake (*Y*).   Conventional modern brakes should be disassembled at least once a year, and all parts thoroughly cleaned.   Examine ratchet teeth and pawl tip and bore for excessive wear.   Replace as necessary.   Examine friction surfaces of ratchet, friction hub, and handwheel for wear.   These surfaces must be free of score marks.

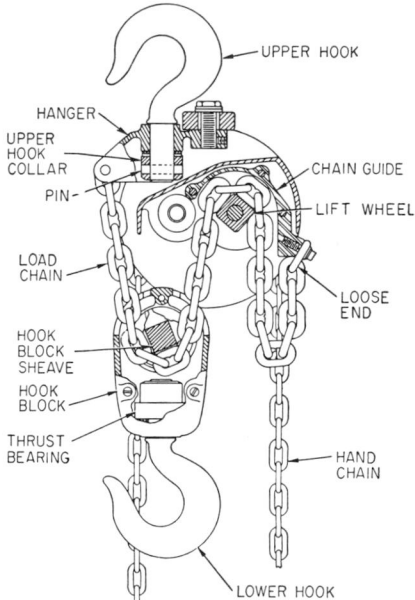

FIG. 10-17. Hoist parts to be inspected and serviced.

Replace as necessary.   Examine friction disks for wear, score marks, and coating of foreign matter.   Foreign matter usually can be removed by buffing with emery cloth. Worn or scored disks should be replaced.   Reassemble in accordance with manufacturer's instructions.

Housing, Frame and Covers (*M*).   Make a general inspection for loose-fitting screws and bolts, and check for cracks or other evidence of physical damage.   See that gaskets on the gear housing, etc., are tight and not leaking lubricant.   Repair as necessary.

Additional Services for Electric Hoists. *Electric Brake (M).* Operate the hoist under load, and check brake holding power, drift, and drag. If the brake does not hold or drifts, adjust in accordance with manufacturer's instructions or replace friction members. If the brake overheats or smokes, adjust in accordance with manufacturer's instructions to eliminate drag. Apply lubricant sparingly to cam and cam followers or linkage, if any, before reassembling.

Magnetic Contactor (Y). Inspect terminals and operating coils to see that they are tight and clean. Clean and inspect line contacts; replace contacts if necessary.

Limit Switches (Y). Check operating linkage, contact points, and terminals. Tighten, clean, and adjust in accordance with manufacturer's instructions.

Electrical Connections and Insulation (Y). See that all screw terminals are tight, securely crimped to wires, and insulation sound. Clean and repair as necessary. An annual check of insulation resistance by a megger or high potential (Hypot) tester is recommended; resistance to ground should be at least 1 megohm.

Motor (Y). Most modern motors are lifetime lubricated and require no service beyond cleaning. Older motors will require cleaning and lubrication.

OPERATING AND SAFETY PRECAUTIONS

General

1. Keep hoist clean.
2. Keep load chain clean and lubricated.
3. Assemble load chain according to manufacturer's instructions.
4. Lift with hoist directly over load and with hooks free to swivel.
5. Follow manufacturer's instructions for inspections, maintenance, and repair.
6. Keep yourself and others clear of load being lifted.
7. Never overload beyond rated capacity.
8. Bent, damaged, worn, or stretched hooks are unsafe. Repair or replace them.
9. Worn, damaged, stretched, or corroded load chain or hand chain should be replaced.
10. Do not use hoist with damaged or unsafe frames or suspension members.
11. Be sure brake holds load properly in suspension.
12. See that upper hook is properly attached to suspension.
13. Lift with load on the throat, not the point of the hook.
14. Never wrap load chain around load.
15. Avoid lowering hook into liquids or loose solids.
16. Make sure that load chains and hand chains are not twisted.
17. New chains should not be installed in worn or damaged lift wheels, idler sheaves, or handwheels.
18. Keep chains and pockets of wheels free of foreign matter such as paint, tar, cement, rust, etc.
19. Load chain should be repaired only by the manufacturer.
20. Make certain that load won't roll or fall before unhooking.
21. All replacement chain should be purchased from the original manufacturer. A substitute may endanger satisfactory operation of the hoist.

Electric Hoists

22. Follow manufacturer's instructions for the specific model and type when making initial installation.
23. Check power supply against hoist name-plate data.
24. Turn power *off* before adjusting or repairing hoist.
25. Under no circumstances should the wiring of a hoist or push button be changed to reverse direction of hook. Wiring is inspected and tested before leaving factory.

To help yourself to maximum safe and satisfactory service, it is wise to request from the manufacturer an instruction book specifically applying to the type and model hoist you have.

Chapter 11

V-BELT DRIVES

By Jack Klingenmeier
Application Engineer
The Gates Rubber Company
Denver, Colo.

Properly designed, correctly installed, and adequately tensioned V-belt drives give dependable power transmission with a minimum of maintenance. This chapter contains basic physical dimensions of V belts and sheaves, installation suggestions, tensioning data, and general maintenance recommendations which will assure top performance. For actual design of V-belt drives, manufacturers' design manuals should be consulted.

Belt Dimensions. V-belt drives used in industrial plants fall into two classifications: Heavy-duty (industrial), and light-duty (fractional-horsepower).

Industrial V belts, in turn, are of two basic types: Conventional (A, B, C, D, E) cross sections, and narrow (3V, 5V, 8V) cross sections. The nominal dimensions of these belts, along with those of the fractional-horsepower V belts, are shown in Fig. 11-1 and Table 11-1.

Table 11-1. Nominal Cross-section Dimensions

V-belt cross section	b_b (Fig. 11-1) (in.)	h_b (Fig. 11-1) (in.)
A	$\frac{1}{2}$	$\frac{5}{16}$
B	$2\frac{1}{32}$	$1\frac{3}{32}$
C	$\frac{7}{8}$	$1\frac{7}{32}$
D	$1\frac{1}{4}$	$\frac{3}{4}$
E	$1\frac{1}{2}$	$2\frac{9}{32}$
3V	$\frac{3}{8}$	$\frac{5}{16}$
5V	$\frac{5}{8}$	$1\frac{7}{32}$
8V	1	$2\frac{9}{32}$
2L	$\frac{1}{4}$	$\frac{5}{32}$
3L	$\frac{3}{8}$	$\frac{7}{32}$
4L	$\frac{1}{2}$	$\frac{5}{16}$
5L	$2\frac{1}{32}$	$\frac{3}{8}$

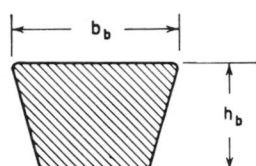

FIG. 11-1. Nominal cross-section dimensions.

Sheave Dimensions. Standardized V-belt sheaves are manufactured for all of the belt types and sizes listed. V-belt sheaves have exact rather than nominal dimensions. Industrial sheave dimensions are shown in Fig. 11-2 and Table 11-2; fractional-horsepower sheave dimensions are shown in Fig. 11-3 and Table 11-3.

Table 11-2. Dimensions, Industrial V-belt Sheaves

| V-belt cross section | Pitch diameter | | Standard groove dimensions (Fig. 11-2) | | | | | |
	Minimum recommended (in.)	Range (in.)	α $\pm\frac{1}{2}$ (degrees)	b_g (in.)	h_g ± 0.031 (in.)	a (in.)	S ± 0.031 (in.)	S_e (in.)
A	3.0	2.6 to 5.4	34	0.494 $\pm .005$	0.490	0.125	$\frac{5}{8}$	$\frac{3}{8}$ +0.070
		Over 5.4	38	0.504				−0.000
B	5.4	4.6 to 7.0	34	0.637 $\pm .005$	0.580	0.175	$\frac{3}{4}$	$\frac{1}{2}$ +0.150
		Over 7.0	38	0.650				−0.000
C	9.0	7.0 to 7.99	34	0.879				+0.150
		8.0 to 12.0	36	0.887 ± 0.007	0.780	0.200	1	$1\frac{1}{16}$
		Over 12.0	38	0.895				−0.000
D	13.0	12.0 to 12.99	34	1.259				+0.250
		13.0 to 17.0	36	1.271 ± 0.007	1.050	0.300	$1\frac{7}{16}$	$\frac{7}{8}$
		Over 17.0	38	1.283				−0.000
E	21.0	18.0 to 24.0	36	1.527 ± 0.010	1.300	0.400	$1\frac{3}{4}$	$1\frac{1}{8}$ +0.250
		Over 24.0	38	1.542				−0.000

| V-belt cross section | Outside diameter range, in. | Standard groove dimensions (Fig. 11-2) | | | | | |
		α $\pm\frac{1}{4}$ (degrees)	b_g ± 0.005 (in.)	h_g +0.010 −0.000 (in.)	a (in.)	S ± 0.015 (in.)	S_e (in.)
3V	Less than 3.50	36					
	3.50 to 6.00	38					+0.094
	6.01 to 12.00	40	0.350	0.350	0.025	$1\frac{3}{32}$	$1\frac{1}{32}$
	Over 12.00	42					−0.000
5V	Less than 10.00	38					+0.125
	10.00 to 16.00	40	0.600	0.600	0.050	$1\frac{1}{16}$	$\frac{1}{2}$
	Over 16.00	42					−0.000
8V	Less than 16.00	38					+0.250
	16.00 to 22.40	40	1.000	1.000	0.100	$1\frac{1}{8}$	$\frac{3}{4}$
	Over 22.40	42					−0.000

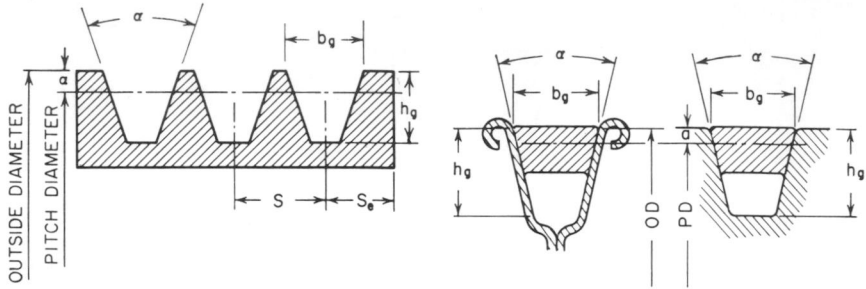

FIG. 11-2. Dimensions of industrial V-belt sheaves.

FIG. 11-3. Dimensions of fractional-horsepower V-belt sheaves.

Drive Installation.   A few important recommendations apply to installing V-belt drives.

1. Make sure sheaves are clean, free of oil and paint, and free of sharp edges or burrs.
2. Install sheaves parallel and in line with each other.   A straightedge across the faces of sheaves should contact the faces at all points.   (But make sure the "edge land" of the first groove is equal on all sheaves for this procedure to give proper belt alignment.)
3. Provide adequate shaft movement for installing V belts and maintaining their tension (see Table 11-4).   (If the driveR or driveN shaft is not movable, idlers may be used for this purpose.   Make sure an amount of idler movement equivalent to the center-distance change is provided.)   V belts should never be pried or rolled onto the sheaves.

Table 11-3. Dimensions, Fractional-horsepower V-belt Sheaves

V-belt cross section	Outside diameter range (in.)	Standard groove dimensions (Fig. 11-3)			
		α (degrees)	b_g (in.)	h_g (in.)	a (in.)
2L	Under 1.5 1.5 to 1.99 2.0 to 2.5 Over 2.5	32 34 36 38	0.240 0.243 0.246 0.250	0.250	0.05
3L	Under 2.2 2.2 to 3.19 3.2 to 4.2 Over 4.2	32 34 36 38	0.360 0.364 0.368 0.372	0.406	0.075
4L	Under 2.65 2.65 to 3.24 3.25 to 5.65 Over 5.65	30 32 34 38	0.485 0.490 0.494 0.504	0.490	0.10
5L	Under 3.95 3.95 to 4.94 4.95 to 7.35 Over 7.35	30 32 34 38	0.624 0.630 0.637 0.650	0.580	0.15

For deep groove sheave dimensions and tolerances on all sheaves, the applicable industry standards may be consulted.   See references at end of chapter.

4. Use matched sets of V belts, from one manufacturer, for multiple-belt drives. The matching tolerances between belts for multiple-belt sets vary with the belt length. They are given in Table 11-5. Light-duty, fractional-horsepower V belts are not generally recommended for use on multiple V-belt drives.
5. Make sure that proper tension is imposed on the belts.

Drive Tension. The total tension required by a V-belt drive is independent of the brand, type, or number of belts. For example, two drives identical except for the

Table 11-4. Installation, Take-up Allowances

Standard length designation	Minimum allowance for installation of belts (in.)					Minimum allowance for maintaining tension—all sections (in.)
	A	B	C	D	E	
26– 35	3/4	1				1
38– 55	3/4	1	1 1/2			1 1/2
60– 85	3/4	1 1/4	1 1/2			2
90– 112	1	1 1/4	1 1/2			2 1/2
120– 144	1	1 1/4	1 1/2	2		3
158– 180		1 1/4	2	2	2 1/2	3 1/2
195– 210		1 1/2	2	2	2 1/2	4
240		1 1/2	2	2 1/2	2 1/2	4 1/2
270– 300		1 1/2	2	2 1/2	3	5
330– 390			2	2 1/2	3	6
420 and Over			2 1/2	3	3 1/2	1.5% of belt length

Standard length designation	3V	5V	8V	Minimum allowance for maintaining tension (in.)
250– 475	1/2			1
500– 710	3/4	1		1 1/4
750–1,060	3/4	1	1 1/2	1 1/2
1,120–1,250	3/4	1	1 1/2	1 3/4
1,320–1,700	3/4	1	1 1/2	2 1/4
1,800–2,000		1	1 3/4	2 1/2
2,120–2,240		1 1/4	1 3/4	2 3/4
2,360		1 1/4	1 3/4	3
2,500–2,650		1 1/4	1 3/4	3 1/4
2,800–3,000		1 1/4	1 3/4	3 1/2
3,150–3,550		1 1/4	2	4
3,750			2	4 1/2
4,000–5,000			2	5 1/2

Standard length designation	2L	3L	4L	5L	Minimum allowance for maintaining tension (in.)
080– 170	3/8	5/8			1/2
180– 240	3/8	5/8	3/4		1/2
250– 370		3/4	3/4	1	1/2
380– 600		3/4	7/8	1	3/4
610– 790			1	1 1/8	1 1/8
800–1,000			1 1/8	1 1/4	1 1/2

Table 11-5. Matching Tolerances for Multiple V-belt Sets

A, B, C, D, E		3V, 5V, 8V	
Standard length designation	Matching tolerance (in.)	Standard length designation	Matching tolerance (in.)
26– 75	0.1	250–1,000	0.125
80–144	0.2	1,060–2,000	0.25
158–270	0.3	2,120–2,800	0.375
300–390	0.4	3,000–5,000	0.50
420–480	0.5		
540 and Up	0.6		

number of belts, require the same total tension, but the drive with fewer belts requires greater tension per belt.

A few simple rules about V-belt drive tensioning satisfy most requirements:

1. The best tension for a V-belt drive is the lowest tension at which the belts will not slip under the highest load condition.
2. Check the tension on a new drive frequently during the first day of operation.
3. Check the drive tension periodically thereafter.
4. Too much tension shortens belt and bearing life.
5. Keep sheaves and belts free from foreign material which may cause slip.
6. If a V-belt drive slips, tighten it.

In the event a numerical tensioning method is desired, the following may be used as an approximation if the design of the drive conforms to recommendations of manufacturer's drive-design manuals:

Step 1. Determine the force required to deflect one belt $\frac{1}{64}$ in. per inch of span length.
   A. Measure the span length of the drive.
   B. At the center of the span (t) apply a force perpendicular to the span large enough to deflect one belt on the drive $\frac{1}{64}$ in. per inch of span length from its normal position. See Fig. 11-4.
Step 2. Compare this deflection force with the range of forces in Table 11-6.
   A. If it is less than the minimum recommended deflection force, the belts should be tightened.
   B. If it is more than the maximum recommended deflection force, the drive is tighter than it need be.

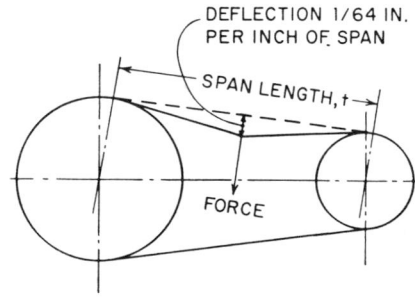

DEFLECTION 1/64 IN. PER INCH OF SPAN

SPAN LENGTH, t

FORCE

Fig. 11-4. Measuring tension of V-belt drives.

Table 11-6. Deflection Forces for Tensioning V-belt Drives (See Fig. 11-4)

Industrial conventional cross section V belts

V-belt cross section		Recommended deflection force, lb per belt	
		Minimum	Maximum
A	....	2	$2\frac{3}{4}$
B	....	4	$5\frac{1}{2}$
C	....	$8\frac{3}{4}$	12
D	....	17	23
E	....	$26\frac{1}{2}$	37

Industrial narrow cross-section V belts*

V-belt cross section	Small sheave diameter range (in.)	Small sheave rpm range	Speed ratio range	Recommended deflection force, lb per belt	
				Minimum	Maximum
3V	2.50 to 3.50	1,200 to 3,600	2.00 to 4.00	3	$4\frac{1}{4}$
	3.51 to 4.50	900 to 1,800	2.00 to 4.00	$3\frac{1}{2}$	$5\frac{1}{4}$
	4.51 to 6.0	900 to 1,800	2.00 to 4.00	$4\frac{1}{4}$	6
5V	7.0 to 9.0	600 to 1,500	2.00 to 4.00	$8\frac{3}{4}$	$12\frac{3}{4}$
	9.1 to 12.0	600 to 1,200	2.00 to 4.00	$9\frac{1}{2}$	14
	12.1 to 16.0	400 to 900	2.00 to 4.00	$10\frac{1}{2}$	$15\frac{1}{4}$
8V	12.5 to 17.0	400 to 900	2.00 to 4.00	$21\frac{1}{2}$	31
	17.1 to 24.0	200 to 700	2.00 to 4.00	$23\frac{1}{2}$	43

Light-duty V belts

V-belt cross section		Recommended deflection force, lb per belt	
		Minimum	Maximum
2L	....	$\frac{1}{4}$	$\frac{1}{2}$
3L	....	$\frac{1}{2}$	1
4L	....	1	$1\frac{1}{2}$
5L	....	$1\frac{1}{4}$	2

* If the drive does not fall within the above small-sheave diameter, small-sheave rpm, or speed-ratio ranges, consult a V-belt manufacturer's design manual for tensioning instructions.

Maintenance. V-belt drives are characterized by low maintenance. It usually is necessary to retension only occasionally. A periodic maintenance check might include the following points:

1. *Tension.* (See paragraphs on tension.)
2. *Alignment.* (See paragraphs on installation.)
3. *Foreign materials.* V-belt drives should be shielded by guards both for safety and to prevent foreign material from entering the drive.
4. *Belt wear.* When V belts begin to show signs of wear (covers frayed, belts worn) they should be replaced. Replace all belts in a multiple V-belt drive, rather than only part of them, with belts from one manufacturer. Store replacement belts in a cool, dark, dry location.
5. *Sheave wear.* When putting on a new set of V belts, make sure the sheaves are in good condition. If there is $\frac{1}{16}$ in. or more wear along one side of a groove (as detected by using the proper sheave-groove gage) poor belt life will result.

Other V-belt Drive Information. There are many facets of V-belt drives that cannot be discussed here because of space limitations: oil and heat resistance, static conductivity, exact belt-length measurement, balancing of sheaves, stock items, and others. Information on any V-belt drive subject can be obtained from the Rubber Manufacturers Association, 444 Madison Ave., New York, N.Y. 10022, or the Mechanical Power Transmission Association, 3525 Peterson Rd., Chicago, Ill.

REFERENCES

"Engineering Standard Specifications for Drives Using Multiple V Belts (A, B, C, D, E Cross Sections)," Rubber Manufacturers Association or Mechanical Power Transmission Association, January, 1964.

"Standard Specifications for Drives Using Narrow V Belts (3V, 5V, and 8V Cross Sections)," Rubber Manufacturers Association or Mechanical Power Transmission Association, July, 1964.

"Standards for Light-Duty or Fractional-horsepower V Belts," Rubber Manufacturers Association, February, 1963.

Chapter 12

MECHANICAL VARIABLE-SPEED DRIVES

By D. B. Rush[1]
Manager Application Engineering
Reeves Pulley Company Division
Reliance Electric & Engineering Company
Columbus, Ind.

There are many variations of mechanical variable-speed drives, but notably common to most is the principle of the sliding cone-faced pulleys permitting belt operation on an infinite variety of pitch diameters.

The almost universal use of this time-proved principle permits several generalizations before treating in greater detail the individual variations of this principle, along with the several other design approaches in current use.

The maintenance problem most often linked with mechanical variable-speed drives is the freezing or sticking of the sliding disks on their shafting so that speed variation cannot be obtained.

A brief review of the series of events leading up to this condition affords an insight into the best approach to preventive maintenance and places in proper perspective recent lubrication improvements designed to combat this condition of sticking disks.

Of the forces illustrated in Fig. 12-1, we are particularly concerned with the radial hub force. It is this pressure that tends to squeeze out the lubricant from between the mating surfaces and leave a bare metal-to-metal contact.

If the grease is squeezed or pounded out, the bare metal-to-metal surfaces will tend to gall, with resultant fusion and tearing out of minute particles of metal. These tiny specks of ferrous metal tend to combine with free oxygen from the air and rapidly oxidize, forming contaminated ferrous oxide (rust). This entire process is termed "fretting corrosion." As expected, the rust or corrosion thus formed occupies greater space than did the metal in its original state. Build-up of this rust gradually fills the area of sliding clearance around the hub, thereby causing the disks to freeze or stick on the hub.

One would imagine that the use of metals other than those of the ferrous family or perhaps one of the ferrous metals in contact with a dissimilar metal would reduce the tendency of the disks to stick. However, exhaustive tests indicate that this is not the case. Many metals are too soft, unable to withstand the pressure involved without deforming. Others have sufficient strength but tend to gall and/or fuse together very rapidly when in bare, oscillatory pressure contact with one another.

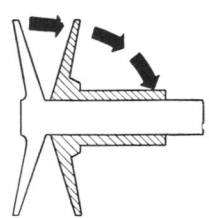

TORQUE LOAD

RADIAL HUB FORCE
(BELT PRESSURE)

Fig. 12-1. Radial hub force tends to squeeze lubricant from mating surfaces.

[1] The author is deceased.

Fretting will occur, regardless of design, whenever the pressure is great enough to squeeze out the entire amount of grease between the two metal surfaces. There is no known method of preventing fretting corrosion when two bare metal surfaces are in oscillatory contact.

It is this tendency toward fretting corrosion that has led to explicit instructions by the various manufacturers of mechanical variable-speed equipment to recommend shifting the drive equipment through its entire speed range at least once each day, if possible, and regreasing every 2 to 5 weeks, depending on the type of duty to which the drive is subjected. The shifting has the effect of spreading the grease over the load-bearing surfaces and so preventing the tiny specks of ferrous metal from being torn out.

FIG. 12-2. "Close grooving" of motor pulley.

Design efforts to meet this problem have taken two forms. One is the use of oil-impregnated bushings to provide a continuous lubricity to the mating surfaces. This has so far been limited to fractional loadings because of the tendency of the bushings to gall under the hub pressures associated with the higher horsepowers. The pores of the oil-impregnated bushings tend to become plugged owing to carbonization of the surface oil and the burnishing action of the disk hub on the bushing. This prevents the oil stored within the bushing from reaching the bearing surface. The lack of lubricant between the contacting surfaces results in rapid failing or, in some instances, in actual seizure of the parts.

The other design effort to meet this problem has been the recognition of the chain of events leading up to the sticking condition in designing a positive lubrication system to prevent its beginning. We shall refer to this design as "close grooving" (see Fig. 12-2).

In the "close-grooved" design the proximity of the grease grooves effectively prevents the build-up of large fretted areas. If fretting corrosion does start, there is an early break-through into the adjacent grease groove. The grease tends to flow into the affected areas, minimizing the action.

Various drives have been undergoing continuous-running life-load tests for several years. Disks incorporating the close grooving have operated for several thousand hours with no stuck disks, even though the units are rarely shifted.

Another advantage of the close grooving is that even a slight shifting will permit the passage of several grease-filled grooves over the relatively narrow load-bearing surfaces.

Proper Type of Grease Important.   Several different types of grease have been tested recently and show marked improvement over the older recommended lubricants. These new greases will not necessarily prevent fretting corrosion; however, they do not tend to bleed off their oils and subsequently cake or solidify in the grooves as did the older lubricants.   This is a distinct advantage, especially after the variable-speed drive has been in operation for an extended period.   These improved lubricants are particularly effective with the close-grooved design because they tend to remain semi-fluid longer and readily flow into adjacent areas that may have started to rust.   Some of the new greases that have been approved and released by the Reeves Engineering Department include:

Socony-Vacuum, BRB-1
Sinclair, Grease No.1
N.Y. & N.J. Lubricant Co., Non-Fluid Oil No. 926
Texaco, Nova No. 1
Standard Oil Co., Stanolith No. 42
Gulf, Precision Grease No. 1

Adjustable-while-stopped Pulley.   Adjustable-while-stopped pulleys are designed for the machine which at the outset may require a slight adjustment in speed to operate at optimum performance, but once set will rarely need adjustment.

The several makes of stationary-control adjustable pulleys fall into two groups: those that are designed for use with the narrow section *A* through *E* V belts and have a limited range of 30 to 50 per cent (see Fig. 12-3) and those that use the wider section V belts to obtain speed ratios up to 3 to 1 (see Figs. 12-4 to 12-6).   Both are available in single- and multiple-groove designs, the former in capacities from fractional to 300 hp, the latter from 100 to 30 hp.

Of significance to the maintenance man is the fact that once adjusted, the various parts are designed to be held together in a fixed relation one to another by setscrews or holding nuts, thus minimizing the wear and lubrication problems men-

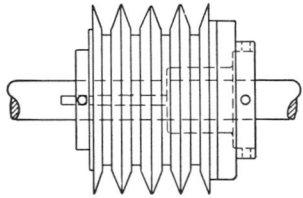

FIG. 12-3. Adjustable-while-stationary control vari-pitch sheave.   (*Courtesy of Allis-Chalmers Manufacturing Co.*)

FIG. 12-4. Adjustable-while-stopped control, speed ratios up to 3 to 1. (*Courtesy of T. B. Wood's Sons Co.*)

tioned above.   Care must be exercised to assure that the holding devices are quite secure, for even the slightest oscillatory motion in the absence of lubrication will quickly result in a seizing of the mating surfaces.

Speed adjustment is somewhat complicated and can be done only while the machine is stopped.   The adjustment usually is made by some form of turnbuckle-type tie-rod arrangement which provides for an equal and synchronized and lateral shifting of all flanges.   The exceptions to this are two approaches which use pulleys designed for section *A* through *D* belts.   In one case, only one set of flanges moves, thus misaligning the belt at one end of the range unless the motor is moved.   Fortunately, the amount of misalignment is not considered critical.   In the other, which is a two-groove style,

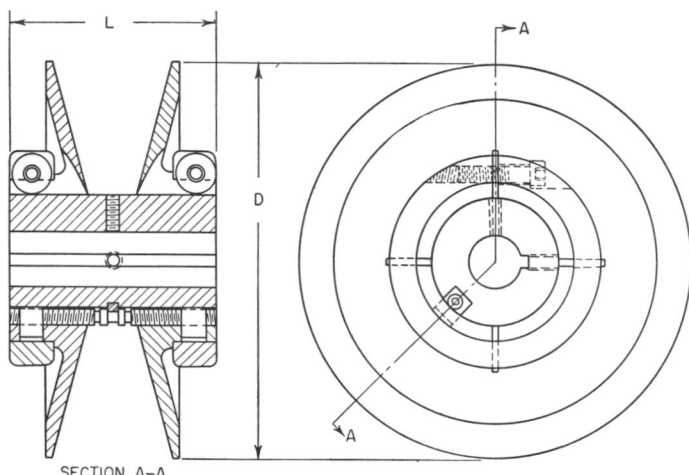

SECTION A–A
FIG. 12-5. Section of control shown in Fig. 12-4.

the outer flanges are thread-mounted onto a common hub, which carries the common center flange.   Since the outer flanges can be independently adjusted, care must be exercised to assure the same pitch diameter for both grooves.   Otherwise, one belt will take all the load and probably an additional load resulting from the dragging action of the other belt.

FIG. 12-6. Adjustable-while-stopped control, speed ratios up to 3 to 1.   (*Courtesy of Dodge Manufacturing Corp.*)

The most critical problem with the wide-section multiple-belt pulleys is the matching of belt lengths to assure a sharing of the load.   Unfortunately, these must be matched more closely than standard tolerances set up by the belt manufacturers, which call for a trial-and-error matching of belts.   This, of course, is not economically practical unless the particular plant is making several installations at the same time.

This, together with the definite stretch a belt will take during its first several hundred hours of operation, calls for replacement of the complete set of belts when any one particular belt goes bad.

This tendency for the belts to stretch during their initial break-in, along with the changing of operating diameters, requires some method of take-up to maintain proper belt tension, which is usually accomplished by adjusting the motor position on slide rails or by some type of idler roll.

Table 12-1 lists troubles, their causes and cures, experienced with the adjustable pulleys, stationary control.

Adjustable Pulley-in-motion Control.   Within its horsepower capacity and speed ranges, the most popular method of speed control is the spring-loaded split pulley which can be adjusted with the drive in operation (see Fig. 12-7).   Generally it is used

Table 12-1. Adjustable Pulleys—Stationary Control

Trouble	Cause	Correction	Prevention
I*a*. Accelerated belt wear.	Excessive misalignment of driver and driven pulleys	Realign pulleys	
I*b*. Accelerated belt wear.	Continuous flexing over small diameters	Select driven pulley of proper diameter to avoid this condition	
I*c*. Accelerated belt wear.	Excessive heat, cold, moisture, acid fumes, abrasives, etc.		
I*d*. Accelerated belt wear.	Overloaded, excessive shock loads, excessive belt speeds		Do not exceed ratings set by manufacturers
I*e*. Accelerated belt wear.	In multiple-belt pulleys one or a few belts taking entire load	Belt lengths must be matched more closely	
I*f*. Accelerated belt wear..	Excessive belt tension	Adjust center distance	
I*g*. Slipping belt.........	Insufficient tension	Adjust center distance, or use idler roll	
I*h*. Slipping belt.........	Pulley faces greasy	Clean	
I*i*. Slipping belt.........	Overloaded		

FIG. 12-7. Spring-loaded split pulley, adjustable with drive in operation.

in conjunction with some type of sliding, swinging, or tilting motor base to provide the means of changing the operating diameters.   Countershaft units are available when the final speeds must be lower or higher than are obtainable with standard drive sheaves.

These pulleys are available with limited speed range (2 to 1) for use with standard *A* and *B* section belts from ⅛ through 1½ hp.   Ranges as high as 4 to 1 are available with pulleys designed around the wider section V belts and are available as such from ½ to 20 hp.

Maintenance men should be especially interested in the two distinct design approaches that have evolved.   One is to design around the maintenance of in-line belt alignment.   The heart of this approach is providing equal lateral movement of the two pulley halves as the speed is adjusted.   This has been accomplished by mechanical linkage systems as shown in Fig. 12-8.   The other school of thought has considered the maintenance problem of sticking disks and moving parts to be of first importance and

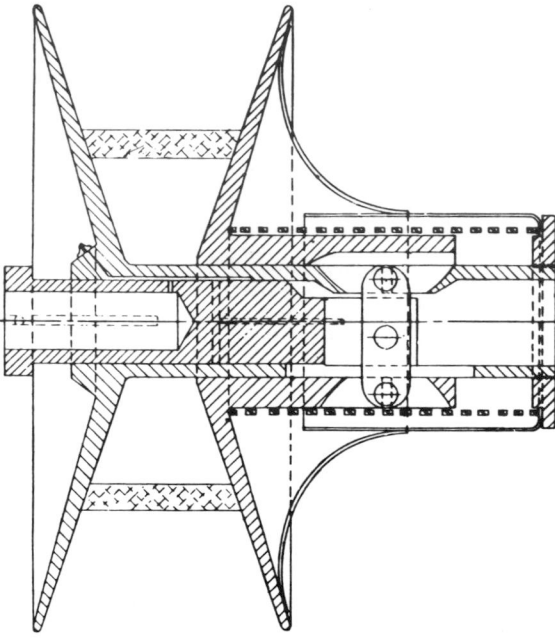

FIG. 12-8. Pulley halves are given equal lateral movement as speed is adjusted.   (*Courtesy of Lewellen Manufacturing Co.*)

has forsaken the in-line belt feature for an absolute minimum of parts to reduce the number of working surfaces to as few as possible and thereby minimize invitation to fretting corrosion (see Fig. 12-9).

In the smaller pulleys designed for use with section A and B V belts, no compensation for belt misalignment is made on the basis that the misalignment is inconsequential and the inexpensive A and B section belts are more expendable than the adjustable pulley.

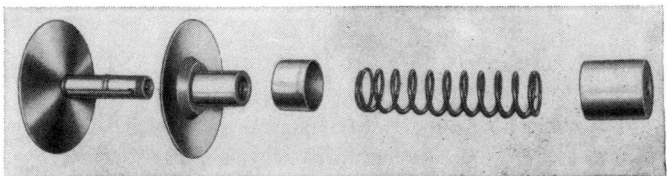

FIG. 12-9. Exploded view of motor pulley disks.

In the larger pulleys designed around the wide-section belts for greater speed range, the degree of misalignment becomes a more important factor when considering the wide cross section of the belt and its consequent resistance to lateral deflection.   Here compensation is accomplished by driving to a flat-faced pulley wide enough to accommodate the lateral movement of the belt as it rides down into the split pulley.

Table 12-2 lists troubles, their causes and cures, experienced with adjustable pulleys controlled in motion.

Compound Floating Sheaves. One method of obtaining a wide speed range at a relatively low first cost is by use of a compounded variable-pitch sheave assembly mounted on an intermediate countershaft between the driving and driven pulleys, as

Table 12-2. Adjustable Pulley—Controlled in Motion

Trouble	Cause	Correction	Prevention
IIa. Accelerated belt wear.	See items Ia, Ib, Ic, Id*		
IIb. Slipping belt.........	See items Ih, Ii*		
IIc. Slipping belt or belt not running level	Spring-loaded disks do not compensate owing to sticking of disks from improper or insufficient lubrication	Stop at once; disassemble; clean until parts slide freely	Lubricate every 2–5 weeks; shift speed range each day if possible

* Reference is to items in Table 12-1.

shown in Figs. 12-10 and 12-11.   Changing the position of the countershaft causes the floating compound flange to shift in position under belt pressure and thereby vary the operating diameters to effect the desired speed change.   These drives are available up to 10 hp, although their widest use is 1 hp and below.

Maintenance of proper belt tension and belt alignment have proved to be the greatest problem with these drives.   Belt tension varies as the countershaft is swung in either

Fig. 12-10. Use of compounded variable-pitch sheave to obtain wide speed range.   (*Courtesy of Speed Selector, Inc.*)

direction from its center position.   One manufacturer has recently designed spring loading on one of the outer flanges into his drive.   Otherwise, the motor should be mounted on a pivoting base, utilizing the weight of the motor to take up belt slack. Care should be exercised to locate the countershaft in a direct line between the driving and driven pulleys to minimize the need for such compensation.

Lateral movement of the common flange is quite substantial and has led most manufacturers to design some type of compensation into their drives.   The floating disks are usually provided with self-lubricating bushings, which tend to gall under the pressures of higher horsepower loadings; for this reason most of these installations are found in the lower horsepower capacities.

Belt Transmissions. Belt transmissions of the type shown in Fig. 12-12 have, through the years, earned a most enviable reputation among plant maintenance men for ruggedness and reliability with a minimum of attention. Stories are related of

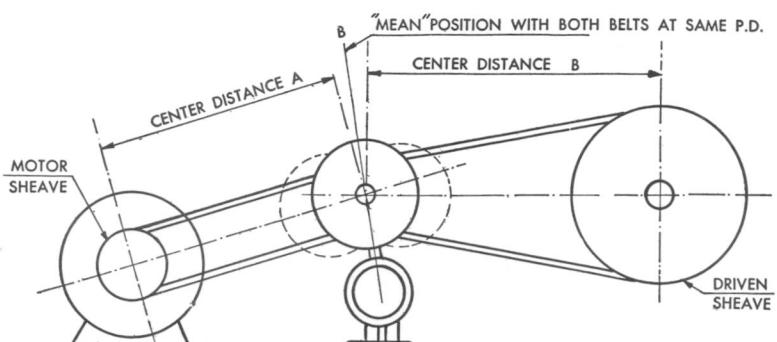

FIG. 12-11. Diagrammatic scheme of drive shown in Fig. 12-10.

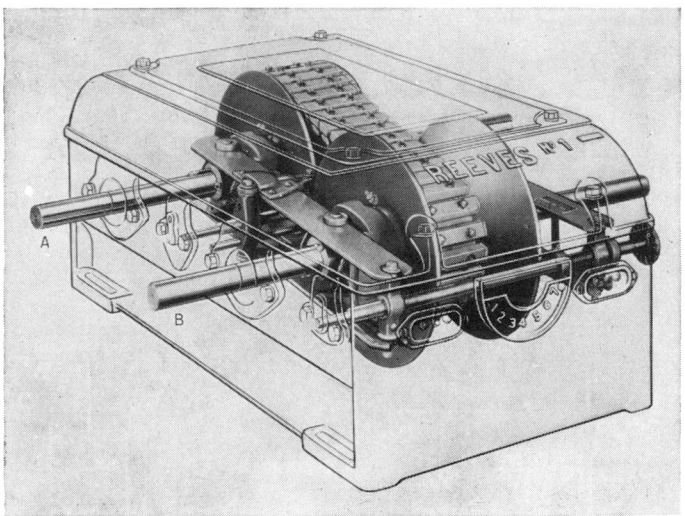

FIG. 12-12. Belt transmission.

such drives operating 7 days a week for 20 to 30 years without changing belts and calling only for periodic lubrication. They are available in capacities from fractional to 87 hp and up to 16-to-1 speed range. Standard variations include vertical or horizontal mountings, open or enclosed, and with a variety of controls.

Usually one shaft is driven at constant speed, speed adjustment being accomplished by a lever arrangement which positively synchronizes the position of all four flanges. Two screw arrangements are provided: one by adjusting speed by controlling the position of these levers, which, in turn, control the pulley operating diameters; the other, for controlling belt tension and horsepower capacity, by adjusting the center distance of the pivotal points of these synchronizing levers.

The heart of these transmissions is the time-honored block-belt design. Wedge-shaped wooden blocks tipped with leather are bolted to and carried on a wide strip of belting.   This design has the advantage of separating the handling of the torque load (belt pull) and the radial wedging forces.   Little attention is required of the belt other than an occasional check to assure that the disk faces are clean and free from grease, acid, or water.   If adverse conditions of dust, water, chemical fumes, or live steam are present, an enclosed type of transmission should be used.   Table 12-3 lists troubles, causes, and cures experienced with belt transmissions.

Table 12-3. Belt Transmission

Trouble	Cause	Correction	Prevention
IIIa. Accelerated belt wear..	Misalignment of disk assembly	Constant-speed and variable-disk assemblies should be parallel at mean speed	
IIIb. Accelerated belt wear..	See also items Ib, Ic, and Id*		
IIIc. Slipping belt.........	Pulley faces greasy, usually from over-lubrication of thrust bearings	Clean	Avoid overgreasing thrust bearings
IIId. Slipping belt.........	Constant-speed shaft too slow	Increase input speed by changing sheaves	
IIIe. Slipping belt.........	Insufficient belt tension	Adjust tension screw, but only while drive is running	Belt should have a slight sag on the loose side
IIIf. Creaking belt.........	Excessive belt tension	Adjust tension screw, but only while drive is running	
IIIg. Bearing failures......	Belt too tight	Adjust tension	
IIIh. Bearing failures.......	Excessive overhung load		Do not exceed loads specified by manufacturer
IIIj. Bearing failures.......	Insufficient or excessive lubrication		See manufacturer's instructions
IIIk. Bearing failures.......	Atmosphere: abrasive particles, moisture, corrosion	Use enclosures where necessary	
IIIl. Bearing failures.......	Bent shaft or improperly assembled		
IIIm. Cannot adjust speed..	"Sticking disks" due to improper or insufficient lubrication	Stop at once; disassemble; clean disk hub and shaft with kerosene	Lubricate every 2–5 weeks; shift through entire speed range each day, if possible

* Reference is to items in Table 12-1.

An all-metal version is available in capacities from fractional to 25 hp with speed ratios up to 6 to 1 (see Fig. 12-13).

Power is transmitted by a unique all-metal laminated steel belt.   These laminations shuffle to mate with radial grooves on the conical pulley flanges.   The pulleys, belt, and shifting levers are fully enclosed in a casing which serves as an oil reservoir for splash lubrication.

FIG. 12-13. All-metal belt transmission—P.I.V.   (*Courtesy of Link-Belt Co.*)

FIG. 12-14. Packaged belt drive.

Its advantage is a more compact design by virtue of using higher input speeds, but this is accomplished at a somewhat higher cost.

The packaged drive, Fig. 12-14, provides a preengineered combination of drive motor, belt transmission, and gear increaser or reducer where necessary for higher or lower than standard speeds.

These drives are cataloged from fractional to 100 hp with speed ranges up to 10 to 1 in the fractional ratings, 6 to 1 up through 30 hp, and 3 to 1 beyond 30 hp. Maximum speeds are as high as 10,000 rpm, and minimum speeds are as low as 2 rpm. All variations of motor characteristics and enclosures, as well as numerous mounting positions and methods of manual or automatic control, are available.

Table 12-4. Packaged Belt Drives

Trouble	Cause	Correction	Prevention
IV*a*. Accelerated belt wear.	See items I*b*, I*c*, I*d*, III*a**		
IV*b*. Slipping belt.........	Broken spring in variable-speed disk assembly	Replace spring	
IV*c*. Slipping belt.........	Pulley faces greasy owing to excessive lubrication of thrust bearings	Clean with kerosene	
IV*d*. Bearing failures......	See items III*h*, III*j*, III*k*, III*l**		
IV*e*. Cannot adjust speed; belt not running level.	See item III*m*		
IV*f*. Chatter in gearing....	Insufficient oil in gear case		Check oil level every 30 days

* Reference is to items in Tables 12-1 and 12-3.

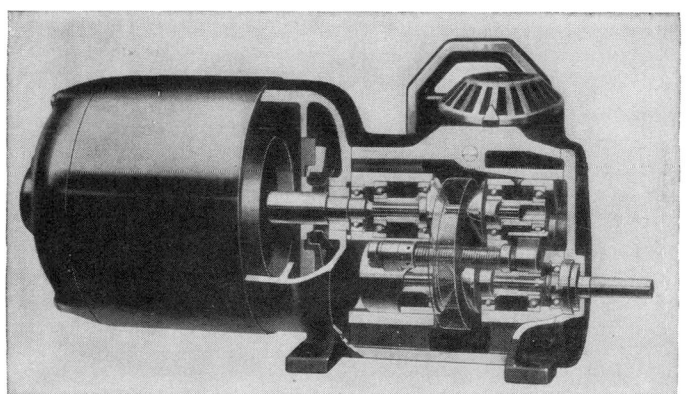

FIG. 12-15. Drive with metal surfaces in frictional contact. (*Courtesy of The Master Electric Co.*)

All three commercially available lines are designed around two sets of variable-pitch sheaves mounted on parallel shafts and driven through a ribbed V belt designed especially for this service.

Except in the case of one manufacturer, the drive motors are of special design to accommodate speed-shifting devices or to eliminate the need of a third bearing on the constant-speed shaft. The line of one manufacturer, except in the fractional-horsepower series, uses motors meeting standard NEMA mounting dimensions, which makes them interchangeable with any other make of NEMA motor. This is done to facilitate replacement if trouble is localized in the motor.

Table 12-4 lists troubles, causes, and cures experienced with packaged belt drives.

All-metal Traction Systems. Several manufacturers have designed mechanical variable-speed drives around the principle of metal surfaces in frictional contact to take advantage of the resulting space savings (see Figs. 12-15 to 12-17). The com-

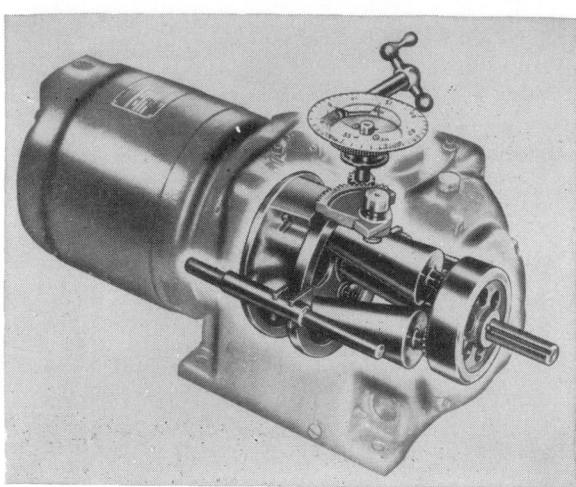

FIG. 12-16. Drive with metal surfaces in frictional contact.   (*Courtesy of Graham Transmissions, Inc.*)

FIG. 12-17. Drive with metal surfaces in frictional contact.   (*Courtesy of The Cleveland Worm & Gear Co.*)

Table 12-5. All-metal Traction Systems

Trouble	Cause	Correction	Prevention
Va. Cannot shift speed; OK if shifted only slightly. Will tend to slide back to original setting	Extended operation at one speed has caused concentrated wear tending to lock the sliding surfaces in a fixed position	Return to factory for replacement of damaged parts	Avoid running at one speed for extended periods
Vb. Pronounced thumping	Sudden load change reversal or overload has caused scoring of contact surfaces	Return to factory for replacement of damaged parts	Avoid use of traction-type drives on this type of application
Vc. Severe overheating...	Insufficient oil	Replenish to proper level	
Vd. Excessive slipping....	Use of too heavy an oil	Flush. Replenish with oil of proper viscosity	Use appropriately thin oil as recommended by manufacturer. Change every 1,000 hr of operation

FIG. 12-18. Differential gearing integrally mounted with all-metal belt transmission. (*Courtesy of Speed Control Div., Fairchild Engine and Airplane Corp.*)

pactness is made possible by the hard and finely finished compact surfaces, which permit the use of smaller parts.

At the same time, the use of metal-to-metal contact imposes limitations which must be carefully recognized by the application engineer if the drive is to give satisfactory service. Most important of these is to avoid applications which involve

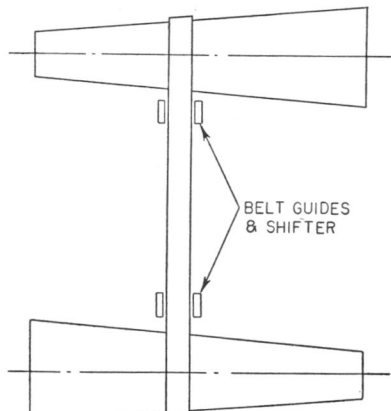

BELT GUIDES & SHIFTER

FIG. 12-19. Flat belt and cone drive.

sudden load changes, overloads, or sudden reversals. These may result in the skidding of the metal parts in contact, which, under the necessary high contact pressures, will cause a scoring of the surfaces.

Operation in temperature in excess of 50°C above ambient should be avoided to maximize the life of the contact surfaces.

Finally, the drive should not be permitted to operate at one speed for any extended period of time in order to avoid highly localized grooving, from which it will then become difficult to shift the drive.

Table 12-5 lists troubles, their causes and cures, experienced with this type of drive.

Table 12-6. Flat Belt

Trouble	Cause	Correction	Prevention
Short belt life...	Inherent slippage; contact surface speed varies across face of belt	None	
Slipping belt...	Overloaded. Remember belts are necessarily narrow to approach theoretically ideal line contact	Reduce loading	Do not overload
Slipping belt...	Belt has stretched	Extend center distance between pulleys or use idler roll	
Slipping belt...	Pulley faces greasy	Clean with kerosene	Keep clean

Geared Differential Drives. Differential gearing can be attached to any parallel-shaft cone-pulley transmission to permit infinite speed variation down to zero speed and with proper selection of components on into the reverse direction. Figure 12-18 shows such a differential integrally mounted with an all-metal belt transmission.

The most important consideration with these geared-differential drives is the proper recognition of the internal circulating power, which may reach as high as six times the input power, and if the motor transmission and gear components are not properly matched, disastrous internal overloading can result. Since each of the components must be of sufficient size and capacity to handle these maximum conditions, the cost of the total unit approaches that of the more familiar electrical variable-speed drives.

For troubles, their causes, and remedies, refer to the tables which give that information for belt transmissions and gear units.

Flat-belt Drives. Occasionally a flat belt, driving between two cone-shaped pulleys of the type shown in Fig. 12-19, will be found as a method of obtaining variable speed. There is no particular manufacturer who merchandises a complete line of these pulleys; rather, they are holdovers from the very early days or are specially designed to meet particular requirements.

Line contact is the theoretical ideal and, as such, requires that the belt width be kept quite narrow, which, of course, limits the power-transmitting capacity of the system. This same consideration means that contact surface speed varies across the face of the belt, producing an inherent slip and its consequent effect on belt life. See Table 12-6.

Chapter 13

AUTOMATIC-TENSIONING MOTOR BASE DRIVES

By WILLIAM STANIAR[1]
Formerly Mechanical Power Engineer
E. I. du Pont de Nemours & Company, Inc.
Wilmington, Del.

The automatic belt tensioning motor base drive is an engineered power-transmission unit built in various designs for the efficient operation of short-center belt drives.   It uses the simplest form of mechanical power transmission: a motor mounted on an automatic tensioning and adjustable base, two pulleys or sheaves, and a strong flexible flat belt (preferably endless) or a set of conventional V belts.   If a drive of this character is properly selected, calculated, and installed, practically no maintenance is required with the exception of periodic lubrication of the motor base movable parts.

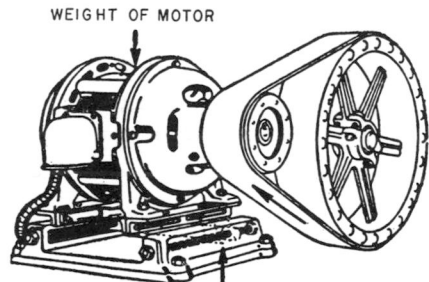

WEIGHT OF MOTOR

MOTOR PIVOTS HERE

FIG. 13-1. Typical pivoted motor base drive.

The selection of the belt for this type of drive should receive careful consideration in that it may be subjected to deleterious atmospheric conditions and mechanical effects such as high starting-torque loads, frequent starting and stopping, and non-flexibility of the belt itself.   From a flat-belt standpoint the best results are obtained from a leather belt of the mineral retanned variety, made endless.   Other types of flat belting can be used, but they should, from a maintenance and life standpoint, be made endless.

In all designs of the pivoted-type base, as shown typically by Fig. 13-1, the motor is bolted to the arms of the base and is free to swing about the pivot point, its weight being supported by the pivot and the belt.   With the motor correctly placed on the arms of the base it automatically maintains the belt tension necessary to ensure an uninterrupted flow of power.   Motor bases of this character are available for practically any normal-size motor, and they can be installed, as shown by Fig. 13-2, to operate vertically or mounted on the ceiling, floor, or wall.   They can be operated at an angle and can be mounted on the driven machine itself.   Automatic tensioning motor bases are adjustable devices which can be used on many types of driving installations such as fans, blowers, compressors, pumps, generators, machine tools, textile spinning frames, beaters, and lineshafts.

Ceiling motor drives of the regular belted type can be troublesome and can be the cause of considerable maintenance.   Because of their inaccessibility they are gen-

[1] The author is deceased.

erally neglected, with the result that the belt stretches and slips, causing burning of the belt and a production slowdown.   An automatic tensioning motor base mounted on the ceiling will prevent such action, since, when it is once correctly installed, belt stretch is automatically taken care of.
The floor-type base can be used as a ceiling mount, but special care should be given to the belt direction.   The tight side of the belt must approach the face of the motor pulley closest to the pivot of the base, as shown by Fig. 13-3.

Vertical motor drives of the regular belted type are another source of trouble and can be the cause of considerable maintenance because of fixed centers with no facilities to take up the slack occasioned by belt stretch.   The down-drive automatic tensioning base, shown by Fig. 13-4, mounted on either suitable brackets or a platform, keeps the belt tight regardless of stretch.   The topside drive base, Fig. 13-5, is used when the center line of the drive is within 45° of the vertical. Both the down drive and top-side drive bases possess all the adjustable features found in the regular floor-type bases.

Belt Stretch or Elongation.   This unavoidable condition of almost all flat power-transmitting belts is caused by centrifugal tension, too much mechanical tension, high humidity, heavy loads, or too small a width and thickness of belt for the load and speed requirements.   It is one of the prime causes of maintenance on all regular types of belt drives.   The

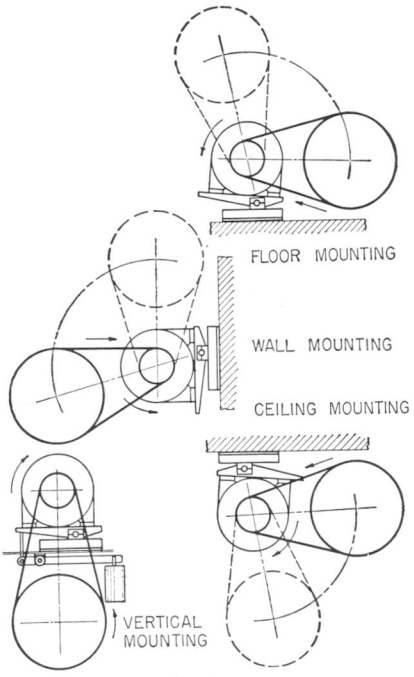

FIG. 13-2. Permissible methods of installing pivoted-type bases.

automatic tensioning motor base overcomes this difficulty to a considerable extent.

The Belt.   While any type of flat power-transmission belt can be used in connection with the automatic tensioning base drive, some give higher efficiency, longer life,

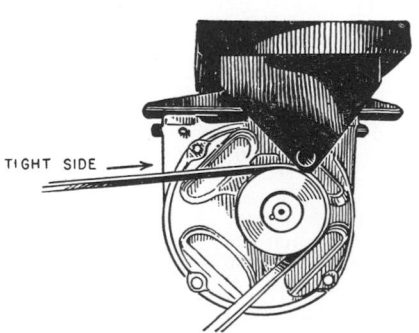

FIG. 13-3. Proper installation of ceiling mounted base.

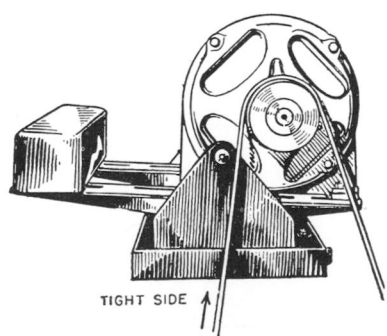

FIG. 13-4. Proper installation of down-drive type.

and lower maintenance.   Endless mineral-retanned leather belting is very flexible, has a high coefficient of friction and therefore a nonslipping grip on the pulleys, can readily be made endless, and has long life.   However, oak-tanned leather, rubber, stitched canvas, solid woven cotton, steel cable, and other types of flat belting have been successfully used.

The Pulleys. While any type of pulley is applicable to the automatic tensioning base drive, those whose driving surfaces have the greatest resistance to slip should be initially considered. The motor pulley should be of either the paper or wood type; the driven pulley also, if the driving ratio is unity. Large driven pulleys can be cast iron, fabricated steel, or wood. All pulleys should be of sufficient diameter and face for the load and speed requirements (see Tables 13-1 and 13-2). Motor pulleys smaller in diameter than those designated introduce high belt tension and bearing pressures. Belt speeds from 2,500 to 4,500 fpm are the most satisfactory. Speeds up to 6,000 fpm and higher are permissible under certain conditions but are not generally recommended. For speeds above 6,000 fpm, belting of the steel-cable construction can be satisfactorily used.

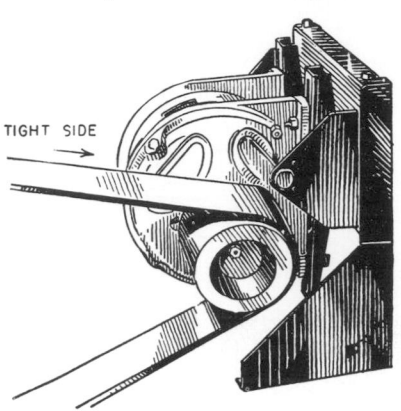

FIG. 13-5. Proper installation of topside-drive type.

TIGHT SIDE

Motor Float or Vibration. With the motor free to follow the load pulsations, the motor must move in unison with such pulsations. The amount of vibration or motion depends upon several factors. If the load is steady, the float may be hardly perceptible. On drives where severe fluctuating loads occur, the use of snubbers will tend to keep the drive steady. A base too small for the motor can cause vibration, resulting in breakage of some part of the base.

Table 13-1. Motor Horsepower Ratings and Recommended Pulley Diameters for Automatic Tensioning Motor Base Drives

Pulley diameter, in.	Horsepower ratings at various motor speeds						
	3,600	1,800	1,200	900	720	600	514
3	1½–2	1–1½	¾–1	½			
4	3–5	2–3	1½–2	¾–1			
4½	7½	5	3	1½–2	1–1½	¾–1	
5	10	7½	5	3	2	1½	¾–1
6	15	10	7½	5	3	2	1½
8	20	15	10	7½	5	3	2
9	.....	20–25, 30	15–20	10–15	7½–10	6–7½	3
10	.....	40	25–30	20–25	15–20	10–15	5–7½
12	.....	......	40–50	30–40	25–30	20–25	10–14
15	.....	......	60–75	50–60	40–50	30–40	20–25
18	.....	......	100	75–100	60–75	60	50
20	.....	......	.....	125	100–125	75–100	60–75
24	.....	......	.....	.....	150–200	125–150	100–125
26	.....	......	.....	.....	.....	200	150

Uneven belt thickness, eccentric pulleys, varying load application and an out-of-balance motor rotor constitute causes for undue motor vibration. With the motor free to follow the load pulsations, the motor, belt, machine, and bearings are freed of harmful load shocks, resulting in longer life for all.

Pulley Centers. The center distance between driving and driven pulleys can be extremely short, only a trifle greater than the diameter of the larger pulley of the drive. Such ultrashort centers are employed chiefly in the textile industry on spinning and twister frame drives where space is limited and the speed ratio is approximately 2.5 to 1 or less with a horsepower range from 5 to 20. Depending on operating conditions, large-horsepower drives generally require long center distances.

Efficiency. The efficiency of the automatic belt tensioning drive varies with the type and quality of the belt being used but it reaches a peak of around 99 per cent over a wide range of tensions. Drives of this character should be designed to accommodate the maximum capacity of the motor, which for most types of motors is generally 150 to 250 per cent of their rated capacity. However, since motors usually operate at less than their rated capacities, the drive is operating most of the time at

Table 13-2. Maximum Belt Widths for Motors, In.

Motor horse-power	Nominal motor speeds, rpm						
	1,800	1,200	900	720	600	514	450
1	2½	2½	4				
1½	4	4	4				
2	4	4	4				
3	4	4	5	6			
5	4	5	6	7			
7½	5	6	7	9			
10	6	7	9	10			
15	7	9	10	10			
20	9	10	10	12			
25	9	10	12	12	12		
30	10	12	12	12	14		
40	12	12	14	14	14		
50	....	14	14	16	16		
60	....	14	14	16	16		
75	....	14	16	18	18	18	20
100	....	14	16	18	18	22	22
125	....	....	18	20	20	22	22
150	....	....	20	20	22	22	24

less than one-half its peak capacity. This load characteristic makes it possible for the drive to maintain its high efficiency under fractional loadings (see Fig. 13-6).

Direction of Rotation and Base Selection. A good rule to follow when selecting an automatic belt tensioning base is "The tight side of the belt must approach the face of the motor pulley closest to the pivot of the base." This rule facilitates the selection of the proper type of base. The most favorable position of the motor is with its center on a level with the driven pulley center.

Installation. The motor base should be placed on its foundation with the pivot shaft moved back about one-quarter of the total take-up. With the pivot in this position, future increase in belt tension, if necessary, can be obtained without changing the center distance. The oil cups should be on the machine side of the motor. Oil should be put in the bearings with the belt in place when starting up the drive. Any small amount of misalignment can be corrected by adjusting one of the take-up bolts. A small amount of tension increase or decrease may be necessary, depending upon how close was the original assumption of the peak load to the actual load. Some very heavy static friction loads, as in a large and heavy fan, may have to be freed before the motor will start such a fan.

Possible Difficulties and How to Correct Them. Correct setting of the pivot shaft center, based on calculations (see Staniar's "Plant Engineering Handbook"), should eliminate most difficulties with this type of drive. In most cases vibration can be reduced to a minimum, since usually the cause suggests the cure. Too much or insufficient belt tension, loose bolts holding the motor to the base, or a worn bearing can be causes of trouble. Checking the period of vibration of the motor against that of the belt or driven machine may help in locating the difficulty.

The following rule will determine if the belt is the cause of the vibration: Divide the belt length in feet into the belt speed in feet per minute, and if it is found that this

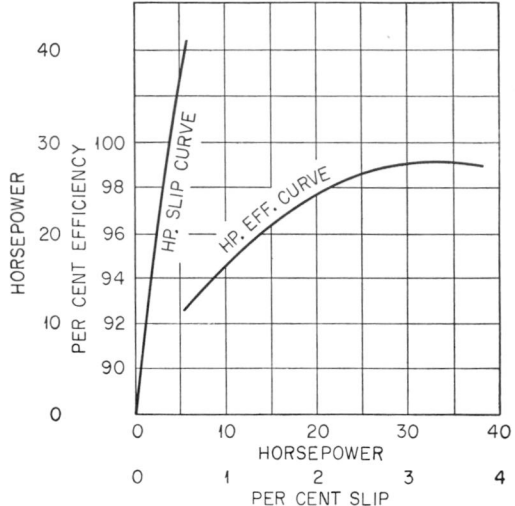

FIG. 13-6. Efficiency and slip chart.

result is the same as the number of vibrations per minute, the belt is the cause of the trouble.

Motor Rotor Float. It frequently happens that misalignment of the drive causes the belt to hold the motor rotor tight against the retaining collars, resulting in no float of the rotor. With correct alignment and with pulleys in the same plane this condition is avoided. Insufficient end play of the motor rotor can cause trouble. This end play should be no more than ⅛ in. or reduced as far as possible by the use of fiber washers. If the belt runs on the center of the pulleys when under load but runs off center with no load, misalignment is the cause. If by turning one of the center-distance adjusting screws of the base the belt will not run true, the drive is out of level with the driven machine or apparatus.

General Advantages

1. Dependability.
2. Low maintenance.
3. Constant correct belt tension.
4. Centrifugal tension overcome.
5. High efficiency maintained over a wide range of loadings.
6. Small amount of space required.
7. Long life furnished to belt and pulleys.
8. Easy drive alignment.
9. Inexpensive to install.

Types.   There are three general types of automatic belt tensioning motor bases available:

1. The gravity type, which depends mainly upon motor weight acting through adjustable lever arms to supply tension to the belt.
2. The reaction torque type, which utilizes mainly the twisting or rotating action of the motor stator which is equal and opposite to the motor rotor action.   The motor weight is offset enough to furnish initial tension, and the load determines the tension in the belt automatically.
3. The spring tension type, which, in reality, takes the place of the regular type of slide rails of the conventional electric motor, utilizes spring tension to control the tension of the belt, and consists of a stationary member, motor plate, tensioning springs, and adjusting screws.

The underlying principles of the first two bases are the same, but motor weight is more important to the gravity type than to the reaction torque type.

The spring-type base was a development that followed that of the gravity and reaction torque types.   In this base, shown by Fig. 13-7, the spring absorbs those

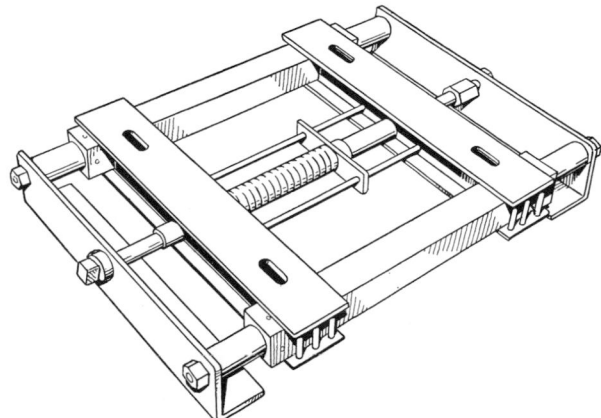

FIG. 13-7. Spring-type base.

shock loads which would otherwise have to be taken by the belt and bearings.   The spring also compensates for a considerable amount of belt stretch before adjustment is necessary.   Tension in the spring and belt is in a state of constant equilibrium regardless of variations which may occur as a result of fluctuations in load.

Chapter 14

GEAR DRIVES AND SPEED REDUCERS

By RUSSELL C. BALL, JR.
President
Philadelphia Gear Corporation
King of Prussia, Pa.

Gear drives and speed reducers are widely used where changes of speed, torque, shaft direction, or direction of rotation are required between a prime mover and driven machinery.

Essentially, gear drives incorporate one or more sets of gears mounted on shafts and bearings, including a positive means of lubrication, and enclosed in a gear casing with appropriate gaskets, oil seals, and air breathers. In addition, gear drives may also be equipped with some combination of electric motor and accessories, base plates or other equipment for mounting the unit, outboard bearings, a device for providing overload protection, a means of preventing reverse rotation; and any other special equipment required.

Gear drives have many advantages when used for industrial power transmission, including (1) economy of operation, (2) adaptability, (3) long service-life expectancy, (4) conservation of power and mounting space required, (5) minimum maintenance required, (6) operating safety, and (7) ability to operate under adverse conditions.

Gear reducers have been used for many years to reduce the speed of shaft rotation between a prime mover and a driven machine. This change in speed produces corresponding increases in torque on the output shaft of the reducer, permitting relatively small, low-cost, high-speed motors to drive machines requiring substantially higher horsepowers and slower speeds.

With the advent of high-speed machinery such as rotary compressors, the volume and importance of gear speed-increaser drives has been growing. In most cases, increasers are not simply speed reducers driven backward but involve design considerations different from those encountered in reducer drives.

Common Gear Types. Common types of gears used in industrial gear drives include spur, helical, herringbone or double-helical, bevel, spiral bevel, hypoid, zerol, worm, planetary, and internal gears (see Fig. 14-1).

Spur gears are used to transmit power between parallel shafts without end thrust or axial displacement. They are commonly used on drives of moderate speeds such as marine equipment, hoisting equipment, mill drives, and kiln drives. Simplicity of manufacture, absence of end thrust, and general economy of maintenance recommend the use of spur gearing wherever practicable.

Helical gear teeth are cut on a helix (oblique) angle across the gear wheel face. Mating helical gears permit several teeth to be in mesh at the same time. This increases load-carrying capacity, assures transmission of constant velocity, and reduces noise and vibration. Helical gears produce end thrust along the axis of rotation, which must be accommodated by the shaft bearings.   Helical gears are used where loads and speeds may be higher than can be conveniently met by spur gearing or where reduced noise and vibration are important.

Herringbone gears are used for transmission of heavy loads at high speeds where continuous service is required, where shock and vibration are present, or where a high

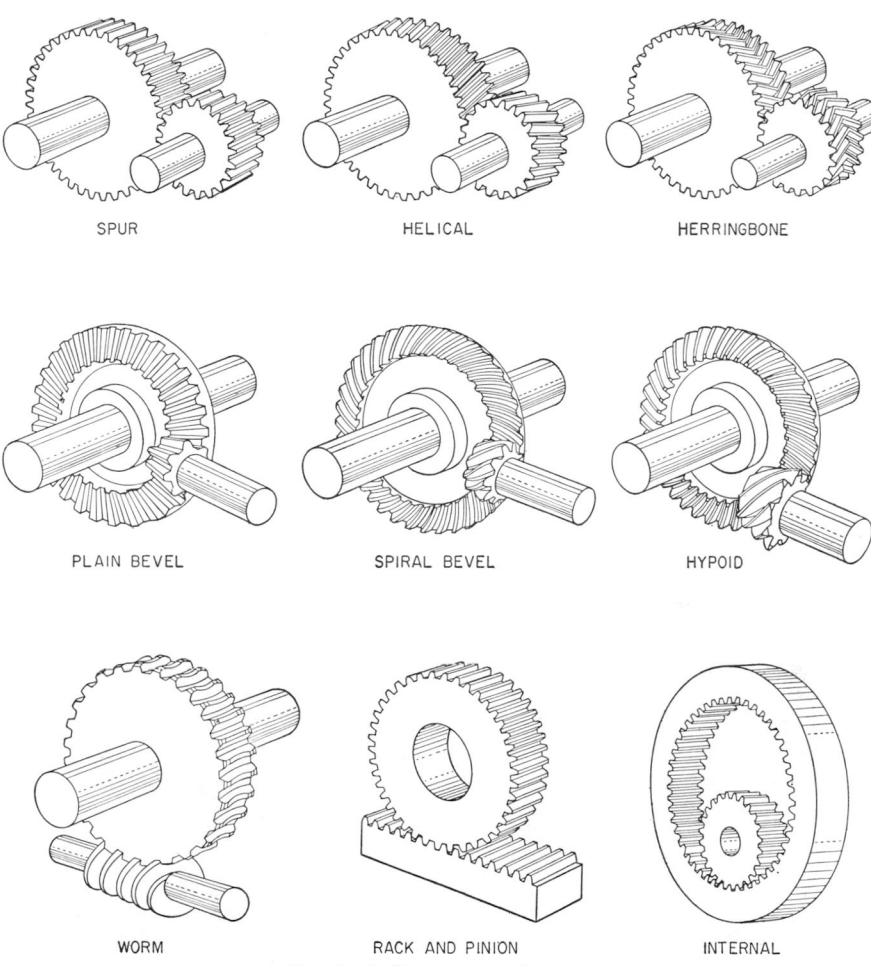

SPUR   HELICAL   HERRINGBONE

PLAIN BEVEL   SPIRAL BEVEL   HYPOID

WORM   RACK AND PINION   INTERNAL

FIG. 14-1. Basic types of gears.

reduction ratio is necessary in a single gear train.   Because herringbone gears are actually opposed helical gears, end thrust is eliminated.   Tooth surface contact is maximized, and load capacity, velocity, and quietness of operation are greatly increased.

Bevel gears transmit power between two shafts, usually at right angles with each other.   However, shafts positioned at other than 90° can be used.   Straight bevel gears may be used for right-angle power transmission where operating conditions do not warrant the superior characteristics of spiral bevel gearing.   Since bevel gearing creates thrust loads along the supporting shafts, adequate bearings must be provided.

Spiral bevel, zerol, and hypoid gears are generally considered under the heading of spiral bevel gear units.   Loading of spiral bevel gears is always distributed over two or more teeth.   Tooth action is smooth and quiet.   Accuracy of tooth contact can be closely controlled through precision grinding and lapping.   Axial thrust of spiral bevel gears is slightly higher than for straight bevel gearing and varies with direction of rotation and hand or cut of the gear and pinion.   Where possible, gears should be designed so that axial thrust tends to move the pinion out of mesh.

FIG. 14-2. Single-reduction herringbone.

Worm gearing has won wide acceptance for industrial drives because of its many advantages of conjugate tooth action, arrangement, compactness, and load-carrying capacity.   Worm gear drives are quiet and vibration-free and produce a constant-output speed.   They are well suited to service where heavy shock loading is encountered.   The many variable mounting arrangements possible with worm gears allow for compactness of design not otherwise obtainable.   Since action between worm thread and the teeth of the driven worm gear wheel is predominantly sliding rather than rolling, greater heat generation and reduced mechanical efficiencies result at higher speed-reduction ratios.

Internal gears are more compact than external gears of the same ratio.   In general, they have greater load-carrying capacity and run more smoothly.   Internal gearing usually employs spur or helical teeth.   In

FIG. 14-3. Double-reduction herringbone.

FIG. 14-4. Triple-reduction herringbone.

rare instances, herringbone teeth can be employed.   Owing to the nature of their construction, internal gears are limited in speed-reduction ratios obtainable on a given center distance.

Basic Gear Drives.   Gear drives are used to transmit power between a prime mover and driven machinery.   In addition to the simple transmission of power, gear drives usually change or modify the power being transmitted by (1) reducing speed and increasing output torque, (2) increasing speed, (3) changing the direction of shaft rotation, or (4) changing the angle of shaft operation.

FIG. 14-5. Single-reduction spiral bevel (top view).

FIG. 14-6. Double-reduction spiral bevel.

Gear drives are generally considered packaged units, manufactured in accordance with accepted and advertised specifications, to be used for a wide range of power-transmission applications.   Published standards of the American Gear Manufacturers Association are accepted as the basis for design, manufacture, and application of modern gear drives.

In addition to general gear drives and speed reducers, the AGMA has established specific standards for certain special types of gear drives which are used explicitly for driving particular types of machinery, such as deep-well pumps, cooling-tower fans, and pinion-stand drives.

Motorized gear drives (commonly called gear motors or motor reducers) are used extensively throughout industry. These units differ from conventional gear drives

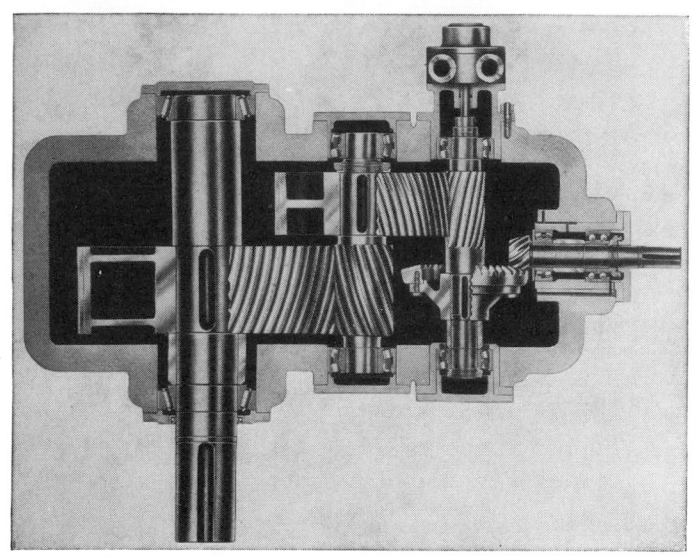

FIG. 14-7. Triple-reduction spiral bevel (top view).

FIG. 14-8. Double-reduction worm gear reducer.

in that the prime mover (usually an electric motor) is designed as an integral component of the unit. Any of the basic gear drives (see Figs. 14-2 to 14-10, inclusive) can be manufactured as motorized units.

Select the Proper Drive. Satisfactory performance of a gear drive depends upon proper design and manufacture of the drive itself, selection of the proper type and size unit for a given application, proper use of the unit in service, and proper maintenance of the unit throughout its entire service life.

The official AGMA identification plate, Fig. 14-11, assures that the unit has been designed, manufactured, and assembled in accordance with the accepted standards of

FIG. 14-9. Double-reduction gearmotor.

FIG. 14-10. Special change-speed reducer.

the AGMA. Do not hesitate to request the assistance of trained engineers from a reputable manufacturer in selecting and properly installing your gear-drive units.

In selecting the proper gear drive for any application, you will need to determine horsepower requirement of the unit and speed ratio between input and output shafts. You will already know (1) the horsepower and speed required to drive your machinery and (2) the output speed and horsepower of the prime mover.

To calculate horsepower required in any gear drive, first adjust for efficiency losses in the unit. Generally speaking, the efficiency of spur, helical, double helical, herringbone, straight bevel, spiral bevel, zerol, and hypoid gears is taken as 98 per cent per gear set.   The efficiency of worm gears in reducers is generally taken as 100 − ratio/2 per gear set where the worm speed is greater than 100 rpm.   Where worm speed is less than 100 rpm, the efficiency is taken as 100 − ratio per gear set.   Where multiple-gear sets are used, the over-all efficiency is the product of the efficiencies of the gear sets.   Most gear-drive manufacturers publish efficiency ratings on their individual units.

Having adjusted required horsepower upward to compensate for efficiency losses, now adjust for the type of service the gear drive must handle.   For standardization and convenience, certain commonly used driven machines have been classified according to the types of drive service they normally require.   Table 14-1 shows this classification, where U = uniform shock load, M = moderate shock load, and H = heavy shock load.

Determine the load characteristics of your application from this table.   Then multiply the horsepower (adjusted for efficiency losses) by the appropriate service factor, Tables 14-2 to 14-4, for that type of unit and service (shock load).   Select a gear drive that will meet this increased horsepower requirement.

FIG. 14-11. AGMA identification plate.

To calculate the speed ratio of any gear drive simply divide rpm of input shaft by rpm required on output shaft.

After a gear-drive unit has been selected for mechanical rating, check the actual horsepower to be transmitted against the manufacturer's thermal rating for that unit. Thermal rating is the maximum average horsepower that can be transmitted continuously without creating a dangerous rise in temperature and without necessitating auxiliary cooling of the unit.

Install Gear Drives Carefully.   When installing gear-drive units, be sure that the units are well supported and securely anchored to prevent misalignment of gears or shafts.

Good-quality, key-locked mechanical couplings should be used to couple the shafts of driving and driven units.   Slight angular or linear shaft misalignments may be overcome by using flexible-type mechanical couplings.   In some cases, torsional stresses at starting or during momentary overloads can be compensated for by use of certain types of flexible mechanical couplings.

Proper loading of gear-drive units is essential to long and trouble-free service life. Assuming that gear drives are properly rated for the particular applications and properly installed, it is important that they should not be subjected to extreme or sustained overloads.

Torque limit switches are available as optional equipment on the gear drives of some manufacturers.   Where the possibility of overloading or machinery jamming (which might produce an overload on the drive unit) is present, it is wise to insist upon torque-limiting devices.

If you have any questions about the load capacities of gear drives on your machinery, do not hesitate to consult the manufacturer of the drive units.

Gear-drive housings are usually designed for proper heat dissipation under normal operating conditions.   Do not allow units to operate where oil temperatures exceed those recommended by the manufacturer.   Where surrounding atmospheric conditions might reduce normal heat dissipation, consult the drive manufacturer for his recommendations.

Some manufacturers ship new gear-drive units with internal parts protected by polar-type rust-preventive film.   There is no necessity to flush out this film, since it is soluble in the lubricant in most cases.   (Consult the supplier of your particular gear drive units for configuration of this fact.)   Merely fill the case with the recommended

Table 14-1. Load Characteristics

Application	Uniform load	Moderate shock	Heavy shock	Application	Uniform load	Moderate shock	Heavy shock
Agitators:				Bucket—cont	U		
Pure liquids	U			Centrifugal discharge	U		
Liquids and solids		M		Escalators	U		
Liquids—variable density		M		Freight		M	
Blowers:				Gravity discharge	U		
Centrifugal	U			Man lifts*			
Lobe		M		Passenger*			
Vane	U			Fans:			
Brewing and distilling:				Centrifugal	U		
Bottling machinery	U			Cooling towers			
Brew kettles, cont. duty	U			Induced draft*			
Cookers—cont. duty	U			Forced draft*			
Mash tubs—cont. duty	U			Induced draft		M	
Scale hopper, frequent starts		M		Large (mine, etc.)		M	
Can filling machines	U			Large (industrial)		M	
Cane knives		M		Light (small diameter)	U		
Car dumpers			H	Feeders:			
Car pullers		M		Apron		M	
Clarifiers	U			Belt		M	
Classifiers		M		Disk	U		
Clay-working machinery:				Reciprocating			H
Brick press			H	Screw		M	
Briquette machine			H	Food industry:			
Clay-working machinery		M		Beet slicer		M	
Pug mill		M		Cereal cooker	U		
Compressors:				Dough mixer		M	
Centrifugal	U			Meat grinders		M	
Lobe		M		Generators (not welding)	U		
Reciprocating, multicylinder		M		Hammer mills			H
Reciprocating, single-cylinder			H	Hoists:			
Conveyors—uniformly loaded or fed:				Heavy duty			H
Apron	U			Medium duty		M	
Assembly	U			Skip hoist		M	
Belt	U			Laundry washers:			
Bucket	U			Reversing		M	
Chain	U			Laundry tumblers		M	
Flight	U			Line shafts:			
Oven	U			Driving processing equipment		M	
Screw	U			Light	U		
Conveyors—heavy duty, not uniformly fed:				Other line shafts	U		
Apron		M		Lumber industry:			
Assembly		M		Barkers—hydraulic-mechanical		M	
Belt		M		Burner conveyor		M	
Bucket		M		Chain saw and drag saw			H
Chain		M		Chain transfer			H
Flight		M		Craneway transfer			H
Live roll*				Debarking drum			H
Oven		M		Edger feed		M	
Reciprocating			H	Gang feed		M	
Screw		M		Green chain		M	
Shaker			H	Live rolls			H
Cranes				Log deck			H
Main hoists	U			Log haul—incline			H
Bridge travel*				Log haul—well type			H
Trolley travel*				Log turning device			H
Crusher:				Main log conveyor			H
Ore			H	Off bearing rolls		M	
Stone			H	Planer feed chains		M	
Sugar†		M		Planer floor chains		M	
Dredges:				Planer tilting hoist		M	
Cable reels		M		Resaw merry-go-round conveyor		M	
Conveyors		M		Roll cases			H
Cutter head drives			H	Slab conveyor			H
Jig drives			H	Small waste conveyor-belt	U		
Maneuvering winches		M		Small waste conveyor-chain		M	
Pumps		M		Sorting table		M	
Screen drive			H	Tipple hoist conveyor		M	
Stackers		M		Tipple hoist drive		M	
Utility winches		M		Transfer conveyors		M	
Dry-dock cranes:				Transfer rolls		M	
Elevators:				Tray drive		M	
Bucket—uniform load	U			Trimmer feed		M	
Bucket—heavy load		M		Waste conveyor		M	
				Machine tools:			
				Bending roll		M	
				Punch press—gear driven			H

Table 14-1. Load Characteristics (Continued)

Application	Uniform load	Moderate shock	Heavy shock	Application	Uniform load	Moderate shock	Heavy shock
Notching press—belt driven*				Pumps:			
Plate planers..			H	Centrifugal	U		
Tapping machine			H	Proportioning		M	
Other machine tools:				Reciprocating			
Main drives		M		Single acting, 3 or more cylinders		M	
Auxiliary drives	U			Double acting, 2 or more cylinders		M	
Metal mills				Single acting, 1 or 2 cylinders*			
Draw bench carriage and main drive		M		Double acting, single cylinder*			
Forming machines			H	Rotary—gear type	U		
Pinch, drier and scrubber rolls, reversing*				lobe, vane	U		
Slitters		M		Rubber and plastics industries:			
Table conveyors				Crackers†			H
Non-reversing				Laboratory equipment†		M	
Group drives		M		Mixing mills†			H
Individual drives			H	Refiners†		M	
Reversing*				Rubber calendars†		M	
Wire drawing and flattening machine		M		Rubber mill (2 on line)†		M	
Wire winding machine		M		Rubber mill (3 on line)†	U		
Mills, rotary type:				Sheeter†		M	
Ball†		M		Tire building machines*			
Cement kilns†		M		Tire and tube press openers*			
Dryers and coolers†		M		Tubers and strainers†		M	
Kilns		M		Warming mills†		M	
Pebble†		M		Sand muller		M	
Rod, plain and wedge bar†		M		Sewage-disposal equipment:			
Tumbling barrels			H	Bar screens	U		
Mixers:				Chemical feeders	U		
Concrete mixers, continuous		M		Collectors, circuline or straight-line	U		
Concrete mixers, intermittent		M		Dewatering screws		M	
Constant density	U			Grit collectors	U		
Variable density		M		Scum breakers		M	
Oil industry:				Slow or rapid mixers		M	
Chillers		M		Sludge collectors	U		
Oil-well pumping*				Thickeners		M	
Paraffin filter press		M		Vacuum filters		M	
Rotary kilns		M		Screens:			
Paper mills:				Air washing	U		
Agitators (mixers)		M		Rotary-stone or gravel		M	
Barker—auxiliaries—hydraulic		M		Traveling water intake	U		
Barker—mechanical		M		Slab pushers		M	
Barking drum			H	Steering gear*			
Beater and pulper		M		Stokers	U		
Bleacher	U			Sugar industry:			
Calendars		M		Cane knives†		M	
Calendars—super			H	Crushers†		M	
Converting machine, except cutters, platers		M		Mills†			H
Conveyors	U			Textile industry:			
Couch		M		Batchers		M	
Cutters—platers			H	Calendars		M	
Cylinders		M		Cards		M	
Dryers		M		Dry cans		M	
Felt stretcher		M		Driers		M	
Felt whipper			H	Dyeing machinery		M	
Jordans			H	Knitting machines*			
Log haul			H	Looms		M	
Presses	U			Mangles		M	
Pulp machine reel		M		Nappers		M	
Stock chests		M		Pads		M	
Suction roll	U			Range drives*			
Washers and thickeners		M		Slashers		M	
Winders	U			Soapers		M	
Printing presses:*				Spinners		M	
Pullers:				Tenter frames		M	
Barge haul			H	Washers		M	
				Winders		M	
				Windlass*			

* Refer to gear manufacturer.
† To be selected on basis of 24 hr. service only.

lubricant to the proper oil level.   Always check to see if gear-drive units are shipped with or without oil from the factory.   Units having bearings requiring grease are generally shipped from the factory with grease in the bearings.

When units furnished with forced-feed lubrication are first put into service, they should be checked to observe that oil is being pumped.   When a pressure gage is furnished with the unit, gage pressure should be approximately 15 to 30 psi with oil temperature at 160°F (5 to 15 psi for high-speed units with sleeve bearings).   Adjust the relief valve if necessary to obtain this pressure.

Table 14-2. Service Factors for Herringbone (Double-helical), Helical, and Spiral Bevel Gear Units

Character of load on driven machine	Electric-motor or steam-turbine drive				Multicylinder internal-combustion engine				Single-cylinder internal-combustion engine			
	8–10 hr per day	24 hr per day	Inter-mittent 3 hr per day	Occa-sional ½ hr per day	8–10 hr per day	24 hr per day	Inter-mittent 3 hr per day	Occa-sional ½ hr per day	8–10 hr per day	24 hr per day	Inter-mittent 3 hr per day	Occa-sional ½ hr per day
Uniform.........	1.0	1.25	0.8	0.5	1.25	1.5	1.0	0.8	1.5	1.75	1.25	1.0
Moderate shock...	1.25	1.5	1.0	0.8	1.5	1.75	1.25	1.0	1.75	2.0	1.5	1.25
Heavy shock.....	1.75	2.00	1.5	1.25	2.0	2.25	1.75	1.5	2.25	2.5	2.0	1.75

1. Ratings shown in horsepower tables are based on a service factor of 1.   For service factors other than 1 it is necessary to multiply the actual running horsepower required under normal full load by the service factor.   The product of these two, which may be called the equivalent horsepower, is to be used when making reducer selection from horsepower table.

2. The horsepower tables permit a maximum momentary or starting load of 200 per cent normal (100 per cent overload).   If peak load on driven machine exceeds twice the normal running horsepower, divide the peak horsepower by 2 and compare with the equivalent obtained by item 1.   If larger, use it instead of item 1 in selecting reducer from tables.

3. Extreme repetitive shock and applications where exceedingly high energy loads must be absorbed, as when stalling, require special consideration and are, therefore, not covered by service factors given in the table.

4. In selecting a unit, the horsepower required should not exceed the thermal rating of the unit. Thermal rating indicates the amount of power that can be delivered through the unit without overheating.

Each unit is usually given a short run-in at the factory as part of the inspection procedure.   However, for complete run-in under operating conditions, it is recommended that the unit be operated at partial load for one or two days to allow final breaking-in of the gears.   After this breaking-in period, the unit can be run under rated load.

After the unit has been operated under rated load for 2 weeks, it should be shut down in order to drain the oil and flush the housing.   If desired, the original oil may be strained and replaced.   Do not use a strainer finer than 25 microinches in order to avoid filtering out the additives.   After the original oil has been drained, fill the case to the indicated level with SAE 10 straight-run mineral flushing oil containing no additives.   The unit should be started, brought up to speed, and shut down immediately as a flushing procedure.   Drain off flushing oil, and fill with recommended lubricant to the proper level.

After this initial oil change, an oil change is recommended after 2,500 hr or 6 months of normal operation, whichever occurs first, unless there are unusually high-temperature conditions combined with intermittent high loads where the temperature of the gear case rises rapidly and then cools off quickly.   This condition may cause sweating on the inside walls of the unit, thus contaminating the oil and forming sludge.   Under these conditions, or if the oil temperature is continuously above 150°F, or if the unit is subjected to an unusually moist atmosphere, oil changes may be necessary at 1- or 2-month intervals, as determined by field inspection of the oil.

Good Maintenance Practice.   Lubricating oils for use with enclosed gears and gear units should be high-grade, high-quality, well-refined, straight mineral petroleum oils, within the recommended viscosity ranges as noted below.   They must not be corrosive to gears or ball or roller bearings.   They must be neutral in reaction.   They should have good defoaming properties.   No grit or abrasives should be present.

Table 14-3. Service Factors for Worm Gear Units

American Gear Manufacturers Association outlines five (5) classes of worm gear speed-reducer services that are based principally upon running time and nature of load to be transmitted.

Class I.   Normal 8- to 10-hr service, free from recurrent shocks, that is, shock loads that recur at even and frequent intervals.   In Table 14-1 this would be Type U service on 8 to 10 hr per day basis.   Service factor equals 1 for service in this classification.   The thermal rating must not be exceeded.

Class II.   8- to 10-hr service where recurrent shock loading is encountered or 24-hr service where no shock load is experienced.   For application to this service classification multiply actual input horsepower or output torque to be transmitted by a service factor of 1.2.   The thermal rating must not be exceeded.   Types M and H loads on an 8- to 10-hr per day service or Type U load on a 24-hr service would be applicable.

Class III.   24-hr shock load service.   For application to this service classification, multiply actual input horsepower or output torque to be transmitted by a service factor of 1.3.   The thermal rating must not be exceeded.   Either Type M or H loads on a 24-hr service would require this service factor.

Class IV.   Intermittent service, where the worm is operated at a speed of 100 rpm or more.   Multiply actual input horsepower or output torque required by the factor in the table depending upon the frequency and the duration of the load.   The thermal rating need not be considered for this class of service.

Total Minutes of Operation Allowed

Per hour multiple cycles per hour	Per cycle 1 cycle per hour	Per cycle 1 cycle per 2 hr or more	Service factors
	5	10	0.6
2	10	20	0.7
5	15	30	0.8
10	20	40	0.9

Example.   A service factor of 0.8 would be used in each of the following cases: (1) More than one start and stop per hour with total time of operation not exceeding 5 min per hr. (2) One start and stop per hour with total time of operation not exceeding 15 min per cycle.   (3) One start and stop in 2 hr or more with total time of operation not exceeding 30 min per cycle.

Class V.   Low-speed service where the worm speed is less than 100 rpm.   For application to service in this classification (service factor equals 1) independent of the nature or duration of the load except where such service is intermittent, then the service factor in the intermittent rating table above will apply.

Ratings of worm gear units permit momentary or starting loads of 300 per cent normal (200 per cent overload).

For high operating temperatures, good resistance to oxidation is needed.   For low temperatures, an oil having a low pour point to meet the lowest temperature expected is needed.   When the operating temperature varies over a wide range, an oil having a high viscosity index is desirable.

For standard worm gear drives, the oil should have an additive of 3 to 10 per cent of acidless tallow or similar animal fats.

When the gears are subject to heavy shock or impact loading, or when the unit is subject to extremely heavy duty, an extreme-pressure (EP) lubricant should be used.

The lubricant should be an extreme-pressure type compounded with lead naphthenate in a well-refined lubricating oil. The extreme-pressure lubricant must meet the general specifications listed above for straight-mineral-type oil and in addition be noncorrosive to a copper strip at 212°F. It must have a pour point of 0 to 5°F.

The viscosity of the extreme-pressure lubricant should be approximately the same as that of the recommended AGMA lubricants given in Table 14-5.

On many types of gear-drive units, pressure fittings are supplied for the application of grease to bearings that are shielded from the oil.

Sufficient grease to form a film over the rollers and races of the bearing is all that is actually required for lubrication of roller bearings; however, ample reservoir space for grease is provided.

Gear-drive units are usually shipped from the factory with grease applied. Bearings should be lubricated at definite intervals. Study will be required to determine how frequently this should be done for a particular application.

Table. 14-4. Service Factors for Gear Motors

The three classes of gear motors and shaft-mounted reducers as defined by the American Gear Manufacturers Association are as follows:

Class I. For steady loads not exceeding normal rating of motor and 8 hr a day service. Moderate shock loads where service is intermittent. Service factor equals 1.

Class II. For steady loads not exceeding normal rating of motor and 24 hr a day. Moderate shock loads for 8 hr a day. Service factor equals 1.4.

Class III. For moderate shock loads for 24 hr a day. Heavy shock loads for 8 hr a day. Service factor equals 2.

The lubricant should not be corrosive to gears or to ball or roller bearings; must be neutral in reaction; should have no grit, abrasive, or fillers present; should not precipitate sediment; should not separate at temperatures up to 300°F; and should have moisture-resisting characteristics. The lubricant must have good resistance to oxidation.

There are many greases suitable as lubricants for roller bearings in gear drive units. The following greases are representative; any equivalent lubricant may be used:

Texaco Regal Starfak No. 2
Esso Standard Oil Co. Andok "B"
Shell Alvania E.P. No. 2
Stanolith M.P. Grease No. 2 (manufactured by Standard of Indiana)

Bearings should be grease-lubricated at definite intervals. Study will be required to determine how frequently this should be done for a particular application.

Every precaution should be taken to prevent any foreign matter from entering the gear case. Sludge is caused by dust, dirt, moisture, and chemical fumes. These are the biggest enemies of proper and adequate lubrication in gear-drive units.

During normal periods of operation, gear-drive units should be given daily routine inspection, consisting of visual inspection and observation for oil leaks or unusual noises. If oil leaks are evident, the unit should be shut down, the cause of leakage corrected, and the oil level checked. If any unusual noises occur, the unit should be shut down until the cause of the noise has been determined and corrected. Check all oil levels at least once a week. The operating temperature of the gear-drive unit is the temperature of the oil inside the case. Under normal conditions, the maximum operating temperature should not exceed 180°F. Generally, pressure-lubricated units are equipped with a filter which should be cleaned periodically.

If it becomes necessary to shut down the unit for a period longer than 1 week, the unit should be run at least 10 min each week while it is idle. This short operation will keep the gears and bearings coated with oil and will prevent rusting due to condensation of moisture resulting from temperature changes.

Table 14-5. Lubrication Table for Specific Gear Drives
Fill to indicated oil level with lubricant as follows

Type of unit	Size of unit	Ambient temperature, °F		
		0–40 Use AGMA No.	41–100 Use AGMA No.	101–105 Use AGMA No.
Herringbone, double-helical and helical gear reducers	3103–3118, 3204–3218, 3305–3318, with splash lubrication	2	4	5
	3121–3135, 3221–3235, 3321–3335, with splash lubrication	3	5	6
	All size units force feed lubrication	3	4	5
Change speed unit	All size units splash and force feed lubrication	3	4	5
High-speed reducers and increasers	All size units force feed lubrication	1	2	3
Spiral bevel gear reducers	3403–3421, 3508–3518, 3605–3618, with splash lubrication	2	4	5
	3424–3432, 3521–3524, 3621–3635, with splash lubrication	3	5	6
	All size units force feed lubrication	3	4	5
Cooling tower drive Worm gear Spiral bevel Helical spiral bevel	All size units splash and force feed lubrication	Lubricating oil for use in cooling tower units should be an extreme-pressure-type lubricant compounded with lead naphthenate in a well refined oil. The recommended viscosity of the lubricant when normal operating temperature of the oil in the speed reducer is not over 180°F is: 1250–1330 SSU @ 100°F, 440–500 SSU @ 130°F, 89–94 SSU @ 210°F		
Motor reducers: Types HS, HC, VS, VC	All size units splash and force feed lubrication	2	4	5
Types HD, VD	All size units splash and force feed lubrication	3	5	6
Planetary reducers: Types RHS, RHC	Sizes 202–324	2	3	4
Types RHS, RHC	Sizes 326–505	3	4	5
Type RHD	Sizes 202–324	3	4	5
Type RHD	Sizes 326–505	4	5	6
Gear motors	All size units	2	4	5
Floating gear motors Types W and HW	All size units	7 comp. diluted*	7 comp.	8 comp.
		or		
		An extreme-pressure-type lubricant compounded with lead naphthenate in a well refined oil. Viscosity range for various AGMA Lubricants and footnotes		
Agitator gear drives*	All size units spaslh and force feed lubrication	2	4	5
Special gear unit				
		0–40	41–90	91–120
Worm gear reducers	Intermittent operation All worm speeds (where period of operation is insufficient to produce any appreciable rise in oil bath temperature)	5	5	7 comp.
	Continuous operation Worm speeds below 600 rpm	7 comp. diluted*	8 comp.	8 comp.
	Continuous operation Worm speeds 600 rpm and over	7 comp. diluted*	7 comp.	8 comp.

* Diluted AGMA No. 7 comp. oil should be diluted with a lighter oil, preferably not exceeding 500 sec viscosity at 100°F, until the desired fluidity is obtained. The lubricant used for dilution should be of the same basic crude as that of the recommended oil. The lubricant supplier should be consulted if there is any doubt.

Trouble-shooting Gears. Someone has observed that "gears wear out until they wear in . . . and then they wear forever." The AGMA describes this phenomenon more precisely as follows:

It is the usual experience with a set of gears on a gear unit . . . assuming proper design, manufacture, application, installation, and operation . . . that there will be an initial "running-in" period during which, if the gears are properly lubricated and not overloaded, the combined action of rolling and sliding of the teeth will smooth out imperfections of manufacture and give the working surfaces a high polish. Under continued proper conditions of operation, the gear teeth will show little or no sign of wear.

Despite the truth of this statement, failure of metallic gear teeth may occur as a result of excessive deterioration of the working surfaces of the teeth or as actual tooth breakage. In many such situations, early recognition may suggest a remedy before extensive damage occurs.

Experience indicates that the vast majority of gear-tooth wear and failure may be summed up under nine basic headings in two classifications:

Classification A.   Surface deterioration:

1. Wear.
2. Plastic yielding.
3. Welding.
4. Surface fatigue.
5. Miscellaneous tooth-surface deteriorations.

Classification B.   Tooth breakage:

6. Cracking.
7. Quenching cracks.
8. Overload.
9. Fatigue.

The following portion (which conforms to AGMA Standard 110.02 nomenclature) may be used as a guide to identification of gear-tooth trouble. If discovered early enough, many gear-tooth failures can be avoided through proper corrective maintenance as indicated. (The illustrations were prepared by the AGMA, which has given permission for their use.)

SURFACE DETERIORATION

Wear

Wear is a general term covering sliding of metal against metal or abrasion by lapping or scratching.

Normal wear, Fig. 14-12, is the loss of metal from the surface of a gear tooth resulting from unavoidable abrasion at rate and degree that will not prevent the gear from performing satisfactorily during its expected life.

Maintenance Procedure. A certain amount of smoothing and polishing is expected during "running in" of new gear sets. This type of wear is less noticeable where gears have been shaved or ground-finished during manufacture. Before gears are run at all, they should be checked for proper installation and to assure that loading is controlled within rating limits as set by the manufacturer.

FIG. 14-12. Normal wear.

The use of recommended lubricants and filters should eliminate excessive gear-tooth wear during the "running-in" period. Most manufacturers of assembled gear drives recommend flushing the gear case frequently to remove any metallic particles and to eliminate any possibility of foreign objects circulating through the gear mesh.

Abrasive wear, Fig. 14-13, is surface injury caused by fine particles carried in the lubricant or buried in the gear-tooth surfaces. The particles may be metal detached from gear teeth or bearings, abrasives not completely removed before assembling, sand or scale from castings, or other impurities in the oil or surrounding atmosphere.

Maintenance Procedure. Whenever abrasive wear is detected, the unit should be stopped immediately. Oil should be drained. The inside of the housing, gear teeth, and oil passages should be thoroughly scraped, flushed, and wiped down. A light flushing oil should be used for a short time, then drained before refilling the oil reservoir

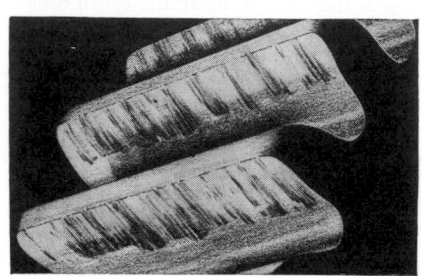

FIG. 14-13. Abrasive wear.

FIG. 14-14. Scratching.

FIG. 14-15. Overload wear.

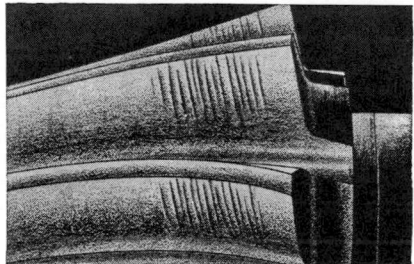

FIG. 14-16. Ridging.

with clean oil of proper grade. In contaminated atmospheres, special air breathers, oil seals, and filters should be considered as means of eliminating the infiltration of foreign particles to the gear case.

Scratching, Fig. 14-14, is a form of wear characterized by deep scratches in the direction of surface sliding, caused by particles that are larger than those associated with abrasive wear.

Maintenance Procedure. Since scratching is an accentuated type of abrasive wear, with comparatively deep and widespread grooves up and down the tooth profile, maintenance procedure is identical with that for simple abrasive wear. Make sure that the case, gears, and lubrication channels are completely free of foreign matter. Protect against recontamination by use of filters, breathers, and oil seals where conditions indicate.

Overload wear, Fig. 14-15, is a form of wear experienced, under conditions of heavy load and low speed, in both hardened and unhardened gears. Metal seems to be removed progressively in thin layers or flakes, leaving surfaces that appear somewhat as if etched.

Maintenance Procedure. The only permanent remedy for overload wear is to reduce unit loading to the rated capacity of the gears. In some cases, extreme-pressure lubricants may be used to reduce the *rate* of wear. Care should be exercised in selecting pressure lubricants which are free from corrosive substances.

Ridging, Fig. 14-16, is a particular form of scratching wear that may occur on case-hardened surfaces of hypoid pinions under heavy load and that shows closely spaced grooves in the direction of surface sliding.

Maintenance Procedure. Since ridging usually results from localized loading, wherever possible gears should be adjusted to distribute the load more evenly over the full tooth surface. In the case of bevel gears, backlash should be altered to reduce impact loading. In some cases, the use of extreme-pressure lubricants may help to reduce the *rate* of tooth-surface deterioration.

Plastic Yielding

Plastic yielding is a deformation of gear-tooth surfaces resulting from heavy loads, characterized by fins on the tip edges or ends of the teeth (not to be confused with shaving fins) and an occasional ridge and matching groove on the mate at the pitch line. It is usually associated with ductile materials but actually occurs with hardened steel as well.

Rolling, Fig. 14-17, is a form of plastic yielding resulting from heavy, even loads and sliding. The "ridging and matching" pattern is generally limited to spur gearing and

FIG. 14-17. Rolling.

FIG. 14-18. Rippling.

is caused by excessive loading at the point where one pair of mating teeth carries the whole load momentarily and where the direction of sliding is reversed (outward from the tooth root).

Peening is a form of plastic yielding caused by localized impacts or by uneven, heavy, or shock loads. The effect is that of a series of "hammer blows," resulting in "flattened" plastic yielding of gear-tooth surfaces at irregular intervals.

Maintenance Procedure. Often peening can be checked by reducing backlash of gear teeth. Occasionally, the addition of a flywheel to the gear shaft will serve to smooth out the hammer-blow effects of spur gear teeth entering and leaving the mesh. Since peening is "localized" surface deterioration, extreme-pressure lubricant sometimes is effective in reducing this destructive type of plastic yielding.

Rippling, Fig. 14-18, is a form of plastic yielding over areas of casehardened steel surfaces under heavy sliding load. It is characterized by a fish-scale pattern.

Welding

Welding is a general kind of surface deterioration occurring when pressure, sliding, and rise of temperature combine to cause the lubricating film to be forced out, allowing metallic surfaces to rub directly against each other to the extent that molecular adhesion, or welding, occurs, followed by immediate tearing apart. Sometimes referred to as "seizing" or "galling," gear-tooth-surface welding usually results from excessive loading and inadequate lubrication. Welding often occurs on relatively soft gear sets where there is no difference in hardness between gear and pinion teeth.

Slight scoring, Fig. 14-19, is a minor impairment of the gear-tooth surface of a welding nature, showing slight tears and scratches in the direction of sliding. Scoring usually starts at a surface area where there is a combination of high surface stress and sliding velocity—generally occurring at or near the tip of the tooth.   (The term *scoring* has been selected in preference to scuffing, seizing, galling, roping, etc.)

Maintenance Procedure.   Correction of slight surface scoring often can be accomplished through use of an extreme-pressure lubricant.   Consult your lubricant supplier for his specific recommendations.   In some cases it may be necessary to polish

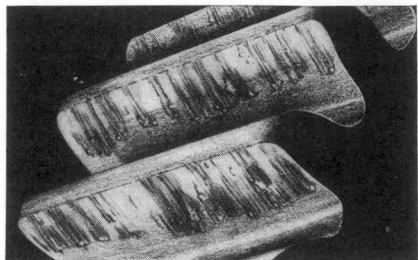

FIG. 14-19. Slight scoring.   FIG. 14-20. Severe scoring.

tooth surfaces in addition to using a pressure lubricant.   Where scoring persists, gear teeth may be metallurgically hardened to resist further damage.

Severe scoring, Fig. 14-20, is a more advanced degree of welding, showing deep scratches and adhesions and leading to rapid gear-tooth-surface deterioration.

Maintenance Procedure.   This is the same as for slight scoring.   If scoring cannot be checked, consult the gear manufacturer.

Surface Fatigue

Surface fatigue is the formation of cavities in the surface of the teeth, usually quite small at first and at separated areas of high compressive stress, often due to surface irregularities.

Initial pitting, Fig. 14-21, may occur when a pair of gears is first started in service and may continue only to the stage where local high spots have been reduced, so that

FIG. 14-21. Initial pitting.   FIG. 14-22. Destructive pitting.

there is sufficient area of contact to carry the load without further impairment.   This type of pitting, according to experience, is not necessarily serious, being corrective and nonprogressive.

Maintenance Procedure.   Usually, initial pitting is observed as tiny cavities at scattered spots on the surfaces of the gear teeth.   In most cases, running-in of gears will tend to polish down surface irregularities, and pitting will cease.   Where pitting continues, metallurgical surface hardening of the gear teeth may be necessary.   On occasion, grinding and polishing of tooth bearing surfaces will help.

Destructive pitting, Fig. 14-22, is defined as pitting that continues to progress after the initial period of gear operation, often at an increasing rate.   It will often progress to the point where remaining unpitted tooth-surface areas are insufficient to carry the load, and rapid destruction of gear teeth will occur if they are continued in operation.

Maintenance Procedure. Destructive pitting may be checked by grinding and polishing gear-tooth surfaces. If polishing fails to retard destruction, metallurgical surface hardening often will eliminate further damage. In some cases, use of extreme-pressure lubricants has met with success.

Spalling, Fig. 14-23, is a more extensive type of surface fatigue in which a considerable area of the tooth bearing surface is progressively undermined and eventually breaks away in flakes. It seems to occur only in casehardened gears. Spalling may start at a crack (in a manner similar to pitting) and does not necessarily follow the junction between case and core.

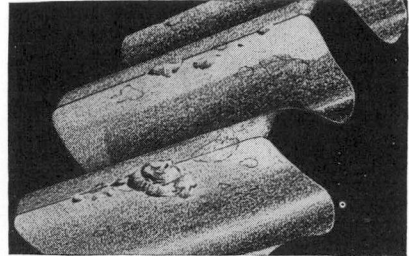

FIG. 14-23. Spalling.

Maintenance Procedure. If damage from spalling is not too extensive, use of an extreme-pressure lubricant may retard further damage. In some cases, surface polishing will provide more even distribution of the load across gear tooth surface and relieve excessive pressure at the point where spalling has occurred. If tooth destruction continues, consult the gear manufacturer.

Miscellaneous Tooth-surface Deterioration

Since corrosive wear, burning, interference, and grinding-check tooth-surface deterioration are independent sources of trouble, not closely related to one another or to the foregoing groups, they are treated independently.

Corrosive wear, Fig. 14-24, is the result of chemical action on metal tooth surfaces by oxidation, through either acid or alkaline contamination or by contamination from inferior or improper lubricants. The destructive effects of corrosive wear may occasionally be accelerated by excessive moisture in the gear case.

FIG. 14-24. Corrosive wear.

FIG. 14-25. Burning.

Maintenance Procedure. Drain and flush gear case and gears to remove the source of existing contamination. Be sure that new lubricant is clean, of high quality, and uncontaminated. If corrosive wear persists, consult the manufacturer for recommendations as to special breathers and oil seals.

Burning, Fig. 14-25, is a discoloration and loss of hardness resulting from high temperature produced by excessive friction caused by overload, overspeed, lack of backlash, or faulty lubrication.

Maintenance Procedure. To reduce friction, look first to the lubricant. In many cases, extreme-pressure lubricants will eliminate gear-tooth burning. Be sure gears are not being run in excess of their rated load and speed capacities. If burning persists, request the gear manufacturer to test for proper backlash and gear-tooth spacing.

Interference, Fig. 14-26, is a type of gear-tooth deterioration caused by extremely heavy contact between the tip edge of one tooth and the fillet surface of a mating tooth. Such interference may eventually cause localized abrasion or gouging.

Maintenance Procedure. Since interference usually is the result of improper gear design or manufacture, or of deflection, or of assembling the gears at too close a center distance for the profile shapes existing on the teeth, remedy for the situation should be left to the gear manufacturer.

 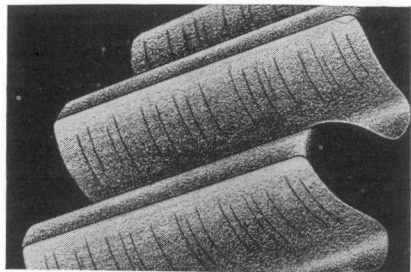

FIG. 14-26. Interference.   FIG. 14-27. Grinding checks.

Grinding checks, Fig. 14-27, are fine cracks usually in a definite pattern, caused by improper grinding technique, improper heat treatment, or both. They are usually not visible until the gears are placed in service.

Maintenance Procedure. In some cases grinding checks will not cause serious gear-tooth deterioration if gears are properly lubricated. Where overloading, high operating velocities, or high-temperature service cause grinding cracks to enlarge, magnetic inspection and polishing may be useful in overcoming the trouble. If damage continues, consult the gear manufacturer.

TOOTH BREAKAGE

Tooth cracking or actual breakage is the end result of gear-tooth deterioration. These conditions are listed for identification purposes only, since their existence indicates a situation already beyond the ability of maintenance procedures to retard.

Cracking, Fig. 14-28, results from residual stresses induced in hardenable material by faulty manufacturing control or from improper operating conditions. One cause

FIG. 14-28. Cracking.   FIG. 14-29. Quenching cracks.

is too soft a core or some other form of improper heat treatment. Chipping and flaking represent various forms and degrees of cracking failure in which portions of the gear teeth eventually will break off.

Quenching cracks, Fig. 14-29, result from improper heat treatment of gears, from extremely sharp tooth fillets, or from tooling marks in mating gears. They usually start at either the roots or the ends of the teeth. Deliberate fracturing of a quench-cracked gear tooth will reveal a discolored area in the metal where the crack existed.

Overload breakage, Fig. 14-30, refers to gear-tooth breakage as the direct result of an unexpected shock overload, such as may be casued by jamming of connected machinery.   Overload breakage is not necessarily attributable to improper design, application, or faulty manufacture of the gears.   Overload gear-tooth breakage can be prevented by use of a torque-control device between the gear drive and the driven machinery.

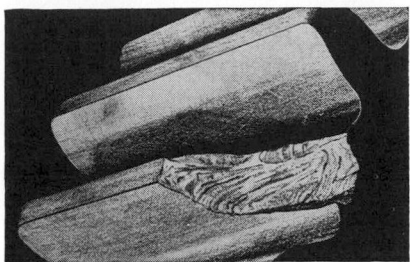

FIG. 14-30. Overload breakage.

FIG. 14-31. Fatigue breakage.

Fatigue breakage, Fig. 14-31, results from a large number of repetitions of a load (revolutions or cycles) rather than being caused by a single application of a shock load.   A fatigue break is of progressive nature, starting as a short crack which continues to extend until a portion of or a whole tooth breaks loose.   Discoloration and rubbing on the fractured surfaces, if discernible, are indications of fatigue breakage. Sometimes design fatigue fractures are characterized by a series of "contour" lines roughly concentric and spreading from a focal point.   This area has a smoother appearance than the surface of the final fracture.

Maintenance of gear drives involves proper selection, proper installation, proper loading of the unit, proper lubrication, and periodic inspection.   Metallic gears have tremendous service life when properly used and cared for.

Occluded bandage. Fig. 141-26 gives the two steps in the actual fixation of an uninterrupted shock dressing, and suction bandage for temporary immobilization. Bleeding bandage is not necessary in these cases except that application of full pressure. The hemorrhage may be controlled with firm pressure. A bandage can be prevented by means of close contact with the new bone and friction may change.

Section **9**

MAINTENANCE OF SERVICE EQUIPMENT

Chapter 1

AIR CONDITIONING

By JOHN H. KOONCE
Manager, Parts and Service Operations
STEWART DOCTER
Editor, Editorial and Technical Writing Services
and ROBERT M. KELLY
Associate Editor, Editorial and Technical Writing Services
Carrier Air Conditioning Company
Syracuse, N.Y.

Air conditioning is the control of temperature, humidity, purity, and distribution within the conditioned area.

TYPES OF EQUIPMENT

There is a great variety of equipment in use to do this job. Some devices are designed to serve a specific type of space; others to perform a specific function; and still others as components to be assembled into a tailor-made system to fit a particular building. Generally speaking, however, they may be grouped into two classifications: unitary and central station.

The unitary equipment classification includes those designs such as a room air conditioner, where all of the functional components are included in one or two packages, and installation involves only making the service connections such as electricity, water, and drains.

Central-station systems, often referred to as applied or built-up systems, require the installation of components at different points in a building and their interconnection (see Fig. 1-1).

TYPES OF COMPONENTS

All air-conditioning systems are made up of two major types of components. In a unitary equipment, for example, the air-handling part of the unit would include the fan, filter, heater, air passages through the unit, and the air outlet. Most of the air outlets have a means of adjusting air flow or direction or both. The refrigeration part includes the compressor and its drive, the cooling coil, and the condensing coil or condenser.

The size of the unit normally is indicated by reference to the refrigeration, and the air-handling capacity is designed to match the refrigeration. Units are made in sizes from ⅓ ton up to 60 tons. Ton, as used here, does not mean the weight of the equipment, but is a measure of the cooling capacity. A ton of refrigeration is equivalent to the cooling effect resulting from the melting of 1 ton of ice in 24 hours. As a rule of thumb, approximately 1 horsepower is required to produce 1 ton of refrigeration at normal air-conditioning temperatures. The size of the refrigeration-machine motor is, therefore, a general guide to the size of the air-conditioning system.

A central-station system employs the same functional components as unitary equipment. Here, the air-handling equipment includes the fan, filter, heater, apparatus for treating the air, dampers for control of air volume, and a distribution system of ducts or conduit. In such a system, the refrigeration, consisting of one or several machines, usually is centrally located, and several air-handling equipments may be served from the central refrigeration plant.

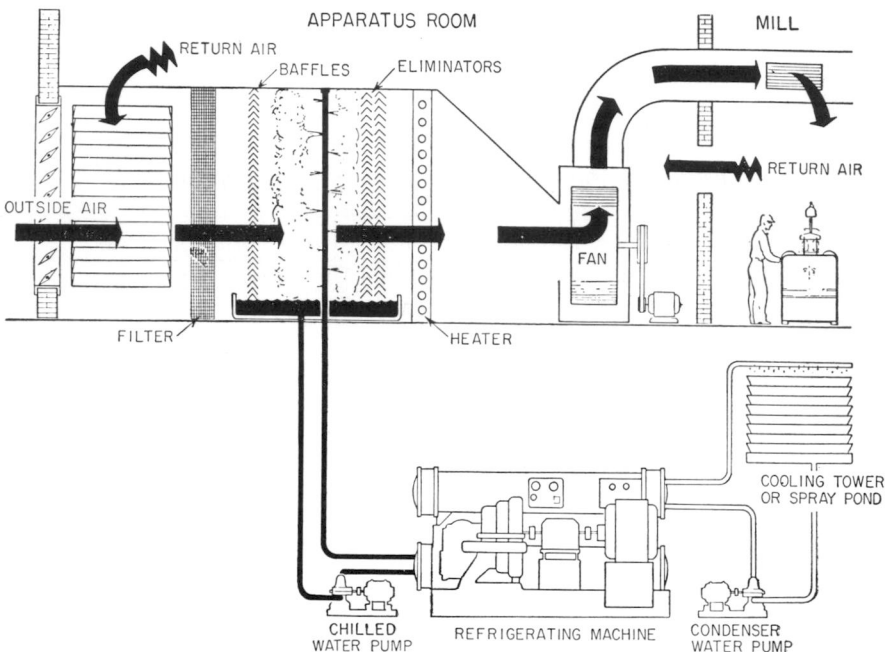

FIG. 1-1. Central-station system. Air from outdoors enters at the left, where it is mixed by automatic dampers with the proper proportion of air returning from the mill. This mixture then passes through filters (if needed) and baffles to the spray chamber, where it is washed and saturated with moisture. Banks of eliminators scrub the air and remove entrained water before the air passes through the heating coils. Here it is heated, if necessary, and then it passes through the centrifugal fan to the ducts and out into the factory or mill.

REFRIGERATION PLANTS

There is wide variety in refrigeration equipment, but most fall into one of three general types. These are: reciprocating, centrifugal, and absorption. Reciprocating and centrifugal refer to the type of compressor used, since both employ mechanical refrigeration cycles. Absorption refers to a fundamentally different cycle, where a cooling effect is produced by the absorption of one fluid by another.

Almost all unitary conditioning equipments use reciprocating compressors. These are driven by electric motors, and a number of different chemicals are used as refrigerants.

Reciprocating compressors are made in sizes from $\frac{1}{6}$ horsepower, like the ones commonly used in the domestic refrigerator, to those requiring as much as 300 or 400 horsepower. Where more capacity is needed in a central refrigeration plant than is available in one compressor, multiple units are used. Several compressors may be interconnected to provide wide flexibility in capacity, or each compressor may operate on its own individual circuit.

Centrifugal compressors are in common use in capacities from about 100 tons to 2,500 tons in one unit. The minimum size limit is set by first cost and operating economics as compared to other types of refrigeration and the practical maximum size by over-all dimension and weight for shipping and handling.

The absorption cycle is used in a range of sizes, from the domestic refrigerator to 1,000 tons at air-conditioning temperatures in one unit. A ready source of heat favors selection of the absorption unit, because the power requirements are limited to circulation of the fluids through the unit. Absorption machines have no major moving parts and may use plain water as a refrigerant.

AIR-CONDITIONING LOAD

An understanding of the source of air-conditioning load and how it is handled is essential to efficient operation, maintenance, and repair of air-conditioning equipment.

The load on an air-conditioning system is the amount of heat that must be removed from or added to a space in a given time. This applies both to the load which manifests itself in terms of the actual sensible temperature of the space, and that involved in the control of humidity, since raising or lowering the moisture content requires the transfer of heat.

If heat is to be added, it is a "heating load." If it is to be removed, it is a "cooling load."

Cooling Loads

To determine the cooling load of a building and thus establish the amount of refrigeration needed, it is first necessary to know what produces the heat and how much is produced. The following sources of heat will be encountered in any building:

Sun Load. The sun shining on a building and through the windows carries heat into the building. Heat coming through the windows is felt much sooner than heat coming through the walls. The rate at which the sun heats up the walls depends upon wall construction. Thick walls increase in temperature much more slowly than thin walls but will hold more heat. This has a definite effect on conditions in the building, since the walls give up their heat slowly and the effects can be felt long after the sun has passed the wall. The sun load varies according to season and exposure. The south exposure has the highest sun load in winter. During both seasons the east-exposure sun load reaches its peak point in the morning and the west reaches its peak in the afternoon. The sun load on the north exposure is due mostly to reflection and is therefore low throughout the year.

Transmission Load. The heat that comes into or goes out of the room through the windows and walls (because of the difference between the outdoor and indoor temperatures) is called transmission load. On a warm day, the heat travels into the room. On a cold day it travels from the room. Transmission load is thought of as separate from the sun load. For example, the sunny side of the building has a sun load and a transmission load while the shady side has only the transmission load.

Occupancy Load. Since normal body temperature (98.6°F) is higher than the desired room temperature, the occupants give heat to the room air. In addition, the occupants release moisture through perspiration and by breathing.

Load from Lights. Electric lights give off heat in proportion to the wattage of the light bulbs. This heat is included when the designer calculates the cooling load.

Miscellaneous Loads. The heat from other sources such as electric motors, business machines, radios, and television sets, also is included as part of the cooling load.

Latent Load. Excess moisture in the room is termed latent load. This load appears from several sources: People breathing and perspiring; ventilation air; moist air infiltrating through the window cracks or building openings; and many miscellaneous moisture-producing pieces of equipment such as steam tables, showers, and sterilizers.

All of these loads, including latent load, are removed by cooling action. In the case of unitary equipment, the action takes place at the cooling coil in the unit, which is fed liquid refrigerant directly from the refrigerating assembly. The refrigerant in vaporizing absorbs heat from the air passing over the coil.

Excess moisture is removed by cooling the air, since air will hold only so much moisture at any given temperature. To control room humidity, the amount of moisture to be removed from the room air must first be determined. The temperature and air quantity at the cooling coil is then planned to establish moisture content of the supply air at the proper level to permit absorption of the desired amount of moisture from room air.

In central-station systems, similar cooling and dehumidifying action takes place at the central air-handling apparatus, either through the use of cooling coils, or coils and fine water sprays combined, or sprays alone. In the larger systems the coils usually employ chilled water from the refrigerating machine rather than liquid refrigerant.

In order to exercise complete control over both humidity and temperature, it is frequently necessary to add a reheat coil to warm up the air after it has been dehumidified, because the reduced temperature required for dehumidification may be lower than that required to maintain proper temperatures in the conditioned space.

In modern high-velocity induction systems of the type used in many of the better office buildings today, an additional means of regulating temperature is provided by means of a coil in the room, through which chilled or warm water may be passed. Room air is "induced" over this coil by the effect of high-velocity air from the central unit and is cooled or heated an additional amount corresponding to the flow of water through the coil. This water flow is regulated by either an automatic thermostat or a manual valve. All dehumidifying, however, is done at the central apparatus.

Another type of central system employs coils in the room to handle all cooling and dehumidifying as in the case of unitary equipment. However, chilled water is piped to the room units from a central refrigerating plant.

Size of the Cooling Loads

For a typical room, the distribution of cooling loads might be as follows:

Sun	50 %
Transmission	20 %
Lights	18 %
Occupancy	12 %
Total	100 %

The above distribution shows that the sun is the largest part of the total room load. It also is a changing load since it moves from one side of the building to the other and, in effect, can turn on or off any time throughout the day. Therefore, it has considerable effect on the control of the system.

The tabulation also shows transmission to be the second largest load. This load can vary as the outdoor air temperature varies. It is zero when outdoor air and indoor air have the same temperature, and negative when the outdoor air is cooler than the indoor air. When the load is negative, heat passes from the room to the outdoors. Transmission is the only load that can reverse. The others can become zero, but none will take heat from the room.

All the loads can vary within certain limits. The sun load varies with weather conditions and seasons; the load from lights varies according to the number and wattage of units being used at a given time.

Occupancy, transmission, latent, and miscellaneous loads cannot be so readily defined. The engineer must, therefore, design the system for the maximum practical load. These conditions are called "design conditions." To limit the occupancy load, the engineer decides how many persons will normally occupy the room. For example, a hotel room might be designed for two persons and an office for three or more.

Transmission load varies with the difference between outdoor and indoor temperatures. The maximum transmission load is based on the maximum design outdoor temperature. The maximum design temperature is determined by studying weather records for the area.

The design engineer bases the system capacity on design conditions only and not on maximum possible conditions. It would be costly and impractical to use a system whose capacity is great enough to meet the demands of an abnormally hot day or an abnormally crowded room, since a larger system than necessary would be required. The oversized system would operate at full capacity only a few hours during the day or the season.

Heating Loads

During cold weather heat must be added to the room to offset the heat loss through the walls and windows. Although heat is still added to the space by occupants, lights, and miscellaneous sources, the transmission loss to the outdoors may be great enough to require additional heat. The effect of direct sunlight may offset the outward transmission load so that cooling may be necessary even during the winter months.

Since outdoor air is used for ventilation, it must be warmed in winter. In a typical system the air is preheated to approximately 50°F as it enters. Air then passes to the room after being further heated to produce the room temperature desired by the occupant. In rooms where the heat gain from sun, light, occupancy, and miscellaneous sources is high, supply air may be used without additional heating.

Size of the Heating Loads

During the winter both heating and cooling loads are present in the building. The sun, lights, and occupancy loads require cooling, while the transmission load and outside air load require heating.

The lights and occupancy loads are the same as in summer. The sun load is less on all exposures except the south. The sun, lights, and occupancy loads will assist in heating the rooms in winter. In a room without these loads, the outside air and the transmission loss remove heat, which must be offset entirely by heating.

EQUIPMENT

As is implied by the preceding review, relatively similar components are used for the same function in any of the several types of air-conditioning equipment, although they may be employed in different arrangements. Identity of the individual component or part, along with an understanding of its function and care, will best give the maintenance engineer a concept applicable to the wide variety of equipments and systems in use.

The assembly pattern of components differs in equipments of the many manufacturers. Thus, there is no fixed sequence for listing. The name of a part or component may vary from one manufacturer to another, so the more commonly used names are employed in the discussion following. Also, there are functions, such as general maintenance, that are not component parts of an equipment but are essential parts of such a treatise.

For easy reference, the function or component is discussed in order of an alphabetic listing, as follows:

Air compressors	Cooling towers	Heat pumps
Air washers	Dampers	Humidifiers and dehumidifiers
Centrifugal compressors	Drives	Pumps
Coils	Fans	Rooftop units
Condensers	Filters	Room air conditioners
Controls	Heaters	Self-contained units
Coolers		

Discussion of the maintenance of service equipment follows under these topics:

Freeze protection
General maintenance
Refrigeration
Water conditioning

There is no discussion of some items, such as electric motors and circuit breakers, for example, because they are treated in other sections of this book.

Air Compressors

Capacity. Air-compressor capacity is stated in cubic feet per minute of free air that the compressor will take in. Spray nozzles, control instruments, and other devices using compressed air are likewise rated in cfm (free) air to give a uniform rating system. Compressed air required depends upon number of instruments served, type of instrument, and the addition of other devices such as spray heads.

Working Pressure. Control circuits generally operate at 18 to 25 psi, and pressure must be uniform for results. Valve and damper motors are sized for proper relation to system only at design pressures.

Control. Most compressors are under automatic control by a pressure switch, which normally operates on a differential of about 15 psi. Normal cleaning and maintenance are needed.

Unloading. Almost all air-compressor units are supplied with a device to relieve the pressure (unload) on the piston until the motor has started and approaches full speed. Unloading is done in some units by the pressure control; in others by a mechanical device operated by centrifugal force related to motion of the flywheel.

Compressor Intake. Compressors are designed for free intake. Long pipe runs, small pipe, or any high-resistance device must not be used on the intake. If a dusty condition might be created in the compressor intake, provision must be made for adequate filtering with a low-resistance filter.

Lubrication. Most compressors used for temperature-control work are splash-lubricated and depend upon correct oil charge in the crankcase. Low oil level means inadequate lubrication. High oil level may cause carry-over of oil into the system, which is very bad for all control devices.

For general use, a good grade of automobile engine oil is suitable, either SAE 10 or 20. The compressor oil reservoir should be drained and refilled after the first 2 weeks of continuous operation. After the compressor is worn in, drain and refill after every 3 to 4 months' operation.

Operating Period. Excessive running time to compensate for a minor cooling load indicates either a leak somewhere in the system or low pumping efficiency. Logical places for leaks to develop are ruptured diaphragms, broken air lines, or open cocks. Low pumping efficiency means trouble in the compressor—probably in the valves.

Removal of Impurities. All dirt pockets, drip legs, filters, and other points arranged for blowoff of oil and water from the system must be attended on a regularly scheduled maintenance basis. All such points should be blown out weekly. One drop of oil or water can put a sensitive control instrument completely out of service

Air Lines. Lines handling compressed air to automatic control devices must be maintained tight and clean. Repair any leakage by remaking the joint. Use only a material that will not crumble, powder, or flake for pipe dope on a threaded joint. Materials like synthetic rubber or shellac—preferably a material that will set in a semiplastic condition—should be used. Flat-face unions with rubber gaskets are preferable. Sweat, imperial, or SAE joints are satisfactory with copper tubing.

Air Washers

Air washers remove lint, dirt, and other contaminants from incoming air and discharge cleaned air. Air enters the unit, passes through the fan, through the diffuser and into the spray section, where it is blanketed by water sprays. The water removes the contaminants and the washed air is discharged from the system. The water used in the washing process must be cleaned before recirculating. This is accomplished by passing the water through a strainer, where foreign material is collected and flushed from the system.

Maintenance of air-washer equipment should include the following procedures:

Cleaning. Remove lint and dirt periodically from damper blades and linkage, if so equipped. Remove all rust appearing on outside damper blades. Check fan and fan motor and remove any accumulation of foreign material. Check the entire spray section at regular intervals. Remove lint and dirt from spray nozzles and piping. Check for any plugged nozzles which could affect pressure, quantity, or distribution of water. Remove lint and dirt from drain sump and from float ball on water-level float switch.

Clean unit standpipes. Remove lint from eliminator blades by directing a stream of water between eliminator blades. Use a wire hook to remove any dirt remaining on the blades. Drain water-storage tank periodically and remove all foreign matter. If strainer is not self-cleaning, clean it weekly to insure a constant flow of water. If strainer is nonautomatic, establish the required cleaning cycle in accordance with needs. Check rubber seal and entering end of drum for tightness and remove any lint or dirt. Clean sludge collection pan.

Fan. Check fan blade angles and clearance. Adjust where necessary. Remove and dismantle fan motor periodically in accordance with manufacturer's recommendations for inspection.

Lubrication. Check fan bearings and lubricate approximately every four months with water-resistant grease. Inspect main shaft bearings of automatic strainer, if so equipped. If bearings are operated continuously under water, lubricate once a year. If operated out of water, lubricate once every three months.

Operating Log. Maintain an operating log with frequent entries to record the schedule of maintenance procedures.

Centrifugal Compressors

Centrifugal compressors are used in large-capacity refrigeration systems. Single compressor capacities normally range from 100 to 3,000 tons. The refrigerants used are R-11, R-12, R-113, R-114, and R-500, depending on the compressor type and capacity.

Centrifugal compressors consist of one or more impellers mounted on a shaft which is rotated at high speeds within a housing. Refrigerant gas entering the eye of the impeller is discharged by centrifugal force (hence the name) to the tip of the impeller at a high velocity. From here the gas is flung to a diffuser, where it is compressed and passed to the system.

Lubrication. Use only high-grade oil that meets the compressor manufacturer's specifications. Check the oil levels daily and maintain the proper levels in all parts of the lubricating system. Check the operating oil pressure and temperature regularly. Adjust these, if necessary, to meet the compressor manufacturer's specifications. Check the oil temperature and pressure cutouts at least once a year for proper operation. During machine shutdown, maintain the reservoir oil temperature recommended by the compressor manufacturer to minimize refrigerant absorption by the oil. Starting the machine with excess refrigerant in the oil will cause excessive foaming, loss of oil, and possible bearing failure. The oil should be changed at least once a year. If the oil becomes contaminated during machine repairs, it should be replaced. Refer to the compressor manufacturer's maintenance instructions before changing the oil. Care must be taken to prevent air entrance into the machine.

Bearings. Bearing maintenance consists mainly of maintaining clean oil in the lubricating system. Oil filters should be changed at least once a year. If bearing temperatures rise above normal, check the oil-cooling system and oil supply to the bearings. Inspect the bearings once a year and replace when necessary.

Oil Heater. The oil heater should be on during compressor shutdown. Refer to the compressor manufacturer's operating instructions.

Leak Testing. Periodically check all compressor joints for refrigerant leaks, and check the purge for air and water leaks. Also, check the oil cooler for water leaks.

Purge. The purge unit and its controls should be checked regularly for proper operation. All parts of the purge unit should be checked regularly for corrosion and wear and replaced when necessary.

Refrigerant. Once every two years a refrigerant sample should be removed from the system and analyzed by a competent laboratory. If the refrigerant is contaminated, consult the compressor or refrigerant manufacturer for recommendations.

Extended Shutdown. Refrigerant absorption by the oil can be minimized by proper operation of the oil heaters, occasional manual operation of the large pump, and occasional operation of the oil pump. If the machine is in an area subjected to freezing temperatures, remove the water from the oil cooler. It may be desirable to remove the oil charge during extended shutdown. *However, if the oil is not removed, do not shut off the oil heater.*

Coils

Maintenance. Cooling coils and heating coils are made with prime or extended surface tubing. Maintenance in either case is essentially the same, and involves two features—tightness and cleanliness.

Tightness. In the case of coils handling refrigerant for direct cooling, a tightness check should include inspection of all joints in the piping connections to the coil, and seasonal inspection for leakage in all return bends and other joints in the make-up of the coil. All leaks should be repaired promptly.

Freeze Protection. Coils handling water should be observed periodically for leakage and must be given careful and thorough attention seasonally to protect against damage due to freeze-up. Positive protection against damage to water coils in the outside air stream can be obtained by removal of all water or by using an antifreeze solution in the coil. Dependence upon a preheater to raise an approaching air stream above freezing is a gamble.

If facilities exist for drainage or circulation of an antifreeze solution, these positive methods should be used. Many factors contribute to make complete drainage of water coils difficult. Coils cannot be designed for high efficiency with large tubes, and small tubes will not drain completely when level. Coils cannot be designed to permit pitching all tubes toward a drainage point. Coils may be installed with tubes level and straight but not remain in such exact position. Water can be completely removed from an average coil only by blowing with adequate air volume; 150 cfm at $\frac{1}{2}$ to 1 psi will satisfactorily remove water from three 10-ft-long coils if the blower connection and air outlet are fully as large as the pipe supplying water to the coils. Blowing should be continued for $\frac{1}{2}$ hr minimum.

Antifreeze acceptable to code and underwriter authorities and in keeping with plant safety rules may be circulated with residual water in the coil and then drained off and reused for the next coil, or next season, until its dilution approaches the minimum concentration for safety. Hand- or power-operated circulating equipment may be used for this antifreeze preparation. Ethylene glycol is a commonly used antifreeze.

Cleaning. Cleaning of coils varies widely as to need and effective methods. The face of any coils over which flows an air stream containing lint, fly, rug nap, or similar fiber will require frequent mechanical cleaning of the entering side. The schedule must be developed for each occupancy, and the maintenance staff for each job should check all coils weekly until a suitable schedule is established.

Coils that are several rows of tubes deep cannot be thoroughly cleaned by brushing, vacuuming, or blowing in some occupancies. Chemical cleaning is available in such instances, and recommendation should be obtained from the water-treatment company handling the job.

Coil surfaces from which water is evaporated will become coated with chemicals left behind by the water in many localities. Evaporative condenser coils are particularly subject to this problem. The removal of some of these deposits is most difficult, and can be satisfactorily done only by removing the coil, and soaking it in a suitable chemical bath. The continued use from the time of original installation of a suitable chemical in minute quantities can prevent adherence of this chemical deposit and is recommended for use with the evaporative condenser.

The inside of coils handling refrigerants will not need cleaning unless subjected to some abnormal operating condition. The inside of water-cooling coils in a closed system will not require cleaning provided suitable water treatment is used.

The cleaning of the inside of any coil or piping system can be accomplished by suitable chemical treatment. Such cleaning will uncover all latent leaks, however, and for that reason, as well as many others, it must be used with judgment.

Air-cooled Condensers

Air passing over finned tubes of an air-cooled condenser removes heat from a refrigeration system. Condensers may be cooled by gravity or by forced-air flow. Forced-air cooled condensers are either draw-through or blow-through. Either a direct- or belt-drive propeller or centrifugal fan may be used to move air through the coil.

Maintenance procedures should include:

Inspection. Condenser must be inspected periodically; how often it must be inspected depends on usage and location. Coil should be inspected for physical damage and air-flow restrictions. Examine fan for bent blades and alignment and clearance with Venturi orifice or cutoff plate. Belt drive (if used) should be inspected for wear and proper belt tension and sheave alignment. Motor power and control wiring should be examined for tight connections and deterioration of insulation (and contacts, where possible). Ammeter and ohmmeter tests should also be made. Inspect motor suspension and support for tightness and isolator deterioration. Bearing wear and fan and/or motor may be checked by ammeter test and by listening to operative unit and by hand when power is off.

Cleaning. The condenser must be cleaned at the beginning of each cooling season and at regular intervals during the season, with length of interval depending on usage and installation location. Air-borne dirt may be removed from the air-inlet screen, coil face, and fan by brushing, vacuum cleaning, or spraying with low-pressure water. Compressed air or refrigerant gas may also be used. Preferable cleaning procedure for dry, nongreasy coils is blowing out coil from outlet face with compressed air, then vacuuming inlet face. In areas where oil and grease have accumulated on the coil, a weak solution of detergent in hot water may be brushed on to the dirty coil face. The motor should also be cleaned of any surface dirt, and vent openings should be cleaned by vacuuming or compressed-air blast. If water is used to clean coil, care must be taken not to spray motor vents. They should be masked shut prior to coil cleaning. Do not use water to clean open-type motors. Finally, clean leaves and debris from condenser base pan and clean drain holes.

Lubrication. Follow manufacturer's lubrication instructions.

Inspection and Maintenance Log. A log should be maintained to reflect unit performance and maintenance requirements. Items recorded should include unit model and serial numbers, condition of components at last inspection, and a cumulative record of inspection, cleaning, and lubrication dates and requirements. Service replacements, including dates, should also be noted.

Evaporative Condensers

In an evaporative condenser, heat is absorbed from the coil by the evaporation of water. Water is pumped from a pan in the base of the unit, passes through a series of spray nozzles, and flows over the refrigerant coil. At the same time, air enters through the inlet at the base, passes through the coil and water spray, through eliminators which remove free water, through the fan, and is then discharged from the unit.

The following maintenance procedures can reduce repair costs and improve the efficiency of the condenser.

Cleaning. Clean equipment when unit is shut down for the season. Year-round systems should be cleaned at least once annually. Air-borne dirt may be removed from the coil surface by washing down with a high-velocity jet of water or steam. *Caution: If steam is used, coil must first be pumped down.* Dirt may also be removed from coil surface with a nylon brush. Swab each coil and flush out with clean water.

Evaporative condensers are particularly subject to chemical surface deposits from local water supplies. A water-treatment program should be employed, if possible, to protect the coil from these deposits. Inspect the coil regularly to detect the presence of scaling. If coil has a deposit of carbonate scale, it should be cleaned by a reputable cleaning company. Check the surface of the condenser regularly to detect any tendency to rust. Clean off all rust spots with a wire brush and paint with a rust-resistant paint.

Air-inlet screen, water-distribution pan, and pump screen should be checked frequently and cleaned if necessary.

Fan Section. Check periodically the current input to the fan motor. Check fan belts at least twice a year. When belts are replaced, replace only in matched sets. Check fan bearings and fan alignment.

Lubrication. If pump motor has grease fittings or cups, check bearings at least twice a year and grease if necessary. Lubricate fan bearings at least twice a year.

Refrigerant Joints. Check regularly the joints of condenser piping and refrigerant-piping connections. Repair all leaks promptly.

Freezing Precautions. Evaporative condensers must not be operated with a wet coil when air circulated is below 32°F. If unit is subjected to freezing temperatures, take precautions to prevent damage to pump, drip pan, recirculating water piping, and supply piping. When unit is shut down, drain all water from the pump. Shut off water supply piping at a point not subject to freezing, and drain supply piping and coil beyond this point. Blow out piping and coil or add antifreeze to insure complete protection.

Operating Log. Maintain an operating log with regular entries to reflect machine performance. Use this log to indicate cleaning or maintenance which may be required at more frequent intervals than those suggested.

Water-cooled Condensers

Proper maintenance can reduce repair costs and improve the efficiency of operation.

Cleaning. The tubes of a condenser used seasonally, as for an air-conditioning system, should be cleaned at the time the equipment is shut down for the season. Systems that operate year-round should be cleaned at least annually. Local conditions may make cleaning at more frequent intervals advisable, but under any conditions cleaning should not be less frequent than once each year.

Cleaning of straight tubes can be done either physically or chemically. The simplest process is to swab each tube with a suitable brush, and flush out with clean water. In this method the brush selected should be of a size and bristle stiffness to remove deposited silt and soft scale, but must not have bristles stiff enough to score the metal of the tube. The materials that have high resistance to corrosion are protected as a general rule by the formation of a fine surface coating. Removal of this coating permits corrosive action until the coating is reformed. The selection of a suitable brush is therefore of great importance. Metallic spinners or other devices that may cut the tube surface should not be used with nonferrous tubes.

Another method, less effective, is the use of a water gun to drive a nonmetallic plug through the tube. Once set up, the cleaning of an average condenser requires only a few hours by this process.

Chemical cleaning involves the circulation of a suitable inhibited acid solution through the tubes, followed by flushing with clean water, circulation of an inhibitor, and flushing with clean water. Time is an important element and varies with each application. The water-treatment companies are generally able to give detailed assistance on this operation. Chemical cleaning has the distinct advantage of being equally applicable to straight or bowed tubes, or to shell and continuous-coil equipment.

Water Treatment. Water treatment should be investigated and employed where local conditions warrant its use for protection of the water circuit.

Refrigerant Joints. Joints of condenser piping and refrigerant-piping connections thereto should be checked regularly for leakage, and all leaks should be repaired promptly.

Operating Log. In many cases, cleaning at more frequent intervals than indicated will be necessary. A schedule to fit the conditions for any job can best be established by comparing day-to-day performance of the refrigerating equipment. This can be done only by maintaining an operating log. A log, to be of greatest benefit, must have entries made regularly and should include readings of all instruments that reflect machine performance.

Freeze Protection. Condensers subject to freezing temperatures must be protected against damage in winter (see Coils—Freeze Protection).

Controls

The control system is the nerve system of air-conditioning installations and must be treated with delicate care.

Good general rules for attending control instruments are: don't tamper; don't blame controls for all the ills of the system; don't permit contact points of electrical devices or delicate valves of pneumatic devices to become fouled with dirt, caked oil, water, etc., but clean them with care.

There are many control devices. Temperature-sensitive instruments are generally called "thermostats." Humidity-sensitive instruments are called "hygrostats" or "humidistats." Pressure-sensitive instruments are called "pressure switches," "differential pressure controls," "pressurestats," etc. A liquid-level control is usually a float. There are also instruments sensitive to light, time devices, and many other similar instruments.

Controls fall into three general classifications, identified by the nature of the power source:

1. The pneumatic system uses compressed air for motive power.
2. The electric system uses electric current as a power source.
3. The self-contained instrument depends upon the force of air pressure or of an expanding gas or liquid for power.

Instrument Sensitivity and Calibration. Many qualities of any type of instrument are available. For example, thermostats sensitive to 0.01° temperature change can be obtained. Instruments that will operate a power device to control temperature conditions within limits of $\pm 2°$ from setting are normally acceptable for commercial use and are obviously less expensive.

The better-quality instruments are made with sensitivity adjustments, and many of them with calibration adjustment. Frequently, experimentation with sensitivity and calibration are essential to obtain best results from a specific application.

Selection and Location. Instruments must be selected for the property that is to be regulated, should provide the sensitivity of regulation that is required but should not be more sensitive than will meet requirements, and must be properly located. The location at which an instrument is to be used establishes its form. Devices that are to be used on the side of a duct, for example, usually are made with a stem for projecting through the wall of the duct. Instruments that are to be used on a wall are arranged for so mounting and usually are finished for better appearance than instruments to be used at the apparatus.

Control Motors. Motors that operate dampers or valves or other devices to create a change in conditions are also part of a control system. These are available to fit the three general types of systems—pneumatic, electric, or self-contained.

Change-over. Since an instrument may be required to do one thing in summer to accomplish a change in conditions and something entirely different in winter to accomplish the desired result, it is common for many instruments to be made with a change-over provision. In pneumatic instruments this may be accomplished by a change in pressure. In electrical instruments it may be a small change-over relay.

Recommendation. The variety of controls is so great, their parts are so delicate, and their operation is so complex that the maintenance engineer should obtain expert help from a competent local controls company.

Coolers

Types. Shell-and-tube and shell-and-coil coolers require essentially the same attention as similar condensers. A cooler may be used on a completely closed circuit where the water introduced to the system is for make-up only. In this case, and with suitable treatment applied to the water, it may be unnecessary to clean cooler tubes with the frequency specified for condensers. An annual inspection of the condition of tubes is nevertheless warranted and should be made to detect any tube weaknesses for correcting in advance of failure.

Coolers supplying water to an open spray should receive the same maintenance attention as recommended for condensers (see Condensers).

Insulation. Coolers are insulated, and care should be exercised to keep this covering in good repair.

Cleaning Inside Shell. The design of some coolers is such that refrigerant is inside the tube and water is circulated through the shell. The water circuit is subject to fouling in this instance, as explained above. This type of cooler is seldom used on an open-spray system, so generally speaking, the cleaning requirements are nominal. The inside of the shell can be cleaned chemically when conditions necessitate cleaning. The water-treatment company handling the job should be able to recommend suitable procedure.

Refrigerant Joints. Joints of coolers and the refrigerant-piping connections should be checked regularly for leakage and all leaks repaired promptly.

Control. Control of the direct-expansion coolers used with reciprocating compression is generally by thermal-expansion valve. Once the valves are adjusted to job conditions, they should not be altered or tampered with.

Flooded coil coolers are frequently controlled by a high-side float installed in a surge drum. This operates on essentially the same basis as any float and ball cock regulating the level of liquid in an enclosure. Maintenance in this type of equipment is nominal.

Flooded shell-and-tube coolers used with reciprocating compressors are generally controlled by a low-side float. This float with the valve that it regulates is as important to the system as a carburetor to an automobile. Adjustment is critical, and the device should not be tampered with or modified once a correct setting has been made.

Oil Return. Oil return from the flooded cooler to a reciprocating compressor is most important. Oil-return lines are normally provided. The rate of flow through this line may be critical. The hand valve should be opened to the point that oil concentration in the cooler will be kept low (as indicated by the color of liquid flowing through the bull's-eye in the oil-return line), and not open any wider than necessary to accomplish this.

Cooling Towers

Cooling towers are made in sizes that will handle the heat rejection from 1 ton of refrigeration up to several thousand tons. The larger units are designed for the specific job and usually are made up of several cells, each with its own operating components.

Towers usually fall into one of three groups: atmospheric, forced- or induced-draft. The atmospheric tower has no fan and is commonly used only in smaller sizes. In a forced-draft tower, the fan forces air through the water spray. An induced-draft tower has a fan to draw air through the spray.

Tower efficiency is related to the effectiveness of air and water contact, and needs finely divided water or a great amount of wetted surface exposed to air flow.   Large air quantities are handled.   Noise is inherent.   Operating weight is considerable. Tower site selection must take these facts into consideration, as well as the requirement of free movement of large quantities of natural outside air.

A forced- or induced-draft cooling tower is an assembly of several functional components.   A fan, sprays, motor, drive, and starter are included.   Some installations are made of an air washer, housed fan, and apparatus casing similar in all respects to air-conditioning equipment.   Maintenance for these parts is given below.

Exposure.   Cooling towers use outside air and are usually outdoors.   Protection must be provided for motor, starter, disconnect switch, and drive.   Also, the structural part must be suitable for such exposure.

Maintenance.   Steel casing, basin, and framework should be painted regularly with a good protective paint.   In some locations such painting will be necessary annually to prevent rust and deterioration.   A regular schedule should be established for such maintenance, and the time between paintings should not exceed 3 years.

Redwood will last without paint.   The life of redwood is shortened by painting all surfaces.   Painting of a redwood tower, therefore, is for appearance and should be attended as needed.   Redwood or cypress fill should not be painted.   Bolts in wood towers should be checked annually and tightened while the parts of the tower are dry.

Fans.   Fans should turn freely.   Propeller-type fans generally can be adjusted for capacity by pitch adjustment of blades.   Uniform pitch of all blades is important, and adjustment must keep power requirements within motor capacity.

Alignment and Lubrication.   Gear-driven fans require an annual check-up of alignment, of motor to gear to fan.   Alignment must be within limits of couplings, or normally within 0.002 to 0.003 in.   Oil level in the gear should be checked weekly. Oil should be replaced annually or after 3,000 operating hours, if the tower is used continuously.

Belted drives should be checked monthly, and belt tension and alignment kept in proper adjustment.   Belts must not be tight enough to impose undue bearing load, but must be tight enough to avoid slipping (see Drives).

Water Distribution.   Water distribution must be checked and kept uniform. Gutter distribution must be checked for obstruction.   Spray distribution must be checked for clean spray nozzles and designed working pressure.   Most cooling-tower sprays (where fill is included in the tower) operate at approximately 3 psi.

Eliminators.   Eliminators must be kept free from algae growth and in good repair. Metal eliminators should be cleaned and repainted annually.

Algae.   Algae growth should be cleaned from all parts of the tower, and water treatment put into use to prevent regrowth and to protect pipe and equipment.

Cleaning.   The water basin should be drained and hosed out weekly.   The strainer should be checked and a regular routine established for cleaning after the frequency of need for cleaning has been determined.

Water Level.   The float valve should be adjusted to maintain the water level high enough in the basin to prevent serious vortex at the water outlet, and the supply must be adequate to make up the loss due to evaporation and drift.

Winter Protection.   The basin and all piping, valves, etc., exposed to weather conditions must be drained for shutdown during freezing weather.

Dampers

Automatic Dampers.   Dampers that are opened or closed by a motor are called "automatic dampers."   They are usually under automatic control.   Sluggish response to command of the controlling instrument means poor regulation of conditions.

Maintenance.   For good results all operating parts of the control system must move in proper relationship.   It is important to lubricate and maintain damper adjustment.   All automatic dampers should be checked for freedom of movement and lubricated at bearing points.   Surplus oil should be wiped off.   Blades should be checked in closed position to be sure that all close tightly, and adjustment should be made to the linkage to close any open blades.   Operating motors should be observed through an operating cycle to check defects.   The damper-motor anchorage should be checked and verified.

Relief Dampers.   A large quantity of outside air is used for conditioning some buildings during certain seasons.   This will build up the pressure inside the building to interfere with distribution, and make the opening and closing of doors difficult. Relief dampers are installed to prevent this pressure build-up.

Relief dampers made up of a series of lightweight aluminum blades are provided in some buildings.   The purpose of these dampers is to permit passage of excess air from the building.

Maintenance.   Trunnion bearings, unless of the oil-impregnated type, should receive a film of light machine oil (with all surplus wiped away) each spring.   Blades may become bent or warped and should be checked for complete closing twice annually.

Damaged blades should be repaired or replaced.   Dirt, soot, lint, etc. should not be permitted to accumulate on blades, as this will increase weight and present an unsightly appearance.   Calking, where it is used to make damper frames tight to the structure, should be checked and repaired as needed.

Fire Dampers.   Fire dampers are installed as a protective feature for life and property.   The hope at the time of installation is that the damper will never be used.   The damper loses all usefulness should it fail in case of fire.   To be sure that the intended safety exists, each damper should be checked annually.   The linkage (with fusible link) should be disconnected, to be sure the damper will close under its own weight. Lubrication of fire-damper bearings is unnecessary; however, the presence of oil film will retard oxidation and for that purpose would be helpful.

Occasionally, a damper will be found closed due to a defective fusible link, a source of heat sufficient to fuse the link, or blade weight in excess of the mechanical strength of the fusible link.   Corrective measures are, respectively, replacement of the defective link, a nonmetallic shield between the link and the source of heat, or the use of multiple fusible links in parallel (arranged so that fusing of either one will release the damper).

Splitter and Hand Dampers.   A multitude of damper arrangements are used to regulate the distribution of air to meet needs.   Under most conditions these dampers are fixed at the time of initial adjustment and will seldom need attention unless the load distribution is altered from the original.   In some instances dampers are altered by hand to adjust for seasonal conditions.   An example is the hand-operated outside-air damper, which is normally closed to minimal position in summer to conserve refrigeration, opened during the intermediate season for the same purpose, and closed to minimal in the winter to save heat.

Drives—Belt and Direct-connected

Service Life of Belt Drives.   The conventional V-belt drive gives exceptionally good service when properly maintained.   Two adjustments are paramount—alignment and tension.   Misalignment causes excessive belt wear, imposes unnecessary load on the motor, and in many cases accelerates bearing wear.   Excess tension imposes overload on the motor and all bearings, while belts too slack wear out rapidly due to slippage.

Alignment.   Realignment should always be carefully done after a pulley is removed, and should be checked annually even though no changes have been made.   Alignment is made by adjusting the respective pulleys so that a taut chalk line touches both edges of the rim of both pulleys simultaneously.   Increasing belt tension causes all motors to assume an out-of-line position.   This must be corrected.

Tension.   A generally applicable rule for correcting tension is difficult to state. The aim should be to run the belts with just enough tension to avoid slippage either at start or during operation.   One method is to loosen the belts just to the point where slippage occurs at the start (usually evidenced by belt squeal), then tighten just enough to eliminate the slippage.

Adjustable Pulleys. Some driver pulleys are arranged for adjusting the width of the slot, which changes the pitch diameter (the diameter of the line of contact between pulley and belt) to change the speed of the driven pulley. In some multigroove pulleys, it is not possible to keep all faces of the slots in line because of the width changes mentioned. In this case the misalignment should be divided so that the center line of the two pulleys is in exact alignment.

Replacement. Minor variation occurs in the manufacture of V belts, which has led to the practice of selection of matched belts for any multibelt drive. As belts are used, they stretch; however, the stretch is about equal for each belt. The result is a pretty well matched set of belts for the life of the drive. Replacement must be made by replacing a complete set of belts.

Couplings in Direct-connected Drives. All direct shaft couplings must be kept in alignment. All direct-connected equipment should be carefully checked each year for alignment.

Only general rules can be given for alignment because all equipments have individual characteristics. But generally, all direct-connected equipment should be in exact alignment when operating at normal full-load conditions, and after having operated long enough to rise to full operating temperature. Allowance must be made for load variation, dimensional variation due to expansion from increased temperature, and any other condition that can alter the relationship of driver and driven equipment.

Rigid couplings will need little attention beyond maintenance of alignment. Some couplings depend upon the flex of a diaphragm for flexibility and require little attention beyond maintenance of alignment and tightness of assembly.

Flexible couplings must be kept in alignment as indicated and must be lubricated in accordance with the manufacturer's direction. Some of these couplings are oil-lubricated, and others are grease-packed. In the absence of detailed instruction, replace with the same lubricant used in the original application.

Fans

Capacity. Fan capacity is measured in cubic feet per minute (cfm). Fans are selected to deliver the required capacity at the operating pressure required for delivery through the distribution system. Any increase in the operating pressure on a fan reduces the capacity. The fan handles more air as the operating pressure is reduced. The horsepower required increases as the cfm increases.

The frictional resistance to air flow which occurs in the outside air intake, coils, filters, washer, duct, etc., combine to fix the operating pressure of the fan. It will be evident that any increased resistance, such as dirty filters, dirty coils, or restriction of any kind, will reduce the air quantity. Any major reduction in operating pressure may overload the motor by permitting the fan to handle more than rated capacity. Some fans are protected from overloading by features of design, but many are not. Operation of the system with filters out, with access doors standing open, with outlets removed, or under similar conditions may cause overloading of the motor. When it is necessary to operate under any such conditions, the motor should be observed frequently for overheating.

Cleaning. In many locations, fine dust particles find their way into the fan and cling to the blades of the wheel. This should never be allowed to build up, as it will increase operating costs by lowering efficiency and by disturbing the balance of the fan wheel. Fan wheels should be checked as often as operating conditions warrant. Under many conditions the entire inside of the fan should be cleaned and repainted annually.

Bearings. The larger housed fans are normally provided with pillow block, sleeve, or ball bearings. Bearings on these fans are almost all self-aligning. The sleeve bearings are ring-oiled. Ball bearings are generally grease-packed, and provide a means for introducing grease.

The bearing liners of the sleeve bearings are split for ease in assembly and are supported by a ball-and-socket assembly. In the replacement of the bearing assembly, care must be exercised to avoid distorting the bearing shell by overtightness of the ball-and-socket adjustment screw.

Should oil be drawn from the bearings, and lubrication instructions have been followed, the felt retainers and slingers should be examined by removing the top housing of the bearing and replacing worn seals.

Direction of Rotation.   Most housed fans will deliver some air when running in the wrong direction.   The quantity will not be up to requirements and the fan efficiency will be very low.   Changes in power source may reverse the motor rotation.   The operating staff should observe and check direction of rotation occasionally.

Adjustment of Wheel in Housing.   The position of the fan wheel with respect to the inlet is important for efficiency and noise.   As a general rule, operation as close as possible without actual striking is the correct position.   On unitary equipment with multiple-fan wheels on a common shaft, care must be taken to adjust the position of bearings to avoid striking, as the assembly is designed to operate with close tolerances.

Alignment.   Alignment of fan and motor as outlined under Drives is important and should be checked.   All bolts in equipment and foundation should be checked annually for tightness.

Lubrication.   Babbitt sleeve bearings in normal room temperatures use a high-grade automobile engine oil, SAE 20.   Bronze sleeve bearings in normal room temperatures use a high-grade automobile engine oil, SAE 40.   Do not use detergent oils. When located in an area of high temperature or when handling air at temperatures over 150°F, special consideration must be given the selection of oil.   The local oil companies will select a suitable lubricant for unusual conditions.

Ring-oiled sleeve bearings have a level indicator and oil-filter cup located on the side of the shaft where rotation is downward.   This cup should be filled to within $\frac{1}{8}$-in. of the top (not overflowing) when the fan is shut down.

Oil should be drained and replaced with fresh clean oil after 2,000 hr operation. If the oil removed is very dirty, the bearing and well should be flushed out with a light machine oil before new oil is added.

Grease-lubricated bearings should be filled with a good grade of soda-base grease at fixed intervals.   Under normal circumstances, grease should be added after 1,200 to 1,500 operating hours.   The bearing should not be overfilled so that the grease retainer felts are forced out, and all excess grease and accumulated dirt should be wiped away.

Vortex Dampers.   Some fans are equipped with special dampers (called "vortex dampers") at the fan inlet.   These dampers are made up of many operating parts, and when used are generally under automatic control.   It is most essential that all moving joints of these dampers be carefully and thoroughly lubricated—at least once each month.   Observation may indicate the need for more-frequent maintenance attention under severe conditions.

Filters

Purpose.   A porous material through which a fluid stream passes for removal of solid particles is called a filter.   Filters used in the air stream are called "air filters"; in the water stream, "water filters," etc.   A filter is used for the very purpose of getting dirty.   The more completely the dirt is removed, the more efficient is the filter.   The more dirt removed by the filter, the greater the need for it.   Filters simply must be cared for, and attended to regularly.

Types.   There are four general types of air filters:

1. The cell type where the filtering medium is thrown away when dirty, and a clean medium installed.
2. The cell type where the medium is cleaned cell by cell and reused.
3. The continuous cleaning type, where some mechanical means is provided to remove dust accumulation from the filtering medium.
4. The electrostatic filter, where dust particles are charged electrically and accumulated on a plate of opposite electric charge.

Examples of the throw-away cell type are the spun-glass mats contained in cardboard frames. Similar cells are made using paper, steel wool, brass wool, or the mats of steel wool without the paper frame. There are also the cells where a heavy porous paper is stretched over a suitable frame. In the latter, paper replacement is furnished in rolls and used as needed to recover the frames.

The cleanable cells are made in variety. A common one is the metal mesh included in a metal frame, which is washed when dirty and recharged with a "sticky" surface by dipping in suitable oil. There are also cleanable cells where a water hose is used for washing down.

An example of the continuous-cleaning type is a series of overlapping perforated plates moving as a belt over upper and lower drums. The assembly is moved slowly by a ratchet mechanism. The lower drum is mounted in a tank of special oil. Each plate is released with a snap into the oil bath, where accumulated dust is washed away.

When to Clean. Commercial filters have a great holding capacity and restrict air flow a relatively constant amount for a fairly long period. Beyond this period resistance to air flow builds up rapidly. Observations of operating conditions at different seasons of the year will indicate the rapidity with which the filter collects dust. From those observations, a regular schedule should be established for attention to filters. A draft gage will show when filters need attention. A gage may be permanently installed at each filter bank or a portable unit may be connected to outlets provided for checking.

Cleaning Procedure. Throw-away cell-type filters anticipate the use of new cells for replacement when dirty. A supply of spare replacements should always be on hand. Many applications use two layers of throw-away cells in series to air flow. Some economy may be effected by replacement of the cells on the air-leaving side with new cells, and reuse of the cells from leaving side on the entering side.

Paper should be replaced on that type of cell when dust has accumulated to build up resistance.

Installations using cleanable oiled cells are usually provided with spare for cells and dipping tanks. Dirty cells should be thoroughly washed with a strong solution of washing soda, allowed to dry, dipped in an oil bath, and drained for several hours before reuse. The oil used is special and should be obtained from the filter manufacturer. *Do not use lubrication oils for coating filters of any kind.*

Cells designed for hose cleaning should be maintained in full accordance with manufacturer's directions. Satisfactory results depend upon careful adherence to routine as established for each job.

The continuous-cleaning filter requires routine removal of sludge from the oil basin, oiling operating motors annually, and greasing of the chain drive as determined by examination. Oil must be added as needed to maintain the level at the indicated point. Use only an oil recommended by the filter manufacturer. *Do not use lubricating oil for replacement.* The filter must be put into operation at least 12 hr before the fan is started so that the filter grid will have time to complete one circuit through the oil bath. The filter should not be turned off overnight or for week-end shutdown.

Electrostatic filters require careful adjustment and maintenance. The manufacturer's written instructions should be followed explicitly. Do not undertake adjustments of the filter without a full understanding of needs. Do not interfere with protective features like the disconnect and manual-reset switches, or the time element on the opening devices of access doors. These are provided for protection from the high electrical potentials at which the filters operate. Cleaning is important and is usually done with a water hose.

Oil and Water Filters. Oil filters of the multiplate or felt-on-wire frame type may be used in circuits of oil or water. This multiplate type is equipped with a lever for rotating alternate plates to clean the strainer. Conditions will vary for each job, and only direct observation can determine frequency for routine attention to these filters. As a starting procedure, the filters should be checked weekly, and the operating lever turned several revolutions to dislodge and collected dirt from the surface of the plates. Operating levers should not be forced, as this will injure the plates and wreck the filter. Cleaning must be done at intervals frequent enough to make forcing unnecessary. Should a filter become so fouled as to need forcing, it should be dismantled and manually cleaned.

The felt-cartridge type of filter, like those commonly used on the oiling system of the automobile, will often be found in liquid circuits. A spare unit should be on hand, and general instructions followed in the establishment of regularly scheduled attention and maintenance.

Many filters are sized to handle only part of the liquid flow through a circuit. The result is the same as using a larger filter, as all of the liquid will eventually pass through the filter. It is common practice to install line and bypass valves as part of such an assembly. The operator must avoid undue restriction of flow; however, the valve in the main liquid line must be throttled enough to give the same friction loss through the valve that exists through the filter.

Heaters

Heating Coils. Lightweight coils with extended fins outside are used for almost all air-conditioning heating purposes. These coils usually are encased in a galvanized metal casing that can be fitted into the equipment or duct work. They are made in standard sizes and many different forms. For certain applications, they must be designed so that stratification does not occur. Stratification means that the air passing over one section of a coil may be heated more than over other sections. Also, coils that are to be used exclusively in air that is above freezing temperatures may be less expensive in construction than coils that are designed against freezing.

Nonfreeze coils in current use are almost always in outside air. The construction of these coils is such as to get the condensate out of the coil before its temperature is reduced to the point of freezing.

While it is important to pipe all coils correctly for condensate removal and to avoid the trapping of air in the coils, greater consideration must be given the quick removal of condensate from preheaters.

Where the automatic control of temperature is included, heaters normally work on steam pressures of not more than 10 lb. Light-weight heaters, however, are designed for high-pressure steam, and especially for industrial plants having high-pressure steam available. This provides an economical approach for space heating.

Expansion provisions must be included in the piping to avoid imposing stresses beyond the strength of modern coils, and this becomes of increasing importance as the steam pressure employed goes up. For heaters that are used in outside air, even of the nonfreeze type, it is of very great importance that the steam pressure be maintained under all conditions. Even a five-minute period when freezing outside air is passing over the coil is sufficient to condense enough subpressure steam to burst the tubes in the heater.

Coil Maintenance. See Coils.

Water Heaters. Two types of steam water heaters are in current use. One is a shell and tube unit. Steam is usually supplied to the shell side, while water is circulated through the tubes. Where these heaters are used on closed water circuits and suitable water treatment is employed, the principal maintenance requirement will be observation and repair of leaks. Where the water circulated through the heater is used in open spray, seasonal cleaning of the water circuit through the heater is recommended.

Control of the output from this type of heater is normally accomplished by regulating the amount of steam admitted. However, a heater-bypass arrangement for a controlled quantity of water may be used in some applications. Examination of the physical plant will reveal the type of control needed and enable the operator to service it as required.

The other general type of steam water heater is arranged for the admission of low-pressure steam directly into a water stream. Maintenance is normal except that the valves for control of the steam admitted to the unit must be kept in first-class order.

The steam line to the heater unit must be closed when water is not flowing through the heater to avoid an open end on the steam line.

Electric heaters are designed for use in either air or water. In either case the heater must be loaded before current is applied. In the case of air heaters, it is necessary to establish an air flow over the heater before the current is turned on, which is generally done by electrically interlocking the fan motor and heater circuit. Maintenance includes keeping the contact and working parts of relays in good working order, cleaning heater elements, and replacing burned-out elements.

Electric water heaters usually depend upon immersion for load. Sometimes the heater control can be electrically interlocked to the water-circulating pump; in other cases, it may be necessary to control power input to the unit by a float-operated switch. Maintenance is comparable to the air strip heater.

Controls on all heaters should be checked seasonally for operation and for calibration.

Heat Pumps

A heat pump is a reversible heating and cooling system. Through a special four-way valve the normal cycle is reversed so that the condenser becomes the evaporator and the evaporator becomes the condenser.

Therefore, the maintenance procedure outlined elsewhere in this chapter for compressor, condenser, and coils also apply to heat pumps. Periodic inspection and maintenance will insure long, trouble-free operation. The following are a few of the recommended procedures:

1. The most important maintenance action is a regular check of the outdoor coil. Since heat is removed from the low-temperature air passing over the outdoor coil, a large amount of frost will be formed on the coil. This frost is regularly removed by reversing the cycle and circuiting the hot refrigerant gas through the coil. The coil should be checked for rapid and efficient defrost action. Poor defrost action may be traced back to the timer, the defrost thermostat, the reversing valve, the defrost relay, or wind effect.

2. The check valve normally used in a heat-pump system forces the refrigerant to go through the expansion device when the flow is in one direction and permits the refrigerant to bypass the expansion device when the flow is in the opposite direction. A slight leak in a check valve will cause a temperature drop across the valve. If the valve is stuck open, refrigerant will flood back to the compressor and high back pressure will result. If the valve is stuck in the closed position, it will tend to back up refrigerant in the condensing coil, thus causing high head pressure and low suction pressure. Pump down before changing a check valve.

3. The reversing valve is a four-way solenoid valve which, when energized, reverses the flow of gas through the indoor and outdoor coils. The valve is energized in the "Heat" position and deenergized in the "Cool" position. An open or burned-out solenoid coil will cause the valve to fail and go into the "Cooling" position. A defective valve should be replaced. No attempt should be made to repair the valve.

4. Replace air filters with new filters of the same size at least four times each year to insure maximum efficiency and air circulation. Inspect the filters every two months or as often as necessary. If the filters are moderately dirty, they may be cleaned by using a vacuum cleaner or by tapping lightly. Replace the filters with the dirtier side facing into the return air stream. The filters are located in the return air stream.

5. Inspect both the indoor and outdoor coil surfaces. If they are dirty, the surface dirt may be brushed off with a stiff brush and the dirt between the fins cleaned with a good vacuum cleaner. The outdoor coil may be washed out with water, blown out with compressed air, or brushed.

6. Inspect the refrigeration piping for evidence of leaks. Check to see that the piping does not vibrate against any surface that would cause any rattle or abrasion of the piping.

7. Clean and check the condensate drain on the indoor coil.
8. Check all wiring for deterioration and all electrical contacts for tightness and corrosion.
9. Check the fan belt on the indoor unit and adjust to a correct tightness if necessary.
10. Check the mounting arrangement of both indoor and outdoor units.
11. Check defrost thermostat for a good, tight, and clean contact with tubing.
12. Check crankcase heaters by running a continuity check at the terminals when they are supposed to be energized.

Humidifiers and Dehumidifiers

Humidifiers and dehumidifiers control the moisture content of air. These units are similar in appearance but differ in spray density, air velocity, and other details.

Many types of humidifiers are available to provide humidifying (and evaporative cooling): (1) central station spray, (2) spray heads at outlet of supply air duct, (3) devices in conditioned area for breaking water into fine particles, (4) steam spray, (5) water pans with steam coil or electric heater, (6) any spray (or spray and coil dehumidifier).

Four general types of dehumidifiers are available: (1) spray, (2) coil, (3) coil and spray, (4) chemical. Dehumidification is accomplished by chilling air to a temperature below the existing dewpoint or by chemical adsorption of air. For effective dehumidification, large wetted areas must be exposed.

To reduce repair costs and maintain peak operating efficiency, follow the maintenance procedures listed below:

Cleaning. Remove lint and dirt periodically from air dampers, fan parts, spray chamber and diffuser, controls, strainer, and eliminator. Clean the eliminator wheel by directing a high-pressure steam of water between blades. Use a wire hook to remove any foreign material which remains. Inspect all components for rust and corrosion, and clean if necessary. Inspect and clean surface of reheat coils and supply air ducts.

Lubrication. Lubricate fan and motor bearings according to manufacturer's instructions.

General Maintenance. Remove and dismantle fan motor periodically (in accordance with manufacturer's instructions) to inspect motor bearings. Adjust fan blade clearance. Inspect entire unit for loose connections and tighten if necessary.

Check equipment for carry-over. Carry-over may be maintained by adjusting eliminator seal gap, altering damper position, or changing air velocity.

Operating Log. Maintain an operating log to record equipment performance. Entries in the log will reflect instances in which maintenance is required at more frequent intervals.

Pumps

Centrifugal-type pumps are used almost exclusively for circulation through sprays and cooling coils, to cooling towers, for the return of condensate to the boiler, and for other air-conditioning services.

Centrifugal pumps are manufactured in sizes that will handle from less than a gallon of water per minute up to several thousand gallons per minute. They are also designed for operating at low heads, such as 2 or 3 ft lift, up to many hundred feet of total operating head. A single-stage pump—that is, with one rotating impeller—will handle almost any requirement in air-conditioning work.

Centrifugal pumps work best when there is suction head. This means that the level of the water from which the pump draws is above the center line of the impeller. There are applications in air-conditioning work where it is necessary to use a centrifugal pump with a suction lift. In this case, the level of the water from which the pump draws is below the center line of the pump.

The larger air-conditioning pumps are rated in gallons per minute (gpm). Very small pumps may be rated in gallons per hour (gph).

If the piping system forms a continuous circuit with no open portions, it is referred to as a *closed water system*. There is no static lift involved. If there is a break in the piping system, however, the difference in elevation between the point at which water is discharged to the atmosphere and the point at which the water returns from the atmosphere to the piping system is referred to as *static lift*, or *static head*. This head must be overcome by the pump. In addition, power is necessary for liquid to flow through a piping system. The resistance flow, measured in feet of head, is referred to as *friction head*. The *total head* against which a pump must work is the *sum* of static head, or lift, and friction head. A pump is rated, therefore, in terms of gallons per minute and *total pumping head*.

The larger centrifugal pumps are usually designed for either belt or direct-connected drive from any standard motor. Many smaller pumps and some in larger sizes are now available with the pump impeller mounted on the end of the motor shaft. This assembly is commonly known as a "close-coupled pump."

Pumps that start up with a suction lift will require priming. Once the pump has been primed or has its design flow of liquid, it will continue to operate and pick up the water from a point below its center line.

Maintenance. Pump bearings must be lubricated, and the information given elsewhere in this handbook is applicable.

Where the shaft on which the pump impeller is mounted passes through the casing, a seal must be established between the rotating part and the shell. This is accomplished by suitable packing in a stuffing box, and it is here that the average pump used on air-conditioning equipment needs most attention. It is common practice to permit the passage of a few drops of water each minute through the stuffing box to act as a lubricant between the rotating shaft and the packing. It is of great importance that pump glands be carefully packed with the correct packing and that the gland be pulled up evenly and just to the right tightness to prevent excessive loss of water or inward leakage of air, but not tight enough to bind the shaft.

It is possible to close either the suction line to the pump or the discharge line from the pump on most centrifugal pumps without causing damage. If it is permitted to operate for an extended period of time without flow of water, however, it will overheat. This characteristic of the centrifugal pump makes it easy to adjust water flow without injury to pump.

All of the nuts on the packing gland should be tightened uniformly. These should be pulled up only a fraction of a turn at a time, keeping the gland parallel to the shaft at all times.

Most pumps used for air conditioning will be direct-connected through a flexible coupling. It is important that alignment of the motor to the pump be checked regularly and carefully maintained. Misalignment will cause excessive wear on bearings and packing glands, overheating of the pump and motor, and unnecessary noise. Each time piping connections are made to the pump or remade, there is the tendency to pull the pump out of alignment with the motor. Also, large rigid conduit for electrical connections to the motor may cause misalignment. After initial installation or at the time that any connections are remade, alignment must be remade. Alignment should be checked at least semiannually.

Trouble Symptoms and Their Correction. *Note:* The *symptom* is given; it is followed by the *probable cause* (in parentheses); then the *correction* is given.

No water or not enough water delivered. (Needs priming—casing and suction pipe not completely filled with liquid.) Start and stop the pump several times. Vent air from the pump while operating. Check for plugged strainer and adequate water level.

Not enough pressure. (Air in water. Mechanical defects, such as wearing rings worn, impeller clogged, or casing packing defective. Wrong direction of rotation. Leaky suction line. Stuffing-box packing worn. Suction lift too high.) Check direction of rotation. Check for an air pocket trapped in the suction line. Replace the stuffing-box packing. Unplug the water seal. Repair any air leak in the suction line.

Excessive packing wear. (Misalignment. Shaft scored. Improper packing. Misadjustment.) Realign. Refinish the journal. Pack in accordance with manufacturer's recommendation. Adjust the packing gland with uniform tightness and allow for slight drip to provide lubrication.

Rooftop Units

Rooftop units are electric cooling units and gas heating units designed primarily for rooftop installation. When available, refer to manufacturer's instructions for inspection and cleaning procedures for heating and cooling sections. Maintenance procedures should include:

Inspection. Heating and cooling sections should be checked periodically; how often they should be checked depends on usage and location. The thermostat should also be examined periodically.

Condenser, evaporator, and filters must be inspected prior to cooling season and periodically during the season, how often depending on operating conditions. Coils and filters should be inspected for physical damage and air-flow restrictions. Examine condenser and evaporator fans for bent blades and alignment and clearance with Venturi orifice or cutoff plate. Belt drive (if used) should be inspected for wear and proper belt tension and sheave alignment. Motor power and control wiring must be examined for loose connections and deterioration of insulation (and contacts, where possible). Ammeter and ohmmeter tests should also be made on motors. Inspect motor suspension and support for tightness and isolator deterioration. Bearing wear on fan and/or motor may be determined by ammeter test and by listening to operative unit and hand turning when power is off. Inspect panels and ductwork for air leakage. Check condensate pan and drain line for restrictions.

Inspect unit sight glass and moisture indicator. If possible, take suction and discharge readings while unit is operative and check with manufacturer's data.

Inspection prior to and during heating season is also essential. In addition to items listed above to be examined for cooling operation, heating components must also be inspected. Combustion air box (and forced draft blower, if used), orifices, pilot, main burners, heat exchangers, and flues must be checked for dirt, sooting, cracks or distortion, and adjustment. Inspect operation of automatic pilot, gas valves, pressure regulator, and other heating controls (air pressure switch, 100 per cent shutoff valves, fan and limit controls, etc.). Burner alignment with heat-exchanger flues should also be checked. Check flames for proper primary air.

Cleaning. Components must be cleaned at the beginning of cooling and heating seasons and periodically as required during the season to insure efficient operation.

Condenser and evaporator coils must be cleaned at the beginning of each cooling season and at regular intervals during the season, the length of interval depending on usage and installation location. Evaporator coil should also be cleaned at the beginning of each heating season. Air-borne dirt may be removed from the air-inlet screen, coil face, and fan wheel and scroll by brushing or vacuum cleaning. Compressed air or refrigerant gas may also be used. The indoor condenser motors should also be cleaned of any surface dirt, and vent openings should be cleaned by vacuuming or compressed-air blast.

Cleanable-type high-velocity filters should be removed and cleaned at the start of each heating and cooling season, and at least once during the season. Periodic inspection may indicate more frequent cleaning is necessary. Flush dirt from filters with hot water or steam. If dirt is heavily caked, soak filters in mild soap or detergent and water solution. (Refer to filter manufacturer's specific cleaning-agent recommendations.) After drying filters, spray with a water-soluble adhesive recommended by the filter manufacturer. Drain off excessive adhesive and reinstall filters. Throwaway filters should never be cleaned more than once. Clean by tapping gently or vacuuming. Replace with dirty side facing into air stream.

Clear and flush condensate drain lines and condensate pan at the beginning of each cooling season or more frequently if necessary. For winter operation, guard against freezing damage due to residual water in the drain line. Protect with antifreeze or dry completely.

Clean combustion air chamber, pilot, main burners, and flues as required. Refer to manufacturer's maintenance instructions for cleaning of heating-section components.

Lubrication. Lubricate motors and bearings periodically, depending on usage. Follow manufacturer's lubrication instructions.

Inspection and Maintenance Log. A log should be maintained to reflect unit performance and maintenance requirements. Items recorded should include unit model and serial numbers, condition of components at last inspection, and a cumulative record of inspection, cleaning, and lubrication dates and requirements. Service replacements should also be noted.

Room Air Conditioners

The room air conditioner is a unitary equipment designed specifically for a room or similar small space. It is unique among air-conditioning equipment in two respects. It is in the electrical-appliance classification, and it is made by a great number of manufacturers.

Types. The more popular type of room air conditioner is designed with an air-cooled condenser. Since it must have an unrestricted source of outside air, it is most commonly installed on a window sill. Floor or console models are made by some manufacturers.

Application. All of the summer air-conditioning load factors must be considered in selecting a room air conditioner. A unit used in a room which is too large or in which the heat load is far beyond cooling capacity will be completely ineffective.

Units are designed for balance between air side and refrigeration equipment at nominal comfort conditions. They should not be expected to reduce room temperature below normal comfort conditions even in mild outside weather. Also, since design conditions must be based on the widest general use, maximum outside ambient temperature must be arbitrarily established. In general, room units should not be expected to operate satisfactorily with outside temperatures above 115°F.

Full voltage at the unit is essential. Almost without exception, existing wiring and power service will be inadequate for the addition of more than one or two room air conditioners.

Leakage around the unit or at any other point into the room seriously impairs effectiveness. Installation should, therefore, seal the unit well in the wall and be neatly done.

Maintenance. Air flow through the unit must not be restricted. During the operating season, filters and coils must be kept clean. Refrigerant charge in the unit is critical. A seasonal check should include a careful leakage test. The drip pan of the unit, coils, and fan blades should all be cleaned seasonally. Fan motors should be checked for free turning. The service cord and service connections should be examined.

Detailed Instruction. The manufacturer's product booklet should be followed for detailed instruction.

Self-contained Units

Self-contained or packaged units are in the unitary-equipment class. Some units are made just for summer cooling; others are made for cooling in the summer and for heating in the winter. The latter type has the widest application in residential work. Either may be suitable, however, for use in offices, shops, specialty stores, and other applications.

Equipments are available with either air-cooled or water-cooled condensers. Normally, air-cooled condensers will not be used in sizes over about 60 tons. Water-cooled units are entering the market up to 120 tons. Water for the units may be obtained from a cooling tower or other available source, such as city water.

Application. Self-contained units in sizes up to 25 or 30 tons are available in highly styled, finely finished cabinets for a wide variety of application. The larger units are normally intended for industrial use where spacesaving is given more consideration than styling or finish.

Self-contained equipments have the application advantages of low initial cost, simple installation, and very limited control.

Such equipment must be selected to handle the air-conditioning load as outlined elsewhere in this text. It is built with direct-expansion cooling and is designed for balance between air-handling and refrigeration equipments at nominal comfort conditions. Units should be selected to operate fully loaded for best economy in first cost and in use.

Installation. Self-contained equipment is styled and finished for good appearance in consideration of frequent use in the occupied space itself. For this same reason, units are designed for the lowest practical noise level. The noise factor still must be considered in determining location and installation.

Full-power voltage is essential to satisfactory operation. Power supply, line sizing, and other electrical components must receive full consideration.

Maintenance. Full air flow must be maintained. Filters must be cleaned regularly. Drip pans inside of unit, coils, and other parts must be cleaned seasonally.

The refrigerant circuit must be kept tight and the refrigerant charge maintained up to requirements. Controls must not be allowed to accumulate dirt. Burners on heating equipment must be kept in order.

MAINTENANCE OF SERVICE EQUIPMENT

Freeze Protection

Damage from Freezing. That damage results from the formation of ice inside a coil, pipe, or other enclosure is generally known. Freeze-up may occur in equipment subject to outside conditions during winter, or in the low side of the water-cooling refrigeration equipment at any time.

Freeze Prevention. Three common methods are used to avoid freeze-up from winter air:

1. Draining water from vulnerable equipment.
2. Lowering the freezing point to a safe limit by adding antifreeze to circulating water.
3. Heating surrounding air to a temperature above freezing.

These principles are in such common use that they are fully understood, so this text can serve best to direct attention to those parts of the air-conditioning equipment where protection is needed.

Precautionary measures in the design of refrigeration equipment usually include positive circulation of water before the refrigeration machine can operate, automatic control devices to hold the operating level above the freeze point, and temperature-sensitive instruments to stop the refrigerating effect (before damage occurs) should the other features prove inadequate. Any freeze-protection device should be accepted as the last line of defense, and equipment *must never be forced to operate when stopped by the protection instrument.* The reason for temperature dropping low enough to actuate the protective device should be determined and the condition corrected before the machine is put back into service.

Where Attention Is Needed. To prevent freeze-up, particular attention should be given the following:

1. Water coils anywhere in the circuit where air below 32°F may be handled.
2. Heating coils in outside air.
3. Water-supply lines and drain lines to evaporative condensers, or other equipments located outside.
4. Pans of evaporative condensers, cooling towers, and other outside equipment.
5. Refrigerant condensers, expansion tanks, and other equipment located in unheated portions of the building, such as penthouses, street vaults, etc.

6. Any and all water lines running through unheated spaces or outside the building.
7. Well pumps and water lines located outside heated spaces.
8. Compressed-air lines and air motors of a pneumatic control system in outside air intakes.
9. Refrigerant coolers of any type when cooling water or brine.

Protecting Water Coils. Preheating coils cannot provide positive insurance against freezing because they can be effective only with adequate steam supply, and uninterrupted steam supply can seldom be guaranteed. Failure of pressure for only two or three minutes (while the furnace is cleaned, e.g.) in extreme weather may permit damage.

Positive return air in sufficient quantity to heat minimum-temperature outside air above freezing, with a suitable means of mixing before reaching the coil, is reliable. But conditions seldom will permit such an over-all design.

The maintenance staff *must* investigate the freeze potential of *every* water coil and exercise the necessary precaution. For details concerning Freeze Protection, see "Coils."

Aerofin Preheating Coils. Improvement in design in recent years has provided coils suitable for use in outside air when properly selected and installed. These non-freeze coils may have the steam supply modulated through a reasonable range to permit better regulation of air conditions, but steam flow must not be reduced below a minimum point under severe outside conditions. Condensate removal must be adequate and effective. Only proven practices of piping installation should be used. Obviously, condensate lines should not pass through the outside-air path.

Water-supply Lines Outside Building. All water lines outside heated space must be completely drained. Water lines passing through an outside-air duct or otherwise crossing the path of outside air must be drained.

Pans of Evaporative Condensers. Pans of evaporative condensers, cooling towers, and other equipment located outside heated space should be drained when shut down for the season, and at that time cleaning, painting, and general maintenance attention should be provided.

Refrigeration Condensers, Expansion Tanks, etc. Any vessel containing water is an item needing attention for freeze protection if located where heat may not be provided for even a nominal period. System design may require the location of an expansion tank in an unheated penthouse; pipelines, storage tanks, refrigerant condensers, or other equipment may be placed in unheated basement spaces; equipment may be in buildings under construction or major alteration where freezing temperatures occur. Under any of these conditions, the maintenance staff must apply the general rules for protection.

Well Pumps and Water Lines. Well pumps and water lines above ground level and in unheated space must be prepared for winter stand-by. If the pump is not to be used during freezing weather, it should be properly drained and conditioned for the next season's use.

Compressed-air Lines and Air Motors. Moisture taken into the pneumatic control system with air condenses within the system, and will seek the point of lowest vapor pressure. The moisture tends to accumulate in any piping, damper, or valve motors located in the outside-air chamber. Continued build-up of moisture at those points leads to the rupture of filled parts when frozen. This problem can be successfully met by periodic blowdown of the compressed-air system (see Air Compressors).

Refrigerant Coolers. Five minutes is plenty of time for careless handling to wreck completely any refrigerant cooler. *Don't do anything to make the machine work when the protective devices have stopped the refrigeration.*

To pump all refrigerant out of a flooded cooler (as an example, for winter stand-by), it is necessary to put the regulating controls out of operation, and operate the refrigerant compressor at lower than normal suction temperatures. This is a hazardous operation in regard to cooler freeze-up and must be carefully done. Since the protective controls cannot protect the equipment, the operator must exercise skilled judgment to be sure that enough load is always applied to the cooler to offset the refrigerating effect. Water should be kept circulating and load should be added to the water. If multiple compressors are connected to a common cooler, only one machine should be operated for pump-down. If the load is inadequate to keep the water above 36°F with the compressor in continuous operation, then the compressor should be run intermittently, giving time for the water temperature to rise between

SUGGESTED FREQUENCY FOR MAINTENANCE SCHEDULE

Column key:
1. ALIGNMENT
2. LUBRICATION
3. OVERHEATING
4. BELT TENSION AND ALIGNMENT
5. BLOW OUT DRIP POCKETS AND ELIMINATORS
6. CLEAN
7. AIR TAKE
8. DUST FROM
9. FILTERS
10. OIL CHAMBERS
11. SCREENS
12. SPRAYS
13. STRAINERS AND TANKS
14. CONTROLS
15. SETTING AND CALIBRATION
16. PROTECTIVE DEVICES
17. DRAINAGE
18. EFFECTIVE OPERATION
19. FREEZE PROTECTION
20. INSPECT GENERALLY
21. LEAK DETECTION AND REPAIR
22. OIL LEVEL
23. OIL PRESSURES
24. OPERATING PRESSURES
25. PUMP DOWN
26. REFRIGERANT LEVEL
27. ROTATION
28. SPRAY EROSION
29. STAND-BY
30. SEALS
31. PH VALUE OF WATER

Equipment	1	2	3	4	5	6	7	8	9	10	11	12	13	14	15	16	17	18	19	20	21	22	23	24	25	26	27	28	29	30	31
1. AIR COMPRESSOR	X	Y	M	W		Y			S	Y	W	M	M	W	Y				Y			M									
2. AIR WASHER											•	.	W	S					S	Y	Y			W				M			W
3. APPARATUS ROOM				W															S	W											
4. CIRCUIT BREAKER OR STARTER	Y													Y	Y				Y		Y										
5. COILS								S									S		S	Y	Y				S						
6. CONDENSERS								S									S		S	Y	Y					D					W
7. CONDITIONED SPACE																	W			W											
8. CONTROLS						W	Y							W	M					S											
9. COOLERS								S					M				S		X	S	Y				D	S	W				W
10. COOLING TOWERS		M	S									S	X	S	W				M	S	S	Y	S	M					S	S	W
11. DAMPERS		S	Y											S					M	Y											
12. DEHUMIDIFIER													M	W	S				S	Y	Y			W							W
13. DISTRIBUTION SYSTEM							X	X											Y												
14. DRIVES	M		M																Y												
15. EVAPORATIVE CONDENSER		S	S										W	S	W				S	S	Y			W				M			
16. FANS	X	M	S	M					Y													X		M				Y			
17. FILTERS				Y	Y				S				X	M					M	Y				W							
18. FREEZE PROTECTION														S			S		S	S											
19. HEATING COILS																	S		S	Y	Y										
20. HUMIDIFIERS													M	W	S				S	Y	Y			W				M			W
21. INSULATION																			Y												
22. LINT SCREENS						X	D												Y												
23. MOTORS		M	S	M					S		Y			Y					Y			M					Y				
24. OPERATING CONDITIONS																			D												
25. OPERATING SCHEDULE																			S												
26. PUMPS	Y	M	S									Y	X		X				S	Y		M								S	Y
27. REFRIGERANT PIPING																					M			S							
28. REFRIGERATION COMPRESSOR	S	M	M	M									X			M			Y			D	D	D	S		W		S	W	
29. ROOM AIR CONDITIONER						W								S	S				S											S	
30. SELF-CONTAINED UNITS				M			X								S				S	S				M						S	
31. STEAM PIPING					S								Y						Y	X											
32. WATER CONDITIONING														W				W	W												
33. WATER PIPING					S								W				S		S	Y										S	W

FIG. 1-2. Suggested frequency for maintenance schedule.

runs. The operator should ask for detailed instruction before pumping down, unless he is familiar with the procedure.

The treatment of coolers handling brine is fundamentally the same. The only difference is a lower freezing temperature above which brine must be maintained.

This text will have served its purpose if the operator recognizes his responsibility. The methods of insuring against expensive damage are easily understandable.

General Maintenance

Responsibility.   Upon the maintenance engineer rests the triple responsibility of operating the air-conditioning equipment available to him to the greatest good of the people or product served, at the minimal operating cost, and for the preservation of the equipment through the greatest useful life.   He will discharge these responsibilities successfully only to the extent that he knows the air-conditioning plant and its ability to serve, and plans wisely.

Records.   Records must be established, and this can be most easily done at the time of initial installation.   These records should be maintained to show additions to the system, changes of any kind, and major repair or maintenance functions.

Planning.   Planning should include consideration of routine and emergency renewal-parts availability, tooling for major functions, and a general time schedule for attention to the many details.   A check list comprehensive enough for all normal systems is shown as Fig. 1-2.   A written plan of maintenance tailored to the individual job should be prepared and rigorously enforced.

Housekeeping.   Housekeeping is an index to the general management ability of an individual in any maintenance position.   Good, clean housekeeping is one of those requirements so simple and so fundamental that every maintenance engineer must develop habits of this kind.

Refrigeration

Definition.   Refrigeration has been defined as "the transfer of heat from a place where it is not wanted to a place where it is unobjectionable."   This transfer usually results in lowering the temperature in the refrigerated space or substance.

Unit of Measure.   The common unit for measuring refrigerating effects is "ton." A ton of refrigeration is equivalent to the cooling effect resulting from the melting of 1 ton of ice in 24 hr.   To get this into measurable units, it must be expressed in terms of smaller units and related to change in temperature or change in state of matter. The smaller unit of heat is the British thermal unit (Btu).   A Btu is the amount of heat required to raise 1 lb of water $1°F$.

Heat will not only change temperature but will change the state of matter.   For example, adding heat to ice will change the ice to water.   Adding more heat will change the water to steam.   This change of state can take place without change in temperature.   For our purpose here, the amount of heat required to change 1 lb of ice at $32°$ into water at $32°$ is 144 Btu.   One ton of refrigeration, then, is equivalent to 2,000 lb of ice times 144 Btu per lb in 1 day, or 24 hr, or 288,000 Btu.

Where a refrigerating plant is cooling water, the amount of water in circulation is known, and the temperature change of the water is indicated, the maintenance engineer can compute the tonnage of the refrigerating plant by use of the formula, gallons of water cooled per minute (gpm) times °F the water is cooled divided by 24 equal tons of refrigeration, or

$$\frac{\text{gpm} \times (T_1 - T_2)}{24} = \text{tons}$$

Where the refrigerating plant is not cooling water, the variations are too great and the computation too complex to be given here.

Types of Systems.   There are three types of refrigerating systems in common use. One of these is the *reciprocating system,* which derives its name from the fact that a reciprocating compressor is used.   The second system is the *centrifugal type;* this derives its name from the use of a centrifugal compressor.   The third common system is a fundamentally different cycle, where a cooling effect is produced with the absorption of one fluid by another; this is called an *absorption system.*   A fourth system is called *steam-jet refrigeration.*   In this system water is cooled as a result of lowering the pressure in a vessel by condensing steam.   The steam-jet system, while being entirely practical, has found use only in specialized fields, where factors such as the ready availability of steam might favor its application.

Refrigerants. A wide variety of chemicals are in current use as refrigerants. Many others have been tried and discarded during the development of the refrigerant industry. Comparative temperature-pressure relations of the more commonly used refrigerants are shown in Table 1-1.

Factors such as safety, cycle efficiency, practical operating pressures, stability, corrosive tendencies, and initial cost must all be considered in selecting a refrigerant. In general, refrigerating machines are designed for use of a specific refrigerant. However, the ability of a machine to handle efficiently several members of the family of halogenated hydrocarbon refrigerants is used to advantage in certain machine designs. In these cases, it is possible with the same base machine to obtain a wide range of tonnage by the change of power supply and certain auxilaries.

Application. First cost, operating cost, maintenance cost, safety, operating efficiency, space and weight requirements, power availability, and many other factors must be considered in the selection of a refrigerating plant.

In the smaller sizes, reciprocating equipment is the only generally available equipment. In sizes up to a little over 100 tons, first cost will normally be in favor of reciprocating equipment. Also, reciprocating equipment adapts more readily than either of the other systems to direct expansion. Direct expansion describes a system in which the refrigerant is expanded in a coil that is located directly in the air stream and thereby directly cools the air. Direct expansion has the advantages of low first cost, but does not provide the safety, flexibility, and ease of control obtained with the water- or brine-cooling system normally associated with the centrifugal or absorption equipments.

Centrifugal equipment, especially in larger sizes, and where a water- or brine-cooling type of system is desired, offers advantages in compactness, flexibility, maintenance and operating costs, and adaptability to available power supply. These machines may be driven by slip-ring, synchronous, or squirrel-cage motors, high- or low-pressure steam turbines, diesel engines, or any other type of engine. Also, the centrifugal machine is easily adaptable to ultralow temperature operation.

Absorption refrigeration cycles offer definite advantages over other types for many water-cooling applications. The machines are compact, light in weight, may use water as a refrigerant, have only very limited moving parts, and operate on low-pressure steam. Whenever low-pressure steam is more readily available or cheaper than electric power, the absorption system may offer the greatest advantages. For example, the heating-steam distribution system may be used in many cases as the power supply to an absorption machine for summer cooling. In some large industrial plants this may permit the use of smaller-size absorption units distributed throughout the plant, thus saving power-distribution cost at the installation and transmission costs over long distances when in operation.

Initial selection of equipment can be made only by careful evaluation of all the factors peculiar to the specific application.

Installation. The factors with which the maintenance engineer should be concerned at the time of installation include: Selection of the right type of system in the proper size units for flexibility of control needed; installation at location or on a foundation suitable to avoid transmission of vibration or noise to occupied areas; location with adequate space for maintaining or repairing the equipment; care in making the installation so that needless dirt is not introduced into the system; an absolutely tight system; complete drying of the refrigerant side of the system by mechanical or chemical means before introducing refrigerant; and a detailed check-out of all safety devices at the time of initial start-up.

Maintenance. The three important maintenance requirements of any refrigerating system are cleanliness, tightness, and effective functioning of safety devices. Cleanliness is important to avoid interference with heat transfer, fluid flow, and adequate lubrication. Tightness is of importance to avoid loss of capacity, loss of refrigerant, and entrance of foreign matter into the system.

Effective operation of the safety devices is important to prevent the machine from destroying itself. By its very nature, a refrigerating machine will continue to pump heat out of the refrigerated substance until a freeze-up occurs unless preventive means are applied when the refrigeration load is light. Protective devices must be understood and checked regularly to be sure they are functioning when called upon to protect the machine.

Systems using modern, high-efficiency, safe refrigerants must be free of all water. Even the small amount of water contained as vapor in the air is enough to contaminate a refrigerant and establish corrosive conditions. At installation all trace of water is removed from the refrigerating system. By careful attention to leak detection and repair at weekly intervals, the maintenance engineer should keep the system free of air or moisture.

Leaks are difficult to find in a system that operates at lower than atmospheric pressure or in which odorless refrigerants are used. This fact imposes on maintenance the obligation to establish and follow rigorously a routine check for leakage. Leaks detected should, obviously, be corrected by positive repair procedures immediately.

The most effective way available to the maintenance engineer of finding a leak in a refrigerating system is with a halide leak detector. Testing with oil or soap bubbles at joints will locate the larger leaks, but this should be followed by the halide torch method for small leaks. The halide leak detector includes a burner, needle valve, exploring tube, and chimney with a copper reaction plate. Two types of torches are in general use—one uses alcohol as a fuel, the other propane. The detector flame should be adjusted so that the top of the flame cone is level with or slightly above the chimney. In checking for leaks, place the end of the exploring tube at the joint or point of test and observe the lamp flame. The exploring tube pulls a sample of air into the burner, where any refrigerant present will decompose into free acids to react with the copper plate and change the flame color. Small leaks give a greenish tint, while larger leaks color the flame a vivid blue. A suitable test torch is one of the essential items on the tool list of every qualified maintenance engineer.

The halide test can be used only when there is one of the hydrocarbon refrigerants and sufficient pressure available inside the system. Reciprocating refrigerating systems using hydrocarbon refrigerants can usually be tested with normal shutdown pressures. The pressure will need boosting in a low-pressure refrigerant system, such as the centrifugal machine or absorption machine, or in a reciprocating system that has not been charged with refrigerant. Test pressure should be as high as practical within the working limits of the equipment. Normally, reciprocating systems can be built up to around 150 psi. Centrifugal systems designed for low-pressure refrigerants should be tested at some pressure below the condenser relief setting. Absorption systems that operate at pressures below atmospheric should be tested at around 15 psi.

The requisite pressure should be established by first introducing a hydrocarbon refrigerant such as R-12 to build up 3 to 5 lb pressure in the system. An inert dry gas such as nitrogen should then be introduced to bring the internal pressure to the desired level.

If correction of the leak necessitates removal of the refrigerant, the interior of the system should be protected with an inert dry gas such as nitrogen or dry carbon dioxide while the leak is being repaired. This is accomplished by introducing sufficient gas to bring internal pressure to atmospheric pressure and continuing a small flow of the inert gas to the system while open for leak repair.

Systems that have been open for major overhaul or leak repair should be dehydrated before being put back into service. It can normally be done to best advantage by the use of a chemical dryer, either as a permanent part of the installation or as a service device to be included as part of the operating cycle for the first several hours after return to service.

Drives, either belted or direct-coupled, must be kept in alignment. The higher the rotating speed, the more critical alignment becomes. Obviously, alignment on relatively high-speed centrifugal equipment is of the greatest importance. Also, some parts of a refrigerating machine get cooler and others hotter when the machine goes into operation. Alignment must, therefore, be correct when the machine is at operating temperatures.

Lubrication is essential to the life of any mechanical equipment. An inherent characteristic of refrigerating equipments is the tendency for lubricating oil to be diluted

Table 1-1. Comparative Temperature-pressure Relations of Common Refrigerants
Saturated vapor pressure

Number	11		12		22		113		114		500		502	
Chemical name	Trichloromonofluoromethane		Dichlorodifluoromethane		Monochlorodifluoromethane		Trichlorotrifluoroethane		Dichlorotetrafluoroethane		Azeotrope of dichlorodifluoromethane and difluoroethane		Azeotrope of monochlorodifluoromethane and monochloropentafluoroethane	
Chemical symbol	$CFCl_3$		CF_2Cl_2		$CHClF_2$		$CCl_2F\text{-}CClF_2$		$C_2Cl_2F_4$		73.8% CCl_2F_2 26.2% CH_3CHF_2		48.8% $CHClF_2$ 51.2% $CClF_2CF_3$	
Temperature, °F	Gage	Vacuum	Gage	Vacuum	Gage	Vacuum	Gage	Vacuum	Gage	Vacuum	Gage	Vacuum	Gage	Vacuum
−40													4.28	
−30													9.40	
−20		27.03	0.58		10.31			29.05		22.91	3.14		15.52	
−10		26.01	4.50		16.59			28.69		20.63	7.76		22.76	
0		24.72	9.17		24.09			28.21		17.79	13.26		31.24	
+5		23.95	11.81		28.33			27.92		16.14	16.38		35.99	
10		23.10	14.65		32.93			27.60		14.31	19.75		41.09	
12		22.73	15.86		34.88			27.45		13.52	21.18		43.24	
14		22.34	17.10		36.89			27.30		12.71	22.65		45.45	
16		21.94	18.38		38.96			27.14		11.86	24.16		47.72	
18		21.52	19.70		41.09			26.97		10.98	25.72		50.05	
20		21.08	21.05		43.28			26.80		10.07	27.33		52.45	

Pressure

22	54.91	28.99	9.12		26.61		45.53	22.45	20.62	
24	57.44	30.70	8.14		26.42		47.85	23.88	20.15	
26	60.04	32.45	7.12		26.22		50.24	25.37	19.66	
28	62.70	34.26	6.07		26.01		52.70	26.89	19.14	
30	65.44	36.12	4.99		25.79		55.23	28.46	18.61	
32	68.24	38.04	3.85		25.55		57.83	30.07	18.05	
34	71.12	40.01	2.69		25.31		60.51	31.72	17.47	
36	74.07	42.02	1.47		25.06		63.27	33.43	16.87	
38	77.10	44.10	0.22		24.79		66.11	35.18	16.25	
40	80.20	46.24		0.52	24.52		69.02	36.98	15.61	
42		48.44		1.18	24.23		71.99	38.81	14.94	
44		50.69		1.86	23.93		75.04	40.70	14.24	
46		53.01		2.56	23.61		78.18	42.65	13.52	
48		55.39		3.28	23.29		81.4	44.65	12.78	
50		57.82		4.03	22.94		84.7	46.69	12.00	
60		70.96		8.13	21.02		102.5	57.71	7.73	
70		85.81		12.87	18.68		122.5	70.12	2.64	
80		102.5		18.34	15.87		145.0	84.06		1.61
90		121.2		24.59	12.53		170.1	99.6		4.99
100		141.9		31.69	8.59		197.9	116.9		8.90
102		146.3		33.22	7.71		203.8	120.6		9.75
104		150.9		34.78	6.82		209.9	124.3		10.63
106		155.4		36.39	5.88		216.0	128.1		11.52
108		160.1		38.03	4.93		222.3	132.1		12.45
110		164.9		39.71	3.95		228.7	136.0		13.39
112		169.8		41.44	2.95		235.2	140.1		14.35
114		174.8		43.20	1.91		241.9	144.2		15.34
116		179.9		45.00	0.83		248.7	148.4		16.37
118		185.0		46.85		0.14	255.6	152.7		17.41
120		190.3		48.74		0.70	262.6	157.1		18.50

by absorbing refrigerant when the machine is not operating. Various approaches are used by manufacturers to avoid damage to lubricated parts at start-up. Since damage can occur in the first few seconds at start, it is desirable to avoid absorption of refrigerant into the oil. Many systems use a small electric heater to keep the surface of the oil in the reservoir warm at any time the machine is shut down. Other systems, especially with reciprocating compressors, are left on the line subject to control of the temperature or pressure device regulating low-side pressure, so that the refrigerant is at all times pumped out of the crankcase. Other systems include oil-refrigerant separating devices. It is of great importance that the maintenance engineer completely understand the provision for lubrication at start-up and operate the system in accordance with the intended provision.

Detailed Instruction. The manufacturer's product booklet or detailed operating instructions should be consulted for guidance in handling the specific requirements of the system in use.

Water Conditioning

The Problem. Water damage in air-conditioning equipment is an ever-present problem which varies widely from area to area, and even from job to job in the same area. Water, especially when recirculated, can be responsible for scale—which interferes with heat transfer; corrosion—which ravages the equipment; algae or slime—which interferes with performance; and erosion. Each of these actions imposes needless cost in operation or maintenance or both, and is therefore a matter that should be given the closest possible attention by the maintenance engineer.

Definitions. In general, the term "scale" applies to deposits which result from crystallization or precipitation of salts from the water.

The term "corrosion" applies to the decomposition of metal caused by electrolytic or chemical attack.

The term "erosion" applies to the impingement of rapidly moving water, particularly where entrained gas bubbles are suspended, abrasive solids are present, or where intermittent cavitation occurs, which may result in the breakdown of protective films and cause corrosion of metal surfaces.

Slime and algae are microorganisms, which are capable of multiplying rapidly, and thus produce large masses of plant material.

Treatment or conditioning of the water used in each of the circuits of an air-conditioning system is of just as much importance as the treatment of water used in boilers. The problem differs in closed recirculating systems from open recirculating systems or once-through systems. Also, because of the very great variety of waters used in air conditioning equipments, it is impossible to give rules that will apply generally.

Corrective Measures. The water that is lost by evaporation in an open circulating system should always be replaced by make-up water. In cooling-tower or evaporative-condenser circuits, for example, there should always be bleed-off water to offset the continual concentration of chemical impurities through the evaporation that takes place in the unit.

Beyond this simple dilution procedure, the counsel and guidance of an engineer capable of establishing exact conditions of the water used and recommending corrective action will be required. The maintenance engineer will best serve his employer by following in detail the recommendations of the most competent local water-conditioning company.

Chapter 2

POWER-PLANT EQUIPMENT

By Frank L. Bradley
Assistant to Engineering Manager
Stone & Webster Engineering Corporation
Boston, Mass.

SCOPE OF POWER-PLANT MAINTENANCE

The supply of steam and power is indispensable to industrial plant operation. This indispensability places a heavy responsibility on management of the power plant to insure its reliability. One of the essentials for reliability is maintenance, adequate both in quality and character. Planned maintenance, with its economy of expenditure in labor and materials, inherently contributes in a positive manner to the dependability of these services.

This type of maintenance as applied to powerhouse operations may be defined as "anticipation and prevention of performance deficiencies and major repairs through design, operation, lubrication, inspection, planning, and upkeep." A definite distinction should be drawn between upkeep and repair. Upkeep places major emphasis on keeping equipment in its original condition. Repair entails mending or replacing of broken or worn-out parts. Therefore, any powerhouse planned maintenance program should stress upkeep. With upkeep as a maintenance objective, major repairs will be widely spaced over the life of the equipment.

DESIGN

One of the most profitable approaches to preventive maintenance is through proper design. To maintain plant or equipment burdened with poor design characteristics is always an uphill struggle. Unless the design is adaptable to change or correction, maximum efficiency is only a mirage, and repair is the order of the day.

Increases in steam pressures and temperatures have resulted in improved thermal efficiencies and savings in the fuel dollar. These improvements in the generation of steam and power have been acquired at a sacrifice of simplicity in design. This makes for increased maintenance in practically every piece of major equipment. Analysis of these increased sources of maintenance will provide ample reasons for simplicity in design as an initial and effective attack on the maintenance of the power plant as a unit.

Improper design may be responsible for excessive repair costs and repair time due to inaccessible equipment locations, lack of handling and moving equipment for heavy machinery, lack of sufficient working space around equipment, and failure to provide adequate working platforms. Intelligent planning during the design stage of a power project will realize substantial savings in maintenance costs throughout the operating life of the equipment. Units designed correctly, from a maintenance standpoint, may be more costly because of wider spacing, platforms, and handling equipment. This additional first cost will be justified by the savings in upkeep costs. It will be desirable to consider the possibilities of redesign of certain features of existing equipment if changes will result in material reductions in maintenance expenditures. The first-cost obligation is met only once, whereas the maintenance-cost obligation is met continuously during the life of the equipment.

OPERATION

The maintenance budget can be raised or lowered by the results of operating practices. Attention to minor repairs or adjustments can prevent major breakdowns. The simple practice of good housekeeping psychologically conditions an operator to good operating procedures. A bearing dripping oil on the floor will not go unnoticed if the operator is responsible for cleanliness in that area. He removes the cause of leakage, or has the necessary repair made by maintenance personnel. The important point is that the bearing received attention before a major repair became necessary.

Intelligent operators can handle equipment in such a manner as to get maximum production without abuse of the equipment. Slicing a fuel bed on an underfeed stoker as is done in hand firing is a sign of improper firing practice and an indication of deficiency in experience on the part of the operator. Further deficiencies of this sort may result in other abuses and premature damage to the stoker itself. Careless backwashing of a filter or a water softener may result in undue disturbance of the bed. Relaying of the bed, a costly labor operation, is the direct result of such malpractice. The indirect damage to boiler heating surfaces from the passage of hard water through the softener before discovery of bed disturbance can be far more costly.

It is a well-known fact that excess fan capacity is a means of obtaining cheap boiler capacity. Stokers and boiler settings take excessive abuse from attempts to get maximum steam rates from equipment on this premise. A well-stocked supply of stoker parts and refractory shapes will help these fans accelerate depreciation on the steam generator. Managements demanding this type operation impose a heavy burden on the power-plant organization.

LIFE OF EQUIPMENT

Efficiency of equipment depreciates in time due primarily to poorly planned or unsatisfactorily executed maintenance operations. Maintenance upkeep extends the life of equipment and sustains its efficiency.

Equipment begins to deteriorate the moment it is installed. The operating unit invariably receives attention even though it must be routine in character. Idle equipment needs special attention with regard to method of "lay up" to protect it against unnoticed acceleration in deterioration, and to have it ready for operation when needed. Each type of equipment presents a special problem. All the vulnerable parts of the equipment need careful analysis to provide effective protection.

As the life curve of the equipment is extended, more maintenance attention is required to retain its operational capacities and efficiencies. Each minor or routine repair raises the question of extent of repair at any given time. Reversibility of parts to take additional wear, as in stokers or pulverizers, may determine the extent of maintenance work on this equipment at any given time. The use of the older equipment in the plan of operation will affect the maintenance decision. The unit used mostly as a spare cannot justify the extensive maintenance given the main operating equipment. Management looks to power-plant supervision for careful analysis of this question, and the expenditure of maintenance funds.

ORGANIZATION FOR MAINTENANCE

The organization for maintenance must be tailored to the requirements of the individual plant. In some plants, the operators do all the maintenance work except that requiring skilled electricians, machinists, and heavy machine-tool equipment. Other plants have a separate maintenance crew within the power plant equipped with all necessary machine tools.

There are variations of the above two approaches to power-plant maintenance organization, and very strong opinions regarding them. The most generally adopted setup is based on the premise that the power plant should have some kind of maintenance crew of its own. Because of its specialized equipment, the power plant cannot be adequately covered by the forces responsible for general plant maintenance. Conversely, the average industrial power plant cannot afford a power-plant maintenance crew large enough to do all its own maintenance work.

The practice of having some maintenance work done by operating personnel is profitable in several respects. A man who has done repair work on power-plant equipment becomes a more intelligent operator of that equipment. Among other advantages, it should be noted that first, the operators know the equipment and may be more efficient in its repair; second, the operators are interested in doing a good job; third, they are available at all times; fourth, on rush jobs they can work on the job through three shifts; and fifth, they know where all the special tools are and how to use them.

One operating force setup that has worked well in several plants consists of a 16-man crew divided into three regular four-man operating shifts and four men for relief and general maintenance duties. This setup makes a flexible operating group, provides for substitutions during sicknesses and vacations, and permits execution of day-to-day maintenance work.

During general plant shutdowns, strict time schedules usually are in effect. The powerhouse may be operated with a skeleton operating crew using most of the operators for major overhaul work. This group, augmented by necessary central shop labor, usually can take care of major overhauls during shutdowns. The experience gained by the operating force is invaluable.

Not only is it essential to have the right man for the job, but the right tools as well. A thorough study should be made of the particular problems encountered, and the special tools provided. Power-driven tools, such as pneumatic wrenches and power lifts, serve to save manpower and expedite the work.

Selection and Training of Maintenance Personnel

The problem of selecting maintenance personnel for power-plant work has increased in proportion to the improvements in power generation, with its complexities and its limitations in spare capacity. The reduction in operating personnel has made it imperative to follow the maxim of fewer but better skilled operators, whether the force be made up of operating crews and maintenance crews, or a combination operator-maintenance crew. Availability of equipment will be contingent to a large extent on the skill put into the maintenance operations. Therefore, power-plant management must give careful consideration first to selection of personnel, and second to adequate training.

The chief engineer should hire, or at least have a decisive part in the interview of the applicants and the selection of the man to fill the job. Selection should be made on the basis of the man progressing through operator, operator-maintenance, and future supervisor stages.

A general list of qualifications is outlined below. Modifications to these may be made to fit the special job requirements.

Education. The applicant for modern powerhouse requirements should have a high-school education, or at least, an equivalent of this in practical experience. He may augment this practical experience by supplementary educational work either through night school or correspondence school. His education should include at least a good background in general mathematics, which should preferably consist of two periods of algebra, two of geometry, and the same in general science. For ability to express himself properly, he should have a good background in English, and show interest in extra reading. While these qualifications might seem rigid for a power-plant operator of thirty or more years ago, they are essential to the applicant if he is going to have the ability to progress through the various stages, and eventually become a supervisor.

Age.   A desirable age bracket would be twenty to thirty years.   This, of course, may be changed to meet some special requirements, or exceptions may be made in the case of an outstanding candidate.   By maintaining the lower limit of twenty years, the young high-school graduate of seventeen has had an opportunity to look around, try out one or more jobs, and at least is more certain of his desires when he applies for the powerhouse work.   It also gives him an opportunity to learn how to work because, with the limited number of personnel in the power-plant crew, time cannot be wasted on the person or individual who doesn't know how to, or want to, apply himself.   The upper limit of thirty is selected for general cases because a man beyond that age is not apt to have the same possibilities for attainment of supervisory roles because of his late start in the organization.

Health.   Of course, the applicant must be capable of passing the physical exami-nation for employment in the company.   However, he should be a fairly robust per-son, with no serious physical handicaps.   Maintenance men are required to work on hard, and often hazardous, jobs.   The work usually is heavy, hot, and dirty.   During breakdowns and emergencies, the applicant may be on the job for long periods. Therefore, he must have the physical stamina to meet these requirements.

Alertness.   Mental alertness is a prerequisite for power-plant operation, to say nothing of power-plant maintenance.   The complex equipment, electronic controls, combustion controls, and other vital operating equipment requires the candidate to have intelligence, initiative, and an ability for logical thinking.   His school record may be one indication of his over-all mental capacity.

Character and Personality.   Sound character and good personality are desirable requisites for candidates in all types of work.   However, it is most important in the case of the power-plant maintenance man.   He is on his own a good part of the time and, therefore, must be in a position to observe the true condition of equipment.   He must know that failure to properly accomplish seemingly simple repair tasks can cause major breakdowns, and possibly involve the safety of others.   He must have the courage to make a complete report to management for a decision.   He must be truthful in reporting his own failures because a tendency to cover up mistakes can grow on a man and possibly lead to disastrous results for himself and the equipment for which he is responsible.   The maintenance man must work with the powerhouse operators, his foreman, and men from the central shop or outside contractors.   If he has the right type of personality he will get along well with these other people and learn much from them.

Aptitude.   There are reliable tests for mechanical aptitude that can measure this quality fairly accurately.   Some men have more of this than others.   The prospect should rank high in this characteristic.

Attitude.   Attitude toward his job is an important indication of his potential success on the job.   If he considers his job as an opportunity to learn and develop rather than simply a means of livelihood, he has real possibilities.   This type of applicant is more apt to feel that his job is an opportunity for him to work for himself rather than to work only for the company or just have a job.   He must be able to give the job all that it requires in the matter of time and effort, even though it is well beyond his actual work schedule.   This type of man is more likely to take advantage of self-development and educational programs offered either by the company or by outside agencies.

Training.   Training usually is divided into two parts, namely, orientation and job training.   In the case of orientation, all subjects such as company history, policies, safety rules, possibilities for promotion, methods used by the company for promoting, and such other general items in connection with job training are covered.   Job train-ing covers procedures or methods that affect the actual maintenance work of the powerhouse.   Training, in its broader sense, can be applied in various ways, and is continuously used by good supervisors in order to give those working for them a better understanding of their jobs.   By this method, the basic responsibilities and duties can be both understood and taught in an informal way, and the men are more apt to accept the responsibility of their jobs to their fullest extent.

Responsibility for Training

The persons directly responsible for training programs are the chief engineer and/or his assistant. The chief must be interested in order to be assured that the programs are being properly applied. The assistant is to be made responsible for their development and application. This latter responsibility also applies to all of the power-plant foremen. It is, therefore, essential that the assistant or person chiefly responsible for developing and applying these procedures be well equipped in ability to assist the foremen to apply these training procedures for the best execution of the maintenance work.

The training program should be developed in two parts: one, on-the-job training; the other, job-supplementary courses. The on-the-job training usually is a direct responsibility of the man's foreman. The supplemental courses are the responsibility, first, of management to provide these courses; second, of the man himself in putting in his own time to take these courses. If a man puts in his own time, it is a measure of his interest in self-improvement and possible advancement to a higher position.

On-the-job training by the supervisor is one of his most important functions. The importance of the foreman's function as a trainer can be gaged by the estimates of management people that training and teaching constitute 50 per cent or more of the foreman's job. Therefore, it is essential that the foreman realize the importance of training, and be able to do this job effectively. Many in supervisory jobs do not understand the principles of training. Training and teaching is a process that involves the following steps:

1. Tell a man what to do.
2. Tell him how to do it.
3. Tell him why he is doing it.
4. Show the man what to do.
5. Show the man how to do it.
6. Show the man why he is doing it.
7. Make the man tell what he is to do.
8. Make the man tell how he is doing it.
9. Make the man tell why he is doing it.
10. Have the man do the job.
11. Correct the man in a friendly way where he has performed erroneously until—
12. The man is able to do the job perfectly even though he does it very slowly and awkwardly.
13. Have the man repeat the performance of the job until he has, by a sufficient number of repetitions, acquired the necessary skill.
14. Check and review to make sure that all the above steps have been fully and carefully carried out.

All the on-the-job training programs in World War II developed one fundamental rule—"No one learns without doing." The training in industry efforts showed that very little is learned by telling a man, or by showing a man. It is not until you allow the man to learn by a number of repeated efforts on his own part that he accomplishes anything in the learning process. Therefore, it is important for the supervisor to check the man's performance in skill in a very sympathetic manner, and to make sure that he has learned the steps thoroughly. The foreman who is a good teacher usually has a well-qualified, highly skilled, and enthusiastic group working for him.

For the formal class teaching, there are available several sources of data. These include first of all manufacturer's drawings of equipment showing details of construction. The manufacturer's instruction book, with its details as to operation and maintenance, supplements the detailed drawings of the equipment. The plant operating and maintenance manual coordinates all these data and describes plant operating and maintenance procedures.

Exploded views of equipment parts are especially helpful in maintenance instruction. Photographic views of each step in the repair of equipment explain repair operations much more effectively than descriptive writing, no matter how simple.

TYPES OF MAINTENANCE

Essentially, power-plant maintenance falls into two categories: breakdown maintenance and planned maintenance. Breakdown maintenance comes under the heading of repairs as noted in the opening paragraphs of this section. It may be defined as making repairs to equipment only when actual failure occurs and making only the repairs necessary to get the equipment into production quickly. This form of maintenance is not only very expensive and inefficient, but it precludes the possibility of obtaining maximum production and availability of the equipment. Planned maintenance would come under the classification of upkeep. This may be defined as a sound, logical, tested system of maintenance to obtain maximum efficiency and availability with existing equipment. It is intended to prevent breakdowns and shutdowns through systematic inspection of equipment, adjustments, and scheduled repairs before failures occur, and thus reduce interruptions to operation.

Maintenance practices in power plants are the practical results of many years of experience of trial and error, of investigation by science and engineering, of failures and successes. Because of its essentiality to production operations, maintenance of power-plant operation must of necessity be planned.

The most important preventive practices include periodic shutdowns, thorough inspection of all equipment, replacement, and repairs as needed. These might be classified as routine maintenance, scheduled inspections and repairs, and scheduled overhauls.

The regular operating force performs the routine inspection and repair work. Because of their knowledge of the equipment and its characteristics, they are able to note changes in performance, or minor difficulties that need immediate attention. This group performs lubrication of machinery and the cleaning operations that are required, such as the cleaning of soot from the boiler-tube surfaces, air-preheater surfaces, and economizer surfaces. They remove the ash from the stoker hoppers before it does damage to the operating equipment. They do the cleaning of condensers and feedwater heaters as performance records indicate this is necessary. Under the classification of routine maintenance, they overhaul leaking valves and traps and make necessary replacements, or grind in seats to prevent extensive damage to the valve or trap due to wire drawing.

Inspections are one of the most important phases of the planned maintenance program. Made at proper intervals, they insure against mechanical breakdown. For general purposes, there are two types of inspections, running inspections, and shutdown inspections. Running inspection is that made on equipment which cannot be shut down for more-complete detailed inspection. The term "running inspection" implies that the unit inspected was operating during this inspection, or that the inspection was limited and not thorough in every detail. Units in operation can be given a running inspection to locate loose parts and check vibration, misalignment, wear, lack of cleanliness, lubrication, and poor operating conditions. Shutdown inspections are made on equipment that is idle, and involves a thorough check of all working parts that can be inspected without dismantling the equipment, including parts that are concealed or in motion during operation. Among these items are bearings, gears, shafts, collars, set screws, pins, and lubrication. While shutdown inspections are much more desirable than running inspections, the latter are important for indicating such deficiencies as vibration and lack of lubricating pressure on turbines and turbine bearings.

The determination of planned maintenance-inspection schedules depends on many factors, such as the age of the equipment, its condition, the hours of operation, and the importance of the equipment. As far as the frequency of these inspections goes, the optimum is probably different for each make of equipment, and for each installation. In most plants, insurance-company inspections are incorporated in the inspection schedule. These cover machinery and boiler equipment.

Scheduled overhauls are much more extensive in nature, and include dismantling of the equipment and all parts necessary to determine the actual condition of the equipment. Equipment covered by scheduled overhauls is of types requiring longer periods for repair and dismantling than is usual in that covered by the running and shutdown inspections. This includes such equipment as steam-generating units, turbines, and deaerators.

SHUTDOWN OPERATIONS

One of the foremost functions of any industrial-power-plant maintenance organization is to provide effective upkeep service to steam and power equipment with a minimum of interruption of service to production facilities. The growing trend to an annual shutdown period of 1 or 2 weeks duration for all production operations facilitates overhaul scheduling. When capacity in the power plant is not a factor, the work can be scheduled without undue influence on production operations.

It is equally important to accomplish these objectives at the lowest possible cost. The effectiveness of a well-organized and planned shutdown program is the best insurance for a low cost and an effective job.

The shutdown operation consists of three important parts: preshutdown work, shutdown work, and postshutdown operations. Each plays an equally important part in the total operation.

Preshutdown Work. The first step at this stage of the operation is the planning of the entire project. Work planning and scheduling consists basically in analyzing the work to be done, and then projecting the work load into the future.

Planning. Planning the shutdown takes place in two stages: preliminary and final.

The preliminary work is done under the direction of the power chief, who is responsible for upkeep in the power plant. This is essentially the job of drawing up the tentative list of equipment to be overhauled, and developing an approximate estimate of time, manpower requirements, supplies needed, and effect of equipment outage on production department activities. The final planning of the work takes place when the preliminary planning has developed a definite scope of work. This preliminary planning may start immediately after the shutdown, and continue through the entire period up to the date of the next scheduled shutdown. During this period, the master work list may be reviewed to ascertain whether subsequent changes in operations have rendered the improvements unnecessary.

The final planning of the work takes place when the preliminary planning has developed a definite scope of work. Items that are not deleted from the master list are carefully analyzed, and if they are of such nature as to require new equipment, plans are made for the purchase of necessary items for delivery well ahead of the anticipated annual shutdown.

Throughout the yearly operating period, the work list is kept up to date. This list serves as an excellent basis for planning the preventive-maintenance work which results from operating changes and suggested improvements. However, this long list also includes all those jobs that are necessarily done during the unit overhaul. This list should include such items as burner repairs and adjustments, external cleaning of fireside deposits, internal cleaning, packing of steam valves, stoker or pulverizer repairs, and items of that nature. As an illustration, there is routine repair work that may be required for the regenerative air preheaters. Past operating records and experience may indicate that a certain number of elements and seals must be replaced during each shutdown. Therefore, all the new materials which will be required are transported to the job and made ready for installation. The inclusion of these items on the master work list is based on the study of the previous unit outages, and the foreman selects those jobs which must be done.

Who is involved in the actual planning work? In addition to the power chief, representatives from the following departments are included in planning work: plant engineering, to provide for any engineering or drafting that may be required, and coordinate the sources of maintenance manpower; production, to determine the effect of shutdown on production, and make necessary production changes and report to top management; plant maintenance mechanical and electrical, to note the scope of their manpower requirements needed to augment the power-plant management personnel.

The Planning Meeting. At least 2 months prior to the scheduled shutdown, copies of the work list are distributed to all craft and maintenance foremen and other persons involved. A general meeting is then held which all foremen are required to attend. At this meeting, each item on the list is carefully discussed, and if the job is to be a major one, the method and manner of handling it are decided. The purpose of this meeting is twofold: first, to acquaint the men with what has to be accomplished; and second, to emphasize how necessary it is that each man carefully plan his work. Such planning should be based upon the premise that the entire shutdown must be handled with a minimum of manpower and minimum of time. Therefore, at this meeting, the program of what is to be done is outlined. All equipment is listed, such as boilers, turbine generators, deaerators, and all other similar power-plant equipment. An individual schedule for each piece of major equipment is prepared. A turbine-generator overhaul schedule is shown in Fig. 2-1. This schedule should list all anticipated operations to fit into the shutdown period or overhaul time allocated to the work. From this schedule and the estimates of man hours required for each operation, the allocations of manpower are made from both the power-plant group and the central maintenance shops. The schedule for each piece of equipment is adjusted with respect to the over-all requirements and manpower available. Each schedule is not meant to be a rigid timetable, since, for many of the operations, it is impossible to know how much work will be required until the machine has been opened up and its condition determined. All the schedule does is to give everyone concerned enough idea of timing so that other operations can be scheduled to fit in with this particular overhaul. The schedule also is useful in checking actual time for each operation against estimated time so that future estimates can be made more accurately.

What is needed? Under the heading of preshutdown planning comes the determination and procurement of what is needed for the various jobs. Manufacturer's drawings are obtained from the files, any necessary drawings covering improvements or changes to equipment are prepared by the design division of the engineering department, tools are listed and allocated to each job, materials and parts are procured or obtained from the storeroom. Work by outside contractors is organized and contracted for through the purchasing department. Also included are the selection and transportation of all tools and equipment needed for each job. This includes the erection of scaffolding, platforms, or special rigging, and hoists. In general, it means the completion of all possible work prior to actual shutdown so that the downtime is held to a minimum.

An excellent illustration of this is air-preheater maintenance. It is known from past experience that before any repair work can be done on this type of equipment it must be thoroughly cleaned. Operating experience has indicated that these units can be safely and efficiently water-washed as the boiler is cooling down. Therefore, when the unit is finally taken out of service, the preheaters are completely cleaned and dried, and ready for inspection and required repairs. Such a procedure is, therefore, a prominent part of the unit operating orders. There is no delay of maintenance forces on this particular work after the unit is shut down. Also, where the equipment provisions and repairs to be made require connection changes in regular operating pumps and lines, corresponding orders are posted for the shutdown schedule so that this equipment will be emptied, steamed out, and cooled down; then there is little or no delay for the maintenance forces when the unit is turned over for repairs.

During the preshutdown period, the practice of tagging equipment and parts has proved unusually successful in conservation of maintenance-force time. The more routine part of the standard repair work is properly marked by an easily identifiable tag prior to the shutdown. With this system it is no longer necessary to point out, for example, the individual valves which must be repacked, since the men assigned to the job are aware of the fact that all tagged valves must be repacked. Upon com-

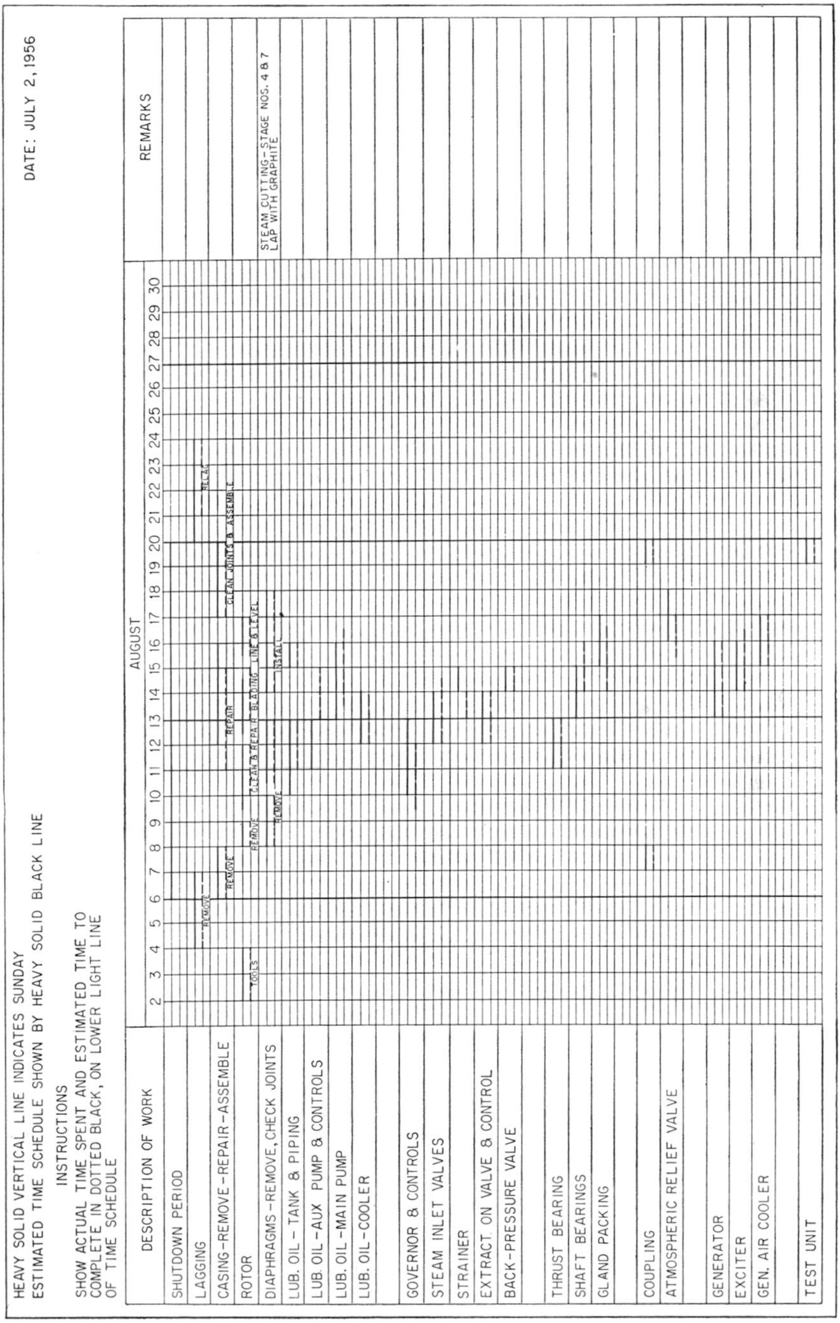

Fig. 2-1. Progress chart—overhaul of No. 3 2,000-kw turbine-generator.

pletion of the job the tag may be removed or the valve handle marked with colored paint. Use of tags is extended to cover all the major repairs, and it has been found that such a procedure considerably expedites the completion of the required work during the shutdown.

```
FORM NO.                                        PLANT _____
                   EQUIPMENT DATA RECORD        INVENTORY NO. _____
                                                LOCATION _____
   ITEM                                         REQ. NO.
   DESCRIPTION


   VENDOR
   MANUFACTURER

   ESTIMATED LIFE

   PROJECT NO.            PURCHASE ORDER NO.              DATE
   SIZE                   CAPACITY                 TYPE /MODEL
   R.P.M.                 SERIAL  NO.              WEIGHT
   PACKING SPECIFICATIONS

   BEARING DATA


   LUBRICATION DATA

   DRIVE  SPECIFICATIONS



   AUXILIARY EQUIPMENT NOS.

   THIS MACHINE IS AN AUXILIARY OF NO.
   FREQUENCY OF INSPECTION                   BY
   ITEMS FOR INSPECTION



                      SPARE  PARTS STOCK LIST
   MFG'S PART                                            MAX. MIN.  UNIT
   NUMBER                                                           COST
```

FIG. 2-2. Equipment data record.

Shutdown Work. As soon as the shutdown period starts, all of the operations scheduled by the various trades are started. The work then proceeds according to the prearranged plan. Although the preshutdown planning is extremely important to the entire operation, the greater part of its usefulness is lost unless it is followed through by daily meetings during the shutdown period, at which attendance by all maintenance foremen is required. Meetings are of short duration and are for the purpose of reviewing the status of the work. Each man has the opportunity to discuss any unforeseen difficulty which he may have encountered. It is then the responsibility of the chief engineer to shift the working hours and readjust work scheduled accordingly. By this system, the over-all progress of the job is expedited, and the situation wherein all but one item of work is completed on time is largely eliminated.

Postshutdown Work. The work allocated to the postshutdown period should include such items as are not essential to returning equipment to service. This work should cover insulation, removing of scaffolds, painting, and similar operations which can be done after the major repair work is completed and the unit is back in service. A careful record of the history of the unit overhauled should be made a part of this postshutdown work. This can become an important aid in the planning of the next shutdown operation.

EQUIPMENT HISTORY

INVENTORY NO. ________________ DESCRIPTION ________________

HISTORY OF ALTERATIONS AND REPAIRS					
DATE	J.O. NO.	DESCRIPTION OF WORK	COST		
			LABOR	MAT'L	TOTAL

FIG. 2-3. Equipment history.

RECORDS, EQUIPMENT DATA, AND HISTORIES

An equipment inventory is the basic data for any planned maintenance program. An equipment number serves as identification to power-plant personnel as well as to the plant accounting department.

It will simplify the inventory of equipment if a form is prepared with space for listing the general data and special data peculiar to each type of equipment. The suggested form given in Fig. 2-2 provides space for nameplate data, a description of the equipment, the serial number, the manufacturer's name and address, purchase-order number, lists of drawings and bulletins pertaining to operation and maintenance, bearing data, lubrication data, and other pertinent details. A record of essential spare parts should be a part of this list.

Equipment history is an important part of this physical record. Figure 2-3 is one form which can be used to keep these data. It provides for the record of repairs and changes, which includes the job-order numbers, notations or types of repairs and changes made, and the cost of labor and materials. The detailed description of shutdown repairs is a vital part of this history.

This equipment record is very valuable either for planned shutdown or in a breakdown. The plant engineer can immediately get accurate machine parts and specifications, the name and address of the manufacturer of the equipment, the purchase-order number, and the date of purchase.   Where there is a question of size, weight, lubrication, current characteristics, or other operating data, the essential details are there.

Performance Data.   The philosophy of upkeep predicates a knowledge of what equipment is capable of doing and comparing today's performance with that.   Each piece of equipment should have a performance record and the guarantee performance data set up for easy comparison with daily and periodic test data.   Daily performance records, as well as periodic heat-rate tests on equipment, serve as a measure of upkeep efforts.

Reports.   Reports to management through the plant engineer or other person responsible for power-plant performance are a means of putting the record of power-plant maintenance and performance before management.   Usually once a month is frequent enough, with perhaps a special report at the end of the year.   These monthly reports from the chief power engineer serve to provide the plant engineer with information upon which to base his report to top management.   Management wants information on where the maintenance manhours were spent, the amount of overtime, jobs completed, estimate variances, and the hours of work of each craft.

These reports can take the shape of simple forms and charts, as well as tables of data and descriptive matter.   This type of report makes an easy understanding of the maintenance performance.   Usual situations affecting performance should be shown or explained so that top management will better understand the maintenance problems.   Many maintenance difficulties stem from the lack of understanding on management's part, and inability on the maintenance supervisor's part to get the point across. A periodic report to management will be read if it is brief and contains the kind of information that is wanted.   An efficient, brisk report creates an impression of an efficient maintenance organization, which is just about the first thing needed for management's backing and support.

Any report if at all lengthy because of amount of data and information included should be accompanied by a letter or memorandum of transmittal, summarizing the findings and conclusions of the main report.   It should contain a brief statement of the purpose of the report and the importance of the problem to management.   A short description of the solution and cost estimates are necessary.   Recommend action and ask for authorization to release the work.

PRINCIPAL EQUIPMENT TROUBLES

Fuel Preparing and Burning Equipment

Coal Bunkers.   Among the various factors that influence the maintenance of coal bunkers are shape of bunker, materials used in construction, sulfur in coal, internal moisture in coal, and mixture of different coals.

A bunker shape which permits pockets or dead areas increases difficulty of complete evacuation of the coal.   This condition causes spontaneous combustion and attack from corrosion.   The presence of moderate amounts of sulfur is sufficient for slow corrosive action.   High-sulfur coals that also retain large percentages of adherent moisture will accelerate this action.   While coal bunkers have been built of tile, reinforced concrete, stainless-steel-clad plate, carbon-steel plate, copper-bearing steel plate, and steel plate with various forms of acid-resisting linings, it is safe to assume that most steel industrial power-plant coal bunkers are made from carbon-steel plate because of the more economical cost of this construction.

Whenever unlined carbon-steel plate is used, a periodic check must be made to determine the extent of the corrosion.   Various forms of bitumastic paints are helpful in retarding this action.   However, a most effective protection is gained by the use of acid-resistant linings, such as gunite with acid-resisting cements, bitumastic linings troweled on, and rubber-coated surfaces.   This latter application is contingent on securing a good clean surface for the rubber lining to adhere to.   The use of any linings should be resorted to only if there is sufficient remaining thickness in the bunker plate to give a safe construction.   This latter factor will be influenced by the shape of the bunker itself.   Coal fires in bunkers are not only dangerous to personnel, but destructive to the bunker and coal-preparatory equipment. This hazard should be dealt with promptly. Steam or carbon dioxide may be piped in directly to the top of the bunkers. This is more effective in totally enclosed bunkers than in open bunkers. However, effective and prompt steps to evacuate all the coal in the affected bunker is the most direct approach to overcoming this hazard. Hot coal should be run through the fuel-burning equipment until the bunker is empty. No raw coal should be discharged into the bunker until all the burned coal is removed. During this process all fuel-handling equipment should be watched closely. The pulverizer or pulverizer feed, if either stops, should be investigated promptly to determine the cause of the stoppage. All valves in connection with the pulverizer should be closed to prevent a draft through the pulverizer. After it has been determined that there is no fire present in the pulverizer, the unit should be placed in service again until the bunker is empty. In connection with stoker-fired units, a continuous flow to the stoker hopper should be maintained so that the chute is sealed, thus preventing an air flow back into the bunker.

Preventive measures are the most effective means of reducing the hazard of coal bunker fires. While it depends on the type of coal, it is generally found that coal should not be kept in the bunker longer than 6 weeks. This turnover period can be determined for each type of coal that a particular plant may be using. Usually, the hand temperature on the coal chutes will be a fairly effective indication of increased temperature in the bunkers.

Coal Chutes. Coal chutes from bunkers to pulverizers or to stokers are a maintenance expense and source of operating difficulties in most industrial plants. These difficulties stem from the use of carbon-steel plate as a material, and in design of the ducts themselves. When bituminous slack is burned and this coal is wet or contains excessive fines or ash, there are frequent stoppages of the flow to the fuel-burning equipment because of coal sticking in the pipes. The corrosive action of the sulfur on the coal chutes aggravates this sticking condition. Chutes made of steel usually have a life of approximately 6 to 8 years. Stainless-steel construction is essential where slack coal with high moisture content is being handled.

The chute should follow the shortest possible path from the bunker to the fuel-burning equipment. It should be tapered or uniformly enlarged as it continues toward the fuel-burning equipment. Where two or more pipes converge into a single pipe, a breakaway section should be used to help the passage of the coal.

The stainless-steel construction shown in Fig. 2-4 includes stainless-steel sheet of $\frac{1}{8}$-in. thickness on all round ducts. On the larger flat panel and spots where there was impact from dropping coal, the thickness was increased to $\frac{3}{16}$ in. Experience indicates that greater stainless-steel thickness is not required for corrosion or abrasive resistance, and that there is sufficient strength and rigidity in this type of construction. If it is necessary to make a design having large flat surfaces, or rectangular ducts, the stainless-steel plate of the $\frac{1}{8}$-in. thickness can be reinforced by mild-steel angles applied to the exterior of the duct. The interior surfaces of the ducts become highly polished from the action of the coal. Frequent inspections show no indication of corrosion or erosion. Any loss of wall thickness that may have occurred is not measurable by ordinary means. In these installations, in so far as can be determined by visual inspection, major repairs or replacements will not be required in the immediately foreseeable future.

In one installation using stainless steel to replace $\frac{1}{4}$-in. thick plate where mild-steel ducts were used, it was found that the $\frac{1}{8}$-in. stainless-steel, type 304, was satisfactory, using mild-steel construction for the flanges. With these modifications, the installed cost with stainless steel was only 15 per cent greater than with full-thickness mild steel.

Pulverized-coal Equipment. Pulverized-coal firing has some definite advantages due to high thermal efficiency, flexibility in operation, and reduction of labor costs. As a result, in the last 20 years it has had a marked increase in use for industrial plants for both power and process steam generation. The three basic principles used for grinding coal are impact, attrition, and crushing. The four commonly used pulverizers are the ball, impact, ring-roll, and ball-race types.

In the early stages of pulverized-coal firing, the bin system was the one predominantly in use.   However, with the development of equipment for direct firing that could match the reliability of the bin system, the direct-firing system was adopted,

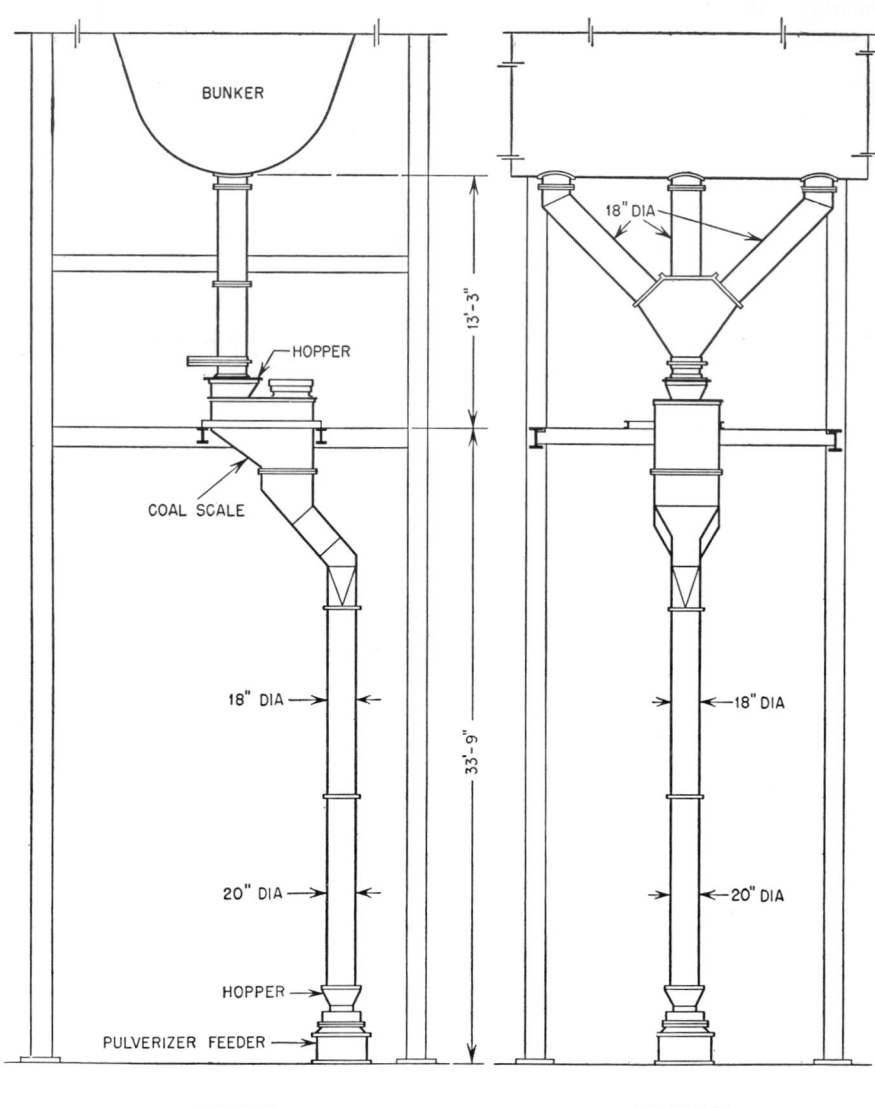

SIDE VIEW   FRONT VIEW

FIG. 2-4. Stainless-steel coal chute.

not only by industrial users, but also by utilities.   The components of the direct-firing system are, in general: (1) an air heater, to supply hot air through the pulverizer for drying the coal as it is pulverized; (2) a pulverizer fan, known as the "primary air fan," arranged either as an exhauster or as a blower; (3)) the pulverizer, arranged to operate under suction or pressure; (4) an automatically controlled raw-coal feeder; and (5) coal and air conveying lines to the burners.

Pulverized-coal Feeders. The maintenance of the pulverized-coal feeder is not a big factor. Both the table and roller-type feeders are usually slow-moving units. The drive is simple, rugged, and capable of long periods of operation. Proper lubrication of bearings and drive gears comprises the principal maintenance operations required.

The operating parts are readily visible, or the unit is provided with doors in the housing for inspection or access for repair to moving parts. The coal flow through the hopper of the feeder supplying coal to the pulverizer may be improved by use of a stainless-steel lining. Take a 16-gage stainless-steel cone, fit it snugly to the inside of the existing steel hopper, and hold it in place by forming around the outside edges of the hopper. Experience with this type of lining has indicated complete elimination of choking in the outlet of these hoppers.

Pulverizers. The ball mill, or "tube mill," is a horizontally rotating cylinder filled to a little less than half with a charge

FIG. 2-5. Exhauster blades. (*Courtesy of Riley Stoker Corp.*)

FIG. 2-6. Ball-tube-mill interior showing pickup tube. (*Courtesy of Riley Stoker Corp.*)

of mixed-size steel balls. The interior is fitted with cast-iron liners, and it is rotated at relatively slow speeds of 20 to 30 rpm. The balls are carried over halfway up the periphery, and cascade toward the center. Coal intermingles with the balls and is pulverized in the cascading process. Hot air passing through the cylinder dries the coal and removes the fines.

Maintenance on a ball mill is characteristically low, and this combined with careful operation will result in excellent over-all performance. Items of operation to watch are:

1. Maintain correct ball charge.
2. Maintain mill discharge temperature at 175°F.
3. Maintain correct coal level in mill.

These factors all combine to keep the coal fineness up to standard, which will in turn decrease wear from coarse coal particles and improve furnace conditions.

Of equal importance with regard to corrective maintenance and scheduling work for annual outage are the following items:

1. An inspection schedule should be established and should include such items as exhauster blades and liners, mill liners, and wear on coal valves and lines.
2. Photographs taken during inspections and shutdowns, with the tonnage and operating hours recorded, will be very helpful in predicting the useful life remaining in pulverizer parts. Figure 2-5 shows exhauster blades with two years' operation.

Photographs are useful in making comparisons, as shown in Fig. 2-6.   This photograph shows a higher ball level in a ball mill.   The gain in ball level during the second year of operaticn indicates a reduction in the rate of adding balls.   The level in these mills should be at the liner ring.   Excessive balls cause an increase in wear, excessive power consumption, and resulting high total costs.

3. The importance of a rigid lubrication schedule cannot be overemphasized.   One operator on each shift should be responsible for all lubrication and the general condition of equipment.

Maintenance of the ball level is essential in order to maintain capacity and fineness. A regular schedule of adding balls should be established based on tons of coal ground. This rate should be adjusted as the ball level shows a gradual increase or decrease.   Removing the small balls and classifying the balls is necessary only if the mill is short of capacity.   Otherwise, the considerable labor involved in removing the small balls is wasted.

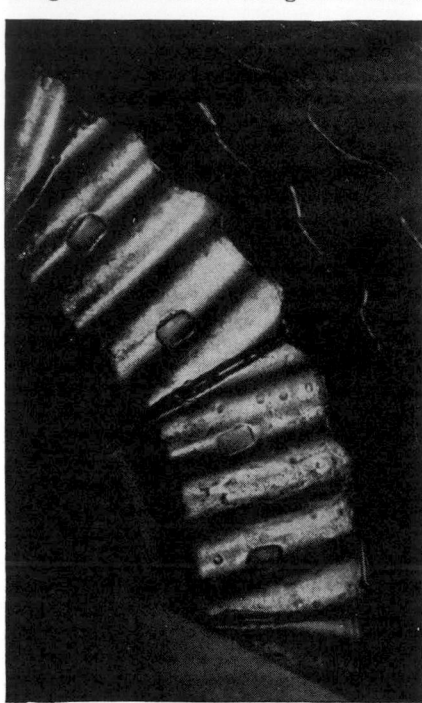

FIG. 2-7. Ball-tube-mill step shell liner.

Maintenance of liners (Fig. 2-7) on the ball tube mill is negligible, with the life often exceeding 10 years.   To realize this long life on liners, it is imperative that the liners be tight against the mill barrel. For this reason, it is recommended that the liners be tightened after the first month of operation, and then periodically at each annual outage.

The pulverizer fan is located in the outlet of the pulverizer and discharges coal fines into the burner piping.   This location subjects the fan to some wear from the coal and air flow.   Proper lubrication of drive and operation of the unit within design capacities usually will result in low maintenace costs.   If this type unit is used for intermittent operation, care must be taken to prevent fires in the idle mill due to the large amount of heat in the coal and ball charge.

Roll-Race Pulverizer.   The principal parts of the bowl mill are the rotating bowl fitted with a replaceable grinding ring, two or more tapered rolls in stationary journals, a feeder, a classifier, and main drive.   This is a type of roll-race pulverizer.   The principal difference from the standard roll-race pulverizer is the method of applying the grinding force on the coal and the load circulation within the grinding zone.   In the standard roll and race pulverizer, the grinding action depends entirely on the centrifugal force exerted to press the rolls against the race, while in the bowl mill the rolls are held in the desired position relative to the grinding ring by mechanical springs, and the centrifugal force acts only to feed the coal between the race and the rolls.   The bowl mill is suitable for the direct-firing systems since the roller journals can be lubricated, and the rolls can be adjusted without shutting the unit down.   Maintenance is very little higher, if any, on the bowl-mill type than with the ball and race type, and about midway between the maintenance of the ball tube mill and the impact mill.   They are not well suited, however, from the cost standpoint for manufacture in sizes below 2,000 to 3,000 lb per hr capacity.

The bowl mill has been designed to operate only under suction, and the pulverizer fan is placed on the outlet side of the classifier.   Heavy scroll liners and rotor blades usually are provided to withstand the abrasive action of the material on the fan. These mills are used extensively in direct-firing systems.

Ball-Race Pulverizer. The ball-race pulverizer employs the same principle of pulverizing as the roll-race type, and is a relatively slow-speed machine. It works on the principle of the roller bearing. Balls used as the grinding element are confined between two races, and pressure for crushing is obtained by springs forcing the races together. The balls may be driven by rotating the upper or lower race, or the intermediate race in the case of the multiring units. Coal circulation is affected by means of preheated air under pressure supplied to the mill by a blower or exhausted from the unit. The coal is fed to a table and swept into the path of the balls. The fines and coarse particles are carried to a classifier, which returns the coarse particles to the grinding area and passes the fines to the burners.

Fineness of coal at the outlet of the classifier is regulated by adjustable vanes. The condition of these vanes due to erosive effect of coal particles will influence the effect of the vane settings on the classification. Other influencing factors are pressure on the grinding elements, wear on grinding elements, and volume and velocity of air passing through the mill.

The parts most vulnerable to wear are the balls and races. They are replaceable as inspection indicates the necessity. Judgment in their replacement is a factor in length of life of these parts. It is good practice with this type of pulverizer to wear down two sets of balls with one set of races. When new balls and races are installed, allow the ball diameter to reduce $\frac{1}{4}$ in., then remove them and install another new set of balls only. Allow this second set to wear down $\frac{1}{2}$ in. and then change to the first set, allowing them to wear an additional $\frac{1}{2}$ in. This procedure keeps the balls within $\frac{1}{4}$ in. of each other in diameter and close enough to the contour of the races. If, however, one set of balls is allowed to wear to the minimum size and is then replaced with new balls, the effect on the contact faces of the races will be such that the races will have to be renewed prematurely. The method of application and amount of pressure applied to the grinding elements will affect the wear on these parts. Pressure in excess of that necessary to obtain required fineness is wasteful of both power consumption and life of these parts. The ease of adjustment of pressure by external means during operation can accelerate wear if the pressure on the movable race is applied unevenly.

The medium speeds of approximately 230 to 275 rpm and the general ruggedness of this type unit promote long life and moderate maintenance costs. The forced lubrication to bearing surfaces and driving parts, as well as thrust bearings, make these parts relatively free from troubles. Frequent inspection of quality and amount of lubricant in the lubrication system is necessary for continued effectiveness. Maintenance costs based on coal of 50 Hardgrove grindability are reported ranging from 0.5 cent to 2.0 cents per ton. In this type of pulverizer, the grinding elements are replaced through the access doors without disturbing the housing as in the case of the roll-race pulverizer.

The life of the pulverizer parts is affected by the grindability of the coal, the moisture content and sizing of the coal, the fineness of the finished product, and the temperature and quantity of air supplied to the pulverizer. The cost of replacement of wearing parts usually is expressed in cents per ton of coal pulverized. The maintenance cost expressed in cents per hour of service is a more representative figure, and gives a better basis for comparing results. It will be found that the cents per ton of coal ground will be the lowest on the pulverizer which can be operated continuously at maximum capacity, and will be the highest on one operated at low capacities. If these maintenance costs are expressed in cost per service hour, the figures will be nearly alike, assuming, of course, that all operating conditions except capacity are the same. The life of various wearing parts based on service hours will be fairly uniform for any given plant, and a replacement schedule can be made up from these figures.

The life of pulverizer wearing parts increases as the fineness of coal decreases, and as the air flow through the pulverizer increases. In order to obtain the lowest-possible pulverizing cost, the fineness of coal must be the lowest that can be satisfactorily used in the burners and the furnace.   This fineness for any plant can be determined only by observation and tests.

In order to keep the maintenance costs as low as possible by careful operation, the following items should be observed:

1. Adjust the spring pressure on the rolls so that the journal arms do not come in contact with the stop bars at the lowest continuous operating rating.
2. Maintain the suction at the mill base under the bowl as recommended by the manufacturer of the equipment.
3. Keep the coal-air mixture at the approximate range of 170 to 180°F.
4. Maintain an air flow through the mill as high as possible consistent with satisfactory burner operation.
5. Establish a definite lubrication schedule.   One operator on each shift should be responsible for checking the lubrication of the roller journals, greasing other bearings, and for general inspection of the equipment.
6. The inspection schedule should be based on sufficiently frequent inspection of all wearing parts until the life of the various parts has been definitely established. These should include such parts as the bowl ring rolls, mill side liners, exhauster blades, and exhauster liners.
7. Keep an accurate record of service hours, as well as total tons pulverized.   Base the life of parts on service hours in order to establish a schedule for inspection and replacement of parts.
8. Bowl rings and rolls receive most of the wear at the bottom.   As capacity drops off, the clearance should be readjusted between the ring and rolls.   The life of the grinding elements of ball-race pulverizers varies from 6,000 to 14,000 hr of operation.   The rate of wear is affected by the sulfur and ash content more than the grindability of the coal.

Impact Mills.   The high-speed pulverizer is based on the principle of both impact and attrition of the coal.   The grinding elements consist of hammerlike beaters revolving in a chamber lined with hard metal plates, to which one or two rows of beaters or stationary pegs are attached.   The coal is fed to the crushing chambers and

FIG. 2-8. Cutaway of pulverizer.   (*Courtesy of Riley Stoker Corp.*)

passes through the grinding zone, where it is pulverized and dried.   The preheated air for drying and transporting the coal is induced by an exhauster fan mounted on the same shaft as the pulverizer.   This class of mill (Fig. 2-8) is compact, low in cost, and simple.   Since it can be built in small sizes, it lends itself readily to industrial applications.   These mills are excellent dryers and give good service for direct firing.

Loading of the mill is a definite factor in the maintenance of this type of unit.   When the loading drops below a point approximately 20 per cent of its rated capacity, the rate of wear increases.   Quality of coal pulverized has a marked influence on wear.   Although grindability is a factor in wear, the presence of increased amounts of ash, sulfur, and tramp material (dirt and stones) increases the maintenance of wearing parts.

Frequent inspections of all wearing parts are necessary to determine the life of these parts and rates of wear.   Based on these findings, an inspection and parts-replacement schedule can be set up.   Inspections will anticipate rupture of parts within the mill and the resultant damage to other parts and the mill itself.

Since capacity and fineness are affected by the wear of hammers and mill liners, these parts should be given the most attention.   An index of wear on these parts is the presence of "stars" or "sparklers" in the furnace, indicating an increase in percentage of larger fines.   This together with physical inspection will determine the need for replacement of parts.

Life of hammers can be increased without unfavorable effect on fineness by reversing

Fig. 2-9. Stationary pegs, impact mill. (*Courtesy of Riley Stoker Corp.*)

the hammers and by changing their position.   An accurate record of tons should be kept, showing tons of coal pulverized, as well as service hours.   The life of parts should be based on service hours in order to establish a schedule of replacement parts.

Developments in metal alloys have contributed to the increase of life in wearing parts.   Tungsten-carbide and nickel-chrome alloys have service records indicating as much as 1,000 per cent increased life for these parts.   Figure 2-9 shows stationary pegs of an impact mill, subject to severe service.

Pulverized-coal Piping.   Lines for conveying pulverized coal generally are of standard-weight steel piping, with average wall thickness of ⅜ in.   Removable liners often are fitted in the areas of the conveying systems subject to excessive wear.   In an effort to reduce pressure drop, the radii of bends are made as large as possible consistent with good design.   However, a more important gain is obtained in the form of elimination or reduction of the erosive effect of coal dust.   If the coal is of uniform fineness and the system is properly designed for bends and velocities through the pipes, the maintenance of the conveying line is very low.   Records indicate that conveying piping of direct-fired installations have operated for 10 to 15 years and, in some cases, 20 years without any maintenance.   The coating of the internal surface of the conveying lines with a graphitelike substance from the coal protects the lines from corrosion and erosion.   This protection usually is effective in straight runs of pipe, where impingement is not severe.   An additional advantage gained by large bends is the allowance for expansion due to temperature changes.   In some cases, expansion joints are necessary to take care of this effect.

Pulverized-coal Burners.   Operators of pulverized-coal equipment expect stable ignition of coal, limitation of unburned combustible to less than 2 per cent, efficient burning of a wide range of coals, and freedom from major repairs.   Most repairs are of a minor nature, and can be affected without waiting for an annual overhaul.   Burner parts subject to abrasion that may require replacement at more frequent intervals should be easily removable and of reasonable cost.   Alloy steels should be used for parts subject to high temperatures.   Accessability for both adjustment and maintenance is a design consideration during layout of the burner arrangements.

The distribution vanes or rosettes of the horizontal-type burner are subjected to the radiant heat of the furnace and, therefore, vulnerable to damage. Straw initially used to seal coal-car gates will sometimes find its way through the pulverizer to the burner rosette. This straw packs behind the rosette vanes and cuts off the cooling air, with resultant burning out of the vanes. Otherwise, a life of at least 4,000 service hours can be expected from the rosette.

Burner tubes and coal valves have a consistent record of long life, i.e., 18 to 20 years. Proper design of coal piping for expansion to prevent binding in the coal valves is essential to low maintenance of these units.

Stokers. The mechanical stoker is an important type of fuel-burning equipment in the production of steam with small and moderate-sized steam generators. In general, it has the capacity for successfully burning a wide range of coals from anthracite and coke breeze to lignite.

Over a period of 30 to 35 years, the stoker has moved from its position as the principal method of automatic coal firing to where it comprises less than 20 per cent of present-day mechanical firing. The spreader-stoker installations over a period of 15 years have displaced the underfeed stoker as the most universal stoker unit. Maintenance has played an important part in this change.

The most common types of stokers are (1) underfeed, (2) chain grate and traveling grate, and (3) spreader or overfeed type. The underfeed stoker is based on the use of a ram or screw which continuously forces coal along a longitudinal channel. Coal fills up the channel or retort and spills over the sides to develop a fuel bed. Rising through the retort, it picks up air, which is admitted through tuyères in the sides of the retort. The heat from the coal burning above on the fuel bed drives off coal gases by distillation. The gases ignite on passing through the burning fuel bed. The coal burns as it reaches the incandescent bed, completing the combustion process as it approaches the ash-discharge grates. This type, supplied in single or multiple retorts, is classified as (1) horizontal feed or (2) gravity feed.

The chain-grate type and the traveling-grate type of stokers are essentially alike in that the grate surface moves continuously in one direction to convey the coal through the furnace. Coal is admitted at one end and discharged at the other end as ash. The grate surface of the chain-grate stoker is made up of series of cast-iron links so connected by pins or bars as to form an endless chain. The chain passes over a driving drum at the front and an idler drum at the rear. The upper surface of the chain or belt carries the fuel bed. In some designs, the links forming the chain have a scissors-like relative movement as the chain passes over the idler drum at the rear. The grate surface of the traveling-grate stoker consists of a series of cast-iron sections mounted on carrier bars. The carrier bars are connected to two or more drive chains, which in turn are supported on steel rails.

The modern spreader or overfeed stoker consists essentially of a feeder, a spreader mechanism, and a grate. It is based on the principle of suspension burning, and burning on a fuel bed. The coal is discharged by the feeder to the spreader mechanism, which throws it into the fire, distributing it in a thin bed on the grate. The fines in the coal are burned in suspension, and the larger particles fall to the surface of the fuel bed. The grate may be of stationary, undulating, or continuous-discharge type. If a traveling- or chain-grate type of fuel bed is employed with the overfeed stoker, in many installations the travel of the grate is from the rear to the front of the furnace, thereby permitting the raw fuel to be distributed on the bed at the rear of the furnace and the ash discharged at the front.

Stoker Maintenance. Maintenance is one of the principal items of cost in operating a stoker-fired boiler. The replacement of overheated and burned-out parts makes up the greater part of this cost.

The causes of excessive maintenance are basically deficiencies in good operating practice. The principal cause is the continuous overloading of the equipment. Insufficient draft, or positive pressure in the furnace as well, contributes to unnecessarily abnormal maintenance of stoker parts.

Overloading of the stoker where excess fan capacity is available should be avoided because of the excessive burning and overheating of stoker parts. Under certain load conditions, extended periods of overloading may be unavoidable. In such cases, careful operation and intelligent maintenance practices are essential to continued operation of the equipment. Under such conditions, maintenance of a satisfactory fuel bed, a negative draft in the furnace, and frequent check of temperature of stoker parts where possible will help to keep maintenance costs in line.

Draft above the fuel bed should not be less than 0.10 in. A positive pressure results in abnormal temperature at the grates and lower wall areas. Draft gages and a CO_2 indicator are essential for control of these conditions. A relatively uniform fuel-air ratio should be maintained throughout the entire stoker. Localized overheating of tuyères and grates, as well as poor efficiency, may result if there is too little air in one section of the fuel bed and too much in another. Some air should pass the grates at all times for cooling the grate parts. During banking, the wind-box access doors should be opened to admit air for cooling purposes.

Damage to grates from fires in the wind box is not infrequent. While the accumulation of fines is contingent on the coal being fired, the siftings should be removed often enough to prevent the possibility of fires. Inspection of wind boxes once each shift should be sufficient to anticipate trouble from this source.

Proper banking methods are an important factor in control of stoker maintenance. The fire should be allowed to burn short as the boiler load is reduced. When the boiler is off the line, fresh coal is run in for the length of approximately 4 ft. The forced-draft fan is stopped, and air is admitted through the compartment side doors to prevent overheating and to sustain combustion in the banked fire. A furnace draft is controlled by the boiler outlet damper of the induced-draft fan control. This should be sufficient only to carry off the gases and maintain a slight draft in the furnace. Fresh coal must be run in as required to keep the coal from burning back to the fuel entrance point.

Exposure of stoker parts to the radiant heat of the furnace is another cause of excessive maintenance. Holes in the fire bed expose parts to this type of overheating. Holes are blown in the fuel bed as the result of overloading the unit and segregation of coal in the stoker hopper, which results in uneven distribution and burning of the fuel on the stoker. The thin fuel bed on underfeed stokers, as well as insufficient cover on the overfeed section next to the ash disposal section, are responsible for radiant-heat damage to parts.

Proper lubrication of all points requiring it helps to limit maintenance costs. A lubrication schedule based on manufacturer's operating instructions and experience with the stoker can be effective in reducing wear on and outage of equipment.

All accessible parts of the stoker should be inspected at least daily. Parts which are not accessible should be inspected when the unit is taken out of service, or at least twice a year.

Daily inspections should show evidence of play or looseness in connections between moving parts. Where movement is transmitted by a shear pin or a safety release, check for freedom of movement and effectiveness of action on this safety device. Make repairs promptly.

Underfeed Stokers. The increases in size and burning rates forced a replacement of all refractory construction of stoker furnaces with water-wall cooling. Water-cooled tubes are used to absorb radiant heat, protect refractory, and prevent clinker adhesion along the sides of the stoker. Extension of water cooling to retorts and tuyères has been employed with success in lowering fuel-bed temperatures and prevention of slag by chilling the ash.

The use of preheated air has had a marked effect on the performance of underfeed stokers. Aside from the increase in efficiency, it has been possible to run with a thinner and more uniform fuel bed and reduced excess air. These gains in themselves were favorable from a maintenance standpoint. On the other hand, grate temperature being contingent on air temperature, the preheated air temperatures must be limited to avoid excessive maintenance.

Published data on this point show the marked influence of combustion-air temperatures on stoker maintenance. Maintenance costs of 3 cents per ton of coal burned with 200°F air was average. An increase of air temperatures to 300°F was accompanied by an increase in cost to 6 cents per ton of coal.   Costs exceeding 12 cents per ton were experienced with air temperatures of 400°F.   Based on these data, combustion-air temperature should be limited to less than 300°F in order to attain a low maintenance cost.

Maintenance costs of underfeed stokers depend on design, correct application, fuel, and quality of operation.   In order to reduce to a minimum the major cost factor, namely, the burning of stoker parts, the fuel bed must be kept in a porous condition to permit an adequate flow of air for cooling.   Maintenance of stokers using preheated air is approximately 100 per cent more than that for using air at room temperatures. There are data on record indicating that an average cost of slightly more than 3 cents per ton of coal burned with air temperatures under 350°F is attainable.   This is contingent on careful operation, maintenance of uniform and correct fuel bed, and air-temperature control.   The grade of coal burned is an important factor in attainment of this goal.   A relatively low-ash coal that has a tendency to cake but breaks into a porous fuel bed when agitated is a favorable coal for use in underfired stokers.

Preventive steps to eliminate or reduce maintenance are dependent principally on reducing exposure of stoker metal to the possibility of burning.   Keep the fire out of the retorts of underfeed stokers.   Except in an emergency, the coal feed should never be stopped while there is air pressure in the wind box, since it would tend to allow the fire to burn down into the retort, damaging tuyères and retort parts.   To this end, banking should be done with sufficient fuel, air supply reduced to a minimum, and intermittent operation of the stoker practiced to keep the fire out of the retorts.

Proper depth of fuel bed will help to prevent burning of metal.   The depth of fuel above the tuyères may vary from 12 to 30 in., depending on the coal characteristics.

When the stoker is taken out of service, a thorough inspection of all parts should be made.   Prompt attention to minor repairs will forestall major breakdowns.   The wearing surfaces of retort sides and boxes and all moving parts should be checked carefully.   Inspection will disclose misalignment of parts and the condition of dump grates, clearances, moving grate bars, and dump plates.

Evidence of binding between parts should be attended to immediately because extensive breakage may result, with the damage affecting other parts in adjacent areas.   The design of the stoker will provide over-all clearances of $\frac{1}{2}$ to 2 in., contingent on stoker size, to provide for growth of grate bars.   The adjusting mechanism controlling secondary rams and overfeed sections should be checked and adjusted to provide actual travel as indicated on the indexing plate.   Compensation for growth through the adjusting device or removal of the grate or filler bars to provide necessary clearance is imperative.   Damage from excessive tightness as a result of metal growth can be far more extensive than the breakage of the parts immediately affected.

Much has been done from a metallurgical standpoint, varying the composition of stoker iron by use of chromium and other elements.   Design of tuyères and all stoker iron exposed to heat is very important.   Many times the maintenance or operating personnel by their experience have added effectively to improvements in design of these parts.

The effect of accurate air control on both operation and maintenance costs, as noted above, points up the importance of proper adjustment of stoker dampers.   They should be checked in their various positions, especially the closed and opened positions.

During operation, the overfeed section of the dumping-type stoker and the grinder rolls of the clinker-grinder type are kept covered to protect against radiant heat.   The grinder bed is cleaned under normal conditions when it is practically full of ash.   At this time, air is admitted to the pit in order to burn any unburned fuel.   A deviation from this practice should obtain when, during emergency stoppage of the steam-generating unit, great quantities of burned coals are dumped into the pit.   In order to avoid damage to the grinder rolls and pit castings, the air should be shut off and the ash removed as quickly as possible.

The grinder rolls are fitted with hardened replaceable teeth.   During shutdown the rollers and cutters are checked for wear to insure proper grinding.

Chain-grate and Traveling-grate Stokers.   Chain-grate and traveling-grate types of stoker installations are designed for either natural or forced draft.   Because of capacity limitations and the desirability to restrict the fuel to coarser coal for adequate air-flow conditions, the natural-draft units comprise only a small percentage of this type of stoker installation.   The forced-draft unit, which can be used with smaller coals and a wider range of fuels, is more generally used.

Low maintenance costs for this type stoker have been reported from numerous sources.   These have been approximately 1 cent per ton for bituminous coal, and under 2 cents per ton for anthracite.   In all cases, the importance of good operating practices was stressed.

Air flow, a basic consideration in good stoker design, is considered of utmost importance, not only for combustion, but for limitation of overheating and burning of stoker parts.   Data presented at the 1954 Annual ASME-AIME Fuel Conference confirmed this point.   "In both chain- and traveling-grate stokers, grate sections are exposed to furnace temperatures less than 50 per cent of the time.   This permits grates to cool and results in low maintenance."   One engineer reported no grate maintenance since installation in 1941.   During the 13-year period of operation, total stoker maintenance consisted of replacing belts on drives.   Another engineer reported practically no maintenance on his traveling stokers since they were installed in 1929.

Free air space through the grate is provided in the order of 6 to 10 per cent.   The normal draft loss through the bed may be 1.0 to 2.0 in. of water.   An unexplained increase in draft loss should be cause for investigation of the condition of the fuel bed during operation, and inspection of the grate during outage of the unit.   Flow of air through the stoker may be restricted either by growth of grate metal or by a matted section of the fuel bed.   This latter condition is often the result of size segregation of the coal entering the stoker.   Areas of coarse coal burn more rapidly, whereas areas of fine coal mat over.   A traversing coal spout or nonsegregating-type spout and hopper will help considerably in the proper distribution of coal sizes in the hopper.

Air leakage into the furnace setting affects the draft above the fuel bed and reduces the air flow through it.   Therefore, frequent checks of the setting should be made, especially at doors and joints, and air leaks eliminated.   One source of air leakage requiring prompt attention is that occurring at the grate line.   The air bypassing the fuel bed at this point sets up a blowtorch action, with accelerated damage to both adjacent stoker metal and furnace.

As noted above, the use of preheated air in stoker installations has resulted in definite operating benefits, such as increased boiler efficiency, better ignition conditions, and greater flexibility in meeting load demands.   The temperature of air must be maintained within definite limits to attain reasonable maintenance costs.   The characteristics of the coal, fuel-bed control, and load conditions are controlling factors in the limitation of preheated-air temperatures.   Air at 250°F may be used without unfavorable effect on maintenance.   Favorable maintenance costs with air temperatures in excess of 300°F are dependent on excellent operating efforts.

Fluctuating load conditions have their effect on maintenance.   While a sudden load increase may result in too-rapid coal need and loss of ignition, a drop in load may result in overheating of the grate.   This load condition requires careful control of air flow.

Proper lubrication is essential to good maintenance.   The right lubricants correctly applied to all exposed bearing areas are simple but effective means of retarding wear. A lubrication schedule should be prepared based on the stoker manufacturer's recommendations and the operator's experience.   Scheduled lubrication should be followed without fail.

During scheduled outage, the complete stoker should be inspected thoroughly. After extended periods of operation, there will be an over-all growth in the parts exposed to the fire.   Stoker links, pins, and ledge plates show the effect of slight degrees of overheating.   In replacement of these parts, allowance for growth in operation is necessary to allow for damage from growth under heat.   Adjustment of the grate over-all growth can be effected by removing the links to restore the lateral clearance in the chain grate.

The tension of chains must be checked and undue tightness corrected.   Neglect of this element will result in binding of parts, wear, and breakage.   Some wear on link pins, joints, grate-bar ends, chains, sprockets, return rails, and wearing strips is inevitable.   Neglect will result in accelerating this wear and increased future damage. Drive sprockets and chains may be reversed to compensate for wear, and the chain take-up adjusted to provide the proper tension.

The fuel-gate tile and supports are susceptible to burning and warping.   Fuel-bed control requires prompt replacement of these parts.

The stoker drive and the drive parts are accessible for inspection and lubrication during operation.   The alignment of shear pin or slip clutch must be checked to insure reliable operation for the protection of the stoker unit.

Spreader Stokers.   The spreader or overfeed stoker is similar in many respects to the chain and traveling-grate stoker.   The major difference is in the method of burning. The fuel bed in the conventional chain-grate stoker travels away from the feed hopper and gate, and the coal burns from top to bottom of the bed.   The spreader stoker with continuous ash discharge spreads the fuel uniformly over the entire grate surface.   The grate serves only to convey the ash continuously and deposit it in an ash pit located either in front or rear of the furnace.   Part of the fuel is burned in suspension, and larger pieces are ignited by the radiation from the hot furnace walls and the burning fuel bed on which it is deposited.   While the traveling-grate or chain-grate stokers have fuel beds ranging from 4 to 12 in. thick, the spreader stoker maintains an extremely thin fuel bed.   The fuel bed should have a minimum average thickness of about 2 in., based on the variation in the thickness of the ash bed from front to rear of the grate, where the traveling grate is used.   Any thicker fuel bed on a spreader stoker indicates poor distribution of fuel, air, or both.

The spreader stoker is inherently low in maintenance.   The traveling-grate unit has all the low maintenance of the chain- or traveling-grate stoker.   The stationary grate is simple in design.   The spreader unit itself is located outside the furnace.   Therefore, its parts are cool and easily accessible for continuous inspection and lubrication.

Operating attention given to the fuel bed will save maintenance expense, not only in connection with the stoker itself, but also with respect to the spreader unit and the furnace.   A level bed retards the formation of clinkers and disturbance of air flow through the stoker.   Adjustment of the spreader should be controlled to avoid the heavy concentration of fire at either the rear of the furnace or the front.   In one case, damage to the refractory results, and in another the spreader and the brickwork arch may be subjected to excessive overheating.

The ash-conveying speed of spreader stokers having traveling grates, shaker grates, or oscillating grates is set to maintain sufficient ash-bed thickness on the grate to insulate the grate metal from furnace temperatures.   In many instances, the minimum thickness is best at 3 in. at the discharge end of the grate.   The removal of ashes from the ash pit is dependent on ash-pit capacity and operating schedule.   The cleaning operation should be accomplished as quickly as possible to avoid undue exposure of grate surface to radiant heat, and disturbance of the over-all fuel bed.   Excessive accumulation of ash in the ash pit exposes the grates and the grate-operating parts to damage.

As in the case of the chain or traveling grate, broken grate sections should be replaced as soon as possible, allowing clearance for growth due to heat.   The spreader-mechanism bearings should be checked each shift.   The alignment of the spreader feed in the rotor should be inspected during outages of the unit.

Experience indicates that coal size has a definite effect on maintenance of the overfeed stoker.   Coarse sizes and large lumps of coal increase the wear of the coal feeder and distributing parts.   While coal segregation in the hopper can be overcome by adjustment of the spreader, this condition imposes an additional responsibility on the operator.   Segregation is prevented more effectively by using a spreading spout for feed to the hopper.

Stoker Operation.   Sound stoker operation is the most effective attack on maintenance costs.   Although this factor has been stressed above with each type of stoker, the importance of proper procedures in lighting-off, banking, and emergency shutdown cannot be stressed too highly.

The stoker manufacturer will supply lighting-off instructions which experience dictates to be best for results with his equipment and the coal to be burned.   Whether burning bituminous or anthracite coal, the fuel coverage of the grate both as to area and fuel-bed thickness is important to well-managed lighting-off procedures. The gate opening of the chain grate, the speed of the underfeed stoker, and the spreader operation on the overfeed unit control the area and thickness of the fuel bed. The kind, amount, and placement of kindling on the fuel bed, and its lighting, will be recommended for each type of unit.

For lighting-off, a light furnace draft is established and the kindling is ignited, while air is admitted to the fuel bed as required to support the burning of the coal. The stoker is run at a slow speed to maintain ignition in the front of the bed. It may be necessary to stop the stoker as a means of stabilizing combustion throughout the initial fuel bed. When the bed is completely covered with fuel, and sufficient ash developed to protect links, tuyères, and dumping grates, the stoker is ready for operation. Procedures to permit accelerated lighting-off should be carefully analyzed for unfavorable effect on personnel, as well as stoker and furnace maintenance.

Banking a fire usually can be anticipated, and the fire is allowed to burn down as the boiler load decreases. If this is properly timed, the banking operation can proceed in an orderly manner. The fuel over the entire bed, except that over the first compartment adjacent to the hopper or gate, should be burned to ash. The air to the first compartment should be shut during the burning-down period. When the bed has burned to ash, the forced draft is cut off and all compartment dampers closed. A slight furnace draft is maintained to carry off the gases of combustion. Fresh coal is added to bring the edge of the banked fire away from the hopper or gate. Bituminous coal is more difficult to control on bank, and care must be taken to prevent the fire burning back under the gate or the hopper, and causing damage at these points. Therefore, it is usual practice to run up the coal in the hopper, leaving only enough to provide a coal seal. Operation of the stoker for several minutes may be necessary to keep the fire away from the hopper. The banked bed on a spreader stoker is maintained in a pile in the middle or forward section of the grate. In all cases, the ash is retained on the grate to protect the metal from overheating.

In the case of an emergency loss of load, prompt action is necessary to reduce the burning of coal as quickly as possible. In all cases, the forced-draft fans are shut off and dampers closed to reduce the air supply to zero. In the case of the spreader stoker, the coal feed as well as air supply is stopped. The small amount of coal on the grate is a favorable factor in reducing the burning rate to a minimum. In this case, the fuel bed can burn to ash without excessive heating of the grate. The stoker and forced-draft fan for the underfeed stoker are cut off and dampers are closed tight. Furnace doors should be opened, admitting air over the fire. This retards the fire and permits the furnace to cool gradually. In the case of chain-grate or traveling-grate units, the air is cut off, but coal feed is increased to a maximum. The burning fuel is dumped into the ash pit. Prompt removal of the hot ash and burning coal from the ash pit is necessary to protect the ash pit and equipment.

Preventive maintenance is necessary to assure trouble-free operation. An inspection check list should be prepared for each piece of equipment so that no items will be overlooked. Operating and maintenance experience, combined with the information contained in the manufacturer's manual, should be worked into the check list. A typical inspection list follows:

SPREADER STOKER

Feeder Drive (Fig. 2-10)

1. Motor—check bearings and lubrication
2. Belts—replace if worn
3. Clutch—clean and adjust

Feeders

1. Bearings—clean and relubricate
2. Gear housing—clean and relubricate
3. Rocker shaft—check rollers, replace if worn

4. Feeder block—replace if worn
5. Water cooling—clean

Grate Drive (Fig. 2-11)

1. Check alignment
2. Oil—check quality
3. Bearings—check wear
4. Lubrication lines—inspect; check location

Grate (Fig. 2-12)

1. Grate surface—remove damaged grate, check expansion clearance
2. Sealing clips (Fig. 2-13)—check for expansion and header clearance
3. Drive shaft—check alignment
4. Internal seals—inspect

Reinjection

1. Hoppers—clean
2. Venturi nozzles and lines—inspect, rotate, or replace if worn

Furnace

Refractories—inspect and repair if necessary
  a. Rear wall
  b. Side walls
  c. Front wall

FIG. 2-10. Feeder drive. (*Courtesy of Riley Stoker Corp.*)

Fuel-oil Equipment. Fuel oil is widely used for steam generation for industrial purposes. It is the residue resulting from distillation of crude petroleum in which the more volatile elements are driven off. It comes in five grades as classified by the Bureau of Standards. The lighter grades, designated as 1, 2, and 3, are used mostly for domestic purposes. Bunker C or grade 6 is the heavier residue, and has a viscosity range from a maximum of approximately 300 seconds Saybolt Furol at 100°F to a minimum of 45. It has a high carbon content, approximately 87 per cent, and hydrogen content of between 10 and 11 per cent.

The common methods of burning fuel oil in industrial installations involve mechanical or steam atomization, and proper mixture of air for supporting combustion. The burner is the gun type with a nozzle tip to give the required oil spray, according to the method of atomization.

Proper preparation of oil for delivery to the burner is vital to good operation. Adequate maintenance of the fuel-oil equipment has a marked effect on efficiency. The oil storage tank, whether small or large, of steel or concrete construction, is relatively free from serious maintenance problems. The usual maintenance consists of periodic cleaning of sludge and removal of water. The heating coils in the storage tank frequently are a source of steam leakage. Excessive accumulation of water in the tank serves notice as to this condition. Water and sludge are removed by pumping. The leaking coil should be repaired promptly to prevent further contamination of oil.

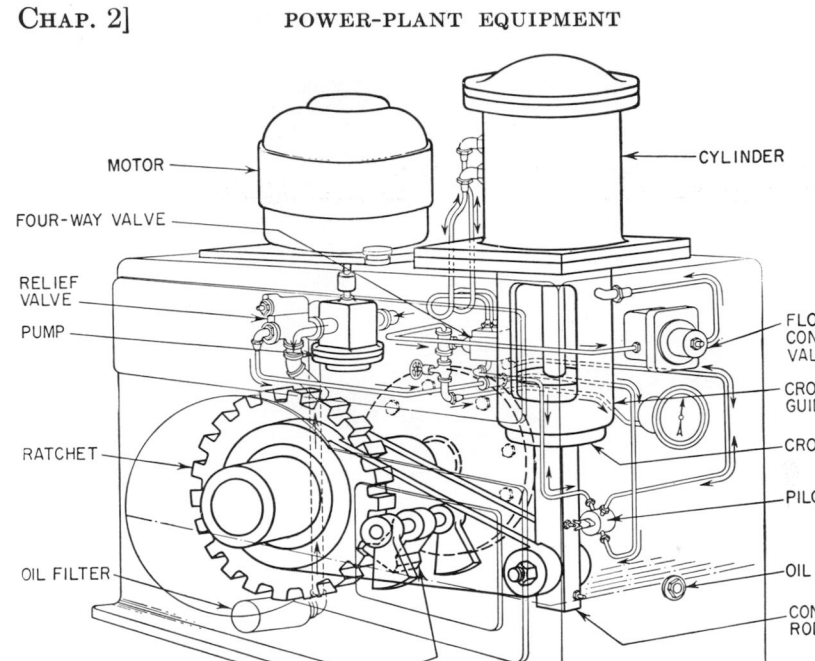

MOTOR

FOUR-WAY VALVE

RELIEF VALVE

PUMP

RATCHET

OIL FILTER

PAWL

CYLINDER

FLOW CONTROL VALVE

CROSS HEAD GUIDE

CROSS HEAD

PILOT VALVE

OIL GAUGE

CONNECTING ROD

FIG. 2-11. Hydraulic grate drive. (*Courtesy of Riley Stoker Corp.*)

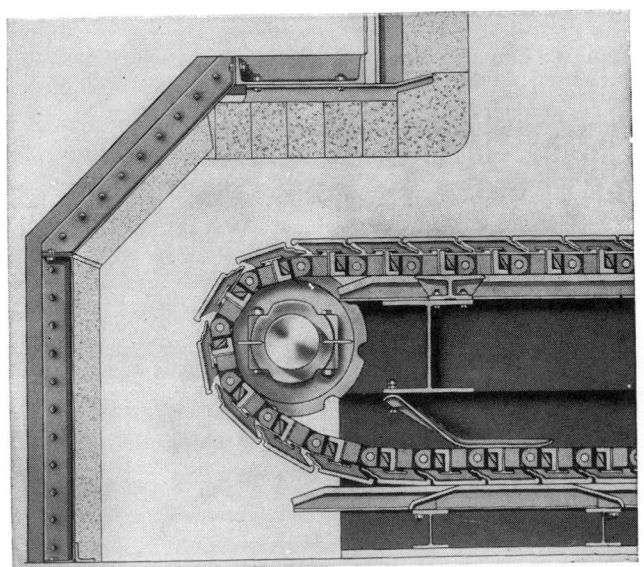

FIG. 2-12. Grate. (*Courtesy of Riley Stoker Corp.*)

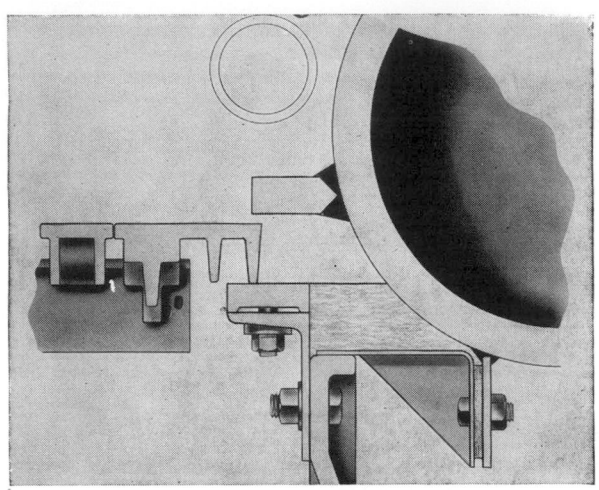

FIG. 2-13. Side seal.   (*Courtesy of Riley Stoker Corp.*)

Before repair work on a fuel-oil tank or heating coil is attempted, a thorough cleaning of all surfaces is necessary to avoid accumulations of oil, and possibility of fires. Chemical cleaning methods have been successful in this service.   Steam and condensate connections to the heater should be broken before chemical cleaning is started. This will prevent the possibility of contamination in the steam and condensate lines.

Fuel-oil heaters utilize either steam or electricity as a heat source.   The steam heater may consist of a bank of tubes rolled-in at one tube sheet and packed at the other. For industrial installations, compact duplex oil-heater pumping and heating units are available, with a steam-driven pump, motor-driven pump, strainers, controls, instruments, and heating units.   Large installations involve separate heater units and pumping units of the screw, reciprocating, or rotating-plunger type.

The oil is heated to 80 to 100°F in the storage tank for delivery to the heater, at a viscosity of approximately 700 Saybolt Furol seconds.   Steam atomizing installations require a temperature of 180 to 190°F for satisfactory flow to the burner.   For mechanical atomization, the oil must be heated to approximately 220°F for adequate atomization.   Heating the oil to temperatures above 240 to 250°F accelerates carbonization of oil in the heater as well as the burner tip.   With temperatures of 220°F or under, the build-up of carbon is gradual.   A drop-off of approximately 20°F in the temperature differential between oil entering and leaving the heater is an indication that the heater needs cleaning.   Both mechanical and chemical cleaning methods are available for this purpose.   Both methods of cleaning may be used by plant personnel with safety, provided necessary precautions are taken.   Heaters with oil in the tubes may be cleaned by either method.   The units having oil in the shell can be cleaned most effectively and quickly without removing the tube bank by chemical methods. The tank, pump, and piping for chemical cleaning should be hooked up to permit reversal of flow of chemical cleaning fluid through the shell and between the two banks to get complete cleaning.   Chemical cleaning should not be attempted except under supervision, and after thorough training of the personnel.

Duplex fuel-oil strainers installed both in the suction of the pump and in the discharge of the heater protect the equipment and especially the burner tips from fouling and plugging.   These units consist of double-wall, wire-mesh baskets and switching valves contained in a cast-iron body with piping connections to control the flow of oil in and out of the strainer compartments.   Bolted covers seal the compartments when in service and permit easy access to the basket for cleaning.   The switching valve consists of a three-way cock with jack for ease in operation and tight seating.   An inner basket having wire cloth of bronze or monel 0.010-in. wire, 40 mesh, is satisfactory for most fuel-oil requirements.

The baskets must be kept in complete repair for full protection of burner tips.   The strainers on the discharge side of the heater should be cleaned once per shift for best service.   Pressure gages may be installed on the inlet and outlet of the strainer to indicate the pressure drop across the unit.   A log can be made of each service period for each basket showing length of time, pressure lost through the basket at start and end of period, as well as quantities of oil passed.   An analysis of this log will indicate whether service periods are correct.

In many situations, the practice is to strain through one compartment until pressure loss on the line indicates that the basket needs cleaning, then switch the flow through the clean basket in the other compartment, and at once open up the compartment that has been in use and clean its basket.   A stricter and better practice is to wash the baskets every day or every watch, or at even shorter periods if the oil supply is carrying large quantities of dirt.   They may be washed regardless of whether the gages show only a small increase of pressure loss through the strainer.   This rule should be followed on all installations where the oil burner must be given the best possible protection.

Care must be exercised in cleaning baskets.   In cleaning and in all handling of double-wall baskets, use all precautions to prevent even the slightest injury to the wire-cloth wall of the heater basket.   A break or even excessive enlargement of even one opening through the wire cloth makes it useless as a protection to the burner nozzle unless the damage is repaired.   A double-wall basket can be washed more completely if the parts are separated during the cleaning process.   The first step is to agitate the basket in a bucket or tank containing light oil or kerosene.   This loosens any matter that is caught on the inner side of the wire-cloth wall of the inner basket.   This accumulation should not be forced through the wire basket, but should be made to fall within the basket.   In order to protect the wire cloth, never use a cleaning jet from the inside, only from the outer side through the mesh.   If cleaning of the baskets is attempted without separating the inner and outer baskets, the cleaning jet should be directed not only straight through the part of the mesh wall exposed by openings in the outer basket, but also at an angle in order to reach parts of mesh covered by the metal of the outer basket.   The next step is to set the baskets unseparated upsidedown.   Direct a stream of hot water or solvent through the openings in the wall of the outer basket and through the wire cloth of the inner basket in order to flush out particles of matter that may be caught in the mesh.   If any stiff or hardened particles adhere to the mesh of the inner basket, these should be softened by soaking the basket in a solvent and not by forcing a jet or by scrubbing.

Fuel-oil pipelines usually are not troublesome.   The piping is arranged for recirculation to maintain oil temperature up to the burner head.   Shutoff and control valves, as well as burner gun connections to the piping, must be maintained free from leakage.

The burner tip is subject to abrasion and carbonizing from the oil and rough treatment from the operators.   If the oil is heated to over 240°F, carbonizing takes place at the burner tip.   The effect of furnace radiant heat increases the tendency toward carbon formation at the tip.   The tip orifice is enlarged by the abrasive action of the oil.   The use of improper cleaning tools, such as a handy jackknife, also enlarges and distorts the orifice.   Burner tips should be stored in a box, with compartments for various sizes, in order to protect the bearing surfaces as well as the orifice from unnecessary mishandling and damage.   Burner tips must not be strung on a wire for storage.   Such handling will cause undue wear and distortion of the orifice.

When the burner is taken out of service, the oil is thoroughly removed from the burner barrel and nozzle.   The barrel and tip assemblies should be removed, thoroughly cleaned, and reassembled.   The unit is hung vertically with the tip immersed in kerosene.   If burners are cut in and out of service frequently, the nozzles usually are kept in place.   In this case, blow out the unit thoroughly with compressed air or steam to prevent clogging and carbon deposits, and retract the nozzles as far as possible to protect them from the heat of the furnace.

The burner tip and tip cap must be maintained in good condition to prevent dripping during operation. Dripping during outage is an indication of a leaking shutoff valve. Both instances of leakage and dripping of oil on the burner tile and furnace front should be corrected promptly to avoid damage from fires in the wind box or on the furnace floor.

In operation, it is essential to position the nozzle for the best mixture of oil spray and air without damage to the burner throat. If the nozzle is moved too far into the furnace, the mixture of air and oil vapor is not complete, and a smoky fire may result. On the other hand, if the nozzle is retracted too far into the throat, the oil spray will hit the refractory tile of the throat and develop a build-up of carbon. In this case, the disturbance of the spray is progressively worse as the carbon deposit increases.

Gas-burning Equipment. Gas makes an ideal fuel for steam generation. While natural gas is most generally used, there is also substantial use of other types that may be burned near their points of generation, such as refinery gas, blast-furnace gas, and coke-oven gas. In general, gaseous fuels are free from solids. However, some raw gases have an appreciable dust contact and require cleaning before being supplied to the burner. The major maintenance on the gas burner is cleaning to prevent clogging or fouling of the gas openings. Some types of burners can be cleaned while in operation. During outage of the boiler, the nozzles should be inspected and cleaned thoroughly.

Burning gas appears very simple, but it is actually more dangerous than other fuels. The invisibility of unburned gas makes explosion hazards an acute possibility. The operating procedures, including adequate purging of the furnace in lighting-off and when ignition is lost, must be strictly followed. Therefore, adequate maintenance of gas controls and valves is essential to safety in operation.

Inspection of burner cock vents will indicate leakage of gas. The cocks must be lubricated with grease as often as inspection and operation indicates its necessity. Exposure of cocks to heat increases the frequency of greasing. During boiler outage, the cocks can be carefully inspected and lubricated. Installation of the gas cocks in tandem should be in such manner as to permit operation of control levers for each cock in the same way. This facilitates duplication of cock settings, and reduces the possibility of mistakes in operation.

The gas regulating controls and safety devices should be tested for positive operation. This procedure can be followed during boiler outages. Regulators should be designed to close in case of failure to control lines or mechanisms. Gas from the main supply lines may be reduced to burner-head-supply pressure at reducing-valve stations. This usually is 30 to 50 psig. These stations should be checked regularly to see that (1) there is no excessive leakage, and (2) the regulating valves work smoothly, providing a steady header-supply pressure. High- and low-pressure alarms in this type of installation warn of undesirable conditions. For a very high pressure drop, reducing valves may stick and freeze. Some means for heating these often must be provided. It may be that traps to drain condensation out of low points in the gas lines are needed. These traps must be checked periodically to see that they are working satisfactorily. The gas-leakage detector manufactured by the Mine Safety Appliance Company has been found highly effective in searching for gas leaks and should be used periodically for this purpose.

Furnaces and Steam-generating Equipment

Maintenance of the refractory-type furnace installed in power boilers 30 or more years ago was a major operating expense. It was kept at a reasonable figure by careful attention to design considerations to meet the service. One of the important design considerations covered the expansion movement of the refractory walls. Failure to provide for expansion resulted in the cracking of the refractory prior to any real defects from heat or erosion. It was necessary to provide expansion joints with seals. The seals and their sealing materials required careful maintenance in order to prevent leakage and air infiltration into the furnace, with attendant unfavorable effect on combustion efficiency.

As steam-generating units increased in size, the problem of structural stability developed. The expansion movement of the brickwork caused cracking and failure of bonds. The higher setting necessary for increased capacity of the unit and the limitations on furnace-heat releases imposed by the refractory posed serious problems for the designer. The load-carrying capacity of the firebrick is reduced by high temperature, and compression failure of the lower courses of brickwork developed. Firebrick with good load-carrying properties is deficient in expansion qualities under heat and tends to spall. Structural-steel bracing and buck stays were increased in size and number to offset the structural deficiencies of the refractory.

Molten ash has a highly erosive effect on refractories. Therefore, increase in furnace temperature with a tendency toward fusion of ash resulted in rapid damage to the brickwork.

While refractory maintenance costs in themselves are substantial, outage of the boiler for maintenance in many instances can be a more important factor. Solid-brick settings are still used for some light-duty boilers. Complete refractory furnaces can be operated successfully. However, the limitations of the refractory materials prevent full use of the unit's design capacity, except at the price of maintenance and availability.

Repair of furnace brickwork is relatively simple and can be done by a skilled mason. Brickwork repairs must be made with full allowance for expansion of the new brickwork. The new refractory must be dried out by a slow fire in the furnace. The duration of the drying-out period is contingent on the amount of new refractory in the furnace. This may take 3 to 10 days. The fire should be sufficient to maintain the water in the boiler hot enough to produce a light vapor at the boiler drum vent. Water in the boiler should be maintained at normal levels. Keep the superheater drains wide open.

Selection of firebrick should be based on the service requirements and location of repair. ASTM specifies seven grades of refractory. Present-day refractory materials are made to meet a wide range of service requirements. A firebrick with minimum deformation under load should be selected for locations such as the lower courses where dead-weight load is heavy. The more porous or less dense qualities are suited to applications where thermal shock is expected as a result of wide-range furnace temperatures. A dense brick tends to spall under these conditions. In locations where molten slag is expected, select a brick with low absorption characteristics.

The development of water cooling has changed the furnace maintenance problem completely. Maintenance costs and boiler outage have been reduced to an insignificant amount. Water-wall design is flexible in that it can be applied in amounts and in furnace locations to meet combustion requirements. In addition to low maintenance costs for furnaces, water cooling favorably affects the maintenance of boiler tubes. The first row of boiler tubes is relieved of excessive heat absorption normally found in an all-refractory furnace. The extension of water cooling to the hopper bottom of the furnace results in maintaining the ash in a granular condition, thus relieving the refractory bottom of erosion from molten ash.

Expansion, the problem inherent in the all-refractory setting, disappears in the water-cooled installation. Expansion problems in the latter type of furnace are minor. The pressure parts, i.e., the boiler and water walls, expand together. Local expansion differences between steel and the refractory parts are offset without the need for expansion joints. Furnace design, based on expansion characteristics of steel and refractory, washes out the expansion differential and permits a continuous refractory casing around the furnace without expansion joints. This type of furnace will remain airtight and require practically no maintenance.

Stoker-fired furnaces, with the exception of the underfeed stoker, all have made use of an arch over the fuel bed. These installations have a unit consisting of a front arch, a rear arch, or a combination arch. The combustion requirements of the fuel and the type of stoker have dictated the arch to be used. These serve a two-fold purpose in burning the fuel in that they reflect radiant heat back into the fuel bed to aid ignition of raw fuel, and they provide turbulence in, and therefore better combustion of, the gases arising from the fuel bed. The increased use of over-fire air jets provides the necessary turbulence. The increased ratings in the furnace aid in the trend toward reduction of the arch areas.

These arches always have been subject to severe service, with arch-refractory maintenance costs exceeding by far similar costs for other parts of the furnace. The belated adoption of water cooling of the arch construction brought a gratifying reduction in arch maintenance. The construction frequently used is one composed of bare tubes with refractory projecting between them to the centerline of the tube. The combination arch-type furnace has a considerable arch area exposed to the fire. Complete water cooling has produced no unfavorable effect on combustion, and has eliminated arch refractory as a maintenance problem.

While water-cooled construction has been relatively free from maintenance, there are definite precautions to be observed in order to prevent an increase in maintenance expense. The amount of water-cooled tube surface exposed to the fire is an important factor in operation and tube maintenance. Exposure of a short length of tube to furnace heat, where the tube is normally covered by refractory, will result in a high concentration of heat at that area. The resultant sluggish circulation at that point is not sufficient to carry off the heat rapidly enough. The tube tends to overheat and early failure results. This same condition may obtain in side-wall tubes of stoker-fired furnaces if the circulation is inadequate because of poor design.

Water-screened tubes in the furnace bottom normally have a long life—20 or more years. They are subject to physical damage from large and heavy pieces of slag falling on them from high points in the furnace. The refractory in the furnace bottom as well suffers damage from falling slag. Burner rings in oil, gas, or pulverized-coal furnaces burn out from radiant heat of the furnace. The burner ring is repaired, usually with a refractory cast in place. Skill in mixing and applying the refractory and proper drying out are important to successful repair and reasonable service life. An average of 4 years' service can be experienced when the work is done properly, which is at least 100 per cent longer than the service life of burner rings repaired by an ordinary mason.

Oil and coal as fuels both present problems in maintenance of clean heating surfaces. Where deposits from the products of combustion collect on the boiler tubes, systematic cleaning of the tubes must be a regular procedure. In the burning of certain coals, there is a tendency to coat the bottom row with a hard, tenacious slag. This type of coating yields only to lancing with either water or steam. The cleaning interval may be best established by using draft loss and exit gas temperatures as a guide. The Detroit Edison Company reported, "Increasing humidity of combustion air to at least 16 lb of water per 1,000 lb of dry air has been found to reduce greatly fireside deposit troubles in stoker-fired steam generators at the Delray Plant. It is believed that by keeping the heating surfaces cleaner than normal, humidification may improve average boiler efficiency sufficiently to compensate thermally for the water added to the combustion air, leaving a pronounced gain in availability and lower maintenance. Humidification appears to increase volatilization from the fuel bed, particularly of silicon compounds."

The deterioration in quality of some fuel oils has brought with it new cleaning problems. Formerly, the fuel oils were relatively trouble-free from ash and slag deposits. Ash from many present-day oils contains large quantities of alkaline sulfates and vanadium pentoxide. Both have low fusing temperatures, and tend to build up slag coatings on the heating surfaces. After each cleaning period, the surfaces are free from this slagging action. However, once it starts, the rate of build-up increases rapidly. These deposits are cleaned off with the unit both in service and out of service by water washing. The in-service washing is effected by using a hand lance and hot boiler feedwater. This should be applied only to carbon-steel surfaces, such as the boiler tubes. There is some danger of damage if used on the surfaces subject to high metal temperatures, such as superheater tubes. High-alloy-steel tubes in high-pressure high-temperature installations should never be water washed in service because of the possibility of cracking from the quenching effect of the water. The out-of-service washing should be followed by adequate drying-out measures to prevent corrosion due to acid formation.

The use of additives to the fuel oil has met with some success in the control of these slag deposits. Studies now in progress indicate further possibilities. The additives used to date with the best results are alumina and dolomite. A report on these studies was given in the paper, Application of Additives to Fuel Oil and Their Use in Steam Generating Units, by McIlroy, Holler, and Lee, presented at the ASME meeting in December, 1952.

When a steam-generating unit is prepared for periodic or annual inspection, certain precautions should be observed for the protection of personnel and equipment. The ASME Boiler Code Committee publication, "Suggested Rules for Care of Power Boilers," outlines a suggested procedure for this inspection.

Before the furnace is opened, the steam soot blowers should be operated just before the fire is extinguished. The furnace draft should be increased above normal during this blowing period. No soot blowing should be done after the fire has been extinguished because of explosion hazards. The walls, baffles, tubes, and drums, should be thoroughly cleaned of slag, ash, and soot deposits to permit thorough examination of all parts.

The fireside inspection is just as important and supplements the inspection of the waterside surfaces. Plate and tube surfaces exposed to the fire are checked for bulging and blistering. The cause of the blisters may be determined by waterside inspection. The repair must be approved by the authorized inspector. Blistered tubes are cut out and replaced with new. Seams and tube ends must be examined carefully for leakage.

Lap joints are apt to crack where plates lap in a longitudinal or straight seam. Evidence of leakage at this point may require removal of the rivets to determine possibility of cracks in the seam. Cracks in shell plates are usually dangerous, except if these are fire cracks which run from the edge of the plate into the rivet holes of girth seams. The extent and seriousness of fire cracks should be thoroughly investigated. The inspector will pass on the seriousness of these cracks.

Tubes are tested by tapping with a light hammer to show up thinness. Tubes in horizontal fire-tube boilers tend to fail at the ends toward the fire. Tubes of vertical tubular boilers develop thinness at the upper ends due to lack of water cooling. Impingement of ash and fuel particles in areas of strong draft will cause erosion of tubes. Leaks in or near the tubes set up corrosive action due to acid from water spray and soot mixtures. Check to see if baffling is in place. Small leaks through the baffles are a source of localized overheating of tubes or erosion by fly ash. Large leaks or displaced tiles will affect the gas temperatures in the various passes of the furnace. Check the clearance between baffles and furnace walls.

The alignment of soot-blower nozzles with respect to the boiler tubes and blowing arcs must be checked and the tubes examined for possible cutting by jet impingement. Checks for bowed tubes may be made by using a straightedge across the tubes. Signs of overheating, sagging, and bulging of tubes may be detected by looking along the tubes.

Superheater supports and clamps should be checked. If slag works in between them and the superheater tube, they lose the cooling effect of the steam in the tubes and may be burned off as a result. Loss of support will result in sagging and misalignment of superheater elements, resulting in damage from exposure to impingement of ash particles or the steam-jet action of soot-blower nozzles.

Where the boiler drums require refractory or insulation protection, they should be inspected carefully for cracks and disintegration. This protection must be maintained in good condition.

Air infiltration, contingent on its magnitude, can be a sizable potential source of operating losses. The design of the steam-generating unit and its furnace influence the effectiveness of efforts to control the point of possible air leakage into the setting. In general, all doors, seals around piping at point of entrance to the setting, seals at drums and headers, expansion joints, and ash-pit openings are potential sources of air leakage.

Rolling of tubes should be assigned only to experienced workmen. It is preferable to underroll rather than overroll new or leaky tubes. The hydrostatic test will detect insufficient rolling. Overrolling may result in damage to the tube-sheet ligaments between tube holes. The cause of leaky tubes should be determined if lasting results are to be attained. Check especially expansion movement of boiler elements.

Repairs by welding should be made only with the approval of the authorized state or insurance inspector. No welding of pressure parts should be done by anyone other than a welder certified and approved by the insurance inspector.

Steam-generating Equipment. The steam-generating equipment in an industrial power plant consists of a boiler as the main steaming-element unit. In addition, it may include one or more of the following: water-cooled furnace, superheater, and economizer units. The water-cooled furnace, if used, is considered as part of the boiler circulating system containing a mixture of steam and water.

The fire-tube boiler is limited to relatively small and low-steam-pressure installations. The water-tube boiler, with its flexibility, can be used for pressures over 150 psi and larger steaming capacities. This design may be obtained in either straight-tube or bent-tube types. The straight-tube boiler has horizontally inclined tubes with either sectional-header or box-header designs. The bent-tube boiler, with its better circulation and its ready adaptability to the addition of water-cooling elements, is more prevalent in installations of higher pressures and higher steaming capacities.

Straight-tube boilers may be either the box-header or sectional-header type. Each is equipped with horizontal steam drums, which may be arranged as longitudinal drums or as cross drums. Tubes are rolled into the headers, which in turn are connected to the steam drum by horizontal and vertical circulators for uptake and downcomer headers respectively.

The bent-tube boiler consists of a bottom water drum and one or more upper steam and water drums. The drums are connected by bent tubes which serve as circulating elements for water and steam. Expansion of the boiler elements must be provided for in the design of the unit. Boiler designs provide for either top or bottom supports. The top-support designs provide either saddles or U hangers under each of the drums. Boiler and furnace cooling tubes are supported from the drums or headers to which they are connected. The supports must have sufficient movement to allow for expansion of the pressure elements. In the bottom-support design, the load is taken by this lower drum, which is supported on saddles. In this instance, the boiler is anchored at only one point. During initial operation of the unit after drying-out and boiling-out operation, the expansion of the pressure parts when under full pressure and temperature must be checked carefully. Any restriction in the expansion movement by structural members in the boiler setting, refractory sections, or external piping may cause damage to either the expanding pressure parts or the elements restricting their movement.

The designer provides a feedwater-supply header in the boiler drum and such other drum internals as may apply to the type of boiler in order to limit or eliminate steam contamination. There are many types of purification equipment in use. They are intended to remove water and foam from the steam. In cases where a high degree of purification is required, the steam is washed by feedwater, which results in final elimination of small particles of moisture and impurities. The internal elements must be inspected for corrosion and dirt deposits. They must be free from leaks, especially in spots where leakage will recontaminate the steam. Since all or portions of these parts must be removed for access to boiler tubes, care must be exercised in reinstalling them to prevent leaks. It is important to understand the principles of operation on which the design is based, in order to check tightness of joints where they must be absolutely tight.

Hydrostatic tests are applied to the boiler, water wall, and superheater elements during installation or after repairs to pressure parts. The usual test pressure is $1\frac{1}{2}$ times design pressure. The test pressure should be applied with a small hand pump, or one with which the pressure may be increased slowly under accurate control. Safety valves should be gagged during hydrostatic testing in order that they may not be opened.

Procedures to be followed during initial operation or after extensive repairs include drying out of the refractory surfaces, boiling out the internal side of the pressure parts, and starting up the unit. They are outlined in detail in the ASME Boiler Code publication, "Suggested Rules for Care of Power Boilers." The suggestions given there are basic rules for safe care and operation of the equipment. Their effect on maintenance is second only to the safety of operation which is the prime objective of the rules.

Corrosion and scale deposits are the main problems of the upkeep of the internal parts of the pressure parts. The feedwater and its proper treatment are the most effective means of preventing these deposits.

Deaeration for the complete removal of oxygen from feedwater is the most effective preventive measure for elimination of potential corrosion. Chemical treatment of boiler feedwater is of such importance to safety of operation and maintenance of steam-generating equipment that it should be entrusted only to a person thoroughly versed in the chemistry involved. The proper chemical treatment and methods of application are best established by the feedwater chemist. Treatment is based on feedwater characteristics, design of the steam generator, and operating requirements. The operator responsible for application of the treatment procedure should be thoroughly trained for it. Frequent internal inspections should be made to check on the effectiveness of the treatment and methods of control.

The usual daily check of oxygen content in feedwater is not conclusive as an indication of satisfactory deaerator operation. A 24-hr check by a recording analyzer may reveal the presence of disturbing amounts of oxygen under varying load conditions. A survey of amounts and causes of oxygen in deaerated feedwater, by Grabowski, Ongman, Willsey, and Nelson, of Combustion Engineering, Inc., Research Department,[1] indicated the following as factors contributing to oxygen in feedwater:

1. Introduction of undeaerated or partly deaerated condensate to the feedwater.
2. Feedwater heaters which operate normally under positive pressure, but drop to vacuum under light loads.
3. The addition of heater drips directly to the condensate system.
4. The presence of excessive gland seal leaks.

The introduction of an oxygen scavenger such as sodium sulfite into the deaerated feedwater is used extensively to remove traces of oxygen remaining in the feedwater. This treatment should be employed only under competent advice.

In the past, hard-scale formations in boiler tubes were normally removed by turbining. The removal of such scale in various thicknesses, some thicknesses too thin for mechanical removal, has been effectively attained by chemical cleaning with an inhibited acid. The actual cleaning by experts in the chemical-cleaning field can be attempted only after the chemical characteristics and amount of scale in the boiler have been determined. A wide range of chemicals are used for solvents, contingent on the scale or deposit to be removed. Oil and grease deposits from steam-engine condensate are removed by an alkaline boil-out. The use of an inhibited acid for removal of scale leaves the boiler metal clean and reveals the true condition of the metal. Cleaning to the metal surface may reveal any stress areas and cracks which may be due to fatigue, embrittlement, or corrosion. In preparation for acid cleaning, certain protective steps should be taken. Valves and boiler auxiliaries having brass or bronze parts must be protected. Table 2-1 shows data covering corrosion factors of some trim materials. Proper venting of acid vapors and gases is necessary. The unit to be cleaned must be positively isolated from all connecting piping. Acid cleaning is followed by draining and thorough flushing, and pumping a neutralizing solution through the unit until the effluent shows a definite alkaline reaction. Chemical cleaning of steam-generating equipment should be performed only by experts in this field in order to effect most efficient cleaning and protect the unit from damage.

Maintenance of adequate circulation in the boiler and water-wall tubes is imperative to successful and continued service of a steam-generating unit. The evidence of lack

[1] Problems in Deaeration of Boiler Feedwater, *Combustion*, March, 1955.

of proper circulation can be determined usually by inspection. The tubes show stripes or water-level markings as an indication of inadequate flow, and the presence of a stratum of steam next to the exposed surface of the tube rather than the cooler mixture of steam and water.

The correction of this deficiency is primarily a boiler design problem. Changes to furnace baffling may correct the trouble. It may require changes to the pressure parts themselves, and even alterations or additions to boiler-drum internals. The boiler manufacturer can provide the most effective corrective measures for inadequate circulation.

Table 2-1. Corrosion Factors

Alloy	Resistance to 5 per cent inhibited hydrochloric acid at 150°F		Acceleration of attack on SAE 1020 steel in contact with the alloy
	Individually	Contacting steel	
Hastelloy "B" (rolled)	Excellent	Excellent	1.0
Hastelloy "D" (cast)	Excellent	Excellent	3.0
316 stainless steel	Good	Excellent	1.4
Stellite No. 6	Good	Excellent	Pitting around stellite
317 stainless steel	Good	Excellent	1.8
310 stainless steel	Good	Excellent	1.4
Hastelloy "B" (cast)	Good	Excellent	2.4
Ni-Resist No. 4	Good	Good	2.4
Ni-Resist No. 1	Fair		
303 stainless steel	Fair	Fair	1.5
420 stainless steel	Fair		
"S" monel	Fair		
"K" monel	Poor	Excellent	2.8
316 stainless steel (nitrided)	Poor		
SAE 1020 steel	Poor		
Beryllium copper	Poor	Excellent	4.1
SAE 8630 steel	Poor		
416 stainless steel	Poor		

From W. G. Steinmiller and H. G. Ebert, Yarnall Waring Co.

Low water in a boiler is the operator's warning of impending trouble and possible damage to the equipment. If the operator loses the water level in the gage glass, he should immediately blow down the water column as an aid in determining the water level. If the water level is low, the decision to keep the boiler on the lines would be made by the person responsible for the shift, who should be fully aware of the existing operating conditions. Section VII of the Boiler Code advises as follows:

When the level of the water is not visible in the water glass, blow down the water column or gage glass to determine whether the existing level of the water is above or below the water glass. If the water level is below the water glass, stop the supply of air and fuel and close the dampers and ash-pit doors, unless fully in touch with the entire situation as to boiler feedwater supply and positively certain that it is safer to continue steaming the boiler than to reduce the steaming rate.

Check feed lines, if found advisable not to stop the steaming rate. If low water is caused by operating conditions, remedy it immediately before resuming normal steaming rates. If any uncertainty exists, do not change the feedwater supply, do not open the safety valves, or change the steam outlet valves, or make any adjustment that will cause a sudden change in the stresses acting on the boiler. In the case of hand-fired boilers, do not disturb the fire except to cover it with green coal or wet ashes. Where stokers are used, stop the fuel feed, shut off the air supply, leave stack damper open, and open the fire doors. After the fire is banked or out, close the feedwater valves. When the boiler is sufficiently cooled, close the fire doors and cut the boiler off the line. Determine the cause of low water and remedy it before the boiler is again placed in service. Carefully examine the boiler for the effects of possible overheating before placing it in service.

In the case of boiler or water-wall-tube failure, the boiler drum will tend to empty although it will still be under steam pressure. The outlet valve should be closed as promptly as possible in order to prevent too rapid a drop in temperature, and to reduce the quenching effect on boiler drums from the cooler feedwater still entering the drum. Therefore, if a tube failure is sufficiently serious to justify taking the boiler off the line, shut off the fire, as noted previously for emergency operation under fuel-burning equipment; completely cut off the feedwater supply, shut the boiler outlet valve, and adjust air if possible through the side doors of the furnace. The unit should be allowed to cool as under normal operation. A complete inspection should be made of the drums and tubes to determine the extent of any incipient cracks on the drums or tubes. All repair work is followed by a hydrostatic test under the supervision of the authorized boiler inspector.

Tube failures and tube bulges are the most common sources of failure and consequential troubles in water-tube boilers. The basic cause of most bulging and eventual tube failure is overheating of the tube. The high heat rates of the water-tube boiler make the tubes vulnerable to overheating with a scale thickness that would not cause trouble in a fire-tube boiler. Through flame impingement, the concentration of heat develops such a high rate of heat input that the water is driven away from the surface of the tube, leaving a blanket of steam. Overheating develops, followed by a bulge, and then the tube ruptures. The alternate overheating and chilling of the tube due to splashing of the boiler water may cause quench cracks.

The repair of a bulge should be undertaken only by an expert, and only with the approval of an authorized inspector. If the bulge is not deep or burned, the bulged area should be heated to a dull red and hammered back to its original tube shape. A 2- or 3-lb hammer is used. Blows should be applied at the periphery of the bulge, gradually reducing it in size. The bulge area must be maintained at a red heat while working it back in shape, so as to keep the metal above the range of "blue brittleness," which occurs at 300 to 700°F.

A bulge that is burned should not be hammered into shape. It should be cut out and a new section of tube welded in its place. The abutting edges should be beveled to form an included angle of approximately 45°. Welding should be done only by a welder certified by the insurance carrier. The work must be approved by an authorized inspector.

When a steam-generating unit is taken out of service for an extended period, special precautions are necessary to protect the boiler, water wall, and superheater parts, as well as the economizer if this is included in the unit. Precautions against corrosion are most important, as well as periodic checks during the outage period.

The internal surfaces may be protected by use of one of two recommended methods. The details of these two methods, i.e., dry storage and wet storage, are outlined in Sec. VII, ASME Boiler Code, under Control of Chemical Conditions.

The external surfaces of the unit also must be prepared for any extended outage period. Pressure parts, and in fact all metal surfaces, should be completely cleaned of all ash and soot deposits. Accumulations of ash, soot, and unburned fuel should be removed from the grates and furnace bottoms, as well as ash hoppers. Although the furnace should be closed up, the difficulty of maintaining a dry condition in the furnace may require the use of coke to maintain conditions above the dewpoint. Frequent checks of furnace conditions are necessary to prevent condensation on metal surfaces.

In addition to routine or other inspections by the plant personnel, an annual inspection is required by the state in which the boiler is registered. This inspection is primarily concerned with safety of the unit. Therefore, since safety is contingent on the condition of the equipment, the results of the inspection have a direct bearing on its maintenance. The inspection covers a meticulous search for evidence of overheating, corrosion, leakage at seams, and leakage at all joints.

The boiler must be opened and prepared for both internal and external inspection. The boiler is emptied and washed out. The unit must be permitted to cool down naturally.   Manhole plates and handhole covers are removed.   The furnace is cleaned and soot removed from tubes and all surfaces to be inspected.   If moisture shows through the insulation, the inspector will want the insulation removed.   Brickwork covering a vulnerable area or part of the boiler must be removed.   Insulation and jacketing along longitudinal seams of shells or drums must be removed so inspector can check the condition of rivets.   Suspected thin spots in the metal may need to be drilled for gaging the thickness of the metal.

The inspector's internal check will cover scale, oil, action of feedwater treatment on metal, corrosion (especially along or next to a seam), grooving, and cracks along longitudinal seams.   The stays are inspected for even tension, and the ends are examined for cracks where stays are punched or drilled for rivets or bolts.   Manholes and all openings are examined both internally and externally for deformity or cracks.   Openings to water-column connections, dry pipes, and safety valves must be free of obstructions.   Manhole covers and drum openings are checked for corrosion on the seat surfaces, as well as cracks.   Tubes inside headers are checked for scale.   Both downcomers and risers are checked for scale and condition of the tubes.   Ligaments between tube holes will be checked for cracks and signs of weakness.   Tube ends are checked for corrosion and erosion.

The attachments on the boiler are on the inspector's list for check.   Safety valves on the boiler and superheater are inspected to note their general condition and freedom from foreign material between coils, and pressure settings of each valve with regard to operating pressures of the boiler unit.   The superheater valve must be set to blow before boiler valves in order to protect the superheater from damage.   Safety valves should be tested by popping only with steam on the unit.   Steam gages must be removed and calibrated and piping to gages blown out.   The water columns, their piping, and attachments require careful inspection for conformity to code requirements.   The steam piping drains toward the column so water cannot accumulate in steam connections and give a false reading.   The check valve and stop valve in feedwater inlet, the main steam stop valve, and blowoff valves must be checked, and they must be in good working condition.   Setting and operation of soot blowers is checked to protect boiler and superheater tubes from damage due to jet action of steam.

The annual internal and external inspection of the steam-generating unit is a most vital check on its condition as to both code safety requirements and satisfactory operation.   The more thoroughly its internal and external surfaces, as well as fittings and attachments, are cleaned, the more complete will be the inspection.   A complete inspection is important in order to effect necessary repair.

Superheater.   Faulty operating methods and internal deposits are the principal causes of superheater-tube failures.

Inadequate steam flow during starting up, shutting down, and banking may subject the superheater elements to excessive gas temperatures without the sufficient cooling effect of the steam.   The control of furnace conditions is essential at these periods to prevent overheating the elements.   During starting up, the superheater tubes are subjected to the heat of the gases, but no steam will pass through them until the boiler water has reached steaming temperature.   As soon as the boiler develops a slight pressure, the drum vent valves are closed, and all vented steam is passed through the superheater.   The drain or vent valve on the superheater outlet header must be fully opened until the unit is placed on the line.   Variations in the opening of this valve should be made in accordance with instructions of the boiler manufacturer.   The firing-up period must provide sufficient time to permit evaporation of condensate trapped in the tubes, especially in the pendant type of superheater.

The superheater safety valve is always set at a lower pressure than the boiler-drum safety valves as a protection for the superheater during sudden loss of load.   This provides for steam flow through the superheater for cooling purposes.

When the unit is shut down, the superheater outlet-header vent valve is opened wide as soon as the boiler stops delivering steam.   The drain valve remains open until the boiler is placed on the line again.

During banking periods, proper control of furnace conditions will help considerably to protect tubes.   At this time, the superheater-outlet vent valve must be opened to provide steam flow until the furnace gas temperatures are reduced to a safe level for the protection of the superheater.   Most warping of superheater tubes and resultant failure result from not following the necessary precautions during starting up, shutting down, and banking periods.

According to boiler insurance records, internal deposits from water carryover cause the greatest number of tube failures.   Solids in the water dry out and tend to build up a layer of concentrated material which insulates the tube metal from the cooling effect of the steam.   Even a thin layer can cause tube failure from overheating.

The source of this carryover is the proper point of attack for prevention of this difficulty.   Feedwater conditioning to prevent foaming and priming is the basic corrective measure.   Concentration of solids in the boiler must be held at a sufficiently low level to prevent carryover.   The condition of steam separators and baffles in the boiler drums must be checked for leakage and steam tightness.   This is especially necessary after a unit overhaul where parts of these elements are removed for access to boiler tubes.   The spray from leaks in the baffles or steam separator contaminate the steam going to the superheater, and the solids separate out in the superheater tubes.

External cleanliness of superheater tubes and supports helps to limit maintenance costs.   The build-up of slag and ash deposits causes laneing of gases and localized overheating, and imposes extra weight on supporting elements.   Slag or ash build-up between superheater supports and boiler tubes insulates the hangers from the cooling effect of the steam and water in the tubes, and may cause burning of hangers.

A check list should be prepared for use during boiler unit outages both of short duration and for overhaul.   This list should include a check of all the elements for alignment, warping, and bulging.   Inspect the condition of hangers, spacers, link supports, and lugs.   Check the superheater tube connections at the inlet and outlet headers for steam leakage.   Failure to repair such leaks promptly will result in steam cutting of the tube seats.   Check the pressure drop through the superheater as an indication of the internal cleanliness of the unit.   Check the alignment, location, and operation of the soot blower nozzles with relation to the superheater elements.

Welding serves as an effective and quick means for repair of a burned-out tube.   The welding must be done by a certified welder under the direction of an authorized inspector.

Economizers.   The economizer is one of the first heat-recovery units to be added to the steaming unit in boiler installations.   Because of its design, it provides lower-cost heating surface than that in the boiler.   It absorbs heat from the flue gases before they pass to the stack or air preheater, if the latter unit is included in the installation. The feedwater is heated in the economizer before passing to the boiler.

Operating pressures, condition of feedwater, and station design all affect the design. Boiler pressures not exceeding 250 psi permit use of cast-iron tubes and headers. Undeaerated water and limitations in chemical treatment favor use of cast-iron for its resistance to corrosion, and restrict the design to straight tubes for mechanical cleaning.   Low feedwater temperatures due to lack of steam-turbine stage-heating facilities impose an internal as well as an external corrosion problem best met by the use of cast iron.

Adoption of higher steam pressures and temperatures brought with it the use of steel, and economizer designs with more economical tube size and spacing as well as improved tube forms and arrangements.   The innovations that made these advances possible were deaeration and proper treatment of feedwater, and preheating of the water going to the deaerator to temperatures above the dew-point temperature of the flue gases.

Internal corrosion will result from oxygen in undeaerated water.   The oxygen in the water is driven off as the water temperature rises in the economizer and attacks the internal surfaces of the tubes.   Deaerating heaters of proper design and capacity will give practically complete elimination of oxygen and reduce carbon dioxide in the feedwater.

Adequate treatment of feedwater is essential to eliminate scale formation and prevent corrosion.   Undissolved solids in the feedwater build up in the economizer tubes, reducing heat transfer and restricting flow through the unit.   The pH of the feedwater should be maintained at a value of 8 or more to reduce its corrosive effect on the steel tubes.

The pressure drop across the economizer is a reliable indication of the internal condition of the tubes. The straight-tube economizer lends itself to mechanical cleaning. However, chemical cleaning can be used in this type of unit, and must be used for adequate cleaning of the continuous-tube type and most of the modern designs.

The external cleanliness of the economizer materially affects its efficiency. Therefore, modern designs provide tube spacing and arrangements to permit effective use of soot blowers. Temperatures of the gases before and after the economizer serve to indicate the condition of the unit. The elements must be carefully adjusted and checked at each boiler outage to maintain the correct position of the nozzles and avoid steam-jet impingement on the tubes.

External corrosion may result from water vapor in the flue gases condensing on the tubes. Sulfur in the gases combines with the condensate and sets up active corrosion of the tubes. This is influenced by the percentage of sulfur products in the flue gases, the type of fuel, and method of firing. The most effective correction of this source of corrosion is through maintaining a feedwater temperature above the dew-point temperature of the gases. It is safe to use a feedwater temperature above 212°F in this instance.

External corrosion of this same type may result from leakage of water at flanged or rolled joints and in combination with sulfur. This type of leakage is the result of rapid and recurring temperature changes due to intermittent feed of water to the unit. Inspection of all joints should be made during outage of the unit.

Air Preheaters. The air preheater commonly used in industrial power plants is a tubular, a plate, or a regenerative type. In the tubular heater, the gas travels in a single pass inside the tubes while the air passes outside the tubes in either single or multiple passes. The plate type is arranged for counterflow of gas and air through narrow alternate lanes. The heating surface in the regenerative air preheater is made up of numerous specially formed steel sheets called heating elements. These elements absorb heat from the flue gas flowing through one-half of the preheater structure and release it to the incoming cold air as it passes through the other half of the structure in counterflow. The heating elements are arranged in a rotor of cellular construction, which revolves slowly within the preheater structure. The rotor moves alternately through the air and gas streams so that transfer of heat is continuous.

The major factors in maintenance of all types of air heaters are cleanliness of surfaces exposed to flue gases and control of corrosion on these surfaces. The characteristics of the fuel burned, as well as the type of firing, have pronounced effects on the ash accumulations on the gas-swept surfaces. Ash from stoker-fired installations seems to cause more difficulty in this respect than ash from pulverized-coal furnaces.

With some coals, the ash deposits set up as hard, cement-like accumulations. In others, the ash is soft and tends to pack. Coals that develop a more abrasive ash tend to keep the tubes or plates clean and highly polished without excessive wear of these surfaces. The short and straight-through passages of the regenerative heater help to reduce the tendency for formation of ash deposits. The increase in both draft loss and the exit-gas temperature are indications of excessive fouling of these surfaces.

Cleaning mediums and methods vary according to the individual installation. Steam, air, and water are used with success. Steam and air are used most generally in coal-fired units. Washing is used with oil-burning installations. Washing with warm water has been used with success in all. Precautions must be used when washing in order to minimize the tendency to produce acid solutions, especially where the washing residue may be held in pockets. Use of an alkaline rinse and drying-out procedures are effective in retarding acid action. Plate heaters are particularly difficult to clean if they are badly plugged. These usually are designed with doors which permit sufficient access for inspection and lancing while unit is on the line.

Special arrangements of steam or air soot blowers have been designed to meet the individual installation requirements.   Precautions must be taken to avoid damage to the heater elements from jet impingement and the use of excessively high blowing pressures.   Tubular heaters may be cleaned very effectively by power-driven tube cleaners during overhaul periods.

Corrosion in air heaters is more likely to occur where the cold entering air reduces the metal temperature below the gas temperature dew point.   The water vapor in the gases condenses at these points, setting up a condition conducive to acid formation due to the presence of sulfur dioxide and sulfur trioxide in the gas.   This condition results in an accumulative corrosive deterioration of tubes and plate sections.   The corrosive effect on crimped sheets and rotor seals in the discharge end of the regenerative heater may be a major maintenance expense in this type of unit.   The design of these latter units provides for their regular replacement when necessary.   Inspection of vulnerable areas must be included in the list of items to be checked during shutdown.

Although tubular heaters cannot be inspected when the unit is in operation, an increase in draft loss through the unit or an unexplained increase in temperature of the gas leaving the heater is indicative of some degree of plugging.

Although many well-balanced air-preheater installations have no troubles from this type of corrosion, it is a major source of difficulty in many.   Where boilers operate over a wide load range, this type of corrosion may occur at low loads due to low gas temperatures prevailing at that point.   In such cases, provision for bypassing the heater with all or a portion of the cold entering air during low loads and starting-up is effective in controlling corrosion.   In other cases a portion of the hot air may be recirculated back to the inlet for mixture with the cold entering air.   Both of these corrective measures can be added in the field if found necessary.

The rotor seals whose function is to limit the loss of the air to the flue gas are subject to the same corrosive conditions as the cold-end heating surface.   Therefore, they should be inspected and replaced, if necessary, at least once a year to insure maintaining the minimum leakage.

The regenerative preheater, being a machine, has moving parts.   Such components as rotor support bearing, guide bearing, rotor drive unit, and electric motors, should be inspected at set intervals to insure that they are being properly lubricated.

Forced- and Induced-draft Equipment.   Forced- and induced-draft fans are of the centrifugal type and as a rule are ruggedly designed.   The service of each, especially the forced-draft fan, is reasonably simple.   The service rendered to the steam-generating unit for long periods of operation is most essential.   Therefore, these units should be inspected when out of service to assure continuity of operation.

Forced-draft fans have experience records of 25 years or more without major repairs.   Induced-draft fans protected by dust collectors have similarly favorable records.   This latter type of fan without such protection on pulverized-coal installations usually requires blade replacement every 6 to 12 months.

The following items should be checked for each type of fan where they apply:

1. Clean blades of fly-ash deposits to prevent shedding of deposits during operation thereby causing fan imbalance.
2. Inspect blades and fan-housing liners to assure that they are firmly attached.
3. Check clearance between stationary and moving parts of fan inlet seals, to prevent excessive leakage or inadequate seal at these points.
4. Clearance between fan-housing cutoff and blade tips should be checked for wear against original settings.
5. Check fan alignment and allowances for differential expansion of fan, coupling, and drive unit.   This should be checked under cold as well as hot conditions.
6. Induced-draft fan-shaft seals must be checked under load to prevent excessive tightness.
7. Check balance of rotor at full speed both with no air or gas flow and with full flow.
8. Check condition of bearings and oil reservoirs as well as water passages in water-cooled bearings.   Clean water passages chemically every 2 or 3 years.   (See comment re positive action of oil rings.)

9. Check fan housing and connecting ducts to prevent accumulation of debris which may adhere to the fan rotor and affect balance.
10. Check control dampers by hand to assure freedom from sticking or partial closing, conformity of damper position with markings on linkage, and excessive play in damper linkage.
11. Paint rotor annually with graphite to protect against corrosion.

The fan unit with a wide speed range may lack positive action of oil rings at extremely low speeds.   If this condition exists for long periods, the effect of inadequate lubrication will be evident on the bearing.   Positive lubrication can be secured

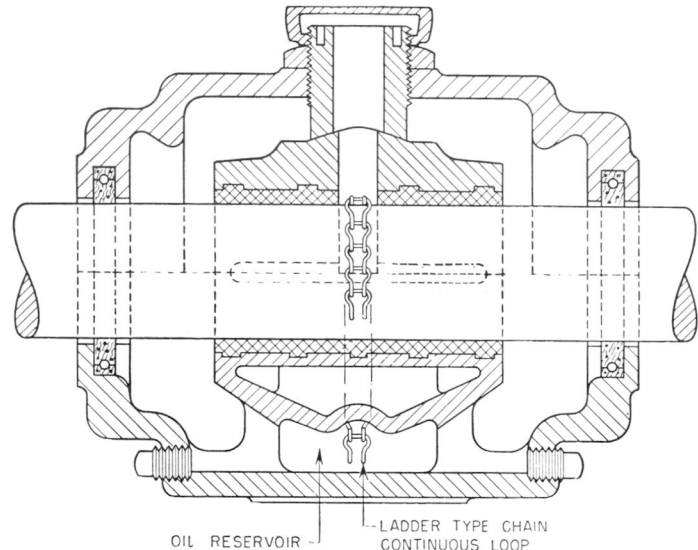

OIL RESERVOIR ⌐   ⌐LADDER TYPE CHAIN
                            CONTINUOUS LOOP

Fɪɢ. 2-14. Link chain in lubrication of water-cooled fan bearing.

through replacement of the oil ring with a continuous wire "ladder" link chain as shown in Fig. 2-14.   The chain starts to move with the first revolution of the shaft. It passes up from the oil reservoir, over the fan shaft, and back to the oil reservoir. This type oil carrier has the additional advantage of 180° contact with the shaft.

Turbine-Generator.   The advantages gained by the increase in industrial turbine-generator speeds from 1,800 to 3,600 rpm brought with them definite problems.   The higher-speed machines have all the problems found in the lower-speed unit, as well as some due to the increased speed.   The rotating mass of one to several tons moving in the casing with only a few thousandths clearance requires precision in manufacturing and installation.   The safety of personnel and equipment justify the utmost care in operation and maintenance.

Safe and economical operation of equipment is the basis of good maintenance.   It includes intelligent operation, good housekeeping, adequate spare parts, planned inspections and repairs, special attention during shutdown, a good operational log, securing adequate information from the manufacturer, insurance, and use of good inspection specialists during major inspections and repairs.   When the equipment involved has high potential power-release capacity such as steam generators, high-speed turbines, generators, air compressors, gas generators, etc., the responsibility and safety consciousness must be highly developed; and therefore, work on such equipment should not be left in the charge of repairmen or machinists.   The man in charge should be specially trained in operation and repair.   Slight flaws, cracks, wear on critical parts, distortions, or misadjustments mean little to the ordinary mechanic and usually escape his observation or attention, but may be the primary or the immediate causes of disastrous accidents to life and equipment, not to mention loss of production and income.

The amount to be spent for repairs on a turbine-generator depends on many factors such as availability of unit, its age, previous care received, accuracy of speed or cycles needed for a particular process, how many more years of service are expected (obsolescence). Regardless of all of these factors, the unit should at all times be in a *safe operating condition.*

The purchaser and manufacturer of a machine may cooperate to overcome any potential mistakes or deficiencies in the installation. For example, the manufacturer will check the design of steam-supply piping and the turbine foundations to prevent any thrust or strain on the turbine that will affect the alignment of the unit during and after installation. Alignment of the unit in the field requires the utmost care to reproduce the same precision in an assembled unit that it had on the factory test stand.

There are several methods that may be used in alignment of turbine-generators. A detailed description of five methods, together with a sag chart for tight-lining turbines and engines, is covered by J. H. Jansen in the 1952 issue of "Engineer's Data Book," published by the National Association of Power Engineers. Close adherence to these instructions should produce satisfactory results in alignment of both three- and four-bearing machines.

Operation of the machine in accordance with the manufacturer's instructions should result in maximum machine availability and help to keep maintenance costs at a minimum. The unit and its auxiliaries should be started in the order specified, and with full regard to warming-up recommendations. Reasonable attention to good housekeeping, such as checking and repairing steam, oil, and water leaks, favorably affect major maintenance costs. Dust and dirty surroundings create conditions that are conducive to development of maintenance work.

A preventive-maintenance schedule starts with operating maintenance. On a turbine-generator unit, the following daily checks should be made:

1. Check operation of the *throttle valve* by partially closing the valve, then reopening it to make sure the stem is free at the packing. Oil all links and connections. On valves with exposed threads on the stem, make sure that threads are clean. To improve operation of stiff valves, "Molycote" or similar lubricating material may be put on threads and bearings; however, avoid its use on free-turning valves, as operation may be eased to the point where slight vibration might close the valve and drop the load.

2. Check *oil level* in the main oil tank, and at the same time note any water condensation on the bottom of the oil-tank cover, as well as general condition of the oil. Check bearing temperatures by feeling with the hand as well as reading the thermometers. Where possible, note bearing return oil. Excessive vibration at governor linkages or bearings should be noted and immediately reported. Note oil leaks.

3. *Listen* with a listening rod or other device at turbine casing and bearings for rubbing noises; note any unusual noises or clicking at governor housing and oil pump.

4. *Excessive leakage* at the packings should be corrected. It may be caused by stopped drains or excessive back pressure at the drains, stuck steam-seal regulator if any, broken rings or springs, and rise in turbine casing pressure (includes loss of vacuum).

5. Check *governor* for hunting, by noting periodic motion of governor levers and linkages. Oil all joints and check operating valve gear for loose or stuck lever parts or stuck valves. Stuck valve stems may be relieved by a small application of beeswax at the packing box, unless more serious defects are present.

6. The *generator temperature* should be checked by feeling the casing or outer shell with the hand as well as testing with any temperature-indicating instruments provided. The collector rings and the exciter commutator should be checked for sparking, heat, and vibration of the brushes. The current (amps) in each phase should be balanced or equal. Loss of current in one phase (single-phase operation) of a three-phase machine for even a fraction of a minute will produce a rotating 120-cycle flux in the

generator field which will cause serious damage to the field core and retaining rings by heating and cracking them, sometimes completely wrecking the generator. Unbalanced load in the three phases tends to have a similar effect.

7. Any *unusual conditions* should be noted in the log book.

In addition to the above, the turbine should be "tripped" once a month by carefully overspeeding it to check trip mechanism, which is usually 10 per cent above operating speed unless otherwise specified by manufacturer. Do not run the unit more than 12 per cent above normal running speed. Stop and have the trip-governor reset to the proper trip speed. On extraction units, also check the nonreturn valve in the extraction line; on the external-lever type, make sure the lever moves freely and that the weight or any other part does not interfere with operation. Automatic or oil-tripped nonreturn valves are checked by tripping the main trip mechanism and noting operation. Before starting or stopping a turbine-generator, it is imperative to *make sure that stop valves in extraction lines are closed*. Extraction stop valves should be opened only after the generator carries load and *must be closed before* the breaker or generator switch is opened.

When starting a unit, warm the turbine by admitting enough steam to turn it over, and then run it at 300 to 600 rpm for the specified time given by the manufacturer, usually 30 to 60 min, depending on size and type. Gradually bring it to speed, noting critical speeds at which vibration takes place. Check trips by overspeeding, let speed drop below runnihg speed, reset the trip mechanism, and put the unit in normal operation. When a machine is taken off the line for only a few hours (say 2 hr or more), the initial drop in temperature of the turbine is such that the normal warming-up procedure should be followed. Excessive vibration may be encountered by rapid starting up under the assumption that the machine is warm enough to bring it up to full speed right away.

Good lubrication is vital to continued operation of the turbine-generator. The auxiliary oil-pumping equipment, as well as the main oil pump at the head end of the machine, must be in reliable operating condition and be operated to maintain specified oil pressure at each bearing. The preparations of the lubrication system for a new turbine are covered by recommendations of the Joint ASTM-ASME Committee on Turbine Lubrication. These provide for complete cleaning and flushing of the assembled system, with draining and complete removal of all flushing oil and contaminants.

An unaccountable rise in bearing temperature is cause for a prompt check of all possible causes. The pressure, temperature, and condition of the oil and the oil level in the reservoir should be checked immediately. The temperature and flow of water to the coil cooler can be checked quickly. If none of these sources is causing it, the trouble may be within the oil-distribution system, or the bearing itself. The oil-supply lines, the cooler, or the filter may be plugged or dirty. As a preventive measure, the oil cooler and filter, as well as the oil supply and drains to the bearings, should be cleaned periodically. While operating conditions will vary, it is considered desirable to hold the bearing outlet temperature at about 145°F, or at least within the range of 130 to 160°F. At the outlet of the oil cooler, the circulating oil should be held to a temperature range of 110 to 130°F. The oil should not be cooled below 100°F. The oil temperatures for any individual unit should be maintained in accordance with the turbine manufacturer's recommendations.

The oil must be maintained in satisfactory condition by adequate purification during service. Periodic inspections of the lubrication system are the best means of determining the adequacy of the maintenance practices. The advent of inhibited oils has caused radical changes in the past practices of handling turbine oils. Records of the Edison Electric Institute indicate that with inhibited oils it is possible to maintain clean oil after 100,000 hr in a turbine system that is in service 95 per cent of the time. Experience indicates that oil coolers will give service periods between cleanings three to five times greater than those where uninhibited oils are used.

Water in the oil is the major cause of oil breakdown. Excess water washes out the oxidation and rust-preventing inhibitors, resulting finally in a complete breakdown of the oil. Gland leakage is the frequent cause of this water contamination. The turbine glands must be maintained properly and the gland ejector equipment operated according to instructions. The gland ejector should be checked for scale and dirt, which is usually the cause of loss of gland vacuum. Moisture also may enter the lubrication system through condensation from the atmosphere in the sump tank. A careful watch should be kept for moisture from this source, and its cause promptly removed. Plugged vent piping on the oil sump will cause moisture to form on the tank sides above the oil level. Daily inspection of the tank will anticipate trouble from this source.

If the oil pressure drops off abruptly, the pump suction should be checked for low oil level. The oil pump should be checked during machine outage for excess wear. Extra care should be taken in making oil piping tight. Oil joints should be made up with a compound that does not dissolve in oil, form brittle beads inside the casing, or harden to a solid mass. Aviation Permatex No. 2 or Babbitt Softset No. 74 are effective for sealing, and can be removed easily.

Inhibitors in the oil may break down and separate out as a sludge, forming a plastic-like coating. The sludge adheres to the bearing surface as a brown deposit. It may be scraped off when new, but if not removed promptly, it then hardens to a glazed finish. The thrust bearing is particularly vulnerable since this coating tends to put a glazed finish on the face of the bearing surfaces. If this occurs, it is necessary to replace the thrust washer. It may be anticipated by inspection of the bearing.

Pittings in the bearings may be due to vibration, dirt in the oil, corrosive action of the oil, or electrolysis. In spite of inhibitors, oxidation in the oil is promoted by high oil temperatures and the presence of oxygen with metals such as brass, bronze, copper, and zinc. The hydrocarbons in the oil react with oxygen to form sludges and deposits. While the oil in this condition deteriorates, it also contains oxidation products that may be corrosive to certain types of babbitt. Bearings having a high lead content may pit as a result of oil-oxidation products. A high-tin babbitt will resist this type of attack. Galvanized tanks and piping, as well as use of copper and copper alloys, should be avoided as a preventive in this situation.

Aside from insufficient warm-up in starting a turbine, vibration is an indication of serious trouble that will require careful investigation by a vibration specialist. Spindle vibration may be produced by any one or more of the following causes:

1. Constant mechanical unbalance due to a bent shaft, missing blading, or rotor unbalance.
2. Variable mechanical unbalance due to rubbing between spindle and stationary section, cool water contacting a hot shaft, variable heat transfer to and from spindle, overheating exhaust by noncondensing operation, or strain on casing from external piping.
3. Coupling unbalance, misalignment, or worn coupling.
4. Blading may be damaged, eroded, or plugged by carry-over.
5. Wheels loose on shaft, loose thrust-bearing collars.
6. Excessive bearing clearance or packing clearance too small.
7. Slugs of water in steam or solids carry-over.

Usually the vibration shows unique characteristics, and if sufficient data are available, a vibration meter definitely will help in localizing the source of vibration. If check of the above possible sources does not reveal the cause, the machine should be opened for an internal inspection.

Rotor and diaphragm blade and shaft erosion may be caused by carry-over of water or solids in the steam. A leaky throttle valve will pass enough steam to set up pitting from corrosion, according to S. T. Powell,[1] feedwater consultant. Even though no corrosion may take place in the boiler, the carbon dioxide discharged from the boiler with steam may cause active corrosion of turbine blading, shafts, and diaphragms. This condition may result from condensation caused by frequent outage of the unit, which permits re-solution of the carbon dioxide. Preventive measures to combat this source of trouble include washing with an alkaline solution and passage of warm dry air through the unit to maintain temperatures above the dew point of the vapors in the

[1] Sheppard T. Powell, "Boiler Feedwater Purification." McGraw-Hill.

casing.   Before adopting any preventive method, the procedure should be discussed with the turbine manufacturer.

In addition to potential troubles from frequent outage of the unit, prolonged inactivity of the turbine can result in serious deterioration due to corrosion.   The turbine manufacturer will prescribe a detailed procedure for protection of the unit and auxiliaries during such periods.

Sticking of governor valves is caused frequently by carry-over of solids and water in the steam.   This in turn may cause the governor to hunt.   The effect on the turbine may be so severe as to cause the unit to trip out, or even may prevent the dropping of the load when required.

The plunger-type emergency governor functions independently of the main governor, and operates to prevent damage to the turbine in the event that the unit overspeeds due to failure of the main governor to operate.   This and the emergency tripping mechanism operate when overspeed occurs, to trip the throttle-valve trigger and close the valve, thereby shutting off the steam flow.   Effective maintenance methods provide for keeping the parts clean and lubricated.   All bearings and pins should be properly oiled.   Frequent inspections should be made of all moving parts, and adjustments made to detect wear and deterioration and variation in adjustment.

The throttle valve usually is packed with packing which requires no setting up on the glands.   If the packing eventually deteriorates, it should be replaced, but in no case should it be set up tight.   The packing must be free enough to permit the valve to trip shut.   Under no condition use a packing containing rubber, as this is quickly deteriorated by high temperatures and gums the valve stem, interfering with its operation.   Test the valve for tightness during turbine overhaul, since steam leaking into the turbine during idle periods will cause corrosion and distortion of the rotor.   The valve seats should be ground to prevent leakage in either the main or bypass valves. If a valve develops sluggishness, it should be disassembled for thorough inspection and cleaning.

The speed governor, with hand and remote control, valve-control mechanism, oil pump, and governor drive, all operate in coordination to maintain the speed of the turbine to meet load variations.   The governor should hold the turbine speed steady without hunting or jerky movements of the governor or its linkage.   Such difficulties may be caused by:

1. Poor adjustment, binding, or wear of governor linkages.
2. Wear in pilot valves or incorrect pilot-valve lead on replacement parts.
3. Excess wear of governor gear teeth or poor tooth contact between drive gears.
4. Low oil pressure.
5. Faulty compensation of lever mechanism of governor.
6. Misalignment of governor or drive shaft.

Faulty control tending to cause the unit to trip out or prevent dropping the load may be caused by:

1. Wear or binding of governor control linkage.
2. Failure of valves in steam chest to close due to sticking of valves in bar lift.
3. Improper adjustment of overspeed trip governor.
4. Low governor oil pressure or level.   On units with low oil level, low oil-pressure control may be the cause.
5. Sticking and leaking governor valves.
6. Faulty governor adjustment.
7. Faulty closure of nonreturn valve in extraction line on extraction or bleeder turbines.
8. Improper setting of throttle-valve trip or worn latches.

The oil pump and governor drive should be carefully inspected during turbine overhaul periods.   Draw all the oil from the tank, and clean the tank, strainer, oil passages, pump, and shaft casing.   Small oil pipes should be blown out with steam or air.   Inspect worm and worm-gear wheel contact.   The gear teeth will show a uniform contact of the worm across the centerline of its face when the proper vertical alignment is maintained. Check the teeth of the gear pump. Inspect the flexible drive or coupling for the worm, and the bearings of the worm shaft, and clean all oil grooves. If there is any doubt about the extent of wear on the bearings, replace them.

There should be no excess play in the centrifugal governor parts. The pivots of the governor normally are well lubricated from oil spill from the pilot valve. Replace worn pivots and pins. It is advisable to renew the governor and pilot valve as a unit. The bearings and pivots of the hand-control unit must be free of friction and lost motion. Check the clutch of the governor motor for defects. Inspect electrical circuit of motor.

Automatic extraction equipment is designed to control the flow of steam through that section of the turbine beyond the extraction opening so as to maintain a relatively constant pressure in the extraction line at any load or extraction flow within specified limits. The pilot valve and cylinder and linkage should be lubricated regularly and checked for wear. Looseness or lost motion in the operating linkage should be checked. During machine overhaul of linkages, pins and bearings should be checked for wear. The adjustment of limiting devices on the piston and cylinder should be checked to prevent any movement that might result in overtravel of the piston, or sticking in one position. If a grid valve is used, the valve and its seat are rubbed down with graphite during manufacture. This process should be repeated any time the valve is dismantled for inspection or repair. The grid valve is designed to pass a sufficient flow of steam even in its closed position to keep the stages beyond the extraction point from overheating. Under no circumstances should the unit be operated without maintenance of normal vacuum on the exhaust, and the normal flow of cooling steam through the low-pressure stages.

All extraction turbines are protected by a nonreturn check valve in the extraction line to protect the turbine from reverse flow of process steam to the extraction stage of the unit when the unit is taken off the line or is shut down by operation of the emergency overspeed governor. In many installations, this valve is operated automatically from the turbine-overspeed trip system to assure positive closure. Inspection of the external linkages should be made daily to assure that the valve is always in dependable condition. Leaking in the valve should be corrected promptly to protect the rotor from the corrosion due to steam when the unit is out of service. Any substantial back flow due to leakage or failure of the valve to close completely may result in overspeeding and wrecking of the turbine when the load is removed.

A thorough inspection requires a shutdown of the unit and dismantling all vital parts. Preferably this should be done every 2 years, but at least every 4 years. Small imperfections, wear, and damage usually can be corrected without much expense at frequent inspections, but become major and costly expense items when the unit is run too long. Oftentimes such neglect results in forced shutdowns, which mean expensive repairs and curtail plant production as well.

Plan the inspection procedure carefully to utilize space as well as manpower efficiently; in most plants both are at a premium. Make a summary of all serious defects as noted by the operational log. Suspected damage should receive priority, as repair or replacement may take time. Normal inspection, however, usually can start after the unit has cooled overnight. First remove the outer metal covering and heat-insulating material, and sweep or blow off all loose dust and dirt. Remove all levers, pipes, and apparatus that interfere with or may be damaged during bolt removal.

Impact wrenches usually pay for themselves on large or medium industrial turbines by saving in time and labor and added safety. Low-pressure units up to 400 psig usually have solid casing bolts that have to be slugged loose with a wrench and sledge. The nuts may be corroded or burned tight. Penetrating oils help to loosen the nuts. However, in some cases, heating the nuts and using beeswax may be necessary. In the severest cases it may be necessary to drill a hole vertically through the small section of the nut and split it. Care should be taken that replacement nuts are made of the material specified by the manufacturer. High-pressure turbines usually have hollow bolts which are stretched by heating. Proper heaters or torches are supplied and used as specified by manufacturer.

After all horizontal joint bolts, as well as packing boxes are removed, the casing is ready to be lifted.   Steel cables are recommended on account of safety.   Open the horizontal joint slightly by the use of jacking bolts in the joint, then adjust the rigging till the joint opening is uniform.   Remove the coupling cover and middle bearing if necessary, and turn the rotor while lifting.   Stop if unusual friction is noticed and check the upper casing for level.   If this procedure is followed, a successful lift may be made; otherwise the stationary parts of the turbine and diaphragms may damage the bucket covers or blading.

Next, remove all bearing caps, oil deflectors, generator end shields, brush riggings, and sometimes the exciter.   Open the main coupling and force the coupling faces apart to clear the coupling rabbet.   Remove the top half of bearing liners, thrust bearing, and connection between the main shaft and governor drive.   Rig and lift out the turbine spindle, using a cable-spreader if necessary so cable slings will not rest against wheels or blading.

Remove diaphragms from the lower half of the casing, and if any damage is noted, remove diaphragms in the upper half after the casing has been turned over.   Usually the last operation is simplified by removing the valve chests first.   Also, the valves may be inspected.

The diaphragms should be free from corrosion and scale, the vanes should be tight and free from pitting and edge erosion; if vanes are corroded and eroded through (so-called "laced") at the exit edges, some cutting back is possible so as to get a smooth, relatively straight edge.   But at this point it should be remembered that no cutting, welding, or machining is permitted on the casing, diaphragms, turbine shaft, wheels, blading, bucket covers, valve seats, or the field, except by direction of the manufacturer, because of limitations in design and material which are under his control.

Wheels, blading, covers, and shaft should be checked for cracks by one of several nondestructive testing methods such as ultrasonic, Magnaflux, Magnaglow, Zyglow, Chek-Spek, Dy-Chek, Spotcheck, etc.   The first four require specialists, the others may be used effectively by average mechanics.   Hammer test (light tapping) will usually detect loose buckets or wheels.   Wheels should have a clear metallic ring if everything is tight and flawless.   On high-efficiency units, the inlet edge of the blades should be worn back less than $1/16$ in., otherwise new blades and covers should be ordered.   A badly worn set of blades will increase thrust pressure and damage the thrust bearing as well as give poor efficiency.

The diaphragm fits in the turbine casing should be smooth without eroded spots indicating steam leakage or corrosion.   If erosion is present the corresponding diaphragm will also be cut.   Slight cutting may be corrected by lapping with grinding compound, but serious cutting (over 0.006 in. deep) will require boring out the casing and using stainless-steel inserts on the diaphragms.   This is an expensive and extensive repair and should be made only under manufacturer's supervision.

Bearings should be examined for wear, wiping, grit-cutting, electrolysis (generator bearing), and static electrolysis (turbine-end bearing or thrust).   Bearing clearances can vary from 0.001 to 0.0025 in. per inch of journal diameter without replacement except in special cases of pressure-type bearings.   Then follow manufacturer's instructions.   Generator-bearing electrolysis (dull and pitted appearance) results from stray shaft currents sparking and breaking down the oil film in the bearing.   Bearing insulation should be 1 megohm or more.   On some units, steam friction in the turbine rotor will generate high-voltage static electricity, which will produce electrolysis in turbine bearings, and sometimes the worm-gear drive.   Grounding devices are needed.   The governor worm-gear drive should be free but cannot stand excessive clearances or end play without producing a high-frequency oscillation of governor parts, resulting in poor governing and excessive wear of linkage pins.   The same result may be caused by too much gear backlash, irregular gear wear, slightly elliptic or off-center gear, bent pump shaft, worn main oil-pump gears, or pump gears rubbing the pump housing.

All governor pins should be just loose, never more than 0.005 in. loose.   Throughout the linkage system good operation cannot be obtained with worn pin connections.

Generator winding should be clean with no cracks in the coil varnish, and there should be no soft spots in the insulation, especially where the coils emerge from the core, as this is an indication of internal friction in the insulation and pulverizing. A smoky appearance of insulation with numerous pinholes is an indication of corona in a high-voltage generator. Slot wedges should be tight and there should be no obstructions in the air slots. Careful examination should be made to see that laminations are tight.

When the unit is reassembled, make sure that the thrust bearing is square and has 0.006 to 0.010 in. clearance for a landed thrust bearing. Other types should be as per instructions. The wheel clearances have to be checked. The wheels should be forced forward and the diaphragms wedged toward the generator so as to produce minimum clearances, which should match the original clearances or those given by the manufacturer. When the spindle and field are coupled up, check the shaft for runout and alignment sidewise by use of a roller rig at the generator end bearing. Check the vertical alignment with a tight line or by bearing reactions. The latter can be supplied by the manufacturer and simply calls for the actual weight of the shaft when it is in its running position.

Examine operating valves for erosion and spinning, and lap them in if necessary. Examine valve guides and bushings for excessive wear and galling. If damage is slight, stoning with an oil stone may suffice, but replace them if wear is excessive. Check valve-seat inserts for looseness and proper locking.

Cam-lift valve gears should be closely examined for loose pins and rollers. Flat spots on the rollers usually are an indication of tight roller pins and excessive turbine vibration.

Valve-chest joints, as well as the main turbine joints, should be well cleaned and slightly stoned before assembly to remove imperfections and burrs. A protective coating of sealing compound should be lightly applied to the joint before bolting up. On steam joints, good results have been obtained with Crane Joint and Thread Compound No. 425. Another effective mixture is composed of equal parts by weight of pulverized graphite and sifted pulverized red lead mixed to a paste in Schracks XXX boiled linseed oil. Oil joints are effectively sealed with Babbitt Softset No. 74, or by Aviation Permatex No. 2.

After overhaul and assembly, special care should be exercised in starting the unit. A unit with new carbon packing requires several hours at slow speed, and a little carelessness may result in a bent shaft. Metal labyrinth packing is not as sensitive and will take only a little more time than normal.

Metallizing by competent mechanics has been successful in repairing limited erosion in turbine shafts and exhaust casings. Metallizing on the shaft should not be attempted if the erosion or the necessary machining is so extensive as to weaken the shaft. The metallizing must be controlled to prevent distortion of the shaft from heating. The adjacent parts must be protected from effects of the spray. The final coating may be finished to size by grinding.

A sample of blade deposits should be taken and analyzed in order that corrective feedwater measures may be taken. Modern feedwater treatment has eliminated the large quantities of baked mud frequently encountered in the early days. However, even with modern methods of treating boiler feedwater and the use of superheated steam, blade deposits may be experienced. Several abrasive compositions may be used in cleaning the deposits from turbine blading. Some of these are fly ash, aluminum oxide, or 140-mesh silica sand applied as a jet of abrasive and water. The equipment commonly used consists of a sheetmetal housing built around the spindle to collect the mixture in a sump from which it is pumped back to the hose and jet.

The turbine casing must withstand pressures and temperatures that are often high and subject to wide variations. In spite of care in machining and adequate bolting, casing flanges develop leaks. When the top half of the casing is removed, leaks show up in the flanged surfaces as irregularly shaped grooves of varying depth. If a leak is not too great, it may be sealed with careful preparation of the joint and the use of one of several compounds. Remove all scale, burrs, dents, rust, and other foreign matter, getting down to bright metal. Thoroughly clean the top casing and lower it to within a few feet of its final position.   Then apply a thin coating of the joint compound with a putty knife or a good stiff brush.   If the casing is worn, do not use a quick-setting compound.   The compound has to remain fluid or plastic until the joint is bolted up tight.   As soon as the joint is covered, the casing is ready to be lowered into place.   A very satisfactory joint compound can be made up as needed, using heavy triple-boiled linseed oil without dryers.   First mix equal parts of powdered graphite and powdered red lead.   The graphite should be very finely powdered, such as US No. 205; or pulverized flake, such as Dixon's microfine; and the red lead should be sifted free of lumps and granules.   Add about $1\frac{1}{2}$ lb of this mixture to a quart of warm XXX heavy oil, and stir until a smooth paste is obtained.   This compound is applied to the joint without addition of thinners.

Molycote and lead coat (80 per cent lead) are used with good results on bolt threads. Cylinder oil and graphite should not be used because the oil carbonizes under heat.

Where the surface is badly steam cut, the use of uncured rubber as a cure is effective, quick, and low in cost.   Plain Usudurian sheet packing is an uncured rubber put out by the U.S. Rubber Co.   Usudurian sheet packing comes in sheets $\frac{1}{32}$ in. thick.   This should be cut in $\frac{1}{8}$-in. strips.   Paint a line on the joint with rubber cement, between the inner edge and the bolting line.   Paint the strips with cement, let them air dry, and then mount them on the casing joint.   Where the strips join, cross or lap them. Do not use butt joints.   Then prepare the joint with compound, and slug it down tight.   The material will spread across the joint to less than 0.002 in. thick, and is not affected by repeated temperature changes.

If a joint has to be scraped down for a fit, always scrape the top of the nozzle diaphragms the same amount in order to close the casing.   Oversize diaphragms may have been the original cause of the leakage.

The steam joint between the stage diaphragms and the casing is a metal-to-metal joint, accurately machined and ground in to make it steamtight.   When the diaphragms are assembled in the casing, they are supported at the center line of the turbine casing on adjustable screws, so that shaft clearances are maintained during temperature changes.

If the diaphragm-to-casing joint is not steamtight, the joint surfaces of both casing and diaphragm may be subject to severe steam cutting.   If not corrected promptly, severe damage to the casing and the diaphragm may result.   The joint may be repaired by inserting a stainless-steel band in the joint surface of the diaphragm.   Both halves of the diaphragm are accurately lined up on a boring mill, and a circumferential groove is cut in the joint surface.   The stainless-steel band is pressed into the groove and fastened with stainless-steel screws, drilled and tapped into both the band and the diaphragm.   The entire assembly is machined to produce a finished surface comparable to the original surface.   The matching surface of the casing is prepared by internal boring.   The top half of the casing is set in place and accurately lined up as in final assembly of the unit.   A boring-bar assembly (obtainable from the turbine manufacturer) is set up outside the turbine and extends into the casing through the rotor opening.   The operation of the boring bar is observed by a man inside the casing.   With both diaphragm and casing surfaces properly machined and lapped, the joint can be made steamtight again.

The axial alignment of the rotor is set by the manufacturer before shipment.   The axial clearances between the sides of wheel and bucket covers and the nozzles, intermediates, diaphragms, and labyrinth-tooth shaft packing are set and maintained by the shims of the thrust bearing.   The position of the rotor should be checked during turbine overhaul.

For illustration one type of thrust bearing shown in Fig. 2-15 may be checked as follows:

Have the turbine at rest and at room temperature.   Remove the bearing cap (13). Unbolt the top half circle of screws (3), and then remove the upper half (14) of the bearing lining.   Then remove the upper half of the casing (8) and also the upper halves of the thrust rings (6) and (22).   Remove the upper half of the packing boxes and the wheel casing.   Bucket-clearance dimensions may be obtained from the nozzle-diaphragm drawing for the machine.

Adjust the axial alignment, if necessary, in accordance with the foregoing instructions.   To reassemble the parts, reverse the foregoing sequence of operations for dismantling.   See that all parts are assembled in their proper positions, particularly with reference to the direction of rotation of the shaft as indicated by the marking of the bearing lining.

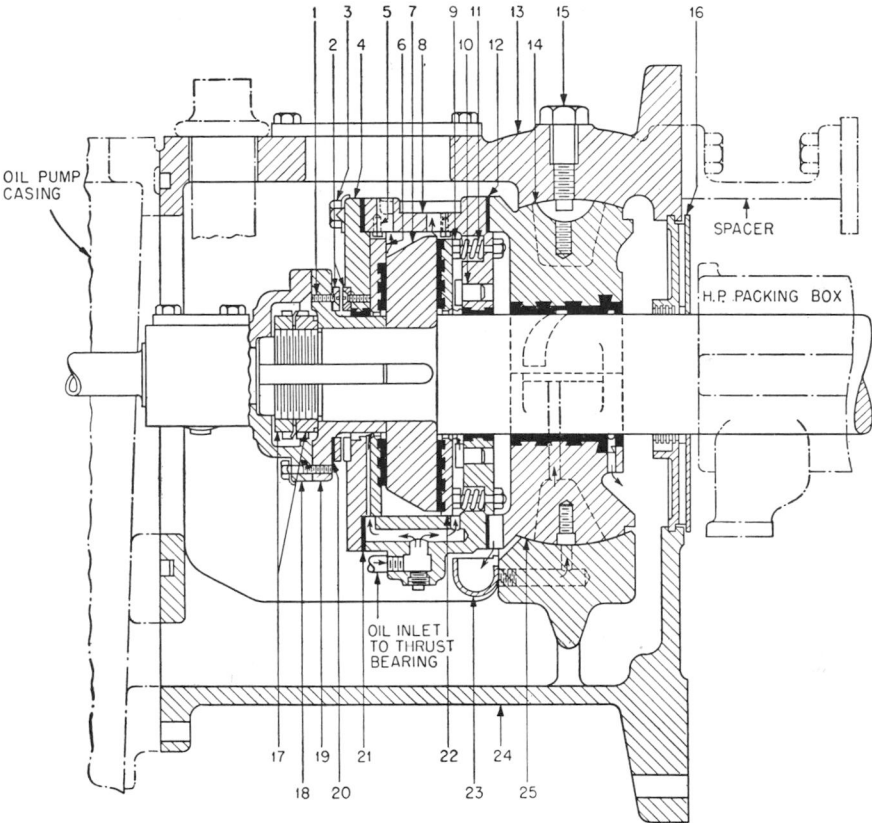

Fig. 2-15. Thrust and shaft bearing, 2000-kw turbine, General Electric Co.   (1) screw; (2) squealer ring; (3) screw; (4) cover; (5) pin; (6) thrust ring; (7) thrust collar; (8) thrust casing; (9) bolt; (10) stop pin; (11) spring; (12) shims; (13) bearing cap; (14) bearing lining—upper; (15) lining screw; (16) oil deflector; (17) nut; (18) casing; (19) sleeve; (20) shims; (21) shims; (22) thrust ring; (23) oil trough; (24) bearing bracket; (25) bearing lining—lower.

With proper lubrication, the parallel surfaces of the lands on the thrust ring should experience little or no wear.   If inspection shows that they are wearing and are encroaching upon the tapered surfaces, the ring should be renewed.   Before reassembling, see that surfaces of the parts are in proper condition, and that all oil passages are clean.

The labyrinth shaft-packing rings require little attention except that they should be carefully inspected when the turbine is opened for inspection.

The steam strainer located in the supply main must be kept clean and with screen intact in order to protect the turbine from damage due to foreign particles in the steam. In a new installation, the main steam line should be thoroughly blown out to free it from solid particles.   In addition, the screen should be inspected after the first month or two of service.   Drain off condensate from the steam main before starting up. Carry-over in the steam or slugs of water will foul up the screen.

The strainer should be inspected at least once a year to check breaking up of the screen and prevent its parts entering the machine.   Use a monel screen and bolts. After each inspection, retap the bolt holes and use new monel bolts.   The strainer in

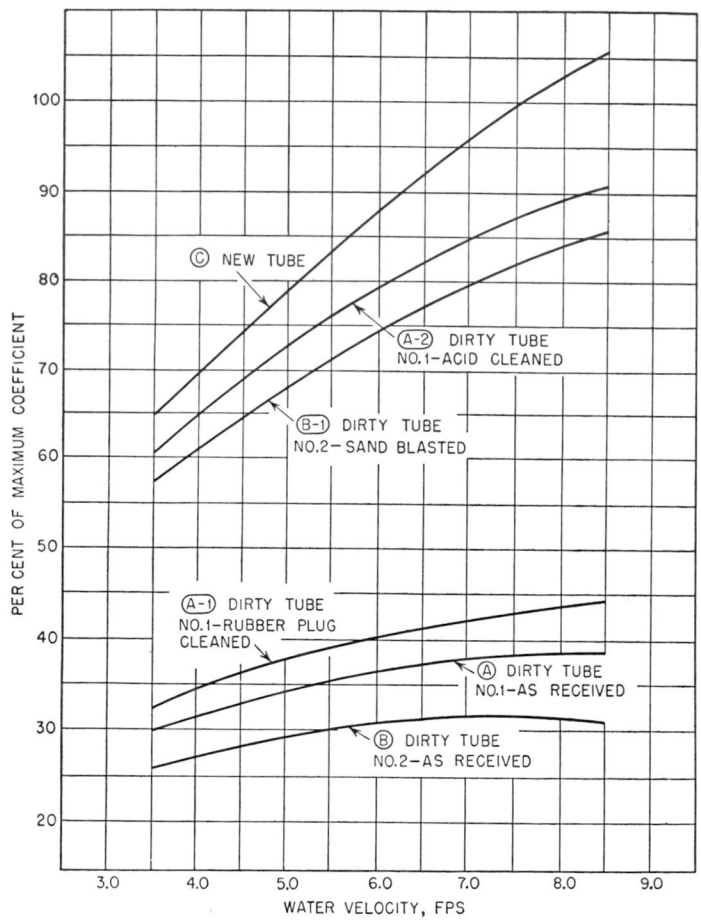

FIG. 2-16. Calorimeter test on condenser tubes.   (*Courtesy of G. H. Putnam, Ingersoll-Rand Co.*)

the turbine steam inlet should be furnished by the turbine manufacturer so that he may be responsible for its design and the materials used in its construction.   Although monel metal has given very satisfactory results, one leading manufacturer is now recommending 13 per cent chrome material for this purpose.

It is most important that no repairs of a major nature be attempted on a modern turbine generator without assistance from the manufacturer of the equipment.

Surface Condensers.   The industrial condenser is fundamentally a heat exchanger used to reduce a vapor to the liquid state through the removal of heat.   The application of this unit in the industrial power plant serves, by means of cooling water, to produce a specified vacuum at the exhaust of a prime mover.   The vacuum produced increases the steam-pressure differential between the inlet and exhaust of the turbine.

The condensing system consists of the condenser proper, air-ejector equipment, and condensate and circulating water pumps. The subject of pumps is treated under another chapter, and therefore will not be covered here.

The condenser unit may be either a direct-contact type, in which steam and cooling water are mixed, or a surface type, in which the steam and cooling water are isolated from each other. The direct-contact type has many uses in the industrial-process field. It is used where it is not necessary to reclaim condensate. The surface type is used more universally in modern power-plant installations because of the need to reclaim the condensate with its heat content and suitability for boiler feedwater. The maintenance on the direct-contact type is relatively low because of the simplicity of design. However, the maintenance recommendations regarding the steam-ejector units in the surface-type unit apply in general to the ejector elements of the direct-contact type as well. Therefore, the following comments refer only to the surface type.

Satisfactory upkeep of surface condenser equipment demands constant attention to five principal sources of trouble. These are:

1. Dirty tubes.
2. Deficiency of cooling water.
3. Tube leakage.
4. Excessive air leakage.
5. Deficiency in air removal.

Figure 2-16 shows the effect of tube cleanliness on heat-transfer coefficient. The curves are based on the actual results of calorimeter tests run on tubes taken out of a condenser in service. The need for a periodic check and inspection of tube condition, followed by adequate cleaning as necessary, is demonstrated by the data shown. A heat-rate test run periodically will serve to indicate the relative condition of the dirty tubes and the loss due to their condition.

Test results show the actual heat transfer. The theoretical heat transfer for identical operating conditions may be calculated from the standards of the Heat Exchange Institute for condensers. The calculated possible heat transfer with clean tubes can be determined also from these standards. With these data, the actual cleanliness of the tubes can be calculated as a percentage of the heat transfer obtainable under identical operating conditions.

Rubber plugs are effective for removing dirt in the form of mud, slime, algae, vegetable matter, or soft, flaky scale. Figure 2-17 shows a hydraulically operated gun and plug which have been used with very

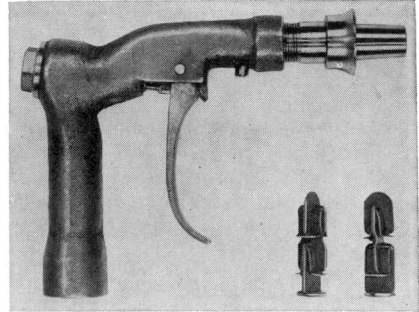

FIG. 2-17. Hydraulically operated gun and plug.

satisfactory results. The gun trigger releases the jet of water which forces a metal spring-leaf plug through the tube.

While hard deposit formations should not be permitted, in some cases, with unusual circulating-water characteristics, they do occur. In such cases, chemical cleaning is not only effective and low cost, but also produces cleanliness approaching new-tube results in heat transfer. Hard scale should never be removed from condenser tubes by turbining.

A reduction in circulating water flow has a promptly unfavorable effect on the condenser capacity. Without sufficient water as a cooling medium, the required vacuum cannot be maintained. This low flow may be caused by tube-sheet fouling, screen plugging, and pump-impeller wear. Although tubes may be clean, the tube-sheet fouling by leaves or foreign matter, or plugging by fish, will definitely reduce the effective condenser-tube surface. Although utility installations are often provided with reverse-flow valves to backwash the tube sheets and water boxes, the average industrial power plant must take the condenser off the line for a thorough cleaning.

If the fouling is due to breaks in the traveling or stationary screen in the circulating-water system, these must be repaired to secure lasting results.

If the screens become plugged, the condition can be taken care of promptly by cleaning the screens themselves. In the case of plants located on fresh-water rivers and lakes, this condition periodically requires more attention. Extended periods following storms, flood conditions, and purging of lakes and streams make the problem of maintaining clean screens a major one.

Tube leakage has been one of the major factors in condenser upkeep. While pinhole leaks can be taken care of temporarily on the run, extensive leakage causes contamination of the condensate, and forces outage of the unit for repair.

FIG. 2-18. Injector to repair small leaks.

A unique method of taking care of small leaks is shown in Fig. 2-18. It makes use of the swelling properties of a fibrous compound injected into the circulating-water inlet piping. It consists essentially of a hopper mounted on a small injector using steam for injection purposes. The unit with compound in the hopper is connected to the inlet circulating-water piping, then the injector valve is opened and steam turned on. The compound is pumped into the water side of the condenser by jet action. The vacuum on the steam side of the tubes helps to plug the small leak with compound. Experience shows that a few ounces of the compound will seal a number of leaks.

Air erosion is one of the worst causes of tube failure. Although various tube metals and alloys successfully resist chemical attack from all types of circulating water, none of these is safe from the effects of air erosion. Air entrained in the water is liberated by turbulence in the circulating water lines and pumps, and as it flows by stay bolts, supports, and blank spaces in the tube sheets. In addition, the minus pressure in the condenser water boxes induces air leakage through gasketed surfaces of the access doors. A recent instance of abnormal tube failure in a large utility prompted an extensive study, the results of which confirmed the damaging effect of air on the condenser tubes. Leaks occurred mostly in the upper part of the tubes, and approximately 3 ft from the discharge end.

One effective attack on the problem of air erosion is through the use of an air-erosion eliminator (Fig. 2-19). This consists of a series of perforated plates fitted in the water boxes in front of the tube sheet. These plates induce extreme turbulence in the water as it passes through the perforations which liberate the absorbed air. The air tends to collect on the under side of the water-box division rib, where it is drawn out by Venturi nozzles. These discharge overboard to the circulating-water outlet.

Another attack on the problem of air erosion may be made through the use of Flowrite nozzles (Fig. 2-20). These are inserts placed in the inlet of the condenser tubes. They serve as replaceable wearing sections. The length of the inserts varies, contingent on the length of attack area in the tube. When the Flowrite insert is almost completely destroyed, it is removed and a new one is inserted. These inserts are made of the same material as the tube, or of plastic. They are shaped in the inlet to fit the tube bell, and are machined to a knife edge at the discharge end to avoid turbulence at that point.

When a tube fails to the extent that it must be plugged, the right type of plug material is important to continued operation of the unit. Wooden plugs are not suitable because wood is porous and water will continue to leak through the plug. Metal plugs, when used, must be driven securely. They may distort the tube sheet and often require drilling out for removal. Screwed plugs lack dependability. Fiber plugs are not suitable because they swell up on contact with water, are not porous, and are easy to remove.

A common method used in detecting leaking tubes is to shut down the condenser with the exception of the steam jets.   The steam jets maintain a vacuum in the steam space, and a candle is passed across the face of the tube sheet to detect the leak. While this method is successful where leaks are fairly large, pinhole leaks with only a small air flow are more difficult to detect by this method.   A more effective procedure

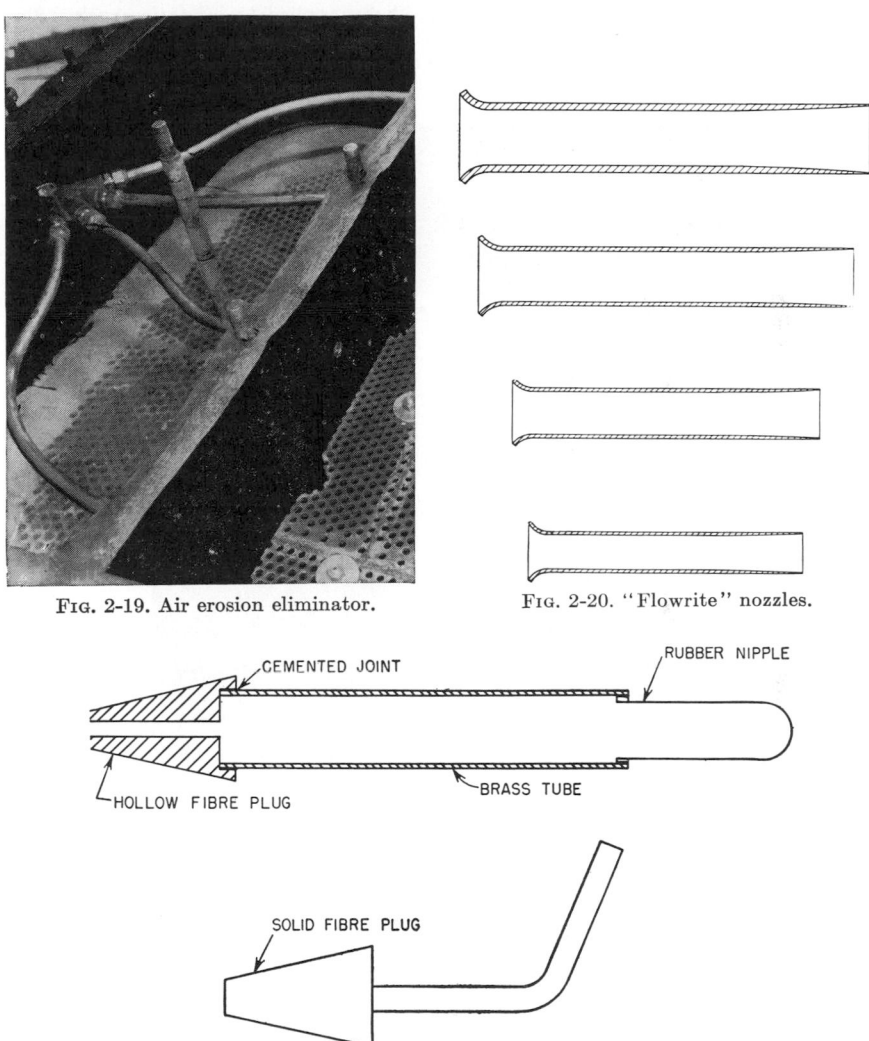

FIG. 2-19. Air erosion eliminator.   FIG. 2-20. "Flowrite" nozzles.

CEMENTED JOINT   RUBBER NIPPLE

HOLLOW FIBRE PLUG   BRASS TUBE

SOLID FIBRE PLUG

FIG. 2-21. "Detect-a-leak."   (*Courtesy of Service & Engineering Co., Inc.*)

is to use the Detect-a-Leak tube shown in Fig. 2-21.   This consists of a solid plug for one end of the condenser tube and a hollow rubber plug for the opposite end.   The hollow plug terminates in a rubber nipple.   The two fittings are attached to opposite ends of the condenser tube.   The vacuum in the steam space will act through a leak in the tube to collapse the rubber nipple.   This method of detecting leaks, using a two-man team, is very effective and can be done with a considerable saving of outage time.

Potential leaking tubes always present a problem. The tubes that actually are leaking are easily detected. The tubes which are about to leak may fail only after the unit is put back in operation. As a result the complete unit may be retubed as a precautionary measure before it is necessary. A hydrodynamic shock tester (Fig. 2-22) has been developed to locate tubes on the verge of failure. Each condenser tube is filled with water and is subjected to a suddenly applied hydrostatic shock. The peak pressure generated by this unit is within safe limits of sound tube material. The tube section with latent defects will be destroyed. In this way, defective tubes

FIG. 2-22. Hydrodynamic shock tester.

that may fail after a short period of operation are located and replaced during a regular outage of the unit.

Excessive air leakage can be checked on the meter normally used in conjunction with the air ejectors. Air enters the condenser through leaks in joints on the vacuum side of the generating unit, particularly at the low-pressure gland. This factor as it increases acts adversely on the heat-transfer coefficient. If unchecked, it can result in a condition where the air-removal equipment is carrying the condenser load in place of the condenser itself. All piping and apparatus under vacuum must be made tight. Periodically inspect and tighten valve packing, stuffing boxes, and all gasket joints. Tighten all joints, and paint them with heavy bitumastic paint or shellac, while the system is under vacuum, so that the paint is drawn into the crevices. A thorough check for air leakage is bound to pay either in improved vacuum or a saving in steam consumption, if spare ejectors are being run to hold a satisfactory vacuum.

Hydrostatically testing the entire vacuum side, including piping, usually will reveal most of the leakage. A finer method is to dissolve a few drops of flourescein dye in the water and then go over all joints, including the face of the tube sheets, with a black light. This method will reveal the most minute leaks.

The steam-jet air ejector is recognized as the most efficient and most reliable method of air removal. Steam jets have no moving parts, are simple and compact in construction, and are low in maintenance costs. Twin-element two-stage units normally are furnished for industrial-power-plant applications.

The air ejector, as shown in Fig. 2-23, consists essentially of a steam nozzle discharging a jet of steam across a suction chamber and through a Venturi-shaped diffuser, or compression tube. Air or gases to be evacuated enter the ejector suction and are entrained by the steam jet through an interchange of energy and momentum. The entire mixture then enters the diffuser where the velocity is converted into pressure. The simplicity of design of the steam air ejector and reasonable care in its operation are factors that make for long life and low maintenance costs for this type of equipment.

Every possible precaution should be taken to prevent dirt in the steam line from reaching the ejector nozzles. The steam-supply connections should be made at the top of a steam header rather than the bottom or end of a long line. An adequate strainer and blowoff connection should be provided at the ejector equipment. All steam piping should drain in the direction of steam flow, and be lagged with suitable insulation. If wet steam is used for supplying the air ejector, a separator should be provided because water in the steam will erode the nozzles, and slugs of water will cause unstable operation of the equipment.

With the surface-type inter- and after-condenser, a strainer should be provided in the water-supply line if there is any chance of water entering the tubes that contain material which may plug them. In starting this equipment, always start the cooling-water flow before turning on the steam, and follow the reverse of this order when shutting down. This is a precaution necessary to avoid subjecting the equipment to full steam temperature.

The ejector steam nozzles must be kept clean and free from obstruction at all times. Their condition should be carefully checked in connection with a new installation, or after an extended shutdown. A twist drill of correct diameter, such as is stamped on each nozzle, is a convenient means of periodically checking the size of the orifice. If the orifice becomes scaled up, oversize, or worn out of round, it will seriously affect the performance of the unit. Periodic inspection of the diffuser throat is necessary to be sure it is clean and not worn, eroded, pitted, or grooved. If scaled or gummed up, it can be cleaned out with a suitable solvent, but if badly worn, replacement will be necessary.

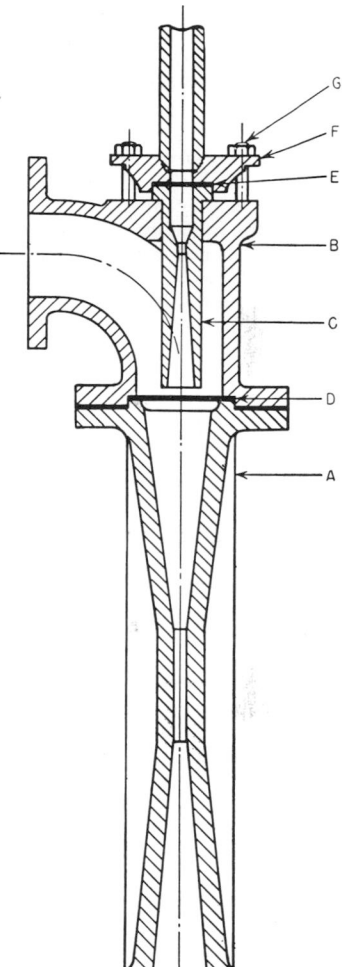

FIG. 2-23. Steam-jet air ejector, Ingersoll-Rand Co. (A) diffusor; (B) suction chamber; (C) nozzle; (D) asbestos gasket; (E) McKim gasket; (F) nozzle retaining flange; (G) stud and nut.

With good operating practices, it is routine to blow down the steam line and strainer before starting up this equipment. In addition, the strainer baskets should be removed and cleaned out periodically. The pressure gage on the steam-supply line should be calibrated frequently to insure the specified steam pressure at the ejector unit.

The tube sheets of the inter- and after-condenser section should be regularly inspected for trash and dirt. In addition, the tubes must be kept clean on both the inside and outside. Soft slime or dirt may be removed with high-pressure air or water jet, but preferably with rubber or metal plugs. Hard scale can be removed only by a weak chemical solution or solvent. Water temperatures often run high in the inter- and after-condensers. This condition accelerates slime and scale formation.

An hydrostatic test applied to the vapor space should be used from time to time, and the tube ends should be inspected for leaks. All flange bolts should be tightened, and in the case of an inter- and after-condenser mounted in the same shell, stay bolts must be checked for tightness to prevent intercompartment air leakage on the vapor side. In such cases, it is recommended to test separately each compartment hydrostatically.

Mechanical-drive Turbines. The small steam turbine, when properly installed and with reasonable care, should give practically no trouble over a long period of time. For satisfactory operation, it is necessary to use utmost care in installation. The foundation must be adequate to support the unit and maintain alignment of the shafts. Do not expect that a combined unit mounted and aligned on a bedplate in the factory will provide perfect alignment when set down on the foundation. The alignment must be checked and established in the field, and the unit doweled and bolted in place. Supply and exhaust piping must be designed to exert a minimum force on the turbine casing.

The preventive-maintenance schedule for small turbines should provide for periodic inspections of vital parts. The bearings, including oil rings and oil level, packing leakage, governor, and throttle valve, should be checked by the operator on each shift. Once a week, the throttle valve, governor valve, and relief valve should be checked for reliability. An annual inspection should include cleaning and overhaul of governor thrust and the speed governor, as well as a thorough internal inspection. The nozzle plate and stationary and rotating buckets should be cleaned and all deposits removed. The packing rings should be removed from the rotor and carefully match-marked so that they can be reassembled to their original position.

The table shown on pages 9–89 and 9–90 is a guide to possible troubles, their causes, and remedies. This check list is provided as a general guide. A check list referring to a specific make of turbine should be prepared along these lines, but based on the operating instructions issued by the turbine manufacturer.

Deaerators. The deaerator heater serves to remove the dissolved gases from the water being processed. It consists basically of a vent condenser, a heating compartment, a deaerating section, and a storage compartment. The water entering through the vent condenser flows downward through the heater and deaerator sections to the storage tank. The steam entering below the deaerator section passes parallel to the water flow up through the deaerator to the vent condenser, where it condenses and the gases pass to the atmosphere.

The pan tray above the heating compartment receives the water from the vent condenser and distributes it evenly over a serrated edge in a thin sheet to the heater trays. Each heater and deaerating tray in turn discharges the water in a thin sheet to the next tray. The deaeration desired is effected by maintenance of maximum contact between steam and water. Therefore, it is essential that all the trays should be set firm and level for even water distribution. These trays in older units were principally cast iron, or an alloy of cast iron. The wear on the sawtooth edges affected the water distribution adversely. The distribution tray and the heater and deaerator section trays, as is necessary, may be replaced with stainless-steel or other corrosion-resistant alloy metals. The modern deaerators are provided with the latest corrosion-resistant metals.

The vent condenser of the tubular type is provided with tubes of admiralty metal, arsenical copper, or other corrosion-resistant metal. The U-tube heater is not subject to maintenance difficulties due to temperature expansion and contraction of the tubes from changes in cold water flow into the unit. The straight-tube type facilitates internal cleaning of the tubes where solids in the water tend to deposit on the tube surfaces.

Trouble	Cause	Remedy
Overspeeding.........	Governor valve stem sticking	Clean and lubricate
	Trip weight stuck	Remove weight and smooth up; clean spring
	Governor out of adjustment	Adjust trigger for operation by governor weights
	Steam leakage through governor valve	Readjust or replace worn parts
	Insufficient governor travel	Readjust so governor can push valve to its seat, without taking full governor travel
Throttle trips without turbine over- speeding	Throttle-valve trip latch worn	Install new latching device
	Trip trigger too close to shaft	Adjust to required clearance
	Latch seats worn	Square up or install new latch seats
	Trigger spring broken	Replace
	Overspeed governor spring not compressed sufficiently	Adjust spring tension as per manufacturer's instructions
Valve does not close when tripping mechanism operates	Latch may be corroded or im- properly engaged	Clean and adjust latch
	Valve stems sticking	Remove and smooth up
Unstable governing...	Sticking or worn parts	Disassemble governor, inspect, and repair; free all parts
	Binding in governor linkage or valve stem sticking	Disassemble linkage and valve, clean, reassemble, adjust, and lubricate
	Leaky governor valve	Remove deposit or remachine valve
	Governor valve loose on stem	Remove and tighten valve on stem
	Friction in speed governor	Disassemble, clean, and replace worn parts
	Clogged drains at operating- valve stem bushings	Clean drains
Throttle valve sticking	Valve-stem packing too tight	Loosen packing or install new and correct packing
	Dirt from steam deposited in valve	Remove dirt, check strainer
	Trip latch fails to unlatch valve	Clean knife edges and adjust linkages for proper travel
	Dirty or damaged valve-stem guides	Clean and repair
Vibration............	Bearings may be worn so as to have excessive clearance	Replace bearings
	Coupling misalignment	Realign unit and redowel
	Coupling worn, producing un- equal torque	Repair or replace
	Piping thrust effect on shaft alignment	Alter piping or its support and realign shafts
	Packing clearance	Increase clearance
	Turbine rotor out of balance	Repair any injury to blades and rebalance rotor
Packing leakage......	Ring wear	Alter ends of ring segments to fit or replace rings
	Broken packing springs	Replace springs
	Dirt between ring and groove of gland case	Disassemble packing and clean side of groove and ring
Water in oil.........	Packing leakage into bearing	Stop packing leakage
	Water leaking into oil from cool- ing jacket or coils	Repair or replace bearing bracket or cooling coils

Trouble	Cause	Remedy
Bearing failure.......	Lack of lubrication from defective oil rings	True up rings to feed oil to bearing
	Oil deterioration and sludge from gland-seal steam contamination	Correct steam leakage from glands and replace oil
	Lack of oil supply	Keep oil at proper level
Turbine unable to carry load	High exhaust pressure	Remove obstructions in exhaust line
	Low inlet steam pressure	Check supply valves to maintain design pressure
	Dirty steam strainer	Clean and check strainer
	Clogged or damaged nozzles and buckets	Remove deposits from nozzles and buckets
	Governor trouble	Adjust governor mechanism
	Excessive wear of nozzles and buckets	Replace
	Governor-valve opening insufficient	Clean valve stem and prevent binding to permit valve full opening
	Hand valve for nozzle control closed	Check for full opening
Thrust bearing failure.	Plugged buckets	Open turbine and clean buckets
	Misalignment between turbine and driver unit	Correct alignment and redowel unit
	Cooling-water failure	Check flow of cooling water, clean water passage
	Insufficient thrust clearance	Repair and adjust thrust for proper clearance

The entire deaerator should be overhauled and cleaned annually, unless poor water conditions require more frequent cleaning. The trays should be removed and thoroughly cleaned by wire brushing. Condenser tubes should be thoroughly cleaned.

The storage tank should be painted with a suitable protective coating which will not affect the water. Float- or diaphragm-operated control valves should be thoroughly overhauled, and floats or diaphragms replaced if leaking or seriously deteriorated.

Strainers. Strainers for power-plant service are widely used to remove foreign matter from cooling water, process water, fuel oil for burners and engines, and lubricating oil. Contingent on the type of service, the fluid to be cleaned, and the material to be removed, the strainer to be used may be single or twin type, of suitable corrosion-resistant metals, and with single or duplex baskets.

The basket may be of the end-inlet type, or the side-inlet type. The end-inlet type may come in perforated sheet or double-wall construction. The side-inlet basket is fabricated of perforated sheet, welded or riveted to the basket inlet casting. This type of basket, which is provided with either perforated top and bottom or open-top construction, is sturdily built. The inlet casting is provided with a tongue on each side which slides in a corresponding groove in the strainer body. An accurate fit is provided between the inlet casting and the grooves to prevent bypassing of unstrained liquid. Baskets with open tops make fitted joints with the body covers to prevent bypassing. These joints must be maintained clean and free from dirt and deposits. Care in handling is important in order to protect the fitted surfaces.

In the double-wall basket, the flow is in the top and out the sides. A seal is made between the shroud and the strainer body, as well as between the shroud and the fine-mesh liner basket. Each seal is a finished metal-to-metal joint, and must be handled with care to preserve the finish. The surfaces must be cleaned thoroughly before the double-wall basket is reassembled and put in place.

The inner basket fits into the shroud and is positioned and secured at the bottom to the shroud basket. The inner basket must be positioned correctly in the shroud, or the assembled basket will not permit complete closure of the strainer cover. The assembled basket in turn must be positioned correctly in the strainer body. Any cocking will prevent a tight seal, and will interfere with closing the strainer cover.

In cleaning, and in all handling of double-wall baskets, use all precautions to prevent even the slightest injury to the wire-cloth wall of the inner basket. A break or even excessive enlargement of even one opening through the wire cloth will impair its effectiveness in straining. If the deposits on the fine-mesh basket tend to harden, soak the basket in a solvent to loosen, and then while wet remove the remaining particles with small, strong air jet.

The seal between the cover and the strainer body is a gasket joint, which must be broken each time the basket is cleaned. The gasket and both joint surfaces on the body and cover must be cleaned thoroughly each time the cover is put in place.

A log should be kept for each turn of service for each basket, length of each period, pressure loss through this basket at start and end of period, and flow through basket. This log may indicate whether the scheduled times for cleaning, and periods of basket service, are shorter or longer than they should be. It also will detect changes in the fluid being strained.

Steam Traps. Steam traps are installed as part of a system intended to recover condensate and its heat content as discharged from a steam-line drain or a heat-exchanger unit using steam as the heating medium. The trap unit may be a great potential means of preventing waste of the above discharges, contingent on its proper operation.

A trap is only part of a recovery system, and any consideration of its performance should be based on analysis of the entire system, not only the trap itself. The right trap must be based on careful consideration of character of service, pressure, size required, and location. To get maximum results, installation of the trap with all the necessary valves and fittings, i.e., unions, test connection, and strainer or dust pocket, is important both for operation and maintenance. Supply and discharge lines on new installations should be blown out thoroughly. Where possible, traps should be located close to the unit being served, and accessible for adequate servicing. Locate the trap below the drip point if possible; otherwise, provide a check valve or a water seal ahead of the trap. Bypass valves, unless maintained tight, may become a source of trap trouble from loss of priming, as well as waste of steam.

Traps should be tested on a regularly scheduled basis. Contingent on type of service and importance, high-pressure traps should be tested at least weekly, and in some instances more frequently. Medium-pressure traps, in general, should be checked on a monthly basis. A 6-month schedule usually is satisfactory for low pressure units except where units they are serving require more frequent testing.

Testing should include the following steps: (1) Operate the test valve with the trap-discharge valve closed. If trap discharge is intermittent, the trap is operating satisfactorily. A continuous steam flow or no flow is an indication of trouble. (2) Trap discharge temperature can be checked against inlet temperature by either the "glove" test or a pyrometer. With a canvas glove in each hand for protection, a quick test can be made to detect definite temperature difference between inlet and outlet. The more accurate pyrometer test requires clean spots filed on the inlet and outlet piping near the trap for instrument contact points. (3) Experience in the use of a multiscope or a plain steel rod as a listening device is effective in diagnosing trap performance. Intermittent discharges of the trap are easily distinguished. Excessive rattle in the trap indicates loss of prime.

Traps should be opened at least once a year. This permits careful check of parts and a thorough cleaning in a suitable solvent. Check the valve and seat for tightness. If either is worn, replace both the valve and seat because these parts are matched. This same procedure should be followed in replacement of all matched or fitted assemblies.

The following chart will be helpful in checking trap troubles:

TROUBLE-SHOOTING CHART FOR STEAM TRAPS[1]

Trap doesn't discharge

1. Steam pressure too high, pressure-regulating out of order, boiler-pressure gage reads low, steam pressure raised without altering or adjusting trap. On the last item consult trap maker; he can supply parts for higher pressure or tell you how to adjust trap.
2. Plugged strainer, valve, or fitting ahead of trap; clean.
3. Internal parts of trap plugged with dirt or scale; take trap apart and clean. Fit strainer ahead of trap.
4. Bypass open or leaking; close or repair.
5. Internal parts damaged or broken; dismantle trap, repair.

Trap won't shut off

1. Trap too small for load; figure condensate quantity to be handled and put in correct-size trap.
2. Defective mechanism holds trap open; repair.
3. Larger condensate load from (a) boiler foaming or priming, leaky steam coils, kettles or other units, or (b) greater process load; find cause of increased condensate flow and cure, or install larger trap.

NOTE: Traps made to discharge continuously won't show these symptoms. Instead, the condensate line to trap overloads; water backs up.

Trap blows steam

1. Open or leaky bypass valve; close or repair.
2. Trap has lost prime; check for sudden or frequent drops in steam pressure.
3. Dirt or scale in trap; take apart and clean.
4. Inverted bucket trap too large, blows out seal; use smaller orifice or replace with smaller trap.

Trap capacity suddenly falls

1. Inlet pressure too low; raise to trap rating, fit larger trap, change pressure parts or setting.
2. Back pressure too high; look for plugged return line, traps blowing steam into return, open bypass or plugged vent in return line.
3. Back pressure too low; raise.

Condensate won't drain from system.

1. System is air-bound; fit suitable vent or trap with larger air capacity to get rid of the air.
2. Steam pressure low; raise to the right value.
3. Condensate short-circuits; use a trap for each unit.

Not enough steam heat.

1. Defective thermostatic elements in radiator traps; remove, test and replace damaged elements.
2. Boiler priming; reduce boiler-water level. If boiler foams, check fires and feed with fresh water while blowing down boiler at $\frac{1}{4}$-min intervals.
3. Scored or out-of-round valve seat in trap; grind seat or replace old trap body with new one.
4. Vacuum pump runs continuously; look for a cracked radiator, split-return main, cracked pipe fitting, or a loose union connection. Or pump shaft's packing may leak.
5. Too much water hammer in system; check drip-trap size. Undersized drip traps can't handle all condensate formed during warm-up so hammering results. Fit larger trap if drip lines are clean and scale-free. Size for warm-up load, not for load with mains hot.
6. System run down; older heating plants are sometimes troublesome because a large number of trap elements are defective. Easiest cure is replacement of all thermostatic elements in the radiators. This is low-cost, sure.

[1] Tyler Hicks, Associate Editor, *Power*.

Traps freeze in winter

1. Discharge line has long horizontal run where water collects; make discharge line as short as possible and pitch away from trap.
2. Trap and piping not insulated; fit insulation to outdoor traps and piping connect to them.

Back flow in return line

1. Trap below return main doesn't have right fittings; use check valve and a water seal, or both, depending on what the trap maker recommends.
2. High-pressure traps discharge into a low-pressure return; flashing may cause high back pressure.   Change piping to prevent return pressure from exceeding trap rating.
3. No cooling leg ahead of a thermostatic trap that drips a main; condensate may be too hot to allow trap to open right.   Use a 4- to 6-ft cooling leg ahead of thermostatic traps on this service.   Fit strainer in cooling leg to keep solids out of trap.

Many difficulties that are experienced with traps after overhaul and repair are not due to faulty conditions of the trap.   To eliminate all doubt of trap condition, make use of a test stand.   A suitable stand can be made with a steam-reducing valve and connections to pipe water and compressed air into a leg feeding the trap.   With this stand, operators are able to test each trap under operating conditions before installing it.

Chapter 3

VENTILATING FANS

By FREDERICK C. JOHNS
Professional Engineer
Buffalo Forge Company
Buffalo, N.Y.

TYPES AVAILABLE

Ventilation may be described briefly as the circulation of air. Implied in this definition are factors such as the supplying of fresh air and the removal of heat, dust, toxic gases, fumes, and odors.

Almost without exception, any modern ventilating system will require a fan to circulate the air. The fans commonly used may be divided into three general types—propeller, axial, and centrifugal. Most fan manufacturers can supply all three. Each type is manufactured in a range of sizes.

Fans can be obtained in a variety of discharge positions and with either clockwise or counterclockwise rotation of the impeller. With few exceptions, they can be furnished for either direct connection or V-belt drive. See Figs. 3-1 and 3-2.

Propeller. This fan consists of a propeller, or disk-type wheel, within a mounting ring or panel (see Fig. 3-3). The direction of air flow is in a straight line parallel to the fan shaft. It is used primarily for moving air from one room to another, to the outdoors, or to bring in fresh air. These fans will handle large volumes of air at low static pressure. Wheel blades usually are formed from sheet metal or plate, although some designs are furnished with cast-metal wheels. Propeller fans seldom are used at static pressures higher than 1 in.

Axial. Essentially a propeller fan enclosed in a cylindrical housing, this fan is available in the two types illustrated by Figs. 3-4, 3-5, and 3-6. The addition of straightening vanes behind the wheel converts a tube-axial to a vane-axial fan. Wheels may be fabricated from sheet metal or plate, or may be cast. They are available for a wide range of air volumes at low to moderate static pressures. The vane-axial fan is capable of developing higher static pressures than the tube-axial and is more efficient. Above 3- to 4-in. static pressures, axial fans are seldom used for ventilating duty.

Centrifugal. The centrifugal fan consists of a wheel enclosed by a scroll-shaped housing. Air enters through the eye of the wheel or rotor parallel to the fan shaft and is discharged through the housing outlet at right angles to the shaft. A centrifugal fan may be of the single- or double-inlet design. In a double-inlet fan, air is drawn through both sides of the housing by a double wheel or by two single wheels mounted side by side. Usually, wheels are fabricated from sheet metal or plate, although wheel hubs often are cast. Rotors are manufactured in a wide variety of designs, but may be classified broadly as to whether the blades are radial, inclined forward, or inclined backward to the direction of rotation.

Forward-curved blade fans handle large volumes of air at low rotative speeds. Radial-blade fans generally are used for high static pressures and for this reason do not have much application in ventilating. Backward-curved blade fans have the distinct advantage of a self-limiting horsepower characteristic.

Centrifugal fans can be selected for almost any volume and pressure required in general ventilation.

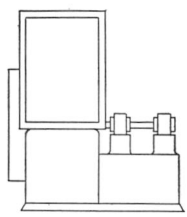

Arr. 1, single inlet. For belt drive or direct connection. Wheel overhung. Two bearings on base.

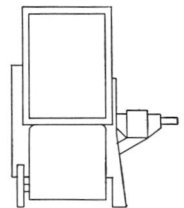

Arr. 2, single inlet. For belt drive or direct connection. Wheel overhung. Bearings in bracket supported by fan housing.

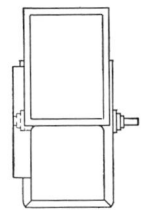

Arr. 3, single inlet. For belt drive or direct connection. One bearing on each side and supported by fan housing.

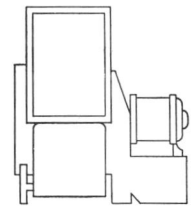

Arr. 4, single inlet. For direct drive. Wheel overhung on prime mover shaft. No bearings on fan. Base, or equivalent for prime mover.

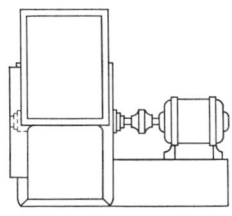

Arr. 7, single inlet. For belt drive or direct connection. Arrangement 3 plus base for prime mover.

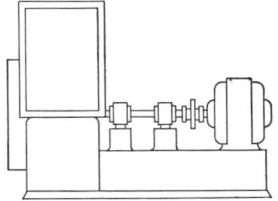

Arr. 8, single inlet. For belt drive or direct connection. Arrangement 1 plus base for prime mover.

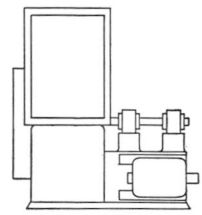

Arr. 9, single inlet. For belt drive. Arrangement 1 designed for mounting prime mover on side of base.

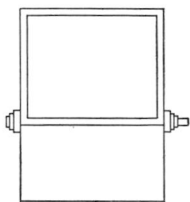

Arr. 3, double inlet. For belt drive or direct connection. One bearing on each side and supported by fan housing.

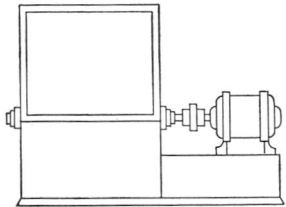

Arr. 7, double inlet. For belt drive or direct connection. Arrangement 3 plus base for prime mover.

FIG. 3-1. Standard arrangements of ventilating fans. (*Courtesy of Air Moving and Conditioning Association, Inc.*)

Special Units. There are a number of general-purpose "package units" available. They consist of fan, motor, and variable-pitch V-belt drive, and usually can be purchased at a saving over the price of the individual components.

In addition, there are various special-purpose fan units available, such as roof ventilators, elbow-type axial fans, portable spot-ventilation or man-cooling fans, multifan units, and many others (see Figs. 3-7 and 3-8). It is a good idea to consult the manufacturer or his representative on special applications. He may have a unit designed for the job which will save time, trouble, and money.

Related Equipment.   Accessories and special features to modify or complete a fan installation also are available.   Among those commonly obtainable are: vibration-absorbing bases (see Fig. 3-9), belt and coupling guards, filters, inlet screens (Fig. 3-10), special paint and coatings, spark-resistant construction, dampers, variable inlet vanes,

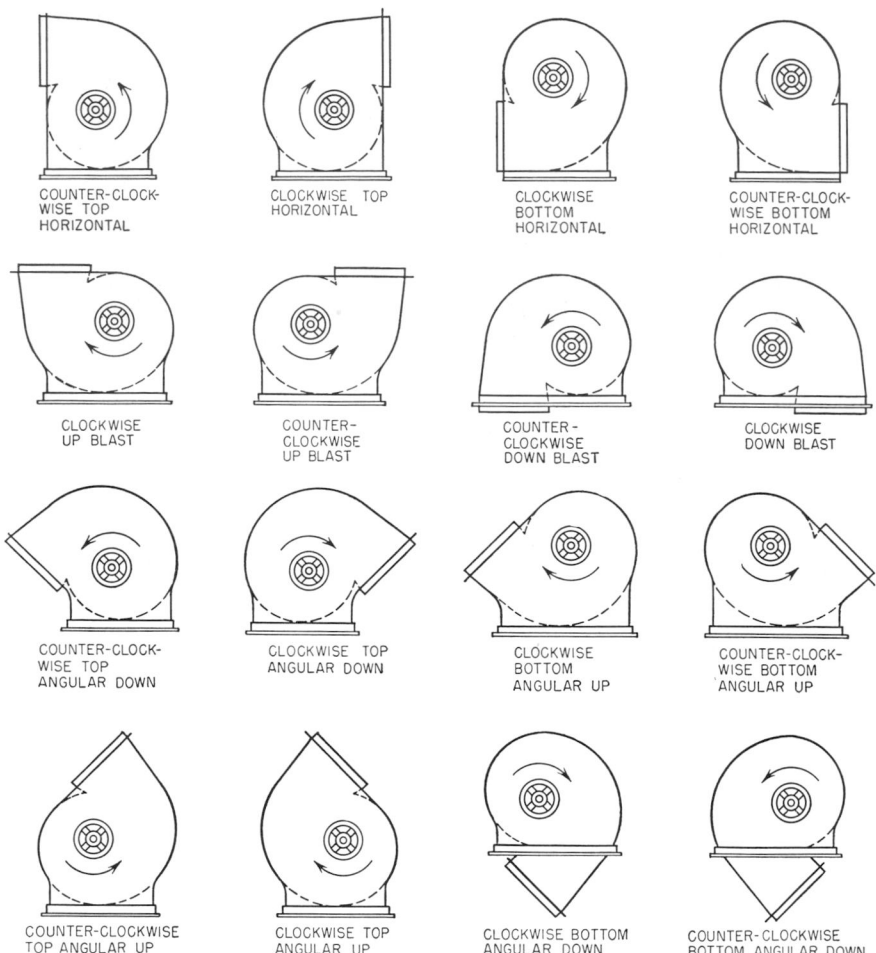

FIG. 3-2. Designations of direction of rotation and discharge.   Direction of rotation is determined from drive side for either single- or double-inlet fans.   The driving side of a single-inlet fan is considered to be the side opposite the inlet regardless of actual location of the drive.   For fan inverted for ceiling suspension, direction of rotation and discharge is determined when fan is resting on floor.   (*Courtesy of Air Moving and Conditioning Association, Inc.*)

access doors, drain connections, shaft seals, special metal construction, various types of bearings, special motors, belt and chain drives, and variable-speed hydraulic, magnetic, and turbine drives.

SELECTION OF EQUIPMENT

Ventilating-system design in all but the simplest cases should not be attempted by anyone not thoroughly trained and experienced in this specialty.   The requirements of a ventilating system depend not only upon the comfort or needs of the individuals involved, but often are regulated by codes, ordinances, or laws. The competent designer or consultant is aware of all the factors involved and assumes responsibility for the adequacy of the design.

FIG. 3-3. Belt-driven propeller fan for medium duty. Most units can be obtained for air flow in either direction. This fan is for wall mounting and will exhaust air from a space, drawing it over the motor and the drive.

FIG. 3-4. Discharge end of a vane-axial fan. Belt drive and bearings are protected from dust in air stream.

Selection of the proper fan for a specific system depends upon the following considerations:

1. The *quantity* of air to be handled.
2. The fan *static pressure* required.
3. The *cost* of the unit.
4. The *space* available.
5. *Noise* limitations.
6. Presence of *corrosive* or *abrasive* elements in the air.
7. High *temperatures*.

Quantity. The first step in the design of any ventilating system is to determine the amount of air required, measured in cubic feet per minute (cfm). Once this quantity is established, there remains the problem of introducing the air into the desired space or rooms, or exhausting it, as the case may be. Often this is a relatively simple matter, but sometimes it becomes quite complex, necessitating a large air-distribution system and the necessary controls.

Static Pressure. Before selecting a fan which will deliver the required capacity, it is necessary to know the pressure the fan will have to develop when delivering the required volume of air. In fan parlance, it is referred to as static pressure (SP) and

FIG. 3-5. Inlet end of direct-connected vane-axial fan. Motor shaft supports and drives wheel. Vanes behind wheel straighten inherent spiraling motion of air as it leaves the wheel and increase static pressure.

FIG. 3-6. Inlet end of direct-connected tube-axial fan. Note electrical connections and grease fittings brought outside housing. Arrows are provided near nameplate to indicate direction of wheel rotation and air flow.

FIG. 3-7. Package-type units such as this belted vent set are furnished complete with motor and variable-pitch V-belt drive. Fan speed and capacity can be varied by adjustment of the motor sheave. Hinged weather hood is raised to show arrangement of drive components.

is measured in inches of water gage, often referred to simply as inches. Air traveling at a given velocity will exert a definite pressure on any object in its path. This pressure, independent of the static pressure, is called velocity pressure. Total pressure is the algebraic sum of the static and velocity pressures. When the resistance to flow is negligible and the static pressure is essentially zero, the fan is said to be operating at "free delivery." An example of this condition is a propeller fan discharging through a wall.

Air will not flow through a duct unless a difference in pressure exists, when it will flow from a region of higher total pressure to a region of lower total pressure. The pressure drop between the two points represents energy used in overcoming the frictional resistance of the duct walls and in dynamic losses resulting from turbulence caused by changes in air velocity and direction in elbows and branches, or by changes

FIG. 3-8. Multifan ventilating units (three-fan shown) are neat and compact. Motor, drive, and bearings are outside the unit for servicing.

FIG. 3-9. Single inlet arrangement with V-belt drive mounted on vibration-isolating base. Fan and motor held in alignment by channel iron. Unit floats on isolation pads. Guide vanes in inlet are fixed and turn air in direction of wheel rotation for minimum shock loss.

in cross-section area. In addition, any obstruction to the air passage, such as air filters, coils, louvers, dampers, or inlet grilles, will also add to the required static pressure. The sum of all these losses is the required fan static pressure. It sometimes is called the system resistance, or system static, and means the resistance offered by that particular system to the flow of a given quantity of air.

Fan manufacturers publish sets of rating tables as a convenience in selecting fans. A fan rating is a statement of performance and includes cfm, SP, rpm, and hp. Each table covers a different size of fan, and the range of cfm and SP over which it is ordinarily used. Fan manufacturers will furnish these tables on request. Usually they are part of a bulletin which contains illustrations, descriptive matter, and dimension prints.

Cost. Careful and detailed analysis of this item always is justified. It should include in addition to the actual purchase price such factors as installation cost, operating costs including maintenance expense, and depreciation.

Space. In general, propeller fans will occupy the least space for a given quantity of air, with axial and centrifugal fans following in that order.

Noise. All fans make some noise. In some installations the sound level may be a very important factor. A fan will operate with minimum noise when it operates at or near its peak efficiency. There is a method of measuring fan noise which has been adopted jointly by the Air Moving and Conditioning Association, Inc., and the American Society of Heating, Refrigeration and Air-Conditioning Engineers. It should be remembered, however, that it gives no indication of the actual fan noise that will be transmitted through a duct, for example, but it is useful in that it can be used to compare the relative noise levels of different sizes or types of fans. Any comparison should be made with the fans handling the same quantity of air against the same static pressure.

FIG. 3-10. Arrangement No. 3 double-inlet fan, using two single-inlet wheels mounted back to back and positioned with blades staggered. Wide-mesh screen causes minimum restriction of air flow.

Corrosion and Abrasion. Corrosion due to moisture alone usually can be controlled with a good asphalt-base or other moisture-resistant paint. Corrosion due to other elements must be treated on an individual basis. Fans of special metals are available. Usually the metals are aluminum, stainless steel, or Everdur. Special protective coatings, such as hard or soft rubber and various plastics, can be obtained. Many types of fans now are available in all-plastic construction, usually a polyester or rigid polyvinyl chloride. Thus it is possible to secure a fan that will be more or less resistant to most common chemicals. Usually the manufacturer cannot guarantee the life of a fan handling corrosive fumes, since the rate of corrosion depends on many factors, such as temperature, concentration, or the presence of other substances that may tend to accelerate the action of the corrosive element.

Abrasion seldom is a serious matter in general ventilation. There are special fan designs and materials available from most manufacturers if abrasion should be an important factor.

Temperature. While high temperatures ordinarily are not a problem in general ventilation, it is worth mentioning that most manufacturers can furnish fans specially designed or modified for high-temperature work.

It is always wise to give the manufacturer all the information you have about a proposed installation. This is especially true if the fan will operate under unusual or severe conditions.

CONTROL

Fan control, which usually means volume control, can be accomplished in several ways. Which is best for a particular installation depends on considerations too numerous and varied for complete discussion here. Briefly, the common methods of control are as follows:

Dampers. Usually they are used with a fan driven at constant speed. They may be manually or automatically operated, and come in a number of designs (Fig. 3-11). Modifications that give more accurate control include the use of splitter plates between damper blades and linkage, causing adjacent blades to rotate in opposite directions.

Dampers are lowest in first cost, but least economical with fan horsepower, since they waste static pressure developed by the fan.

Variable-inlet Vanes. They consist of a number of vanes positioned around the fan inlet and joined together by linkage which causes them to operate in unison (see Fig. 3-12). They cause the air to spin, or "whirl," in the same direction as the wheel rotation. The volume of air delivered and the static pressure developed depend on the whirl imparted to the entering air-stream, and it may be controlled manually or automatically. They are moderate in first cost, save power by not wasting static pressure, and are as simple to operate and maintain as ordinary dampers.

Variable-speed Drivers. Varying the fan speed to exactly meet varying cfm requirements is the most efficient method of control. Hydraulic and magnetic variable-speed couplings are available that will give stepless control over the entire operating range of the fan. Steam turbines sometimes are used, especially where they can be fitted into a plant heat balance at good economy. Direct-current motors can also be used and are easy to regulate. Auxiliary dampers or variable inlet vanes may be required with the last two if control over a wide range is required.

Multispeed and Slip-ring A-C Motors. These are other alternatives, and they, too, usually require dampers or variable-inlet vanes for regulation at intermediate points.

FIG. 3-11. Outlet damper with stream-lined blades and linkage arranged to move adjacent blades in opposite directions for even throttling.

The curves in Fig. 3-13 show an approximate comparison of the power required with various methods of fan control.

FIG. 3-12. Single inlet arrangement with variable inlet vanes. Vanes rotate in unison when control lever is moved, varying amount of "spin" imparted to air and modifying fan performance. Access door is equipped with quick-opening latches.

CARE OF FANS

Receiving. A thorough inspection should be made at the time of delivery to check for completeness of the order and any damage that may have occurred in transit. The carrier should be informed immediately if there is any shortage, breakage, or damage. Watch for dents in the housing, bent wheel blades, shaft or bearing damage, and the like.

Small and medium-size fans usually are shipped completely assembled. Large units are shipped knocked down, but are completely assembled before shipment. All parts of the fan are match-marked at disassembly to assure correct reassembly on the job. These marks are painted or stamped on the various parts. The manufacturer will furnish assembly prints.

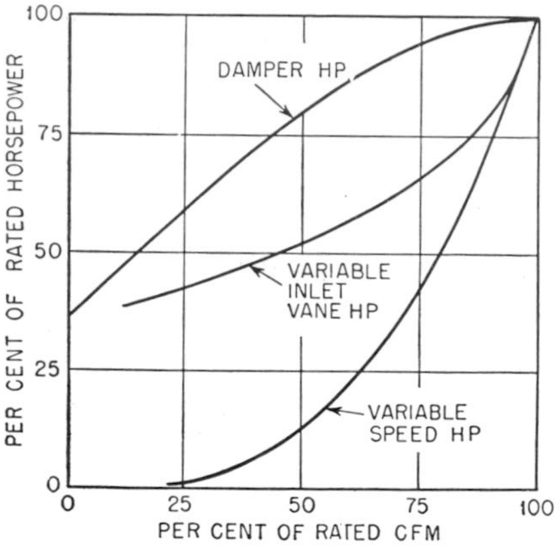

FIG. 3-13. Comparison of power required with various methods of control.

Handling. Fans require extra care in handling, especially when they are lifted with a hoist. Large fans or assemblies should be lifted in such a manner as to prevent distortion of any of the parts. When it is necessary to lift a wheel or housing with a single hoist, a spreader bar should be used to prevent pressure against the sides of the object.

Shafts must not be nicked or scratched, particularly on bearing surfaces and thrust collars. Any small marks that may be incurred should be removed with fine emery cloth or a stone and carefully cleaned. Generous use of padding when handling a heavy shaft will prevent this sort of damage.

It is extremely important to see that the rotor is installed correctly in the housing. An arrow painted on the rotor indicates the correct direction of rotation, which should be the same as indicated by another arrow painted, stamped, or fastened on the housing. Serious overloading of the driving motor may result if the rotor is installed with the wrong rotation.

Fans are furnished with such a variety of blade designs that it is risky to guess at the correct rotation from their shape or curvature. If there is the slightest doubt about correct wheel rotation, the manufacturer or his representative should be consulted.

Similar precautions apply to fans equipped with either fixed or variable inlet vanes. Both are designed to give spin to the air in the same direction as the wheel rotation before it enters the eye of the wheel. Again, serious overloading of the motor may result if the vanes are installed so as to whirl the air against the wheel rotation. Correct installation of inlet vanes is easily determined by inspection when the proper wheel rotation is definitely established.

While it is not likely that there would be any room for doubt about proper wheel or inlet-vane installation on a new fan, these precautions should be observed when a fan is disassembled. All parts should be marked so they will be reassembled in the same positions.

Storage. If the fan will not be installed promptly, it should be protected against rusting and dirt. Special attention should be given the shaft and bearings. The shaft should be coated with grease or rust-preventive compound and the bearings covered and sealed.

The housing should be protected against the entry of any material that might cause damage by striking the wheel while the fan is running.

Never allow material of any kind, particularly heavy objects, to be piled on top of a **fan** housing or bearing base.

If it is necessary to store the fan outdoors, it should be covered with a tarpaulin, heavy waterproof paper, or plastic film.

Foundations.   A good, rigid foundation, as level as possible, is a must for every fan installation.   It will insure permanent alignment of the fan and driving equipment and freedom from excessive vibration, thereby minimizing maintenance costs.

The best fan foundation is poured concrete under the fan and all drive components. A generally accepted rule of thumb is that the weight of a concrete fan foundation should be at least three times the total weight of the equipment it will support.

Anchor bolts set in concrete should be surrounded by pipe sleeves to allow for some adjustment in case they are displaced during pouring.   An allowance of $\frac{1}{2}$ to 1 in. for grouting and shims to level the fan should be made.

When it is necessary to use a structural-steel foundation, it should be sufficiently rigid to insure permanent alignment.   It must be designed to carry with minimum deflection not only the weight of the equipment but the loads imposed by the centrifugal forces set up by the rotating elements.   The entire structure should be welded or well riveted to eliminate the possibility of loosening and distortion.

Fans installed above the ground floor of a building should be located above a rigid wall or heavy column if possible.   When an overhead platform must be used to support the fan, it should be strong and rigid, with particular emphasis on all the precautions mentioned under structural-steel foundations.

Fans shipped knocked down are assembled on the foundation, following the manufacturer's detailed instructions.   The procedure is similar to that followed with completely assembled units.   Before placing the fan over the foundation, the locations of all anchor bolts should be checked to see that they will match up with the holes provided in the fan-base angles.   Place the fan over the foundation, using shims or wedges as required.   Level and align all components, tighten anchor bolts, and recheck level and alignment.   Grout now can be poured in and allowed to harden.   Recheck for final level and alignment of all components after making certain that all anchor bolts are tight.

Vibration-isolating Bases.   Such bases often are used when it is desirable to reduce the transmission of sound and vibration from a fan and motor to other areas of a building.   The isolating elements consist of a resilient material, steel springs, or both, which deflect under load, absorbing vibration and structurally borne sound.   When they are used, the following requirements should be met to obtain the longest and most satisfactory service:

1. The fan and motor should be mounted on a rigid base which in turn is supported by the vibration isolators.
2. A sufficient number of isolators should be used, and they should be properly spaced so that adequate mechanical support is provided for the fan.
3. Flexible connections from the fan to ductwork should always be used.

Prestart Inspection and Adjustment.   Prior to shipment, all fans are completely assembled and all bearings, couplings, and drives are properly aligned.   However, all these items should be rechecked before the fan is started.   Rough handling or a severe jolt in shipping could cause misalignment of any or all of these parts.   The wheel should be rotated by hand to make sure that it turns freely and does not strike the housing or inlet.   Check to see that the wheel has not shifted on the shaft, and tighten all set screws.

Bearings.   Fans may be furnished with either antifriction or sleeve bearings, depending on the user's preference or what the manufacturer normally furnishes. Small fans often are equipped with sealed or self-lubricating bearings, which should require no attention other than to make sure they are properly aligned and sealed against leakage of lubricant or the entry of dirt.

Grease-lubricated bearings receive their initial lubrication at the factory, but this usually is not true of oil-lubricated bearings.   They should be filled to the proper level with the recommended grade of oil.   Bearings shipped separate from the fan or as replacements are almost never lubricated before shipping.   When there is the slightest reason for doubt, the safe practice is to assume that the bearing has not been lubricated.

It is impossible to give any general information about lubricants that would apply to the many different makes and types of bearings in use today.   This information should come directly from the fan or bearing supplier.   As a rule, complete lubrication instructions are furnished with every new fan.

Many bearings, both antifriction and sleeve, have the self-aligning feature.   It should be emphasized, however, that they are designed only to compensate for normal shaft deflection.   They will not take care of bearing misalignment.   When they are carelessly or improperly installed, leakage of lubricant, overheating, or complete failure may result.

Couplings.   Couplings require little attention if they are properly installed and kept in alignment.   They are called flexible couplings, but are not intended to function as universal joints.   It is extremely important that they be installed with both halves perfectly concentric and parallel.   Poor installation will damage the coupling and may damage the fan, motor shaft, and bearings.   Parallelism should be checked with a feeler gage at four points between the coupling halves—at top, bottom, and sides.   A

Table 3-1. Suggested Fan-vibration Tolerances

Fan speed, rpm	Vibration displacement, mils			
	Smooth	Fair	Rough	Very rough
600	2	4	8	15–20
900	1.5	2.75	6	8–10
1,200	1.0	2	4.5	6– 8
1,900	0.75	1.5	3.5	5– 7

NOTE: *Fair* is not bad, but should be improved.
  Rough should be corrected as soon as possible.
  Very rough is too rough to operate.

straightedge used at corresponding points on the outer periphery of the two halves will check concentricity.   Follow the coupling manufacturer's instructions regarding lubrication.

V-belt Drives.   Sheaves must be installed and maintained in perfect alignment. Fan and motor shafts must be parallel and the centers of the grooves on both sheaves must be in perfect alignment.

When installing belts, always move the motor so the belts can be easily placed in their grooves.   Never pry or force them on.

Belt drives depend on friction and must be under some tension to function properly. If too loose, they will slip and overheat.   If too tight, they will place an extra strain on shafts and bearings and may stretch excessively.   Adjusting a belt drive for initial tension is largely a matter of judgment and experience.   Correct adjustment is attained when the belts have just enough tension to prevent them from slipping when they are operating at full speed and load.   Belt slippage can be detected by squealing or overheating of the smaller sheave.

V-belt drives should be protected from oil and grease.   No dressing of any kind should be used.

Belt guards that allow some circulation of air around the drive are preferable.

All the slack should be on one side of the drive, or the entire load may be carried by one or two belts when starting, causing them to break after a few revolutions.

Replacement drives for multi-V-belt drives should be purchased and installed in matched sets.   They are matched for length by the manufacturer.   New belts will not ride as deeply in their grooves as worn belts, and will be considerably shorter.

Selecting drives with two few belts or sheaves that are too small is uneconomical. These two factors will materially reduce belt life.   Maintenance cost will be increased because of more frequent adjustment required by more rapid belt stretching and wear.

Finally, remember that variable-pitch sheaves are intended to provide for speed regulation, not belt-tension adjustment.   Move the motor on this type of drive when adjusting for tension.

Initial Run.   When the fan is ready to be run, it should be started under light load if possible.   Outlet dampers or variable inlet vanes should be partially, not completely, closed.   This will reduce the power required.

Axial-flow fans should never be completely dampered, as they may require as much or more horsepower than under normal conditions.

At first power should be applied only long enough to determine that the wheel is rotating in the proper direction.   Then the fan should be allowed to come up to operating speed.   It should be stopped immediately if unusual noise or vibration develops, and the cause should be determined.   The fault should be corrected.   Watch for overheating of bearings or drive during this preliminary period.

A small amount of vibration is inherent in any fan, and should cause no concern. Excessive vibration can be injurious to bearings and shaft, sometimes to the entire fan. Permissible vibration can be felt with accuracy by a maintenance man familiar with fans.   Portable instruments are available that will indicate vibration displacement in mils (1 mil = 0.001 in.).   Table 3-1 can be used as a guide to determine when a fan is operating with too much vibration.   The common causes of excessive vibration are itemized in the check list at the end of the chapter.

Fan rotors are balanced statically and dynamically by the manufacturer, and if undamaged should require no further balancing.   Before rotor unbalance is suspected, the other items listed above should be checked and the rotor examined for deposits of dirt or other foreign material.   Sometimes a thorough cleaning of the rotor is all that is necessary.

Portable instruments are available to aid in field balancing of rotating machinery. Some will indicate the location where the weight should be added, but not the amount. Others enable the determination of both location and weight.   It is possible to balance a fan without instruments by a cut-and-try method.   It consists of holding a sharpened piece of chalk or soapstone so the point just touches the shaft while the fan is running.   When there is unbalance, the shaft will be forced to deflect outward by the unbalanced weight.   The chalk will scribe a line on the shaft, the length of the line indicating the amount of unbalance.   A short line indicates poor balance.   A line even all around the shaft indicates proper balance.   It is best to make three or four lines at each reading to secure a good average.   The chalk must be held firmly, so it will be touched only by the high spot, not allowed to "ride" the shaft.

The actual balancing is accomplished by adding trial weights to the rotor on the light side.   A set of trial weights can be made up from sheet metal or bar stock bent into a U shape and varying from a fraction of an ounce upward.   Weights should be made so they can be forced on the heel (inside) of a blade where they will not fly off. Where both bearings are on the same side of the housing, the shaft should be chalked between the housing and the inboard bearing.   Shafts on arrangement 3 and double-inlet fans (see Fig. 3-1) must be chalked on both sides between the rotor and the bearing and balanced accordingly.   When the position and amount of weight are established, the trial weights, or equal weights may be welded or riveted to the wheel, preferably on the back of the blades.   The weight of the weld bead or rivets should be taken into account.   While this method requires time, patience, and good judgment, excellent results can be obtained.

A new fan should be watched carefully for the first few hours of operation.   After a few days or a week of continuous running, a complete inspection should be made, with particular attention to the following:

1. Check for excessive vibration.
2. Check lubricant level and look for leaks.
3. Check bearing operating temperatures.   Remember that a bearing uncomfortably hot to touch is not necessarily too hot to operate.   Consult the fan or bearing supplier if there is any question.
4. Check and tighten all set screws.

5. Check all bolted and riveted joints for tightness, particularly on bearings, coupling, motor mounting, and foundation.
6. Inspect belt drive for proper tension.
7. Observe the general condition of the unit. Look for dirt accumulation, especially on the rotor. Check for any signs of corrosion, especially inside the housing and on the rotor. Clean and paint where necessary.

Good maintenance is largely a matter of good housekeeping combined with regular inspection designed to prevent major failures. A complete inspection, such as the one described, takes little time. It should be performed regularly, on a definite schedule, with perhaps a simple printed report in the form of a check list filled out for each piece of equipment. The man ultimately responsible for its maintenance should receive these equipment reports and initiate whatever action is indicated.

The frequency of inspection depends on the severity of operation and the location of the unit. Fans operating under dusty conditions, in outdoor locations, or in corrosive atmospheres should, of course, get more frequent attention than fans handling clean air in a dry location. On the other hand, too frequent inspection may be uneconomical. A combination of good judgment and experience and an analysis of the relative costs involved should determine the program to be followed. Once determined it should be adhered to strictly to get its full benefit. It is over a long period that the advantages of a systematic inspection and maintenance program become impressive.

HINTS ON PROPER OPERATING PRACTICES

Never run a fan at a speed higher than the manufacturer sold it for. Always consult him if you want to speed up a fan to increase its capacity. The rotor may be operating near its maximum safe speed and may fail under the higher stresses induced at the higher speed. The higher speed may be in or near the critical range for the shaft, and may cause excessive vibration. The higher speed increases bearing temperature. The power required by the fan may increase enough to overload and burn out a driving motor.

A fan operating in a fixed system follows definite laws, called "fan laws." The cfm is directly proportional to the rpm ratio, the pressure developed is proportional to the square of the rpm ratio, and the hp required is proportional to the cube of the rpm ratio. Thus, if the speed of a fan is doubled, the pressure becomes four times and the horsepower becomes eight times what it was.

Remember that any air exhausted from a space must be replaced. If a fan is installed to exhaust from a room where no provision is made for air to enter, there won't be any ventilation.

SAFETY DEVICES

Safety devices should protect personnel from contact with rotating elements, while causing a minimum of interference with normal functioning of the equipment. Also, they should protect the equipment from accidental damage.

Protective Screens. Screens may be used to cover the inlet or outlet on a centrifugal or axial fan, or to completely enclose the fan, motor, and drive on a propeller fan. Screens are obstructions in the air stream and will reduce fan capacity considerably if the mesh is too fine. If possible, do not use finer than 1-in.-square mesh for a flat screen. If a finer mesh must be used, the screen often can be made in a box form, or with a dished or cylindrical shape to provide greater free area. When this is done, the screen should be made large enough that its free area is at least equal to the fan inlet or outlet area, as the case may be.

Belt Guards. A V-belt drive is a friction drive, and as such will generate heat. Air should be allowed to circulate freely around all parts of the drive to help dissipate this heat. It is not good practice to completely enclose V-belt drives. Use open-mesh guards if possible.

Coupling Guards. They should be strong enough to provide complete protection yet allow easy access to the coupling for inspection and servicing.

The following check list itemizes the most common fan troubles and the possible causes:

Capacity or Pressure Below Rating

1. Total resistance of system higher than anticipated.
2. Speed too low.
3. Dampers or variable inlet vanes not properly adjusted.
4. Poor fan inlet or outlet conditions.
5. Air leaks in system.
6. Damaged wheel.
7. Incorrect direction of rotation.
8. Wheel mounted backward on shaft.

Vibration and Noise

1. Misalignment of bearings, couplings, wheel, or V-belt drive.
2. Unstable foundation.
3. Foreign material in fan causing unbalance.
4. Worn bearings.
5. Damaged wheel or motor.
6. Broken or loose bolts or set screws.
7. Bent shaft.
8. Worn coupling.
9. Fan wheel or driver unbalanced.
10. 120-cycle magnetic hum due to electrical input.   (Check for high or unbalanced voltage.)
11. Fan delivering more than rated capacity.
12. Loose dampers or variable inlet vanes.
13. Speed too high or fan rotating in wrong direction.
14. Vibration transmitted to fan from some other source.

Overheated Bearings

1. Too much grease in ball bearing.
2. Poor alignment.
3. Damaged wheel or driver.
4. Bent shaft.
5. Abnormal end thrust.
6. Dirt in bearings.
7. Excessive belt tension.

Overload on Driver

1. Speed too high.
2. Discharging over capacity because existing system's resistance is lower than original rating.
3. Specific gravity or density of gas above design value.
4. Packing too tight or defective on fans with stuffing box.
5. Wrong direction of rotation.
6. Shaft bent.
7. Poor alignment.
8. Wheel wedging or binding on fan housing.
9. Bearings improperly lubricated.
10. Motor improperly wired.

Chapter 4

VENTILATING EXHAUST SYSTEMS

By E. C. Englert
Vice President—Sales
D. D. Herrman
Vice President—Engineering
Hartzell Propeller Fan Company
Division of Castle Hills Corporation
Piqua, Ohio

The importance of ventilation exhaust systems in all types of industry has been greater since the beginning of World War II than ever before. Actually, industrial ventilation other than as material handling was once looked upon as pampering the employee. Now industry has come to realize that proper ventilation pays handsome dividends in improved production, less absenteeism, better employee relations, cleaner plants, and longer productive machine life. Good ventilation is obtainable with many types of units, each designed to do a specific job. Many of the larger equipment manufacturers maintain staffs of experts to design and install systems and equipment. Industrial hygienists have done much to promote proper application and design of ventilating systems.

Generally, the exhaust equipment used can be divided into propeller fans, tube-axial blowers, vane-axial blowers, centrifugal fans, and the related equipment that normally is used with these air movers. The related equipment includes heating and cooling coils, shutters, guards, penthouses, ventilators, and many other items.

Propeller fans are made in many styles and types for specific jobs. Regular exhaust fans may have from 2 to 16 blades, depending on the particular function of the fan. Generally, the units with a small number of blades are used for low-pressure fans and the units with a larger number of blades are used for pressure applications. Blade width, blade angle, tip speed, and number of stages are all factors in design, and capacities range from a few hundred to 1,500,000 cfm of free air. Static pressures run from zero to 4 in. water gage in properly designed fans. Many mountings are available, including direct drive, belt drive, extended shaft, tube-axial, and other variations. Applications include general factory ventilation and specific process ventilation, as well as man cooling and product cooling.

Vane-axial blowers are used for moderate to high-pressure applications, from ½ to 16 in. water gage. To oversimplify, a vane-axial blower is simply a special tube-axial fan to which either intake or discharge guide vanes or both have been added to straighten the flow of air out of the unit. By taking advantage of the conversion of the rotational component of the air stream, the fan can reach higher statics than a straight propeller type at the same tip speed, and do it more efficiently. Vane-axial units have found wide use not only in general exhaust systems, but in such special applications as oven exhausts, spray machines, plating tanks, water-wash spray-booth exhaust, supply fans for high-velocity product cooling, and many others. The ease of mounting and straight-line air flow make them ideal for many applications.

Centrifugal blowers function differently than the types described above in that air enters the blower at the center, is picked up by the wheel, and then is literally thrown around and out of the casing by centrifugal force at right angles to the original direction of flow. These blowers are divided into three broad classes: forward-curved fans, backward-curved fans, and radial-bladed fans. The forward-curved units are used for pressures from $\frac{1}{4}$ to 3 in. water gage and find some use in industry. Air-conditioning systems, office exhaust, and related uses where low noise level and low speed are required are the usual field for this type of fan. Some small sizes are made direct-connected but generally these fans are belt driven as utility sets.

Backward-curved centrifugal fans find much wider use in industry, since the blades lend themselves to a sturdier construction, have nonoverloading characteristics, and run at higher speeds, making use of simple drives. They can be furnished in many sizes as direct-connected units, also as utility vent sets, and many other belted arrangements. These blowers are used for pressures from $\frac{1}{2}$ to 16 in. water gage at volumes up to several hundred thousand cfm.

Radial-bladed centrifugal fans are high-speed high-pressure units. Often they are direct-connected units, such as those used for air supply to melting furnaces, small high-pressure exhaust systems, etc. Such fans have an overloading power curve, but are very sturdy, compact units. They are relatively low-volume, high-pressure fans, with large-diameter, narrow blades.

All fans and blowers should be purchased from reliable manufacturers who test their equipment in accordance with the Standard Test Code for centrifugal and axial fans of the American Society of Heating and Air Conditioning Engineers, and the Air Moving and Conditioning Association. Unless fans and blowers are properly rated, it is impossible to design proper exhaust systems. Copies of the Standard Test Code are obtainable from the Air Moving and Conditioning Association, 2159 Guardian Building, Detroit 26, Mich.

Obviously, without Code ratings it is impossible to determine the performance obtainable from the fans and blowers, and usually an inadequate system results. Most reliable manufacturers have well-equipped laboratories for testing fans and blowers and are in position to guarantee performance on all equipment they manufacture.

Further effort has been made by the U.S. Department of Commerce to protect purchasers of fans and blowers. The Department of Commerce recommends that fans and blowers purchased should be in accordance with Commerical Standards 178-51, Amendment 1. Copies of this Commercial Standard are available either direct from the U.S. Department of Commerce or from any of the Department's field offices.

Practically all plants require some ventilation today. The amount of ventilation, of course, depends on the type of manufacturing or processing being done. An assembly plant obviously needs far less ventilation than a foundry. However, during summer months ventilation in an assembly plant plays an important part in obtaining high performance from the employees. As examples of various requirements in plants, the following occur frequently: man cooling, product cooling, paint-spray exhaust, fume and gas removal, heat removal, tank ventilation, fume control, and many other similar applications. Frequently, the fans and blowers are required only for health and comfort of workers, but in many instances it is found beneficial for plant maintenance, elimination of explosive hazards, prevention of injury to machinery, and plant cleanliness.

INSTALLATION OF EXHAUST SYSTEMS

Probably the simplest method of exhausting fumes and heat from a plant or an area is the mounting of an exhaust fan in a window or wall. Under certain conditions, where the size of the room and the building itself are adaptable, the use of exhaust equipment of this type does an excellent job. Generally, such fans are equipped with accessories such as automatic shutters and guards to meet safety codes devised by the plant and various states. Considering the amount of air that can be removed with exhaust fans of this type, it is the least expensive and has the lowest maintenance costs yet is very effective where it can be used.

An extension of the system described above is the installation of exhaust fans in roof ventilators. Ventilators usually are spotted effectively over the plant, with sizes and locations being determined by the heat and operating conditions in the plant. They can be placed anywhere on the roof of the building. Types and kinds of ventilators will be described later. An example of roof ventilators for general ventilation is shown in Fig. 4-1. Here the ventilators are fan-powered, and are removing excess heat and fumes from a diesel plant.

Specific ventilation for the removal of fumes, dust, etc. at the source usually is handled by duct systems of various types, depending on the particular problems involved.

Specific exhaust systems vary from very simple single-fan, single-hood units to very complex duct systems. Examples of simple booth or hood exhaust include spray

FIG. 4-1. Roof ventilators removing heat and fumes from diesel repair plant.

FIG. 4-2. Tube-axial blower exhausting acid fumes from cleaning tank.

booths, booths for welding-fume and heat exhaust, furnace hoods, and exhaust hoods for solder pots. Generally, the static pressure requirements in simple exhaust ducts are very low, ranging from $\frac{1}{4}$ to approximately $\frac{3}{4}$ in. water gage. In the complex systems, where many hoods or tanks are tied together, and particularly where slots, baffles, water eliminators, etc., are used in the duct systems, the pressures rise to as high as 4 or 5 in. water gage. A good example of such a system would be the tying together of as many as 10 or 12 plating and cleaning tanks into a single ductwork system that is handled by one vane-axial blower. Many problems arise in these complicated systems, and the calculation of the static pressure drop through the system is often quite elaborate.

Figure 4-2 illustrates the use of a belt-driven tube-axial blower exhausting through a slot-type arrangement over a cleaning tank. This is a simple method of fume removal that allows ready access to the entire face of the tank. The crane or hoist above the tank is not complicated by this method. Single-side ventilation is satisfactory for 6 or 8 ft of tank width. Tanks wider than 8 ft should have slots on both sides. Figure 4-3 illustrates a portion of a complicated duct system handling vapors from cleaning tanks in a rather elaborate setup. The ductwork shown is overhead, but to gain working space in some plants the ducts are placed in or under the floor. The static pressures required on the system shown in Fig. 4-3 run several times that of the static pressure of Fig. 4-2 and necessitate the use of a vane-axial blower or a backward-curved centrifugal rather than a tube-axial unit.

In the larger plants, the system requirements, material specifications, and fan selections depend on static pressures involved and are decided by the plant ventilation engineer together with the fan engineer from the equipment supplier.

Specific ventilation consists of capturing the fumes, heat, or dust at the source, whereas general ventilation consists of replacing the vitiated air in an entire plant with clean, fresh air at stated intervals. Both of these systems have their application in industry and frequently are applied in the same plant at the same time.

Fig. 4-3. Portion of cleaning-tank vapor exhaust system.

ROOF VENTILATORS

Roof ventilators for general plant ventilation include two types—powered roof ventilators and gravity ventilators. The gravity ventilator depends on wind velocity over the ventilator, and height of the ventilator off the floor, and temperature differential in the building between floor and ceiling.

These ventilators work very well where high heat is experienced and there are good wind velocities, but they are influenced by outside weather conditions over which the plant operator has no control.

Powered roof ventilators, while generally used for exhaust purposes, are now being built for intake as well and are completely controlled by push-button operation regardless of weather conditions.

In industrial plants propeller-type or tube-axial-type roof ventilators are usually furnished because of high outlet velocities or air movements. Special adaptations can be made by some manufacturers using reversible fans to bring air into the plant through the ventilators at certain times of the year. The same ventilator can be used for exhaust when required. Most manufacturers furnish roof ventilators for curb, slope, or peak mounting, depending on the type of roof involved. Generally, galvanized iron is used, although other materials such as copper, aluminum, asbestos-coated sheet, and monel or stainless can be furnished. Roof ventilators are furnished either direct-connected or with motors placed out of the air stream where fumes are encountered. On direct-connected units, temperature must be given consideration, with maximum of 115°F for a Class A motor, 160°F for a Class B motor, and 200°F for Class H motor. On higher temperatures, belt-drive units are used, although some manufacturers use breather ducts to bring outside air over the motor to assist in cooling.

Since the fire at the Lavonia, Mich., plant of General Motors,[1] fire underwriters have

---

[1] Hydra-matic transmission plant. 1.5 million sq ft of unobstructed manufacturing area destroyed. Direct damage more than $50 million; cost of lost production estimated an a minimum of $150 million more.

changed their thinking in connection with roof ventilators. The underwriters now require that the ventilators go to an open position automatically when a fire starts or excessive heat occurs, whether the electrical system in the building is operating or not. This is a reversal of the thinking of several years ago, when devices were furnished to close off the dampers.

The direction of air discharge in some instances is very important. As an example, the removal of lead fumes from a brass foundry should be directed vertically, with the idea of pushing the air as high as possible for complete dispersion of the fumes. Failure to observe this simple rule can easily result in the fumes returning to an adjacent building, causing employee health problems.

EXHAUST REQUIREMENTS

Average Air Changes Required for Good Ventilation. Table 4-1 is a list of industrial and commercial establishments indicating air-change requirements normally

Table 4-1. Average Air Changes Required for Good Ventilation

	Minutes per change		Minutes per change		Minutes per change
Assembly halls....	2–10	Forge shops.......	1–5	Plants:	
Auditoriums.......	2–10	Foundries:		Furniture.........	2–5
Bakeries..........	2–3	Aluminum......	3–5	Plastic...........	1–3
Banks............	3–10	Brass..........	1–3	Plating rooms.......	1–5
Barns............	10–20	Gray iron.......	1–3	Poolrooms.........	2–5
Bars.............	2–5	Garages..........	2–10	Pressrooms.........	1–3
Beauty parlors.....	2–5	Generator rooms...	2–5	Projection rooms.....	1–3
Boiler rooms.......	1–5	Glass plants.......	1–3	Recreation rooms....	2–10
Bowling alleys.....	2–10	Gymnasiums......	2–10	Residences.........	2–5
Churches.........	5–15	Kitchens:		Salesrooms.........	2–10
Clubs............	2–10	Hospital........	2–5	Theaters...........	2–8
Dairies...........	2–5	Resident........	2–5	Toilets.............	2–5
Dance halls.......	2–10	Restaurant......	1–3	Transformer rooms...	1–5
Dining rooms.....	3–10	Laboratories......	1–5	Warehouses........	2–10
Dry cleaners.....	1–5	Laundries........	1–3	Welding shops.......	1–3
Engine rooms....	1–3	Markets..........	2–10		
Factories:		Offices...........	2–10		
Assembly.......	3–5	Packing houses....	2–5		
Welding.........	1–3	Paper mills........	1–5		
Machine........	2–5				

accepted as good practice. It should be mentioned, however, that the variations of from 1 to 5 min or more per change really depend on the circumstances surrounding the installation.

In such cases there is no substitute for the experience and knowledge of a qualified fan engineer to determine where changes and how many minutes per change are required. Careful consideration of all factors must be considered before the cfm required and the placement of fans are determined.

Some of the rules to be observed in installing fans for general ventilation can be followed in all ventilation. Fans should be located wherever possible to blow with the prevailing wind. The intake areas in the plant should be so placed as to take advantage of the positive pressures created by prevailing winds if possible. Also, the fans for exhaust in such cases should be located so that there is no short-circuiting from openings direct to the fan. Often, in roof monitors, the fans will be so installed that they exhaust with the adjacent windows open. This does not help the workers or the situation existing in the main or working portion of the building; it merely allows air to be pulled in through the open monitor windows and exhausted by the fan.

Intake areas generally should be at least 50 per cent greater than the fan-wheel discharge area and even greater than this amount where possible. They should be located so that drafts will not be objectionable to workers who are placed near the areas. If filters are used on the intakes, they should be arranged as far as practical to keep the pressure loss from filter resistance at a minimum. The velocity through filters will vary from 350 fpm for the ordinary throwaway glass type to as high as 550 or 600 fpm through some special types of washable filters. The static resistance usually runs approximately .2 in. clean up to 0.3 or 0.4 in. when the filters are dirty.

In general ventilation it often is necessary to provide fans with external cooling tubes over the motors because of high ambient temperatures encountered or to use Class B or Class H insulated motors (glass-wound or silicone-wound) to enable the motor to stand up under the heat in conditions where the fan is mounted. Also, there are times when the air is hazardous due to gaseous fumes or dust concentrations, and in these cases, explosion-proof motors must be used. In such cases, non-sparking construction on the fan wheels is a must, and for belt-driven exhaust equipment, spark-proof belts must be used.

In corrosive or wet atmospheres the fumes generally are collected by specific ventilation, but in some cases general ventilation is used. In these cases acid-resisting motors and special coatings and materials are available and should be used in the ventilating systems.

Recommended Velocities for Exhaust Hoods. Table 4-2 shows some processes and types of hoods that are used in industry. Note that the required air velocities are rather wide in range, and it is often necessary to have an experienced fan engineer consult with the plant engineer on such jobs.

Some of the practices to be followed in placing exhaust hoods, slots, and canopies are commonsense requirements. It is obvious that fumes and heat should be collected as near the source of their generation as possible. Also, it is well to make all runs of ductwork as direct and as short as possible. Often these two factors are overlooked in laying out the exhaust systems. However, many times it is not practical to pick up fumes directly at their source because of working conditions, crane operation, etc. For the same reasons duct systems sometimes require many turns.

Another practical rule is to keep the duct velocity as low as possible, considering, of course, the fumes to be handled and the length of run. When conveying materials, this cannot be followed, as there are definite requirements for each type of material as to velocity. In any duct system where turns are necessary it is well to use long-radius elbows or splitters or turning vanes to keep the elbow resistance at a minimum. Also, after calculating the resistance of such an exhaust system, it is well to suggest a fan having a reserve capacity 10 to 15 per cent beyond the pressure-volume point selected.

The engineer should be sure in specifying the setup for a specific ventilation system that the hood area is ample and that the height of the hood and the overlap are such that effective working conditions and effective collection are maintained. This also applies to slot-type tank ventilation systems and other specific hood jobs. If corrosive fumes, abrasive conditions, or high temperature are encountered make sure that the fan and duct parts are properly treated to secure long life. In addition to special materials such as stainless steel, monel, transite, and rigid polyvinyl chloride, there are many plastic coatings, special paints, and rubber coatings that are available.

With reference to both specific and general ventilation, there are several excellent guides available. The "Industrial Ventilation Guide," published by the Air Moving and Conditioning Association, Detroit, Mich., is an excellent guide to both types of ventilation. In addition, there is a manual of "Recommended Practice on Industrial Ventilation," prepared by the Committee on Industrial Ventilation, Lansing, Mich., that presents the requirements for different systems and outlines duct-design procedure for the plant engineer. Actually, this excellent manual was prepared in cooperation with government industrial hygienists, plant engineers, and fan and blower engineers, and it represents a compilation of the best thinking on industrial ventilation.

Examples of specific ventilation are shown in Figs. 4-4 through 4-8.

Table 4-2. Recommended Velocities for Exhaust Hoods

Area of slot or face (sq ft) × velocity (fpm) = cfm required

Location	Hood	Required air velocity (fpm), average
Aluminum furnace......	Enclosed, open one side	150–200 fpm over open face
	Canopy	200–250 fpm over face
Bottle washing.........	Enclosed booth, open one side	150–250 fpm over face
Brass furnace..........	Enclosed, open one side	200–250 fpm over open face
	Canopy	250–300 fpm over open face
Chemical laboratory....	Enclosed, door front	100 fpm over door opening
	Enclosed, open front	100–150 fpm over face
	Down draft, table type	150–200 fpm over table gross area
Degreasing............	Canopy	150–200 cfm over face
	Slot type for tanks up to 4 ft wide (slot one side)	2-ft width, use 1,500–2,000 fpm thru 2-in. slot
		3-ft width, use 1,500–2,000 fpm thru 4-in. slot
		4-ft width, use 1,500–2,000 fpm thru 6-in. slot
		For tanks over 4 ft use slots on 4 sides
Dryers...............	Canopy	125–150 fpm over face
	Slot type at each end of continuous dryer	150–200 fpm over 6- to 8-in. slot
Electric welding.......	Enclosed booth, open front	100–150 fpm over face
	Canopy	125–150 fpm over face
Electroplating..........	Canopy	125–175 fpm over face
	Slot type for tanks up to 4 ft wide (slot one sid)	2-ft width, use 1,500–2,000 fpm thru 2-in. slot
		3-ft width, use 1,500–2,000 fpm thru 4-in. slot
		4-ft width, use 1,500–2,000 fpm thru 6-in. slot
		For tanks over 4 ft wide use slots on 4 sides
Foundry shakeout......	Enclosed booth, open front	150–200 fpm over face
	Down draft, grill type	300–500 fpm
Grain dust, wood flour, etc.	Slot type	2,000 fpm thru 2- to 4-in. slot
	Canopy	500–600 fpm over face
Grinding (disk) and sanding	Down draft, grill	400 fpm over open face
	Bench type with slot one side	2,000–2,500 fpm thru 4-in. slot
Hand forge	Canopy	150–250 fpm over face
	Enclosed booth, open one side	200–300 fpm over face
Kitchen ranges.........	Canopy	125–150 fpm over face
Metal spraying.........	Enclosed, open one side	200–250 fpm over face
Paint spraying.........	Enclosed booth, open one side	125–200 fpm over face
Paper machine.........	Canopy	100–300 fpm over face*
Pickling tanks.........	Canopy	200–250 fpm over face
	Slot type for tanks up to 6 ft wide, slot one side only	Minimum 4-in. slot, 2,000–2,500 fpm thru slot
Quenching tanks.......	Canopy	200–300 fpm over face
Rubber mixing rolls....	Canopy	150–200 fpm over face
	Slot type	2,000–2,400 fpm thru 2-in. slot
Soldering booths.......	Enclosed both, open one side	150 to 200 fpm over face
Steam tanks...........	Canopy	200 fpm over face
	Slot type for tanks up to 6 ft wide, slot one side only	1,500–2,000 fpm thru minimum 4-in. slot
Stonecutting...........	Enclosed booth, open face	400–500 fpm over face
Varnish kettles.........	Canopy	250–350 fpm over face
	Slot type—all around slot	2-in. minimum slot, 2,000 fpm thru slot

* Must be calculated from water-pickup method.

FIG. 4-4. Fumes being removed by slot-type hood in a galvanizing plant.   Note that duct-work must be offset to permit effective use of the cranes.

FIG. 4-5. Long hood over conveyor carrying freshly painted barrels.   Fumes are removed and paint film is dried rapidly.   Tube-axial blowers are driven through belts by explosion-proof motors.

SUPPLYING REPLACEMENT AIR

Intake Requirements.   Generally speaking, exhaust systems of all types work very well during the summer or when windows or doors are open in the factory.   A different problem, however, occurs once the windows and doors are closed for winter operation. Then, if exhaust is required in the plant, which so often happens, there is likely to be starvation of the inlet air, static pressure will be built up, and the efficiency of the units will be lowered.

This condition is easily noticed on entering many plants, where it is found almost impossible to open doors.   Also, when an outside door is open, a tremendous rush of cold air comes into the plant.   Naturally, an exhaust system without supply air is very inefficient.   Particularly bad conditions exist in plants where toxic or acid fumes exist or in cleaning plants where dust is a problem.   Paper mills, plating rooms, etc., have a severe problem in connection with condensation on walls, windows, and roof.

It is difficult to specify the exact amount of intake air required for particular applications.   In most cases a supply of 75 per cent of the cubic feet of air per minute exhausted is sufficient.   The other 25 per cent of the fans' requirements can come from infiltration, or it may even be possible to cut down the exhaust system by 5 or 10 per cent of normal capacity, since comfort-cooling effects are not needed in the winter.

In other cases, such as the supply to paint spray booths, varnish rooms, paint-mixing rooms, etc., where the principal object of the fans is to exhaust explosive or hazardous fumes, the intake should be kept at a maximum of 75 or 80 per cent of the exhaust-fan requirements.   If the intake units supply more air than the exhaust fans can

Fig. 4-6. Vane-axial blower with considerable ductwork removing oil fumes from screw machines.

remove, the fumes within the room being ventilated will spread throughout the building.

In other instances, such as transformer rooms, switchgear rooms, or rooms containing any device subject to deterioration by dust or abrasive material in the air, it is necessary to filter the intake air and provide slightly in excess of the cfm being exhausted by the ventilating fans.   This keeps the room under positive pressure and allows air to leak out of the room through cracks and other openings, in order to make the air flow out and keep dust or dirt from entering.

Various types of steam-intake equipment are available, most of which are equipped with nonfreeze coils, unit heater coils with extra condensate tubes on the outside of the steam-supply tube so that the supply tube continuously warms the condensate.   A more accurate name for this type of coil would be "distributing coil" rather than nonfreeze unit.   Actually the unit can freeze if pressures drop below 5 lb.   A safety device should be built into the system to cut off the supply fan and possibly close supply dampers when the steam pressure fails or the controls call for zero flow.   The coils can be equipped with housings containing propeller-type fans, vane-axial blowers, or centrifugal fans, and may be equipped with intake air filters or air diffusers, or with ductwork to pipe the incoming air to various portions of the building.   In many cases it is impossible to merely "dump" the air flow into the room, so to speak, whereas in others it is necessary to use diffuser heads or ductwork to divert the incoming air to sections where the heated air does not come in direct contact with people.

One example is that of paper mills, where intake air is brought in heated, ducted to the underside of the paper machine, permitted to mix with the heat from the paper machine, and then exhausted. Some installations are made near the roof, bringing air in from the roof and forcing it down to the floor level. Here again it is necessary to avoid direct throw on employees. This method is particularly advantageous in extremely wide buildings where the supply of air is needed near the center.

Care must be taken in the piping of installations of this type to make sure they are properly trapped. It is generally necessary to put a control thermostat bulb a considerable distance ahead of the coil or shield it from radiant heat so that it will operate properly. Should the thermostat bulb be unshielded or too close to the heat source, it may turn the unit off, causing freezing of the core and failure. Manufacturer's recommendations in connection with control valves should be followed closely, as too large a valve will result in too frequent opening and closing of the valve and cause premature failure. A valve that is too small will lead to insufficient heat or freezing of the core.

The use of intake units is relatively new but is increasing. Almost all new plants are being equipped with supply units. A word of caution is necessary in connection with these units. It takes approximately 75,600 btu per hr to heat 1,000 cfm from 0 to 70°F. Obviously, this means considerable boiler load and must be considered before purchase of intake equipment. Frequently it is possible to cut down on ventilation requirements during the winter months, reducing the amount of intake air necessary to do a satisfactory job.

Thus far, only heated-air intake has been discussed. In the South and in other parts of the country during summer months, there are many cases where an unheated air supply that is controllable must be used. As mentioned above, in many large, wide buildings, it is often necessary to bring air into the building to satisfy exhaust fans. To bring this air in properly and to control it is the job of the plant engineer and the fan engineer.

FIG. 4-7. Typical hood in a rubber calendar mill removing fumes and heat. The blower is mounted above roof.

Many units have been developed for this application and there are some on the market that can be used for both supply and exhaust depending on the time of the year and the nature of the job to be done.

Good examples of supplying unheated air are the new large powerhouses that are being built all over the country. In these, air is brought in at various levels in the powerhouse walls and blown without louvers, diffusers, or ductwork. Then the exhaust fans at extreme high levels, together with the forced- and induced-draft boiler fans, take this air and exhaust it from the building.

It has been found necessary to augment the general ventilation of forge shops, rolling mills, steel works, and glass factories with pressure systems which supply small streams of cool outside air to certain operations and to certain operators. This is used not only for comfort ventilation but, in many cases, to cool press molds, glass molds, and rubber-curing molds in production. Such intake air is also used to cool aluminum extrusions and other materials in various operations.

The use of steam-type heating coils for intake units has been described. Natural-gas, liquid-petroleum-gas, and oil-fired units also are available for approximately the same service.

FIG. 4-8. Vane-axial blowers exhausting from wet-spray booths in motor-manufacturing plant. Supply fans (not shown) are used to prevent negative pressure in building.

EXHAUSTING CORROSIVE FUMES

The problem of exhausting corrosive fumes is persistent and serious from the stand-point of maintenance because fan and blower equipment is subject to corrosion. Various metals have been used by fan and blower manufacturers. No one metal will withstand all of the acids found in various plants, but usually a metal or material can be found to withstand most acids and corrosive fumes for a reasonable period.

Some of the factors which affect the deterioration of metals are type of acid or alkali present, temperature of the fumes, concentration, amount of aeration, and location. Some metals used for corrosive fumes are stainless steel, monel metal, bronze, cast iron, inconel, nickel, and cast alloy. The proper alloy to combat the particular corrosive fumes should be specified. For example, not all stainless steel is resistant to the same degree. The fan and blower manufacturer can combine his experience with that of the customer in offering the proper metals.

Table 4-3 indicates the resistance to corrosion of two types of stainless steel, monel metal, and low-carbon steel by some of the more common corrosives at certain temperatures.

Other fan materials are available for acid and alkali conditions. A canvas-base phenolic resin is excellent in its resistance to many acids and salt water, but is poor against high concentrations of caustics. Rigid polyvinyl chloride was first used in France for ductwork and is now being used in this country under various trade names for fan casings, ductwork, and hoods in a limited way. It is practically inert to most industrial acids and alkalis, but most types of this material tend to become soft over 150°F and lose most of their strength. The material can be welded with a rod of the same material by applying heat, but it must be formed under heat to the proper shape. It has very low tensile strength and impact strength.

Other materials, such as glass fabric or mat reinforced with polyester, have been used for ductwork and, of course, transite material has been used for ducts and hoods for many years.   Transite is impervious to most industrial acids and can be fabricated into many shapes, but it is quite expensive.   Glazed acid-proof tile is often used for square duct, particularly underground.   This is also available in round forms for some types of extremely corrosive ductwork.

Any special metal for use in fan or ductwork, as well as many of the plastics discussed, are expensive.   But in many severely corrosive applications the extra life

Table 4-3. Resistance to Corrosion of Fan Materials

Fumes handled	Temperature	Stainless 18–8	Stainless 35–15	Monel metal	Low-carbon steel
Ammonia	Room temperature	Good	Good	Fair	Fair
	Over 120°F	Good	Good	Fair	Fair
Caustic soda	Room temperature	Good	Good	Good	Not recommended
	Over 180°F	Good	Good	Good	Not recommended
Chlorine	Room temperature	Fair	Fair	Good	Not recommended
	Over 120°F	Fair	Fair	Good	Not recommended
Hydrochloric acid	Room temperature	Not recommended	Fair	Good	Not recommended
	Over 180°F	Not recommended	Fair	Good	Not recommended
Sulfuric acid	Room temperature	Not recommended	Fair	Good	Not recommended
	Over 180°F	Not recommended	Fair	Good	Not recommended
Nitric acid	Room temperature	Good	Good	Not recommended	Not recommended
	Over 120°F	Good	Good	Not recommended	Not recommended
Chromic acid	Room temperature	Good	Good	Not recommended	Fair
	Over 180°F	Good	Good	Not recommended	Fair
Acetic acid	Room temperature	Good	Good	Not recommended	Fair
	Over 180°F	Good	Good	Not recommended	Fair

from air-moving equipment and ductwork and trouble-free operation will overshadow first cost.

Many special coatings are available for air-moving equipment, ductwork, and supporting structures.   These materials range from ordinary black asphaltum stack paints to very complicated and high-priced resins, as well as natural rubber and Neoprene coatings.   Some of the more successful coatings include Neoprene rubbers, modified phenolics, epoxy resin coatings, and plastisols made of polyvinyl chloride. Other vinyl coatings and some of the polyesters have been used with success.

Fan casings and ductwork are relatively easy to protect.   There is not too much difficulty encountered in coating these parts.   There is little abrasion except at corners or at entrance points.   Rotating fan parts, however, are severely abraded and eroded by water droplets.   The softer coatings which will not peal off the blade will resist the abrasive effect of water droplets and dirt particles much better than the harder coatings.   When a hard coating is used, the first effect is for the water droplet actually to chip the coating, and then the acid or alkali gets under the coating and eats the base metal.   With the softer coatings, the particle of water dents the coating but slides off.

It is important to have all set screws, bolts, and shafts either coated or made of a metal that will resist the corrosion.

It is practically impossible to predict the life of equipment under corrosive conditions. Temperatures and concentrations play a very important part. Locate the fan as far as possible from the source of the fumes when a duct system is used, and arrange to flush down the duct system periodically. A corrosion-proof water eliminator should be used if possible between the fan and the source of fumes. Plugs should be provided, sloped to drain away from the fan.

EXHAUSTING EXPLOSIVE OR FLAMMABLE FUMES

We find in many plants today a requirement for special equipment for the removal of explosive or flammable fumes. Spark-proof or explosion-proof motors with underwriters labels are required. The most common types of explosion-proof motors are Class 1, Group D, which can be used in applications covering gasoline and petroleum fumes, dry cleaning and dyeing plants, paint and varnish factories, gas plants, and chemical plants, where the gas involved is no more dangerous than high-test gasoline or lacquer-solvent vapor. Class 2, Group G, motors are for hazardous grain-dust conditions, and Class 2, Group F, for hazardous carbon-dust conditions. Other motors not as commonly known are Class 1, Group A, for acetylene; Class 1, Group B, for hydrogen; and Class 1, Group C, for ether.

Generally speaking, nonsparking impellers are used in hazardous conditions of this kind to prevent a possible explosion where two ferrous metals might rub or hit. Aluminum, copper, brass, and monel are good examples of nonsparking materials that can be used for impellers.

Centrifugal blowers usually are equipped with nonsparking rubbing plates and aluminum and brass wheels. Frequently, belt-drive units are required for such installations, and covers for the belts can be furnished as well as nonsparking belts.

Fans or blowers should be located as near as possible to the source of fumes or explosive materials to prevent them from flowing throughout the plant. With some materials, care should be taken to insure that the condensate from the fumes is drained out of the ductwork. Fusible-link dampers frequently are used to close off the system or open it in case of fire. Some large systems even employ blowout doors as an added protection. It is recommended that for special applications of this kind, a reliable manufacturer be consulted for his recommendations and suggestions as to proper installation and maintenance.

COOLING-TOWER AND HEAT-EXCHANGER FAN PROBLEMS

Many large fans are used in the cooling of water in cooling towers and heat exchangers. The requirements in the oil industry frequently call for fans in diameters from 10 to 22 ft. The scarcity of water in many parts of the country means that air-conditioning units, power plants, and large processing industries cannot be operated there without recirculating the water. Generally, the units are propeller type and are used to move large volumes of air at low static pressures. Fans in the smaller towers for air-conditioning use run from 2 to 12 ft in diameter, and are frequently of aluminum or steel, although fans from 2 to 22 ft are being furnished in stainless steel, monel, plastic, aluminum, wood, and possibly other materials. The problem in a cooling tower is extreme from a maintenance standpoint in that it is a 24-hr operation, with water vapor passing over the blades and causing erosion and corrosion.

Not only the fans but the couplings, drive shafts, gears, and motors are subject to extremely punishing service.

Inspection should be made at regular intervals, hubs should be wire-brushed and painted when necessary, and the blades painted and kept in good repair. Manufacturers' recommendations in connection with maintenance and upkeep should be followed carefully. Maintaining oil levels in the gear reducer and proper lubrication of the motor are essential. Many years of trouble-free operation can be obtained from most cooling-tower fans if they are properly maintained.

Figure 4-9 shows an installation of 20-ft fans in an induced-draft cooling tower installed in a power-generating plant.

FIG. 4-9. Cooling-tower installation, power-generating plant.

CLEANING OF FANS AND BLOWERS

The periodic cleaning of fan and blower blades and housings is necessary for efficient operation in many applications. Build-ups of foreign material on a propeller blade cut down the efficiency of the unit and lead to severe unbalance. An extreme case is the paint spray booth, where much of the spray material passes through the fan. Paint builds up on the fan-blade supports and in the ductwork. Many strippable coatings are available for protecting the fan and enabling it to be cleaned easily. These coatings are placed on the clean fan and then either washed off with water or stripped off by means of a putty knife after sufficient accumulation.

The forward-curved centrifugal with a multitide of vanes is particularly susceptible to the collection of lint and dust, which build up in an uneven manner and will soon throw the blades out of balance unless removed.

Care should be taken in the cleaning of any fan blade to see that the blade is not harmed. Never use a chisel and hammer on an aluminum blade, or even a steel blade, as it is very easy to start cracks or bend the blade and cause an out-of-track or out-of-balance condition.

If intake screens or discharge screens are used on a fan application, care should be taken that these are not plugged or filled with debris and dirt. Accumulation of dirt, lint, leaves, and trash will materially affect the performance of the fan.

Where moisture, acid, or abrasive conditions exist, or in any application where it is noted that the fan housing as well as the propeller has corroded, the unit should be wire-brushed and painted with a material that will withstand the particular conditions involved. Paint must be carefully applied on the propeller or blower wheel to make sure that balance is not affected. Many new maintenance paints and coatings are available that are quite effective, and the fan manufacturer usually will offer recommendations.

MOTOR MAINTENANCE

The totally enclosed motor should be kept free from accumulations of paint over-spray, lint, and general shop dirt. Such accumulations cut down the heat transfer from the motor shell and actually insulate it. On fan-cooled motors, the fans on the motor should be kept clean, and the air channels through which the cooling air passes should be cleaned out periodically.

On open-end motors, care should be taken that the inlets and outlets of air to the motor are not plugged at any time. Sometimes it is necessary to place insect screens or rat screens over inlets. Motors in steamy atmospheres or in atmospheres where there are severe temperature fluctuations should be provided with drain holes or drain tubes to permit condensate to drain out. This is difficult to do at times on explosion-proof motors, but explosion-proof drains with breather tubes are available.

ROOF VENTILATORS

Galvanized roof ventilators should be permitted to weather for several weeks before painting. Ventilators made of black iron or other materials should be touched up after installation if there are any bare spots or scratches in the paint. Ventilators should be checked periodically to see that screens are clear of debris and that flashing on the roof is in good condition to prevent leaks. Regular fan maintenance, assuming that the ventilators are powered units, is required. If the ventilators are for summer use only, the dampers should be checked, the fan motors lubricated, and a complete check of the unit made prior to the start of a new season. Drain holes and weep holes in the condensation gutter should be cleaned and opened. Usually, checking the ventilator twice a year is sufficient.

MAINTENANCE ON UNIT HEATERS AND INTAKE UNITS

It is important on steam unit-heater coils and intake unit-heater coils, particularly those of the fin type, that the small finned openings be kept free of lint and dust. At times, and in many plants, this need only be done every 2 to 3 years, but in a very dusty or linty operation such as a textile mill, it is necessary to blow the lint off the fins and tubes every 4 to 5 weeks. On oil-fired and gas-fired unit heaters and intake units it is necessary to check the starting and safety equipment periodically and to make sure that flues are in good order. In connection with this, it is sometimes overlooked that when gas-fired or oil-fired unit heaters are not operating correctly a vacuum exists within the plant. The best way to correct this is to provide warmed intake air to supply the exhaust fans that are causing the vacuum, or at least to provide a supply of air to the burner element of the gas- or oil-fired unit heater.

On steam units, traps, check valves, and air vents should be checked before the start of the heating season. If there is any possibility of scaling in the unit, this should also be checked. This is very easily taken care of by dropping the dirt trap on the unit and checking to see if any corrosion or lime deposits exist in this portion.

Steam unit heaters generally are used on low-pressure steam for heating but at times may be used on high-pressure steam up to 150 psi for processing work. In this case, it is important to make sure that the piping is properly installed and then main-tained to provide continuous service. The fan and blower motors on such applica-tions, as well as the filters, intake screens, dampers, and controls, should be checked just as carefully as any other fan. Many times unit heaters and intake units are installed and forgotten, but they are an integral part of the plant's heating and venti-lating system and require care at least once a year.

Intake-air units of the steam type generally are furnished with what is known as a nonfreeze heating coil. This is a steam-distributing-tube type where the incoming steam enters the heater and warms the condensate at the same time. These dis-tributing-tube types of heater coils are quite effective, but the small orifices that are used require clean steam that is oil-free and that will not scale up. If scale is found on a periodic inspection, then boiler compound will have to be used to clean the units.

IMPORTANCE OF MAINTAINING PEAK SYSTEM EFFICIENCY

The main reason for an industrial plant to maintain peak efficiency on the ventilating systems is an economic one. Many large power companies and industries calculate that 1 hp means to them a $450 cost over a 10-year period. When systems are allowed to deteriorate, clog up, or become so dirty that the static pressure rises, either the proper amount of air is not used—thus cutting down plant operating efficiency—or the fan must be speeded up in order to move the proper amount of air through the system. When this happens the amount of horsepower absorbed varies approximately as the static pressure ratio. For example, if a system was originally designed to work at 1 in. static pressure and has become so clogged that, in order to move the proper amount of air, the static pressure is raised to 2 in., double the horsepower must be used. The investment in new motors, in rewiring and changing speeds, and in spending money to run such a system could have been saved if the system were maintained properly.

A second and no less important point is that the investment in equipment has been made. Therefore the ventilating system or systems should be maintained to obtain the maximum performance from the employees who benefit by the improved working conditions.

Chapter 5

DUST-COLLECTING EQUIPMENT

By JAMES R. KAYSE
Staff Analyst
DAVID E. BONN
Manager, Dust Control Department
American Air Filter Company, Inc.
Louisville, Ky.

There are two general classes of air-cleaning devices—air filters and dust collectors. The first are used in air-supply systems for heating, ventilating, air conditioning, and intakes of engines and compressors. Air filters normally are designed to handle atmospheric dust loadings from 1 to 4 grains per 1,000 cu ft of air. The second are designed for much heavier concentrations originating from local exhaust systems or stack-gas effluents found in industrial processes. Dust collectors normally will be used for concentrations 100 to 20,000 times greater than those for which air filters are designed. This chapter deals with dust collectors only.

Dust collectors are installed for one or more of the following purposes: (1) prevent nuisance or damage to property; (2) prevent reentry of contaminants to workroom; (3) reclamation of usable material; (4) reduce fire or explosion hazards; and (5) permit recirculation of cleaned air to working space. An outline of dust-collector characteristics is given in Table 5-1.

TYPES OF EQUIPMENT

There are 50 or more companies in the United States alone manufacturing dust-collecting devices. Designs are varied, often employing more than one of the known principles of separation of a solid, fume, mist or vapor from a gas stream. Operation will rely, in all probability, on more than one of the following mechanisms: interception; impingement; diffussion; gravity settling; humidification; condensation; wetting; electrostatic precipitation. Therefore it is much simpler to group the collectors in the following classes:

Inertial or dry centrifugal
  Simple cyclone
  Multiple centrifugal
  Dry dynamic
  Louver
Wet
  Packed tower
  Wet centrifugal

  Wet dynamic
  Orifice type
  Nozzle type
  Venturi scrubber
Fabric arrester
  Conventional
  Reverse jet
Electrostatic

Inertial or Dry Centrifugal

Dry-centrifugal collectors are usually found in applications emitting coarser dusts in light to moderate concentrations. They are often used as primary collectors in conjuction with final high-efficiency devices.

Simple Cyclone.   Relies on centrifugal force to spin the dust particles against the side walls of the collector, with the collected dust leaving the air stream through the dust outlet at the apex (see Fig. 5-1).

Table 5-1. Dust-collector Characteristics

	Cyclones	High-efficiency centrifugals	Wet collectors	Fabric arresters	High-voltage electrostatic
Effect of dust variations					
Efficiency:					
Particles less than 1 micron.....	Poor	Poor	Poor to fair	Good	Good
Particles 1–10 microns..........	Poor	Poor to fair	Fair to good	Good	Good
Particles 10–20 microns..........	Poor	Good	Good	Good	Good
Particles over 20 microns.......	Fair to Good	Good	Good	Good	Good
Abrasion resistance..............	Fair	Fair	Good	Good	Fair
Handles sticky, adhesive materials.	Fair	Poor	Poor to good	Poor	Poor
Bridging material gives troubles...	Slight	Yes	No	Yes	Yes
Fire or explosion hazard minimized.	Fair	Fair	Good	Poor	Poor
Can handle hygroscopic materials..	Yes	Fair	Yes	With care	With care
Large foreign materials cause plugging	Seldom	Yes	Seldom to yes	Seldom	Yes
Effect of gas stream variation					
Maximum temperature (standard construction).................	750°F	750°F	No limit	180–600°F	750°F
Troubles from condensed or entrained mists or vapors	Slight	Considerable	Slight	Not recommended	Some
Corrosive gases attack standard construction...................	Slight	Slight	Severe	Slight	Slight
Collector					
Space.........................	Large	Modest	Modest	Modest to large	Large
Pressure drop....................	1–2 in.	3–5 in.	3–6 in.	2–6 in.	1–2 in.
Reduced volume adversely affects collection efficiency	Yes	Yes with most designs	Depends on design	No	No

Multiple Centrifugal.   Greater centrifugal forces are obtained by using a number of small-diameter tubes with identical elements in parallel (see Fig. 5-2).

Dry Dynamic.   Dust is precipitated by centrifugal and dynamic forces on numerous specially shaped fan blades.   The collected dust travels along the blade surfaces and is discharged into a separate dust circuit within the fan housing.   It is then conveyed pneumatically to the dust storage hopper (see Fig. 5-3).

Louver Type.   Centrifugal force can be applied to a particle by a rapid change in direction of air flow by a series of plates set at an angle to the air stream, as illustrated in Fig. 5-4.   Coarser particles traverse the air stream and are projected back into the dirty-air side by the rebound vector and the aerodynamic spin that can be produced from such an impact.

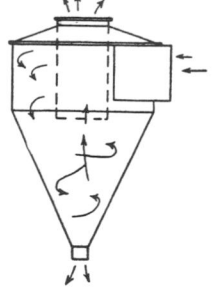

FIG. 5-1. Simple cyclone.

Wet Collectors

Wet collectors usually offer the advantages of constant exhaust volume, no secondary dust problem during disposal, and the ability to clean high-temperature, moisture-laden gases.

Packed Towers.   Packed towers (Fig. 5-5) have been largely restricted to the chemical industry, where they still are used extensively as gas scrubbers to remove gases and vapors.   Removal of the contaminant relies on long contact between the entering gas stream and the wetted surface of the packing.   Water flow usually is downward, with water rates of 5 to 10 gal per 1,000 cfm of standard air.   Packing material may be irregularly shaped ceramic saddles, although coke, gravel, and similar products have been used.

Wet Centrifugal.   Two types of wet centrifugal collectors are shown in Fig. 5-6.

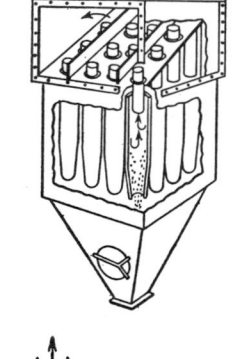

Collection relies on throwing the heavier particles against wetted collector surfaces by centrifugal force. Water rates usually are 3 to 5 gal per 1,000 cfm of gas cleaned.   Water distribution can be from nozzles, gravity flow, or induced water pickup by the air stream.

Wet Dynamic.   The wet dynamic precipitator (Fig. 5-7) combines the dynamic and centrifugal forces of a rotating fan wheel to cause the contaminant to impinge on the numerous specially shaped blades, on whose surface a film of water is maintained by spray nozzles at the inlet.

Orifice Type.   Collection efficiency in orifice-type wet collectors (Fig. 5-8) relies on the pickup or delivery of large water quantities to a collecting zone, where centrifugal forces, impingement, or collison causes wetting of the contaminant before its removal from the air stream.   Water quantities in motion are high, running from 10 to 40 gal per 1,000 cfm.   Much or all

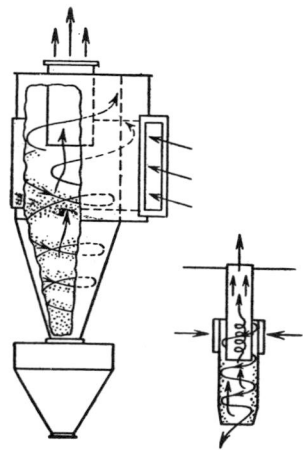

FIG. 5-2. Multiple centrifugals.

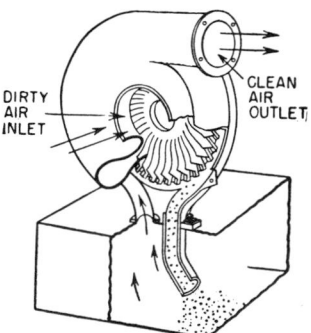

DIRTY AIR INLET

CLEAN AIR OUTLET

FIG. 5-3. Dry dynamic.

of this water can be recirculated without the use of distribution spray nozzles or recirculation pumps.

Nozzle Type.   High-pressure nozzles normally are installed in tower types of centrifugal collectors.   A large number of small nozzles is involved, using water pressures

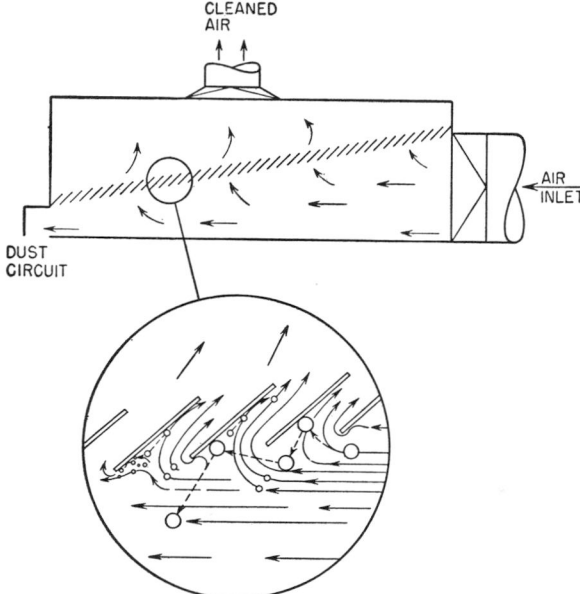

FIG. 5-4. Louver.

of 250 to 600 psi and water volumes of 5 to 10 gal per 1,000 cfm. Distribution of the droplets must be such that dispersion increases the chances of impact between water droplet and contaminant particle, rather than droplet against droplet to form larger, less effective droplets. The use of small nozzle orifices makes recirculation of water impractical for most industrial operations.

Venturi Scrubber. In the venturi design, the shear stresses of the air stream traveling at velocities of 12,000 to 20,000 fpm are used to break up water introduced through open supply pipes in the venturi throat. The turbulence in the venturi is utilized to disperse and cause impact with contaminant within a short time interval.

Fabric Arrester

The effectiveness of passing air or gas through a fabric at low velocity has been recognized, and the method has been used for many years in cleaning devices. Fabric is arranged in envelope or tubular (stocking) shapes, as illustrated in Fig. 5-9. While removal appears to take place by a straining action of the media, actually collection is obtained by building up a mat of the material on the dirty side of the media which provide the filtering or straining bed.

Conventional. Sectional arresters, as indicated in Fig. 5-10, allow continuous

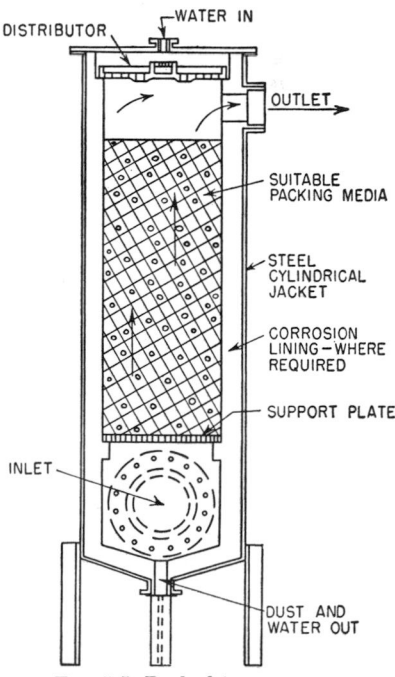

FIG. 5-5. Packed tower.

operation of the exhaust system, as automatic dampers periodically take one section out of service for vibrating the fabric while the remaining sections handle the

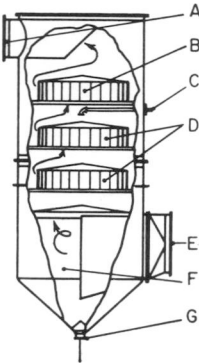

SYMBOLS	PARTS
A	CLEAN AIR OUTLET
B	ENTRAINMENT SEPARATOR
C	WATER INLET
D	IMPINGEMENT PLATES
E	DIRTY AIR INLET
F	WET CYCLONE FOR COLLECTING HEAVY MATERIAL
G	WATER AND SLUDGE DRAIN

Fig. 5-6. Wet centrifugal.

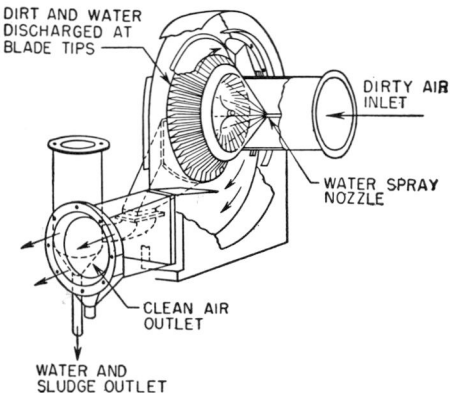

Fig. 5-7. Wet dynamic.

entire gas volume. The use of reverse air flow to increase effectiveness of removing adhering material usually is incorporated.

Reverse Jet. This type differs from the conventional in its use of high-pressure air jets from a moving "blow ring," dislodging the material from the inside of the stocking-shaped fabric (see Fig. 5-11).

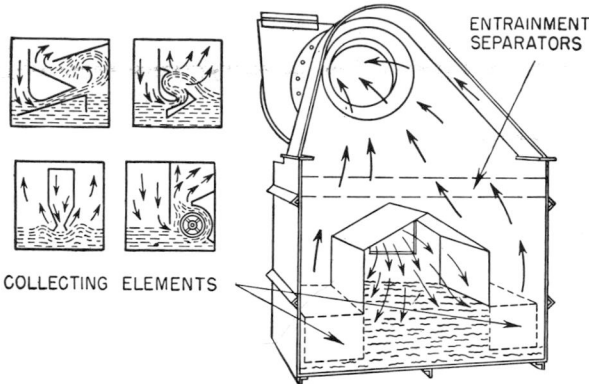

Fig. 5-8. Orifice type.

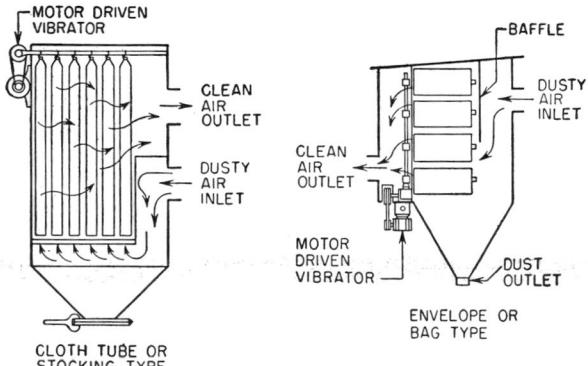

Fig. 5-9. Conventional fabric arrester, intermittent duty.

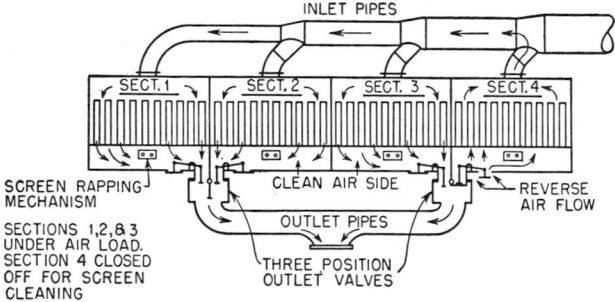

Fig. 5-10. Conventional fabric arrester, continuous duty.

Electrostatic

The high-voltage electrostatic precipitator (Fig. 5-12) is the predominant collector in this group. It should not be confused with the low-voltage, small dust-holding designs used in air filtration. The principle of collection relies on the ability to impart a negative charge to the particles in the gas stream, causing them to move and adhere to the grounded or positively charged collector plates. Voltage difference between

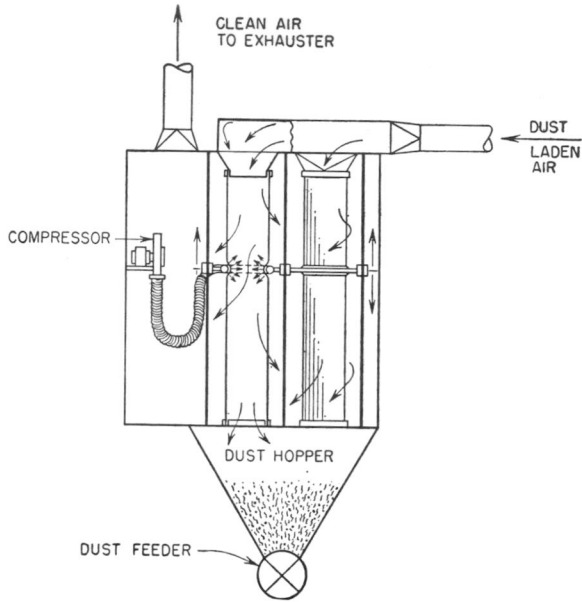

FIG. 5-11. Reverse-jet fabric arrester.

electrode and plate is 60,000 to 75,000 volts in most designs. Collector plates of cylindrical shapes surrounding the electrode rod are provided, where water is used to wash off collected material and where the gas stream is under high pressure or vacuum. Removal of the collected material is obtained by rapping or vibrating the elements either continuously or at predetermined intervals. Vibration or unloading usually takes place without stopping air flow through the precipitator, although some loss in the cleaned air can be expected in most applications during the cleaning cycle.

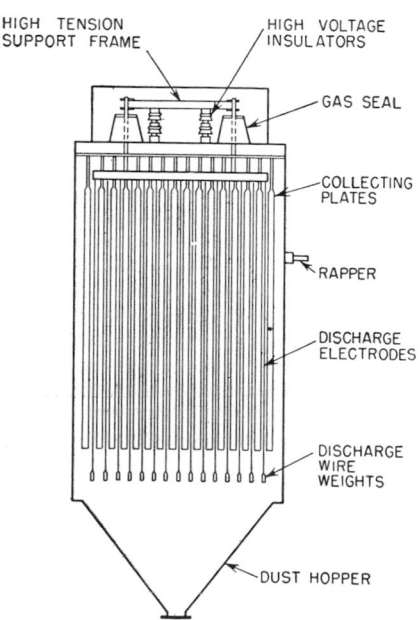

FIG. 5-12. Electrostatic precipitator.

MAINTENANCE OF DUST-CONTROL EQUIPMENT

Adequate and convenient maintenance begins on the drawing board. The eventual removal of parts which wear out or are damaged by other equipment should be taken into consideration by the draftsman and the design engineer. Parts normally exposed to maximum wear or mechanical abuse should be protected with extra-heavy construction. Employee safety and convenient maintenance are readily provided by adequate service catwalks, platforms, and ladders. The initial installation and future repair of any fan or motor always are aided by the installation of a simple monorail or bridge crane. Proper upkeep will be insured by following three general rules:

1. Cleaning the dust-collector storage hoppers at regular, predetermined intervals.
2. Definite scheduling of inspection for preventive maintenance.
3. Repairing, replacing, and cleaning all parts where indicated by the regular inspection.

Inertial or Dry Centrifugal

Simple Cyclone and Multiple Centrifugal. Because these units frequently are used as primary collectors ahead of a more efficient final collector, they usually are subjected to heavy abrasive-dust loadings. Rugged construction is essential, and sometimes wear plates or rubber liners are installed in the areas subjected to greatest wear. Installation and repairs are aided by bolted-flange construction.

Multiple centrifugals should have the outlet tubes tightly sealed into the header sheet to prevent short-circuiting. Centrifugals, having multivaned swirl rings to impart a swirling motion to the air stream, should be protected against large or foreign articles by using a ¾-in.-mesh wire screen at the hoods. Build-up in the tubes can sometimes be prevented by suspending chains in the center of each cyclone. Typical maintenance on both units will include:

1. Emptying the storage hoppers at regular intervals to avoid reentrainment.
2. Avoiding leakage at the dust-discharge point, especially if the unit is under negative pressure.
3. Giving routine inspection for build-up and points of extreme wear.
4. Keeping uniform air volume to maintain constant efficiency. Obstruction at the hoods or in the ducts will cause the volume to decrease proportionally.

Dry Dynamic. Routine maintenance will include:

1. Keeping the dust storage hopper vented back to the collector.
2. Inspection of the impeller at scheduled intervals for accumulation and wear on the blade tips.
3. Emptying the dust storage hopper regularly to avoid recirculation of the collected dust, which would reduce efficiency and cause extreme wear.
4. Because this unit is a combination fan and dust collector, the preventive maintenance outlined under Fans regarding bearings and V-belt drives should be followed.

Wet Collectors

As most wet collectors are in the high-efficiency group, they normally provide a nonhazardous dust discharge, but the equipment must be maintained to prevent undue wear, corrosion, and accumulation of sludge. Corrosion is frequently due to moist air, therefore all collector surfaces in contact with water or the air stream can be treated with a water-resistant or rust-retarding coating. Sheet rubber has been applied to areas subjected to severe abrasion with some success. A crust will sometimes form on the internal surfaces; it should be removed and the protective coating should be renewed. A periodic flushing will dislodge most accumulations.

Wet Centrifugal. Maintenance will include:

1. Insurance of adequate water supply at all times when the fan is operating.
2. Where recirculation of water is used, adequate settling tanks providing relatively clear water should be used
3. Water should be allowed to flow for a half hour after the fan is shut down to flush the equipment adequately.
4. Equipment should be inspected regularly for accumulations, and thoroughly cleaned when required.
5. Spray nozzles, when used, should be checked at least once a week for plugging.
6. Check all drains for accumulations. A plugged drain may form a water trap which could reduce the air volume.

Wet Dynamic. The same maintenance requirements as stipulated for wet centrifugals apply to the wet dynamic. Recirculation of the water is not recommended because of the type of nozzles used to provide the proper spray pattern. Since it is a combination fan and dust collector, see the section under Fans for proper maintenance of bearings and V-belts.

Orifice Type

1. The baffles or orifices that force the air to travel through the water should be checked regularly for wear, corrosion, and accumulation.
2. A high-pressure water jet should be used periodically for hosing down the interior.
3. Moisture-entrainment baffles should be removed and cleaned. They must be replaced properly, by having the hooked lips opposite the direction of air flow.
4. Water-overflow pipe should always be open to prevent reduced air volume resulting from excessive water in the collector.
5. Water-level control device should be regularly inspected for proper operation. Improper water level will affect efficiency, air volume, and performance of the unit.
6. Orifice-type collectors incorporating sludge ejectors for removal of the collected dust should be inspected for the same items mentioned in the section Sludge Settling Tanks.

Fabric Arresters

Items to be checked in routine maintenance of both the conventional and reverse-jet types include:

1. Dust leakage through holes in the fabric.
2. Unusual wear, or holes in the baffle plates, if used.
3. Unusual wear in the spark screens, if used.
4. Excessive build-up or accumulations in the dust storage hoppers.
5. Leaky or inoperative dust discharge valves.
6. Routine inspection of the fabric-rapping mechanism in conventional units to insure adequate shaking or cleaning action.
7. Proper operation of the jet ring and secondary air supply of the reverse-jet units.

Dust leakage from holes in the fabric normally will reveal itself on the clean air side of the unit by staining of the fabric and dust accumulations near the leak. With the fan installed on the air-discharge side of the collector, excessive leakage will cause undue wear on the impeller and fan casing. With good fabric maintenance, a set of tubes or envelopes should last for several years on most applications. Premature wearing or tearing of the fabric can be avoided by not stretching too tightly during installation. The tubes should never be under tension when the shaker mechanism is in operation.

The pressure differential in fabric arresters should not exceed the design pressure drop just before the shakedown cycle for the conventional unit and the design maximum for the reverse-jet unit. Excessive pressure differential can be caused by: overloading the arrester; plugging of the pores on the fabric by moist or sticky materials; and defective shaker mechanism or jet ring.

A permanently installed U tube will quickly indicate an inoperative condition and provides an easy method for the maintenance men to check visually the condition of the unit.

Electrostatic Precipitators

In maintaining electrostatic units, attention must be given to the *mechanical system* and the *electrical system*.

The mechanical system consists of the rapping mechanism. It should receive the same maintenance given fabric arresters.

The electrical system is complex, and maintenance should be carried out only by personnel equipped with knowledge of high-voltage electrical equipment. Before opening or entering any part of the unit, it is essential that the current to that portion of the collector be shut off by locking the switch in either the off or the grounded position. A fatal shock from high-voltage current is possible without physical contact because the charge may jump a 6- to 8-in. gap.

Even with the current turned off, it is not safe to enter the equipment until the static electricity has been dissipated by grounding. Proper grounding procedure consists of connecting a heavy wire to the grounded steelwork and then hooking it to the disconnected high-voltage point. In explosive atmospheres, the high-tension points should be grounded to the outside. If this cannot be done, the entire rectifier and transformer must be shut off and the high-voltage line grounded at the rectifier with all high-voltage switches closed.

All grounding procedures should be followed whenever maintenance personnel:

1. Clean the line insulators.
2. Clean precipitator insulators.
3. Contact any high-voltage part.
4. Enter the rectifier screened enclosure.
5. Perform work inside the precipitator chamber.

After all the precautionary measures have been taken, normal maintenance inspection will include:

1. Checking for excessive accumulations on the ionizing and grounded plate section.
2. Checking inoperative dust outlets and storage hoppers.
3. Checking performance of the electrical system for good ionization.

SLUDGE-SETTLING TANKS

Such equipment may be incorporated with the wet centrifugals and wet dynamic collectors. Routine maintenance includes:

1. Periodic removal of the sludge before the tank becomes completely filled.
2. Removing the silt from the bottom of the clean-water chamber.
3. If drag-type chain sludge conveyors are used, they should be checked for broken links and bent paddles.
4. Check for accumulations in the hopper bottom to avoid binding of the conveyor.
5. Automatic timers normally are used with sludge ejectors to permit operation for 2 hr after the fan has been turned off. The timer mechanism should be checked for proper operation.
6. Chain guides and hopper wear plates should be given routine checkup for excessive wear.
7. Chain links should be removed whenever proper tension is lacking in the conveyor.
8. Pumps handling the water from sludge-settling tanks should be checked for abrasion.

FANS

One of the most important items of any exhaust system is the fan. Most fan troubles are caused by:

1. Abrasive cutting of the fan impeller and housing.
2. Improper maintenance of V-belt drive and bearings.
3. Accumulations causing vibration.

Heavy-duty industrial fans are recommended for dust-collecting systems. Although paddle-wheel fans are not as efficient as the centrifugal type, they give better service and have a more rugged construction. Proper maintenance has to do with:

1. Vibration caused by accumulations or improper mounting on a platform of light construction.

2. Abrasive wear and corrosion of the blades, rivets, and bolt heads. This usually will appear near the impeller disk.
3. Proper rotation. Most fans will discharge some air when running backward, so air movement is not an adequate test for correct fan rotation. Most manufacturers now mark direction of rotation on the housing.
4. Proper tension on V-belts. In the event of a belt break in a multiple-belt drive, all the belts should be changed at the shutdown period. Multiple V-belts should have matching numbers to avoid having a few of the belts carry all the load.
5. Routine schedule for greasing the bearings. Follow the schedules and methods outlined by the bearing manufacturer. Remember that overgreasing can be as detrimental as lack of greasing.

All fans should be equipped with service doors built into the housing or into the inlet and outlet ducts. These doors should be provided with sturdy clamps and effective seals.

When making repairs to the fan wheels by welding on wear or patch plates, it is essential that the wheel be carefully balanced before reinstalling or operating. All patches should be of the same weight and of a uniform pattern. Balancing is easily done by adding arc-weld beads to the patches. It is possible for the wheel to be in balance in the balancing rolls (static balance) but wobble when the fan is run at operating speed (dynamic unbalance).

MAINTENANCE OF EXHAUST HOODS AND DUCTS

Hoods and ductwork must not only convey the material safely and efficiently, but should be low in first cost and should require a minimum of maintenance work. Factors such as the characteristics of the material to be handled (sticky, abrasive, toxic, oily) determine the type of hood or enclosure.

Future requirements can influence design and maintenance costs. An installation cannot be properly operated and maintained when branches are added indiscriminately. Additions destroy air balances and change velocities; pluggage and other malfunctions are multiplied. Additions should be estimated when the system is designed. If this has not been done, it may be found advisable, from a maintenance point of view, to install a separate main for additional hoods.

Cleanout provisions are necessary. Good design can minimize the number of cleanouts required, but it cannot completely eliminate them. When adequate cleanouts are built into the system, maintenance is simplified. Types of cleanouts in common use are the slide-door, hinged-access, and dead-end cap. They should be placed so that all of the header or main can be inspected and cleaned as required. They can be placed in either the side or the bottom of the ductwork. Side cleanout has the advantage of allowing inspection and cleaning without excessive spillage on machinery or personnel.

The plant maintenance department cannot properly determine the condition of an exhaust system unless it knows how the system is to perform. After installation, a check sheet (Table 5-2) should be prepared. It should include the following basic information:

1. Location of the system can be indicated by bay, column, machine, or department numbers. Manufacturer's equipment, operating, and installation instructions are recorded or filed for reference in maintenance and ordering spare parts.
2. Operating data. The design volume on each hood, branch, and connection is recorded, and the total volume, pressure, horsepower, and rpm are noted.
3. System characteristics. Pressure readings are taken at all check points after the system has been balanced. These figures are used for comparison when checking performance at future scheduled dates.

Strangely enough, check points frequently are lost. Painting a circle of white or yellow around the hole and giving it an identifying number will correct this difficulty.

Pressure readings are a guide to system maintenance. When taken at all hood entries, branches, and collection-equipment inlets and outlets, they show not only the requirements for maintenance but indicate plugged collection equipment, slipped belts on exhausters, and other minor ailments.

Week-end work can be largely eliminated when check points are built-in features of the system. The system card and a U gage can discover troublesome conditions without shutdown during regular hours. A comparison of the original readings with those made periodically will point out any need for maintenance work. When one hood check point, or the check points on one branch, show lower readings, while other

Table 5-2. Dust-control System Check Sheet

System No........Location..................Dwg. No.....................

Date started......................{ Col. No. }
....{ Bay   }

Equipment exhausted..

....

Collection equipment:

  Make................Type............Size.........Arr..........Serial.........
  Miscellaneous data................................Design rpm...................

Exhauster:

  Make................Type...........Size..........Arr..........Serial.........
  Shaft diameter............kw...........Design rpm........................
  Design bhp..................Actual bhp........................(at start up)

Motor and base:

  Make.................Type...........Enclosure............................
  hp...........rpm............Volts...........Phase.........Cycle..........
  Shaft diameter..............kw..

V-belt drive:

  Motor sheave pd............No. grooves..........................Belt section
  Bore....................kw...
  Exhauster sheave pd.........No. grooves..................Belt section
  Bore....................kw...

System data Check point No.	Design volume (cfm)	Design pressure (in. water gage)	Balanced system (in. water gage)
1			
2			
3			
etc.			

branches give higher readings, an obstruction is indicated. This build-up can be located and removed, for it is obvious that it must lie somewhere between the lower reading points and the air mover. The general condition of hoods, pipe hangers, and ductwork can be determined visually at the time of reading.

It is important that hoods be properly replaced after work has been done. A hood properly designed can be replaced in only one way.

In cleaning ductwork, the light-gage type can be taken down by removing the drawbands. It can then be emptied into a hooded container if the material is dry. If material containing oil mist or a condensate must be cleaned from ductwork, spray washing may be required. This generally is satisfactory only for short runs of duct.

Condensation in pipes often is a problem, and no certain preventive method has been found. Different plants have tried lower velocities, higher velocities, insulation, heating of the ducts, and built-in scrapers or nozzles. Perhaps the best solution is to keep the ducts as short as possible and mix the high-humidity air with warm, dry air from some other nearby operation. Short runs mean that ductwork can be removed easily and washed out. Strip heaters can be placed on ductwork to warm it before air is pulled through. Auxiliary heated air may be introduced into the duct, but the operation is expensive.

The check-point method will more than pay its way.

DONT'S

Don't hope to provide a dust collector by tying a burlap bag over a discharge pipe or directing the discharge duct into a barrel of water or into a settling chamber. Factors involved in the collection of small particles do not lend themselves to such elementary treatment. Hundreds of times each year hopes are blasted in such attempts, at high cost in dollars and man-hours, and loss of face.

Don't put two collectors of the same order of efficiency in series; the second collector will not remove enough material to alter discharge appearance, public nuisance complaints, or settlement in the plant area, unless the initial unit is not functioning satisfactorily. Exceptions could include installations where agglomeration of particles is involved, or where a second collector is used to remove material concentrated in a carrier air stream from the first collector.

Don't visualize discharge appearance based on efficiency data. Fine particles have many, many more light-reflecting surfaces per pound than coarse particles. Appearance of effluent air will be governed by efficiency of the collector, particle size of the contaminant, and concentrations of the solid particles. Often the removal of 85% of the solids from a local exhaust system will make no visual change in the discharge-stack appearance.

Don't expect dust-collection equipment design to be more advanced than production-machine design. Generally, the higher the degree of effectiveness, the more certain the need of periodic servicing, inspection, and part replacement. Such operations will not receive proper attention where (1) collectors are placed in inaccessible locations without ladders, working platforms, and lighting, and (2) in outdoor locations where workmen are exposed to rain or winter weather.

Don't wait for dust collectors to fail before ordering replacement parts. Periodic inspections will give ample warning. Under present-day working conditions, failure of a dust collector can mean the halting of production lines while long-distance calls and air-express shipments attempt to reduce the downtime.

Don't expect collectors employing principles used for lower-efficiency primary collection to be developed that will give efficiencies equal to those of more expensive, high-efficiency units—hopes of the purchaser and enthusiasm of the inventor notwithstanding. The cost to American industry each year is a tremendous figure based on such hopes and enthusiasm.

Don't expect replacement of the exhaust-air volume to slip in through cracks in windows and doors without creating cold drafts in winter months, and often starving exhaust systems so that effectiveness is reduced. Make-up air-supply systems can improve control, eliminate drafts, and warm the incoming air efficiently.

Don't attempt to recirculate cleaned air from dust collectors handling toxic material without careful investigation of the policing required to be assured of maintaining effectiveness.

Don't install unit collectors on heavy-duty production operations without careful evaluation of the frequency of servicing required.

REFERENCES

"Engineering Manual for Control of In-plant Environment in Foundries," Sec. II, American Foundrymen's Society.

"Industrial Ventilation," 8th ed., American Conference of Governmental Industrial Hygienists, 1964.

Kane, John M., Guideposts Tell How to Select Dust Collecting Equipment, *Plant Eng.*, November, 1954.

Kane, John M., Operation, Application and Effectiveness of Dust Collection Equipment, *Heating and Ventilating*, August, 1952.

Chapter 6

CENTRIFUGAL PUMPS

By H. W. Linneman
Administrative Assistant to Chief Engineer
Gardner-Denver Company
Quincy, Ill.

Successful and efficient operation of centrifugal pumps depends greatly upon proper selection and installation. This chapter primarily treats maintenance; however, the selection of the correct pump for each application or service is essential to efficient and trouble-free performance. To insure the most efficient operation and the least maintenance, submit complete data on your prospective application to the pump manufacturer so that he can properly select a pump to fulfill your requirements.

Most pump manufacturers supply instruction books covering installation, operation, and maintenance of their pumps, so the following information is general in character, to apply to all makes.

Installation. Locate the pump in a place that is easily accessible for regular inspection during operation. The pump should be placed as near the liquid supply as possible, to permit use of short and direct suction pipe (see Suction Piping). Ample head room should be provided for a crane, hoist, or tackle. Pits in which pumps are placed should be safeguarded against floods.

It is of paramount importance that the pump be placed on a good foundation, preferably of concrete. Foundation bolts should be placed according to the method shown in Fig. 6-1 and according to dimensions furnished on a certified drawing. Pipe sleeves used should be about two and one-half diameters larger than the size of the anchor bolts being used.

Alignment. Pumps are properly aligned at the factory by leveling the base and bringing the pump and driving unit into exact alignment with shims. Experience has proved, however, that all bases, no matter how rugged, will spring and twist during shipment. Therefore, there is no guaranty that the original alignment will be maintained. Consequently, it is necessary that the factory alignment be reproduced when the unit is erected on its foundation.

1. Place the pump unit on its foundation, allowing approximately 1 in. between top of foundation and bottom of base, using wedges to obtain proper spacing (see Fig. 6-1).
2. Remove coupling pins (if used) and check top of base for degree of level, using the wedges for adjustment.
3. Tighten foundation bolts evenly and firmly so that the base rests solidly on wedges.
4. Check the alignment at the coupling by placing a straightedge across the coupling flanges. This should be done at four points on the coupling, the points being 90° apart. The distance between the faces of the coupling halves should also be checked at four points with a thickness gage. See coupling sketches, Fig. 6-2.

The coupling halves are to be brought into perfect alignment by adjusting the wedges under the base, the base at the same time being level.

5. If the pump is to be connected to the prime mover by gears or chains, the alignment should be checked by a straightedge across the faces of the gears or sprockets. This should be done in two directions at an angle to each other as large as permitted by the relative size of the gears or sprockets. When pumps or prime movers are to be heated in operation, i.e., steam-driven prime movers or pumps handling hot water, the unit should be aligned under the thermal conditions in order that contraction and expansion due to these changes in temperature may be taken into account.

6. Build a form or dam around the foundation and fill it with grout to a point about 1 in. above the bottom of the base. Allow grout 48 hr to set.

Connecting Piping. Pipes must line up naturally. Do not force them into place with flange bolts, for this may draw the pump out of alignment. Pipes should be supported independently of the pump so as not to put any strain on the pump casing. After the piping has been installed, alignment should be checked again and, if necessary, correction made. For unusually long discharge lines, a packed slip joint should be provided to compensate for elongation of pipe due to pressure. Also, when piping is subject to temperature changes it should be arranged so expansion and contraction do not place a strain on the pump casing. Air-conditioning and service pumps installed in buildings where any noise is objectionable should be insulated from the steelwork and walls in such a way that vibration cannot be transmitted to the building, and the discharge pipe should be insulated from the pump so that no noise or vibration can be transmitted to it.

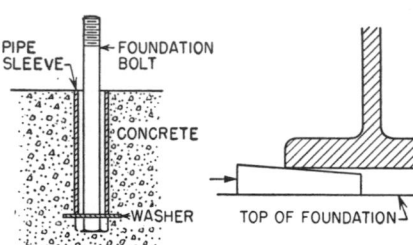

FIG. 6-1. Method of placing foundation bolts.

Discharge Piping. To protect the pump, a gate valve and a check valve should be installed in the discharge pipe close to pump. The check valve should be placed between the pump and the gate valve.

If increasers are used on the discharge side to increase the size of discharge piping, they should be placed between the check valve and the pump. The selection of the

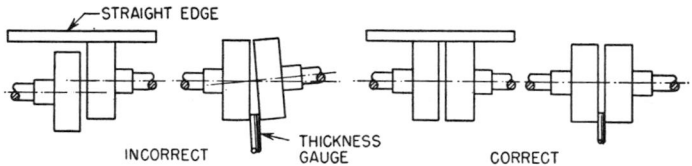

FIG. 6-2. How to check alignment of coupling.

discharge pipe should be made with due reference to friction losses. The discharge pipe should never be smaller than the pump discharge and preferable one or two sizes larger.

Suction Piping. The suction piping should be as direct and short as possible. It should be at least one or two sizes larger than the pump nozzle. Length and size are determined by the maximum allowable suction lift, which should never exceed 15 ft (friction included). If changes from one pipe to another are necessary, standard ASME suction reducers should be used. Hot liquids must flow to the point of pump suction by gravity. Pipe should be laid out so that air pockets are eliminated. Refer to Figs. 6-3, 6-4, 6-5, and 6-6, showing correct and incorrect methods of installing piping at the pump. Pipe should be tested with pressure for leaks.

A foot valve in the suction line will keep the pump primed. The net area of the foot valve should be at least equal to the area of pump suction but preferably larger.

Care should be taken with new suction lines to see that no foreign material such as chips, rocks, etc., are in the piping or near the entrance to it, as this debris will be drawn into the pump and cause damage and trouble. To protect the pump from being clogged with foreign material, a strainer should be installed with a net area of at least three or four times the area of the suction pipe.

Final Check on Alignment. Check the alignment after the piping has been completed, using the straightedge and thickness-gage method. As the unit has been aligned before completing the piping, the chances are that piping strains are the cause of any misalignment found, and changes should be made accordingly. If the stuffing box is properly adjusted and the pump drives are properly aligned, the unit can be turned over easily by hand.

Rotation. The pump must be run in the direction indicated by an arrow on the casing, which is always toward the discharge nozzle. Rotation, right-hand or left-hand, is determined by facing the pump from the drive end. See Fig. 6-7, showing rotation toward the discharge nozzle and the rotation of the impeller vanes indicated by dotted lines. You will note that the impeller rotates in the direction away from the vane curvature.

Starting. Fill the pump with water. (This is called priming.) Before starting a centrifugal pump, the casing and the suction pipe must be completely filled; unless this is done, the pump will not operate, as air will be pumped instead of water. Centrifugal pumps can be primed in three ways:

1. By filling the casing and suction pipe with water and holding the water with a foot valve.
2. With a vacuum pump.
3. With a steam, air, or water ejector.

When starting the unit, the discharge valve should be set so that the least load is thrown on the driver when the pump is started. For radial or Francis-type impellers this occurs at shutoff or when the discharge valve is closed, and for mixed-flow or propeller-type pumps the valve should be fully open. Opening a closed valve should be gradual, to avoid throwing a large sudden load on the driver and to prevent a sudden surge in the discharge line.

Stopping. Before stopping the prime mover, the discharge valve should be in the same position as when starting, so that less horsepower is dropped from the line and any sudden surges in the pipe system are avoided.

Locating Causes for Faulty Operation. In operating a centrifugal pump, apparently serious troubles may arise, but close and careful inspection usually will reveal the fault to be some minor oversight, and investigation for irregular conditions should be made. See Table 6-1.

Belt Drive. When installing a pump for V-belt drive, belts must be in perfect alignment; any slight misalignment will cause excessive belt wear. This will shorten materially the life and use of the belts. V-belts should be only tight enough to prevent slippage.

Bearings. It would be impossible to overemphasize the importance of proper lubrication of bearings. For grease-lubricated ball bearings, it is recommended that regular ball-bearing grease be used. A good general-purpose grease for ball-bearing lubrication has the following characteristics: It is clean and neutral, with a mineral soap base free from acids, alkalis, fillers, or impurities. It has good film strength and a consistency of about No. 1 to No. 2, which is a little stiffer than petroleum jelly. It should be chemically stable, and there should be no separation of the oil from the soap base in the container or during use. It does not oxidize from standing or in service. It has low internal friction, good adhesive qualities, is water resistant, and has an operating temperature range from -40 to $200°F$.

Ball bearings require only a small amount of lubricant, and the lubrication intervals generally are long. How long a bearing can run without grease being added or replaced depends upon the grease properties, the size and design of the bearing and housing, the speed, and other operating conditions. It is not possible to establish any general rule as to when new grease must be added. The reason for this is that grease

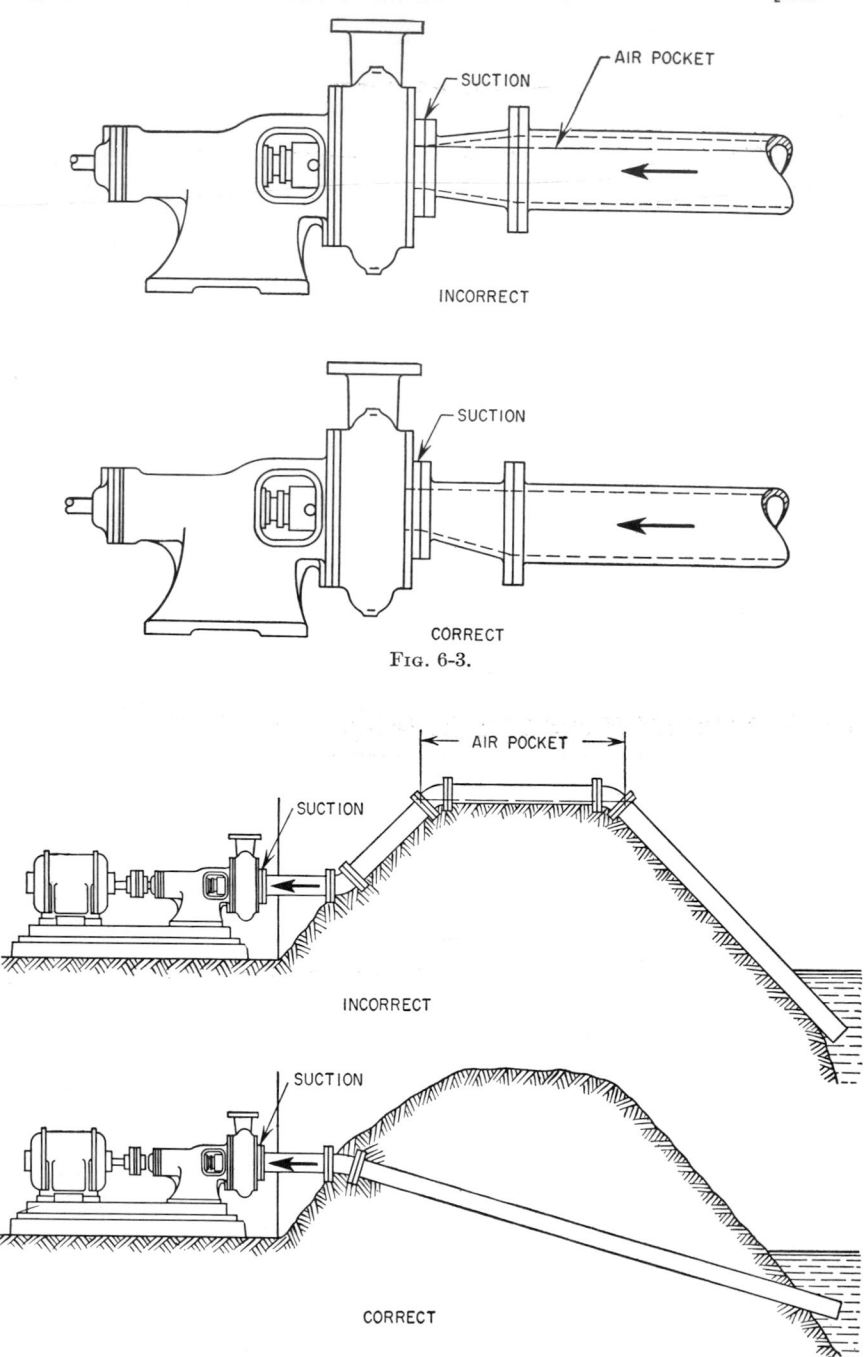

FIG. 6-3.

FIG. 6-4.

FIGS. 6-3 to 6-4. Correct and incorrect methods of installing piping at pump.

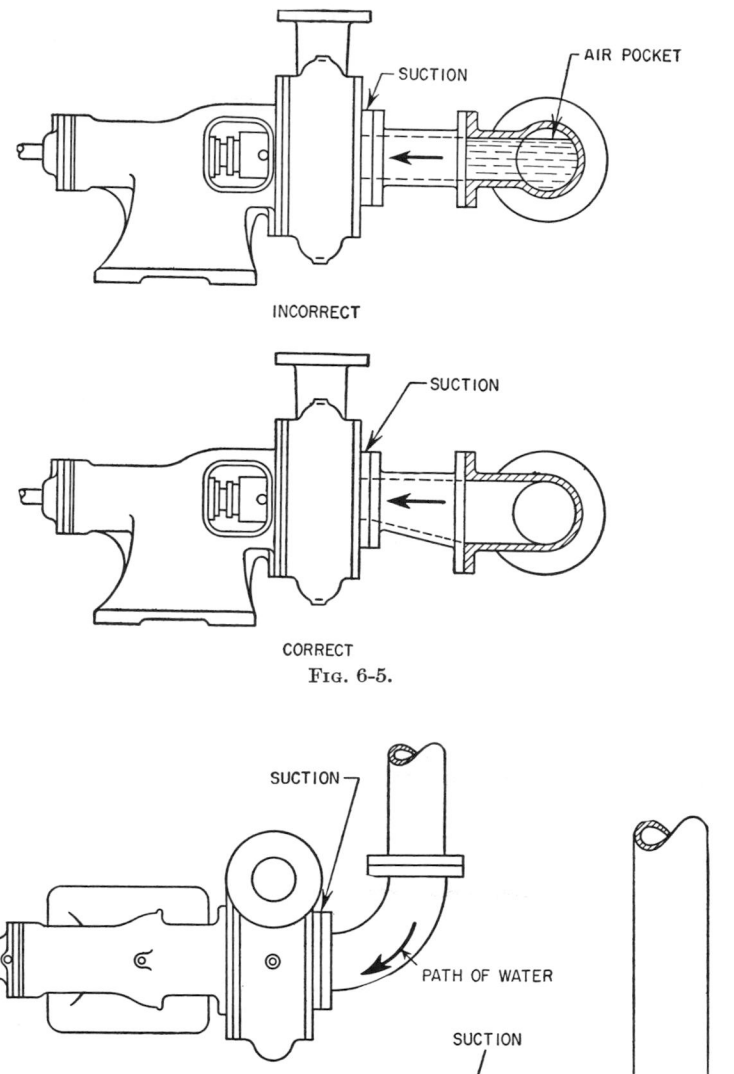

INCORRECT

CORRECT
Fig. 6-5.

INCORRECT

CORRECT
Fig. 6-6.

Figs. 6-5 to 6-6. Correct and incorrect methods of installing piping at pump (*Continued*).

in the bearing does not suddenly lose its lubricating ability or life; rather, it is reduced gradually.   For pumps operating under severe service, perhaps greasing is required every 3 months; and for normal service, 1 year.   To be on the safe side, the addition of grease should be determined from experience.

Heating of bearings invariably means too much grease instead of an insufficiency, and careful inspection to determine the trouble should be made before more grease is added.

Great care should be exercised to keep the bearing housing immaculately clean, and only clean grease should be used.   Under no circumstances should grease which has been used before be applied.   Foreign solids or liquids invading the housing can completely ruin the bearings in a short time.   It is important to use clean instruments and cloths when cleaning housing.   The housing should be flushed clean, using gasoline or a high grade of water-free kerosene.

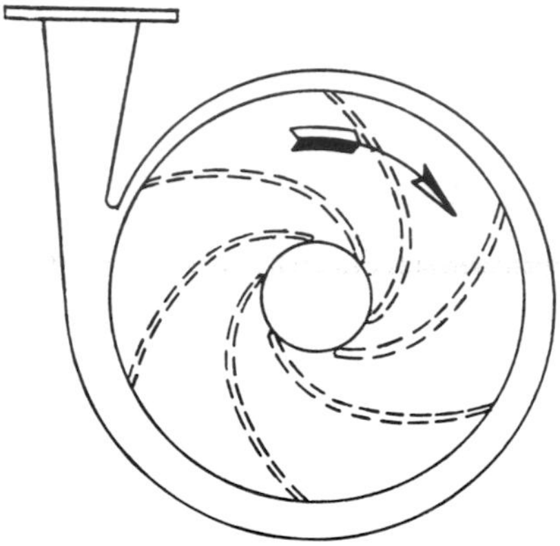

For oil-lubricated ball bearings, mineral oil of the best quality should be used, such as automobile- and aircraft-engine oil of the better grades.   For general use, an SAE 30 oil usually will be satisfactory.

Bearing housings with oil-bath lubrication or with an oil sump which is to be filled to a given level, ordinarily are equipped with oil gages.   Oil is added when the oil level, due to loss, has dropped below the established low limit.   In general, the oil level should never reach higher than the center of the lowest rolling element when the bearing is not rotating.

FIG. 6-7. Direction of rotation of inpeller vane.

How soon the oil must be drained and new oil added depends on the operating conditions.   For temperatures below 120 to 140°F, if there is no contamination, a lubrication interval of 1 year can be considered normal.   For higher temperatures, the oil must be replaced after a shorter time, ordinarily 2 to 3 months.

For oil-bath lubrication, drain off the old oil and flush the bearings out with an oil of low viscosity.

Wearing Rings.   Wearing-ring clearances should be checked from time to time, depending upon the liquid handled.   Liquids containing gritty or corrosive materials may make monthly inspection necessary, whereas when handling clear cold water, inspection annually may be sufficient.

When the wearing-ring clearances increase, a loss in capacity and head is caused. If the clearance is approximately twice the original, or if the loss in capacity and head does not meet requirements, it is time to replace the rings.

Shaft Sleeves.   Shaft sleeves should be replaced when it becomes difficult to control leakage without tightening the glands excessively.   When pumping water containing gritty particles, such as sand, silt, slurries, etc., the life of sleeves can be increased by the following procedure:

1. Plug the water-seal passage to the stuffing box, as illustrated in Fig. 6-8 for single suction pumps.
2. Provide either an outside source of clear cold water or grease lubrication.   The pressure for sealing and flushing must be slightly greater than stuffing-box pressure. Care should be exercised in determining this, as some types of pumps have stuffing boxes operating at pressures approaching the discharge pressures.
3. Select the sleeve material for the best wearing qualities.   Special materials with hardness of approximately 400 to 450 Brinell are available.

Figure 6-9 illustrates a typical water-seal arrangement for the stuffing box of horizontal split-case pumps.   The stuffing boxes on single-stage horizontal split-case

Table 6-1. Locating Causes for Faulty Operations

Trouble	Cause	Correction
No water being delivered	Pump may not be primed.	Refer to text paragraph or Starting.
	Speed may be too low.	Check whether motor is directly across the line and receiving full voltage. In case of steam turbine check governor and determine if receiving full steam pressure.
	Discharge head too high.	Check operating conditions. See that pipe friction and suction and discharge heads are as specified.
	Suction lift too high.	Check with gages. Normal suction should not exceed 15 ft.
	Impeller and/or piping may be plugged.	Inspect piping, suction strainer, and impeller.
	Impeller may be rotating in wrong direction.	Refer to text paragraph on Rotation.
Not enough water being delivered	Air leaks may exist in suction line or stuffing box.	Plug inlet and put line under pressure. A gage in line will indicate leakage with a drop in pressure. A 1% air leak may cause the capacity to decrease 10%.
	Speed may be too low.	Refer to text paragraph on Starting.
	Discharge head may be higher than anticipated.	Check operating conditions. See that pipe friction and suction and discharge heads are as specified.
	Suction lift may be too high.	Check with gages. Normal suction should not exceed 15 ft.
	Impeller or suction line may be partially plugged.	Inspect piping, suction strainer, and impeller.
	May not be sufficient suction head for hot liquid.	Hot liquids in almost all cases must flow by gravity and have sufficient head or submergence to eye of impeller. Refer to pump manufacturer for complete information on suction piping, size and type of liquid, and amount of submergence available.
	Wearing rings may be worn.	Refer to text paragraph on Wearing Rings.
	Impeller may be damaged.	Repair or replace.
	Foot valve may be too small.	Inspect. Net area should be at least equal to area of pump suction but preferably larger. Suction-strainer area should be at least three or four times the area of suction pipe.
	Casing packing may be defective.	Replace all worn packing.

Table 6-1. Locating Causes for Faulty Operations (*Continued*)

Trouble	Cause	Correction
Not enough pressure....	Foot valve or suction opening not be submerged enough.	Submerge entrance of suction pipe at least 3 ft below surface of the liquid.
	Speed may be too low.	Check whether motor is directly across the line and receiving full voltage. In case of steam turbine check governor and determine if receiving full steam pressure.
	May be air in the water.	Plug inlet and put line under pressure. A gage in line will indicate leakage with a drop in pressure. A 1% air leak may cause the capacity to decrease 10%.
	Wearing rings worn.	Refer to text paragraph on Wearing rings.
	Impeller damaged.	Repair or replace.
Pump works for a while and then loses suction	Casing packing defective.	Replace all worn packing.
	May be a leak in the suction line.	Plug inlet and put line under pressure. A gage in line will indicate leakage with a drop in pressure. A 1% air leak may cause the capacity to decrease 10%. (An 8 to 10% air leak will cause pump to lose its prime)
	Water seal may be plugged.	Inspect line and position of seal cage in stuffing box.
	Suction lift may exceed 15 ft.	Check for obstruction in suction line and for low water level.
	Air or gas may be found in the liquid.	Vent suction back to source of supply.
Pump takes too much power	Speed too high.	Check speed of driver or, in case of belt drive, sheave or pulley diameters.
	Head is lower than rating, and pump capacity increases.	Have pump manufacturer calculate impeller diameter required, and then turn impeller outside diameter.
	Liquid may be heavier than water	Check the specific gravity and also viscosity of the liquid.
	Mechanical defects such as a bent shaft.	Check runout of shaft. Total runout allowed depends upon pump design and speed. Approximately 0.003 in. for high-speed and 0.006 in. for slow-speed units.
	Rotating elements may be binding.	Check for too tight stuffing boxes, wearing-ring fit, and defective packing.

pumps operate under suction pressure. The above procedure is applicable for horizontal split-case pumps except for the substitution of lubrication. If the pump is operating under a suction lift, air leakage into the pump through the stuffing box may be expected unless seal pressure is provided. Therefore an outside source of water with pressure slightly greater than suction pressure is required. In cases where an outside source of clear water is not available, an alternate method would be to install a filter in the water-seal tubing lines.

Packing. The packing normally recommended for clear cold water is long-fiber asbestos, square-braided and well impregnated with oils and graphite. When

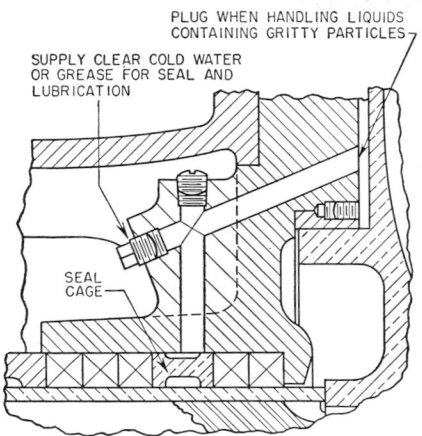

Fig. 6-8. Plug water-seal passage as shown when pumping water containing grit.

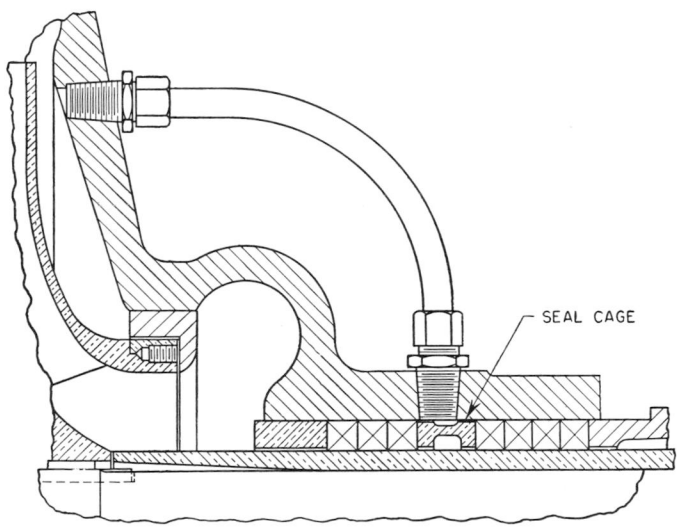

Fig. 6-9. Typical water-seal arrangement of stuffing box of horizontal split-case pump.

handling liquids other than water, special packing is required. Consult the pump manufacturer or a manufacturer of packing for recommendations.

The following procedure should be followed in repacking a pump: After the glands have been removed, the packing, cut to the proper length and compressed just enough to slide readily without being smashed while placing, is inserted into the stuffing box. Pressure with the hand and fingers should be sufficient for pushing the rows of packing into place. If it is not, either the packing is too large or some obstruction exists. The rings are spaced so that the splices are staggered. After all rings are placed, glands are put into position and inserted into the stuffing box tight enough to permit just a few drops of water to drip out per minute.   This slight amount of water helps to lubricate the pump shaft at the packing joints.

The packing should be replaced after it becomes hard and tends to score the shaft. Also, it is good practice always to fully repack the pump; never add only one or two rings.   Be sure the water-seal cage is withdrawn to remove packing at the bottom of the stuffing box.   Make note of the number of rings so the water-seal cage will be installed in the correct position.   This must be in line with the water-seal passage as shown in Fig. 6-8.

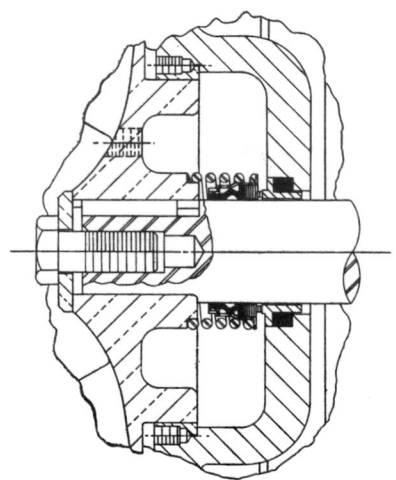

Fig. 6-10. Seal cavity requiring no adjustment.

Mechanical Seals.   Mechanical seals are steadily gaining in popularity and acceptance and, in many cases, replacing packing as standard equipment.   They are particularly recommended when absolute control of leakage is required.   When properly installed, mechanical seals provide a sealing method which eliminates the human element.   The only maintenance required is lubrication for seal faces, which may be either oil or grease, depending upon the design and service of the seal.   Method of lubrication and type of lubricant depend upon service and, therefore, the recommendation of the pump manufacturer should be followed.

There are many applications that require no lubrication other than the liquid being pumped.

Because of the numerous types of seals, no general rule for replacing seals can be established.   However, extreme care should be exercised and instructions as provided by the pump manufacturer followed carefully.   Some seals are installed in seal cavities requiring no adjustment (see Fig. 6-10), while others employing locking collars require positioning.   Before disassembly, note the position of the seal on the shaft or make sure you know what dimensional setting is required.   It is essential that seals be installed in the correct position, otherwise there may be too much load on seal faces, causing rapid wear; or too little load, causing seals to leak.   Assuming that correct design and materials are used for the application, the seal should give carefree service. For severe service, an average seal life of 3 to 4 months may be expected, and for clear liquids approximately 24 months.

Chapter 7

RECIPROCATING AIR COMPRESSORS

By M. F. BAECKER
Engineering Department
Gardner-Denver Company
Quincy, Ill.

An inadequate or undependable supply of air always is a handicap for continuous and economical operation of air tools. A specific compressor-maintenance program will go a long way toward obtaining the maximum efficiency from a compressor and eliminate unnecessary shutdown periods. The modern compressor is a precision-built machine, and it should be operated and maintained as such. Too many compressors are installed in out-of-the-way locations and are practically forgotten until trouble develops.

Each major air-compressor manufacturer furnishes an "installation and operation" instruction book with each unit. Many hours of preparation and years of experience are represented in these books. They are included with the compressors so that owners and operators will have sufficient information to install, operate, and maintain the equipment for maximum efficiency. Read the instruction book carefully and become familiar with the compressor construction so that minor adjustments and emergency repairs can be made. Also know whom to contact should serious difficulty develop.

Location. For good maintenance a clean, well-lighted location should be selected with enough space allowed to dismantle any parts that may need to be removed for servicing. Too often compressors are located so that it is impossible to remove the pistons, rods, or cylinders without breaking through a wall or moving the compressor. Outline and foundation drawings show the necessary service clearance. Maintenance and costs are materially reduced where these recommendations are followed.

Foundation. An adequate compressor foundation (Fig. 7-1) is a necessity for satisfactory operation and maintenance of a compressor. A foundation that is designed without sufficient mass and bearing surface will cause vibration of the compressor, resulting in discharge-, suction-, and water-line breakage and excessive wear of compressor parts.

For compressors requiring concrete foundations, the compressor vendor furnishes prints showing the foundation above the floor line plus the weights of the parts to be mounted on the foundation, also the out-of-balance forces that must be absorbed by the foundation. The amount of foundation will depend on the type of soil upon which it is being set. To determine the depth and size of the foundation below the floor line, a competent foundation engineer should be consulted who will take test cores and from these calculate the soil carrying capacity. With this information, along with the weights and out-of-balance forces, a foundation can be designed for satisfactory compressor operation.

Many small vertical compressors are installed on existing concrete floors and usually operate very well this way, as the large area of the floor forms a more than sufficient mass to offset any out-of-balance forces of the compressor.

At some locations it is impossible to set the compressor on a foundation or concrete floor that is poured on the ground. It must be located on a floor that does not have a solid base under it. For this type of installation, isolation dampeners are used under the base supporting the compressor and its driver. Suction, discharge, and water lines should be attached with good flexible connections to prevent vibration and noises

Fig. 7-1. Compressor on proper foundation.

Fig. 7-2. Air cleaners mounted on compressor.

from being carried through the building. There are many manufacturers of isolation dampeners, and their engineers should be consulted for recommendations for this type of application.

Air Cleaners and Suction Lines. Every compressor must be equipped with an air cleaner which should be the most efficient type made for the service it is applied to. The air cleaner must be located so that an adequate supply of cool, clean water and acid-free air will be had at all times, with explicit instructions for servicing the air cleaner posted where the maintenance personnel will always be reminded of the regular servicing required for good maintenance (see Fig. 7-2).

At some locations it is necessary to place the air cleaners away from the compressor due to unfavorable surrounding conditions. Care must be used in providing a suction line to a compressor. It must be tight, free of dirt, chips, and scale, and of correct size for the length necessary to reach compressor suction.

Air-friction loss in a suction line increases approximately in proportion to the length of the line and the square of the velocity.   From this it is evident that a suction line as short as possible is most advisable.   When a large compressor is housed in a small room or building, it is essential to run the suction line outside to prevent collapse of the building.   If the suction line is more than 10 ft long, the line will need to be increased in size to eliminate a possible resonant condition.

This resonant condition can occur in the suction line if length of line, velocity of air, and compressor rpm happen to bear a critical relation to each other, resulting in supercharging and excess horsepower.   To overcome the resonant condition it is necessary to use a larger suction line reduced to fit the air-cleaner size at the air-filter end and reduced to fit the suction opening at the compressor.   A good rule to follow is to increase the size 1 in. in diameter for every 10 ft of length.

The time interval for cleaning an air filter depends on the type of cleaner and its location, and must be determined by checking the cleaner for dirt accumulation.   No set time can be made to cover all installations and types of air cleaners.

Air-receiver Location and Capacity.   Air receivers often are considered accessories to air compressors and, for many applications, are not correctly installed or properly sized.   Proper installation and proper sizing are very important for both compressor and air-line systems.   An air receiver absorbs pulsations in the discharge line from the compressor and smooths the flow of air to the service lines.   It serves as a reservoir for the storage of compressed air to take care of sudden and unusual momentary demands in excess of the capacity of the compressor.   Another of its functions is to precipitate moisture that may be condensed in the receiver and prevent it from being carried into the air-distribution system.

The location of a receiver is, in most cases, a problem.   It is recommended that it always be located as near the compressor as possible so that the discharge line can be of minimum length, eliminating pressure drop between the receiver and compressor. Many receivers are located outside the compressor room and are exposed to the weather, offering difficulties when the temperature drops low enough to cause freezing.   An ordinary top-outlet pop valve can be frozen shut, creating a hazard; the valve should be placed with opening down, thereby keeping water out and allowing the valve to function if necessary.   Should the compressor be shut down, allowing no air to pass through the receiver, the drain valve or mechanism can freeze, perhaps breaking the parts making up the drain.   The only solution is to heat the drain line or drain it when allowing it to stand idle.

The size of the receiver usually is recommended by the compressor vendor, who has charts listing the necessary receiver sizes for various compressor sizes.   Start-and-stop compressors require larger receivers than do continuously operated compressors, to keep them from starting too often.   Each start requires electrical inrush to the motor, which can cause expense by increasing electrical requirements beyond normal electrical demand.

Air from the compressor should flow into the receiver at the bottom and out at the top.   Condensate will stay near the bottom, giving drier air from the top opening.   If excess condensate is a troublesome factor in the system, use an efficient water-cooled aftercooler and separator between the compressor and receiver.   The aftercooler will condense the moisture and collect most of it in the separator, which can be drained by hand or automatically.   The aftercooler dries and cools air, which promotes efficiency and safety.   Most fire and explosion hazards are eliminated.   Most aftercoolers will cool the air to within 15°F of the incoming cooling water.   Where water supply is short or expensive, air-cooled aftercoolers are available.   They are not as efficient as the water-cooled, but if properly sized and of good quality, usually will cool to within 20 to 30°F of the ambient temperature.

Always consult the compressor vendor about receiver problems.   Many states are exacting about pressure-vessel requirements; pressure vessels must meet the codes for safety and pass inspection by the insurance companies.

Starting a New Compressor.   Before starting a new or repaired compressor, careful check must be made of the lubricating system, making certain all places needing lubrication have been oiled per manufacturer's requirements.   On compressors having a forced mechanical lubricator, crank or pump by hand until it is certain the oil is getting to the parts requiring lubrication, as some initial lubrication is required before the unit is started. Tighten all bolts, nuts, and cap screws. Turn the compressor over by hand wherever possible to determine that there is no interference or binding of working parts.

In the case of compressors requiring cooling water from a water main, turn on the water and check for leaks and for circulation through all parts requiring cooling water. For compressors having a self-contained water-cooling system, fill it and check to see that all air is out of the cooling system.

Check the discharge line from the compressor to the receiver, and if there are any globe, gate, or check valves anywhere between the compressor and receiver, be sure the valves are open and there is a pop safety valve between the compressor and valves. The pop safety valve is a necessity, as it is possible that a valve could be left closed and the compressor started, resulting in an explosion should there be sufficient power in the driver, or should the overload protection fail to act.

If all points have been checked, apply driving power momentarily and let the machine coast to rest. Close observation during the coasting period will reveal any excessive tightness in the moving parts. The time that the unloaded machine continues to roll after driving power has been removed gives a fair indication of no-load friction; if no trouble is evident, the unit can be run without load.

After running from 1 to 2 hr unloaded, with periodic stops to check for any heating of bearings or other working parts, apply partial load and build up to maximum load and pressure gradually. The entire breaking-in period should consume a minimum of 4 hr.

The importance of a break-in run cannot be stressed too strongly. The time and care spent in giving the running surfaces a polished finish pay dividends by increasing compressor life. After the initial run, compressor operation resolves itself into maintaining a clean air supply, feeding sufficient cooling water, and supplying adequate lubrication.

Operating a water-cooled compressor with too much cooling water through the system will cause excess condensate and cylinder wear because a cold cylinder will not lubricate properly; and because lubrication is affected, excess horsepower is required, adding to both maintenance and operating costs. A good rule is to hold the outlet temperature of the water between 120 and 130°F. This range will allow for good cooling and lubrication and also keep condensation in the cylinder to a minimum.

All the foregoing requirements are necessary to get a compressor ready for efficient operation and to hold maintenance costs to the minimum. Routine maintenance must now be set up and a definite pattern followed.

Lubrication. The most important check for any compressor is the lubrication system (see Fig. 7-3). Keep the compressor well lubricated, check the oil level at least once every 24 hr of operation. Use only oils and greases as recommended by the compressor manufacturer. The oil used should have a low carbon and sulfur content and contain an oxidation inhibitor. It is important to use the correct weight of oil, which is determined by the surrounding ambient temperature. The instruction book has these conditions listed.

Because dust, dirt, and atmosphere conditions are different at various locations, it is not practical to state definitely how often the oil should be changed in the crankcase or power end of an air compressor. Oil will become contaminated with foreign materials held in suspension and will also oxidize. The time for oil changes is regulated by local conditions and must be determined by the discoloration and physical condition of the oil.

When oil changes are made, it will always pay to remove a handhole or cover plate and wipe the inside of the crankcase or power end clean with lint-free rags. Never use mechanics' waste. If impossible to wipe out, use a good grade of flushing oil to remove any particles that may have settled on the crankcase floor. When refilling the compressor oil sump, be certain the filling container is free of all dirt, grit, or dust. This simple point often is overlooked.

Valves. In a reciprocating compressor the valves must be kept in first-class operating condition, as leaking or inoperative valves cause loss of net air delivered. Heating often over-loads the driver. It is therefore important to check the valves periodically and be certain they are always in good operating condition (see Fig. 7-4).

The checking time for valves depends on several conditions, such as efficiency of the air cleaner, carbon content of oil used, and the over-all condition of the compressor. If the air cleaner is efficient and regularly serviced, excess dirt will be kept out of the air stream and dirt will not lodge in the valves. By using low-carbon-content oil, the carbon build-up on the valves is held to a minimum. For single-acting vertical compressors, the pistons, rings, and cylinder walls should be kept in good condition so that excess oil will not pass these parts. Low oil consumption adds to valve life by eliminating unnecessary carbon deposit. No set checking time can be recommended but will need to be determined by actual investigation by the maintenance personnel. On a new unit the valves should be checked after 200 hr of operation.

FIG. 7-3. Lubrication points.

Many compressor owners have found it pays dividends to have a spare set of valves so that a change of valves can be made immediately, and the replaced set reconditioned when time allows.

When valve troubles occur, there are several means of locating the valve or valves causing the difficulty. The first symptoms usually are low net air delivery and heating around the valve compartments. On a single-stage compressor, the usual method used is to feel the valve cover plates and examine the valve under the cover plate that is the hottest. If suction valves are leaking, a definite blow-back noise can be heard in the air cleaner when the compressor is operating under load.

On two-stage compressors, the intercooler pressure gage is used as a guide to locate defective valves. When low intercooler pressure occurs, examine the valves on the low-pressure cylinders, and when high intercooler pressure is found, examine those on the high-pressure cylinders. By feeling the valve cover plates, the defective valve can be located under the cover plate that is the hottest. If high-pressure suction valves are leaking, the intercooler gage hand will fluctuate above normal intercooler pressure and the intercooler safety valve will pop. If high-pressure discharge valves are leaking, the intercooler gage hand will rise steadily and pressure will build up in the inter-cooler until the intercooler pop safety valve will release it.

When low-pressure suction valves leak, the air will blow back through the suction line and air cleaner if the compressor is operating under load. Leaking low-pressure discharge valves will cause the intercooler pressure gage to fluctuate below normal intercooler pressure.

Since the valves are such an important part of the compressor, the information given in the instruction book must be followed when removing and installing them.

Wear between the valve disk or plate and the valve seat appears as indentations in the valve disk or plate, leaving a shoulder. These formations start as soon as the compressor first operates, which makes it necessary to return each individual disk or plate to its original location after dismantling for inspection and cleaning.

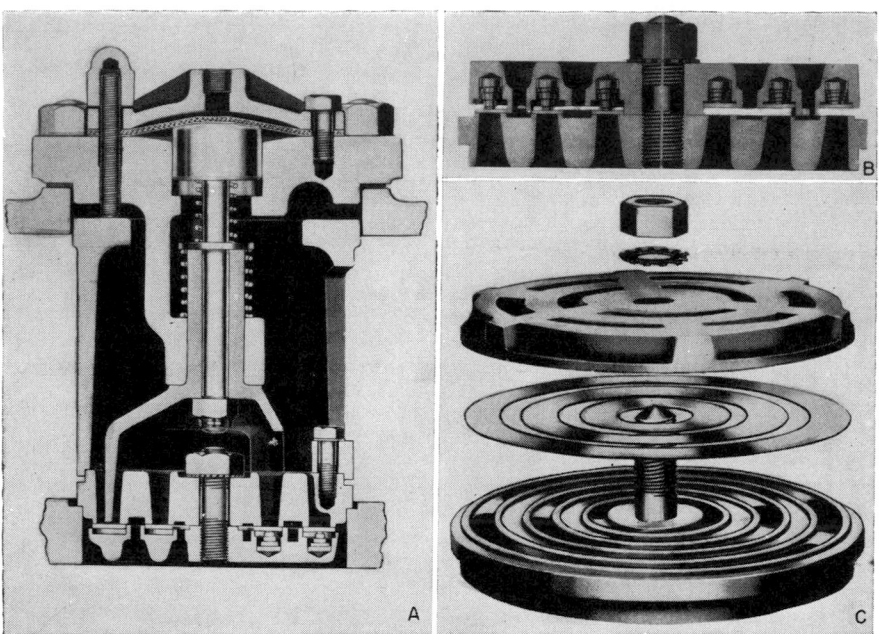

FIG. 7-4. Compressor valves: (A) suction-unloading valve assembly—safety spring type; (B) three-plate discharge valve shown with valve disks in closed position (left) and with valve disks in open position (right); (C) exploded view of discharge valve.

Because compressor valves operate hundreds of times each minute, the valve parts are subject to considerable wear. When a valve disk or plate wears to less than one-half its original thickness, it should be replaced. Valve seats can be resurfaced to remove wear. On some types of valves it is necessary to check the lift of the valve after resurfacing the seat, and if found to be more than recommended by the vendor, the bumper will need to be cut down to get the correct lift. Too much lift causes rapid wear and breakage.

Duo-plate disk-type valves usually have raised valve seats, and when the seat is refinished it is not necessary to do anything to the bumper as the lift will still be to manufacturer's specifications.

Whenever a valve has been overheated, replace all the valve disks or plates and springs, because excessive temperature resulting from this heat will reduce the life of these parts and may result in breakage, causing damage to the compressor.

Most compressor valves have a gasket under the seat. This gasket must be in first-class condition; should it show any imperfection, replace it, as a leaking valve-seat gasket will eventually blow out.

The cover-plate gaskets also are important, and when installing valve cover plates, be sure the gaskets are in good condition.   It is imperative that the valve cover-plate nuts or cap screws be pulled down evenly.   Do not completely tighten one side and then the opposite side, as this will cause uneven gasket pressure, resulting in leaks or sprung cover plates.

Several types or designs of valves are used by different compressor manufacturers, and in order to get the proper installation in the compressor, refer to the instruction book that was furnished with the compressor.   Too much care cannot be used when installing the valves and the component parts.

Piston Rings.   Valves often are the cause for lost compressor efficiency, but should the valves be known to be satisfactory, the lost efficiency could well be in the piston rings.   Piston-ring wear usually is very slow when the rings are properly lubricated, but operating time will eventually wear them so that the gap increases and the piston-ring lands wear to the point where some of the ring valving action is lost, allowing for blow-by through the gap and around in back of the ring.

One way to check rings is to put air pressure on top of the piston and listen or feel for blow-by past the piston and rings.   For checking a double-acting cyclinder, one

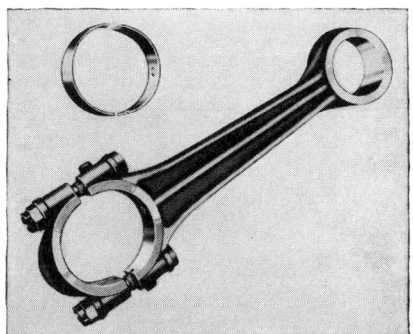

FIG. 7-5. Crankpin bearing and insert.

valve can be removed on one end and air applied at the other end, and then check for blow-by on the end with the valve removed.   *Caution!*—Do not put a hand in the cylinder, as air pressure on the opposite end may cause the piston to move, resulting in a crushed hand and arm.

When excess blow-by is found, remove the pistons and check the piston-to-cylinder-wall clearance and the piston rings for the amount of wear, determining the parts that will need to be replaced.   In the case of scored cylinders and pistons, the cylinders should be rebored to a standard oversize, then new pistons and rings fitted.   Scored cylinders always will allow excess blow-by, adding to operating costs due to lost horsepower and fast wear.

Standard oversize pistons and rings usually are available in 0.005-, 0.010-, 0.020-, and 0.030-in. oversizes.   When reboring over 0.030 in. oversize, it is well to check the compressor manufacturer, even though most cylinders can be rebored considerably over 0.062 in. oversize.   This is particularly true for horizontal cylinders, which have a relief in the valve section to clear the portion of the piston that extends beyond the piston-ring travel.   Too much oversize can cause the piston to strike the valves.

Compressors having automotive-type pistons should have the wrist-pin fits checked when new piston rings are installed and, if found loose, the pin bushings should be replaced.   Often the added drag on the cylinder walls caused by new piston rings will result in a pin knock when too much clearance is allowed.

Bearings.   Crankpin bearings on vertical compressors usually are the automotive type, either steel-back babbitt-lined inserts or spun babbitt (see Fig. 7-5).   To correct noise in the insert type, the installation of new inserts will serve.   Should the crankpin be damaged, it can be reground undersize, and undersize inserts can be used to get correct fit.   Spun-babbitt rods should have shims to get correct running clearance.

Horizontal compressors have several types of crosshead and crankpin bearings (see Figs. 7-6, 7-7, 7-8, and 7-9).   One common type is the split-box, wedge-adjusted

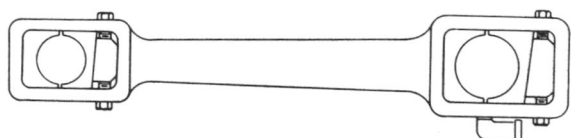

FIG. 7-6. Connecting rod.

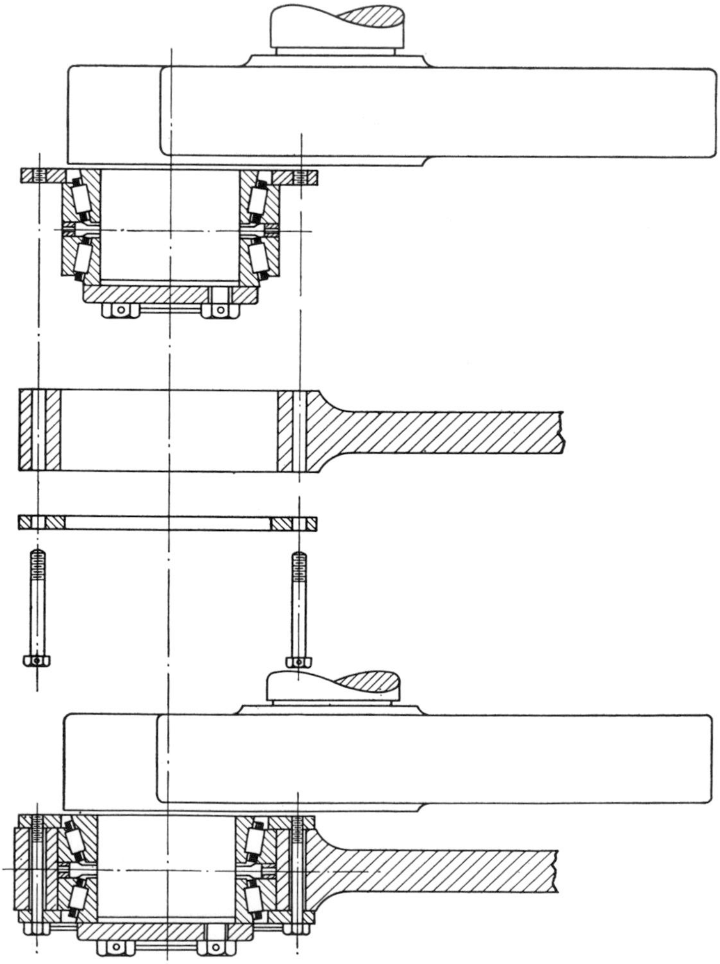

FIG. 7-7. Connecting-rod bearing.

bearing; to adjust this type is simple, as all that is needed is to wedge the movable
half toward the pin by raising the wedge with the adjusting screws.   Care on this
type of bearing must be used not to get the bearing too tight, especially the crosshead pin bearing, as a tight fit here will cause crosshead rocking, resulting in damage to
the crosshead shoes and guide.   If the crankpin bearing is adjusted too tight, the
bearing will fail.   The trial-and-error method for adjusting wedge-type bearings is
the usual means used (see Fig. 7-6).

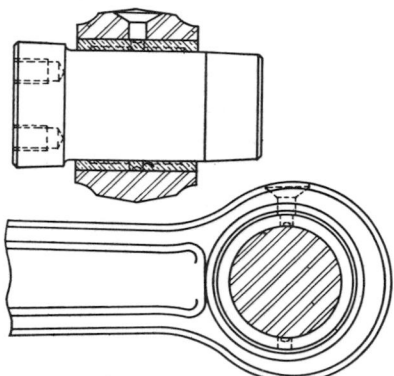

FIG. 7-8. Crosshead-pin bearing.

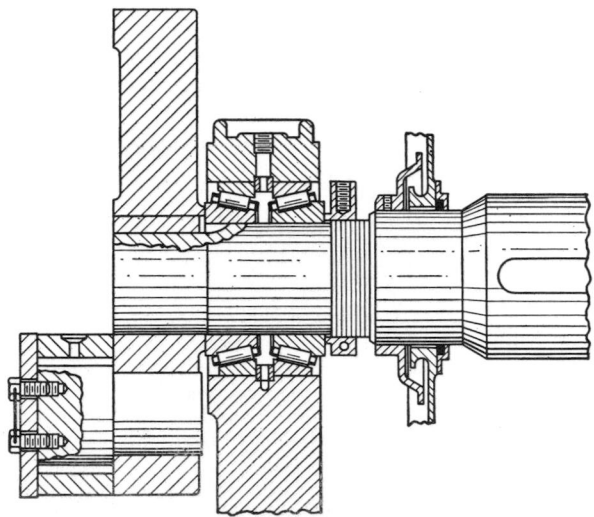

FIG. 7-9. Crankshaft bearing.

For horizontal compressors having steel-backed, babbitt-lined inserts on the crankpin, use new inserts.   Never file a cap or rod having the precision-type bearing inserts,
as new inserts will never fit in a rod that has been filed because the bore will be out of
round and the bearing is apt to burn out.

Some designs use tapered roller bearings for the crankpin when it is a side-crank
design.   Adjustment of these bearings is by means of removing or adding shims.
This moves the outer cone in or out to get running clearance, which for this application is approximately 0.0015 in. over the free rolls (see Fig. 7-7).

For compressors having crosshead pins which operate in a crosshead-pin bushing having no adjustment, it is necessary to replace the bushing. Because of different fit requirements of different compressor manufacturers, the running fit must be obtained from the compressor vendor (see Fig. 7-8).

Many different constructions are used for main bearings in both vertical and horizontal compressors, no matter whether they are sleeve or antifriction bearings. For sleeve bearings, shims are installed between the cap and the body of the bearing housing, and adjustment is made by removing or adding shims. Antifriction single-row taper-roller-bearing adjustment is made by removing or adding shims. Double-row taper roller bearings have adjusting nut locked on the shaft. Unlock the nut and turn it to move the cone in on the cup. For trial purposes use a feeler gage and get about 0.002 in. over the free rolls. Check bearings for heat and noise after starting, as it may be necessary either to tighten or to loosen them slightly (see Fig. 7-9).

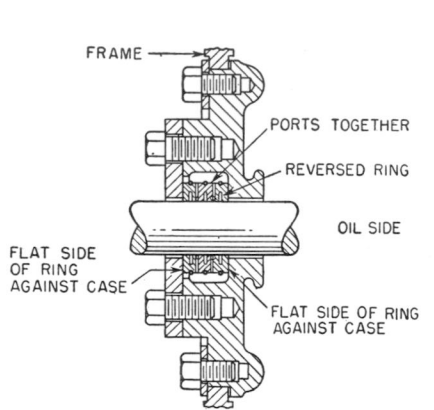

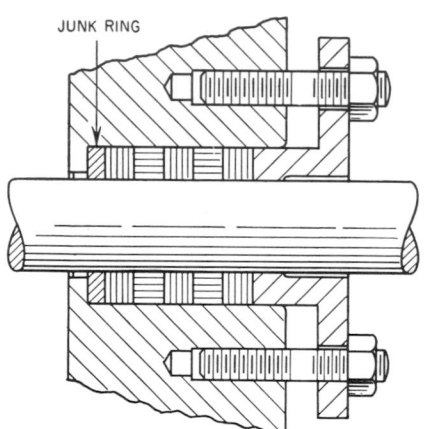

FIG. 7-10. Oil-stop head packing. The packing in the crankcase-oil-stop head is a metallic oil-scraper ring type. It consists of three identical tangential rings. It requires no attention and will last for years. Oil-stop head packing must be assembled as shown.

FIG. 7-11. Braided packing in gland.

Intercoolers and Aftercoolers. These are important compressor parts that often are neglected to the extent that they become inefficient. The most important maintenance is simple, and that is the proper draining of the moisture traps or compartments. Any type of cooler is a condenser, and the condensate, if not drained regularly, will build up until water is carried over to the high pressure cyclinders in the case of an intercooler, and on into the air receiver and air lines in the case of an aftercooler. Coolers should be drained regularly, according to existing humidity condition. The surest way to insure draining is the use of automatic drain traps on the intercooler, aftercooler, and air receiver.

Tube-type intercoolers and aftercoolers are subject to build-up from the mineral content in water, which, if not removed, will eventually affect cooling; therefore these coolers need inspection for deposit removal.

Air-cooled intercoolers and radiators must have the core sections cleaned on the outside because dirt will lodge in the core, reducing heat dissipation. For removal of dust, air blown through in a direction opposite the usual flow will do; but in case the dirt is contaminated with oil, a solvent should be applied, allowed to soak for a while, and then blown clean.

Cleaning. An important item for proper compressor maintenance is keeping the compressor clean on the outside surfaces. Dirt and oil will make an insulation which hinders heat dissipation to atmosphere; this is especially true for an air-cooled compressor, which must depend on all heat dissipation through the cyclinder and cylinder-head surfaces. When dirt is allowed to accumulate on the surfaces of a compressor, it is certain some will find its way into the working parts. A well-kept clean compressor will pay dividends with a good appearance plus reduced operating and maintenance costs.

Unloading. Practically every compressor manufacturer has his own type of air-unloading and control system; to cover all types would require complete data for each system. Some compressor vendors use several types, so for servicing the unloading system and its control, the instruction book should be referred to.

Some common unloading systems are suction unloading valves, suction throttling device, centrifugal unloaders, and by-pass systems. Most of these controls are operated by means of a pressure switch, solenoid, and a three-way valve actuated by the solenoid. Another means of actuating the unloading device is a pneumatic pilot, of which there are several types on the market.

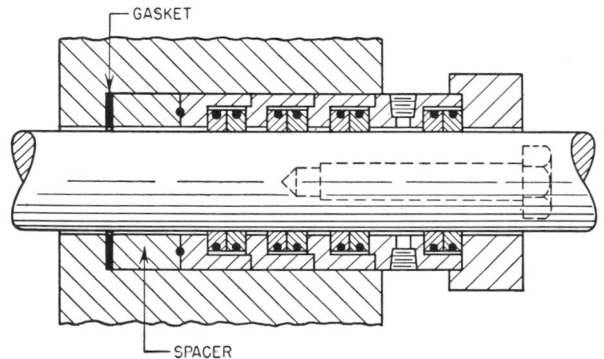

FIG. 7-12. Metallic packing in gland.

Packing. Double-acting compressors using piston rods have oil-stop-head packing and cylinder-head packing which require periodic checking. The oil-stop-head packing usually is a set of metallic scraper rings. They require very little attention because they are designed to scrape oil off the rod, yet get excellent lubrication. Should the piston rod become damaged, the packing will be ruined and new packing required. Never put new scraper rings on a piston rod that is nicked, scratched, or worn, as it will pay to install a new rod (see Fig. 7-10).

The cylinder-head packing usually is the square-braided asbestos packing or the metallic type. Braided asbestos packing often is pulled too tight and results in excess heat, which burns the piston rod. This type of packing should be pulled up until the packing gland is tight, then the packing gland nuts loosened until they are just finger-tight. This will allow the packing to self-adjust and wear in properly. After running, it can be adjusted to stop any leaks that may occur (see Fig. 7-11).

Metallic packing, after it is installed and worn in, requires little attention. However, the piston rod should be checked when it passes through the packing and, if any scratches are present, the packing must be removed and inspected for imbedded material causing the scratches. As long as the packing does not leak or show any signs of marking the rod, it should not be disturbed, as the metal rings are self-adjusting for the slight wear that occurs under normal operation (see Fig. 7-12).

The Service Check Chart (Table 7-1) lists the common causes of derangements of mechanical parts of compressors.

Table 7-1. Service Check Chart, Mechanical Parts

1. Low oil pressure.
   a. Low oil level.
   b. Plugged oil-pump strainer.
   c. Leaks in suction or pressure lines.
   d. Worn-out bearings.
   e. Defective oil pump.
   f. Dirt in oil-filter check valve.
   g. Broken oil-filter-check-valve spring.
   h. Oil-pressure-bypass leaks.
2. High oil pressure.
   a. Plugged oil-pressure lines.
   b. Defective oil-filter mechanism.
   c. Excessive spring tension on filter check valves.
   d. Excessive spring tension on oil-pressure adjusting mechanism.
3. Incorrect delivery of mechanical lubricator.
   a. Dirty or gummed valves.
   b. Broken spring in check valve at cylinder.
   c. Leak in lines or sight feed.
   d. Low oil level.
   e. Plugged vent in lubricator reservoir.
4. Overheated low-pressure cylinder.
   a. Insufficient cooling water.
   b. Scored piston or cylinder.
   c. Broken valves or valve springs.
   d. Excessive carbon deposits.
   e. Packing too tight.
   f. Insufficient lubrication.
   g. Corroded or clogged cylinder water passages.
5. Overheated high-pressure cylinder.
   a. Insufficient cooling water.
   b. Scored piston or cylinder.
   c. Broken valves or valve springs.
   d. Excessive carbon deposits.
   e. Insufficient lubrication.
   f. Packing too tight.
   g. Corroded or clogged cylinder water passages.
6. Water in cylinders.
   a. Leaking head gaskets.
   b. Cracked cylinder or head.
   c. Condensate caused by too much cooling water.
7. High intercooler pressure.
   a. Broken or leaking high-pressure valves.
   b. Defective gage.
   c. Defective or leaking valve-seat gaskets.
8. Low intercooler pressure.
   a. Broken or leaking low-pressure valves.
   b. Leak in intercooler.
   c. Piston-rod-packing leaking.
9. Knocks.
   a. Excessive carbon deposits.
   b. Scored piston or cylinder.
   c. Defective lubricator.
   d. Foreign material in cylinder.
   e. Piston hitting cylinder head.
   f. Loose piston or piston pin.
   g. Burned-out or worn rod bearings.
   h. Loose main bearings.
   i. Scored crosshead or crosshead guides.
10. Scored cylinder, liner, or piston.
    a. Foreign material.
    b. Dirty or inefficient air cleaners.
    c. Lack of lubrication.

Table 7-1. Service Check Chart, Mechanical Parts (*Continued*)

    d. Too much and too cold cooling water causing excess condensate and washing out lubrication.
    e. Excessive heat.
    f. Plugged water jackets.
11. Broken valves and springs.
    a. Too much condensation, causing rust.
    b. Carbon deposits.
    c. Foreign materials not removed by air cleaners.
    d. Incorrect assembly.
    e. Acid condition prevailing at location of suction air inlet.
12. Control trouble.
    a. Suction-valve unloader stuck open or closed.
    b. Pressure switch defective.
    c. Solenoid burned out.
    d. Foreign material in three-way valves.
    e. Vibration of control.
    f. Voltage drop or loss of power.
    g. Plugged air line or strainer.
    h. Incorrect voltage or cycle.
13. Incorrect operation of suction-valve unloaders.
    a. Leaks in unloader line.
    b. Foreign material in guides or seats.
    c. Worn plungers.
    d. Leaking or ruptured diaphragms.
    e. Broken springs.
    f. Manual shutoff partly closed.
    g. Wrong pressure-switch setting.

Note: Remember to read the instruction book carefully and to keep it and the parts list in an accessible place so that when information to make adjustments and repair is needed, shutdown time can be held to a minimum.

Chapter 8

ELEVATORS

By H. R. OTTO[1]
General Service Superintendent
Otis Elevator Company
New York, N.Y.

A preventive maintenance program is of paramount importance in the care of elevators. The requirements of such a program are: qualified personnel; methods; records; spare parts; tools; ability to handle emergency conditions; and safety for the elevator maintenance mechanic.

QUALIFIED PERSONNEL

Since the elevator plant of a building is composed of a variety of electrical, mechanical, and hydraulic equipment, most of which is not common to any other business, even highly trained mechanics and electricians will not have the proper background or knowledge to service without special training. It is of the utmost importance that the owner or manager place the maintenance of his elevator plant in the hands of a competent elevator mechanic or company. Failure of the elevator to operate as designed will seriously affect the transportation and safety of personnel and materials.

Figure 8-1 shows how a freight-elevator installation appears with the hoistway enclosure removed. Although the control apparatus is relatively simple compared with a high-speed, operatorless passenger elevator, it must also fulfill all the requirements for safe, dependable, vertical transportation.

The elevator mechanic must be sure that he understands just what the safety features, such as safeties, governors, gates, contacts, and door locks, are designed to do and how wear and tear will affect their operation. He must understand the functions of the machine, the controller, the operating, signal, and door devices, the operational sequence, and the wiring diagram, so he may readily localize and correct troubles. He must be able systematically to inspect, clean, lubricate, adjust, and replace parts of the entire elevator equipment.

METHODS

With a knowledge of the component parts of the elevator to be maintained, a schedule must be prepared which will insure that each part is inspected at the proper intervals. Such a schedule as used by Otis examiners for the company's maintenance service on more than 40,000 elevators is illustrated in Fig. 8-2.

The primary intent of such a check chart is to serve as a guide to the maintenance man and assist him in establishing a set routine for the items of work which must be

[1] Author is retired.

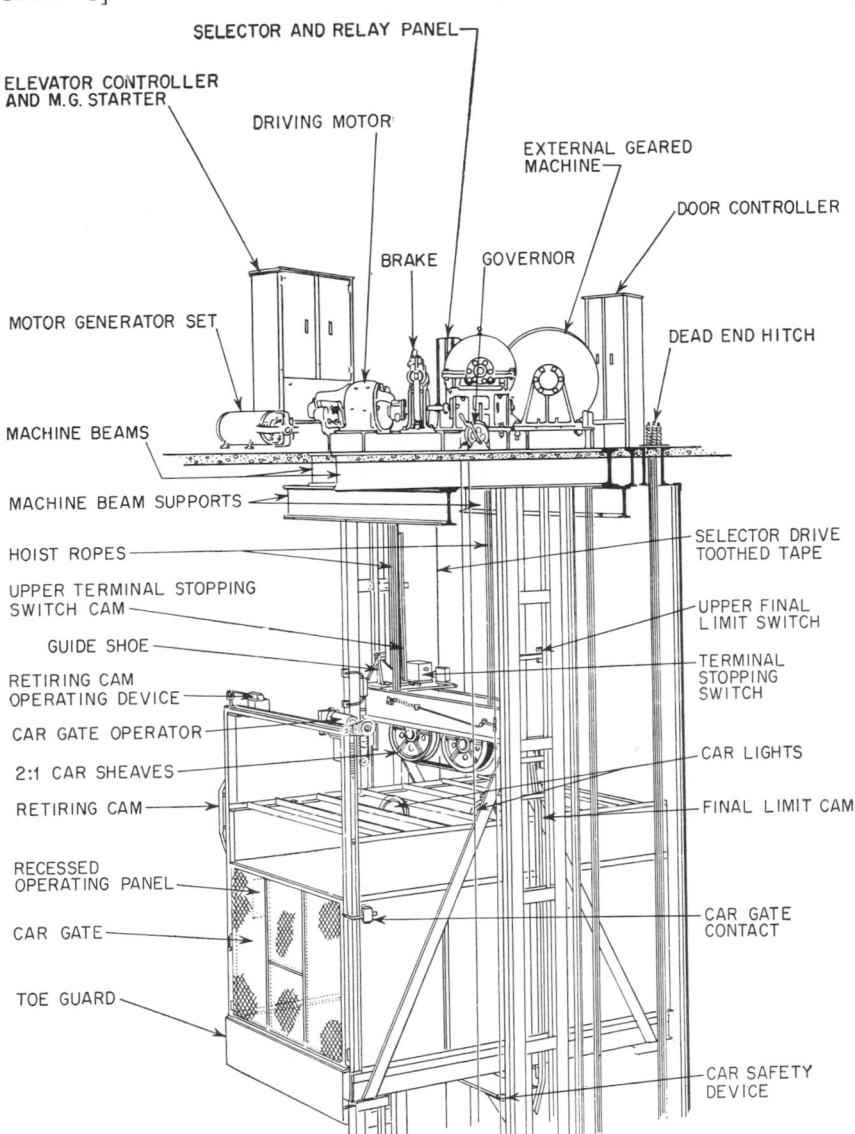

SELECTOR AND RELAY PANEL

ELEVATOR CONTROLLER
AND M.G. STARTER

DRIVING MOTOR

EXTERNAL GEARED
MACHINE

DOOR CONTROLLER

BRAKE   GOVERNOR

MOTOR GENERATOR SET

DEAD END HITCH

MACHINE BEAMS

MACHINE BEAM SUPPORTS

HOIST ROPES

SELECTOR DRIVE
TOOTHED TAPE

UPPER TERMINAL STOPPING
SWITCH CAM

UPPER FINAL
LIMIT SWITCH

GUIDE SHOE

TERMINAL
STOPPING
SWITCH

RETIRING CAM
OPERATING DEVICE

CAR GATE OPERATOR

2:1 CAR SHEAVES

CAR LIGHTS

RETIRING CAM

FINAL LIMIT CAM

RECESSED
OPERATING PANEL

CAR GATE

CAR GATE
CONTACT

TOE GUARD

CAR SAFETY
DEVICE

FIG. 8-1. Otis heavy-duty freight elevator (external geared machine 2:1 roping, unit multivoltage control).

performed at prescribed intervals with a minimum of record keeping. It requires the complete cooperation of the maintenance man to be effective.

The check chart is divided into three sections: (1) the work that is to be performed on each visit; (2) the operations that are to be done during any particular calendar month, with a notation as to frequency, such as monthly, quarterly, semiannually, or annually; and (3) a check list where semiannual and annual items are checked as the work is

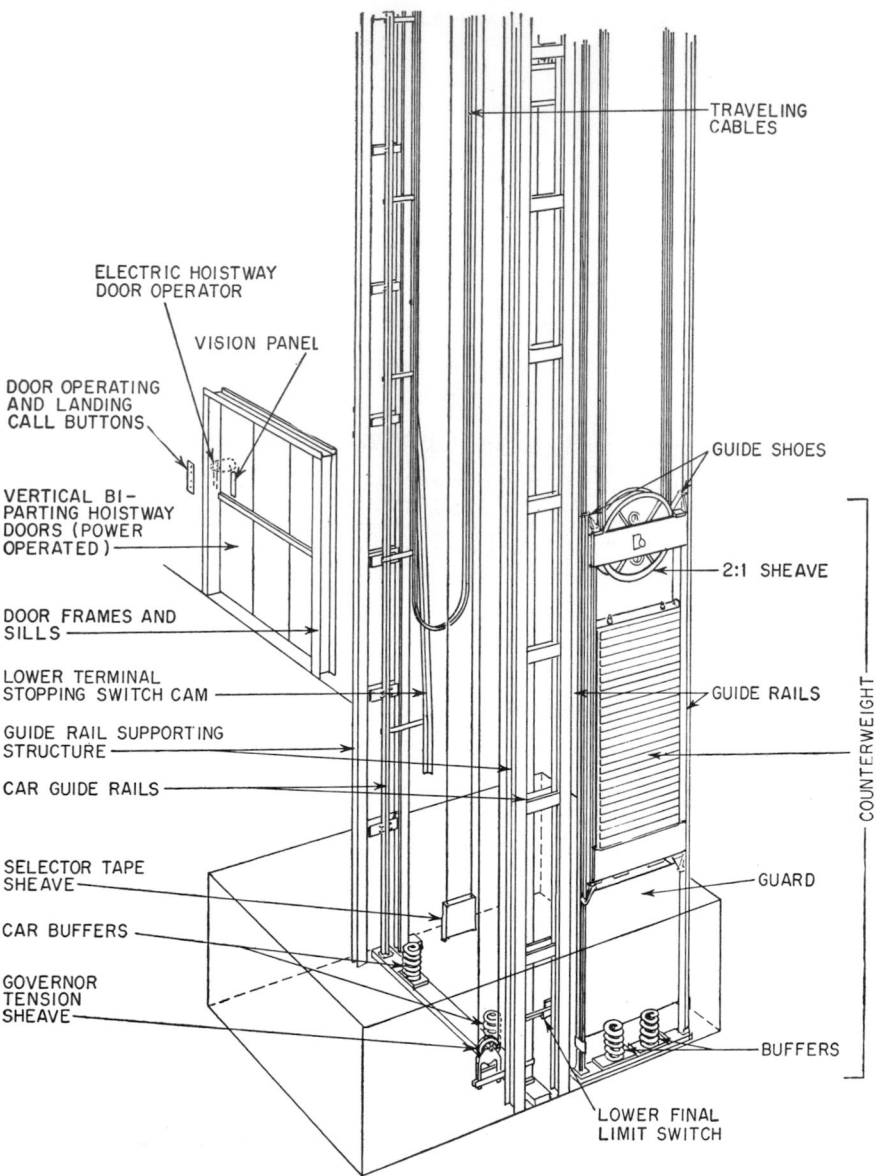

FIG. 8-1. (*Continued*).

performed.   In using the charts:

1. It must be understood that the make-up of the chart is based on average conditions; therefore, adjustments must be made to the frequencies where unusual conditions exist.
2. The routine is based on the assumption that the elevator can be taken out of service to perform this work.

ON EVERY VISIT . . . . *it is essential that the following be properly executed.*

1. SEE CUSTOMER OR HIS REPRESENTATIVE; CONTACT STARTER AND OPERATOR.
2. RIDE CAR, OBSERVING STARTING AND STOPPING, OPERATION OF DOORS AND GATES; CHECK FOR UNUSUAL NOISES.
3. INSPECT ALL EQUIPMENT IN MACHINE ROOM PAYING PARTICULAR ATTENTION TO CONTACTS, CONNECTORS, REVERSE PHASE RELAY.
4. MAKE CORRECTIONS AS INDICATED BY THESE INSPECTIONS OR COMPLAINTS RECEIVED. REPORT REQUIRED REPAIRS TO OFFICE.
5. CLEAN MACHINE ROOM AND FLOOR WHEN NECESSARY.
6. CHECK CONDITION OF PIT AND CLEAN FLOOR AND BOTTOM OF CAR IF NECESSARY.
7. KEEP CAR TOP CLEAN.
8. USE PERSONAL PROTECTIVE EQUIPMENT AS REQUIRED.

it is also important, on every visit, that the items in guide below receive systematic attention.

MACH., SELECTORS, MG SETS, CONTROLLERS	General inspection of mach., sheaves, worm & gear, motor, brake, also selectors or floor controllers when used, lub. as reqd.
	Empty drip pan. *NOTE:* Oil should not be reused.
	Observe brake oper., check brake linings, adj. brake when necessary.
	Inspect & lub. mach. automatic, contacts, linkage & gearing.
	Clean coll. rings, brush rigging, commutators & undercutting as reqd.
	Clean & lub. contr. contacts, connectors & holders, as reqd.
OVER-HEAD	Lub. bearings, remove grease from around sheaves, bearing boxes.
	Inspect governor working parts & lubrication, check gov. switch.
	Clean & lub. signal drive mechanism when used.
CAR	Check car flooring for wear that would create tripping hazard.
	Check car gate contacts for operation, when used.
	Lubricate car & cwt. sheave bearings when used.
	Check condition of car switch handle, replace emergency release glasses if required.
HOIST-WAY	If rails are lubricated, check condition and lubrication.
	Check governor & tape tension sheave lubrication.
HOISTWAY ENTRANCES	Inspect. gate ropes or cables, gate body, tracks, posts.
	Observe operation of door locks, contacts, checks, Rixson hinges, if used.
	Replace any broken or worn pull straps on bi-parting doors.
	Check oper. of car call bell system when used.
MISC.	Drain air lines.

Form 2921B

FIG. 8-2a. Inspection schedule. Lists the work to be performed on every visit.

CHECK CHART FOR GEARED 2 SPEED AND UMV CONTROL PASSENGER OR FREIGHT ELEVATORS

Operations To Be Performed During First Quarter . . . .

JANUARY

DOOR & GATE OP.	Clean, lubricate, check brake, operation of checks, check keys & setscrews, contacts.	(M)
DOOR CL.	Clean & lubricate pivot points & sill trips as required.	(M)
SEL.&SIG. COMM.	Check brushes, dashpots, traveling cables, chain, brush & pawl magnets, lubricate as reqd.	(M)
	Observe operation of signal system, as used.	(M)
MISC.	Inspect drum buffers, rope clamps, slack cable switch, coupling, shafts, keyways.	(M)
	Check main line switch fuses for heating.	(Q)
	Check compensating chain hitches, when used.	(Q)
	Lubricate indicator dials & pulleys.	(SA)
	Clean car grille & stile channels visible from inside of car.	(SA)
LVLG.	Check leveling switches and leveling operation.	(Q)
MACHS.	Observe micro gear case bearing for wear & end play.	(Q)
	Observe gear backlash, thrust end play & bearing wear.	(Q)
	Remove, clean & lubricate brake cores on DC brakes, clean linings if necessary, check wear.	(A)

FEBRUARY

DOOR & GATE OP.	Clean, lubricate, check brake, operation of checks, check keys & setscrews, contacts.	(M)
DOOR CL.	Clean & lubricate pivot points & sill trips as required.	(M)
SEL.&SIG. COMM.	Check brushes, dashpots, traveling cables, chain, brush & pawl magnets, lubricate as reqd.	(M)
	Observe operation of signal system, as used.	(M)
MISC.	Inspect drum buffers, rope clamps, slack cable switch, coupling, shafts, keyways.	(M)
ROPES	Check all fastenings, inspect all ropes for wear & lubrication.	(Q)
TAPE DRIVES	Clean & lubricate tape drive, clean tapes as necessary.	(Q)
	Check hitches & broken tape switch.	(SA)
C.O.BOX	Check contacts, switches, clean & lubricate car oper. box.	(SA)
MACHS.	Seal small leaks.	(SA)
MOTORS GEN. EXCITERS	Clean all comm., renew or reseat brushes if necessary.	(Q)
	Clean armatures, motors with blower or vacuum.	(A)
	Check armature & rotor clearances.	(A)
	Check motor & mg. set connections, change oil in bearings.	(A)

MARCH

DOOR & GATE OP.	Clean, lubricate, check brake, operation of checks, check keys & setscrews, contacts.	(M)
DOOR CL.	Clean & lubricate pivot points & sill trips as required.	(M)
SEL.&SIG. COMM.	Check brushes, dashpots, traveling cables, chain, brush & pawl magnets, lubricate as reqd.	(M)
	Observe operation of signal system, as used.	(M)
MISC.	Inspect drum buffers, rope clamps, slack cable switch, coupling, shafts, keyways.	(M)
CAR	Check alarm bell system, when used.	(Q)
	Clean light fixture globe.	(Q)
	Check retiring cam device, chain, dashpots, commutators, brushes, cam, pivots, fastenings. Check oil level of AC cam devices.	(Q)
	Check emer. switch.	(Q)
	Check safety parts, pivots, setscrews, switch.	(Q)
	Check adjustment of car shoes.	(Q)
G. SHOES	Lubricate guide shoe stems & adj. if necessary.	(A)
CONTRS.	Clean with blower, check align. of sws., lub. hinge pins.	(SA)
	Check all resistance tubes & grids.	(SA)
	Check oil in overload relays, settings & oper. of overloads.	(SA)
	Clean & check fuses & holders; check other contr. connections.	(A)

Form 2921A

FIG. 8-2b. Operations to be performed during first quarter of year M, monthly; Q, quarterly; SA, semiannually; A, annually.

CHECK CHART FOR GEARED 2 SPEED AND UMV CONTROL PASSENGER OR FREIGHT ELEVATORS

Operations To Be Performed During Second Quarter . . . .

APRIL		
DOOR & GATE OP.	Clean, lubricate, check brake, operation of checks, check keys & setscrews, contacts.	(M)
DOOR CL.	Clean & lubricate pivot points & sill trips as required.	(M)
SEL.&SIG. COMM.	Check brushes, dashpots, traveling cables, chain, brush & pawl magnets, lubricate as reqd.	(M)
	Observe operation of signal system, as used.	(M)
MISC.	Inspect drum buffers, rope clamps, slack cable switch, couplings, shafts, keyways.	(M)
	Check main line switch fuses for heating.	(Q)
	Check compensating chain hitches, when used.	(Q)
LVLG.	Check leveling switches and leveling operation.	(Q)
MACHS.	Observe micro gear case bearing for wear & end play.	(Q)
	Observe gear backlash, thrust end play & bearing wear.	(Q)
BI-PART. DOORS	Clean chains, tracks & sheaves, lubricate as required.	(SA)
	Check door contacts.	(SA)
PIT	Lubricate compensating sheave & check hitches.	(SA)
	Check oil level in oil buffers.	(SA)
	Check governor & tape tension sheave fstngs.	(SA)
SHEAVES	Overhead, Deflector, 2:1 (car & cwt.) See that sheaves are tight on shafts, sound spokes and rim with hammer for cracks.	(A)
MAY		
DOOR & GATE OPER.	Clean, lubricate, check brake, operation of checks, check keys & setscrews, contacts.	(M)
	Check shaft brgs., tapered pins, align., operation of cams, rollers.	(SA)
DOOR CLOS.	Clean & lubricate pivot points & sill trips as required.	(M)
	Check fastenings, operation of checks, interlocks.	(SA)
SEL.&SIG. COMM.	Check brushes, dashpots, traveling cables, chain, brush & pawl magnets, lubricate as required.	(M)
	Check traveling nut & gears for wear.	(SA)
	Observe operation of signal system, as used.	(M)
MISC.	Inspect drum buffers, rope clamps, slack cable switch, couplings, shafts, keyways.	(M)
MOT.GEN	Clean all comm., renew or reseat brushes, if necessary.	(Q)
TAPE DR.	Clean & lubricate tape drive, clean tapes as necessary.	(Q)
ROPES	Check all fastenings, inspect all ropes for wear & lubrication.	(Q)
	Check all rope hitches, shackles, equalize rope tension.	(SA)
HALL	Check hall button contacts, springs, wiring, clean & lubricate.	(A)
JUNE		
DOOR & GATE OP.	Clean, lubricate, check brake, operation of checks, check keys & setscrews, contacts.	(M)
DOOR CL.	Clean & lubricate pivot points & sill trips as required.	(M)
SEL.&SIG. COMM.	Check brushes, dashpots, traveling cables, chain, brush & pawl magnets, lubricate as required.	(M)
	Observe operation of signal system, as used.	(M)
MISC.	Inspect drum buffers, rope clamps, slack cable switch, couplings, shafts, keyways.	(M)
	Check alarm bell system, when used.	(Q)
	clean light fixture globe.	(Q)
	Check retiring cam device, chain, dashpots, commutator, brushes, cams, pivots, fastenings. Check oil level of AC cam devices.	(Q)
	Check emerg. switch.	(Q)
	Check safety parts, pivots, setscrews, switch.	(Q)
CAR	Check adjustment of car shoes.	(Q)
	Check stile channels for bends or cracks, also carframe, cams & supports.	(SA)
	Lubricate moving parts of vert. rising or collapsible car gates, also check pivot points, sheaves, guides & track for wear.	(SA)
	Check car enclosure steadying plates.	(A)
	Check clearances for car safety shoes.	(A)

Form 2921A-1

FIG. 8-2c. Operations to be performed during the second quarter of year.

CHECK CHART FOR GEARED 2 SPEED AND UMV CONTROL

PASSENGER OR FREIGHT ELEVATORS

Operations To Be Performed During Third Quarter . . . .

JULY

DOOR & GATE OP.	Clean, lubricate, check brake, operation of checks, check keys & setscrews, contacts.	(M)
DOOR CL.	Clean & lubricate pivot points & sill trips as required.	(M)
SEL.& SIG. COMM.	Check brushes, dashpots, traveling cables, chain, brush & pawl magnets, lubricate as required.	(M)
	Observe operation of signal system, as used.	(M)
MISC.	Inspect drum buffers, rope clamps, slack cable switch, coupling, shafts, keyways.	(M)
	Check main line switch fuses for heating.	(Q)
	Check compensating chain hitches, when used.	(Q)
	Lubricate indicator dials & pulleys.	(SA)
	Clean car grille & stile channels visible from inside of car.	(SA)
LVLG.	Check leveling switches and leveling operation.	(Q)
MACHS.	Observe micro gear case bearing for wear & end play.	(Q)
	Observe gear backlash, thrust end play & bearing wear.	(Q)
HOIST-WAY	Clean & check guide rails, cams & fast'ngs, also counterweight.	(A)
	Inspect limit & terminal stop. switches; lub. pins & rollers.	(A)

AUGUST

DOOR & GATE OP.	Clean, lubricate, check brake, operation of checks, check keys & setscrews, contacts.	(M)
DOOR CL.	Clean & lubricate pivot points & sill trips as required.	(M)
SEL.& SIG. COMM.	Check brushes, dashpots, traveling cables, chain, brush & pawl magnets, lubricate as required.	(M)
	Observe operation of signal system, as used.	(M)
MISC.	Inspect drum buffers, rope clamps, slack cable switch, coupling, shafts, keyways.	(M)
MOT.GEN	Clean all comm., renew or reseat brushes if necessary.	(Q)
ROPES	Check all fastenings, inspect all ropes for wear & lubrication.	(Q)
TAPE DRIVES	Clean & lubricate tape drive, clean tapes as necessary.	(Q)
	Check hitches & broken tape switch.	(SA)
C.O.BOX	Check contacts, switches, clean & lubricate car oper. box.	(SA)
MACHS.	Seal small leaks.	(SA)
TRAV. CABLE	Check wear, insulation, hanging, junction box connections.	(A)

SEPTEMBER

DOOR & GATE OP.	Clean, lubricate, check brake, operation of checks, check keys & setscrews, contacts.	(M)
DOOR CL.	Clean & lubricate pivot points & sill trips as required.	(M)
SEL.& SIG. COMM.	Check brushes, dashpots, traveling cables, chain, brush & pawl magnets, lubricate as required.	(M)
	Observe operation of signal system, as used.	(M)
MISC.	Inspect drum buffers, rope clamps, slack cable switch, couplings, shafts, keyways.	(M)
CAR	Check alarm bell system, when used.	(Q)
	Check light fixture globe.	(Q)
	Check retiring cam device, chain, dashpots, commutator, brushes, cams, pivots, fastenings. Check oil level of AC cam devices.	(Q)
	Check emerg. switch.	(Q)
	Check safety parts, pivots, setscrews, switch.	(Q)
	Check adjustment of car shoes.	(Q)
CONTRS.	Clean with blower, check align. of switches, lubricate hinge pins.	(SA)
	Check all resistance tubes & grids.	(SA)
	Check oil in overload relays, settings, & operation of overloads.	(SA)

Form 2921A-2

FIG. 8-2*d*. Operations to be performed during the third quarter of year.

CHECK CHART FOR GEARED 2 SPEED AND UMV CONTROL PASSENGER OR FREIGHT ELEVATORS

Operations To Be Performed During Fourth Quarter ....

OCTOBER

DOOR & GATE OP.	Clean, lubricate, check brake, operation of checks, check keys & setscrews, contacts.	(M)
DOOR CL.	Clean & lubricate pivot points & sill trips as required.	(M)
SEL.&SIG. COMM.	Check brushes, dashpots, traveling cables, chain, brush & pawl magnets, lubricate as required.	(M)
	Observe operation of signal system, as used.	(M)
MISC.	Inspect drum buffers, rope clamps, slack cable switch, coupling, shafts, keyways.	(M)
	Check main line switch fuses for heating.	(Q)
	Check compensating chain hitches, when used.	(Q)
LVLG.	Check leveling switches and leveling operation.	(Q)
	Observe micro gear case bearing for wear & end play.	(Q)
MACHS.	Observe worms & gears for end play; also observe wear in machine bearings.	(Q)
BI-PART. DOORS	Clean chains, tracks, sheaves, lubricate as required.	(SA)
	Check door contacts.	(SA)
HOIST-WAY DOORS	Clean, lubri. tracks, hangers, check upthrust & adj. if necessary.	(A)
	Fill & adj. checks. Check bott. gibs, struts, sills, headers & fastngs.	(A)
	Adjust door contacts.	(A)
PIT	Lubricate compensating sheave & check hitches.	(SA)
	Check oil level in oil buffers.	(SA)
	Check governor & tape tension sheave fstngs.	(SA)

NOVEMBER

DOOR & GATE OP.	Clean, lubricate, check brake, operation of checks, check keys & setscrews, contacts.	(M)
	Check shaft brgs., tapered pins, align., oper. of cams, rollers.	(SA)
DOOR CLOS.	Clean & lubricate pivot points & sill trips as required.	(M)
	Check fastenings, operation of checks, interlocks.	(SA)
SEL.&SIG. COMM.	Check brushes, dashpots, traveling cables, chain, brush & pawl magnets, lubricate as required.	(M)
	Check traveling nut & gears for wear.	(SA)
	Observe operation of signal system, as used.	(M)
MISC.	Inspect drum buffers, rope clamps, slack cable switch, coupling, shafts, keyways.	(M)
MOT.GEN	Clean all comm., renew or reseat brushes if necessary.	(Q)
TAPE DR.	Clean & lubricate tape drive, clean tapes as necessary.	(Q)
ROPES	Check all fastenings, inspect all ropes for wear & lubrication.	(Q)
	Check all rope hitches, shackles, equalize rope tension.	(SA)

DECEMBER

DOOR & GATE OP.	Clean, lubricate, check brake, operation of checks, check keys & setscrews, contacts.	(M)
DOOR CL.	Clean & lubricate pivot points & sill trips as required.	(M)
SEL.&SIG. COMM.	Check brushes, dashpots, traveling cables, chain, brush & pawl magnets, lubricate as required.	(M)
	Observe operation of signal system, as used.	(M)
MISC.	Inspect drum buffers, rope clamps, slack cable switch, coupling, Shafts, keyways.	(M)
	Check alarm bell system, when used.	(Q)
	Clean light fixture globe.	(Q)
CAR	Check retiring cam device, chain, dashpots, commutator, brushes, cams, pivots, fastenings. Check oil level of AC cam devices.	(Q)
	Check emerg. switch.	(Q)
	Check safety parts, pivots, setscrews, switch.	(Q)
	Check adjustment of car shoes.	(Q)
	Check stile channels for bends or cracks, also carframe, cams & supports.	(SA)
	Lubricate moving parts of vert. rising or collapsible car gates, also check pivot points, sheaves, guides & track for wear.	(SA)
R. GUIDE	(Car & Cwt.) Lubricate wheel bearings, small amount as required.	(A)

Form 2921A-3

Fig. 8-2e. Operations to be performed during fourth quarter of year.

INDICATE WITH A √ MARK PERIOD IN WHICH ▶ EACH ANN. & SEMI-ANN. ITEM IS TAKEN CARE OF ▶	CAR_____ QUARTER 1 2 3 4				CAR_____ QUAR 1 2	
MACHS.	Remove, clean & lubricate brake cores on DC brakes, clean linings if necessary, check wear. (A)					
	Seal small leaks. (SA)					
MOTORS GEN. EXCITERS	Clean armatures, motors with blower or vacuum. (A)					
	Check armature & rotor clearances. (A)					
	Check motor connections. (A)					
	Change oil in bearings. (A)					
CONTR.	Clean w/blower, check align. of sws., lub. hinge pins. (SA)					
	Check all resistance tubes & grids. (SA)					
	Check oil in overload relays, setgs. & oper. (SA)					
	Clean & check fuses & holders; check cont. conns. (A)					
SEL.	Check traveling nut & gears for wear. (SA)					
SHEAVES	See that sheaves are tight on shafts, sound spokes and rim with hammer for cracks. (A)					
TAPE DR.	Check hitches & broken tape switch. (SA)					
CAR	Check stile channels for bends or cracks; also car-frame, cams & support. (SA)					
	Lub. moving parts of vert. rising or coll. car gates, also check pivot points, sheaves, guides & track for wear. (SA)					
	Check car enclosure steadying plates. (A)					
	Check clearances for car safety shoes. (A)					
DOOR OPER.	Check shaft brgs., tapered pins, alignment, oper. of cams, rollers. (SA)					
D. CL'SER	Check fastenings, operation of checks, interlocks. (SA)					
C.O. BOX	Check contacts, switches, clean & lub. car oper. box. (SA)					
ROPES	Check all rope hitches, shackles, equal. rope tension. (SA)					
	Check all fastenings, inspect all ropes for wear. (SA)					
G. SHOES	Lubricate guide shoe stems & adjust if necessary. (A)					
R. GUIDE	(Car & Cwt.) Lub. wheel brgs., small amt. as reqd. (A)					
HOIST-WAY	Clean & check guide rails, cams & fstngs., also cwt. (A)					
	Inspect limit & term. stop sws.; lub. pins & rollers. (A)					
TRAV. CABLE	Check wear, insul., hanging, inspect junc. box conns. (A)					
BI-PART. DOORS	Clean chains, tracks, sheaves, lubricate as reqd. (SA)					
	Check door contacts. (SA)					
HOIST-WAY DOORS	Clean, lub., tracks, h'gers, ch'k upthrust & adj. if nec. (A)					
	Fill & adjust checks. (A)					
	Check bottom gibs, struts, sills, headers, fastenings, adjust door conts. (A)					
HALL	Check hall button contacts, springs, wiring, clean & lubricate as required. (A)					
MISC.	Lubricate indicator dials & pulleys. (SA)					
	Clean car grille & stile chan'ls visible from inside car. (SA)					
PIT	Lubricate compensating shv. & check hitches. (SA)					
	Check oil level in oil buffers. (SA)					
	Check governor & tape tension sheave fstngs. (SA)					

FIG. 8-2f. Check list to be used where semiannual and annual items are to be checked as the work is performed. May be used for any number of elevators of same type.

3. The chart does not include methods of adjustment, lubrication, cleaning, and minor repairs, which information is available to the mechanic from other sources. It is expected that the chart will direct his attention to items that may seem relatively unimportant to him.

Some of the items which a thorough inspection will uncover follow.

Motors and Generators: Oil-soaked armatures or stators; clogged vent holes; improper brush-spring pressure; poor brush seating; brushes stuck in holders; incorrect brush type and grade; high mica; commutator flat spots; high bars or pitting; bearing wear affecting armature air gap and rotor clearance; brushes of d-c motors off neutral point; undercut commutator slots filled; ground clamps missing.

Brakes: Will not hold 125 per cent of full load; noisy lifting and application; worn linings; pins frozen with rust or paint; pulley rough or dirty; shafts loose in the brake couplings; excessive brake-shoe clearance; misalignment of brake shoes with pulley; brake switch contacts improperly set.

Machines: Gear rim bolts broken or loose; excessive backlash or binding between worm and gear; excessive side or end thrust; uneven sheave grooves; ropes bottomed in sheave grooves; gland packing ineffective; gear oil dirty or has lost its lubricating qualities; loose foundation bolts; cracked sheave spokes.

Controllers: Incorrect fuse capacity; broken leads; loose connections and lugs; loose or broken resistances; improper contacts; worn contacts; weak springs; improper contact-spring tension; no contact wipe; worn pins, bushings, and walking beams; switches sticking due to residual magnetism and gummy cores; overheated coils; circuits open or short-circuited.

Car: Worn flooring; emergency exit missing or improperly secured; cracked fixture glass; broken buttons; car switch handles not locking in neutral position; alarm or stop buttons not working; gates dragging threshold; gate contacts plugged; bottom door guides worn.

Top of Car: Loose steady plates and platform fastenings; vibration of ropes; lost lay in ropes at schackles; guide shoes with excessive float; worn gibs; door operators out of alignment; oil leakage; switches inoperative.

Hoistway: Worn traveling cables; worn or rusted hoist and governor ropes; doors with broken glass or structural defects; excessive wear in door pins, chains, bushings, and shoes; broken springs; missing door bumpers; doors improperly balanced; trucking-sill bent; tracks loose, worn, or out of alignment; worn interlock fingers, springs, bases, tumblers, cams, and rollers; loose and missing bolts and screws; hoistway door operators out of adjustment; insufficient oil in counterweight buffer; dirty and sticking counterweight buffer piston; worn limit-switch rollers; rails out of alignment; loose rail fastenings, brackets, and fishplates.

Pit: Insufficient oil in car buffer; dirty and sticking piston; worn sheave bearings; water and debris in pit; switches out of adjustment; rope stretch.

Bottom of Car: Worn safety shoes; frozen safety drums; insufficient turns on safety drum; crossed safety rope; missing safety rollers; loose lead sheaves; car shoes out of adjustment; worn gibs.

Hallways: Broken buttons, lamp fixtures, and emergency-key glasses; missing emergency keys; inadequate lighting.

Lubrication: Of course lubrication is an important factor, and the proper lubricants must be used. Usually each installation receives a lubrication chart from the manufacturer, showing recommendations and the normal interval for attention (Fig. 8-3).

Cleaning is an important part of preventive-maintenance operations. It cannot be overemphasized because it requires the maintenance man to handle parts of the equipment which are usually only glanced at casually. As a result, loose nuts and worn and broken parts are discovered and corrections made before trouble occurs.

One of the items which is not always taken care of as a part of ordinary maintenance is the cleaning of hoistway equipment and hoistways. The failure to do this work periodically creates a serious fire hazard, as considerable flammable dust and lint gather on the oil and grease used in lubricating guide rails and on the equipment.

When loads permit, the introduction of roller guides, which run on bone-dry rails, has to a large extent eliminated this condition.

External wear is readily recognized by the maintenance man and is corrected first by adjustment of the affected parts, where adjustments are available. Where correction is not possible with adjustment, new parts are installed or surfaces machined as required. Proper lubrication minimizes the wear. It is important that any preventive-maintenance program combat the effects of airborne dust, humidity, gases, extremes of temperature, and liquids such as water, steam, brine, blood, and urine. Ventilation, heating, waxes, paints, and chemical coatings of various kinds are used to overcome or ameliorate the effects of these destructive forces.

In addition to external wear, the preventive-maintenance program must recognize that certain parts and controller components have definite limited built-in life, and that their deterioration is not apparent to the eye. In this category we find springs, light bulbs, electronic tubes, dry cells, capacitors, rectifiers, and insulation values. Where this equipment is involved we have to rely upon instruments and judgment as to whether or not we ought to replace after we obtain a certain amount of life rather than wait for failure or make frequent repetitive adjustments to compensate for the deterioration.

Among the most essential and major components of an elevator are the hoist ropes, which require renewal from time to time. The life of an elevator rope depends to a large extent on the care it receives. Abrasion is damaging to ropes; therefore, it is essential that ropes do not rub or drag over obstructions. Corrosion also is a destructive factor, which can be prevented or retarded by periodic application of a good wire-rope lubricant. Differential sheave diameters, caused by grooves of unequal depth, bring about very rapid wear and breakage of wires in a rope, as one or more of them may be badly overloaded while the balance of the ropes just drag over the grooves. Unequal tension also causes rapid wear of ropes and grooves, as one or more ropes may be carrying a considerable overload. Worn sheave bearings, which will cause the drive or any other sheave to tilt, will cause abrasion of the ropes, as the rope will not seat properly in the groove. Too rapid acceleration and retardation of the elevator also take their toll of rope life.

It is essential that ropes be of the correct length, so that the counterweight will not land in the pit, as this produces a severe shock when the car arrives at and leaves the top landing. Where drum machines are involved, the resocketing of the ropes at the proper frequency is essential because of the fatigue which occurs in the wires of the hoist ropes at their connections.

Rope inspection and condemnation require considerable skill and experience if ropes are not to be condemned prematurely. The method most generally used is to count the broken wires per rope lay, a rope lay being the distance required for one strand to make a complete revolution. For $\frac{5}{8}$-in. cable this is approximately 4 in. of rope length, and for $\frac{1}{2}$-in. cable approximately 3 in. When the number of broken wires in a 6-strand rope is found to be 24 to 30 wires per rope lay, evenly distributed, and in an 8-strand rope 32 to 40 wires, the rope should be removed. These are maximum figures, but if the factors of abrasion and corrosion are present, if there is a loss of diameter, if there is a concentration of breaks in a single strand, or if 5 or 6 adjacent wires are broken across the crown of the strand, the ropes should be removed before these figures are reached.

In any preventive-maintenance program, safety devices must be checked to see that they will operate properly They include terminal stopping devices, to automatically retard and stop the car at the terminal landing; final limit switches, to cut off the power from the motor in the event of failure of the terminal stopping devices; hoistway door interlocks at each landing; a compensating-rope switch, to indicate excessive stretch or an obstruction which tends to lift the sheave out of its guides; and a broken-tape switch. In the car there is a manual emergency stop switch, to shut off the power, and a car door or gate contact, to insure that the door is closed before starting and while the car is running. In all of these the function is to prevent motion of the car when these devices are in the "off" or "open" position, and they are tested by placing the device in the "off" or "open" position and trying to operate the elevator.

On the other hand, the safety and governor (Fig. 8-4) are designed to operate in case of overspeeding. The governor, which measures the speed of the moving car and trips to actuate the safety when a certain speed is reached, is set in the factory and is sealed to prevent changes after an acceptance test. If any repairs are made to the governor it must be recalibrated to conform with code requirements and resealed.

The safety should be checked annually, the type of check varying with the construction of the device, but generally it consists of tripping the governor by hand with the car operating at rated speed in the down direction with no load. With a type of safety which functions as the result of breaking or slackening of the hoist ropes, slack rope is obtained by mechanical means to cause the device to operate.

Car oil buffers (Fig. 8-5) should be checked every 2 years

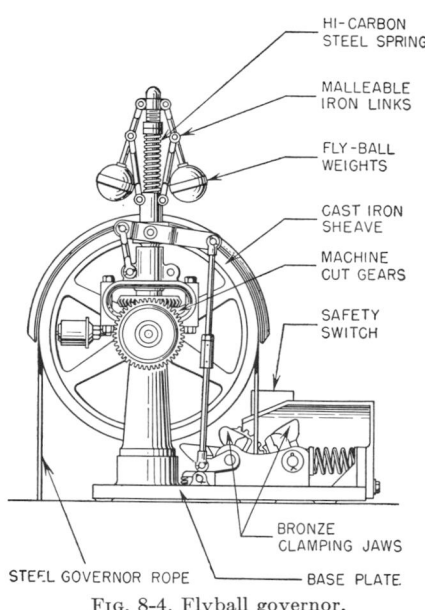

HI-CARBON
STEEL SPRING

MALLEABLE
IRON LINKS

FLY-BALL
WEIGHTS

CAST IRON
SHEAVE

MACHINE
CUT GEARS

SAFETY
SWITCH

BRONZE
CLAMPING JAWS

STEEL GOVERNOR ROPE

BASE PLATE

FIG. 8-4. Flyball governor.

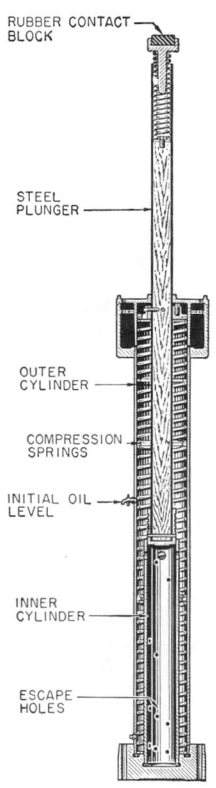

RUBBER CONTACT
BLOCK

STEEL
PLUNGER

OUTER
CYLINDER

COMPRESSION
SPRINGS

INITIAL OIL
LEVEL

INNER
CYLINDER

ESCAPE
HOLES

FIG. 8-5. Oil buffer (spring-return type).

for drum-type elevators and every 5 years for traction-type elevators by running the car onto its buffer at rated speed with rated load in the car.

Major repairs such as renewals of worm and gear, bearings, drive sheave, motors, and ropes require extra manpower and specialized knowledge of materials handling and techniques that can usually be provided only by large organizations or by companies specializing in elevator work.

Despite the preventive-maintenance program it is usually necessary on the more complicated equipment to make a periodic complete readjustment of the entire elevator plant. These adjustments should be made by a specialist if the elevator is to give optimum performance and the service for which the engineers designed it.

RECORDS

Records are of advantage, other than historically, only if they can be used to plan the work for repetitive operations or for pointing up the life and cost of renewable parts so as to obtain comparisons for future action.

The check chart, as shown in Fig. 8-2, is adequate for the purpose of recording examination work.

It is also important that a record be kept of service interruptions because they provide an index of possible weaknesses in the maintenance program, such as lack of knowledge by the maintenance man; repairs that may be needed; misuse by the employees or the public; or inferior materials.   A second service interruption for the same difficulty indicates that additional review of the situation and corrective measures are necessary.

For those items of maintenance that are replaced periodically as they wear or as difficulty occurs, such as ropes, brake linings, thrust bearings, and guide-shoe gibs, a record like that shown in Fig. 8-6 is of value in deciding whether the proper life is being obtained.

SPARE PARTS

In addition to the supply of lubricants required by the particular installation, wiping cloths of good absorbent quality and a nontoxic cleaning compound with a high flash point should be on hand.   Fuses and lamps should be available.

The spare-parts inventory for the individual elevator is dependent upon the type of usage, the degree of importance placed by the owner on the elevator's quick return to service, and the availability of manufacturer's facilities.

Small parts subject to damage, wear, and replacement at intervals, such as switch contacts, switch bushings, conductors or leads, motor brushes, guide-shoe gibs, door-pull straps, door chains, push-button or car-operating-device contacts, should be placed in a cabinet or locker in the machine room where they will be readily available if needed.   Then the maintenance man is more likely to make an immediate correction than to wait until the next time.

Other items which may be designated as spare parts, such as complete switches, relays, coils, resistors, capacitors, gland packing, thrust bearings, locks, and motors, must be decided upon by the individual plant.

TOOLS

The tools required in the maintenance of elevators are customarily of three types: (1) hand tools; (2) meters; and (3) tools required for heavy repairs.

Hand Tools: The following is a recommended basic kit of tools to be carried by the maintenance man.   The kit or toolbox should be solidly constructed with rounded corners, equipped with a tray for small items, a carrying handle, and shoulder strap.

1 pressure oil can (pistol grip), small
1 8-in. mill file, second cut
1 1-lb ball-peen hammer
1 pair 7-in. lineman's pliers
1 vise-grip wrench
1 pair channel-lock pliers
1 pair 6-in. needle-nose pliers with side cutters
1 4-in. caliper rule
1 6-ft rule
1 ½-in. cold chisel
1 offset screwdriver, four angles
1 two-cell flashlight
1 fuse puller
1 3-ft jumper with test clips attached
1 small hack saw
1 8-in. round file
1 1-in. round dust brush
1 3-in. screwdriver
1 6-in. screwdriver

1 stubby screwdriver
1 set of thickness gages
1 spin-tight socket-wrench set
3 small box wrenches
1 6-in. adjustable wrench
1 8-in. adjustable wrench
1 grease gun

Miscellaneous items

1 tube of Permatex No. 2
1 roll of Scotch electric tape
1 spool of binding wire
1 can soldering paste
1 ¼-lb string solder
1 small first-aid kit
1 tube Practi-Kreme
Sandpaper and sandpaper sticks
Miscellaneous screws, nuts, washers, cotter pins

NAME						CONTRACT NO.		
ADDRESS						SERVICE NO.		
MACH. SIZE		TYPE		LOCATION		CONTROLLER		
ROPED		CAPACITY		SPEED		A.C. OR D.C.		

RECORD OF ROPE RENEWAL

HOIST GOV. ETC.	NO.	SIZE	LENGTH	MATERIAL	CONST.	MAKE	INSTALLED	REMOVED	MO. OF SERVICE

REPAIRS TO OR RENEWALS OF WORMS AND GEARS

RENEWED GEAR	RENEWED WORM	CUT WORM	RENEWED BEARINGS	RENEWED THRUST	

GENERATOR AND MOTOR REPAIRS

RENEWED ARMATURE	REPAIRED ARMATURE	RENEWED FIELDS	REPAIRED FIELDS	REWOUND STATOR	REPAIRED ROTOR	RENEWED BEARINGS

MISCELLANEOUS REPAIRS

BRAKE LINING	BRAKE COIL	REGROOVE DRIVE SH.	RENEW DRIVE SH.			

Fig. 8-6. Record of replacements by which service life may be checked.

Meters and Gages: These are dependent upon the extent and nature of work the plant intends to perform.   For trouble shooting, an all-purpose test meter, such as Simpson or Weston, should be available.   Other items required for more extensive tests and adjustments include ammeter, voltmeter, megger, tachometer, and stop watch.   A set of groove gages for measuring rope grooves is also helpful.

Repair Tools: Here it is possible to make either a long or a short list.   Each job will require an analysis of the requirements as to hoisting and handling materials, the work that will be performed at the job site, and other factors, so only a few tools are listed here:

2-ton chain fall	Heavy-duty vacuum cleaner
½-ton puller	Wire-rope cutter
10-ton hydraulic jack	Insto-gas tank complete with hose and torch
Slings	½-in. electric drill
Landing blocks	Motor crank
2- by 10-in. clear spruce planks	Thrust nut wrench

HANDLING EMERGENCY CONDITIONS

The elevator maintenance mechanic should know how to handle emergency conditions swiftly and surely if and when they occur.   These conditions include the need for rapid entrance to the hoistway or pit; car stalled away from the landing; car safety device set; a person caught between car and hoistway; car or counterweight striking the buffers; loads that are too long to be placed in the car; handling heavy safes or similar equipment.

It is not feasible to describe the infinite variety of equipment that is in the field or may be in a particular plant.   The above is merely a listing of the most common problems which will face the elevator mechanic.

SAFETY FOR THE MAINTENANCE MAN

The elevator maintenance man should be thoroughly indoctrinated in the safe use of hand and power tools; housekeeping practices; proper methods of hand lifting, rigging, and hoisting materials; the use of ladders and stepladders; and how to climb stairs or fixed ladders.

He should be required to wear personal protective equipment such as proper clothing, safety shoes, and safety glasses at all times.   Other safety equipment required for special work, such as goggles, welder's mask, respirators, hand-protective creams, leather-palmed gloves, and hard hats, should be available.

Precautions to be followed while working in the machine room, in the hoistway, on top of the car, in the pit, and in the car are to be understood by the maintenance man so that he will be able to perform his functions safely.

CONCLUSION

A complete detailed description of elevator maintenance covering every piece of equipment and operation would fill a volume.   The subject has, therefore, been treated in a general way to indicate the scope of preventive maintenance and the importance of a regularly scheduled examination of the elevator equipment, not alone to obtain safe, dependable elevator service, but to extend the useful life of the elevator. The routine, while general, may be applied in connection with any elevator installation.

Chapter 9

VALVES

By THEODORE H. PYLE
The Lunkenheimer Company
Cincinnati, Ohio

Valves are simple in conception, and the various designs are developed from one idea. This idea consists of placing a disk over a seat opening in such a way that the resulting closure is tight. This one idea branches out into the three basic designs of valves, namely, globe valves, check valves, and gate valves. An exterior view of a standard bronze gate valve is shown in Fig. 9-1. Cross sections of the three basic designs are shown in Fig. 9-2. Each design places the disk over the seat in a different manner.

Valves usually are made of one of three different metals, for the following reasons:

Bronze, for temperatures up to 550°F. Bronze is corrosion-resistant to a large majority of fluids, and it is easy to cast and machine. Bronze valves are usually 3 in. and smaller in size.

Cast iron, for temperatures up to 450°F. Cast iron is cheaper than bronze, hence the cost of cast-iron valves over 2 in. in size is decidedly reduced. These cast-iron valves usually have either a bronze or all-iron trim. Valves with a bronze trim are called "I.B.B.M." (iron body, bronze-mounted) valves, while valves with an iron trim are called "A.I." (all-iron) valves. All-iron valves are used for solutions that attack bronze but not iron, such as caustic soda and concentrated sulfuric acid.

Cast steel, for temperatures up to 1050°F. Steel is stronger at high temperatures than bronze or cast iron.

In addition to three basic designs and three basic metals, valves are available in various steam-pressure ratings, as follows: 125, 150, 200, 300, 350, 400, 600, 900, 1,500, and 2,500 lb. For instance, there is a line of 125-lb bronze valves available in globe-

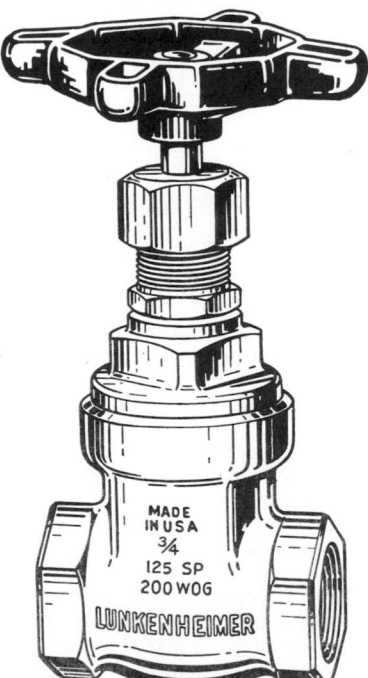

MADE
IN USA
¾
125 SP
200 WOG

LUNKENHEIMER

FIG. 9-1. Typical bronze gate valve.

valve, check-valve, and gate-valve design, sizes ¼ to 3 in.   There is also a line of
125-lb I.B.B.M. valves available in globe-valve, check-valve, and gate-valve design,
sizes 2 to 24 in.   The larger sizes, above 14 in., are in gate valves only.   These
I.B.B.M. valves are made with either screw ends or flange ends.   Similarly, there are
other lines of valves for other pressures.

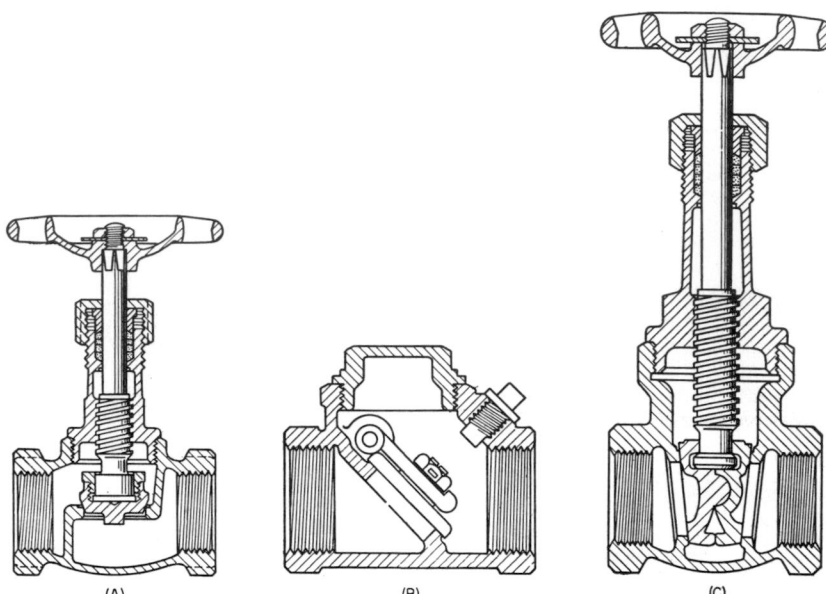

(A)   (B)   (C)

Fig. 9-2. Three basic designs: (A) globe; (B) check; (C) gate.

In order to understand the operation, application, and maintenance of valves, it
might be well if the definition of a valve were taken up first.

WHAT IS A VALVE?

For the purposes of this discussion, *a valve is a mechanical device usually used in connection with a pressure-containing vessel to stop completely or regulate flow.*

As a mechanical device, a valve should be properly installed and should be selected
to do the job expected of it.   It will then give long and lasting service before it starts
to leak or wear out.

When wear or leakage shows up, it will require some maintenance to restore the
valve to its original efficiency.   Wear occurs more frequently in globe or check valves,
and features are built into these valves to facilitate maintenance or renewal of parts.
Gate valves are installed where they are not operated very often, and hence do not
wear out quickly, and they do not as a rule have the maintenance features of globe and
check valves.

Mechanical devices should be operated occasionally.   If you store your automobile
and do not use it for 6 months, it is probable that the engine will not start, and it
should be gone over thoroughly before it is used.   Valves which are placed in lines and
then forgotten may become hard to operate.   This is especially so in hot-water lines,
hard-water lines, or any other lines in which there is a tendency to deposit scale or
solids.   Valves actually have been known to scale up or coke up so badly over a period
of years that they had to be disassembled and cleaned before they were usable.

The statement that a valve is used in *connection* with a pressure-containing vessel
deserves some thought.   There are various connections available, such as screw end,

flange end with flat or raised face, butt-welding end, socket-welding end, solder end, and union end. The selection of the proper end connection on a valve frequently eliminates a lot of maintenance.

As to *pressure-containing vessels*, these are of various kinds. The most common are:

1. A boiler for *steam*.
2. An air compressor and tank for *air*.
3. A water tower on an elevation for *water*.
4. A well containing *natural-gas* pressures, indicated by an oil derrick.

Each one of these media for conveying pressure—steam, water, air, and gas—requires consideration as to what valve to use. Each one requires different valve construction to function properly. Notice that each one of these media shows up in the pressure rating of a valve. Valves are rated by steam pressure (the SP rating), and water, oil, and gas (the WOG rating). The WOG rating usually is twice the steam-pressure rating. Why? Because the higher steam temperatures lower the tensile strength of the metal in the valve. At 150 lb pressure, saturated steam has a temperature of 366°F. Water at room temperature uses the full tensile strength of the metal. By considering the temperature at which the valve is to operate, the cost of installation can frequently be lowered by using the WOG rating of the valve on cold lines.

The statement that a valve is used to *stop completely* or *regulate flow* deserves consideration, as it indicates when a globe valve or when a gate valve is to be used. A globe valve is used to regulate flow and a gate valve should be used where the service requires the valve to be in full open or closed position.

PROPER INSTALLATION OF GLOBE AND GATE VALVES

When an ordinary globe valve is used to regulate flow, throttling results and wears the seat and the disk. After use, the valve does not close tightly. For tight closing it is better to use two valves on the line, one for throttling and one that is either full open or closed. A typical case is an air nozzle on the end of an air hose. The hose is fastened to the air supply through a cock. The cock is either open or closed; the air nozzle is used continuously. The air nozzle may develop leakage, so the cock is closed each night and opened each morning. It closes tightly with no leakage.

Also, due to the construction of the valve, a globe valve is recommended when the valve is to be operated frequently. The disk in a globe valve touches the seat only at the instant of closing. In a gate valve, the disk travels over the full face of the seat, and consequently sliding wear will develop. Therefore, in all good engineering specifications, you will find, "Globe valves are to be used on throttling service or where the valve is to be opened and closed frequently. Gate valves are to be used for full-flow conditions, or where the valve is normally in an open or closed condition." This is amply illustrated in the Fig. 9-3.

BRONZE GLOBE VALVES

After the theory of valves, the next consideration should be design, application, and maintenance. In Fig. 9-4 are shown five cross sections of various globe valves, each a little different in design. Notice that the seat of all globe valves is directly opposite the top opening in the body. This means it is easy to get at the seat for inspection, maintenance, or repair.

Threaded-bonnet Globe Valve. It has a pressure rating of 125 lb SP and is designed for use on inexpensive installations where the valve is not used frequently. Contractors often use it in low-pressure heating systems and on plumbing lines. *Maintenance* is very limited. Due to the construction of the threaded bonnet, it is practically impossible to regrind the valve. This valve can be repacked while under pressure by turning the valve stem full open.

Union-bonnet Regrinding Valve. It is made in two different pressure ratings, 200 lb and 350 lb SP. It was originally designed for easy *maintenance*, without removal from the line.   It can be reground and repaired.   A small metal plate clamped between the end of the stem and the disk is used to prevent the disk from swiveling on the stem during the regrinding operation.   The handwheel is used for the tool, the bonnet lip is used for a guide in the body neck.   Valve-reseating tools, which can be obtained in sets from any industrial-supply house, can be used to dress up the seat if disk and seat are too worn for regrinding.   The hardness of the bronze seat and disk is 85 Brinell, which makes the use of the reseating tool possible.   The valve can be repacked under pressure.

GLOBE THROTTLED

GATE WIDE OPEN

GATE THROTTLED

FIG. 9-3. Diagrams of flow condition.   These diagrams illustrate the answer to the question as to where you use globe valves and where gate valves.   Globe valves are used to throttle flow.   Note that the flow is around the entire periphery of the disk, giving even wear. Globe valves are easily repaired or reground.   Gate valves are used when you want unobstructed flow and little line loss.   The illustrations show the uneven wear when gate valves are misused for throttling.

Plug-type "Renewo" Globe Valve.   It is designed for severe throttling, drain, drip, water-column blowdown, and other services demanding high resistance to destructive action on seat bearings.   *Maintenance* consists of renewing the seat and disk.   Because of their hardness, these valves present quite a regrinding problem by hand.   They are cone-shaped and are always installed in pairs.   Their hardness is 500 Brinell.   The valve can be repacked under pressure.   It is made in three pressure ratings, 200 lb, 300 lb, and 350 lb SP.

600-Brinell Flat-seat Globe Valve.   This valve has a pressure rating of 150 lb SP. There is practically no *maintenance* on the valve except for repacking.   It is of revolutionary new design and will give extremely long life and trouble-free service.   The flat seats have never been known to show leakage, and the stem is of a material that has shown practically no wear with over 100,000 openings and closings of the valve.   It is useful on steam, air, water, oil, gas, or other media, and will be equally tight on all of these services.   A newer valve has a pressure rating of 200 lb SP.

Nonmetallic-disk Globe Valve.   This valve is one of the most popular globe valves because of its easy maintenance.   It has a pressure rating of 150 lb SP.   It is known as a nonmetallic-disk or composition-disk globe valve.   *Maintenance* consists principally of renewing the disk as it wears out.   It can be easily removed from the disk

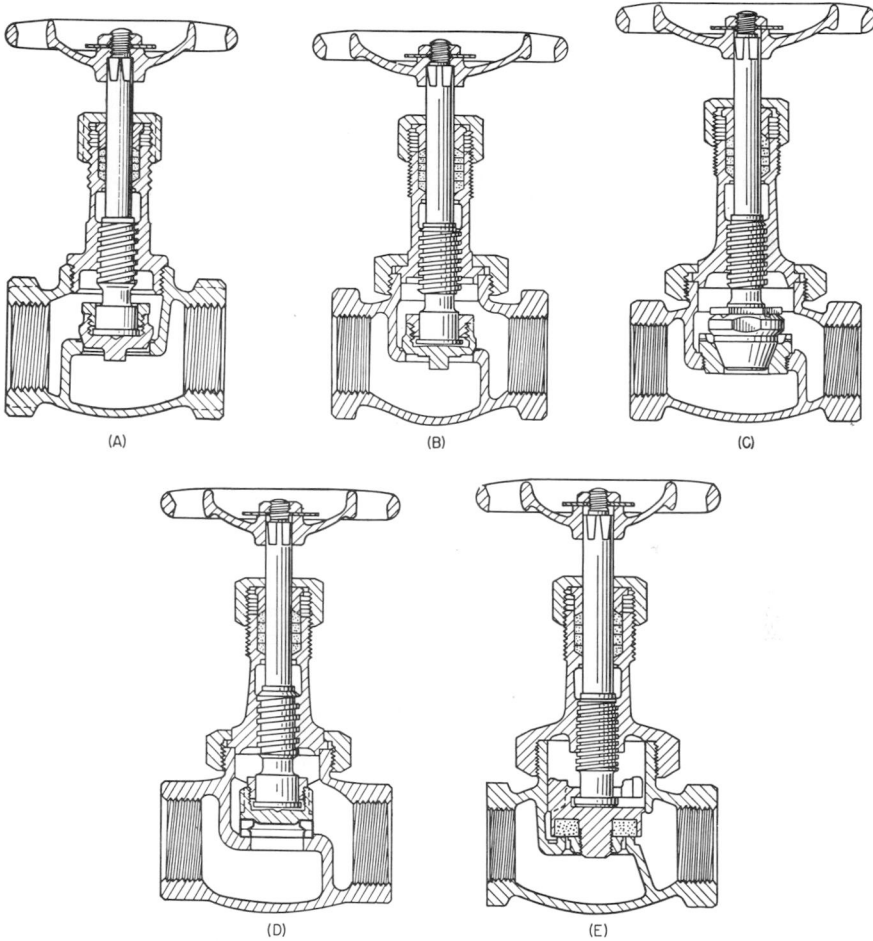

Fig. 9-4. Bronze globe valves: (*A*) threaded-bonnet globe.   (*B*) Union-bonnet regrinding globe; (*C*) "Renewo" globe, plug type; (*D*) flat-seat globe, 600 Brinell; (*E*) nonmetallic-disk globe.

holder, and a new disk inserted.   Three kinds of disks are available: one for steam, one for cold water and air, and one for oils and gasoline.   If the raised seat becomes worn or grooved, it can be resurfaced with a reseating tool.   Brinell hardness is 85. The valve can be repacked under pressure.

BRONZE CHECK VALVES

Check valves are the guardians against back flow in a pipeline.   They are entirely automatic in action and are of various designs, some of which are illustrated in Fig. 9-5.

They fall into two general groups, commonly known as "swing check" valves and "lift check" valves.   A swing check valve is usually used where full flow is desired.   A lift check valve is usually used on air or gases, or when the operation of the check valve is quite frequent.   A discussion of check valves and their maintenance follows.

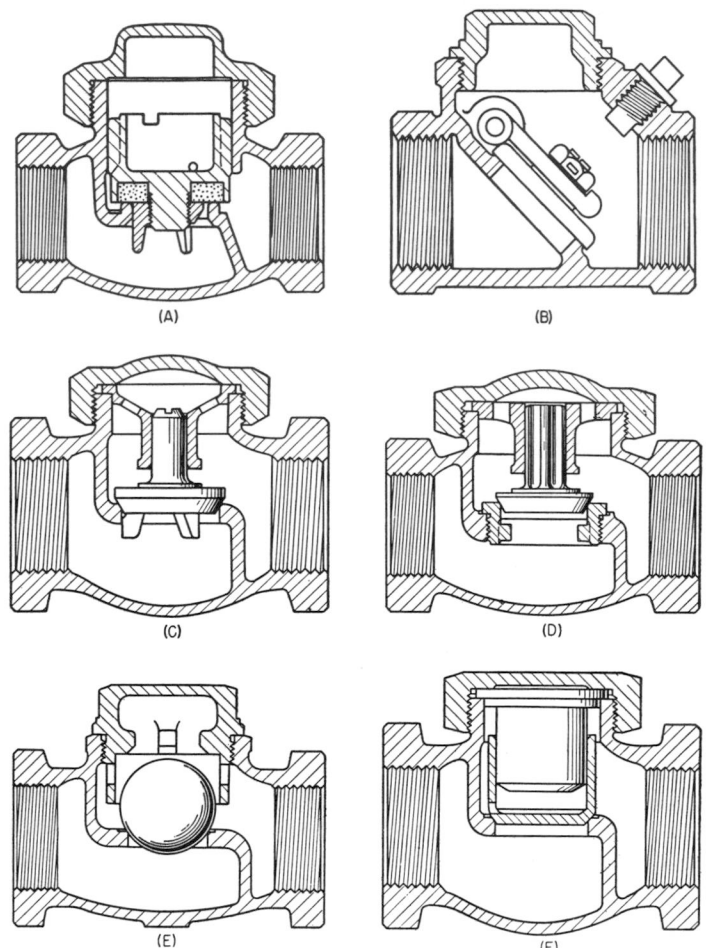

FIG. 9-5. Bronze check valves: (*A*) N-M-D lift-check nonmetallic disk; (*B*) swing-check regrinding seat; (*C*) lift-check regrinding seat; (*D*) lift-check renewable seat; (*E*) ball check; (*F*) air-compressor check.

Nonmetallic-disk Lift Check Valve.   The seat is rounded to give line contact on the disk, in comparison to the flat seat in a similar globe valve.   The line contact is necessary, as there is usually little pressure to hold the disk to its seat.   Sometimes a spring is inserted to act on the disk to increase this pressure.   *Maintenance* of this valve consists of renewing the disk when necessary, smoothing the upper and lower disk guides when necessary, and removing grooves or worn places from the seat with a reseating tool.

Swing Check Valve.   Swing check valves are probably the most popular and the most used of all check valves.   They can be installed in either horizontal or vertical lines.   *Maintenance* consists of regrinding the disk to its seat by applying a screwdriver to the slot in the top of the disk and using a grinding compound.   If carrier pin, side plugs, or disk carrier become worn, they can be easily and inexpensively replaced with new parts.   These maintenance suggestions apply also to I.B.B.M. swing check valves.

Regrinding Lift Check Valve.   This is a good check valve in that it has both upper and lower guides to guide the disk to its seat.   All parts are renewable except the seat, which is integral.   *Maintenance* of this valve consists of regrinding the disk to its seat by means of the screwdriver slot in the disk stem.   Brinell hardness of seat and disk is 85 Brinell, allowing for the use of a valve-reseating tool.

"Renewo" Lift Check Valve.   This check valve has renewable seats and disks of nickel alloy, Brinell hardness 185.   The disk has only an upper guide, so it is not as accurate in seating as the regrinding lift check valve.   *Maintenance* consists of regrinding the disk to its seat or replacing it if too badly worn.

Ball Check Valve.   Some people consider the ball check valve as the ideal check valve.   But in the opinion of valve men, it should be used only on viscous or heavy liquids, such as varnish, molasses, muddy water, or liquids containing solids.   Any of these would clog the mechanism of the other check valves.   There is little *maintenance* on a ball check valve, as there is no means of holding the ball for regrinding the seats. This ball must be as perfect a sphere as possible, and the seat must be perfectly round.

Air-compressor Check Valve.   This check valve is especially designed for this service, which is the hardest known for check valves.   An ordinary check valve opens and closes once at each revolution of the compressor.   Swing check valves have been known to disintegrate in 5 minutes with this frequency of operation.

The air-compressor check valve shown. (Fig. 9-5f) incorporates a stainless-steel disk operating over a bronze plug.   This plug dampens the movement of the disk so the disk opens when the compressor starts, and stays open until the compressor shuts down.   The disk then eases itself to its seat and is held tight by back pressure.   Carry-over oil in the air line helps this check valve in numerous ways.   There is practically no *maintenance* on this valve.   All parts are renewable except the seat, which can be reseated.   It is best to install the valve as far from the compressor and as near the receiving tank as possible.   This will reduce pulsations acting on the disk.

BRONZE GATE VALVES

Gate valves are by far the most popular and the most frequently used of the three types of valves—globe, check, and gate.   As their correct installation calls for usage where they are opened and closed only infrequently, they last a long time and do not require much maintenance.   If a gate valve is operated over ten times a day every day, it will quickly wear out, and a globe valve should be substituted for it.   The wear will be found on the downstream faces of the seat and the disk, because the line pressure forces all the wear on these surfaces.   The upstream faces frequently will be found to be in good condition.   Very often, worn gate valves can be reversed 180° and they will be as good as new.   Gate valves should be installed with the stem vertical if at all possible.   Installation with the stem in a horizontal position is permissible, but is not as good.

The three gate valves shown at the top of Fig. 9-6 are kindred valves, in that all use the same body.   The first one shown is the most popular valve known.   It is a standard 125-lb double-disk bronze gate valve with rising stem.

Double-wedge-disk Rising-stem Gate Valve.   The double wedges are of ball-and-socket construction.   They readily adjust themselves to the taper seats, insuring a tight valve.   It should be evident that line strains could distort the angle of the taper seats in the bronze body.   Slight distortion will not affect the tightness of double-disk valves.   The rising stem indicates whether the valve is open or closed.   There is little *maintenance* to be done on a gate valve.   It should be taken apart occasionally over the years, and cleaned; especially, valves on hot-water lines.   The valve can be repacked under pressure by opening the valve to the limit of the stem travel.

Solid-wedge-disk Rising-stem Gate Valve.   This valve is used on heavy liquids such as molasses or varnish or any other liquids that would tend to make ball-and-socket disks inoperative.   The solid-wedge-disk bronze gate valve is not as tight on

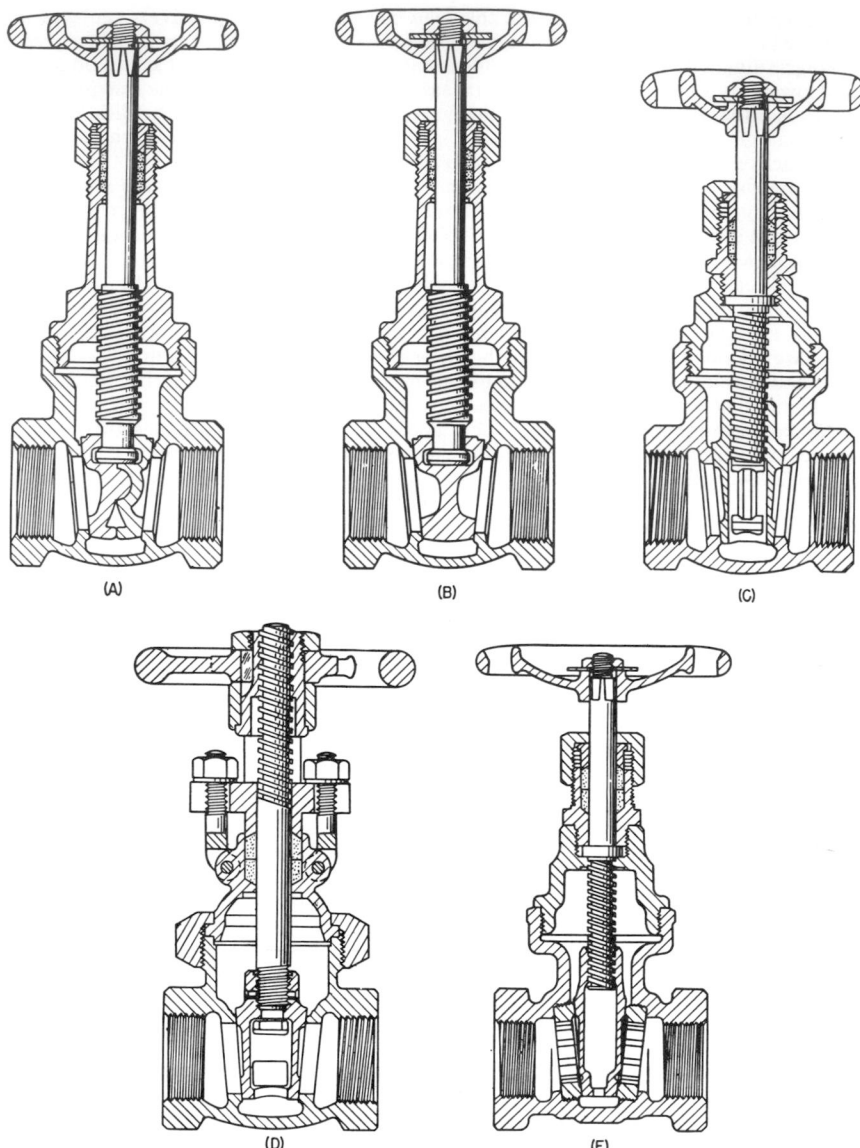

FIG. 9-6. Bronze gate valves: (A) rising-stem, double-wedge disk; (B) solid-wedge-disk, rising stem; (C) nonrising stem, single-wedge disk; (D) outside screw and yoke, union bonnet, single-wedge disk; (E) nonrising stem, single-wedge disk, renewable seat rings.

thin liquids or gases as is the double-wedge-disk.   *Maintenance* is the same as for the double-wedge-disk rising-stem gate valve.

Single-wedge-disk Nonrising-stem Gate Valve.   This valve is popular with contractors, and is extensively used on marine service.   The nonrising-stem feature allows the valve to be used in cramped spaces where overhead construction interferes with the operation of a rising-stem valve. *Maintenance* is the same as for the double-wedge-disk rising-stem gate valve.

Small Outside Screw-and-yoke Rising-stem Gate Valve. Note that this valve has a union bonnet and a single-wedge disk. It is required by code on the lines leading to the top and bottom connections on the water column of a boiler. It must be locked in open position by means of a chain and padlock, so there is no wear on it. It is an emergency valve; hence its *maintenance* consists in test operation and inspection to see that it is in working condition. It can become limed up rather quickly; especially the valve on the lower line, as this line contains hot water.

Renewable-disk-and-seat Bronze Gate Valve. The valve shown has a nonrising stem and renewable nickel-alloy seats and disks. It is popular in the chemical industry, as the seats and disks can be renewed as they become unsatisfactory in operation. The valve should be removed from the line during this repair. Gate valves are not like globe valves, which can be repaired while on the line.

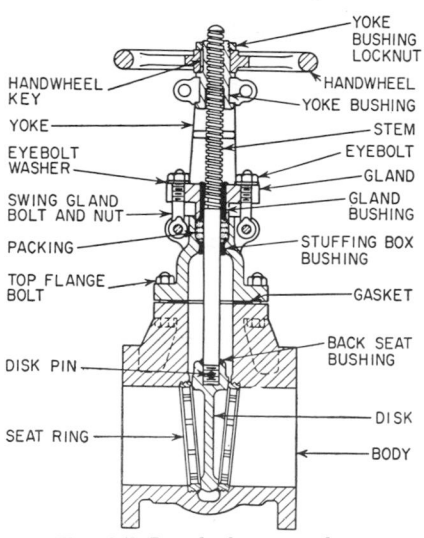

YOKE BUSHING LOCKNUT
HANDWHEEL KEY
HANDWHEEL
YOKE BUSHING
YOKE
STEM
EYEBOLT WASHER
EYEBOLT
GLAND
SWING GLAND BOLT AND NUT
GLAND BUSHING
PACKING
STUFFING BOX BUSHING
TOP FLANGE BOLT
GASKET
BACK SEAT BUSHING
DISK PIN
DISK
SEAT RING
BODY

FIG. 9-7. Iron-body gate valve.

IRON-BODY GATE VALVES AND STEEL GATE VALVES

A 6-in. iron-body bronze-mounted (I.B.B.M.), outside Screw-and-yoke (O.S. & Y.), flanged-end (F.E.) gate valve is the most popular in size and design of all the large valves (see Fig. 9-7). Other sizes are available from 2 to 24 in. and larger, and in screw ends in sizes 6 in. and smaller. This gate valve is included here due to its popularity.

The *maintenance* of the valve follows commonsense lines. The stem threads should be kept lubricated and free from dirt. When the valve is wide open for a long period of time, the exposed stem threads should be protected by a light sheet-iron tube placed over them.

To repack the valve, move the swing gland bolts out of the way. The gland is raised and rests on the ledges provided for that purpose. The stuffing box is then accessible for renewal of the packing. Each ring of new packing should be compressed by the gland before another ring is added. The valve can be repacked under pressure.

Should the downstream seat and disk become scored, the upstream seats will frequently be found to be in good condition. Reverse the valve 180° and the valve will be as good as new.

Should it become necessary to replace the seat rings, remove the valve from the line and prepare a correct-size pipe with square notches to fit the lugs in the seat rings. As the pipe with lugs is twisted (by means of a bar), tap the body smartly with a hammer to help loosen the ring. Clean all threads and seating surfaces with a wire brush before installing new rings. Graphite or pipe dope can be used. A new disk should be installed with new rings. It may have to be lapped in.

The *maintenance of steel gate valves* is very similar to the maintenance of this iron-body gate valve.

VARIATIONS OF BASIC VALVES

In Fig. 9-8 are shown valves of different designs. Figure 9-9 shows different methods of operation (breech-lock steel gate valves with butt-welding ends are used in high-pressure, high-temperature steam and water service in power plants). Figure 9-10 shows different applications. Figures 9-11 and 9-12 show butterfly and ball valves.

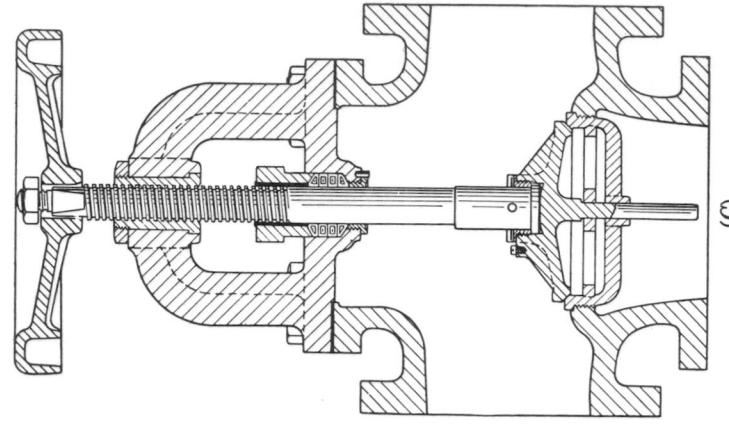

(C)

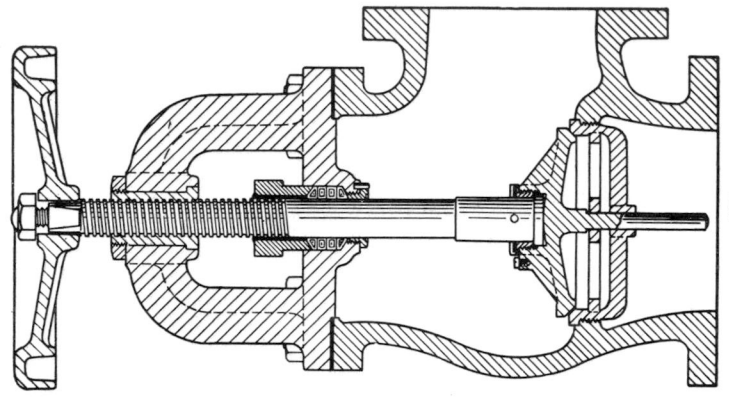

(B)

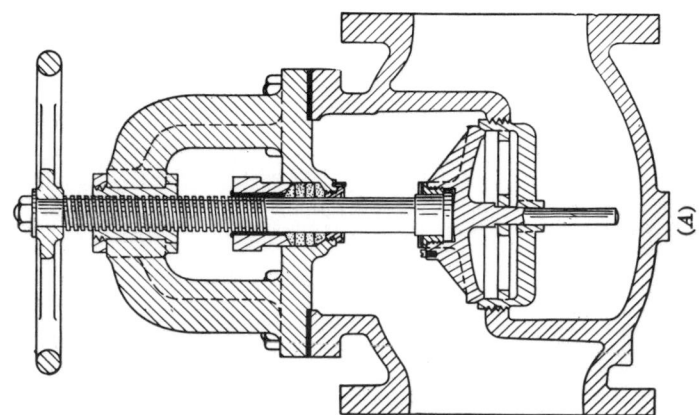

(A)

FIG. 9-8. Variations of basic valves as to design: (A) globe; (B) angle; (C) cross.

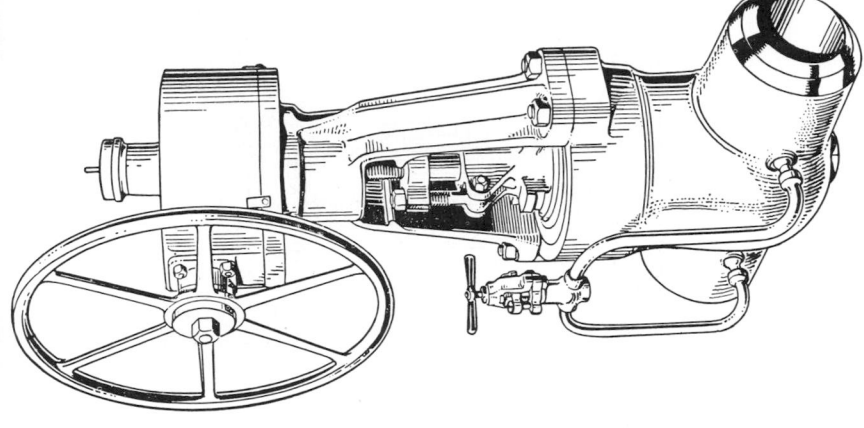

(C)

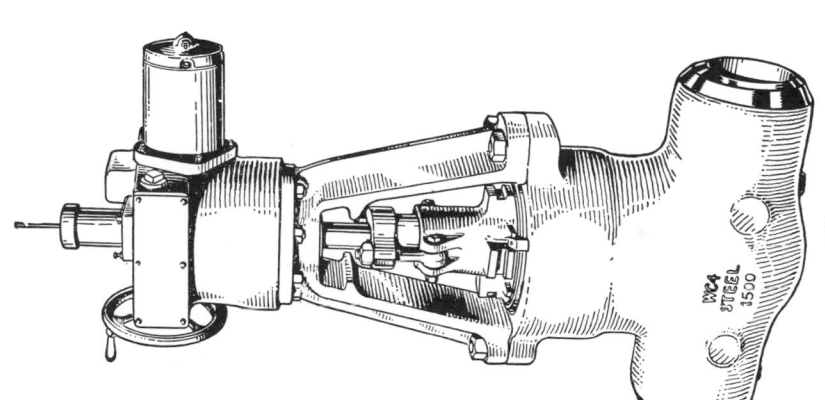

(B)

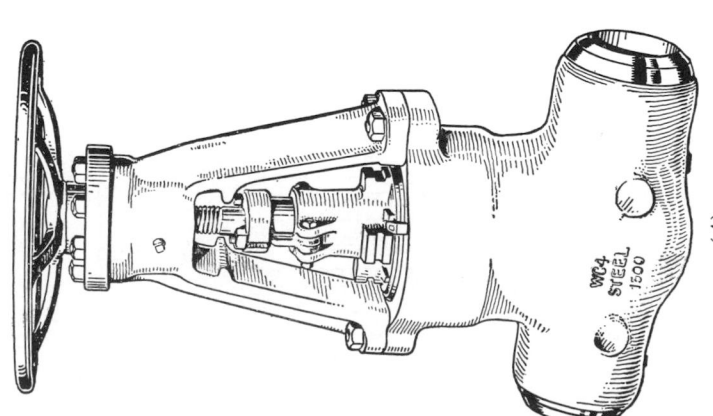

(A)

FIG. 9-9. Variations of basic valves as to methods of operation: (A) breech lock, hand-operated; (B) breech lock, motor-operated; (C) breech lock with by-pass, bevel-gear-operated.

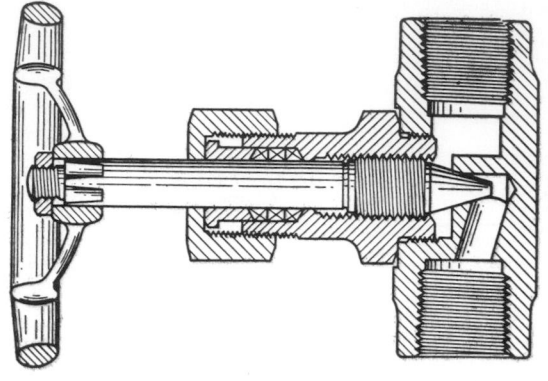

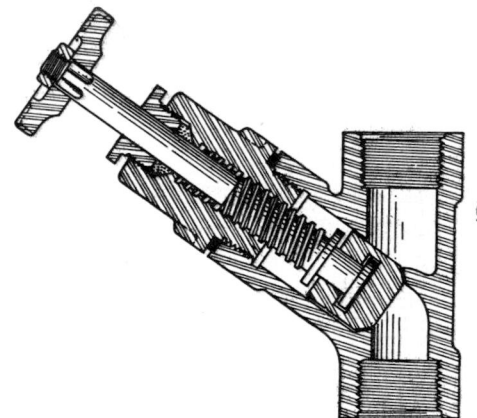

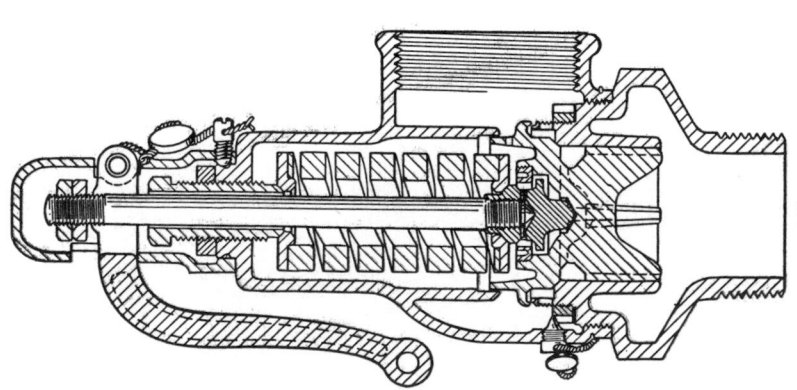

FIG. 9-10. Variations of basic valves as to applications: (A) pop safety (a spring-loaded angle valve); (B) Y valve (made of plastic); (C) bar-stock needle valve (made from steel bar stock).

Ball Valves. The ball valve is an adaptation of the taper-seat plug cock. Instead of the taper plug, a perfect sphere with a hole for passageway is used. The ball is rotated on a renewable seat of Teflon. The ball valve is quicker in action and tighter on shutoff than a conventional gate or globe valve; it is a combination of the perfect sphere rotating on a practically frictionless seat. Ball valves are used in many services where conventional valves would have been used formerly.

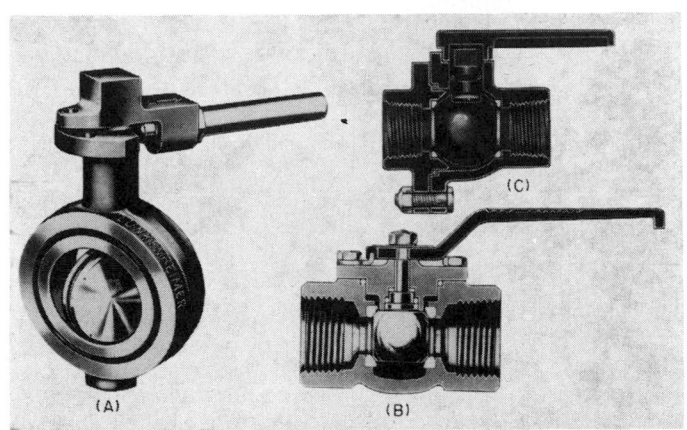

FIG. 9-11. Variations of basic valves (cocks): (A) butterfly valve with O-ring disk seal; (B) top-entry ball valve; (C) end-entry ball valve.

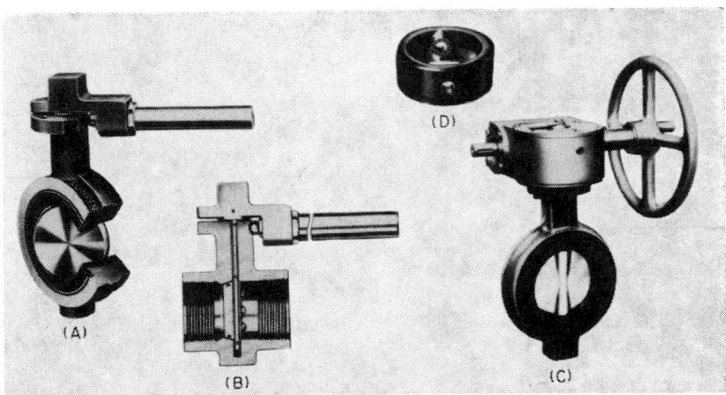

FIG. 9-12. Variations of butterfly valves: (A) wafer-type with bonded rubber lining; (B) body-type with screw ends, O-ring disk seal; (C) wafer-type with replaceable resilient seat, gear operated; (D) replaceable resilient seat.

Actually, a ball valve is a gate valve with a renewable seat and a renewable disk. Ball valves are available in many valve metals, with many sealing elastomers, and in many designs. They come in sizes from $\frac{1}{4}$ in. up to 24 in. and larger. The two major designs differ in method of getting the ball into the body. One design is called "top entry," and the other is called "end entry." Each has its advantages. The valve with top entry can be repaired without removing it from the line, while the end-entry valve offers a built-in union, which sometimes is desirable. The end-entry design usually results in a valve in which the flow can be in one direction only. When the flow is cut off, the line pressure forces the ball against the downstream seat, in an action similar to that of a gate valve. When the ball is in the open position, it is held in place by a spring against the upstream seat. In the top-entry design, the ball is sprung between the two Teflon seats, and thus no springs are required. The flow can be in either direction.

A ball valve, therefore, has these advantages:

1. It offers the unobstructed flow of a gate valve.
2. It offers the bottle-tight shutoff of a globe valve.
3. It offers the quick-acting, quarter-turn operation of a cock.

The maintenance of ball valves is simple. Should the valve show leakage, the seats, seals, and balls can be replaced easily, thus giving you a new ball valve.

Butterfly Valves. Basically, there are two types of butterfly valves. There is the *body type*, which generally has pipe-threaded connections for connecting to pipe lines. And there is the *wafer type*, which is bolted into the pipe line between standard ASA Class 125 plain-faced cast-iron flanges or ASA Class 150 steel flanges.

There are distinct advantages to butterfly valves:

1. They are compact, and their face-to-face dimensions are very short. For example, a 6-in. wafer-type valve measures $2\frac{1}{8}$ in. face-to-face and weighs approximately 27 lb.
2. They are quick-closing. A quarter turn suffices from the open to closed position. Handles are used on small valves, and gear actuators are recommended on 8-in. and larger valves.
3. The pressure rating generally is 150 psi WOG. The valves are economical with regard to cost, installation, maintenance, and repair.

Butterfly valves may be obtained with various metal inserts, trims, and seating materials or elastomers, depending upon the specific installation. Proper selection can be made through knowledge of the pressure, temperature, and fluid to be handled. They may be obtained with bonded resilient seat, replaceable resilient seat, or metal seat with O ring inserted in the disk for tight closing.

For throttling service, the rubber-lined valve generally is recommended. Throttling handles are obtainable which operate in notches, each 10° in a 90° arc. A lock which engages any of these notches is built into the handle, thus preventing the disk from moving from its desired throttling position. Gear operators are obtainable also and can be used for infinite throttling positions.

Butterfly valves find applications in most categories where valves are used. They are used extensively in the gathering lines in oil country installations. They are also used throughout industry and for all fluids with which they are compatible.

The maintenance of butterfly valves is quite simple. No lubrication is necessary until such time as stem O rings need replacement. Disks and stems are readily replaceable, as are disk O rings and replaceable resilient seats. Replacement of the bonded resilient seat is a factory job; but usually when that type of seat deteriorates, it is more economical to purchase a complete new valve, since the cost of butterfly valves is low.

ORDERING SPARE PARTS

Whenever it is necessary or advisable to order spare or replacement parts, the first problem that arises is to identify the part, and the second problem is to identify the valve.

Identifying the Parts. It is well to specify the correct name of the part wanted; and for this reason, most valve catalogs carry illustrations naming the parts. This type of information is shown in Fig. 9-13 in the cross sections of the gate and globe valves, with the size and figure number being a necessary part of the information. If you have a valve catalog of one manufacturer and are ordering parts for another make of valve, specify the catalog and page number you are using to identify the parts. The names of each part of a valve are not identical with all the various valve manufacturers.

Most valve catalogs also show exploded views of their valves with each part illustrated. This makes it a little easier to identify the part desired. This type of information is shown in Fig. 9-14 for a swing check valve.

Identifying the Valve. Most modern valves carry a name plate, which makes it easy to identify the manufacturer and figure number. Name plates originated with

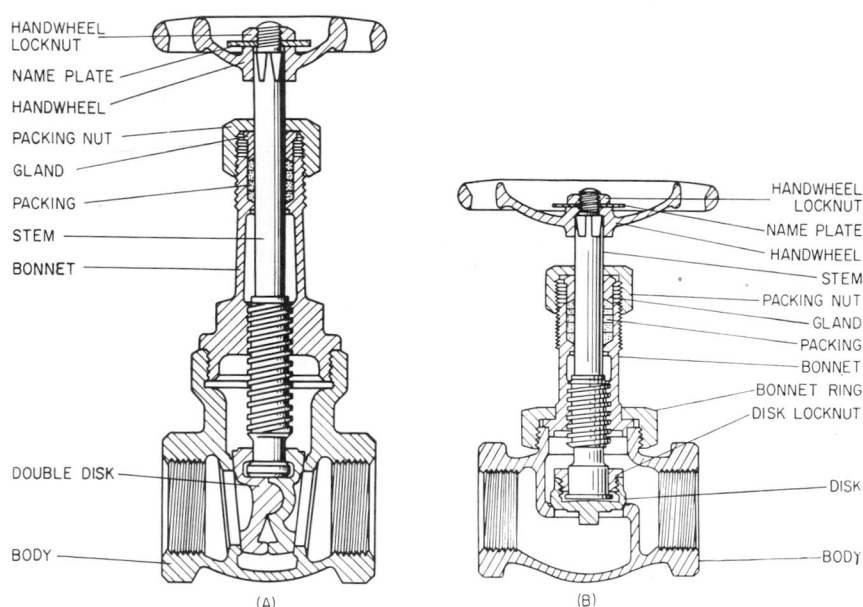

FIG. 9-13. Parts identification: (*A*) rising-stem, double-wedge-disk gate valve; (*B*) union-bonnet regrinding globe valve.

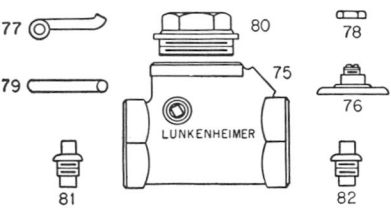

FIG. 9-14. Ordering parts. Illustrated is bronze regrinding swing check valve, Figures 554 and 596 in maker's catalogue (complete valves on page 24 of same). Orders should specify part number, size, and figure number of the valve for which part is intended. Part No. 75, bodies, screwed; 76, disks; 77, disk carriers; 78, disk locknuts; 79, disk carrier pins; 80, caps; 81, side plugs; 82, top plugs.

steel valves; but after the close of World War II, they were placed on bronze and iron valves, also. Unfortunately, many of the valves without name plates have not worn out, and we are forced to identify the valve in some other way. If the valve is covered with insulation, it will be necessary to remove this to view the markings on the body.

There you will probably find the name of the manufacturer, the size of the valve, and the steam pressure, and other ratings. This information may be on both sides of the body. The figure number is rarely found on the body casting, as the same casting is often used to make valves carrying various figure numbers.

Copy all this information and include it with the order, which should specify the metal the valve is made of, a brief description together with the type of valve (globe, check, or gate), and the type of ends (screw or flange).   In the case of flanged valves, the type of face (whether flat or raised face), the diameter of the flange, the diameter of the bolt circle, the size of the bolts or bolt holes, and finally the face-to-face dimension of the flanges should be given.   If possible, give the approximate date of the installation of the valve.   Valve designs and details and figure numbers change over the years, and all of the above information suggested will be helpful, especially in the case of an old valve.   Sometimes it may be necessary to call in a representative of the valve manufacturer to help identify an old valve.

Writing the Order.   In writing the order, it is well to specify first the part wanted, and let the other information follow, thus:

> 1 Disk only, Part 76,
> for $1\frac{1}{2}''$ Lunkenheimer Fig. 554, 200-lb S.P. bronze swing check
> valve, screw ends.   Part shown on page 450, Catalog 53.

Frequently repair-parts orders read, "One $1\frac{1}{2}$-in., Fig. 554, disk only."   This will probably result in a complete valve being shipped, unless some well-informed order checker scans the order.

RECOMMENDED PIPING PRACTICE

Clean the inside of the pipe before installing or repairing a valve.   This will remove rust, scale, welding beads, and dirt, which could be carried into a valve and cause trouble.   Do not remove flange or thread protectors from the valve until ready for installation.   When threading pipe, do not cut the threads too long.   Long threads allow the pipe to enter the valve too deeply and distort the seat.   Apply pipe dope to male threads only when making up a threaded joint.   When installing a screw-end valve, do not employ enough force to distort the valve body.   Use a crescent wrench or monkey wrench on the valve end that is being made up.   Employ a pipe wrench on pipe only.   Allow a new valve to warm up gradually.   Packing glands are assembled hand-tight at the factory, and on installation should be tightened only enough to prevent leakage.

On open-end and drain lines, it is recommended that globe valves be installed with the pressure on top of the disk.

Finally, it is extremely important that a valve be closed tightly by hand only.   Do not use a wrench or persuader.   Dirt under the disk can usually be flushed out by operating the valve a number of times.   A valve that is cracked open is subject to the most severe wire drawing or throttling conditions possible, decreasing valve life and increasing maintenance.

Chapter 10

WIRE ROPE

By C. H. Layton
Chief Engineer
Wire Rope Divisions
American Chain & Cable Co., Inc.
Wilkes-Barre, Pa.

When it receives proper care and attention, wire rope is a faithful servant that gives generously in long life, easy handling and installing, safe operation, and economy. To know how to use wire rope correctly, one should know what it is and what types are available.   To get the most use from wire rope, the right type must be selected for the particular job to be done.   The wrong type, no matter how carefully used, will not give the service available from the proper rope.

Wire ropes are designed to meet specific service requirements as defined by operating conditions and usage.   Figure 10-1 shows cross sections demonstrating constructions. Figure 10-2 shows the differences between lays and other details of construction.   The following grades are available:

Iron.   A low-carbon steel with a tensile-strength range up to 100,000 psi.
Mild Plow Steel.   A medium-carbon steel with a range to 200,000 psi.
Plow Steel.   Slightly higher carbon content than mild plow steel and tensile strength of 240,000 psi.
Improved Plow Steel.   A high-carbon steel with tensile strength of 260,000 psi. Weights and breaking strengths of improved plow steel wire ropes are given in Tables 10-1, 10-2, and 10-3.
V.H.S. (Very-high-strength).   A newly introduced grade of wire rope 15 per cent higher in breaking strength than the strongest previous wire rope.

There are more than 100 wire-rope constructions.   Fortunately, the problem of selection has been simplified by the manufacturers in their recommendations booklets, with which the user can be assured of getting the best rope for his needs.   Most manufacturers have the same recommendations for the same services, and any differences usually are not too far apart.

In general, wire rope can be classified in this way:

1. The coarser constructions and the least flexible can be put under the 6 × 7 heading. The first numeral designates the number of strands, and the second numeral the number of wires per strand.   Ropes of these types are used for operations where abrasion is the principal factor to combat, and for guy rope, where strength and price are the prime requisites.   They also find considerable use in water- and oil-well drilling operations as sand lines.

2. Flexible wire rope, or the 6 × 19 classification. Under this heading are all the ropes whose individual strands contain more than 12 wires but less than 29. Most of the tonnage falls into this group for use in mining, contracting, marine, oil, industrial, and logging work.
3. Extra-flexible wire rope, or the 6 × 37 classification. Wire rope in this group contains more than 29 wires per strand but not over 46 wires. These ropes usually are used as crane ropes, large-shovel ropes, for winch lines, and in other services where flexibility is an important factor.

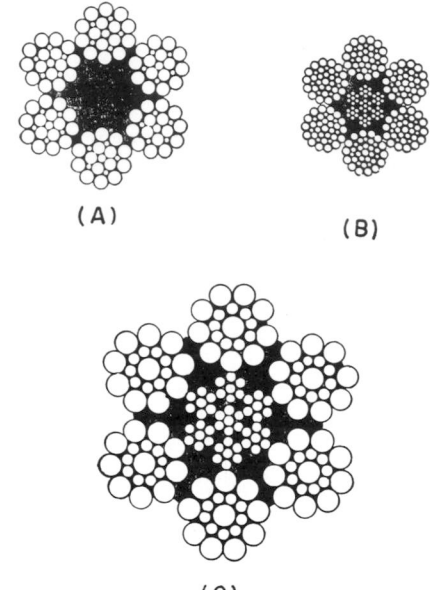

(A)   (B)

(C)

FIG. 10-1. Wire-rope construction. It is determined by the number of strands and the number of wires in each strand. The ropes illustrated have six strands with 21, 36, and 19 wires in each strand and are known as (A) 6 × 21 filler wire, (B) 6 × 36 Seale, and (C) 6 × 19 Seale, respectively. First figure gives number of strands; next two figures give number of wires per strand. Filler wire means that small wires are run into the interstices between outer and inner wires of strands. Different structures are obtained by changing the number of strands, the number of wires per strand, and the arrangement of the wires.

Under each general classification there are several constructions, each of which has a geometrical pattern of wire arrangement which qualifies that particular rope for a specific usage requirement. In this connection, and in order to simplify the product for the purchaser, the wire-rope industry recently has agreed to a standard nomenclature for the various constructions. The new system includes in the title the number of strands and the number of wires per strand, along with symbols for construction differences. The classification 6 × 19FW has been changed to 6 × 25FW, and 6 × 37FW has become 6 × 46FW.

Each grade, construction, and size is available with the following types of centers:

1. *Fiber Core.* This type of core can be made from sisal, manila, or cotton fibers. Its appearance is about the same as that of an ordinary hemp-fiber rope, although in features of construction and lubrication it will differ somewhat. For years this type of core, because of its wearing qualities and resiliency, was the most popular wire-rope center. New conditions and more severe requirements have lessened the demand.

2. *Independent Wire-rope Core* (IWRC).　This type of wire-rope center is actually a fabricated wire rope made specifically for use as a wire-rope core.　It increases the rope strength by at least $7\frac{1}{2}$ per cent over the rope with fiber core, and offers greater resistance to crushing and distortion.　Wire ropes with IWRC are used on all installations where strength and ruggedness of construction are desirable.　They have approximately the same flexibility as fiber-core wire rope and can be used interchangeably with it without changing sheaves or drums.

3. *Plastic Core.*　This is the newest type of center, and is made from polyvinyl chloride compounds.　It has gained considerable favor because of its resistance to practically all fluids.　It will not absorb or retain moisture.　Wire ropes with plastic cores have the same rated breaking strength as ropes with fiber cores.

With this background, and remembering that wire rope is composed of wire made from high-carbon steel of high tensile strength, consider its care and use.

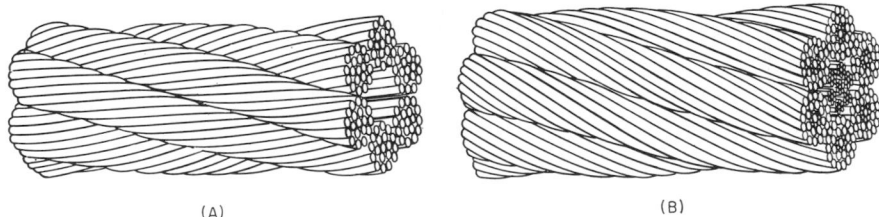

(A)　　　　　　　　　　　　　　　　　　(B)

Fig. 10-2. Wire-rope differences.　(*A*) Regular lay with fiber center where strands are "laid up," or manufactured around a center of hemp or jute fibers.　(*B*) Lang lay, with center composed of an individual wire rope, commonly termed a "steel core."　Hard fiber cores are used for maximum elasticity under repeated loads.　Independent cores are used for greater strength; they are 7.5 per cent stronger than similar wire-core ropes and offer maximum resistance to crushing.

Wire rope is made to do the unusual.　It will transmit great force through all planes and angles.　Because the work required of it is heavy and rugged and, in its normal operation it is subject to overloads, abuse, and abrasive wear, the service life of wire rope is definitely limited.　However, there are certain precautions that can be taken which will result in longer service.　For instance, in winch-line service, either truck or tractor, corrosion can be combated by keeping the rope well lubricated.　Corrosion not only can cause failures by weakening the rope to a point where normal loads can no longer be sustained, but often will result in individual wire failures which make the rope extremely dangerous to handle.　When a wire rope becomes corroded, its wires have neither their original strength nor their ability to resist bending fatigue and abrasion.

When storing wire rope, keep it in a clean, dry place away from acids or other compounds which would tend to deteriorate it upon contact.

When installing a new wire rope, if received in a coil, uncoil it along the floor or ground.　Do not just pull a loose end and let twists develop.　If received on a reel, jack up the reel so the rope can be pulled off straight.　Do not throw wraps off the reel flange.

By making an attempt to keep the rope level-wound on the winch drums, many doglegs, bends, and kinks can be eliminated.　These not only contribute to the general rope deterioration but often result in distortion which will cause failure.　If the winch line is used in conjunction with a truck A frame, it is advisable to use the largest sheaves possible.　Bending wire rope around sharp corners and small sheaves reduces the breaking strength and safe working load.　In winch-line use, try to have a straight-line pull.

In the interest of securing maximum rope service, an analysis of the installation is in order.　Rope stress analysis should be made to determine proper working loads and adequate rope diameters.　Sheaves of proper diameters, as established by the wire-rope manufacturers, should be used.   Rope travel should be checked and points of wear eliminated.   In many installations wear in specific rope sections cannot be prevented.   In these cases, distributing this wear over a greater length can be accomplished by reversing the rope end for end or instituting a system of cutting off one end while paying out on the other.

Table 10-1. Weights and Breaking Strengths of 6 × 25 Flexible Improved-plow-steel Wire Rope

Diam, in.	Weight per foot, lb		Breaking strength, lb			
			Bright		Galvanized	
	IWRC*	FC†	IWRC	FC	IWRC	FC
$\frac{1}{8}$	0.029	0.025	1,500	1,390	1,350	1,250
$\frac{5}{32}$	0.045	0.039	2,330	2,170	2,100	1,950
$\frac{3}{16}$	0.065	0.056	3,340	3,110	3,010	2,800
$\frac{1}{4}$	0.11	0.10	5,891	5,480	5,301	4,932
$\frac{5}{16}$	0.18	0.16	9,159	8,520	8,243	7,668
$\frac{3}{8}$	0.25	0.23	13,110	12,200	11,800	10,980
$\frac{7}{16}$	0.34	0.31	17,780	16,540	16,000	14,890
$\frac{1}{2}$	0.44	0.40	23,000	21,400	20,700	19,260
$\frac{9}{16}$	0.56	0.51	29,020	27,000	26,120	24,300
$\frac{5}{8}$	0.69	0.63	35,900	33,400	32,310	30,060
$\frac{3}{4}$	0.99	0.90	51,170	47,600	46,050	42,840
$\frac{7}{8}$	1.35	1.23	69,230	64,400	62,300	57,960
1	1.76	1.60	89,870	83,600	80,880	75,240
$1\frac{1}{8}$	2.23	2.03	113,100	105,200	101,800	94,680
$1\frac{1}{4}$	2.75	2.50	138,900	129,200	125,000	116,300
$1\frac{3}{8}$	3.33	3.03	167,000	155,400	150,300	139,900
$1\frac{1}{2}$	3.96	3.60	197,800	184,000	178,000	165,600
$1\frac{5}{8}$	4.65	4.23	230,000	214,000	207,000	192,600
$1\frac{3}{4}$	5.39	4.90	266,600	248,000	239,900	223,200
$1\frac{7}{8}$	6.19	5.63	303,100	282,000	272,800	253,800
2	7.04	6.40	344,000	320,000	309,600	288,000
$2\frac{1}{8}$	7.95	7.23	384,800	358,000	346,400	322,200
$2\frac{1}{4}$	8.91	8.10	430,000	400,000	387,000	360,000
$2\frac{1}{2}$	11.00	10.00	524,600	488,000	472,100	439,200
$2\frac{3}{4}$	13.31	12.10	627,800	584,000	565,000	525,600

* Independent wire-rope core.
† Fiber core.

After the installation has been checked for the factors mentioned, and reasonable steps have been taken by the user to assure the best or most practical working conditions, further study should be made to keep the rope in its best working condition.   In many installations, corrosion and corrosion fatigue are the principal causes of rope retirement.   The wire-rope manufacturer takes particular care during the fabrication process to protect his product from corrosion in storage and shipping by thoroughly lubricating all the rope components.   In most services, the manufacturer's lubrication must be augmented from time to time.   The use of continuous lubricators has proved to be one of the best methods of rope preservation.   Where this method is impracticable, other ways, such as swabbing or brushing the lubricant on the rope, have been found satisfactory.   However, to be effective, a regular schedule of lubrication must be maintained.   Frequency usually is based on a visual inspection of the rope's condition and is dependent on the extent of activity.

For operations where conditions are particularly bad, galvanized-coated wire or

Table 10-2. Weights and Breaking Strengths of 6 × 37 Improved-plow-steel Wire Rope

Diam, in.	Weight per foot, lb		Breaking strength, lb			
			Bright		Galvanized	
	IWRC*	FC†	IWRC	FC	IWRC	FC
¼	0.11	0.10	5,568	5,180	5,011	4,662
5⁄16	0.18	0.16	8,664	8,060	7,798	7,254
⅜	0.24	0.22	12,400	11,540	11,160	10,390
7⁄16	0.33	0.30	16,810	15,640	15,130	14,080
½	0.43	0.39	21,930	20,400	19,740	18,360
9⁄16	0.54	0.49	27,730	25,800	24,960	23,200
⅝	0.67	0.61	33,970	31,600	30,570	28,440
¾	0.96	0.87	48,590	45,200	43,370	40,680
⅞	1.31	1.19	65,790	61,200	59,210	55,080
1	1.70	1.55	85,570	79,600	77,010	71,640
1⅛	2.16	1.96	107,700	100,200	96,940	90,180
1¼	2.66	2.42	132,200	123,000	119,000	110,700
1⅜	3.22	2.93	159,300	148,200	143,400	133,400
1½	3.84	3.49	189,000	175,800	170,000	158,200
1⅝	4.50	4.09	221,400	206,000	199,300	185,400
1¾	5.23	4.75	255,800	238,000	230,300	214,200
1⅞	6.00	5.45	292,400	272,000	263,200	244,800
2	6.82	6.20	331,100	308,000	298,000	277,200
2⅛	7.70	7.00	371,900	346,000	334,700	311,400
2¼	8.64	7.85	414,900	386,000	373,400	347,400
2½	10.7	9.69	507,400	472,000	456,700	424,800
2¾	12.9	11.72	610,600	568,000	549,500	511,200
3	15.3	13.95	720,200	670,000	648,200	603,000

* Independent wire-rope core.
† Fiber core.

drawn galvanized wire are used in rope fabrication.   The regular wire-rope lubricating compounds should also be used with this type of rope.

In addition to taking steps to insure longer serviceability, the user must consider the problem of determining the service end point of his wire rope.   Unless this problem is considered in its proper perspective, he can lose money by retiring his ropes too early. On the other hand, extending the service too long, thereby reaching a point where the rope cannot sustain normal operating loads and allowing actual rope failures to occur, can be tremendously costly.   In many cases it is not easy to determine when a wire rope should be replaced.   Manufacturers are glad to cooperate with their customers with consultation and testing services.   After a representative number of samples have been tested, a safe and economical criterion can be established.

To make any plan effective, all parties must cooperate fully. The user should keep accurate service records of the work done, or the time in service, or a combination of the two. Because working conditions are subject to change, by either wearing of the equipment or physical changes in the installation, the user should institute regular

Table 10-3. Weights and Breaking Strengths of 7 × 7 and 6 × 7 Improved-plow-steel Wire Rope

Diam, in.	Weight per foot, lb		Breaking strength, lb			
			Bright		Galvanized	
	7 × 7	6 × 7	7 × 7	6 × 7	7 × 7	6 × 7
1/16	0.0075	0.0068	365	340	330	305
5/64	0.011	0.010	570	530	515	480
3/32	0.016	0.014	820	760	735	685
7/64	0.022	0.020	1,110	1,030	1,000	930
1/8	0.028	0.025	1,450	1,350	1,300	1,210
5/32	0.043	0.039	2,250	2,090	2,020	1,880
3/16	0.062	0.056	3,220	3,000	2,900	2,700
7/32	0.083	0.075	4,370	4,060	3,930	3,660
1/4	0.103	0.094	5,676	5,280	5,108	4,752
5/16	0.165	0.150	8,815	8,200	7,933	7,380
3/8	0.231	0.210	12,600	11,720	11,340	10,550
7/16	0.319	0.290	17,050	15,860	15,340	14,270
1/2	0.418	0.380	22,140	20,600	19,930	18,540
9/16	0.528	0.480	27,950	26,000	25,150	23,400
5/8	0.649	0.590	34,180	31,800	30,770	28,620
3/4	0.924	0.840	48,800	45,400	43,920	40,860
7/8	1.26	1.15	66,000	61,400	59,400	55,260
1	1.65	1.50	85,300	79,400	76,820	71,460
1 1/8	2.09	1.90	107,000	99,600	96,360	89,640
1 1/4	2.57	2.34	131,100	122,000	118,000	109,800
1 3/8	3.12	2.84	157,200	146,200	141,400	131,600
1 1/2	3.72	3.38	185,300	172,400	166,800	155,200

inspections. Frequency and thoroughness would be dependent upon the type of service, damage caused by accidental rope failure, whether or not loss of life might be involved, and cost of shutdown time for emergency replacements. All these factors should be weighed.

Chapter 11

SLINGS—WIRE ROPE AND CHAIN

By W. B. Lashar, Jr.
Manager, Technical Sales
American Chain & Cable Company, Inc.
York, Pa.

Because slings are considered, in many cases, as expendable items of somewhat erratic characteristics, they rarely receive the necessary study. Just a few minutes in a busy shop will prove that slings are actual materials-handling tools, and are responsible for the safe, continuous movement of material from one production operation to the next. Also that they are called upon to move much valuable equipment which, if damaged, could cost many times the value of the slings for repair or replacement.

The amount of maintenance required and the effectiveness of the methods employed are determined by the correctness of the equipment for the purpose, the amount of use given, and the abuse it receives. Since the last two factors are not normally under the control of the maintenance department (although resulting costs may be charged to it), the principal means for reduction of maintenance costs is through assurance of maximum suitability of the equipment for operating conditions. Therefore the selection of slings is a serious responsibility and one demanding consideration of all factors involved, for no maintenance or subsequent care can overcome improper selection.

Maximum strength, low deterioration in use, and effective inspectability for determining strength loss are built into their products by the principal sling manufacturers. The strength of slings made in this manner is certified, and deterioration characteristics are defined. It is on the basis of having such information that the recommendations which follow are made, for without it you can only guess at the steps necessary for safety, efficiency, and economy.

Selecting Slings. In selecting slings two materials, chain and wire rope, will be found to develop the high strength required to efficiently handle today's loads and at the same time give the freedom from hidden deterioration necessary for low maintenance costs and safe service life. When correctly designed and manufactured, chain and wire-rope slings give equal safety and dependability. In the majority of lifting operations choice is dictated by individual preference alone.

However, the short, individual-link structure of sling chain and the large number of continuous wires laid up to form the body of the wire-rope slings give certain characteristics to slings of each material. By comparing these characteristics with the conditions of the application, it is possible to obtain slings giving the highest efficiency and lowest maintenance cost for the job. The most basic characteristics of standardized sling chains and wire-rope slings are compared in Table 11-1 to help in this selection.

Table 11-1. Basic Characteristics for Consideration in Selection of Slings

Characteristic	Alloy-steel sling chain	IPS–IWRC wire rope*
Abrasion resistance.........	Good	Fair
Cutting resistance..........	Good	Should be protected by padding
Corrosive-atmosphere resistance:		
Moderate concentrations..	Fair unless special alloys used, then good	Poor unless stainless is used
Heavy concentrations.....	Good with special alloys	Fair with special stainless
Crushing resistance.........	Good	Fair
Ease of attaching to load....	Bridle hitch—good; difficult to pass under or around load using larger sizes of sling	Good
Ease of effective inspection...	Good, but chain must be handled	Good
Efficiency:		
In bridle hitch...........	Good	Good
In basket hitch...........	Poor grip if load is smooth unless lifting beam used	Good, unless load is oiled
In choker hitch..........	Poor grip if load is smooth	Good
Heat resistance:		
Under 1000°F............	No permanent injury to chain—strength lower when hot	Not recommended over 300°F
Over 1000°F.............	Good, but requires special alloys	Fair with special stainless
Impact resistance...........	Good within overload limitations	Good within overload limitations
Normal service life..........	Good, unless overloaded or abused	Relatively short in choker hitches, fair to good in basket hitches, good in bridle hitches
Overload to permanently damage	Approx 100% over working-load limit†	Approx 300% over rated capacity†
Protection required for load..	Pad machined or thin sections	Pad polished surfaces or thin sections
Protection required for sling.	None, except against overloading	Pad sharp corners, avoid bends of very short radii, avoid excessive overloads
Usual reason for retirement..	Overloaded or worn out	Localized cutting from lack of proper protection, wear from excessive abrasion, or cranky
Weather resistance..........	Good	Fair, if frequently lubricated

* Improved plow steel, independent wire-rope center.
† Overload given is based on total stress in sling regardless of source, whether weight of load, angle of lift, acceleration, or impact. It is also based on all attachments and fittings having strength equal to or in excess of sling body.

Care and Maintenance. Once slings proper for the application have been selected, their length of life and safety in use require two things—regular inspection to insure safety, and regular maintenance to prolong service life.

Regular inspection should be based on the amount and severity of use. Sling chains elongate under overload, and therefore the first check should be measurement (preferably with chain hanging vertically) of the reach of the chain and comparison of length with that shown on the ring or tag with which all first-rate slings are equipped.

Wear in the chain, as well as overload, will cause increase in length, and each link should be inspected for interlink wear, cuts or nicks, and deformation.

Wire-rope slings are not as subject to overloads as sling chains and, unless the sling is actually broken, little damage results.   Therefore, inspection of wire-rope slings is concentrated on any areas of localized damage resulting in concentrations of broken wires, which, by lowering the metallic cross section, lower the sling strength.   Check,

Fig. 11-1. Stator being lifted with single-leg sling.

Fig. 11-2. Combination chain and wire-rope slings, as shown, usually are the best means of handling loads with sharp edges. To avoid cutting the wire rope and subsequent "crankiness," a section of chain is inserted into the area where cutting normally occurs.

also, should be made for kinks, corrosion or rust, and damage to the endings, for these also lower strength.

On both sling chains and wire-rope slings careful attention must be given to the end fittings.   Links, where used, should be checked for distortion, gouges, and nicks. Hooks should be checked for any sign of opening, and splices on wire rope should be checked for any sign of "working" or damage to collars or ferrules where used.   The actual determination of suitability of the sling for continued service must be based on the rules set up by the safety department of the particular plant.   All responsible sling manufacturers are glad to furnish specific information on recommended procedures and wear limitations for their own sling products.

Inspection is extremely valuable to maintenance, not only in determining suitability of the chain for further use, but in detecting the abuse given to the sling.   If abuse can be prevented, sling life can be prolonged.   If, however, the abuse is inherent in the application, it may be necessary to change the type of sling used to one less likely to be damaged under the operating conditions.   This can effect material savings.

Care and Storage. If inspection determines the suitability of a sling chain for further use, it should be lightly oiled. This will increase interlink resistance to wear and, by retarding rust, make the sling easier to handle.

Wire-rope slings normally are given a light lubrication when the wires pass through the "closing operation." However, this lubrication may be removed from surface wires during use, and a light oiling at time of inspection is advisable. If wire-rope slings are continually exposed to weather, coating with a mixture of one-half boiled linseed oil and one-half light engine oil will retard corrosion and lower deterioration.

One of the most costly mistakes in sling maintenance is having more slings than necessary in use on the "floor." This encourages leaving slings under loads, where

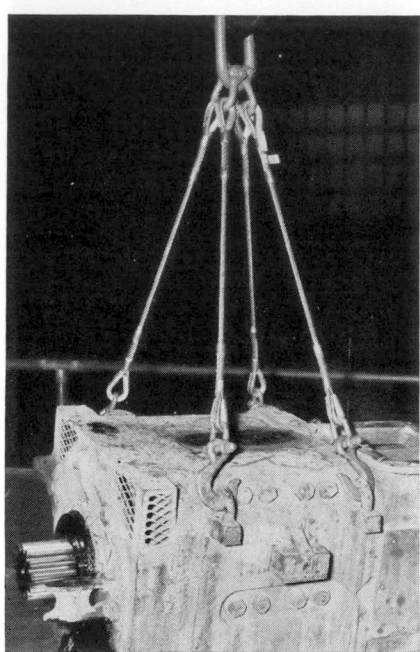

Fig. 11-3. Transmission housing and four-legged bridle sling with shackles and hooks.

Fig. 11-4. Boiler section and four-legged bridle lift.

they are lost, or tossing them into corners, where they may become damaged. It is highly advisable to require return of the old sling before issuing a new one for the same job. Unless this requirement is enforced there can be no control over the number of slings in use. In addition, a situation of actual danger can be created by slings unfit for service being continued in use.

If possible, a rack should be provided for hanging "floor slings" when not in actual use. This practice minimizes accidental damage and will allow a quick check of sling condition between regular inspections. Such a rack will save time by allowing larger slings both of chain and wire rope to be picked up and returned by the crane, instead of manually handling them and the heavy fittings that may be attached. The savings in inspection time by the use of such a rack are obvious.

Slings not in active service should be inspected and, if found suitable for reissue, lubricated and placed in dead storage. New slings should be held in such storage until issued. Usually, chain slings can be stowed conveniently in barrels or similar containers. Wire-rope slings will be more conveniently handled if hung from racks.

Your sling supplier will be glad to advise on storage and preservation procedures for his products. Quite frequently he can assist in lowering your costs for sling maintenance.

Use. Proper lifts are illustrated in Figs. 11-1 to 11-4.

Chapter 12

PORTABLE AIR TOOLS

By Warren M. Black
Marketing Manager
The Rotor Tool Company
Cleveland, Ohio

Portable tool equipment, particularly high-production air tools, tend to decline in efficiency and power because of wear. Moreover, this type of equipment receives extremely hard usage, and sometimes abuse and neglect, as well as being subject to the usual accidents. Since the operators of portable tools are paid approximately $2 an hour, and since their production is tied directly to the efficiency of the tools, the importance of top maintenance is obvious.

SELECTION

The starting point in the maintenance program is in the original purchase of the tool. Units that will require low maintenance should be selected. For example: bearings should be held in steel inserts in aluminum housings (the inserts permit easy bearing replacement); renewable parts, such as end plates, should be reversible; to save expense, parts of the tools should be split (the handle from the cylinder, for example) so that if one is broken it will not be necessary to buy the two parts as a one-piece unit. Maintenance experience should be recorded and reported to buying personnel, to insure selection on a service basis, as well as on price.

SETUP OF MAINTENANCE DEPARTMENT

For effective upkeep of portable air tools, proper equipment should be provided, and it should be manned by competent workmen under adequate supervision. Sufficient space should be allocated to this maintenance work, and it should be well lighted. The benches, as shown in Fig. 12-1, should be equipped with power supply, arbor press, tachometer, hand tools, and cleaning facilities. There should be a reasonable stock of spare parts. Plants with only a few tools of a given type will stock only the parts that wear out most frequently (the tools being designed so the wear will take place on those parts). If ten or twenty tools are in use, the stock of parts will be larger, and will include more parts, such as handles. Large, well-equipped maintenance shops keep their parts in bins, with maximum and minimum quantities.

For preventive maintenance, a periodic check of tools should be established. As the scheduled inspections are made, the dates and the repairs can be entered in simple fashion, say on 5- by 7-in. cards. The frequency of inspection will depend upon the extent and severity of use. As the tools are treated, they can be marked for easy identification.   One plant has its tools inspected each month and puts a dab of color on the tool to indicate the month in which it was inspected.   If the color for May is green, and tools with green dabs are found in service in June, they will be returned to the maintenance department at once.   A normal practice in preventive maintenance is to keep complete tools on hand as spares, the number depending upon the total number in use and the frequency with which they are out of service.

Fig. 12-1. Properly equipped maintenance bench, with 360- and 180-cycle outlets.

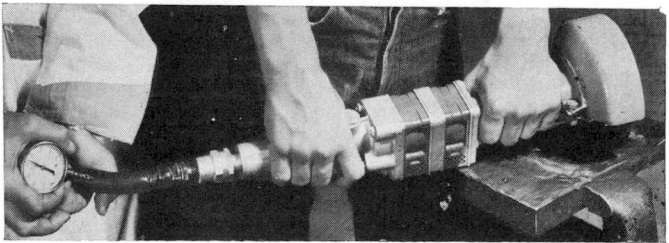

Fig. 12-2. Needle pressure gage, inserted in hose just ahead of the tool, registers pressure of the air while it is flowing.

Conditions under which the tools operate should be right. Most of them are designed to operate on 80 to 100 lb pressure.   Even though the gage at the compressor shows the correct pressure, there may be considerable loss by the time the air gets to the tool.   Leaks in air lines are not the only cause of reduced pressure.   Transmission lines may be too long.   They may be corroded, with consequent reduction of inside diameter and delivery of insufficient volume of air.   The drop line from the main transmission line may be too small to deliver required volume.   The hose line from the drop line may be too small or contain restrictions, such as hose menders.   Valves and couplings may be at fault.

To check pressure, inject a needle pressure gage into the hose line just ahead of the tool; it will register the air *while it is flowing*.   See Fig. 12-2.   If pressure drops below 80 lb, correction should be made by installing larger transmission line, larger drop line, larger hose, or larger valves and couplings.   See that there are no obstructions to air passage.

Most air tools come equipped with an air strainer to keep dirt out of the motors. Screens should be used, they should be kept clean, and they should be replaced when necessary. Figure 12-3 shows such a screen that was not treated properly.

LUBRICATION

Lubricants differ for different kinds of air tools. It is not safe to use just any lubricant, whether the tool is of the rotating or the percussion type. Use the oil and grease recommended by the manufacturer. For most air tools the best means of lubrication is the line oiler (Fig. 12-4). It is installed in the line just ahead of the hose connection to the air tool. It gives a constant flow of lubricant while the air is flowing. It can be regulated to give just the desired amount. When it has a transparent bowl, as most of them do, there never is any excuse to run dry. In some types the oil can be seen to drop into the transmission line. To gage the flow of oil, hold a piece of white paper near the exhaust of the air tool while it is running, and observe the amount of oil that collects. Many tools of the rotating type have an oil reservoir in the handle.

For percussion tools, a light oil, in most

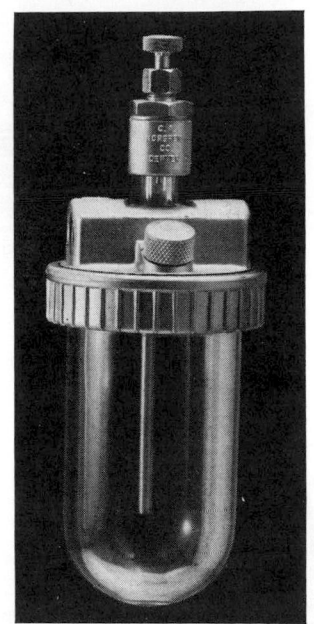

Fig. 12-3. Air-cleaner screen (the hole was punched by operator instead of cleaning screen to permit passage of air).

Fig. 12-4. Line oiler (½-pint) to be installed in the line just ahead of the hose connection to the air tool.

cases SAE 10 machine oil, is suitable. Heavier oil might make the valves stick or hesitate. But be guided by the recommendations of the manufacturer.

The worst enemy of lubrication is water in the compressed air. Traveling along the pipe lines at high velocity, it tends to wash the lubricant out of the tool. It causes corrosion, particularly if the tool lies idle for some time without being conditioned by an internal bath of lubricant.

Moisture can be eliminated to a large extent by the use of an aftercooler at the compressor and by water traps along the lines. The main transmission line should be sloped back to the compressor, to direct water into the receiver to be drained away. Down pipes should be taken off the top of the transmission line so that a minimum amount of water will be picked up. If the compressor is not equipped with an aftercooler and if the main transmission lines are not installed so that the water will flow by gravity to the receiver, the installation of water traps at low points along the transmission line will be helpful. They may be in the form of legs made of a length of large pipe, with a cap on the bottom and with a petcock for draining. Probably the best is the automatic trap, which dumps the accumulated water with no attention. These traps also catch sludge from the compressor.

MAINTENANCE PROCEDURES

Percussion Tools (Chipping Hammers, Scalers, etc.).   The chipping hammer is shown in Fig. 12-5 as a typical percussion tool.   In such tools the piston usually is the most important part; if badly worn, the blow will not be effective.   Pistons usually wear most at the ends.   Sometimes replacing a worn piston will restore the tool to good operating condition.   However, in many cases, the bore of the barrel may be

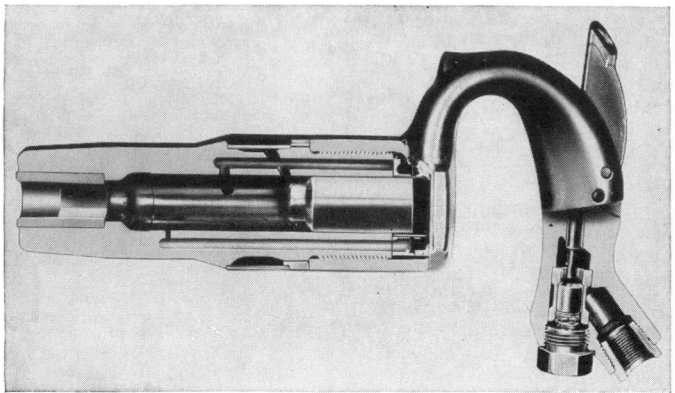

FIG. 12-5. Chipping hammer, back position.

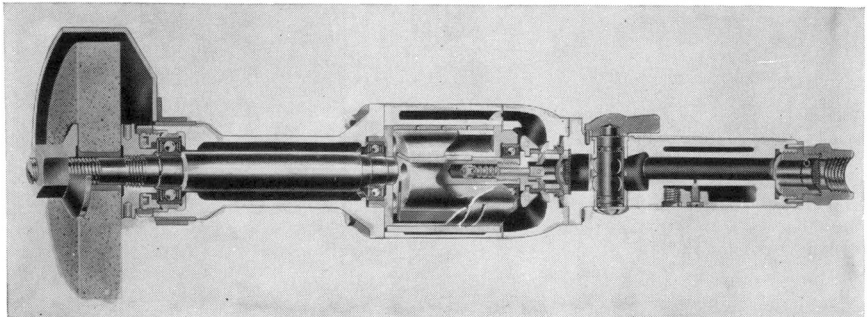

FIG. 12-6. Internal-blade grinder, 6-in. wheel.

worn (most wear takes place at the middle).   When the design permits, the barrel can be rebored and fitted with an oversize piston.   The usual procedure is grinding or honing.   In the case of hammers with replaceable bushings, for example a chipping hammer, replacement should be made when the wear becomes appreciable, because the fit in the chisel shank in the bushing makes an air seal to create a cushion at the end of the piston stroke.

The valve block which controls the action of the piston should be carefully inspected, because in certain types of valve blocks a worn valve will reduce the effectiveness of the piston blow.

The throttle-valve mechanism in the handle should be inspected frequently, and worn parts should be replaced so that the throttle will act to start the action promptly, open full, and shut off completely.

It is advisable to carry in stock a calculated amount of parts, such as chisel bushings, pistons, valves for the valve block; and throttle parts such as the compression spring, trigger pins, valve stems, and valves. Initial advice can be secured from the manufacturer, but experience and records will dictate the extent of the spare-part stockroom after the tools have been used for a long enough time to completely cover their work requirements.

Rotating Tools (Grinders, Drills, etc.). The internal-blade grinder is shown in Fig. 12-6 as a typical rotating tool. Nearly all such tools have ball bearings. It is advisable that the bearings be replaced before being badly worn; otherwise they are likely to cause misalignment, which will accelerate the wear of other parts. Preferably, replacements should be of the same make put into the tool by its manufacturer, who may have selected them for their close tolerances, type of grease seal, or retainer.

Rotor blades, or vanes, usually will wear out first. They should be checked with reasonable frequency and replaced promptly if at fault, so the motor will give peak power output. A fairly liberal supply should be kept on hand. Figure 12-7 shows a tool opened for the insertion of blades.

Nearly all motors have end plates against the ends of the rotors to seal the air within the chamber created by the rotor blades contacting the cylinder liner. Air which escapes around the ends of the rotor, or rotor blades, is wasted, so worn end plates should be replaced. Some types are interchangeable end for end to give double life.

The key which holds the rotor to the shaft should be replaced if it shows the slightest wear. There should be a close sliding fit; too much play will cause the rotor shaft, in contact with the rotor bore, to wear too rapidly.

Most air grinders do not have gears, and operate at relatively high speeds. It is essential that the spindle which carries the grinding wheel run true, and that the bearings be in good condition; otherwise it will vibrate considerably, causing rapid wear and increasing the possibility of wheel breakage. It is advisable to be sure that spindle attachments such as chucks, collets, and arbors run true with the spindle to avoid vibration.

FIG. 12-7. Inserting blades, or vanes, in grinder.

In tools with gears, inspect them and the ball bearings in which they are mounted when changing or replenishing grease. If wear is allowed to go on too long, it will increase at an accelerating pace, and maintenance cost will become unduly high. Sections of drills with gears and ball bearings are shown in Figs. 12-8 and 12-9.

Often the maintenance department needs guidance. Should the tool be repaired or a new one purchased? A correct estimate of the cost of repairs is needed and a comparison of this estimate with the output of a new tool and its cost. There is a fairly general acceptance of the policy of replacing when the cost of repair is approximately half the cost of a new tool. There should be considered, also, the fact that the discarded tools can be cannibalized, the parts that are good enough for further use being stored.

When are parts good enough to be put back into service? The maintenance department should consult with the service experts of the manufacturers, who are acquainted with the experiences of many users and have access to all the research and experimental information gathered by their plants. Repair sheets should be secured from the manufacturers. They show drawings of the tools, list part numbers, and give suggestions on removing spindles and other parts, how to avoid damage to parts by clamping, how to fit rotor blades, and so on.

SAFETY

It is a responsibility of maintenance to see that the tools are in safe operating condition. This is particularly true of grinders. With the exception of cone-shaped wheels, all wheels should be operated under guards. The diameter of the wheel arbor should be of the correct size for the kind and size of grinding wheel it will carry. The wheel washer and collar should be of the correct diameter and thickness and made with the

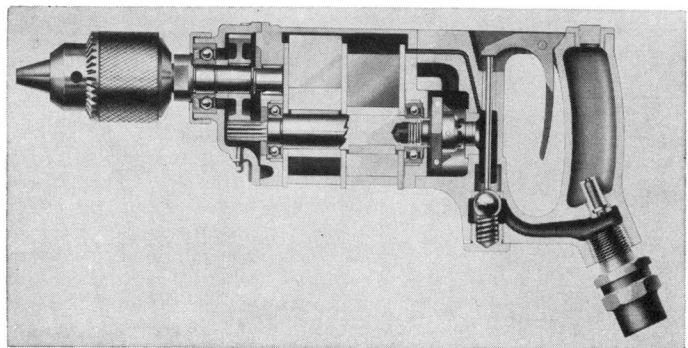

FIG. 12-8. Ball-bearing drill.

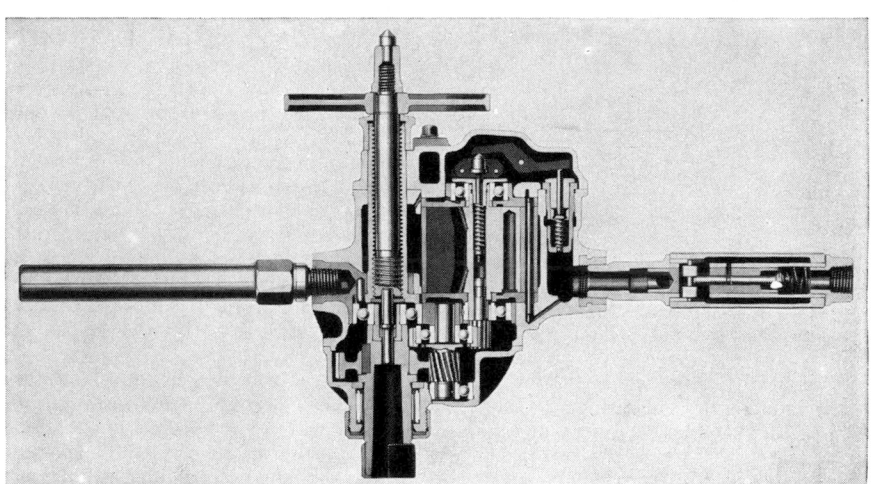

FIG. 12-9. Nonreversible drill (ball-bearing).

proper recess to grip the wheel firmly. Never should the two be of different diameters. The nut which holds the wheel on the arbor and the washer against the wheel must be of ample size and strength to do the job.

There are two kinds of grinding wheels commonly used on portable grinders— "slow-speed" wheels, which are vitrified bonded to be operated at 5,500 to 6,500 surface feet per minute, depending upon the hardness of the bond; and "high-speed" wheels, which are organic bonded, rubber or bakelite, which can be operated at speeds of 6,500 to 9,500 surface feet per minute, depending upon the hardness of the bond. Wheels almost always have circular blotters around the arbor hole which tell the kind of wheel and permissible speed.

Portable grinders use straight, recessed, raised-hub, disk, and cone wheels.   Wheel manufacturers furnish charts giving information as to applications and speeds.

A wheel may be chipped or cracked in transportation or in storage.   Hold the wheel loosely on a finger slipped through the arbor hole and tap lightly with the wooden handle of a hammer to see if the ring is clear.   If it is, mount it on the arbor, drawing the nut up firmly, but not so tight as to cause fracture.   Hold the tool under a bench and run it; if fractured, and failure results, injury will be avoided.   If OK, test the speed with a tachometer to be sure it conforms to the Safety Code.   The Grinding Wheel Manufacturers Association issues "American Standard Safety Code for Abrasive Wheels," which gives detailed explanation of the care, handling, mounting, and operation of grinding wheels.

Chapter 13

PORTABLE ELECTRIC TOOLS

By J. L. BENNETT
Technical Research Manager
The Black & Decker Manufacturing Company
Towson, Md.

Proper maintenance of portable electric tools is necessary for their efficient operation. If not properly maintained, they can be dangerous to operate. Most manufacturers of portable electric tools furnish an instruction book with each tool indicating proper use and maintenance. These instructions should be read and followed. A preventive maintenance program will reduce service costs and aid in keeping tools on the job.

BEARINGS

Motor and gear shafts rotate in bearings. Spindles and mechanism components rotate or slide in bearings. Portable electric tool bearings may be of the ball, roller,

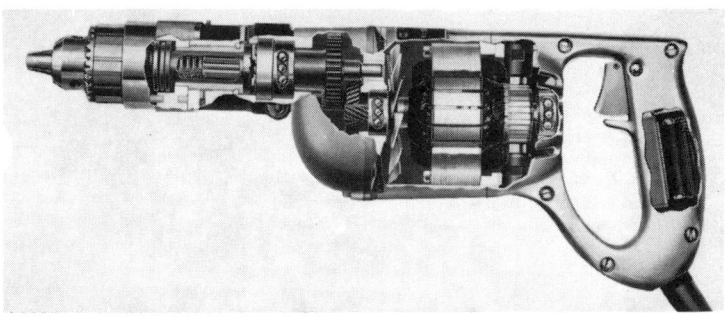

FIG. 13-1. Motor and gear shafts rotate in bearings; spindles and mechanism components rotate or slide in bearings.

needle, or sleeve type. Proper lubrication of these bearings is essential to their life. Excessive lubrication is often as contributory to trouble as is too little lubrication. The frequency of lubrication will depend on the type of bearing and the length of time tool is in use.

Most ball bearings are prelubricated by the manufacturer and do not require further lubrication. Roller, needle, and sleeve bearings require the addition of lubricant. Often these are located in a gear chamber, where lubrication is automatically supplied by the grease in this chamber. If additional lubrication is necessary, an oiler is provided. Instructions for the addition of lubricants will be found in the manufacturer's instruction book.

When bearings show signs of wear, they should be replaced. If tools are operated for any length of time with worn bearings, damage may occur to other parts, such as gears and armatures. It is economical to replace worn bearings before other damage occurs.

GEARING

The most frequent types of gears used in portable tools are spur, helical, spiral bevel, and worm. Gearing is generally housed in a gear box, which contains grease or oil for lubrication. The manufacturer has determined the correct type of grease or oil and the correct amount to be used for longest life of the gears in any particular

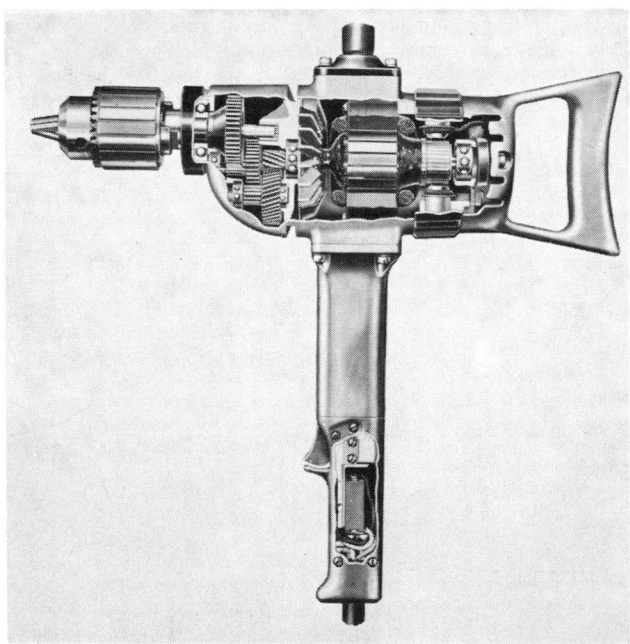

Fig. 13-2. Example of gearing.

tool. It is advisable to follow the instructions in the manufacturer's instruction or maintenance book concerning the type and quantity of lubricant. Gear lubricants should be changed periodically. When this is done, old grease should be removed and the gear case and gears cleaned completely. New lubricant should be added in accordance with the manufacturer's recommendation.

Worn gears will be noisy. They should be replaced when definite signs of under-cutting appear on the gear teeth.

ELECTRIC CORD

The electric cord on a portable tool is its life line. Cords should be kept clean and free of oil and grease. Tools should be stored so that cords do not have sharp bends. Worn cords can fail and present shock hazards to the user. They should be replaced.

Metal-housed tools are equipped with three-wire cords and three-prong plugs.

The green wire is provided for the grounding of the tool. This is necessary to provide operator safety from shock hazard should a ground fault occur within the tool. The manufacturer's recommendation concerning the grounding of electric tools should be followed carefully. The preventive maintenance schedule should include a check of the continuity of the ground wire and cable from the grounding prong on the plug to the motor housing.

All-insulated tools have only two-wire cords. In this type of tool, the third, or grounding, wire is not necessary, since the insulated housing and other built-in insulation provide the operator safety from shock hazard.

When replacing an electric cord, it is preferable to use the manufacturer's cord set. If this is not available, be sure to use the same size and type of cable provided originally with the tool. Most tools are provided with cord protectors where the cable enters the tool housing. These protectors prolong the life of the cable. It is important to replace them when installing new cable.

When it is necessary to use an extension cord, it is important that the proper size cord be used in order to prevent low voltage at the tool. Check the tool's ampere rating, which appears on the name plate, and make reference to the table below for determining the proper size extension cord. If the tool has a three-wire cord, be sure to use a three-wire extension cord so that the continuity of the ground circuit is retained.

Extension cord length, ft	Ampere rating					
	0 to 2.0	2.10 to 3.4	3.5 to 5.0	5.10 to 7.0	7.10 to 12.0	12.1 to 16.0
	Wire size (A.W.G.)					
25	18	18	18	18	16	14
50	18	18	18	16	14	12
75	18	18	16	14	12	10
100	18	16	14	12	10	...
150	16	14	12	12	...	...
200	16	14	12	10	...	...

BRUSHES

Motor carbon brushes have been selected by the manufacturer for maximum life and best motor performance. They should, therefore, be replaced with the manufacturer's part when worn. Substitutes can cause poor motor performance or excessive commutator wear. Brushes should be checked on a preventive maintenance schedule. They should be replaced before they are completely worn out. If they are allowed to wear completely out, excessive commutator wear will occur. The condition of the commutator on which the brushes ride should also be checked frequently. If commutators are deeply grooved, the life of new brushes will be low. Grooved commutators should be turned and reundercut.

SWITCHES

The switches in portable electric tools are selected by the manufacturer to match the motor characteristics. When replacing them, it is important to use the equivalent of the original switches. It is preferable to obtain replacement switches from the tool manufacturer.

There are two basic types of switches used in electric tools—a-c–d-c, which have quick make-and-break contacts, and a-c only, which have slow make-and-break contacts.   If the a-c only switches are used with direct current, short contact life will result.

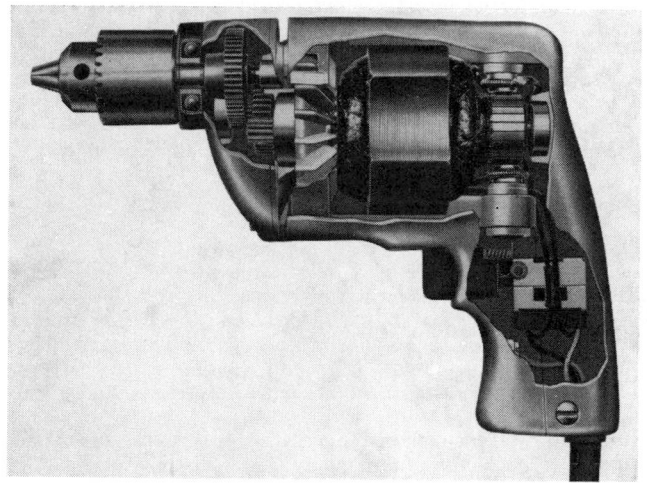

FIG. 13-3. The electric cord is the life of the tool.

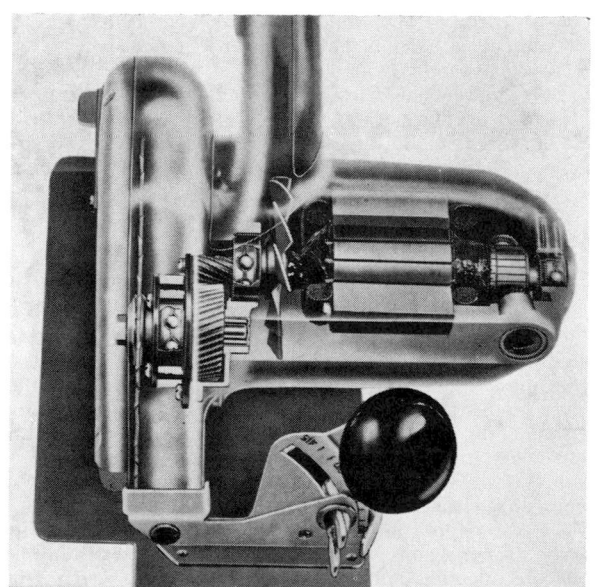

FIG. 13-4. The motor—showing armature, commutator, brushes, bearings, and fan.

Double-pole switches are employed on heavy-duty portable electric tools.   Single-pole switches are often used on lighter-duty tools.   The double-pole switch breaks both sides of the line, whereas the single-pole switch breaks only one side.   In connecting a single-pole switch, the hot line should be connected to the switch with the neutral bypassing.

Three basic types of terminal connections for switches will be found in portable electric tools. The most popular one utilizes a screw-type connection. It is important to use a proper terminal on the leads for fitting under the screws. "Push in" type switches are frequently used on electric tools. For this type of switch, the leads are tinned and forced into the slots provided. To release this type of connection, a wire is inserted into the release slot and then the leads pulled out. A third type of switch has wire leads permanently connected internally. Exterior connections are then made to the motor and cable with splicing connectors. It is important to use the same type of terminals on the leads for connection to switches as those provided in the original equipment.

Repairing of small switches is not practical. If they have failed, it is more economical to replace them with new switches.

MOTOR

Three basic types of motors are used in portable electric tools—series, shunt, and induction. The series type is the most widely used.

The series motor consists of a stationary field and a rotating armature equipped with a commutator on which the carbon brushes ride. The stationary field can fail because of open circuit, short circuit, or ground. Failures may be caused by severe overload, overheating due to lack of cooling air, or excessive exposure to abrasive or conductive dirt.

The armature, or rotating member, may also fail because of open circuit, short circuit, or ground. Mechanical failure may occur because of wear on the pinion or the bearing journals. Excessive sparking at the brushes may be caused by poor commutator surface. If the surface is rough or dirty, it may be cleaned with fine sandpaper or a glass brush. The use of emery cloth is not recommended. If the commutator is deeply grooved, it should be turned on a lathe.

Direct-current motors in portable electric tools generally utilize a permanent-magnet field. These have no windings and are, therefore, not subject to the same type of failures as a wound field. They can, however, lose their magnetism because of shock or overheating. If this occurs, they should be remagnetized by the manufacturer. The armature, or rotating member, of a d-c permanent-magnet shunt motor is identical to that of a series motor and should be maintained in the same manner.

When d-c permanent-magnet shunt motors are employed in portable electric tools intended for operation on a-c lines, a rectifier is included in the tool. These rectifiers utilize diodes. If the tool does not operate properly, the rectifier should be checked. Repairing these rectifiers is not practical. It is more economical to replace the complete rectifier unit.

Induction motors have cast or fabricated rotors. These rotors are virtually indestructible and should not have need of maintenance. The field or stator of an induction motor can fail because of overloading, overheating, or exposure to conductive dirts and abrasives just as the field or stator of a series motor can fail. Single-phase induction motors generally have starting windings which are removed from the circuit after the motor reaches full speed. This switching is accomplished by a relay or a centrifugal switch. If a starting winding has failed, it is advisable to check the relay centrifugal switch, since either could have been the cause of failure.

Most portable electric tool motors have cooling fans. It is quite necessary for them to receive the proper amount of ventilation in order not to fail because of overheating. Ventilating openings and passages should be cleaned periodically so that the supply of air is not restricted.

CORDLESS

Cordless electric tools are powered by self-contained, rechargeable batteries. It is important that the batteries be maintained on full charge. Manufacturer's instructions concerning the frequency of charging and the charging times should be followed carefully. It is advisable to have batteries on charge whenever the tools are not in use.

Chargers for the batteries of cordless electric tools generally contain a transformer, rectifier, and necessary control devices. Repairing chargers is not recommended. They should be returned to the manufacturer's local service facility if maintenance is required.

The motors in cordless electric tools are of the d-c permanent-magnet shunt type. They are designed for the low voltages produced by the batteries. Maintenance procedures will be the same as those indicated above under "Motors" for d-c permanent-magnet shunt types. It is quite important that the motors in cordless tools

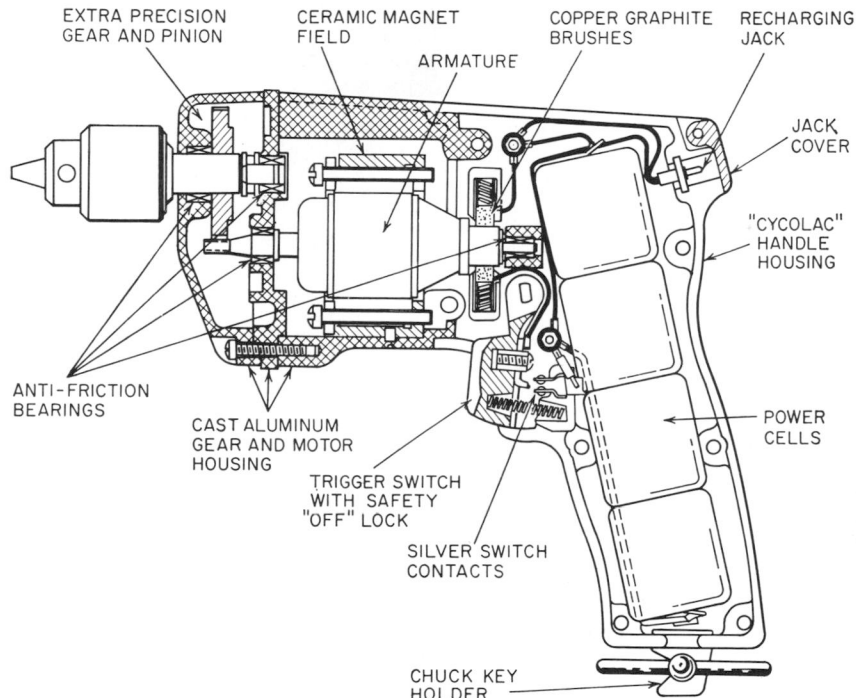

EXTRA PRECISION
GEAR AND PINION

CERAMIC MAGNET
FIELD

ARMATURE

COPPER GRAPHITE
BRUSHES

RECHARGING
JACK

JACK
COVER

"CYCOLAC"
HANDLE
HOUSING

ANTI-FRICTION
BEARINGS

CAST ALUMINUM
GEAR AND MOTOR
HOUSING

POWER
CELLS

TRIGGER SWITCH
WITH SAFETY
"OFF" LOCK

SILVER SWITCH
CONTACTS

CHUCK KEY
HOLDER

FIG. 13-5. Cordless electric drill.

be maintained in tiptop shape, since poorly operating motors can cause undue drain on the batteries and thereby shorten their life.

ALL-INSULATED TOOLS

All-insulated tools have no ground wire and thus have only two-prong plugs. Safety of the operator from electric shock is insured by insulated housings and insulation of the spindle. The spindle insulation is attained by an extra insulating member on the armature shaft, in the gear train, or at the spindle itself.

Since safe operation depends on the insulation provided, it is important that it be checked carefully. Damaged housings should be replaced. A preventive maintenance schedule should definitely include a periodic ground check with the switch on. Potential should be applied from a plug terminal to the housing and to the spindle.

To guarantee protection against electric shock, it is important when maintaining this type of tool to use only manufacturer-supplied replacement parts.

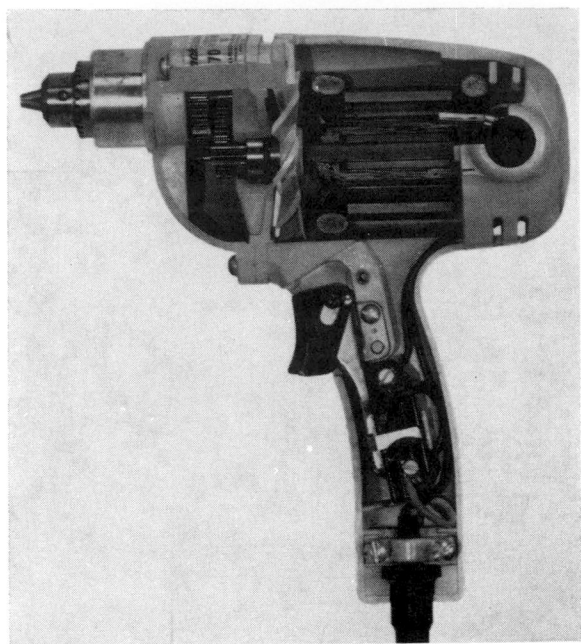

FIG. 13-6. The all-insulated tool (shown, a $\frac{1}{4}$-in. drill).

VARIABLE-SPEED TOOLS

Speed change on portable tools is accomplished either mechanically or electrically.

Mechanical speed change is generally accomplished in a two-speed gear box using syncromesh drives. Service procedures on these gear boxes will be the same as on a normal gear box. Speed-changing motors employ various methods. The simpliest arrangements utilize series-parallel field coil connections or coil tapping. The more sophisticated types use rectification to direct current with control of the rectified current. Semiconductor devices and capacitors are frequently used in the control circuits. If these devices are to be replaced, it is important to use components with ratings identical to those supplied with the original equipment.

INSPECTION

A proper preventive maintenance schedule will keep portable electric tools in continuous operating condition. During periodic inspections, the following should be checked:

1. *Ground test at 500 volts.* This should be performed with the switch on, testing from each line prong of the plug to the housing.
2. *Continuity test of the ground circuit.* This should be performed with a continuity tester from the grounding plug to the housing.
3. *Cable.* Cable should be checked for worn or frayed spots and always replaced if in poor condition.
4. *Brushes and commutator.* Carbon brushes should be checked and replaced if excessively worn. Commutators should be cleaned frequently and if excessively grooved, should be turned on a lathe.
5. *Ventilating openings.* Cooling air is important to the motor operation. Ventilating openings should be cleaned if they become clogged with dust or dirt.

6. *Conductive dust.* Accumulations of carbon or other conductive material inside the motor housing can lead to shock hazards. These accumulations should be periodically blown out or wiped out.

If a portable electric tool will not run, the problem will generally be found in one of the following: plug, carbon brushes, electrical connections, cord, armature, or field.

If motor overheats, the problem will generally occur in brushes, commutator, armature, field, or ventilating openings.

If the unit is noisy, gears and bearings should be inspected.

If the unit is grounded, the problem will generally be located in the armature, field brush holder, or cable.

If the motor lacks power, a check should be made of the brushes, commutator, armature, and field.

Armatures can be checked for short on a growler and for open circuit with a continuity tester. Field coils can be checked with a resistance meter or bridge.

FACTORY SERVICE

While there are a number of items of maintenance that can be easily taken care of, there are some that require equipment not available in all the plants of portable-tool users. Also, there are some for which only the manufacturer has the equipment. In such cases, the matter of repairs should be taken up with the tool manufacturers through their service stations. Also, even though the user can take care of much of the maintenance on his portable tools, it is good practice to send the tool back to the manufacturer once in a while for an overhaul by factory-trained service men.

All plants that do their own service work should use only those parts supplied and recommended by the tool manufacturer if they want to avoid unnecessary trouble and expense. Finally, always follow religiously the manufacturer's instructions for care and maintenance of the portable electric tools.

MAINTENANCE OF SPECIFIC TYPES OF TOOLS

Particular types of tools may require specific maintenance, owing to the nature of their construction. The usual types are treated below.

Drills. The portable electric drill is distinguished primarily by being equipped with a chuck. Chucks are assembled to the spindle with a tapered fit, male thread, or female thread. They are generally of the gear type, although there are other types known as keyless, which can be hand tightened or impact tightened. The jaw-type gear chuck can be repaired. The majority of the parts for them are obtainable from the manufacturer.

Very large drills are often equipped with a Morse taper socket instead of a chuck. These sockets should be kept clean and free from burrs in order to maintain the proper grip on the drill shank.

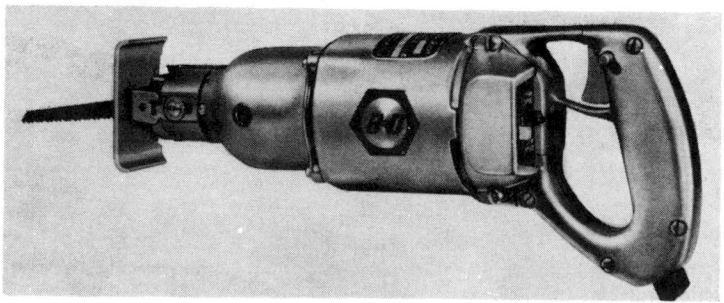

FIG. 13-7. Variable-speed tool (shown, a sabre saw).

Screwdrivers. Screwdrivers are similar to drills but have a ratcheting type of clutch which provides the impact for screw tightening. The positive type of clutch depends on operator pressure for resulting torque. The adjustable type of clutch is provided with a spring which can be adjusted for controlled torque. The clutches

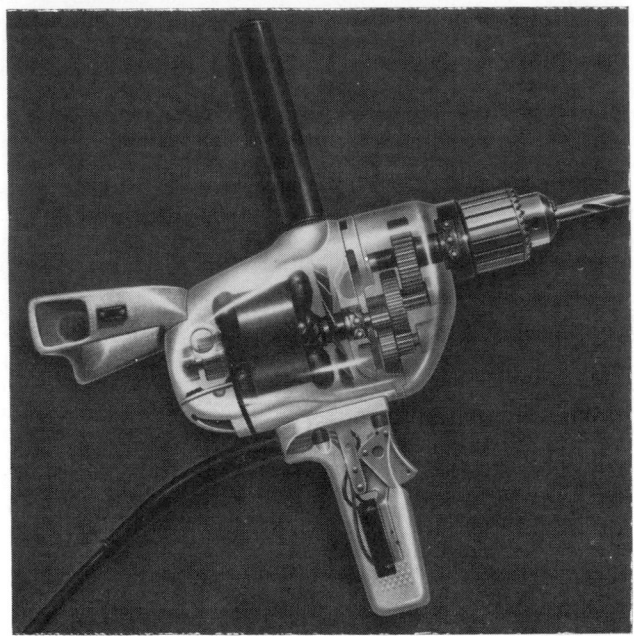

Fig. 13-8. Drill (equipped with gear-type chuck).

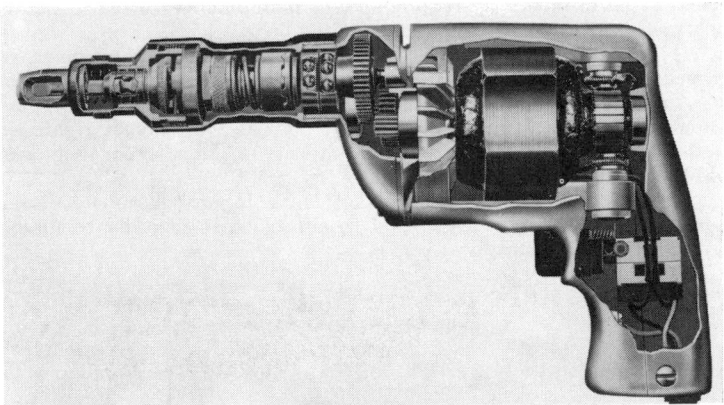

Fig. 13-9. Screwdriver (can be equipped with either positive or adjustable clutch).

are made of hardened steel for long life. Lubrication, however, is quite necessary to their life. It is important to follow the lubrication instructions provided in the manufacturer's manual. Worn clutch teeth will result in loss of torque. When this occurs, clutches should be replaced.

Impact Wrenches. Impact wrenches have mechanisms designed to provide high torque on large nuts and bolts. Impact energy is accumulated in a hammer member between blows.   Special alloy steels are used in the impacting members.   Lubrication is quite necessary for long life of these mechanisms.   It is quite important to follow the lubrication instructions provided in the manufacturer's manual.   Spindle ends on impact wrenches are either square or splined for the acceptance of commercial sockets.   It is important to use impact-classified sockets.   One of the most prevalent reasons for loss of torque is worn sockets.   They should be replaced if they are loose on the spindle or if they fit the bolt head or nut sloppily.

Sanders and Portable Grinders.   All tools which are used to drive abrasives are subject to damage from the resulting dust.   It is important to clean the ventilating

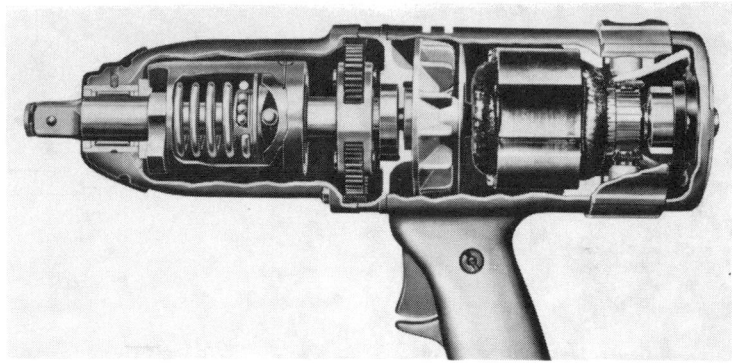

FIG. 13-10. Impact wrench (designed to provide high torque).

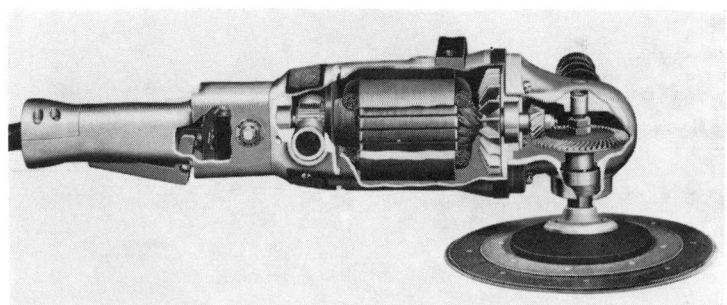

FIG. 13-11. Sander (should be cleaned frequently with air hose).

system and moving parts frequently.   This can be done with an air hose.   Occasionally, sanders and portable grinders should be disassembled and all parts cleaned. Gears should be relubricated at this time.   If units are used continuously, this procedure is recommended every sixty to ninety days.

Shears and Nibblers.   Properly adjusted and sharp cutting blades are most important to the proper performance of shears.   Manufacturer's instructions for adjustment and sharpening should be accurately followed.

Sharp punches and dies are most important to the proper performance of nibblers. Manufacturer's instructions for sharpening of punches and dies should be accurately followed.   Worn spindle bearings can cause improper clearance between the punch and die.   This can result in poor cutting, excessive loads, or damage.   Check this clearance frequently.

Circular Saws.   The lower retracting guards on circular saws must operate freely in order to cover the blade when the saw is removed from the work.   These should be

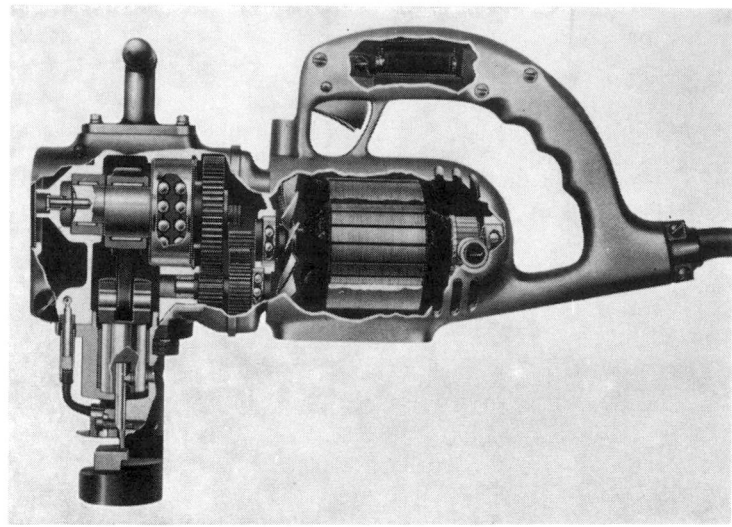

FIG. 13-12. Shears and nibbler (sharp cutting blades most important).

FIG. 13-13. Professional circular saw.

checked carefully to make sure they operate properly. The lower shoes on circular saws are frequently bent. Misalignment of the blade with guide markings can occur and the accuracy of angle cuts impaired if this happens. Bent shoe structures should be straightened or replaced.

Saw motors are frequently overloaded and burned-out because of the use of dull blades. It is most important to keep circular saw blades sharp to prevent motor failures and retain cutting ease.

Reciprocating Saws.   Blade holders and blade clamps on reciprocating saws should be carefully checked.   If they do not grip the blade properly, breakage of blades can occur and erratic cutting can result.   If spindle bearings are worn, excess play between

Fig. 13-14. Reciprocating saw.

Fig. 13-15. Router (high-speed spindle is driven directly by the motor).

the reciprocating shaft and the spindle will cause difficult cutting.   Worn spindle bearings should be replaced.

Routers.   Routers have high-speed spindles directly driven by the motor.   The collet which grips the cutter must be true in order to prevent excessive vibrations. Worn or wobbly collets should be replaced.   Spindle bearings on routers are subject to very heavy loads. If they become rough or sloppy, they should be replaced. Dull cutters can cause motor overloads and burning of the work. It is important that router cutters be kept sharp.

Hammers. Demolition hammers, rotary hammers, and percussion drills all produce heavy blows on the accessory being used. The mechanism parts are designed to withstand these heavy impacts. They require good lubrication, however, for long

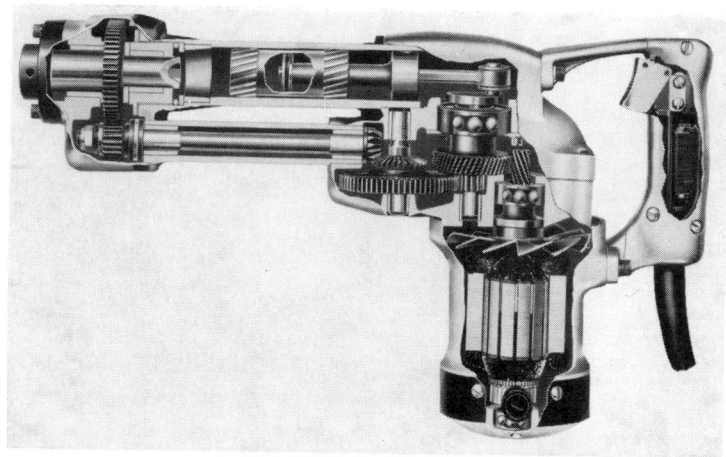

Fig. 13-16. Hammer (periodically should be dismantled and cleaned).

life. It is most important to follow the manufacturer's instructions for the lubrication of hammers. When hammers are used for concrete work, the resulting dust can be very damaging to the mechanism and motor. A good preventive maintenance schedule on hammers will materially reduce service costs. Periodically, this type of tool should be dismantled and thoroughly cleaned. Worn parts should be replaced before they fail and cause damage to other parts.

Chapter 14

SCAFFOLDS AND LADDERS

By V. W. MENG
President
Patent Scaffolding Company
Division of Harsco Corporation
Long Island City, N.Y.

Important strides have been made in reducing plant maintenance costs, despite rising material prices, through good management of labor. Where cleaning, painting, and repairs go overhead, however, systematic labor management alone cannot provide the worker efficiency needed for minimum cost. The worker must be properly equipped—and the basic item of this proper equipment should be correct means of support. Greatest efficiency—hence the greatest saving—is achieved by the use of supporting equipment that permits minimum job time due to freely moving, confident workers; and assures properly done jobs, faster erection and dismantling of equipment, and reduced time loss from accidents.

Modern scaffolds and ladders are designed to meet the requirements of these overhead maintenance operations. There are portable, demountable, metal scaffolds; ladders and allied equipment; and swinging scaffolds. Which of these should be chosen for most efficient accomplishment of any one job depends upon such factors as:

1. How high is the work?   Is it in or out of normal ladder range?
2. Is there a wall to afford support or bracing?
3. Is the area below the work suitable for giving support?
4. Must people or conveyances pass unobstructed beneath the work?
5. Is frequent moving of the support necessary?
6. Does work range horizontally or vertically, or is it spot work?
7. How many men and how much equipment must be supported?

To illustrate how these factors affect choice of equipment, assume that the windows on a one-story building are to be cleaned.

1. The work is within ladder range.
2. There is a wall for support.
3. The area below the work will afford support.
4. No traffic must pass beneath the work.
5. Shifting of the support is unnecessary.
6. The work ranges horizontally.
7. One man with light equipment can do the work.

All factors except number 6 suggest that either a ladder or ladder scaffold would be most practical for this job. But factor 6 indicates that a ladder scaffold is the ideal choice. A man with a ladder scaffold can clean a much greater area from one placement with freer movement and no obstruction, and then more easily *roll* his scaffold to the next location to continue his work.

Similarly, it can be shown that work of considerable vertical scope, such as exterior wall cleaning, pointing up masonry, etc., can be accomplished most efficiently with swinging scaffolds, or that low-height spot work, such as cleaning transoms or light fixtures, is best done with the ladders. Other maintenance operations, too, can be resolved into classes requiring different means of support for most efficient accomplishment.

FIG. 14-1. Folding aluminum ladder scaffolds are designed so that the end frames will not fall over at any point during the erection or dismantling process. It is a completely freestanding unit at all times.

FIG. 14-2. Outrigger supports should be used when working at platform heights greater than four times the smallest dimension. Shown is an aluminum sectional scaffold 4-ft 6-in. wide.

SCAFFOLDS

The most desirable scaffolds are prefabricated from high-strength metal tubing and are equipped with casters when casters are necessary for easy mobility of the erected scaffold. The types usually most practical for maintenance work are aluminum rolling scaffolds with internal stairways and aluminum ladder scaffolds.

Folding scaffolds (Fig. 14-1)[1] are built in one-piece base sections which speed the erection and dismantling process. The ladder-type base sections are 29 in. or 4 ft

[1] Illustrations in this chapter show the equipment of Patent Scaffolding Co., Division of Harsco Corporation.

6 in. wide, with spans of 6 ft, 8 ft, or 10 ft between frames.   In this type of unit, the
two diagonal braces and one horizontal brace are integral parts of the folding unit.
Intermediate, extension, and guard-rail sections can be placed atop the folding unit,
using individual end frames and braces.

A larger folding-type scaffold has base dimensions of 4 ft 6 in. by 6 ft.   This unit
has an internal stairway, and the upper sections as well as the base section are one-
piece folding units.   When the scaffold must be erected higher than recommended for a
base of this size, outriggers can be used.   They clamp to the legs of the base section.

FIG. 14-3. Sectional rolling scaffold.   Steel
frames are 5 ft wide and are joined by diagonal braces.

FIG.   14-4. Aluminum ladder scaffold·
Basic unit consists of 6-ft ladder frames,
diagonal braces, platform, and adjustable
casters.

Means for leveling, to compensate for uneven ground, are part of the leg equipment.
The casters on the legs are locked at both wheel and swivel.

Sectional aluminum stairway scaffolds are designed with end frames of various
heights to provide different working levels, adjustable bottom sections with casters,
intermediate sections, half sections, and guard-rail sections.   All components are
sectionalized for ease of erection and dismantling.   Internal stairways are used.
Outriggers may be used to increase the base area (see Fig. 14-2).

Sectional steel scaffolds (Fig. 14-3) are recommended where heavier load conditions
are likely.   The welded-steel end frames are trussed for additional load-bearing
capacity.   Some end frames have integral exterior ladders.   Adjustable extension
legs may be used for leveling.   Casters lock at wheel and swivel.

FIG. 14-5. Swinging scaffold. Steel wire rope, mechanical raising and lowering device.

Steel ladder scaffolds, similar to the aluminum, are used for greater loads. Steel cross bracing is used. An often useful accessory for the steel ladder scaffold is the bridging trestle. This replaces the diagonal cross braces and permits the scaffold to clear obstructions or permits the passage of traffic beneath the scaffold without interference.

The folding, sectional-stairway, and ladder scaffolds are used for outdoor cleaning and maintenance work—ladder scaffolds for low to medium height and one-man jobs, and folding or sectional-stairway types for higher or heavier work. They are especially suitable when the work is horizontal. Indoors, they simplify work on walls and ceilings, and often are suitable for group lamp replacement.

Swinging scaffolds (Fig. 14-5) are essentially steel-reinforced wood platforms suspended from above by steel cable with mechanical raising and lowering devices at platform level. The most satisfactory swinging scaffolds from the standpoint of safety and ease of operation are those supported by steel wire rope raised and lowered by all-metal drum and ratchet or geared-winch mechanisms located at the ends of a factory-made reinforced platform.

Swinging scaffolds are particularly suitable for cleaning and painting, tuck pointing, window washing, and similar jobs on exterior walls or tanks where large vertical range and quick up-down mobility are required. They are used also where the surface below the work is crowded, or where conditions are unsuitable for support of ground-based scaffolding. They are recommended for light and medium loads.

FIG. 14-6. Tube and coupler scaffolding applied to cylindrical tank.

Tube and coupler scaffolds (Fig. 14-6), providing the greatest versatility in scaffolding odd shapes and in erecting to extreme heights, are erected from four basic components. They are: steel base plates, interlocking steel tubing or pipe, couplers for making right-angle connections, and adjustable couplers for making connection at other than tight angles.

Since horizontal runners can be placed at any point on the vertical posts and, in turn, bearers at any point on the runner, maximum versatility is obtained. This type of equipment is used in scaffolding spheres, cylinders, and other odd-shaped vessels found in refineries. It also can be used to build storage racks with any size of bay.

This scaffold also is available in all-aluminum components, making it particularly useful in corrosive atmospheres. Both types can be used as rolling scaffolds.

Safety Requirements. Almost all present-day steel and aluminum scaffolds for plant maintenance are inspected and approved by Underwriters' Laboratories, Inc. The UL seal on maintenance scaffolds means that the product not only is properly designed to sustain the loads for which it was intended, but also that certain manufacturing standards are being maintained to assure maximum strength. So one of the first things a maintenance department should look for is UL approval. After purchase of the equipment, it becomes the department's responsibility to make sure that the scaffold is not only used properly, but also that it is maintained properly.

Maintenance. Aluminum scaffolds of all types require minimum maintenance. Stairways, ladders, and platforms should be inspected frequently, and any grease or oil should be removed immediately. Make sure the plywood platforms or platform planks are solid, with no splits. Do not store platforms near excessive heat, to avoid drying and warping. Casters should be cleaned and lubricated, and brakes should be checked for satisfactory operation. Threads on extension legs should be cleaned and lubricated periodically for smooth operation. Coupling pins used to join frames vertically should be kept clean so that upper frames slip over the pins easily and freely.

With aluminum scaffolds, slight bends in the tubing due to severe impact or mishandling should be straightened. The spring-lock devices used to fasten the braces should be kept free from dirt to insure proper operation of the lock. On the more popular types of aluminum scaffolding, this mechanism is exposed and can be cleaned easily with a wire brush.

The steel types of scaffolding should be kept clean by scraping or wire brushing; any rusted spots on frames or braces should be scraped and touched up with quick-drying enamel. Stud threads should be lubricated, and wing nuts run off and on to insure fast, secure fastening during erection. All frames should be checked frequently for missing vertical-coupling sprockets and the pins that lock them in place, as well as wing nuts. Cross braces should be straightened if bent, and the alignment of the tops of the frames should be checked and braces realigned if necessary.

For maximum safety, swinging scaffolds must be properly maintained. The operating mechanism, or winch, should be kept free of dirt and grit at all times. A wire brush usually is satisfactory for this work. All operating parts should be properly lubricated as outlined in the manufacturer's instructions. The safety devices in the winches should be inspected frequently. Pawls and pawl springs should be checked for proper working condition. Teeth on the drum casting should be inspected, and if broken or worn, the manufacturer should be consulted about replacement. The steel cable should be run off and checked for excessive damage and kinks and then rewound through an oily rag to clean the cable and give it a thin coat of oil. Worm and gear mechanisms should be checked for excessive play, cleaned, and repacked with fiber grease. The stirrup should be checked for alignment and straightened, and all painted surfaces of the machine should be recoated where necessary for rust prevention.

Wooden platforms require careful inspection and maintenance. Grease or oil spilled on the platform should be removed immediately. After a job, the platform should be placed across horses for inspection, overhaul, and repair. Mortar, concrete, and paint should be removed with a wire brush and scraper. Broken rungs, slats, and damaged or missing toeboards should be replaced, as should missing hinges and hooks and eyes. After necessary repairs have been made, the platform should be given a

STEEL SCAFFOLDING SAFETY RULES

as Recommended by

STEEL SCAFFOLDING AND SHORING INSTITUTE

Following are some common sense rules designed to promote safety in the use of steel scaffolding. These rules are illustrative and suggestive only, and are intended to deal only with some of the many practices and conditions encountered in the use of scaffolding. The rules do not purport to be all-inclusive or to supplant or replace other additional safety and precautionary measures to cover usual or unusual conditions.

I. **POST THESE SCAFFOLDING SAFETY RULES** in a conspicuous place and be sure that all persons who erect, dismantle or use scaffolding are aware of them.

II. **FOLLOW LOCAL CODES, ORDINANCES** and regulations pertaining to scaffolding.

III. **INSPECT ALL EQUIPMENT BEFORE USING**—Never use any equipment that is damaged or deteriorated in any way.

IV. **KEEP ALL EQUIPMENT IN GOOD REPAIR.** Avoid using rusted equipment—the strength of rusted equipment is not known.

V. **INSPECT ERECTED SCAFFOLDS REGULARLY** to be sure that they are maintained in safe condition.

VI. **CONSULT YOUR SCAFFOLDING SUPPLIER WHEN IN DOUBT**—scaffolding is his business, **NEVER TAKE CHANCES.**

A. **PROVIDE ADEQUATE SILLS** for scaffold posts and use base plates.

B. **USE ADJUSTING SCREWS** instead of blocking to adjust to uneven grade conditions.

C. **PLUMB AND LEVEL ALL SCAFFOLDS** as the erection proceeds. Do not force braces to fit—level the scaffold until proper fit can be made easily.

D. **FASTEN ALL BRACES SECURELY.**

E. **DO NOT CLIMB CROSS BRACES.**

F. **ON WALL SCAFFOLDS PLACE AND MAINTAIN ANCHORS** securely between structure and scaffold at least every 30′ of length and 25′ of height.

G. **FREE STANDING SCAFFOLD TOWERS MUST BE RESTRAINED FROM TIPPING** by guying or other means.

H. **EQUIP ALL PLANKED OR STAGED AREAS** with proper guard rails, and add toeboards when required.

I. **POWER LINES NEAR SCAFFOLDS** are dangerous—use caution and consult the power service company for advice.

J. **DO NOT USE** ladders or makeshift devices on top of scaffolds to increase the height.

K. **DO NOT OVERLOAD SCAFFOLDS.**

L. **PLANKING:**

1. Use only lumber that is properly inspected and graded as scaffold plank.

2. Planking shall have at least 12″ of overlap and extend 6″ beyond center of support, or be cleated at both ends to prevent sliding off supports.

3. Do not allow unsupported ends of plank to extend an unsafe distance beyond supports.

4. Secure plank to scaffold when necessary.

M. **FOR ROLLING SCAFFOLD THE FOLLOWING ADDITIONAL RULES APPLY:**

1. **DO NOT RIDE ROLLING SCAFFOLDS.**

2. **REMOVE ALL MATERIAL AND EQUIPMENT** from platform before moving scaffold.

3. **CASTER BRAKES MUST BE APPLIED** at all times when scaffolds are not being moved.

4. **DO NOT ATTEMPT TO MOVE A ROLLING SCAFFOLD WITHOUT SUFFICIENT HELP**—watch out for holes in floor and overhead obstructions.

5. **DO NOT EXTEND ADJUSTING SCREWS ON ROLLING SCAFFOLDS MORE THAN** 12″.

6. **USE HORIZONTAL DIAGONAL BRACING** near the bottom, top and at intermediate levels of 30′.

7. **DO NOT USE BRACKETS ON ROLLING SCAFFOLDS** without consideration of overturning effect.

8. **THE WORKING PLATFORM HEIGHT OF A ROLLING SCAFFOLD** must not exceed four times the smallest base dimension unless guyed or otherwise stabilized.

N. For "PUTLOGS" and "TRUSSES" the following additional rules apply:

1. **DO NOT CANTILEVER OR EXTEND PUTLOGS/TRUSSES** as side brackets without thorough consideration for loads to be applied.

2. **PUTLOGS/TRUSSES SHOULD EXTEND AT LEAST** 6″ beyond point of support.

3. **PLACE PROPER BRACING BETWEEN PUTLOGS/TRUSSES** when the span of putlog/truss is more than 12′.

thick coat of quick-drying paint. Finally, clean and examine the S and L hooks from which the scaffold is hung, clean and inspect center stanchions, and replace missing or defective wing nuts and bolts.

Tube and coupler scaffolding should undergo a systematic inspection. Bent tubes should be strengthened and, in case of seriously damaged tubes, discarded or cut into shorter lengths for short bearers. Very dirty or rusty tubes should be cleaned with a wire brush. During this operation, inspect the male and female fittings for damage which would affect their safety and then clean with a wire brush. Remove damaged couplers from stock. Studs should be kept covered with a light film of oil, and catch bolts should be checked for stripped threads.

LADDERS

Some things are so simple, both in the way they are made and in the ways they are used, that the scientific principles upon which they are based are barely visible. With all the simplicity it has constantly retained, the ladder as we know it in its best form today represents a high degree of engineering skill, scientific accuracy and, most important, dependable safety.

Vital differences in ladders may not be detected except by the expert; hence industry finds it profitable to seek expert ladder advice. Proper weight, exact balance, scientific proportions, dependable quality of materials, character of workmanship and, of utmost importance, adaptability of a certain type of ladder to the particular kind of service for which it is intended—these factors are essential in the modern ladder even though they may not always be visible to the uninitiated.

Most of the states and principal industrial groups take the ladder question seriously, and have acknowledged the importance of ladder efficiency and safety by establishing rigid codes designed to insure the use of ladders built for the special kind of service required.

A program of ladder upkeep and care should be as much a part of any company's safety program as is its maintenance of equipment or any other efficiency or safety devices. The proper use of ladders must be considered no less than the matter of choice when purchases are made.

Three Ladder Groups. Generally, ladders can be classified in three groups: extension ladders, single (straight) ladders, and stepladders. Also, there are special-purpose ladders, which may constitute a fourth classification.

Extension ladders are used in building construction, painting, plastering, maintenance, and almost everywhere that an adjustable ladder is needed.

Single ladders, which of course are not adjustable for height, are generally used when one type of work is to be done at a more or less standard height.

Both extension and single ladders should be fitted with ladder feet to prevent slipping.

Stepladders are what the name implies. They also are self-supporting. Selection for both efficiency and safety is of prime importance. The use of the proper type of stepladder, whether standard classification or special purpose, is receiving more and more attention from industrial executives responsible for their selection.

For design and construction details, the "Safety Code for Wood Ladders" (A-14.1—1959), published by the American Standards Association, is a reliable guide. Since not all ladders meet the standards of safety necessary in industrial plants, the following condensed information on the most important types of ladders should be helpful to those responsible for procurement and factory maintenance. In addition, Underwriters' Laboratories, Inc., approval of a ladder indicates it meets basic standards of design and construction for safety for various categories of use.

Extension Ladders. Extension ladders (Fig. 14-7) consist of two sections with three-section ladders also available for longer lengths. The strength and safety of such ladders come from the type and quality of wood used in the side rails, as well as their size. Rung size also is important. The required thickness of the side rails depends on the length of the ladder and the type of wood used. The distance between the side rails of the bottom section of a parallel side ladder should be at least 14½ in. inside to inside for ladders of extended lengths up to 28 ft. Between 28 and 40 ft it should be a minimum of 16 in., and for ladders over 40 ft it should be 18 in. Two-section extension ladders longer than 60 ft are not allowed under the ASA code.

Good-grade rope (⁵⁄₁₆-in. diameter minimum) and pulley (1¼-in. diameter minimum) for raising the upper section are essential features of well-built extension ladders, because weakness at this point may result in serious injuries. All holes to hold the wood rungs must either extend through the side rails or be bored to give at least ⅞-in. length of bearing to the rung tenon.

Extension ladders should be equipped with automatic spring locks, which enable the worker who is on the ground or floor to raise and lower the upper section. No manual adjustment is necessary. This automatic spring lock, like all other ladder hardware, is better if plated to resist rust.

Single Ladders. Single ladders longer than 30 ft are not permitted under the ASA code. Rungs should be not more than 12 in. apart, and all holes for rungs should be drilled in the same manner as for extension ladders. Rungs must be tight in the hole and secured in place with nails to prevent turning. Pressed-steel rung braces under several rungs is one earmark of a good single ladder. The width between side rails at the base, inside to inside, must be at least 11½ in. for all ladders up to and including 10 ft. This minimum width increases 14 in. for each additional 2 ft of length.

Because ladders are subjected to rough usage in such trades as masonry and building construction, the extra-heavy-duty single ladder is preferred. Both the side rails and the rungs are heavier than in the standard single ladder, although the length is limited to 30 ft. Mason's ladders should measure at least 12 in. between side rails (inside to inside) up to 10 ft, with ¼ in. for each additional 2 ft of height. Rungs must be between 8 and 12 in. apart.

Stepladders. Stepladders should be made so that the treads will be level in the open position. Good-quality stepladders are designed so that, when open, the slope of the front section is at least 3½ in. per ft and the slope of the back section at least 2 in. per ft for each

Fig. 14-7. Extension ladder proportioned to meet ASA codes and approved by UL.

12 in. of side rail. Stepladders, in accordance with ASA and UL code requirements, should never be furnished in lengths greater than 20 ft, and steps should be uniformly spaced not more than 12 in. apart. Good-quality ladders are equipped with steel safety spreaders, so designed that they will not injure hands when opening and closing. The spreaders also act as braces between the front and rear side rails.

The inside to inside measurement of side rails at the top should be at least 11½ in., with an increase of at least 1 in. for each foot of ladder length. This assures a safe, wide base.

Safe footing is assured in high-quality ladders by reinforcing steps by means of trussing and bracing, substantially attached by rivets, bolts, or screws. Ladders should be checked frequently to make sure that steps are securely fastened.

Stepladders for heavy-duty use are usually identified by a rung-type back, this construction being more rigid than the slatted back. It permits working from either side.

The minimum dimensions of parts of the heavy-duty ladder (or equivalent cross section developing an actual working stress per square inch as required by the ASA Code) are shown in the table on page 9-235.

The platform stepladder (Fig. 14-8) is by far the most popular, having proved itself by reducing the number of accidents resulting from falls and dropped objects. The 14- by 19-in. platform gives the worker a firm footing and a "guard" on three sides, at the same time permitting him to work with both hands.

	Length 12 ft and less		Length 14 to 20 ft	
	Thickness, inch	Depth, inches	Thickness, inches	Depth, inches
Side rails.......	$2\frac{5}{32}$	$3\frac{1}{4}$	$1\frac{1}{16}$	$3\frac{1}{2}$
Back legs.......	$2\frac{5}{32}$	$2\frac{1}{4}$	$1\frac{1}{16}$	$2\frac{1}{4}$
Steps..........	$2\frac{5}{32}$	$3\frac{5}{8}$	$2\frac{5}{32}$	$4\frac{1}{4}$
Tops..........	$2\frac{5}{32}$	$5\frac{1}{2}$	$2\frac{5}{32}$	$5\frac{1}{2}$

In the safety platform ladder, steps are truss-rodded and also knee-braced. The steel spreader is of the safety type, a shield over the joint preventing injury to the worker's hands. Good spreaders do not permit the ladder to accidentally fold up. Holes in the top are used as a tool rack, thus reducing danger from falling tools.

Special-purpose Ladders. There are many types of special-purpose ladders, such as shelf, fruit pickers', trolley, decorators' and paperhangers', and others. One of the more familiar types is the sectional which, as the name implies, is made in interlocking sections, either continuous taper or interchangeable. It is used widely by window cleaners. A big advantage is portability, since it can be knocked down into small units. Sectional ladders should not be longer than 31 ft and should have an overlap of at least 1 ft.

All special-purpose ladders should conform to the ASA standards.

Metal Ladders. In recent years, single, extension, and stepladders made of aluminum or magnesium alloys have come on the market. They are light in weight and resist climatic conditions. However, because they are conductors of electricity, they should not be used around electrical equipment. It is well to tag or paint instructions to this effect on the ladder.

Upon receipt, metal ladders should be examined for sharp edges and burrs on the side rails, tops, and bottoms; such defects can cause painful cuts. The bottoms should be protected to prevent the marring of floors. The best method is to use safety shoes, which also help to prevent slipping.

Metal ladders are now covered by ASA code A14.2, effective Oct. 5, 1956.

Precautionary Measures. Where special groups are using ladders, such as plumbers, electricians, and millwrights, the ladders

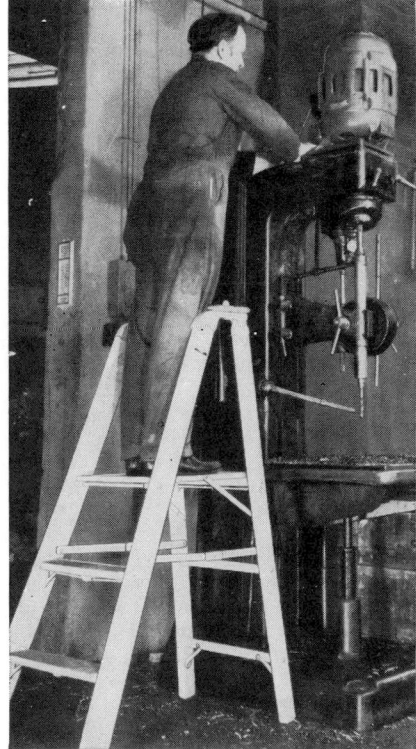

Fig. 14-8. Platform step ladder. Safe because it permits worker to have both hands free.

should be properly identified, with the members of each craft held responsible for their particular ladders. The use of just any ladder the worker comes across is likely to lead to costly disaster. Instructing workers as to ladder usage is extremely important.

Information relative to choosing the right ladders for specific kinds of work is easily obtained from concerns whose business it is to apply scientific principles to this field of manufacture.   Many factors must be considered, including materials, hardware, safety shoes, and other accessories as well as design, measurements, proportions, and construction.   Any company that has made a specialty of quality ladder manufacture may be relied upon as a source of information.   Many of their ladders exceed ASA code requirements.

Care of Ladders

1. Always inspect a ladder before using it.   Do not load-test a ladder, because this procedure subjects it to a more severe load than it was designed for, or intended to carry, and wood members may be permanently injured.   New ladders should be checked to make certain that such defects as pitch pockets, knots, and cross grain do not exceed the ASA code limits.
2. Inspect periodically for defects inherent and developed.   Ladders found to have defects should be withdrawn from use and marked, "Do not use."
3. Store in locations not exposed to the elements.   Do not place near excessive heat or in damp areas.
4. Store in such position that they can be readily inspected and properly supported to prevent warp or sag.
5. Replace worn or frayed rope.
6. Keep hardware and fittings tight, although movable parts should operate freely.
7. Do not let grease or oil accumulate on rungs.

Use of Ladders

1. Ladder should be placed so that the distance from its foot to the wall is one-fourth the length of the extended ladder.
2. Place so that both side rails have a secure footing.
3. Ladder feet of the proper type should be used on single and extension ladders.
4. Do not place ladders in front of doors or doorways, which open in the direction of the ladder, unless they are locked or blocked open.
5. Never place a ladder on boxes or other unstable bases to get additional height.
6. Always face a ladder when ascending or descending.
7. Both hands should be kept free for climbing.   Use hand line where practicable to raise or lower light materials.
8. Do not use ladders with faulty steps, rungs, or side rails.   Improvised repairs should not be made.
9. Never splice together two short ladders to provide longer sections.
10. Do not use ladders as skids, guys, or for any purpose foreign to that for which they were intended.
11. Two-section extension ladders measuring up to 36 ft always have at least 3 ft overlap; 36-ft to 48-ft ladders should have an overlap of 4 ft; and 48- to 60-ft ladders should have an overlap of at least 5 ft.   Lengths of extension ladders are designated by the combined length of sections.
12. Tops of ordinary stepladders should not be used as steps.
13. For your own safety do not overload any ladder.

Chapter 15

HEATING EQUIPMENT

By John S. Wendt
Senior Development Engineer
Engineering and Construction Department, Ore Processing
J. J. Mehler, Jr. and H. W. Lutz
Application and Development Department
Machinery Division
Dravo Corporation
Pittsburgh, Pa.

Space heating is accomplished by passing air over a hot surface (heating element), where it picks up heat by convection and radiation, and circulating the air to or through the space to be heated, where it gives up its heat. A space-heating system must provide:

1. A means of moving the air from the heating surface to and through the space to be heated.
2. A means to guide the air to be heated over the heating surface.
3. A heating surface.
4. A transfer of energy from a source such that it heats the heating surface.
5. A means of supplying a source of energy to the heating surface.

The source of energy is fuel, the combustion of which gives up energy in the form of radiation from the flame and convection, as the products of combustion pass over the heat-exchange surface, designed to extract energy from these products. The energy thus released during combustion is transferred to the heating surfaces of a piece of heating equipment in one of two ways: (1) *Directly*—the heating surfaces of the heating unit receive the energy released by combustion directly, and the air to be heated passes over these same surfaces. Such units are called "direct-fired heaters." (2) *Indirectly*—the energy released by combustion is used to heat a fluid which in turn gives up its energy to the heating surface of the piece of heating equipment over which the air to be heated is passed. Such heating units are named from the fluids used to convey the energy to the heating surface, i.e., steam, hot water.

Direct-fired units are built in a wide variety of sizes and shapes, which fall into three general categories: built-up units (usually used in central-heating installations, packaged unit heaters, and suspended unit heaters.

Built-up units range in capacity from approximately 400,000 to 8,000,000 Btu per hr and are usually assembled at the point of application. They are of two general constructions: either built-up like a boiler (brick-set); or steel-cased, insulated, and having a combustion chamber lined with refractory. Secondary heating surfaces can be built up out of cast-iron sections, or may consist of steel tubes arranged so that the products of combustion pass through the sections or tubes, and the air to be heated passes over the outside of the surfaces. The air to be heated is moved over the heating surfaces by large blowers. Because these large units are generally used as central-heating units, the air passing over the unit is distributed throughout the space to be heated by a system of ducts. Fans and drives are usually engineered by the manufacturer to accommodate the duct system. These units can be obtained equipped for burning coal, oil, or gas.

The advantages of this type of unit, when applied for central heating, are: centralized maintenance, centralized fuel handling and storage, occupies space not needed for production (if incorporated into the original building design).

Disadvantages are that the installation is relatively permanent, lacks flexibility in the event of building expansion or changes in layout, requires extensive air-distribution system, and depends upon a single unit for heat security.

Packaged-type heating units range in size from about 200,000 to 2,500,000 Btu per hr. They are completely assembled at the factory, usually having been test fired, and require external fuel, electrical, and vent (flue-gas) pipe connections.

Combustion chambers are constructed of carbon steel (refractory lined) or stainless or aluminized steel, and are connected to carbon-steel flue-gas passages, generally in the form of tube banks.

The air to be heated is moved over the combustion chamber and secondary tubes by multiblade fans, usually located in the base of the unit, with discharge at the top. The heater outlet may be equipped for a duct connection or for air nozzles, which discharge air directly to the space to be heated. The fan drive is usually engineered by the supplier to meet such external static pressures as may be imposed on the unit by ductwork, filters, and dampers.

These units can be equipped with oil, gas, or combination oil-gas burners, and utilize mechanical draft to effect the flow of combustion products and the supply of combustion air to the burner. They are usually supplied as vertical (floor-set) units; may be suspended in horizontal or inverted position; and can be equipped with filters and dampers as the application requires.

They have the following advantages: mobility (can be easily moved to new locations); flexibility of operation (can be used to heat a portion of a structure without running a large central system); ease of installation due to factory assembly; and, in larger installations involving a number of units, the heat security of the structure is not dependent upon a single source. The disadvantages are extensive fuel distribution system and dispersion of points of maintenance.

Suspended unit heaters are built in capacities from 25,000 to approximately 200,000 Btu per hr for operation on natural gas or light fuel oil. Basically, they consist of a natural-draft burner firing in a cast-iron or aluminized-steel combustion chamber having vertical tubular flue-gas passages, comprising the heating surface. The products of combustion are collected in a top header for venting to atmosphere. Air circulation through the heater is usually provided by a direct-driven propeller-type fan. The air is discharged through louvers to the space being heated. Units can be obtained for limited duct installations, with or without a fan.

Advantages of this type of unit are: flexibility for small-area applications; ease of installation; and light weight. Disadvantages are: extensive fuel-distribution system in large-area installations; lack of temperature uniformity at working level; excessive air movement in vicinity of the blow from the unit; and points of maintenance relatively inaccessible.

Application Notes—Direct-fired Units. The passing of the proper amount of air over a direct-fired unit is of paramount importance; too little air permits the combustion chamber to overheat and shortens the life of the unit. The *use of air filters* necessitates a regular inspection schedule to prevent clogging and subsequent damage.

Units arranged for *tempering make-up air* should be equipped with modulating burners to conserve fuel in mild weather.

The working level is best served when outlets deliver heated air at approximately 2,000 ft per min velocity parallel to the floor and above workers' heads; return air should be taken low, as near to floor level as practicable. With extensive duct distribution systems, low-velocity outlets may be preferable, and should be equipped with diffuser vanes and located so as not to blow on personnel.

Fuel-distribution piping (oil and gas) is usually carried overhead. *Dirt and drip legs* should be provided ahead of the control equipment for each unit in the form of an extension of a down-flow leg.

The *pressure drop* allowed for in *gas* distribution systems is a function of the available pressure and its expected downward fluctuations: *low pressure* available (6 to 8 oz)—pressure drop throughout the system 0.2 in. water column; *high pressure* (over 1 lb)—usual practice is to reduce pressure to 8 oz and then distribute within the plant with

Table 15-1. Capacity of Gas Piping
Cu Ft per Hr with a 0.6 Sp Gr Gas and Pressure Drop of 0.3 in. Water Column

Length of pipe, ft	Nominal diameter of pipe, in.				
	¾	1	1¼	1½	2
15	172	345	750		
30	120	241	535	850	
45	99	199	435	700	
60	86	173	380	610	
75	77	155	345	545	
90	70	141	310	490	
105	65	131	285	450	920
120	...	120	270	420	860
150	...	109	242	380	780
180	...	100	225	350	720

Reprinted by permission from "Heating, Ventilating, Air Conditioning Guide," 1955, Chap. 15.

Table 15-2. Multipliers for Various Specific Gravities
For Use with Table 15-1

Specific gravity	Multiplier	Specific gravity	Multiplier	Specific gravity	Multiplier
0.35	1.31	0.75	0.895	1.40	0.655
0.40	1.23	0.80	0.867	1.50	0.633
0.45	1.16	0.85	0.841	1.60	0.612
0.50	1.10	0.90	0.817	1.70	0.594
0.55	1.04	1.00	0.775	1.80	0.577
0.60	1.00	1.10	0.740	1.90	0.565
0.65	0.962	1.20	0.707	2.00	0.547
0.70	0.926	1.30	0.680	2.10	0.535

Reprinted by permission from "Heating, Ventilating, Air Conditioning Guide," 1955, Chap. 15.

0.5 in. water column pressure drop to heating units. All heating units should be equipped with pressure regulators adjusted to equipment manufacturer's recommendations. Tables 15-1 and 15-2 give the capacity of various pipe sizes for pressure drop of 0.3 in. water column with gas of 0.6 sp gr and multipliers for various specific gravities.

Flues, stacks, and vents for the products of combustion from each type of direct-fired heating equipment are sized by the manufacturer to handle the rated volume of combustion products. Suspended unit heaters are usually designed with built-in down-draft diverters. A barometric draft-control damper is not needed when a diverter is present. A barometric damper acts to limit the overfire draft to the required level, tending to reduce the stack temperature of natural-draft units. *Barometric dampers* should be designed to open only when the draft increases above the desired setting. Dampers should be located downstream from devices which limit high stack temperatures. *Horizontal runs* of flue should be avoided, but when necessary should be pitched upward at least ½ in. per ft in the direction of flow. Stack height should be carried at least 2 ft above the highest point of roof within 10 ft of the stack location for natural draft units.

The *clearance* of the unit, metal flues, and stacks from combustible material is based upon maintaining a maximum temperature of combustible surface not over 160°F. Considerations of accessibility dictate greater distances when locating the heating unit. *Minimum clearances* from direct-fired, floor-mounted units are given in Table 15-3.

Table 15-3. Minimum Clearances from Direct-fired Floor-mounted Units
In Inches

	Above	Sides and rear	Front	Breeching
Mechanical units with 250°F bonnet control:				
Burning oil or coal....................	3	6	48	18
Burning gas...........................	3	6	18	9
Natural draft units without bonnet control:				
Burning liquid or solid fuel.............	18	18	48	18
Burning gas...........................	18	18	18	9

Vertical stack runs should be kept at least 18 in. away from combustible material. The recommended arrangement for passing a stack through a combustible roof structure is shown in Fig. 15-1. The sleeve may be omitted when the unit is fired with gas

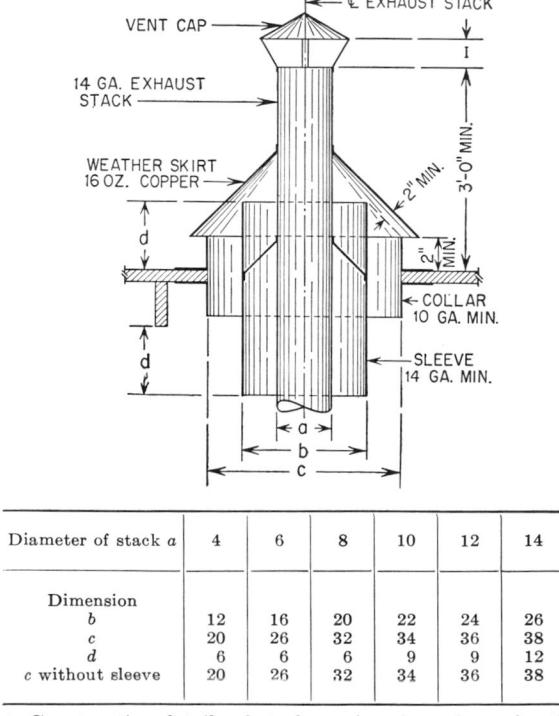

Diameter of stack a	4	6	8	10	12	14
Dimension						
b	12	16	20	22	24	26
c	20	26	32	34	36	38
d	6	6	6	9	9	12
c without sleeve	20	26	32	34	36	38

FIG. 15-1. Construction details of stack passing through combustible roof.

only and is equipped with a high-limit bonnet control having a maximum setting of 250°F.

STEAM HEATING SYSTEMS

Generally, industrial steam heating systems may be classified as high-pressure, low-pressure, vacuum, or vapor systems, with the first three types more prevalent than the fourth. They are further classified in accordance with one or several features, e.g., one-pipe system, two-pipe system, up-flow, down-flow, dry return, wet return, gravity condensate return, or mechanical condensate return. A *one-pipe system*, which is rarely used industrially, is one in which both the steam supply and the condensate

Table 15-4. Steam-pipe Capacities for 30-psig Steam Systems*
Capacity Expressed in Pounds per Hour
(Steam and Condensate Flowing in Same Direction)

Pipe size, in.	Drop in pressure—pounds per 100 ft in length					
	$\frac{1}{8}$	$\frac{1}{4}$	$\frac{1}{2}$	$\frac{3}{4}$	1	2
$\frac{3}{4}$	15	22	31	38	45	63
1	31	46	63	77	89	125
$1\frac{1}{4}$	69	100	141	172	199	281
$1\frac{1}{2}$	107	154	219	267	309	437
2	217	313	444	543	627	886
$2\frac{1}{2}$	358	516	730	924	1,030	1,460
3	651	940	1,330	1,630	1,880	2,600
$3\frac{1}{2}$	979	1,410	2,000	2,450	2,830	4,000
4	1,390	2,000	2,830	3,460	4,000	5,660
5	2,560	3,640	5,230	6,400	7,390	10,500
6	4,210	6,030	8,590	10,400	12,100	17,200
8	8,750	12,600	17,900	21,900	25,300	35,100
10	16,300	23,500	33,200	40,600	46,900	66,400
12	25,600	36,900	52,300	64,000	74,000	104,500

* Steam at an average pressure of 30 psig is used as the basis for calculating the table.
Reprinted by permission from "Heating, Ventilating, Air Conditioning Guide," 1955, Chap. 21.

return are conveyed within a single pipe, which must be relatively large and generously pitched in the direction of condensate return, thus limiting its flexibility or adaptability to industrial space. The *two-pipe system* most commonly used is one in which the steam supply and the condensate flow in separate mains and branches. Further identification is made dependent upon the flow of steam in risers (up-flow or down-flow), and general location of the condensate mains as to their being above or below boiler or condensate-receiver water-level line (dry return or wet return). A *gravity-return* system is one in which the condensate is returned to the boiler by gravity, requiring a height differential in proportion to the resistance to flow in the system, and generally it is not adaptable to industrial applications. A *mechanical-return* system is one in which the condensate is pumped to the boiler under pressure of atmosphere or above (condensate-pump-return system), or under vacuum conditions (vacuum-pump-return system). The flow of condensate in return piping of a dry-return system is based on the gravity principle in the mechanical-return system as well as in the gravity system.

High-pressure Steam Heating Systems. High-pressure systems are those in which the steam pressure is *above 15 psig*. They usually are operated between pressures of 30 and 150 psig and are used in large industrial-type buildings equipped with unit heaters or large built-up fan units, or where high-pressure steam is required for process use. Temperatures are generally controlled by modulating or throttling-type thermostatic valves controlled by the air temperature in the room; by fan inlet or outlet; or by on-off operation of fans from a thermostat.

Since this type of system operates under relatively high pressures, and there is a pressure differential between the steam and return mains, it becomes possible to lift the condensate to returns located above the heating units. The height at which the condensate line may be carried above the unit is dependent upon the pressure differential available at the steam side of the trap and the pressure in the return line at the location. For determining this height differential, 1 lb pressure differential can safely be associated with 2 ft of height.

Table 15-5. Steam-pipe Capacities for 150-psig Steam Systems*
Capacity Expressed in Pounds per Hour
(Steam and Condensate Flowing in Same Direction)

Pipe size, in.	Drop in pressure—psi per 100 ft in length						
	$\frac{1}{8}$	$\frac{1}{4}$	$\frac{1}{2}$	$\frac{3}{4}$	1	2	5
$\frac{3}{4}$	29	41	58	71	82	116	184
1	58	82	117	143	165	233	369
$1\frac{1}{4}$	130	185	262	320	370	523	827
$1\frac{1}{2}$	203	287	407	497	575	813	1,290
2	412	583	825	1,010	1,170	1,650	2,600
$2\frac{1}{2}$	683	959	1,360	1,650	1,920	2,710	4,290
3	1,240	1,750	2,480	3,020	3,500	4,940	7,820
$3\frac{1}{2}$	1,860	2,630	3,720	4,550	5,250	7,420	11,700
4	2,630	3,720	5,260	6,430	7,430	10,500	16,600
5	4,860	6,880	9,730	11,900	13,800	19,500	30,800
6	7,960	11,300	16,000	19,500	22,600	31,900	50,400
8	16,600	23,500	33,200	40,600	47,000	66,400	105,000
10	30,800	43,400	61,700	75,600	87,300	123,000	195,000
12	48,600	68,800	97,300	119,000	138,000	194,000	307,500

* Steam at an average pressure of 150 psig is used as the basis for calculating the table.
Reprinted by permission from "Heating, Ventilating, Air Conditioning Guide," 1955, Chap. 21.

Condensate at a pressure above atmosphere may be flashed into steam for use at low pressure, or passed through an economizer heater (water) before being discharged to a vented receiver to obtain the maximum heating value from the system.

High-pressure steam systems must provide for the elimination of air, as in low-pressure systems, and the ends of mains and riser faces must be dripped. Piping can be sized from Tables 15-4 to 15-7.

In general, *steam-supply piping* for two-pipe high-pressure systems can be sized for a total pressure drop between 5 and 10 psi on a system using steam at 30 psig, and between 25 and 30 psi on a system using steam at 150 psig. Condensate-return lines are generally sized on a 5-psig total pressure drop for a 30-psig steam system, and about 20 psi for a system utilizing steam at 150 psig. An average figure for sizing return lines on a high-pressure system is to size on the basis of $\frac{1}{2}$ psi per 100 ft of pipe for a 30-psig system, and 1 psi per 100 ft of pipe for a 150-psig system. Pitch of main should not be less than $\frac{1}{4}$ in. in 10 ft and not less than $\frac{1}{2}$ in. per ft of horizontal runouts to risers and/or heating units.

Traps generally used on the high-pressure system are of the bucket, inverted-bucket, float, or impulse types. During normal trap operation, the float and impulse traps under heavy load discharge condensate continuously because of their construction, and the upright-bucket, inverted-bucket, and impulse traps, under light or normal condensate load, discharge condensate intermittently.

Low-pressure Steam Heating Systems. Low-pressure systems are those employing operating pressures between 0 and 15 psig. A low-pressure system is similar to a vapor system, with the exception that the vapor system operates at pressures varying from 20 in. vacuum or more to 15 psig without the use of a vacuum pump. Once the air is removed from a tight system, it remains air-free, enabling operation under vacuum conditions at lower temperatures. By definition, a low-pressure system often includes the vapor system; however, a true low-pressure system cannot operate at pressures

Table 15-6. Return-pipe Capacities for 30-psig Steam Systems*
Capacity Expressed in Pounds per Hour

Pipe size, in.	Drop in pressure—pounds per 100 ft in length				
	$\frac{1}{8}$	$\frac{1}{4}$	$\frac{1}{2}$	$\frac{3}{4}$	1
$\frac{3}{4}$	115	170	245	308	365
1	230	340	490	615	730
$1\frac{1}{4}$	485	710	1,025	1,290	1,530
$1\frac{1}{2}$	790	1,160	1,670	2,100	2,500
2	1,580	2,360	3,400	4,300	5,050
$2\frac{1}{2}$	2,650	3,900	5,600	7,100	8,400
3	4,850	7,100	10,300	12,900	15,300
$3\frac{1}{2}$	7,200	10,600	15,300	19,200	22,800
4	10,200	15,000	21,600	27,000	32,300
5	19,000	27,800	40,300	55,500	60,000
6	31,000	45,500	65,500	83,000	98,000

* The table is based on steam at pressures of 0 to 4 psig.

Reprinted by permission from "Heating, Ventilating, Air Conditioning Guide," 1955, Chap. 21.

Table 15-7. Return-pipe Capacities for 150-psig Steam Systems*
Capacity Expressed in Pounds per Hour

Pipe size, in.	Drop in pressure—psi per 100 ft in length					
	$\frac{1}{8}$	$\frac{1}{4}$	$\frac{1}{2}$	$\frac{3}{4}$	1	2
$\frac{3}{4}$	156	232	360	465	560	890
1	313	462	690	910	1,120	1,780
$1\frac{1}{4}$	650	960	1,500	1,950	2,330	3,700
$1\frac{1}{2}$	1,070	1,580	2,460	3,160	3,800	6,100
2	2,160	3,300	4,950	6,400	7,700	12,300
$2\frac{1}{2}$	3,600	5,350	8,200	10,700	12,800	20,400
3	6,500	9,600	15,000	19,500	23,300	37,200
$3\frac{1}{2}$	9,600	14,400	22,300	28,700	34,500	55,000
4	13,700	20,500	31,600	45,000	49,200	78,500
5	25,600	38,100	58,500	76,000	91,500	146,000
6	42,000	62,500	96,000	125,000	150,000	238,000

* The table is based on steam at pressures of 1 to 20 psig.

Reprinted by permission from "Heating, Ventilating, Air Conditioning Guide," 1955, Chap. 21.

below atmospheric by virtue of the incorporation of air vents or vented receivers, permitting readmission of air at pressures below ₽tmospheric (under condition of reduced steam). True low-pressure systems have the disadvantage of corroding to a greater extent than vapor systems because of the readmission of new air and inability to hold heat under reduced steam conditions.

In low-pressure heating systems, the supply mains may be carried at elevations higher than the heating units, with branch take-offs from the top of the steam mains. However, due to the relatively low pressure differential between supply main and condensate return, the condensate lines must be carried below the heating unit level and generously pitched in the direction of flow for return to boiler or receiver by the action of gravity. Simplified tables for sizing steam and return or condensate piping

Table 15-8. Steam-pipe Capacities for Low-pressure Systems*

Pipe size, in.	Capacities of steam mains and risers								Special capacities for one-pipe systems only		
	Direction of condensate flow in pipeline								Supply risers up-feed	Radiator valves and vertical connections	Radiator and riser run-outs
	With the steam in one-pipe and two-pipe systems						Against the steam, two-pipe only				
	$\frac{1}{32}$-psi or $\frac{1}{2}$-oz drop	$\frac{1}{24}$-psi or $\frac{2}{3}$-oz drop	$\frac{1}{16}$-psi or 1-oz drop	$\frac{1}{8}$-psi or 2-oz drop	$\frac{1}{4}$-psi or 4-oz drop	$\frac{1}{2}$-psi or 8-oz drop	Vertical	Horizontal			
A	B	C	D	E	F	G	H†	I‡	J§	K	L‡
	Capacity expressed in pounds per hour										
¾	......	......	8	......	....	......	8	......	6	...	7
1	10	12	14	20	28	40	14	9	11	7	7
1¼	22	25	31	43	61	87	31	19	20	16	16
1½	34	39	48	67	95	135	48	27	38	23	23
2	68	79	97	137	193	273	97	49	72	42	42
2½	112	130	159	225	318	449	159	99	116	...	65
3	206	237	291	411	581	822	282	175	200	...	119
3½	307	355	434	614	869	1,230	387	288	286	...	186
4	435	503	614	869	1,230	1,740	511	425	380	...	278
5	806	928	1,140	1,610	2,270	3,210	1,050	788	...	...	545
6	1,320	1,520	1,870	2,640	3,730	5,280	1,800	1,400			
8	2,750	3,170	3,880	5,490	7,700	11,000	3,750	3,000			
10	5,010	5,790	7,090	10,000	14,200	20,000	7,000	5,700			
12	8,040	9,290	11,400	16,100	22,700	32,200	11,500	9,500			
16	15,100	17,400	21,200	30,300	42,400	60,500	22,000	19,000			
	All horizontal mains and down-feed risers						Up-feed risers	Mains and un-dripped run-outs	Up-feed risers	Radiator connections	Run-outs not dripped

* Steam at an average pressure of 1 psig is used as a basis for calculating capacities. All drops shown are in psi per 100 ft of equivalent run—based on pipe properly reamed.
† Do not use col. H for drops of $\frac{1}{24}$ or $\frac{1}{32}$ psi; substitute col. C or col. B as required.
‡ Pitch of horizontal runouts to risers and radiators should be not less than $\frac{1}{2}$ in. per ft. Where this pitch cannot be obtained, runouts over 8 ft in length should be one pipe size larger than called for in table.
§ Do not use col. J for drop $\frac{1}{32}$ psi except on sizes 3 in. and over; below 3 in. substitute col. B.

This table is based on pipe-size data developed through the research investigations of The American Society of Heating and Ventilating Engineers.
Reprinted by permission from "Heating, Ventilating, Air Conditioning Guide," 1955, Chap. 21.

for these types of systems are given in Tables 15-8 and 15-9 based on the condensation of ¼ lb of steam per square foot of equivalent direct radiation (EDR).

Traps for draining condensate from items of equipment such as unit heaters, blast and coil heaters, and steam separators should be of the float and thermostatic type. Thermostatic-type traps are used for draining condensate from radiators, convectors, small pipe coils or unit heaters, drip legs, and other relatively small heating equipment.

Vacuum Systems. Vacuum systems are those operating under vacuum or low-pressure conditions, and employ the use of a vacuum pump to maintain subatmospheric

Table 15-9. Return-pipe Capacities for Low-pressure Systems
Capacity Expressed in Pounds per Hour

Pipe size, in.	1/32-psi or 1/2-oz drop per 100 ft			1/24-psi or 2/3-oz drop per 100 ft			1/16-psi or 1-oz drop per 100 ft			1/8-psi or 2-oz drop per 100 ft			1/4-psi or 4-oz drop per 100 ft			1/2-psi or 8-oz drop per 100 ft		
	Wet	Dry	Vac.	Wet	Dry	Vac.	Wet	Dry	Vac.	Wet	Dry	Vac.	Wet	Dry	Vac.	Wet	Dry	Vac.
M	N	O	P	Q	R	S	T	U	V	W	X	Y	Z	AA	BB	CC	DD	EE
Mains																		
3/4	....	....	....	....	....	42	....	....	100	250	....	142	....	....	200	....	....	283
1	125	62	....	145	71	143	175	80	175	425	103	249	350	115	350	....	....	494
1 1/4	213	130	....	248	149	244	300	168	300	675	217	426	600	241	600	....	....	848
1 1/2	388	206	....	393	236	388	475	265	475	1,400	340	674	950	378	950	....	....	1,340
2	700	470	....	810	535	815	1,000	575	1,000	2,350	740	1,420	2,000	825	2,000	....	....	2,830
2 1/2	1,180	760	....	1,580	868	1,360	1,680	950	1,680	3,750	1,230	2,380	3,350	1,360	3,350	....	....	4,730
3	1,880	1,460	....	2,130	1,560	2,180	2,680	1,750	2,680	5,500	2,250	3,800	5,350	2,500	5,350	....	....	7,560
3 1/2	2,750	1,970	....	3,300	2,200	3,250	4,000	2,500	4,000	7,750	3,230	5,680	8,000	3,580	8,000	....	....	11,300
4	3,880	2,930	....	4,580	3,350	4,500	5,500	3,750	5,500	....	4,830	7,810	11,000	5,380	11,000	....	....	15,500
5	....	....	....	....	....	7,880	....	....	9,680	....	....	13,700	....	....	19,400	....	....	27,300
6	....	....	....	....	....	12,600	....	....	15,500	....	....	22,000	....	....	31,000	....	....	43,800
Risers																		
3/4	....	48	....	....	48	143	....	48	175	....	48	249	....	48	350	....	....	494
1	....	113	....	....	113	244	....	113	300	....	113	426	....	113	600	....	....	848
1 1/4	....	248	....	....	248	388	....	248	475	....	248	674	....	248	950	....	....	1,340
1 1/2	....	375	....	....	375	815	....	375	1,000	....	375	1,420	....	375	2,000	....	....	2,830
2	....	750	....	....	750	1,360	....	750	1,680	....	750	2,380	....	750	3,350	....	....	4,730
2 1/2	....	....	....	....	....	2,180	....	....	2,680	....	....	3,800	....	....	5,350	....	....	7,560
3	....	....	....	....	....	3,250	....	....	4,000	....	....	5,680	....	....	8,000	....	....	11,300
3 1/2	....	....	....	....	....	4,480	....	....	5,500	....	....	7,810	....	....	11,000	....	....	15,500
4	....	....	....	....	....	7,880	....	....	9,680	....	....	13,700	....	....	19,400	....	....	27,300
5	....	....	....	....	....	12,600	....	....	15,500	....	....	22,000	....	....	31,000	....	....	43,800

This table is based on pipe-size data developed through the research investigations of The American Society of Heating and Ventilating Engineers. Reprinted by permission from "Heating, Ventilating, Air Conditioning Guide," 1955, Chap. 21.

pressures in the condensate-return line. In addition to maintaining subatmospheric pressure in the return line, the vacuum pump withdraws the air and water from the system, separates the air from the water and releases it to the atmosphere, and pumps the water to the boiler or condensate receiver. As in the vapor system, the vacuum maintained within limits of the vacuum pump is dependent upon the tightness of the system and the temperature of the returns. These items are interrelated, dependent upon the anticipated air leaking into the system and the capacity of the vacuum pump, usually within the range of 0.3 to 0.5 cfm of air removal, and 0.5 gpm of water per 1,000 sq ft EDR served by the system when operating on a vacuum of $5\frac{1}{2}$ in. mercury with condensate at 160°F.

Systems maintaining vacuum up to $5\frac{1}{2}$ in. mercury are classified as low-vacuum, requiring a commonly termed low-vacuum pump; and systems maintaining vacuums

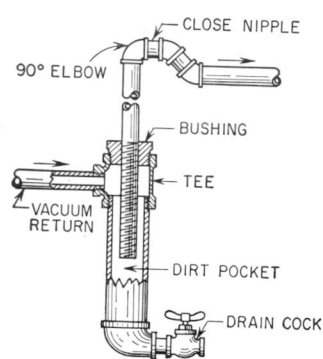

FIG. 15-2. Detail of main return lift at vacuum pump. (*Reprinted by permission from "Heating, Ventilating, Air Conditioning Guide," 1955, Chap. 21.*)

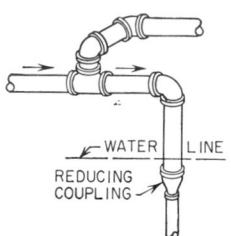

FIG. 15-3. Dripping main where it rises to higher level. (*Reprinted by permission from "Heating, Ventilating, Air Conditioning Guide," 1955, Chap. 21.*)

above $5\frac{1}{2}$ in. mercury are classified as high-vacuum systems, using a high-vacuum pump. Usually, a vacuum pump is controlled by a vacuum regulator in conjunction with a float control. The vacuum regulator will start the pump when the vacuum drops to a predetermined setting and stop it when the vacuum rises to the vacuum desired in the system. Or the pump will be placed in operation through the action of the float control when sufficient condensate has accumulated in the receiver, independent of the vacuum within the system. In addition, vacuum pumps are usually provided with a selector switch for operation as condensate pumps (for night or small-load requirement) or to give manual or continuous operation if desired.

As in the low-pressure heating system, the supply mains may be carried at elevations higher than the heating units, with branch take-offs from the top of the steam main, and the condensate-return lines must be carried below the unit served and generously pitched in the direction of flow to the vacuum pump. There should definitely be no connection between the steam supply and the condensate-return lines except through a trap, and where conditions dictate that a condensate line be carried below the vacuum pump inlet, this can be provided dependent upon the vacuum maintained in the system. This connection should be limited to a single lift at the vacuum pump (see Fig. 15-2). However, if possible, it is more desirable to place an accumulator or receiver tank at the low point of the return, incorporating a float switch to operate the vacuum pump as required.

Generally, dependent upon system size, total drops vary from $\frac{1}{4}$ to $\frac{1}{2}$ psi, and in any case should not exceed $\frac{1}{8}$ psi drop for 100 equivalent feet of run. Mains are to be pitched not less than $\frac{1}{4}$ in. in 10 ft, and horizontal runouts not less than $\frac{1}{2}$ in. per ft without going to the next size larger than indicated in Tables 15-8 and 15-9. Steam specialties for the vacuum-type systems are similar to those used in the low-pressure system.

General Piping Notes for Steam Heating Systems. Steam-supply mains should be pitched in the direction of flow, and the ends should be dripped separately through a trap into the condensate return. Where it becomes necessary for the steam main to

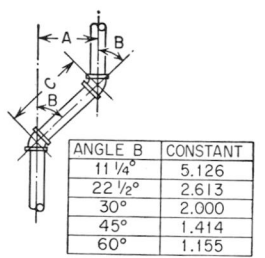

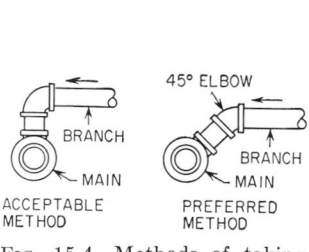

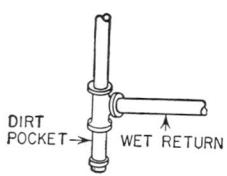

ANGLE B	CONSTANT
11 ¼°	5.126
22 ½°	2.613
30°	2.000
45°	1.414
60°	1.155

TO FIND LENGTH C, MULTIPLY A BY CONSTANT FOR ANGLE B

FIG. 15-4. Methods of taking branch from main. (*Reprinted by permission from "Heating, Ventilating, Air Conditioning Guide,"* 1955, *Chap.* 21.)

FIG. 15-5. Constants for determining length of off-set pipe. (*Reprinted by permission from "Heating, Ventilating, Air Conditioning Guide,"* 1955, *Chap.* 21.)

FIG. 15-6. Dirt-pocket connection. (*Reprinted by permission from "Heating, Ventilating, Air Conditioning Guide,"* 1955, *Chap.* 21.)

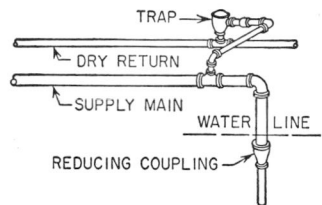

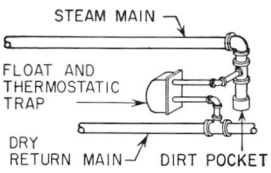

FIG. 15-7. Dripping end of main into wet return. (*Reprinted by permission from "Heating Ventilating Air Conditioning Guide,"* 1955, *Chap.* 21.)

FIG. 15-8. Dripping end of steam main into dry return. (*Reprinted by permission from "Heating, Ventilating, Air Conditioning,"* 1955, *Chap.* 21.)

rise, the base of the riser should be separately dripped through a trap into the condensate return, generally using a float and thermostatic-type trap. Take-offs from steam mains should be along the vertical center line or not more than 45° from the vertical, and where branch take-offs must drop into the unit, thus forming a riser, the bottom should be dripped and returned through a trap in the condensate return. All branch lines to the condensate return should enter the main on the vertical center line or at an angle of not more than 45°, and all mains should be generously pitched in the direction of flow. The branch take-offs from steam mains and condensate mains to heating units should be connected so as to provide for expansion and contraction of piping without undue stress on the pipe or branch line by means of using 90° ells to form a swing connection (see Figs. 15-3 to 15-9).

As the name implies, a *drip* is to return any condensed water from steam mains to the condensate main without interrupting or blocking the flow of steam in the pipe. A drip consists of a vertical leg off the bottom of the main or at the bottom of the riser of sufficient height to include a dirt leg to prevent scale and impurities from entering the main trap.   The bottom of the dirt pocket should have a removable cap or blow-off valve for cleaning out foreign particles, especially in a new installation.   From the drip leg, above the dirt pocket, a trap leg can be installed and connected to the condensate-return line.

Trap rigs installed after heating equipment or on drips to return condensate generally include a cleanable-type strainer ahead of the trap and after the dirt pocket as a

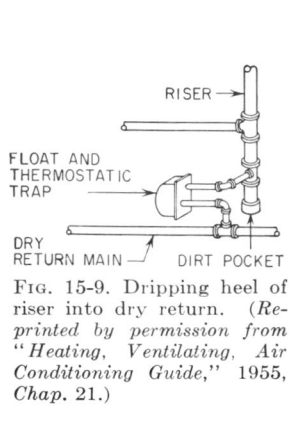

Fig. 15-9. Dripping heel of riser into dry return. (*Reprinted by permission from "Heating, Ventilating, Air Conditioning Guide," 1955, Chap. 21.*)

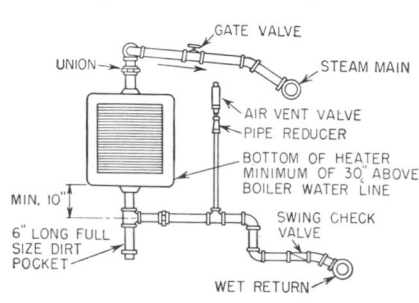

Fig. 15-10. Unit-heater connection to low-pressure steam gravity system. (*Reprinted by permission from "Heating, Ventilating, Air Conditioning Guide," 1955, Chap. 25.*)

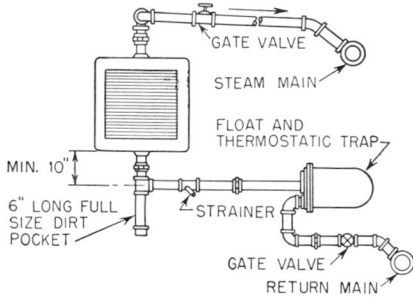

Fig. 15-11. Unit-heater connection for vacuum or vapor steam system. (*Reprinted by permission from "Heating, Ventilating, Air Conditioning Guide," 1955, Chap. 25.*)

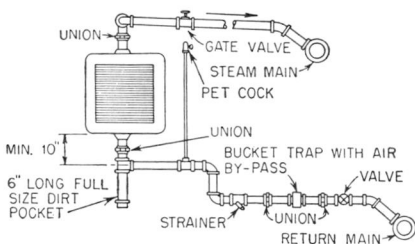

Fig. 15-12. Unit-heater connection to high-pressure steam system. (*Reprinted by permission from "Heating, Ventilating, Air Conditioning Guide," 1955, Chap. 25.*)

further protection against foreign particles entering the trap and making it inoperative. Also, they include unions before and after the trap for ease of removal and cleaning, and a gate valve to isolate the condensate line when maintenance is required.   Dependent upon the type of installation, an additional gate valve may be required ahead of the strainer, particularly where several units are served by one steam-supply line having one gate valve to shut off the whole bank.   On blast heating installations controlled by an automatic device, it is often advantageous to include a vacuum breaker across the trap rig, consisting of a swing check valve installed opposite the normal flow.   This vacuum breaker need not be greater than a ⅜-in. line and check valve, and serves the purpose of breaking the vacuum in the heating coils produced when the steam supply has been shut off and the existing steam in the coils has condensed.

Supply connections to the heating units employing the use of a regulating valve controlled from a thermostat should include the use of a strainer ahead of the regulating valve to prevent foreign particles from clogging or making it inoperative, in addition to shutoff valves and unions for ease of maintenance.   For steam-supply and return connections to small units such as radiators or convectors, it may be impossible to install strainers prior to control valves and thermostatic traps, in which case the run-outs should be installed in the form of drip legs and dirt pockets.   In addition, several manufacturers of small traps used for this purpose include a strainer in the inlet. Typical supply and return connections employed in conjunction with various steam heating units are shown in Figs. 15-10 to 15-12.

HOT-WATER HEATING SYSTEMS

Hot-water heating systems are those in which water is used to convey heat to spaces through piping to heat-dispersing units.   These hot-water heating systems are classified by type of circulation (gravity or forced) and by piping arrangement (one-pipe system; two-pipe, direct-return system; or two-pipe, reverse-return system).

The gravity-type system, with its circulation dependent upon the difference in weight of water in the supply and return mains because of respective water temperatures, is

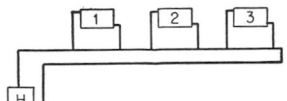

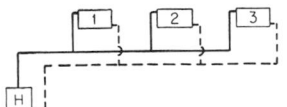

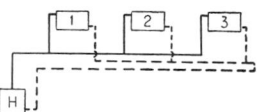

Fig. 15-13. One-pipe hot-water system. (*Reprinted by permission from "Heating, Ventilating, Air Conditioning Guide,"* 1955, *Chap.* 22.)	Fig. 15-14. Two-pipe direct-return hot-water system. (*Reprinted by permission from "Heating, Ventilating, Air Conditioning Guide,"* 1955, *Chap.* 22.)	Fig. 15-15. Two-pipe, reversed-return hot-water system. (*Reprinted by permission from "Heating, Ventilating, Air Conditioning Guide,"* 1955, *Chap.* 22.)

limited in industrial usage because of the relatively small circulating head available. In addition, exacting design is required, plus the use of larger piping and heating equipment for effective heat dissipation.   There is also the disadvantage of slow circulation and large temperature drop in the piping system.

In the *forced-circulation system,* a mechanical device is utilized, such as a pump, to circulate water from the boiler to the heating device and return.   Depending upon the selection of the circulating pump, available pressure heads permit higher water velocities, resulting in relatively small pipe sizes.   In addition, forced-circulation systems can employ high-temperature water under relatively high pressures, resulting in smaller radiation units and having the added advantage of requiring maximum boiler temperatures for maximum-heating-requirement conditions which occur for relatively short periods.

The forced-circulation systems are further identified as one-pipe systems; two-pipe, direct-return systems; or two-pipe, reverse-return systems.   In the *one-pipe forced system,* a single main in one or more circuits is used to circulate the water, and branch take-offs to individual heating units are equipped with special fittings at their connections to the main.   These special fittings introduce the correct amount of resistance to insure proper diversion of hot water into the radiator or convector, and should be used in accordance with manufacturer's recommendations pertaining to capacities, pipe sizes, etc.   Basically, the one-pipe system is a loop-type system wherein the single-size main is used throughout and returned to the heating source, with radiator supply and returns both connected into this main as indicated in Figs. 15-13 to 15-15.

The *direct-return system* employs a graduated-pipe-size supply main and return main, but it is relatively difficult to obtain a proper distribution of heat due to its inherent lack of balance.   The first radiator taking from the supply is also the first radiator to return its load, and the last radiator supplied is the last to return into the common main.

In the *reversed-return system,* heat balance is greatly simplified, in that the first radiator off the line is the last to return and, similarly, the last radiator off is the first to return.   The piping on this type of system is graduated in accordance with required flow, reduced by the amount required for branch take-off.

The term commonly used to depict the measure of heat loss is equivalent square foot of direct radiation (EDR), indicating any surface that will emit 240 Btu per hr when maintained at an average temperature of 215°F.   However in modern hot-water heating systems, this term loses its meaning as a measurement of heat emitted from the system, since a specified surface will emit more or less than 240 Btu per hr as the average temperature of the water is raised or lowered from 215°F.

Hot-water systems are generally designed to cool the water 20° between the inlet and the outlet of the radiator, and since the water enters the radiator at approximately boiler temperature, the average radiator temperature may be assumed to be boiler temperature less 10°.   On this basis, knowing the building heat loss, radiators can be selected from Table 15-10.

Table 15-10. Data for Use in Selecting Hot-water Radiators

Emission, Btu per sq ft	Av radiator temp, °F	Boiler temp, °F
240	215	225
225	210	220
200	197	207
180	190	200
160	175	185
150	170	180

Forced-circulation average design temperatures vary between 170 and 250°F, and water velocities within the piping fall between 4 and 5 ft per sec (200 to 600 mil-in. per ft), although higher temperatures and velocities can be utilized, dependent upon the system pressure available.   In industrial spaces, velocities in excess of 5 ft per sec, especially in larger pipe sizes, may range as high as 8 ft per sec, especially where noise is not objectionable.   In office areas or similar spaces where the smaller pipe sizes may be encountered, velocities in excess of 4 to 5 ft per sec may cause disturbing noises.   In hot-water heating systems, the mil-inch is used to express friction values instead of "feet of water" because of the relatively small system drops used.   The mil-inch eliminates the fractional values of pressure drop and indicates 0.001 in., or 0.0012 ft; therefore, 12,000 mil-in. represents the pressure exerted by a column of water 1 in. high (0.435 psi).   Piping capacities, at various mil-inch pressure drops, are given in 1,000 Btu, based on a 20° water temperature drop, as indicated in Fig. 15-16.

A further design consideration is the equivalent length of the system, taking into account the various resistances of the fittings.   Where several mains are involved, the over-all system pressure drop is based on the main having the longest run, and for a forced-circulation system where friction is not an absolutely critical item, the equivalent length of run can be figured at $1\frac{1}{2}$ times the actual length.   This equivalent length of run is divided into the available pump head converted into mil-inches to obtain the friction drop in mil-inches per foot, upon which the pipe size should be selected.

All hot-water systems should include an expansion tank to permit change in volume of water caused by increase in temperature to take place without producing undesirable pressure stresses.   The expansion tank may be of open construction, vented to the atmosphere, and located at least 3 ft above the highest radiator; or it may be of closed construction, located either above or below the highest radiator.   An open expansion tank, in addition to being vented, should include an overflow from the upper portion of the tank, piped to a suitable waste connection, and an expansion line from the system to the bottom of the tank, a gage glass for viewing the liquid level, and, if desired, an automatic-fill connection to maintain the correct amount of liquid in the system. The tank should have a capacity 50 per cent in excess of the actual increase in volume of water in the system due to increase in temperature from 40°F to system temperature. When the maintained system temperature is approximately 200°F, the minimum contents of an open tank should be 0.06 per cent of the total volume of water in the entire system.

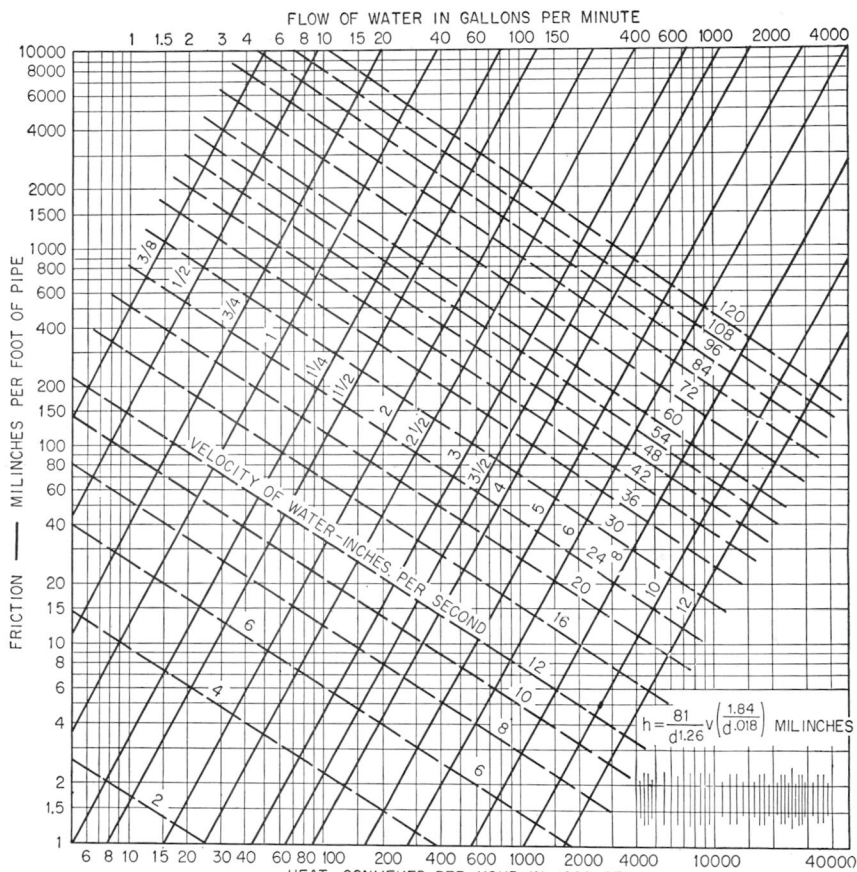

$$h = \frac{81}{d^{1.26}} v \left(\frac{1.84}{d^{.018}}\right) \text{ MIL INCHES}$$

THE DIFFERENCE IN TEMPERATURE OF THE WATER IN THE FLOW AND RETURN RISERS BEING 20F

FIG. 15-16. Friction in black-iron pipes. Lower scale of chart is based on 20° temperature difference between flow and return risers. To find friction when temperature drop is other than 20°, multiply the actual heat conveyed by 20 ÷ actual temperature drop and read the corresponding friction. (*Reprinted by permission from "Heating, Ventilating, Air Conditioning Guide," 1955, Chap. 22.*)

A closed expansion tank is one that is sealed against free venting to the atmosphere, permitting the expansion of water caused by temperature increase to be cushioned against a reservoir of compressed air above the water level in the tank. The size of a closed expansion tank will vary, depending upon its general location. A tank located above the highest radiator will be smaller than one located below the lowest radiator or at any point between. It should be designed to take care of variations in air volume within the tank caused by changes in air pressure, as well as changes in volume of water. A rough method of determining the size of a closed expansion tank located above the highest radiator is to divide the square feet of radiation by the factor 40 to obtain the required capacity in gallons. For a tank located in the basement, the capacity should be equal to 0.1 times the volume of water in the entire heating system for one-story buildings, 0.13 times the volume for two-story buildings, 0.17 times the volume for three-story buildings, and 0.23 times the volume for four-story buildings. When utilizing a closed expansion tank, a means must be provided to adjust and to observe the proportion of air within the tank, thus requiring an air-inlet valve, a water gage, and a relief valve. A source of supply of compressed air for renewing the air cushion is highly desirable in large high-pressure systems where it is impossible to drain down water so as to permit the introduction of atmospheric-pressure air.

General Notes on Piping Hot-water Units. When designing or installing a hot-water piping system, it must be kept in mind that piping must be pitched so that all

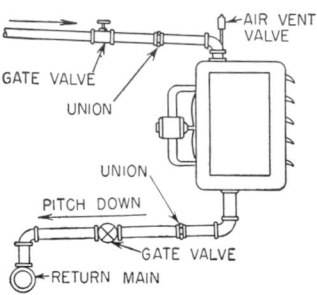

FIG. 15-17. Connection of horizontal unit heater to hot-water system. (*Reprinted by permission from "Heating, Ventilating, Air Conditioning Guide," 1955, Chap. 25.*)

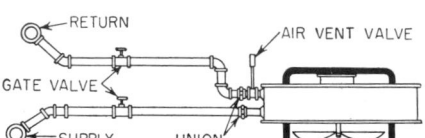

FIG. 15-18. Connection of vertical unit heater to hot-water system. (*Reprinted by permission from "Heating, Ventilating, Air Conditioning Guide," 1955, Chap. 25.*)

air in the system can be vented through an open expansion tank, automatic relief valve, or manual vents at high points of the system.   Free passage of air along the pipe must be possible.   Eccentric fittings should be used on horizontal runs when changing pipe sizes, with the top of the pipe maintained in line.   Piping must be installed to allow for expansion and contraction without producing undue stresses in the piping or connections, and generally can be installed for a variation of 1 in. in length for 100 ft. of pipe.   Where several circuits are required, piping should be sized for balanced water distribution, and main branches should pitch up and away from the source of heat, generally not less than 1 in. per 10 ft.   Branch connections should be taken out of the top of mains at 45 or 90° from the horizontal plane and, generally, supply connections to radiators should be made at the bottom of radiators to prevent stoppage of circulation from an air block, which a top supply might cause.   Sufficient stop and drain valves should be installed in convenient locations to isolate parts of the system for repairs and, unless used as a heating surface, the supply and return should be insulated.   Where there are variations in heat requirements throughout a system, improved control and economy can be effected by zoning the system into sections and using steam in water heat exchangers for each zone, controlled by the zone or section requirement.   General piping diagrams for hot-water units are shown in Figs. 15-17 and 15-18.

RADIATORS AND CONVECTORS

Radiators and convectors supply heat by radiation and convection to the occupied space at a specific rate when steam or hot water is circulated through them.   These heating units should be placed so that output will be directed at the greatest heat loss, which normally occurs along the outside walls and windows.

Radiators are those units which give off the greater portion of their heat by radiation, and include cast-iron units, pipe coils, and fin-tube elements. (Baseboard "radiators" really are "convectors.") Convectors are those units which give off a

Table 15–11. Btu per Hour per Linear Foot of Plain Pipe
Steam at 215°F, Surrounding Air at 70°F

	Size of pipe		
	1 in.	1¼ in.	1½ in.
Single row	132	162	185
Two rows	252	312	348
Four rows	440	545	616
Six rows	567	702	793

Table 15–12. Finned-tube Convector Capacities

Element designation	No. rows high	Minimum installed height (from floor to top fins)	Steam rating, IPSI (215°F) and 65° air	
			EDR per finned lin ft	Btu/ hr/ finned lin ft
1¼ in. IPS, 3¼ × 0.032 to 0.035 in. thick fins, 32 fins/ft	1	9	4.25	1020
	2	15	7.75	1860
	3	20	10.40	2500
1¼ in. IPS, 4¼ × 0.35 to 0.040 in. thick fins, 32 fins/ft	1	10	6.20	1495
	2	17	11.00	2645
	3	23	14.20	3415
1¼ in. IPS, 4¼ × 0.035 to 0.040 in. thick fins, 40 fins/ft	1	10	6.65	1590
	2	17	1.30	2710
	3	23	14.65	3525
2 in. IPS, 4¼ × 0.035 to 0.040 in. thick fins, 24 fins/ft	1	10	5.25	1260
	2	17	9.15	2195
	3	23	12.40	2980
2 in. IPS, 4¼ × 0.035 to 0.040 in. thick fins, 32 fins/ft	1	10	5.95	1425
	2	17	9.90	2370
	3	23	13.05	3125
1¼ in. copper, 3¼ × 0.025 to 0.030 in. thick fins, 32 fins/ft	1	9	5.00	1200
	2	15	9.00	2160
	3	20	12.20	2920
1¼ in. copper, 4¼ × 0.025 to 0.030 in. thick fins, 32 fins/ft	1	10	7.10	1700
	2	17	12.45	2990
	3	23	16.60	3980

Water rating
Btu/hr/finned lin ft

Av water temp	(factor × steam rating)
215°F	1.00
210°F	0.95
200°F	0.86
190°F	0.78
180°F	0.69
170°F	0.61
160°F	0.53
150°F	0.45

For Installed Heights Other than Minimum Multiply Ratings by Indicated Factor Below

36 in. or more 0.870   24 in. or more 0.948
32 in. 0.887   22 in. 0.965
30 in. 0.896   20 in. 0.983
28 in. 0.913   18 in. or less 1.00
26 in. 0.930

For expanded metal cover, multiply bare or adjusted installed height rating by 0.96.

majority of the heat by means of convection, and are of the cast-iron or fin-tube-element type enclosed in a cabinet. In shop areas, the tendency is to use radiation fin-tube elements, and at times plain coils. For offices, the fin-tube-type convector is used with a cabinet enclosure, utilizing steam or hot water. To obtain the amount of heat required from convectors or radiators, it is often necessary to stack horizontal sections vertically against the wall; however, it must be remembered that each element emits less heat than the one immediately below. For best results, a single-row element should be located approximately 18 to 20 in. above the floor line, and not less than 9 in.; a double-row element should not be installed with the top row less than 15 in. from the floor. These figures may vary slightly with different manufacturers.

Table 15-11 indicates the heat radiated by plain pipe of various sizes when used in a system containing steam at 215°F in surrounding air at 70°F.

The fin-tube-convector capacities given in Table 15-12 may be used as a guide in selecting elements to suit specific requirements. For more accurate ratings of elements with convector enclosure, consult manufacturer's information on capacities.

Table 15-13. Data for Use in Obtaining Unit Capacities for Steam and Air Conditions Other Than Standard Given

Steam, psi	Entering air temperature, F				
	0°	20°	40°	60°	80°
Blow-through type					
2	1.5	1.32	1.16	1.00	0.85
5	1.55	1.37	1.21	1.05	0.90
15	1.71	1.53	1.34	1.19	1.04
30	1.87	1.68	1.51	1.35	1.19
60	2.09	1.90	1.73	1.56	1.39
100	2.31	2.11	1.93	1.75	1.58
150	2.50	2.30	2.11	1.93	1.76
Pull-through type					
2	1.44	1.29	1.14	1.00	0.86
5	1.49	1.33	1.19	1.05	0.91
15	1.61	1.46	1.31	1.17	1.03
30	1.73	1.57	1.42	1.28	1.15
60	1.90	1.75	1.60	1.46	1.33
100	2.07	1.92	1.77	1.63	1.49
150	2.20	2.05	1.91	1.77	1.63

Multiply the output capacity for standard conditions by the factor given for actual steam and entering air conditions.

UNIT HEATERS

Steam unit heaters are normally classified by the type of fan employed, propeller or multiblade (centrifugal) type. Small units are usually of the propeller blow-through type, and larger units may have several centrifugal fans incorporated within the unit, either blowing or pulling through the coil. Capacities of propeller-fan units range from 20,000 to 500,000 Btu per hr, and centrifugal-fan units from 130,000 to 2,300,000 Btu per hr.

Almost all modern steam heating units employ the finned-tube type of heat exchanger, consisting of tubes having strips of metal wound around them on edge in the form of a helix. Some units are made of cast-iron sections; they are suitable for relatively lower-pressure service. Maximum allowable pressure and temperature are specified by the manufacturer and are in the range of 150 psig and 400°F for copper finned-tube coils.

Nonfreeze coils are available for steam units, permitting their use where air temperatures may fall below freezing.   Under this condition the minimum steam pressure should not fall below 5 psig at the unit; or a vacuum should be maintained to give a pressure differential across the unit of 5 lb minimum.

Steam units are rated on the basis of dry saturated steam at 2 psig pressure, entering air temperature of 60°F, and free air delivery.   Table 15-13 provides a means for obtaining unit capacities for steam and air conditions other than the standard given above.

Discharge-air velocity and temperature are variable: Propeller-type units are designed to deliver a fixed quantity of air; the discharge temperature of the air will

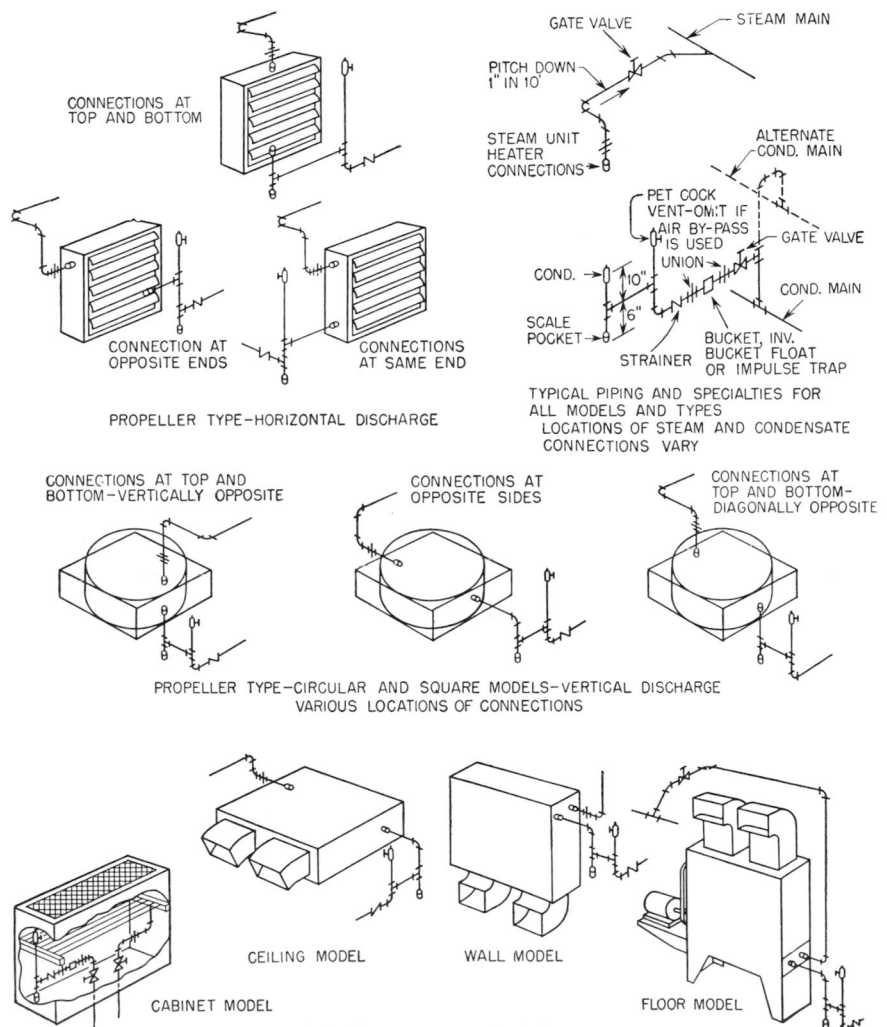

FIG. 15-19. Unit-heater piping connections.   Steam supply, medium and high pressure—above 15 psig; condensate, return to open receiver or feedwater heater.   (*Courtesy of Air Conditioning, Heating and Ventilating, August, 1955, and Industrial Unit Heater Assoc.*)

vary as the steam temperature. Some manufacturers build units with reduced heating elements to provide low discharge temperatures when operating on high-temperature steam. Centrifugal-fan units may be either direct-driven or belt-driven; direct-driven units deliver a fixed quantity of air, belt-driven units can be arranged to deliver an air volume which results in a suitable discharge temperature when operating on high or low steam temperatures.

Maximum coverage per unit is achieved with floor-mounted units having the heated-air discharge parallel to the floor and located above the working level. High discharge air temperatures tend to reduce the coverage of the heater and to promote higher ceiling or roof temperatures; fewer units will satisfy the heat loss. For floor-mounted units the *inlet-air temperature* can be taken as the control temperature; for suspended units the inlet-air temperature is somewhat higher, nominally 1° higher for each 2 ft of elevation of the intake.

For piping connections to steam unit heaters, see Figs. 15-10 to 15-12 and 15-19.

Temperature control of steam unit heaters is usually accomplished by on-off control of the fan by a thermostat. Larger units and units handling outside make-up air are usually equipped with throttling valves controlled from a thermostat, in which case the fans are operating continuously.

Maintenance of steam unit heaters involves the following: Heating elements should be blown off or washed off to maintain heat-transfer efficiency; the frequency of cleaning depends upon the dirt and dust in the atmosphere.

Fans should be brushed off or blown out to prevent an accumulation of imbalance, and set screws should be checked to prevent slippage and scoring of fan shafts.

Motors should be serviced in accordance with the manufacturer's recommendations.

Fan shaft bearings and V-belt drives should be checked for lubrication and belt tightness. New belts usually stretch somewhat and require tightening after a few hours of operation.

Steam specialties should be checked for worn parts.

Air filters should be replaced or cleaned when dirty, so that the air volume handled by the unit may be maintained and the temperature rise over the heating coil not become excessive.

Hot-water unit heaters are of the same construction as steam units. The output of the units when hot water is used is generally lower than when steam is used as the heating medium, except in the case of a hot-water system operating at relatively high pressure and temperature. Hot-water unit heaters are usually rated on the basis of 180°F entering-water temperature and 60°F entering-air temperature; the drop in temperature of the water as it passes through the unit varies with the rate of flow or the pressure differential between supply and return mains at the unit location. Some manufacturers base their capacity tables on a flow rate (gallons per minute) others on a water temperature drop (degrees F). Manufacturers' capacity tables include tables of conversion factors for determining unit output under conditions other than those given for their capacity ratings.

Hot-water units should not be used where the entering-air temperature can be expected to drop below freezing.

Control of hot-water units is effected by on-off operation of the fan from a thermostat.

Piping connections for hot-water units are shown in Figs. 15-17, 15-18, and 15-20.

PANEL HEATING

Panel heating systems are those which emit heat to spaces or areas by means of relatively low-temperature forced water (80 to 140°F) being passed through pipe coils imbedded in floors, sidewalks (in the case of snow melting), walls, or ceilings. Panel heating also includes the passing of warm air through plenums behind walls, ceilings, or floors, and the use of electric-resistance elements imbedded in walls, ceilings, or floor surfaces. The predominant tendency in industrial practice is to employ warm water as the heating medium rather than warm air or electric elements, primarily because of lower operating cost in the larger systems.

The effect of radiant-heat emission from a panel is to heat objects in the path of the

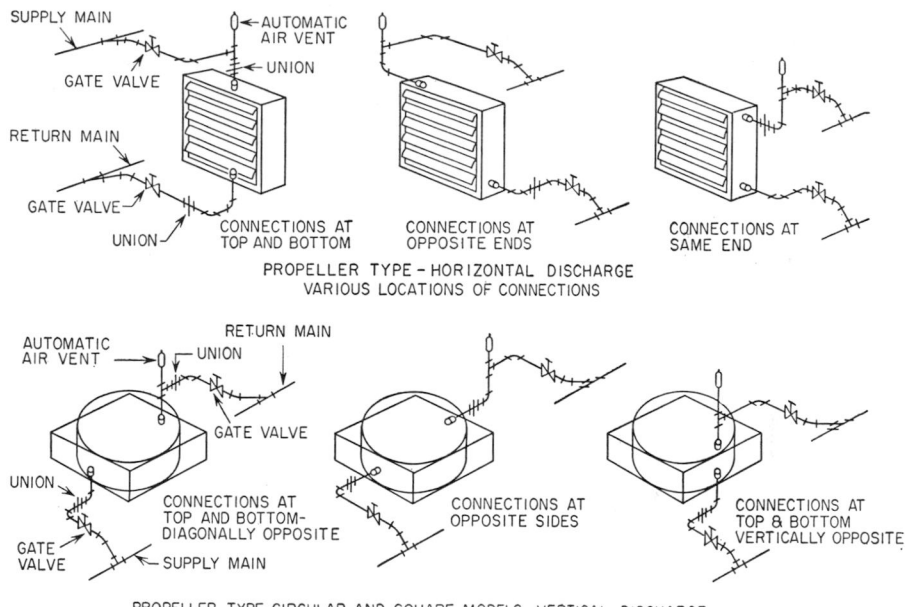

PROPELLER TYPE – HORIZONTAL DISCHARGE
VARIOUS LOCATIONS OF CONNECTIONS

PROPELLER TYPE–CIRCULAR AND SQUARE MODELS–VERTICAL DISCHARGE
VARIOUS LOCATIONS OF CONNECTIONS

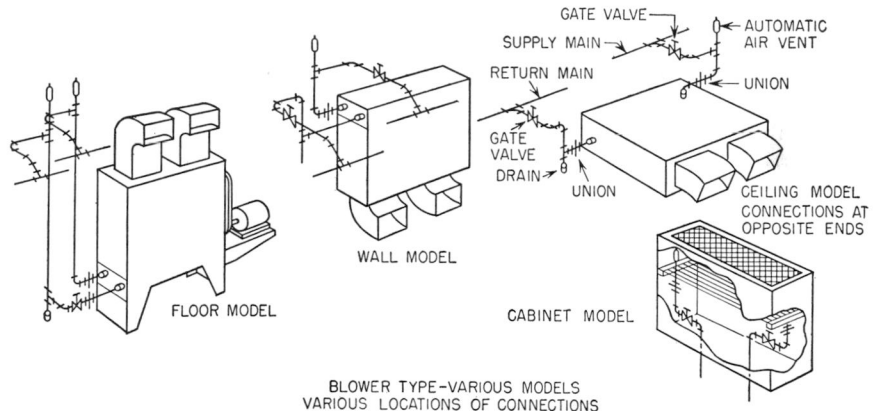

BLOWER TYPE–VARIOUS MODELS
VARIOUS LOCATIONS OF CONNECTIONS

FIG. 15-20. Unit-heater piping connections. Hot-water supply, forced circulation. (*Courtesy of Air Conditioning, Heating and Ventilating, August, 1955, and Industrial Unit Heater Assoc.*)

radiation. For comfort heating, a suitable effect is produced with lower air temperatures than when hot air is the ultimate heating medium. *Floor installations* are usually controlled to provide a *panel-surface temperature* of approximately 85°F. Higher temperatures tend to induce perspiration of the feet and create a health hazard.

The *air temperature* resulting from a given panel temperature is derived from convection currents emanating from the panel itself and objects radiantly heated. It is affected by the heat loss of the enclosing walls and (what is quite important) by the rate of infiltration of unheated air. *Control of infiltration* and the introduction of tempered make-up air to produce an air temperature of approximately 65°F produces an optimum effect.

Air-temperature stratification from floor to ceiling is less with panel heating than with other heating arrangements, and the relative effects of floor or ceiling panel location are negligible in this regard.

Ceiling installations have a disadvantage in office spaces in that the radiant energy is cut off from the feet and legs of people sitting at desks, producing discomfort.   Ceiling panels are advantageous in warehouses in that the radiant energy is received by the exposed surface of the stored material, enhancing the effect of convection for heating the air.

In multistoried structures, ceiling panels located within concrete slabs exposed above and below provide a tempered floor, but the major portion of the heating effect is derived from above.

Wall installations should be located on the most exposed side, and adequate insulation should be provided between the heated panel and the exterior construction.   Wall panels have the advantage of transmitting a greater portion of the heat by convection; a disadvantage is that any large object located near the panel wall will block radiation to a portion of the space, producing an uneven heating effect.

Operation of a panel heating system is identical to that of a recirculating hot-water system incorporating a circulating pump, hot-water boiler, expansion tank, and the necessary fittings and valves to control distribution of hot water throughout the system.

Control of the heating effect is accomplished in one of two ways: Intermittent operation of the circulating pump; or variable water temperature, by mixing of return and hot water, each to be controlled from a thermostat.   In some installations both control mechanisms are employed.   Radiant-heating panels have a greater thermal inertia than convectors or unit heaters; therefore, to overcome the time lag between the requirement for heat and the production of heating effect, it is customary to use both outside and inside thermostats.   The outside thermostat operates as a primary control (starting the recirculating pump or increasing the circulating-water temperature on a drop in outside temperature), and the inside thermostat operates as a high limit, cutting off the water-circulating pump.   In general, the heavier the panel construction, the greater the thermal inertia, and the more elaborate the control system required.   If the space to be heated is divided into zones requiring different heating effects or having different exposures, it is necessary that each zone have a circulating pump and a separate control setup.   An aquastat is placed downstream from the mixing valve, providing a high-limit control of supply-water temperature in order to limit the panel temperature.

Snow melting is accomplished by locating a suitably designed radiant-heating panel in the specific surface to be affected.   Because of the possibility of freezing the heating medium, an *antifreeze* solution (ethylene glycol) must be added.   The slightly toxic nature of the antifreeze and its cost dictate that a snow-melting system be installed and maintained separate from the building heating system.   *Rust inhibitors* also are added, because ethylene glycol tends to become corrosive in water solutions.   Solutions should be tested annually.

Some snow-melting systems use *light fuel oil* for the heating medium, eliminating the freezing and corrosive problem.   Heat is applied to the fuel oil by a heat exchanger, using hot water or steam from the building heating system.   Suitable petroleum distillates have a flash point of 260 to 280°F.

Slab construction consists of concrete having sufficient thickness to provide a minimum of 2 in. above and below the pipe or tubing.   Snow-melting grids have been standardized to ¾-in. pipe or tubing spaced 12 in. apart.   Variations in the severity of conditions are accommodated by adjustment of the temperature of the heating medium.   The pipe grid should be pitched to provide drainage; since pipe elements are usually arranged in parallel to reduce the required pump pressure, it is considered unsafe to depend on blowing out the system with air.

General Piping Notes for Radiant Panels. *Drain lines* should be generously pitched, terminating in a sump pit.   High points in the panel piping should be provided with a means of *bleeding air* from the system; the air-bleed lines are usually brought back to the expansion-tank riser. *Expansion tanks* are located within a heated space and vented to the atmosphere.

Since the piping on radiant panels is usually inaccessible, *welded joints* are preferred over screwed joints for ferrous pipe, and *soldered joints* are used for nonferrous pipe. Where pipe crosses expansion joints in the slab, the pipe should be wrapped in felt and sealed for a distance of 18 in. on each side of the joint to allow for movement of the pipe to accommodate the stress. Where possible, each heating grid should be contained by a single concrete-slab section. Typical arrangements of panel heating elements are shown in Fig. 15-21.

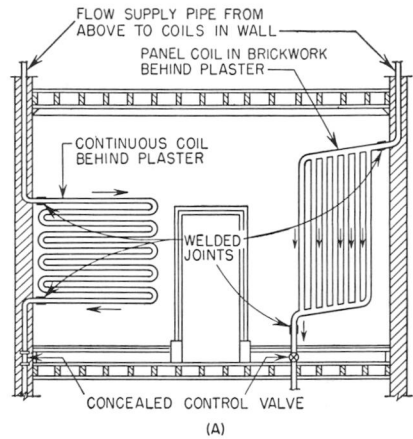

(A)

ESTIMATING THE HEAT LOSS

Accurate calculation of heat loss is the first essential step in determining the size of the heating plant. Modern construction tends to reduce heat losses. Rule-of-thumb methods usually lead to oversizing the heating plant, with consequent high costs of installation and reduction of operating efficiency.

Heat Units. The most common heat unit used, the British thermal unit, is the amount of heat required to raise 1 lb of water 1°F. A frequently used unit in steam-heating practice is the EDR (equivalent direct radiation), which is equal to 240 Btu. This unit was based upon the output of a square foot of cast-iron radiation when supplied with 1 lb of steam pressure. In hot-water heating practice the Btu is generally used, and outputs are related to the water temperature.

Required information for making a proper estimate of heat loss includes: (1) dimensions of the building; (2) materials from which external building walls are constructed; (3) ventilation requirements; (4) temperature to be maintained inside building; and (5) mean low outside temperature to be expected. The items are used in the following manner:

1. The *dimensions of the building* determine the amount of surface of each type conducting heat to the outside. The smaller the building, the more accurate these dimensions should be.

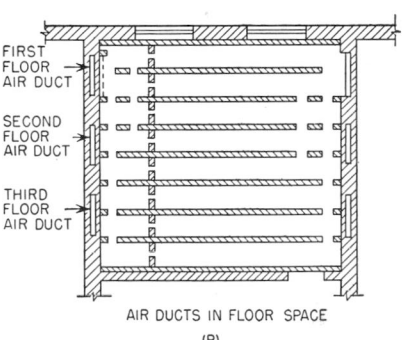

AIR DUCTS IN FLOOR SPACE

(B)

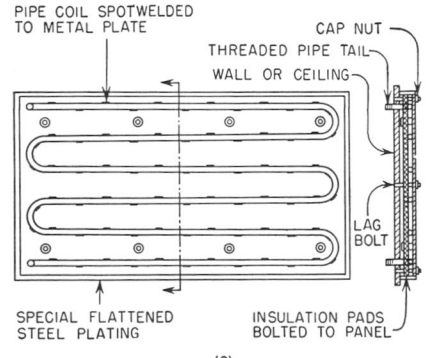

(C)

FIG. 15-21. Typical arrangements of panel heating elements. (*A*) In usual panel heating, pipes are embedded in wall, floor, or ceiling. (*B*) Shallow ducts for warm-air heating may be under floor or above ceiling. (*C*) A variety of heated panels may also be employed for radiant heating. (*Courtesy of Power magazine.*)

2. Every *building material* has its own particular rate of heat transmission. The rate of heat transmission (k), which has been determined by laboratory tests, is expressed in Btu per hour per square foot per degree of temperature per inch of thickness. When two or more dissimilar materials compose a wall section, the rate of heat transmission is not the rate peculiar to any one of these materials, but a rate derived for the combination. For a detailed exposition of this procedure, reference is made to the ASHRAE Guide.[1] Over-all U factors for most types of industrial building materials are given in Tables 15-14 to 15-19.

Table 15-14. Coefficients of Transmission (U) of Light Industrial-type Walls

Material	Finish	U
3/8-in. corrugated transite	None	1.16
	1/2-in. insulation	0.34
	25/32-in. insulation	0.27
	25/32-in. wood sheathing	0.42
3/8-in. flat transite	None	1.10
	25/32-in. wood sheathing	0.42
Corrugated sheet iron	None	1.40
	1/2-in. insulation	0.36
	25/32-in. insulation	0.28
	5/8-in. wood	0.49
	3/4-in. wood	0.46
	7/8-in. wood	0.43
	Sheathing + tongue and groove	0.25
	Two layers of wood + paper	0.29
	Flat iron	0.75
Flat iron	None	1.30
Corrugated aluminum	None	1.30
	1-in. insulation	0.26
	1/2-in. insulation	0.44
3/4-in. wood siding	None	0.58
	3/4-in. wood	0.28

These coefficients are expressed in Btu/(hour)(square foot)(Fahrenheit degree difference in temperature between the air on the two sides), and are based on an outside-air velocity of 15 mph.

3. *Building ventilation* contributes in large measure to the heating load. Experience has dictated certain minimum requirements necessary for each of various types of buildings. Ventilation is generally expressed in terms of air changes per hour (the cubic content of the building or space to be heated per hour). All replacement air must necessarily be heated from outside-air temperature to the desired inside-air temperature. Table 15-20 gives suggested criteria for inside temperatures and infiltration loss. Infiltration is caused by the stack effect of a building and is usually attributable to loosely fitted windows, doors, and unsealed joints in the building construction. Infiltration loss is difficult to calculate. A door in constant use might double the normal infiltration heating load of a building. Mechanical exhaust ventilation can be more accurately appraised. In the event that exhaust fans create a negative pressure within the building, the exhaust-fan capacities may be used for determining the ventilation heating load. It is possible to have both infiltration and mechanical exhausting, and in buildings with over 20,000 sq ft of floor area it is recommended that approximately one-quarter to one-half air change per hour be added to the mechanical exhaust load. Gravity exhausters or ventilators utilize the stack effect of the building. The volume of air exhausted is proportional to the difference in temperature between the air inside and the air outside the building; the capacity is also dependent upon the relative pressures inside and outside. It is not uncommon, when gravity ventilators and powered exhausters are simultaneously in use, to find that air is being drawn in through

[1] American Society of Heating, Refrigerating and Air Conditioning Engineers, 345 East 47*th* St., New York, N.Y. 10017.

the gravity ventilators, producing ineffective ventilation. The capacity of gravity exhausters must be based on manufacturer's capacity data, adjusted to the actual conditions.

4. *Inside temperature*—for a more extensive treatment of optimum temperatures for various building usage and occupancy, refer to the ASHRAE Guide.

Table 15-15. Coefficients of Transmission (*U*) of Masonry Walls

Material	Finish·	6 in.	8 in.	10 in.	12 in.	16 in.
Hollow tile..............	None	....	0.40	0.39	0.30	0.25
	Plaster on wall	....	0.37	0.37	0.29	0.24
	Metal lath and plaster	....	0.27	0.27	0.22	0.19
	½-in. insulation	....	0.20	0.20	0.17	0.16
Solid brick..............	Plain	....	0.50	....	0.35	0.28
	Plaster on wall	....	0.46	....	0.34	0.27
	Metal lath and plaster	....	0.32	....	0.25	0.21
	½-in. insulating board	....	0.22	....	0.19	0.17
Solid concrete...........	Plain	0.79	0.70	0.63	0.58	
	Plaster on wall	0.71	0.64	0.58	0.53	
	Metal lath and plaster (furred)	0.42	0.39	0.37	0.35	
	½-in. insulating board	0.27	0.26	0.25	0.24	
Concrete block:						
Gravel aggregate........	Plain	....	0.56	....	0.50	
	Plaster on wall	....	0.52	....	0.46	
	Metal lath and plaster	....	0.34	....	0.32	
	½-in. insulating board	....	0.24	....	0.22	
Cinder aggregate........	Plain	....	0.41	....	0.38	
	Plaster on wall	....	0.39	....	0.36	
	Metal lath and plaster	....	0.28	....	0.26	
	½-in. insulating board	....	0.21	....	0.20	
Lightweight aggregate....	Plain	....	0.36	....	0.34	
	Plaster on wall	....	0.34	....	0.33	
	Metal lath and plaster	....	0.26	....	0.25	
	½-in. insulating board	....	0.19	....	0.19	
4-in. brick veneer on concrete	Plain	0.59	0.54			
	Plaster on wall	0.54	0.50			
	Metal lath and plaster	0.35	0.33			
	½-in. insulating board	0.24	0.23			
4-in. brick veneer on hollow tile	Plain	0.35	0.34			
	Plaster on wall	0.34	0.32			
	Metal lath and plaster	0.25	0.25			
	½-in. insulating board	0.19	0.19			

These coefficients are expressed in Btu/(hour)(square foot)(Fahrenheit degree difference in temperature between the air on the two sides), and are based on an outside-air velocity of 15 mph.

5. *Outside design temperatures* for various geographic locations can be had in the form of tables, which also give altitudes. The effect of altitude on heating equipment is to reduce its capacity. It is recommended for locations having an altitude above 2,000 ft above sea level that the capacity of heating equipment be considered to be reduced by 4 per cent per 1,000 ft above sea level. Usually a reduction in capacity is not considered for altitudes below 2,000 ft above sea level.

Heat-loss calculations are made, using the foregoing data, in the following manner: Tabulate the sum total of exposed areas of each building material. For each building material (wall construction, glass, roof construction, etc.) select the proper *U* factor. Opposite each material list the applicable temperature difference. Normally the design temperature difference applies at the floor level, and the temperature difference

Table 15-16. Coefficients of Transmission (U) of Interior Partitions

Material	No finish	Single partition (inside finished)	Double partition (both sides finished)
Metal lath and plaster............	....	0.69	0.39
⅜-in. gypsum board..............	....	0.67	0.37
Wood lath and plaster...........	....	0.26	0.34
⅜-in. plywood...................	....	0.59	0.33
½-in. insulating board...........	....	0.36	0.19
3-in. hollow clay tile.............	0.50	0.47	0.43
4-in. hollow clay tile.............	0.45	0.42	0.40
3-in. hollow gypsum tile..........	0.35	0.33	0.32
4-in. hollow gypsum tile..........	0.29	0.28	0.27
3-in. cinder block................	0.50	0.47	0.43
4-in. cinder block................	0.45	0.42	0.40
4-in. brick......................	0.50	0.46	0.43
Corrugated sheet iron...........	0.83	0.83	0.83

These coefficients are expressed in Btu/(hour)(square foot)(Fahrenheit degree difference in temperature between the air on the two sides), and are based on an outside-air velocity of 0 mph.

Table 15-17. Coefficients of Transmission (U) of Roofs (Without Ceilings)

Material	Thickness of insulation				
	None	½ in.	1 in.	1½ in.	2 in.
Built-up roofs					
Flat metal roof deck.......................	0.94	0.39	0.24	0.18	0.14
Precast cement tile........................	0.84	0.37	0.24	0.18	0.14
2-in. concrete.............................	0.82	0.37	0.24	0.17	0.14
4-in. concrete.............................	0.72	0.34	0.23	0.17	0.13
6-in. concrete.............................	0.65	0.33	0.22	0.16	0.13
2-in. gypsum..............................	0.58	0.30			
2½-in. gypsum............................	0.38	0.24	0.18	0.14	0.12
3½-in. gypsum............................	0.31	0.21	0.16	0.13	0.11
1-in. wood................................	0.49	0.28	0.20	0.15	0.12
1½-in. wood..............................	0.37	0.24	0.18	0.14	0.11
2-in. wood................................	0.32	0.22	0.16	0.13	0.11
3-in. wood................................	0.23	0.17	0.14	0.11	0.096
Plain roofs					
Corrugated sheet iron......................	1.40	0.36	0.28		
Corrugated sheet iron, ⅝-in. sheathing......	0.49				
Corrugated sheet iron, ¾-in. sheathing......	0.46				
Corrugated sheet iron, 1-in. sheathing........	0.43				
Corrugated aluminum......................	1.30	....	0.26		

These coefficients are expressed in Btu/(hour)(square foot)(Fahrenheit degree difference in temperature between the air on the two sides), and are based on an outside-air velocity of 15 mph.

to be applied across the roof is usually 10° greater or more.   Multiply the three factors:

$$\text{Area} \times U \times \text{temperature difference} = \text{Btu per hr}$$

The sum of these heat losses for each building material is the total *transmitted heat loss*.

To the transmitted heat loss must be added the heat loss due to ventilation, as follows: Having determined the ventilation rate in terms of cfm (number of air changes × building volume ÷ 60), the quantity of heat required to raise the infiltrating air to the

Table 15-18. Coefficients of Transmission (U) of Roofs (With Ceilings)

Material	Thickness of insulation				
	None	½ in.	1 in.	1½ in.	2 in.
Flat metal roof deck......	0.46	0.27	0.19	0.15	0.12
Precast cement tile.......	0.43	0.26	0.19	0.15	0.12
2-in. concrete...........	0.42	0.26	0.19	0.15	0.12
4-in. concrete...........	0.40	0.25	0.18	0.14	0.12
6-in. concrete...........	0.37	0.24	0.18	0.14	0.12
2½-in. gypsum..........	0.27	0.19	0.15	0.12	0.10
3½-in. gypsum..........	0.23	0.17	0.14	0.11	0.097
1-in. wood..............	0.32	0.21	0.16	0.14	0.11
1½-in. wood.............	0.26	0.19	0.15	0.12	0.10
2-in. wood..............	0.27	0.17	0.14	0.11	0.097
3-in. wood..............	0.18	0.14	0.12	0.19	0.087

These coefficients are expressed in Btu/(hour)(square foot)(Fahrenheit degree difference in temperature between the air on the two sides), and are based on an outside-air velocity of 15 mph.

Table 15-19. Coefficients of Transmission (U) of Windows, Doors, and Floors

Material	U Factor
All-glass and wooden doors............	1.13
Glass block.........................	0.65
Steel doors.........................	1.30

Floors: Use a coefficient of 0.10 with the following ground temperatures:

Zone	Ground Temperature, F
+20	45°
0	50°
−20	55°

These coefficients are expressed in Btu/(hour)(square foot)(Fahrenheit degree difference in temperature between the air on the two sides), and are based on an outside-air velocity of 15 mph.

inside design temperature is given by the formula

$$\text{cfm} \times 1.08 \times \text{temperature difference} = \text{Btu per hr}$$

where 1.08 = specific heat × density × 60 min per hr

The sum of the transmitted heat loss and the ventilation heat loss is the *total heat loss* of the space under consideration.

Other sources of heat such as personnel, electric motors, process heat in the form of ovens, furnaces, etc., are usually not figured in the heating load of a building because of their intermittent nature or the fact that the source of heat is vented to the outside, and may from time to time actually increase the heat load by virtue of the exhaust capacity.   For electric motors,

$$\text{horsepower rating} \div \text{motor efficiency} \times \text{load factor} \times 2,544 = \text{Btu per hr}$$

In unvented ovens and furnaces, the amount of heat stored in the material processed is

Table 15-20. Temperature and Ventilation Design Standards in Common Use in Industrial and Commercial Heating Systems

Type of building	Inside temperature usually specified, F	Infiltration loss, est air change per hr	
		Tight construction	Loose construction
Assembly halls.................	70°	$\frac{1}{2}$	1
Auditoriums....................	70°	$\frac{1}{2}$	1
Barns.........................		2	4
Churches......................	70°	1	2
Factories:			
Under 20,000 sq ft...........	65°	$1\frac{1}{2}$	3
Over 20,000 sq ft.............	65°	$1\frac{1}{2}$	3
Foundries:			
Under 20,000 sq ft...........	60°	3	4
Over 20,000 sq ft.............	60°	$2\frac{1}{2}$	3
Garages.......................	65°	3	4
Gymnasiums...................	65°	1	$1\frac{1}{2}$
Laboratories..................	70°	2	$2\frac{1}{2}$
Offices.......................	70°	1	$1\frac{1}{2}$
Schools.......................	75°	1	$1\frac{1}{2}$
Stores........................	70°	1	$1\frac{1}{2}$
Warehouses:			
Under 20,000..............	60°	$1\frac{1}{2}$	2
Over 20,000...............	60°	1	$1\frac{1}{2}$

relatively small, and this same material usually remains within the building during the cooling cycle; therefore the heat input to the furnace is normally used. The heating effect of personnel is relatively small, as follows:

Seated, very light work........... 200 Btu per hr per person
Moderately heavy work.......... 300 Btu per hr per person
Heavy work.................... 460 Btu per hr per person

FUELS

Fuels fall into three classifications, based upon their natural physical properties, solid, liquid, and gaseous.

Solid Fuels. Coal is classified in various ways by variety, rank, and grade, and can be obtained in various lump sizes. Bituminous coals are usually used for heating purposes. Commercial varieties of bituminous coal are:

Common Banded Coal. The common variety of bituminous and subbituminous coal. It consists of a sequence of irregularly alternating layers of homogeneous black material having a brilliant vitreous luster, grayish striated material, usually of milky luster, and generally thinner bands of soft, powdery, and fibrous particles of mineral charcoal.

Splint Coal. A variety of bituminous or subbituminous coal, commonly having a dull luster and grayish-black color, often containing a few thin, irregular bands with vitreous luster. It is hard and tough and free burning and does not swell on heating.

Cannel Coal. A variety of bituminous or subbituminous coal of compact, fine-grained texture, with a general absence of banded structure. It is dark gray or black in color and has a greasy luster. It is noncaking, ignites easily, and burns with a luminous, smoky flame.

Boghead Coal. A variety of bituminous or subbituminous coal resembling cannel coal in appearance and in behavior during combustion. It is characterized by a high percentage of algae remains and volatile matter.

Coals are classified according to rank, i.e., according to their degree of metamorphism or progressive alteration, in the natural series from lignite to anthracite. The basic scheme of classification is according to fixed carbon and heat value. The higher-rank coals are classified according to fixed carbon on the dry basis, and the lower-rank coals according to Btu on the moist basis. Table 15-21 gives the range of characteristics of coal.

In nearly all localities, coal is obtainable in all lump sizes suitable for mechanical feeding or hand firing. Local ordinances or codes may limit the variety of coals to be used to the extent of requiring the use of processed coal (devolatilized).

Table 15-21. Some Characteristics of Coal

Class	Group	Limits of fixed carbon or Btu	Dry volatile matter, %
Anthracitic..........	Anthracite	Dry, 98% F.C.	2 or less
	Anthracite	Dry, 92–98% F.C.	8 to 2
	Semianthracite	Dry, 86–92% F.C.	14 to 8
Bituminous..........	Low volatile	Dry, 78–86% F.C.	22 to 14
	Medium volatile	Dry, 69–78% F.C.	31 to 22
	High volatile A	Dry, less than 69% F.C.; moist, 14,000 Btu or more	More than 31
	High volatile B	Moist 13,000–14,000 Btu	
	High volatile C	Moist, 11,000–13,000 Btu	
Subbituminous......	Subbituminous A	Moist, 11,000–13,000 Btu	
	Subbituminous B	Moist, 9500–11,000 Btu	
	Subbituminous C	Moist 8300–9500 Btu	
Lignitic.............	Lignite	Moist, less than 8300 Btu	

Coal Storage. Coal is subject to spontaneous heating; the liability to self-heating is greatest among coals of lowest rank. The finer sizes of coal, having more surface area per unit of weight than the larger sizes, increase the opportunity of oxidation. Spontaneous heating can be prevented or lessened by compressing the pile in layers, as with a road roller, to limit the access of air; storing large-size coal; storing in small piles; keeping storage-pile height as low as possible (6 ft is the limit for many coals); and moving the coal when a temperature of 120°F is reached within the pile.

Most bituminous coals are only slightly affected by weathering. Coals of higher grade or processed bituminous coal weather to a lesser degree.

Liquid Fuels. The pertinent qualities of liquid fuels are: viscosity, distillation range, gravity, ignition temperature, fire point, pour point, Btu value, carbon residue, and sulfur content.

Viscosity is the internal resistance of any liquid to flow. Viscosity of fuels is usually expressed in seconds Saybolt Universal. The datum is the time, in seconds, required for 60 cubic centimeters of the oil at a given temperature to flow through the Universal-size orifice under its own (constantly decreasing) pressure. Fuel up to and including No. 5 is generally measured in seconds Saybolt Universal (SSU) at 100°F. No. 6 fuel oil is generally measured in seconds Saybolt Furol (SSF) at 122°F. (These data are obtained similarly using a Furol orifice.)

Distillation range is the index of the volatility, or the tendency of an oil to vaporize, and is generally measured in increments of 10 per cent, which includes the end point, or the maximum temperature recorded by the distillation thermometer to complete vaporization. The distillation range provides a good indication of the burnability of the fuel. The narrower the distillation range, the better the over-all performance of the fuel in a suitable burner. An exceptionally wide distillation range indicates a

Table 15-22. National Bureau of Standards Specifications for Fuel Oils

Grade No.	Description	Flash point, °F	Pour point, °F	Water and sediment, % max	Carbon residue on 10% residuum, %	Ash, %	Distillation temperatures, °F			Viscosity Saybolt			
							10% point	90% point	End point	Universal at 100°F Max	Min	Furol at 122°F Max	Min
1	Distillate oil intended for vaporizing pot-type burners and other burners requiring this grade	100	0	Trace	0.15	....	420	....	625	....	....		
2	Distillate oil for general-purpose domestic heating for use in burners not requiring No. 1	100	20	0.10	0.35	....	....	675	....	40	....		
4	Oil for burner installations not equipped with preheating facilities	130	20	0.50	....	0.10	....	....	....	125	45		
5	Residual-type oil for burner installations equipped with preheating facilities	130	....	1.00	....	0.10	....	....	....	....	150	40	
6	Oil for use in burners equipped with preheaters permitting a high-viscosity fuel	150	....	2.00	....	....	....	....	....	....	....	300	45

Local codes may require a higher flash point than shown.

Because of the necessity for low-sulfur fuel oils used in connection with heat-treatment, nonferrous metal, glass and ceramic furnaces, and other special uses, a sulfur requirement may be specified in accordance with the following table:

Grade of Fuel Oil	Sulfur, Max
No. 1	0.5%
No. 2	1.0%
Nos. 4, 5, and 6	No limit

Other sulfur limits may be specified by mutual agreement between buyer and seller.

It is the intent of these classifications that failure to meet any requirement of a given grade does not automatically place an oil in the next lower grade unless in fact it meets all requirements of the lower grade. However, these specifications shall not require a pour point lower than 0°F under any conditions.

Lower or higher pour points may be specified whenever required by conditions of storage or use. Maximum for use in other than atomizing burners.

The 10 per cent point may be specified at 440°F.

The amount of water by distillation plus the sediment by extraction shall not exceed 2.0 per cent. The amount of sediment by extraction shall not exceed 0.50 per cent. A deduction in quantity shall be made for all water and sediment in excess of 1.0 per cent.

blended oil which may make combustion difficult; a portion of the fuel will burn at a temperature too low to ignite the heaviest ends, which will remain as unburned carbon residue in an excessive amount.

Specific gravity of oil is commonly referred to in degrees API (American Petroleum Institute), which is obtained from an empirical formula.

Ignition temperature (flash point) is the temperature to which an oil must be heated in order to yield sufficient vapor to form a flammable mixture with air.

Fire point is the temperature to which an oil must be heated before a continuous flame can be established.

Pour point of a fuel is the lowest temperature at which all parts of the oil will flow.

Btu value of a fuel oil varies according to its weight. No. 1 and No. 2 fuel oils contain approximately 140,000 Btu per gal, whereas No. 4 fuel oil contains approximately 148,000 Btu per gal and No. 6 fuel oil contains approximately 154,000 Btu per gal.

Carbon residue is the free unburned carbon which has not been oxidized as the result of combustion. If excessive, it can cause carbon build-up in flue-gas passages and induced-draft fans.

Table 15-23. Btu Values and Specific Gravities of Gas Fuels

Type of gas	Btu/cu ft	Specific gravity
Natural.....................	900 to 1150	0.50 to 0.70
Coke-oven..................	500 to 550	0.40 to 0.45
Manufactured...............	500 to 600	0.40 to 0.60
Liquid petroleum gas.........	2500 to 3200	1.50 to 2.00

Sulfur content refers to the sulfur in combination contained in the oil. As a result of combustion, this sulfur will unite with other elements, including water vapor, and form an acid which may cause damage to flue-gas passages or induced-draft fans.

A classification of liquid fuels was introduced by the U.S. Department of Commerce in 1950. Liquid fuels are classified as No. 1, No. 2, No. 4, No. 5, and No. 6. Table 15-22 gives data for the fuel classifications.

Gaseous Fuels. Gaseous fuels may be classified as: natural, manufacturers, coke-oven, and liquid petroleum. Many localities are supplied with mixtures of gases whose characteristics will not conform to the above, and burners should be adjusted to the specific gas.

Fuel gases differ principally in their Btu content per cubic foot and their specific gravity. The specific gravity of a gas is the ratio of the density of that gas to the density of air. Combustion-equipment manufacturers design burners specifically for each of the above fuel gases.

The Btu values and specific gravities of these fuels are given in Table 15-23.

COMBUSTION

Four elements must be present before combustion can take place: Combustible material (fuel), oxygen (air), temperature, and time. Complete combustion is obtained when all the combustible elements in the fuel are combined with oxygen. Not all of the oxygen present need be utilized; however, excess air should be limited to produce higher furnace efficiencies. The vigor and rate of mixing of air and fuel determine the rate and completeness of combustion; the better the mixing, the less excess air will be required for complete combustion.

Approximately 15 lb of air are required to burn 1 lb of fuel oil. This is equivalent to 1,400 cu ft of air, under standard conditions, for each gallon of fuel oil. Approximately 12 cu ft of air are required to burn 1 cu ft of natural gas containing 1,000 Btu per cu ft. If the gas is manufactured, containing 500 Btu per cu ft, 6 cu ft of air will be required to burn 1 cu ft.

It is necessary to bring a combustible substance to its ignition temperature before it will unite in chemical combination with oxygen to produce the reaction. The most important condition governing the process of combustion is temperature.

The time necessary to complete combustion is determined by the rate of combustion. This rate depends partly upon the specific rate of reaction of the combustible substance with oxygen, partly upon the rate at which oxygen is supplied (mixing), and partly upon the temperature obtained because of surrounding conditions.

HEAT TRANSFER

Heat flows from a substance at an elevated temperature to a substance at a relatively lower temperature by three methods: convection, conduction, and radiation.

Convection is the transfer of heat by the circulation of a fluid over a surface which either gives up heat or absorbs it. The circulation may be either forced or natural. Fluid flowing over a surface transmits its heat to the surface by conduction through the fluid. At the boundary of fluid and surface there is a stagnant film which impedes the flow of heat. In order to bring the highest-temperature fluid in contact with the transmitting surface, it is necessary to break down the stagnant films. This is accomplished by promoting turbulence in the fluid stream. Therefore, in general, the greater the velocity of fluid, the greater the heat transfer per square foot of transfer surface.

Conduction is the transmission of heat through and by means of matter, unaccompanied by any observable motion on the part of the matter. The flow of heat in any material is an intramolecular action, the motion of one molecule imparting its energy to its neighbor. The conductivity of any material is the ease with which it permits heat transfer. The physical properties of the material determine its conductivity.

Radiation is the transmission of heat through space by wave motion from higher- to lower-temperature bodies. The rate of transfer is proportional to the temperature difference and inversely proportional to the square of the distance separating the source from the receiver. The nature of the radiating surface influences the rate of heat transmission (a reflective surface transmitting more than a dull surface).

THE MAKE-UP AIR PROBLEM

The removal of large volumes of contaminated air from a plant requires introduction of an equal amount of fresh replacement air. Otherwise resultant "air starvation" creates negative pressure within the building and any or all of the following undesirable conditions:

1. Reduced volumes handled by the exhaust fans and consequently inadequate removal of contaminants.
2. Back drafts in natural draft flues, ventilators, and stacks.
3. Dispersal of contaminants throughout the work area by high-velocity crosscurrents from openings in the outside walls.
4. Uncomfortable, and in many instances unhealthful, working conditions.

The Most Economical and Practical Solution. It is relatively simple and, with natural gas available, modest in cost. *For each cfm exhausted, introduce and temper to design conditions 1 cfm of fresh air distributed as required.*

Direct-flow gas-fired make-up heaters have been specifically designed for this job. These package units are listed by Underwriters' Laboratories for either outdoor or indoor installation. Standard catalog sizes range from 2,500 to 80,000 cfm. Maximum standard catalog capacities are shown up to 80,000 cfm and 12,500,000 Btu per hr; special order units, also UL-listed, are available up to 150,000 cfm and 16,800,000 Btu per hr.

Figure 15-22 shows a typical side elevation of a direct-flow heater. Arranged as a pull-through unit, single or twin-blower fans draw fresh air from outside, through filters if required, across an open-flame line burner, modulated up to maximum turndown of 30 to 1 for close temperature control.　Motorized dampers on discharge close when fans are not operating in order to prevent cold air leakage into the building.

Safe.　Detailed analyses of the products of combustion have been made with the following results: The amount of carbon monoxide detected in the air stream with the

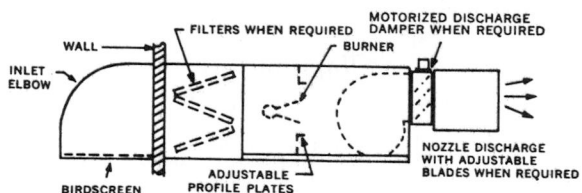

FIG. 15-22. Typical side elevation of direct-flow heater.

burner properly adjusted was not sufficient to measure.　With the burner deliberately and extremely maladjusted, the maximum amount of carbon monoxide detected was less than .001 per cent or less than 10 ppm.　These figures are well below the standard of 100 ppm set by the Bureau of Standards (in Technical Paper 212) and by the American Conference of Goverment Industrial Hygienists.

Chapter 16

PIPING[1]

By TYLER G. HICKS
Mechanical Engineer
Hicksville, L.I., N.Y.

The first step in any piping maintenance program involves eliminating, as far as possible, basic conditions that make excessive maintenance necessary. These may include severe corrosion, water hammer, or poor piping layout. In the case of both corrosion and water hammer, little can be done until one understands the cause.

Corrosion. Probably the biggest single piping-maintenance problem is corrosion. Books have been written on its theory, but the important point is that internal corrosion of piping is generally caused by atmospheric oxygen dissolved in water, and it stops when oxygen is removed or used up by its attack on the metal. Water coming into a system from the outside is always saturated with oxygen, and will continue to corrode the piping until the oxygen is consumed in the process. That is why service-water lines (always supplied with new water and new oxygen) rust faster than hot-water heating lines, which constantly recirculate the same water.

In the steam-water circuit of power plants, dissolved air (oxygen) enters through the make-up water, and through leaks, into parts of the system under vacuum. The accepted cure is to minimize all such leaks by joint and packing maintenance, and then deaerate the feedwater in a suitably designed heater. Sometimes sodium sulfite is used to remove the last traces of oxygen. Corrosion of condensate lines of heating systems is usually caused by air getting in (through vents, reliefs, and joints) at points where the system is under vacuum.

External corrosion may be rapid where a pipe is frequently wet from "sweating" or other moisture—and particularly if the wet surface is repeatedly exposed to air containing sulfurous or acid fumes. To cure it, remove the cause of the sweating or waterproof the pipe. Pipe buried in cinders or soil will often corrode, particularly if the soil is damp and acid. A practical protection is a watertight covering, generally of asphaltic or similar material, applied directly to the pipe or a spiral wrapping of strong fabric. Normally pipe with perforations or cracks from corrosion or other causes is replaced at once. Where this is not possible because of operating conditions, emergency patches, like those shown in Fig. 16-1, may save a shutdown. These are used on iron and steel pipes.

United States Navy practice for a substantial brazed repair of leaking copper or brass pipe is as follows: Shape the copper patch to fit. Clean the mating surfaces with a file, emery cloth, and hydrochloric acid. Wire patch securely in place. Brick

---

[1] For much of the information in this chapter, the author is indebted to the magazine *Power*, New York, and Crane Company, Chicago; also to other manufacturers who participated from time to time in the preparation of the *Power* material.

in an enclosure to confine the heat.   Heat with an acetylene torch, but do not burn patch or piping.   Run in spelter solder (with borax flux) between surfaces.   Keep turning pipe back and forth so spelter will run between all parts of braze.   When patch is cool, test with water pressure.

A small hole in brass or copper pipe may be closed with a rivet or screw plug.   Small weak areas may be temporarily reinforced by tightly wrapping with wire thoroughly soldered together in layers to make a solid band.

Water Hammer.   This occurs when a moving column of water in a pipe is suddenly stopped or retarded.   If the cause is too sudden closing of a valve, the cure is either a mechanical speed limit on the valve or a tag urging cautious handling. Where a pipe is being constantly hammered by connected reciprocating equipment, anchor the pipe firmly and try relieving the shock by air chambers, surge tanks, or similar devices.

Drainage.   Failure to remove condensate from steam lines is a major cause of water hammer.   Drain all condensate pockets.   Make sure that the traps are operating and that no pipe sags so far as to create a pocket.   Watch out for condensate caught above closed valves in vertical lines or in back of globe valves in horizontal lines.   If water hammer occurs only when steam is admitted to a cold system, it indicates that the system is not adequately pitched or trapped to take care of the large initial condensation.   Gradual preheating may ease the situation.   Where water hammer has continued for some time, inspect the pipe guides, anchors, and adjacent walls for serious cracks.

When the more obvious ills of a piping system have been remedied, it is time to set up an orderly maintenance procedure to forestall future trouble.   In piping, as with other equipment, proper maintenance means preventive maintenance—fixing things before they break.   That, in turn, implies organization, records, and definite inspection schedules. The starting point should be a complete set of drawings of the piping system, on which changes and repairs can be noted and dated as made.

Organization.   It is not enough to have good piping mechanics, important as this is.   Failure to organize maintenance can cause much trouble and unnecessary expense. Complete drawings of the system, with all changes and corresponding dates indicated, will repeatedly save ripping out this or that piece to rediscover facts that should be in the office files.   Moreover, recorded installation dates on piping elements will warn the experienced maintenance engineer when trouble may be expected from the everyday causes that lead to piping failure.

When a leak occurs, the adjacent piping should be studied to locate anything else that needs repair, so that the whole job may be done at one time.   If the hookup is deficient in unions, or otherwise difficult to maintain, the situation should be remedied while making necessary repairs.   General routine inspection crews should check leaks, look for signs of corrosion or weakness, make sure anchors are holding and expansion joints working freely, and check hangers for alignment and distribution of load.

Temperatures.   Inspection of an old system should consider any increased pressure or temperature since installation, because these may exceed the safe limits of the materials installed.   The ASA "Code for Pressure Piping," B31.1, sets the upper temperature limits for all common piping materials used in industrial plants.   Consult

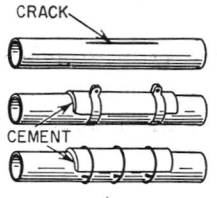

CRACK

CEMENT

1

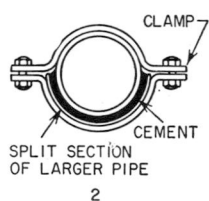

CLAMP

CEMENT

SPLIT SECTION
OF LARGER PIPE

2

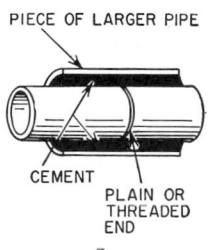

PIECE OF LARGER PIPE

CEMENT

PLAIN OR
THREADED
END

3

Fig. 16-1. Emergency repairs for piping leaks.   (1)   To seal pipe crack, apply iron cement and bind it tight with a metal sheet.   (2) Clamp on a half-shell cut from next larger pipe size and seal with cement or soft gasket.   (3) For an emergency pipe joint, slide ends into larger pipe and calk with iron cement.

the latest edition of the Code to determine the proper operating temperature for various materials.   Note that compliance with Code requirements is purely voluntary.

Pipe Threads.   Any detailed discussion of piping maintenance must start with the practical art of pipe threading for two reasons: (1) Badly made threaded joints increase maintenance and endanger plant operation; and (2) the pipe maintenance man is always a piping erector to some degree.

Good threaded joints are mainly a matter of making good threads.   These, in turn, require a clear understanding of the proper shape and dimensions of the desired thread and of the die or cutting head that forms it.   A brief review of the general scheme of standard American pipe and thread dimensions may bring out certain points often overlooked.   Pipe 14 in. or larger is named by its actual outside diameter.   Usual OD sizes are 14, 16, 18, 20, 24, 30 in., and larger.

Pipe Data.   For 12-in. and smaller, the nominal pipe size is very roughly the inside diameter of so-called "Standard" pipe.   The two heavier series called "Extra Strong" and "Double Extra Strong" have the same external diameters but smaller internal diameters.   These traditional names will eventually be displaced by the more logical nomenclature of the American Standards Association, which sets up a series of pipe schedule numbers of progressively increasing thickness to cover the great variety of modern conditions.   For pipe sizes up to 8 or 10 in., Schedule 40 is identical with "Standard"; "Schedule 80" with "Extra Strong"; "Schedule 160" with "Double Extra Strong."   The complete size schedules and other specifications for piping are contained in the ASA "Code for Pressure Piping."   Regardless of "weight" or "schedule," pipe of a given nominal size follows the outside and thread dimensions given by the American Standard pipe threads.

Most threads are cut with a set of four or six chasers mounted in a hand die or a machine-operated head.   The lip angles are important, and Fig. 16-2 shows lip rake and cutting angles.   Note that the cutting angle equals the lip angle only when the face of the chaser lies along a diameter of the pipe.   If the chaser is not in this position, allow for it when grinding the lip angle.   Since the chaser acts much like a lathe tool, there are similar variations in cutting angle.   The cutting angle should be very small for brass, not over 16° for wrought iron, from 15 to 20° for bessemer pipe, and at least 25° for open-hearth pipe.

Heel clearance (Fig. 16-2) is formed in the chaser threads at the factory and cannot be altered or restored with maintenance tools.   Clearance reduces as the front part of the chaser wears away with long use.   The only cure is a new set.   To get the chasers well started on the pipe, they are beveled at the entrance end with a heavy "lead" angle (Fig. 16-2) to a diameter larger than the end of the pipe.   Figure 16-2 also shows the lead ends of four successive chasers from the same head.   The lead angle is the same in all four, but the cutting edge of each is advanced a little over the next one so that the cutting load is distributed evenly.   Maintaining this equal cutting by proper grinding is a matter of first importance.

Figure 16-3 shows how to grind the lip angle on a narrow chaser such as is used in a hand die.   This method (using the side of the wheel) is not suitable for the wide, flat chasers used in machine-threading heads.   These can be ground on a surface grinder or equivalent rig.   Proper grinding of the lead requires the fixture shown (or equivalent), in which the table can be turned about either horizontal or vertical axes to give universal adjustments.   Before grinding chaser leads arrange them in serial order 1, 2, 3, 4.   Test the angles of the fixture to make sure the wheel bears squarely on the existing face of metal to be ground.   Then take chasers in rotation and remove the same amount of metal from each.   If any in the set is then found to be insufficiently ground, start back with number one and give each an equal additional grinding.   This even treatment should be watched and tested to make sure each chaser carries its share of the cutting load.

Figure 16-4 gives a number of useful pointers in the care of broken and damaged threaded joints of many different types.   Figure 16-5 shows ways to salvage the flanges of pipes in which the threads rust, preventing easy removal of the flange.   The normal engagement to make tight joints is given in Fig. 16-6.

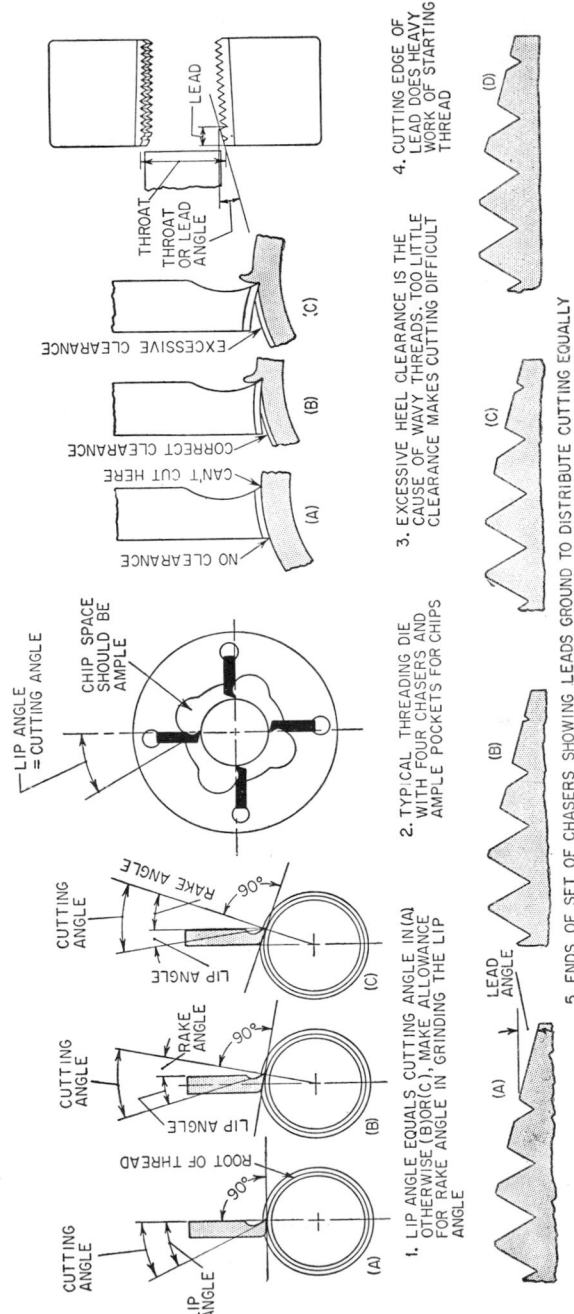

FIG. 16-2. Lip rake and cutting angles for thread chasers.

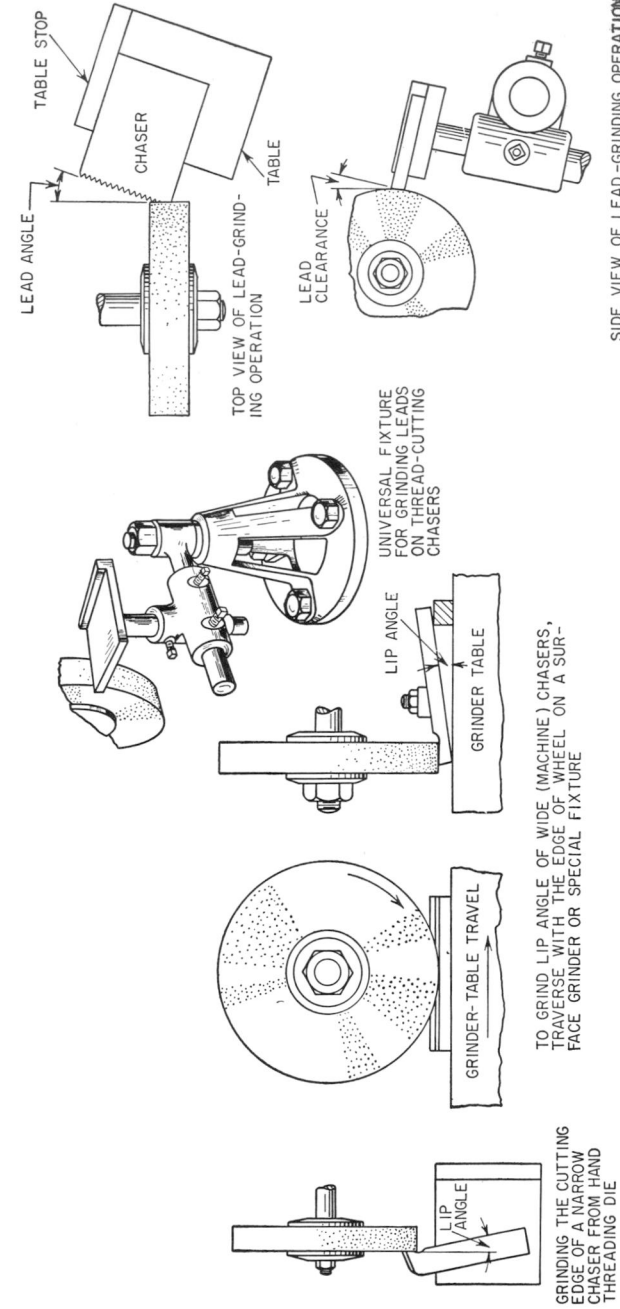

TABLE STOP

CHASER

TABLE

LEAD ANGLE

TOP VIEW OF LEAD-GRINDING OPERATION

LEAD CLEARANCE

SIDE VIEW OF LEAD-GRINDING OPERATION

UNIVERSAL FIXTURE FOR GRINDING LEADS ON THREAD-CUTTING CHASERS

LIP ANGLE

GRINDER TABLE

TO GRIND LIP ANGLE OF WIDE (MACHINE) CHASERS, TRAVERSE WITH THE EDGE OF WHEEL ON A SURFACE GRINDER OR SPECIAL FIXTURE

GRINDER-TABLE TRAVEL

LIP ANGLE

GRINDING THE CUTTING EDGE OF A NARROW CHASER FROM HAND THREADING DIE

FIG. 16-3. Steps in grinding chasers.

Flanges. These are designed to ensure a tight joint that can conveniently be broken for piping changes and repairs. Yet poor selection of flanges, bolts, and gaskets, plus careless joint make-up, can cause endless trouble. Once the desired face has been selected (see Fig. 16-7a), flange dimensions and materials are established by the ASA "Code for Pressure Piping." The customary flange bolt for low-pressure piping is square-headed with a hex nut and American Standard Coarse Thread Series threads. Above 160 psi and 450°F, alloy-steel studs with hex nuts on both ends are often used.

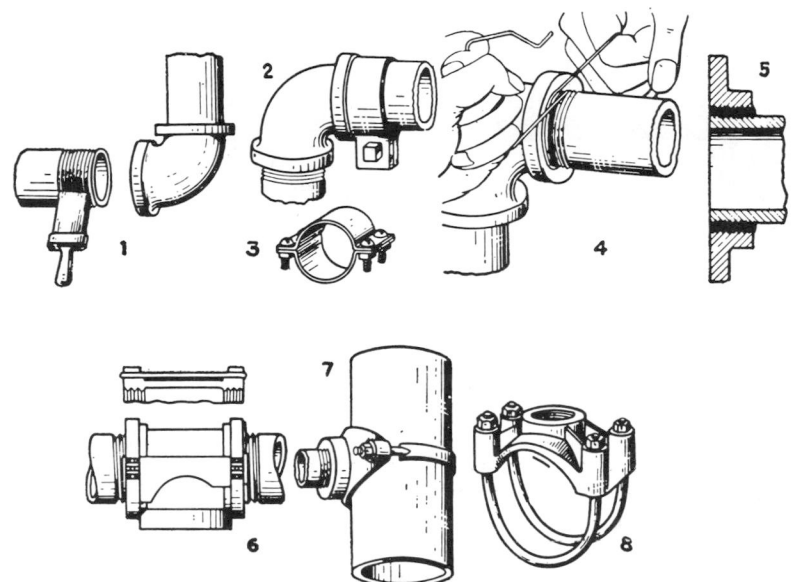

Fig. 16-4. Repairs for threaded joints. Iron cements specially compounded for the service may be applied as paste or putty to seal pipe joints and cracks. Cement used thin makes a good new-thread dope (1). For best results, leaking joint should be *remade* with cement; otherwise cement can be calked under pipe clamp (3) alongside leaky thread (2). Another thread-leak repair involves winding soft wire (4) around cement putty at leak. Allow cement to harden before using. In emergency, a threaded pipe may be cemented into a flange of larger pipe size (5). Tamp cement solidly in place. Crack in fitting (6) sealed with cement backed by metal plate. Outlet saddles for water (7) and steam (8) are clamped to pipe over drilled holes to make emergency branch connections. Saddles may be packed with soft gaskets or cement.

These nuts are generally of carbon steel or at best a less-strong alloy than the studs. Extreme strength is not needed and the difference in metals in contact reduces chances of thread "freezing."

For high-pressure-flange studs the 8-pitch thread series, which provides eight threads per inch for all bolts 1 in. or larger, is often used. Standard flange-drilling templates come in multiples of four holes—four, eight, twelve, sixteen, etc. The flange holes in valves and fittings are set to straddle the center line. Of the flange faces shown in Fig. 16-7a some engineers prefer the raised face or the pipe-lap, with a ring gasket, because these joints (unlike the male-female and tongue-and-groove) do not have to be sprung apart to break a joint or remove a gasket. Grooved joints with thick, soft gaskets are often used for low-temperature, high-pressure hydraulic joints. With either male-female or tongue-and-groove joints, the gasket should be thinner than the depression to avoid "mushrooming."

Gaskets. Widely used gasket materials range from soft rubber for cold water to narrow, solid iron rings for high-pressure steam joints. Table 16-1 shows typical uses and limiting temperatures.   Hand-cut gaskets for raised-face flanges should fit neatly inside the bolts and extend to, but not beyond, the edge of the pipe opening.   If the joint has to be broken frequently, coat one side of the gasket with graphite to prevent

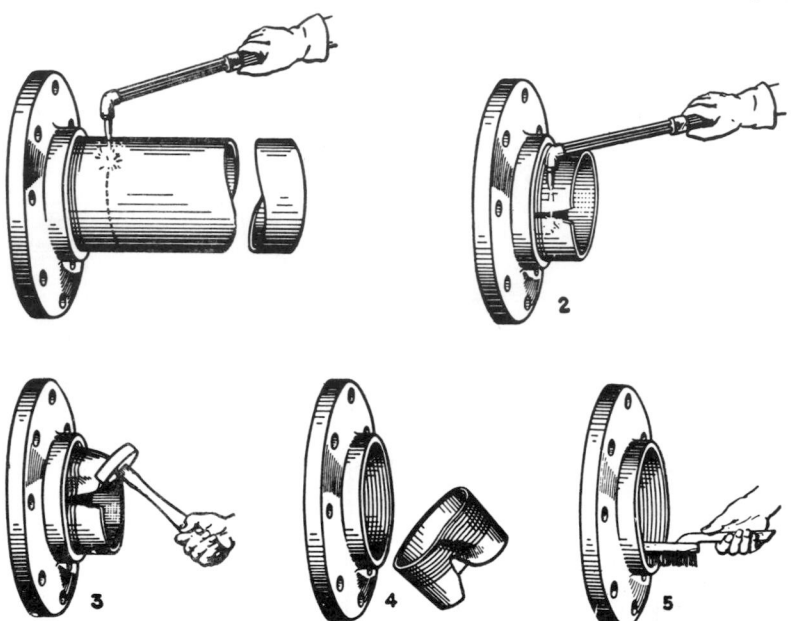

FIG. 16-5. Salvaging flanges when the threads are frozen.   (1) Sever pipe near flange. (2) Cut V notch in pipe stub.   (3) Collapse pipe with hammer.   (4) Pipe falls out, leaving flange threads unharmed.   (5) Clean threads thoroughly.

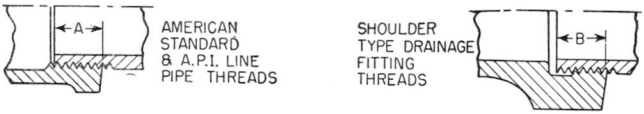

DIMENSIONS, IN INCHES

Dimensions given do not allow for variations in tapping or threading.

Size	⅛	¼	⅜	½	¾	1	1¼	1½	2	2½	3	3½	4	5	6	8	10	12	14
A	¼	⅜	⅜	½	9/16	1 1/16	1 1/16	1 1/16	¾	1 5/16	1	1 1/16	1⅛	1¼	1 5/16	1 7/16	1⅝	1¾	
B*						9/16	⅝	⅝	⅝	⅞	1 5/16	1	1 1/16	1 3/16	1¼	1⅜	1 9/16	1 11/16	1⅞

* Using American Standard Taper male thread with Crane shoulder-type drainage fittings.   The external thread, however, should not be threaded small to gage and not more than one turn large.

FIG. 16-6. Normal engagement between male and female threads to make tight joints. (*Courtesy of Crane Company.*)

sticking.   When a joint has been newly made with soft packing, take up on the bolts again after the line has been hot for some time.

Thin gaskets are less likely to blow than thick.   If flanges fail to meet, it may be risky to fill the gap with a thick, soft gasket.   It is better to use a metal filler, gasketed on both sides.   Raised faces of flanges are often serrated.   These serrations, like corrugations in gaskets and the use of narrow gaskets, are means for increasing the gasket pressure per square inch by reducing contact area.   Most leaky joints are the result of insufficient bolt tension and gasket pressure.   According to Crocker* the initial gasket pressure should be at least 4,000 psi for rubber, 12,000 psi for laminated asbestos in serrated joints, and 30,000 to 60,000 psi for solid-metal gaskets.

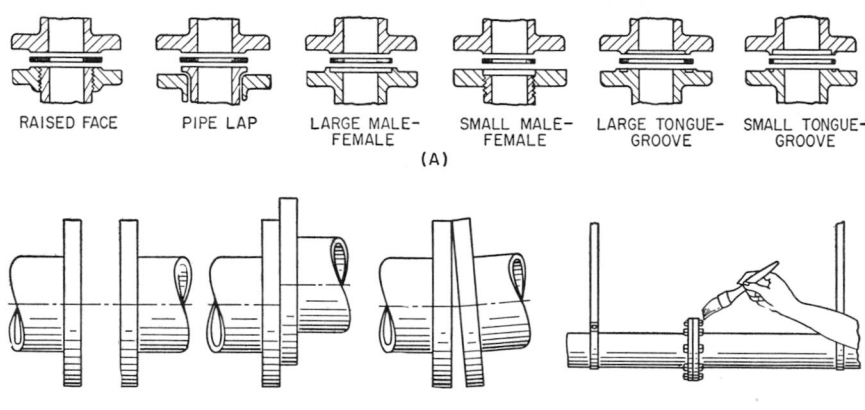

RAISED FACE   PIPE LAP   LARGE MALE-   SMALL MALE-   LARGE TONGUE-   SMALL TONGUE-
                                     FEMALE   FEMALE   GROOVE   GROOVE
(A)

(B)

FIG. 16-7. (A) Standard cast-steel flanges.   (B) Align flanges to avoid trouble; careful aligning before bolting prevents excessive bolting stresses in valves, fittings, and pipe flanges.   Use of thread lubricant cuts friction, protects threads, and makes joints easier to break for necessary repairs.

Ordinarily a tensile stress of about 7,000 psi in the bolt would balance the actual steam pressure, yet the alloy-steel bolts of high-pressure joints are often stressed to 30,000 psi and sometimes to 60,000 psi to flow the gasket into the uneven surface of the flange and thereby ensure tightness.   Tests have been made and tabulated showing how much wrench pull will create a given bolt tension in well-lubricated threads of a

Table 16-1. Gasket-material Selection

Gasket material	Fluid	Usual maximum temp, °F
Red rubber	Steam, air, water	250
Asbestos composition	Steam, water, oil	750
Fiber and paper	Oil	200
Synthetic rubber	Oil	200
Copper, corrugated or plain	Steam or water	600
Steel, corrugated or plain	Steam or water	1000
Stainless steel, 12–14% chromium, corrugated	Steam or water	1000
Hydrogen-annealed furniture iron	Steam or water	1000
Monel, corrugated or plain	Steam or water	1000
Ingot iron, special gasket for ring-type joint	Steam, water, oil	1000

From Crocker, "Piping Handbook," 4th ed., McGraw-Hill Book Company, Inc., 1954.

given pitch.   The practical value of such tables is limited because of the great variation of pull with thread lubrication and also because it is rarely convenient to measure wrench pull, particularly where the wrench must be sledged.   From the practical angle, in the case of all medium- and low-pressure work, the fitter may as well continue to tighten by "feel" and experience.   When this will not do, as with 1,400-psi steam

* "Piping Handbook," 4th ed., McGraw-Hill Book Company, Inc., 1954.

lines, the only reliable determination of bolt tension is by micrometer measurement of bolt elongation, using studs with machined micrometer pads and taking care that before-and-after measurements are taken cold and at the same temperature. The measured elongation must be referred to the grip distance between the nuts and not to the full length of the stud.

For steel of any composition a stress of 30,000 psi corresponds closely to a stretch of $\frac{1}{1000}$ in. per in., with other stresses and stretches in proportion up to the elastic limit.

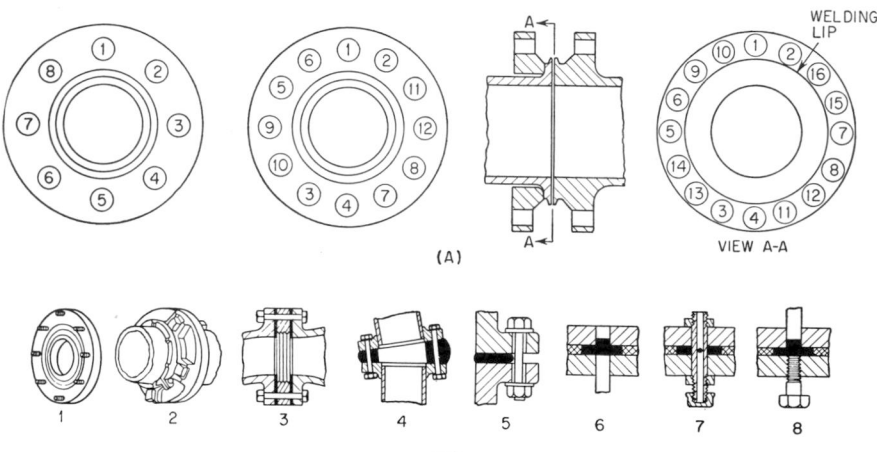

Fig. 16-8. (A) Two sequences of bolt tightening. In either case, first set nuts finger tight. For method at left, tighten nuts moderately in order 1, 2, 3, etc. Then make another round to set bolts a little tighter—and so on until bolts are equally and sufficiently tight and feelers show equal flange separation all around. Many prefer crossover method (right). Bolt tightening for seal-welded joint: First put in temporary bolts all around, hammer tight. Remove 1 and 2, seal weld there, and replace temporary with alloy bolts set up hammer tight. Repeat this operation at 3 and 4, 5 and 6, etc., criss-crossing as shown. Follow same general procedure for a different number of bolts, criss-crossing as before. (B) Iron cement aids in making and repairing flanged joints. Corrugated-iron gasket coated both sides with iron cement will make tight joint (1) despite irregular flange faces. To plug leaky thread at flange, set band clamp with flat edge against flange (2) and tamp groove full of cement. If flanges cannot be aligned, turn a metal "Dutchman" (3, 4) and seal it on both sides with iron cement or cement-plastered gaskets. To make a tight joint with rough-cast flanges (5) separate flanges by rope or soft spacers; then fill joint with cement. Localized leaks in flanges or gaskets may be plugged through adjacent bolt holes (6). Remove bolt, plug one side of hole, and force cement through other side by hammering on a close-fitting rod. Or (7) inject cement with grease gun through pipe nipple with locknuts and a central side-outlet hole. If stud screws into flange, reverse stud (8), making a backstop for cement.

Thus, for a bolt with 3-in. grip, the total stretch should be 0.002 in. to create a unit tension of 20,000 psi in the bolt.

Leaks. Like other piping leaks, those in flange joints grow rapidly. Fix them at the start. A frequent cause is poor alignment of piping. It should not be necessary to spring flanges into line (Fig. 16-7B). All steamfitters agree that nut tightening should follow a definite sequence. Two are shown in Fig. 16-8A—one "round and round," the other "criss-cross." Either should be satisfactory. An improvement on the second might be to tighten a single bolt on one side, then on the opposite—then move 90° and repeat. Figure 16-8B gives a number of pointers on the maintenance of flanged joints.

Valves. Damage in storage or handling and poor installation handicap a valve from the start. Complete wrapping, wooden crating, or thin metal caps over the ends pro-

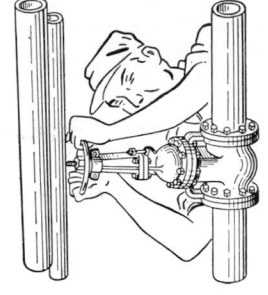

BE SURE TO ALLOW AMPLE CLEARANCE FOR RISING-STEM VALVES, INCLUDING ROOM TO REMOVE STEM AND BONNET FOR INSPECTION. IF LACK OF CLEARANCE PREVENTS FULL OPENING, EXCESSIVE PRESSURE DROP, DISK VIBRATION, AND SEAT WEAR WILL RESULT

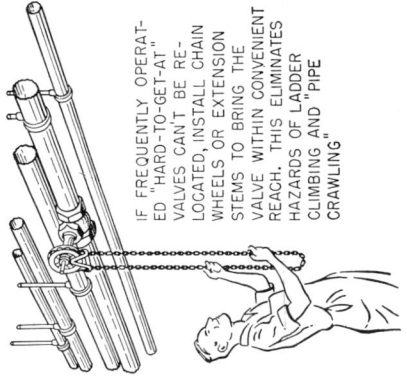

IF FREQUENTLY OPERATED "HARD-TO-GET-AT" VALVES CAN'T BE RELOCATED, INSTALL CHAIN WHEELS OR EXTENSION STEMS TO BRING THE VALVE WITHIN CONVENIENT REACH. THIS ELIMINATES HAZARDS OF LADDER CLIMBING AND "PIPE CRAWLING"

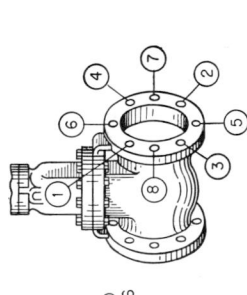

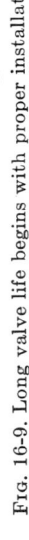

TIGHTEN BOLTS ACCORDING TO CROSS-OVER METHOD SHOWN. THIS INSURES TRUE BEARING OVER THE FLANGE FACES AND REDUCES STRESS ON FLANGES AND OTHER VALVE PARTS

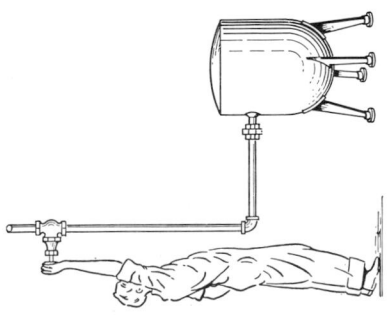

LOCATE VALVES WHERE THEY CAN BE REACHED CONVENIENTLY, TO INSURE PROPER OPERATION. VALVES WON'T BE OPENED FULLY, CLOSED TIGHTLY, OR REGULATED PROPERLY IF THE OPERATOR CAN'T DO THE JOB WITH CONVENIENCE AND SAFETY

FIG. 16-9. Long valve life begins with proper installation.

tect valves as shipped from the factory.   Keep this protection in place and store the valve under cover until it is installed.   Penetration of sand into working parts often follows storage on the ground, exposed to the weather.   Rough handling easily damages valves; place them where they cannot fall and where other material cannot fall on them.

Installation starts with removal of the valve's protective covering; then clean all grit and dirt from the inside.   Pipe cleaning is just as necessary if damage to seats and

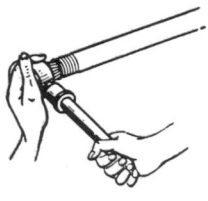

Be sure to ream out burrs that impede flow and sometimes damage equipment

Blow dirt and sand from pipe before making up joints; foreign matter may score valve seats

Apply dope on male threads only to keep it from getting into pipe and equipment

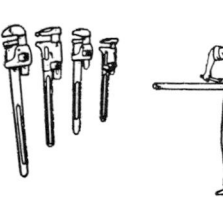

Use right-size wrench; too much leverage may twist valve bodies or crack cast fittings

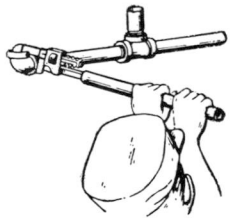

Never use a hickey except to *break* a stubborn joint in taking down a line

FIG. 16-10. Suggestions for pipe fitters.

disks is to be avoided.   Blow out the valve with compressed air or flush it with water; clean the pipe in the same manner, or pull a swab through, to remove dirt and metal chips left from threading operations or storage.

Future troubles can be minimized by mounting valves properly, protecting them against outside damage, and locating them at the most suitable point in the line. Except for split-wedge and double-disk gates, most valves can be mounted at any angle, although it is always better, from the valve standpoint, to mount it with stem pointing upward.   Any position with the stem pointing downward brings the bonnet under the line of flow, forming a pocket to catch pipe scale and other foreign matter. This soon cuts and destroys inside stem threads.   On lines exposed to freezing temperatures, moisture trapped at this point may cause frozen and burst bonnets.   Even when the valve is mounted with its stem upright, take the precaution of installing a drain plug in the bottom of the body.   Figures 16-9 and 16-10 show a number of installation pointers.

Flow Direction.   Direction of flow through globe valves depends on the nature of service and can usually be determined by asking the question, "Should the valve open or shut if the disk and stem part company?"   The ASME "Boiler Code" requires pressure under the disk for globe valves in boiler-feed lines so that the loose disk will not act as a check and stop water flow.   If the valve controls equipment which might overspeed, applying pressure over the disk forms a check valve which will shut down the unit if the disk comes loose.   Drain valves with pressure under the disk will vibrate open if not tightly closed.   If a valve is persistently left cracked open, reversing it to put pressure over the disk will ensure tighter closing.

To summarize: Unless the service clearly requires pressure under the disk, install the valve to put pressure on top of the disk.   Pressure over the disk aids in keeping the valve closed, tending to compensate for any stem contraction caused by temperature changes.   Valves of large size, 12 in. and over, present generous disk areas to line pressure. In unbalanced service, such as discharging from high to low pressure, this pressure makes valve operation increasingly difficult as exposed disk area increases.   This is less pronounced in gates than in globes, because disk movement in the former crosses the line of flow (Fig. 16-11), whereas in the latter it opposes the flow.   To minimize pressure difficulties, equip all gate valves 12 in. and over and all globe valves over 6 in. with throttling-globe bypass valves.

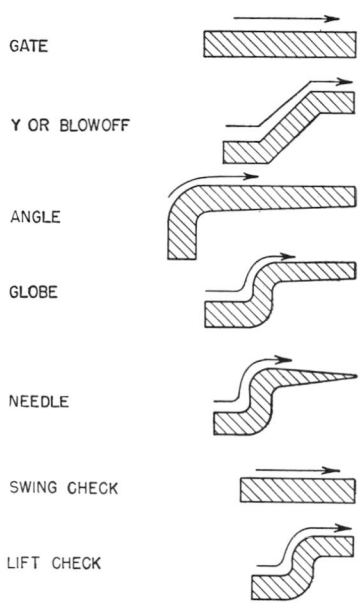

GATE

Y OR BLOWOFF

ANGLE

GLOBE

NEEDLE

SWING CHECK

LIFT CHECK

FIG. 16-11. Valve flow chart.

In pipelines handling sludge or other suspended matter, keep valves out of vertical lines whenever possible; stoppage of flow allows suspended matter to settle and choke a closed valve.   This is especially troublesome when it interferes with check-valve operation.   Never install a valve without thought as to access.   To be sure valves are opened and closed correctly, make it convenient and safe to do so.   Do not expect a man standing on a ladder reaching for an overhead valve to exert any great amount of force.   Install the valve horizontally, and fit it with a chain operator which can be reached from floor level.   Overhead valves on large lines, requiring two-man operation, should be vertical, to permit operators to stand on the pipe.   If possible install a working platform, extend the valve stem through the floor above, provide an impactor hand-wheel or a power operator.

Beware of valves just within finger-tip reach of a normal man; rather than hunt for something to stand on, he'll stretch just enough to reach the handwheel.   The valve cannot be closed tight and leakage will develop.   Always allow sufficient clearance for rising stems and for removing the bonnet and stem.   It is much easier to leave the valve in the line and remove only internal parts for inspection and cleaning.   Providing easy access to all valves represents the first step to correct operation, regular inspection, and careful maintenance.   Good check-valve service depends to a large extent on meeting special needs.   Correct position is most important; install swing and tilt checks with the pin horizontal and so that gravity will close the disk; place lift checks so that the lift is vertical.

Diaphragm-operated control valves present problems connected with the diaphragm as well as with the inner valve.   Inverted installation on oil or chemical lines exposes the diaphragm to leakage through the stem packing.   Heat from adjacent steam lines may cause early deterioration of the rubber.   On steam-operated valves, protect the diaphragm against steam contact by installing a water leg or accumulator and filling it with water before admitting steam.   When using the regulated pressure as the actuating medium, connect the pilot line, controlled by a lock-shield globe valve, on the downstream side of the valve.   Do not make the connection in an elbow or pipe bend, because erratic pressures occur at these points.   Select as a connection point a straight section of pipe at least 10 ft from the valve. The globe valve permits throttling the pilot supply to smooth out pressure pulsations, and the lock shield protects against tampering.

Regulating-valve bodies, marked as to flow direction, must be inserted in the line to conform with the marking (Fig. 16-12). A correctly chosen valve will not necessarily match the pipe size. For the connections, reducing flanges or bushings save space, but bell or venturi reducers give better flow conditions. Install a strainer ahead of the valve to remove foreign matter and protect the seats. Impingement noises can be minimized by installing the valve in a straight pipe run. Do not install an elbow or bend immediately downstream of the valve. To facilitate the regular inspection regulating valves deserve, connect a throttling globe valve as a bypass.

Check every valve installation for ways to simplify maintenance. When applying pipe insulation, end the permanent covering at bonnet bolts. Use a removable section to cover the bonnet, otherwise internal inspection may be neglected because of hesitation in breaking a perfect-looking insulated joint. After the system has been heated to operating temperature, tighten all body and bonnet bolts and adjust the stem packing.

Valve Maintenance. Neglecting a valve until it must be replaced or fitted with new parts wastes expensive materials; frequent and regular inspections uncover leaks and reveal other conditions, such as corrosion, incrustation, and wiredrawing, that mean future trouble unless corrected. Caught early, these defects can be repaired without major difficulty or expense; allowed to go unattended, they may require expensive parts and materials and can cause production shutdowns. A good maintenance program includes correct operation, regular and systematic inspection, proper lubrication of all rotating or sliding parts, replacement of stem packing when leakage or excessive friction develops, and refacing leaking seats and disks. Valve parts such as stem threads, thrust washers, and disk-spacing wedges or cams must be kept free of corrosion, incrustation, or foreign materials and must be adequately lubricated as recommended by the manufacturers. Plug cocks, with their large metal surfaces, require frequent lubrication to prevent galling and seizing of the sliding parts.

Packing. Proper maintenance of packing and correct adjustment of packing nuts are essential to satisfactory stem life and good valve performance. New packing, impregnated with graphite, lubricates the stem; after this lubricant disappears, friction between the stem and packing increases. If the packing nut must be tightened to a point where it is difficult to turn the stem, the packing has become dry and hard or is otherwise unsuitable for the service. In either case it should be discarded; it imposes an additional burden that will rapidly shorten stem-thread life. Excessive packing compression causes uncertainty as to whether or not the valve is fully seated. As a result, operators frequently seat valves tighter than they need be. This excessive closing effort, often applied with a wrench, injures the stem threads.

Stem packing that has been subjected to high-temperature steam and then allowed to cool often leaks a small amount when the line goes into operation again. Expansion and contraction of bonnet, stem, packing, gland, and packing nut cause this condition. It does not necessarily call for adjustment of the packing nut or gland; as soon as the valve becomes hot it will, in most cases, stop leaking. Packing maintenance is particularly important on automatically operated valves; excessive friction causes erratic movement. When lubricators are provided, keep the stem and packing adequately lubricated. Use stem packing that fits; preformed rings enter easily and draw up evenly. When winding coil packing spirally around the valve stem, force it to the outer edge of the stuffing box instead of wrapping it tightly to the stem. After adding the maximum number of rings, draw up the gland evenly, with a wrench, until the packing is forced into snug position. Then slack off on the gland and make the nut finger tight. A good valve stem, sufficient packing of the right kind, and a finger-tight gland will hold all moderate pressures. Higher pressures require a tighter gland to prevent the applied pressure from getting in under the packing.

Many valves contain a back seat closing off the packing gland against pressure, when the valve is open. This arrangement permits repacking the stem with the valve under pressure. Be certain a valve has this feature before attempting to repack under pres-

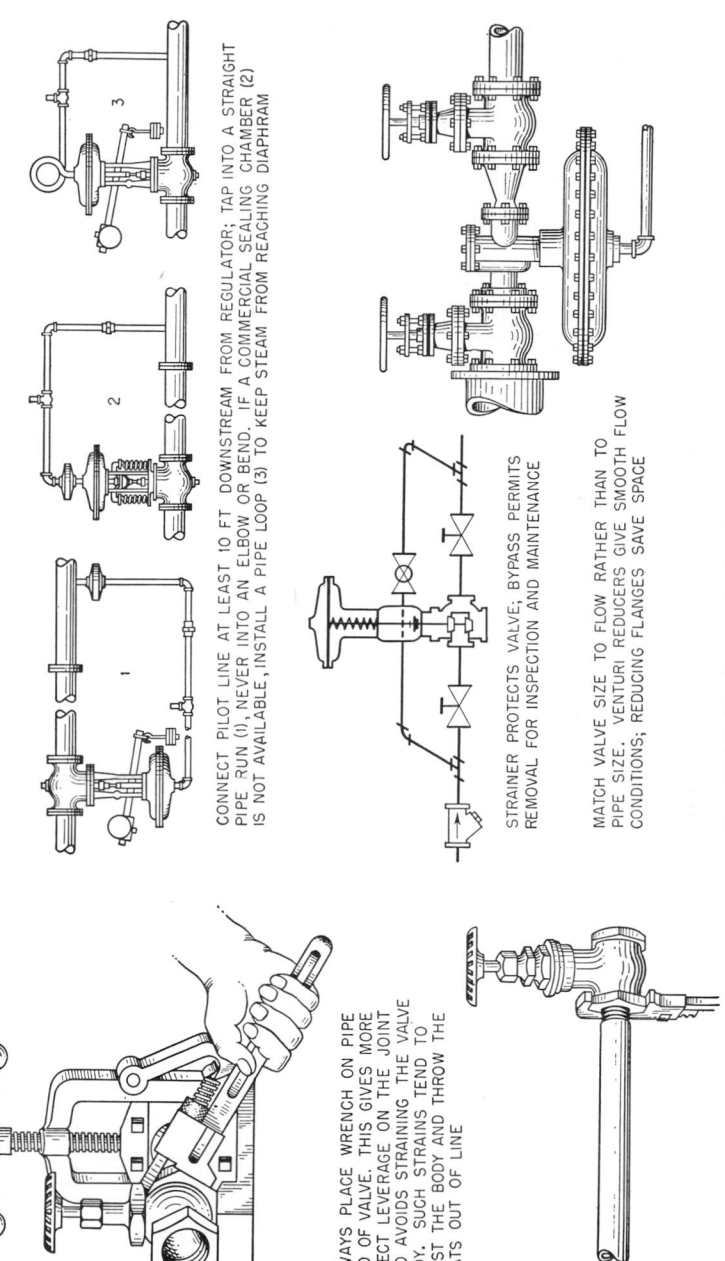

CONNECT PILOT LINE AT LEAST 10 FT DOWNSTREAM FROM REGULATOR; TAP INTO A STRAIGHT PIPE RUN (1), NEVER INTO AN ELBOW OR BEND. IF A COMMERCIAL SEALING CHAMBER (2) IS NOT AVAILABLE, INSTALL A PIPE LOOP (3) TO KEEP STEAM FROM REACHING DIAPHRAM

STRAINER PROTECTS VALVE; BYPASS PERMITS REMOVAL FOR INSPECTION AND MAINTENANCE

MATCH VALVE SIZE TO FLOW RATHER THAN TO PIPE SIZE. VENTURI REDUCERS GIVE SMOOTH FLOW CONDITIONS; REDUCING FLANGES SAVE SPACE

FIG. 16-12. Good regulator hookups.

ALWAYS PLACE WRENCH ON PIPE END OF VALVE. THIS GIVES MORE DIRECT LEVERAGE ON THE JOINT AND AVOIDS STRAINING THE VALVE BODY. SUCH STRAINS TEND TO TWIST THE BODY AND THROW THE SEATS OUT OF LINE

sure. Maintenance and inspection involve frequent dismantling and reassembling of valves. Knowing the best way to do these operations simplifies the job and avoids damage to valves from improper handling. Before starting to remove a bonnet, open the valve so that no bending stress is placed on the stem during removal. Likewise, put the stem in the "open" position before replacing a bonnet. U-clamp gate-valve bodies have been split by tightening the bonnet joint with the wedge in its extreme closed position; union-bonnet gate-valve seats have been sprung apart by wedging action in the same manner.

Bolt Tension. On valves designed for high-temperature high-pressure service, bonnet bolts are usually tightened until a known tension is imposed on the bolt. Before loosening nuts, clean the bolt ends and measure the bolt length with a micrometer. Keep a record of individual bolt lengths, and elongate them the same amount when reassembling the valve, making sure the valve and bolt temperatures are the same as before. Always draw up body bolts evenly until the bonnet is true and square with the body. Most actual maintenance and repair operations are concerned with keeping seats and disks in leakproof condition. The specific methods used depend on the valve construction, condition of seats and disks, and equipment available. Modern methods of building up metallic surfaces (hard soldering, brazing, or welding) now offer means of salvaging valves with badly eroded seats and disks. Such building up makes repair possible without removal of the parent metal, greatly extending valve life.

Build up bronze seats with hard solder or bronze rod; alloy-steel seats for temperatures below 750°F can be repaired by brazing, which, although not as resistant as the original metal, will give good service. Building up alloy trim with supposedly identical metals can easily lead to trouble unless complete information is available as to the composition and hardness of the parent metal. Before building up disks on automatic valves for service on high pressures and temperatures, consult the manufacturer, because any major change in seat or disk contour may cause serious operating difficulties. If facilities for building up special trim metal are not available, the valve can be returned to the factory, although this practice may interfere with plant production. When it is absolutely necessary to buy new parts, buy seats and disks in pairs so that only a minimum amount of grinding is needed. Salvage all good parts of damaged valves for use as spare parts to rebuild other valves when they become damaged.

Seats and disks can be ground or refaced in many ways. The procedure for grinding seats and disks in union-bonnet globe valves is, perhaps, the simplest (Fig. 16-13). It is necessary only to pin the stem and disk together and use the bonnet as a guide for lapping the disk against the seat. Screwed bonnets cannot be used as guides for grinding; this job requires a grinding kit or a drill press. If a drill press is available, remove the stem from the bonnet and insert it in the drill chuck. Clamp the valve body in the drill-press vise; level on the top edge of the body-bonnet joint which parallels the seat surfaces. Pin the disk and stem, apply compound, and grind with the drill press at low speed and light spindle pressure.

Check Valves. Check-valve disks can be lapped against the seats; the disk usually contains a slot for a screwdriver to apply the turning movement. When lapping stainless iron disks and seats against each other, mix white lead and oil with the grinding compound to provide lubrication, otherwise the metal will drag and ruin the surfaces. The use of a grinding compound with small grain size reduces the tendency to gall. Grind with light strokes, lifting the disk frequently to a new position and cleaning the surfaces often. Stellited seats and disks can be ground in the same manner as that recommended for stainless iron, except that in some cases it may be necessary to use silicon-carbide grit.

Balanced-pressure double-seat regulating valves require particular care in grinding. Both seats must be established at the same time. Watch the disks to see which seat touches first; put compound on this disk with just a trace on the other. Grind until both seats are established uniformly. To produce a true seat under operating conditions, provide a steam connection to heat the body and stem to operating temperature, before grinding.

Machining. On globe valves which are badly worn, or where eroded areas have been built up, machining eliminates excessive lapping. Seats can be machined in a lathe, or ground with an emery-cloth-covered metal disk mounted in a drill press. A similar grinding disk, mounted on a motor-driven flexible shaft, can also be used on small valves. Repeated machining or grinding may reduce seat thickness dangerously. On

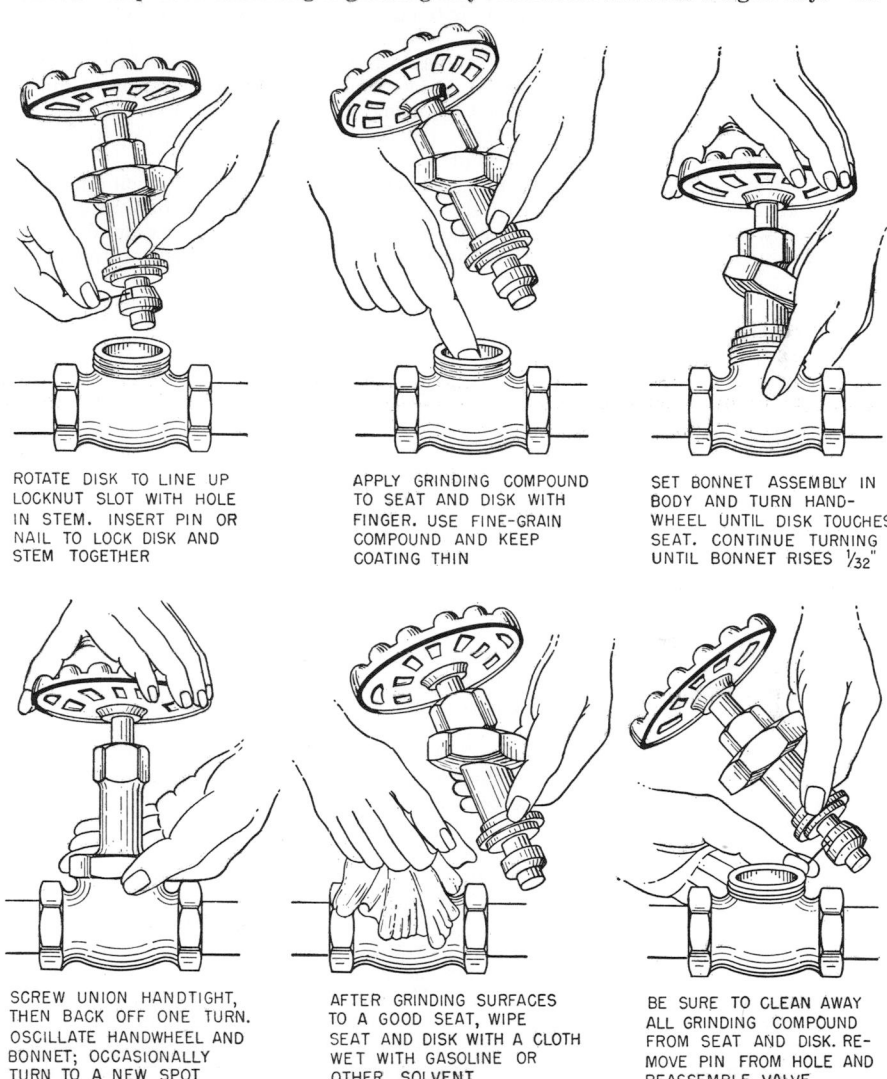

ROTATE DISK TO LINE UP LOCKNUT SLOT WITH HOLE IN STEM. INSERT PIN OR NAIL TO LOCK DISK AND STEM TOGETHER

APPLY GRINDING COMPOUND TO SEAT AND DISK WITH FINGER. USE FINE-GRAIN COMPOUND AND KEEP COATING THIN

SET BONNET ASSEMBLY IN BODY AND TURN HAND-WHEEL UNTIL DISK TOUCHES SEAT. CONTINUE TURNING UNTIL BONNET RISES $\frac{1}{32}"$

SCREW UNION HANDTIGHT, THEN BACK OFF ONE TURN. OSCILLATE HANDWHEEL AND BONNET; OCCASIONALLY TURN TO A NEW SPOT

AFTER GRINDING SURFACES TO A GOOD SEAT, WIPE SEAT AND DISK WITH A CLOTH WET WITH GASOLINE OR OTHER SOLVENT

BE SURE TO CLEAN AWAY ALL GRINDING COMPOUND FROM SEAT AND DISK. RE-MOVE PIN FROM HOLE AND REASSEMBLE VALVE

Fig. 16-13. Regrinding globe-valve seats.

integral-seat globe valves too small to insert soldering or brazing equipment, the seat opening can be reamed and threaded to take a renewable seat ring, which can be made up from material available in the plant shop. While it is desirable to replace the seat with the same metal, a different one can be used in an emergency. It is not advisable to use stainless iron of the same hardness for both seat and disk unless the valve is to handle oil.

Seat Rings. Repeated refacing of shoulder-design seat rings reduces the shoulder thickness to a point where metal contact pressure against the under side causes concaving of the outer or seating surface.   The remedy lies in replacing the ring or increasing its thickness by welded overlays.   Leakage past seat-ring threads must be repaired immediately; it can be done by welding and rethreading or by reaming and threading to take an oversize ring.   If the damage is too great for these remedies, weld the ring solidly in the valve body.

Good service from composition globe-valve disks depends on care.   When one side of such a disk is eroded, either machine it to a new face or reverse it and use the opposite side.   Disk stocks can be stretched by using substitutes such as leather, scrap rubber belting, or lead machined smooth.   Although not ideal, these materials will give satisfactory service until new disks arrive.

Refacing.   Refacing of gate-valve seats and disks usually requires machining in a lathe or grinding in a drill press, although disks with surfaces not too badly worn can be refaced with a sanding wheel or by hand grinding, and seats can be ground with a hand brace.   Lathe machining offers no major difficulties for parallel-seat gate bodies,

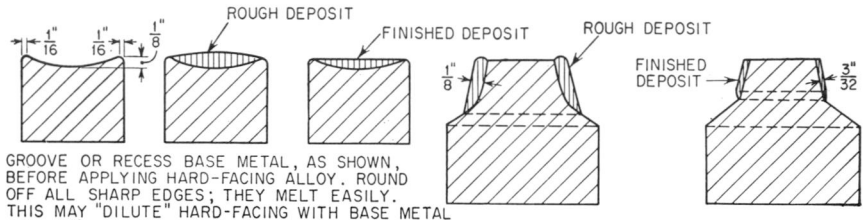

FIG. 16-14. Correct preparation means good hard-facing.

but wedge-gate bodies require cumbersome holders.   The drill-press grinding method is convenient.

Parallel-seat disks may be chucked readily for lathe refacing; a taper block to fit the faceplate helps with wedge disks.   The drill-press grinding method can be used on wedges as well as seats.   Special holding jigs, milled out to hold the wedge snug and level and keep it from turning, offer maximum convenience, but a jig is required for each valve size.   One flat tapered plate, with clamps, will serve for many sizes and can be used on either a drill press or a lathe.   Wedge disks can also be refaced by holding the surface against a motor-driven sanding or grinding disk.   Keep the wedge centered on the disk and hold it with uniform pressure, or uneven grinding will ruin the taper. Hand grinding on an emery-cloth-covered flat surface proves satisfactory where only light scratches or machine marks need be removed.

Reseating Kits.   Most of the methods described so far require that the valve be removed from the line.   Valve reseating kits are available for refacing seat rings without removing the body from the line.   This eliminates the need for breaking pipe joints, reduces possibilities of leaks, and saves time and labor.

Valves subjected to corrosive conditions soon become covered with "barnacles" which build up around seat and disk rings.   If allowed to increase to any great extent, the barnacles soon creep over the seat edges and prevent the valve from closing tight. Cleaning the valve with a sandblast and applying a good paint or metal-spray coating on the areas around the seats greatly retards this growth.   Timely repairs make valves last longer and save metal.

Hard-facing.   This is a useful maintenance tool for protecting steel valve parts against severe abrasive wear and wiredrawing action.   Cobalt-chromium-tungsten alloys (stellite) retain their hardness at red heat, making them particularly suited to surfaces in friction and to parts exposed to high temperature.   Before applying hard-facing alloy, prepare the part by grooving the surface to a depth of from $\frac{3}{32}$ to $\frac{1}{8}$ in. (Fig. 16-14), leaving a ridge on each side.   Round off all sharp corners, because sharp edges melt easily and interalloying between the base metal and the hard-facing alloy might occur.   Such "dilution" results in decreased wear resistance and frequently causes blowholes.   If the seat or part is too narrow for grooving, machine it flat and round off the edges.　After grooving, clean the surface thoroughly, removing all dirt, scale, and grease.

If the part is small, say under 3 in. in diameter, and the welding flame is large enough to keep it red hot during welding, no furnace preheating is necessary; preliminary heating can be done with the torch.　Larger parts require preheating with several torches or in a temporary furnace.　Raise temperature slowly to 800 to 1200°F, or just under the point where steel begins to scale.　This is a faint red heat, just visible in a dark room.

Maintain Heat.　If possible deposit the alloy while the valve part is in the furnace; when this is impractical, reheat whenever the part cools to 600°F.　Fixtures can be purchased or made that will rotate the work during the hard-facing.　Such a device is not absolutely necessary; a helper can turn the part.

Hard-facing requires an excess acetylene flame (Fig. 16-15).　Adjust the acetylene feather length, measured from the blowpipe tip, to three times the inner-cone length,

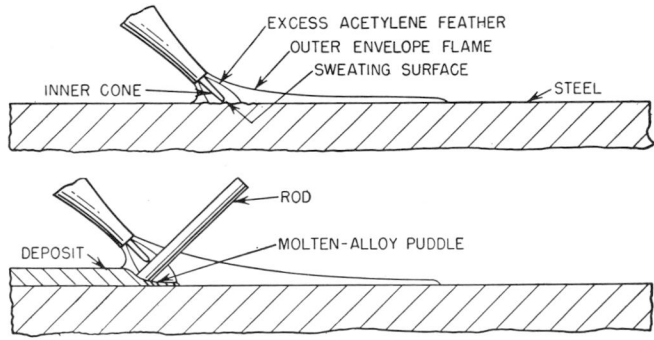

FIG. 16-15. Sweating work surface with a torch.

measured from the welding-tip end.　This flame prepares steel by melting an extremely thin surface layer, giving the steel a watery, glazed appearance called "sweating."　This sweating, produced only by an excess acetylene flame, is necessary for successful hard-facing on steel.

Torch Angle.　Hold the torch to direct the flame at a 30 to 60° angle to the surface, with the inner-cone tip about ⅛ in. from the steel.　Keep this position until the steel under the flame suddenly glazes.　The extent of sweating area varies with size of welding tip, but for a medium tip, steel will sweat about ¼ in. around flame.　Withdraw the torch slightly, and bring the welding rod between the inner cone of flame and the steel surface.　The inner-cone tip should almost touch the rod, and the rod should lightly touch the sweating area.　The melting rod forms a puddle on the steel.　If the first few drops foam or bubble, or do not spread evenly, the steel is too cold and should be brought to the recommended temperature.

Some steels foam slightly when brought to sweating heat.　When this occurs, do not deposit metal until foaming stops.　If deposit is started before foaming is noticed, direct the torch at the foaming spot and agitate the molten metal with flame until foaming stops.　Depositing metal during foaming causes blowholes and poor results. To spread molten alloy over the area, remove the rod from the flame and direct the flame into the puddle.　Return the rod and melt off more alloy as required.　Now direct the flame so that it plays partly on the edge of the puddle and partly on the adjoining steel surface.　As steel approaches sweating heat, a puddle of hard-facing alloys spreads.　As it spreads, bring the rod quickly into the flame again to add more metal as needed.　If any dirt or scale appears on the steel or in the puddle, float it to the surface with the flame or dislodge it with the end of the welding rod.

With a little practice the right amount of alloy can be added to make the desired thickness.　It is better to do this in one operation than to go back over the entire job

to add another layer.   During the operation, move the flame back to melt a thin surface layer of the deposit, to smooth out high spots as the work progresses.   Do this
quickly, without letting the front edge of the puddle solidify and without interrupting
the steady forward travel of the work.   After completing the deposit, use the flame to
smooth out remaining rough surfaces.   On this second pass, take care to melt only the
hard-facing surface and not the base metal.   This avoids bringing iron from the base
metal to the hard-facing deposit.

Prevent Cracks.   When the deposit reaches desired size and thickness, remove the
flame slowly to prevent formation of shrinkage cracks and blowholes.   If these occur,
remelt the deposit and remove particles of scale from the pool.   If holes still show,
grind the alloy deposit down to steel, heat the area with flame, gradually, and deposit
additional metal.   Make sure that no slag, dirt, or scale is covered or embedded in the
deposit to cause pinholes.

Slow cooling is absolutely essential to produce a deposit free from cracks and internal
stresses.   Parts showing a strong tendency to crack, such as large gate-valve wedges
and seat rings, or parts on which the deposit is circular or large in area, should be
returned to the preheating furnace while still hot from welding.   Bring them slowly
to a low red heat, then let them cool in the furnace.   If a furnace is not available,
place the part in dry powdered lime, ashes, or other insulating material, so that at
least 2 in. of material covers and protects every point of the part.

Some alloy steels used for valve trim require heat-treatment in order to maintain
corrosion resistance.   When this is necessary, follow the steel manufacturer's instructions, with but one exception: never cool hard-faced parts by quenching in water or in
an air blast.   This will set up strains and cause cracks in hard-facing.   If quenching is
considered necessary, use only oil.   After the hard-faced part has cooled, excess metal
must be removed.   This can be done by grinding or by machining with a tungsten-
carbide tool.

Traps.   With these, too, good operation and low-cost maintenance starts with
proper installation.   For example, hard-to-get-at traps will be neglected; easy access
encourages regular inspection.   If a trap is exposed to low temperatures, protect it
against freezing.   Install impulse or thermostatic drains in the trap or piping inlet to
release all water when pressure is shut off and the condensate temperature falls.

Trap location directly affects operation.   Wherever physically possible, install
traps below equipment to be drained, so condensate can flow by gravity.   Avoid
U bends or water seals; they obstruct free flow and cause "steam binding."   A slug
of water flowing toward the trap immediately after discharge lies in the pocket until
steam, remaining beyond the pocket and in the trap chamber, condenses.   Where
traps must be installed above equipment to be drained, install a check valve and water
seal or U bend in the connecting piping.   The check prevents backflow and loss of
prime and also prevents back drainage from a common-return header, or entrance of
air when the unit is shut off.   The water seal, although acting as an obstruction, serves
as a sump for condensate collection, allowing it to be carried to the trap in slugs.
Without the seal it would be possible for the bottom coil to remain partly filled with
condensate.

Where traps discharge into common lines and connections do not require a check
value in the inlet line, a check in the discharge prevents backflow from other units or
drainage back to an idle unit when the trap has an individual overhead discharge line.
Even when condensate flows vertically downward to a trap, a heavy rush of condensate
chokes the line, prevents backward escape of trapped steam, and requires time for
steam to escape or condense before water enters the trap.   Although obstructing bends
installed on steam lines only delay trap action, more serious trouble occurs on air lines
unless the trap vents back to the vessel being drained.   Such vent lines can be used
only when the trap stands below the drained equipment.

If allowed to enter traps, pipe scale and sediment prevent tight seating and cause
blow-through.   Cleaning the pipe before installation fails to protect fully because
temperature changes and flow loosen other particles.   Install a strainer ahead of the
trap or, if this is not possible, fabricate a "dirt leg" from pipe, to act as a catch pocket
(Fig. 16-16).   Uniform piping connections help in removing or exchanging traps for

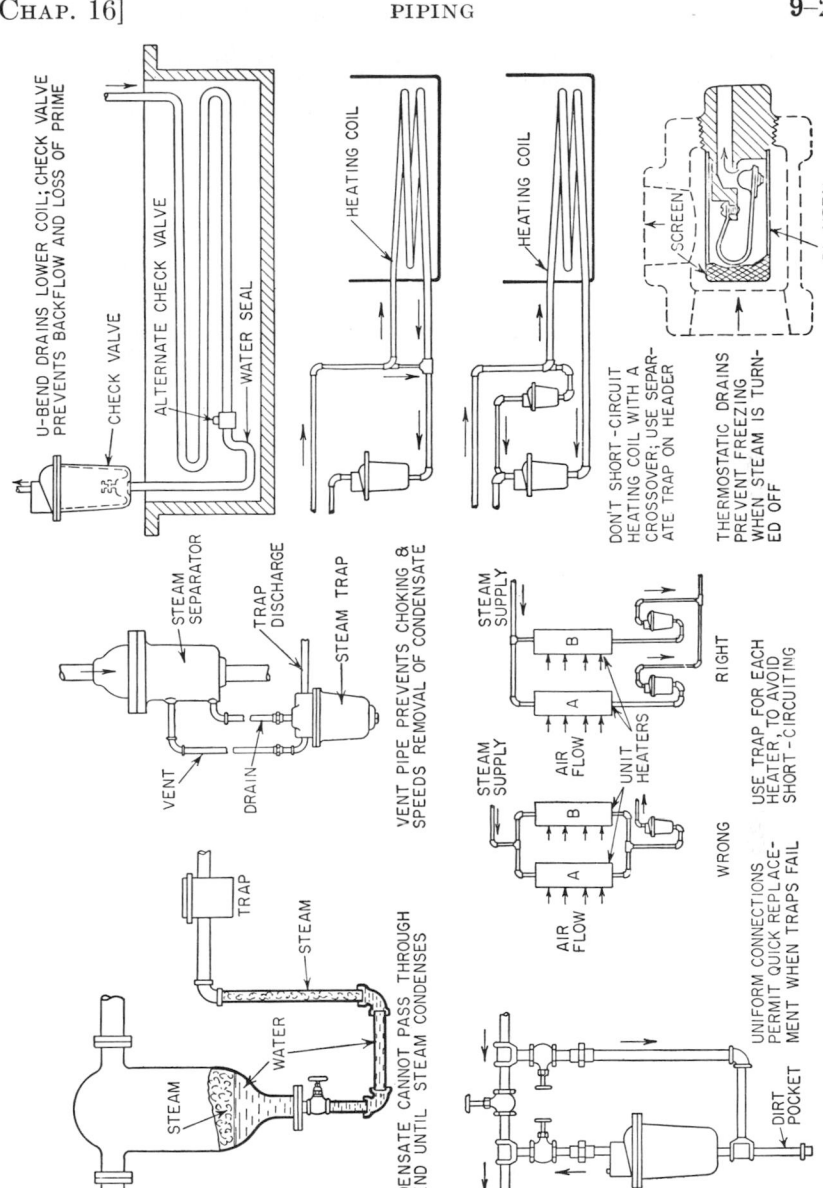

FIG. 16-16. Pointers for trap installation.

inspection and repair.   Test valves and a tee in the discharge from each trap facilitate checking trap action.   Installing a bypass around the trap permits adequate drainage and removal for repair when no spares are available.

Many traps include a valve, an operating device (bucket, float, bellows, etc.) and, if necessary, a linkage and bearings between valve and operator.   Trap maintenance usually involves cleaning to remove foreign matter that might interfere with valve or linkage action, reseating valves when necessary, removing lost motion from linkage,

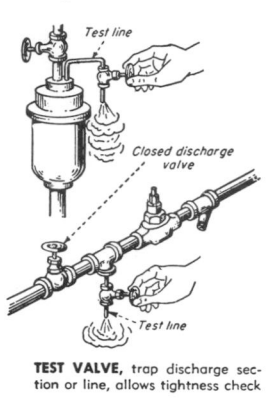

TEST VALVE, trap discharge section or line, allows tightness check

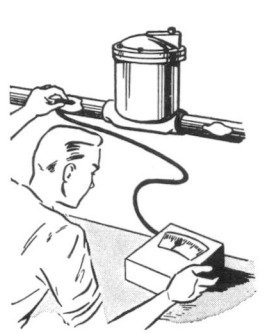

PYROMETER checks inlet, discharge temperature. File two spots

STEEL ROD held against trap body helps you to hear discharge action

GLOVE TEST checks inlet, outlet temperature; it is easy to make

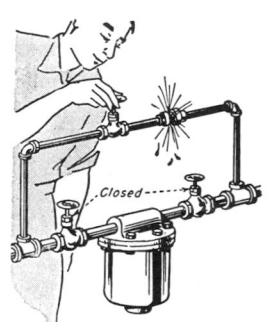

LEAKY BYPASS valve wastes plenty steam. Check tightness regularly

CLEAN TRAP parts in suitable fluid for good system operation

FIG. 16-17. Trap maintenance tests.

and renewing the body gaskets.   Moving parts located inside the body, in contact with moisture, offer lubrication difficulties and may show considerable wear.   Excessive wear and lost motion, if allowed to continue, prevent positive operation and may reach the stage where the valve no longer seats.

Normal wear of some valves gradually enlarges the seat area at the point of disk contact.   This increases the surface acted on by differential pressure across the valve, making it more difficult to operate.   The area may increase to such an extent that the operating device is no longer powerful enough to move the valve.   When this happens the valve must be refaced to regain the original area.   Whenever a trap fails to operate, and the reason is not readily apparent, observe the trap discharge by opening a test cock or breaking the discharge connection.   Live steam usually indicates a leaking valve; it may be caused by the trap losing prime.   Failure to discharge can be caused by a leaking bypass valve, inlet piping or trap obstructed by sediment and pipe scale, return line too small, or an obstructed outlet.   Figure 16-17 shows a number of steps in trap care.

Valve leakage represents a common cause of trouble; worn seats are not so much to blame as are particles that prevent tight closure. Other trap troubles include rusting and sticking of the mechanism, lost motion in linkage, gasket and connection leaks, float leaks, and bent lever arms. Wear in levers and pins of a continuous-discharge trap causes intermittent operation. For most of these difficulties, simple mechanical

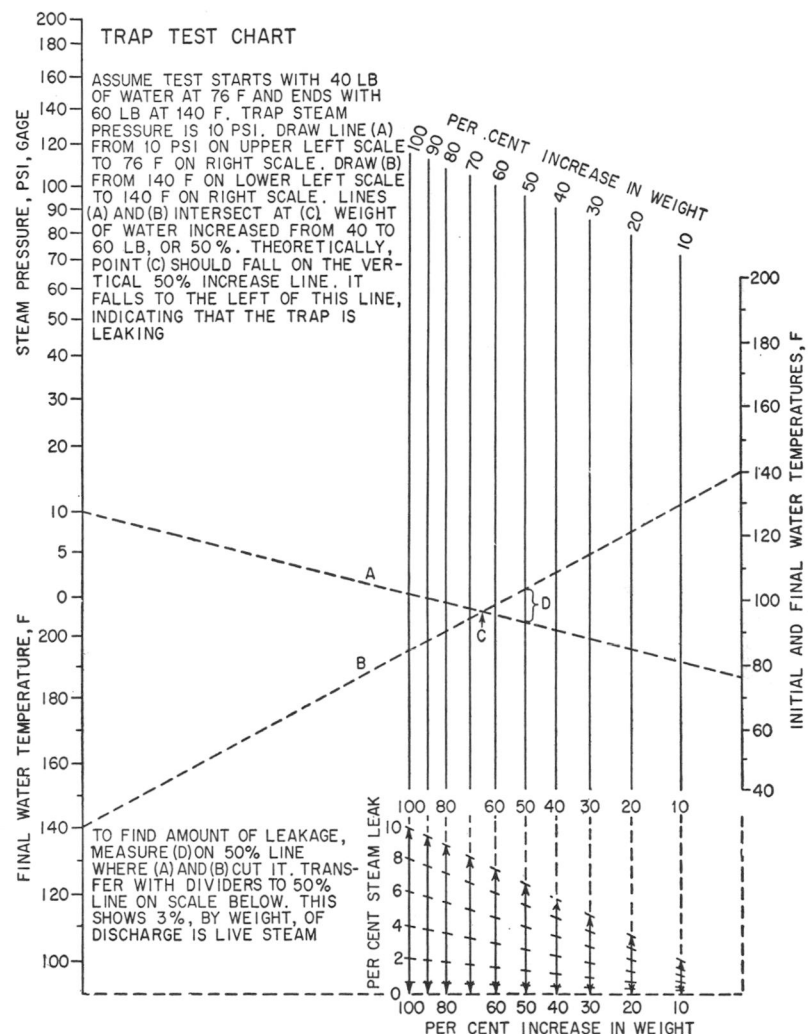

Fig. 16-18. Trap test chart.

remedies suffice, once the cause of the trouble is spotted. When valves do not seat properly yet appear to be in good condition, check linkage and stem length. Repeated regrinding may have shortened the stem. Make adjustments of stem length at or near full operating temperature.

There are numerous ways of checking trap operation. A slight temperature difference between inlet and outlet indicates a working trap; no difference indicates a leaking trap; a large change in temperature indicates no condensate passing. Intermittent-discharge traps produce a light clicking sound at each operation; constant-discharge traps can be checked with a listening rod or a stethoscope applied to the trap body. When visible discharge is not satisfactory evidence, passing the discharge into a vessel of water forms a positive test. Weigh the original quantity of water and check its temperature. After discharge, weigh the water again and check its temperature. Heat given up by trap discharge in falling to final temperature equals heat gained by original water quantity rising to same temperature. The chart in Fig. 16-18 simplifies computations, eliminating the use of steam tables. Table 16-2 gives trap trouble-shooting data.

Pipe Supports. An ideal piping system would float like a layer of logs on a smooth pond, each part self-supported and imposing no stress on any other part. All elements in the system would hold their correct relative positions and alignment despite thermal expansion and contraction. Actual well-built systems approach this theoretical ideal by the intelligent use of anchors to fix certain points of the system, and expansion joints, supports, and guides to combine support with free movement for all the rest of the piping in the system. Without being an expert in the mathematical design of piping systems, the maintenance engineer should understand the duty to be expected of each part of the system under his care so he can check whether that job is actually being performed as it should.

First take the system as it stands, cold or at some fixed temperature. Anchors should securely lock the anchored points in the piping to heavy steelwork or other dependable footing. Between each pair of anchors should be an expansion joint or bend designed to absorb all possible movement from temperature differences. Pipe supports should be spaced closely enough to prevent undue sag in the span. All steam and air lines should be properly pitched for condensate drainage and checked to make certain that sag does not bring the center point of any span below its lower support, thus forming a condensation pocket leading to water hammer and other troubles.

Check each hanger or other support to make sure that it carries its share of the load; that pipes track truly on fitted rollers or other guides; and that supports and their attachments are amply strong for the load and set to carry the weight, yet permit free pipe movement in the direction of expansion. To avoid trouble these conditions should be met whether the line is hot or cold. To make a single set of adjustments serve for both extremes of temperature is a most difficult job both for the designer and the maintenance engineer. One requirement is an understanding of thermal expansion, and here are the main points:

When an unrestrained steel body is uniformly heated no forces whatever are set up, either internal or external. The body expands gently and proportionately in all directions. Thus, if a piping system is completely unrestrained except that the weight is carried at all points by fully "floating" supports, heating to a higher temperature will produce no forces whatever, nor any change in the proportions of the layout. All dimensions will be slightly increased, as if the new layout were a slightly enlarged photograph of the original. The coefficient of expansion for any grade of iron or steel is approximately 0.000007 per degree F. This simply means that the expansion is 7 parts per million per degree. For example, if the temperature of a steel pipe is raised by 400°F, its length will increase by about $400 \times 7 = 2,800$ parts per million, or about 0.28 in. per 100 in. The coefficient of expansion varies somewhat with the actual temperature, so expansions should be taken directly from Table 16-3 or similar data if accurate results are desired.

With either corrugated-metal or well-lubricated sliding expansion joints, the forces to be handled by the anchors are substantial, but much less than with the expansion pipe bends commonly used for the higher pressures. Figuring such bends is a rather mathematical branch of design engineering, but the maintenance engineer may be able to learn from the designer how much force the bend exerts for each inch of compression as the connected piping expands.

Expansion. When piping is heated it moves straight out from the anchor by an amount proportional to the temperature rise and to the distance from the anchor. In an elaborate piping system many complications can arise. If a long horizontal run without an expansion joint ends in a riser, expansion will push the riser out of plumb

Table 16-2. Trouble-shooting Chart for Steam Traps

Trouble   *Possible Cause and Cure*

Trap doesn't discharge....... 1. Steam pressure too high, pressure regulating out of order, boiler pressure gage reads low, steam pressure raised without altering or adjusting trap. On the last item consult trap maker. He can supply parts for higher pressure or tell you how to adjust trap.
2. Plugged strainer, valve, or fitting ahead of trap; clean.
3. Internal parts of trap plugged with dirt or scale; take trap apart and clean. Fit strainer ahead of trap.
4. Bypass open or leaking; close or repair.
5. Internal parts damaged or broken; dismantle trap, repair.

Trap won't shut off.......... 1. Trap too small for load; figure condensate quantity to be handled and put in correct-size trap.
2. Defective mechanism holds trap open; repair.
3. Larger condensate load from (*a*) boiler foaming or priming, leaky steam coils, kettles or other units, or (*b*) greater process load; find cause of increased condensate flow and cure, or install larger trap
Note: Traps made to discharge continuously won't show these symptoms. Instead, the condensate line to trap overloads; water backs up.

Trap blows steam............ 1. Open or leaky bypass valve; close or repair.
2. Trap has lost prime; check for sudden or frequent drops in steam pressure.
3. Dirt or scale in trap; take apart and clean.
4. Inverted bucket trap too large, blows out seal; use smaller orifice or replace with smaller trap.

Trap capacity suddenly falls.. 1. Inlet pressure too low; raise to trap rating, fit larger trap, change pressure parts or setting.
2. Backpressure too high; look for plugged return line, traps blowing steam into return, open bypass or plugged vent in return line.
3. Back pressure too low; raise.

Condensate won't drain from 1. System is air-bound; fit suitable vent or trap with larger
system   air capacity to get rid of the air.
2. Steam pressure low; raise to the right value.
3. Condensate short-circuits; use a trap for each unit.

Not enough steam heat....... 1. Defective thermostatic elements in radiator traps; remove, test, and replace damaged elements.
2. Boiler priming; reduce boiler-water level. If boiler foams, check fires and feed with fresh water while blowing down boiler at quarter-minute intervals.
3. Scored or out-of-round valve seat in trap; grind seat or replace old trap body with new one.
4. Vacuum pump runs continuously; look for a cracked radiator, split return main, cracked pipe fitting, or a loose union connection. Or pump shaft's packing may leak.
5. Too much water hammer in system; check drip-trap size. Undersized drip traps can't handle all condensate formed during warm-up so hammering results. Fit larger trap if drip lines are clean and scale-free. Size for warm-up load, not for load with mains hot.
6. System run down; older heating plants are sometimes troublesome because a large number of trap elements are defective. Easiest cure is replacement of all thermostatic elements in the radiators. This is low-cost, sure.

Traps freeze in winter....... 1. Discharge line has long horizontal run where water collects; make discharge line as short as possible and pitch away from trap.
2. Trap and piping not insulated; fit insulation to outdoor traps and piping connected to them.

Table 16-2. Trouble-shooting Chart for Steam Traps (*Continued*)

Trouble   *Possible Cause and Cure*

Back flow in return line...... 1. Trap below return main doesn't have right fittings; use check valve and a water seal, or both, depending on what the trap maker recommends.

2. High-pressure traps discharge into a low-pressure return; flashing may cause high back pressure. Change piping to prevent return pressure from exceeding trap rating.

3. No cooling leg ahead of a thermostatic trap that drips a main; condensate may be too hot to allow trap to open right. Use a 4- to 6-ft cooling leg ahead of thermostatic traps on this service. Fit strainer in cooling leg to keep solids out of trap.

Courtesy of *Power* magazine.

unless the top end is so suspended that it can move out too. If the weight of a riser, when cold, is equally distributed over several rigid hangers, one above the other, heating the line will expand the pipe and thereby unload all upper hangers, shifting the entire load to the bottom hanger. Many other similar effects will be observed, and generally can be sized up on the spot by the exercise of commonsense mechanics.

Here are some practical points to remember: Supports for a horizontal pipe (Fig. 16-19), far from an anchor must allow ample roll, slide, or swing in the direction of the pipe expansion. If temperature changes cause any piping (whether horizontal or vertical) to rise and fall, such sections must be carried on properly designed spring supports. For large movements in a vertical direction, the springs must be "soft." Such springs permit substantial up and down movement with only a moderate change in the support delivered to the pipe.

Maintenance of a piping system will naturally start with obvious ills—leaks, water hammer, swaying, and vibration. Leaks may be caused by joints improperly designed or made up, by expansion forces, or improper support. Piping should always be supported on both sides of every large valve. Where leaks persist or recur despite good joint technique, check the alignment and condition of neighboring anchors, supports, and expansion joints to make sure the leak is not caused by external forces. Other common causes of leaks are pipe swaying and water hammer. Water hammer may result from reciprocating pumps or the too-quick closing of valves. A common cause, traceable to poor maintenance, is undrained condensate caught in low points of the

Table 16-3. Thermal Expansion of Steam Pipe

Table gives total expansion above −20°F in inches per 100 ft of pipe. To get expansion per 100 ft between two given temperatures, subtract tabular value for lower temperature from that for higher.

Temp, °F	Cast iron pipe	Steel pipe	Wrought iron pipe	Copper pipe
−20	0	0	0	0
0	0.127	0.145	0.152	0.204
100	0.787	0.898	0.939	1.338
200	1.495	1.691	1.778	2.500
300	2.233	2.519	2.630	3.665
400	3.008	3.375	3.521	4.870
500	3.847	4.296	4.477	6.110
600	4.725	5.247	5.455	7.388
700	5.629	6.229	6.481	8.676
800	6.587	7.250	7.508	9.992
900	7.579	8.313	8.639	11.360
1000	8.617	9.421	9.776	12.741

Condensed from Crocker, "Piping Handbook," 4th ed., McGraw-Hill Book Company, Inc., 1954.

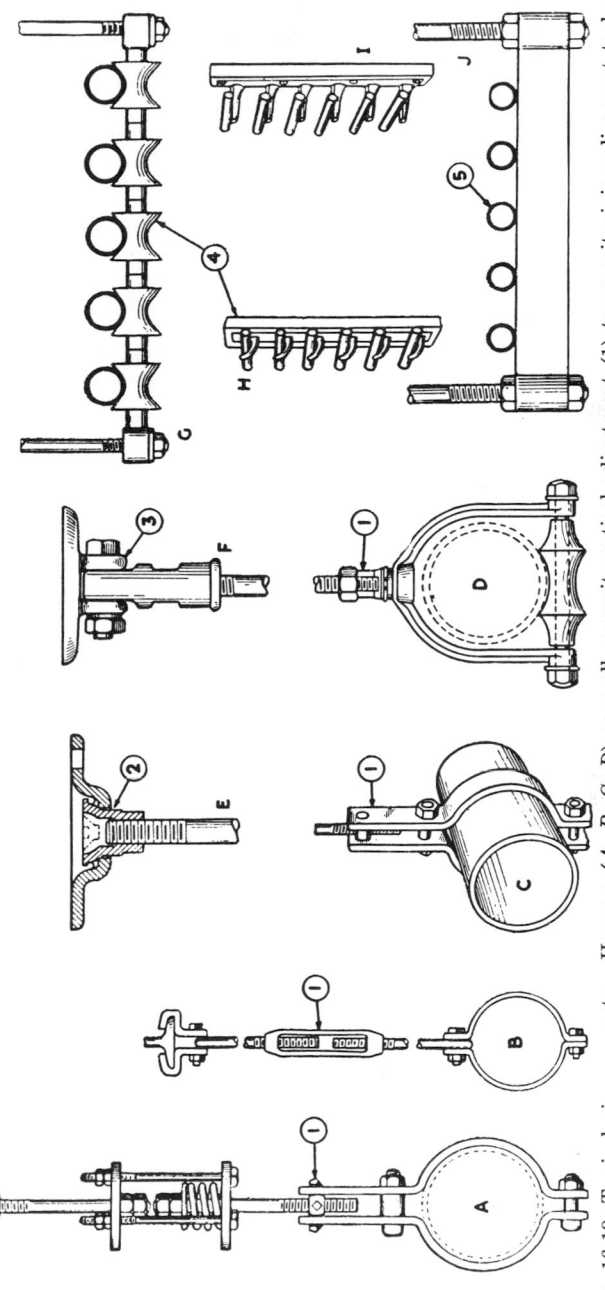

FIG. 16-19. Typical pipe supports. Hangers (A, B, C, D) generally permit vertical adjustment (1) to permit piping alignment to be maintained and to allow for proper division of load among supports. Pivoted hangers (E, F) may permit universal movement (2) or may permit one-way movement as shown at (3). Multiple supports (G, H, I, J) for banks of small pipe may be grooved for axial movement only (4) or may have a flat surface (5) to allow a certain amount of sidewise movement.

piping, back of globe valves, etc.   Check the system to make sure that low points are raised and all other pockets drained.   Sags caused by misalignment can usually be cured by simple hanger adjustments.

When all such obvious ills have been cured, the job shifts to preventive maintenance —regular routine inspection to make sure that anchors are holding and showing no signs of breaking or slipping; that walls and footings near anchors are not showing distress cracks; that sliding expansion joints are not leaking or sticking; that supports everywhere are in line with pipe and tracking true; that supporting rolls turn freely and support their share of the load whether the line is hot or cold; and that bolts, turn-buckles, and other stressed members give no sign of distress or possible early failure.

Pipe Insulation.   A good maintenance program keeps insulation in perfect condition because necessary inspections and repairs save many times their cost in fuel.   Here are practical pointers on maintaining and repairing covering of piping, valves, and fittings —chiefly those containing steam or hot water:

A good job of hot-pipe insulation will have the following characteristics: (1) efficient insulating material applied to economic thickness, (2) material able to stand ordinary handling, (3) inner layer able to stand pipe temperature, (4) insulation bound securely to pipe, (5) joints closely fitted and staggered (if double layer), (6) insulation well covered and painted, if necessary, and (7) complete waterproofing for outdoor or underground lines.

Materials.   Widely used heat-insulating materials for plant piping include 85 per cent magnesia, laminated asbestos-felt, and various forms of mineral wool (both molded and felted), including glass wool, as well as other materials.   The magnesia covering is molded in sections or blocks, and contains about 85 per cent basic carbonate of magnesia with 10 to 15 per cent of long-fiber asbestos as a binder.   Both magnesia and laminated-asbestos coverings may be used safely up to 600°F.   Mineral-wool insulation can withstand temperatures higher than 1000°F.

For pipes above the temperature limit of magnesia and asbestos, double-layer insulation is common.   An outer layer of 85 per cent magnesia or asbestos is protected from overheating by an inner layer of molded covering composed of calcined diatomaceous silica, asbestos fiber, and cementing materials.   This high-temperature covering looks like magnesia and has lower insulating efficiency and the ability to resist temperatures well above 1000°F.   Both mineral wool and laminated asbestos are particularly suited for points subjected to heavy vibration or shock.   Table 16-4 gives the insulation thickness commonly recommended for laminated-asbestos and magnesia coverings. Note that the correct thickness increases with both pipe size and temperature.

Figure 16-20 shows standard methods of covering piping and fittings.   Such applications are fairly simple for any mechanic.   Magnesia and other molded coverings can be easily sawed to trim length and beveled with a knife at the ends that face the flanges. Coverings on bends, fittings, and other irregular surfaces can be built up by wiring on odds and ends of magnesia blocks or pipe coverings and filling the remaining spaces with magnesia cement.   Since this cement is of exactly the same composition as the solid pieces, the mass sets as a homogenous whole.

Apply 85 per cent magnesia cement in thin layers, letting each dry before applying the next.   If the surface is smooth, wire mesh may be needed to hold the cement in place.   In general it is difficult to make magnesia cement or ordinary asbestos cements stick directly to metal surfaces (particularly hot metal surfaces) without wire reinforcements.   For quick insulation of flanges and fittings, by direct application of insulation to the metal without reinforcement, use a cement specially compounded for high adhesive capacity.   First dab or throw it on in spots.   When these dry they will help anchor the next layer.   This, in turn, should not be applied too thick.

Asbestos and mineral-wool cements are available in a great variety of types and prices.   In general, the cements of highest insulating value will tend to be light, soft, and difficult to apply, while the harder and stronger cements will have low insulating value.   That is why the use of so-called hard-finish cements is largely confined to finish-coating for hardness and good appearance.   In general, insulation on fittings, bends, etc., is finished with either canvas or hard-finish cement.

Insulation for cold lines may range all the way from a simple antisweat jacket for cold water to elaborate built-up, thick insulation for low-temperature refrigerating lines. Materials used include hair felt, cork, and mineral-wool felt. An essential characteristic of low-temperature insulation is complete sealing against the penetration of moisture that would otherwise destroy the insulation. Check periodically to make certain that such coverings remain hermetically sealed and completely free of internal

Table 16-4. Recommended Thicknesses of Pipe Covering

85 Per Cent Magnesia

(Plus inner layer of H.T. for high temperature)

Pipe size, in.	Temperature of hot surface, °F														
	170	270	370	470	570	670		770		870		970		1070	
	Temperature difference, °F														
	100	200	300	400	500	600		700		800		900		1000	
	85 % magnesia					HT	Mag	HT	Mag	HT	Mag	HT	Mag	HT	Mag
1	S	S	1½	2	2	2	...	2	...	2	...	2½	...	2½	
2	S	S	1½	2	2	1½	1½	1½	2	2	2	2½	2	2½	2½
3	S	S	1½	2	2	1½	1½	1½	2	2	2	2½	2	2½	2½
4	S	S	1½	2	2	1½	1½	1½	2	2	2	2½	2	2½	2½
5	S	S	2	DS	DS	1½	2	1½	2	2	2	2½	2	2½	2½
6	S	S	2	DS	DS	1½	2	1½	2	2	2	2½	2	2½	2½
8	S	S	2	DS	DS	1½	2	2	2	2	2½	2½	2½	3	2
10	S	S	2	DS	DS	1½	2	2	2	2	2½	2½	2½	3	2
12	S	S	2	DS	DS	1½	2	2	2	2	2½	2½	2½	3	2
14	S	S	2	DS	DS	1½	2	2	2	2	2½	2½	2½	3	2
16	S	S	2	DS	DS	1½	2	2	2	2	2½	2½	2½	3	2
18	S	S	2	DS	DS	1½	2	2	2	2	2½	2½	2½	3	2
20	S	S	2	DS	DS	1½	2	2	2	2	2½	2½	2½	3	2
Flat........	1½	1½	2	2½	3	1½	2	2	2	2	2½	2½	2½	3	2

NOTE: HT = high-temperature covering, S = standard thick, DS = double standard.

Laminated Asbestos

Temperature of heated surface, °F	Pipe size		
	Under 2 in.	2 to 4 in.	4½ in. and up
Up to 300	1 in.	1½ in.	1½ in.
301 to 400	1½ in.	1½ in.	2 in.
401 to 500	2 in.	2 in.	2½ in.
501 to 600	2 in.	2½ in.	3 in.

water or ice. The application of refrigeration insulation is a specialty for experts, as is most heat insulation.

Maintenance. Routine maintenance of warm-pipe insulation should include prompt repair of damaged surfaces, repainting and waterproofing, tightening bands and wires, and repairing torn canvas jackets. Look out for shrinkage, loosening, and the effect of moisture, fumes, and vibration. Make sure that steam temperatures have not been raised above the safe limit for the material used. Check carefully for steam and water leaks concealed by insulation.

Often a casual inspection will reveal bare flanges—either originally bare or left so by a recent replacement of the gasket.   A single large bare flange can waste a ton of coal per year, so all such should be covered—preferably with replaceable covers.

Flanges.   The preservation of flange covering is a major maintenance problem. Even supposedly removable covers are often broken in removal, particularly when an

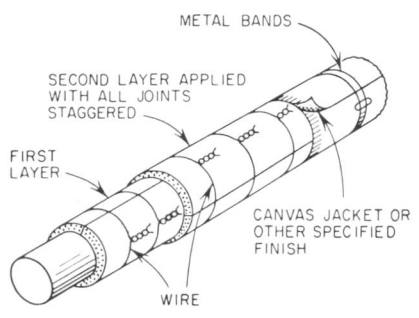

TWO-LAYER SECTIONAL MINERAL-WOOL COVERING

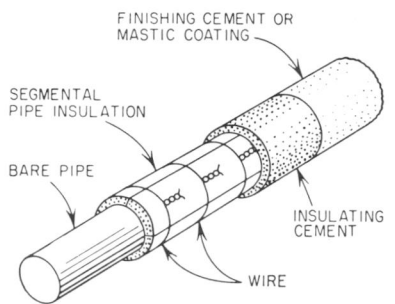

SEGMENTAL MINERAL WOOL WITH CEMENT FINISH

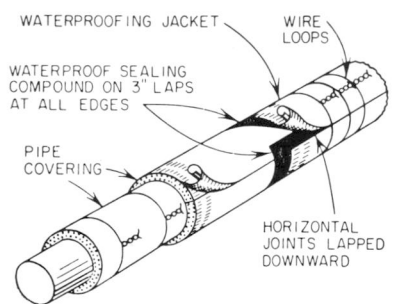

APPLICATION OF WEATHERPROOF JACKETING

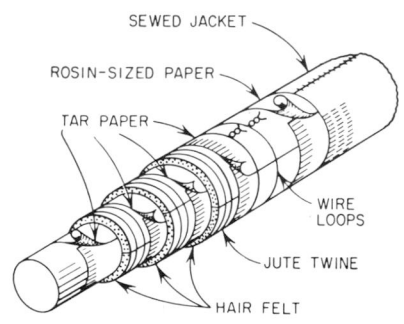

BUILT-UP HAIR-FELT ANTI-FREEZE COVERING

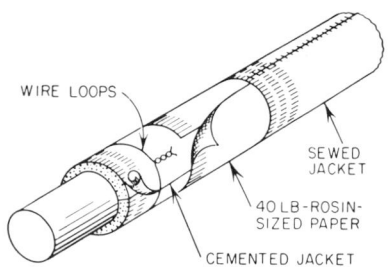

HAIR-FELT ANTI-SWEAT COVER FOR COLD WATER

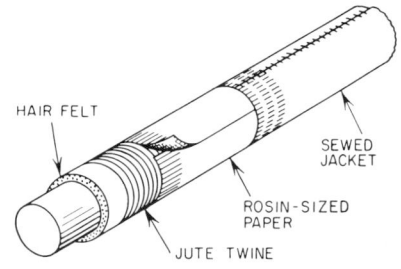

TYPICAL INSULATION FOR COLD-WATER LINES

FIG. 16-20. Methods for applying some typical pipe insulations.

emergency requires quick access to the flange.   Replacement of the insulation is a nuisance, too often delayed or omitted because the plant can run without it.   It should be a standard rule to protect flange covers as far as possible and replace them promptly.

Silicate of soda (water glass) is a convenient and powerful adhesive for cementing tears in asbestos laminations or canvas jackets.   Where magnesia covering is broken, a monolithic repair can be made by wiring in a magnesia "Dutchman" and filling

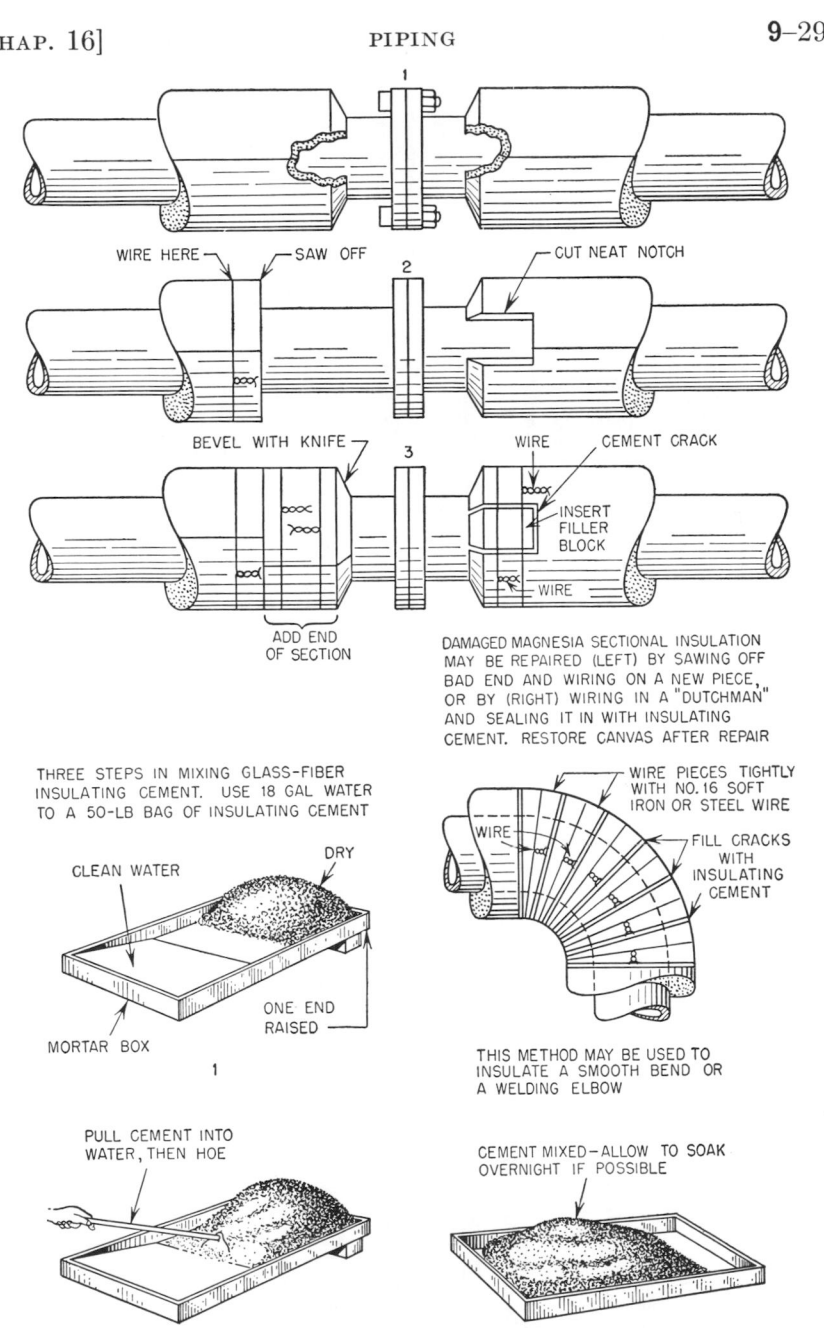

FIG. 16-21. Pointers on insulation maintenance.

THREE TYPES OF BUTT WELDS

60° to 90°

Chill ring

V-groove with chill ring

60° to 90°

Flush chill ring

V-groove without chill

U-joint with flush chill ring and reinforced end for high-velocity high-pressure steam (before and after)

Cup joint for field joints, where lining-up is inconvenient

THREE WAYS TO ATTACH FLANGES

Weld

Weld

Pipe end kept back of face

Weld

Slip-on flange field-welded to pipe end

Weld-neck flange

Welding nipple with pipe lap

SPECIAL-PURPOSE SLEEVES

Screwed coupling, back-welded for extra tightness

Butt weld plus welded sleeve, used only for unusual stress

HOW TO WELD LEAKS UNDER PRESSURE

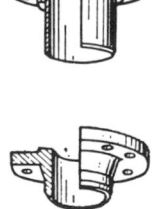

1

2

A

A

Weld

Leak

3

Nut

Leak

4

Plate

Nut

5

Weld all around

Fig. 16-22. Use of welding in piping maintenance. Electric-arc welding is a quick way to stop leaks in pipe under pressure. To close pinhole leak (1), weld an ordinary square-head machine nut around leak (2, 3). This permits water, etc., to escape through the hole in the nut during welding, making it possible to complete the weld. To stop the leak, screw a bolt into the nut with sealing compound. A cracked or split pipe (4) can be closed in the same way. This kind of leak usually is too large to be covered by a nut, so a piece of plate stock is applied as a patch. Drill a small hole in the plate and shape the plate to the pipe. Next, weld a nut over the hole and weld the plate to the pipe (5). Then screw in a bolt or plug, using sealing compound.

voids with magnesia cement, which has the same composition as the block. See Fig. 16-21 for pointers on insulation maintenance.

Maintenance Welding.   Each element of piping maintenance has two aspects: (1) how to select and install to reduce maintenance, and (2) how to maintain.   In the case of welded joints the second is practically eliminated.   If the joint is rightly selected and made it should need no maintenance for the life of the plant.   In general, maximum use of welding means minimum maintenance except where joints must be broken from time to time.   Flange connections should be used at such points.

Most engineers are familiar with the standard lines of welding fittings—ells, tees, crosses, flange necks, etc.—also values with welding necks.   No attempt will be made

Table 16-5. Corrosion Questionnaire

1. What is the name or composition of fluid to be handled?
2. What is the concentration (percentage strength, specific gravity, pH value, etc.)?
3. What is the operating temperature and pressure in pipelines?
4. If the fluid is not a water solution but a gas, organic fluid, etc., is water or water vapor apt to be present at any time or at any particular location?   If so, explain.
5. If the fluid is a water solution, are substances other than water (abrasive solids, oil, etc.) present at any time or at any particular location?   If so, explain.
6. Is there much opportunity for air-in leakage?
7. Is the flow through the system intermittent or continuous?
8. If intermittent, is the system ever drained entirely of fluid and allowed to dry?
9. Is the piping system washed or rinsed at regular intervals, and if so, with what materials?
10. Is a slight amount of corrosion objectionable from the standpoint of contamination or discoloration of product?
11. If so, what metals are particularly objectionable?
12. What materials are being used or proposed for piping, tanks, etc.?
13. Has any specific trouble been experienced with these materials?
14. What materials have been used for valves and fittings?
15. In general, what is the comparative life of the different materials which have been used?
16. What packings give the best service?

Courtesy of Crane Company.

here to show how to make pipe welds.   That information is available in concise booklets issued by the manufacturers and in standard codes for the making and testing of welds and for the qualification of welders.   The ASA "Code for Pressure Piping" covers welded joints from the specification aspect.

The elaborate sleeves, patches, and reinforcements of the early days of welding reflected the user's lack of confidence in the process.   Modern practice favors the plain butt weld, made by officially qualified welders following standard welding and testing procedures.   Results have been so good that welding is preferred today for the highest pressures and temperatures.   In such lines flanges are used only where joints must be breakable.

Joints.   In low-pressure work, welding has the disadvantage that cast-iron valves cannot be welded in, so one must either use the more expensive steel valves or install the cast-iron valves with flanged joints.   For pipe wall up to $\frac{3}{4}$ in. thick, the sides of the standard butt joint are beveled $37\frac{1}{2}°$, with a $\frac{1}{16}$-in. land.   For thicker pipe the bevel is U-shaped to avoid the need for excessive welding.   Chill rings ensure full penetration of the weld without the formation of dangerous "icicles" in the pipe.   Except for high-velocity steam, the extra cost of a flush chill (Fig. 16-22) is rarely warranted.

Flanges can be installed in a welded system in the three ways shown in Fig. 16-22. The lap-joint stub end, welded to the pipe and backed by a slip-on flange, gives the highest type of lap joint.   A quick field connection can be improvised by joining a slip-on flange to the pipe end by two fillet welds as shown.   Welding may be used also to seal the thread where a flange is screwed onto a pipe.

In high-pressure work it is best to build up welds in $\frac{1}{8}$-in. layers, cleaning and

Table 16-6. Recommendations for Piping Materials to Be Used in Handling Fluids

	Iron and steel	Ni-Resist cast iron	18-8 Mo	Monel metal	Nickel	Red brass	Acid-resisting bronze	Aluminum
Acetate solvents, crude..	C	C	C	A	A	C	A	A
Acetate solvents, pure...	C	A	A	A	A	A	A	A
Acetic acid, crude......	C	C	A	C	C	C	A	C
Acetic acid, pure.......	B	B	A	A	C	B	A	A
Acetic acid vapors[1].....	B	B	A	C	D	C	B	C
Acetic anhydride.......	C	A	A	A	D	B	C	A
Acetone...............	A	A	A	A	A	A	A	A
Acetylene[2].............	A	A	A	A	A	B	B	A
Alcohols...............	A	A	A	A	A	A	A	A
Aluminum sulfate alums.	B	C	A	A	D	C	C	C
Ammonia gas[3].........	A	A	A	A	A	B	B	A
Ammonium chloride....	C	A	C	A	A	C	C	B
Ammonium hydroxide, ammonia liquors.....	A	A	A	C	C	B	B	A
Ammonium nitrate[4].....	A	C	A	C	C	B	B	A
Ammonium phosphate (monobasic).........	B	C	A	C	D	C	A	B
Ammonium phosphate (dibasic)............	C	A	A	A	D	C	C	A
Ammonium phosphate tribasic.............	A	A	A	A	A	C	C	A
Ammonium sulfate.....	A	A	C	A	A	C	A	
Asphalt...............	A	A	A	A	A	A	A	D
Beer[5].................	C	C	A	A	A	A	A	A
Beet-sugar liquors......	A	A	A	A	A	C	C	A
Benzene or benzol......	A	A	A	A	A	A	A	A
Benzine...............	A	A	A	A	A	A	A	A
Borax.................	A	A	A	A	A	C	C	C
Boric acid.............	B	C	A	A	A	C	A	A
Butane, butylenes, butadiene[6]...............	A	A	A	C	C	A	A	A
Calcium bisulfite[7].......	B	B	A	B	B	B	C	C
Calcium chloride[8].......	A	A	C	A	A	A	A	B
Calcium hypochlorite...	C	C	C	C	C	C	C	D
Cane-sugar liquors......	A	A	A	A	A	A	A	A
Carbolic acid or phenol..	C	C	A	A	A	C	C	A
Carbon dioxide, dry....	A	A	A	A	A	A	A	A
Carbon dioxide, wet....	C	C	A	A	A	C	A	A

KEY. A. Can be and is being successfully used. B. Should not be used. C. Proceed with caution. Used where corrosion is permissible; for temporary installations; where cost of better materials is too high, etc. D. Information lacking.

[1] Severe corrosion sometimes experienced at locations where liquid changes to vapor and vice versa.

[2] Iron and steel used, but combinations that produce sparks should be avoided at valve seats. High-copper alloys prohibited by codes. Yellow brass acceptable.

[3] These recommendations apply to the industrial use of ammonia gas and to low-temperature stages of its manufacture. They do not all apply to the handling of hot gases in its manufacture by the synthetic process.

[4] Iron and steel used. Some trouble experienced with hot solutions, especially adjacent to welds. Wherever possible welds should be stress-relieved. Stainless steel is first choice.

[5] Iron and steel used for handling beer in the alcohol industry but not permissible in the beverage industry.

[6] Recommendations do not apply to handling of these compounds at high temperatures. Behavior when hot depends largely on amount and nature of impurities. See notes 16 and 17.

[7] Commonly encountered as pulping liquor in the pulp and paper industry. Copper and brass have been used in the past and can be used again in emergency. Stainless steel (Type 316 or 317) preferred. Bronze valves should be trimmed with stainless steel.

[8] Iron and steel used for refrigerating brines. Severe corrosion indicates need for control of solution.

Table 16-6. Recommendations for Piping Materials to Be Used in Handling Fluids (*Continued*)

	Iron and steel	Ni-Resist cast iron	18-8 Mo	Monel metal	Nickel	Red brass	Acid-resisting bronze	Aluminum
Carbon disulfide	A	A	A	C	D	B	B	A
Carbonic acid, carbonated beverages	B	B	A	A	A	C	C	A
Carbon tetrachloride[9]	C	C	C	A	A	C	C	C
Chlorine, dry[10]	A	A	C	A	A	C	C	D
Chlorine, wet[10]	B	B	B	B	B	B	B	B
Chlorex	A	D	D	A	D	A	A	D
Chromic acid[11]	C	C	A	C	C	B	C	C
Citric acid	B	C	A	A	A	C	A	A
Coke-oven gas	A	D	A	C	D	C	C	A
Copper sulfate[12]	B	C	A	C	C	B	B	B
Core oils	A	D	D	D	D	A	A	D
Cottonseed oil	A	A	A	A	A	C	A	D
Creosote, crude	A	A	A	A	A	C	A	A
Doctor solutions	A	A	A	A	D	B	B	B
Ethers	D	D	A	A	A	A	A	A
Ethylene glycol	A	A	A	A	A	A	A	A
Ferric chloride[13]	B	B	B	B	B	B	B	B
Ferric sulfate[12]	B	B	A	C	C	B	C	B
Formaldehyde	C	C	A	A	A	A	A	A
Formic acid	B	D	C	C	C	B	C	B
Freon, wet	C	A	C	A	A	A	A	A
Freon, dry	A	A	A	A	A	A	A	A
Furfural	A	D	D	A	A	A	A	A
Gasoline, sour	C	C	A	C	D	B	B	A
Gasoline, refined	A	A	A	A	D	A	A	A
Gelatine	D	D	A	A	A	B	C	A
Glucose	A	A	A	A	A	A	A	A
Glue	A	A	A	A	A	A	A	A
Glycerine or glycerol	A	A	A	A	A	A	A	A
Hydrochloric acid or muriatic acid[14]	B	B	B	C	C	B	C	B
Hydrocyanic acid or hydrogen cyanide	C	D	A	A	D	D	A	A
Hydrofluoric acid[15]	C	B	B	C	C	B	C	B

KEY. A. Can be and is being successfully used. B. Should not be used. C. Proceed with caution Used where corrosion is permissible; for temporary installations; where cost of better materials is too high, etc. D. Information lacking.

[9] These recommendations are based on industrial uses of the solvent. Galvanized steel commonly used for tanks, piping, etc. Iron and steel are widely used in manufacture of solvent, with good success.

[10] Industrial applications of "dry" chlorine frequently involve locations where moisture is present. Steel gives good results as piping material but something better is needed for critical parts. Steel valves trimmed with monel or Hastelloy C give good results. Nonmetals required for wet gas and aqueous solutions.

[11] Steel, with or without lead lining, used for tanks, piping, etc. Corrosion of unlined steel adjacent to welds is common. Wherever possible welds should be stress-relieved if steel is not to be lined. Impingement by rapidly moving solution—especially when hot—may cause severe corrosion.

[12] See Water, acid mine. Presence of copper sulfate and/or ferric sulfate in dilute sulfuric acid inhibits the attack of this acid on stainless steel.

[13] Nonmetals usually indicated. Hastelloy C used with some success.

[14] Nonmetals usually indicated. Hastelloys used with excellent results. Hastelloy B used as trim in steel valves in hydrochloric alkylation. Red brass or bronze valves with nickel-alloy trim work well with dilute solutions (<1%). Do not use Hastelloys with acid that has previously been in contact with copper alloys and has become contaminated with copper salts.

[15] Steel standard for piping in hydrofluoric acid manufacture and in hydrofluoric alkylation. Steel valves should be trimmed with monel metal or Hastelloy B.

Table 16-6. Recommendations for Piping Materials to Be Used in
Handling Fluids (*Continued*)

	Iron and steel	Ni-Resist cast iron	18-8 Mo	Monel metal	Nickel	Red brass	Acid-resisting bronze	Aluminum
Hydrogen gas[16]	A	A	A	A	A	A	A	A
Hydrogen peroxide	B	B	A	A	A	B	C	A
Hydrogen sulfide and organic sulfur compounds[17]	A	A	A	C	C	B	B	A
Hydrogen sulfide, wet	C	C	A	C	C	B	B	A
Lacquers and lacquer solvents	C	A	A	A	A	A	A	A
Lime-sulfur	A	A	A	A	A	B	B	
Magnesium chloride	C	C	C	A	A	C	A	B
Magnesium hydroxide	A	A	A	A	A	C	C	B
Magnesium sulfate	A	A	A	A	A	A	A	A
Mercuric chloride	C	C	B	C	C	B	B	B
Mercury	A	A	A	A	A	B	B	B
Milk	B	B	A	C	A	B	B	A
Molasses	A	A	A	A	A	A	A	A
Natural gas	A	A	A	A	A	C	C	A
Nickel chloride[18]	D	D	C	C	C	B	B	B
Nickel sulphate[18]	D	D	C	C	C	C	C	B
Nitrating acids (water <20%; sulfuric >15%)	C	C	C	B	B	B	B	B
Nitrating acids (water >20%; sulfuric <15%)	B	B	C	B	B	B	B	B
Nitrating acids (water >20%; nitric <15%)	B	B	B	B	B	B	B	B
Nitrating acids (sulfuric + nitric = 1% or less)	B	C	A	B	B	B	B	A
Nitric acid, crude	B	D	C	B	B	B	B	C
Nitric acid, pure[19]	B	D	A	B	B	B	B	C
Oleic acid	C	C	A	A	D	C	A	A
Oxalic acid	C	C	D	A	D	C	A	A
Oxygen	A	D	A	A	D	A	A	A
Palmitic acid	C	C	A	A	D	C	A	A
Petroleum oils, not refined	A	A	C	D	D	C	C	
Petroleum oils, refined	A	A	A	A	A	A	A	A
Phosphoric acid, crude	C	D	C	C	C	B	B	B
Phosphoric acid, pure (<45%)	B	D	A	C	D	B	C	B
Phosphoric acid, pure (<45%, cold)	B	D	A	C	D	B	B	B
Phosphoric acid, pure (<45%, hot)[20]	B	D	C	C	B	B	B	B

KEY. Can be and is being successfully used. B. Should not be used. C. Proceed with caution. Used where corrosion is permissible; for temporary installations; where cost of better materials is too high, etc. D. Information lacking.

[16] Recommendations apply to gas when used at ordinary temperatures. Extreme care should be exercised when the gas is to be handled at elevated temperatures, as in hydrogenation and dehydrogenation processes, etc.

[17] Recommendations apply to dry gas at ordinary temperatures. Nickel alloys very susceptible at elevated temperatures.

[18] Commonly encountered as constituents of nickel-plating solutions, when equipment should be lead, lead-lined Duriron, or rubber-lined.

[19] Straight chromium alloys used in preference to chromium-nickel alloys when feasible.

[20] Special high-chromium–nickel alloys required.

Table 16-6. Recommendations for Piping Materials to Be Used in Handling Fluids (Continued)

	Iron and steel	Ni-Resist cast iron	18-8 Mo	Monel metal	Nickel	Red brass	Acid-resisting bronze	Aluminum
Picric acid (molten)	A	D	A	B	B	B	B	D
Picric acid (aqueous solution)	C	D	A	B	B	B	B	A
Potassium chloride	A	A	C	A	A	A	A	C
Potassium hydroxide	C	A	C	A	A	B	B	B
Potassium sulfate	A	A	C	A	A	A	A	A
Propane gas[6]	A	A	A	A	A	A	A	A
Rosin dark	A	A	A	A	A	C	A	A
Rosin, light	B	C	A	A	A	B	B	A
Shellac, orange	A	A	A	A	A	A	A	A
Shellac, bleached	B	C	A	A	A	C	C	A
Soda ash or sodium carbonate	A	A	A	A	A	C	C	B
Sodium bicarbonate or baking soda	C	A	A	A	A	C	A	C
Sodium bisulfate	B	C	C	A	A	C	A	C
Sodium chloride	A	A	C	A	A	A	A	C
Sodium cyanide	A	C	A	C	C	B	B	B
Sodium hydroxide	A	A	C	A	A	C	C	B
Sodium hypochlorite	B	C	C	C	C	B	B	B
Sodium metaphosphate	C	D	A	A	D	C	A	A
Sodium nitrate	A	A	A	A	A	C	C	A
Sodium perborate and sodium peroxide	C	A	A	A	A	C	C	A
Sodium phosphate (monobasic)	C	D	A	A	A	C	A	A
Sodium phosphate (dibasic)	C	A	A	A	A	A	A	A
Sodium phosphate (tribasic)	A	A	A	A	A	B	B	B
Sodium silicate	A	A	A	A	A	B	B	B
Sodium sulfate	A	A	C	A	A	A	A	D
Sodium sulfide	A	A	A	A	A	B	B	B
Sodium thiosulfate ("hypo")	C	D	A	C	C	B	B	C
Sludge acid	B	C	B	C	D	B	C	B
Stearic acid	C	C	A	A	A	C	C	A
Sulfate liquors[21]	A	A	A	A	D	B	B	B
Sulfur	A	C	C	C	C	B	B	A
Sulfur chloride	C	A	C	A	A	B	B	
Sulfur dioxide, dry[22]	A	A	A	A	D	A	A	A
Sulfur trioxide, dry[23,24]	A	A	A	A	D	A	A	A
Sulfur acid[23] (98% to fuming)	A	A	C	B	B	B	B	C

KEY.　A. Can be and is being successfully used.　B. Should not be used.　C. Proceed with caution. Used where corrosion is permissible; for temporary installations; where cost of better materials is too high, etc.　D. Information lacking.

[21] Includes black, green, and white liquors encountered in kraft paper mills. Iron and steel used for general piping. Low nickel (1 to 2 %) cast iron much superior to nickel-free cast iron and widely used for valve bodies, fittings, etc. Stainless steel used for valve trim. Evaporator tubes may require special alloys.

[22] When gas is wet apply recommendations for sulfurous acid.

[23] When gas is wet apply recommendations for sulfuric acid (<10 %).

[24] Sulfur trioxide, either as a constituent of fuming sulfuric acid or when being handled as a gas, is capable of penetrating cast iron along the grain boundaries and causing intergranular cracking. Much cast-iron equipment is used, but safety considerations suggest that steel should be used wherever possible.

Table 16-6. Recommendations for Piping Materials to Be Used in Handling Fluids (*Continued*)

	Iron and steel	Ni-Resist cast iron	18-8 Mo	Monel metal	Nickel	Red brass	Acid-resisting bronze	Aluminum
Sulfuric acid (75–95%)[25]	A	D	B	B	B	B	B	B
Sulfuric acid (10–75%)[25]	B	C	B	A	C	B	C	B
Sulfuric acid (<10%)...	B	C	C	A	C	C	A	B
Sulfurous acid..........	B	D	A	B	B	B	A	C
Tar....................	A	A	A	A	A	A	A	A
Tartaric acid..........	B	C	A	A	A	C	A	A
Toluene or toluol......	A	D	D	A	D	A	A	A
Trichloroethylene[9].....	C	C	C	A	A	C	C	D
Turpentine............	C	A	A	A	D	C	C	A
Varnish...............	C	C	A	A	A	C	C	A
Vegetable oils.........	A	A	A	A	A	A	A	A
Vinegar...............	C	C	A	A	A	C	C	C
Water, acid mine (containing oxidizing salts)	B	C	A	B	B	B	B	B
Water, acid mine (no oxidizing salts).......	C	A	B	A	A	C	A	B
Water, fresh (boiler feed, etc.)................	A	A	D	A	A	A	A	C
Water, distilled (laboratory grade)[26]........	B	B	A	C	A	B	B	A
Water, distilled (return condensate)..........	A	A	A	A	A	A	A	A
Water, salt (sea water, etc.)................	C	A	C	A	C	A	A	C
Whiskey and wines.....	B	C	A	C	A	C	C	C
Zinc chloride..........	C	C	B	A	D	B	B	B
Zinc sulfate...........	C	A	D	A	D	C	C	D

KEY. A. Can be and is being successfully used. B. Should not be used. C. Proceed with caution. Used where corrosion is permissible; for temporary installations; where cost of better materials is too high, etc. D. Information lacking.

[25] Special high-chromium–nickel alloys having good resistance to a wide range of concentrations are being used. Ordinary iron and steel are good where concentration remains over 90%. Absorption of moisture from the air dilutes exposed acid and makes it more corrosive to iron.

[26] Current practice in many cases where a mineral-free water is required is to use the effluent from a softener employing "hydrogen" zeolites. Such water may be distinctly "acid" and correspondingly corrosive. Final application may require that it be handled in rubber-lined pipe or in piping made of stainless steel, monel metal, etc.

Courtesy of Crane Company.

inspecting after each layer. This catches defects before they are buried. Moreover, the heat of each layer improves the grain structure of the underlying layer.

It is considered unsafe to weld "carbon-moly" steel without preheating, so induction and resistance electric heaters have been designed to keep the pipe at 300 to 600°F throughout the welding. Similar heaters are used to stress-relieve high-strength welds at 1200°F.

Corrosion-resistant Piping. In recent years a number of nonmetallic materials have been introduced for corrosion-resistant service—plastic, glass, etc. Older corrosion-resistant materials include transite, stainless steel, cast iron, and coated piping. The coating may be plastic, bitumastic, rubber, etc. The general maintenance procedures for piping and fittings made of special materials resemble those for iron and steel piping, except for differences resulting from the materials involved. For specific procedures in maintaining special piping materials, consult the manufacturer. There

Table 16-7. Flange-bolting Data

Size of alloy-steel bolt-stud*	Average stress applied manually, psi†	Approximate torque to obtain stress, ft-lb‡	Elongation, in. per in. of effective length§
¾	52,000	175	0.00173
⅞	48,000	255	0.00160
1	45,000	370	0.00150
1⅛	42,500	500	0.00142
1¼	40,000	665	0.00133
1⅜	38,000	860	0.00127
1½	36,500	975	0.00122
1⅝	35,000	1,285	0.00117
1¾	34,000	1,700	0.00113
1⅞	33,000	2,200	0.00110
2	32,000	2,350	0.00107

* Coarse thread series, 1 in., and smaller; 8-pitch thread series, 1⅛ in., and larger.
† Average stress applied by maintenance men in assembly, using a lever and wrench or by sledging.
‡ Based upon well-lubricated threads.
§ Based on a modulus of elasticity of 30,000,000. The effective length of bolt-stud equals the distance from center of one nut to center of the other.

Courtesy of Crane Company.

are many variations in procedures and methods which must be carefully observed. The corrosion questionnaire, Table 16-5, can be helpful as a reminder of factors to be considered.

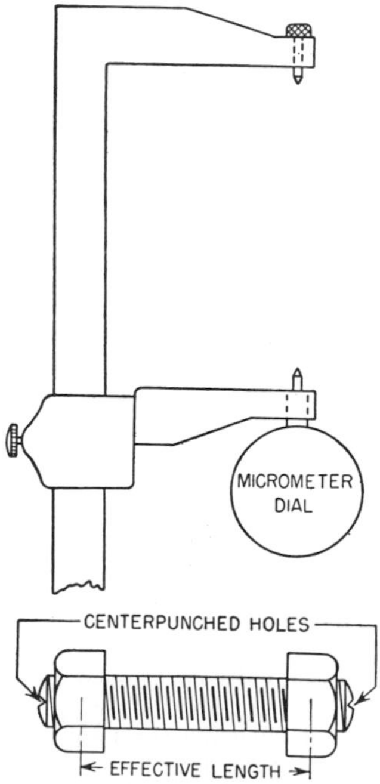

Pipe Materials. For a comprehensive list of piping materials see the "Code for Pressure Piping." For maximum safety it is advisable to design all industrial piping in accordance with Code requirements, even though local regulations may not make this mandatory. Correct design, with adequate provisions for maintenance, is the key to long trouble-free operation with minimum attention. Routine inspection of piping systems and their associated equipment ensures finding minor defects before they become major ones. Table 16-6 gives the general recommendations of one manufacturer of piping materials for the construction to be used for handling various liquids. Data presented are to be used only as brief indicators of some materials that have been found suitable for various liquids. It is impossible in such a brief table to cover all the variables that might be met under different service conditions.

Flange Bolting. Table 16-7 gives data determined by the Crane Company in a number of extensive surveys of field-erected flanged joints. Experience shows these stresses are satisfactory for American Standard steel flanges. It is recommended that the initial bolt stress be about 45,000 psi. Figure 16-23 shows a micrometer for measuring bolt-stud elongation.

This company also recommends that the bolting in all flanged joints operating at temperatures over

MICROMETER DIAL

CENTERPUNCHED HOLES

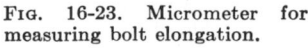

EFFECTIVE LENGTH

Fig. 16-23. Micrometer for measuring bolt elongation.

Table 16-8. Water Velocities to Reduce Piping Maintenance

Conditions to be prevented	Type of flow	Pipe or ditch material	Velocity limits, ft per sec
Deposits of silt and mud	Vertical upward	All types of pipes and ditches	24 min
	45° upward		13 min
	9° upward		5 min
	3° upward		4 min
	Horizontal		3.3 min
	3° downward		2.6 min
	9° downward		Almost zero
Rust formation......	All types	All corrosive pipe materials	26. min
Deterioration of pipe walls	All types	Concrete pipe, carrying pure water	20 max
		Concrete pipe, carrying sand-laden water	10 max
		Steel and cast-iron pipe	50 max
		Wood-stave pipe	40 max
Deterioration of ditch walls	All types	Fine-grained sand	0.6 max
		Coarse sand	1.2 max
		Small stones	2.4 max
		Coarse stones	4.0 max
		Rock	25 max
		Concrete carrying sandy water	10 max
		Concrete ditch, carrying pure water	20 max
		Sandy loam, 40% clay	1.8 max
		Loamy soil, 65% clay	3.0 max
		Clay loam, 85% clay	4.8 max
		Soil, 95% clay	6.2 max
		Clay	7.3 max
Formation of ice in ditch or race.......	All types	All types of ditches or races	5.0 min

These velocities realize special conditions:

Conditions to be realized	Velocity limits, ft per sec
Formation of ice cover in ditch or race..............	3 max
Desilting..	1 max

Minimum velocity to prevent pipe freezing:

$$v = \frac{A(0.5T_w - T_a + 16)}{18,000D^2(T_w - 32)}$$

where v = minimum velocity, ft per sec; T_w = water temperature, °F; T_a = air temperature, °F; A = exposed pipe surface area, sq ft; and D = pipe inside diameter, ft.

Courtesy of *Power* magazine.

500°F be pulled up after the first shutdown. At high temperatures, where creep may be expected to occur, it is recommended that bolting be pulled up at least once during the first 200 hr of service, regardless of whether the line has been shut down or not. Check bolt stress periodically during the life of the installation, as part of the routine maintenance program.

As a general rule, it is only necessary to check the elongation in two or three diametrically opposite bolt-studs, using the average of the values obtained as the elongation for the remainder. If the bolt elongation is to be determined while the joint is in service, one bolt should be checked and pulled up before another is loosened. Measurements should be taken immediately after releasing the load before the bolt temperature decreases. The following procedure should be used in checking bolt elongation:

(1) Determine the length of the bolt in the assembled joint. (2) Release the load on the bolt by loosening the nut, and remeasure the length. (3) Subtract the second reading from the first. (4) Divide this value by the effective length of the bolt. (Effective length equals the distance from the center of one nut to the center of the other.) If the residual elongation is less than 70 per cent of the values given in Table 16-7, the bolts should be pulled up so that the final elongation approximates the figures shown.

Liquid Velocity. Table 16-8 gives condensed data from the experience of two hydraulic organizations with liquid velocities for pipes and ditches of many different types. It is useful in choosing or changing velocities to reduce pipe maintenance and deterioration.

Leak Detection. Where leaks are difficult or impossible to detect visually, radioactive isotopes are widely used to determine the general location of the opening in the pipe. The isotope is injected into the liquid stream and its flow traced by a Geiger counter. A leak is detected by a change in the radioactivity level. Since this method

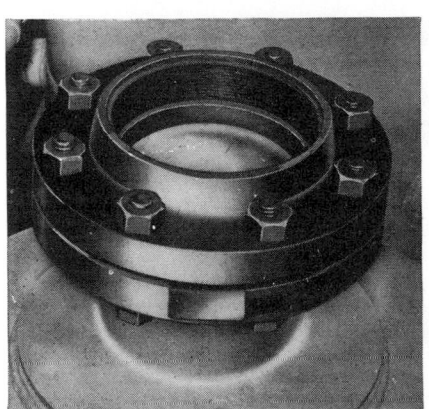

(A)	(B)

Fig. 16-24. (A) Safety heads on compressed-air bottles. (B) Ruptured safety head. (*Courtesy of Black, Sivalls & Bryson, Inc.*)

exposes personnel to some radioactivity and requires special equipment, it is usual practice to have a firm specializing in this type of testing do the work.

Acid Cleaning. Piping, valves, heat exchangers, process vessels, etc., are often cleaned today by means of acid. This is pumped through the piping and vessels under controlled conditions of concentration, velocity, temperature, and time. After the acid is removed from the system a neutralizing agent is generally applied, followed by a flushing with clean water. Since a rather specialized knowledge and equipment setup is required for acid cleaning, it is usual practice to have this work done by a firm having the required experience and machinery. Since portable equipment is suitable, acid cleaning can be done in the plant during a routine shutdown. Correctly applied acid cleaning can often reduce piping-system maintenance costs considerably.

Pipe Identification. Colored bands in accordance with the ASA "Scheme for Identification of Piping Systems" are valuable in plant maintenance operations. They permit more ready identification of the piping, eliminating errors.

Relief Devices. Safety and relief valves must be kept in good working order at all times to ensure safe operation and prevent the loss of valuable liquids. Routine tests of relieving capacity should be part of the piping maintenance program. Safety heads (Fig. 16-24a) must be replaced immediately after function (Fig. 16-24b).

Plastic Piping. Metal piping is being replaced in many applications by plastic piping of various types. Plastic piping has internal, external, and electrolyte corrosion resistance. It is easy to install, is not subject to caking of the fluid on the walls, and cannot be pitted by tuberculation. Since plastic pipe does not corrode, it is ideal for high-purity systems.

Plastic pipe, however, has both temperature and pressure limitations. The usual maximum-allowable operating temperature is in the 200°F range and depends on the material of which the pipe is made. Certain glass-fiber reinforced pipe can withstand temperatures up to about 250°F; asbestos-reinforced pipe can operate at temperatures in the 400°F range. New plastic materials are rapidly being introduced—some allow operation at over 500°F. In general though, plastic piping is usually confined to operating temperatures less than 200°F.

Allowable working pressure of plastic pipe decreases as operating temperature increases. Most plastic pipe manufacturers recommended that the working pressure not exceed 20 per cent of the bursting pressure. Typical bursting pressures range from a high of about 1,500 psi at 70°F for smaller-diameter pipe to a low of about 100 psi for 6-in. pipe at 70°F. Plastic pipe is more expensive than galvanized metal pipe, but the many advantages of plastic often make the extra investment worthwhile.

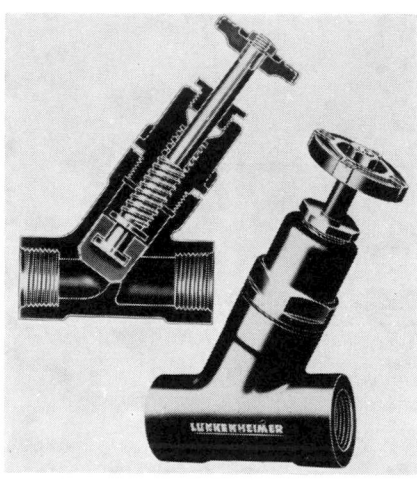

FIG. 16-25. Polyvinyl chloride molded plastic Y-type globe valve for use in plastic piping systems. (*Courtesy of The Lunkenheimer Company.*)

Valves, elbows, tees, flanges, and other pipe fittings are also made of plastic. Figure 16-25 shows a typical molded plastic valve. These parts have the same advantages as plastic piping and are subject to the same general pressure and temperature limitations.

Maintenance of Plastic Piping. Relatively little maintenance is required for plastic piping. Since the external surface of plastic piping resists corrosion, painting is never required for protection, though the surface may be painted for purposes of appearance.

Inspect plastic piping regularly for leaks, sagging, or out-of-roundness. Any of these conditions can be caused by excessive operating temperatures or pressures. Repair leaks using the solvent cement recommended by the pipe manufacturer. Be certain to drain pipe and dry it thoroughly before applying cement. Brush the cement carefully over the entire surface being repaired. Apply liberal amounts of the cement to insure complete repair of the leaking joint. At least a 10-hr drying time is required before the pipe can be subjected to operating pressure and temperature. Where possible, allow a 48-hr drying time for development of full strength in the pipe.

Leaks caused by sagging or out-of-round pipes cannot be repaired without replacing the affected section of pipe, unless the damage is only minor. Sagging is caused by too few supports. Figure 16-26 shows the usual support spacing for polyvinyl chloride plastic piping recommended by one pipe manufacturer.   Note that the recommended spacing is a function of flow temperature, pipe thickness (schedule number), and pipe diameter.   Where pipe sagging causes leaks, check the distances between supports, the flow temperature, and the ambient temperature at the pipe.   Fit more support if the distance between the existing supports exceeds that recommended in Fig. 16-26. Continuous supports are sometimes used for short spans in place of spaced supports. All supports should allow the pipe to expand axially without damage to the exterior surface of the pipe.   Therefore, the support must not clamp the pipe tightly.

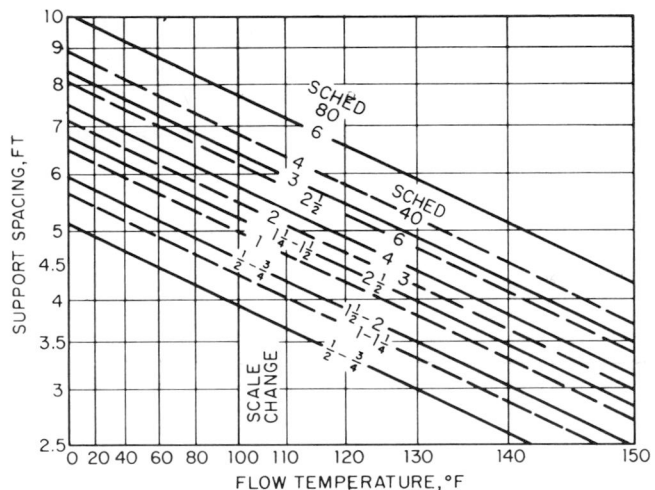

FIG. 16-26. Recommended support spacing for uninsulated polyvinyl chloride piping. Chart is for plastic pipe carrying fluids of up to 1.35 gravity.   For insulated piping reduce spans by 30 per cent.   (*Courtesy of Tube Turns Plastics, Inc.*)

Where sagging is caused by excessive flow or ambient temperature, reduce the fluid or air temperature.   Excessive temperature can cause sagging even when the pipe has properly spaced supports.

Out-of-roundness usually results from excessive operating temperature.   Reduce the fluid or air temperature before installing replacement sections for the out-of-round pipe.

Since plastic piping is particularly sensitive to shock resulting from being struck by a hard object, protect the piping in areas of heavy traffic.   Use a guard railing or low wall to protect the piping from fork-lift trucks and other vehicles used in industry. Plastic pipe used in outdoor service is often buried under ground to protect it from moving vehicles and the ultraviolet rays of sunlight.   Direct sunlight will shorten the life of plastic piping made of certain materials.

Chapter 17

AUTOMATIC SPRINKLER SYSTEMS[1]

By NATIONAL FIRE PROTECTION ASSOCIATION
Boston, Mass.

An automatic sprinkler system provides for the extinguishment of fire in a building by the prompt and continuous discharge of water directly upon all burning material. This is effected by means of an arrangement of pipes to which are attached outlet devices known as sprinklers. These sprinklers are constructed to open automatically whenever the surrounding temperature reaches a predetermined point.

In general, there are two types of automatic sprinkler equipment—dry-pipe systems and wet-pipe systems. In wet-pipe systems, the pipe lines contain water under pressure. This is the more common arrangement, but in buildings or portions of buildings which are subject to freezing temperatures, the dry-pipe system is ordinarily used. In this type of system, water is admitted to the pipes automatically when fire occurs.

Automatic sprinkler systems employing standard devices and installed in accordance with the established rules are sturdy and durable and require a minimum of expenditure for maintenance. However, like other types of equipment, they may suffer deterioration or impairment through neglect or from certain conditions of service. Definite provision for regular and competent attention to maintenance is a prime requirement if the system is to serve its purpose effectively.

SUMMARY OF IMPORTANT FACTORS

Controlling valves must be kept open and water supplies must be maintained in service. Automatic sprinklers will open in vain if there is no water or its flow is cut off.

When fire occurs, sprinkler control valves should not be closed until the fire is out or under control by other means. Haste to close sprinkler valves before proper investigation has been made or with the hope of preventing damage by water has resulted in many serious fires which would otherwise have been controlled by the sprinkler systems. The amount of water discharged by sprinklers is small compared with that from hose streams, which may be needed if fire rekindles.

When, of necessity, sprinkler protection is interrupted, every effort must be made to limit the extent and duration of the interruption. Contracts for fire insurance state or imply the requirement for the exercise of such precautions by the insured. Insurance inspection service organizations stand ready to advise property owners regarding measures that may be taken to maintain protection in emergencies. It is important that owners advise their insurers when there is interruption of sprinkler protection.

---

[1] Reproduced by permission from "Care and Maintenance of Sprinkler Systems (NFPA No. 13A)," copyright by the National Fire Protection Association. Copies of the latest issue of this pamphlet are available from NFPA, 60 Batterymarch St., Boston, Mass., 02110.

Sprinkler protection must be complete in the areas to be protected. Sprinkler action may be ineffective if fire gains headway in an area where water from sprinklers will not reach. Sprinklers should be extended to cover new areas before they are occupied.

Obstruction by stock or partitions to the distribution of water discharge from sprinklers must be avoided. Arrangements should be made to keep all stock piles, racks, and other possible obstructions the proper distance below sprinklers. (The minimum distance below sprinklers is 18 in., with increased clearance up to 36 in. over large, closely packed piles of combustible cases, bales, cartons, or other combustible stock.) To extinguish a fire, the water from the sprinklers must reach the burning material.

Sprinkler equipments must be protected against the freezing of water in pipes or other devices. Freezing, even in minor areas, may stop the flow of water to sprinklers or may render control and alarm devices inoperative. Serious damage may be done to the equipment, resulting in expensive repairs and interruption of sprinkler protection.

OWNERS' ORGANIZATION

It is not necessary to have a trained engineer to look after a sprinkler system, but the job does require a competent, intelligent, and reliable employee who has been given the responsibility of regularly inspecting the system and reporting any troubles or defects to his employer. This employee must have a certain amount of instruction and training and a general understanding of the mechanical requirements of operation.

The importance of having some one person responsible for maintenance cannot be overemphasized. A large part of the troubles that have been experienced with sprinkler systems has been due to lack of responsibility rather than lack of knowledge.

There are two basic considerations in delegating responsibility for maintenance. The property owner, company official, or anyone else responsibile for the installation of the sprinkler system—and from a business and financial standpoint directly interested in fire protection, maintenance, and cost of repairs—should be directly represented by some one person in authority, with whom insurance organizations, the sprinkler installing company, or other interested parties can cooperate. Also important is the appointment of an employee to be responsible for the condition of the sprinkler system and anything else affecting control of fire by sprinklers. This employee must be made familiar with all such matters, must make periodic inspections, and must report regularly to his superior officer. The selection and supervision of this man is of vital importance. Sufficient time should be allotted to such a man to permit him to give the necessary attention to this work.

Weekly inspections of sprinkler equipments are recommended, and a written report of the conditions found should be made. This report should be signed and dated by the inspector, and attested by his superior officer, who should then see that reported defects are corrected. These reports should be filed for reference. Sample inspection report forms may be obtained from insurance inspection organizations.[1]

When a watchman is employed, he should be a competent and trustworthy man, and should be instructed in the operation of the sprinkler system and what to do in case of fire.

Although the foregoing stresses the importance of having some one person responsible for maintenance, other persons should be trained in this matter and should be fully capable of taking over the function at any time the authorized individual is unavailable.

Where central-station supervision of sprinkler alarm and control devices is provided under contract, a specially valuable aid to maintenance is afforded. The outside agency reporting to the owner or manager each incident involving water flow or gate closure keeps a constant check on the condition of the equipment and stimulates care on the part of the plant employees.

Fire insurance inspection service organizations, as well as the manufacturers and installers of automatic sprinkler equipment, stand ready to advise and guide owners in the provisions to be made for the maintenance of sprinkler systems. The owners who benefit from the provision of sprinkler protection, however, should recognize

[1] Figures 17-1 and 17-2 show two sample forms.—Ed.

FORM 10-20A
SHEET 1 OF 2

(Standard Form of the National Automatic Sprinkler and Fire Control Association, Inc.)

REPORT OF INSPECTION

Inspection Contract

No. _____

For _____

Street _____ City _____ State _____

Date _____ Inspector _____

ALARM VALVES - No._____ Make & Model?_____ Condition?_____
   Alarm control open?_____ Sealed?_____ Insp. test conn.?_____
DRY PIPE VALVES - No._____ Make & Model?_____ Condition?_____
   Air pressure?_____ Alarm control open?_____ Sealed?_____ Insp. test conn.?_____
   Priming water at proper level?_____ Date last trip tested?_____ Periodic Trip Test Report Attached?_____
   Low point drains blown out?_____ Valve house & heater?_____ Condition?_____
   Accelerator or exhauster - No._____ Condition?_____ Control valve open?_____ Sealed?_____
RATE-OF-RISE SYSTEMS - No._____ Make & Model of valve?_____
   Air pressure?_____ Alarm control open?_____ Sealed?_____ Sup. high-low air pressure alarm tested?_____
   Date last trip tested?_____ How?_____ Condition?_____ Size?_____in.
HEAT ACTUATING DEVICES - (tripping time in sec. by systems)   Heat source used?_____

VALVE SERIAL NO.	A	B	C	D	E	F	VALVE SERIAL NO.	A	B	C	D	E	F
VALVE SERIAL NO.	A	B	C	D	E	F	VALVE SERIAL NO.	A	B	C	D	E	F
VALVE SERIAL NO.	A	B	C	D	E	F	VALVE SERIAL NO.	A	B	C	D	E	F
VALVE SERIAL NO.	A	B	C	D	E	F	VALVE SERIAL NO.	A	B	C	D	E	F

   Automatic Releases - No._____ Type?_____ Location?_____ Time_____ Sec.
   No._____ Type?_____ Location?_____ Time_____ Sec._____ Monitor Switches_____ Tested?_____
WATER MOTOR & GONG - No._____ Tested?_____ Condition?_____
ELECTRIC ALARM - No._____ Tested?_____ Condition?_____
OPEN SPRINKLERS - Condition?_____
STRAINERS - Condition?_____ Cleaned out?_____
COLD WEATHER VALVES - No.?_____ Date closed?_____ Date opened?_____
NON-FREEZING SYSTEMS - No.?_____ Condition?_____
NON-FREEZING SOLUTION TESTED?_____ Date?_____ Freezing point?_____
AIR COMPRESSOR - plant or system?_____ Condition?_____
   Manual or automatic_____ Cuts in_____ lbs. Cuts out_____ lbs. Low air alarm?_____
FIRE DEPT. CONN. - No._____ Condition?_____ Checks tight?_____
   Caps in place and couplings lubricated?_____ Accessible?_____
GRAVITY TANKS - No._____ Condition?_____
   Structure - condition?_____ Altitude gauge - condition?_____
   Heating equipment - condition?_____ Temperature?_____ Tank high & low alarm?_____
   Level of water in gravity tank?_____ Date last cleaned?_____
PRESSURE TANKS - No._____ Condition?_____ Level of water?_____
   Air pressure?_____ Water level gauge - condition?_____
   High and low air alarm - condition?_____ Tank house - condition?_____
FIRE PUMP - No._____ Type?_____ Condition?_____
   Suction - discharge - priming - condition?_____
   Date pump last tested?_____ Condition?_____
   Any interruption of steam or electric power since last inspection?_____ Explain_____
CITY WATER MAIN - direct connection?_____ Size?_____in. Pressure?_____PSI
SUPERVISORY ALARM SERVICE?_____ Type?_____ Direct connection to?_____
SPRINKLERS - PIPING - HANGERS - Condition?_____ Extra heads on hand?_____
   Drain valve - Condition?_____ Check valves - condition?_____
   Hand hose (on sprinkler system)_____ Condition?_____
   Hydrants - No._____ Condition?_____ Date last flushed?_____
   Hydrant house equipment - complete?_____ Condition?_____
   Fire extinguishers in good condition?_____ No._____ Date recharged?_____
   Pressure gauges - No._____ Condition?_____ Valve pits - No._____ Condition?_____

FIG. 17-1. Form for report of inspection. (*By courtesy of the National Automatic Sprinkler and Fire Control Association, Inc., 60 E. 42nd St., New York, N. Y. 10017.*)

FORM 10-20A
SHEET 2 OF 2

(Standard Form of the National Automatic Sprinkler and Fire Control Association, Inc.)

REPORT OF INSPECTION

Inspection Contract

No. _____

CONTROL VALVES

	NO.	TYPE?	OPEN Yes | No	SEALED Yes | No	SUPERVISED Yes | No	SIGNS Yes | No	CONDITION
City Connection Control Valve							
Tank Control Valves							
Pump Control Valves							
Sectional Control Valves							
System Control Valves							

2" Water Flow Test

Water Pressure - City_____PSI   Tank_____PSI   Fire Pump_____PSI

Water Flow Test Made?_____(If None Made, Why?)_____

FLOW TEST TAKEN AT	SIZE TEST PIPE	PRESSURE BEFORE	FLOW PRESSURE	PRESSURE AFTER	FLOW TEST TAKEN AT	SIZE TEST PIPE	PRESSURE BEFORE	FLOW PRESSURE	PRESSURE AFTER

Any changes in sprinkler system since last inspection?

Any Addition to Building?

Any new fire hazards?

Any stock, fixtures, etc. within 18" of ceiling?

Any areas protected by wet system not properly heated?

Any fires since last inspection?   Date?   Number of sprinklers operated?

How long was system off?   Area where fire occurred?

Minor Adjustments or Corrections Made

Suggestions to Subscriber for improvements

Remarks:

Copy of the Foregoing Report Received This Date

By _____
    SUBSCRIBER   DATE

FIG. 17-2. Form for report of inspection. (*By courtesy of the National Automatic Sprinkler and Fire Control Association, Inc., 60 E. 42nd St., New York, N. Y. 10017.*)

that the costs and responsibility for the maintenance of this protection rest with them.

The routine testing of sprinkler systems and devices, witnessed at regular intervals by insurance inspection organizations, is a service extended by the insurance companies to insured property owners in the common interest of both. By these routine tests, the equipment is either shown to be in good operating condition or any defects or impairments are revealed. Such tests are made, however, at the owner's responsibility and risk. Intelligent cooperation in their performance is evidence of interest in maintenance.

The efficiency and reliability of the protection offered by automatic sprinkler system is promoted when there is regular and competent inspection by automatic sprinkler contractors. Inspection procedures by automatic sprinkler contractors should include:

1. A minimum of four inspections, at approximately regular intervals, yearly.
2. Sealing of valves where seals are broken during the inspection.
3. Tripping of dry-pipe valves at least once every year.
4. An inspection report form used in conformity with the standard form of the automatic sprinkler industry, with copies furnished the property owner and the insurance authority having jurisdiction after each inspection.

DETAILS OF MAINTENANCE

In order that property owners and those charged with responsibility for proper maintenance of sprinkler systems may have useful information readily available, there are presented herewith recommendations and suggestions with regard to each of the principal features and devices commonly found in sprinkler installations.

Control Valves. *Secure each control valve in the sprinkler system in its normal or open position by means of wire and seal or a leather strap padlocked at the ends. Examine all control valves of the sprinkler system at regular intervals, preferably at least once each week.*

Control valves should be numbered and each should have a sign indicating the portion of the system that it controls. An inspection should be made at regular intervals, and the condition of each valve recorded on a report blank that lists the valves according to number. A valve inspection report should show that the valves are (1) open or closed, (2) properly secured or sealed, (3) in good operative condition, turn easily, and do not leak, (4) readily accessible. It should also show that wrenches are in place. If the examination of a valve shows any unsatisfactory condition, proper notice should be given to those in authority and the condition should be corrected as soon as possible. Valve stems should be greased at least once a year.

A valve sealing and tag system may be used in connection with the supervision and maintenance of a sprinkler system. Instructions for the establishment of such a system should be secured from the inspection department having jurisdiction.

Post Indicator Valves. These should be tried with a wrench at each inspection but should be left about one-quarter turn from the wide-open position so they will not be jammed open. When they are tried with a wrench, they should be brought to the wide-open position to get the spring of the rod, since sometimes this becomes detached from the valve itself and the indicator may read "Open" when the valve is closed. The stems and indicating mechanism of these valves should be oiled at least once each year. Wrenches should be fastened to the valve or kept near by.

Hub Valves (**Underground**). The location of each such valve should be clearly indicated by a sign on a nearby wall or by a marker. The road box for the valve should always be readily accessible, and the cap should be kept in place. The wrench should be located nearby and properly marked.

Outside-screw-and-yoke Valves. The position of the stem indicates whether the valve is wide open or not. These valves need not be given a one-quarter turn at each weekly inspection. The valve stems should be kept clean.

Valves in Pits. These should receive the same attention at each inspection. Access to the pits should be free, and care should be taken that the pits are kept clear of water and properly protected against freezing. If valves are of the outside-screw-and-yoke (O.S. & Y.) type, the protruding stems should be cleaned frequently.

Gages. *At the weekly inspection of control valves, read the gages showing water and air pressure on the system to make sure that normal pressures are being maintained.* The maintenance of proper pressure is of vital importance. Provision should be made to check the system gages with an inspector's gage once each year to insure reliability of readings.

Flow Tests. *Provide for regular water-flow tests to be made from test pipes at the top of the systems and the main drain valves of the systems.* Regular testing of sprinkler systems by water flow may best be made in cooperation with the inspection department having jurisdiction. Proper flow from the test pipe at the top of the system indicates the water supply at that point. Testing at the main drain valves includes noting of pressure-gage readings with unrestricted flow of water with the drain valve wide open and comparing it with the reading with the drain valve closed. If the readings vary materially from previously established or normal readings, the condition should be investigated. These tests are designated to show whether or not the normal water supply is available and to indicate the possible presence of closed valves or other obstructions in the supply pipe. (Note: Water-flow testing of a system having a direct connection to central station or fire department should be made only after proper notice is given to the signal station.)

Alterations and Repairs. *If a sprinkler valve is closed, shutting off any part of the system, notify the owner or the manager of the property immediately. Keep valves open and the sprinkler system in service to the greatest extent possible during alterations and repairs. After any alterations or repairs, make a special inspection to make sure that the valves are open, properly secured, and the system in order.*

When any alterations, additions, or repairs are to be made involving interruption of part or all of the sprinkler protection, the insurers should be notified and the inspection department having jurisdiction should be consulted in advance of making such changes. The inspection department may be able to give valuable advice about the maintenance of the protection and the requirements for any new work.

When building extensions, new partitions, decks, platforms, or enclosures are erected, the required extension of the sprinkler system to the new areas should be completed promptly. When repairs or alterations affecting the sprinkler system are in progress, special provisions should be made to keep the sprinkler system in service in all areas not affected. When the sprinkler system is shut off during the day to allow for work in progress, it should be restored at night. When the normal water supply to the system is interrupted, it is frequently possible to provide emergency supplies or connections. If any part of the sprinkler system must be shut off overnight, it is proper precaution to post a specially instructed watchman to guard the areas without sprinkler protection. Sprinkler valves are frequently left closed after alterations or repairs have been completed. A special inspection should be made to check the condition of the system following any such work, to make sure that all the control valves are open and properly secured.

Changes in Class of Work. Any proposed changes of this nature should be referred to the inspection department having jurisdiction in order to determine whether changes in the sprinkler protection will be required. Such changes in the class of work may require alterations on part or all of the sprinkler system. Special types of protection, including changes in location and temperature rating of sprinklers and protection against corrosion, loading, and mechanical injury, are sometimes necessary.

Changes in Heating, Lighting, or Mechanical Equipment. These changes may also necessitate changes in the sprinkler system. The installation of unit heaters, heating ducts, or high-power lighting units may require a change to higher-test sprinklers at such locations. Any changes in equipment or occupancy which might result in temperatures at the sprinklers over 100°F, or less than 32°F with wet-pipe systems, should be given immediate attention in order to guard against premature operation or freezing.

Changes in Exposure to Fire. Additional sprinkler protection may be required because of changes in exposure to fire. Any changes such as new buildings, sheds, and lumber yards or any conditions which might affect spread of fire to the property equipped with sprinklers should be taken up with the inspection department having jurisdiction.

Automatic Sprinklers. *Check the sprinklers regularly to make sure they are in good condition, clean, free from corrosion or loading, not painted or whitewashed, and not bent or damaged.*

It is of prime importance to keep sprinklers in good condition. If they are subject to loading with dust or foreign material (Fig. 17-3), the inspection department having

Fig. 17-3. Examples of loaded automatic sprinklers.

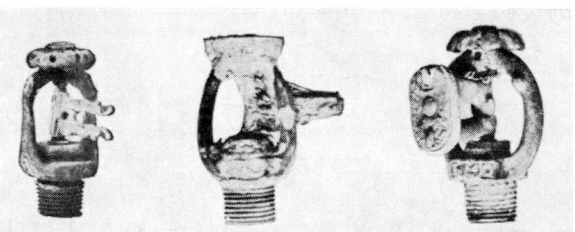

Fig. 17-4. Examples of corroded automatic sprinklers.

jurisdiction should be consulted. Where sprinklers are exposed to corrosive atmospheres (Fig. 17-4), special types of sprinklers, which are protected to prevent or retard corrosion, should be used. Tests of the reliability of operation of sprinklers that have been affected by corrosion may be arranged through the inspection department having jurisdiction. Sprinklers should be protected against mechanical injury. Where there is danger of this, approved guards should be provided.

Sprinklers of the proper temperature rating must be used, and changes in temperature conditions may require changes in sprinklers. The standard temperature ratings of automatic sprinklers are as follows:

Rating	Operating temp., °F	Color	Max ceiling temp., °F
Ordinary............	135, 150, 160, 165	Uncolored*	100
Intermediate........	175, 212	White*	150
High..............	250, 280, 286	Blue	225
Extra-high..........	325, 340, 360	Red	300
Very extra-high......	400, 415	Green	375
	450	Orange	425
	500	Orange	475

* The 135°F sprinklers of some manufacturers are half black and half uncolored. The 175°F sprinklers of the same manufacturers are yellow.

Sprinklers of Intermediate, High, Extra-High, and Very Extra-High ratings shall be used only when necessary. When used, the following rules should be followed:

1. For ceiling temperatures exceeding 100°F but not exceeding 150°F, install Intermediate rating sprinklers.
2. For ceiling temperatures exceeding 150°F but not exceeding 225°F, install high rating sprinklers.
3. For ceiling temperatures exceeding 225°F but not exceeding 330°F, install extra-high rating sprinklers.
4. For ceiling temperatures exceeding 300°F, install very extra-high rating sprinklers, as indicated in the table.

Always use the sprinkler wrench in removing or installing sprinklers. Other types of wrenches may injure the sprinkler.

Extra Sprinklers. *Always have on hand an adequate supply of extra sprinklers.* This supply should be kept together with sprinkler wrench in a cabinet provided for that purpose. The cabinet should be so located that it will not be exposed to moisture, dust, or a temperature exceeding 100°F. The supply of extra sprinklers should include sprinkler heads of the different temperature ratings that may be required for replacements. The extra sprinklers should be supplied by the installing contractor and replenished when necessary. It is necessary that this supply be maintained in order that replacements may be made in an emergency and the sprinkler protection restored.

Piping. *Keep piping in good condition and free from mechanical injury.* Sprinkler piping should not be used for support of ladders, stock, or other material. When the piping is subject to corrosive atmosphere, special protection may be needed. When the age or service conditions of the sprinkler equipment warrant, an internal examination of the piping should be made in accordance with instructions of the inspection department having jurisdiction. When it is necessary to clean out or flush out a part or all of the piping system, it is well to have this work done by experienced workmen or contractors in accordance with the instructions of the inspection department.

Hangers. *Keep hangers in good repair. Promptly replace any broken hangers and refasten any that become loose.* Broken or loose hangers may put undue strain on piping and fittings, cause breaks, and interfere with proper drainage.

Dry-pipe Valves. *Check the air pressure on each dry-pipe system at least once a week and pump up the systems when necessary.* Instruction charts are provided for the maintenance of dry-pipe valves by the sprinkler installing company and should be posted at or near these valves. It is necessary to watch the maintenance of air pressure on dry-pipe systems carefully. If pressure is lost rapidly, making frequent pumping necessary, the piping system should be gone over and made tight. It is desirable to maintain dry-pipe systems on dry-pipe service throughout the year in order to reduce corrosion and accumulation of foreign matter in the pipe systems. If water is admitted to a dry-pipe system, alarm devices will ordinarily be out of service until the dry system is restored.

Make sure that the priming water is maintained at the proper level above the dry-pipe valve. In cold weather, make sure that the valve closet is properly heated and that the heating equipment is safe and in order. Slight freezing of a dry-pipe valve may cause it to be inoperative. It is extremely important to make sure that adequate provision is made for the heating of the valve enclosure or the room in which it is located.

Before and during freezing weather, make sure that all low-point drains of the dry-pipe system are kept free of water. Dry-system piping should be thoroughly drained before freezing weather and kept free of water during the winter. The freezing of a small amount of water in the piping may cause rupture of the piping or sprinklers and prevent the operation of the valve.

Thoroughly clean and reset each dry-pipe valve once each year during the warm weather. Operating tests of dry-pipe valves, including quick-opening devices, if any, should be made from time to time, and this work should be done either by a sprinkler installing company or qualified personnel with the approval, or under the observation, of the authority having jurisdiction. At the time of such a test, occasion may be taken to thoroughly clean and properly reset the valve, performing any necessary service with regard to renewal of rubber parts or the adjustment of gages, alarm devices, connecting piping, and quick-opening devices.   In general, it is recommended that the servicing of dry-pipe valves be entrusted only to men experienced in this work or to representatives of the sprinkler installing company.

For proper maintenance of the valve in good condition, careful cleaning and resetting once each year is advisable.   On such occasions, the valve body should be throughly washed out, preferably with warm water, care being taken to make sure that the small ports and piping leading to the alarm connections are free from obstructions. No grease or other sealing materials should be used on seats of dry-pipe valves in an effort to stop leaks.   Force should not be used in an attempt to make dry-pipe valves tight.   Dry-pipe valves should carry a tag or card to show the date on which the valve was last tripped and to show the name of the organization making the test. Such tags are usually available from the installing company or the insurance authorities.

Quick-opening Devices.   The operation of quick-opening devices usually can be tested either with or without operating the dry-pipe valve itself.   The manufacturer's instructions for testing and resetting the device should be carefully followed.   If the device does not operate properly on test, it can, if necessary, be removed and the sprinkler system kept in operative condition without it.   Repair parts can be ordered from the manufacturer, or the device can be sent to the manufacturer for repair or adjustment.

Deluge and Preaction Systems.   Complete charts showing in detail the proper method of operating and testing thermostatically controlled systems are furnished by the installing company.   Only competent men fully instructed with respect to the details and operation of such systems should be employed in their repair and adjustment.   It is highly advisable for the owner to arrange with the installing company for regular periodic inspection and testing of the equipment.

The automatic valves controlling the flow of water into these systems operate through the effect of fire temperatures on actuating devices.   Ordinarily, when it is necessary to repair the actuating system as distinguished from the piping system itself, the water may be turned into the sprinkler piping and automatic sprinkler protection thus maintained, provided there is no danger of freezing.

Water-flow Alarm Devices.   *Test water-flow alarm devices at regular intervals by opening the inspector's test pipe or bypass test connection.*   Test electric alarm devices weekly by means of test switch or contact.

Keep the small valves or cocks controlling the water supply to alarm devices secured in the normal open position.   The frequency and method of testing alarm devices may be established after consultation with the inspection department having jurisdiction. It is not advisable to test water-motor gongs in cold weather if the piping to the gong is exposed to freezing.   Care should be taken to maintain properly the electric wiring, gongs, and transformer or batteries in the electric alarm equipment.

Central Station Supervisory Service.   *Always notify the central station before operating any valve or otherwise disturbing the sprinkler system.*   The central station sprinkler supervisory is so arranged that the operation of a control valve or the flow of water from a sprinkler, drain, test connection, or other abnormal condition in the system gives an automatic signal at the central station, and certain signals may be transmitted direct to the fire department.   Special arrangements must be made with the proper authorities before water flow or other tests are made which might result in an alarm signal being received at the central station.

The supervisory service provides monthly inspection of devices and tests.   Other tests that may be advisable should be made subject to the approval and supervision of the inspection department having jurisdiction.

Gravity Tanks.   *Make periodic inspection to check the maintenance of water at proper level in the tank.*   Constant maintenance of a full supply of water in gravity tanks is necessary not only to insure proper performance of the sprinkler system in the event of a fire but to prevent shrinkage of wooden tanks and unnecessary corrosion of steel tanks.

Make sure that the tank roof is kept tight and in good repair with the hatches fastened closed and that the frost-proof casing of the tank riser is in good repair and makes a tight joint with bottom of tank.   Keep heating devices in order and check the maintenance of proper temperature in the tank during freezing weather.   The prevention of freezing in the riser and formation of ice in the tank itself is extremely important.   Freezing in the riser may cut off the supply of water to the sprinkler system, while the formation of a layer of ice on the water may impede or prevent the flow from the tank.   The formation of heavy icicles because of leakage from the tank is dangerous.

The space at the top of the tank, the valve pit at the bottom of the tank riser, and the entire area about the bases of the columns of the tank must be kept free of dirt, rubbish, and waste material.   The steelwork of steel tanks, the hoops and grillages of wooden tanks, and the structures of supporting towers should be carefully examined annually and should be kept properly painted.   The entire tank equipment—piping, control valves, check valves, heating system, mercury gage, expansion joints, and all other accessories— should be inspected carefully.   Through bolts and hidden surfaces of built-up columns should be inspected for corrosion or weakening.   Instructions regarding the cleaning or repainting of a tank should be obtained from a tank-erection company or the inspection department having jurisdiction, and any such work should be done by a reputable concern with experience in this line.

When repair work is done on the tank or its covering, special care should be exercised to prevent any debris from falling into the tank.   When the tank is drained for internal painting, the outlet to the discharge pipe should be covered with a few sheets of paper to prevent material from falling into the riser.   When the tank has been refilled after emptying, the main tank valve should be opened wide and the discharge pipe should be thoroughly flushed through a drain or hydrant to make sure that no debris or other foreign material remains in the riser.

Insurers or their representatives should always be notified in advance if for any reason the tank is to be out of service.

Pressure Tanks.   *Inspect pressure tanks regularly, checking the water level, air pressure, and, during freezing weather, the heating of the tank enclosure.*   Consult safety codes of the particular state or municipality involved regarding the maintenance and testing of pressure tanks as unfired pressure containers.   Gage cocks of pressure tanks should be kept closed, except when test for water level is being made.   *Examine and paint the tank and its supports periodically, as recommended for gravity tanks.*

Fire Pumps.   *Steam or rotary pumps.   Start the pump once each week and operate until water is discharged freely from the relief valve.   Inspect regularly, checking the maintenance of ample pressure, proper supply of lubricating oil, operative condition of relief valve, and level of water in the priming tank.   Keep the pump room clean, accessible at all times, and at proper temperature to prevent freezing.*

Fire pumps should be operated only in connection with fire protection service and not for plant use.   Each pump should be tested to capacity with hose streams at least once a year during the warm weather.   Accumulation of water, through condensation, in the stream supply line or drainage equipment may be dangerous and should be avoided.   The suction pipes, intakes, foot valves, and screens of fire pumps should be examined frequently to make sure that they are free from ice or other obstruction.   Mud, gravel, leaves, and other foreign material entering the suction pipe may cause damage to the pump or obstruction of the sprinkler-system piping.

Centrifugal Pumps.   The pump room and equipment should be checked regularly, as recommended for steam pumps.   The examination should be extended to include the condition and reliability of the electric power supply and, if the pump is engine-driven, the storage batteries, lubrication system, and oil and fuel supplies.

Fire Department Connections.   *Inspect fire department connections regularly.*   Make sure that caps are in place, threads are in good condition, ball drip or drain is in order, and check valve is not leaking.

Open Sprinkler Equipment.   *Test outside or open sprinkler equipment once each year during warm weather.*   These tests should preferably be made in conjunction with the inspection department having jurisdiction and, if desired, with representatives of the fire department.   Before making operating tests, care should be exercised to make sure that all windows and doors through which water might enter are tightly closed. Proper precautions must be taken to prevent damage from discharge or accumulation of water to sidewalks, streets, areaways, or adjoining buildings. Determine by test whether the sprinklers and the system piping are in good condition and free from plugging. Any piping or sprinklers that are found clogged should be at once removed, cleaned, and replaced.

Flushing of Underground Water-supply Connections. Underground piping connecting water supplies to sprinkler systems should be flushed at periodic intervals using sufficient flow of water to remove any obstructions from the piping.

Spring Inspection. Annually, as soon as danger of freezing weather is past, a special inspection of the sprinkler system should be made to make sure that all is in proper condition for the summer.

At this time, the cold weather valves should be opened. Dry-pipe valves should be opened, thoroughly cleaned, carefully serviced, and properly reset by a competent sprinkler mechanic or by the sprinkler-installing company. The electric and water-motor, water-flow alarms should be tested. Any needed repair work or painting on the sprinkler equipment should be given prompt attention.

Fall Inspection. Annually, in October or at the approach of freezing weather, a special inspection should be made covering each building, its sprinkler system, and its water supplies to make sure that all conditions are proper for winter service and that all needed precautions are taken to prevent impairment of the sprinkler protection by freezing.

Control valves should be checked to make sure that they are open and properly secured. Post indicator valves should be examined to make sure that they are properly oiled and turn easily and that there is no leakage around the stem. Cold-weather valves should be closed, and the exposed pipes drained out. The drain valves on the exposed piping should be left slightly open.

Dry-pipe valves should be checked to make sure that the systems are holding air properly and that the electric and water-motor alarms are in order. The drains at low points of the dry piping should be checked to make sure that they are properly clear of water. The heating provisions for the dry valves should be checked.

Alarm valves should be tested for operative condition, and the valves or cocks controlling the alarm devices should be left secured in the proper position.

The gravity tank and its protection against freezing should be checked, and the heating system should be tested for operative condition.

Fire-pump rooms should be checked for proper condition. Attention should be given to the intake and suction reservoir.

Buildings should be looked over to make sure that windows, skylights, doors, ventilators, etc. are in proper repair and that cold air will not enter or unduly expose sprinkler piping to freezing. Heating equipment should be made ready for winter service. Special care should be given to the heating of any idle or vacant portions. Arrangements should be made for adequate maintenance of heat in extreme weather, at night, and on Sundays and holidays. Blind or unused attics, stair towers, low spaces under buildings, and roof houses are especially subject to freezing.

Watchman. *Instruct the watchman about the sprinkler equipment and the location and use of the shutoff valves, drains, and the alarm devices. Instruct the watchman to give the alarm at once and summon aid if he discovers fire or if the sprinkler alarms operate.* The watchman should be told how to give the alarm, which is his first duty. He should also be told how to notify someone in authority in case of fire or other trouble.

Serious fires and losses have occured because the watchman shut off the water before the fire was extinguished, allowing the fire to spread and to get beyond the control of sprinklers. If sprinkler alarms operate, it is important that the sprinkler valves shall not be closed until it has been definitely ascertained that there is no fire or that the fire is out. It is of vital importance to determine the cause of water flow from the sprinkler system before shutting off the water. Although the watchman may give valuable service in extinguishing incipient fires, he should not attempt emergency work of this character without first giving an alarm or summoning aid.

The watchman should be instructed to inspect on his first round as many of the sprinkler control valves as possible to make sure that they are open. If any are found closed, he should at once notify someone in authority. During cold weather, the watchman on his first round should make sure that windows or other outside openings are closed and that proper temperature is being maintained to prevent freezing of the sprinkler system.

Public Fire Department. It is advisable to have the fire department notified of the installation of automatic sprinkler equipment and that they become familiar with the layout of the system. The fire department should know the extent of the protection and the location and arrangement of control valves and connections for fire department use. At the time of a fire, inadequate knowledge of the sprinkler equipment on the part of the fire department may lead to faulty operations.

Restoring Systems to Service after Disuse. Occasionally, automatic sprinkler systems in idle or vacant properties are shut off and drained during the winter months or for longer periods. When the equipments in such properties are restored to service, it is recommended that such work be performed by a responsible and experienced sprinkler contractor. In such cases, the following procedures are recommended as good practice.

1. All lines of sprinkler piping should be traced from the extremities of the system to the main connections, with a careful check for blank gaskets in flanges, closed valves, corroded or damaged sprinklers or piping, insecure or missing hangers, and insufficient support. Proper repairs or adjustments should be made, and needed extensions or alterations of the equipment should be completed.

2. Water should be admitted slowly to the system, with proper precautions against damage by escape of water from previously undiscovered leaks. When the system has been filled under normal service pressure, drain-valve tests should be made to detect any closed valve that possibly could have been overlooked. All available test pipes should then be flushed, and where such pipes are not provided in accordance with the present standards, the proper equipment should be installed.

3. Where the sprinkler system has been long out of service, has been damaged by freezing, or has been subject to extensive repairs or alterations, the entire system should be hydrostatically tested in accordance with the Standards for the Installation of Sprinkler Systems (NFPA Publication No. 13). Special care should be taken to detect any sprinklers showing minor or dropping leaks and to make replacements where necessary.

4. Dry-pipe valves, quick-opening devices, alarm valves, and all alarm connections should be examined, put in proper condition, and tested. Fire pumps, pressure and gravity tanks, reservoirs, and other water-supply equipment should receive proper attention before being placed in service. Each supply should be tested separately.

5. An investigation for obstruction or stoppage in the sprinkler-system piping should be made as in the manner outlined in the pamphlet, "Internal Cleaning of Sprinkler Piping" (National Board of Fire Underwriters, 85 John St., New York, N.Y. 10038).

6. Finally, all controlling valves should be operated from closed to fully open position and should be left secure in the open position by means of a strap riveted or padlocked to the ends or by means of a seal attached by the inspection department or sprinkler contractor.

REFERENCES

The following publications are among the many dealing with fire protection and maintenance of fire-protection equipment issued by the National Fire Protection Association:

"Fire Protection Handbook," 12th ed.
"NFPA Inspection Manual," 2nd ed.
"Industrial Fire Loss Prevention," NFPA no. 6.
"Maintenance and Use of Portable Fire Extinguishers," NFPA no. 10A.
"Care of Fire Hose," NFPA no. 198.
"Centrifugal Fire Pumps," NFPA no. 20.
"Operation and Maintenance of Steam Fire Pumps," NFPA no. 21.
"Outside Protection (Yard Piping)," NFPA No. 24.

Chapter 18

EFFECTIVE USE OF PLANT FACILITIES

By A. M. Beebee, Jr.
Plant Engineer
Rochester Products Division of General Motors Corporation
Rochester, N.Y.

A reasonable utility cost can be 20 per cent of direct-labor cost or, in some industries, 100 per cent of labor cost or even higher. But in the manufacturing industries as a whole, the cost of utilities is twice as much as the net profit. In all plants there is a potential for saving from 10 to 50 per cent on utilities.

A program seeking to reduce the cost of utilities should be labeled with a term more acceptable than "Utility Conservation." It should be thought of in terms of "Effective Use of Plant Facilities." Such a program is not a campaign to end waste, although no successful program can tolerate it. It must be an engineering concept, and skilled technicians are necessary to arrange, plan, execute, and perpetuate it. It is not a one-shot affair and it is not a part-time job. It is big business, and will succeed only in proportion to the effort that is expended. Such a program requires constant attention, but there is no end to its possibilities. For those who have the energy to seek it, improved performance in this field is as certain as increased productivity. There are two ways to go about it:

1. Hire an engineer and make the problem his whole assignment. He has to be a qualified engineer with wide practical experience and, above all, an abundance of initiative and ingenuity. He will pay for himself many times over.
2. Establish a committee. All committee members should be experts in their fields of plant maintenance and engineering to assure committee effectiveness.

The latter way has several advantages. A committee automatically gets more people committed to action. Each member becomes a salesman for the project. Follow-up is more efficient. A chairman of the committee must be appointed by management and must be accountable to management. No one with less responsibility than that of the plant engineer should hold this position. Subcommittee chairmen, one for each utility, should be appointed by the chairman and should be from the regular line organization and report to the chairman.

With the decision made about which way to go, objectives should be established. With either the individual or the committee approach, this is a joint venture with management. For each utility it is necessary to establish a record of costs for a period of years. To evaluate this information properly, it is necessary to correlate it with some measure of plant activity, expressed in well-defined and readily available dollar costs, such as dollars of sales or direct-labor costs. Correlation can be on a plant-wide or a department basis, depending on how the utility is billed or metered. It is imperative that the value be actual and not include any estimates.

The smallest quantities available (meter readings by department instead of for total plant) will provide a series of records which can help to direct effort and to measure results in the most fruitful areas.

With this history, it is necessary for the subcommittee chairmen to establish concrete programs for its effective use.   To help in this endeavor, it sometimes is desirable to

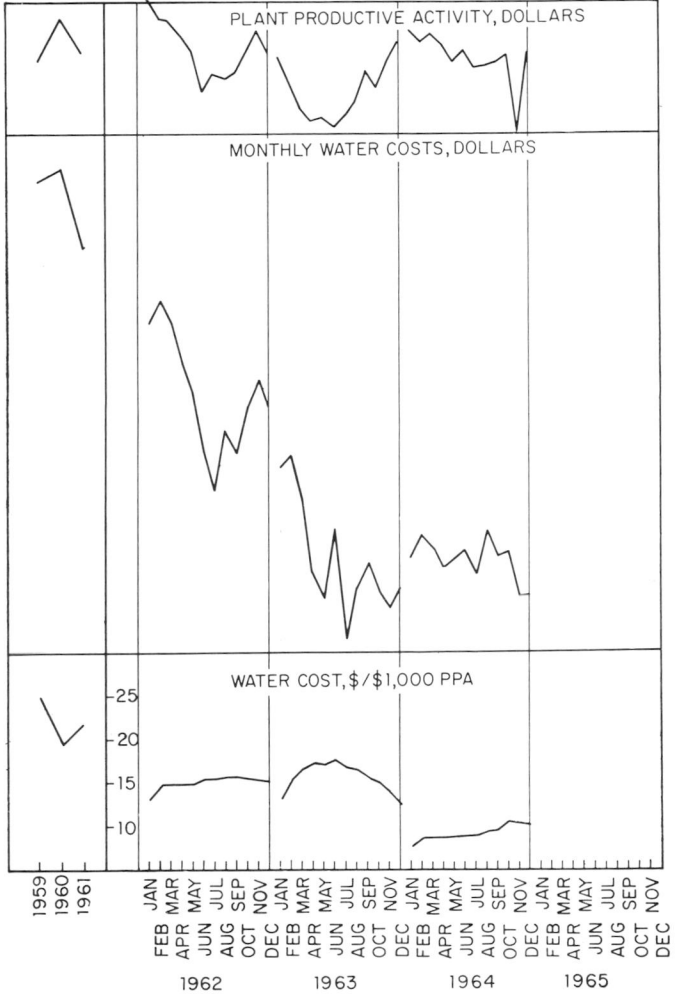

FIG. 18-1. Plant engineering objective: reduce water costs.

calculate and plot monthly and cumulative ratios of utility costs to plant activity. Examples are shown in Fig. 18-1.   Sometimes it is surprising how the effects of effort to save on utilities change these ratios.   For example, after considerable action, utility costs which formerly varied directly with plant activity have no relation to them at all after installation of conserving facilities.   On the other hand, some utility costs have a consistent straight-line relation to plant activity.   In the average industry this may be the case with compressed air and electricity, while the general pattern for steam may not be similar to the patterns for compressed air or electricity and may depend on the seasons, as might be expected.   Industrial steam usage is likely to be quite independent of plant activity.   This is understandable because in most instances its consumption has little dependence on machine capacity and varies only according to whether the machine is running or not.

Such known or discovered facts are combined with plant-survey information, and a list of possible savings through change of methods can be studied.   Analysis of proposals will indicate possible savings, and goals can be established and interpreted in terms of expected utility dollar costs or reduction in ratio of costs to productivity or both.   This information, recorded on a chart by periodic plotting, provides a ready record of progress.   The method varies with the utility.   In general, each program is directed by the full committee.   The committee evaluates each proposal and either dilutes or strengthens it to make sure that it is reasonably attainable.   The existence of an aggressive spirit, good cooperation, and proper timing influences achievability.   When problems of organization and objectives are solved, the stickiest part of the work is completed.   The goals are in focus, and the following sections offer suggestions of lines to follow.

STEAM

Powerhouse.   A measure of the effectiveness of the powerhouse can be gained from frequent evaluations of total operating costs per 1,000 lb of steam generated. Because several fixed operating costs are amortized by gross steam send-out, it would be easy to report possible false progress by reducing unit costs when increasing send-out.   Therefore it is extremely important to evaluate total generating costs also. It may be suggested that an objective of reduction in both unit costs and total costs would be correct and challenging.   An effectively scheduled maintenance program will be as rewarding in a powerhouse operation as it will be in any other operation.

Look at housekeeping and maintenance practices.   If they are not in top shape, costs are not minimum.   Labor controls also may be in order; the shift engineer should be responsible for housekeeping and maintenance as well as operating.   In eliminating demurrage charges as well as reducing fuel costs for shipments, it is important to schedule trainload or 1,000-ton shipments, which receive attractive freight rate adjustments.

Survey the plant condensate system and recover every bit of condensate.   Conductivity indicators can indicate contamination, and if there is a high probability, automatic condensate-dumping to sewer may be included when plating and other applications fail.   Frequent proximate analyses for checking and adjusting coal-specification techniques are important for controlling the big increment of fuel costs.   One simple axiom is to try to recover all the Btu possible.   The ways are almost limitless.   They include improving boiler efficiency by means of heat traps such as economizers and air heaters, continuous and surface blow-down heat exchanging to make-up water, heating overfire air with flue gas, and reducing excess air by using ash-pit or flue gas for turbulence.   These and other procedures must be augmented by frequent calculations of boiler efficiency, continuous flue-gas analysis, and other techniques well-known in powerhouse operation.

Cold Chemical Cleaners.   New chemical cleaners reduce or eliminate the need for, and cost of, hot cleaning solutions.   In many severe applications, if heating cannot be eliminated, the temperature can be reduced.   Losses are strictly proportional to temperatures.

Balanced Make-up Air.   Process-air exhausts near the center of the plant can create a negative pressure.   If there isn't enough make-up air, cold air pulled in through the cracks and openings in the building makes peripheral areas chilly and hard to heat.   Low-hanging peripheral outlets can be provided to allow enough air to relieve the situation.   Moreover, it is now possible to shut down the make-up heating system during weekends and warm the plant quickly on Monday mornings.   Because the make-up air must be heated sooner or later, comfort is achieved with little or no operating-cost increase, and there can be an actual saving if Btu otherwise lost can be recovered in the process.   Relative utility rates and equipment costs should be checked.   Direct-fired gas units approach 100 per cent efficiency because products of combustion are released to the heated space, and they should be considered for use in providing make-up air.

Tank Heat Seals.   The use of mineral-oil heat seals on top of hot, liquid-filled, open tanks can cut surface radiation losses drastically.   The heat seal forms a foam insulating layer that is nonmiscible.

Thermal Insulation.   The economies of insulation are well known, but it is all too easy to overlook the many bare spots on hot containers and pipelines.   Studies of uncovered areas show that thermal insulation of these areas would pay off in less than a year.

Control of Exhaust Air.   Spray booths consume large amounts of in-plant air.   It is possible to minimize the amount of exhaust (as well as the amounts of wash water and electric power) by the use of a "mat switch," like those at supermarket doors.   This is placed under a rubber mat on which the operator stands.   When he steps off the mat, the switch shuts off the fan and water-wash pump.

Exhaust-system Design.   Large hoods over an entire work-station area should not be used.   They throw away too much warm air.   All hoods should hang low and be designed specifically for the problem.   For example, in a process that generates kerosene fumes, the use of a small-diameter Inconel tube will permit sucking off of the fumes close to their origin.   This high-velocity design can replace a large hood and cut air waste by 99 per cent.

Recuperation.   Many designs for air-to-air heat exchangers are available.   Hot-spot exhausts, such as heat-treating furnaces, drying ovens, atmosphere generation, and the like, may be excellent sources of energy for tempering incoming air or recirculated air.   The higher the exhaust temperature, the greater the saving.

Heat Exchangers.   Heat Exchangers have many applications.   They can be used for tempering incoming water used for washing and rinsing, for domestic purposes, or even for boiler make-up.   The use of exchangers for coolants, hydraulic systems, lubrication temperature reduction, and even refrigeration condensing water offers excellent opportunities.

WATER

Methods for Recovery and Reuse.   Techniques for recovery and reuse of water have been found that produce big and obvious savings.   Some require capital investment which, for water reclamation, usually can be regained within two years.   The recovered cooling water may be reused in many ways—for mold cooling in die-casting machines, air compressors, and refrigeration condensers, for hydraulic cooling and process-bath cooling, and for atmosphere generator, capacitor, and transformer cooling, which are only a few of the low-rate applications.   Treated effluent from industrial-waste plants, closed-water systems using cooling towers, evaporative coolers, direct-expansion absorption machines, wells, cooling ponds, and lakes are some of the source facilities.   Water treatment and control is imperative, and its cost must be calculated as part of incremental operating costs in justifying the adoption of methods for recovery and reuse.

Modified Wash Basins.   A 40 per cent saving can be realized if the holes in the peripheral hot-water feed of circular wash basins are plugged.   The holes in the areas where personnel cannot stand are the ones plugged.

Spring-loaded Valves.   Spring-loaded valves can be installed on all manual make-ups and at hose outlets, thereby effecting substantial saving.   This method is useful for air hoses, also.

Platers.   Although more costly, rinse water conductivity controllers are more positive washwater controls, and usually they will pay for themselves in less than a year.   A counterflow principle of rinsing that uses cascade flow from the last to the first tank can cut wash water demand 50 per cent or more.

Direct Mixing.   Whenever possible, the use of a direct-mixing valve instead of a heat exchanger to temper water to specified temperatures is advantageous.   It not only saves water and Btu, it eliminates pumps, refrigeration, heat exchangers, and valving.   One of its applications concerns the water used for sealing vacuum pumps. The outlet water (which has gained heat in the process), can be mixed with cooler water from a cooling tower and tempered down to a consistent temperature for reuse.

Temperature-rise Controls.   Waste water can be eliminated in all cooling systems of hydraulic equipment by temperature-rise controls.   Placed in the discharge water line, they restrict flow unless water temperature is at least 10°F higher than inlet temperature.

Water Conditioning.   Treating water for hardness reduces scale deposits.   Thus, when conditioned water is used for heat transfer, less water is needed.   One major benefit is lower cost of maintaining equipment.

Mechanical Refrigeration.   In operations where cooling by water alone is not sufficient it is possible that the second stage of cooling can be accomplished by mechanical refrigeration.   If this method is chosen, a use for the hot condensing water should be sought.

COMPRESSED AIR

Blower Drying and Cooling.   High-volume, high-velocity blowers can be used for washing and drying parts.   The cost of using compressed air for this purpose should not be tolerated.   The maximum velocity of air through a nozzle is approximately 1,125 fps.   Nozzle pressure above 10.4 psi will not raise the throat velocity; therefore the energy expended in compressing air to a higher pressure is lost.   Frequently the drying operation is adjacent to, or a part of, a system of dryers using high temperatures.   The exhaust, or even flue gas, can be recompressed by a blower to retain Btu otherwise lost.   The process will be improved in this manner.

Leaks.   The need for elimination of leaks is obvious, but it needs emphasis.   Sometimes weekend operations, with maintenance support, are necessary.   These are ideal occasions for scheduling specific sections of the plant to be surveyed for compressed-air leaks and for repairing these leaks.

Compressed Air for Cooling.   Frequently, air is used for cooling that could be done better and more cheaply by water, blowers, or refrigeration.   This is illustrated by the following two examples: (1) Compressed air was blown on a long run of 2-in. tubing to keep it from overheating.   The tubing enclosed a run of smaller, welded tubing in its travel from a welder to an annealing furnace.   Substituting finned outer tubing and blowing low-pressure air on it from small blowers was just as effective. (2) A compressed-air stream was used to cool hot die-cast parts on a conveyor.   A portable blower, similar to a tank-type vacuum cleaner, did the job just as well.

Proper Air Pressure.   Most air cylinders on shop equipment can be oversized when exact sizes are not obtainable.   In such cases the air-line pressure can be reduced by a regulator which fits the pressure to the needs of the job, affording reductions in air usage.

Dry Compressed Air.   Water and oil vapor that condense in distribution lines can cause trouble with controls on pneumatic equipment.   One of the advantages of the installation of dryers is the elimination of the waste of compressed air used in blow-down operations in attempts to remove the moisture from the system.

Intermittent Usage.   The development of photoelectric and proximity switches that are sensitive to any mass has allowed the installation of intermittent-use facilities that regulate use of compressed air, with savings of usually more than 50 per cent.

GAS

Engineered Reductions.   Frequently an engineering study for saving in one utility can mean savings in companion utilities.   As an example, second-stage mechanical refrigeration was applied to allow use of reclaimed water rather than raw city water in the condenser heat exchangers of heat-treating atmosphere gas generators.   The resulting lower dew point made possible by mechanical refrigeration eliminated costly enriching and saved gas costs as well as water costs.   Questions which may be considered are: Is the gas being used efficiently?   Is it needed at all?   Will a cheaper substitute or a different method do?

Combustion Control. Flue gas from any combustion operation using gas should be analyzed. The best gas-air mix (neither to much nor too little air) for efficient combustion should be achieved. An inefficient mix may require adjustments of air inlet, cleaning of burner, changing the size of orifice, or other modifications.

Effective Use. The design of combustion chambers and flues can greatly affect their efficiency, as can the location of firing. Most local utilities have experts in this field to give advice. Temperature controls and proportioning equipment often need calibration and adjustment.

Recuperators. One of the most effective facilities for gas saving is an air-to-air heat exchanger, when flue-gas energy can be used to preheat combustion air. Readjustments of combustion apparatus are required because of the resultant reduction in air density, but efficiency can be increased approximately 1 per cent for every 30°F rise in combustion-air temperature. Ordinarily, costs, including those for ductwork and equipment, can be justified in less than one year.

ELECTRICITY

Power-factor Correction. Such correction can be a source of big power savings. Many plants tackle the problem by using capacitors and synchronous motors or by judicious sizing of induction motors. Maximum power factor may be obtained by controlling the excitation of several synchronous motors used as prime movers. This may be supplemented by the use of capacitors on all bus-duct distribution lines (which increases their carrying capacity).

Motor Checkup. Every motor which is 100 hp or over should require reviewing regarding load demands to determine whether it is suitably applied and whether individual power-factor correction is justified. The attempt should be made to apply motors for full load; the tendency to overdesign horsepower results in poor power factor when a motor is running partially loaded.

Voltage Regulation. Significant savings may be obtained by a periodic check of voltage conditions. Distribution voltages can be adjusted to their best settings by changing the voltage taps on substation transformers. Voltage that is too high reduces equipment life. Occasional adjustments are necessitated by major alterations in plant loading. If plant voltage is above rating, downward adjustment saves power by decreasing motor-starting current and running kilowatts and by raising power factor. (Overvoltage causes poor power factor.) By reducing feeder voltages 2.4 per cent, the life of incandescents, solenoids, and similar equipment may be increased by as much as 25 per cent.

Rate Studies. Detailed studies of utility rates can result in significant savings. Plant operations usually can be coordinated more advantageously with the rate structures. As a rule, it is wise to:

1. Purchase every required load through one meter in order to utilize the low end of the rate to the greatest extent.
2. Adjust equally throughout all shifts where possible in order to decrease peak demand charges.
3. Avoid repeated starting of large equipment because of the effect of this on demand. It can be more economical to continue running a motor than to make repeated starts.
4. Purchase power at the primary rate and reduce voltages in user's substations.

Lighting Controls. It is possible to cut power consumption by replacing manual lighting controls with timers, clocks, and photoelectric controls so that power is used only when needed. This policy also extends bulb life.

Stray Current Losses. By continual alertness and correction of grounds in plating, stray currents can be eliminated, thus saving lost energy. This field often is overlooked until there is major trouble.

Recuperators. Heat-treating furnaces that are fired by ribbon elements, Glo-bars, or other types of electrical equipment nearly always are supplied with controlled atmosphere, and heat balances will show that upward of 50 per cent of the energy dissipated is lost in heating this controlled atmosphere. Energy savings will be enjoyed in direct proportion to the ability to use heat from sources where it would otherwise be lost in preheating the atmosphere. One application that is attractive economically is the use of air-to-air exchangers on hot-exhaust operations.

GENERAL

Attention should be directed toward automatic controls, like timers, for starting and stopping air-conditioning units and heating and ventilating units and interlocking utilities with equipment operations so that these facilities are provided without reliance on memory. Many times it may be necessary and desirable to connect indicating devices to the plant alarm systems to provide unlimited surveillance, particularly where large losses are probable.

Provision of equipment for cutting utility costs is of little value unless it is properly operated and maintained. This requires adequate training of operators and service people. Without such training, it is appalling how original design or instructions are misinterpreted as a piece of equipment passes down the levels of supervision. Operating instructions and a schematic diagram of the system should be posted (framed under glass) at every machine or process. Thus, in a three-shift operation, the "guide book" is always available to operators and maintenance men. Maintenance men are trained in servicing all special equipment.

Knowing how to maintain conservation equipment is not enough. Consider a control such as an automatic make-up valve. It has to be maintained, calibrated, and adjusted when necessary to make sure it fulfills its function. This can be done through a program of scheduled maintenance and checking of operating conditions. It is not suggested that inspectors check equipment and report defects for later repair. Trained maintenance men, on the job, should detect any malfunction from visual or recorded data (such as maximum temperature or minimum pressure). If adjustments are needed, they are made right away.

All people in the plant can help in this program, and any efforts to enlist their assistance will unearth possibilities that could require months of study to find otherwise. A suggestion program is excellent in this regard. Training programs, booklets, management directives, publicity, utility billings, and formal presentations will serve a real purpose.

The applications suggested here are only a few of the many that are possible. Each suggestion needs evaluation of its proposed application. Engineering analysis will lead to unusual, intriguing, and highly challenging charges involving savings.

Section 10

MAINTENANCE OF TRANSPORTATION EQUIPMENT

Chapter 1

ELECTRIC INDUSTRIAL TRUCKS

By E. J. Swanson
Product Service Manager
Baker Division
Otis Elevator Company
Cleveland, Ohio

Because industrial-lift-truck equipment is ruggedly built, its care is often on the basis of "when it breaks down we'll fix it," rather than a planned preventive-maintenance program. It is estimated that 50 per cent or more can be saved in maintenance and downtime costs with a planned preventive-maintenance program. Some of the more important preventive-maintenance procedures are illustrated by Figs. 1-1 to 1-13, inclusive.

Any industrial lift truck can pay dividends only when it is in operation; downtime can lose 1 to 2 weeks of operation. Compare the time lost and parts costs with a planned preventive-maintenance program of 1 or 2 hr weekly. No infer-

FIG. 1-1. This sprocket represents more than a hundred-dollar replacement cost. Don't permit misalignment to ruin it.

FIG. 1-2. This shaft wear permitted misalignment of sprockets and chain with ultimate breakage.

ence is made that preventive maintenance will eliminate all breakdowns. Early discovery of potential trouble allows replacement-parts ordering and scheduled repair to keep downtime costs at a minimum.

Some mechanics look askance at an electric lift truck because they feel that it is complicated and that electrical components are intricate and involved. Nothing could be further from the truth. Actually there are about 120 fewer moving parts in an electric lift truck than in its gasoline- or LP-powered counterpart. In reality this means less adjustment, less repair, and fewer replacement parts required.

The care and maintenance of an electric lift truck should be placed in the hands of a competent mechanic. He should be instructed and charged with the responsibility of maintaining a log, or record, of each truck. This log should record in detail all adjustments, repairs, overhauls, lubrications, and inspections made on each vehicle. The name or initials of the individual performing such functions should be recorded. A periodic review of this record can determine potential trouble areas, and corrective action can be taken.

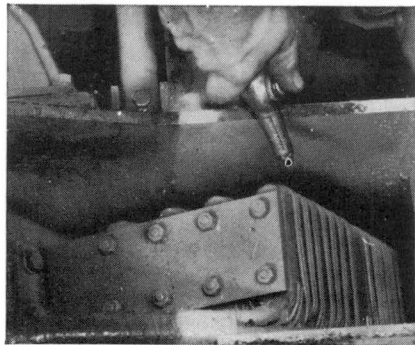

FIG. 1-3. Use dry air to keep resistors clean.

FIG. 1-4. Inspect commutator for burning and pitting.

Many forms have been devised to record this information; their details depend on the type and quantity of information the specific company requires. It can be merely a simple form as shown in Table 1-1 or a more sophisticated form showing accumulative costs by month, quarter, or year, with costs per hour of operation computed directly on the record. A further refinement can be devised, such as a

Table 1-1. Sample Maintenance Form

FORK TRUCK _____ MODEL _____ SERIAL NO. _____ CAPACITY _____

DATE IN SERVICE _____ DEALER _____ TEL. NO. _____

DATE	HOUR METER	LABOR PER.	PARTS USED	REMARKS	NAME
9/1	100	A	—	Adjust Brakes	EJS

Table 1-2. Sample Code for Preventive Maintenance Form

A—Clean electrical system with air—no parts used
B—Check motor brushes—list parts if used
1—Inspection—no parts used
L—Lubrication—no parts used
O—Complete overhaul of unit—list parts used

code for the most common tasks performed. The code can be devised to suit individual preference; a sample is shown as Table 1-2.

Fig. 1-5. Keep motor terminals tight and coated with insulating paint.

Fig. 1-6. Motor coupling should be free in action and properly lubricated.

COSTS

Maintenance costs are an important item in the over-all profit and loss statement of any company, which is why control of these costs is so important. Maintenance costs generally fall into two categories: *normal* and *excessive*.

Normal. Normal maintenance costs consist of those charges for labor, material, and downtime necessary to keep the equipment in reasonable and safe operating condition.

Excessive. Excessive maintenance costs are a result of one or more or a combination of the following:

1. Tinkering (whether by operator or mechanic).
2. Neglect of minor repairs.
3. Faulty or inadequate lubrication.
4. Bad floor conditions.
5. Overloading.
6. Careless operation.
7. Poorly maintained skids.
8. Careless or poorly stacked loads.

Items one through three can be eliminated by a planned preventive-maintenance program. The last five items come under the heading "Reasonable Care and Operation." Though they are operating problems, their neglect by management will result in increased maintenance costs.

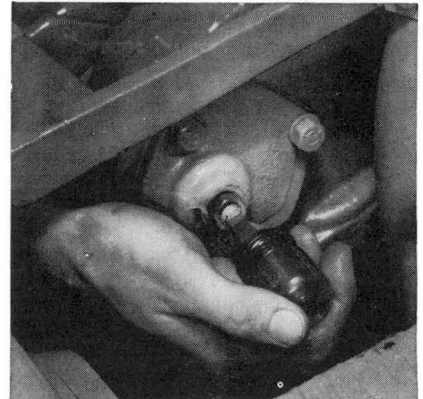

Fig. 1-7. Keep excess play out of steering reduction unit.

PREVENTIVE MAINTENANCE

Because it is not always possible to determine the beginning of trouble in the course of truck operation, regular periods of inspection should be established as an aid in detecting trouble before it gets out of hand. These established periods vary according to the number of hours the truck is in operation and working conditions (dust, dirt, moisture-laden atmospheres, etc.), Also, some parts require more frequent inspection than others. It is an excellent idea to completely clean the truck with air and/or steam prior to any inspection, lubrication, or repair.

Frequency of Inspection. The best yardstick to determine frequency of inspection

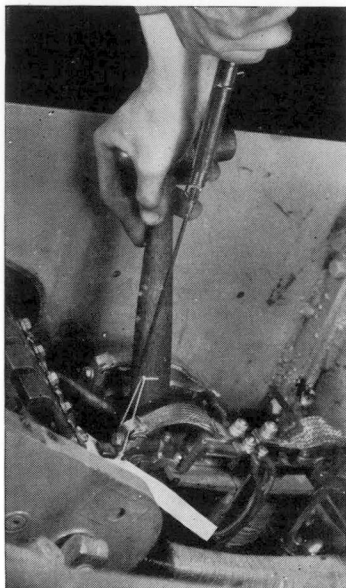

is "hours of operation." It is axiomatic that a truck operating 7 days a week, 24 hr a day, will require more frequent periods of inspection than a truck operating 5 days a week and only 8 hr a day. These periods again should be modified by actual working conditions. Operation in a foundry sandblast room will necessitate more frequent inspections than operation in a grocery warehouse, for example.

Preventive maintenance actually starts with

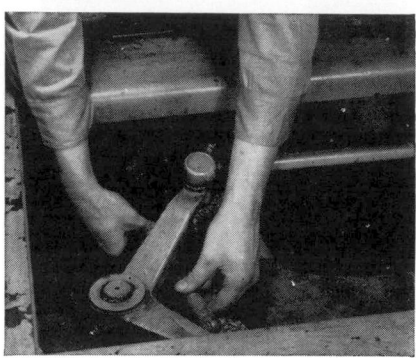

FIG. 1-8. Check spring tension and gap on contactors.

FIG. 1-9. Steering connections should be checked with wheels at center, extreme left, and extreme right.

the truck operator. Daily checks on the following items, at the start of each shift, should be mandatory. If anything is amiss, it should be reported to the maintenance department for immediate action.

1. Check steering for proper operation.
2. Check hydraulic system for leaks.
3. Check truck for proper operation in travel and hoisting speeds.
4. Check all lights for proper operation.
5. Check all attachments for proper operation.
6. Check battery terminals and connections.
7. Check battery for proper fluid level.
8. Check seat brake and operating brakes for proper operation.

As stated before, hours of operation is the best yardstick to use in determining frequency of inspection. A suggested frequency of inspection under normal operating conditions is 100 hr; this we will call Inspection X. At the 500-hr period we will have Inspection Y and at the 5,000-hr period Inspection Z. These suggested time periods should be reduced by 50 per cent when excessive ambient heat is encountered as one of the operating conditions. They should be reduced by 25 per cent where abnormal dirt or dust is present.

The following is a list of items that should be covered during Inspection X. However, because of heavy- or light-duty operations, these may be done at more or less frequent intervals, depending on experience.

Inspection X

Clean truck completely with air and/or steam, wipe off all oil holes, and grease fittings.

Differential. Jack up one drive wheel; start directional motor. Check for excessive noise. Check backlash.

Wheel Bearings. Check wheel bearings for looseness. Loose wheel bearings can cause damage to the differential, tires, and brakes.

Tires. Check for uneven wear. Drive tires should be roughly the same diameter, or damage to the differential and bearings can result. Check for cutting and gouging; remove imbedded chips.

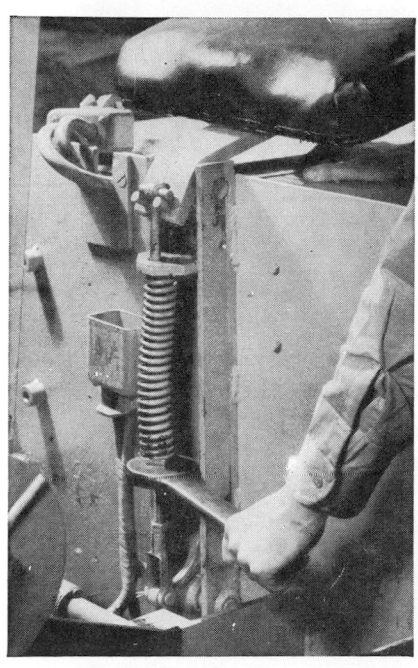

FIG. 1-10. Where seat interlock is used, maintain proper adjustment to brakes and switch.

FIG. 1-11. Check for equal chain adjustment; sprockets should run free.

Chain Rollers. Check for lubrication and free running.

Chains. Check for equal adjustment; check anchors. Use wire brush to remove caked dirt or grease. Recoat with light oil or special roller-chain lubricant. *Note:* Chain should be replaced in full lengths *only.*

Hydraulic Cylinders. Examine for leaks at stuffing box and connections. Tighten or replace as required.

Electrical. Disconnect battery plug from receptacle; remove all covers from motors and controls. Blow out dust before working on any component.

Motor. Check insulation on armature and field coils; if burned or in bad condition, return to the manufacturer for rewinding or repair. Check terminals, tighten if required, clean, and recoat with insulating compound.

Commutator. Inspect for burning or pitting. Burned commutators cause sparking and excessive heating. Pitted commutators result in short brush life. In either case remove and turn down the commutator sufficiently to clean up and remove high or low spots.

Motor Coupling.   Check for free action and proper lubrication.

Contactors.   Check tips for burning or pitting.   Do not file tips, as this changes the contour and prevents proper wiping action.   Some transfer of metal is normal and need not be removed if no interference with proper seating is apparent.   Check for proper gap and spring tension.   Tips will not seat properly if the springs are weak; the result is arcing and tip burning.   The heat generated by arcing is sufficient to remove the spring temper, thus reducing the contact pressure and causing further arcing.   Check the manufacturer's recommended spring pressures.

Resistors.   Blow dust from resistors. Check insulators for cracks or grounds. Replace as required.   If overheated for too long a time, resistor wires will scale and change in ohmic value.   Replace as required.

Hydraulic Lines.   Examine for leaks, chafing, wear, or cracks; tighten or replace as required.

Hydraulic Pump and Valve.   Check for leakage at fittings and seals.   Tighten fittings; replace seals if required.   Check valve for return to neutral; if not operative, check for dirt under seats or a broken spring.

Operating Brakes.   Keep in proper adjustment at all times.   Examine lines for

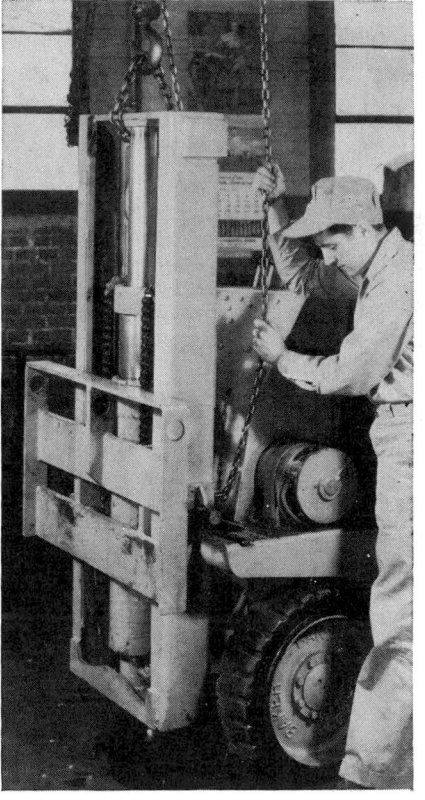

FIG. 1-12. Examine forks for bends and cracks.   *Do not* use heat to straighten bent forks.

FIG. 1-13. Remove mast assembly for annual check.

wear, cracks, oil, or grease.   If lining is glazed, roughen its surface with a wire brush. If the lining glazes constantly, check with the manufacturer for a different lining.

Seat Brake.   Check adjustment for brake drag or failure to hold on a ramp with the seat up.

Seat-interlock Switch.   Check switch operation to be sure that the switch disconnects the electric current as the seat rises.

Battery.   Keep battery clean and dry.   Check each cell weekly for fluid level; add fluid as required.   Make sure that vent plugs lock securely in place and that vents are clear and open.

Inspection Y

Inspection Y covers all work performed in Inspection X with the following additions:

Motor Brushes. Examine brushes for proper wearing and pressure. Poorly seated brushes and insufficient pressure will cause arcing and consequent heating. Brushes should have at least 60 per cent bearing surface and from 28 to 40 oz pressure. The exact pressure will be determined by the manufacturer. Use only those brushes recommended by the manufacturer. Be sure that the pigtails do not restrict free action of the brushes and do not short out against the frame or cover.

Steering-gear Unit. Check unit for tightness and lack of play. Jack up the steering end of the truck; turn full in both directions for freedom or movement. If roughness or sticking is found, dismantle, wash out, and check for worn or broken components.

Steering. With steering end jacked up, check for equal turning in each direction; if not equal, examine the drag link and tie rods for bending or loose or tight adjustment at joints. Wheels should line up parallel without camber or caster.

Wiring. Check for chafed or worn insulation, burning, and loose connections. Proper clamping will prevent chafing and subsequent grounds or shorts. Check for grounds with test light or voltmeter.

Hydraulic-system Oil. Check oil for contamination. Drain and flush system; refill with clean oil if contamination is found.

Inspection Z

In addition to the X and Y inspections slow-wearing parts should be completely checked. This inspection is essentially an overhaul and involves the dismantling of many of the units to permit a thorough visual inspection, repair or replacement of worn parts, and proper adjustment of all units.

Forks. Examine for bending or cracks. *Note:* Forks must be straightened cold, as application of heat will remove the heat treating.

Upright (Mast). Remove from truck; completely dismantle; check all welds on the mast and carriage for cracks. Check chain rollers and carriage rollers for wear or flat spots. Wash all bearings; thoroughly replace if worn or if brinelling appears on the bearing race. Check bronze wear pads; replace as required.

Chains. Clean with kerosene; examine for plate and/or roller wear or breakage. Check for stretching. *Note:* Do not replace sections of worn chain; *always* replace in full-length sections.

Hydraulic Cylinders (Hoist and Tilt). Dismantle and clean with kerosene or solvent. Examine packing glands for wear; replace as required. *Note:* Always replace packing; do not tighten beyond manufacturer's recommendations.

Power Axle. Remove and dismantle. Check bearings, gears, and shafts for wear; replace as required. Check backlash on reassembly; follow manufacturer's directions. *Note:* Replace all oil seals when reassembling.

Motor. Dismantle and thoroughly clean all parts. Inspect terminals for tightness. Check insulation and insulator bushings. Check leads for chafing or loose terminals.

Brush Holders. Inspect for tightness, radial position, angle, and spacing.

Brushes. Check the same as Inspection Y.

Armature. Inspect "growler" for starts and inspect for grounds. Check insulation for fraying, also for charring, which indicates possible breakdown from overheating.

Examine the commutator for discoloration, which indicates possible annealing. Inspect for high or low bars and for looseness. Check the soldered connections on the commutator risers. Check wire banding for tightness; reband if necessary. High-tensile wire must be used, preferably with wire obtained from the manufacturer.

Inspect the armature shaft for straightness and examine the bearings for wear. Replace all parts as required. If the commutator requires truing, take a very light cut on a lathe and undercut the mica separators $\frac{3}{32}$ in. Inspect for dynamic balance.

Field Coils. Inspect connections. Test for insulation shorts, grounds, and open circuits.

Motor Coupling. Clean and inspect for wear. On reassembly make sure that all moving parts are free. Repack with the proper lubricant and reseal as required.

Motor-anchor Screws. Make sure that the proper length screws are used, especially for a saddle-mounted motor; extra-length screws may short out the field coils.

Brush Covers. Before replacing the brush covers make sure that the brush pigtails are not shorting on the frame or cover.

Contactors. Remove and inspect bearings and shafts. Check coils for shorts, opens, or grounds. Replace tips if required. Check the shunt cable; clean, reassemble, adjust proper air gap in magnetic circuit, and test.

Switches. Remove and clean; check snap action, springs, and operation. Replace as required.

Master Accelerator (Controller). Clean; check cam and gear action and dash pots for fluid level. Check for proper spring tension, reassemble, and test.

Trailing Axle (Steering). Remove and dismantle; remove, wash, and inspect wheel bearings. Examine for cracked or broken rollers or brinell marks on bearing race. Check for excessive wear. Replace as required. Repack bearings with proper wheel-bearing grease. Check wheel spindles for wear or cracks. Check thrust bearings. Check kingpins for wear; replace if required.

Reasonable Operating Care

Good housekeeping pays dividends. Not only does it create better working conditions and employee morale but it also contributes to reduced operating costs.

While the following conditions do not come under the heading of lift-truck maintenance, their neglect by management can and does contribute to lift-truck maintenance costs.

Bad Floor Conditions. Smooth floors with ample aisles should be provided wherever possible. Mark aisles clearly and keep clear at all times. Eliminate chips, oil, material in process, or any obstructions that could cause damage to tires or steering. If trucks must be used outside, keep aisles or roads clear of ice or snow; spinning wheels deplete battery life. If steel plates are used to cover floors, make sure that the abutting edges are securely fastened down to prevent tire cutting and abnormal wear.

Overloading. Every lift truck is designed to carry a specific capacity with a calculated safety factor. Any overloading imposes extra strains and stresses, which in turn leads to premature failure of components. Premature failure causes excessive maintenance costs. The time saved in overloading a truck can never be justified, owing to these excessive costs. Common causes of overloading that are usually overlooked are off-center loading and failure to carry the load within the load center as specified. Excessive tire replacement is usually an indication of overloading.

Careless Operation. Much damage can result from careless operation. Ramming loads, hitting curbs, skidding or plugging to a stop contribute to high maintenance costs. Avoid tire slippage with its attendent wear. Accelerate the truck through its various speeds to start, and apply brakes gradually to stop. When descending a ramp, use the dynamic brake. If the truck is not equipped with dynamic brakes, the controller should be placed in neutral and the brakes applied sufficiently to contain the truck at a controllable speed.

Poorly Maintained Skids. Damage to material and equipment can result from poorly maintained skids. Discard skids or platforms that are not firm and do not nest properly. Consult with the pallet and rack manufacturers to determine the best type of equipment to use with your product and application.

Carelessly Stacked Loads. Damage to manufactured goods, raw materials, equipment, and personnel can result from careless or improper stacking. *Never* rack up more weight than the bottom skid or tube can withstand.

Chapter 2

GAS-POWERED INDUSTRIAL TRUCKS

By GLEN R. JOHNSON
Director, Material Handling Development Center
W. A. CROFOOT
Field Service Supervisor
ROBERT BARTLETT
Service Training Instructor
Industrial Truck Division
Clark Equipment Company
Battle Creek, Mich.

Industrial trucks for materials handling are specialized types of equipment purchased by management for the purpose of increasing production, speeding up the flow of materials, reducing nonproductive costs, and providing safer working conditions for the employees. If the equipment is not able to handle the material quickly and efficiently, then production time, material, and manpower will be wasted.

A rigid preventive-maintenance program is a major step in securing from the equipment all the service the manufacturer built into it. If material-handling equipment is to be kept at its highest efficiency and the life of each vehicle is to be prolonged, it is mandatory that preventive maintenance be performed regularly and systematically. If that is done, most major repairs and costly breakdowns will be eliminated.

A preventive-maintenance program properly administered then becomes productive maintenance, since it adds dollars and cents to the over-all profit picture. Productive maintenance for trucks is the process of eliminating the causes of machine failures and breakdowns in order to keep the truck from going out of service.

Productive maintenance encompasses routine inspection of the equipment at regular intervals, preferably at the beginning of each work shift. It also includes cleaning the equipment, complete lubrication, and making minor adjustments at regular specified periods plus keeping records which show all these services performed and the dates on which they were done. Qualified mechanics working under competent supervision are essential to the success of the program.

There are four aspects to the program of using and maintaining industrial-lift-truck equipment:

1. The productive-maintenance program.
2. Hiring and training qualified mechanics.
3. Hiring industrial-truck operators and training them in the care and use of the equipment.
4. Selecting and evaluating the correct equipment.

MANAGEMENT RESPONSIBILITIES

To assure achievement of the desired results, management must first develop the proper attitude toward the program in its own mind and in the minds of the employees. Employees follow the example set by the superintendent and the foremen; therefore, supervision must believe in the program before the workers can be expected to accept it.   Management must:

1. Delegate the authority to administer and carry out the preventive-maintenance program.
2. Provide adequate maintenance facilities and equipment.
3. Control the working conditions of the plant, warehouse, or terminal.
4. Properly train operating and maintenance personnel.
5. Enforce safety.
6. Select initially the correct industrial-truck equipment.

Management must select a maintenance supervisor and then delegate to him complete authority and control over all industrial-truck equipment.   The maintenance supervisor usually reports to the director of material handling or one who has complete charge of the material-handling program.   The maintenance supervisor must have the authority over the industrial-truck operators, their training program, hiring and training qualified mechanics, and maintaining the records necessary to control the program.

Management must provide space and proper equipment for a truck-maintenance department.   Without adequate space and tools, a preventive-maintenance program becomes mediocre.   A well-equipped truck-maintenance department should have adequate cleaning facilities, proper lubrication equipment, tools and gages, hoisting equipment, parts bins, workbenches, and a filing cabinet for safekeeping of parts books, maintenance manuals, and machine records.   Spray-painting equipment and a space for an industrial truck to be used as a loaner are desirable, but not essential.

Management must control the conditions in the truck-operating areas to prevent damage to material or handling equipment or injury to personnel.   If good housekeeping is allowed to disappear, the effects of a good preventive-maintenance program wear off quickly.   If hazardous working conditions are permitted to remain, fatal accidents can easily happen.   The maintenance supervisor must have the cooperation of other departmental heads to ensure that trucks are available for regular maintenance checks at the prearranged time.   Management must take the responsibility for seeing that equipment is released to the maintenance department according to schedule. Frequently an extra machine is purchased and assigned to the maintenance department, usually one for every ten in service.   This machine can be loaned to other departments while their equipment is in for a regular maintenance checkup.

To assure the best possible results, management must assume the responsibility for properly training equipment operators and mechanics.   Personnel may be sent to training schools conducted by equipment manufacturers, or training schools may be established within their own organization.   Most equipment manufacturers provide training manuals for both mechanics and operators and supply instructors to assist in establishing a training program.   A few have full-fledged service schools of several weeks' duration to which equipment users can send their personnel without obligation for a complete schooling in maintenance and repair procedures.   Some provide a traveling service school which visits the larger cities on regular schedule and presents a condensed service-procedure program.

A complete list of general operating and safety instructions will be found elsewhere in this chapter, but following are some of the precautions management must enforce in the interest of safety:

1. Reckless and careless truck operators should be removed from their jobs.
2. Drivers' overhead guards should be mandatory on lift trucks performing high stacking operations.

3. Adequate refueling facilities should be provided, and correct truck refueling procedures should be enforced to prevent fires.
4. Gas-powered trucks should be prohibited from operating long periods of time in unventilated areas to prevent the possibility of carbon monoxide poisoning, or suffocation because of lack of oxygen.
5. The use of heavy machines on weak floors should be prohibited.
6. Improper use of industrial trucks, such as towing railroad freight cars, should be prohibited.
7. The practice of overloading a fork-lift truck should be prohibited. There is danger of overturn, with injury of personnel.
8. Floors should be kept clean and in good condition. A floor which is rutted or cracked is a safety hazard to personnel and subjects an industrial truck to severe shock, causing abnormal wear.

Management must be sure the industrial lift truck purchased has adequate capacity to handle the loads. Overloaded equipment is a hazard to personnel. Its deterioration is accelerated, and subsequent downtime is greater. Industrial trucks should not be purchased on a price basis with the idea of overloading them. Operators should know and observe the rated capacity of the equipment they are driving.

Administration of a Productive-maintenance Program. In a one- or two-truck operation, authority for the maintenance program can be the plant superintendent, a department foreman, or, in special circumstances, the truck operators. However, generally speaking, truck operators should not be permitted or expected to make repairs on their machines. Routine inspection and lubrication can be within their scope of activities.

Frequently, industrial-truck franchised dealers will contract with the user to undertake maintenance and repairs and keep records. This type of service pays dividends to the truck owners who do not wish to go to the expense of assuming the responsibility themselves.

When a fleet, considered to be three or more units, is involved, a maintenance supervisor is required. In the smaller fleets, the responsibility often is placed with a supervisor who also has charge of other rolling stock, such as highway-truck equipment, but as the truck fleets become larger, a maintenance supervisor responsible solely for industrial-truck equipment is a necessity.

The maintenance supervisor should control all the records, the repair shop personnel, maintenance schedules, and truck operators. While he may not have immediate supervision over the truck operators (who report to department foremen), he should have the right to remove a truck operator from his job should he abuse a truck.

The maintenance supervisor should be an important member, sometimes the prime authority, on a committee selecting industrial-truck equipment. He has the complete performance records and is the best informed individual on the relative merits of the various makes of industrial trucks. His opinion should be given priority standing.

Adequate and accurate records are essential in the management of a productive-maintenance program. Elaborate and detailed records are required with large fleets; simpler records with small fleets.

Each organization should develop its own record forms to meet its particular requirements. However, the end result should be an up-to-date, cumulative, operational cost on each piece of equipment and a sum total for the entire fleet. These final figures must be supported by detailed records for purposes of analysis.

Figure 2-1 is an example of a daily summary of the operating cost of a fleet. This form can be maintained by departments to which various machines are assigned, or it can be kept on a plant-wide basis. It should show the machine number; the quantity and cost of fuel consumed, engine oil, and lubrication; the material and labor costs for maintenance or repairs, accidents, and unclassified items. Do not include capital expenditure, such as the cost of adding accessories or an attachment. The same form can be expanded and used as a monthly, quarterly, or annual cost summary for a truck fleet.

On the form shown in Fig. 2-2, the data are kept by individual trucks to show the number, manufacturer's serial number, type, department to which assigned, and foreman's name. For convenience, this form usually is kept on a monthly basis with provisions for showing daily expenditures. The data accumulated can be transferred by sum totals to the form in Fig. 2-1 on a monthly or annual basis.

It is also common practice to maintain a separate form by individual machines showing the annual charges for each cost segment listed on the two forms.

Important data that can be recorded are the number of operating hours by day, week, month, or year or the number of hours at the time of each repair. Several manufacturers provide engine-hour meters on gas-powered trucks to give an accurate

		DAILY OPERATING COST SHEET							
DATE_____		CLARK GASOLINE POWERED INDUSTRIAL TRUCK					DEPARTMENT_____		
Date	Mach. No.	Gasoline Quant. Cost.	Engine Oil Quant. Cost.	Grease & Lub. Quant. Cost.	Maintenance Matl. Labor	Accidents Matl. Labor	Misc. Item Cost.	Total Costs	Remarks

FIG. 2-1. Form for recording costs daily.

	MONTHLY OPERATING COST SHEET											Month_____ 19___	
Truck No._____ Serial No._____ Type_____	GASOLINE POWERED CLARK INDUSTRIAL TRUCKS											Dept._____ Foreman_____	
DATE	Maintenance Parts Labor		Accident Parts Labor		Gasoline Quant. Cost.		Motor Oil Quant. Cost.		Grease & Lub. Quant. Cost.		Misc. Item Cost.	Labor	Total Costs
1													
2													
3													
4													
5													
28													
29													
30													
31													
Total													

FIG. 2-2. Form for recording costs monthly.

recording of the operating hours. A few manufacturers have changed their warranty provisions to include not only a calendar period of time but also operating hours, whichever occurs first. Also, actual operating hours give a definite cost-per-hour figure rather than a cost figure governed by the number of hours in a work shift.

Once in a while it is desirable to maintain an analysis of repair and maintenance costs. A form for listing these data is illustrated in Fig. 2-3. The record for one truck is kept on each card. It gives a running analysis showing frequency of occurrence of the items that go to make up the operational cost. The information on this form is taken from the shop order and the daily operating cost sheets. There are provisions to show the date, the shop order number, the parts cost, and the various components of an industrial truck along with the engine hour reading and the cause for the repair. A breakdown of the total parts cost would be made under the appropriate column heading. Under the column labeled Cause would be shown such terms as Driver, Operation, Routine Repair, so the cause of repairs can be pinpointed and corrective action taken if necessary. This record form is also valuable to the maintenance supervisor in his report to management when recommending purchase of industrial-truck equipment.

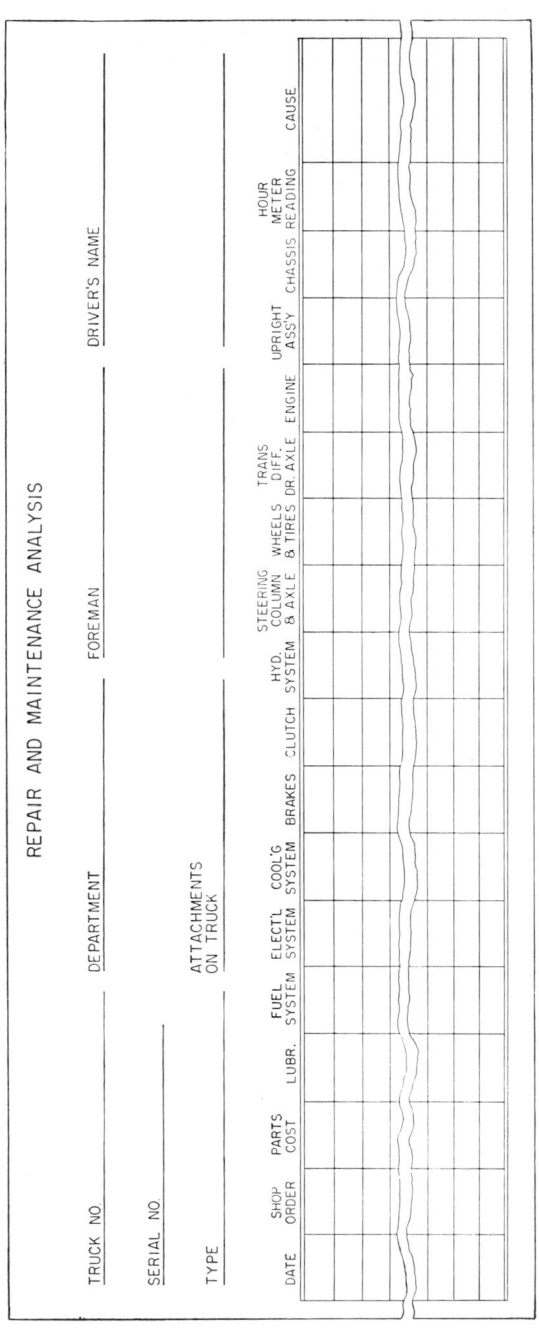

FIG. 2-3. This record facilitates cost analysis.

CLARK EQUIPMENT COMPANY, SERVICE DIVISION

INSPECTION AND SERVICE ORDER
GAS AND ELECTRIC FORK TRUCKS AND TOWING TRACTORS

DRIVE AXLE AND DIFFERENTIAL	8	40	300	1000
Clean and Repack Gears and Bearings				
Wheel Ends (Hypoid Axles)				
Check Oil Level			■	
Drain and Refill			■	■
Drive Axle Air Vent				

BRAKES				
Service Brakes	■			
Seat Brake	○			
Master Cylinder and Lines		■		
Check Shoes Linings and Connections				
Brake A ment				
Check Hand Brake or Brake Lock	■			
Power Brakes (Hydrovac & Air Cleaner)			✕	

CLUTCH OR DYNATORK DRIVE				
Throwout Bearing Grease Cup	✕			
Clutch Pedal Adjustment		✕		
DYNATORK DRIVE: CLEAN HOUSING SCREENS BRUSHES & COLLECTOR RINGS		✕		

COOLING SYSTEM				
Radiator, Water Level & Anti-Freeze	✕			
Examine Core, Hoses, Check for Leaks		✕		
Water Pump, Check Lube and Mounting			✕	
Fan and Fan Belt Tension		✕		

ELECTRICAL SYSTEM				
WATER LEVEL, HYDROMETER READING CABLES, RECEPTICLE AND TERMINALS	○			
WATER LEVEL, HYDROMETER READING CABLES, AND TERMINALS		✕		
Pump and Drive Motor Brushes			○	
PUMP AND DRIVE MOTOR: INSPECT, CLEAN AND REPACK OR REPLACE BEARINGS				○
Gauges: Ammeter and Etc.	■			
Contactor Panel, Clean & Adjust Points		○		
Generator Lubrication		✕		
Starting Motor Lubrication			✕	
Gen. and Start. Motor. Check Brushes			✕	
Lubricate Distributor		✕		
DISTRIBUTOR: ADJUST POINTS INSPECT: ROTOR, CAP & CONDENSER			✕	
Ignition Timing			✕	
Spark Plugs: Check Gap & Clean			✕	

ENGINE				
Check Crankcase Level	✕			
Drain Oil & Refill, Check Oil Filter		✕		
Valve Tappets, Inspect & Adjust			✕	
Engine Compression			✕	
Cylinder Head Nuts, Gasket & Leaks			✕	
Manifold, Nuts, Gaskets & Leaks			✕	
Muffler, Mounting, Condition			✕	
Governor, Speed & Surge			✕	

FUEL SYSTEM	8	40	300	1000
Carburetor Adjustment			✕	
Air Cleaner	■			
Fuel Pump			✕	
Fuel Supply	■			
Fuel Filler Cap: Clean Screen		✕		
Check Fuel Oil Filters (Diesel Only)		✕		

HYDRAULIC SYSTEM (NOT TOWING TRACTORS)				
Operation Tilt & Lift: Oil Level				
Check Pump, Valve & Tank				
Clean Tank Filler Cap				
Lift Chain Adjustment				
Lift Brackets and Slides			■	
Check Tilt & Lift Cylinder Drift				
TILT CYLINDER: CHECK GLANDS, BOOTS, MOUNTING PINS				
Lift Cylinder, Packing Boots & Vent				
Inner Slides (Lubricate)				
Inspect Lift Forks				■

STEERING SYSTEM				
Wheel Bearings				
Axle Grease Fittings				
Steering Gear, Lube & Mounting				
Drag Link Adjustment				
Check Turning Radius				
Inspect Tie Rod Ends				
Inspect Pivot Pins & Spindles				
Power Steering: Pump & Valve			✕	
Power Steering Booster			✕	

TRANSMISSION				
Hydratork: Check Oil Level				
Hydratork: Drain and Refill			✕	
Hydratork: Check Oil Pressure			✕	
Standard: Drain & Refill			✕	
Standard: Check Level		✕		
Drop Gear Case, Check Level			✕	

MISCELLANEOUS				
Check Electrical Connections and Tips		○		
Check Tires	■			
Lights: Head and Stop	■			
Lubricate All Grease Fittings	■			
Miscellaneous Linkage & Clevis	■			
Steam Clean Machine	■			
Inspect Spring Shackles U Bolts & Clips	■			
Tighten All Bolts, Nuts & Capscrews	■			
Inspect U Joints			✕	
CHECK FLUID COUPLING (GAS TOWING TRACTORS ONLY)			✕	

DATE _____ MACHINE SERIAL NO._____

DRIVER _____

SERVICEMAN _____

FOREMAN _____

CODE: All Machines ■ Gas Models ✕ Electric Models ○

Time Intervals For Inspection Are Either _____ | 8 | 40 | 300 | 1000

REMARKS _____

372-Z

FIG. 2-4. A form that is used for both history and upkeep.

Figure 2-4 is a composite record form of an inspection and service order check sheet. This form is arranged to show the checks and adjustments to be made at the time intervals of 8, 40, 300, and 1,000 operating hours. Some companies use a separate form for each time-interval inspection. Regardless of the record form make-up, it is recommended that such a system be used for scheduling maintenance work on individual trucks. It also serves as a reminder to make sure that each item is inspected and none overlooked.

Figure 2-5 frequently is used with large truck fleets. It is a service order which the driver fills out with check marks to show the maintenance department where he believes adjustments or repairs are necessary. With this order in hand, the maintenance department can go over each item checked; make repairs or replacement, if necessary; list the part numbers, quantity, and description; and comment as to whether or not further corrective action is necessary. The information accumulated on the driver's service order can then be transferred to the repair and maintenance analysis record shown in Fig. 2-3 in the daily operating cost summary.

Some companies use operational cost figures to determine time for equipment replacement. They keep the running record of cost per operating hour on each truck. As long as this cost figure remains relatively steady, the truck is kept in the fleet. If the cost per hour shows a sudden increase, the cause is investigated. If the cost figure continues to increase month by month over a 6-month period with no decrease in that period of time, then the piece of equipment is scheduled for replacement.

Maintenance Procedures. It is desirable for each company to work out the details of a productive-maintenance system to meet best its own conditions and problems. Each make and type of industrial truck has individual characteristics which determine to a great extent the routine maintenance procedure required. It is wise to follow as closely as possible the maintenance procedure recommended by the manufacturer in his charts and service manuals, but sometimes the details of the manufacturer's recommendations must be modified in order to establish an adequate system to meet local needs. The important thing is to establish a definite program, stress the importance of an effective system, and record each maintenance or repair activity to ensure continuous and regular performance as well as information concerning the costs involved.

A strict program of cleaning the equipment, making periodic checks, lubricating, and changing oil should be enforced. A major portion of a preventive-maintenance program is visual work, making inspection checks and minor adjustments. It has been repeatedly demonstrated that the job is half done if the equipment is clean. A mechanic's time is reduced 50 per cent on any repair job on a clean machine as compared with a dirty one. It has been demonstrated that mechanics can make the 40-hr inspection check and lubrication in 20 per cent less time on a clean machine. Defects show up more easily, and lubrication fittings are not overlooked. Frequently a dirty machine will hide cracks in castings or welds, and this weakness is not discovered until an unexpected failure occurs.

A weak alkaline solution applied under steam pressure is a good method for cleaning industrial trucks. There are also several cleaning compounds which can be mixed with water for the same purpose.

After cleaning, a thorough inspection check should be made according to the manufacturer's recommendations. Minor adjustments should be made at the same time as the inspection. It is common experience that no more than 1 hr per truck per week should be required to thoroughly clean, inspect, and lubricate.

After the cleaning and inspection procedures are finished, then the equipment should be lubricated according to the chart furnished by the manufacturer of the truck. It is highly desirable to display these charts in a prominent location for ready reference. Follow the recommendations of the manufacturer. Often the wrong grease or oil can cause rapid or premature failure of a working part.

To keep the engine trouble free, change the oil regularly. Every 40 to 50 hr of operation is the correct frequency provided the truck has good maintenance, the engine oil is of high quality, the oil filters are changed regularly, and the truck works on a steady operation. If any of these factors is not present, then the engine oil should be changed more often. Engine oil becomes contaminated and corrosive by reason of:

1. Dirt drawn in through the crankcase system or carburetor.
2. Unburned fuel, particularly as a result of choking in cold weather starts.

DRIVER SERVICE ORDER

MACHINE SERIAL NO.

DEPT.

DATE

DRIVER

HOUR METER READING

CONDITION GOOD

NEEDS ATTENTION

INSPECTION TO BE PERFORMED

8 40

300 1000

SERVICEMAN

FOREMAN

USE REVERSE SIDE TO LIST PARTS USED AND FOR REMARKS

REMARKS

PART NUMBER | QTY. | DESCRIPTION

G&E BATTERY
E CONTACTOR POINTS
G&E BRAKE LOCK
G HAND BRAKE
E SEAT BRAKE
G&E SERVICE BRAKES
G&E HYDRAULIC VALVE
G&E HYDRAULIC PUMP
E PUMP MOTOR
G&E HYDRAULIC OIL
G&E LIFT
G&E TILT
G&E UPRIGHT
G GOVERNOR

G ENGINE
G&E TRANSMISSION
G CLUTCH
G&E DYNATORK
G&E STEERING
G CARBURETOR
E RADIATOR
E DRIVE MOTOR
G&E FORWARD AND REVERSE SWITCH
G&E LIFT CHAINS
G&E LIGHTS
G&E HORN
G FUEL
G&E STEAM CLEAN MACHINE

G ANTI-FREEZE
G GAUGES
G&E TIRES
G&E LUBRICATION
G ENGINE OIL
G AIR CLEANER
G FAN BELT
G MUFFLER
G OIL FILTER

OTHER

* CHECK THESE ITEMS EACH TIME TRUCK IS SERVICED   G=GAS TRUCKS.   E=ELECTRIC TRUCKS.   G&E=BOTH GAS AND ELECTRIC TRUCKS.

FIG. 2-5. Driver's report, generally used with large fleets.

3. Water vapor from combustion gases bypassing pistons into the crankcase and from air drawn through the crankcase ventilating system.
4. Carbon from combustion, especially during idling or because the carburetor or ignition system is out of adjustment.
5. Lead compounds from burning gasoline sometimes causing the oil to become gray or brown.
6. Products of oil oxidation that may form gummy or sticky deposits of varnish or sludge which tend to clog oil lines and screens.
7. Metal particles from engine surfaces. Because of these contaminants, some of which the filter cannot eliminate, it is more economical to replace the oil and oil filters at regular intervals.

Repair is another phase of the well-run productive-maintenance program. Even in the best-regulated maintenance program, repairs are necessary because of worn parts

Table 2-1. Primary Tool Set

Quantity	Size, in.	Type
1	$7/16$	Wrench combination box—open end
1	$1/2$	Wrench combination box—open end
1	$9/16$	Wrench combination box—open end
1	$5/8$	Wrench combination box—open end
1	$11/16$	Wrench combination box—open end
1	$3/4$	Wrench combination box—open end
1	8	Wrench adjustable
1		Wrench universal drain plug
1	6	Pliers
1	$7\frac{1}{2}$	Pliers, diagonal
1	$13/16$	Socket, spark plugs
1	$5/16$ by 6	Punch drift
1	$1/2$	Hammer, ball peen
1	6	Screwdriver
1	10	Screwdriver

and damage caused by accidents. Repairs should be performed only upon the authority of the maintenance supervisor when he has been given the responsibility by management. Sometimes repairs could total so much that it would be more economical to purchase new equipment, and only the maintenance supervisor can advise management of this situation.

It is essential to have a clear understanding of terms, especially when contracting with an outside concern for maintenance work.

Tune-up means to perform necessary adjustments to a truck already in good repair but which does not operate smoothly.

Repair means the replacement of a worn or broken part with an identical new part. Repairing is confined to the process of replacing parts.

Overhaul means to put in top-operating condition all the parts visibly needing attention. It does not necessarily mean to disassemble and inspect a component assembly.

Rebuild means the complete disassembly of the entire machine or a major assembly into its basic component parts and replacement of all necessary parts with new material and reassembling. A rebuilt truck or assembly is essentially a remanufactured unit and should carry a warranty provision equal to that of the original manufacturer.

When contracting with outside concerns, be sure to have a firm understanding of exactly what work is to be performed and how much latitude will be given the repair shop to follow its own judgment.

Table 2-2. Secondary Tool Set

Quantity	Size	Type
1 set	$\frac{3}{8}$–1$\frac{1}{2}$ by $\frac{1}{16}$ in.	Wrench, combination open-box end
1 set		Wrench, ignition kit
1	14 in.	Wrench, pipe
1	18 in.	Wrench, pipe
1 set		Wrenches, hollow-head setscrew
1 each	$\frac{9}{16}$, $\frac{5}{8}$, 1$\frac{1}{16}$, $\frac{3}{4}$, 1$\frac{5}{16}$, 1 in.	Wrenches, tappets
1	0–200	Wrench, torque
1 set	$\frac{1}{4}$–$\frac{3}{4}$ by $\frac{1}{16}$ in.	Sockets, $\frac{3}{8}$ in. drive—complete with ratchet speed handle and with 2, 4, 6, 8 in. extensions
1 set	$\frac{7}{16}$–1$\frac{1}{4}$ by $\frac{1}{16}$ in.	Sockets, $\frac{1}{2}$ in. drive—complete with ratchet 18 in. flexible handle and extensions to 12 in.
1	6 in.	Pliers, standard
1	10 in.	Pliers, water pump
1	6 in.	Pliers, diagonal
1	9 in.	Pliers, vise grips
1	6 in.	Pliers, snap ring
1	14 in.	Tongs, brake spring
2	16 in.	Pry bar, lady slipper
1	$\frac{5}{16}$ by 6 in.	Punch, drift
1	$\frac{3}{8}$ by 8 in.	Punch, drift
1	$\frac{5}{8}$ by 11 in.	Punch, drift
1 each	$\frac{1}{4}$, $\frac{5}{16}$, $\frac{3}{8}$, $\frac{7}{16}$, $\frac{1}{2}$, $\frac{9}{16}$, $\frac{5}{8}$ in.	Punch, gasket
1	$\frac{1}{2}$ by 6$\frac{1}{2}$ in.	Punch, prick
1	$\frac{5}{16}$ by 5 in.	Chisel
1	$\frac{1}{2}$ by 6$\frac{1}{2}$ in.	Chisel
1	$\frac{5}{8}$ by 7$\frac{1}{2}$ in.	Chisel
1	$\frac{3}{4}$ by 9 in.	Chisel
1	$\frac{5}{16}$ by 5$\frac{1}{2}$ in.	Chisel, cape
1	$\frac{1}{2}$ in.	Hammer, ball peen
1	1$\frac{1}{2}$ in.	Hammer, ball peen
1	1$\frac{3}{8}$ in., 17 oz	Hammer, rawhide
1 set	6$\frac{1}{4}$, 7$\frac{1}{2}$, 9$\frac{1}{2}$ in.	Puller, universal gear and bearing
1 set		Pilot, shaft universal clutch
1	9 by 11 in.	Valve lifter
1	2$\frac{1}{2}$ by 5 in.	Compresser, piston ring
1	2$\frac{1}{2}$–4$\frac{1}{2}$ in.	Ring groove tool
1 set		Carburetor universal tool kit
1	2$\frac{3}{16}$–3$\frac{3}{16}$ in.	Reamer, cylinder ridge
1 set	0.001–0.025 in.	Gage, tappet, feeler, and ignition
1		Gage, spark plug
1	Standard	Gage, vacuum
1	Standard	Gage, compression
1	0–2,000 psi	Gage, hydraulic pressure (Schrader 8318 or equal)
1	12 in.	Hack saw
1 set	4, 6, 8, 10 in.	Screwdrivers
1 each	Nos. 2–3	Screwdriver, Phillips
1 set	$\frac{5}{16}$–1$\frac{1}{16}$ in.	Screwdriver, offset
1	6 in.	Hone, ignition
1	Standard	Grinder, valve
1	1 by 10 in.	Scrapper, flexible wire carbon
1	14 in.	Brush, hand wire
1	0–500 rpm	Tachometer electric (Sun model 4 or equal)
1	20$\frac{1}{2}$ by 9$\frac{1}{4}$ by 10$\frac{1}{4}$ in.	Box tool
1	$\frac{1}{8}$, $\frac{3}{16}$, $\frac{1}{4}$, $\frac{5}{16}$, $\frac{3}{8}$, $\frac{1}{2}$1 in. OD	Cutter, tube
1		Flaring tool, tube
1		Creeper

HIRING AND TRAINING MECHANICS

Select a mechanic with a basic practical experience of at least 2 or 3 years. The applicant should be one who is ambitious and willing to spend time studying maintenance manuals, bulletins, etc., to learn about the servicing of the equipment. He should be interested enough in his job to study about new developments in engines, power transmission, and gear trains and keep himself current on industrial-truck progress.

Table 2-3. Additions to Tools Listed in Tables 2-1 and 2-2

Quantity	Type
1	Reboring bar, Van Norman or equal, portable $2\frac{1}{2}$–4 in.
1	Refacer, valve, wet-sioux or its equal
1	Grinder with wire brush, pedestal type
1	Press, hydraulic, 75 ton or more
1	Lathe, South Bend or equal, 13-in. swing, 6-ft bed, mounted on cabinet with drawers, all accessories
1	Gage, volts, amperes, Sun model CB-10 or equal
1	Diagnosis test unit, Sun model UDT or equal
1	Generator and regulator test unit, Sun or equal
1	Charger, low ampere, 6 batteries capacity
1	Drill press, floor model, high-speed, slow-speed attachment, No. 2 taper spindle, Jacobs chuck, vise attachment.
1	Drill motor, $\frac{3}{8}$ in. slow speed
1 set	Drills, high speed, $\frac{1}{16}$-in.–$\frac{1}{2}$-in. by $\frac{1}{64}$-in. steps
1 set	Drills, high speed No. 2 shank, $\frac{1}{2}$-in. –1-in. by $\frac{1}{64}$-in. steps
1 set	Drills, high speed, Nos. 0–60
1	Thread chaser, or renew, 8 thread sizes 11, 12, 13, 14, 16, 18, 20, and 24
1 set	Taps, spark plug, 18, 14, 10 mm
1 set	Remover, studs, $\frac{5}{16}$, $\frac{3}{8}$, $\frac{7}{16}$, $\frac{1}{2}$, $\frac{9}{16}$, $\frac{5}{8}$, $\frac{3}{4}$ in.
1 set	Reamer, expansion, spiral flute, pilot type, sizes $\frac{1}{4}$–$1\frac{1}{16}$ in., (15 reamers)
1	Welder, acetylene and oxygen torch with all tips, cutting attachments, glasses, lights, welding rods
1	Jack, hydraulic 6,000 lb movable
1	Chain hoist, overhead and car, 2,000-lb capacity
1	Washer, power, with all attachments and compounds
1	Lubrication power equipment with air hoses, greases, motor oils, drain receptacles
1	Stand, motor test
1	Stand, rebuilding, metal 4 by 4 ft by 30 in. high on wheels
2	Vises, 4-in. jaws, swivel base
1	Can, gasoline, 5-gal, fireproof
1	Carburetor solvent, 5 gal
1	Rack, air dispenser
4	Lamps, extension cords
1 set	Micrometers, 1–6 in. (outside and inside)

There are several means of adding to his basic fundamental knowledge. One has been mentioned—studying manuals and bulletins. He can also attend service schools conducted by manufacturers at their home plants or their mobile training schools which visit the metropolitan centers from time to time. For a complete indoctrination in truck-maintenance techniques, it is highly recommended and well worth the investment to send a mechanic to the manufacturer's service school.

EQUIPPING AN INDUSTRIAL-TRUCK MAINTENANCE SHOP

Adequate space for a truck-maintenance shop and a good set of tools are elements essential to the success of any company-sponsored productive-maintenance program. The primary tool set, Table 2-1, for one mechanic permits him to make minor adjustments and repairs. The secondary set, Table 2-2, permits him to perform overhaul jobs also, and the third list, Table 2-3, in addition to the primary and secondary tool kits, would equip a shop and enable it to handle a complete rebuilding program.

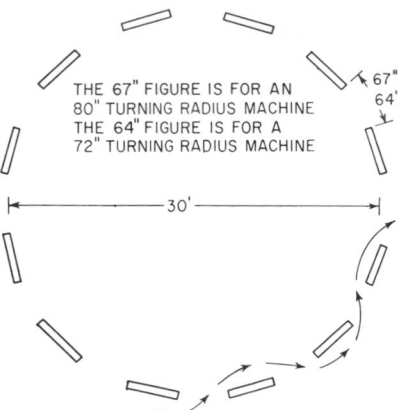

FIG. 2-6. Close operating is essential training. Stand pallets on side. Have students pick up pallets they tip over. The most training is obtained in the short time allowed by having students learn to turn in and out of pallets working around the circle. Three machines can be operated safely at the same time in this course provided they are driven slowly.

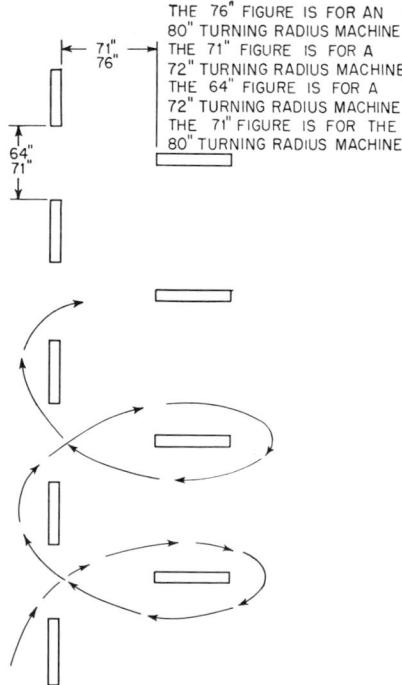

FIG. 2-7. Have students operate as close to pallets as possible. Stand pallets on their sides. Have students pick up pallets they knock over. Few pallets should be overturned by any one student, as this indicates they are operating too fast. Teach them to be sure of every move. If they learn correctly, they need not learn twice. Where possible, insist on 90° turns.

THE 76" FIGURE IS FOR AN
80" TURNING RADIUS MACHINE
THE 71" FIGURE IS FOR A
72" TURNING RADIUS MACHINE

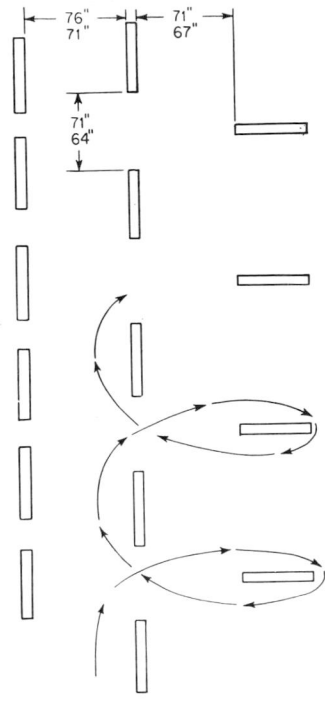

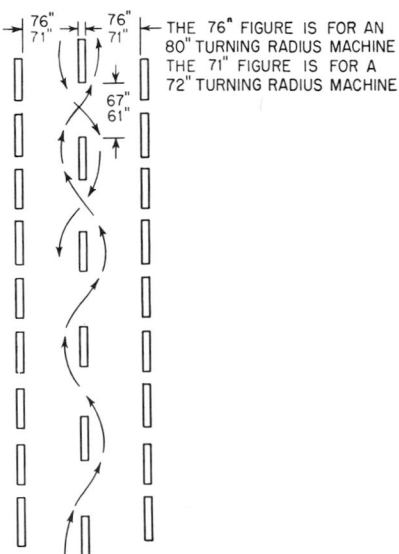

THE 76" FIGURE IS FOR AN
80" TURNING RADIUS MACHINE
THE 71" FIGURE IS FOR A
72" TURNING RADIUS MACHINE

Fig. 2-8. Pallets are to stand on their sides. Students should pick up pallets they knock over. Operators should practice on course with all available makes of lifts. Operators are to make 90° turns where possible. Operate trucks forward and backward. Discourage all signs of speed. Insist on accuracy, and operate trucks close to the pallets.

Fig. 2-9. The load should generally be pulled in this course. Train operators on all makes of fork trucks available. Encourage accuracy in operation. Pallets that are moved or knocked over must be accurately replaced. Close operating is essential training.

HIRING AND TRAINING INDUSTRIAL-TRUCK OPERATORS

All too frequently little consideration is given to the selection and training of the operator who is going to run the industrial-truck equipment. It is unthinkable in well-run manufacturing operations to hire inexperienced men to operate expensive machine tools, yet this is the practice frequently followed when selecting industrial-truck operators. Perhaps the attitude prevails that since an industrial truck operates like an automobile, anyone can drive it properly. This is far from the truth. An industrial truck is a production tool; it is no better than the man who operates it.

The question frequently arises, "How big do you have to be before an operator-training program is needed?" If a company owns one industrial truck, then it is large enough to have a trained operator. One truck in a small company can cause bodily injury, damage to materials, and unnecessary repair expense just as easily as one truck in the big company.

Applicants should be well adjusted, mature, and dependable. They must be indoctrinated with the purpose and importance of their jobs and be given a sense of job security.

After the applicants have been carefully screened, they should be given a physical examination, including checks for vision, field of vision, steadiness, reaction time, and distance judgment.

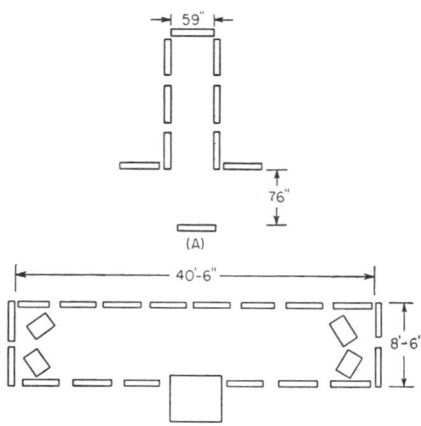

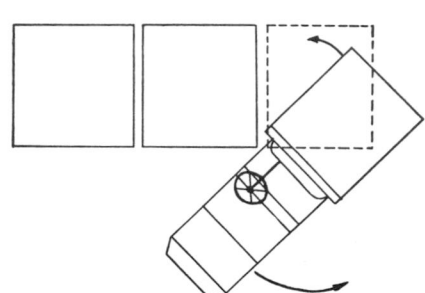

FIG. 2-10. (*A*) This part of the lesson can be properly executed only by making 90° turns. Instruct students as to proper point at which to pivot. Use all available makes of trucks. Operate forward and backward. (*B*) Operators must learn to enter and leave simulated boxcar without moving car plate. They must learn to pick loaded pallets from both ends of car. There should be no unnecessary movements of the truck. Discourage all indications of speed and recklessness.

FIG. 2-11. Operator must learn to set loaded pallets close together. Use two loaded pallets for instruction, and have operators alternate by placing loaded pallet first to the right of stationary pallet and then to left. Operator must approach stationary pallet at a slight angle just clearing edge with moving pallet. When moving pallet almost reaches line of stationary pallet, turn the steering mechanism hard over, bringing the moving pallet in swinging motion, in line with and against stationary pallet. This method is used in order to prevent edges of materials from catching as moving pallet is brought into position. Moving pallet must clear floor not more than 2 in. during this operation. The reverse procedure is used in removing loaded pallets.

The next step is to give them a formal training program consisting of lectures and tests, both written and operational. A well-rounded training course would include the following:

1. Lectures on driving techniques, including the types of hazards encountered and ways to avoid them.
2. Conference periods devoted to a discussion of lectures, quizzes, and the applicant's experiences.
3. Written tests.
4. Operational tests driving industrial trucks over obstacle courses.
5. Operational driving problems consisting of situations staged to represent actual driving conditions. The purpose is to present the trainee with potentially hazardous situations which he is required to solve.
6. Verbal coaching given to the trainee during driving sessions.
7. Printed handout sheets stressing safety and operation techniques.

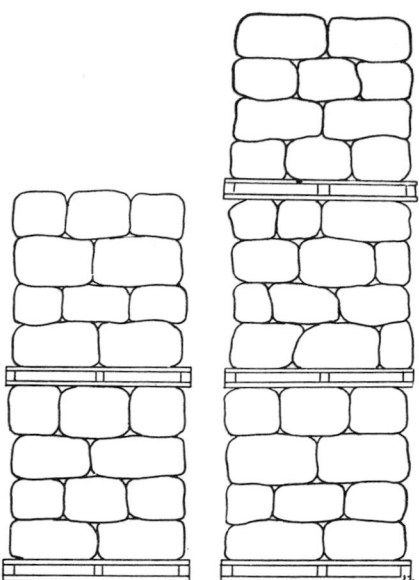

FIG. 2-12. Fork truck must be stopped before pallet is lifted for stacking. Load must be lowered before fork truck is moved, except for clearance space for lowering pallet. Care must be exercised in removing upper pallets in that supplies on lower pallet are not dragged off. Fork truck must not be suddenly moved while load is in the air. Insist on neatness and caution to prevent damage and uneven stacks. Proper stacking means utilization of space.

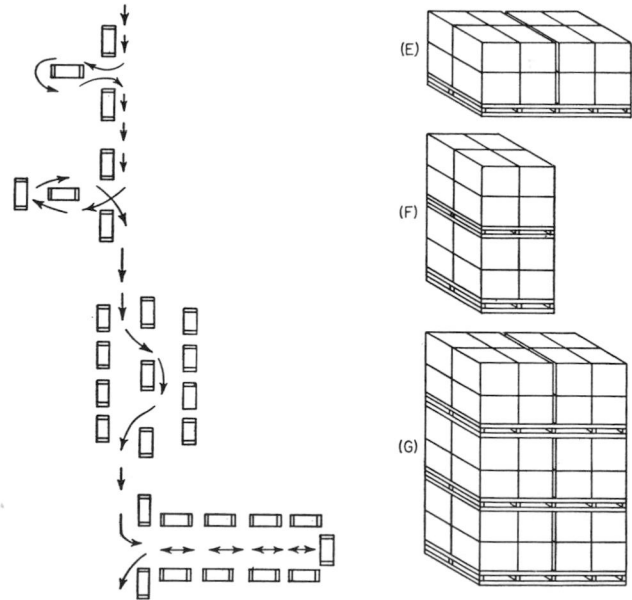

FIG. 2-13. Test drivers on fork trucks on which they had the least amount of training. Watch for signs of recklessness. This obstacle test course is a review of former lessons and should be executed as before. Operator should cover course in about 20 min. Use loaded pallets on tests *E*, *F*, and *G*. Written test should be given to students during the time they are not operating on obstacle course. In test *G*, operator must remove and replace upper pallet on left stack without disturbing upper pallet on the adjacent side.

Figures 2-6 to 2-16, inclusive, show sample obstacle courses, operational problems, and written tests which can be used as a nucleus for building an operators' training program. Figure 2-17 gives the answers to the written tests. Figure 2-18 is a test score card for the course. Figure 2-19 is a check chart for daily use in preventive maintenance.

Obstacle Course
Fork Truck Test Score Card

Name: _____ Dept: _____ Experience: _____
Type truck: _____

Test 1—10%: Deduct _____
  a. Pallets displaced:
    Forward   ( ) @ 0.5 _____
    Reverse   ( ) @ 0.5 _____
Test 2—16%:
  a. Pallets out of line   ( ) @ 2.0 _____
  b. Excess backing, etc.   ( ) 2.0 _____
Test 3—14%:
  a. Pallets displaced   ( ) 01.0 _____
  b. Encounters difficulty   ( ) 4.0 _____
Test 4—10%:
  a. Pallets displaced:
    Forward   ( ) 02.0 _____
    Reverse   ( ) 02.0 _____
Test 5—10%:
  a. Pallets displaced   ( ) @ 2.0 _____
  b. Encounters difficulty   ( ) 4.0 _____
Test 6—20%:
  a. Improper approach   ( ) @ 0.5 _____
  b. Improper leaving   ( ) @ 0.5 _____
  c. Quality of tiering   ( ) 10.0 _____
  d. Cases lost   ( ) 2.0 _____
  e. Improper approach to place pallet   ( ) 2.0 _____
  f. Improper direction to remove pallet   ( ) 2.0 _____
General 7—20%:
  a. Poor starting technique   ( ) 1.0
  b. Poor driving position   ( ) 1.0
  c. Rides pedals   ( ) 2.0 _____
  d. Stalls engine   ( ) 1.0 _____
  e. Clashes gears, reverses controls for brake   ( ) 2.0 _____
  f. Races engine   ( ) 1.0 _____
  g. Too (fast-slow) operation   ( ) 4.0
  h. Careless operation   ( ) 4.0
  i. Inefficient operation   ( ) 4.0 _____

Total deductions _____
Grade _____

Below 65%, Not Passing
65–75%, Fair
75–85%, Good
85–95%, Very Good
95–100%, Excellent

FIG. 2-14. Score card, used after obstacle-course instruction.

The time required for the complete training program will vary with the experience of the driver. On the average, 16 hr total time in classroom and operating instruction will be sufficient for operators who have already had some experience. Inexperienced trainees should receive at least 32 hr of instruction. In either case it is much better to have the training sessions run consecutively on a full-day schedule rather than space the program over several weeks.

Some companies have found that it pays dividends to issue drivers' licenses to qualified industrial-truck operators. The license shows the type of equipment the operator is qualified to drive, and frequently some identification with a colored coding is posted in a conspicuous place on the truck to show that the driver is qualified to operate that particular piece of equipment.

Some companies have also found it to their best interests to post in a conspicuous place on the equipment its original capital cost. If the operator knows the amount of money invested in the equipment he operates, he seems to give it better care.

Fork Truck Operator's Questionnaire 1

Date_____

1. If an operator cannot start his truck immediately, he should   10%
   a. Fix it himself.
   b. Call the mechanic.
   c. Report the trouble.
2. If mechanical deficiency develops, he should   10%
   a. Fix it himself.
   b. Keep on driving.
   c. Report the trouble.
3. Forks on an empty parked truck must always be   10%
   a. Two inches from the floor.
   b. Four inches from the floor.
   c. On the floor.
4. Forks on a moving truck must always be   8%
   a. Two inches from the floor.
   b. Four inches from the floor.
   c. Reasonably low yet high enough to miss any floor obstruction.
5. Anyone may ride the forks of a fork truck or hitch a ride in any manner   8%
   a. If absolutely necessary.
   b. Absolutely in no case.
6. Fork trucks may be driven with the forks elevated above 2 in. from floor   8%
   a. To avoid wear on hydraulic system.
   b. Only to avoid hitting obstructions.
   c. Never in any case.
7. Operators will drive their trucks   8%
   a. Two truck lengths behind other vehicles.
   b. Three truck lengths behind other vehicles.
8. When tractor-trailer train is used, it shall never be made up of more than   5%
   a. Two trailers.
   b. Four trailers.
   c. Eight trailers.
9. Riding on tractor-trailer train is prohibited unless in rare instances when instructed to do so by the foreman. When passengers do ride, they will ride   5%
   a. In the first trailer-truck.
   b. In the center tailer-truck.
   c. In the last trailer-truck.
10. Explain what procedure you would follow if you were to leave the seat of your fork
    truck   5%
11. Explain what you will do when approaching to cross an aisle.   8%
12. In case of an accident, what procedure do you follow?   10%

Fig. 2-15. Written test for operators.

General Operating and Safety Suggestions for an Industrial Truck. There are many rules and regulations written, published, and made into motion pictures which govern the operation of industrial trucks. Following are 28 of the most important regulations which should be observed by industrial-truck operators:

1. Only qualified operators should be permitted to operate trucks.
2. No one should operate a truck other than the person to whom it is assigned.
3. Forks on moving trucks should be within 2 in. of the floor.
4. Forks on parked truck should be flat on the floor. Machine should be parked outside the working area, off the aisle, with levers in neutral positions, ignition switch off, parking brake set.

5. The operator should face or look in the direction in which he is traveling.
6. When a load obstructs the driver's vision, he should drive in reverse.
7. The truck or tow tractor should not be left unattended with the engine running.
8. Do not use reverse as a brake.
9. Do not drive with wet or greasy hands.
10. Slow down for wet or greasy floors.
11. Avoid bumping into objects, especially when backing.
12. Refuse to move unsafe loads, and do not overload the machine.
13. Check gas, oil, and water at the beginning of each shift.
14. Do not ride the clutch or inching control pedal or pump the foot accelerator when truck is in motion.

Fork Truck Operator's Questionnaire 2

	True	False	True-or-false questions
6%	☐	☐	1. Fork truck operators shall wipe off their machines when the machine is not operating sometime during their working shift.
6%	☐	☐	2. Operators will check gas, oil, and water at the beginning of each shift.
6%	☐	☐	3. Operators will not have to watch for pedestrians and workers while in motion.
6%	☐	☐	4. Trucks will not be left unattended with the engine running.
6%	☐	☐	5. Operators must fix immediately any mechanical deficiency.
6%	☐	☐	6. Operators will use "reverse" to stop their machine rather than the brake.
5%	☐	☐	7. The forks may be used to bump a loaded pallet into position.
6%	☐	☐	8. Fork trucks shall be driven in "reverse" at all times except when stacking, to remove a stack, or to enter a boxcar.
6%	☐	☐	9. Bent or damaged dock plates must never be used.
6%	☐	☐	10. Travel in the left-hand side of an aisle whenever possible.
6%	☐	☐	11. Operator must face in the direction in which his machine is traveling.
5%	☐	☐	12. Fork truck should never be driven into a boxcar or semitrailer to get material.
6%	☐	☐	13. It is not permissible for an operator to let his left foot ride the clutch or inching pedal.
6%	☐	☐	14. Operator should pump the foot accelerator while the truck is in motion.
6%	☐	☐	15. Operator should elevate his load while in motion to the stack.
6%	☐	☐	16. Fork trucks should be operated at "full" speed at all times.
6%	☐	☐	17. It is permissible to start, turn, or stop a fork truck suddenly.
____ %	Total		

FIG. 2-16. True-or-false written test for operators.

---

15. If an operator cannot start his engine in a few minutes, he should report the trouble to his foreman.
16. Operators must report immediately any apparent mechanical deficiency.
17. Gasoline-powered trucks should be serviced in designated areas, and the operator should always shut off the engine.
18. Before restarting the engine, all spilled gasoline must be cleaned up.
19. In no case shall anyone ride the forks of a truck or hitch a ride in any manner.
20. If forks are used to elevate a workman to the top of a stack, a pallet must first be placed on the forks.
21. Keep to the right whenever possible.
22. Slow down at cross aisles and exits, and sound horn at blind intersections.
23. Keep three truck lengths behind when following other vehicles.
24. Do not park in nonparking areas.
25. Keep feet inside running line of truck.
26. Do not engage in stunt driving or horseplay.

Answers to Fork Truck Operator's Questionnaire 1

1. (c)
2. (c)
3. (c)
4. (a) In nearly all cases.
   (b) On ramps or rough areas.
5. (b)
6. (b)
7. (b)
8. (c)
9. (c)

10. (a) Park in a parking area.
    (b) Place gear shift levers in neutral; set parking brake
    (c) Place forks flat on floor.
    (d) Turn off ignition switch.
11. (a) Slow down at approach to aisle or corner.
    (b) Stop at intersection.
    (c) Sound horn, if blind intersection.
    (d) Proceed with caution.
12. (a) Stand by for protection.
    (b) Send someone to report accident.

Answers to Fork Truck Operator's Questionnaire 2

1. True
2. True
3. False
4. True
5. False
6. False
7. False
8. False
9. True
10. False
11. True
12. False
13. True
14. False
15. False
16. False
17. False

Fig. 2-17. Answers to written tests given in Figs. 2-15 and 2-16.

Fork Truck Operators Test Score Card

Name _____ Date _____
Department_____ Building _____ Age _____
Total operating time _____Score _____
   Score—Questionnaire 1 _____ %
   Score—Questionnaire 2 _____ %
   Score—Obstacle Course _____ %
Instructor's remarks:_____
_____
_____
_____

Recommendations: _____
_____
_____

Fig. 2-18. Score card for instruction course.

Daily (8 Hr) Preventive Maintenance

Truck No. _____   Date _____
Operator _____
Checked By _____
1. Crankcase _____ ☐ Oil level _____ ☐ Qt added _____ ☐ Oil condition _____ ☐
2. Air cleaner _____ ☐   Oil cup cleaned _____ ☐   Body cleaned _____ ☐
3. Brakes _____ ☐ Service _____ ☐ Pedal reserve _____ ☐
4. Horn _____ ☐   5. Radiator _____ ☐ Water level _____ ☐ Antifreeze _____ ☐
6. Clutch throwout bearing _____ ☐   One turn of grease cup _____ ☐
7. Instruments _____ ☐ Fuel level _____ ☐ Water temperature _____ ☐
   Transmission oil pressure _____ ☐ Engine oil pressure _____ ☐ Ammeter _____ ☐
8. Lift operation _____ ☐   9. Tilt operation_____ ☐
10. Lights (if used)_____ ☐   11. Hydraulic attachments _____ ☐
12. Tire condition _____ ☐   13. Steering booster sump tank _____ ☐
14. Steering booster sump tank oil level _____ ☐
15. Steering booster operation OK _____ ☐

Fig. 2-19. Check sheet for daily use in preventive maintenance.

27. The operator must watch for workers and pedestrians while in motion.
28. Empty pallets should not be stacked higher than eye level at the car or where they are used for loading.

SELECTING AND EVALUATING INDUSTRIAL-TRUCK EQUIPMENT

There are several basic factors which should be observed when recommending equipment for purchase. They are probably in the following order of importance:

1. Plan the operation.
2. Use available equipment if possible and avoid custom-built jobs.
3. Select equipment with adequate capacity to handle the maximum-sized loads. Do not select equipment on the basis of its ability to handle average-sized loads.
4. Select equipment that meets safety requirements.
5. Observe manufacturers' recommendations.

Here are some of the most important measuring sticks by which to determine what to buy:

1. Will it do the job?
2. Does it meet safety requirements?
3. What is the reputation of the manufacturer and his representatives?
4. What is the availability of local service?
5. What has been the past experience with the manufacturer and his product?

Section 11

MAINTENANCE STORES AND THEIR CONTROL

Chapter 1

MAINTENANCE STORES CONTROL

By JOHN C. MARTIN
Staff Assistant
Headquarters Manufacturing Controls Department
Westinghouse Electric Corporation
Pittsburgh, Pa.

The policies and procedures relating to the maintenance stores function need to be designed carefully to fit conditions that exist within a specific plant. There are many aspects to be considered, ranging from basic organization to clerical forms. This chapter will describe approaches for developing an integrated system that will help provide the desired level of maintenance service in an economical manner.

Importance of Cost Considerations. Maintenance stores control requires making comparisons between various material inventory costs and the costs that are likely to be incurred without such inventory. Some of the cost factors are definite, while others require judgment to evaluate. The concept of over-all costs should be emphasized in making plans for storeroom operation. This means the labor and material required for plant servicing and repairs *plus* the cost to production departments for equipment downtime or subnormal operating condition.

Importance of Systems and Procedures. Systematic approaches are necessary in the control of storeroom costs. This chapter first describes the factors that need to be considered in a control program. Next, the principles of stores control are outlined. Finally, some detailed procedures are given to illustrate specific applications of the principles.

In developing a stores control system for plant maintenance, two steps are important: (1) determine the storeroom and related functions considered necessary to assist in minimizing total maintenance costs; and (2) develop the most effective procedure that will accomplish these objectives.

MAINTENANCE STORES COMPONENTS

Five basic categories of material would normally be included as part of the stock within maintenance storerooms:

Spare Parts. These are the "insurance" items that are stocked for specific plant equipment to guard against prolonged equipment downtime. Although wide variations properly occur, it would not be uncommon for about half the dollar value of maintenance stores material to be made up of spare parts. The items in this category may be further described in the following ways:

1. Relatively expensive compared with normal stock.
2. Specialized for use on one or a limited number of equipment items.

3. May be difficult to obtain promptly from suppliers.
4. Likely to have longer average turnover intervals than normal stock.
5. Used in equipment for which prolonged downtime is considered costly or unsafe.

Examples of such parts are special bearings or cams, special motors, gear replacements, and single-purpose electronic tubes.   Compared with the relative certainty of normal stock usage, the need for spare parts is somewhat of a gamble.   They should be stocked only when the risks involved in doing without them are considered to outweigh the total cost of carrying them in stock for a predicted interval.   This interval may be taken as the average time in stock of similar parts, based on past experience.

Normal Maintenance Stock.   These are items which have generally less specialized usage, more definite requirements, and shorter stock turnover intervals than spare parts.   Examples are pipe fittings and standard valves, commonly used bearings, bar stock for machining, electric wire and switches, lumber and plywood, bolts, welding rod, and electrical conduit.   The decisions that must be made concerning what to stock, how much to stock, or when to reorder can be handled in a more routine manner than with spare parts.   Other sections of this chapter will discuss procedures that are applicable.

Janitor Supplies.   This category includes paper towels, cleaning compounds, toilet tissue, etc. which are commonly a part of the maintenance stores.   Because of their closely predictable usage and different handling requirements, they may be classified separately.

Tools.   In small or medium-sized maintenance departments, it is common practice to require that the maintenance storeroom handle and control the special-purpose tools that are issued on a loan basis.   While this is not the same as the material control functions, it is a practical possibility and justifies attention in developing the over-all storeroom plan.

Nonmaintenance Items.   A large maintenance storeroom might be expected to carry in stock some of the supplies required by production departments.   This could be a relatively minor function.   The opposite situation could also occur, as in a job-shop manufacturing plant which required the use of a wide range of pipe fittings, electrical supplies, steel plate, sheet metal, etc.   It is probable that many of the items normally stocked in such a plant for use by manufacturing sections would be the same as those needed regularly by the maintenance crafts.   If so, the maintenance men might be required to use the manufacturing storerooms for some of their material needs.   There are disadvantages in such combined stores functions as well as obvious advantages.   A following section will discuss this in more detail.

CONDITIONS TENDING TO INCREASE MAINTENANCE STORES INVENTORY

As previously noted, sound stores control procedures involve the analysis of a number of factors.   This section discusses some of the factors that tend to increase the amount of stock carried in the storeroom.

Cost of Production Downtime.   When equipment failures occur and equipment remains down through lack of spare parts or materials, the resulting losses may be serious.   This is particularly true if required capacity is affected or if production operators cannot be reassigned to other work.   A systematic record of equipment downtime throughout the plant should be maintained where there is a problem to enable realistic evaluation of policy.

Requirements for Maintenance Scheduling.   An important factor in effective control of maintenance costs is the systematic planning and scheduling of maintenance jobs.   This can insure a full day's work for each man, avoid assignments when equipment is not ready, reduce waiting among various crafts on the same job, insure proper crew sizes, and obtain other results that combine to reduce costs.   One of the keys to maintenance planning and scheduling is to have normal stock items on hand without needing to check the availability of every minor item.   Maintenance scheduling quickly bogs down or becomes expensive if more than a few special items have to be separately ordered and accounted for ahead of scheduling or during progress of the job.

Economics of Quantity Purchasing. The fact that many items cost less when bought in large quantities is one of the influences toward an increase in inventory. A similar influence comes from the cost of issuing a purchase order, checking receipts, and making payment. Quantity purchasing often can work in the direction of total cost reduction but only if the savings are greater than the added costs incurred by carrying the inventory over the increased period of time.

Lack of Parts Standardization. Examples are different makes of motors or pumps which have approximately the same performance specifications; different electric controls which do the same thing; various solenoid valves or electric relays with essentially the same functional properties; or an unnecessarily wide range of sizes or grades of such materials as lumber, sheet metal, steel plate, or welding rod. While standardization of maintenance parts and materials will always be less than desired, there are approaches which can be taken to advantage. A following section will discuss some of these.

Multiple Storage Depots. With decentralized maintenance storerooms, duplication of stock is likely to exist. This may not be serious in the case of craft supplies that are stored at a single location for each craft since materials used by any one craft are somewhat specialized. The duplication becomes more pronounced, however, with area storerooms that carry maintenance supplies for various crafts. The effect on inventories in such cases is equivalent to that of the lack of parts standardization.

Inadequate Attention to Inventory or Order Quantities. Without records of inventory quantities, casual inspection at varying intervals usually is relied on to indicate when orders should be placed. It is easy to "be on the safe side" in such cases. The same tendency occurs when reordering without the aid of predetermined order quantities (discussed in a following section). Although the simpler approaches may eliminate some clerical time, they do not provide the degree of control that can be attained with a more orderly system of records.

Lack of Nearby or Dependable Suppliers. Many plants are close enough to supply houses for rush orders of certain items to be picked up or delivered in an hour or so when emergencies arise. Similarly, some of the suppliers of specialized spare parts—even though not located near the plant—can be depended on to furnish parts from their own stock without delay. When such conditions do not exist, there may be valid reasons to consider increasing selected stock inventories.

Size, Nature, and Condition of Production Facilities. Justifiable maintenance stock inventories are obviously increased when conditions exist such as the following:

1. Large investment in plant equipment or facilities.
2. Process equipment used continuously as in the case of refineries, steel mills, or power plants.
3. Production equipment must have a high usage factor as in highly automated facilities, tape-controlled machine tools, or bottleneck facilities.
4. Old or worn equipment must remain in use to handle production needs.
5. Lack of spare facilities.

Small Amount of Work Handled by Outside Contractors. Plant policies vary in this respect. Large jobs occur at frequent intervals in many plants. If the regular maintenance crews normally handle such work, then stock quantities are likely to be set somewhat higher to avoid stock-outs that may affect rush jobs.

CONDITIONS TENDING TO REDUCE MAINTENANCE STORES INVENTORY

Availability of Cash. Most plants have a backlog of possibilities for investing money in new tooling, machines, or equipment which will reduce costs through resulting methods improvements. If the cutoff point for such investments is, say, a

20 per cent annual return, the money which is invested in carrying marginal stores inventories should be expected to pay off at about the same rate, after deducting expected costs. It is admittedly difficult to estimate the probable return in specific cases where decisions are required about inventories. This line of thinking is a sound one to follow as a policy guide, however.

Cost Associated with Storeroom Activity.   Some of the expected storeroom costs are listed as follows:

1. *Plant space* occupied by the storeroom.
2. *Labor costs* of required storeroom attendants, clerks, or material handlers.
3. *Storeroom facilities* involved (bins, cranes, fork trucks, etc.).
4. *Obsolescence* of stored parts. As new technology or old age causes replacement of specific plant equipment, the spare parts for specialized use on such equipment become obsolete.
5. *Depreciation and depletion* of stock material. Handling within the storeroom may cause damage to fragile parts. Some items have a limited shelf life. There will be occasional misuse of expensive parts. Stealing can be a problem particularly where there is ready access to stored material or where inventory records are controlled by stores attendants.
6. *Costs of insurance and any applicable taxes.*

Good Service from Suppliers.   This acts to reduce maintenance stock needs, as previously discussed. The cost of picking up stock items from nearby vendors must be given due consideration, however.

Equipment Downtime Infrequent or Unimportant.   Some process plants are equipped with spare equipment to take care of repair needs. Capacity requirements for a particular plant or section of the plant may be such that some equipment downtime is unimportant. New production facilities may require little replacement of parts for a number of years. Such conditions will obviously act to reduce needed repair parts inventory.

ADVANTAGES OF CENTRALIZED MAINTENANCE STOREROOMS

A basic step in establishing control procedures is to decide whether the various categories of material should be: (1) stocked centrally in one location; (2) stocked in various decentralized maintenance storerooms; (3) stocked with supplies for production departments; or (4) handled by some combination of these approaches. To properly make this decision for a specific case involves considering a number of factors. The possible advantages to be gained from centralized storerooms are listed below:

Duplication Avoided.   While a single stores location does not in itself assure minimum inventories, it does provide the basis for controls that will keep total stock at a minimum. This is not the case when specific items are stocked in more than one storeroom location.

Inventory Control Systems More Practical.   Workable control systems involve requisitions, inventory records, and other procedures that will be covered later in detail. Accurate, conscientious clerical work is required. This can seldom be achieved without one or more storeroom attendants plus interested supervision. Small substorerooms make it more difficult to justify the kind of staff that will apply controls to achieve desired results.

This is particularly true for second-shift work. Only the largest maintenance functions could justify assigning second-shift attendants within various area storerooms. Yet a second-shift man might properly be used in a centralized storeroom for a medium-sized maintenance department.

Fewer Stores Attendants Required.   There is less work to disburse the stock and control the stock quantities for a central supply of various pipe fittings (for example) than to do so for identical fittings in several different areas. This would be true even if the total number of withdrawals were the same in each case.

While attendants may not be used in decentralized storerooms, there is an equivalent handling time on the part of craftsmen or maintenance foremen. With good supervision, a centralized storeroom can be operated more economically.

The rush and slack periods for obtaining maintenance material are generally quite consistent within a plant. After identifying these periods, it is often practical to transfer a clerk from some other work temporarily to help fill stores requests, say for two separate hourly periods each day. This is one of the many ways that over-all costs can be lowered—through a centralized stores function.

Losses Reduced from Various Sources. On the assumption that there will be better supervision and more orderly handling within a central storeroom, the losses that occur from depreciation and depletion of stock would normally be less than for subdivided stores. A higher stock turnover rate could be expected.

Delivery Service More Practical. One way to avoid the need for maintenance men to walk to a storeroom and wait there for service is to make frequent deliveries from telephoned requests. This service is easier to provide on a justifiable basis if the storeroom is a large one with frequent calls for stock.

One practical way of establishing the delivery service is to select and identify a number of delivery points in the plant area and set up a truck route that contacts these points at intervals such as every half-hour. Telephone calls to the storeroom would then be filled promptly and placed at a dock for truck pickup and subsequent delivery. Requisitions could be signed or collected as deliveries are made.

More Reliable Cost Accounting. Because of the tendency to operate small storerooms without a regular attendant on all working shifts, the larger stores functions tend to provide better control of cost allocation for material that is issued. This is not automatic with size, of course, but requires close supervision and careful handling. Such details as the following need to be controlled:

1. Consistent use of material requisitions.
2. Regular checks to see that requisitions show the proper account charge and have been approved in the manner designated.
3. Enforcement of rules to permit only the attendants or other designated individuals within the storeroom.
4. Proper accounting for receipt and disbursement of salvaged or returned items.
5. Transmittal of all requisitions to accounting for prescribed handling.

More Efficient Space Usage. This advantage would hold in comparing centralized stores with substorerooms that have overlapping stock items.

More Orderly Planning for Large Jobs. For large repair, construction, or rearrangement jobs by plant maintenance crews, good advance planning may require setting aside certain amounts of stock items to be sure they are available when needed. This is easier to accomplish in an orderly manner when there is one central maintenance storeroom rather than several small ones.

Simplified Handling into Storeroom. The receiving point and receiving inspection may be where production materials are received or at the central maintenance storeroom. In the latter case particularly, but also in both cases, handling is reduced when only one maintenance stores location is involved.

ADVANTAGES OF DECENTRALIZED MAINTENANCE STOREROOMS

There are two general approaches. One is to locate all or a portion of a specific craft's specialized material at or near the shop location of the craft involved. The other approach is to locate spare parts and/or material within specific plant areas for convenience to the point of usage. There may also be combinations of these approaches. It is not possible here to discuss separately all of the variations. Consequently, the advantages noted below may apply in some cases and not in others:

Less Walking and Waiting Time for Craftsmen. This is an obvious advantage and is perhaps the primary reason for area storerooms. In considering this advantage over centralization, however, the possibility of material delivery should be kept in mind, as previously noted. With an hour's advance planning of material needs, it may be easier for maintenance men to get material from a central storeroom than from the nearest area storeroom.

Closer Control by Craftsmen Concerned.   This occurs where material is turned over to craft departments for handling by the maintenance men concerned.   If there are both close supervision and responsible maintenance craftsmen, this can work out well, though not without losing some of the advantages listed for central storerooms.   Examples that have been observed to function satisfactorily are:

1. A welding- and burning-torch repair station in a large plant where the assigned maintenance man controls all the repair parts involved.
2. A fork truck repair station in a medium-sized plant where parts used by the assigned mechanic are stocked and handled in an orderly manner.
3. A repair station for small tools where the boiler room attendant makes such repairs at intervals and stocks the necessary parts.

Closer Control by Supervision Concerned.   This may apply when spare parts are stored at the point where they will eventually be used.   In such cases, the line management involved can see what is available and presumably can be held more closely accountable for downtime due to waiting for spare parts.   It should be recognized, however, that central storeroom procedures could include regular reviews by line management of repair parts stocked for their departments.

A similar situation can occur in the case of separate maintenance storerooms that are located next to decentralized maintenance shops.   Craft foremen involved can supervise the handling of stock material more closely, but this requires time on their part and is not necessarily an advantage.

More Likely to Get Correct Material for a Job.   When maintenance men regularly inspect and handle the stored material themselves, there is an advantage in being able to select the most suitable items for conditions at hand.   This advantage may be counteracted, however, by the resulting interference with precise record keeping or by waste from poor handling practices.

For example, a large research laboratory provides several decentralized storerooms and allows maintenance men and technicians to have access to most items so they can determine by inspection what will fit their needs.   The same laboratory has one large storeroom, however, to which only the attendants have access.   This is because the cutting of metal plate and bar stock, micarta, plastic, etc. requires special handling and would involve undue waste without regular operators being used.

FACTORS INVOLVED IN COMBINED STOREROOMS

As previously mentioned, one of the possible approaches is to stock part of or all the maintenance supplies within production storerooms.

Advantages.   To the extent that this is done, there is obviously less duplication in parts storage.   It permits use of the same inventory control procedures and tends to reduce the number of stores attendants that would be needed.

Disadvantages.   The chances are that storerooms which issue parts or material to both production and maintenance personnel will be located for the convenience of the production departments.   The result is likely to be a scattering of some maintenance supplies all over the plant.   There could be time lost from excessive travel to get material in such cases.

Another disadvantage is that the stores inventory control procedures will normally be oriented in the direction of production requirements and may not closely fit maintenance needs without some alterations.   If it is found that such combinations of stores functions are advisable from an over-all standpoint, steps should be taken so that adequate service is provided for the maintenance department.

ORGANIZATION FOR MAINTENANCE STORES CONTROL

In the past, there have been at least three different organizational concepts regarding maintenance stores control.   One of these recognizes the need for sound purchasing by placing the storeroom personnel and material control procedures within the organization of the purchasing department.   A second approach stresses cost accounting and safeguarding of the investment within the storeroom by delegating the organizational control to the accounting department.   The third approach recognizes the importance of material control in providing a sound basis for adequate maintenance service by placing the storeroom function within the plant maintenance organization.

The last of these three organizational concepts is a sound approach that can be applied while retaining the needed assistance and control from other departments. Typical procedures would include buying material through the purchasing department and developing inventory records through the accounting department.   The plant maintenance manager would normally retain the authority to select items and quantities to be stocked (within policy limitations) and to insure adequate storeroom service through supervision of storeroom personnel.

PRINCIPLES OF MAINTENANCE STORES CONTROL PROCEDURES

The principles for systematic control of maintenance stores are listed under headings that follow.   As in all cases of maintenance control, it is the *total* cost figure that should be considered.   Controlling spare-parts cost, for example, might include demonstrating the need for adding to such stock in specific cases in order to reduce the costs of equipment downtime.

The Stores Requisition.   This is considered an essential step in withdrawing most material from the maintenance storeroom because it provides:

1. Authority for stores attendants to issue stock.
2. Basis for a maintenance man to obtain approval at the designated level to withdraw stock (usually his maintenance foreman).
3. Systematic basis for cost accounting and inventory records.
4. Means of reducing mistakes or lost time by stores attendants.

The requisition format should be as simple as possible.   One copy will normally suffice.   Spaces for the following should be considered:

1. Material description and quantity.
2. Material code number (may be combined with bin location reference).
3. Account charge number and/or work-order number.
4. Date, user's name, and approval space.

The high cost of many repair parts or normal stock items justifies a careful check of material used on specific jobs.   It may be practical to repair existing parts, use salvaged parts, use less expensive material, or use different material that is better for the job.   For these reasons, it is sound practice to require that maintenance men obtain their foreman's approval before withdrawing material.

Because of the lost time that is often involved in locating a busy foreman within a large plant, some compromise with this approach may be necessary.   A substitute control plan is to issue material for requisitions signed by maintenance men, collect all requisitions during the shift, and have them signed by the respective foremen later as evidence that they are familiar with the withdrawal and approve use of the material as specified.

Inventory Record.   Most control procedures make use of a continuous or perpetual inventory record on which receipts are added and withdrawals subtracted.   This may be done through:

1. *Hand posting* to a form having columns for date, order reference number, receipts, issues, and balance on hand.   Such a procedure is simple and relatively inexpensive to install.
2. *Machine posting,* using standard bookkeeping machines.   Both the computations and printing of the inventory record are done by the machine.   This helps reduce errors which may occur with hand posting.
3. *Data processing methods,* utilizing tabulating machines or electronic computers. The input is usually in the form of punched cards for each transaction.   This

information is applied automatically to update the records of quantity and other details which are part of the data processing system. An advantage of this method is that various other forms of output data can easily be obtained as a by-product. Examples are total material cost on individual work orders, dollar value of spare parts or normal stock inventory, and a listing of items for which the inventory quantity has reached a specified level.

Verifying the Inventory Records. A physical inventory of stored material is essential at periodic intervals to detect errors in the continuous inventory records. This also serves as an indication of possible stock depletion. If there are serious, unexplained shortages, the need for corrective action is indicated. A yearly period between physical counts is common, with more frequent checks if conditions dictate.

The physical inventory may be at a single period, such as when the plant is shut down for vacation or over a weekend. This will require a crew large enough to complete the job in a few days. An alternate method is to make provisions for continuous inventory during the year on a part-time basis. Using this approach, the checking of various items would be scheduled so that all are covered within a designated interval.

Deciding What to Stock. When the plant is new, it will be necessary to use judgment in determining material and parts which should be stocked. The recommendations of equipment manufacturers should be reviewed concerning spare-parts needs but not followed blindly. The past experience of craft foremen will assist in selecting normal stock material. Decisions made along this line should be on a conservative basis, but it should be recognized that usage records will provide a more definite picture in the future.

The usual high cost of spare parts plus the judgment involved in deciding whether to stock them or take the risk of downtime indicates that a suitable management level should be specified to authorize stocking such parts. Typically, the maintenance manager would be expected to screen all such requests. Approval of production management where the equipment is located might properly be required also before spare parts are classified as regular stock items.

Order Points. These are numerical values that are established through careful analysis by the plant maintenance manager or his organization. When an order point is reached on the inventory record, a new order should be initiated. If desired, a somewhat lower stock quantity (minimum) can be designated as the point at which urgent checking should be initiated to expedite delivery. The order points should take into consideration peak usage requirements, as shown by past records, plus the time to obtain delivery. They are subject to periodic revision as conditions change.

Order Quantities. The stock quantities to be recorded when a low point is reached should be developed through an analysis of factors such as:

1. Average usage quantity, determined from past records.
2. Costs of purchasing, including related handling and clerical costs.
3. Costs of carrying inventory in stock.
4. Points at which quantity discounts apply.

The approximate interrelation of the first three of these factors is illustrated by Fig. 1-1, subject to the following definitions:

P = Total cost of purchasing and receiving one order quantity, including:
    1. Cost to request, process, and issue the required purchase order.
    2. Cost to receive, identify, inspect, and handle the incoming material.
    3. Accounting and clerical costs to make payment, prepare records, handle purchase-order copies, etc.
Y = Number of pieces used per year.
I = Yearly inventory carrying cost in per cent of dollar value, expressed as a decimal fraction. This normally includes:
    1. Cost of capital invested, which may be considered somewhere between bank interest rates and the return expected if an equivalent investment were made in other phases of the business.

2. Increased depreciation and depletion due to carrying extra amounts in stock.
3. Increased obsolescence risks.
4. Insurance and taxes.
5. Cost of space, facilities, heat, etc.
6. Cost of labor for handling in storage.

C = Cost per piece, including freight.

T = Cost per year to carry items in stock, over and above the purchase price. T_1 is the portion of T due to inventory and storage costs. T_2 is the remaining portion of T due to purchasing and receiving costs.

L = Number of parts in a single order. The value of L which minimizes T is called the "economic order quantity," or EOQ.

While the curves in Fig. 1-1 are typical for various items, the values charted are those which might apply to a hardware item costing \$2.00 each and used in quantities

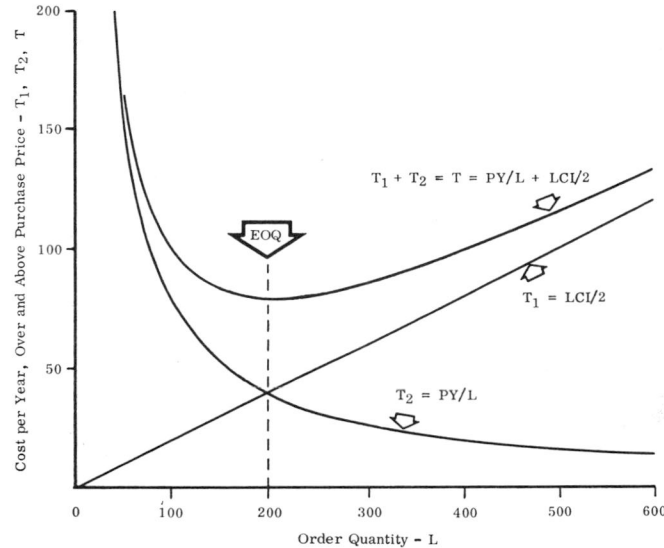

FIG. 1-1. Variation of inventory and purchasing costs with respect to order quantities.

of 400 per year. The curve for T_1 is based on $I = 0.20$, and the curve for T_2 is based on a purchasing and receiving cost of \$20 per order. From the graph, it is clear that the minimum added cost occurs with an order quantity of about 200.

It is possible to derive an equation that may be used to calculate the economic order quantity directly for cases of this nature. The EOQ may be defined as the low point of the curve, or the point at which the derivative of T with respect to L is zero.

$$\frac{dT}{dL} = -\frac{PY}{L^2} + \frac{CI}{2} = 0$$

$$\frac{PY}{L^2} = \frac{CI}{2}$$

$$L = \text{EOQ} = \sqrt{\frac{2PY}{CI}}$$

The derived equation may be used generally, subject to the limitations noted. For the specific example of Fig. 1-1 the EOQ may be calculated to be 200, or a supply of six months.

Fig. 1-2 is an alignment chart which may be used to calculate economic order quantities within the range of costs and usage for typical maintenance materials.

Exceptions to Inventory or Requisitioning Procedures. The clerical effort involved in the usual procedures is not significant compared with the benefits gained in most

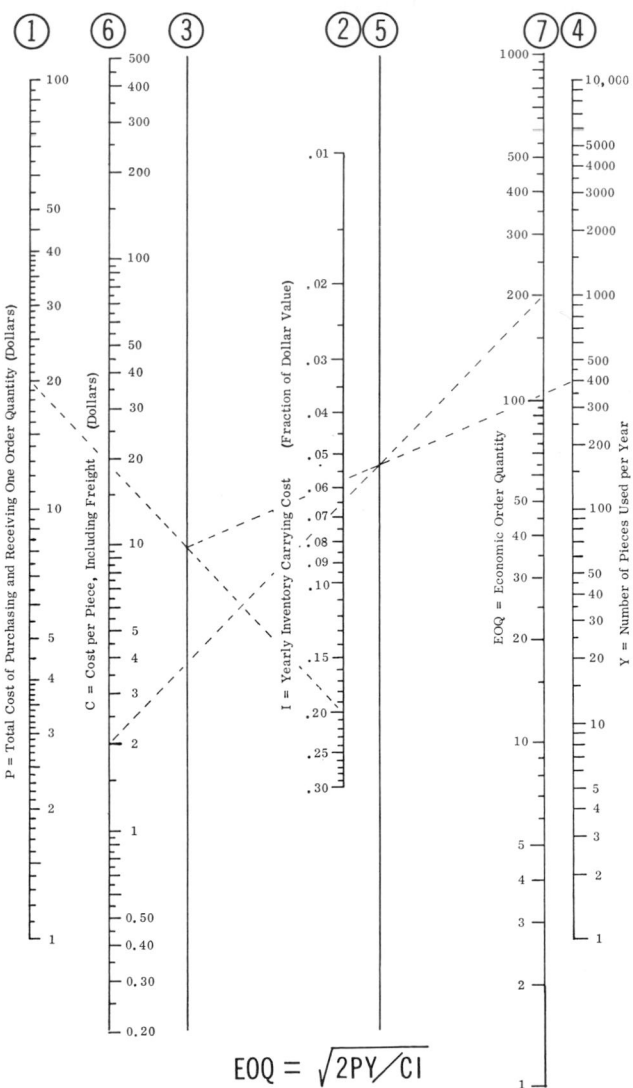

$$EOQ = \sqrt{2PY/CI}$$

Fig. 1-2. Alignment chart for calculating economic order quantity.

cases. It should be recognized, however, that some categories of items within the maintenance stores may not justify being controlled either by requisitions or by continuous inventory.

Typically, these are low-cost items used in relatively high volume such as bolts and nuts in common sizes, washers, sandpaper, nails, etc. This "free stock" may be charged to general expense when received and either issued on request or located where maintenance men have access to it.   Periodic checks of supplies on hand will suffice for reordering.

A simple version of the inventory control procedure is called the 2-bin system.   One sealed bin contains the number of items equivalent to the order point, and the second bin contains the usual excess above this quantity.   Stock is withdrawn from the second bin until it is empty, which signals the need for an order to be initiated.   With only one bin available for an item, the order point quantity may be sacked or tied together to achieve the same signal for reordering.

What may seem at first to be even simpler is the casual inspection of stock items at intervals to initiate required orders.   This is suitable as a means of control only in limited storeroom applications, however, and cannot be depended on either to minimize stock quantities or stock-out situations.

Parts Catalog.   When maintenance functions are large enough to justify storeroom attendants, it is desirable to assign definite responsibility to the stores organization for correct inventory records, orderly arrangement of stock, lost or stolen items, etc. This is not easy to do in a clear-cut manner.   The complex nature of many items tends to require personal selection on the part of craftsmen.   Even if a maintenance man could give the generic names of unusual items exactly, only the most experienced storeroom attendants would be able to locate the correct parts consistently.

An approach that is often worthwhile is to prepare listings of part names, descriptions, and storeroom locations, so that maintenance men can specify code numbers to designate the desired parts.   Such catalogs may be prepared by data processing from punched cards, in which case new copies can be issued without delay when changes occur.   The catalogs may be typed, of course, and are commonly illustrated where necessary with drawings, pictures from vendors' catalogs, photographs, or sketches. Extra copies of the catalogs may be made available to craft offices, material planning personnel, or maintenance men in area locations.

Stock Code Numbers.   Code numbers for each different item in the maintenance storeroom are needed for catalog reference as described above.   They are also desirable for precise inventory control purposes, for use in positive identification to purchasing, and as an aid in locating parts within the storeroom.   The detailed illustration in a following section, Stock Code Numbers, shows how one plant developed stock code numbers to serve a variety of purposes.

Accounting for Material Usage.   It is customary to charge the cost of material or parts placed in the storeroom to an undistributed inventory account.   When finally used, specific items of material are then charged to departmental expense or capital accounts, as dictated by the intended usage.   One way to itemize material charges is simply to enter the account charge on the material requisition copy.   The required costing of items listed can be done manually or through data processing methods.

There is another way to allocate material charges which simplifies verification of the charge and permits the accumulation of charges against specific jobs.   This method involves (1) work-order copies for all maintenance jobs, preferably in connection with a work planning and scheduling procedure; (2) verified departmental or other charge numbers on each work order; and (3) reference to the work-order number on material requisitions.   It would then be the function of accounting, using data processing procedures, to match together various items of the following data as needed for cost accounting, work-order performance records, equipment repair records, control reports, etc.:

1. Work-order number.
2. Cost-account charge number.
3. Equipment record number.
4. Hours worked.
5. Material cost.
6. Abbreviated or coded work description.

This approach is further explained in the case history in a following section, Stores Requisition.

Coordination with Purchasing Department. It is common practice to require that requisitions for replacement stock or spare parts be routed through the purchasing department. The paper work involved can be greatly simplified through use of a *traveling requisition* format. This is typically a card which contains the following data:

1. Material description and reference number.
2. Approved vendors.
3. Approved order quantities.
4. Reference dates as needed.

Such cards are normally kept on file in the storeroom office. When the inventory record (which may be handled by accounting) shows that the order point for a specific item has been reached, the traveling requisition card is withdrawn, dated, and sent to purchasing. After an order has been placed, the traveling requisition card is returned to the storeroom where it is filed separately until receipt of the material. The card is then refiled to complete the cycle of its usage.

To avoid confusion, one should indicate clearly the repair parts which are to be ordered by purchasing from a specific vendor and the normal stock items which can be obtained wherever advantageous. It is also good practice for the purchasing department to contact the storeroom or maintenance supervisor concerned before ordering quantities that are appreciably different from those specified.

A close working relationship is essential among the storeroom supervisor, maintenance department personnel, and the purchasing department. Each should have fixed responsibilities, including cooperation as required to eliminate delays and help control costs.

Special Material Requisitions. When nonstock material is needed for special jobs, requisitions should be channeled through purchasing in most cases. For common items obtainable from nearby supply houses and required on a rush basis, a simplified approach can be worked out that retains the needed control. For example, purchasing might investigate prices on typical items at one or more supply houses and establish blanket purchase orders with each to cover specific types of material within a given price range. Then the maintenance manager or his representative would be authorized to order small lots by telephone, giving as charge reference the number from a prenumbered requisition which would be initiated for internal-record purposes.

Obtaining material quickly from nearby vendors can be simplified still further by making use of telephone line facilities which accept prepunched cards at a maintenance department transmitter and duplicate such cards at a selected vendor's transmitter. Restrictions would be needed of course to prevent lack of control with such installations.

Salvaged Parts and Material. It is sound practice to route such items back into the maintenance storeroom for subsequent issue in the same manner as new material. Applicable accounting practices are covered in another chapter of this handbook.

Standardization Where Possible. Continuing efforts should be made to obtain the maximum degree of equipment or parts standardization within the plant. The maintenance manager should be expected to coordinate and promote such efforts. This is not an easy job, but tangible results can be achieved with some effort. A key step is to review requests for new plant equipment at a stage which will provide the needed maintenance background when making decisions between competitive items of equipment. Standard equipment parts such as controls, motors, hydraulic units, pumps, etc., may properly be specified on certain equipment.

Another approach, as repair needs become evident, is to make replacements with standard parts wherever practical, even though some minor equipment revisions are required in doing so.

An aid in working toward standardization of parts is to enlist the cooperation of manufacturing engineers who investigate new equipment possibilities or plant engineers who design new facilities. If we make the parts catalog available to such men, the selection of standard parts and materials for new equipment can be made where practical.

Control Indexes. Records of the total inventory cost and average turnover interval are important and should be developed regularly. The average turnover can be calculated by dividing the cost of stock disbursed during the year into the total inventory cost.

When we determine such figures, it is important that we classify spare parts separately from normal stock. The average turnover interval for the latter may be expected to fall into the 2- to 6-month range while the average spare parts turnover may properly be much longer than this. The necessary separation in reporting will be facilitated if distinguishing symbols are used in the stock codes for each of the two classes.

The control of inventory csot and turnover can be facilitated by investigating in detail the most active items involved. In most cases, a small percentage of categories stocked (say 10 per cent) will account for a large per cent of inventory investment.

Other reports should be developed to provide information such as the following:

1. Variances between perpetual inventory records and periodic physical inventories.
2. The number of stock-outs that occur.
3. Stock losses through obsolescence and deterioration.

Use of Equipment Repair Records. Adequate maintenance control procedures usually include some form of equipment repair records. Such records may be as simple as completed work-order copies filed by equipment number. A step beyond this would involve hand or mechanized posting to equipment record cards of data such as summarized work-order descriptions plus labor and material costs. Going still further, data processing by means of computers may provide equivalent records.

One important use of this information is to review it regularly to determine what steps can be taken to reduce repair needs. It may be found that corrective-maintenance work is needed on some equipment to prevent recurring breakdowns. In other cases, preventive-maintenance inspection or servicing should be initiated. Systematic approaches of this kind are an integral part of the maintenance control program.

ILLUSTRATIONS OF PROCEDURAL DETAILS

Several examples of stores control forms and detailed procedures are described in this section.

FIG. 1-3. Stock catalog and file of cards for computer printing when changes are required.

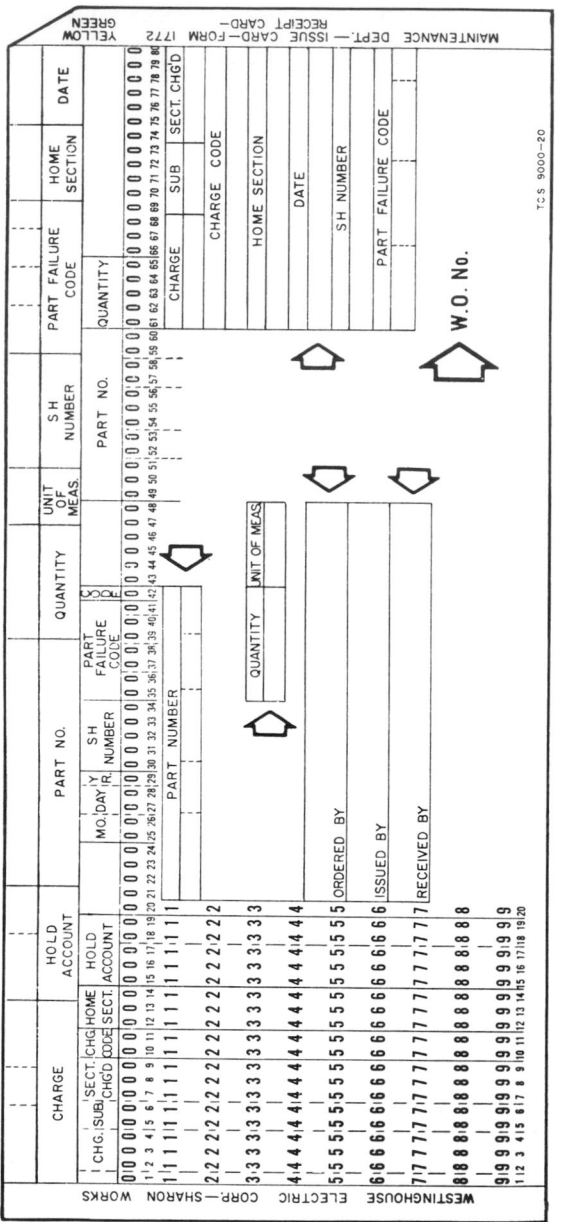

FIG. 1-4. Stores requisition showing data required for computer processing.

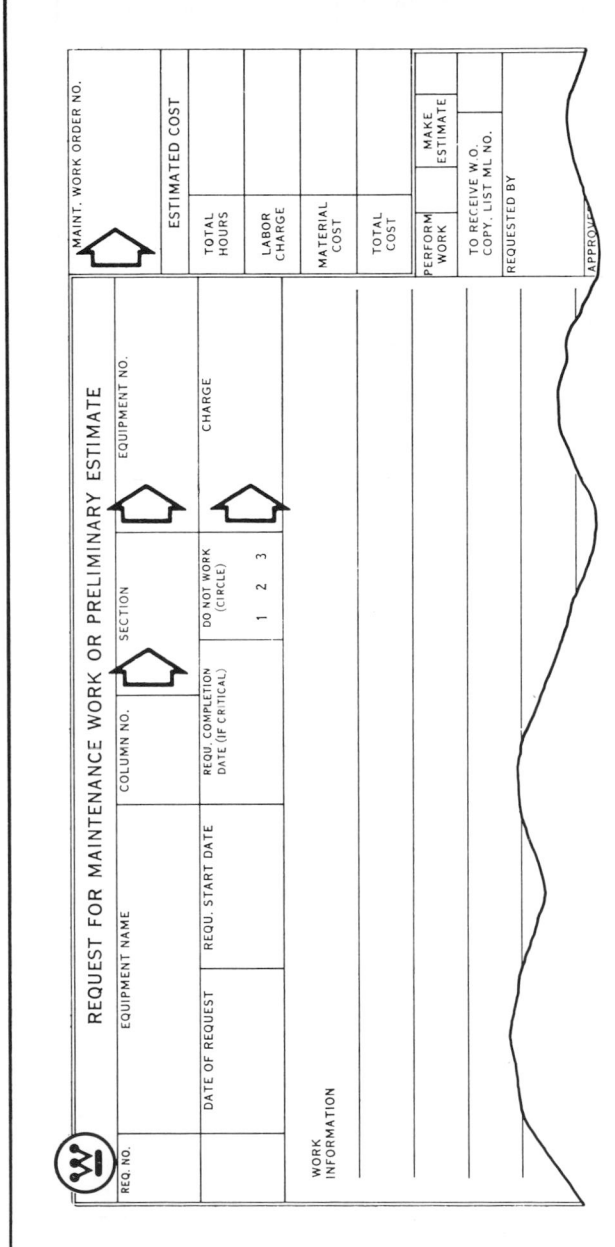

Fig. 1-5. Portion of work order showing data required for computer processing.

CHARGE	PART DESCRIPTION	UNIT	ORDER AMT.	PART NO.
576-Gen.	NIPPLE PHN 4-1/4 MALE	PC	00075	SP180250

SUFFIX	SUPPLIER	QUANTITY	UNIT PRICE	ORDER DATE	SHIP DATE	REQ'D. DATE	REC. DATE
F90	ABC Supply Co.	75	.30	6-12-64	6-27-64		6-22-64
F91	ABC Supply Co.	75	.30	8-18-64	8-30-64		8-29-64
F92	ABC Supply Co.	75	.30	11-5-64	11-17-64		11-18-64

MAINTENANCE STOREROOM TRAVELING REQ.

TCS 9000-39

FIG. 1-6. Traveling requisition format.

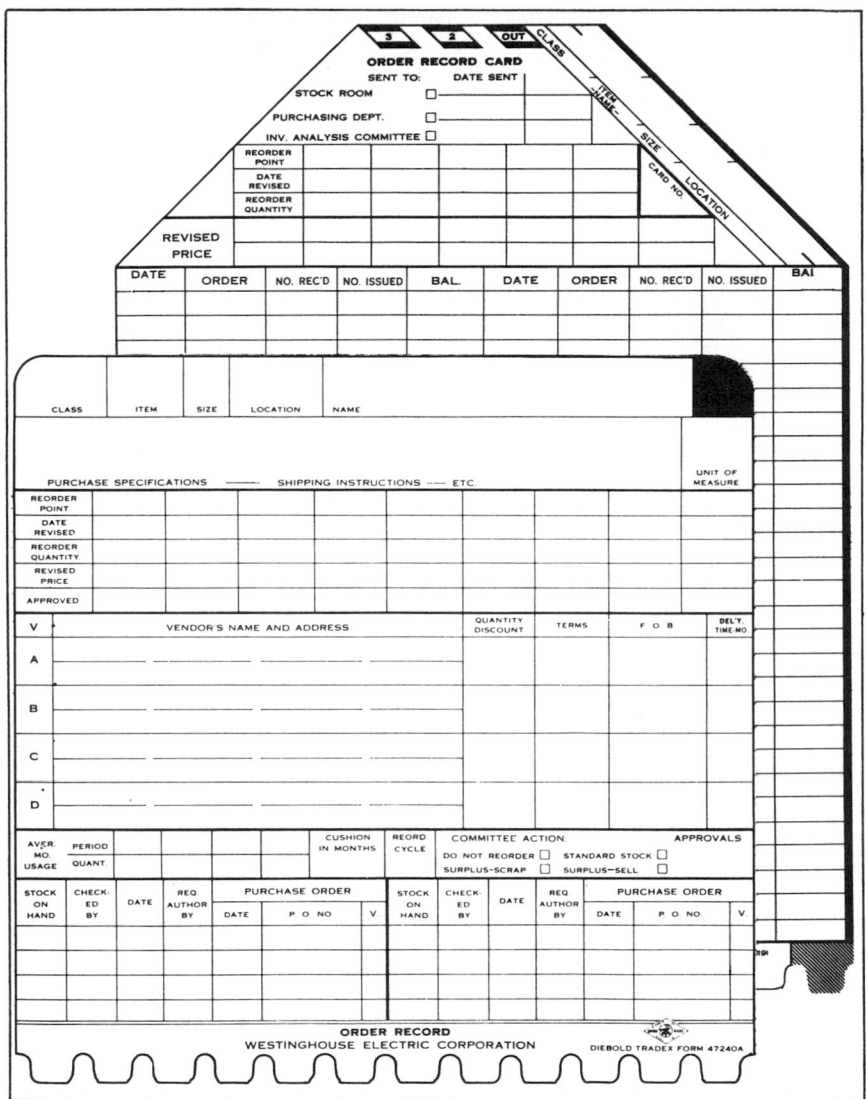

FIG. 1-7. Stores ledger cards, with traveling requisition at left.

Stock Code Numbers. One plant has developed a method of applying reference numbers to identify specific stock items for different purposes. They are an aid in costing procedures; they are a means of positive identification for catalog reference, for easy location within the storeroom, and for inventory control record keeping. This system of coding is described as follows:

1. The prefix letters R or S designate repair parts or normal stock, respectively. This tells purchasing which parts need to be ordered from a single source. It provides a routine way to separate the reporting of inventory values so that reports have more meaning.

2. A second prefix letter designates the maintenance craft chiefly concerned with the stocking of parts. This helps in checking inventory requirements.
3. A final series of six digits designates the location within the storeroom. The first two digits indicate the row of bins, the next two specify the location along the row, the next digit indicates the vertical location in the row, and the final digit shows either an open bin (zero) or the position in a drawer (1 to 9).

Stock Cátalog. Figure 1-3 shows a stock catalog obtained by means of computer print-out. The clerk is withdrawing a set of punched cards used for a one-line entry in the catalog. The file of similar punched cards is maintained for reprinting the catalog when additions or corrections have been made.

Stores Requisition. Figure 1-4 shows a stores requisition form that is in use. A separate card is prepared for each different stock category involved. The spaces indicated on the card are those normally filled in when withdrawing stock. The same card will be punched later by the tabulating section for computer input data. This will be used by the computer to update the master inventory record for the stock category that applies.

Where this requisition is used, practically all maintenance jobs are covered by a work order. In such cases, the work-order number (lower right corner of Fig. 1-4) eliminates the need for filling in most other spaces on the right side of the card. Work-order copies (Fig. 1-5) also go to tabulating, where the data indicated by arrows is punched on tab cards. The computer matches this data with that from both the stores requisitions and labor time reports. It is then possible to obtain from the computer material and labor changes for:

1. Cost accounting.
2. Each completed work order.
3. Repairs made on individual units of plant equipment.

Traveling Requisition Card. The form shown in Fig. 1-6 is used in connection with the inventory system described above. When an order point is reached, the computer causes a signal card to be issued. This is sent to the maintenance department. The traveling requisition card corresponding to the stock number on the signal card is then pulled, the signal card filed in its place, and the traveling requisition card sent to purchasing. When the order has been issued, the traveling requisition card is returned to maintenance.

Stores Ledger Card. For hand posting of stores receipts and disbursements, forms such as that shown at the top of Fig. 1-7 may be applied. The lower form in Fig. 1-7 serves as a traveling requisition, being used approximately as described previously. Equivalent record cards are commercially available to fit various types of filing systems.

Chapter 2

MAINTENANCE STOREROOMS

By JOHN C. MARTIN
Staff Assistant
Headquarters Manufacturing Controls Department
Westinghouse Electric Corporation
Pittsburgh, Pa.

The previous chapter dealt largely with procedures for effective maintenance-storeroom service at minimum over-all cost. This chapter is concerned with the facilities and equipment that serve to implement the established procedures.

PRELIMINARY ASPECTS OF STOREROOM DESIGN

Before it is possible to deal with specific storeroom buildings, facilities, or layout, decisions are required concerning (1) the degree of stores centralization; (2) the extent of inventory control to be established; and (3) the scope of related functions that stores personnel will be expected to handle.

Centralized or Decentralized Storerooms. Since this subject is basic to any form of control procedures, it was discussed in detail in the preceding chapter. A centralized maintenance storeroom permits considering many cost-reduction techniques that might not be practical with smaller subdivided storerooms. Some of these techniques involve administrative procedures. In addition, there are refinements in storeroom facilities and handling equipment which could hardly be justified unless given maximum use in a centralized location.

The Question of Storeroom Attendants. There are several possible approaches to be considered, each of which has an influence on how the storeroom should be partitioned or otherwise arranged:

1. *Trained attendants* to receive, store, and disburse all items that are stocked. This approach requires partitions to keep out those not authorized to enter. One or more issuing windows or counters are needed. In addition to the obvious improvement in stores records and prevention of losses that such an approach helps provide, a more efficient and space-conserving layout within the storeroom becomes possible. With less need for visual inspection to find the desired material, bin arrangement can be more compact, vertical space can be utilized more effectively, and handling equipment of a specialized nature can successfully be applied.
2. *No attendants, with stores area open* to maintenance men concerned. This is the other extreme. There isn't much control this way, but neither is there the added labor cost for issuing material. This is a frequent method for establishing small area stores locations. In cases of this kind, simplicity of arrangement is desirable. Stock should be out in the open, where it can be identified and selected easily. The

facilities should be such that they make orderly upkeep as easy as possible. Figure 2-1 shows a portion of the stores facilities in a large research laboratory where both maintenance men and laboratory technicians have ready access to certain classes of material and supplies. Requisitions are prepared to cover the material that is taken.

3. *No attendants, with limited access to stores area.* In such cases, the facilities involved are usually locked in some manner. Examples range from small storage cabinets to sizable storeroom areas. Typically, a craft foreman would have the key and authorize withdrawals as needs arise. This would be a commonly applied arrangement for small storerooms near craft shops or within plant areas. It would also be common for larger storerooms that are attended during busy shifts to be locked and entered by a maintenance foreman on the second or third shift.

Fig. 2-1. Portion of a self-service storeroom showing items arranged for ease of selection.

Facilities for Receiving Stock Shipments. In a manufacturing plant, the volume of maintenance material might be far exceeded by production supplies. The receiving function would be likely to be consolidated in such cases to avoid duplication of services. Its location would no doubt be established for maximum convenience to the production storerooms. Most maintenance material would require plant transportation to the point of storage. While disadvantages from a maintenance standpoint are obvious, this might be the best arrangement.

In a chemical plant or petroleum refinery, to take another example, incoming hardware shipments would normally be for maintenance usage. A receiving area might well be established at the maintenance storeroom, particularly if it were set up on a centralized basis.

In any case, provision should be made for adequate facilities. This will include one or more docks for truck and perhaps rail shipments. Consideration should be given to providing a hoist or crane in at least one dock area for handling heavy equipment replacements or repair parts. Space will be required for the usual temporary storage during the processes of shipment identification and subsequent inspection. The facilities should be planned so that unnecessary handling is avoided.

Tool Crib Combination. It may be an advantage to combine the issuing of special tools for temporary use with the issuing of maintenance material. This is more likely to be the case if the tool control duties do not justify a separate, full-time attendant. The location of craft shops with respect to the maintenance storeroom will also influence whether such a combination of duties can properly be made. If so, the storeroom layout should provide for the required space and racks.

Location of Spare Parts. The preceding chapter brought out the advantages possible from centralized storing and record keeping for spare parts as well as regular maintenance material. It was indicated, however, that parts storage near the equipment concerned is sometimes desirable. Decisions along this line will be necessary in firming up the requirements for maintenance-storeroom facilities and space.

Spare parts are relatively expensive. If they are not kept in attended storerooms, they should be locked in cribs or cabinets except where their size or nature precludes their being lost, stolen, or misused.

Location of Salvaged Stock. Such items as valves, pipe fittings, motors, etc. may have a value after salvage that compares closely with the value of new stock. In

Fig. 2-2. Small delivery truck suitable for use either in plant aisles or between buildings.

many cases, the material can be substituted for purchased stock inventory and should be stored and controlled in a suitable manner. This can properly be done through the same storeroom facilities as for purchased material. Adequate planning for maintenance stores facilities will consider the salvaged items in specific categories.

Provisions for Pickup or Delivery. The maintenance storeroom in a small plant may need only the issuing window plus a locking gate for occasional entrance or exit of transporting equipment. In a large plant, however, it is often desirable to establish a material delivery system. This may involve either regularly scheduled or requested trips by a pickup truck or smaller plant-delivery truck. Figure 2-2 shows a type of truck suitable for inside or outside use.

In any case, but particularly where scheduled pickups are anticipated, the storeroom facilities should provide space for truck-load accumulation. In a multibuilding plant, dock space for loading of the truck may be needed.

Storage for Specific Large Jobs. Advance planning for large maintenance or construction jobs usually requires the ordering of certain nonstock items. After checking the receipt of these, they should be stored temporarily until the respective jobs are scheduled. Some items can be stored at the job site or out-of-doors. Others need to be kept in a locked crib until they are required.   Space for this purpose should be allocated so that over-all handling requirements are at a minimum.

It may also be advantageous to withdraw from regular stock certain items which will be required in unusually large quantities on planned projects.   It is common practice to place these in the temporary storage crib with nonstock items.

Free Stock.   As noted in the preceding chapter, some high usage items are not worth dispensing by stores attendants in the usual manner.   There is still the need to maintain inventory levels through visual inspection, however.   Accordingly, it may be appropriate to store such material at the central storeroom but outside the restricted area.   The stores layout should provide for such space as required.

High Value Items.   In addition to a storeroom enclosure in which only the attendants are normally admitted, a locked crib or storage cabinet may be required within the storeroom to which only designated individuals have access.   This will serve to

F̲ɪɢ̲. 2-3. Power hacksaw in metals storeroom, used with other cutting equipment to issue requested lengths and sizes.

control the items, such as new drill bits or hand tools, which are subject to being stolen.

Bulky, Heavy, or Weather-resistant Items.   Not all maintenance material must go in an enclosed storeroom.   Heavy equipment parts that are not easily transported may be kept where they will eventually be used.   Material such as lumber, pipe, and steel plate is commonly stored near the shops that use it, sometimes out-of-doors.   A survey of items in this category will assist in minimizing the maintenance stores area without making it inadequate.

Need for Cutting to Length or Size.   It is common practice for the maintenance shops to do what cutting is required on steel bar stock, steel plate, sheet metal, pipe, plastic, etc.   In such cases, the shops would provide storage for the partially used lengths or sheets.   For closer control, however, particularly where more than one shop location is involved, it is advisable for the central storeroom to do some cutting to length or size according to indicated needs.

Figure 2-3 shows one of several cutting tools within the storeroom of a large research laboratory which are used to prevent waste of steel sheet, plate, bar stock, and materials such as stainless steel, aluminum, brass, laminated plastic, etc.   The cutting operations are part of the assigned duties of stores attendants.   In addition to the power hack saw shown, there are metal band saws, a power shear, abrasive cut-off equipment, and plate-burning equipment.

Clerical Functions and Office Space. The preceding chapter covered the procedures involved in clerical stores control functions. The storeroom layout should make adequate provision for needed personnel and office equipment. Sufficient counter space is required for the attendants to receive requests and issue stock without crowding. Clerks who work at a desk should have facilities with which they can do an effective job. Supervisors' offices should be close to those with whom they are concerned.

BASIC STOREROOM DESIGN CONSIDERATIONS

The functional requirements of storeroom facilities will be indicated by analysis along the lines discussed in the preceding section. The next step is to develop the basic building and equipment requirements.

Location in Plant. Unless existing unused space requires making a compromise, the most practical location should be determined by considering points such as:

1. The flow of material into and out of the storeroom.
2. The flow of individuals served by the storeroom. Unless material delivery is emphasized, the time for maintenance men to make a round trip for needed material becomes important.
3. Integration with maintenance shop facilities. If the shops are centralized, for example, an adjacent or included stores facility would probably be needed.

Type of Building. One aspect is the choice between single and multistory buildings. When ground space permits, use of single-level storerooms will provide advantages such as:

1. Less handling by elevators, chutes, or hoists.
2. Ease in supervising personnel and using them effectively.
3. Greater load-bearing capacity for vertical stacking.

Handling Equipment. This should be suited to the type of material. It should be recognized that physical lifts of 50 lb for men or 35 lb for women are suggested as approximate upper limits.[1] These figures are subject to variations according to industry practice. State laws may be applicable in some cases. For small items that can be lifted by hand, simple grocery-type carts are ideal when filling orders.

Fork-truck handling of palletized loads is a common way to transport heavy material and store it so as to make use of vertical space. Figure 2-4 shows typical equipment in use for very high lifts. Figure 2-5 shows a smaller unit designed for lifting and storing plate stock. Permanently installed cranes or hoists may be justified where lifts occur frequently within a definite storeroom area.

A labor-saving, mechanized handling device for specialized uses is the stacker crane shown in Fig. 2-6. This kind of equipment may be adapted for pallets or other unit loads and serves to maximize the use of vertical storage space.

Storage Facilities. These should be designed for protection of stock, ease of access, minimum use of floor space, and accommodation of quantities to be stored. Some of the commonly applied types are as follows:

1. *Shelves and bins.* While they may be constructed of wood, the flexibility and relatively low cost of sheet-metal shelving or bins makes this form of small-item storage popular. They may be rectangular or circular, as shown in Fig. 2-7. Bin configurations range from tiers of built-in drawers to simple arrangements such as in Fig. 2-7, which shows inexpensive containers for orderly storage on shelves.
2. *Movable bins.* To reduce the required space, roller-mounted bins may be installed on parallel tracks, as in Fig. 2-8. The extra time to open an aisle space for access to parts must be weighed against floor space savings. This method would normally be considered only for very slow-moving items.

[1] Karger and Bayha, "Engineered Work Measurement," The Industrial Press, New York, N.Y.

FIG. 2-4. Fork truck used for high vertical lifts of palletized material.

FIG. 2-5. Small fork lift used for handling metal plate and similar material.

FIG. 2-6. Stacker crane used to reduce both handling time and floor space in the storage of maintenance material and manufactured stock.

FIG. 2-7. Typical rectangular and circular sheet-metal bins for material storage.   Extra space has been provided for future needs.

FIG. 2-8. Movable bins, equipped with rollers on floor tracks.

FIG. 2-9. Trailer used to store gaskets and other material near the work location in a petroleum refinery.

3. *Racks.* Various forms of specialized racks may be purchased or constructed for orderly storage of pipe, bar stock, sheet metal, steel plate, etc. Heavier, rectangular racks for palletized-load storage, (Fig. 2-4) are commonly installed to utilize air space rather than floor space. If the palletized material is uniform and sturdy, pallets may be stacked without racks. When fork trucks are used, aisle space is

required for truck turning.   This space may be reduced, vertical storage height increased, and handling time decreased by using stacker cranes as in Fig. 2-6.

4. *Portable facilities.*   Bringing the storeroom to the work site is practical to a limited extent, utilizing special-purpose trailers.   Figure 2-9 shows such an installation as applied in a petroleum refinery.

5. *Flammable liquids, chemicals.*   Separate storage areas may be required.   The types of containers should be developed to fit specific needs.

6. *Identification.*   In all cases, provision should be made for easy and precise identification of stored material.   The use of a comprehensive catalog is desirable, as previously discussed.   Item numbers should be visible on bins and racks where practical.   Use tags or direct marking on parts when needed for positive identification.   Color coding of bar-stock ends is a standard approach to designate the alloy content.   Identify material so that the required physical inventory can be taken by stores personnel with a minimum of confusion.

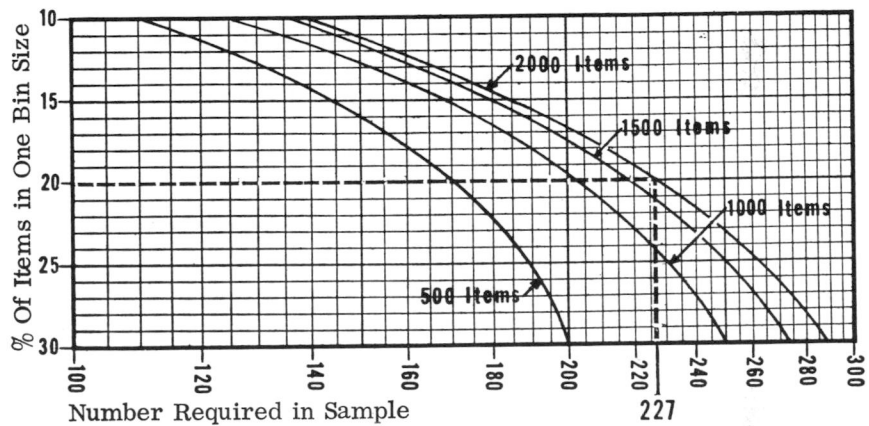

Fig. 2-10. Curves for determining number of parts to be sampled in the estimation of total bin requirements.

Capacity of Storage Facilities.   After you determine the items to be stocked, the quantities involved, and the types of storage facilities needed, the quantity of required facilities should be estimated.   This may be done for shelves and bins on a sampling basis as follows:

1. Obtain a list of (1) the total number of items to be stocked in bins, (2) the estimated number of times per year each item will be issued, and (3) the order point and order quantity of each.

2. From Fig. 2-10, determine how large a sample must be analyzed for valid checking of bin capacity needs.   The sample curves on this chart are calculated for a 95 per cent confidence level.   For example, if a storeroom carries 2,000 items and 20 per cent is the estimated maximum stored in any one bin size, some 227 items should be sampled at random from the stock list.

3. Compute the maximum quantity of each item sampled, which will be the order quantity plus approximately one half the order-point quantity.

4. Decide what bin size is needed for each of the maximum quantities.   Standardize on a bin depth, say 2 ft.   Estimate the width and height of opening required. Three or four bin sizes would normally be sufficient plus large bins for bulk items and roto-bins or drawers for small, loose parts.

5. Classify the samples by frequency of issue, for later use in storeroom layout. Generally, about 20 per cent will fall into the most-often-used group (A), 60 per cent into the less-often-used group (B), and 20 per cent in the rarely-used group (C).

6. Tabulate this information in chart form similar to that in Fig. 2-11, assigning each item to a bin just large enough to hold the maximum quantity. Indicate by letter which group the item belongs to. For the example charted, 49 of the items sampled will require a 12- by 12-in. bin, 42 a 12- by 18-in. bin, etc.
7. Compute the number of bins of each size needed to handle all 2,000 items. Thus, $\frac{49}{227}$ times 2,000 equals 432 bins of No. 1 size.
8. Allow a safety factor and a factor for future expansion as considered desirable. For example, 432 plus 20 per cent equals 518 bins of No. 1 size. Compute the total area of shelf opening and the total bin floor space.
9. Estimate the space requirements of palletized items, those requiring racks, etc.

ITEM	MAX. QUANTITY	BIN SIZES					
		#1 12 x 12	#2 12 x 18	#3 12 x 24	#4 24 x 24	Bulk 3' x 4'	Roto Bin
		1A					
						1C	
			1A				
					1A		
				1B		1C	
							1
TOTAL ITEMS FOR EACH BIN SIZE		49	42	46	25	26	39

Fig. 2-11. Method of tabulating samples of individual bin requirements to estimate total bin space needed.

Layout. In developing the storeroom layout, keep Group A items up front and Group C items in the rear. Movable bins might properly be specified for the latter to conserve space. The group letters of Fig. 2-11 will show how many bins of each size are needed for each classification.

Keep the aisles as narrow as practical. Keep allied items, such as nuts and bolts, together. Put heavy items and bulk materials in ground-level bins. Put the fastest-moving items at eye level.

Provide adequate space and facilities for all forms of storage and for the functions previously noted such as receiving, counter space, cutting equipment, clerical work, and accumulation for delivery.

Chapter 3

INVENTORY

By ROBERT W. FLESCH
Senior Management Systems Analyst
Space and Information Systems Division
North American Aviation, Inc.
Downey, Calif.

The quantity of materials stocked in company storerooms is maintained at its most economical levels through astute inventory planning. This presupposes careful and considerate coordination between independent plant groups which are concerned, to some degree, with the receipt or issuance of materials.

The sales department exerts the primary influence on inventories. This premise sometimes appears to be too remote to accept, but the current sales data of this group and its analysis of the future market are the factors which establish operating requirements. On this sales forecast, the planning group sets a production schedule.

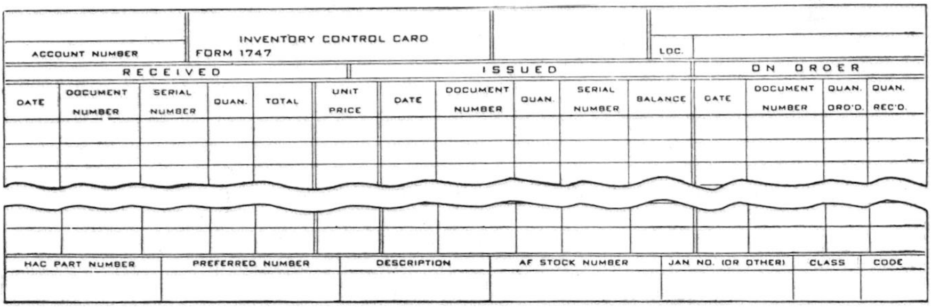

		INVENTORY CONTROL CARD									LOC.		ON ORDER		
ACCOUNT NUMBER		FORM 1747													
		RECEIVED					ISSUED								
DATE	DOCUMENT NUMBER	SERIAL NUMBER	QUAN.	TOTAL	UNIT PRICE	DATE	DOCUMENT NUMBER	QUAN.	SERIAL NUMBER	BALANCE	DATE	DOCUMENT NUMBER	QUAN. ORD'D.	QUAN. REC'D.	
HAC PART NUMBER		PREFERRED NUMBER		DESCRIPTION			AF STOCK NUMBER		JAN NO. (OR OTHER)		CLASS	CODE			

FIG. 3-1. Inventory control card. Used by material control to record material transactions.

Scheduling of operations is planned to provide for an integration of the numerous activities involved. One of these activities is to assure that all the proper materials will be on hand at the right time. If certain materials are very expensive or exceedingly bulky, it is wise to order specified amounts to be delivered at the time needed. This prevents the needless tie-up of working capital and also the overloading of storerooms or warehouses.

The material-control section is the proper center for focusing inventory quantity control. This group is the link between the production planning group and the purchasing department. It maintains records, Fig. 3-1, similar to those in the storerooms, which indicate material quantity balances on hand. In many companies these records also show the material unit cost and the total cost of each balance. Records for materials not primarily concerned with production (maintenance, repairs, and operating

11–31

supplies) may indicate minimum and maximum limits.   When balances of these items drop to or below the minimum figure, reorders are automatically authorized to restore the balances to the maximum quantity shown.

The personnel functions and location of material-control operations should be kept entirely separate from storekeeping activities.   This will discourage any opportunities for collusion in false recording to cover up shortages.   Actually, it will lead to more accurate balances when any variances between material-control and stores records are checked and corrections made.

Record quantity balances are determined by material control through posting all material transactions (receipts and issues) from documents used for this purpose. When balances on hand drop to the reordering point or new requirements are established, a material procurement or purchase requisition is completed.   This sets forth in detail the specific items needed, the total quantity required, and the lead time allowed (how much time is permitted to get the material on hand).   Sometimes, a specific vendor or trade name is recommended.   The requisition is sent to the purchasing department to negotiate buying terms.   Where restrictions are not imposed, purchasing selects the vendor on the basis of price, quality, or ability to meet delivery schedules.   Purchase and material records, Fig. 3-2, are kept.

At the time inventories are taken, some of the materials to be considered are found in the receiving department.   They might be recently arrived or undergoing test and inspection.   If found damaged in transit or not meeting the requirements of the purchase order, they may be rejected and returned to the vendor or accepted subject to certain conditions.   Rejected materials must not be included in the inventory records.

Financial control is a second phase of inventory control.   The most accurate quantity records are of little value unless they are accurately costed to agree with the ledger control.   Pricing the inventory tags and other media to determine inventory valuations is the function of the accounting or cost control department.   It is the responsibility of material control, however, to price the material documents for the transactions of each day's business unless standard prices are used.   Documents relieving stores for material issues at standard prices may be valued electronically by a tabulating means.

Some of the principles to follow for better inventory control are:

1. Establish a storeroom of ample size in a location close to operations.
2. Provide protection for the materials against all losses.
3. Employ only honest, competent, and intelligent stores personnel.
4. Permit no one to be within the storeroom at any time except authorized personnel.
5. Document all material transactions by an accounting form approved to provide required information.
6. Keep all stores- and material-control inventory records up to date.
7. Be sure that all material records are *accurately* posted.
8. Use inventory control as a tool of management rather than as an end in itself.
9. Eliminate surplus and obsolete materials from the storeroom to save valuable space, avoid confusion, and improve inventory accuracy.
10. Practice good housekeeping methods in stores to reduce possibilities of loss.

Use of Stores-control Systems.   Efficient storekeeping depends upon an effective control system.   Material must be maintained in usable condition, easy to locate when needed, and properly recorded for inventories.   The first step in storeroom control is to establish material classifications.   These individually designate each item stocked by a number referenced to a catalog file record or bin card.   Some classifications are based on a group number for each major material type, such as abrasives, paints, or hardware.   These are then divided into smaller subgroups on down to individual units.   Any stock or code number readily gives the key to the location and type of item it identifies.

When materials are stocked in numerical or coded sequence, items of the same type are grouped together.   Thus, sandpaper, sanding belts, and grinding wheels are all listed under the general heading of abrasives.   The group method leads to careful

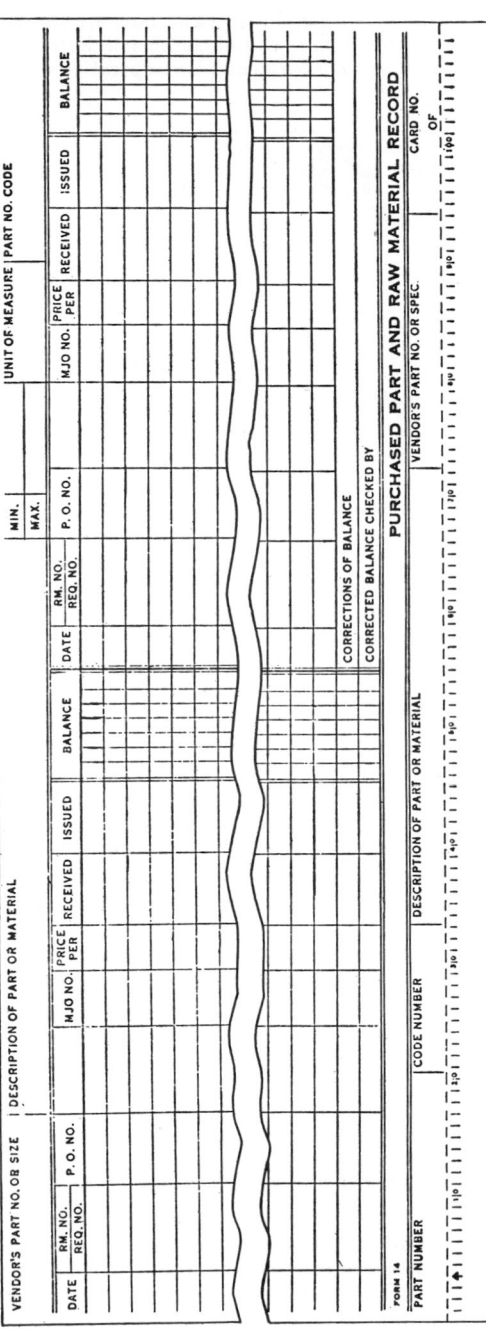

Fig. 3-2. Purchased parts and raw material record.   Stores inventory record of receipts, issues, and balance on hand.

planning of the layout of the storage bins. The bins are designated by numbered rows, numbered sections within each row, and the shelves lettered within each section. These are arranged in a protected area near plant operations where they are readily accessible for issuing material.

FIG. 3-3. Move tag. Identifies material moved by the transportation department or by others off company property.

To follow the movement of materials in and out of the storerooms, various types of documents, under accounting control, are required. Materials purchased from vendors (or returned from customers) are shown on *receiving reports*. Fabricated parts are noted on *move tags*, Fig. 3-3. Completed items are recorded on *finished units transfers*. Excess issues are returned by *credit slips* or requisitions, Fig. 3-4. Materials brought in from other accounts or from branches are entered on *stock transfers*, a similar form. All these receipts are debited to the stores inventory account.

Credits to the stores inventory arise from withdrawals. *Stores requisitions,* (a form almost identical with Fig. 3-4) issue materials for repairs, maintenance, operating supplies, etc. *Stock transfers* remove obsolete and surplus materials or items needed at branch facilities. All these documents are listed in sequence by control number and type in a daily log or register. This listing is invaluable for tracing lost documents and in verifying the cutoff for physical inventories.

The detailed information on material documents must fill the requirements of audit cost controls. These accounting forms all have a date, material description, unit of measure, and quantity. A serial number, approval signature, issue stamp, and the

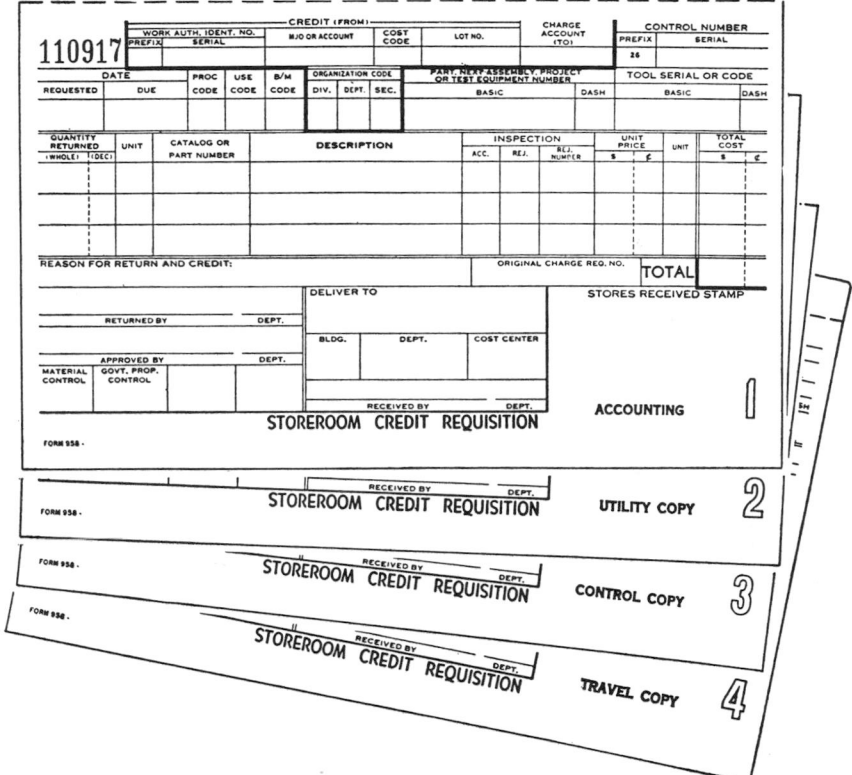

FIG. 3-4. Storeroom credit requisition. Records return of excess materials to stores.

value are also needed. The stores operate like banks, with controlled deposits and withdrawals. The inventories are statements of the balances on hand. If the deposit slips and checks have been correctly computed and applied, the accounts will agree with the financial controls.

All storeroom transactions are recorded from the material documents to ledger cards. To discourage fraud, these cards should not be located where store clerks have access to them. Good inventory clerks maintain adequate records for each material in stock. Cards for items currently on hand are sequenced in the "live" files. Formerly stocked materials are recorded in a "dead" file. An "on-order" file is used in some companies for items being reordered or temporarily out of stock. Bills of material or production schedules guide purchases of product materials. An effective way of handling nonproductive materials is to note reorders in the "live" records and carry maximum and minimum purchasing limits on each inventory card.

Each inventory card, Fig. 3-5, lists the material classification number, name of the item, and unit of measurement. It also has the date and quantity of each receipt and issue. When properly posted to record all material moving documents and adjusted for any errors or omissions, it will correctly show the balances on hand in the store bins. If these records are duplicated in the accounting department, they will also indicate the unit price and extended value of the current balance.

PART No._____				DESCRIPTION_____								
LOCATION_____							CARD No._____					
INVENTORY A/C No._____							UNIT OF ISSUE_____					
REC. MEMO PREPOST	DATE	R. M. NUMBER OR Requisition No.	P.O. NUMBER	ACCT. NUMBER	RESERVED	UNRESERVED	UNIT PRICE	AMOUNT		BALANCE
								RECEIVED	ISSUED	
BALANCE CARRIED FORWARD										

FIG. 3-5. Part record card. Store ledger card for material transactions.

Stores ledger records are not concerned with inventory values, but only with physical quantities. They are used for determining how much material is available for issue, without physically checking quantities at the time of each material issue, and to assure storekeeping accountability. Bin cards kept with materials are never reliable records. Store clerks, in their haste to fill orders, often forget to note issues and receipts or to compute the new balance. There is no need for bin cards if a good stores-inventory system is in use. Only in a very small company with inadequate inventorycontrol methods can bin cards be justified.

FIG. 3-6. Hold tag. Earmarks material for specific use until it can be removed from stores.

Where it is necessary or desirable to relate materials to their corresponding shop order, purchase order, shipment, etc., *identification tags* or *labels* are often used. *Lot release* or *hold tags*, Fig. 3-6, are also in common use for reserving materials to be set aside for a specific use.

An important stores-control function is to verify the usability of materials. Items which are damaged or destroyed are deleted from the records and cleared from the storage areas by transfer documents. Periodic physical inspections are made by a qualified materials engineer to discover and remove from the bins all deteriorated stock for salvage or scrapping. Records are also reviewed at regular intervals to note slow-moving items. Reports are then submitted for management investigation of those seldom-used materials, which can be reclassified for disposal as surplus or obsolete.

Costing. Costing is primarily an accounting function. It concerns the maintenance engineer, however, in relation to the efficiency of his department. This efficiency is influenced to some extent by the way in which maintenance operations affect plant overhead. To stay within the bounds of his budgeted expense, he must be certain that the material unit costs and units of measurement correctly reflect his inventories.

Maintenance materials are valued according to established units of measurement normally used. Lumber is counted by "board feet," plywood by "square feet," and rope by "lineal feet." Small items go by "each," "inches," or "square inches." Nails are inventoried by the "pound," paint by the "gallon," etc.

All unit costs are shown to three decimal points in the inventory ledgers. The number of identical items on hand multiplied by the unit cost produces the inventory cost. As an example, the inventory cost on 100 gal of machine paint priced at $5.717 per gal would be $571.70. This becomes the "extended cost" of the balance on hand. The total cost of an inventory is equal to the sum of the extended costs of all the items listed.

There are several methods which can be used for costing materials relieved from inventories. The one followed should be selected by company financial management to best fit its particular needs, subject to government tax restrictions and other requirements. A popular basis for costing purchased materials is the last-in–first-out (LIFO) method. A second very popular choice is the first-in–first-out (FIFO) plan. The average cost computation is also widely used.

Average unit costs may be determined on a weighted, arithmetic, periodic, or variable basis. The moving (variable) average unit cost is computed by first determining the extended values of the units on hand and of the newest quantity purchased. The sum of the two amounts is divided by the new total number of units on hand. To illustrate, if there are 100 sanding belts in stock at an average price of $0.400 each and an additional 100 are purchased at $0.350 each, the value of the two lots will be $40 and $35, respectively. The total value of the 200 belts, $75, averages out to $0.375 for each unit.

Taking Physical Inventory. Physical inventories confirm to management that material assets are reasonably intact. They are used to get accounting records certified by outside auditors and to compute a basis for insurance rates. Performed regularly, they show up both costly surplus or dangerous shortage. They also point out possible losses through waste, theft, obsolescence, or deterioration.

Inventories must be taken very accurately. Poorly handled inventory work confuses management as to the true status of materials storerooms. Large differences in the records might be interpreted as incompetent or fraudulent storekeeping. This will be avoided by sound planning and careful, intelligent operations. Audit control assures that all materials to be inventoried are counted and that the counting is reliable.

Physical inventories are usually made periodically. These counts are taken once or more annually, such as at midyear and year end. They can also be taken continuously on a perpetual (cycle) basis. The second method is used to advantage when there are many items to count, also where it is necessary or desirable to keep interruption of production at a minimum or where frequent discovery of material deterioration is required. There is a wide difference in the manner in which these two methods are employed.

Special inventories are taken at any time during the year when there is a particular need for the quantity information. Some companies also count certain items when the quantities are unusually low, during slack periods, or when a reorder is being considered.

Detailed preparation is required for physical inventories taken at stated periods. First, specific dates are scheduled, usually by the treasurer or controller. A plan for the inventory program is then developed. This can be modest or elaborate, as required by circumstances within each plant. It assigns definite functions for counting and audit control. The financial executive reviews, coordinates, and evaluates all details to assure that they are adequate and complete. He also arranges to have auditors present to observe the inventory.

Plant management sets a cutoff date, after which no materials move in or out of storerooms until the inventory is completed. This is to prevent double counting of the same items in more than one location. All paper work which issues or receives materials by the stores prior to the cutoff is noted as "before inventory." When all the before-inventory transactions have been posted, the material control records should agree, in quantities, with the inventory counts. Any variances are adjusted to the general ledger.

Serially numbered tags, Fig. 3-7, or listing sheets, under audit control, are used for noting the quantities of each item. For this work it is better to have counters teamed in pairs. One person counts, and the other writes down the figures, followed by his employee number or initials. Auditors observe the counting and verify the accuracy and honesty of the inventory teams. This is done by taking random tests of counted materials according to statistical sampling techniques.

Any tag or listing sheet number missing at the end of the inventory is considered lost, destroyed, or covering material not recorded in the count. The use of three-part inventory tags assures greater accuracy and speeds counting operations. When the auditors approve the count in an area, the original copies of the tags can be detached and sorted into numerical sequence. They are then checked at tag control for missing numbers and forwarded to accounting for pricing. The duplicates are sent to material control to verify quantities on the card records. The third copy remains with the material until all the original copies have been located and returned to audit control.

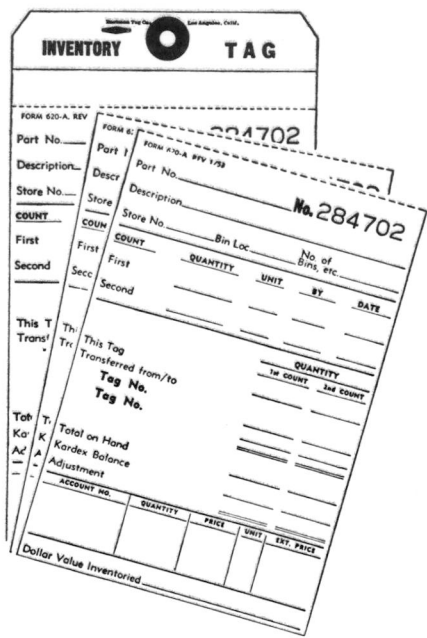

If listing sheets are used, inventoried items are identified to prevent double counting. Where tags are utilized, a control is established to account for every tag issued. All tags and listing sheets, including those voided or unused, must be returned to the auditors. Missing tags are located, to account for all inventoried material, before the inventory is acceptable. For this reason, *no tags are to be destroyed.* Erasures are not permitted, since they might indicate tampering with a count. An error on a tag requires that it be voided and replaced with a new tag. Errors on listing sheets are lined through, and the correct entry noted below.

To save time, large inventory areas are divided into small sections. This enables auditors to follow closely behind the counters. They can test each section as it is counted instead of waiting for the whole area to be completed before starting their check. It also restricts the quantities to be recounted if the auditors find too many errors. Areas (or sections) indicating excessive counting errors are rejected and completely recounted.

FIG. 3-7. Inventory tag. Used in taking physical inventory.

Materials en route to the storerooms or directly to their end use must also be counted. Items found in the receiving or inspection areas are identified by packing sheets or receiving reports, and the quantities inventoried. These can be accurately checked by preparing an extra yellow copy of all receiving reports for materials received during the two weeks before the inventory. These yellow copies, collected in large envelopes by the auditors, represent part of the receiving-area inventory. They and the material from which they are removed should be rubber-stamped "after inventory" to prevent double counting when the materials are received in the storeroom. Materials arriving too late for preparing a receiving report are assigned receiving report numbers and noted on listing sheets. These lists cover the balance of the inventory for those areas.

The before-inventory yellow receiving reports are detached from the material in the storeroom. They are forwarded, with the regular copy, to material control. There they are destroyed after the quantities are posted to card records or punched on tabulating cards from the regular copy. The receiving- and inspection-area inventory is processed through the storeroom in the normal way and posted to the records as "after inventory." This latter group, plus the quantities in the storeroom and in-transit material with an F.O.B. at shipping point, comprise the total physical inventory.

Perpetual inventories are scheduled to complete one or more full cycles each year. A selected number of items are counted each month. The results are posted to storeroom ledger cards, and material-control records are adjusted to correct errors. When the entire inventory has been counted, the cycle is repeated.

Perpetual inventories are tested periodically to maintain a check on their accuracy. Discrepant balances may be due to:

1. Errors in accounting figures.
2. Failure to record transactions for issues or receipts.
3. Use of wrong materials, in issues or receipts, through misidentification.
4. Loss of materials through waste, theft, deterioration, etc.

Where the auditors are assured that the records are reasonably accurate, a physical inventory is not always necessary at the year end.

Pricing. The principal methods of pricing inventories are (1) cost, (2) market, and (3) the lower of cost or market. Market value usually means either *replacement market* or *selling market*. These two terms are subject to certain restrictive interpretations. The proper pricing basis to use is a decision for the company accounting executive to make. The cost method appears to be the most favored in industry.

Prices are a measure of value only. They can change almost from day to day. It is hardly possible to price an entire closing inventory, however small, at the actual value as of any one day. There is always a time lag in entering price changes in the records. The fastest personnel and finest calculators can do little in overcoming this handicap.

Even with the use of authentic prices, clerical errors creep into inventories through faulty computations or inaccurate transcriptions. The wrong amount posted from an invoice, an error in the invoice or source document, and a transposition of figures are common mistakes. Where many different materials are stocked, tests are made to assure that the right inventory figures are taken from the records or original invoices. The correct amounts must be used in extending an accurate count to arrive at a valid inventory total. If either the unit price or quantity count is falsely stated, inventory values (considering any adjustments for market) will not agree with general ledger control accounts.

With the physical count or pricing out of balance, no true accounting of the company's material assets can be attained. A good physical inventory is almost useless when the prices by which it is valued are misstated. Variances will then exist which must be correctly computed. These variances are properly applied to the ledger control to reflect the actual inventory values.

Section 12

LUBRICANTS AND LUBRICATION

Chapter 1

LUBRICANTS

By ALLEN F. BREWER
Consultant in Lubrication, Eden, Fla.
Formerly Editor of The Texas Company Publication "Lubrication"

Lubrication is of interest to the maintenance engineer because it has an influence upon his personal comfort and the costs he must charge to maintenance. Any machine will operate most dependably when it is properly lubricated. Under such conditions the maintenance engineer has only to note (in company with the operating engineer) that lubrication is being properly maintained and that lubricants most suited to the operating and constructional conditions are being used. This leads to minimum cost of maintenance, fewer headaches for the maintenance engineer, and low-cost production.

As a rule the maintenance engineer is not consulted when the plant is purchasing lubricants. That responsibility belongs to the purchasing and operating people. In all fairness the maintenance department also should be included. But to cooperate, the latter should be adequately informed as to how lubrication and lubricants fit into the picture. Let the purchasing and operating people bother about the details; the maintenance engineer is concerned chiefly with how successfully these details (as to viscosity, pour test, carbon-residue content, penetration, melting point, etc.) will obtain lubricants which will so thoroughly protect the machine parts that his responsibilities for maintenance will be within reason.

The Conventional Tests. For lubricating oils these include viscosity, flash and fire points, pour-point test, carbon-residue content, emulsification and demulsibility, and acidity or neutralization number, color, sulfur content, and saponification number. For greases the base, the penetration, and the dropping or melting point are most significant.

Viscosity as an indication of the relative fluidity of any lubricating oil is discussed regardless of the service. Machinery builders develop their lubrication recommendations around viscosity; it is the number one test when purchasing. Viscosity, however, does not denote quality; it indicates simply how the oil will flow at the temperatures under which lubrication must be maintained. This is of decided interest to the maintenance engineer. He does not care about the viscosity of a hydraulic oil, for example, at 100°F, the usual laboratory temperature of test; his interest is in the fluidity at the operating or working temperature on the machine. Unless the fluidity is right for the unit and the oil is resistant to foaming and oxidation and able to protect the machine against rusting, parts failure may result.

Viscosity changes with temperature, and the rate of change is denoted by the viscosity index (VI). The higher the viscosity index, the less change in fluidity with change in temperature.

Flash and fire points are customarily quoted in listing the characteristics of a lubricating oil, but unless it is to be used under very high temperature conditions where vaporization could be a factor, the flash and fire points are of little interest to the maintenance engineer. Flash point is the temperature at which the vapors given off by the oil when gradually heated will ignite momentarily when a flame is applied. Fire point is the somewhat higher temperature at which the vapors will ignite and burn steadily. The flash point of any well-refined petroleum lubricating oil, regardless of base but with respect to viscosity, is above 300°F. Normally the higher the viscosity, the higher the flash and fire points. Like viscosity, these tests do not tell much as to the lubricating ability, but they can be useful in deciding upon the viscosity of any make-up oil required when consistently high temperatures in the oiling system promote vaporization and subsequent increase in viscosity of the oil remaining in the system.

Pour-point test is another temperature test which should be considered with respect to the viscosity of an oil. In contrast to flash and fire points, the pour test interests the maintenance engineer because it indicates how fluid he can expect the oil to be at very low temperatures. In the laboratory the pour test is run to develop the lowest temperature at which the oil will pour or flow. The lower the viscosity (for oils of like base), the lower the pour test. With straight mineral oils (without use of pour depressant additives or special dewaxing) naphthenic-base oils will show lower pour tests (for the same viscosity) than paraffin-base oils. Pour test is most useful in selecting refrigeration-grade lubricating oils for normal industrial service or when machine or bearing oils are to be used in circulating systems which may be exposed to low atmospheric temperatures. In small-diameter piping, an oil of inadequate pour test could become so congealed during a cold overnight shutdown as to result in starved lubrication and the need for bearing replacement. The maintenance engineer is particularly concerned with such a possibility.

Carbon-residue content of an oil is a factor in internal-combustion-engine service. Being an indication of residual matter, it becomes allied with the lubricating ability of the oil. For clean engine performance it should be as low as possible. With the modern detergent and dispersant types of heavy-duty engine oils, engine cleanliness is more positively assured by the quality and additive make-up of the oil than by the carbon-residue content of the base oil. In internal-combustion-engine maintenance it is very important to watch the cleanliness of the air intake and the water temperature. Dirty air or condensation of moisture in the crankcase can contribute far more to cause a dirty engine and need for frequent overhaul than the fraction of a per cent of carbon residue which may be indicated by the laboratory test.

Emulsification and demulsibility are tests which definitely relate to lubricating ability when the oil is to be used for steam-turbine lubrication, in steel- or paper-mill circulating systems, and in hydraulic operations. Emulsification indicates the tendency of an oil to mix intimately with water to form a more or less stable emulsion. Demulsibility indicates the readiness with which subsequent separation will occur. As oil-water emulsification is a prelude to oil oxidation when other oxidizing conditions such as air and high temperature are present, an oil which will break such an emulsion most readily is desirable under these conditions. Additives are available to assist in breaking such emulsions. Normally, oils for the service indicated above are known as "turbine grade." The maintenance engineer can assure best performance of such oils if he sees to it that oil temperatures in the system do not get too high (say 150 to 160°F maximum), that the oil-reconditioning system is operating effectually in removing water and other contaminants, and that the rate of water flow to the oil coolers is adequate to enable returning oil to the system at around 100°F.

Neutralization number is related to acidity. The laboratory measures this characteristic in a lubricating oil by noting the number of milligrams of potassium hydroxide required to neutralize 1 g of oil. Usually this is very low in a well-refined oil, normally less than 0.10. The basic figure in the new oil, however, if of far less interest to the maintenance engineer than subsequent increase after the oil has been put in service in a turbine or hydraulic system. Abnormal rise can be taken as an indication of oil oxidation. Good practice is to arrange for regular laboratory testing of the oil in service for its neutralization number and to plot charts showing the rate of rise for hours of service. If this is considered abnormal, the lubrication engineer should be

Table 1-1. Lubricating Greases—Their Characteristics and Properties*

	Older, specialized greases				Newer, multipurpose greases	
Specifications:	Calcium	Sodium	Mixed base	Aluminum	Barium	Lithium
Type of soap	Calcium	Sodium	.....	Aluminum	Barium	Lithium
Texture	Smooth buttery	Fibrous or buttery	.....	Smooth to stringy (never fibrous)	Smooth to fibrous	Smooth to buttery
ASTM dropping point (approximate)	190°F	325°F (plus)	.....	185°F	350°F (plus)	350°F (plus)
Service qualities: Maximum continuous usable temp.	160°F	250°F (plus)	Specific data as to texture, dropping point, temperature limitations, etc., are not given in this column because variations in the percentages and types of ingredients used and methods of manufacture employed make it impossible to state with any degree of accuracy what the characteristics of the finished product will be	180°F	275°F (plus)	275°F (plus)
Resistance to water (average)	Good	Fair		Good	Good	Good
Resistance to breakdown and softening by working	Fair to good	Fair to excellent		Poor to fair	Poor to fair	Good to excellent
Behavior after subjection to 250°F and cooled (under working conditions)	Separates	No change		Liquefies	No change	No change
Principal uses	Cup Pressure gun Heavy duty (For general purpose industrial use)	Antifriction; plain bearings Flat surfaces (For moderately high temp. lubrication)	Life-lubricated bearings Specialized lub. (For widely varying, unusual demands)	Chassis fittings Oscillating bearings, etc. (Where insolubility or extreme tackiness is needed)	Multipurpose "All bearings" (For general automotive lubrication)	Air-craft lub. Multipurpose (For superior performance at extreme temperatures)
Remarks	Most calcium-base greases contain water of hydration'. Above approximately 160°F, they tend to lose this water, which is necessary to their stability, and separate into the original oil and a hard curdy soap. Below 160°F, calcium greases show good mechanical stability	Soda-base greases give good performance at moderately high temperatures. When short-fibered or buttery, they are excellent for high-speed antifriction bearings. When made from well-chosen materials, they resist mechanical breakdown and oxidation	Mixed-base greases vary widely, in performance with variations in the kind and percentage of ingredients used—and manufacturing methods. This classification includes the very stable, oxidation-inhibited greases used in 'lifetime' lubricated bearings	Aluminum greases maintain their consistency and texture up to the melting point. However, they may 'set up', if heated above this point and then cooled. They are very 'tacky', but never fibrous. The popularity they enjoyed some years ago for certain applications, has been transferred to other types of greases	Barium greases bring together many of the best characteristics of various other greases and hence are good multipurpose lubricants. However, because of their high soap content, they may cause trouble in grease-dispensing systems, in very high-speed bearings, and in low-temperature operation.	Lithium greases, of special composition, have the best available low-temperature characteristics and are also excellent for high-temperature uses. However, their temperature characteristics may vary widely, depending on the kind of materials used. Certain lithium greases have the highest known mechanical stability

* Courtesy of Shell Oil Company.

consulted. It may be most economical to drain the system, flush, and install a new charge of oil. Meanwhile the maintenance engineer should be investigating the cause, i.e., abnormal temperature, above 160°F; stray electric currents; effectiveness of the oil-reconditioning system; steam leaks plus boiler compounds; excess air in the oiling system.

Color is most significant where transparent cutting oils are involved; it is of relatively minor importance in machine oils and circulating or hydraulic oils because today such products are all of relatively light color due to their degree of refinement. Although color does not necessarily indicate quality in a lubricating oil, it is definitely a factor when selecting a transparent cutting oil for metal working, where the operator must observe the action of the tool upon the work during the cutting process in the interest of more positive control of surface finish accuracy.

Sulfur Content. Sulfur is a factor in a sulfurized cutting oil, *but* it must remain in *noncorrosive* form. To assure this, the oil must be held at a reasonably constant temperature during storage and circulation to obviate variation in solubility and possible change in the chemical make-up. Corrosive sulfur is objectionable because contact with water and oxygen (from the air) could lead to formation of sulfurous and sulfuric acids. In such oils 3.00 per cent is normally regarded as the acceptable maximum sulfur content.

Saponification Number. Saponification is a chemical reaction involving the action of an alkali upon a fat or fatty acid; the resultant combination is called a soap. Saponification will rarely occur in a well-refined mineral oil and then only where fatty acids may have resulted because of oxidation or chemical breakdown. In effect, the principle of saponification is the basis for the manufacture of certain greases.

The tendency which a petroleum lubricating oil may have to saponify is determined by neutralization and is measured by the equivalent amount of caustic potash required to react with or neutralize one gram of the oil under test. In terms of milligrams of caustic the resultant figure is called the saponification number of the oil. Obviously this should be as low as possible. Increase in the tendency toward saponification may have a like effect upon the tendency toward oxidation and gum formation in the oil.

Lubricating-grease Characteristics—Tests. *Base.*[1] Lubricating greases are classified broadly according to the type of soap used in their manufacture. The more conventional products include the calcium (lime) base or general-purpose greases usable up to around 160°F, sodium base products usable up to at least 250°F, and the soda-lime (mixed base) greases which are so widely used for service where the combined features of their respective elements are enhanced by inclusion of antioxidation additives.

In addition there are the more recently developed multipurpose greases of primarily lithium, barium, or strontium base, as well as the aluminum and lead soap products which are designed for more specialized service where good resistance to water is required along with high temperature durability up to 275°F (plus).

Among the nonpetroleum materials which are applicable to grease service are the bentones, which can be compounded with certain petroleum products, and molybdenum disulfide, which has excellent high-temperature stability, good film tenacity, and low coefficient of friction. The latter is effective at high sliding velocities. The average operating conditions to which bearings on industrial or power-plant machinery along with machine tools are subjected permit the use of any of these types of grease, all of which have excellent lubricating ability when used according to these conditions and the means of application. Table 1-1 shows in detail the conventional types of lubricating greases, their characteristics, and, as will be noted, the base.

Penetration relates to the consistency of a grease, also to some extent to its texture. The maintenance engineer is concerned with grease consistency because the grease must continually reach the parts to be lubricated. Too heavy or inert a grease in a roller bearing could channel in the housing and develop an inadequate lubricating film on the rollers. In a pressure system serving a considerable number of bearings, a grease too heavy for the diameter of the piping or pumping ability of the pump could

[1] Allen F. Brewer, Lubricants and Coolants. (Courtesy of "Machine and Tool Blue Book," Hitchcock Publishing Company, Wheaton, Ill.)

cause clogging of the lines and, again, inadequate lubrication, which could mean only parts renewal later.

Dropping or melting point is a temperature measurement for a grease; it indicates the tendency for the product to soften with increase in temperature. The percentage and type of soap used in manufacture, the viscosity of the mineral oil, and type of alkali affect the dropping point of the finished grease. As a rule sodium- and lithium-soap greases show higher dropping points than those of calcium base. To some extent this indicates that the former are better suited for higher temperature service, although the dropping point should not be assumed to indicate the maximum usable temperature. This requires laboratory study taking into consideration the maximum expected operating temperature, the speed, type of bearings, method of lubrication, and type of bearing seals. Modern high-speed heavy-duty service which prevails on machine tools, textile machinery, and other precision units requires most careful preanalysis of the expected operating conditions in the interest of ensuring dependable operation and low-cost maintenance in service.

TYPES OF LUBRICANTS

Petroleum lubricants are broadly classified according to the service for which they are most widely used. Some are virtually specialties; others can be successfully applied to such a wide variety of machinery as to become multipurpose in nature.

The maintenance engineer is interested in the following classifications:

Circulating oils.
Gear oils.
Machine or engine oils.
Refrigeration-grade oils.
Spindle oils.
Steam-cylinder oils.
Wire-rope lubricants.
Greases of calcium, sodium, aluminum, lithium, or barium base.
Solid and synthetic lubricants.

Circulating Oils. These are probably the highest quality lubricants available today. They are obtained over a comparatively wide range of viscosities, i.e., from around 21 to 550 centistokes (100 to 2,500 seconds Saybolt Universal[1]) viscosity at 100°F. In this category are included:

Steam-turbine-grade oils.
Hydraulic oils.
Steel-mill circulating oils.
Paper-machine circulating oils.
Heavy-duty internal-combustion-engine oils.

Circulating oils may be of paraffin or naphthenic base according to the service. For turbine, hydraulic, and steel-mill service the former predominate. Either naphthenic- or paraffin-base oils are used for paper-machine and heavy-duty engine service. The viscosity range at 100°F is given in Table 1-2.

Circulating oils contain additives. Turbine and hydraulic oils are fortified to enable them to resist oxidation and to retard rusting in the system; they also usually contain a foam dispersant.

Steel-mill and paper-machine oils must have high-demulsibility properties the same as turbine and hydraulic oils. They also are inhibited by additives to improve their resistance to oxidation and to enable them to retard rusting; some also may contain a foam dispersant.

The modern heavy-duty internal-combustion-engine oil is specifically refined to function under high engine temperatures and bearing loads. These oils are highly resistant to oxidation and are fortified with detergent and dispersant additives.

[1] Hereafter to be indicated as SSU.

Gear Oils. These may be straight mineral oils of widely varying viscosity or compounded oils containing extreme-pressure additives to improve the film strength and load-carrying ability.

Straight mineral gear oils for plant service range normally from SAE 80 to 250. They are suitable for enclosed gear sets of spur, bevel, helical, spiral bevel, herringbone, or annular type where there is provision for splash or force-feed lubrication. The lower viscosity grades are used for low-temperature service, the heavier grades, i.e., SAE 140 or 250, being selected for service which will normally range above 100°F. Such oils are best suited for average tooth loads and pinion speeds.

Where gears of the above type are exposed and bath or hand lubricated, the viscosity of the lubricant must be increased to enable the film to resist throwoff. Exposed gear sets generally do not run too fast, but because of their location, they may be exposed to wide temperature ranges, viz., the swing gear on a power shovel or turning gear on a bessemer converter. For such gears a straight mineral residual petroleum product is used which may be compounded with a small percentage of pine tar to

Table 1-2. Viscosity Range of Circulating Oils

Service	Viscosity at 100°F	
	Centistokes	SSU
Steam turbine:		
Direct connected..................................	32–40	150-185
Geared..	65-110	300-500
Hydraulic:		
Light service.....................................	21–54	100 250
Machine tools.....................................	30–121	140-550
Heavy duty..	Up to 154	Up to 700
Steel mill:		
Oil film roll neck bearing according to service...........	54–550	250–2,500
Paper machine:		
Drier end roller bearings and calender stack..............	87–187	400–850
Internal-combustion engines:		
Heavy-duty SAE 30 to SAE 60 according to service.......	110 -370	500–1,700

improve the adhesiveness. Some such lubricants are cut back with solvents to facilitate application. These thinners later evaporate from the film, but as some solvents may be flammable, it is well not to use such lubricants in enclosed areas. The question of toxicity also is important.

When the hypoid gear came into usage and later when other types of industrial gears were designed to carry heavier tooth loads, the extreme-pressure type of lubricants were developed. Hypoid gear oils are of the heavy-duty type in order to stand up under the extremes of load and temperature which prevail in modern automotive service.

The mild noncorrosive type of extreme-pressure gear oil is more of a lubricant for use in industrial plants. Such a product may have the same load-carrying ability and film strength as a hypoid gear oil, but the nature of the additives puts it into the mild E-P category. This type of gear oil is useful not only for conventional steel-on-steel gears but also in worm gear sets where nonstaining of the bronze gear is important. In fact it is the nonstaining feature of such lubricants which fostered the noncorrosive identity and which makes such products virtually multipurpose in nature.

Machine or Engine Oils. The straight mineral red oils come under this classification. They came into usage for general lubrication of external operating parts of engines, pumps, compressors, and general machinery when unit lubrication by oil can or oil cup was practiced. Later they were adapted to ring oilers, but on modern machines where circulating oiling systems are installed, the higher quality turbine-grade oils are used.

The average so-called machine or engine oil is a good lubricant for "once-through" lubrication, but since the resistance to oxidation is lower than that of the modern premium-grade circulating oils, ordinary machine oils are not recommended for service where formation of sludge or gummy residues could add to the troubles of the maintenance engineer.

Refrigeration-grade Oils. Refrigeration service involves low temperatures in certain parts of the system where oil may be present. Normally, refrigeration compressors are run so that as little oil as possible will pass over with the compressed refrigerant. Most of the oil which may pass over should be trapped by the oil separator, but some may get by to be deposited on the surfaces of the expansion coils and reduce refrigerating efficiency.

Low pour test used to be the primary requirement provided the oil was of the recommended viscosity. During recent years the floc point has become a primary test when Freon or other similar types of refrigerants are used. The floc-point test is made to determine the presence of congealable wax. Normally it is desirable for this test to be at least $-60°F$, especially if deep-freeze or other very low temperature service is involved.

Refrigeration-grade oils are of comparatively low to medium viscosity, ranging from 15 to 121 cs (80 to 550 SSU) viscosity at 100°F. They may be of either paraffin or naphthenic base, but in any event they should be virtually free from moisture. Normally they are refined and packaged to show a dielectric strength of at least 25,000 volts.

As the maintenance engineer is actively concerned with good refrigeration efficiency, he should watch the oil separator to be sure it is doing its job and that not more than a trace of oil is going over to the expansion side of the system. Cleaning coils is a costly maintenance procedure; an oil of unduly high wax content, as indicated by high pour and floc points and churning or foaming in the compressor, can overload the oil separator and aggravate this condition. It is well also for the maintenance engineer to check on how the operators add make-up oil. If they handle it carelessly from the shipping drums or cans (exposing it to the air), it will probably go off dielectric by absorbing some moisture. This can freeze in the system or accelerate sludge formation in the crankcase.

Spindle Oils. These involve the relatively light- to medium-viscosity straight mineral oils which are designed primarily for textile spindle service where speeds upward of 10,000 rpm may prevail. For spinning motors and ring-type spindles the oil will range from around 10 to 32 cs (60 to 150 SSU) viscosity at 100°F. For mule spindles a heavier oil is required, i.e., from around 38.5 to 76 cs (180 to 350 SSU) viscosity. Spindle oils are among the most carefully refined products of the petroleum industry and are always regarded as premium-grade lubricants. They must be highly resistant to oxidation and gum-forming tendencies because any drag on the fast-turning spindles has a definite effect on power consumption.

Steam-cylinder Oils. The necessity for lubricating steam cylinders with something more dependable than the time-honored tallow pot became evident when steam engines were operated on high-pressure steam and when multistaging or expansion was adopted. By that time the petroleum industry had perfected methods of refinement and residual lubricating stocks were available so that compounding with a few per cent of fatty (animal) oil such as lard oil, tallow, or wool fat to improve the wetting ability of the finished oil became standard practice. The principle remains the same today, although the petroleum chemist has isolated certain base stocks such as bright stock and the fire stocks dewaxed more or less, which with steam-refined stock make available a variety of products for compounding according to the nature of the steam (i.e., pressure, temperature, moisture content), the utilization of the exhaust, and whether or not very rapid atomization is desired.

Being residual in nature steam-cylinder oils are necessarily of higher viscosity than distilled oils such as turbine oils. They can be grouped into three broad classifications according to viscosity, i.e.:

Table 1-3. Characteristics of Synthetic Lubricants*

	Low-temperature flow properties	Inhibitor susceptibility	Resistance to oxidation	Water solubility	Thermal stability	Lubricating ability	Viscosity index
Hydrocarbons	Fair to 0°F, although some are OK to −40°F	Poor to good according to type	Fair to good according to type	Immiscible	Poor to good according to type	Comparable with equivalent petroleum oils	Slightly above petroleum paraffin-base oils
Polyalkylene oxides and polyethers (glycols)	Generally good to −40°F	Generally fair	Low	Mostly water-soluble to insoluble	Suitable for high-temperature work	Good where high-temperature usage requires vaporization with minimum residue	Up to 150
Esters	Generally good to −70°F	Good	Fair	Mostly immiscible	Have high flash point		Up to 150
Silicones	Good to −70°F	Poor	Good up to 390°F; above this they oxidize rapidly	Immiscible	Good	Most effective only when one surface is nonferrous. Additives improve	High
Fluorocarbons	Fair	....	Excellent	Immiscible	Excellent but volatility may be high	Not too well known	Below 100

* From Allen F. Brewer, "Basic Lubrication Practice," Reinhold Publishing Corporation, New York.

Light—100 to 120 SSU at 210°F.
Medium—120 to 150 SSU at 210°F.
Heavy—150 and above SSU at 210°F.

They are used by injection into the steam line by hydrostatic or mechanical force-feed lubricator. When a suitable injection quill is installed in the line, the steam atomizes the drops of oil as they pass onto the quill thereby to carry a so-called fog or mist of oil to all parts of the cylinder walls, pistons, valves, and valve seats. Engineers call this "lubricating the steam."

The maintenance engineer can judge how effectually a steam-cylinder oil is lubricating by noting if the engine groans or is unduly noisy, if the condensate has a milky appearance, if there is a light film of oil on the piston rod.

Wire-rope Lubricants. Lubrication of wire rope has undergone quite a transition. At one time it was felt that best protection resulted from using a comparatively heavy residual-type lubricant similar to a heavy gear lubricant. Today the idea of using lighter-bodied oils is popular, applying them by spray to assure better penetration between the rope strands. For this purpose a specially prepared fluid lubricant of around 600 SSU viscosity is adaptable. Inclusion of a few per cent of pine tar gives it added stickiness and also penetrative ability. This type of lubricant is especially suited for wire rope which must be exposed to the weather and low temperatures as on aerial tramways.

For less severe service a somewhat heavier straight mineral product is satisfactory; this type of lubricant can be applied by drip, brush, or split box.

The maintenance engineer is particularly concerned with good wire-rope lubrication because strand breakage can require removing the rope from service and installing a new rope. Safety precautions require rigid inspection.

Greases. The American Society for Testing Materials defines a lubricating grease as "a combination of a petroleum product, and a soap or mixture of soaps, suitable for certain lubrication applications." The metal used in making the metallic soap constituent of a grease denotes its base, i.e., calcium, sodium, aluminum, lithium, or barium. In addition a mixture of calcium plus sodium produces what is called a mixed-base grease. Table 1-1 indicates the features and serviceability of modern greases.

Greases are further identified by the type and viscosity of the petroleum oil used in their make-up, by their degree of plasticity, and by their dropping or melting point. A combination of these factors scientifically worked out will produce a grease of remarkable stability and endurance over a wide range of temperature conditions. The multipurpose grease is the ideal, as it reduces the possibility of misapplication and is a factor in storage.

There used to be a popular conception that greases were chosen for a job where a fluid oil could not be retained owing to the nature of the housing or inadequacy of the seals. Modern design has relegated this idea to the past. Today in the ball- and roller-bearing field, for example, precision manufacture is so fine and seals are so perfect that lifetime lubrication by just a few grams of grease in a bearing is practicable. Furthermore greases are available which will function over very wide temperature ranges. Installations of this type are a boon to the maintenance engineer. *But* when any such bearing is to be disassembled from the other parts of a machine during overhaul procedure, the sealed ball or roller bearings must be carefully handled. An effective seal is effective only as long as it is not abused. Careless handling or soaking in solvents may lead subsequently to entry of abrasive dust due to windage.

In maintenance work the protection of a grease lubrication system is just as important as protection of the bearings or other parts being lubricated. Modern pressure-greasing systems, which involve many fittings, control outlets, long lengths of piping, and a suitable pumping element, cost thousands of dollars. Careless usage of tools around these parts or inadvertent striking while moving a beam or scaffold might render some one or more outlets inoperative because of stricture or grease leakage. The resultant cost for repair could be alarmingly high. For this reason the maintenance engineer should be on the alert and work with the operating people to see that machine personnel are fully aware of the importance of respecting all parts of the pressure-greasing systems on their units.

Table 1-4. Solid Lubricants*

Product	Nature and characteristics	Lubrication service adaptability
Bentones	Produced by reacting hydrous magnesium aluminum silicate (montmorillonite) or bentone clay with an ammonium salt. Features are stability at high temperatures, water resistance; do not liquefy	Effective in compound with petroleum greases. Prepared by a gelling process. No soap is involved. Well suited for high-temperature service and extreme water conditions
Fuller's earth	Silica base—finely divided	Can be used dry or mixed with water, light oil, or grease. Effective in retarding fretting corrosion. High temperature resistant up to around 700°F
Graphite	Produced from coke or anthracite coal. Milled to obtain colloidal graphite usable for lubrication. The flake nature in form of sheets piled on top of each other imparts the lubricating effect as these sheets slide over one another in motion	Can be used dry or mixed with oil or grease. Its chemical inertness enables its use where high thermal stability is required. Maximum usable temperature is around 1500°F. Not too effective in preventing corrosion when used dry
Molybdenum disulfide (MoS₂)	Stable at high temperatures. Good film tenacity. Low coefficient of friction	Effective in reducing friction at high sliding velocities. May be mixed with a solvent for application to parts to be lubricated. To obtain best results from a chemically active lubricant of this type the metal surfaces should be *clean*
Mica	A natural mineral which is ground very finely	Can be used like talc as a lapping material to obtain high surface finish of machine parts. Sometimes added as a filler or thickener in certain lubricants
Talc	Powdered soapstone	Suitable as a lapping material for finishing or working in machine parts
Zinc oxide (ZnO₂)	White in color. Particle size very small—requires no milling. Has low coefficient of friction	Usable as a component with mineral oil for lubrication of parts where perishable products are being produced as in food handling and meat processing

* From Allen F. Brewer, "Basic Lubrication Practice," Reinhold Publishing Corporation, New York.

Synthetic and Solid Lubricants. Names and characteristics of nonpetroleum lubricants are given in Tables 1-3 and 1-4.

THE OPERATING CONDITIONS—ADDITIVES

In addition to knowledge of the basic characteristics of petroleum lubricants it is necessary to consider the operating conditions and their relation to additives. There have been drastic changes in design, construction, and operation during the past 25 years. Modern machinery is precision built, and lubrication is planned when the layouts are on the drawing board. Wartime production called for overspeed and overload. These conditions often required or resulted in higher temperatures. Steel came to the runout tables hotter; faster paper drying and calendering called for the use of higher temperature steam; metal presses working on heavier gage stock developed greater reaction pressures on gears and bearings; gear sets were enclosed to enable use of more fluid extreme-pressure-type gear oils; ball and roller bearings were precision built to run at speeds upward of 100,000 rpm and over temperature ranges from −75 to 400°F; bearing seals were improved to enable lubrication for life; synthetic materials came into active competition with metals.

Maintenance schedules had to be arranged to fit in with these requirements and often round-the-clock operation. It all hinged on lubrication. A new era developed in lubricant manufacture. Additives became a byword because straight mineral oils and conventional greases simply could not stand up under the conditions involved. So the maintenance engineer should know how modern lubricants are fortified to give them the required stability.

Additives serve a variety of useful purposes; accordingly there are a variety of additives.

Pour-point Depressants. These are added to lubricating oils to enable them to flow at and be usable at lower temperatures than would be possible with the base oil. Such additives retard or change the action of formation of wax crystals at low temperatures so that they do not interfere with the fluidity of the oil.

Viscosity-index Improvers. Viscosity-index improvers are added to an oil to improve the viscosity-temperature relationship, in other words to obtain as little change in viscosity as possible over the expected service-temperature range.

Antioxidants. Antioxidants, often called inhibitors, are widely used to fortify steam-turbine, hydraulic, and circulating oils, also ball- and roller-bearing greases, against oxidation when subject to oxidizing conditions. Oxidation of lubricants vitally concerns the maintenance engineer because the resulting gums, lacquers, and sludges generally call for considerable expensive machine overhaul and cleaning of the working parts.

Foam Depressants. These additives are useful in turbine and circulating oils to prevent foaming when they are agitated with air; foam depressants also accelerate foam dispersion when it has once formed.

Anticorrosion Additives and Rust Preventives. These serve a very useful purpose especially when added to circulating oils and to some types of greases. They retard metal corrosion and rusting when the surfaces are exposed to moist air or to water. Some condensation must occur in practically every machine housing as a result of breathing. The greater the humidity and wider the temperature range, the more moisture may result. Ordinary lubricants exert a certain amount of wetting action upon metallic surfaces, but the protective films are not lasting when much moisture is present, especially when the parts are idle. So the petroleum industry includes rust-preventive and anticorrosion additives in premium-grade lubricants to increase the preferential wetting ability and to neutralize any acidity.

Extreme-pressure (EP) Additives. Extreme-pressure additives are most widely known probably because they are so closely associated with the automotive hypoid gear. An extreme-pressure additive is a chemical compound which increases the load-carrying ability of the lubricating film when subjected to high rubbing speeds and heavy tooth loads. Extreme-pressure additives reduce friction and wear especially at high temperatures, where they are most effective. When metal-to-metal contact occurs between meshing gear teeth, so-called spot welding develops between the surfaces under the extremely high spot temperatures which prevail. This can lead to serious tearing away of surface metal and to serious malfunctioning of the gear set. Then a maintenance problem results, usually calling for gear replacement. An extreme-pressure additive in the gear oil imposes a sufficiently protective and easily sheared lubricating film between the teeth. In other words the ideal of tooth surface sliding plus rolling at the line of contact is maintained; the oil film resists wiping off at high rubbing speeds and squeezing out under high pressures.

Engine-cleanliness Additives. *Detergents* and *dispersants* are included in this category. They are used in the make-up of modern heavy-duty motor and engine oils. *Detergents* are cleaners. They ensure most satisfactory performance of a circulating oil by preventing residual nonlubricating matter, such as sludges and lacquers which result from oil decomposition and fuel combustion, from accumulating around piston rings, in bearing clearances, and elsewhere on the engine parts. Regardless of the original degree of purity of the oil ultimately it will get dirty because of entry of road dust via the crankcase breather or air cleaner, water of condensation, and the natural results of service under high temperatures. The oil filter removes some of these contaminants, but some will remain to develop the sticky gummy substances which ultimately bake onto the hot metal surfaces. A suitable detergent in the oil prevents this by virtue of its continual dissolving and cleansing action. To assist in this function a companion additive known as a *dispersant* is included to keep these finely divided insoluble materials dispersed in the oil until drain-out. No harm to the engine results from this action because after filtration the dispersed material is virtually nonabrasive.

Engine maintenance is costly. The modern heavy-duty oil is a boon to the maintenance engineer in giving better and longer engine performance between overhauls. As the oil filter and air filter are valuable assistants, he should see that they are cleaned or renewed at regular intervals according to the severity of the service and dust content of the air.

MAINTENANCE AND LUBRICATION[1]

Maintenance is directly affected by operating conditions. The cost of maintenance, in turn, is directly influenced by lubrication. Higher maintenance costs must be expected when the operating conditions impose severe loads on the running parts of any machine.

As parts turn faster with respect to each other, their surfaces tend to wear faster. Structural members may change physically because of the vibration or the stress and strain of increased loading.

While lubrication can retard wear, it cannot entirely prevent it. Wear can be due to dust contamination or failure of the lubricating system to maintain a proper film on operating parts. Furthermore, the load on a lubricant under severe operating conditions is equally as heavy as it is on the machine. Adequate maintenance and proper design, however, can control the effects of these loads.

What Is Maintenance? Maintenance consists of any measures designed to keep a machine in good operating condition. Primarily it is just a job of housekeeping. Furthermore, maintenance can become more costly under severe operating conditions. It also can become more costly under dirty or sloppy conditons. Sometimes these conditions cannot be avoided; however, regular cleanup schedules will keep dirt and oil from accumulating on the machine and in the work area.

Cleanup is sometimes charged to maintenance; when this is done, it is low-cost insurance. The cost of a few man-hours a day for cleanup plus cleaning equipment is far less than the cost of machine downtime.

Maintenance must be planned. It is false economy to run any machine until it requires mechanical attention. Inspection, lubrication, adjustments, and cleaning at regular intervals will keep the average machine running a lot longer and with lower production costs. This is preventive maintenance. When planning such a schedule, the first step is to organize the inspection procedure. That is when to decide how often various machine parts should be lubricated and to what extent. At inspection time, loose fittings can be spotted and adjusted. Once a week is often enough for a routine inspection, although certain critical points may require daily inspection. The lubrication engineer, machinist, or millwright is the logical person to make this inspection.

Management Responsibility. A general inspection should be made once a month. At every third such inspection, the plant superintendent or chief engineer should invite an engineer from the lubricant supplier to accompany the maintenance people on their inspection tour. By working together they can determine where the use of an improved type of bearing or lubricating device would make a machine run smoother, longer, and more economically; where a more suitable grade of lubricant would

[1] Allen F. Brewer, Lubricants and Coolants. Courtesy of "Machine and Tool Bluebook."

reduce the frequency of lubrication; or where the housing of overexposed gears would improve safety, reduce fire hazards, and cut the cost of removing dripped lubricant. Management also can promote preventive maintenance by praising operators personally for keeping their machines and working areas clean of dirt and oil. The spoken words "well done" are often much more appreciated than an impersonal memo from the front office with the same message.

Employee Responsibility. Machine operators also have a responsibility in machine lubrication. They should not squirt oil around carelessly or turn down grease cups with a wrench. Sure, this keeps critical machine parts lubricated, but it also wastes lubricant; it may break bearing seals; it can cause slippery footing around a machine; and it can adversely affect the plant's fire-risk rating.

LUBRICANT PROTECTION

Protection of lubricating oils and greases in service is just as important as selecting products of the right characteristics to meet the operating conditions of speed, load, and temperature. This is a requirement which too often is neglected. Premium-grade products are purchased and then stored in some dirty storeroom or even out of doors, drums on end, to accumulate water and dirt. Subsequently it is almost impossible to draw oil or scoop out grease from such a container without some contamination occurring. Obviously the answer is to provide a special location *indoors* for storing lubricants and to plan a definite schedule for taking stock, refilling containers or lubricating systems, and cleaning, with assigned plant personnel responsible for this schedule.

Industry is taking this matter of lubricant protection more and more seriously. Many plants now have experienced lubrication engineers on their operating staffs. The lubricating-equipment people, in turn, have developed devices and procedures for handling and distributing lubricants which are equally as progressive. It is to the interest of the maintenance engineer to see that lubricant protection is practiced, not merely preached. Machine failure due to lubrication can easily start at the point of storage by contamination of the lubricants with abrasives or water or even sometimes acids from fumes in the air.

The best procedure in planning a program for lubricant protection is to decide on a location for storage. This should be done with consideration of the volume of lubricants used and the facilities for delivery—in the average plant assume by truck. The storage area should be not too far away from the working area, although in mining or construction work this might not hold true.

The Location and Personnel. A clean, well-lighted room or building is advisable with provisions for heating in cold weather. It should be specifically kept for lubricant storage and reserve lubricating equipment. In this way the responsibility for cleanliness and proper location of lubricant containers can be assigned to one or two individuals who, in reality, become assistant lubrication engineers. They can be trained by the maintenance engineer to appreciate his problem should a bearing or gear set fail as a result of contaminated lubricant. Likewise they can be schooled in appreciating the value of quality lubricants and the reasons why such products are virtually specialties for the service to be performed. When lubricating systems are to be serviced, these people may also have that responsibility in some plants. In others they may fill the orders from the area supervisors or foremen, the actual job of checking the lubricating systems being detailed to head operators, millwrights, or other members of the lubrication department.

Facilities for Handling Containers. One-level handling is an important item wherever possible in planning for lubricant-container storage. If practicable the floor level should be the same as a delivery truck floor. This facilitates rolling of drums into the storeroom, where racks can be arranged along one or more walls so that oil drums can be raised by a lift truck and spotted in order to draw the contents off with the least effort into distribution containers. Grease drums normally are stored on end because the contents are removed by paddle, scoop, or pressure pump, according to the consistency of the grease.

In large plants, where a considerable volume of lubricants must be stored, a set of parallel rails (see Fig. 1-1) are useful for handling full drums to service racks as well as empties for return.

Lighting—Relates to Good Records. The lubrication and maintenance departments can function most effectually when they have complete records as to lubricant consumption per machine or plant area. This requires careful inventory (monthly) and recording of amounts of oil and grease issued. Lighting plays an important part. If the storeroom is painted with gloss white, if light outlets are well located to obviate glare, and if a comfortable record desk is installed, the personnel logically will keep more careful records. These records all must be considered periodically when the maintenance engineer is preparing his cost-of-maintenance report for the management.

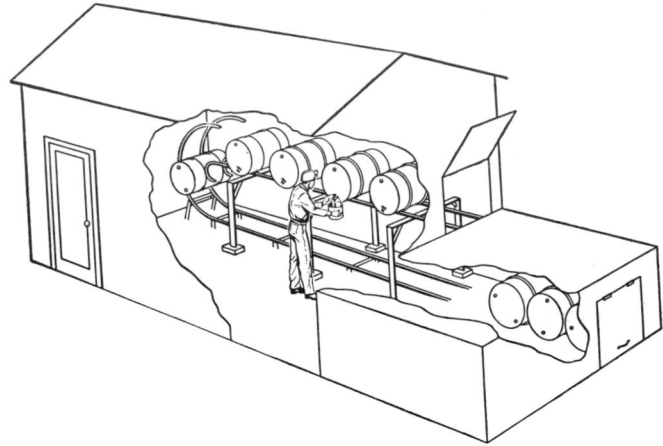

FIG. 1-1. Parallel rails for handling both full drums and empties. (*Courtesy of The Texas Company.*)

Fire Protection. The possibility of fire in a well-planned lubricant-storage area is remote, assuming that *no smoking* rules are observed, that casual visits from other plant people are prohibited, that oil drip is prevented or cleaned up promptly, that waste or wiping rags are stored in metal containers and in *minimum* quantity, that sparking or arcing tools are used only under conditions of good ventilation. Even so, insurance regulations will require installation of suitable fire-extinguishing equipment. The accepted foam-type device for smothering oil fires is best. In a small storeroom one or two hand units may suffice. In a larger area a multiple-gallon foam cart with adequate hose may be required.

Lubrication Terms. Table 1-5 makes available definitions of the most used terms in the field of lubrication. They are compiled by the American Society of Lubrication Engineers Educational Committee.

Table 1-5. Lubrication Terminology
Courtesy ASLE Educational Committee

Additive. A chemical compound or compounds added to a lubricant for the purpose of imparting new properties or of enhancing those properties which the lubricant already has.

Alkali. Any substance having basic properties. In a restricted sense it is applied to the hydroxides of ammonium, potassium, and sodium.

Aluminum-base grease. A grease prepared from a lubricating oil and an aluminum soap.

API gravity. A gravity scale established by the American Petroleum Institute and in general use in the petroleum industry, the unit being called the "API degree." This unit is defined in terms of specific gravity as follows:

Table 1-5. Lubrication Terminology (*Continued*)

$$\text{Degrees API} = \frac{141.5}{\text{sp. gr. } 60/60°\text{F}} - 131.5$$

Axial-load bearing. A bearing in which the load acts in the direction of the axis of rotation.

Ball bearing. A rolling-type bearing containing rolling elements in the form of balls.

Barium-base grease. A grease prepared from lubricating oil and a barium soap.

Black oil. Any dark colored lubricating oil which is used for the lubrication of machine parts under exposed conditions.

Bleeding. The tendency of a liquid component to separate from a liquid-solid or liquid-semisolid mixture, as an oil from a grease.

Block grease. Generally, a grease of high dropping point which, under normal temperatures, is firm to the touch and can be handled in block or stick form.

Bright stock. A term referring to high-viscosity lubricating oils which have been refined to make them clear products of good color.

By-pass filtration. A system of filtration in which only a portion of the total flow of a circulating fluid system passes through a filter at any instant or in which a filter having its own circulating pump operates in parallel to the main flow.

Centralized lubrication. A system of lubrication in which the lubricant or lubricants for the bearing surfaces of a machine or group of machines are supplied from a central location.

Circulating lubricant. A system of lubrication in which the lubricant, after having passed through a bearing or group of bearings, is recirculated by means of a pump.

Clearance bearing. A journal bearing in which the radius of the bearing surface is greater than the radius of the journal surface.

Coefficient of friction. The number obtained by dividing the friction force resisting motion between two bodies by the normal force pressing the bodies together.

Cold test. As referred to an oil, a test by which the pour point is determined.

Compounded oil. A petroleum oil to which has been added animal or vegetable oil, or other substances.

Consistency. The degree to which a semisolid material such as grease resists deformation (see ASTM Designation D 217). Sometimes used qualitatively to denote viscosity of liquids.

Coolant. A fluid used to remove heat (see **Cutting fluid.**)

Corrosion. Destruction of a metal by chemical or electrochemical reaction with its environment (Corrosion Handbook).

Cutting fluid. Any fluid applied to a cutting tool to assist in the cutting operation by cooling, lubricating, or other means.

Detergent. In lubrication, either an additive or a compounded lubricant having the property of keeping insoluble matter in suspension thus preventing its deposition where it would be harmful. A detergent may also redisperse deposits already formed.

Dispersant. In lubrication, a term usually used interchangeably with detergent.

Drop-feed lubrication. A system of lubrication in which the lubricant is supplied to the bearing surfaces in the form of drops at regular intervals.

Dropping point (of grease). The temperature at which a grease passes from a semisolid to a liquid state under specified test conditions (ASTM Designation D 566-42).

Emulsibility. The ability of a non-water-soluble fluid to form an emulsion with water.

Emulsion. A mechanical mixture of two insoluble liquids as oil and water.

EP (extreme-pressure) lubricants. Lubricants which impart to rubbing surfaces the ability of carrying appreciably greater loads than would be possible with ordinary lubricants without excessive wear or damage.

Fiber grease. Grease having a distinctly fibrous structure which is noticeable when a sample of the grease is pulled apart. Greases having this fibrous structure tend to resist being thrown off gears and out of bearings.

Filler. Any substance such as talc, mica, or various powders, which is added to a grease to increase its weight or consistency.

Filter. Any device or porous substance used as a strainer for cleaning fluids by removing suspended matter.

Fire point (Cleveland open cup). The temperature to which a combustible liquid must be heated so that the released vapor will burn continuously when ignited under specified conditions (ASTM Designation D 92-57).

Flash point (Cleveland open cup). The temperature to which a combustible liquid must be heated to give off sufficient vapor to form momentarily a flammable mixture with air when a small flame is applied under specified conditions (ASTM Designation D 92-57).

Fluid friction. Friction due to the viscosity of liquids.

Force-feed lubrication. A system of lubrication in which the lubricant is supplied to the bearing under pressure.

Fretting. Wear phenomena taking place between two surfaces having oscillatory relative motion of small amplitude.

Table 1-5. Lubrication Terminology (*Continued*)

Fretting corrosion. Corrosion which results from fretting. Sometimes called friction oxidation.

Friction. The resisting force encountered at the common boundary between two bodies when, under the action of an external force, one body moves or tends to move relative to the surface of the other.

Full-flow filtration. A system of filtration in which the total flow of a circulating fluid system passes through a filter.

Graphite. A crystalline form of carbon having a laminar structure. It may be of natural or synthetic origin.

Grease. A lubricant composed of an oil or oils thickened with a soap, soaps, or other thickener to a semisolid or solid consistency.

Gum. A rubber-like, sticky deposit, black or dark-brown in color, which results from the oxidation of lubrication oils or from unstable constituents in gasoline which deposit during storage or use.

Heavy-duty oils. A term designating a type of oil having the oxidation stability, bearing corrosion preventive properties, and detergent dispersant characteristics necessary to make it generally suitable for use in both high-speed diesel and gasoline engines under heavy-duty service conditions (SAE Handbook).

Hydraulic oil. An oil specially suited for use as a power transmission medium in hydraulically operated equipment.

Hydrodynamic lubrication. A system of lubrication in which the shape and relative motion of the sliding surfaces cause the formation of a fluid film having sufficient pressure to separate the surfaces.

Hydrometer. An instrument for determining either the specific gravity of a liquid or the API gravity.

Hydrostatic lubrication. A system of lubrication in which the lubricant is supplied under sufficient external pressure to separate the opposing surfaces by a fluid film.

Hypoid gear lubricant. A gear lubricant having extreme pressure characteristics for use with a hypoid type of gear as in the differential of an automobile (SAE Handbook).

Imperfect-film lubrication. A condition of lubrication in which the lubricant film is not continuous over the bearing area.

Inhibitor. A substance which slows or prevents such chemical reactions as corrosion or oxidation.

Lacquer. A deposit resulting from the oxidation and polymerization of fuels and lubricants when exposed to high temperatures. Similar to, but harder than, varnish.

Lead naphthenate. A lead soap of naphthenic acids, the latter occurring naturally in petroleum.

Lime-base grease. A grease prepared from a lubricating oil and a calcium soap.

Lithium-base grease. A grease prepared from lubricating oil and a lithium soap.

Lubricant. Any substance interposed between two surfaces in relative motion for the purpose of reducing the friction and/or wear between them.

Mechanical lubricator. A mechanical device for supplying lubricant to various parts of a mechanism. With this device, the lubricant is not usually recirculated.

Mixed-base crude or **intermediate-base crude.** Crude oil, not predominantly paraffinic or naphthenic in character, found in the mid-continent and other districts.

Mixed-base grease. A grease in which the thickening agent or base is generally a mixture of sodium and calcium soaps, although other soaps may be used.

Naphthenic base. A characterization of certain petroleum products prepared from naphthenic-type crudes (crudes containing a high percentage of ring-type aliphatic hydrocarbon molecules).

Neutral oils. Lubricating oils of low or medium viscosity obtained in petroleum distillation and prepared without chemical treatment. They derive their name from the fact that they have not been treated with either an acid or an alkali, but have been purified by simple filtration.

Nonsoap grease. A product similar to grease in appearance and consistency, but containing only heavy residual stocks and mineral oil.

Oil. A greasy, unctuous liquid of vegetable, animal, mineral, or synthetic origin.

Oiliness. That property of a lubricant which produces low friction under conditions of boundary lubrication. The lower the friction, the greater the oiliness.

Oil ring. A loose ring, the inner surface of which rides a shaft or journal causing the ring to rotate. The ring dips into a reservoir of lubricant from which it carries lubricant to the top of the shaft for distribution to a bearing.

Paraffin base. A characterization of certain petroleum products prepared from paraffin-type crudes (crudes containing a high percentage of straight chain aliphatic or paraffinic hydrocarbon molecules).

Pad lubrication. A system of lubrication in which the lubricant is delivered to a bearing surface by a pad of felt or similar material.

Penetration or **penetration number.** The depth, in tenths of a millimeter, that a standard cone penetrates a semisolid sample under specified conditions (ASTM Designation D 217-60T). (See **Worked Penetration.**)

Table 1-5. Lubrication Terminology (*Continued*)

Penetrometer. An instrument for measuring the penetration of semisolid substances.

Pivoted pad bearing. An axial or radial load type of bearing in which the bearing surface consists of one or more pads or shoes which are pivoted in such a manner to permit them to tip and thus promote the establishment of a hydrodynamic film.

Plain bearing. Any simple sliding type of bearing as distinguished from fixed-pad, pivoted-pad, or rolling-type bearings.

Porous bearing. A bearing made from porous material, such as compressed metal powders, the pores acting either as reservoirs for holding or passages for supplying lubricant.

Pour point. The lowest temperature at which a lubricant will pour or flow under specified conditions (ASTM Designation D 97-57).

Ring lubrication. A system of lubrication in which the lubricant is supplied to the bearing by an oil ring.

Roller bearing. A rolling-type bearing containing rolling elements in the form of rollers.

Rust-prevention test (turbine oils). A test to measure the effectiveness of an oil in preventing the rusting of ferrous parts in the presence of water (ASTM Designation D 655).

SAE numbers—SAE oil-viscosity classification. Numbers applied to crankcase, transmission, and rear-axle lubricants to indicate their viscosity range.

Saponification. A process in which a fat (or other compound of an acid with an alcohol) reacts with an alkali to form a soap and glycerine or other alcohol.

Saybolt Universal viscosity (SUV) or Saybolt Universal seconds (SUS). The time in seconds required for 60 cubic centimeters of a fluid to flow through the orifice of the Standard Saybolt Universal viscometer at a given temperature under specified conditions (ASTM Designation D 88-56).

Saybolt Furol viscosity. The time in seconds required for 60 cc of a fluid to flow through the orifice of a Saybolt Furol viscometer at a given temperature under specified conditions (ASTM Designation D 88-56). The orifice of the furol viscometer is larger than that of the universal viscometer and is used for viscous liquids.

Semifluid. Any substance having the attributes of both a liquid and a solid. Similar to a semisolid but being more closely related to a liquid than to a solid.

Semisolid. Any substance having the attributes of both a solid and a liquid. Similar to a semiliquid but being more closely related to a solid than to a liquid.

Sludge. Insoluble material formed as a result either of deterioration reactions in an oil or by contamination of an oil, or both.

Slushing oil. An oil- or grease-like material used on metals to form a temporary protective coating against rust, corrosion, etc.

Soap. A compound formed by the reaction of a fatty acid with an alkali.

Soda-base grease. A grease prepared from lubricating oil and sodium soap.

"Soluble" cutting oil. A mineral oil containing additives which enable it to be mixed readily with water to form a stable emulsion for use as a cutting fluid.

Specific gravity. The ratio of the weight in air of a given volume of a material to the weight in air of an equal volume of water at a stated temperature.

Spindle oil. A light-bodied oil used principally for lubricating spindles and light, high-speed machinery.

Splash lubrication. A system of lubrication in which parts of a mechanism dip into the lubricant and splash it on to themselves and/or on to other parts of the mechanism.

Sponge grease. A soda-base grease differing from the smooth, buttery soda-base greases in that it is more fibrous and sponge-like in structure.

Steam emulsion number (SE No.). The number of seconds required for an oil to separate from water when emulsified with steam and then allowed to separate under specified conditions (ASTM Designation D 157).

Steam refined. With reference to lubricating oils, a term applied to unfiltered residual cylinder oils from which the lighter fractions have been distilled by the direct application of steam.

Step bearing. A plane surface bearing which supports the lower end of a vertical shaft.

Strong acid number (SAN). The quantity of base, expressed in milligrams of potassium hydroxide, required to neutralize the strong acid constituents present in the gram of sample (ASTM Designation D 664-58).

Synthetic lubricant. A lubricant produced by synthesis rather than by extraction or refinement.

Tacky. A descriptive term applied to greases which are particularly sticky or adhesive to metal surfaces.

Thin-film lubrication. A condition of lubrication in which the film thickness of the lubricant is such that the friction between the surfaces is determined by the properties of the surfaces as well as the viscosity of the lubricant.

Unworked penetration. The penetration at 77°F of a sample of grease which has

Table 1-5. Lubrication Terminology (*Continued*)

received only the minimum handling in transfer to the test apparatus and which has not been subjected to the action of a grease worker (ASTM Designation D 217-60T).

Varnish. When applied to lubrication, a deposit resulting from oxidation and polymerization of fuels and lubricants. Similar to, but softer than, lacquer.

Viscometer or **Viscosimeter.** An apparatus for determining the viscosity of a fluid.

Viscosity. That property of a fluid, semifluid, or semisolid ˙ substance which causes it to resist flow. It is defined as the shear stress on a fluid element divided by the rate of shear. The standard unit of viscosity in the English system is the *reyn*, which has the units of lb sec/in.². The standard unit of viscosity in the cgs system is the *poise*, which has the units of dyne sec/cm². 1 reyn = 6.895 × 10⁴ poises.

Viscosity index (VI). A commonly used measure of a fluid's change of viscosity with temperature. The higher the viscosity index, the smaller the, relative change in viscosity temperature.

Viscous. Possessing   viscosity. Frequently used to imply high viscosity.

Waste lubrication. A system of lubrication in which the lubricant is delivered to a bearing surface by cloth waste or yarn.

Wick lubrication. A system of lubrication in which the lubricant is delivered to a bearing surface by means of a wick.

Worked penetration. The penetration of a sample of lubricating grease immediately after it has been brought to 77°F and then subjected to 60 strokes in a standard grease worker (ASTM Designation D 217-60T).

Yarn grease. Cup, sponge, or residuum greases containing strands of wool or cotton yarn.

DESIGNING FOR LUBRICATION[1]

The function of the machine designer with respect to lubrication is to relate the objective—maximum production—to the systems of lubrication best suited to the operating conditions and to the lubricants which will most effectively protect the proposed mechanisms. The production value of any machine is of major concern to management. There must be assurance of adequate return on the investment to cover operating and maintenance costs, amortization, and dividends to stockholders; otherwise the machine is not paying its way. Since design and lubrication are tied in with operating and maintenance costs, it is necessary to design for lubrication at the time of planning for production.

Naturally this requires familiarity with the types, capabilities, and limitations of lubricating systems. In this regard the lubrication engineer can help the machine designer lay out a coordinated system of lubrication at the same time he is planning for coordinated operation of the mechanisms which will be required in the completed machine. In effect, designing for lubrication should begin on the drafting board.

Operating conditions are the predominant factors which must be considered from the beginning. These involve the speeds at which rotating parts must turn in their bearings or at which reciprocating parts must ride over ways and guides, load conditions in gear trains, the probable temperature ranges, and cleanliness or the chance of lubricant contamination. Then there is the possibility of overload in order to speed up production after the machine is in service. This could increase the severity of these conditions. Factors of safety are included when strength of materials is being considered. There is no numerical factor of safety in regard to lubrication, however, except to use the most suitable product available after consideration of how severe the duty may become. Fortunately the modern systems of centralized lubrication contribute to this assurance. They are designed to protect lubrication and to insure against lubricant contamination. However, they must be able to handle the most protective lubricant. In other words, don't expect a gear oil intended for usage on exposed gears to be effective in a high-speed bearing oil-circulating system.

Safety Considerations. Safety of operating personnel also must be considered. Usually it is practical to plan for inclusion and installation of modern systems of lubrication so that operators will not have to take a chance when adjusting fittings or going through the normal relubrication procedures. Intricate parts which require hand lubrication can involve personal hazard, especially if this is done while the machine is in operation. The designer should forestall this possibility by putting

[1] Allen F. Brewer, Lubricants and Coolants. Courtesy of "Machine and Tool Blue Book."

such parts on the centralized system, even though it may require external service lines from the main source of oil or grease supply. Furthermore it will be assurance that such parts will be receiving adequate lubricant to prevent undue wear and premature replacement of parts.

Tolerance and Speed. The machine designer assumed added responsibilities when mechanized production required the use of more specialized alloys of steels and nonferrous metals, which in turn called for higher cutting-tool speeds. This brought the soluble oils into the picture. As distinguished from cutting oils, the soluble or emulsifiable oils are complex compounds capable of forming emulsions when mixed with water. While limited to temperature extremes, they are applicable to an extensive variety of both ferrous and nonferrous metal-cutting requirements.

The availability of new cutting and grinding soluble fluids has enabled the machine designer to plan for surface finishes hitherto not attainable. It made no difference whether he was planning for the inclusion of miniature ball bearings on an aircraft control mechanism or heavy-duty roller bearings as required in steel mills. The ultimate contact surfaces of the rolling elements must be comparable, in the former because extreme operating speeds are the objective, and in the latter because of the higher operating temperatures under which subsequent lubrication must be maintained.

With the increase in operating speed which has attended rising production requirements, lower tolerances or clearances also have become desirable in the interest of maintaining alignment. Precision finish of gear teeth, ball or roller bearings, and some types of shafting designed to run on sleeve bearings also assures that higher speeds can be attained with greater load-carrying capacity. This is especially true when the film strength of the prospective lubricant is increased by inclusion of a suitable extreme-pressure (EP) additive, plus rust prevention and oxidation-retarding materials to increase the chemical stability.

Relation to Heat Transfer. Since heat transfer is an important function of fluid lubrication, this factor also must be considered when any system of oil circulation is being studied. Elevated temperatures, for instance, can lead to serious metallurgical changes which can reduce hardness of gear teeth and steel shafting. There is evidence that this ultimately could result in gear-tooth failure due to wear if the oil does not have sufficient film strength.

Sometimes provisions for water cooling by means of coils in oil reservoirs are practical; otherwise the designer could plan for a longer rest period of a circulating oil by increasing the reservoir capacity. This is a phase of the design and lubrication procedure which must not be overlooked. Oftentimes designing to enable adequate radiation will suffice, as in the case of unit lubricated ball or roller bearings where heat developed within the housings is transmitted to the external race with subsequent cooling by heat transfer to the surrounding air, provided there is adequate ventilation.

ENDURANCE VALUE OF PETROLEUM LUBRICANTS[1]

The petroleum chemist goes beyond the usual conventional laboratory procedures in considering tests to predict lubricating or endurance value. He considers those factors which will denote the wetting ability of the product, its film-forming ability, its behavior when exposed to water, and its tendency to form sludge or saponifiable by-products. Service considerations will dictate the relative importance of each of these factors.

Wetting Ability. The wetting ability of the lubricating film is regarded as probably its most important function if dependable and protective lubrication is to be maintained. In other words, the extent to which effective lubrication can be expected depends upon the extent to which the lubricating film actually wets the surfaces of the metal parts between which motion is taking place.

Wetting ability as a function of adhesion can be illustrated by wetting steel-strip surfaces with oils which are to be compared. The surface which is wet or coated with a satisfactory oil will retain this film when dipped in water, the water clearly draining

[1] Allen F. Brewer, Lubricants and Coolants. Courtesy of "Machine and Tool Blue Book."

off when the steel strip is removed.   When a steel strip is coated with an oil of poor wetting ability, the water will displace the oil film.   Increase in temperature (use of warm water) hastens this displacement effect.

Surface Tension.   Surface tension in a liquid involves the cohesive action of the component particles.   It is related directly to viscosity, temperature, and emulsion-forming tendency.   Inasmuch as it is an indication of the relative strength of the lubricating film, higher viscosity oils (of comparable degree of refinement and without film-assisting additives) can be expected to produce films of greater strength at the same temperature.   As the temperature is increased, the surface tension is reduced. The emulsion-forming tendency is a factor since an oil of low surface tension will form smaller droplets than an oil of the same viscosity but of high surface tension.

Interfacial Tension.   Interfacial tension in petroleum oils is affected by oxidation. The compounds formed during this reaction tend to reduce the interfacial tension. As these compounds usually have an emulsifying attraction for water, a low interfacial tension may well indicate its presence.   It is not an infallible indication, however, because some of the additives which are currently used to inhibit rust and oxidation also may tend to reduce interfacial tension of the oil.   Thus, low interfacial tension is not as positive an indication of oxidation as an increase in the more practically observed neutralization number would be.

The torsion balance is the customary device used to study both interfacial tension as well as surface tension.   Measurement of the upward force (in dynes per centimeter) required to pull a platinum wire ring through the interface of a layer of oil floating on a layer of water in a suitable container denotes the interfacial tension. The force required to draw the ring free from the oil surface and into the air by continued pull on the wire gives a measurement of the surface tension.   From a practical point of view, and of most significance to the lubrication engineer, the surface tension of an oil indicates a relationship to wetting ability and potential film strength.

Adhesion.   Adhesion already has been mentioned as being associated with wetting ability in a lubricating film.   If good wetting ability prevails, one may assume that the adhesion property is good.   To some extent, however, this will depend upon the surface finish of the contact metals and the way in which the lubricant has been refined.   Too much polish or surface finish is not conducive to good wetting ability or adhesion.   The same holds true for overrefinement of an oil.

Saponification and Emulsification.   These conditions, as they relate to the lubricating value and utilization of petroleum lubricants and coolants, have already been discussed as to test procedure.   While saponification is a characteristic which is relatively negligible in petroleum lubricating oils, organic acids may exist or may develop to react with an alkali.   An oil with a comparatively high saponification number may be susceptible to emulsification.   This would be undesirable in a hydraulic system.

The demulsibility test is probably the most practicable and informative when endurance value of a petroleum lubricant or hydraulic oil is to be predicted if there is any possibility of contact with water.   Every precaution must be taken to keep water out of circulating and hydraulic systems, by checking seals, glands, and coolers for possible leakage.

Chapter 2

LUBRICATING SYSTEMS, DEVICES, AND PROCEDURES

By ALLEN F. BREWER
Consultant in Lubrication, Eden, Fla.
Formerly Editor of The Texas Company Publication "Lubrication"

Lubrication procedure involves the means provided for lubrication, the timing according to the nature of the lubricants and requirements of the machinery, training of personnel as to the resultant benefits, arrangement of records, and analysis of failures which may be traced to faulty lubrication.

The Means Provided for Lubrication. When the lubrication equipment employed on any piece of machinery is suited to the operating conditions and to the type of oil or grease designed for these conditions, most dependable production should result. The maintanance engineer is involved because lubrication failure ties right in with the operating costs of his department. He is well advised, therefore, to study available methods of lubrication along with his study of lubricants. Table 2-1 indicates present-day types of devices intended for automatic lubrication with details as to service and type of lubricant. Automatic lubrication is the rule today rather than the exception. It has been promoted and accepted by the extensive development of industrial and power-plant machinery and the trend toward higher speeds, heavier loads, and closer tolerances in the assembly of precision bearings and gears.

Pressure has been used to good advantage in the application of lubricating oils and greases since the early part of the century. The development from the early types of force-feed oilers and hand-pressure grease guns paralleled the development of auto-motive transportation and mass-production machinery. At first, hand pressure by means of the conventional screw-down grease cup was satisfactory. Naturally there were limitations to this procedure, dependent upon the strength of the operator, the body or consistency of the grease, the prevailing temperature, and the accessibility of the parts to be lubricated.

Hand-pressure Grease Guns. When grease guns of the hand-pressure type came into usage, they made possible considerably higher pressures than had previously been attainable with compression cups; 1,000 to 2,000 psi was not unusual. The modern pressure gun provides application pressures as high as 10,000 to 12,000 psi and therefore is capable of pumping greases of heavier body even up to the NLGI No. 4 range. Such guns can be used either with or without hose connections according to the type of fitting and the location of the part to be lubricated. Pressure can be applied either before or after attaching the gun to the fitting. The usual method of developing pressure in a hand gun is to force a plunger against the grease in the barrel, the stem of the plunger being threaded so as to enable a screw-down action when the handle is turned. This type of gun develops more pressure than could be obtained by leverage.

When pressure is to be developed before attachment of the gun to the fitting, a check valve is installed in the tip.　In such a gun the act of attachment opens this valve and permits grease to be forced automatically to the bearing.

The purpose of designing rigid-connection guns with check valves is to eliminate the necessity for relieving the pressure before detaching the gun from the fitting and to enable pressure to be raised before attachment; this eliminates the possibility of twist-

Table 2-1. Automatic Lubrication*

Type	Typical service	Oil viscosity at 100°F		Grease NLGI‡ No.
		Sec. Saybolt	Centistokes	
Waste pad	Trunnion bearings in cement mills, textile mandrel bearings	300–800	65–176	
Sight-feed oilers	Engine, pump, and compressor crosshead guides	250–550	54–121	
Wick-feed oilers	Line shaft bearings	250–400	54–88	
Ring, chain, or collar oilers	Plain bearing electric motors, pillow blocks	200–400	43–88	
Gravity systems	Industrial steam-engine crankcases, marine turbines	300–550	65–121	
Mechanical force-feed lubricators	Steam cylinders, horizontal compressors	† 300–550	† 65–121	
Hydrostatic lubricators	Steam cylinders	†	†	
Splash oiling	Engine and compressor crankcases	300–550	65–121	
Pressure circulating systems	Steam turbines	140–350	30–77	
Oil-mist or oil-fog systems	High-speed bearings, plain or antifriction; enclosed gears, chains, slides, and ways	75–1,000 (can be straight mineral or EP type of oil. *Do not* use compounded oils)	14–220	
Automatic metered lubrication	Enclosed bearings and gears on textile machinery, machine tools, bottling and food-processing machinery, and printing machines	100–800	21–176	
Compression grease cups	Line shafting	. . . .	. . . . . .	1 or 2
Pressure-gun application	Machine-tool bearings, etc.	. . . .	. . . . . .	2
Centralized pressure-grease systems	Ball or roller bearings on food-handling or steel-mill machinery, etc.	. . . .	. . . . . .	2

* From Allen F. Brewer, "Basic Lubrication Practice," Reinhold Publishing Corporation, New York.
† Indicates use of steam cylinder oil of viscosity in accordance with operating conditions.
‡ National Lubrication Grease Institute.

ing off the fitting.　Direct connection also reduces the possibility of leaks which might develop in flexible hose.　These are important features when bearings may have to be cleared of grease contaminated with dirt or oxidized or gummy residues or suffering loss of oil through separation and leakage.

Power Guns.　Where a considerable amount of machinery is involved with numerous grease fittings, the portable mechanical or power gun is often more suitable than the hand gun.　Power guns are of considerably greater capacity, holding up to 100 lb of grease. Some of the latest designs are planned to work directly from the grease container.

Smaller types of power guns are akin to hand guns in that pressure is developed and grease is discharged by the operation of a pump handle or lever. They also employ a ball or check valve at the base of the pump which closes automatically at the end of each stroke so as to avoid loss of pressure. Obviously this check valve must be free of foreign matter if it is to operate successfully. Power guns of this type can develop up to 2,000 to 3,000 psi. Pressures of this range are capable of pumping most of the conventional industrial- or automotive-type greases up to NLGI No. 3 grade.

Later developments perfected the electric- and air-powered guns which have become popular in handling greases compounded with heavier-bodied mineral oils. Such lubricators normally are of 100-lb capacity, the containers or cartridge adapters being equipped with a follower plate to force the grease down in the container so the gun suction will be covered continually. Multilead discharge manifolds can be installed on such guns to enable simultaneous lubrication of a number of points. As stated, they can be electrically driven or designed to take air from an adjacent compressed-air line.

Centralized Pressure. Manifold lubrication is the feature of the centralized pressure oil or grease system. Pressure circulation of oil to a considerable number of bearings from a central pumping system is widely favored in the paper and steel industries. Filtration and reusage of the oil are dominating factors where several thousand gallons of oil are involved in the system and where protection of bearings having a replacement value as high as $2,000 to $3,000 is involved.

Centralized-pressure grease lubricating systems paralleled to some extent the development of steel-rolling-mill machinery. This means of lubrication is virtually universal on heavy units where bearings are exposed to severe loads and temperatures considerably above normal. Power is developed hydraulically for grease circulation through a manifold and one or two supply lines to the metering valves. Upward of 100 points or bearings can be served simultaneously by such a system, with assurance of positive lubrication and minimum loss of grease provided bearing seals are properly installed and adjusted. Measured lubrication by metering is one of the predominating features of such a system.

Oil Mist. Most recently, oil mist or fog lubrication from a central system has become widely accepted, especially for high-speed precision service as in grinding machinery, woodworking, and aircraft compressors. The principle involves injecting oil drop by drop into a stream of low-pressure air to circulate just enough oil to wet the operating surfaces.

Timing. Timing is important in lubrication even where the completely automatic type of system is involved. Delivery of lubricant must be assured in sufficient amount to avoid any possibility of starved lubrication. Timing begins with the establishment of a suitable schedule. This requires study of the machine, the extent to which its parts are housed or protected to enable conservation of lubricants, the speed of the various parts, the possibility of lubricant contamination, and the ability of the lubricant to act as a flushing agent. Then the nature of the prospective lubricant must be noted. Operating experience is vastly important in planning any lubrication schedule. Where the plant has adequate records of production, costs of maintenance, and lubrication, a schedule of timing for relubrication unit by unit can be readily worked out. Oil-company lubrication engineers can be most helpful in this regard in view of their extensive experience with a wide variety of plants and operating conditions. They can be especially helpful where a condition unique for the service is involved.

The lubrication engineer is a valuable ally of the plant maintenance engineer. Normally the average plant purchasing executive is not too familiar with the operating conditions in his plant and the service to which the lubricants are subjected. Where he buys by specifications or code, he may be overlooking service conditions which have a vital effect upon the ability of the lubricant to give dependable performance. This state of affairs can react directly upon maintenance and the degree of success the maintenance engineer has in keeping costs down.

Education of executives who are prone to regard first cost of lubricants as of primary importance can be well undertaken by the maintenance engineer in company with his oil supplier's lubrication engineer. Working together, with production and cost data developed through related lubrication schedules, they can usually present convincing argument in favor of the now-accepted idea of *buying lubrication* rather than just buying lubricants.

MAKE C.M.M. No. 3 Pl. H/S D/T. Mill				LOCATION	2774	

B. T. No. 4875			CHANGE PERIOD—6 Months		MOS.

REMARKS—

QUANTITIES & TYPES OF EACH LUBRICANT USED

	DATE	BY	P-55	P-50			DATE	BY			

M-1234-1	CMM									

FIG. 2-1. Record card (front) used by machine-repair-department oilers. (*From A. L. Hartley, "Advantages of a Planned Lubrication Program," presented at the fall meeting of ASME, Milwaukee, Sept. 8–10, 1954. Courtesy of Cincinnati Milling Machine Co.*)

The petroleum industry calls this lubrication engineering service. Backed by expert technical and field experience it is of inestimable value in establishing the desired schedules which will indicate frequency of lubrication by automatic units, timing of delivery by metering systems, checking of oil levels in centralized circulating systems of gravity or force-feed type, and evaluating work of oil-reconditioning units.

PARTS TO HAVE OILS CHANGED	INSTRUCTIONS HOW TO DRAIN	INSTRUCTIONS HOW TO FILL	TYPE OILS
Column	On left side of Column	On left side of Column-fill to top of L	P-55
Knee	1 plug to remove to drain	Fill to Gauge	P-55
Vertical Screw		Give several turns of Gun	P-50

FIG. 2-2. Reverse of card shown in Fig. 2-1. (*From A. L. Hartley, "Advantages of a Planned Lubrication Program," presented at the fall meeting of ASME, Milwaukee, Sept. 8–10, 1954. Courtesy of Cincinnati Milling Machine Co.*)

Charts have been perfected for keeping records pertinent to lubricant usage by machine, covering periods for relubrication and various information as to handling the type of lubricant. Some go as far as indicating the latter according to an accepted color code to ensure against misapplication. Figures 2-1 and 2-2 show front and back of typical record cards for machine repair oilers. Figure 2-3 shows a permanent master record card. It is part of the Alemite Coloroute system of identifying lubrication points by means of symbols and colors painted on the equipment.

Lubrication Personnel. There is a decided trend in industry to pay more attention to the status of the lubrication personnel—those who do the actual work of lubrication. The American Society of Lubrication Engineers and the American Society of Mechanical Engineers are doing much to promote this trend. Obviously it is a worthwhile objective. Machinery is costly, and newer models designed for greater precision and faster production certainly require as complete protection as possible by lubrication. Unless this protection is assured by an organization educated to the importance of its job, a unit worth tens of thousands of dollars may fail owing to misapplication of possibly a dollar's worth of lubricant.

Organization and training are important factors in developing a lubrication-minded staff of people. The idea of "grease monkey" must be completely discarded, along with the idea of regarding the oiler as an inferior in the operating group. His job is

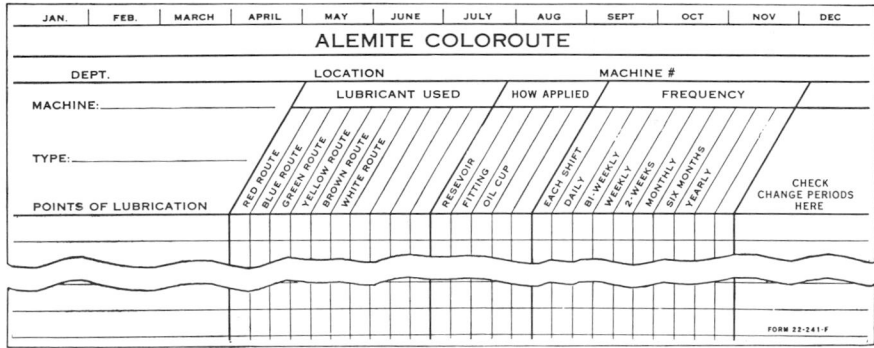

FIG. 2-3. Lubrication guide card. Properly filled out, it is attached to each important piece of equipment. It is protected by a transparent envelope, having a grommet in each end for a screw or rivet. A duplicate card is put into a file to serve as a tickler that ensures against neglect or carelessness. (*Courtesy of Stewart-Warner Corporation, Chicago.*)

as important as the operator's or millwright's. Unless he is trained to do his job thoroughly, to realize the importance of guarding against contamination and the need for following the lubrication schedules as instructed, the operator may loose production while the millwright is taking care of repair and maintenance.

The wisdom of promoting such a program of education in lubrication has been proved by the results in the steel industry. Here many of the largest mills hold regular courses in lubrication, some with textbooks especially prepared for their personnel. The people are encouraged to study machine design, the refining processes, methods of testing lubricants, bearing alloys, gears, and maintenance procedures. Some of the outstanding lubrication engineers in industry have graduated from such courses.

Supervision. Quite naturally good supervision is required. *Factory Management and Maintenance** exemplified this by a table of "Do's" a few years ago, reproduced here as Table 2-2. It is as live today as it was then.

Lubrication Failures. Effective lubrication is a means of insurance that the life expectancy of machinery will be increased. Planning for effective lubrication is as important to the maintenance engineer as timing in the application of lubricants. For lubrication to be effective it must be planned. This means that the prospective operating conditions must be considered, preferably while a machine is being designed. Speed, pressure, temperature, and the possibility of contamination of lubricants constitute the usual operating conditions. They may affect lubricant deterioration (1) internally, as a result of chemical decomposition, or (2) externally, on account of contamination or dilution.

* From Plant Operation Library 99, by Carroll W. Boyce, assistant editor of *Factory*, November, 1946.

Table 2-2. What the Lubrication Supervisor Must Do

The "supervisor of lubrication"—whatever his actual title—should know what his duties are.   Usually, he should be responsible for supervision or execution of these things:

1. Use correct lubricants in every case and as few types as possible for the plant as a whole.
2. Apply lubricants properly.
3. Apply the correct amount of lubricant.
4. Apply lubricants at proper intervals.
5. Develop schedules of items 1-4 for each machine, distribute or post them, and see that they are followed.
6. Train and instruct the oilers; arrange for lubrication clinics if the number of oilers warrants—suppliers' sales and engineering representatives can frequently render valuable assistance in the preparation and execution of such programs.
7. Install and use lubricating devices correctly.
8. Keep lubricants clean, by keeping the oil room clean and by keeping lubricant containers covered.
9. Dispense lubricants through clean, properly identified equipment.
10. Practice preventive maintenance.
11. Cooperate with the maintenance and production departments on lubrication problems.
12. Collect used oils for purification or for resale or reclamation if quantity warrants.
13. Keep complete consumption records.
14. Record and analyze all lubrication-connected failures and breakdowns.
15. Eliminate all accident hazards connected with lubrication.
16. Keep abreast of new developments and practices in the lubricating field by periodic consultation with a qualified lubrication engineer—staff, consultant, or supplier's representative.
17. Minimize the total cost of lubrication, remembering that the price of an improper lubricant is a small fraction of its final cost in terms of poor service.

Lubrication failures can be postponed and often prevented by adoption of a system of "good housekeeping" and complete cooperation between management and the engineering, operating, and maintenance personnel.   Otherwise lubrication may fail because:

1. The grade or type of lubricant is not suitable for the prevailing operating conditions.
2. The lubricating system may not be suited to the design of the machine.
3. The lubricant may be the wrong type for the lubricating system.
4. Contamination by dust, dirt, or water or dilution by fuels or gases may have occurred.
5. The benefits of properly timed schedules for relubrication may not have been realized, resulting in oil film failure due to starved lubrication or damage to seals due to overlubrication.

Industrial or power-plant machinery is operated at temperatures which will vary with room temperatures and at speeds in accordance with the loads.   *Temperature* has an influence upon lubrication because it affects the fluidity or consistency of the lubricant.   Under lower than the normal temperatures for which the lubricant may have been selected, it will tend to become sluggish.   In a ring-oiled motor bearing this might cause too little oil to be carried over by the ring, and starved lubrication could result.   In a pressure grease lubrication system, where long lengths of pipe may be exposed to sudden reductions in temperature, the pumping units may be incapable of handling grease which has become chilled to virtual solidity.   Here, likewise, the result could be starved lubrication.   Usually it is impracticable to do anything about a temperature drop due to weather conditions, but it is sensible to use a lubricant which will be least affected.

Oxidation Can Cause Lubricant Failure.   High operating temperatures can be equally detrimental to effective lubrication owing to the possibility of eventual oxidation unless the lubricant has been strongly fortified with oxidation inhibitors.   Oxidation occurs progressively, being affected by oxidizing conditions, such as heat, and exposure to moisture and oxygen (from the air), in the presence of catalytic metals such as copper or brass.   Once oxidation has started, the oxidized materials speed it

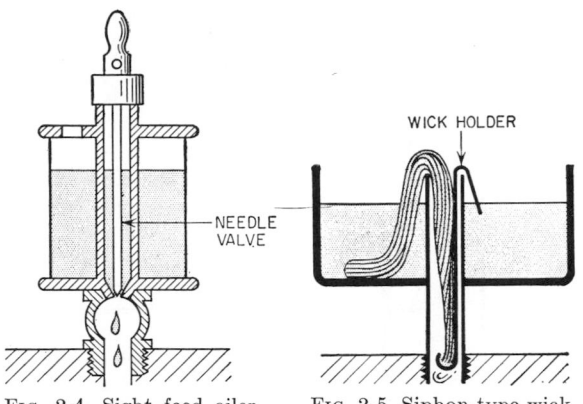

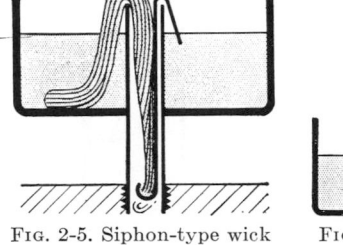

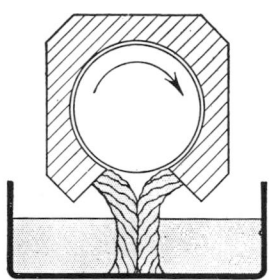

FIG. 2-4. Sight feed oiler. (*Reproduced by permission of Factory Management and Maintenance.*)

FIG. 2-5. Siphon-type wick oiler. (*Reproduced by permission of Factory Management and Maintenance.*)

FIG. 2-6. Bottom-feed wick oiler. (*Reproduced by permission of Factory Management and Maintenance.*)

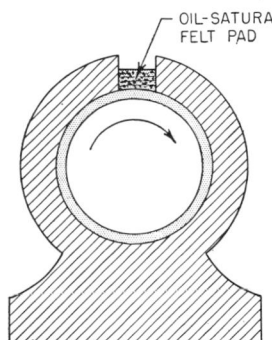

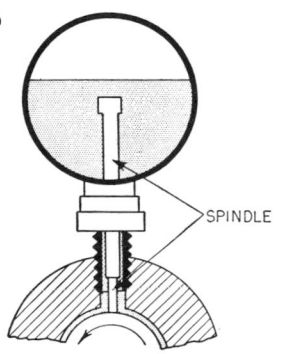

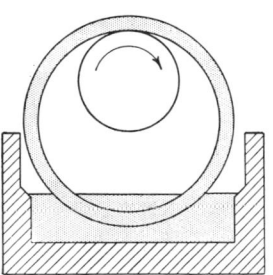

FIG. 2-7. Pad oiler. (*Reproduced by permission of Factory Management and Maintenance.*)

FIG. 2-8. Bottle oiler. (*Reproduced by permission of Factory Management and Maintenance.*)

FIG. 2-9. Ring oiler. (*Reproduced by permission of Factory Management and Maintenance.*)

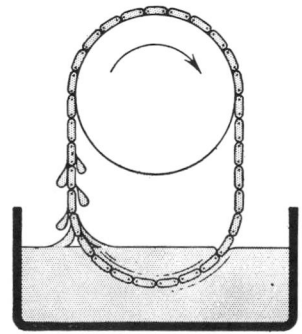

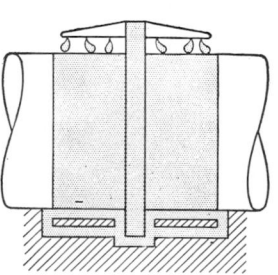

FIG. 2-10. Chain oiler. (*Reproduced by permission of Factory Management and Maintenance.*)

FIG. 2-11. Collar oiler. (*Reproduced by permission of Factory Management and Maintenance.*)

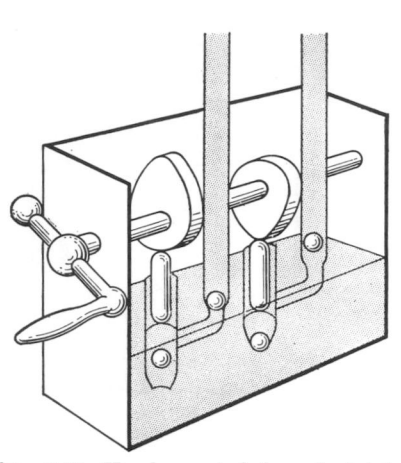

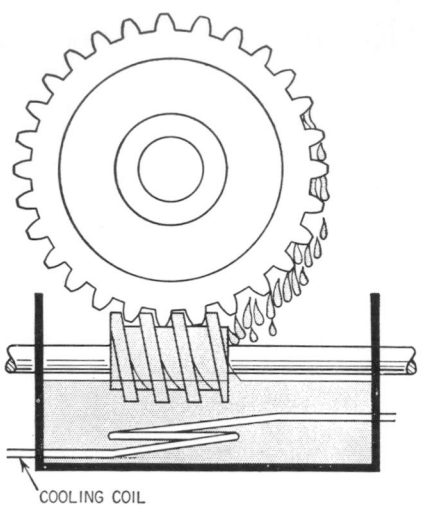

Fig. 2-12. Hand-operated force-feed lubricator. (*Reproduced by permission of Factory Management and Maintenance.*)

Fig. 2-13. Worm gear bath oiler. (*Reproduced by permission of Factory Management and Maintenance.*)

COOLING COIL

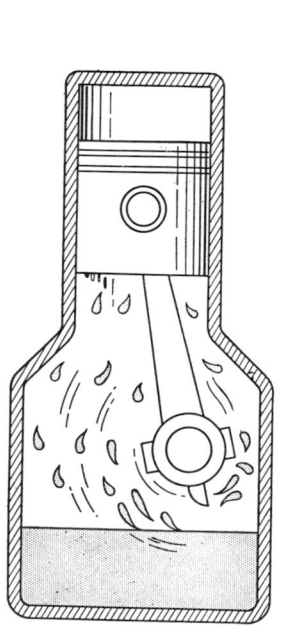

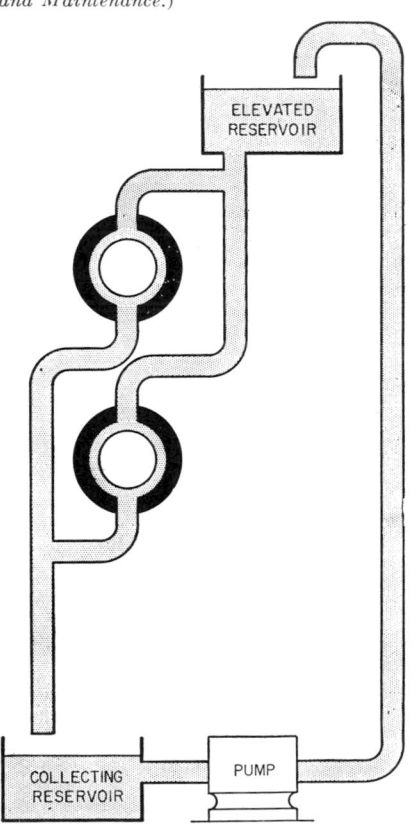

ELEVATED RESERVOIR

COLLECTING RESERVOIR

PUMP

Fig. 2-14. Splash lubricating system. (*Reproduced by permission of Factory Management and Maintenance.*)

Fig. 2-15. Gravity circulation system. (*Reproduced by permission of Factory Management and Maintenance.*)

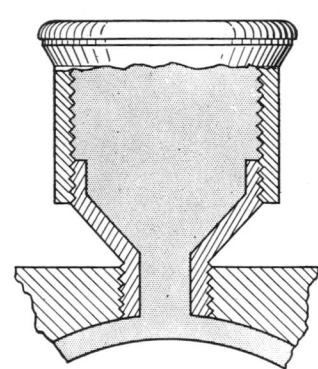

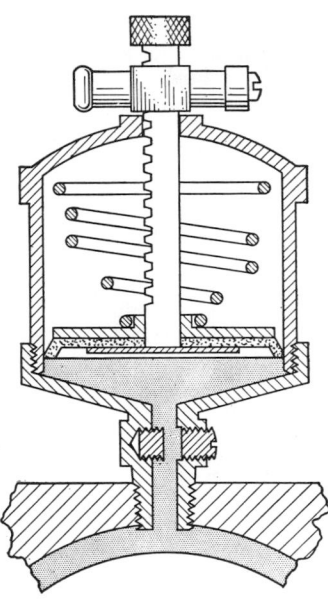

FIG. 2-16. Grease cup, screw-down type. (*Reproduced by permission of Factory Management and Maintenance.*)

FIG. 2-17. Grease cup, spring-compression type. (*Reproduced by permission of Factory Management and Maintenance.*)

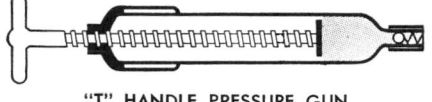

"T" HANDLE PRESSURE GUN

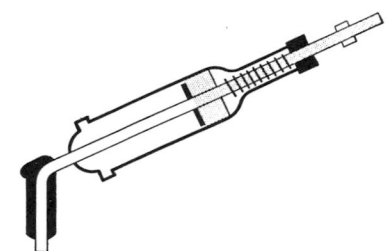

AUTOMATIC HYDRAULIC-TYPE PRESSURE GUN

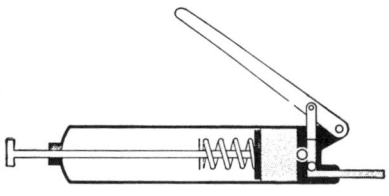

LEVER-TYPE PRESSURE GUN

FIG. 2-18. Pressure grease guns. (*Reproduced by permission of Factory Management and Maintenance.*)

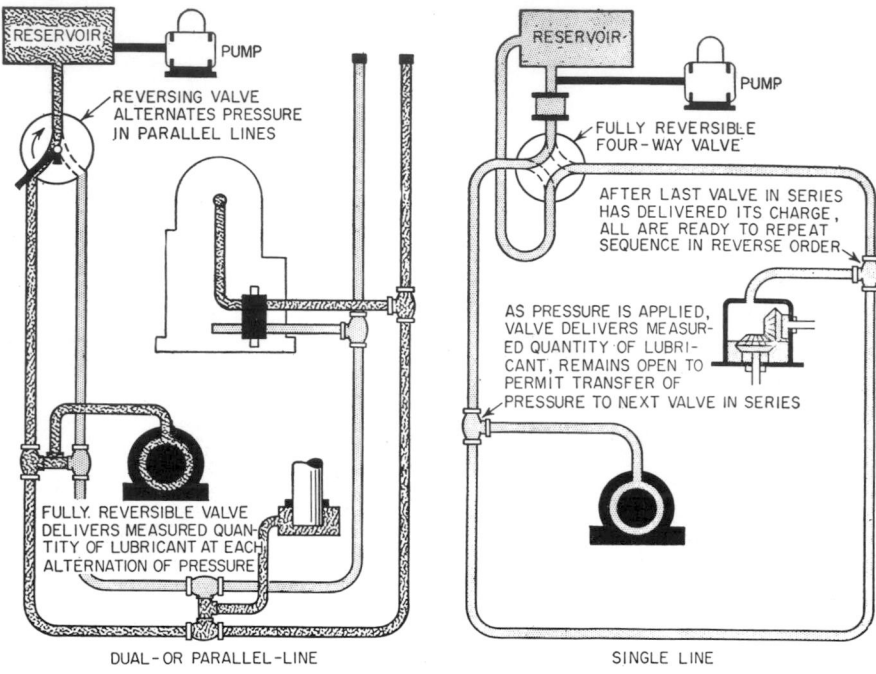

RESERVOIR
PUMP

REVERSING VALVE
ALTERNATES PRESSURE
IN PARALLEL LINES

FULLY. REVERSIBLE VALVE
DELIVERS MEASURED QUAN-
TITY OF LUBRICANT AT EACH
ALTERNATION OF PRESSURE

DUAL- OR PARALLEL-LINE

RESERVOIR
PUMP

FULLY REVERSIBLE
FOUR-WAY VALVE

AFTER LAST VALVE IN SERIES
HAS DELIVERED ITS CHARGE,
ALL ARE READY TO REPEAT
SEQUENCE IN REVERSE ORDER

AS PRESSURE IS APPLIED,
VALVE DELIVERS MEASUR-
ED QUANTITY OF LUBRI-
CANT, REMAINS OPEN TO
PERMIT TRANSFER OF
PRESSURE TO NEXT VALVE IN SERIES

SINGLE LINE

FIG. 2-19. Centralized greasing systems.   (*Reproduced by permission of Factory Management and Maintenance.*)

up further. The progressive results are sludge, resin, varnish, and, ultimately, a hard, carbonaceous residue.

Speed and Load. These are relatively fixed conditions in the average machine, being established according to the service which it is to perform. Normally the operator should not attempt to change these conditions because they have been built into the machine by the designer to enable all related parts to function in synchronism. An overload on one bearing or speed up of the unit by changing the size of the power-transmitting device could throw the entire mechanism off balance.

Internal or fluid friction in the lubricant itself also must be considered. At higher speeds there will be more agitation among the molecules which constitute the oil film, and in a heavier oil the sluggishness of this action would probably cause the bearing temperature to rise until the oil film is reduced in viscosity to flow more freely.

Figures 2-4 to 2-20, inclusive, show devices and systems referred to in the text.

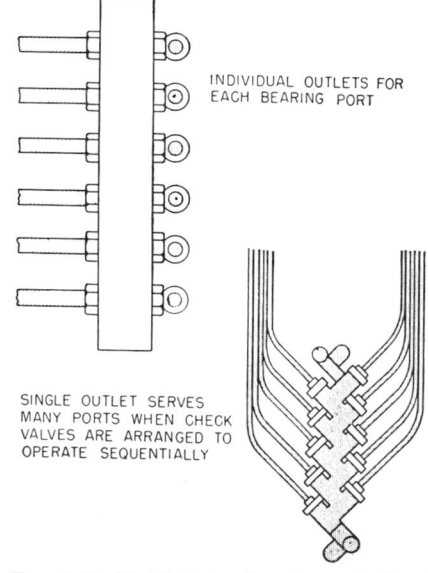

INDIVIDUAL OUTLETS FOR
EACH BEARING PORT

SINGLE OUTLET SERVES
MANY PORTS WHEN CHECK
VALVES ARE ARRANGED TO
OPERATE SEQUENTIALLY

FIG. 2-20. Multiple headers for centralized greasing. (*Reproduced by permission of Factory Management and Maintenance.*)

Section 13

INSTRUMENTS AND INSTRUMENTATION

Chapter 1

MECHANICAL INSTRUMENTS FOR MEASURING PROCESS VARIABLES

By LOUIS GESS
Technical Services Consultant
The Philadelphia Division
Honeywell, Inc.

Mechanical instruments provide an accurate and economical method for measuring and recording or indicating the state of nearly all process variables. In addition they can initiate either pneumatic or electric control action. With these instruments, variations of the process variable result in movement of the measuring element. By means of a linkage mechanism the position of a pen or pointer is changed, or control action is initiated.

Mechanical instruments are widely used in pneumatic transmission systems. In these, the movement of the measuring element changes a pneumatic signal, which is measured by a pressure gage, generally located at some distance in a control center. The measuring unit is known as a transmitter and the pressure gage as a receiver.

The output from the transmitter is manufacturer-standardized 3 to 15 or 3 to 27 psig (pounds per square inch, gage), i.e., proportional from the minimum to the maximum range of the process variable. Although both recording and indicating transmitters are available, the number installed is insignificant compared to the blind type. The transmitted signals are recorded on charts or indicated on scales that are calibrated in terms of the process variable. The transmitted signal can also initiate control action.

Most process variables can be measured with mechanical instruments and include flow, pressure, temperature, level, and positions. The limitations are few, e.g., pressures in the micron ranges, temperatures above 1000°F, and analysis of fluids.

New designs and materials for actuating elements provide acceptable accuracy and sensitivity suitable for most applications. These factors, in addition to ruggedness, low cost, and ease of maintenance, have resulted in an increasing use of mechanical instruments in the expanding market for instrumentation.

TYPES OF INSTRUMENTS

Industrial instruments are classified by case size, type (recorders or indicators), and form (chart or scale). In addition to the record or indication of the process variable, instruments can provide automatic control, integration of flow, and adjustable alarm signals for abnormal operating conditions.

A variety of case designs and sizes are available. Designs generally have a rectangular or square front. They can be mounted flush on a panel or on a wall. Mounting accessories are supplied with cases. Rectangular cases are approximately 14 in. wide by 18 in. high and 4 to 6 in. deep. A commonly used smaller size is 14 by 12 in. Figure 1-1 illustrates a single-pen recorder. In addition, 12- by 12-in. square cases are also available. Since the smaller instruments perform the same functions as those in a rectangular case, the depth also runs from 4 to 6 in. Instruments with smaller case sizes, classified as miniature instruments, are used extensively. They are available in a variety of sizes with width and height of 3 by 6, 4 by 6, and 6 by 6 in. Because of their small cross-sectional area, the depth generally is about 20 in.

Instruments of the sizes listed above are all available as recorders or as indicators. When the pneumatic control function is included, the case assembly includes two 2-in. pressure gages, which continuously indicate the air supply to the control unit and the output pressure to the final control element.

Charts are either round or strip in form. Round charts are available in 3-, 4-, 6-, 8-, 10-, and 12-in. diameters. The smaller sizes are used when accuracy of recording is of secondary importance. The larger sizes provide greater accuracy in reading the state of the process variable and adjusting the set point for automatic control. Most mechanical instruments using strip charts are of the miniature type. Strip charts come in widths of 3 and 4 in. While direct process-variable actuation of the pens is available, most recorders are pneumatic receivers.

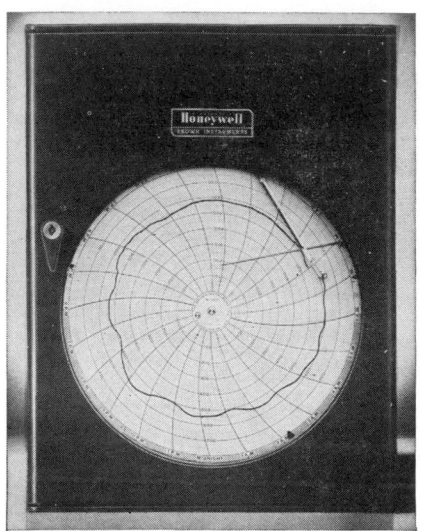

FIG. 1-1. Single-pen recording thermometer.

Indicators are available with concentric and eccentric scales. Concentric scales normally are calibrated for a pointer movement of 270°. Indicators are also available with eccentric scales in the upper or lower portion of the case. A large number of concentric-scale indicators provide only one function—indicating the state of the process variable. Conversely, practically all eccentric-scale indicators provide two functions—indication of the process variable and automatic control. Small-case concentric-scale indicators are also available for automatic control.

Indicating Instruments. Indicating instruments are used when it is not necessary to keep a record of the trend of the process variable for operating use or for future study. Typical applications are to provide operating information of such general-purpose utilities as plant steam, water, and air pressures. Single-point concentric-scale indicators are used for this application.

Where process upsets are not likely to occur, and accordingly no record of process trends is required, indicators provide an economical means for automatic control. Not only is the initial cost less, but also there is no additional cost for charts.

In some applications of indicating controllers process variables may be recorded separately. This is usually done on three-pen rectangular-, round-, or miniature-case strip-chart recorders. Variables may be recorded continuously or on a selective basis, using plug-in connections when a process upset occurs.

Recording Instruments. A relatively small number of recorders are used to record only the state of the process variable. A large number of these record flow, where the amount is made available by a totalizing mechanism. The majority of recording instruments are used for automatic-control applications. For these applications 10- or 12-in. charts are the most suitable because of greater accuracy in reading and positioning the set point and more distance for observing process trends.

Recorders are available with one, two, three, or four pens. Inks of different colors can be used and the record is made on a white chart.   Time lines and graduations may be either white or blue.   By the use of an eccentric scale, following the time line of the chart, and a pointer on the pen arm, it is possible to have a combined recording-indicating instrument.

Printed charts have been in use for so long that they are now available with literally thousands of calibrations, including those for a single variable and those having separate sections for two or three variables.

The standard chart speed is the 24-hr revolution, but many other speeds and the required drive mechanism are available.   The drive mechanism may be electric, hand-wound spring drive, or pneumatically operated.

Miniature Mechanical Instruments.   A separate classification of these instruments is warranted by their frequent use.   Only a few are used to measure the state of the process variable by a direct connection.   The vast majority, known as receivers, are actuated by a 3- to 15-psig pneumatic signal from transmitters which measure the state of the process variable.   These instruments are available as recorders and indicators. Recorders are supplied with 3- and 4-in. wide strip charts, which move either vertically downward or horizontally from right to left.   Indicators have either concentric or narrow vertical scales.   In addition to recording and indication, automatic control of the pneumatic type is also available in all the forms supplied in the larger instruments.

MECHANICAL FLOW METERS

Mechanical flow meters are classified as rate meters because they measure and record, or indicate, the rate of flow.   When measuring liquids or gases, they are in direct contact with the actuating elements.   When steam is measured, it condenses to water in the connecting piping at atmospheric temperatures and is in contact with the actuating element.

The rate of flow is determined by measuring the drop in pressure of the variable flowing through a restriction in the flow line.   This restriction is known as the primary element.   The flow meter is known as the secondary element, and the two complete the system.

Several designs of secondary actuating elements are available.   An early design is a mercury manometer, with float resting on the surface of the mercury in one leg of the manometer.   The float position changes as the flow varies, and by a linkage mechanism the pen or pointer is moved to correspond to the new rate of flow.   For several reasons, such as lower cost and easier installation and maintenance, the use of mercuryless meters is increasing rapidly.   There are two general types.   One has a bellows for measuring the pressure drop and mechanically positions the pen or pointer.   The other measures the pressure drop with a capsular assembly and transmits the standard 3- to 15-psig pneumatic signal.

Most manufacturers publish an accuracy of ±1 per cent full scale for bellows meters. When an installation requires better accuracy, it can be obtained by recalibration. The general published accuracy for pneumatic transmitters is ±0.5 per cent full scale. Both types can be operated to 250°F ambient temperature.

Design of Bellows-actuated Flow Meters.   The general design is shown in Fig. 1-2.   It consists of high-pressure and low-pressure chambers that are separated by a liquid-filled bellows assembly.   The left-hand assembly includes a calibrated range spring whose primary function, in conjunction with bellows movement, is to measure the pressure drop across the primary element.   A rod extending from the bottom of the left-hand, or high-pressure bellows, is connected to a spring, which in turn is fastened to the right-hand, or low-pressure, bellows.

A cable, which always is in tension, connects the bellows rod to the upper end of the cone-shaped torque arm.   The lower end of the torque arm is connected to a torque tube.   Any horizontal movement of the bellows rod is then transmitted by the torque arm to the torque tube.   At this point the horizontal movement is changed to angular rotation and transmitted outside the pressure chamber by the torque tube.   The angular rotation is approximately 8° for all makes.

Most bellows flow meters are of the same general design as that shown.   The bellows are hydraulically formed; those of another make are of a welded construction.   The internal parts of all available, including the bellows, are made of type 316 stainless steel to provide maximum resistance to corrosion.

Various fill materials are used by different manufacturers for ambient temperatures from -40 to 250°F.   The manufacturer should be consulted regarding the special fills available for oxygen measurement and for lower and higher temperatures.

A wide range of springs is available for measuring the pressure drop across the primary element for flow measurement.   In addition, ranges in terms of pounds per square inch are available for measuring pressure drop across process vessels.   Meters are available for operating pressures to a maximum of 6,000 psig.

Fig. 1-2. Bellows-actuated flow meter.

Operation of Bellows-actuated Flow Meters

1. Under no flow, there is no pressure drop across the primary element and the high and low pressures are equal and applied to each of the bellows.
2. When flow starts, the high pressure remains fixed and the low pressure decreases to a value determined by the rate of flow.
3. When this difference in pressure occurs, the forces at the ends of each bellows are no longer equal because of the reduction of pressure applied to the end of the low-pressure bellows.
4. The force of the pressure on the high-pressure bellows compresses the bellows and forces liquid to move past the pulsation check into the low-pressure bellows.
5. When the high-pressure bellows is compressed, the range spring, of which one end is anchored and the opposite end is free to move and is fastened to the bellows, is subjected to increasing tension as it is elongated.   This elongation continues until the difference in forces across the bellows, created by the pressure drop across the primary element, is balanced by an equivalent force in the spring.
6. When the bellows and the bellows rod move to the right under the above conditions, the torque arm is rotated in a clockwise direction.   Since the bellows

assembly is located on the back in both the mechanical flow meter and the pneumatic transmitter, the torque-tube rotation will be counterclockwise when viewed from the front of these instruments.

7. The rotation of the torque tube, by means of suitable linkage mechanism, serves to position a pen or pointer of a mechanical flow meter or actuates a pneumatic or electrical transmitter for remote transmission of measurement.

The volume of the liquid fill in the bellows will change with variations in ambient temperature. This will result in an increase of internal pressure with an increase in ambient temperature and a decrease in internal pressure with a decrease in ambient temperature. Since the internal pressure of the bellows should remain the same as the static pressure of the fluid in the manometer chamber, any variations of the fill pressure will cause errors in measurement. An increase of internal pressure, resulting from a rise of ambient temperature, will result in a high-measurement error. Conversely, a

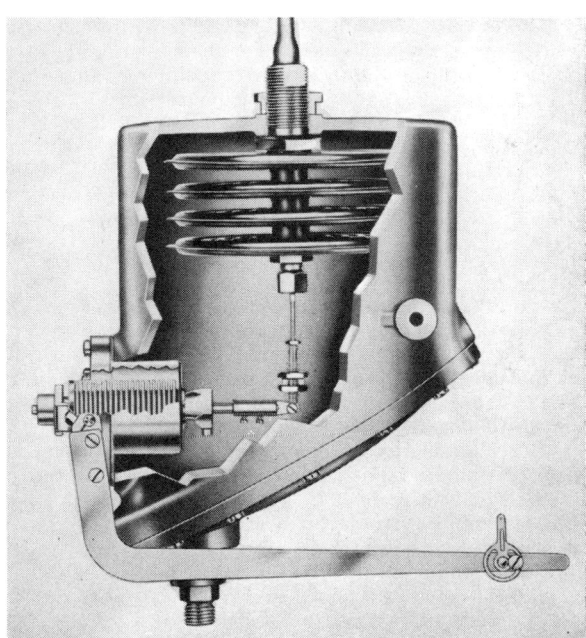

Fig. 1-3. Flow meter with pneumatic transmission.

decrease in ambient temperature will result in a low-measurement error. A standard ambient temperature, from which the above variations are considered, is that of the Bureau of Standards adopted for standards of calibration based on 77 ± 5°F variation.

In order to eliminate the above errors all bellows-actuated manometers are equipped with compensators for changes in ambient temperature. Compensation in the design illustrated is obtained by a combination of unequal cross-section areas of the high- and low-pressure bellows and the spring construction of the bellows rod. With an increase in internal pressure, as the ambient temperature rises, the force developed by low-pressure bellows will be greater than by the high-pressure bellows. If the two bellows were connected by a solid rod, it would move to the right and, through the operation previously explained, the measurement would be in error on the high side. The spring, however, has a gradient equal to that of the low-pressure bellows. When the difference in forces occurs, the spring elongates and allows an increase in the volume of the low-pressure bellows equal to the volumetric increase due to the change in ambient temperature. Since the spring elongates and the solid portion of the rod, to which the cable connection to the torque arm is attached, remains stationary, only negligible errors occur with changes in ambient temperature. With a decrease in ambient temperature the reverse occurs.

Two different methods of compensation are used by other manufacturers. One method makes use of a partially expanded convolution of the low-pressure bellows. Then, with changes in ambient temperature, the convolution expands more or less, as required to maintain a constant internal pressure of the bellows assembly. A second method makes use of a bimetal connection between the bellows rod and the torque tube. Compensation is obtained by a movement of the bimetal connector that is opposite to the bellows movement caused by changes in ambient temperature.

Compensation by all three methods described is adequate for most applications. For extreme operating conditions or for a high degree of compensation, the manufacturer should be consulted.

Flow Meters with Pneumatic Transmission. Most mechanical flow meters, such as the bellows type previously described, are available with pneumatic transmission. Most transmitters, however, are designed for transmission only, operate on a null-balance principle, and cannot position a pen or pointer. They can only measure flow and transmit a proportional 3- to 15-psig pneumatic signal. Figure 1-3 illustrates such a transmitter. Transmitters of this design have extremely low volumetric displacement, about 0.10 cu in., when measuring the full pressure drop across the primary element. As a result, they are highly sensitive to small changes in flow and have very low hysteresis. Both these factors make them excellent for control applications. Because these transmitters are light in weight, they are easy to install.

MEASUREMENT OF TOTAL FLOW

In addition to recording or indicating the rate, it is often necessary to measure the total flow over a period of time. An example is an accounting of steam used in various departments of a plant.

The total flow is determined by means of an integrator. It observes the pen or pointer position or measures a pneumatic signal and changes numbers on a counter in direct proportion to the rate of flow in relation to elapsed time. The operating principle may be either mechanical or electronic. Integrators that observe the pen or pointer position are within the instrument case. Those operating on a pneumatic signal are separate from the instrument.

Figure 1-4 illustrates an electronic integrator. Although shown for an electric flow meter, it is also used on mechanical meters. This integrator consists of three major assemblies: (1) A scanning unit, located to the left of the coil, checks the flow rate, as shown by the pen position, once every 5 sec without interfering with pen motion. (2) An electronic detector relay, located to the right of the coil, is actuated by the scanning unit, which operates the line-voltage motor-driven counting mechanism. (3) The motor-driven six-digit counter mechanism, located in the lower left-hand corner of the case, totalizes the successive output impulses from the detector relay, thus integrating the flow measurements.

Figure 1-5 shows an integrator which receives a signal from a pneumatic flow transmitter. It operates independently of a recorder, indicator, or controller, and can be installed at almost any desired location.

Principle of Operation

1. A 3- to 15-psig pneumatic signal from the flow transmitter is applied to the integrator receiver bellows A.
2. The force exerted by the bellows positions a force bar B in relation to nozzle C.
3. With an increase in flow the force bar approaches the nozzle; and the resulting back pressure at the relay D regulates the flow of air to drive the turbine rotor E.
4. As the rotor revolves, the weight F, which is mounted on a flexure-pivoted bell crank G on top of the rotor, develops a centrifugal force. This force feeds back through the thrust pin H to balance the force exerted on the force bar by the bellows.

5. The turbine rotor is geared directly to the counter J through gearing K. Changes in flow continuously produce changes in turbine speed to maintain a continuous balance of forces.
6. The centrifugal force is proportional to the square of the turbine speed. This force balances the signal pressure, which is proportional to the square of the flow. Therefore, turbine speed is directly proportional to flow; and integrator count, which is a totalization of the number of revolutions of the turbine rotor, is directly proportional to the total flow.

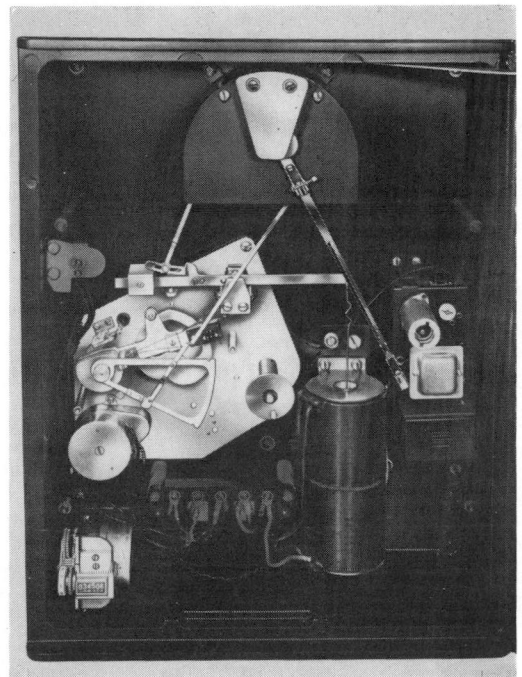

FIG. 1-4. Electronic integrator.   As shown it is for an electric flow meter, but it is also used on mechanical meters.

PNEUMATIC INTEGRATOR

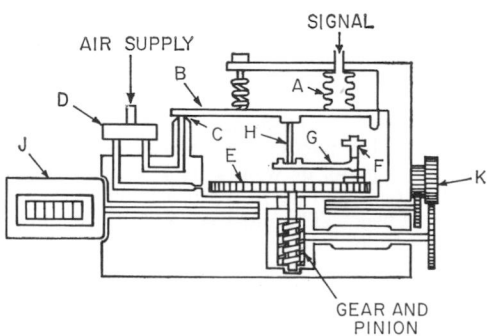

FIG. 1-5. Pneumatic integrator.

Integrators are available with auxiliary attachments for batch control and electric pulse output.

MECHANICAL PRESSURE INSTRUMENTS

The practical range for mechanical pressure measurement is about 0 to 6 mm Hg (millimeters of mercury) absolute pressure to 0 to 100,000 psig. Mechanical instruments often are classified as follows:

Positive pressure.
Vacuum.
Compound, vacuum and pressure.
Absolute pressure.

Measurement of pressure is that of a differential in reference to barometric pressure. Positive pressures are those measured above the barometric pressure, and vacuum is measured below it. Compound pressures are those measured above and below atmosphere pressure. Absolute pressure measurement takes into consideration the variations of barometric pressure.

FIG. 1-6. Concentric scale indicator. (*Courtesy of Marsh Instrument Company, Skokie, Ill.*)

FIG. 1-7. Eccentric scale indicating pressure gage. (*Courtesy of Taylor Instrument Company, Rochester, N.Y.*)

TYPES OF INSTRUMENTS

Figure 1-6 shows a concentric-scale indicator that is the most widely used of all pressure gages. The one shown has a plain case and normally is installed on the process unit and directly supported by the pressure connection. It is available in different cases for flush mounting on a panel or with a back flange for wall mounting. The standard dial sizes are 4½, 6, 8, and 12 in. with a 270° scale. Pressure ranges are from 0 to 15 to 0 to 100,000 psig. The most commonly used actuating element is a Bourdon tube made of brass, alloy and stainless steel, and Monel. Diaphragm seals are available when process variables must not be allowed to enter the Bourdon tube. These gages are suitable for most applications in the process industries, including pressure measurement of air, steam, water, and hydrocarbons under most operating conditions.

Figure 1-7 shows an eccentric-scale indicating pressure gage with pneumatic control.

This type is available for direct measurement of nearly every pressure used in processing and also as a pneumatic receiver for a 3- to 15-psig pneumatic signal.

PNEUMATIC TRANSMISSION SYSTEMS

The pneumatic transmission system shown schematically in Fig. 1-8 is basically the same for all low-volume flow-meter transmitters. The principal parts are a member that moves in response to changes in flow, a pneumatic rebalancing system, which also generates the transmission signal, and a means for changing the range of measurement.

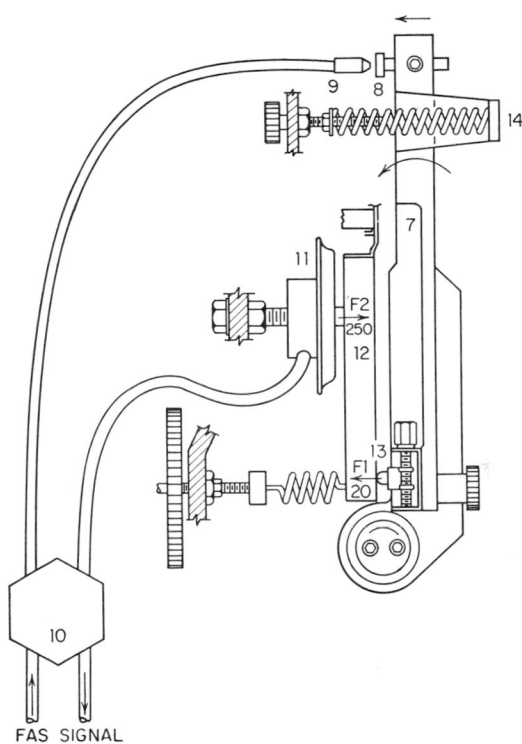

Fig. 1-8. Pneumatic low-volume transmission system.

In the system shown, the primary beam (7) is the member that moves in response to changes in flow. The rebalancing system consists of a baffle (8), a nozzle (9), the pneumatic amplifier or pilot (10), the rebalancing capsule (11), and the secondary beam (12). The rebalancing pressure, produced by the pilot for most transmission systems, is 3 to 15 psig for zero- to maximum-flow measurement. The nozzle pressure may vary with different makes of transmitters but is generally about 20 per cent of the transmission signal. FAS stands for "filtered air supply," and this is normally 20 psig.

The range of the transmitter shown is continuously adjustable from 0 to 20 to 0 to 1,000 in. H_2O. Other ranges, or spans, for most transmitters are available from a minimum of 0 to 1 to 0 to 1,000 in. H_2O for the flow measurement. The range of the transmitter is determined by the position of contact point (13) on the secondary beam (12). The spring and thumb wheel is the zero adjustment. The thumb- and micrometer-screw assembly on the primary beam is the range or span adjustment.

The spring assembly (14) at the upper end of the primary beam is the suppression adjustment. By turning the screw, a force is applied to the primary beam to prevent movement until a desired range is measured. For example, on a 0- to 100-in. range, the adjustment can be such that primary-beam movement will not occur until a range of 50 in. is reached.

Suppression is normally used only on flow transmitters for reverse-flow applications. That is, to measure flow in either direction, a center-zero chart is used, and when there is no flow, the transmitted signal is 9 psig. With flow in one direction the transmitted pressure will increase; when the flow reverses, the pressure decreases. The main use of suppression is when flow transmitters are used to measure liquid level. When the density of the liquid in the outer fixed leg is greater than that of the liquid in the tank, the difference must be suppressed.

With an increase in flow the primary beam moves in a counterclockwise direction, as shown by the arrow. This places a force $F1$ on the primary beam. As the baffle approaches the nozzle, it raises the nozzle back, which in turn increases the output pressure of the pilot. This increase in pressure is not only the transmitted signal but is also applied to the rebalancing signal. A force $F2$ is applied to the primary beam. The output pressure from the pilot increases until $F2$ equals $F1$, and at this point the transmitted signal remains fixed until a change in flow occurs.

PNEUMATIC TRANSMISSION OF PRESSURE MEASUREMENT

The use of central control centers has increased the use of pneumatic transmission for pressure measurement. One advantage is that the cost of the tubing for transmitting the 3- to 15-psig pneumatic signal is considerably less than that of piping suitable for the process pressures from the point of measurement to the instrument. In addition, possible danger due to leakage of high process pressures in the control house is eliminated. A very important operating advantage is that pneumatic

FIG. 1-9. Indicating-type pneumatic pressure transmitter.

FIG. 1-10. Transmitter that operates on a force balance principle; available only in nonindicating form. (*Courtesy of the Foxboro Company, Foxboro, Mass.*)

transmission eliminates freezing of water lines and decreased sensitivity of measurement due to increased viscosity of liquids at low ambient temperatures.

Figure 1-9 illustrates an indicating type of pneumatic pressure transmitter. A nonindicating form is also available. Pressure ranges from low absolute pressures to 10,000 psig can be measured.

Transmitters of this type are often installed at the point of measurement and supported by a bracket attached to a flow line or process vessel. The design, therefore, is such that the transmitter will operate under high vibration. The case design provides good protection for the internal mechanism for locations in corrosive atmospheres.

Figure 1-10 illustrates a transmitter that operates on a force-balance principle and is available only in a nonindicating form. If indication is required, a pressure gage is connected to the transmitted-signal line.

The transmitters shown are available in a series of ranges with spans that are adjustable for various ratios within the span limits of their actuating elements. The transmitter has a capsule-actuating element with the following range and span limits:

Range limits, psig	0–350	0–+750	0–+1,500	0–+3,000
Span limits, psig	25–250	50– 500	100– 1,000	200– 2,000

The representative span limit could then be 250 to 350, 400 to 600, 800 to 1,200, and 1,500 to 2,300 psig.

ACTUATING ELEMENTS FOR PRESSURE GAGES

The actuating elements of pressure gages must perform two main functions: measuring the pressure of the process variable and providing sufficient force to position a pen or pointer or to initiate the generation of a signal by a pneumatic transmitter.

Inherent in the design of the actuating elements must be the ability to withstand the pressures being measured. In addition, they must provide the necessary accuracy, sensitivity, and repeatability required for satisfactory recording, indication, and control. To meet these requirements a variety of actuating elements are available.

Commercial pressure gages have a standard accuracy of ± 1 per cent of the full-scale rated pressure. By more careful calibration, accuracy can be increased to ± 0.5 per cent. Special test gages, at a higher cost, provide greater accuracies. The sensitivity and repeatability of commercial gages is ± 0.25 per cent or better.

Bourdon Tubes. The Bourdon tube (Fig. 1-11,) is used for measuring the widest range of pressures of any, actuating from 15 to as high as 100,000 psig. Its greatest use is in concentric-scale indicators. It is seldom used to actuate recording gages. When correctly designed and made, it meets all the requirements for accuracy, sensitivity, and repeatability.

For high pressures Bourdon tubes are made of steel, stainless steel, and other materials to withstand the severe service of fluctuating pressures. They are designed to withstand an overload of twice their rated pressures without permanent damage. When subjected to overload pressures, only a zero adjustment is required. For lower pressures Bourdon tubes are generally made of phosphor bronze or brass. In order to provide the operating forces, the width may be at least twice that of tubes for higher pressures.

When pressure is applied to a Bourdon tube, it tends to straighten out. This movement, by means of a link connection, plus a pinion and gear assembly, rotates the pointer of the indicating gage. The usual pointer movement is about 270°.

Helix. This unit is another form of Bourdon tube but several times as long and wound in a compact helical form. It is made in this form in order to occupy a minimum amount of space in the instrument case, thus providing room for several actuating elements, controllers, chart-drive mechanism, and other devices. It is used to actuate the eccentric-scale indicating controller (Fig. 1-7).

The element is formed by flattening a round tube to an elliptical shape, heat-treating to provide the spring characteristics, and then winding in a helical form.

It is available in phosphor bronze, brass, steel, stainless steel, and beryllium over copper for a wide variety of applications.

Helix tubes are available for ranges from as low as 0 to 30 to 80,000 psig. When pressure is applied, the helix unwinds, and this movement actuates a pen or pointer or initiates the generation of a signal by a pneumatic transmitter.

Spirals. These actuating elements are similar to helices, except that they are flattened, as shown by Fig. 1-12. The principal design feature of spirals is that they can be installed in an instrument case of considerably less depth than that required for helices. This is important when flush-mounted instruments are installed on panel boards, because of the reduction in the distance behind the board.

A spiral permits the use of suppressed-range, narrow-span measurements where lower pressures are of no value and it is desired to measure higher pressures with greater accuracy. For example, spans of 50 to 100, 400 to 600 psig, etc.

Spiral actuating elements are available in the same materials as helices. The maximum pressures that can be measured

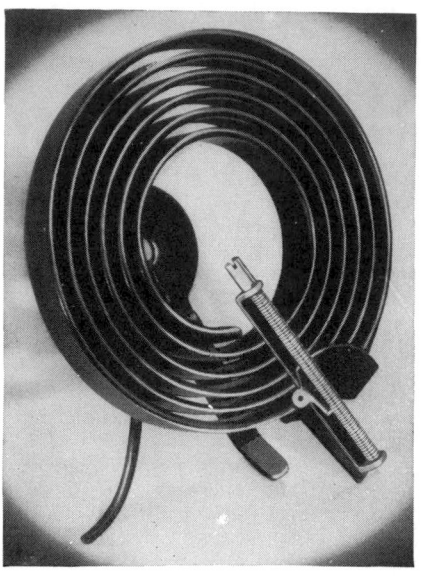

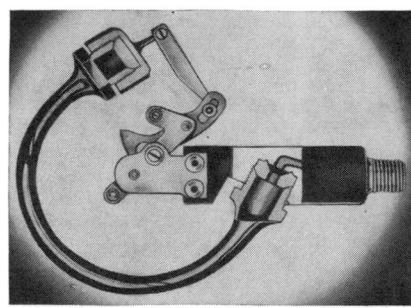

FIG. 1-11. Bourdon tube.   FIG. 1-12. Steel spiral.

are less, with a limit of about 5,000 psig. The range of phosphor bronze or brass spirals generally is limited from 0 to 30 to about 500 psig.

Spring and Bellows. For pressure ranges from about 0 to 5 to 0 to 40 psig an actuating element of an entirely different design is used. In order to obtain the required actuating forces the measuring element must have a larger area against which the lower pressures are applied.

The several designs, providing the larger effective areas, are illustrated by Figs. 1-13 and 1-14. The design shown in Fig. 1-13 consists of an enclosure around a bellows. The source of pressure being measured is connected to the enclosure. Within the bellows, and touching its bottom, is a calibrated steel spring. The spring is supported at its top, and the calibration is such that for any desired pressure ranges the bottom of the bellows moves the same distance. A commonly used distance is 0.375 in. By means of a linkage connection to the bottom of the bellows the desired actuation is obtained. This design is suitable for measuring pressures from about 0 to 100 in. H_2O to 0 to 40 psig.

Figure 1-14 is a similar design except that exterior enclosure of the unit is the bellows, and the can of the enclosure is within the bellows. This design also makes use of a calibrated spring, and the actuation is the same as for the measuring element previously discussed.

These two designs have several important features. One is that the calibrated spring is never in contact with the fluid whose pressure is being measured. It therefore can be made from spring steel to obtain the best calibration, since it will not be affected by corrosive fluids. The second feature is that the bellows and other portions of the enclosure can be made of different materials as required by the application. For example, to measure the pressure of a noncorrosive fluid a lower-priced gage can be supplied by making the enclosure of brass and the bellows of phosphor bronze. For corrosive applications, the enclosure can be supplied of stainless steel at a higher price.

The use of a spring and bellows makes for better calibration than use of a bellows alone. The spring gradient of a bellows not only is poor but also varies from one to another. Conversely, the calibration of springs is good from one to another. The combined gradient of the spring and bellows enters the calibration. To obtain good calibration, a gradient ratio of 85 per cent for the spring and 15 per cent for the bellows is used.

For pressure ranges from 0 to 1 in. to about 10 psig, diaphragm elements (Fig. 1-15) are used. Two diaphragms, made of a spring material, are joined together at their circumference to form a compartment. When subjected to pressure, each

Fig. 1-13. Intermediate-range spring and bellows.

Fig. 1-14. Low-range spring and bellows.

compartment expands a slight amount. Depending on the full-scale range, a number of compartments are stacked together to provide the proper movement for actuation. In order to obtain the required forces, diaphragms having different effective areas are used. The lower the pressure, the greater the area, and consequently the larger the diameter. Diaphragms are available in a number of different materials such as brass, phosphor bronze, and stainless steel.

For the measurement of pressures from 0 to 0.2 to 10 in. H_2O the inverted bell (Fig. 1-16) is used. The lower, or open, end of the bell is sealed by a light oil, and the pressure to be measured is connected to its underside. In most instruments of this type no springs are used, and the movement of the bell with changes in pressure is counterbalanced by weights. In one design the bell, having thick steel walls, is submerged in mercury. With an increase in pressure the bell moves upward, and the change in pressure is balanced by the loss in buoyancy of the walls emerging from the mercury.

To measure differential pressure two bells are used, one suspended from each end of an arm that is center-pivoted.

Absolute Pressure. The actuating elements previously described are suitable for the measurement of vacuum. For some applications they are not suitable because they measure the difference between pressure in a vessel and atmospheric pressure. Since atmospheric pressure varies constantly, it may often be necessary to make

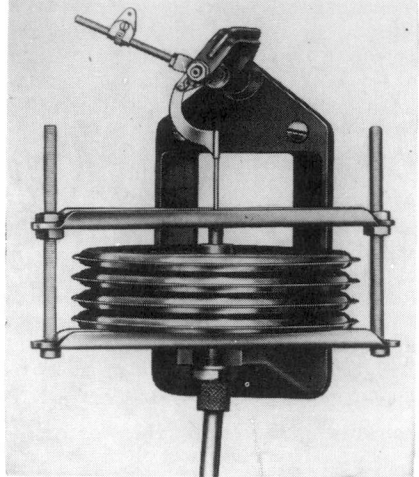

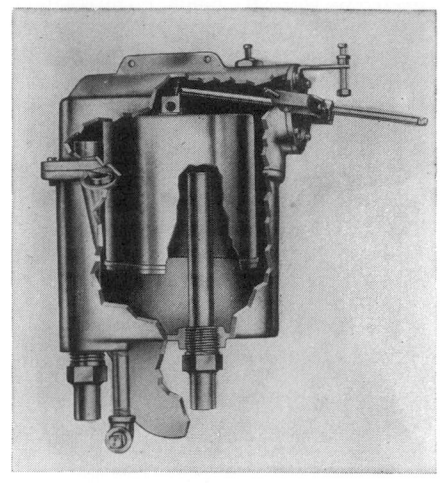

FIG. 1-15. Diaphragm measuring element. (*Courtesy of the Bristol Company, Waterbury, Conn.*)

FIG. 1-16. Inverted-bell measuring element. (*Courtesy of the Bristol Company, Waterbury, Conn.*)

repeated barometer readings and correct vacuum readings or change the set point of controllers on critical processes. The absolute-pressure gage (Fig. 1-17) eliminates the need for repeated readings by automatically correcting the vacuum reading for variations in atmospheric pressure. It is suitable for measuring pressures as low as 0 to 5 mm Hg absolute.

The capsular element is evacuated as completely as possible through tubing extending from the bottom of the assembly and then is sealed. It is enclosed in a pressure-tight housing that is connected to the source of pressure to be measured. With variations in pressure the length of the capsular element changes, and this movement is brought out through the bellows seal. This element will also change its length with changes in barometric pressure, since its free length depends on the difference in internal and external pressure. Thus, with absolute zero pressure inside the element, its length will be a direct measure of the absolute pressure bearing upon its outside.

FIG. 1-17. Absolute-pressure measuring element.

DIAPHRAGM-ACTUATED FLOW-METER TRANSMITTER

The use of diaphragm-actuated flow-meter transmitters (Fig. 1-18) exceeds that of the previously described bellows- and mercury-actuated flow meters by a ratio of 100 to 1. The one shown is a pneumatic transmitter with a signal range of 3 to 15

FIG. 1-18. Diaphragm-actuated flow meter transmitter.

psig for a flow from zero to maximum value. These flow meters are also available with an electric signal such as 4 to 20 ma.

These transmitters have two main parts. One is the meter body, shown at the rear of the case. The other part, within the case, and shown by Fig. 1-19, is the pneumatic-signal-generating unit. To operate the transmitter, a supply of clean air is required, and this is provided by a filter regulator as shown at the right of the case. The supply pressure must be maintained at 20 psig and a gage is installed at each transmitter for setting the regulator. Often a second gage is installed to indicate the pressure of the transmitted signal.

The meter body measures the differential across a restriction such as an orifice, flow nozzle, or venturi in the flow line, by means of capsular diaphragm assembly. This measurement is transmitted to the transmitter unit by means of a torque tube, force bar, or other mechanical methods.

These meter bodies have a low volumetric displacement, generally about 0.10 cu in. This is the change in volume required within the meter body for full-range measurement of the flow for which the primary element is designed. Low volumetric displacement has several impor-

FIG. 1-19. Pneumatic signal-generating unit of diaphragm-actuated flow meter transmission.

tant advantages. One is that the cost of installation is materially decreased because it is not necessary to provide condensers when measuring the flow of steam or pots for liquid-level measurement. Equally important is the speed of response in measuring changes of differential pressure. Small volumetric changes also provide inherent sensitivity of measurement. Other advantages of this type of flow meter transmitters are listed below.

1. Low initial cost.
2. The meter body is available in a number of materials such as carbon steel, type 316 stainless steel and Monel as a standard product. As a special product it can be supplied in other materials for measurement of corrosive fluids.
3. They are small, compact, and light in weight. The average weight of pneumatic transmitters is about 20 lb; that of electric type about 30 lb.
4. Installation is easily effected, either with the pipe bracket shown in the figure or with support from the orifice-pipe connections.
5. The time required for maintenance has been reduced to a minimum. In several designs the fluid being measured does not wet any of the working parts. Cleaning requires only the wiping off of barrier diaphragms.
6. The accuracy of calibration is ± 0.50 per cent full scale or better. Compensation for effects of ambient temperature on the accuracy of calibration is provided, and the error generally will not exceed 1 per cent for a 100°F change. The hysteresis will not exceed 0.25 per cent, and sensitivity is 0.10 per cent or better.
7. This type of transmitter will withstand an overload equal to the rated pressure of the meter body without damage or effect on the calibration.
8. As explained later, the range is continuously adjustable from the minimum to maximum of any meter body.

The transmitter mechanism is shown by Fig. 1-8, and the operation is described under Pneumatic Transmission Systems. The design is simple and rugged, and the number of adjustments required for calibration is reduced to a minimum. Parts are generally of stainless steel or die-cast aluminum in order to permit installation in the corrosive atmospheres of chemical plants and petroleum refineries.

MINIATURE MECHANICAL INSTRUMENTS

Many instruments used in the process industries are of the so-called "miniature" type. They generally require only a 6- by 6-in. panel-board cutout, with the instrument front having somewhat larger dimensions. They are supplied by six or more companies.

Figure 1-20 illustrates a miniature recording control station that receives a 3- to 15-psig pneumatic signal. This control station has all the functions of the larger instruments but requires only about one-quarter of the panel-board area.

The use of these instruments not only reduces the over-all costs but also permits the operator to run the process better. The reduction in size allows the use of shorter panel boards, which in turn reduces the size of the control house and results in a considerable saving in costs. The smaller control house results in further savings in the heating and air-conditioning load.

Use of miniature instruments means that more of them are within the direct observation of the operator, permitting closer supervision of the process and generally resulting in the improved operation of the plant. Their use also reduces operator fatigue because the amount of walking required by the operator is sharply reduced. In some cases further savings result by reducing the number of operators.

The instrument shown is the front view of a recorder for two process variables with control of one of them. The second record on a control station is generally that of a related variable. For example, the variable controlled may be fuel gas to a heater, with the second variable being gas pressure. Another frequently used application is controlling the flow from a tank, with the second variable being the level in the tank.

The following information is provided to the operator by this instrument. The most important is the record of the two process variables. Since the instrument is a pneumatic controller, the upper pointer indicates the air pressure to a control valve. The amount of pressure indicated is a measure of the valve opening, which is a helpful guide in the operation of a process.   The letters *C* and *O* indicate the closed and open positions of the valve.

The lower pointer is the "set-point index" and is manually positioned at the point where the process variable is to be controlled.   When the control is at this point, the process-variable pen is under the set-point index.   Any deviation from the set point is immediately evident to the operator.

Moving the set-point index along the scale operates a pneumatic transmitter.   With the set point at zero on the lower scale the output of the transmitter is 3 psig.   At 100 the output is 15 psig.   The transmitter output is the standard 3- to 15-psig pneumatic signal.

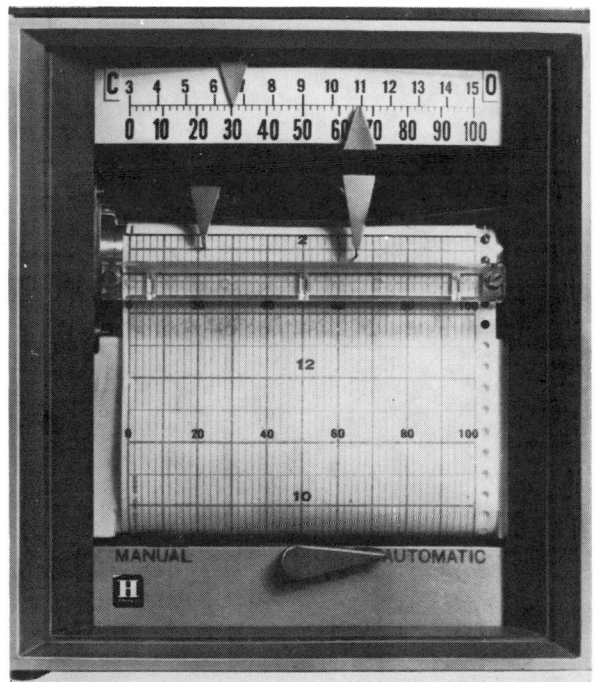

FIG. 1-20. Miniature recording control station that receives a 3- to 15-psig pneumatic signal.

The bottom lever has two positions, automatic or manual.   When the lever is in the position shown, the process is under automatic control.   When it is in the manual position, the operator manually controls the pressure to the valve.   To change to manual control the operator turns the lever from automatic to the manual position.

After switching from automatic to manual control the set-point index lines up with the air-to-valve pressure indicator.   The transmitter-output pressure becomes equal to the previously automatically controlled air pressure to the valve.   To change the air pressure to the valve the operator simply moves the set-point index up- or down-scale, and the air pressure to the valve is indicated by the upper pointer.   To return the variable to automatic control, the operator simply turns the lever to that position.

The calibrated width of the chart is 4 in.   This provides approximately the same pen travel as on 12-in.-diameter round charts of the large instruments.   The chart length is sufficient for 30 days at a chart speed of ¾ in. per hr.   Chart reroll and daily tear-off are available on all recorders.   Pens are of the capillary type with about 6 months' ink supply under normal operating conditions.   Chart drive can be either electric or pneumatic.

In addition to recording control stations, with one or two pens, one-, two-, and three-pen recorders are also available. If no record of the process variable is required, concentric-scale indicators and indicating control stations can be used.

To provide an instrument meeting the requirements for small panel area the depth is increased. The distance behind the panel, including the controller, varies from 20 to 24 in. This depth, plus the close mounting of instruments, presents a maintenance problem. Accordingly, the operating mechanism is mounted on a chassis that can be pulled out from the case when maintenance is required. When the chassis is entirely removed, the pneumatic connections are automatically sealed.

In the design shown the control is either automatic or manual, or it can be switched from one to the other with the chassis withdrawn. On other designs the control must remain on automatic or manual.

The controllers are mounted on the rear of the case, as shown by Fig. 1-21. They can be removed after going on manual control. Controllers are available as proportional plus manual reset, proportional plus automatic reset, and proportional plus automatic reset plus rate. Optional controllers are also available, such as with

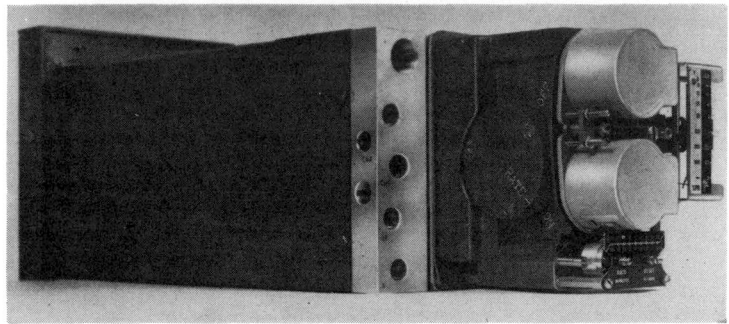

Fig. 1-21. Controller mounted on rear of case.

external reset where override control is required and controllers with means to prevent reset accumulation.

All controllers can be locally mounted in the field where transmission lag is objectionable.

Back-set control adjustments are standard on most controllers. Optional front set is available on some at an additional cost.

The control system used with miniature instruments has an outstanding advantage and generally results in better control than that obtained with large instruments. This is the separation of the recording and control functions and the method used in detecting the error signal and initiating control action. The error signal is, of course, the difference between the set point and process-variable pressures. The process-variable pressure is sent to both the pen-actuating element and the controller.

In the controller the process-variable pressure is compared to that of the set point. Any difference in these pressures initiates control action with a minimum use of links or levers, generally only one. As a result, the sensitivity of the controllers is exceptionally good, and this results in outstanding controller operation.

PNEUMATIC VERTICAL-SCALE INDICATORS

A new concept in process instrumentation is the use of indicating control stations, as illustrated in Fig. 1-22, and a reduction in the use of recorders. Previously most of the variables controlled were recorded. In this new concept the recording capacity, while varying with the type of process, averages only about 35 per cent of variables controlled.

When the control board is designed, permanent recording is not usually assigned to any controlled variable. Instead, plug-in connections are provided so that the operator can select and record any variable in order to follow the trend when an upset occurs. This is known as "trend recording."

When permanent recording is assigned, it is the practice to group three indicating control stations and one three-pen recorder on the panel board. This will require a panel area of about 6 by 12 in., compared to 7 by 20 in. for the previously described miniature recording control stations. Two savings result from this practice. One is the saving in panel-board area. The second, and greater saving, is the lower cost of the instruments of about 15 per cent over the cost of three single-station recorders. Additional savings are the lower cost of the control house and those for heating and air conditioning.

Two types of panel boards are used: one, the conventional vertical board and, two, a console design. Two methods of installing the instruments are followed. One is known as a "saturated board," and the control stations are installed adjacent to each other, both horizontally and vertically. The trend recorders are installed in a separate wing of the panel or in the sloping console.

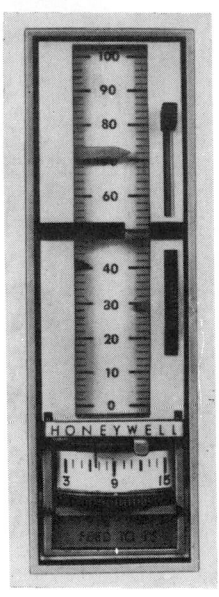

The saturated installation results in the largest reduction in panel-board size. Some engineers, however, concerned about possible operator fatigue in working with this type of board, prefer an installation with bare panels between groups of instruments. In this type of installation recorders are generally adjacent to the indicating control stations for operator convenience.

The design shown occupies a 2- by 6-in. front-of-panel area, and nine can be installed in a row in a 19-in.-relay rack opening. The depth behind the panel is 25 in. A similar design has a panel area of 3 by 6 in. and extends about 20 in. behind the panel. A third design, having a 5- by 5-in. panel area, has concentric- instead of vertical-scale indication.

All designs provide visual indication of the state of the process variable, set point, and air-to-valve pressure on either automatic or manual control. In addition, automatic to manual and back to automatic control is provided.

The set-point signal to the controller is a pneumatic pressure, which is changed by turning the thumb wheel at the right and is indicated by the pointer at the right-hand side of the scale. The process variable is indicated at the left-hand side of the scale and is positioned by a signal from a field-mounted pneumatic transmitter.

Fig. 1-22. Indicating control station.

This design also includes a deviation indicator, which is the pointer above the dark center line. It is operated by a differential-pressure unit, shown by Fig. 1-23, with the process-variable signal applied to one side and that of the set point to the other.

As shown, the process variable is about 10 per cent above the set point. Since the process variable is higher, the deviation indicator is above the dark center line. If the position of the process variable in relation to set point were reversed, the deviation indicator would be below the center line. When the controller is lined out and no error exists between process variable and set point, the deviation indicator is at the null position behind the center line.

Note that while the difference between process variable and set point is only 10 per cent, the deviation indicator is 20 per cent above the center line. This 2 to 1 amplification is made in order to indicate small deviations to the operator.

Before switching from automatic to manual control it is necessary to balance the output of the pressure regulator against the automatically controlled air pressure to the valve. A comparison of these is made by depressing the balancing lever at the upper right, which admits regulator output and controlled air pressures to the previously mentioned differential-pressure unit.   If the pressures are unequal, the deviation indicator will appear up- or down-scale from the center band.   The thumb wheel below the horizontal gage is then turned until the deviation indicator returns to the null center position.   The two pressures are then equal, and the switch lever is moved from the automatic to the manual position.

On manual control the operator changes the air pressure to the valve by means of the thumb wheel below the horizontal gage.   This will change the process variable, and a deviation in respect to set point will occur and be shown by the deviation indicator.   When returning to automatic control this error signal must be made zero prior to switching.   This is done by adjusting the vertical thumb wheel until the deviation indicator returns to the null position.   The switch is then moved from the manual to the automatic position.

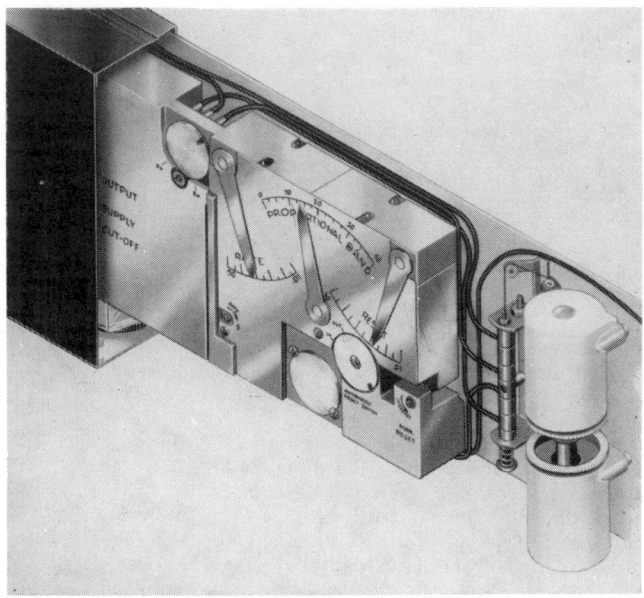

Fig. 1-23. Differential pressure unit for operating deviation indicator.

As with miniature recording control stations, maintenance cannot be done with the mechanism inside the enclosure.   The operating mechanism is mounted on a chassis that is withdrawn from the front of the panel for making adjustments or changing the controller settings.   In this position the station can be on either automatic or manual control.

Figure 1-23 shows the differential-pressure unit and balancing switch at the right and the plug-in controller at the left.   The controller shown has proportional, plus automatic reset, plus rate functions.   Switch action is provided to remove both automatic reset and rate functions, as well as direct and reverse control action.

In addition to the three-mode controller shown, vertical-scale indicating control stations are supplied with all modes of control available with large- and miniature-case controllers.   As with miniature-case recorders, the indication and controller operations are separated.

Concentric gage indicators do not use a chassis, and the controller is plugged in from the back.   With this design the controller adjustments are made at the back of the panel.

FILLED-SYSTEM THERMOMETERS

A filled-system thermometer consists of a recording or indicating instrument, with its pen or pointer actuated by a Bourdon tube, spiral, or helix connected by a small-bore capillary tube to a bulb, as shown by Fig. 1-24. The combination of actuating element, capillary tubing, and bulb is called a "thermal system."

The thermal system may be filled with a liquid, a volatile liquid, or a gas under pressure. Since the system is closed, the internal pressure will change when the bulb is subjected to variations in temperature. These changes in pressure result in the movement of the actuating element, which, by means of a connecting link, positions a pen or pointer or initiates a signal in a pneumatic transmitter.

The minimum temperature indicated on the scale shown in Fig. 1-24 is at the right and the maximum temperature at the left. With an increase in temperature of the bulb, the increasing pressure of the fill will cause the end of the spiral to move to the left and the pointer upscale, as indicated by the arrows.

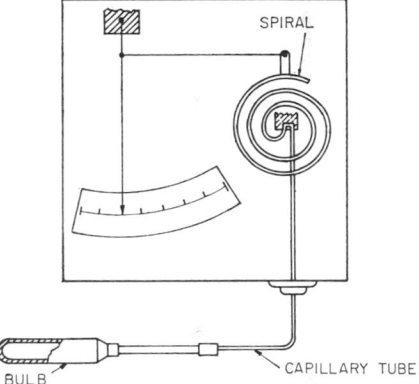

These thermometers are supplied for temperature measurement from −350 to +1200°F. Their accuracy, sensitivity, and other functional factors make them suitable for many industrial applications, for indication, recording, controlling, and pneumatic transmission of temperature. They are reasonable in cost and require only nominal maintenance.

Classification and Descriptions of Filled-system Thermometers

A number of manufacturers of filled-system thermometers have adopted a classification based on the fills. These have been published by Recorder-Controller Section, SAMA in RC 6-10-1963.

FIG. 1-24. Filled system thermometer.

The classifications and figures that follow are taken from this standard.

Liquid-filled (Class I B). Figure 1-25 illustrates a Class I B thermal system, which is completely filled with a liquid (other than a metal such as mercury) and operates on the principle of liquid expansion with changes in temperature. Various liquids may be used for the fill, such as distilled water, alcohol, xylene, etc. The fill used depends on the temperature range to be measured. The temperature range is from −300 to +600°F.

Class I B thermometers are particularly adaptable for applications where narrow spans and small bulbs are required and conditions prohibit the use of mercury-filled thermal systems.

The accuracy is affected by ambient-temperature changes of the spiral and the connecting tubing. The effects on the spiral can be eliminated by use of the bimetallic compensator attached to the end of the spiral, as shown in Fig. 1-25. This is known as case compensation. With an increase in ambient temperature the internal-system pressure will increase and the end of the spiral will move to the left, causing the pointer to move upscale, and the indicated temperature will be in error. The compensator is designed to move to the right a distance equal to the movement of the spiral tip, and the temperature indicated remains that measured by the bulb. Because of effects of ambient-temperature change on the connecting tubing, the maximum length is limited to about 15 ft.

Fully Compensated Liquid-filled (Class I A). Figure 1-26 shows a Class I A, fully compensated liquid-filled thermal system. It has two thermal systems. The one on the left is the measuring system and is complete with a bulb. The compensating system on the right is similar except that it does not have a bulb. This system fully compensates for ambient-temperature changes of the measuring spiral and connecting tubing to the bulb.

The measuring spiral is pivoted at point A and is held in position by the link to the tip of the spiral of the compensating system. The connection from the tip of measuring spiral to the pointer is shown at point B. With changes in ambient temperature the tips of both spirals will move. They are selected, therefore, on a basis of reasonably close matching of movement of each over the range of temperature compensation.

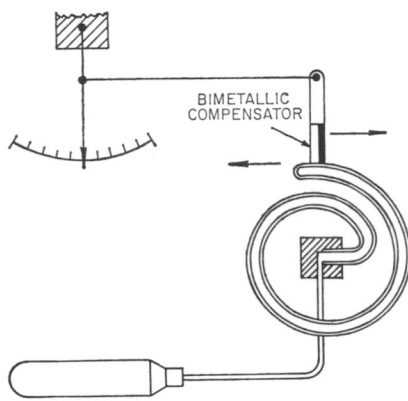

Since changes in the ambient temperature of the tubing will also change the internal-system pressure, in order to obtain good compensation the internal volume of the two tubes should be as nearly equal as possible. For this reason tubing is used from the same draw for both systems. Since spiral movement and tubing volumes cannot be matched exactly, calibration adjustments are also provided to obtain compensation.

FIG. 1-25. Case-compensated, liquid-filled thermal system, Class I B.

With the bulb at a constant temperature and a change in ambient temperature of the spirals, point B would move to the left, and indication would be in error. It is prevented from moving because the movement of A rotates the measuring spiral about pivot C and point B remains fixed. With an increase in the ambient temperature of the connecting tubing the internal-system pressure will increase. Tip movement of each spiral will occur, and compensation will be made as described above.

Tubing lengths up to 200 ft are supplied.

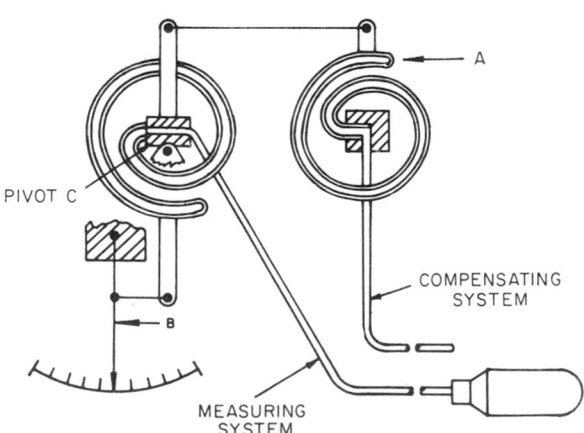

FIG. 1-26. Fully compensated liquid-filled thermal system, Class I A.

Vapor-pressure Thermal Systems (Class II). The system is partially filled with a volatile liquid and operates on the principle of vapor pressure. With changes in temperature of the bulb, variations of vapor pressure within the system occur. Depending on the application, four types are used.

The accuracy of Class II thermometers is unaffected by changes of ambient temperature of the spiral or connecting tubing, because the internal-system pressure is that of the boiling point of the volatile liquid in the bulb.

Class II thermometers have expanded scale or chart graduations within an increase in temperature, as shown by Fig. 1-27. This expansion permits more accurate reading of pen or pointer and adjusting the set-point position of controllers.

A Class II A system (Fig. 1-27) is used on applications where the bulb will always be at a higher temperature than the rest of the system. The spiral and connecting tubing are completely filled with liquid. A Class II B system (Fig. 1-28) is used on applications where the bulb will always be at a lower temperature than the rest of the system. All the liquid is in the bulb, and the spiral and tubing are filled with vapor. A Class II C system (Fig. 1-29) is used on applications where the bulb temperature may be either above or below that of the rest of the system. Note that as the bulb temperature changes, the vapor-volatile liquid positions become the same as for Classes II A and II

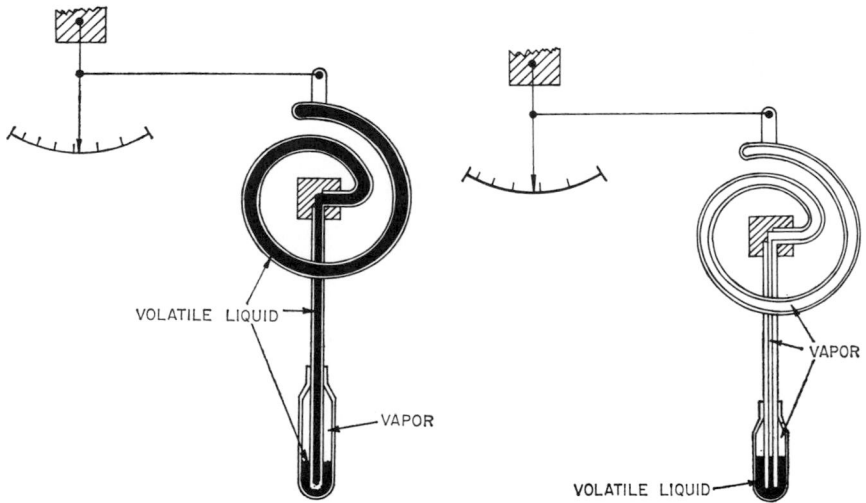

Fig. 1-27. Vapor pressure thermal system, Class II A.   Fig. 1-28. Vapor pressure thermal system, Class II B.

B. A Class II D system (Fig. 1-30) is used on applications when it is necessary to measure the temperatures below, at, or above that of the rest of the system. In this system the volatile liquid and vapor and a second relatively nonvolatile liquid are used in the system to transmit the vapor pressure to the spiral.

In general the bulb sizes for Class II systems are larger than for Class I. They can be supplied with tubing lengths up to 200 ft.

Class II A thermometers must be compensated for the difference in elevation between the bulb and instrument because of the head effect of the liquid in the connecting tubing. If the bulb is below, the instrument will read low. It will read high if the bulb is above. If the difference in elevation is specified when ordering, compensation can be included in the factory calibration. Compensation in the field requires placing the bulb in a bath at a known temperature and making a zero adjustment.

Gas-filled Thermal Systems (Class III). Class III thermal systems are gas-filled and are suitable for temperature ranges from -350 to $1000°F$. While practices among manufacturers vary, nitrogen is used for temperatures from -100 to $1000°F$. For temperatures down to $-350°F$ the gas may be helium or nitrogen.

Figure 1-25 also illustrates a Class III B thermal system with case compensation

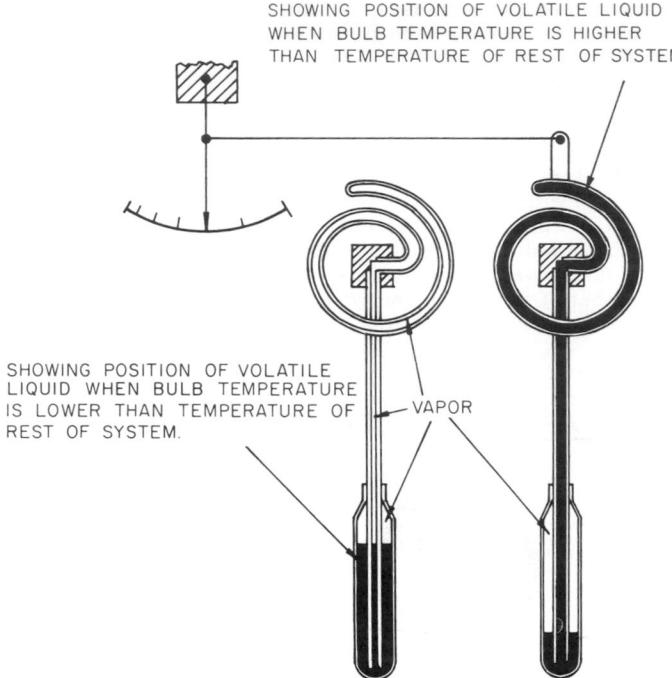

SHOWING POSITION OF VOLATILE LIQUID
WHEN BULB TEMPERATURE IS HIGHER
THAN TEMPERATURE OF REST OF SYSTEM.

SHOWING POSITION OF VOLATILE
LIQUID WHEN BULB TEMPERATURE
IS LOWER THAN TEMPERATURE OF
REST OF SYSTEM.

VAPOR

FIG. 1-29. Vapor pressure thermal system, Class II C.

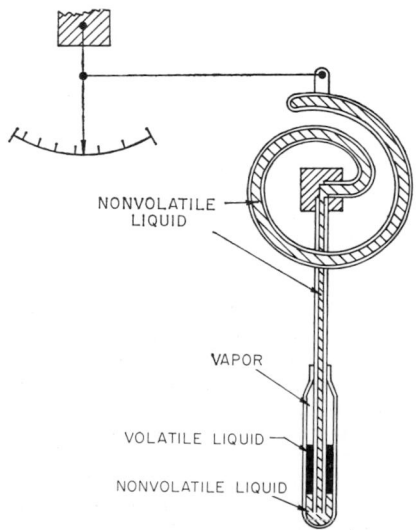

NONVOLATILE
LIQUID

VAPOR

VOLATILE LIQUID

NONVOLATILE LIQUID

FIG. 1-30. Vapor pressure thermal system,
Class II D.

that has been previously described. It is used on all Class III thermometers except those that are fully compensated. Partial compensation for effects of ambient-temperature changes on the connecting tubing is obtained by a large ratio of bulb to tubing volume, generally about 10 to 1.

Class III A is a fully compensated system and uses the same method as shown by Fig. 1-26. Compensation is the same as previously described.

Class III thermometers require larger bulbs than any other thermal system. One reason is the large ratio of bulb to tubing volume required with case-compensated systems. A second reason is the need to have sufficient gas volume remain in the bulb at high temperatures to produce the required system pressures.

Mercury-filled Thermal Systems (Class V). A mercury-filled, Class V B, case-compensated thermal system is also illustrated by Fig. 1-25. This system is completely filled with mercury or a mercury-thallium eutectic amalgam and operates on the principle of liquid expansion. Partial compensation for ambient-temperature changes of the connecting tubing is accomplished by the ratio of bulb to tubing volume, but tubing length is limited to about 25 ft.

Figure 1-31 shows two fully compensated mercury-filled thermal systems. The double thermal system on the left operates on the same principle as that previously described for Class I and III fully compensated thermometers. The method shown on the right uses only one capillary-tubing connection from spiral to the bulb. A metal wire having an extremely small coefficient of expansion with changes of ambient temperature is inserted in the tubing, which also is filled with mercury. The ratios of the wire area to the internal area of the tubing are selected so that with changes of ambient temperature, the volume around the wire always equals that of the mercury. Therefore, the pressure in the bulb due to expansion of the mercury is transmitted to the spiral without change, regardless of the ambient temperature of the connecting tubing.

Mercury-actuated thermometers are used to measure temperatures from −40 to 1000°F. The lower limit is established by the freezing of mercury. The higher limit is based on the expansion of bulb materials, which increases their internal volume and

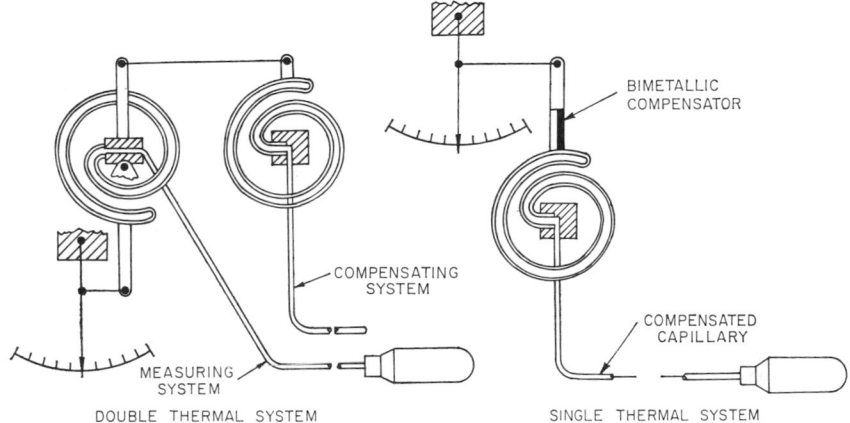

FIG. 1-31. Fully compensated mercury-filled thermal systems, Class V A.

lowers the required pressure in relation to temperature. The minimum span is 25°F over the temperature range from −40 to 1000°F.

Scales and charts used with Class V thermometers are evenly graduated. For most spans the same ones can be used as for Class II and III thermometers.

Bulb sizes are small, but do not approach the size of Class I. Their size, however, does not increase with the length of connecting tubing, as it does for Class II and III thermometers.

The system pressures are high, varying from about 500 psig at minimum to 2,000 psig at maximum temperature, regardless of the span. As a result of these high pressures the calibration and sensitivity of Class V thermometers is excellent.

Thermal-system Bulb Designs

Bulbs are available in a wide variety of designs and materials to meet the requirements of most applications. The principal designs are plain, union-connected, coiled, and averaging type. They are available in steel, various types of stainless steel, copper, brass, and Monel. Most of the above materials are also available with Teflon, Kel-F, Tygon, and other plastic coatings. Coatings serve two functions: they provide additional corrosion resistance or they prevent sticking of materials, thus eliminating an increase of heat transfer through the bulb wall.

The bulb is joined to the connecting tubing by means of an extension neck, usually of much smaller diameter but made of the same material as the bulb. The connecting tubing is of two types. The commoner type is a capillary tube of small diameter, about $\frac{1}{16}$ in., that is protected by a flexible armor of copper or stainless steel. The armor can be provided with the same coatings as the bulbs. The second type, known as plain or smooth tubing, is made of the same material as the bulb and extension neck. It is generally about twice the diameter of capillary tubing and does not have the flexibility of armored tubing.

Flexibility of connecting tubing is important when making the installation, especially where long lengths are concerned. When a thermometer is installed, the instrument and thermal system cannot be separated. The instrument must be installed first and the bulb and tubing "threaded" to the point of temperature measurement. For this reason flexible armor may be preferred over smooth tubing.

Bulb designs for different applications are described below.

Plain Bulb and Extension Neck. These are used where the bulb can be installed from the top of an open tank. The extension neck may be bent over the top edge of the tank.

Union-connected Bulbs. These have a union connection at the top of the bulb or on the extension neck. They are used on tanks under pressure. If pressure cannot be removed when the bulb is to be withdrawn, the bulb must be installed in a socket. The socket is screwed into the tank wall, using a pipe thread, or is welded in position.

Coiled Bulbs. Coiled bulbs are made of small-diameter tubing and formed into a coil about 2 in. in diameter and 4 in. long. They are used principally to present more surface for the heat transmitter and obtain faster response.

Averaging Bulbs. Averaging bulbs are also made of small-diameter tubing and may have a length of 10 ft or more. As the name implies, they are used to measure average temperature of air or other gases in ducts or chambers. Generally they are installed in a crisscross pattern.

HUMIDITY MEASUREMENT

The measurement and control of relative humidity has become very important in many industries, such as textile and paper manufacturing, food processing, and printing, because of rigid product specifications. It is also very important for the control of environmental test chambers.

The three principal methods of measuring relative humidity use hair hygrometers, wet- and dry-bulb thermometers, and dew-point measurement.

Hair Hygrometers. Hair hygrometers, as shown by Fig. 1-32, record relative humidity directly, without the use of psychrometric charts. As shown, they are often supplied to record ambient temperature using a coiled bulb, with a liquid- or mercury-filled system in order to use a linear chart. The actuation is by means of a hygroscopic element made of human hair located below the recorder. The length increases with an increase in relative humidity and contracts with a decrease. One end of the element is fixed, and the pen is positioned by means of a linkage connection to the moving end.

The practical measuring range is from about 30 to 90 per cent relative humidity to an accuracy of ± 2 per cent provided the range of ambient temperature does not exceed 60 to 90°F. The accuracy of temperature recording is ± 1 per cent of span.

The primary application of these recorders is to check on the operation of humidity control of rooms, chambers, etc., where the actual control is by other apparatus.

Wet- and Dry-bulb Thermometers. Relative humidity can also be measured by means of a two-pen thermometer. One bulb, known as the wet bulb, is kept wet at all times, either by covering it with a wick, the lower end of which is immersed in water, or by inserting the bulb in a porous tube into which a regulated supply of water is introduced internally. The passage of air over the wet bulb causes evaporation, which results in a lowering of temperature. The second, or dry, bulb is adjacent to the wet bulb, and both temperatures are recorded by the thermometer. At every temperature there is a definite relationship between relative humidity and the temperature difference between wet and dry bulbs. Tables giving these relative-humidity values are available. Standard psychometric charts, which make it possible to determine relative humidity, dew point, vapor pressure, and other quantities, are also available.

These two-pen thermometers are used for humidity control. One controller is actuated by the dry bulb and maintains a constant temperature. The second controller is actuated by the wet bulb and introduces steam or water into the chamber where the atmosphere is being controlled. The individual set points of the two controllers are positioned to obtain the required relative humidity.

Dew-point Measurement. For some applications it is more desirable to measure and control dew point instead of relative humidity. A thermometer bulb inserted in a sensor unit measures the dew point. The operating principle is based on the fact that a lithium chloride salt solution conducts electricity to a greater or less degree depending upon its concentration. A bifilar winding is applied to a cloth sleeve over a nonconducting tube. This device is impregnated with the lithium chloride solution and is then connected to a power limited a-c source. The device heats by ionic conduction to its operating temperature. After that, the device will self-regulate to maintain an equilibrium. When the temperature of the sensor is below this value, the salt absorbs moisture, its conductivity increases, causing a small current to flow between the wires, and the element is heated until its temperature is such that moisture is neither gained nor lost to the surrounding air. The converse occurs when the salt gives up moisture.

It is this temperature that is measured by the thermometer bulb. The conversion from operating temperature to actual

Fig. 1-32. Hair hygrometer.

dew-point temperature is accomplished either by special calibration curves or through standard direct-reading instruments.

MAINTENANCE OF MECHANICAL INSTRUMENTS

Mechanical instruments are designed so that maintenance has been reduced to a minimum. An inspection program will determine the amount of maintenance required and when it should be done. Protective maintenance, where components are replaced before failure occurs, should be included in this program.

Too often instruments are blamed when the causes lie elsewhere and are not something the instrument can correct. For example, flow cannot be controlled at the proper rate if a sufficient supply of fluid is not available. If the calibration is found to be correct, or has been corrected, and trouble remains, look elsewhere in the process for the source.

An important factor in maintenance is well-trained instrument-service people. Most manufacturers offer free training classes at their plants and district offices, and many provide training at customer plants. Taking advantage of this training will result in considerable reduction in maintenance costs.

To reduce maintenance costs it is essential to follow installation instructions as closely as possible. They are based on actual installations of thousands of instruments in many industries. If they cannot be followed, it is important to discuss the installation with the manufacturer; he will be pleased to be of assistance.

Flow Meters

The manufacturer's instructions for the installation of flow meters should be carefully followed. This is very important in the installation of the primary element in respect to the upstream and downstream piping conditions. Instruction books carefully specify the length of straight pipe required in relation to the ratio of the diameter of the restriction to the internal pipe diameter. Should either the upstream or downstream distance to elbows, bends, valves, etc., be less than that specified, the manufacturer should be consulted.

All primary elements are designed for specific operating conditions, which may include pressure, temperature, specific gravity, and other factors. If these conditions change, measurement will be in error, and correction factors must be applied to either the rate or totalized flow. Most instruction books include tables of correction factors or formulas for calculating them.

If the rate of flow must be frequently used by the operator, as in changing the set point of a controller, applying a correction factor is inconvenient, and the meter should be recalibrated. For example, assume that the correction factor is 1.02 for a meter calibrated for a differential pressure of 100 in. H_2O. Recalibrating the meter to a differential of 104 in. H_2O will eliminate the need to use a correction factor for the new operating conditions.

Field Maintenance. The need for field maintenance and when it should be done depends solely on operating conditions. The time intervals between checkings can be determined only after the meter has been installed. When clean liquids are being measured and flow is relatively steady, quarterly or semiannual inspections will probably be sufficient. When fluids are viscous, and possibly carry foreign matter, and flow fluctuates over 20 to 30 per cent of full scale, more frequent inspections may be required.

After the meter has been installed, a timed program of inspection, as outlined below, should be followed.

Checking at Zero. Stability of calibration is inherent in present-day flow meters and flow transmitters. After the meter has been in service for one week, it should be equalized (using the method given in the instruction book), and the zero reading observed. If not at zero, allow some time for pressures to equalize in the high-pressure and low-pressure chambers. If zero is not correct, check connecting piping for leaks and stop them. Only then make the zero adjustment as directed by the instructions.

If the zero adjustment is 1 per cent full scale or less, it is safe to assume that calibration is satisfactory and no further adjustments are necessary. This can be verified in other ways, e.g., the total flow appears to be correct, or the controlled rate of flow is that expected for a particular process. If a considerable zero adjustment is required, the calibration should be checked; this procedure is discussed below.

After the second week of operation recheck zero. If there is little or no change in zero, this checking procedure can be safely extended for several weeks. By following this procedure it is possible to establish a plan of maintenance and eliminate the cost of unnecessary steps.

Checking Calibration. The calibration can be checked either in the instrument shop or at the installation. Bellows meters, because of their size and weight, generally are better calibrated at the point of installation. Since a complete overhaul includes disassembly of the meter body and cleaning, it should be done in the instrument shop.

Flow transmitters can also be calibrated in the field. Because of their light weight and ease of installation, it is recommended that a shop-calibrated replacement unit be installed. This procedure eliminates taking checking equipment to the field, where setting up and operation sometimes are difficult. Under some weather conditions it is often difficult to duplicate shop calibrations in the field.

Calibration Equipment and Use. To obtain the accuracy of calibration inherent in the design of present-day flow meters and flow transmitters, standards for pressure measurement must be of high quality.

1. The input differential pressures should be measured with a water column to pressures up to 50 in. H_2O. For higher pressures, a mercury column may be used, but it should be equipped to read pressures with the same accuracy as an equivalent

water column.   The mercury column (Fig. 1-33) is designed and built for accuracy
and ease of observation.   Readings to a fraction of a millimeter make it ideal for
precise calibration.   It is designed to be used as a manometer, a differential-pressure indicator, or a differential-vacuum gage.

2. The transmitted pressures should be measured on a mercury column that can be
read to an accuracy of ±0.10 psig.   This is ±2.8 in. H_2O, or about ±0.5 per cent
full scale of the 12-psig span.   An equivalent indicating gage (Fig. 1-34) is excellent
for shop calibration.   This gage is available in ranges from 0 to 120 in. H_2O to 0 to
300 in. Hg.   It can be used for the measurement of pres-
sure, differential pressure, or vacuum.   An important
feature is the elimination of backlash.

3. For accurate reading, glass tubes of columns must be kept
clean.   Mercury and water must also be clean.

4. To avoid errors, read columns at same level as the height
of liquid.   For 100-in. H_2O differentials, a double column
is more convenient to use than a single one.

5. After setting pressures on column, allow pressure in meter
body to stabilize before reading pen position on chart or
transmitted pressures.

Installation Recommendations.   The instruction books
supplied by manufacturers provide installation information
in considerable detail.   A number of general, but very important, instructions that are frequently violated are given
below.

1. Follow instructions as closely as possible.   If there is a
wide discrepancy, be sure to consult the manufacturer.

2. When measuring steam or water, protect the meter body
and connecting piping from freezing.   If freezing occurs,
the pressures developed may blow out gaskets or damage
the meter body.

3. Install pneumatic transmitters as close as possible to the
primary-element connections.   This eliminates possible
decrease in speed of response or failure to measure small
changes in differential due to pressure loss in the connecting piping.

4. When measuring fluids that can become viscous at low
temperatures, heat the connecting piping and meter body
in order to eliminate sluggish operation.

5. When measuring gas containing entrained vapors, install
the primary-element connections on the top of the pipe
and install the transmitter above them.   Condensed
liquids will drain back into the pipe.   Under these conditions, if the meter body is installed below the flow line,

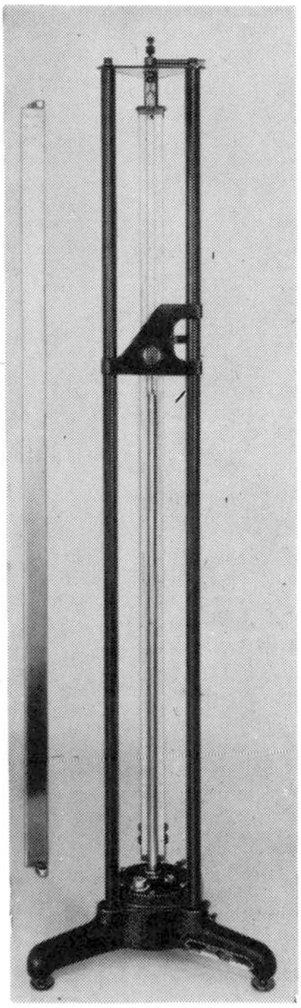

Fig. 1-33. Mercury
manometer. (*Courtesy
of Wallace & Tiernan,
Inc., Belleville, N.J.*)

unequal heads of liquid in the vertical connecting lines will cause measurement
errors.

6. Do not attempt to measure flow from reciprocating compressors or pumps.   Errors
in measurement will result, for which there are no correction factors.

7. If at all possible, avoid excessive vibration of the flow line.   If this cannot be done,
use flexible connections in orifice piping at the meter body.

8. Leaks in connecting piping, especially on the low-pressure side of the meter body,
will result in positive errors.   This is especially true with low rates of flow.

9. When measuring liquids, the maximum distance from primary element to meter
body should not exceed 100 ft.   When measuring gas, it should not exceed 50 ft.
Longer distances may result in sluggish action.

10. When measuring liquids, slope the piping at least 1 in. per ft from the primary-
element connections to the meter body.   A lesser slope may result in accumulation
of air or vapor that will cause errors in measurement.

FIG. 1-34. Indicating pressure gage.   (*Courtesy of Wallace & Tiernan, Inc., Belleville, N.J.*)

Thermometers

Filled-thermal-system thermometers differ from flow meters and pressure gages in that the process fluids are not in direct contact with the actuating element.   The only contact is external, and then when a plain bulb is immersed in the process fluid. If a protecting socket is used, there is, of course, no direct contact.

Since the tubing lengths generally are short, the instrument may be located in the process area and not in a control house, which means that corrosive vapors may be present.   While every effort is made by manufacturers to use corrosion-resistant materials for components, together with the best possible door gaskets, considerable maintenance may be required for some applications.

The connecting tubing is particularly susceptible to corrosive action, which is the result of the previously mentioned process vapors, and mechanical abuse, which comes from various sources.   The most prevalent cause is the manual changing of bulbs from one tube to another in order to measure several temperatures.   Since the tubing cannot be run through conduit because of the bulb size, it is exposed to all manner of damage due to plant operation and maintenance.

Checking of Calibration.   The checking of calibration is more difficult than for flow meters or pressure gages, because an external signal cannot be applied, and the bulb must be placed in baths at several temperatures.   This presents two requirements: a well-agitated liquid bath and correct measurement of the bath temperature. Unless the system has been overranged or temperatures shown are obviously incorrect, calibration normally need not be checked more than twice a year.

If the temperature shown appears to be in error, it can often be determined and corrected by recalibration at a single point, assuming that the same error exists throughout the temperature range.   Correction is made by checking the calibration at one-third to one-half the maximum temperature and using the zero adjustment to make a correction at that point.

For a thermometer with a range of 0 to 600°F, the bulb would be immersed in boiling water.   The water temperature, as indicated by a glass-stem thermometer, would be compared with that displayed on the instrument.   The glass-stem thermometer should be adjacent to the thermometer or fastened to it, so that both will measure the same temperature.

If the temperature shown must be corrected, this is done with the zero adjustment, which is identified in the instructions. If the required adjustment is large, it should be made by rotating the actuating element about its center.

After this procedure has been followed, the thermometer should be returned to service. If the operating temperature shown appears to be only slightly in error, further correction can be made using the zero adjustment. If the error is considerable, that is, more than 5 per cent, complete recalibration is recommended.

For complete calibration, baths at approximately 25, 50, and 75 per cent of full scale should be available. They should be well agitated, and suitable means for temperature measurement should be provided. Glass-stem thermometers are available for high temperatures, but they are sometimes difficult to read above the surface of a hot bath. The use of a thermocouple, wired to the bulb, and an extension lead to a portable potentiometer is a satisfactory method.

The high temperature should first be checked and corrections made, using the span adjustment on the actuating element. If the adjustment required moves the follower on the micrometer screw a considerable distance from its center position, the angular position of the actuating element must be changed. The first step is to return the span adjustment to approximately its mid-position. The actuating element is then rotated until the temperature shown is approximately that of the bath. A precise adjustment at this time is not necessary.

The next step is to check at the low temperature, and the zero adjustment is used to make the correction. Since there may be some interaction between zero and span adjustments, the calibration at the higher temperature should be checked and a precise span adjustment made. It may be necessary to make several zero and span adjustments to obtain the desired accuracy.

Following this the calibration should be checked at mid-scale. If it is not within the desired limits the zero and span adjustments must be changed to obtain the best possible calibration.

Instrument Maintenance. Since the instrument is in the process area, corrosive vapors may enter the instrument case when the door is opened for changing the chart or the set point. Snap-on links, pivot holes, and other connection points should be periodically examined for corrosion or deposits that may cause friction. Instruction books give directions for cleaning.

Installation Recommendations. Manufacturers' instruction books provide installation information in considerable detail. A number of general, but very important, instructions that are frequently violated are given below.

1. Install the bulb where it will quickly sense changes in temperature. Avoid a location in stagnant areas because a lag in sensing temperature changes will generally result in poor control.
2. Do not place tubing of uncompensated liquid-, gas-, and mercury-filled thermal systems near hot pipes or process vessels because radiant heat will result in high readings. Conversely, supporting the tubing on building walls that become cold at low atmospheric temperatures will cause low readings.
3. Protect against breakage. If the capillary tubing is broken, the thermal system will have to be replaced, and the thermometer will be out of service until it is. Armor protection will help avoid damage from general operation or plant maintenance that can lead to time out of service and cost of system replacement.
4. Select internal socket diameters to have a minimum air gap in respect to outside bulb diameter. If bulbs are used in sockets with a greater gap, sluggish operation, and possibly incorrect temperature readings as well, may occur.
5. Sockets are supplied with extensions of various lengths between the top of the thread and the socket end for installation on insulated pipes and process vessels. If the socket extends any distance beyond the insulation, it must be insulated in order to avoid a low reading.

Pressure Gages

Most pressure gages, like flow meters, have the pressure fluid in direct contact with the process fluid. Exceptions are those equipped with a diaphragm seal located at the pressure tap and connected to the actuating element by capillary tubing. This closed system is liquid-filled, the same as a Class I B thermometer. Because of the cost of the sealed type, they are used only where the process fluid cannot be allowed to enter the connecting piping and the actuating element and it is necessary to measure a pressure.

Because the process fluid is in contact with the actuating element, pressure gages can be subjected to severe service. These include corrosive action, the possibility of solidification of fluids under certain ambient-temperature conditions, high overloads, the effect of rapid pressure fluctuations, and the high temperature of the process fluid on the actuating element.

Figure 1-35 represents a method of installation that has many desirable features. It is too costly, however, for most applications, and could be modified to a considerable extent. For example, when measuring the pressure of low-temperature water with a concentric-scale indicator, the gage connection would be screwed directly into the shutoff valve, thus eliminating the rest of the piping shown. When measuring steam pressure, a gage with a female connection would be screwed to the upper end of the siphon. The system shown is very convenient for field calibration, and its use is explained below.

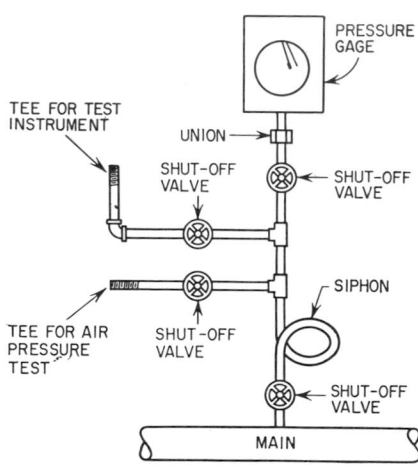

FIG. 1-35. Pressure-gage connections

Checking of Calibration. Two methods are used: one avoids removing the gage from service, and the second involves checking the gage in the instrument shop. There are also two ways of using standards for checking calibration. One uses a primary standard, such as a water or mercury column or a dead-weight tester. The other uses test gages, which, in turn, are periodically calibrated against a primary standard. These gages have very high accuracy, and one type is illustrated by Fig. 1-34, discussed under flow-meter calibration.

When a considerable amount of checking and recalibration is done, a number of gages may be used to provide a series of increasing ranges. Thus several gages can be used at the most accurate portion of their range. For example, a 0- to 400-psig gage may be checked against test gages having ranges of 0 to 100, 0 to 300, and 0 to 600 psig, respectively.

Field Calibration. The piping arrangement shown by Fig. 1-35, as previously stated, is very convenient for field calibration. The pressure source for checking can be that in the main, or if the fluid should not be permitted to come in contact with the actuating element of the test gage, an external source must be provided, such as plant air, water pressure, or a nitrogen bottle. The most common method, using pressure from the main, is described below.

1. Close the shutoff valve at the main and open the upper left shutoff valve. If the connecting line to the gage is filled with a liquid, close the valve immediately when the pressure drops to zero so as not to drain the line. If gas pressure is being measured, the upper shutoff valve need not be closed.
2. Do not make any zero adjustments at this time, because with the gage located above the main it may have been adjusted for the downward head effect of the liquid in the connecting piping.

3. Connect the test gage at the point shown.
4. Apply increasing pressure in successive steps by alternately cracking and closing main shutoff and record the readings of the two gages. Decrease pressure in successive steps by alternately cracking and closing the lower left shutoff valve and record the readings of the two gages.
5. Separately average the up- and down-scale readings of each gage. Compare the values of the two gages. This will determine the accuracy of the operating gage compared to that of the test gage. *Note:* If the connecting piping is filled with liquid, the readings of the test gage must be corrected by the pressure equivalent to the elevation between main shutoff valve and the center of the test gage. The correction factor for water is 1 lb for each 2.31 ft of elevation, and this is to be added to the test-gage reading. The data obtained are used to determine whether recalibration is necessary.
6. For low-pressure ranges, especially where gas pressures are being measured, a water or mercury column is substituted for the test gage. No corrections are required for elevation.
7. If the fluid whose pressure is being measured cannot be allowed to enter the test gage, the system must be completely drained by first closing the main shutoff valve and then opening the lower left shutoff valve. An external source of pressure must be provided at the lower left-hand shutoff valve. The method of checking calibration is the same as that previously described.

Shop Calibration. Checking and recalibration in the shop is better than that in the field. Not only can it be done more accurately and in less time, but it also provides an opportunity for careful inspection of components and their replacement if required, as well as general cleaning.

Water and mercury columns should be provided, and can be considered as primary standards for checking low-range gages. They should be designed so that they can be used for measuring positive pressure and vacuum. A panel of test gages, as previously described, should also be provided if a sufficient number of gages will be checked to warrant their cost.

When test gages are used, they are connected in parallel with the one being checked. Plant air is used for actuation within its available pressure. For higher pressures a light oil is used, and pressures are generated by a manually operated hydraulic jack. A suitable valve must be installed between the jack and the gage to hold pressures.

If the use of test gages is warranted, a dead-weight pressure-gage tester (Fig. 1-36), which is a primary standard, should be provided. It will also be necessary for periodic checking of test gages. The tester shown is a conventional type, and can be furnished for pressures as high as 25,000 psig. A dead-weight tester consists of a vertical cylinder and piston. On the upper end of the piston is a tray, on which one or more standard test weights are placed. A plunger, operated by a hand screw, applies pressure to the liquid inside the piston. This liquid is oil or glycerin, stored in a reservoir connected to the cylinder through a two-way valve.

The gage to be tested is mounted on the dead-weight tester and is connected to the cylinder through a three-way cock, so that it is subject to the same pressure as the liquid in the cylinder. While measurements are being made, the cylinder carrying the weights is rotated to reduce friction. The pressure in pounds per square inch applied by the dead-weight tester is the sum of the weights and plunger in pounds divided by the cross-sectional area of the plunger in square inches.

The calibration is essentially at three points—zero, and about 70 and 90 per cent of the full-scale pressure—and is made as follows. (These directions apply only to rectangular-case instruments. For concentric-scale gages refer to the manufacturer's instructions.)

1. Both zero and span adjustments, which will probably be of the micrometer-screw type, should be set at mid-travel.
2. Apply a pressure equal to 90 per cent full scale. Use the span adjustment to indicate approximately the correct pressure. If an appreciable movement of the

span adjustment is required, return the span adjustment to its center position and rotate the actuating element about its axis to indicate the pressure approximately.

3. Release the pressure and use the zero adjustment to obtain the correct indication.
4. Apply pressure equal to 50 per cent full scale and use the span adjustment to obtain the correct indication.
5. Recheck at zero and readjust, if necessary. Since there may be interaction between span and zero adjustments, several trials may be required to obtain the desired calibration.
6. Check the calibration at 70 per cent full scale. If the indication is not within the limits desired, it will be necessary to compromise on the indication at 90 per cent.

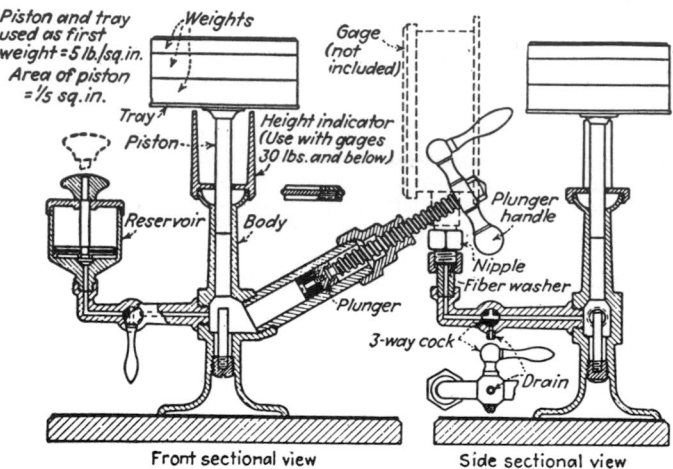

FIG. 1-36. Dead-weight pressure-gage tester.

Installation Recommendations. The instruction books supplied by manufacturers provide installation information in considerable detail. A number of general, but very important, instructions that are frequently violated are given below.

1. When measuring steam, always install a siphon, as shown by Fig. 1-35. It serves two purposes: to prevent high-temperature steam from damaging the actuating element when the gage is first placed in service and following start-up after the main has been shut down. Prior to start-up, and with the main shutoff valve closed, the siphon is filled with water and the gage connected. To place the gage in service, the main shutoff valve is opened. Line pressure then forces water ahead of the steam into the actuating element and protects it from the steam temperature. When the main is shut down, and not under pressure, the siphon acts as a trap and remains partially filled with water. When the main is pressurized, the actuating element will again be protected.
2. When measuring steam or water, both gage and connecting piping must be protected from freezing. The pressures developed may rupture both actuating element and piping.
3. Select a range so that maximum operating point is approximately 75 per cent of the full-scale value. Longer life can be expected because of lower material stresses of the actuating element, and the extent of overload protection will be increased.
4. Where pressures being measured fluctuate rapidly and over a considerable portion of the scale, pressure snubbers should be installed. They are available from several manufacturers.
5. When fluids in the actuating element and piping become viscous at low ambient temperatures, the response will be sluggish. It will be necessary to insulate and

possibly heat the connecting piping and provide a heated enclosure for the gage.

6. Whenever possible install the gage where it is not subjected to vibration from compressors, pumps, or pipes. It is desirable, under such conditions, to use a flexible connection in the piping to the gage.

7. When measuring liquids, if the gage is installed below the point of pressure measurement, slope the connecting piping at least 1 in. per ft to avoid formation of gas pockets. Their formation may cause errors in measurement.

Relative-humidity-measuring Instruments

As previously stated, two mechanical instruments are used in making measurements of relative humidity: the hair hygrometer and filled-system thermometers. Since the installation and maintenance of filled-system thermometers has already been discussed, this section will cover only the hair hygrometer.

Checking of Calibration. Calibration can be checked by means of a sling psychrometer. If consists of two glass-stem thermometers, mounted on a board, with a suitable handle that permits the thermometers to be whirled rapidly. One thermometer bulb is covered with a wick saturated with water. During the whirling the water evaporates from the wick, and this thermometer will indicate a lower temperature than the other. This is known as the wet-bulb temperature. The relative humidity is related to the difference between the two temperatures, and the values can be obtained from tables. The value obtained is then compared with the instrument.

This method of checking must be used with caution. Because of the stratification of air, the relative humidity may differ at the instrument site and at the level where the sling is operated. Such a check is useful, however, for if several values show wide discrepancies, recalibration of the instrument is indicated.

Field calibration is not recommended because calibration should be done in a cabinet where several values of humidity can be controlled and measured, and will be observed by the instrument. All manufacturers have means for doing this.

Field Maintenance. Generally little maintenance will be required. The amount necessary will depend on the ambient conditions of the installation. The major effect on measurement is coating of the element with oil, dust, etc. The hair elements should be cleaned periodically using a clean brush and distilled water. If they cannot be cleaned with water, chemically pure ether should be used. The elements should never be touched with the fingers.

Installation Recommendations. The installation should be made where the instrument will be in the path of air currents. Avoid installation in a stagnant pocket. Forced circulation by means of a small fan is helpful in obtaining increased speed of response.

LIQUID-LEVEL MEASUREMENT

Level is measured under a variety of conditions. The liquid may be under atmospheric pressure, as in an open tank or reservoir, or in a process vessel under pressure.

One of the most flexible and convenient ways to measure liquid level is the static-pressure method. It is based on the fact that the static pressure exerted by a liquid is directly proportional to the height of the liquid above the point of measurement, regardless of the volume. A pressure gage, then, can be calibrated in terms of height of a given liquid and used to measure level under atmospheric pressure. When liquids are under pressure in a closed vessel, a different pressure-measuring gage must be used.

Measurement under Atmospheric Pressure. Figure 1-37 shows the use of a pressure gage to measure level in a tank under atmospheric pressure. The pressure tap is located at the approximate minimum level. If the liquid contains entrained solids, this location decreases the possibility of plugging the connecting lines. If the liquid is corrosive, a seal should be used, as shown, and the sealing liquid should have a higher specific gravity than that of the liquid being measured.

If the gage must be located below the tap, the difference in elevation, which is an additional head on the gage, can be compensated for by the zero adjustment to a maximum value of about 10 to 20 per cent of the instrument range. Gages are also available with a compensation several times the range being measured. For example, the head compensated for may be 90 ft, and the level measured only 20 ft.

For some applications, such as measuring the level in a reservoir, a connection cannot be made at the minimum level. On these applications, level can be measured by means of a diaphragm box shown by the installation on the left in Fig. 1-38. As shown on the right, it can also be connected at the minimum level in order to isolate the gage from the liquid whose level is being measured.

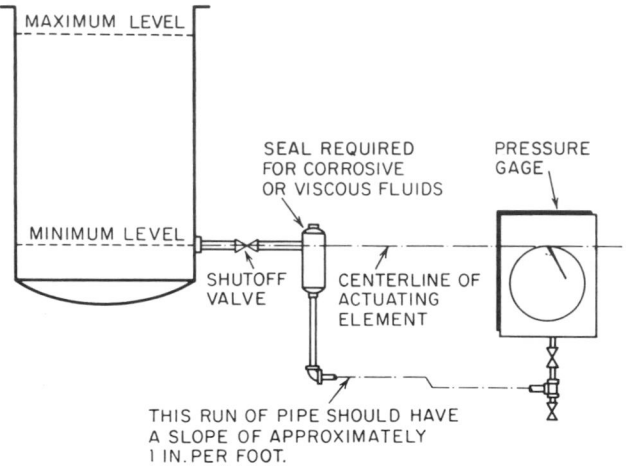

Fig. 1-37. Liquid level measurement in an open tank.

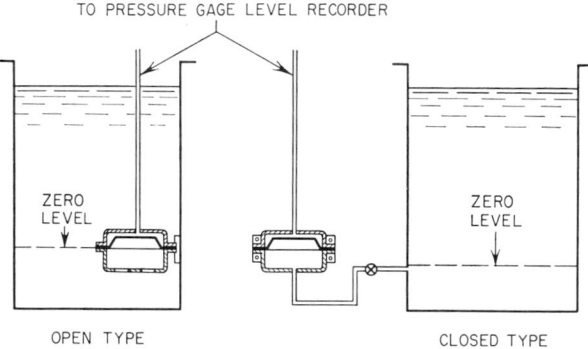

Fig. 1-38. Liquid level measurement with diaphragm boxes.

Within the box is a flexible diaphragm made of rubber, neoprene, or other corrosion-resistant material. The box is connected to the gage by small-bore tubing. The volume in the box is large compared to the volume in the tubing and actuating element.

In operation the pressure of the liquid head is exerted against the underside of the diaphragm, resulting in an upward movement of the diaphragm until the pressure within the closed system is equal to the head of liquid. The gage measures the air pressure but is calibrated in terms of liquid level.

The submerged box shown can be used only with clear liquids. If liquids contain suspended matter, it may collect around or on the diaphragm and cause incorrect readings. The external box should be used for these applications, and when considerable suspended matter is present, a periodic or continuous water back-purge may be necessary. Neither type should be located more than 90 ft from the gage.

Figure 1-39 illustrates an air-purge system. With this system the location of the gage in relation to the point of measurement is not limited, and the level of corrosive liquids or liquids with large amounts of suspended matter can be measured. A probe is immersed in the liquid to the minimum level, with the pressure and volume controlled by a differential regulator to assure a slow bubbling of air through the liquid. The air pressure is then equal to the back pressure exerted by the head of liquid. The gage measures the air pressure but is calibrated in terms of liquid level.

This method makes it possible to measure level where the probe cannot be inserted in the tank because of agitator blades or other reasons. A connection is made in the side of the tank at the minimum level, as shown for the diaphragm-box connection, at the right in Fig. 1-38.

The gage can be located up to 100 ft or more from the point of measurement. The longer the distance, however, the slower the response to measuring changes in level.

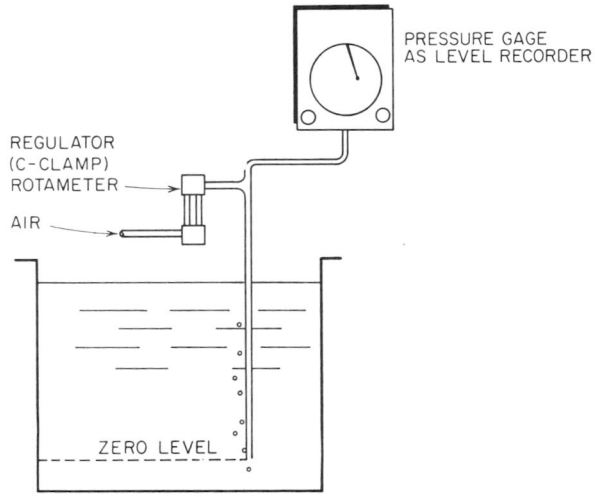

Fig. 1-39. Bubble-type liquid level measurement.

The air purge should always be at or near the point of measurement and not at the gage. Location at the gage causes measurement error due to the friction loss of the air flow through the connection tubing.

The use of a differential regulator plus rotameter indicator is recommended. The differential regulator results in the same rate of air flow regardless of the level in the tank. If it is not used, larger rates of flow at low level can cause errors in measurement due to friction losses. Its use also decreases the amount of air required. The rotameter provides an indication of whether or not air is flowing and is convenient in adjusting the rate of flow.

Measurement in Closed Tanks under Pressure. Liquid level can also be measured in closed tanks under pressure, using the static-pressure method. The static pressure above the level is added to the liquid head and must be compensated for. If the pressure changes, the measurement will be in error, and differential pressure measurement is required.

A differential type of flow can be used, either a bellows meter (Fig. 1-2) or one with pneumatic transmission (Fig. 1-3). While the bellows meter can also actuate a pneumatic transmitter, the low-volumetric-displacement type shown by Fig. 1-3 is used on nearly all applications.

Bellows-type differential flow meters can be used for measuring the level in open tanks for applications shown by Figs. 1-37 and 1-39. Not all can be used with the diaphragm boxes because the volumetric displacement is too large in some designs. Diaphragm-actuated flow meters with low volumetric displacement can be used for all applications shown by Figs. 1-37 to 1-39.

Figure 1-40 shows the installation of a bellows meter. The meter body is mounted on the rear of the instrument case. This arrangement provides indication or recording of the level, with or without pneumatic control. In addition, pneumatic transmission can be supplied with the above functions.

The constant-reference head $H1$ is applied to the high-pressure side of the meter body and the variable level $H2$ to the low-pressure side. The meter body simply

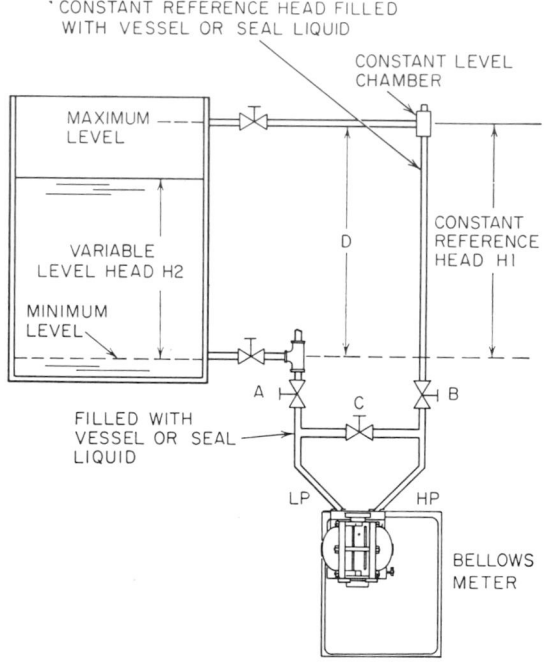

Fig. 1-40. Installation of bellows meter on a closed tank under pressure.

measures the differential between $H1$ and $H2$. The meter is calibrated to read in terms of level which can be indicated, recorded, or transmitted.

The piping is arranged so that the pressure above the liquid is applied to both the high- and low-pressure sides of the meter body and all effects are cancelled. Therefore, regardless of variations in pressure, only changes in level are measured.

For accurate measurement, the constant-reference head must remain fixed. Some bellows meters are designed with an internal volumetric change when measuring changes in differential. For example, for a differential from minimum to maximum, the volume in the high-pressure chamber will increase and that in the low-pressure chamber decrease by the same amount.

With the installation shown by Fig. 1-40, a decrease in level will increase the volume in the high-pressure side. This will cause a decrease in the constant-reference head $H1$. The volume in the low-pressure side will increase, but this volume is insignificant in respect to the volume in the tank and will not have a measurable effect on the variable head $H2$.

In order to eliminate the error, a constant-level chamber is installed at the top of the constant-reference head.   It should have sufficient area so that the head change will be small for full-range measurement.   For example, in a chamber 3 in. in diameter and with 100 in. of water differential, the error will be about $\frac{1}{4}$ per cent full scale.

Because of the low volumetric displacement of diaphragm-type transmitters, constant-level chambers generally would not be required for a constant-reference

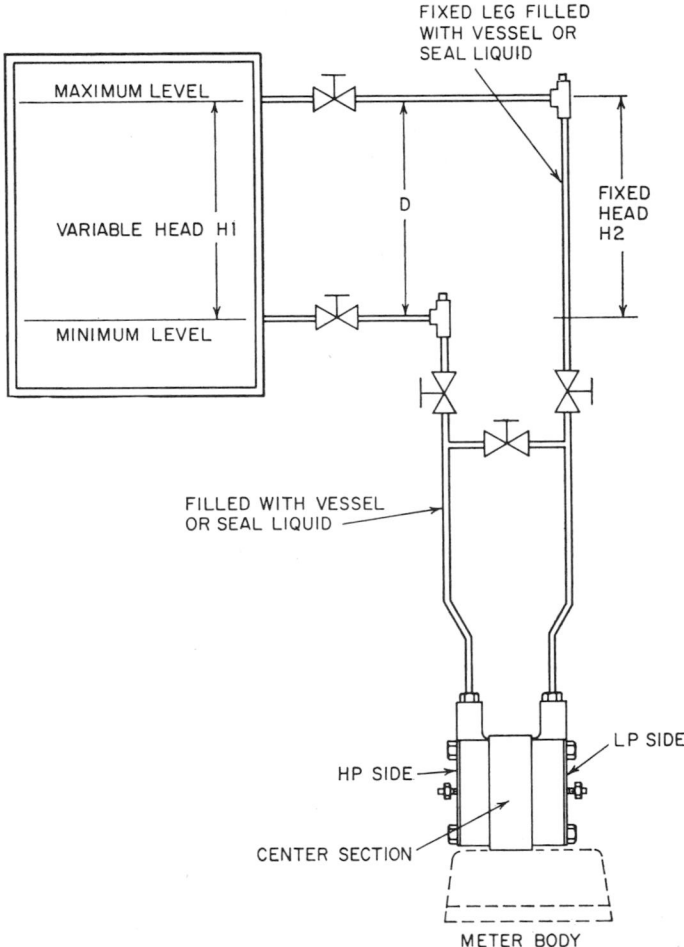

FIXED LEG FILLED
WITH VESSEL OR
SEAL LIQUID

MAXIMUM LEVEL

VARIABLE HEAD H1

MINIMUM LEVEL

D

FIXED
HEAD
H2

FILLED WITH VESSEL
OR SEAL LIQUID

LP SIDE

HP SIDE

CENTER SECTION

METER BODY

FIG. 1-41. Installation of a diaphragm-type transmitter on a closed tank under pressure.

head made of 1-in. pipe.   As shown by Fig. 1-41, the constant-level chamber is replaced by a tee.   This reduces the material and installation costs.

Figure 1-41 shows the installation of a diaphragm-type transmitter on a closed tank under pressure.   The transmitter case, shown by dotted lines, has been displaced in order not to obscure the meter body; it actually is in a vertical position.

Note that the piping for both meters is the same except for the constant-level chamber shown by Fig. 1-40.   The valves and tees shown are required for filling, placing in service, and checking at zero.

Sealing Liquids. Measuring the level of volatile liquids such as butane, propane, and other hydrocarbons is complicated by the fact that these liquids may be unstable in the constant-reference leg with changes of ambient temperature. Boiling of the liquid may occur in the outer leg, and it will be only partially filled with a liquid. When this occurs, the measurement will be in error.

The error can be eliminated by the use of a stable liquid, such as water, in the outer leg. If there is a difference, however, in the specific gravity in the vessel and the leg, it must be compensated for. Almost without exception the stable liquid will have a greater specific gravity than that in the tank. As a result, with the differential designed for the tank liquid for a distance D in inches of water, head $H2$ will not balance

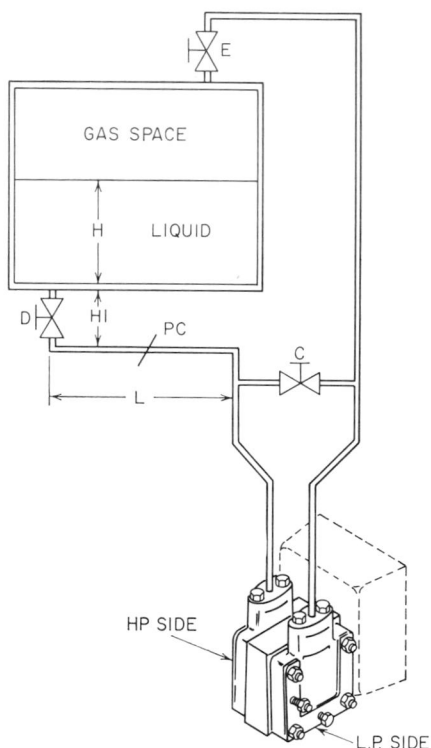

Fig. 1-42. Cryogenic liquid level measurement.

$H1$, and with a maximum level the pen or pointer will not reach full scale or the maximum transmission signal will not be generated.

It is necessary to compensate for the difference in specific gravities by what is known as suppression. The means for doing this either are inherent in the design of level meters or transmitters or can be added in the field.

Cryogenic-liquid-level Measurement. Of increasing importance is the measurement of the levels of cryogenic liquids, such as oxygen, nitrogen, and helium. A typical installation for a transmitter is shown by Fig. 1-42. On most applications the connections on the vessel are at the top and bottom, as shown by Fig. 1-41. Fortunately, under most ambient-temperature conditions the connecting piping is filled with gas. It is important, however, that the lower connection be of sufficient length that PC, the phase change between liquid and gas, be in this run and not in a vertical connection, so that as the position of PC varies with changes of ambient temperature, it will not affect the accuracy of level measurement.

The elevation $H1$ in the vertical line at valve D must be compensated for because this head is also to be measured in addition to head H. Compensation for this elevation is integral in the transmitter design. While Fig. 1-41 shows the transmitter below the vessel, it will also measure the level if located above. The bottom connection should also be such that PC occurs in a horizontal run.

Purge-type Liquid-level Measurement. It is often necessary to prevent the liquid whose level is being measured from entering the connecting piping or meter body. Otherwise the liquid might solidify in the piping at ambient temperatures, suspended matter might plug the vessel connections, or corrosive fluids might enter the meter body. Under these conditions the system can be purged with water, gas, or a light

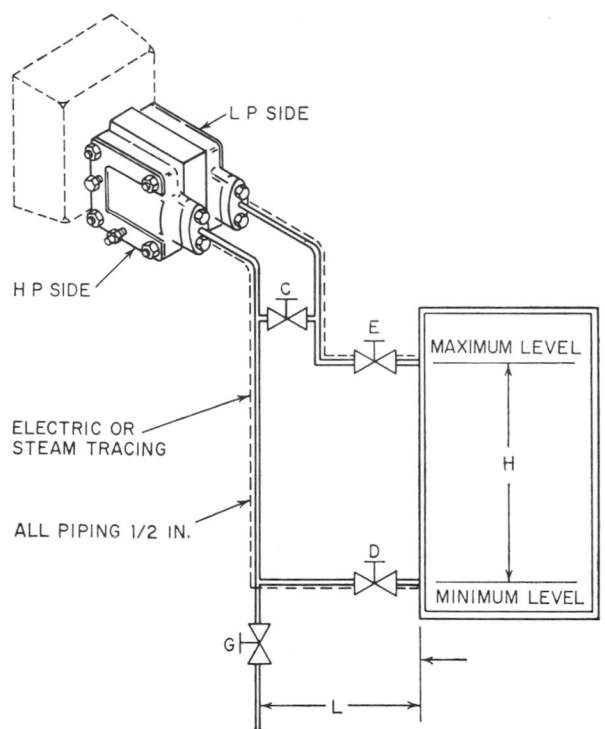

FIG. 1-43. Self-purged liquid level system.

oil at a higher pressure than that of the vessel. The purge connections, as shown by Fig. 1-41, are made at the meter body. Purged systems operate satisfactorily provided the purge is not interrupted.

Figure 1-43 shows a self-purged liquid-level system. It differs from the system shown by Fig. 1-42 for cryogenic liquids in that the connecting piping is heated to higher temperatures than the ambient temperatures to insure that it is filled with gas. The distance L must be sufficient to permit the location of PC in it and not in the vertical connection.

This system has advantages over those using an external purge. The adjustment at zero is more easily made because it is not necessary first to adjust the purge flow to insure equal friction loss in each connecting pipe. Another advantage is that if heating is interrupted, piping will again become gas-filled when heating is resumed.

Chapter 2

ELECTRICAL MEASUREMENTS,
SERVICING, AND TESTING

By R. C. LANGFORD[1]
Assistant Chief Engineer
Weston Electrical Instrument Corporation
Newark, N.J.

Even without the advent of automation and electronics, servicing and maintenance problems in modern factories have multiplied many times in the last few years. It is within the ken of many maintenance staffs when a multimeter, a clamp-on ammeter, and a "Megger" were the only diagnostic tools of the profession. To suit today's needs, it is not enough to describe the instruments in current use—rather it is vital to describe some of the leading measurements required to be made, how to make them, and the instruments best suited for the purpose. Additional information must also be given about safeguards and precautions requisite to these measurements and instruments.

A fairly recent phenomenon has been the growth of preventive maintenance. In this field, electrical instruments have played the role of diagnostician with such success that their initial cost has been more than covered often in a single maintenance job.

Important measurements required comprise those of d-c and a-c voltage and power, together with the circuit parameters of resistance capacitance and inductance and the physical functions of speed and temperature. These and their particular connection to servicing problems are listed below:

CONTINUOUS EMF MEASUREMENTS

Potentiometers. Among the leading features of this class of d-c voltage-measuring device is the ability to measure emf in the range 0 to 1 volt to extremely high precision, i.e., to about 0.001 per cent, without drawing current from the source to be measured. This high accuracy is achieved by measuring all voltages with respect to the emf of a Weston standard cell. These high-precision instruments are usually associated with high-sensitivity galvanometers of very fragile construction, so that apparatus of this kind is limited in location to a fixed position in the laboratory. Portable forms, Fig. 2-1, are available, however, for servicing use.

When the potential to be measured is greater than the range of the potentiometer (usually 1.5 volts), a volt box is used. It consists of a number of resistance coils connected in series, with the taps brought out to binding posts. Figure 2-2 shows the diagrammatic arrangement in two forms. In (A), the potentiometer is connected to the posts marked " + " and " −." When the potential to be measured is between 1.5 and 15 volts, it is connected to the " + " and "15" posts, between which the resistance is

[1] The author is now Director of Research, General Precision, Inc., Aerospace Group, Little Falls, N.J.

just ten times that between " + " and " −." Hence, only one-tenth of the unknown potential is applied to the potentiometer, the readings of which must therefore be multiplied by 10. Similarly, when the potential is between 15 and 150 volts, it is connected to the " + " and "150" posts and the ratio becomes 100. In (B), Fig. 2-2, the potential to be measured is always connected to one pair of posts, designated " + " and " −," and the potentiometer connections are shifted to obtain the desired ratio.

FIG. 2-1. Portable potentiometer.

Theoretically the former method is the better because the resistance in parallel with the potentiometer is constant and the sensitivity is therefore constant. In the latter case, the sensitivity varies, being a minimum with the lowest ratio or when the maximum amount of resistance is in parallel with the potentiometer. On the other hand, in (B), the unknown emf is always connected to a high resistance, and hence, there is no danger of burning out the volt box; this occasionally happens with the first form (A), owing to accidental connection with the wrong terminals.

Precautions in Use. Normally precision potentiometers are kept in one position because of the delicacy of the associated galvanometer. The main precautions in use for both high-precision and portable types are regular cleaning of the main slide-wire

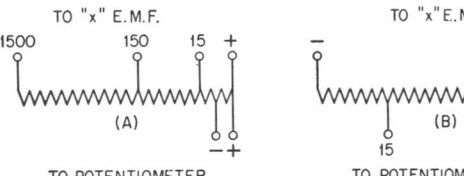

FIG. 2-2. Volt boxes.   (*From " Standard Handbook for Electrical Engineers.*")

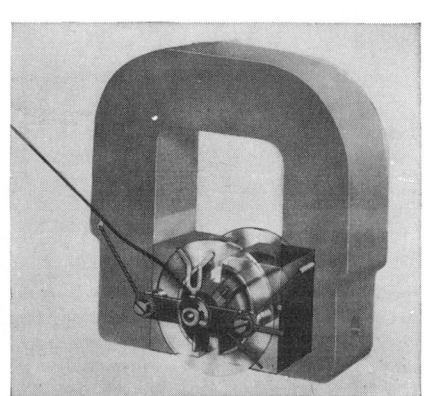

FIG. 2-3. Moving-coil mechanism.

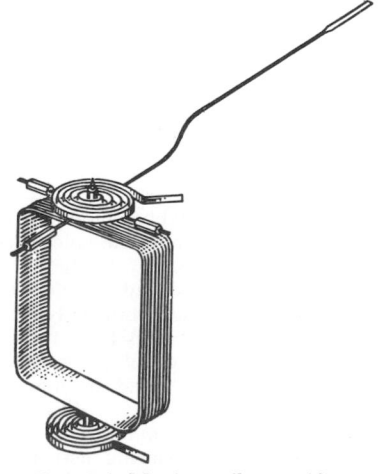

FIG. 2-4. Moving-coil assembly.

and switch contacts and careful operation of the potentiometer to prevent undue slamming of the galvanometer, which could result in considerable damage thereto.

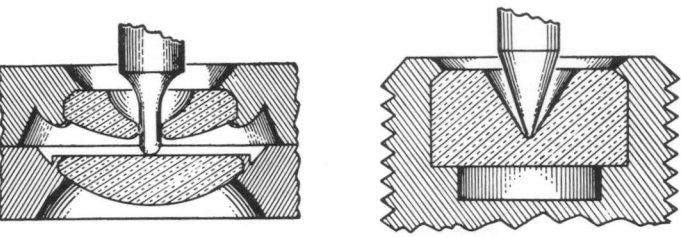

Fig. 2-5. Jewel bearings in instrument mechanisms.

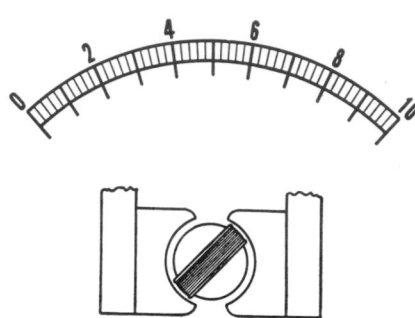

Fig. 2-6. Linear pole piece and associated scale.

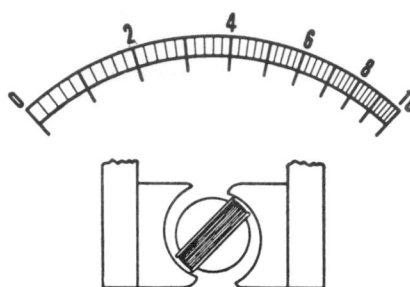

Fig. 2-7. "Cut" pole piece and resultant scale.

Voltmeters. Indicating instruments called voltmeters are used in most industrial measurements. In nearly all cases the basis of measurement is the permanent-magnet moving-coil instrument shown in Fig. 2-3. This consists essentially of a light rectangular coil of copper wire wound upon an aluminum frame as in Fig. 2-4, pivoted in jeweled bearings, Fig. 2-5, and capable of rotating in the circular space between the soft-iron core and the pole pieces of a permanent magnet. Being a closed secondary circuit, the aluminum frame acts as a brake or damper during the period while the coil is deflecting. The pole pieces are normally concentrically shaped, so that the magnetic field is uniformly distributed in the space in which the coil moves. This normally (see Fig. 2-6) gives a uniformly spaced scale to the instrument. (It should be noted that for many types of voltmeter the pole pieces are appropriately shaped, or "cut," so that the magnetic field and therefore the scale shape are no longer uniformly graduated, as in Fig. 2-7.) A light tubular pointer attached to the coil moves over a graduated scale, and the current to the coil is introduced by two spiral springs which also provide the controlling force of the instrument.

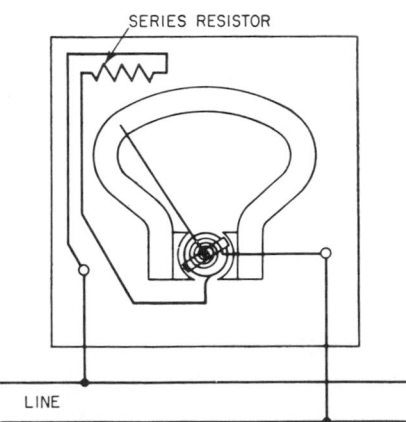

Fig. 2-8. D-c voltmeter.

Voltmeter Sensitivity and Range. The moving-coil instrument described above is basically a current-measuring instrument, and the connection of series resistance as in Fig. 2-8 extends the range to various voltages. Thus, the same basic instrument can be made suitable for a wide range of voltages by changing the tapping point on the series resistor, which is usually made of a wire of low-temperature coefficient.

The sensitivity of a voltmeter is basically an expression of the amount of current taken from the voltage source when full-scale voltage is applied to the instrument. The higher the sensitivity, the smaller the current required for full-scale deflection.

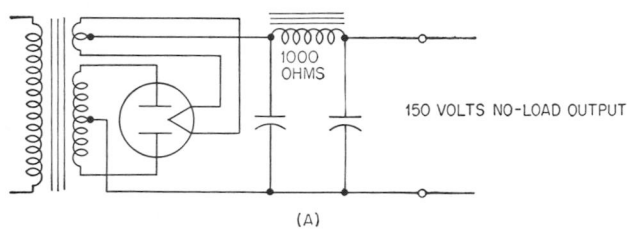

(A)

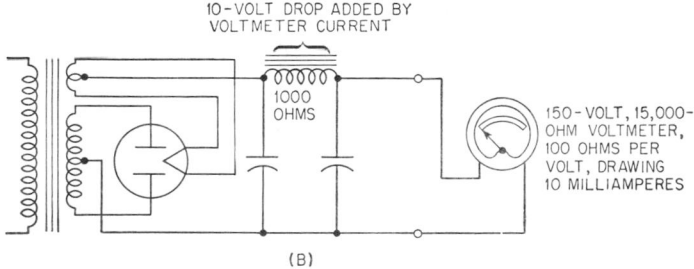

(B)

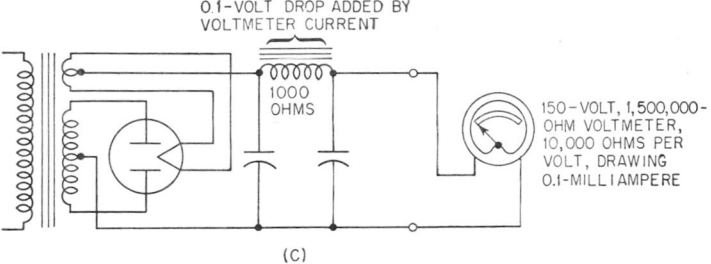

(C)

Fig. 2-9. Voltmeters.   (A) Power unit no-load output 150 volts; (B) low-resistance voltmeter drawing 10 ma increases filter drop 10 volts, thus introducing a measurement error of about 7.5 per cent; (C) high-resistance voltmeter drawing only 0.1 ma increases filter drop 0.1 volts—thus no appreciable measurement error is introduced by load of instrument.

Sensitivity normally is expressed in ohms per volt—the ratio of total resistance to full-scale voltage rating.   For example, the sensitivity of a typical voltmeter may be described as

$$\frac{15{,}000 \text{ total ohms}}{150 \text{ full-scale volts}} = 100 \text{ ohms per volt}$$

The full-scale current is thus the reciprocal of the ohms per volt; i.e.,

$$\tfrac{1}{100} = 0.010 \text{ amp}$$

or 10 ma.   Direct-current voltmeters are most commonly manufactured in sensitivities of 100 and 1,000 ohms per volt, although other standard sensitivities are 200, 5000, 10,000, and 20,000 ohms per volt.

The reason for making voltmeters in different sensitivity ratings can be appreciated when it is recognized that the current required for instrument operation contributes to the total load on the voltage source. If the source is a large generator or a conventional storage battery, the current drain of even the least sensitive voltmeter represents no significant additional load and accurate voltage readings can be made regardless of instrument sensitivity. If, however, the voltage source has only a small current-output capacity, i.e., high internal resistance, the current required by the voltmeter may represent an excessive load on the voltage source and thus prevent accurate voltage measurement.

A practical example is found in the measurement of voltages in the plate-power-supply unit of a radio receiver. Such a unit is normally loaded practically to its full capacity, which may be as little as 20 or 30 ma. Hence, the additional load of a

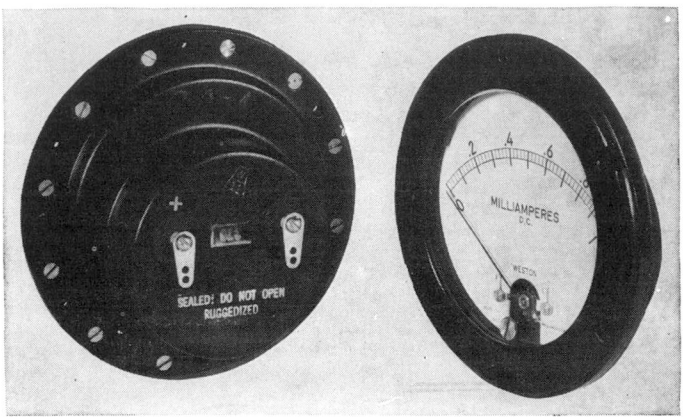

FIG. 2-10. Ruggedized instruments.

100-ohm-per-volt instrument, drawing 10 ma, would load the voltage source to such an extent that the over-all regulation of the power unit would cause an erroneously low voltage to be read. The internal resistance of the power unit may be such that the current taken by the voltmeter will unduly increase the voltage drop in the circuit (see Fig. 2-9A and B), thus giving an incorrect indication of voltage that exists under normal conditions.

The use of a voltmeter of higher sensitivity, as in Fig. 2-9C, requiring less operating current, will increase the accuracy of the voltage readings by reducing the loading effect of the voltmeter. Because of this fact, voltmeters are now manufactured in sensitivities of 10,000 or 20,000 ohms per volt, which permits such instruments to be used in many types of circuits without seriously affecting them. For the highest sensitivities, special electronic instruments are used (see page 13–54). This is particularly required for most forms of trouble shooting in electronic equipment.

Voltmeter Characteristics. Laboratory standard voltmeters are similar to portable instruments except that they are larger, have a longer pointer, and are more accurate.

Switchboard instruments are essentially the same as portable instruments except that they are more rugged and are mounted in shielded cases to reduce the effects of stray magnetic fields due to heavy currents in adjacent bus bars.

Precautions in Use. Instrument mechanisms, although designed to be as rugged as possible, are sensitive to prolonged vibration and shock. Precautions should be taken to prevent abuse of this nature, but if working conditions dictate usage in these hazardous conditions, mechanisms of the ruggedized type with rubber shock mounting should be used (see Fig. 2-10). These are necessarily more expensive than the normal type but can offer considerable savings in the long run should the maintenance department suffer a consistently high breakage rate.

Stray magnetic fields, as described under Micro- and Milliammeters, can permanently or temporarily demagnetize the working magnet.   Accordingly, no indicating instrument should be placed on the steel bedplate of operating electrical rotating machines or near current-carrying bus bars.

Ambient effects of temperature and humidity also exert a considerable effect on the working life of any instrument.   Sealed ruggedized instruments should be considered if these extremes of temperature and humidity are likely to be consistently met.

CONTINUOUS-CURRENT MEASUREMENTS

Again the basic instrument used is the D'Arsonval type of mechanism of Fig. 2-3. However, the details of each instrument depend greatly on the magnitude of the direct current to be measured.

Galvanometers.   These measure the smallest currents, generally using a mirror, lamp, and scale for the most sensitive ranges.   These sensitivities may range down to

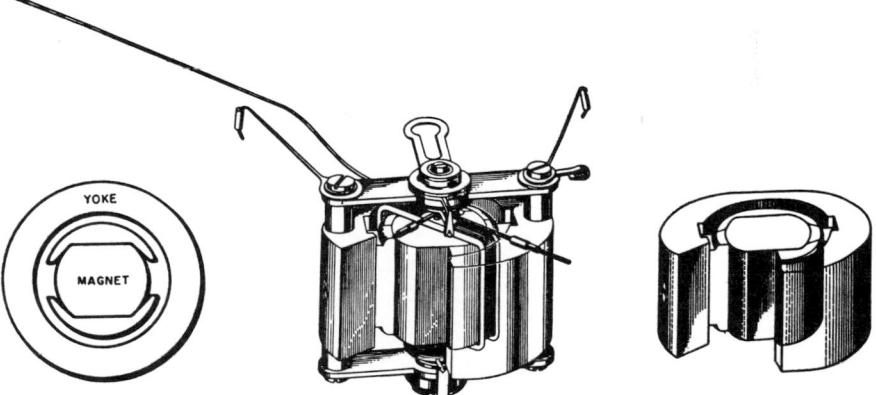

FIG. 2-11. Internal- or core-magnet construction.

0.00001 μa per mm deflection of a light spot on the scale 1 m away from the galvanometer.   Suffice it to say that this instrument is of extremely delicate construction, usually quite unsuited to being carried about, but nevertheless indispensable for sensitive current detection.

Micro- and Milliammeters.   These probably comprise the largest group of instruments in use.   They are again D'Arsonval-type instruments but now can be made so rugged that they can be used for all forms of industrial testing.   Of recent years a new form of design, Fig. 2-11, known as the internal- or core-magnet construction, has shown much utility, particularly in areas requiring rugged construction and freedom from stray magnetic-field effects.   This is achieved by the use of modern high-strength magnets and the self-shielding action of the soft-iron outer action in preventing stray magnetic fields from neighboring bus bars from reaching and thus affecting the magnet.

Ammeters.   Basically, an ammeter is a milliammeter with a shunt in parallel, as in Fig. 2-12.   By this means, self-contained instruments, with the shunt inside the case, can be made up to about 25 amp.   With a variety of these instrument internal shunts, the instrument usually can be arranged to give a multiplicity of ranges as in Fig. 2-13. Above 25 amp, external shunts are almost exclusively employed, as in Fig. 2-14, because of space requirements.

These heavy-current shunts are made of strips of low-temperature-coefficient material, soldered between massive copper blocks and adjusted to give an output of 50 or 75 mv.   By this means one indicating instrument can be used with a variety of shunts to give a variety of ranges, thus cutting down the cost of measuring high direct currents.

Precautions in Use.   These are almost identical with the case of voltmeters.   However, ammeter shunts are instruments together with their associated leads; the two should always be ordered together and kept in one place, since the resistances of all these components are carefully matched for the highest accuracy.

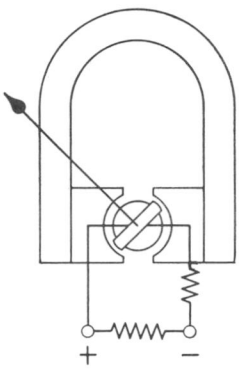

FIG. 2-12. D-c ammeter.

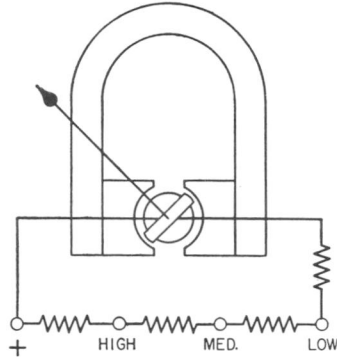

FIG. 2-13. Multirange d-c ammeter.

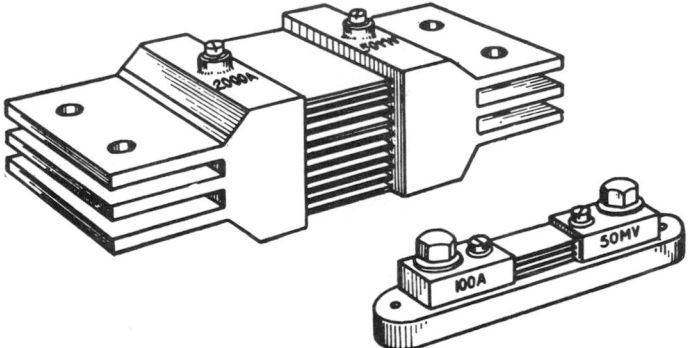

FIG. 2-14. External shunts.

ALTERNATING EMF MEASUREMENTS

In alternating emfs, there are three different values to be considered.   These are the average value, the peak-to-peak value, and the root-mean-square value.   The first usually is encountered in a-c measurements involving high sensitivities, i.e., rectifier-operated instruments.   The second usually is encountered when trouble shooting on electronic equipment where irregular wave shapes are met.   The third, or rms, is the almost invariable value used in electrical power measurements where true sine waves are usual.

Average-reading Voltmeters

These almost invariably are the rectifier-operated class of instrument.   The rectifiers are inserted into a circuit as in Fig. 2-15 with d-c milliammeter and a tapped series resistor for various voltage ranges.   Rectifiers used vary from copper oxide types in earlier instruments to the latest types using germanium and silicon rectifiers. With this class of instrument high sensitivities of up to 20,000 ohms per volt can be obtained.   Normal operating frequencies up to 30 kc may be had with copper oxide rectifiers, but this may be extended for low-voltage ranges up to about 1 megacycle by using germanium and silicon rectifiers.

Precautions in Use. It should be noted that although the scale of this class of instrument usually is calibrated in rms values, it is still essentially an average-reading instrument, so that errors will result if the instrument is used to measure nonsinusoidal quantities.

In addition to the precautions under voltmeters for the d-c instrument, it should be noted that permanent damage to the rectifiers will result if fuses are fitted in series

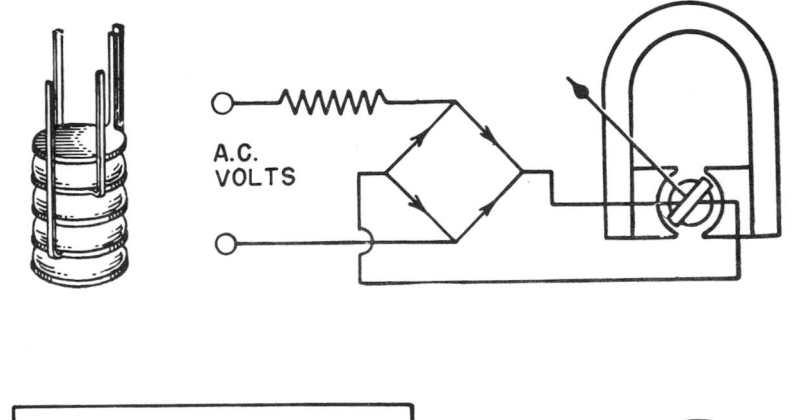

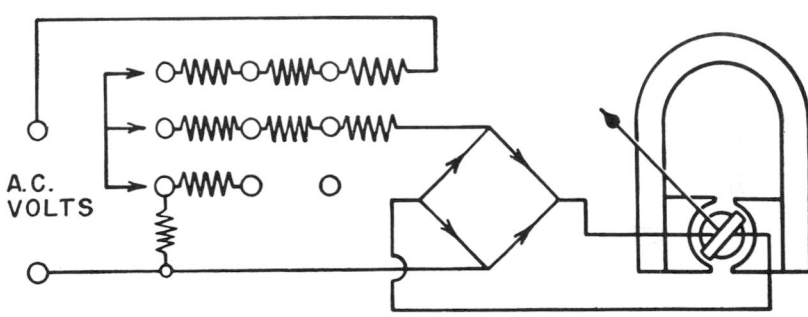

Fig. 2-15. A-c rectifier voltmeter.

with the d-c instrument or if alternating current is applied to the network terminals without having the d-c milliammeter in circuit. Rectifiers have a poor temperature coefficient, so that this class of instrument should not be operated above 65°C.

Peak-to-Peak Voltmeters

These measure the peak-to-peak double amplitude of a-c signals. The signals measured usually are nonsinusoidal and often very badly distorted. Special electronic equipment is used (see Vacuum-tube Voltmeter).

RMS-reading Voltmeters

Measurements of this type encompass the principles of thermocouple and moving-iron instruments, dynamometers, and electrostatic and induction instruments although the two last types are falling out of use.

Thermocouple Instruments. These consist of a series resistor, a heating element, a thermocouple which generates a d-c emf, and a d-c instrument for measuring this emf as in Fig. 2-16. This type of instrument normally is used for the measurement of high-frequency current or voltage, being virtually independent of frequency up to about 1 megacycle.

Precautions in Use. Although this type of instrument is mainly useful for high-frequency measurements, it can be used to measure d-c voltages provided two readings are taken with the measuring leads reversed. The mean reading should be taken as the correct value.

Probably the chief limitation in use is the low overload capacity of these devices. Only about twice full-scale voltage should be applied for brief instants; otherwise the thermocouple may burn out.

Moving-iron Voltmeters. To a considerable extent, the moving-iron instrument is just the antithesis of the moving-coil type. The coil through which the measuring current flows is not movable but is fixed in position on the instrument frame; the "magnet" is the moving member and is attached to the shaft which carries the indicating pointer (Fig. 2-17). But the magnet is not a permanent magnet because, if it were, the instrument would measure only direct current, so that an alternating current

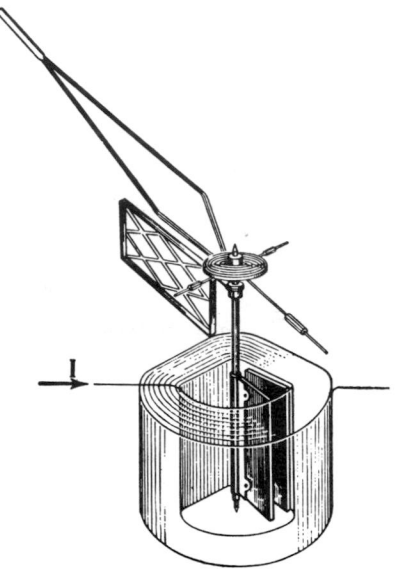

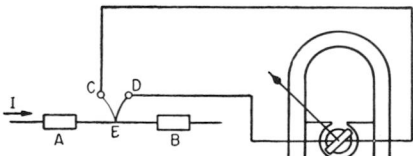

FIG. 2-16. Thermocouple instrument.   FIG. 2-17. Moving-iron instrument.

in the field would cause the magnet to move first in one direction and then in the other with each reversal of polarity, with the result that the pointer would merely vibrate about the zero point on the scale. To allow operation on alternating current, the magnet of the moving-iron instrument is made of soft iron or special alloys, so that it receives magnetism of whatever polarity and strength induced from the field coil but retains only the minimum of this magnetization. When direct current flows in the field, the soft iron is inductively magnetized with a strength dependent upon the magnitude of field current and with a polarity dependent upon the direction of current flow through the field coil.

When alternating current flows in the coil, the polarity of the magnetism induced in the iron reverses with each reversal of the alternating current, and its strength, at any instant, is proportional to the instantaneous value of the current. However, the polarity relationship between the field flux and the vane flux is always the same, regardless of the direction of current in the field, because the magnetism of the iron is produced (induced) by the current in the field coil. Consequently, the moving-iron instrument can be calibrated for both alternating current and direct current, although obviously it will not indicate the polarity of the direct current.

Since both the primary flux of the field coil and the flux resulting from the induction of magnetism in the iron vane are proportional to the direct or alternating current in the coil, the instrument is calibrated in terms of this current. For voltage measurement, the conventional series resistor is added.

It should be noted that the forces acting on the moving iron always tend to move it to the position that results in maximum flux in the coil. This applies for any shape of iron armature or field coil. These forces are greatest when the iron is nearest the position for maximum flux, and this fact has considerable bearing upon the scale distribution of moving-iron instruments.

Because of the elimination of the permanent magnet, the field coil must now supply all the energy necessary to operate the instrument; hence, moving-iron instruments require more power than permanent-magnet moving-coil types of corresponding ratings.

The operating current in the moving-iron instrument flows through a wholly stationary circuit. Consequently, the instrument can handle current of a much higher order

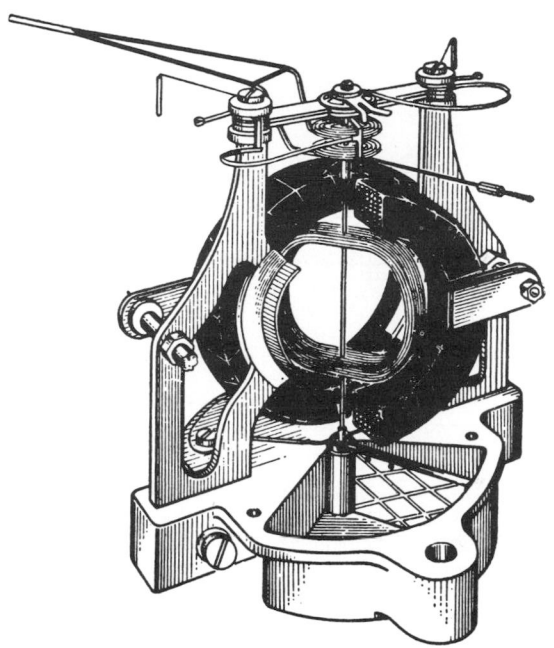

FIG. 2-18. Single-structure dynamometer.

of magnitude than is possible in a moving-coil instrument, in which springs or conducting spirals must carry the measured current. Since the spring in the moving-iron instrument is required only to provide a control torque, a single spring is sufficient, and its design need not be complicated by electrical requirements, such as resistance and current-carrying capacity.

As with permanent-magnet, moving-coil instruments, magnetic shielding is required to avoid interference from external magnetic fields, jeweled bearings are necessary to minimize friction, and accurate spacing of all parts is essential to provide consistent performance. The damping of this class of instrument is not inherent as is the case with d-c instruments, the general method used being that of air damping. This mechanism measures true rms current and has great ability to withstand heavy overloads.

Precautions in Use. As a voltmeter, the low sensitivity of the moving-iron principle often precludes its wide use; however, its ability to withstand rugged service is often of use in servicing electrical power equipment of uncertain overload factor.

Dynamometer Voltmeters. Electrodynamometers (see Fig. 2-18), also termed electrodynamic instruments, depend for their operation upon the reaction between the current in one or more moving coils and the current in one or more fixed coils. Because of the diversity of circuit relationships obtainable through the utilization of this principle, electrodynamometer instruments find widespread use in the measurement of a-c quantities. They are extensively used for measuring power as well as reactive volt-amperes in both single-phase and polyphase circuits, they are employed for high-accuracy voltage measurement, and they provide a convenient means of measuring power factor and frequency. The name electrodynamometer or electrodynamic instrument is colloquially shortened to "dynamometer" instrument, and in this text, the colloquial term is used synonymously with the formal name.

As stated, deflecting torque is produced by the interaction of magnetic fields. One of these magnetic fields is produced by current in a moving coil and the other by current in a stationary coil, as in Fig. 2-19, and the resultant torque is proportional to the product of these two currents and the resultant power factor. As in moving-iron

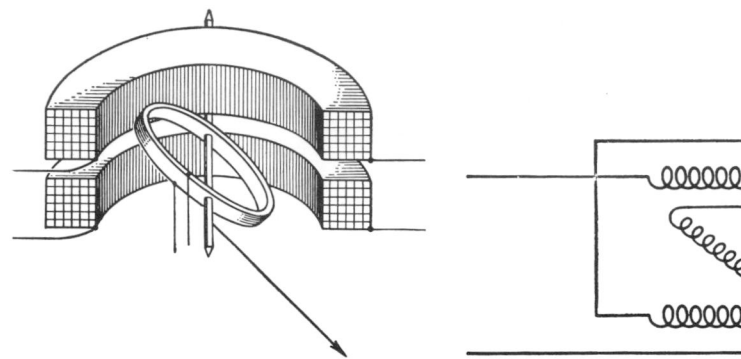

FIG. 2-19. Dynamometer coil structure.   FIG. 2-20. Series connection of dynamometer windings for a-c voltmeters.

instruments, damping is not inherent in this system, and indeed, metal objects in the magnetic field are most undesirable. Accordingly, air damping is most often used, with the damper box far removed from the moving and stationary coils as shown in Fig. 2-18. For voltage measurement, the coils are connected in series, and a true rms reading results with the usual square-law scale as in Fig. 2-20. The sensitivity of such a voltmeter is less than that of a d-c voltmeter because of the higher current required, but compared with the moving-iron instrument, a more efficient and higher accuracy system results.

Precautions in Use. Owing to the low operating fields, dynamometers are peculiarly sensitive to stray magnetic fields. The usual precautions should be observed to keep well away from the iron beds of rotary electrical machinery and heavy-current-carrying bus bars.

ALTERNATING-CURRENT MEASUREMENT

Basically these are the same as their equivalent voltmeters, the main differences being in the method of measuring the various magnitudes required.

Average-reading Current Measurement

Normally the circuit of Fig. 2-21 would be used, i.e., the average-reading voltmeter of Fig. 2-15. Rectifiers small enough to mount in most instruments rarely exceed 50 ma in capacity; hence most average-reading instruments are made in the range from 100 μa to 50 ma. Because of poor temperature coefficient and wave-shape distortion troubles, shunt resistors must never be used to extend the range of such instruments. Ammeters therefore always demand the use of current transformers.

Precautions in Use. As before, the circuit must never be energized without the d-c instrument in series; otherwise damage will be caused to the rectifier.

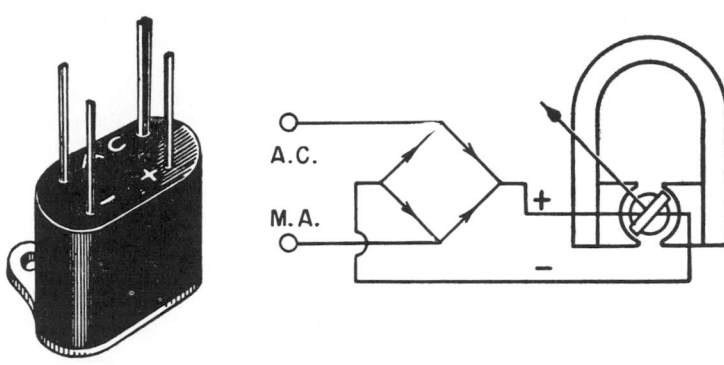

FIG. 2-21. A-c rectifier milliammeter.

Peak-to-peak Current Measurements

Although rarely required, these may be obtained by measuring voltage drops across a resistance inserted in the circuit with the electronic instruments given under Vacuum-tube Voltmeters.

RMS-reading Current Instruments

Thermocouple Current Measurements. This is the element of the voltmeter discussed under Thermocouple Instruments without the series resistor. Usually the minimum full-scale current is of the order of 2 ma, thermocouples of these low current values being enclosed in vacuo in a glass enclosure as in Fig. 2-22.

Precautions in Use. Because of low inherent overload capacity, the usual care must always be exercised if high replacement costs are not to be encountered. Thermocouples, however, offer one of the few ways of measuring true rms currents of a few milliamperes, particularly at higher audio frequencies.

Moving-iron Current Measurements. The physical size of the instrument normally gives an upper limit on the current rating, as it determines the amount of heat that can be dissipated. The principle used is exactly as under Moving-iron Voltmeters. Normally 50 ma is the minimum range and 100 amp the maximum in self-contained instruments. Extension of the current range both up and down may be had by using current transformers.

Precautions in Use. Resistive shunts should not be used to extend the current range because of contact resistances and frequency error trouble. Direct currents may, however, be measured if two readings with reversed connections are averaged. Stray magnetic fields should be avoided as mentioned previously.

FIG. 2-22. Glass-enclosed vacuum thermocouple.

Dynamometer Current Measurements. The dynamometer device discussed under Dynamometer Voltmeters without the series resistor also measures true rms current when the two coils are connected in series. The normal minimum current is of the order of 50 ma. Since only a limited amount of current can be carried through the moving coil, it is usual to supply the moving coil from a shunt for high-current measurement or alternately use a current transformer for the two windings in series.

POWER MEASUREMENTS

The field of power measurements in industrial plants is concerned mainly with the electrical loading of machines and equipment, supplied from the power source. In virtually all cases this power source is a 60-cycle single- or three-phase supply, and measurement demands the determination of true rms quantities. For these reasons the dynamometer instrument virtually dominates the field in view of its versatility as a voltmeter, ammeter, wattmeter, varmeter, etc. In a wattmeter, irrespective of the number of phases, the stationary coils are supplied with the current to the load and the moving coil with the potential across the load.

Single-phase Connections. Figure 2-23 shows the two possible ways of connecting the watt-meter in circuit. Each connection, however, includes the loss of the coil next to the load in the power indicated on the meter. Normally it is easier to correct for

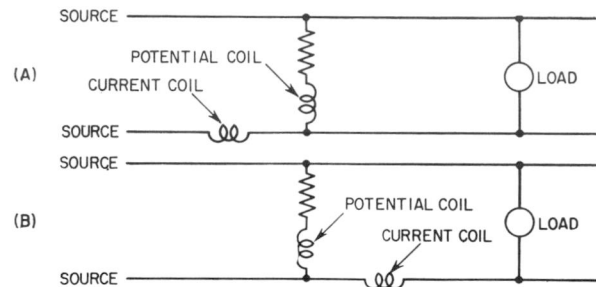

Fig. 2-23. Two possible connections of a simple, single-phase wattmeter. (*A*) Instrument measures load plus power consumed in potential circuit; (*B*) instrument measures load plus power consumed in current coil.

the relatively constant load in the potential circuit, hence the usual connection in this form as per Fig. 2-23*A*. A special type of wattmeter is available that automatically compensates for this error, but in the measurement of power in industrial plants the above errors are usually insignificant.

To provide instruments having maximum utility in power measurements, it is customary to build portable wattmeters with multirange ratings for the current coil, the potential circuit, or both. The scales of multirange wattmeters normally are graduated for the lowest full-scale rating, and the readings for the higher ranges are determined by multiplying the reading on the low scale by a factor called the "scale constant."

Instruments having multiple ranges for both current and voltage have scale constants for each range, and the scale reading must be multiplied by both applicable scale constants for the final determination of the power measured. When it is desired to measure power in circuits in which either the current or the voltage (or both) exceeds the ratings of self-contained instruments, the range of a wattmeter can be extended by the use of current or potential transformers in much the same manner as has been described in connection with moving-iron instruments. There is this important difference, however: Phase relationships must be carefully observed if correct readings are to be obtained and if the instruments are to be protected against excessive voltage.

Use of Current Transformer. Although wattmeters having current ratings up to 600 amp are manufactured, most power measurements involving high current are made by using a suitable current transformer in conjunction with a wattmeter having a current rating of 5 amp. The transformer used must have a turn ratio such that its secondary current is within the ampere rating of the wattmeter current coil, and it must be connected in the correct polarity to ensure maintenance of the original phase relationship between the stationary and moving coils of the instrument. The terminals of current transformers normally are marked to indicate direction of current.

Use of Potential Transformer.   For potentials up to 750 volts, series resistors are used in the potential circuit to increase the range of a wattmeter; for higher voltages, potential transformers are employed.   As with current transformers, it is essential that the correct polarity be observed in connecting the instrument, the transformers being carefully marked to indicate polarity.

When a wattmeter is used with a current or a potential transformer, or both, the operator must be careful to include all the applicable multiplying factors in the final evaluation of the wattmeter reading.   It is necessary to take into consideration the ratio of each transformer and to include in the calculation of indicated watts a multiplying factor corresponding to the ratios.

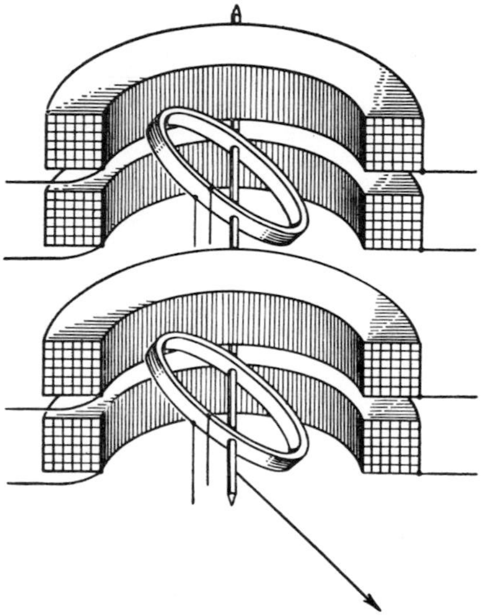

Precautions in Use.   Wattmeters are rated not only in watts full-scale deflection but also in amperes and volts.   The ampere ratings indicate the maximum current that should be passed through the field coil, and the voltage ratings indicate the range of potential-circuit voltage for which the instrument is designed.   The ampere rating is established by the number of turns and the cross-sectional area of the conductor in the field coil, and the voltage rating is established by the permissible size and heat-dissipating capacity of the moving coil and its series resistors.   A wattmeter having a 5-amp current rating would have a full-scale rating of 250 watts at 50 volts, 500 watts at 100 volts, and 1,000 watts at 200 volts. It is easily seen that if the 200-volt instrument were operated at 50 volts, a reading of only 250 watts would be obtained with

FIG. 2-24. Double-structure dynamometer.

the maximum rated current of 5 amp in the field coil.   To reach the full-scale reading of 1,000 watts, a current of 20 amp would be required.   Thus, the instrument might be so severely overloaded that it would be seriously damaged, even though its deflection did not exceed full scale.

Three-phase Wattmeter.   If it can be assumed that the load is evenly balanced with respect to all phases, a single-phase wattmeter may be used in one phase as before and the result multiplied by 3.   This is not, however, usually to be relied upon, and for most circuits where the condition of unbalance is uncertain, a double-element dynamometer is used.   This is accomplished by mounting two sets of stationary potential coils on a single shaft and mounting two sets of coils on the instrument frame in correct relation to the armature coils.   Thus, each mechanism develops torque proportional to the power in the circuit to which it is connected, and the torques of both mechanisms add to indicate the total power in the three-wire circuit.   An instrument constructed in this manner (Fig. 2-24) is called a "two-element" wattmeter, because it consists of two electrically independent dynamometer mechanisms.

This double mechanism is applicable to the measurement of power in a three-phase three-wire circuit with either balanced or unbalanced load.   Its connection for such measurement is shown in Fig. 2-25.   Note that mechanism *A* produces a torque proportional to the line potential (1-2) and the vector sum of the current from phases *a* and *c*.   Mechanism *B* produces a torque proportional to line potential (3-2) and the vector sum of the current from phases *b* and *c*.   The sum of the torques of the two mechanisms is thus proportional to the total power in the circuit.   As with the single-element instrument, the phase differences of voltage and current (power-factor angle) produce corresponding differences in torque of each mechanism, with the result that an indication of true power is obtained.

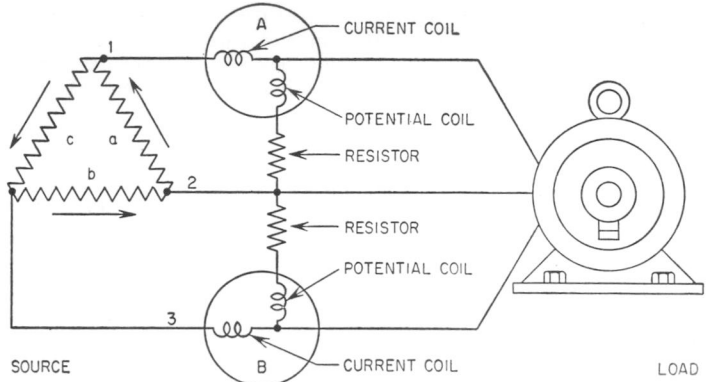

FIG. 2-25. Simple three-phase three-wire system with two-element watt-meter measuring load.

Precautions in Use. Great care should be exercised in making the proper connections to the load in order to avoid incorrect indication.

RESISTANCE MEASUREMENT

There being no sharp distinction between conductors and insulators, resistance measurements are required throughout the whole gamut of microhms to megohms.

Intermediate Resistance Determination

Simple Ohmmeter. Figure 2-26 gives the circuit diagram of the conventional ohmmeter consisting of a milliammeter or microammeter, a series resistor, a small battery, and means for setting the current so that the instrument reads zero ohms, i.e., full-scale deflection, with a short circuit across the ohmmeter terminals.

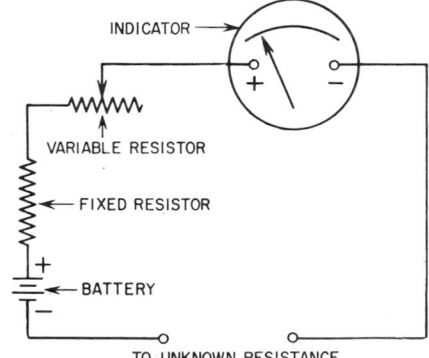

FIG. 2-26. Diagram of simple ohmmeter.

In this circuit, the deflection of the instrument pointer varies inversely with the value of the unknown resistance, and for a given voltage, the scale can be graduated in terms of the series resistance added to the circuit by the test specimen. Full-scale deflection is zero ohms, half-scale deflection shows a resistance equal to the instrument circuit resistance, and zero deflection indicates infinite resistance. Hence, the scale distribution and the range through which satisfactory accuracy is obtainable depend on the resistance connected in series with the indicating instrument. A high-range ohmmeter would, therefore, employ a relatively high value of resistance in series with the indicator. The voltage of the battery is determined by the indicator current sensitivity.

Precautions in Use. Always switch off battery when not in use, as accidental short-circuiting of terminal leads could discharge the battery.

Megger. This is another portable piece of equipment widely used for detecting insulation weaknesses. Shown in diagram form in Fig. 2-27, the hand generator serves as a source of emf. The normal maximum value of this emf is 500 volts, although it may go as high as 2,500 for special models.

The instrument is of the crossed-coil-ratio type of design which has two crossed coils fixed on the same shaft.   Coil A, in series with resistance R, is called the current coil and is connected from one side of the generator to the line terminals.   The operating torques tend to turn these coils in opposite directions until a position of equilibrium is reached.   When the instrument is operated, i.e., when the crank is turned, and with an infinite resistance connected between the earth and line terminals, no current will flow in the current coil.   The potential coil alone, then, will control the motion of the crossed-coil assembly in the gap in the C-shaped iron core until the pointer indicates infinity.

However, when a resistance is connected across the terminals, a current will flow in the current coil, and the corresponding developed torque in the current coil will draw the potential coil away from the infinity position into a field of gradually increasing

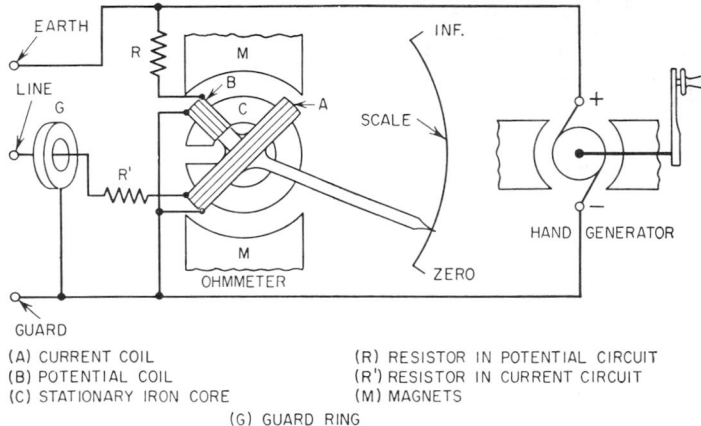

(A) CURRENT COIL   (R) RESISTOR IN POTENTIAL CIRCUIT
(B) POTENTIAL COIL   (R') RESISTOR IN CURRENT CIRCUIT
(C) STATIONARY IRON CORE   (M) MAGNETS
                    (G) GUARD RING

FIG. 2-27. Simplified circuit diagram of Megger insulation tester.

magnetic strength until a balance is obtained between the forces acting on the respective coils.   In this manner, the potential coil acts like a restraining spring.   When resistances of different known values are introduced across the terminals of the instrument and the corresponding position of the pointer is marked in each case, a scale calibrated in resistance can be obtained.   If a very low resistance is connected between the earth and line terminals or should the latter become short-circuited, the pointer simply moves to zero, or off the lower end of the scale of the high-range Megger instrument, the ballast resistance R' offering ample protection against excessive current in the current coil.   Because the two elements of the true ohmmeter receive current from the same source, namely, the generator, any change in generator voltage will affect both coils in the same proportion and, therefore, the pointer will move to the same position for a given resistance under test.   Consequently, the calibration of the instrument is unaffected by the speed at which the crank is turned or by the strength of the permanent magnets.   This is one of the outstanding advantages of the Megger true ohmmeter.

Precautions in Use.   The moving system is mounted in the usual spring-supported jeweled bearings; however, no controlling springs as such are used.   Fine filaments are necessary to bring current in and out of the moving coil, but these are made as fine as possible to allow the moving system to reach the final equilibrium position without any spring influence.   When the generator is not being turned, therefore, there is no controlling torque to return the pointer off scale.   Readings thus must be recognized only when the generator is actually turning.

Wheatstone Bridge.   A more accurate, though a somewhat less convenient, means of measuring most commonly encountered values of resistance is the Wheatstone bridge. The apparatus, available in portable form, Fig. 2-28, comprises a battery, a galvanometer, and three resistance elements, any or all of which may be adjustable in known steps, as shown schematically in Fig. 2-29. With the unknown resistance connected at X, one or more of the other resistances is adjusted until zero reading on the galvanometer shows that g_1 and g_2 are at the same potential with respect to b_1 and b_2. Since the voltages in a series circuit are proportional to the resistance of the various

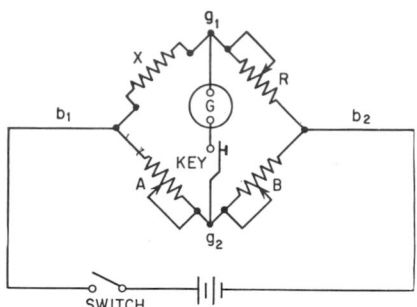

FIG. 2-28. Portable Wheatstone bridge.   FIG. 2-29. Wheatstone-bridge schematic diagram.

elements, the value of X is obtained from the formula $X = (A/B)R$. For convenience in solving this equation, two of the resistance arms usually are made adjustable in ratios of 1 to 10, 1 to 100, 1 to 1,000, etc., and the third is made adjustable in unit values.

Precautions in Use. The battery switch should always be closed before the galvanometer key in order to prevent any momentary rush of current through the galvanometer should the unknown resistance be inductive.

Low-resistance Determination

When extremely low values of resistance are to be measured, the ohmmeter is seldom accurate enough and the Wheatstone bridge is not satisfactory because of the error introduced by contact resistances and the connecting leads. The Kelvin double bridge (Fig. 2-30) measures resistance down to 0.0001 ohm accurately and conveniently and is available in portable form.

In the double bridge (Fig. 2-31), the unknown resistance X is connected in series with a known resistance K and a battery such that a relatively heavy current flows, producing a voltage drop across the known and the unknown resistances. A galvanometer is connected across the two voltages by two ratio arms so arranged that the ratio a/b always equals c/d. The effect of the voltage across X is to produce a galvanometer deflection proportional to $IX/(a + c)$, and the effect of the voltage across K is to produce an opposite deflection equal to $ID/(b + d)$. For the galvanometer to give zero deflection, these two factors must be equal, and since I is the same in both equations, the balance condition can be stated as $X = K(a + c)/(b + d)$.

The ratio arms normally are made with a plugging or switching arrangement for obtaining the various ratios (multiplying factors), and the known resistance K is arranged so that any desired part of its total voltage drop can be applied to the galvanometer circuit. For maximum sensitivity, the current in the measuring circuit is made relatively large, but its exact value does not influence the actual measurement.

The double bridge is provided with four terminals for connection to the unknown resistance.

An instrument commonly used in this field is the "Ducter" low-resistance ohmmeter. It has five ranges, the most sensitive of which has a full-scale reading of 100 microhms which is accurate and reliable to 1 microhm.

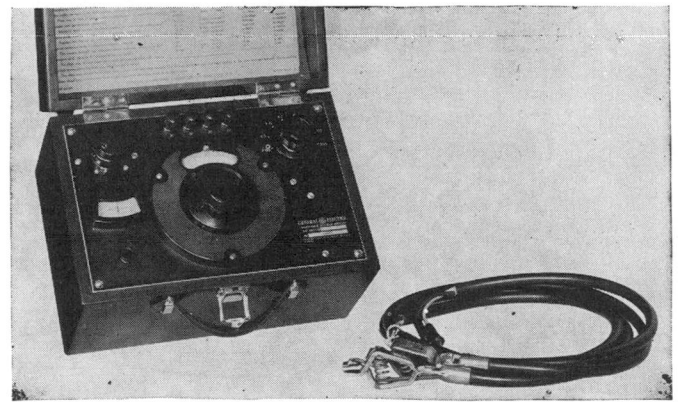

Fig. 2-30. Portable Kelvin double bridge.

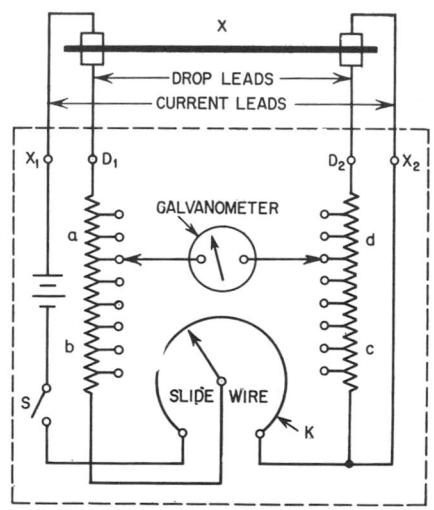

Fig. 2-31. Internal and external connections of portable double bridge.

High-Resistance Determination

In this realm of measurement of high resistance, insulation measurements predominate. For this reason the voltage applied to the insulator is of the utmost importance, being in almost all cases the determining factor in the test equipment used.

Simple Ohmmeter. Using a higher voltage battery, say 15 volts, the circuit of Fig. 2-26 can indicate up to 100 megohms.

Vacuum-tube Voltmeter. Here, as described later, the higher sensitivity of the vacuum-tube voltmeter is used in conjunction with a 1.5-volt battery for resistance determination up to 1,000 megohms.

Megohmmeter. Using the electronic circuitry of Fig. 2-40, a scale indication up to 10,000 megohms may be easily attained.

Megger. This general-purpose instrument described previously is available with generator voltages of 500 to 2,500 volts and is capable of measurement up to 10,000 megohms. Voltages up to 2,500 volts are available for standard rather than "special" hand-operated units and up to 10,000 volts for standard rectifier-operated units.

Important Resistance Measurements

Resistance of Earth Connections. These may be measured, conveniently and accurately, by the three-electrode method. In Fig. 2-32, A is the connection of which the resistance to earth is to be measured; it is temporarily disconnected from the distribution system while the ground connection of the system is preserved through a connection at D, which may be either temporary or permanent. Two additional "grounds," B and C, are established, separated from each other and from A by not less than 15 ft. These auxiliary grounds may be pieces of metal buried in the earth, making sufficient contact with the ground to give a good current reading. The resistances between the three electrodes, taken by pairs, are now measured by the fall-of-potential, voltmeter-ammeter method. Let r_{ab}, r_{bc}, and r_{ac} be the three resistances so measured. Then the resistance

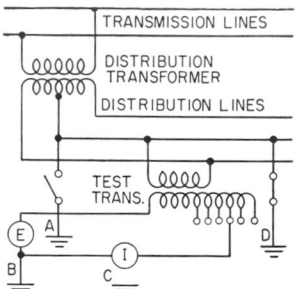

FIG. 2-32. Resistance of earth connections. (*From "Standard Handbook for Electrical Engineers."*)

At A is $\qquad R_a = \dfrac{r_{ab} - r_{bc} + r_{ac}}{2}$

At B is $\qquad R_b = \dfrac{r_{ab} - r_{bc} - r_{ac}}{2}$ ohms

At C is $\qquad R_c = \dfrac{r_{bc} - r_{ab} + r_{ac}}{2}$

This measurement should be made with alternating current, which can be taken from the distribution system through an insulating transformer with secondary taps, as illustrated. A low-range voltmeter usually is required.

Location of Line Faults. Faults in electric lines for the transmission and distribution of power, speech, etc., may be divided into two classes: closed-circuit faults and open-circuit faults. Closed-circuit faults consist of "shorts," where the insulation between conductors becomes faulty, and "grounds," where the faulty insulation permits the conductor to make more or less perfect contact with the earth. Open-circuit faults, or "opens," are produced by breaks in the conductors.

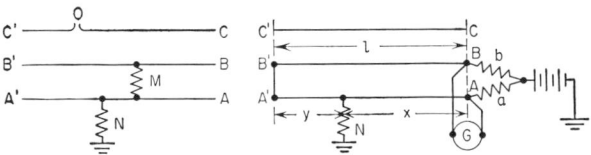

FIG. 2-33.   FIG. 2-34.

FIG. 2-33. Line faults. (*From "Standard Handbook for Electrical Engineers."*)

FIG. 2-34. Murray loop. (*From "Standard Handbook for Electrical Engineers."*)

1. When the short is a low-resistance union of the two conductors, such as at M in Fig. 2-33, the resistance should be measured between the ends AB; from this value and the resistance per foot of conductor, the distance to the fault can be computed. A measurement of resistance between the other ends, $A'B'$, will confirm the first

computation or will permit the elimination of the resistance in the fault if this is not negligible.

2. The location of a ground, as at N in Fig. 2-33, or of a high-resistance short is made by either of the two classical "loop" methods, provided a good conductor remains. Figure 2-34 shows the arrangement of the Murray loop test which is suitable for low-resistance grounds.   The faulty conductor and a good conductor are joined together at the far end, and a Wheatstone-bridge arrangement is set up at the near ends with two arms a and b comprised in resistance boxes which can be varied at will; the two segments of line x and $(y + l)$ constitute the other two arms; the battery current flows through the ground; the galvanometer is across the near ends of the conductors.   At balance,

$$\frac{a}{b} = \frac{x}{y + l} \qquad \text{or} \qquad \frac{a + b}{b} = \frac{x + y + l}{y + l} \qquad \text{ohms}$$

The sum $x + y + l$ may be measured or known.   If the conductors are uniform and alike and x and l are expressed as lengths, say in feet,

$$x = \frac{2al}{a + b} \qquad \text{ft}$$

If the ground is of high resistance, very little current will flow through the bridge with the arrangement of Fig. 2-34; in that case, battery and galvanometer should be interchanged and the galvanometer used should have a high resistance.   If ratio arms a and b consist of a slide-wire (preferably with extension coils), the sum $(a + b)$ is constant and the computation is facilitated.   Observations should be taken with direct and reversed currents, especially in work with underground cables.

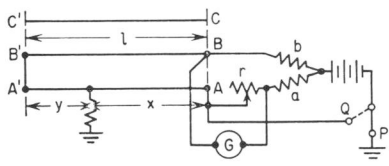

Fig. 2-35. Varley loop.   (*From "Standard Handbook for Electrical Engineers."*)

In the Varley loop, shown in Fig. 2-35, fixed ratio coils, equal in value, are employed, and the bridge is balanced by adding a resistance r to the near leg of the faulty conductor.

$$\frac{a}{b} = \frac{r + x}{y + L} \qquad \text{or} \qquad \frac{a + b}{b} = \frac{x + y + l + r}{y + l} \qquad \text{ohms}$$

if $a = b$,

$$x = y + l - r \qquad \text{or} \qquad x = \tfrac{1}{2}(x + y + l - r) \qquad \text{ohms}$$

The total line resistance $(x + y + l)$ is conveniently determined by shifting the battery connection from P to Q and making a new balance, r' The equation then becomes $x = \tfrac{1}{2}(r' - r)$.   When a and b are slightly unequal, a second set of readings should be taken with a and b interchanged, and the average values of r and r' substituted in the foregoing equations.

3. Opens, such as O in Fig. 2-33, are located by measuring the electrostatic capacitance to ground (or to a good conductor) of the faulty conductor and of an identical good conductor; the position of the fault is determined from the ratio of the capacitances.

4. Shorts and grounds may be detected by sending through the defective conductor an alternating current of audible frequency, say 1,000 cps.   A "pickup" coil connected to a telephone receiver worn on the head of the tester is then carried along the line; the note in the receiver will cease when the fault has been passed.

ELECTRONIC INSTRUMENTS

In this category such a bewildering variety of testing and servicing instruments exists that it is difficult to know where to stop.   The following paragraphs discuss those of most use to maintenance personnel.

Vacuum-tube Voltmeter. In general the vacuum-tube voltmeter is characterized by its ability to read voltage across points in an electronic system without drawing current from the circuit. A typical input impedance for vacuum-tube voltmeters of 10 megohms, for example, gives a sensitivity of 10,000,000 ohms per volt on a 1-volt range—a most valuable feature for electronic trouble shooting. Normally the power to operate such an instrument is drawn from the a-c power mains. In one of the latest devices, Fig. 2-36, however, a long-life, battery-operated device has been introduced giving freedom from dependence on the a-c mains. The d-c voltage-measuring circuit of Fig. 2-37 has a 10-megohm input impedance at full-scale input voltages of 1.6, 8, 40, 160, 400, 800, and 1,600. The feature of battery operation allows complete

FIG. 2-36. Vacuum-tube voltmeter.

freedom from spurious response resulting from stray a-c fields and circulating ground currents. Furthermore, the electronic circuit using a cathode follower inherently protects the indicating instrument from damage, since it saturates before currents of dangerous magnitudes can be reached. The operation of the ohmmeter closely resembles that of the ohmmeter of Fig. 2-26 except that the electronic instrument now permits resistance determination up to 1,000 megohms.

Alternating-current voltage ranges on this class of instrument can be measured on a peak-to-peak basis. The circuit is of the reflex type which adds the signals from the negative- and positive-going portions of the input wave and then supplies them as a d-c voltage to the d-c voltage-measuring circuit. This method of measurement gives the true peak-to-peak amplitude of all types of waveform, be they positive-going pulse, negative-going pulse, sinusoid, squares or saw-tooth shape up to a frequency of approximately 300 kc.

Tube Checker. Statistically, the greatest percentage of failures in electronic equipment is due to tube failure. For this reason a tube checker is a "must" for any maintenance department. Tube checkers may be of two generic classes: absolute and proportional. In the first category, voltages are set on the elements of the tube in question exactly as in the condition of operation and the true transconductance of the tube measured. The second type, i.e., the proportional type, is a smaller portable piece of apparatus which applies standard voltages as normally specified in data sheets by the manufacturer of the tube, and the instrument will indicate the performance as a percentage of the manufacturer's rated guarantee. Use of this equipment on a

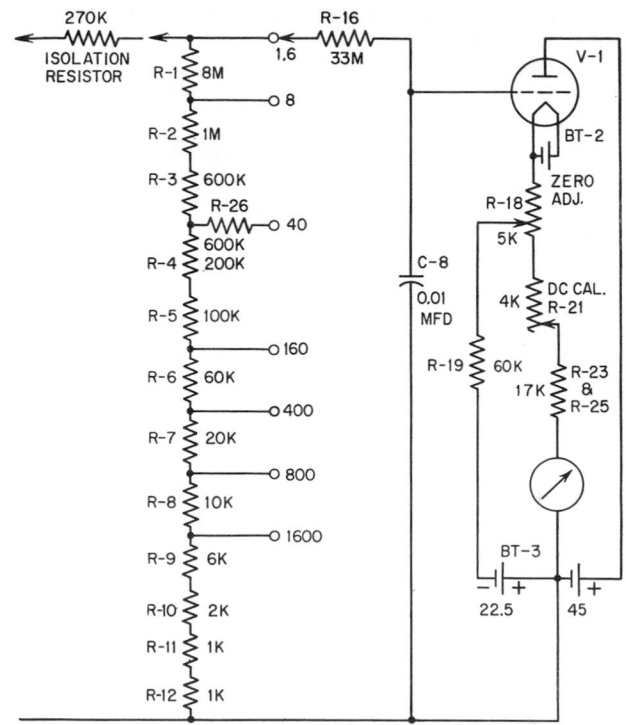

FIG. 2-37. D-c voltage circuit of vacuum-tube voltmeter.

FIG. 2-38. Mutual conductance tube checker.

regular basis can give preventive maintenance indicating slow failure of any tube before actual breakdown takes place.

The proportional conductance checker of Fig. 2-38 is constructed to test almost all the receiving-type tubes made. A multiplicity of tube sockets are available to accommodate the tube in question, be it Octal, Loctal, Acorn, or subminiature. The switches shown are arranged to supply the correct potentials to heaters and all the elements of a vacuum tube as stated in manufacturer's data sheets and conveniently repeated on a roll chart on the front of the unit. The instrument then gives the transconductance, or g_m, value. Additional tests are available for determining leakage, with the heater of the tube energized, for

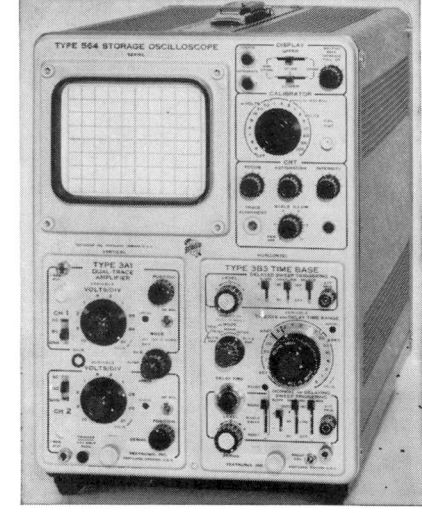

Heater to cathode.
Suppressor to all other elements.
Plate to all other elements.
Screen grid to all other elements.
Control grid to all other elements.

Leakage resistance as high as 10 megohms can be measured by this test. Diodes and rectifiers may also be tested for emission, and voltage-regulation tubes for control.

FIG. 2-39. Oscilloscope. (*Courtesy of Tektronix, Inc., Beaverton, Ore.*)

Oscilloscope. The modern cathode-ray oscilloscope has become almost as common in the laboratory as the multimeter. It is capable of presenting a "picture" of the electrical phenomena from DC to even beyond 1,000 Mc when using sampling amplifier and time base. The instrument illustrated by Fig. 2-39 can plot a wide range of input signals and store the image to permit detailed study and measurement of transient phenomena. Plug-in amplifiers and time-base units provide a broad selection of sensitiveness, bandpass, multitrace, sweep speeds, etc.

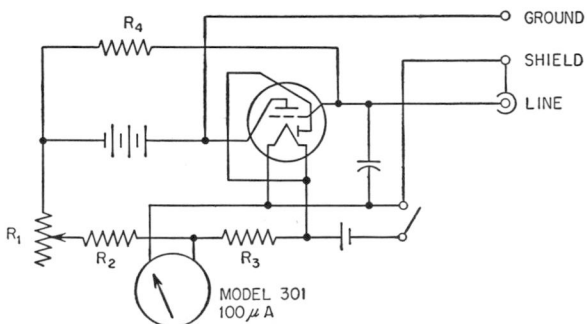

FIG. 2-40. Megohmmeter circuit.

Megohmmeter. An interesting application of electronic methods to maintenance is that of a vacuum tube connected as a grid-current amplifier for measuring insulation resistance in the range 0.1 to 10,000 megohms. A logarithmic scale is used with end marks at zero and infinite resistance. The small values of current through the unknown resistance are amplified and indicated in terms of megohms on a calibrated microammeter. This current is injected into the grid of the tube of Fig. 2-40, and this grid current plus the resultant plate current deflects the meter.   The resulting characteristic gives an approximately logarithmic scale to the indicating instrument of 5 decades of resistance.   The unit, as shown in Fig. 2-41, is completely portable with a 67½-volt plate battery and a 1½-volt cell for the filament energy.   The potential applied to the resistance under measurement is approximately inversely proportional to the current through the indicating instrument.   This is, of course, quite similar to usual ohmmeter practice, in which the applied potential is zero at zero resistance, one-half the plate battery voltage at half scale, and full battery voltage at infinite resistance.

A leakage-shield binding post is provided for use where a guard circuit is required. For best leakage shielding the shield circuit potential should equal the line terminal potential.   Since in this instrument the cathode potential of the vacuum tube closely follows the grid potential of the tube, it is thus selected as the point used for the shield terminal connection.

FIG. 2-41. Megohmmeter.

FIG. 2-42. Multimeter.

COMBINATION CURRENT AND VOLTAGE INSTRUMENTS

In industrial usage where servicing and trouble shooting are prime requisites, it is almost a necessity to have a combination of some of the previously mentioned instruments in one portable case.   This is particularly true when one instrument mechanism is used with a variety of electrical networks to measure current and voltage.   The following classes can be observed:

1. Multimeters.
2. Clamp-on ammeters, voltmeters, wattmeters.
3. Multirange a-c instruments.

Multimeters.   These are characterized by a single d-c milliammeter fitted in a case with a large number of shunt and series resistors and usually a rectifier and a battery. By this means we are able to measure direct and alternating current and voltages as well as ohms.   Figure 2-42 gives the over-all appearance of such an instrument.   Its uses may be broken down into its constituent operations.   The d-c voltage circuit of Fig. 2-43 operates at a sensitivity of 20,000 ohms per volt for full-scale ranges of 1.6, 8, 40, 160, 400 and 1,600 volts.   The a-c voltage circuit of Fig. 2-44 uses a two-disk

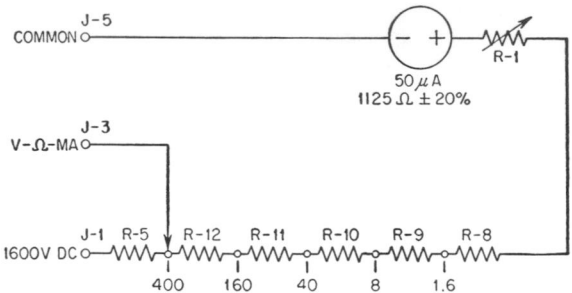

FIG. 2-43. D-c voltage circuit of multimeter.

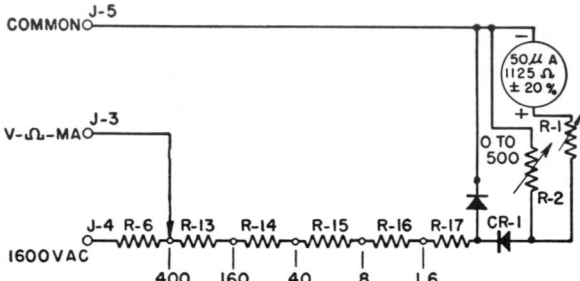

FIG. 2-44. A-c voltage circuit of multimeter.

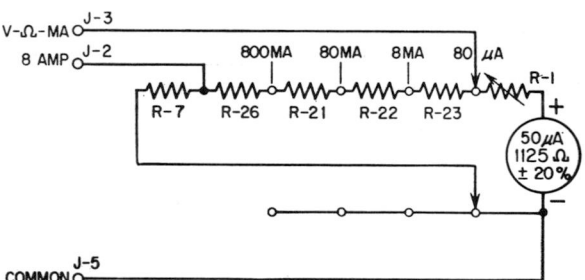

FIG. 2-45. D-c circuit of multimeter.

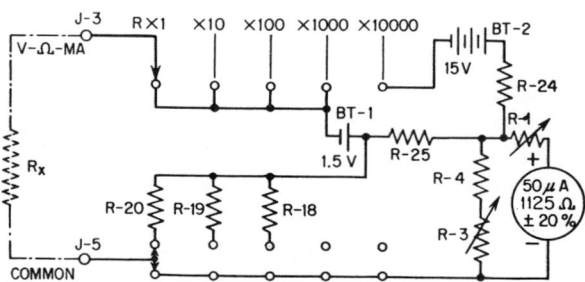

FIG. 2-46. Resistance circuit of multimeter.

rectifier operating at a sensitivity of 100 ohms per volt for the same full-scale ranges as d-c operation.   Direct-current circuit is shown in Fig. 2-45 giving full-scale ranges of 80 μa 8, 80, 800 ma and 8 amp.   Finally the ohmmeter circuit of Fig. 2-46 gives full-scale ranges of 1,000, 10,000, 100,000 ohms; 1 megohm; and 10 megohms.

Precautions in Use.   Instruments of this class are light in weight and use the core-magnet construction described under Micro- and Milliammeters.   This renders them entirely suitable for trouble shooting and servicing problems.   Apart from the obvious care in not dropping such an instrument, little is needed in the way of upkeep except to provide replacement of the 1.5- and 15-volt batteries for the ohmmeter circuit.   It is advisable not to leave the instrument in the ohmmeter position when not in use, as

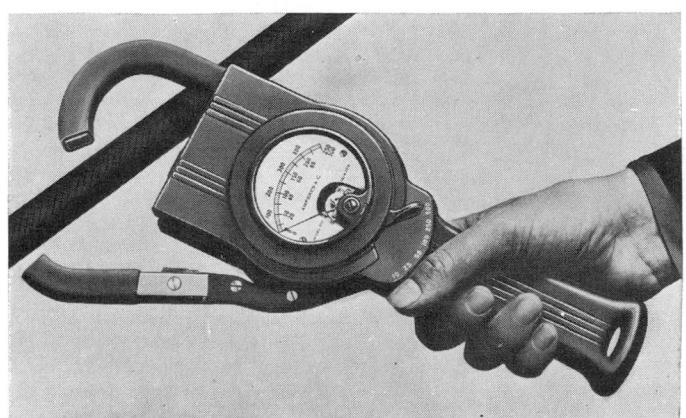

Fig. 2-47. Clamp ammeter.

accidental short-circuiting of the test leads could cause current to be drawn from the battery and unduly shorten its working life.

Clamp on Instruments.   *Clamp Ammeter.*   Conventional instruments for measuring current are connected in series with the measured circuit.   There are, however, many occasions when it is not convenient or desirable to open the circuit so that an ammeter can be inserted.   For such applications, an a-c instrument has been developed which is inductively coupled to the circuit to be measured.

Construction.   This type of ammeter utilizes a rectifier-type instrument connected to the secondary of a split-core current transformer so constructed that the core can be conveniently closed around a current-carrying conductor which then forms the primary winding of the current transformer.   The method of using a hook-on instrument to measure current is shown in Fig. 2-47.   The electric circuit of the instrument is shown in Fig. 2-48.

The secondary of the current transformer, as well as the indicator-moving coil, is tapped to provide several current ratios.   Current below the maximum calibrated range of the instrument can be measured by looping the line conductor through the transformer opening two or more times; this increases the transformer ratio, so that the output indication is increased by a factor equal to the number of primary turns. To increase the utility of the hook-on instrument, it is sometimes provided with built-in resistors which can be connected in the circuit by means of the range switch, thus making available a rectifier-type a-c voltmeter.   The switch circuit is so arranged that the instrument can be left connected for both current and voltage measurement and the range and quantity being measured can be selected by operating the switch.

The construction of the split-core transformer has a major bearing on the performance and convenience of hook-on instruments.   In the instrument shown in Fig. 2-47, the split core of the transformer is provided with a toggle-acting hinge, so that the core can be opened without the use of a trigger or latch mechanism.   The core is opened manually and snaps shut when the instrument is pushed against the conductor. A gentle pull springs the core open and releases the conductor. The core is designed so that there is only one complete break in the magnetic circuit; this break is a dovetail joint. This type of joint minimizes the effect of any dirt and accumulation of non-magnetic material in the joint, since it assures minimum variation in the reluctance of the magnetic circuit.

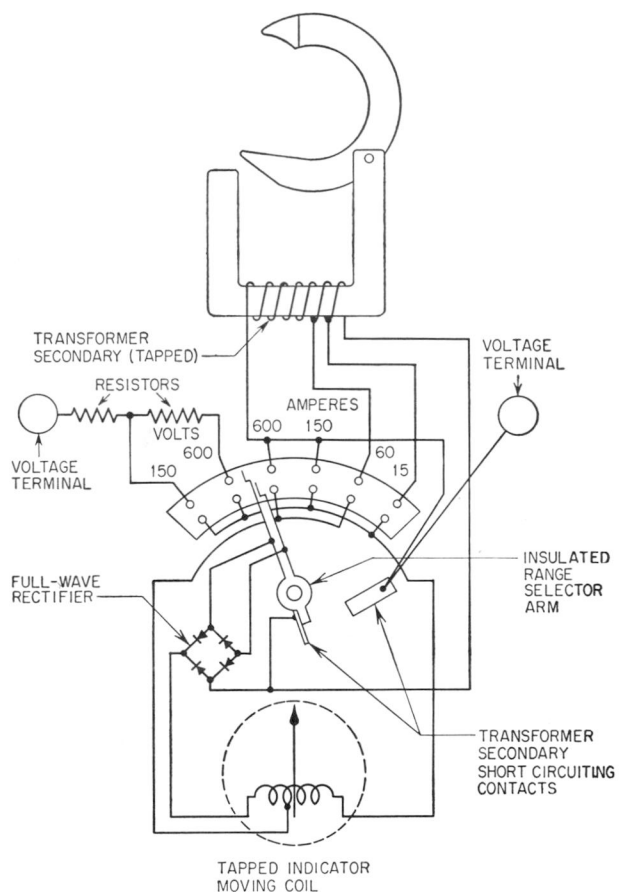

FIG. 2-48. Schematic diagram of volt ammeter.

Although the rectifier instrument can ordinarily be used in the audio-frequency band when it is incorporated in a hook-on instrument, the characteristics of the transformer influence frequency response. Consequently, these instruments normally are rated for use between 50 and 70 cycles, although they can be used from 25 to 90 cycles with only slight decrease in accuracy.

Clamp Wattmeter. Another instrument with a built-in split-core transformer is the hook-on wattmeter for measuring watts in both single-phase and polyphase circuits. Similar in appearance to the hook-on volt-ammeter, its construction consists of a ferrodynamic wattmeter, the field of which is energized by the conductor carrying the current through the hook. By use of a spring-controlled moving system, the resulting scale capacity is directly proportional to the potential circuit resistance. With this design, range selections can be made by simple one-hand switching of the potential circuit. Figure 2-49 shows a schematic connection diagram of this instrument.

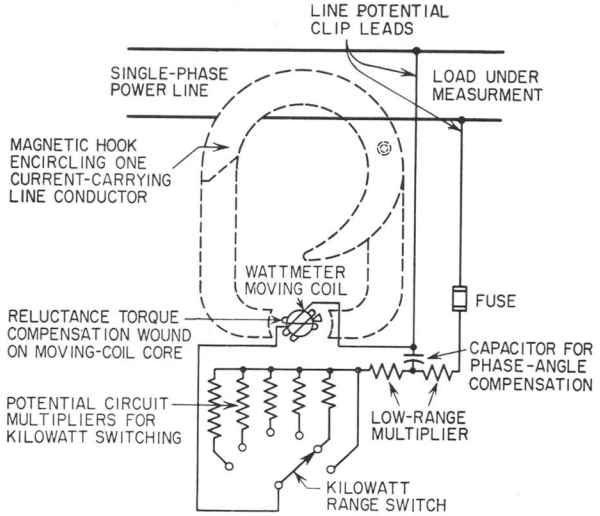

Fig. 2-49. Schematic connection diagram for hook-on wattmeter.

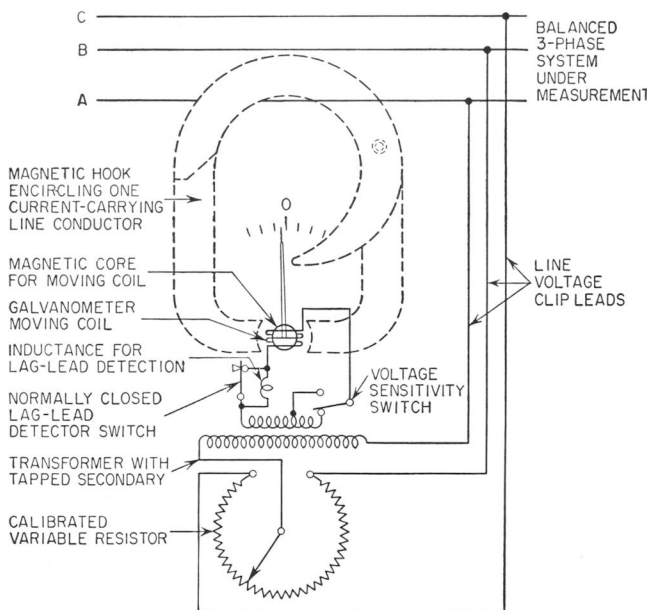

Fig. 2-50. Schematic connection diagram for hook-on power-factor meter.

Clamp Power-factor Meters. Another instrument in this family is the hook-on power-factor meter. It measures the leading or lagging power factor on any balanced three-phase circuit of 100 to 600 volts and 15 to 600 amp.

The basic instrument is a ferrodynamic galvanometer whose coil moves in the magnetic field produced in the hook by the current in one line conductor. The coil is energized from the potential circuit. Phase relation of the coil voltage is controlled by a potentiometer connected cross phase. Rotation of the potentiometer dial, until the galvanometer is balanced (zero center), produces a 90° displacement of the coil voltage with respect to the current.   Under this condition, power factor can be read directly on the calibrated potentiometer dial.   See Fig. 2-50, for a schematic connection diagram of this instrument.

Multirange A-c Instruments.   As distinct from multimeters, this class of instrument is primarily concerned with 60-cycle measurements of voltage, current, power, and power factor in single- and three-phase measurements.   Such a power analyzer has wide acceptance among plant maintenance personnel when these many features are combined in a single package.

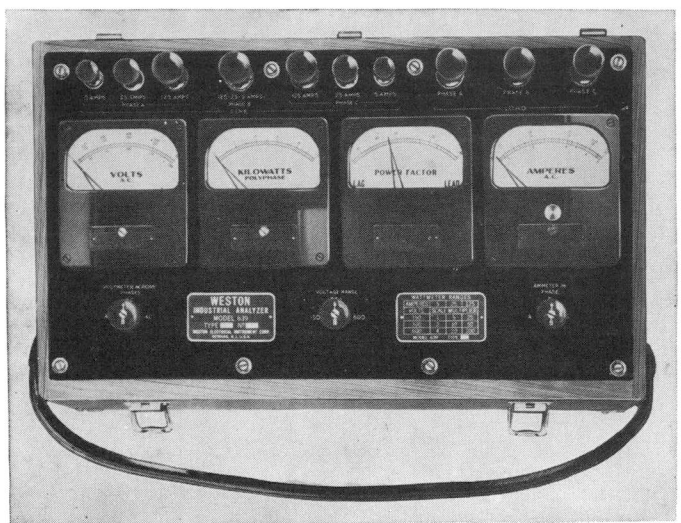

Fig. 2-51. Power analyzer.

Power Analyzer.   The mechanisms of four instruments are contained in one case as seen in Fig. 2-51.   The voltmeter, ammeter, wattmeter, and power-factor meter allow analysis of performance of equipment at potential ranges of 150/300/600 volts, current ranges of 5/25/125 amp, and their corresponding wattmeter ranges.   The power-factor meter is for three-phase three-wire circuits only.

MISCELLANEOUS INSTRUMENTS AND MEASUREMENTS

Temperature Measurements.   In the chemical laboratory, temperature measurements are made almost exclusively by means of glass thermometers.   In industrial usage, however, the electrical temperature-measuring devices play a greater role by virtue of their greater ruggedness and use in recording and controlling purposes. Particularly in all forms of preventive maintenance, the temperature of equipment serves as a final check on the load carried.   Should the temperature rise unduly, insulation will suffer.   Hence, there is a great field for application of these useful devices.   Two principles are most used: the thermocouple pyrometer and the resistance pyrometer.

Thermocouple Pyrometer.   A thermocouple is fundamentally a pair of conductors of dissimilar metals jointed together at two junction points so that an emf is produced if the junctions are at different temperatures.   Usually the wires are welded together at the hot junction, and a sensitive d-c millivoltmeter joined in at the cold junction as in Fig. 2-52.   As shown, the thermocouple pyrometer is relatively simple and possesses the advantage of operating without any additional source of energy; i.e., complete freedom of movement is obtained.   It should be noted that this device does not measure absolute temperature, but rather temperature difference between the hot and cold ends.   The combination of metals chosen depends greatly on the type of service required.

Metals and Alloys for Thermocouples

Type of thermocouple	For long-time service, °C	For short-time service, °C
Platinum to platinum—10% rhodium................	0–1450	1700
Platinum to platinum—13% rhodium................	0–1450	1700
Chromel to alumel................................	0–1100	1350
Iron to constantan...............................	0– 900	1100
Chromel to constantan...........................	0– 900	1100
Copper to constantan............................	−190– 350	600

In general the temperature difference between the hot and cold ends should not be less than 200°F for satisfactory operation of the d-c instrument.

Resistance Thermometer. This method makes use of the variation in electrical resistance of various conductors with temperature and is capable of great sensitivity. In distinction to the previous method, a source of energy (often a few dry cells) is now

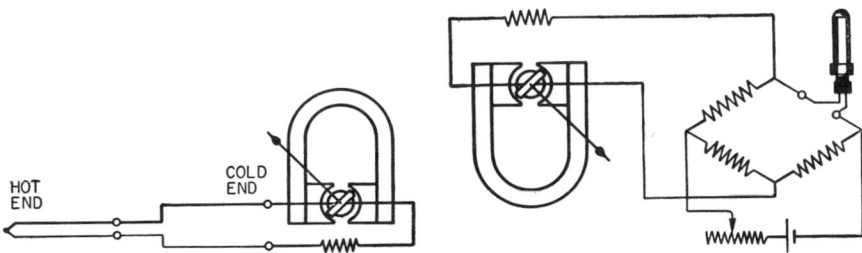

FIG. 2-52. Thermocouple circuit.   FIG. 2-53. Resistance bulb circuit.

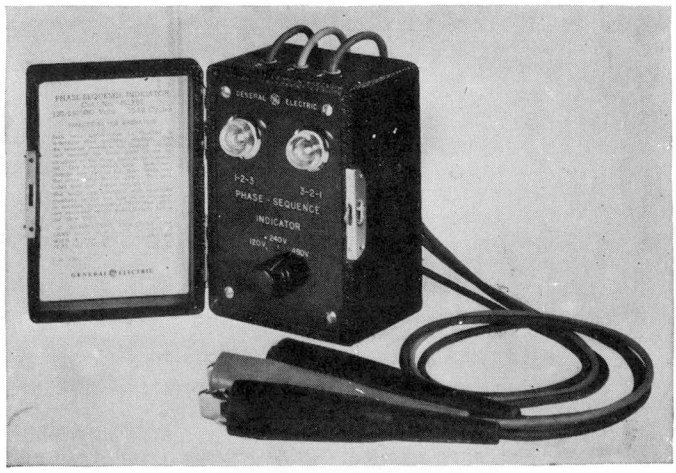

FIG. 2-54. Phase-sequence indicator.

needed.   When the instrument is connected in a Wheatstone-bridge circuit as in Fig. 2-53, absolute temperature may be referenced in terms of one arm of the bridge when it is balanced.   For this purpose, the instrument is normally a sensitive galvanometer detecting balance.   In an indicating-instrument form of this bridge, a ratio instrument to replace the galvanometer is used, and with the bridge arms set, temperature may be read directly on the scale.

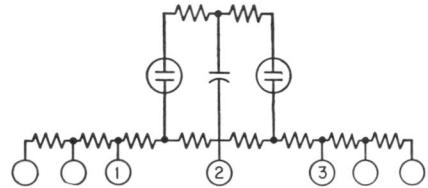

Fig. 2-55. Schematic diagram of phase-sequence indicator.

Phase-sequence Indicator.   The phase-sequence indicator is used to determine the phase rotation of polyphase a-c circuits.   The indicating system has no moving parts but utilizes a simple electric circuit in which neon lamps show phase sequence.   The instrument is shown in Fig. 2-54, its electric circuit being given in Fig. 2-55.   When the instrument is connected across the three-phase circuit which is to be checked, the voltages across the three arms of the Y network are unevenly distributed, with the result that the voltage across one neon lamp is considerably greater than that across the other for a given phase sequence.   The circuit constants are such that the lower voltage is below the ignition voltage of the neon lamp.   Consequently, only one lamp glows at a time.   The one that glows indicates the phase sequence of the applied voltage.

Chapter 3

DIAGNOSTIC INSTRUMENTS

By G. C. Quinn
Senior Editor, Plant Electrical and Utilities Services
Factory
New York, N. Y.

Through the years, and particularly since about 1950, there have come into use a large number of different kinds of instruments that can be grouped under the general name of diagnostic instruments.

No single precise definition exists for classifying these devices as such. The field embraces simple and inexpensive instruments like the stethoscope and complex and expensive instruments like noncontacting vibration analyzers. Some, like temperature-sensitive crayons, require virtually no skill in their use. Others, like certain types of ultrasonic flaw detectors, require weeks of training and months of experience before an operator reaches full proficiency. All diagnostic instruments, however, have these characteristics:

1. They diagnose or predict equipment failure, diagnose causes of equipment failure, or measure the extent of substandard performance.
2. They are designed for portable use under shop conditions.
3. They are primarily for temporary diagnostic purposes, not for monitoring or controlling.
4. They generally do not require that the equipment under test be disassembled for diagnosis.

Thus process controllers, switchboard or laboratory instruments, vibration monitors, or production-test floor equipment would not be considered diagnostic instruments in the context of this chapter.

There are several hundred types of diagnostic instruments. Manufacturers number in the hundreds, and dozens of significant new maintenance instruments are placed on the market yearly. As a result of this fast-changing pace, any maintenance department that is anxious to lead in cost cutting through quicker recognition of off-normal equipment performance or in faster diagnosis of trouble needs to keep in close touch with the field through vendors and technical publications.

Most of the widely used diagnostic instruments are listed on the following pages, together with descriptions of how they work and some of the ways in which they can be utilized. Instruments described in greater detail in other chapters are either omitted or listed for reference purposes only.

SINGLE-PURPOSE INSTRUMENTS

Analyzers. The commonest types of diagnostic instrument are the special-purpose analyzers supplied by vendors of complex equipment to speed trouble shooting, adjustment, or preventive-maintenance testing. The advent of complex numerically controlled machine tools in small shops has forced development of these analyzers. Many are designed to plug directly into available sockets in the control console. Accompanying instructions list acceptable meter or gage readings or oscilloscope waveforms and explain where to look for trouble if readings are off normal.

The purchase of these special-purpose analyzers for complex equipment should always be seriously considered when recommended by the equipment vendor. This is true even though the analyzer may duplicate other test equipment available to the maintenance department. Convenience and faster and more accurate diagnosis can easily justify the purchase when downtime penalties are high. One of the largest numerical-control manufacturers reports that although about one-third of the purchasers specify an analyzer at the time of the tool purchase, over three-fourths of the users have ordered the analyzers within a year after purchase.

OPTICAL EQUIPMENT

Microscopes and Magnifiers. Few people have keen enough eyesight to discern the pattern left by foreign particles on precision surfaces, subtle changes in surface macrostructure, or the presence of hairline cracks. Yet even casual inspection with proper magnifying equipment under high-intensity light (several hundred foot-candles) can enable an average mechanic to trace the causes of many elusive troubles. Microscopes for shop use are generally in the 10 to 50× range, with long focal length (to see into deep recesses) and double eyepieces to reduce eyestrain. Pocket-sized instruments with dimensioned reticles are widely used for quick inspection. Part of the barrel of the pocket microscope generally extends beyond the objective lens to allow the device to be held against the surface under inspection. Tilting the barrel brings the surface in focus.

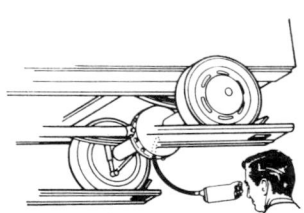

Fig. 3-1. Fiber optic cystoscope with battery light source.

Magnifiers are limited to about 6×. Higher-magnification lenses have edge distortion and short focal length, requiring the lens to be inconveniently close to the surface. Magnifiers vary from pocket reading glasses to lenses with dimensioned reticles integrated with a flashlight to simplify inspection in darkened areas.

Typical uses for both instruments are to look for leakage paths on the surfaces of valves in hydraulic and refrigeration equipment, to find hairline cracks in welds or castings where leakage or failure is suspected, to check orifices in diesel injectors or fuel nozzles in oil burners, and to find current-leakage paths on circuit boards. Microscopes are essential in determining the source of contaminants (gasket, seals, paint, eroded metal) filtered out of hydraulic-system fluid.

Borescopes and Fiber Optic Cystoscopes. These devices are designed to provide close-up visual inspection of remote or inaccessible areas. Borescopes up to 10 ft long or more are rigid light-transmitting tubes constructed like a periscope at the inspection end (see Fig. 3-1). The internal surface of long cylinders or deep cavities in castings can be viewed with ease. Either the observed area is flooded with light, or a tiny lamp at the end of the borescope provides the necessary high-intensity illumination.

Fiber optic devices resemble borescopes except for the fact that the image-transmitting fiber bundle can be bent or twisted without affecting the quality of the eyepiece image. A parallel light-transmitting bundle allows use of a high-intensity external lamp. Fiber optic devices make possible the inspection of cylinder walls, valves, valve seats, and piston heads through spark-plug holes or pressure-gage tappings in engines or compressors. Gear teeth can be inspected without disassembling gear housings. Corrosion or erosion damage can be assessed inside valves, and internal loose parts or leaks can be located in crankcases or other inaccessible enclosures.

Alignment Telescopes and Autocollimators. These instruments are essentially precision-made telescopes used in maintenance for alignment of bearings, leveling ways of long machine tools, checking level of craneways, aligning long multiple-bearing shafts before mounting of couplings, etc. Distance of use may be up to 50 ft. Both normally include built-in illumination which projects the image of the internal scales or cross hairs to an optically flat mirror mounted on the object being aligned. When the reflected image coincides with the internal cross-hair image, the two parts of the instrumentation are in perfect angular alignment. Accuracies to less than 1″ of arc can be achieved. The more elaborate instruments include micrometric adjustments to measure (and compensate for) minor angular misalignment of the mirror.

Regular surveying instruments, of course, are widely used for alignment of long shafts, etc., but they lack the precision and convenience of alignment equipment. And the target must be properly illuminated.

Misalignment Detectors. These devices use monochromatic and polarized light to measure, to less than 1″ of arc, the angular displacement of two rotatable objects.

Stroboscopes. Though more frequently thought of as speed-measuring devices, stroboscopes are essentially optical instruments. Two types are in common use. In the first, two disks, one fixed, the other rotating, are equipped with narrow radial slits. When the speed of the rotating disk corresponds to that of a rotating object, the object appears to stand still. Slight changes in the disk speed will cause the object to appear to rotate forward or backward.

The second, commoner, type uses a flashing light coupled to a power supply capable of varying the rate of flashing over a wide range. To be effective, the flash must be intense (much brighter than ambient light) and of very short duration (to avoid blur caused by movement of the object during the flash). Flashing-light stroboscopes are among the most widely used diagnostic instruments in industry

Fig. 3-2. Using stroboscope to check speed of cam-shaft grinder to assure optimum grinding rate. As diameter is reduced, speed must be increased yet held within safe limits. (*Courtesy of General Radio Company, West Concord, Mass.*)

(see Fig. 3-2). They are highly portable, relatively low in cost, put no load on the object observed, and require no skill to operate. They provide instantly available information, and if a record is needed, photographs can be taken with standard camera equipment. Any repetitive motion, rotary or linear, can be "stopped."

Several convenient attachments are available. One, a photoelectric pick-off, can be used where an external circuit cannot be connected conveniently to trigger the flash. A photocell picks up reflected light from a chalk mark or reflective tape on the moving part under observation. Thus, regardless of variations in speed, the stroboscope remains in synchronism. Similarly, an externally triggered switch or a magnetically sensitive switch can be used to trigger most stroboscopes. Another attachment, variable-flash delay, enables adjustment of the time delay between the instant of photoelectric pick-up and the flash. Observing a high-speed cam, the operator can adjust the delay to stop the cam at any point in its rotation.

Stroboscopes can be used for speed measurement if equipped with a precision oscillator and calibrated dial. Once the object observed is "stopped," speed can be read from the dial. Speed range can be extended by counting harmonics (e.g., multiple chalk marks) beyond the top range of the instrument.

Except for speed reading, the stroboscope is not a quantitative instrument. It is an ideal tool with which to observe transient conditions, such as the slip of a sheave during transitory loads or the whip or overshoot of a reciprocating object. At slow speeds (below about 1,000 rpm) the operator may find that flicker is somewhat annoying or that he requires a few seconds for his eyes to adjust to the pulsing light. Above 1,000 rpm (about 17 cps), flicker seldom presents any problem.

Diagnostic Cameras. The exact path of fast-moving parts often can be studied only from high-speed motion pictures or from a single multiple-exposure photograph under a series of flashes from a stroboscopic lamp. High-speed movie cameras, taking up to 5,000 frames per sec, are reasonably portable for in-plant use and will produce acceptable pictures with about 1,000 watts of lighting on close-up studies, if color contrast between parts is good. Such cameras are useful in studying flutter or vibration of wires, threads, webs, or structures. They are unexcelled for diagnosing and measuring bounce, action, overtravel, or bending in components like relay armatures, vibrators and shakers, loom parts, springs, or hydraulic cylinders. Strobe-flash exposures (using accurately tuned stroboscope flashes) show speed, acceleration and deceleration rate of any nonrepetitive, fast-moving event, such as the action of mechanical snubbers.

SPEED-MEASURING DEVICES

Except in the very low ranges, both rotary- and linear-speed measurements in maintenance work are made with some form of tachometer. Linear speed can be derived from rpm by means of a wheel mounted on the tachometer spindle, the circumference of which bears some integral relationship to the unit of measurement. For instance, a 6 in.-circumference wheel will produce tachometer rpm readings that can be converted to fpm by dividing by 2.

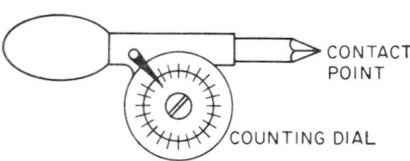

FIG. 3-3. Revolution counter. (*From "Handbook of Applied Instrumentation," McGraw-Hill.*)

Very slow linear and rotary travel rate, such as that of cross-feeds or carriage on machine tools, can be checked with motion-indicating devices. These units can detect variations of less than 1 per cent in speeds below 1 in. per min. Since readings made with these motion transducers often need further study, they are frequently used with graphic recorders. Typical of the maintenance uses are tests to find sponginess in hydraulic feeds on machine tools or erratic motion due to faulty lubrication, worn ways, or loose gibs.

Tachometers are among the most essential of all diagnostic instruments. They detect slip in belt drives and loss of speed under load for nonsynchronous motors. They check the accuracy of speed settings on machine tools, conveyor drives, fans, adjustable-pitch shears, and engine governors.

Three general classes of tachometers are in use: stroboscopic (described under optical instruments), mechanical, and electrical.

Mechanical Tachometers. The different types relay on three operating principles. The revolution counter (Fig. 3-3), the simplest and cheapest of all, indicates average speed over a time period. The centrifugal-force device employs rotating flyballs to compress a spring as a function of speed and position a pointer accordingly. The resonance-type unit employs a series of tuned reeds, the ends of which are visible along a scale marked in rpm. The reeds tuned to the frequency of the rotating object will show the greatest deflection.

Each of these types has advantages and handicaps from a maintenance viewpoint. The revolution counter in its simplest form is very low-priced and durable, and can be carried in a shirt pocket. But it does not show short-term speed variations, and its accuracy depends on precise timing at the instant of starting and stopping. It also requires the use of an easy-to-read timer. Other variations of the revolution counter include the tachoscope, in which the counter is integrated with a built-in timer.

Centrifugal-force tachometers cover the range of about 50 to 40,000 rpm, over several scale ranges achieved through shifting gear ratios. They are convenient to use and require no operator skill (see Fig. 3-4). They can be damaged by speeds beyond the top of their rating. At lower speed ranges they place a substantial torque load on the shaft being measured, enough to cause an error in subfractional motor readings. Meant for short-term test use, some types require regular lubrication.

Resonance tachometers are very durable

FIG. 3-4. Centrifugal-force tachometer. (*Courtesy of Herman H. Sticht Company, Inc., New York.*)

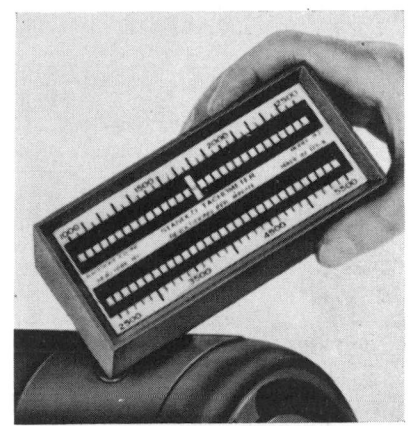

FIG. 3-5. Vibrating-reed tachometer. (*Courtesy of Herman H. Sticht Company, Inc., New York.*)

and can be left in use indefinitely without concern for wear. They also require that the measured device have some vibration. They can be fastened to, or held against, any point of the machine as long as its vibration frequency is the same as that of the shaft. With accuracy as high as 0.5 per cent or better, and available in ratings from 600 to 100,000 rpm, they are well suited for detecting small deviations above and below a known speed (see Fig. 3-5).

Electric Tachometers. An electric tachometer consists of a transducer which converts rotating motion into a signal that is fed to an indicator. A transducer may produce one or more pulses for each revolution of the spindle, in which case the output is digitally counted as so many revolutions in a unit time, or an analog signal proportional to speed, which is read on a meter calibrated in rpm.

FIG. 3-6. Electric-generator tachometer. (*Courtesy of Standberg Engineering Laboratories, Inc., Greensboro, N.C.*)

Electric-generator-type tachometers (Fig. 3-6), involve a miniature generator with permanent magnet field producing either an a-c or d-c output fed through a two-conductor cable to a microammeter. Several speed ranges are typically achieved in a single instrument by various resistance shunts across the meter terminals.

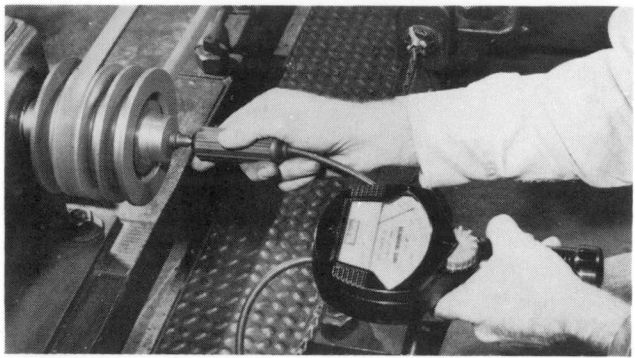

FIG. 3-7. Capacitor-switching tachometer. (*Courtesy of Metron Instrument Company, Littleton, Colo.*)

Eddy-current, magnetic-cup tachometers use a principle similar to that used in automobile speedometers. A flexible shaft couples the speed-measuring spindle to a rotating cup-shaped magnet in the instrument itself. A spring-loaded iron vane inside the cup is connected to the pointer on the rpm scale.

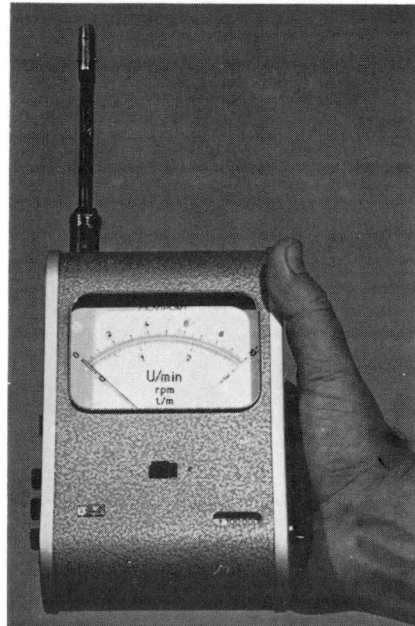

FIG. 3-8. Contactless tachometer. Shown is an electronic rpm meter equipped with photoelectric probe. (*Courtesy of Moviport Company of America, Charlotte, N.C.*)

The capacitor-switching instrument (Fig. 3-7), consists of a flashlight battery, a capacitor and a d-c milliammeter in hand-held unit, connected by a four-conductor cable to a small rotating reversing switch in the speed-driven spindle attachment. The faster the speed of rotation, the more capacitor-stored energy pulses from the battery are fed to the meter. Ranges are 20 to 100,000 rpm.

Several variations of contactless tachometers are available. The photocell probe type is sensitive to variations in light from a reflective spot on the rotating surface. Magnetic probe types sense magnetic-field variations caused by a keyway, gear teeth, a taped-on iron slug, or a vane attached to the shaft (see Fig. 3-8). The capacitive type senses similar variations in capacitance between the shaft and the probe. All these types produce digital pulses, which are amplified and either fed into a digital-to-analog conversion circuit and read on a current-indicating rpm meter or into a counting circuit which is gated to totalize and display on a read-out the number of pulses over a preset time interval (typically 1 sec). With the advent of transistors, pulse-sensitive instruments (Fig. 3-9), have become increasingly popular.

Single hand-held instruments (with multiple scales) are capable of measuring 50 to 800,000 rpm. For increased accuracy, some types use hand-held probes that generate many pulses (typically 60) per revolution.

A variation of the pulse-forming tachometers is used in engine-servicing work.

FIG. 3-9. Digital tachometer. (*Courtesy of Avtron Manufacturing, Inc., Cleveland, Ohio.*)

Here, the pulses in the ignition-coil primary caused by the distributor points are already available, so the signal can be fed directly to a damping circuit and read as rpm on a meter.

Maintenance. All tachometers require reasonable care and calibration checks commensurate with the accuracy needed for the most critical job they perform. Oil mist, dust (especially magnetic particles), and dropping are the greatest hazards. Most types come in a tailor-made case. Use of the case in storing and carrying the instrument from job to job should be encouraged, because it engenders recognition of the precision nature of the instrument. Except where extreme accuracy is needed, any synchronous motor can be used as a calibrating-speed source. Power-line frequencies on large systems seldom deviate more than 0.1 per cent from the base frequency.

TORQUE-MEASURING INSTRUMENTS

Typical of the situations in which torque must be checked are these: torque output (and runout-clutch calibration) of portable power tools; stall and running torque capabilities of electric motors following repair; starting torque of hydraulic and pneumatic motors and electric starting motors; dynamic torque output of gas and diesel engines after repair. Full torque capability is particularly important in portable tools, since product-quality control or worker output is dependent on tool output.

FIG. 3-10. A modified prony brake can be built in any shop from available parts to check torque of small motors at various speeds. (*Courtesy of The Rotor Tool Company, Cleveland, Ohio.*)

Small Prony Brake. Dynamic- or running-torque values are obtained with some form of a prony brake. Small motors and typical portable tools can be tested with a variation of the prony brake in which a smooth-surfaced drum is mounted on the spindle. A flexible cord or fabric webbing, with one end attached to a hanging scale, is wrapped around the drum, then controlled tension is put on the loose end of the webbing. The torque in inch-pounds at any load is equal to the radius of the drum in inches times the scale reading in pounds (see Fig. 3-10). Instructions for building well-suited components for such a device are available from some portable-tool manufacturers. However, the parts can be made up from surplus equipment readily available to most maintenance shops.

Torque Meters. Bench-mounted torque meters are available for convenient checking of torque output of small motors and portable power tools. Both stall-torque and dynamic-torque types are used. Stall-torque units use a spindle into which a properly lubricated test bolt (or nut) or shaft coupling can be fitted. The tool under test with proper chuck socket is fitted on the bolt (or nut). When the bolt is run up tight, either the tool stalls or, in the case of a clutch-type tool, the throwout clutch operates (see Fig. 3-11). Maximum torque

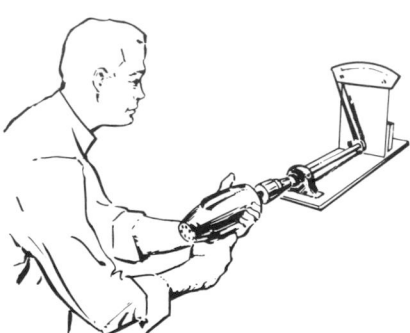

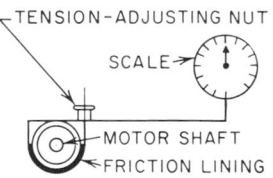

FIG. 3-11. Typical stall-torque meter checking throwout clutch on impact wrench.

FIG. 3-12. Basic prony-brake elements. (*From "Handbook of Applied Instrumentation," McGraw-Hill.*)

reached is read out on the torque meter. A simple form of starting-torque indicator can also be made from a torque wrench adapted to accept the motor shaft.

Dynamic-torque units are placed between the motor and the load. The twist distortion of the power-carrying shaft is amplified through a leverage system to produce a reading on the output gage. The load may be the normal load of the motor, such as a pump or fan; it can be a test load whose friction characteristics are not known, such as a speed reducer which has been repaired; or it can be a stall load with one end of the torque-meter shaft locked.

Some form of torque-measuring apparatus is essential in a shop overhauling portable tools, particularly air tools, as a check on quality of workmanship and to help determine the most economic time for tool overhaul.

Large Prony Brake. Because of their size, simple construction, and infrequent use, large prony brakes often are built by the maintenance shop. A typical one involves a large-diameter drum or flat pulley attached to the motor or engine shaft and a stiff beam, to which is attached at one end a metallic band lined with brake-drum lining. The outboard end of the beam is attached to an accurate scale, either in compression or tension, depending on the direction of rotation. Load is increased by varying the tension on the band while reading the scale. Torque (in foot-pounds) is the product of the beam length in feet times the scale reading (corrected to compensate for beam weight). Basic prony-brake elements are illustrated by Fig. 3-12.

Two important points must be kept in mind when using shop-made prony brakes. The brake drum must be capable of absorbing all the horsepower available from the motor, at least for the period of test. And all the structural members and mounting of the brake must be sturdy enough to handle the peak torque deliverable.

Dynamic torque available from a motor or engine can also be determined from any test in which both the motor speed and the horsepower absorbed by the load are known, using the formula

$$\text{Torque (ft-lb)} = \frac{\text{hp} \times 33,000}{6.283 \times \text{rpm}}$$

Maintenance and Accuracy. Routine lubrication and periodic calibration is the only maintenance required of the typical torque meter. Calibration kits for static testing consist of a precision diameter pulley and suspended calibrated weights. Dynamic-torque testing requires careful alignment of shafts, often difficult under fast maintenance-shop conditions. So double universal joints are recommended. Testers used in dusty atmospheres will require periodic cleaning to eliminate errors that could accrue from increased friction within the instrument.

TENSION- AND COMPRESSION-MEASURING DEVICES

The classic tension- or compression-measuring instrument is the spring scale and, for a great many tests of thrust, spring scales are quite satisfactory. Many places, however, require the use of other devices. Typical of the maintenance applications of thrust-measuring instruments are the following:

1. Checking grip of vacuum and magnetic chucks and grips.
2. Checking unknown weight of components while lifting to avoid overloading lifting device.
3. Overload-stressing critical shop-built and purchased equipment before installation to assure safety.
4. Testing drawbar pull of locomotives, tractors, or industrial trucks.
5. Checking tension on guy wires and overhead wires before anchoring.
6. Setting slip-clutch tension on chain conveyors.
7. Measuring peak thrust load of presses or brakes.
8. Checking uniformity of pressure across faces of squeeze rolls.
9. Determining nonuniform loading of dies in place during press operation.

Mechanical-force Gages. These are either a coil spring whose elongation or compression is measured on a scale or a semirigid U frame with dial indicator to measure deflection under load (see Fig. 3-13). Both kinds are simple, light in weight, and durable. U-frame gages are typically designed to withstand 300 per cent of rating, and include a resettable pointer, which remains at the maximum reading reached during a test.

Load Cells. Both hydraulic and pneumatic types are essentially hydraulic jacks in reverse, with a pressure gage calibrated in units of weight replacing the pump element. The read-out gage, connected by tubing, can be up to about 100 ft away. Similar magnetic load cells produce remote electrical read-out. Where a single cell will not handle total load, totalizing converters are available.

Capacitance or Resistance Cells. Where space is limited and fast response is essential (as in measuring peak pressures during press strokes) resistance and capacitance force sensors the size of a postage stamp can be used. They require the use of amplifying and read-out equipment calibrated to the cell in use. Typically they consist of a wafer-thin pressure-sensitive resistor or capacitor, which is connected in one leg of a Wheatstone-bridge circuit, balanced at zero force and room temperature. The bridge unbalance due to pressure is amplified and registered on a current-sensitive meter or digital read-out.

In many cases the cells are small enough to be slipped under the point of support, as with die blocks, or fed through squeeze rolls (inserted in an outline-sized hole cut in the material being rolled). Pressure build-up in large rolls of paper, film, etc., can be measured by rolling the cells up right in the product. Ceramic or piezoelectric sensor cells are also used in the same way, as the electrical charge of a crystal is proportional to pressure. Forces from a few grams to several tons can be measured with ceramic cells.

Strain Gages. When used as load cells, strain gages are excellent force-measuring devices, particularly when the force is not steady. They measure strain by sensing the deflection of the member to which they are bonded. The techniques of bonding and temperature compensation require specialized experience, however. Both pressure-sensitive semiconductors and wire-wound type of strain gages are in general use. For both types the auxiliary circuitry is quite complex.

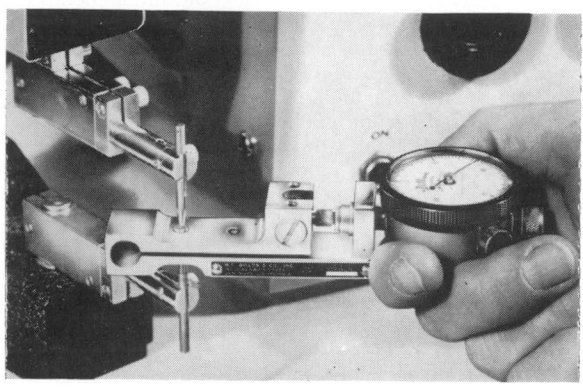

FIG. 3-13. Mechanical-force gage checking clamping pressure of a spot welder. (*Courtesy of W. C. Dillon & Company. Inc., Van Nuys, Calif.*)

Tension Gages. Tension in suspended or stretched thread, wire, cable, or rope can be measured with tension meters. These devices measure deflection of the strand under pressure of an out-of-line capstan. Typical maintenance uses include setting of tension during coil winding or armature banding on electrical repairs and checking for excessive tension caused by dirt accumulation under tensioning disks in textile machinery.

Portable Accelerometers. Also called an impact recorder, this device can be used to spot careless truck or lift-fork handling or damaging bumping of railroad shipments. Attached to the thrust member of a stamping or molding press, it senses the slightest sideward movement, a sign of excessive wear or oncoming damage to the die. Figure 3-14 shows an impact recorder used in adjusting the acceleration of an automatic-elevator car.

The impact recorder consists of three acceleration-sensitive elements with pens attached, one sensitive to acceleration in each plane. Where counting and timing of impacts is needed, a design with pens which trace their deflection on clock-driven recording paper is used.

FIG. 3-14. Impact recorder being used during adjustment of positive and negative acceleration of automatic-elevator car. (*Courtesy of Impact-O-Graph Corporation, Cleveland, Ohio.*)

Pressure-sensitive Paint. Two kinds of pressure-sensitive paint are in use. Electrically resistive paint has a large change in resistance for minute changes and dimension. It can be applied to any insulated surface and will indicate any deformation due to pressure or tension. It must be connected into an auxiliary bridge-amplifier circuit, and the hookup must be calibrated beforehand, asking known loads. Strain-sensitive paint is an extremely brittle coating that cracks instantly whenever the painted surface is deformed beyond the rated elasticity of the paint.　Various elasticity ratings are available.　The paint is useful to record evidence of overload on structures or critical members in presses, other tools, or processing machinery.

NOISE-MEASURING INSTRUMENTS

The reduction and measurement of noise is frequently a responsibility of the maintenance function.　Quantitative noise measurement is becoming increasingly necessary in avoiding damage to the hearing of employees who must work near high-noise-level equipment.　Measurements are necessary in determining the acceptability of motors, fans, pumps, transformers, lighting ballasts, and other equipment where noise is particularly undesirable.　Acoustic tests are the only way to measure the effectiveness of various baffles or sound-absorbent materials.　And in any noise-reduction effort, quantitative readings are essential to permit clearing up of the worst noise

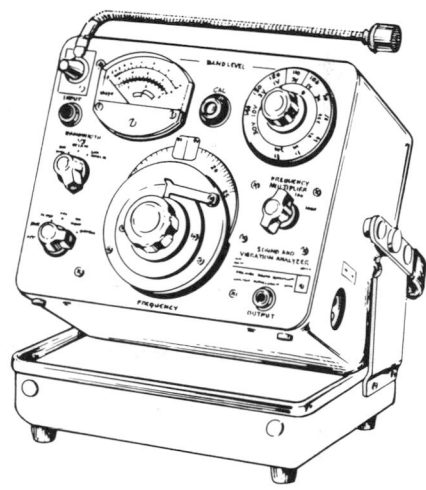

FIG. 3-15.　Typical hand-held sound-level meter.

FIG. 3-16. Octave-band noise analyzer with microphone attached.

sources first.　The human ear often is too subjective in its judgment to be used as an accurate guide.

Acoustic and vibration analysis are closely related.　Any machine vibrating at audio frequencies will produce noise, some of which may be absorbed by baffling or shielding around the machine.　However, equipment may produce extreme noise levels without any appreciable vibration in the machine structure, e.g., a well-balanced siren.

Sound-level Meters.　The instrument consists of a built-in microphone, battery-powered amplifier, filter circuits and switching, attenuator control, and output meter. Three sets of filters correspond to scales designated A, B, and C.　These in turn correspond to the deviations from true (flat) amplification as prescribed by ASA standards for more accurate simulation of the effect of noise of different frequencies at different levels on the human ear.　A typical hand-held sound-level meter is shown in Fig. 3-15. Detailed instruction with the sound-level meter and in ASA standards on acoustic measurements explain which scale is applicable in different noise measurements.　The output meter totalizes all sound energy (after filtering) over the range of the instrument (typically 40 to 8,000 cps).　Sound-level-measurement capability generally ranges from 40 to about 140 db.　Some designs of sound-level meter provide accessories to extend the frequency or decibel-level capabilities of the instrument.　Typical accessories are vibration pickups and amplifier, calibration-noise sources, extension microphones, and a-c power supply.

Sound-level meters are small and durable enough for constant in-plant or outdoor use. Outdoor use requires shielding the microphone from wind noise. Although unskilled operators can make readings, experience and skill may be required to interpret the readings when the purpose is to track down specific noise sources from among many noise sources.

Noise Analyzer. This unit is designed primarily for measuring the amplitude and frequency of the components of complex noise phenomena (see Fig. 3-16). In the octave-band-analyzer version a selection switch is provided to measure the total sound energy within each of several frequency ranges. It is useful where accurate data on individual frequencies are not required. The spectrum-analyzer type provides level readings of any specific frequencies across the audio spectrum by means of a tunable amplifier. Some analyzers are equipped for use with vibration-pickup apparatus.

Sound-spectrum analyzers are useful in tracking down specific sources of noise amidst many noises. For instance, the evidence of an annoying 200-cps noise coming from an 1,800-rpm motor-driven blower indicates the noise source is probably a 10-blade fan. If the blower itself is not a 10-blade unit, the cooling fan within the motor is probably the source of trouble.

VIBRATION-ANALYZING INSTRUMENTS

Analysis of vibration is so frequently encountered in maintenance work that the subject is treated separately in Sec. 13, Chap. 5.

DIMENSION-VARIATION INSTRUMENTS

This class of device covers a wide range of tools, from the simple micrometer caliper to electronic instruments. Only the more complex ones are described here.

Electronic Gages. Although primarily used for production gaging, these sensors are frequently used in checking dimensions on precision maintenance jobs and in setting up dies and fixtures. The gaging head usually is separate from the amplifier-meter unit. The stylus in the typical gaging head is linked to a sensor, which varies the output signal as a result of changes in electrostatic, magnetic, or capacitive properties. Accuracy to better than 0.00001 in. is readily obtained with battery- or a-c-operated portable gages.

Profile Recorders. Roughness of the surface of precision seals or bearings occasionally must be checked with accuracy. Profile recorders use a sensitive piezoelectric or magnetic head that sweeps across the surface at a fixed rate. Recording paper moves under the pen at a fixed speed in relation to the travel rate of the stylus.

Electronic Levels. These devices make it possible to check any deviation from true level without requiring magnification or waiting, as bubble-type levels do. The leveling sensor is available separate from the center-zero-indicating meter and amplifier. With this arrangement, the meter can be placed convenient to the installation mechanic when large or sensitive machines are being leveled, while the level unit is some distance away.

Strain gages, strain-sensitive paint, autocollimators, and misalignment detectors, all described previously, also can function as dimension-variation sensors.

FLAW-DETECTING SYSTEMS

This group of devices includes equipment for nondestructive test to find internal fissures, surface and subsurface cracks, and thickness changes in metal vessels, structural parts, and mechanical components in moving equipment. The equipment varies from highly complex ultrasonic flaw detectors to spray-on dye-penetrant systems.

Ultrasonic Testers. When a short pulse of mechanical vibration (sonic) energy is fed into an air, liquid, or solid medium, the pulse continues to travel throughout the medium until it is dissipated by distance or by reflection from a discontinuity. The discontinuity may be either an internal flaw or an opposite surface. Ultrasonic test devices make use of this phenomenon to find flaws or to measure wall thickness. Figure 3-17 shows an ultrasonic flaw detector being used to check a large press shaft.

A typical ultrasonic test unit for maintenance use is made up of a portable tester and a cable-connected ceramic-crystal transducer. The tester consists of several separate circuits. First is an oscillator of adjustable frequency output (perhaps 0.5 to 15 Mc) capable of emitting 100 to 1,000 pulses of this ultrasonic energy per second. The oscillator output is fed via the cable to the crystal transducer (called the search unit). After the search unit has given off this burst of vibration, it acts as a receiver to detect reflected vibrations. These, in turn, are converted to electrical signals by the search unit, fed back via the cable to an amplifier within the test unit, and displayed as "pips"

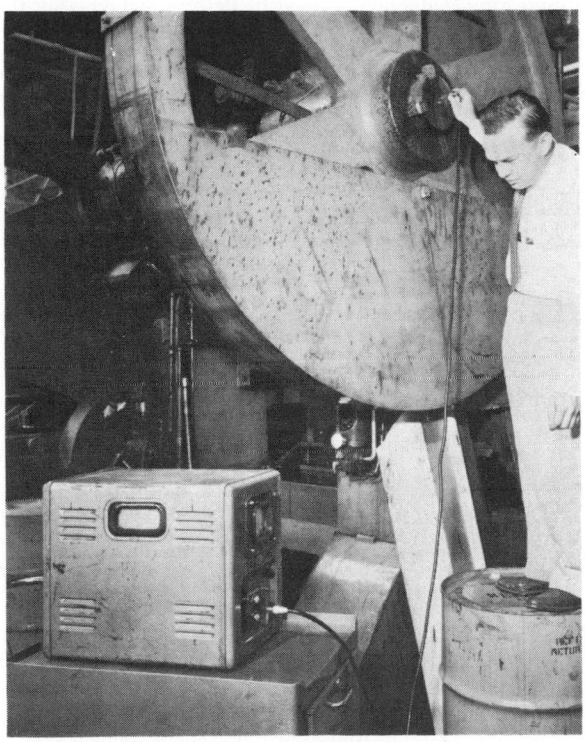

FIG. 3-17. Ultrasonic flaw detector being used to check a large press shaft. (*Courtesy of Sperry Products Company, Danbury, Conn.*)

on the screen of the tester's cathode-ray tube. The pips reflected from internal flaws will appear at a different place on the screen from the echos from the opposite surface. Since the elapsed time for the sound to reach "reflectors" in the material is directly proportional to the distance involved, the location of defects in the material can be accurately determined.

The relative height of the pip is a clue to the size of the flaw. Accuracy in gaging flaw sizes can be achieved by comparing them with drilled holes or notches machined in calibrated plates or weld samples. For greatest ease of recognition, the search unit should be placed so that the pulse strikes the flow surface at as close to 90° as possible.

Ultrasonic testing is so versatile a process that many variations of the principle have been embodied in the types of equipment on the market. Some of these include ultrasonic-resonance testing for thickness measurements, with the frequency being varied until the time between pulses corresponds exactly to the time lapse between two pulses.   Measurement of this frequency makes measurement of the thickness possible. In some types of resonance tester, the cathode-ray screen is eliminated in favor of simpler read-outs such as determining the frequency from flashing lights.

Other variations use different searching techniques.   Search units are available in many different shapes, materials, and characteristics.   All portable ultrasonic testing units have the following limitations in common, however:

1. A liquid coating such as oil, grease, glycerin, or water usually is needed to provide an effective coupling between the search crystal and the surface.
2. Technicians need training in order to interpret test results.
3. Any given search-unit set-up has a certain minimum flaw size below which it cannot sense.   (Before testing is planned, it must be determined whether this could pose a handicap.   This limitation is particularly noticeable with coarse-grain castings.)

Here are typical maintenance jobs for which ultrasonic testers are now being used: finding spalled or defective surfaces in babbit bearings without removal; checking

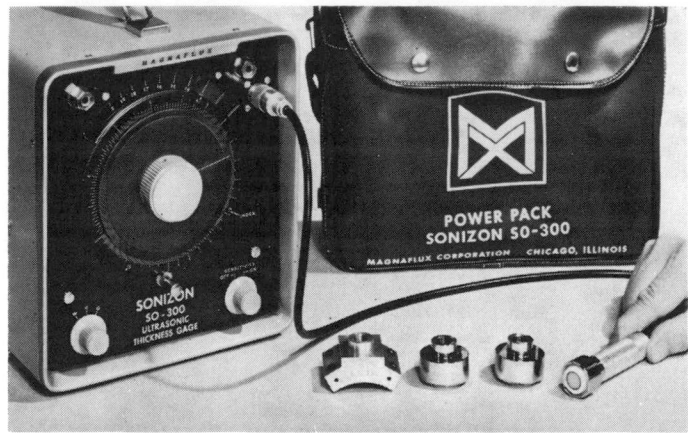

Fig. 3-18. Typical direct-reading ultrasonic-resonance gage with transducers for different surfaces.   (*Courtesy of Magnaflux Corporation, Chicago, Ill.*)

shafts and columns of presses, finding stress cracks in repair welds; checking for evidence of forthcoming fatigue failure in high-speed, critical, or public-use equipment.

Sonic-resonance Gages.   These units operate on a principle similar to the ultrasonic-resonance thickness tester.   Resonance frequency depends on thickness and type of material.   These testers cost less than ultrasonic devices but are more limited in their capabilities.   They are not suitable for complex surfaces.   An example is shown in Fig. 3-18.

Field Discontinuity Meters.   These portable devices use a magnetic probe that senses variations in eddy-current losses in the adjacent surface.   Any crack or defect open to the surface, even invisible ones, will show through variations in the meter reading.   Use is not limited to ferrous materials.

Magnetic-particle Detection.   When magnetic-particle powder or a fluid containing a suspension of iron particles is flowed across a magnetized surface, the particles will concentrate along any crack, even ones slightly below the surface.   Maintenance magnetic-particle detectors typically use a portable d-c yoke-type electromagnet to set up a powerful magnetic field across the surface of castings or forgings.   For improved visibility, fluorescent particles can be used.   They stand out clearly under ultraviolet light (see Fig. 3-19).

Instead of an external magnetic-field source, some systems make use of either alternating current or half-wave direct current flowing through a flexible cable coiled around the iron part under test. Others pass current directly through the part itself, setting up a magnetic field at right angles to the direction of current in the part. In any magnetic-particle inspection system the result is the same—the particles cling to the edges of cracks, marking their location.

While magnetic-particle inspection is unable to find deeply buried flaws, and can be used only on ferrous parts where the surface is accessible, it is usually cheaper than ultrasonic testing. It is also simpler to use on complex-shaped parts or threaded surfaces. Positive location of the crack is somewhat easier than with ultrasonic equipment, too. One technique uses a particle solution that hardens into a strippable plastic sheet, with the crack locations permanently recorded. Typical of the maintenance

FIG. 3-19. Magnetic-particle inspection of lift-truck forks. Magnetic field is developed by high current flowing through the cable coiled around fork. Magnetic particles are sprayed from a container. (*Courtesy of Magnaflux Corporation, Chicago, Ill.*)

jobs performed with magnetic-particle inspection are searching for cracks in critical hand tools, lift-truck forks, crane hooks, valve seats, engine blocks or heads, railroad wheels, and all kinds of structural parts.

Dye-penetrant Systems. These techniques use high-visibility crack-seeking particles suspended in a quick-evaporating or wipe-off solution. Following dye application, a "developer" coat is applied. Dye particles trapped in tiny surface cracks will migrate up through the chalky developer coat to show up as contrasting-colored lines (see Fig. 3-20). Fluorescent dye is widely used to improve visibility. The method is particularly suited to nonferrous surfaces or where minimum investment is essential.

Surface-coating Flaw Detectors. These units use a high-voltage, high-frequency current applied to a wire-whisker brush as it is passed over insulated metal surfaces. Any "holidays" in the porcelain, epoxy, or other coating show up as a spark, detectable by eye or ear or by reading a meter at the high-voltage source.   The technique is used widely in chemical plants and pipelines.   The process is fast, and equipment is relatively inexpensive.   Another type uses voltage and high amplification of any resistance change.   The probe is an electrically conductive water-soaked sponge.

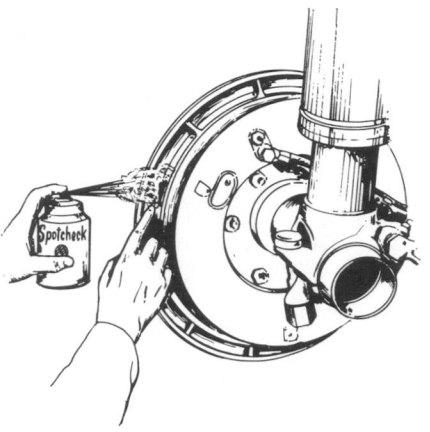

Electrostatic-particle Detection.   This type of system makes use of the principle that charged particles flowed (or blown) across an insulated surface (such as glass-coated steel) will migrate toward flaws or thinner areas in the coating.   The detection process is similar to that used in magnetic-particle testing.

Portable Radiography.   X-ray equipment up to 250,000 volts is available in sizes small enough to fit through manhole covers in tunnels or vessels.   Equivalent shielded sources of isotopes for gamma-ray radiation are even smaller.   Radiography has the advantage of providing positive records of internal conditions of complex assemblies, regardless of the materials involved (see Fig. 3-21).   Typical of the maintenance uses is the radiographing of splices and pothead terminations in high-voltage cables, the detection of product

FIG. 3-20 In the dye-penetrant inspection method spray-on developer brings out the dye, which is embedded in the crack.

bridge-over around the internal mechanism of safety valves in chemical lines, and the quality of repair welds in high-pressure or critical equipment.   Radiography requires control over access to the area to prevent stray radiation from striking nearby workers. It also requires considerable training in both radiographic setup and the reading of radiographs.   Because of this complexity, much of the X-ray work done in maintenance is handled by contract firms specializing in the field.

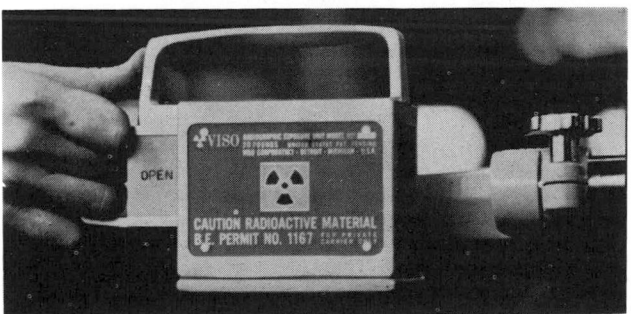

FIG. 3-21. Typical portable isotope source for radiography.   The source, radioactive ytterbium 169, is shielded by tungsten in a stainless-steel housing.   The slide at the left is reinserted for safety.   (*Courtesy of Viso Corporation, Detroit, Mich.*)

FLUID MEASUREMENT

Leak Detectors

Most maintenance operations calling for the measurement of fluid flow involve the detection of small flows such as occur at leaks.   As a result there are several widely used types of leak-detecting systems.

Halogen Detectors. The chlorine-containing compounds widely used as refrigerant fluids have several distinctive properties that facilitate their use in detection. One is that they turn a gas flame a distinctive color when burned in the presence of a hot, reactive metal such as copper. Torch-type leak finders burn acetylene or propane gas in a small shielded flame. In these, flow of the gas to the tip creates suction on a small flexible hose which is used as a probe to search for any sign of the halogen gases. Flame detectors are simple and have the advantage in refrigeration-system leak detection of being sensitive to the gas already in use. "Freon," a typical halogen-containing refrigerant, is relatively inexpensive and does not react with most common metals. Liquid at low temperature or moderate pressures, it can easily be fed into any tight system from refillable steel tanks or from small aerosol-type cans using a piercing needle valve. Since "Freon" in a 12-oz. aerosol can will expand to 2.4 cu ft at room temperature and pressure, it is simple to add enough of the gas even to large vessels to make halogen leak detection practical. A good operator in semidarkened surroundings can see a distinctive change in flame color when the probe tube draws in a mixture of

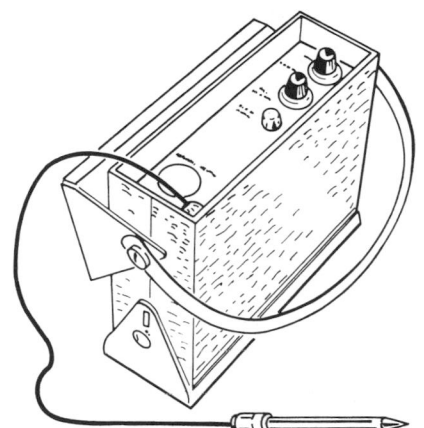

FIG. 3-22. Typical electronic leak detector sensitive to halogens and other ionized gases. Flashing light indicates leak.

FIG. 3-23. Thermal-conductivity leak detector being used to sense gas leaks in a pressure vessel. The belt-mounted tank is hand-pumped to furnish suction at the probe for 30 min.

air and "Freon" mixture containing 1 part in 10 of the refrigerant. After leaks have been found and sealed, the gas will dissipate if the system is left open to the air. "Freon" is inert and nonpoisonous.

Halogens are also highly ionized gases. Electronic leak detectors, being sensitive to changes in ionization, take advantage of this fact. In a typical electronic tester, such as shown by Fig. 3-22, a battery-driven vibrator pump draws in air samples through a plastic tube, passing it over an ion-emiting hot element. Any ionized gas will raise ionization rates around the element, showing up as an increased meter reading or as noise in the detector earphone or speaker.

Halogen leak detectors are widely used in refrigeration work. Electronic-type units are particularly handy in motor-vehicle maintenance. "Freon" can be added to a drained radiator and the probe used to locate the point of leakage precisely. Head-gasket leakage can be sensed by pouring a cup of trichloroethylene into the radiator and allowing the engine to heat up. Leakage will be shown up by probing the exhaust stream. The exact source of the leak can be found by "sniffing" through individual spark-plug holes.

Thermal-conductivity Leak Detectors. The typical leak finder employing this principle uses two conductivity cells in a bridge circuit, one attached to the probe tip inlet, the other to a reference inlet (see Fig. 3-23).   Each cell consists of an electrically heated thermistor, which is cooled by the gas (or air) passing over it.   Since thermistor resistance varies greatly with temperature, any change in the cooling rate of the probe-tip thermistor changes the amount of current flowing in that circuit.   After amplification, the read-out can be made with a meter, speaker, or earphone.   Suction for the probe is provided by a battery-driven pump or by a hand-pumped evacuated reservoir.

Thermal-conductivity detectors are durable and relatively cheap to operate.   They sense the presence of any gas having a thermal conductivity different from air. Cheaper gases, like ammonia, carbon dioxide, or methane, can be employed as tracers in pressure systems.   For extreme sensitivity, high-conductivity gases like helium or hydrogen can be used.   Often the system gas under pressure will be satisfactory.

Ultrasonic Detectors.   The movement of gas molecules through a small orifice releases a substantial amount of sonic energy in the 30,000- to 50,000-cycle region.

Fig. 3-24. Ultrasonic noise from a leak picked up by the ultrasonic leak detector is translated to audible frequencies by the amplifier and fed into the operator's earphone.   (*Courtesy of Delcon Division, Hewlett-Packard Company, Palo Alto, Calif.*)

Ultrasonic detectors or translators make use of this principle to detect and locate leaks.   A typical detector (Fig. 3-24), uses a ceramic microphone sensitive to ultrasounds, a battery-powered portable amplifier, and a filter circuit to screen out all audio-frequency sounds.   The output is read on a meter.   In the translator, the ultrasounds are converted to audio frequencies of about one-tenth their original frequency, amplified, and fed into earphones or a speaker.   Both types of device are lightweight and portable.

Because ultrasonic translators are highly directional and insensitive to most machine-originated mechanical noise, an operator can detect and locate a small leak in a compressed-air system from a distance of 50 ft or more.   With room noises shut out and guided by the increasing volume in the earphones, he often can walk directly to the source of the leak.

The units are less effective in locating large leaks or ones with smooth edges, where intense molecular action along the gas-orifice boundary does not occur.   They will also detect inleakage in vacuum systems, but the energy radiated to the atmosphere is not so great as with pressure leaks.   Ultrasound radiation from vacuum leaks can be increased manyfold if the area surrounding a suspected leak is blanketed with a finely divided mist of water or other liquid.

The use of ultrasonic detectors in maintenance is widespread.   Telephone and power-utility personnel use them to locate leaks in overhead and underground gas-filled cable.   For overhead cables the microphone is mounted at the end of a long pole. For work around hazardous voltages, an ultrasonic relay is available.   This unit at the end of a "hot stick" senses the leak and amplifies the sound, feeding it to a speaker at the opposite end of the relay.   This relayed sound is again sensed by a regular ultrasonic detector several feet away at the base of the hot stick near the operator.   Since there is no electrical connection between the two, there is no electrical hazard.

The type of gas used in the pressure system has little effect on the ease of finding leaks.   Bottled-gas manifolds, steam lines, low-pressure air or gas containers, compressed-air systems, and valve leakage within a closed system can all be checked for leaks as part of a routine preventive-maintenance program.

Because many other malfunctions or undesirable conditions radiate high-frequency sonic energy, ultrasonic detectors are used in other types of maintenance diagnostic work.   In many cases of bearing failure, the actual failure is preceded by hours or days of ultrasound from bearing distress.   This can be picked up effectively by using a pencil-type probe that makes mechanical contact with the bearing housing.   Nearby

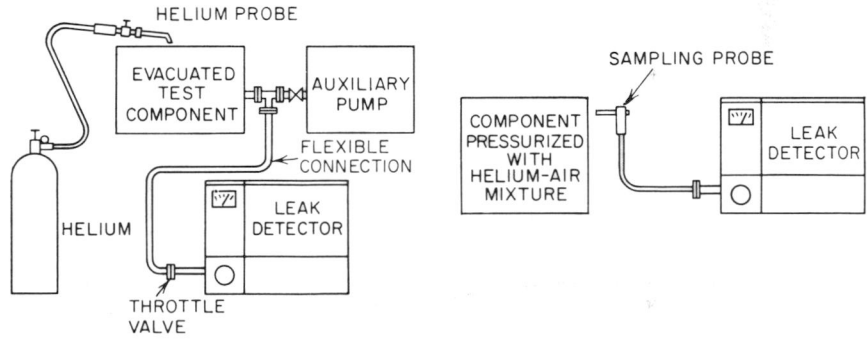

FIG. 3-25. Two methods of using the mass spectrometer for leak detection.   The technique at left is adapted to larger components but usually requires more helium if the entire surface must be probed.   The technique at right is better adapted to finding leaks in pressure vessels.

machine noise does not come through to the operator.   Through experience, operators learn to distinguish between future failures caused by faulty lubrication and those due to defective balls or rollers.   Ultrasonic detection also discloses the presence of insulation-damaging corona discharge in high-voltage transformers, cables, or other electrical equipment.

Sonic Detectors.   These units use a sensitive directional microphone, a battery-powered amplifier, and earphones, speaker, or meter to detect the noise emanating from a leak.   The method is often used to detect leaks in gas and air lines.   The microphone is often mounted on an extension probe to eliminate stooping or reaching.

Mass Spectrometers.   For detection of extremely small leaks in evacuated systems the mass spectrometer is probably the most widely used instrument (see Fig. 3-25). The unit is normally connected with a vacuum-tight coupling to the container or system under test.   The instrument includes its own vacuum-pumping system and generally operates at a lower pressure than the test vessel, so that at all times the spectrometer is being fed a sample of the molecules remaining in the vessel or leaking into it.   A light, easily dispersed gas such as helium is sprayed around the area of the vessel surface suspected for leaks.

Some of the gas molecules entering the instrument are ionized by an electron beam from the filament in the mass-spectrometer tube and are accelerated toward a narrow target at one end of the tube.   Because the instrument is "tuned" beforehand for sensitivity to helium ions (or whatever other gas is used) only the helium ions strike the target. (Heavier or lighter ions from other inleaking gases are deflected by magnetic or electrostatic fields.) The small ion charge reaching the target is amplified by a very-high-gain amplifier and read on a meter. The tuning and calibration required at intervals are done with a gas source and a fixed leak calibrated in atmospheres per cubic centimeter per second. A typical helium leak has a rating of 5×10^{-8}, a typical argon leak has a rating of 5×10^{-6} atm per cu cm per sec.

The versatility of the mass spectrometer can be extended by using it backward, as it were, attaching an adjustable needle-valve probe (instead of the vessel under test) to the instrument inlet. The vessel is then filled with the tracer gas under pressure, and the probe is passed over the surface in the manner of the other leak detectors.

The success of the mass spectrometer is dependent on the extreme velocity of molecular movement in an evacuated system. Leaks of modest size located 100 ft away through a maze of piping and internal baffles, will produce an output meter reading less than a second after the tracer gas is turned on at the leak. A typical spectrometer is capable of locating leaks as small as 5×10^{-11} atm per sec. (A leak this size would require 630 years to admit 1 cu cm of air at atmospheric pressure.)

Some operator training is required, particularly to prevent error in opening the mass spectrometer to atmosphere while it is pumped down and turned on, thus contaminating the unit's diffusion pump and spectrometer-tube components (which requires a time-consuming cleaning and overhauling of the unit).

Stethoscope. The stethoscope, equipped with a pencillike probe placed on the valve body, can be used to detect internal leakage in valves. The physician's type uses hollow flexible tubes to transmit sounds directly to the eardrums. It is simple, rugged, and inexpensive. Tunable models use a variable-length resonance column to increase sensitivity to a single frequency sound and decrease volume of other frequencies. Though primarily designed for tracing mechanical vibration, tunable stethoscopes are useful in tracing leaks.

Electronic stethoscopes are fountain-pen-sized pocket instruments containing a pencil-probe point, a crystal pickup, high-gain transistorized amplifier, penlight battery, and miniature earphone. The units are inexpensive, and can be adapted to pickup elements that are sensitive to magnetic fields, light beams, and various other forms of energy. Output can be fed into an oscilloscope when the input energy must be analyzed in greater detail.

Pipe-thread-leakage Gage. In use, this tester is attached to the plant air system. If a female thread is being tested, a male test gage attached to a flexible hose is screwed into it and controlled air pressure is fed into the system. Special configuration of the thread gage allows a predetermined amount of air to escape. Imperfect threads permit passage of extra air, shown on the sensitive gage. The unit is particularly adapted for finding thread leakage in hydraulic components before assembly.

Other Leak-detection Methods. Many times leakage can be traced without using elaborate instruments. One obvious method is to flow a soap solution over suspected leaks in a pressurized vessel and watch for bubbles. Some maintenance departments successfully trace leaks in air systems by pouring essence of mint or other aromatics into the air receiver and following their noses. Tiny leaks in liquid vessels can be located by adding fluorescent dye to the liquid and searching with ultraviolet light. Some gases, such as ammonia or sulfur dioxide, produce readily observable chemical reactions when a blotter or cloth impregnated with the proper chemical is laid over the leak.

Gas-flow Indicators

Measurement of air velocity is essential in balancing hot-air heating systems, finding air-duct leakage, determining boiler-draft and stack velocities, checking blowers and air-handling systems to see if they meet rated capacities, searching for inleakage around windows and building openings, and determining if annoying drafts exist in occupied areas. Gas-pressure instruments can be converted to flow-measuring devices by use of a venturi-type probe that converts flow to pressure difference.

Moving-vane Meters. Inside the typical moving-vane air-velocity measuring instrument is a lightweight vane. Air impinges on the vane to deflect the pointer up the scale in proportion to the air velocity (see Fig. 3-26). Vane movement compresses a hairspring, and in the more expensive instruments the vane is counterbalanced and suspended on jewel pivots so that the unit can be used in any position. Air is fed into the instrument either directly from a port in the side or from a flexible tube tipped with a jet calibrated to match one of the instrument scales. Jets are available in a wide variety of configurations for either draft or pressure flow, including velocity-averaging types and units designed for fitting in inconvenient duct openings. Where static pressure is backed up by an adequate pressure source, moving-vane meters can be used for static pressure gages as well. Typical ranges of sensitivities are from 20 to 24,000 fpm and 1 to 20 in. of water static pressure. For accurate work the units require correction for temperature and barometric-pressure difference.

Thermopile Flow Meter. One flow meter with a very wide range of sensitivity is the thermopile unit. It has a bridge-sensing circuit similar in principle to the thermal-conductivity leak detector, in which air moving past variable-resistance thermocouples

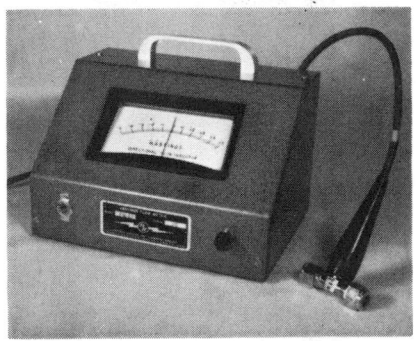

Fig. 3-26. Measuring air velocity at a ceiling diffuser with a moving-vane air meter.

Fig. 3-27. Thermopile-type directional flow indicator and probe. (*Courtesy of Hastings-Raydist, Inc., Hampton, Va.*)

varies their d-c output. Thermocouples are located in the probe itself, which is connected by cable to the instrument (see Fig. 3-27). Both omnidirectional and single-directional probes are available. The omnidirectional unit with a recording instrument is particularly useful for measuring annoying drafts at workplaces over long periods of time. Design of the probe includes compensation for temperature variations. Range of ratings is typically 1 to 20,000 fpm.

Floating-ball Meters. At higher velocities, air can be picked up by a probe (pressure or suction) and caused to pass through a vertical or inclined tube in which a lightweight ball climbs in proportion to the velocity. A scale alongside the tube is calibrated in feet per minute (see Fig. 3-28). This is one of the most inexpensive and durable of all air-flow meters, but for accuracy the scale must be held vertically. Dust getting into the tube destroys accuracy, too.

Diaphragm-pointer Pressure Gages. Though designed for measurement of static pressures, these devices, using a pitot-type probe and flexible hose, make convenient draft-measuring instruments. Sensitivities down to 0.01 in. H_2O are available.

Manometers. These units use some version of a U tube to measure pressure differences between the top surfaces of the two columns. The flexible hose and probe are connected to the top of the column and the pressure difference is read along the scale on one tube. Water, alcohol, mercury, and other fluids are used, depending on the sensitivity needed. The lighter the density, the greater the sensitivity. Ease of reading the scale can be increased by using an inclined scale. Where pressure readings are taken in one direction only, the manometer may use a large-diameter reservoir of fluids at its base and only one column.   Manometer ranges cover 0.05 in. H₂O up to about 20 psi.   Many of the units designed for maintenance use flexible plastic tubing and can be rolled up to be carried in the pocket.   It is also quite simple to make a reasonably accurate manometer by bending glass tubing and mounting it on a board.

Contamination is an enemy of manometers and must be kept out of the U tube.

Hypodermic-needle Gages.   In maintenance work, it is frequently necessary to measure actual air pressure right at the inlet connection of a portable tool, because

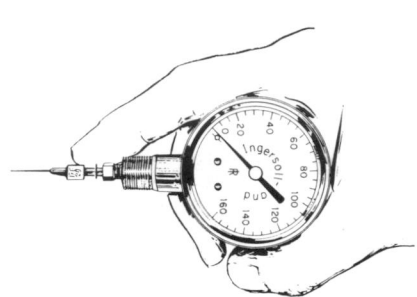

FIG. 3-28. Measuring suction-grille air velocity with floating-ball air-velocity meter.

FIG. 3-29.   Hypodermic-needle pressure gage.   (*Courtesy of Ingersoll-Rand Corporation, New York.*)

undersized or clogged hoses or fittings will reduce air flow (and consequently air pressure) to the tool under full load.   A drop of 10 psi below the rated 90 psi needed will reduce output about 20 per cent.   Hypo-needle gages consisting of a standard Bourdon-tube gage attached to a hollow needle can be pushed through reinforced rubber hose.   When they are removed, the hole is small enough to heal itself.   These gages can also be used on hydraulic lines within the range of their pressure rating (see Fig. 3-29).

HYDRAULIC TESTERS

Most hydraulic-system diagnostic work is performed by disassembling connections and inserting standard pressure and flow gages.   Where high transient pressures are

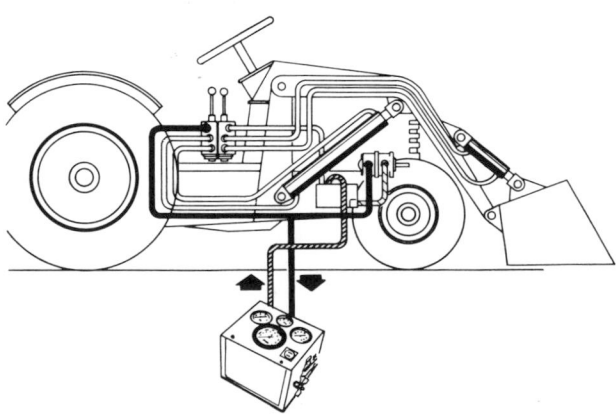

FIG. 3-30. Hydraulic analyzer connected in a tractor loader's pump circuit to check capacity and efficiency.   (*Courtesy of Owatonna Tool Company, Owatonna, Minn.*)

suspected of causing damage to the system or mountings, they can be accurately measured only with some fast-responding sensor such as a strain gage or crystal pressure pickup.   Sensors are available to fit tapped holes of $\frac{1}{8}$ in. NPT or smaller.   They generally require an amplifier.   Actual pressures are read on a cathode-ray or recording oscillograph after calibration and temperature compensation.   Although these setups are perhaps more widely used in laboratories, maintenance departments that have taken time to develop skill in their use have found them both simple and capable of providing a meaningful insight into peculiar hydraulic-system problems. Typical of the problems arising from high transient pressure are breakage, wear, and wiredrawing of valves, cracking of fittings and tubing, and rupturing of heat-exchanger tubes.

Hydraulic Analyzer.   A typical hydraulic analyzer combines pressure, flow, and temperature gages with a throttling valve and convenient hose and fitting connections. The device is connected into the hydraulic system (up to 5,000 psi) and the system is loaded.   Leaking or jammed valves or faulty pumps or heat exchangers will show up quickly (see Fig. 3-30).

HEAT-SENSING INSTRUMENTS

Observing and drawing proper conclusions from changes in operating temperatures is one of the key marks of an experienced trouble shooter.   Every change in equipment operating temperature has some significance.   Often, of course, it is a result of a change in load or ambient conditions.   But the really skilled maintenance technician or engineer recognizes that a bearing, or resistor, or transformer, or air-compressor intercooler, or truck tire that suddenly rises beyond its normal operating-temperature range is trying to tell him that something has changed and that probably something isor—was—wrong.

In spite of the wide variety of instruments available, the hand remains a remarkably fast and accurate means of spotting off-normal temperatures.   It's no trick at all with experience to tell the difference between two surfaces when one is 140 and the other 150°.   (But always use the back of the fingers, not the palm of the hand, to avoid unexpected burns.)   The experienced technician has learned to be wary in predicting the temperature of polished surfaces, because they radiate less infrared energy as a warning than do dull or dark-colored surfaces of the same temperature.   Today the maintenance department seldom needs to rely on "feel" for temperature accuracy. Besides the liquid-filled thermometer, accurate, inexpensive, and durable pocket-type bimetallic dial instruments are also available.   Some of the other temperature sensors are described below.

Thermocouple and Thermopile Pyrometers.   Heat applied to the junction of many combinations of dissimilar metals (a thermocouple) produces a small d-c current, proportional to temperature, which can be read on a meter (see Fig. 3-31).   A group of thermocouples in series (a thermopile) is needed to produce enough output when temperature is near room levels.   Temperature to above 5000°F can be measured with available thermocouples.   Probes can vary in shape from hypodermic needles to flat, flexible saddles that rub against rotating rolls, and they may be several feet or more from the read-out instrument.   Normally the thermocouple needs no amplification or power supply.   Response to temperature change is quite fast, depending on the mass of the thermocouple itself.

Thermistor or Resistance-sensitive Temperature Indicators.   Certain electrically resistant alloys and compounds show a large variation in resistance for a small increase in temperature.   When combined with a battery, a bridge-amplifier circuit, and output meter, they offer an economical and lightweight means of measuring temperature at the tip of the probe.   Probes can be built in almost any configuration and very light in mass.   They are available with pocket-sized read-outs that will accurately indicate a 100°F temperature change in a few seconds (see Fig. 3-32).

Optical Pyrometers.   At temperatures of about 1400°F objects begin to radiate so much of their energy in the visible wavelengths that color comparisons serve as an accurate temperature guide.   The typical optical pryometer compares the color of the

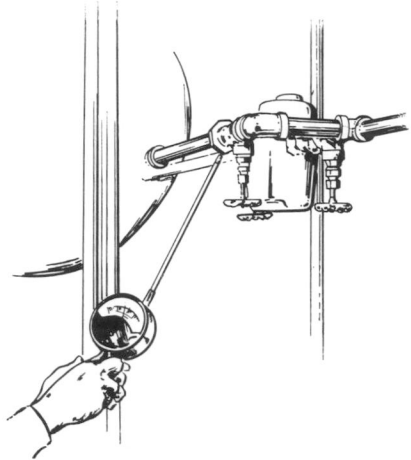

FIG. 3-31. Measuring steam-line temperatures with a rigid-arm thermocouple pyrometer. Flexible-cable types are available.

test object against the color of a built-in filament lamp fed from a variable-current power supply. Once calibrated, the filament-current setting serves as a measure of temperature. In maintenance, optical pyrometers are used primarily for measurements of very hot sources such as furnaces and weldments.

Infrared Thermometers. All molecules at temperatures above absolute zero radiate energy. At low temperatures all this radiation is in the long-wavelength, low-frequency infrared end of the spectrum. It is difficult and expensive to measure the level (temperature) of this energy when it is less than about 75° above the temperature of the instrument.

However, highly portable infrared thermometers made to be aimed optically like

FIG. 3-32. Typical thermistor-type thermometer with three probes and selector switch for simultaneous measurement of temperatures of three different points. (*Courtesy of Simpson Electric Company, Chicago, Ill.*)

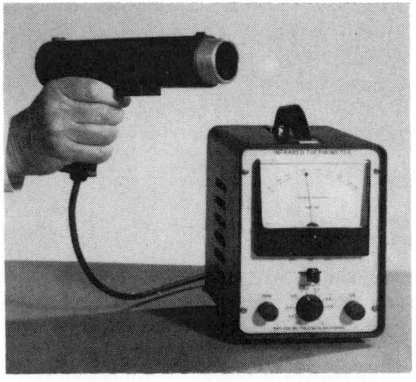

FIG. 3-33. Infrared thermometer senses temperature of distant surfaces "seen" by lens of hand-held probe. (*Courtesy of Ray-Tek, Inc., Palo Alto, Calif.*)

a gun can sense the average temperature of the area within their field of vision (see Fig. 3-33). Output from the infrared cell is fed to a battery-powered amplifier and read on a meter. Typical beam spread is about $\frac{1}{2}$ in. per ft of distance from the infrared lens. Distance from the surface makes little difference unless steam or smoke contamination is serious. Infrared thermometers are still relatively new to the maintenance field, but typical jobs they can handle include quickly searching for hot spots on large surfaces or hot bearings or plugged-up coils in heat exchangers and reading temperatures of surfaces that are dangerous or difficult to reach, such as energized electrical connections or pole-mounted transformers. One drawback of infrared instruments is that correction must be made for emissivity variations in passing from one type of surface to another, but this can be overcome by spraying all routine test points with flat black paint. They are extremely fast in response, however, requiring only time enough for the meter needle to come to rest.

Temperature-sensitive Crayons, Paint, Pellets, and Paper. Widely used in welding, ceramic, and other industries, these handy devices are often overlooked as a maintenance diagnostic tool. They remain inert until their predetermined temperature rating is exceeded, whereupon they irreversibly change color or melt. They are particularly handy in detecting whether equipment was overloaded or heated beyond safe levels between routine preventive maintenance checks. Lack of evidence of overheating between checks may eliminate the need for disassembly or further inspection of electrical equipment, certain bearings, and a wide variety of mechanical equipment.

COMBUSTION AND GAS ANALYZERS

Makeup of various gases in furnaces, boilers, kilns, engine exhausts, and heat-treating areas is a measure of their efficiency or operating performance. Frequently, and particularly in the case of boilers and engine exhausts, adjusting inputs to maintain optimum operation is a maintenance function. A wide variety of analyzers are available.

Combustibles Analyzers. These instruments generally provide a continous readout of per cent of combustibles (hydrogen, carbon monoxide, hydrocarbons) remaining in stack gas. The sampled gas is burned in the analyzer chamber, usually in the presence of a catalyst. Temperature rise is sensed, amplified, and read on a calibrated meter scale. Combustibles analyzers are sometimes combined with an oxygen analyzer (in which the oxygen reacts with hydrogen from a built-in generator to produce temperature rise proportional to oxygen content). The analyzer is used for sampling exhaust gas from furnaces, boilers, kilns, and internal combustion engines. Following evidence of incomplete combustion, operating adjustments are made until optimum burning conditions are achieved.

Smoke Gages. When a predetermined amount of smoke from the stack is forced through a filter paper, the soot and ash deposited on the paper can be compared with standard samples to give a measure of smoke density. High smoke densities are serious causes of air pollution and evidence of faulty boiler combustion.

Gas Analyzers

Specific-gravity Analyzers. Where a definite relationship exists between the change in density and the percentage of a known diluting gas, gas analysis can be accomplished by using a specific-gravity analyzer. The typical unit passes a sample of the gas between two impellers, one of which is belt-driven by a constant-speed battery-driven motor. As a result of gas viscosity, the other impeller exerts a torque against a spring-loaded lever arm. Adjacent to this pair of impellers is a duplicate set through which ambient air is passed. The output impellers have counterrotating shafts and are linked to a common lever arm and scale pointer. The difference in specific gravity between air and the sampled gas deflects the pointer up or down from the center scale point. Specific-gravity analyzers are used to check carbon dioxide in boiler stacks, heat-treating-furnace atmospheres, for spot checks around oil and gas producing and refining, and in engine-exhaust analysis.

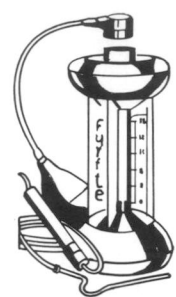

FIG. 3-34. Typical oxygen and carbon dioxide analyzer.

Orsat Apparatus. These widely used analyzers check discrete samples of any gas or exhaust mixture. They work on the principle of selective absorption of gases bubbled through various chemical solutions. Oxygen, carbon dioxide, and carbon monoxide are common gases whose percentage by volume is indicated. The devices are portable and inexpensive (see Fig. 3-34). Chemical solutions need routine renewal.

Thermal-conductivity Analyzers. These units operate on the same principle as the thermal-conductivity leak detector. Calibrated to measure the difference in thermal conductivity between air and a known percentage of sampled gas, they provide a fast, continuous reading of percentage of gases such as carbon dioxide, methane, carbon monoxide, and oxygen in air (or some other reference gas).

Other Gas Analyzers. Several other types of gas analyzers are in maintenance use. Some of them use some visible reaction such as the degrees of change of color, to indicate the percentage of a specific gas (e.g., carbon dioxide or hydrogen sulfide) in the sample. Others measure the current produced from electrochemical reactions to determine the amount of electrochemically active gases such as chlorine, ozone, or nitrogen dioxide in a sample.

ENGINE ANALYZERS

Time-averaged Engine-pressure Indicator. This instrument is designed to be screwed into the individual cylinder indicator valves to balance work load among cylinders in large diesel, natural-gas, or gasoline engines. The flexible bourdon-tube in the indicator is coupled to an internal shock-absorbing, pressure-averaging mechanism. Water cooling is provided to keep instrument parts at temperatures within safe levels (see Fig. 3-35).

Cylinder-pressure Transducers. While these devices are primarily used by experimental laboratories, some of the more advanced industrial-maintenance operators are

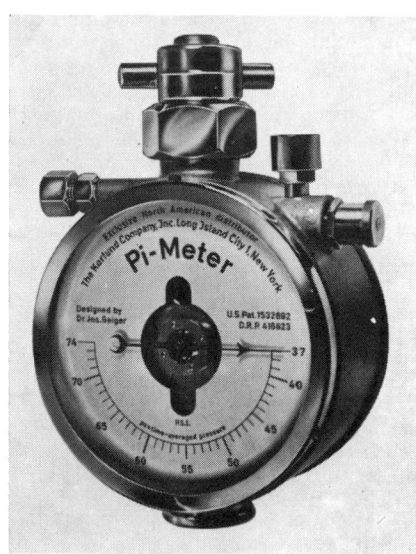

FIG. 3-35. Time-averaged engine-pressure indicator. Pressure connection to engine cylinder is at top; water-cooling connections are at left. (*Courtesy of The Korfund Dynamics Corporation, Westbury, L.I., N.Y.*)

beginning to make use of them for routine testing and trouble diagnosis in critical vehicle or stationary engines. The typical transducer consists of a quartz crystal built into a modified spark plug (or into a pipe plug for use with air compressors or hydraulic systems). Output from the crystal is amplified and fed into the vertical deflection circuit of a cathode-ray oscilloscope. The oscilloscope's horizontal sweep rate is matched to the rpm of the engine. Screen-trace pattern shows up worn cams, leaky valves or rings, faulty ignition, and carburetor or manifold abnormalities. Experience is required to achieve skill in interpreting the trace in terms of diagnosing exact off-normal engine condition. The transducer-amplifier equipment is expensive, but the technique is probably the most versatile of all engine-analysis methods. It is, in a sense, a modern high-speed, high-accuracy version of the card indicator used in testing stationary diesel and gas engines.

Other Engine Analyzers. Analyzers of considerable variety are available to measure various aspects of engine performance. Most are designed for automotive maintenance, and some fall short of the accuracy expected in industrial-maintenance instruments. Nonetheless, a great many useful diagnostic devices can be procured inexpensively to speed engine servicing of industrial and over-the-road trucks and vehicles. Included are ignition-dwell meters, thermal-conductivity exhaust analyzers, fuel-flow-rate transducers, and spark-plug-timing and voltage indicators (on an oscilloscope screen).

MOISTURE-SENSING INSTRUMENTS

Besides the familiar sling psychrometer and wet- and dry-bulb thermometer, several other types of instruments are available to measure moisture content of air. Some are also suitable for use on the surface of loose nonconductive fibrous material or buried within it. Humidity measurements are needed in maintenance checking of air-conditioning systems, refrigerated food-storage areas, air dryers for instrument air systems, and dehumidifiers used in moisture-sensitive areas like paint booths.

Electrolytic Hygrometer. This instrument continuously measures the moisture content of various gases to accuracies of less than 1 ppm. In a typical unit, water vapor in the sampled gas is absorbed by a phosphorus pentoxide film coated between two platinum electrodes. Direct current is applied to the electrodes, causing the water to dissociate into hydrogen and oxygen. Current used in dissociation is a direct measure of the moisture content of the gas. Gases which can be analyzed with the electrolytic-type unit include air, carbon dioxide, hydrogen sulfide, nitrogen, hydrocarbons, and halogens.

Absorption Humidity Meters. Animal fibers and human hair elongate with increases in humidity. Hair can be bundled and mounted in a suitable linkage to operate a pointer for indicating or recording humidity. Top temperature limit is about 160°F. Useful relative humidity range is 30 to 90 per cent. Animal membranes are used in much the same way as human hair in other humidity meters. Top temperature range is about 140°F, and humidity range is 20 to 85 per cent.

Dew-point Indicators. One of the most accurate measurements of the moisture content of a gas is the temperature at which the moisture within it condenses. Dew-point indicators typically use a polished surface cooled by refrigerant or expanding carbon dioxide. The operator watches carefully to observe the surface temperature at which moisture begins to form.

Conductivity Cells. When a conductive salt such as lithium chloride is coated between two closely spaced electrodes on a probe, the resistance between the two will vary in proportion to the moisture content of the air, gas, or fibers surrounding the cell. With amplifier and compensation for temperature, these units have become increasingly popular for quick, relatively accurate reading of humidity.

Chapter 4

NUMERICAL CONTROL

By Alan R. Davis
Vice President and Chief Engineer
Time-Trol, Inc.
Van Nuys, Calif.

WHAT IS NUMERICAL CONTROL?[1]

"Numerical control" is the name given to a fundamental concept of control. This concept is applicable to any kind of process or equipment which must be directed in its operation by human intelligence. Metalworking equipment provides a major field of application for this new control concept, which is also used in petroleum processing, food preparation, and to direct chemical installations. Wherever equipment must be instructed to perform its function, there is likely to be a use for numerical control. Every item of equipment now controlled by an operator offers a potential application for numerical control.

The advantages in numerical control to a manufacturing operation are as follows:

1. Fully automatic performance of all machining operations which lie within the capability of the basic machine tool.
2. Rapid interchangeability of control equipment from one job to another by simply inserting a new set of previously prepared instructions.
3. Smaller number of work set-ups and reduced set-up time.
4. Accuracy unlimited in preparing control instructions.
5. Multiple machine control by a single system, and control need not be located near the machine tool.
6. Instructions do not deteriorate with use, are readily modified through patching techniques, are conveniently stored, can be shipped (or mailed) anywhere with speed and economy, and may be transmitted between plants by conventional tele-type circuits.
7. Of commercial grade, most of the system components are readily available at moderate cost.
8. Inherent mathematical accuracy.
9. Minimum human error in machining procedures.
10. Process preparation remote from machine tool.
11. Part duplication is constant and accurate.
12. Increased machine-tool utilization.
13. New business opportunities in previously unprofitable work.

Numerical control is just what the term implies, *control* by the *numbers*. "Control" and "numbers"—two words—define a revolution in manufacturing.

[1] Portions of this chapter are reprinted by permission of *American Machinist/Metalworking Manufacturing*.

Control, according to Webster, means to exercise directing, guiding, or restraining power over something.   To give directions or guidance is to communicate information in the form of advice or commands.   These commands can provide instructions (It's time to get up!), include directions (Go left to the traffic light, then turn right), involve color (Wear a green tie), or include a numerical value (Give me six eggs).

In every metalworking shop, millions of commands are given by people to people and by people to machines.   Most of these instructions to the machines are given manually.   Pressing a button orders the power supply to start the motor.   Raising a lever may cause the spindle to rotate clockwise.   Turning a handwheel commands a cutting tool to move 0.010 in. into the work.

And that 0.010 in.-instruction takes us into a whole new area of control, the finite commands involving *numbers*.   As complicated as they may appear, numbers provide information symbols for only three functions, *counting, measuring, and predicting*.   It is extremely important to remember that numbers are only symbols for values—they are not values in themselves—and that arabic numerals provide only one of many ways to symbolize these values.

Counting and measuring, in normal uses, are fairly simple functions.   Predicting can be simple, but it is likely to be a more complicated function.   It may call for higher mathematics and even for a computer.

Numerical control in the broad sense requires only the *counting and measuring functions* of numbers.   While there has been much talk of computers in relation to numerical control, they are necessary only for complex programming or as means to speed up tape preparation.   Computers are tools of the advanced programmer. They are not an inherent part of the simpler numerical-control systems.

FIG. 4-1. Converting physical dimensions to numerical values. (*Courtesy of American Machinist/Metalworking Manufacturing.*)

Man is the most versatile control system ever devised, but he is not by any means the most accurate, nor is he the fastest.   In terms of modern manufacturing accuracy requirements, human ability to repeat dimensions and to coordinate two or more dimensions (to produce a cam, for example) is extremely limited.   Nevertheless, man as a control device complete with computer and a set of manipulators is highly flexible.   Numerical control provides accuracy, speed, and flexibility.

Any control system can be said to provide numerical control if it can directly convert symbolic numerical values into physical values, such as quantities or dimensions (Fig. 4-1).   The difference may seem confusing, but the separation is distinct.   When you turn a handwheel, set a length stop, put in a length measure, shift the gears, you are putting in a physical value, not a numerical value.   You determine the limits of value.

POINT-TO-POINT VS. CONTOURING

Three forms of numerical control exist: simple counting, discrete positioning (also called point-to-point), and continuous-path, or contouring.   Between the simplest and the most complex systems many degrees of control are possible.   Machine-tool control is concerned primarily with positioning in two or three dimensions and with contouring in two or more dimensions.

Positioning controls are fundamentally point-locating systems (Fig. 4-2).   They are used to locate a point, or a series of points, by moving independently in two dimensions (called X and Y), without regard to the path of their motions, to meet at the desired point.   Once that point is reached, a third, vertical, motion (called Z) may come into play to provide depth control.   Only the end point is important; the tool path is not

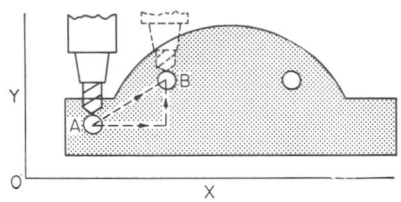

FIG. 4-2. Point-to-point control causes a machine member (here, a drill-press table) to move from one point to another in an X and Y coordinate system so that operations can be performed at the desired points.   Any path of movement can be taken because the tool does no work during movement.   (*Courtesy of Westinghouse Electric Corporation.*)

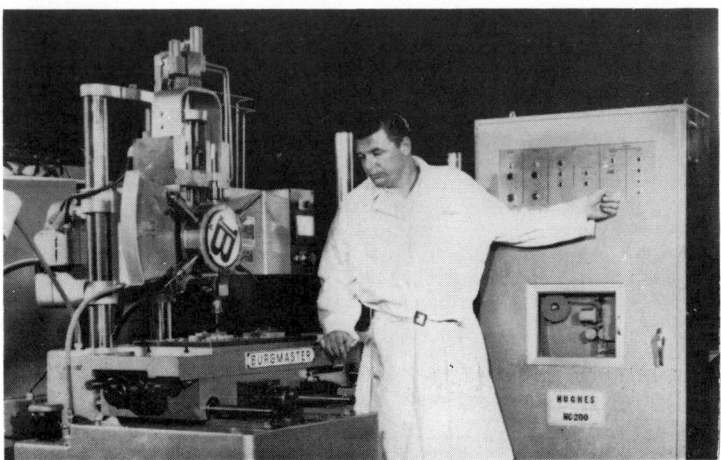

FIG. 4-3. Automatic hydraulic turret drilling, tapping, boring machine with two axis numerical positioning controls.   (*Courtesy of Burgmaster Corporation.*)

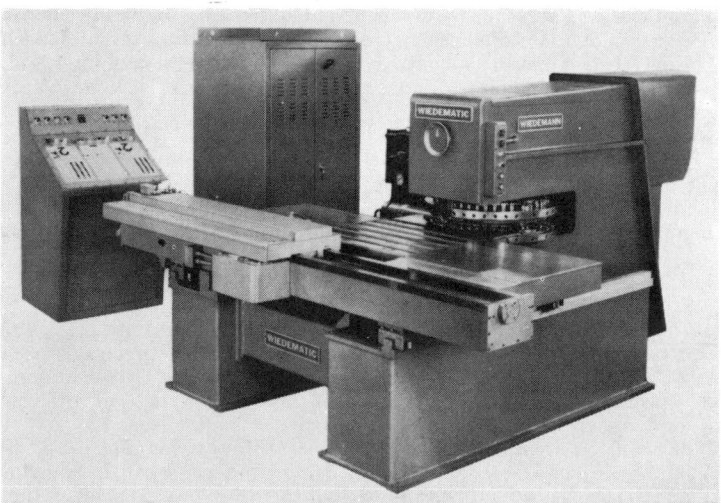

FIG. 4-4. Numerically controlled turret punch press, 15-ton capacity, operating speed of 60 holes per minute.   (*Courtesy of Wiedemann Machine Company.*)

controlled.   Machine tools such as drill presses, jig borers, turret drills, turret lathes, boring mills, riveters, etc., commonly use positioning systems (Figs. 4-3 to 4-5).

Contouring, or continuous-path control, is of a higher order of complexity than positioning (Fig. 4-6).   In contouring, the path of the tool through the work is important.   Thus, the two dimensions (X and Y), or the three dimensions (X, Y, and Z), needed to determine the desired curve or form must be closely coordinated.   They

FIG. 4-5. Four-axis numerically controlled boring, drilling, tapping, and milling machine with automatic tool changer.   (*Courtesy of Kearney & Trecker Corporation.*)

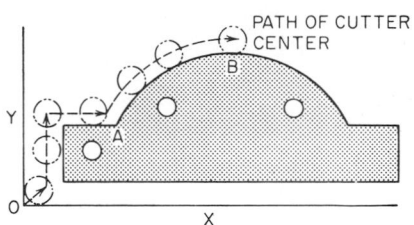

FIG. 4-6. Contouring control also causes a machine member (here, a milling cutter) to move in X and Y coordinates.   The path taken is critical, because the tool cuts as it moves. (*Courtesy of Westinghouse Electric Corporation.*)

must be synchronized by the system after being put into the system as individual dimensions.   Figures 4-7 to 4-9 are typical continuous path machine tools.

Standard Machine-axis Nomenclature.   Numerical control for machine tools depends upon programmed data.   A basic part of these data is the descriptive information coordinating the various machine-tool motions.   The language used to program these data must be standard, hence the machine-axis nomenclature shown in Fig. 4-10 was developed to form the basis for a consistent standard of communication suitable for the most complex machine motions now foreseeable.

Because the part is placed on the machine for the machining cycles, whatever system of description is used for the machine is also imposed on the part.   This nomenclature is designed, therefore, to fit machine motions.   Continual reference to machine axes is made in specifications, data sheets, conversations, proposals, etc., necessitating some universally consistent means of expression.   The *cartesian-coordinate system* has been selected because it is compatible with all branches of science and it is able to satisfy the need to envision machine tools resting on terra firma (Fig. 4-11).

The linear axes of this system are X, Y, and Z.   They are always stated in alphabetical order, and once the X axis has been oriented, and the XY plane established with relation to the machine tool, the rest of the geometry falls naturally into place.   The X axis is the basic reference axis.   Similarly, the first and most important motion of a machine-tool slide is its longitudinal travel, normally seen as traveling from left to

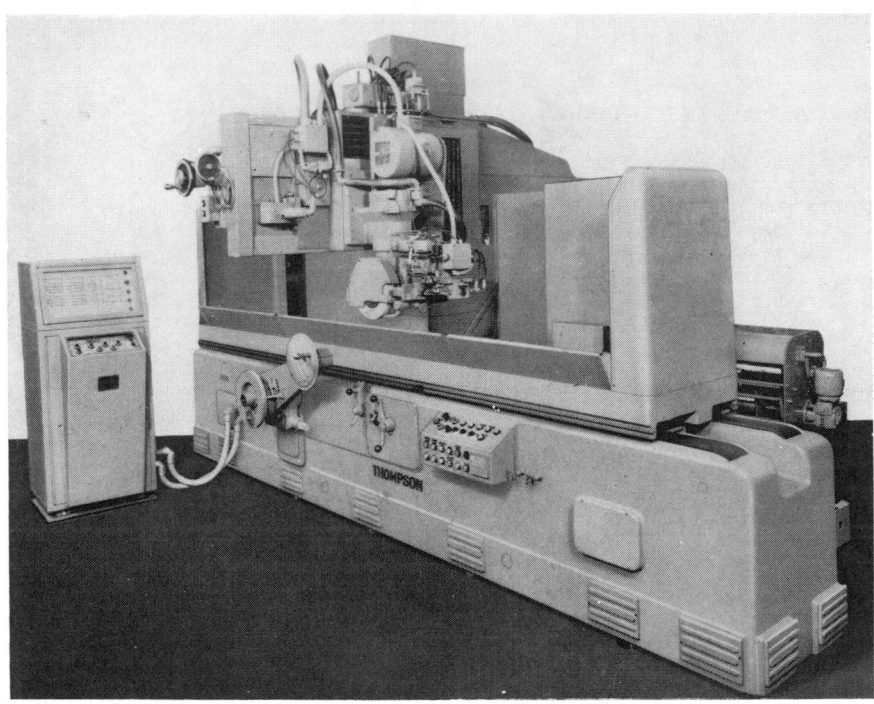

Fig. 4-7. Numerically controlled machine for grinding sophisticated continuous-path contours in both vertical and horizontal planes.   (*Courtesy of The Thompson Grinder Company.*)

right with respect to the operator's conventional position.   This certainly applies to basic machine types such as lathes, milling machines, shapers, planers, and horizontal boring mills, where carriage, table, ram, and platen movements are involved.

To the layman this statement may seem inconsistent because, in machine-tool jargon, the table motion of a horizontal boring mill is called "cross-travel."   Actually, cross-travel is a misnomer and can be construed as longitudinal travel because this motion, as named, is seldom used other than for set-up.   Bar travel may be, and usually is, substituted in its stead.   Left-to-right movement of the table is used more often, is judged to be more important to the purpose at hand, and should be considered comparable to the table travel of a standard horizontal milling machine.

Assignment of the secondary horizontal cross-slide motion as the Y axis fixes the XY plane as horizontal and the Z axis as perpendicular for rise and fall.   Other machine motions requiring description are the simple angular-rotation and compound-angular (tilt) motions.

Simple angular rotation corresponds to the angles a, b, and c.   Angle a is revolution about the X axis; b is revolution about the Y axis; c is revolution about the Z axis. Each is generated in a counterclockwise direction when looking in the plus direction down its corresponding axis.   Such angular rotation "positions" the spindle "axis" so

FIG. 4-8. A five-axis Variax® contour milling machine.   (*Courtesy of Giddings & Lewis Machine Tool Company.*)

FIG. 4-9. A triple-gantry multiple-head skin mill.   (*Courtesy of The Cincinnati Milling Machine Company.*)

that it is no longer along an X, Y, or Z direction.   Thus, the spindle axis is angularly positioned and is labeled P.

Similarly, compound-angular rotation (tilt) of the spindle axis is defined by the angles d, e, and f and is thought of as occuring after one of the simple angular-rotation motions.

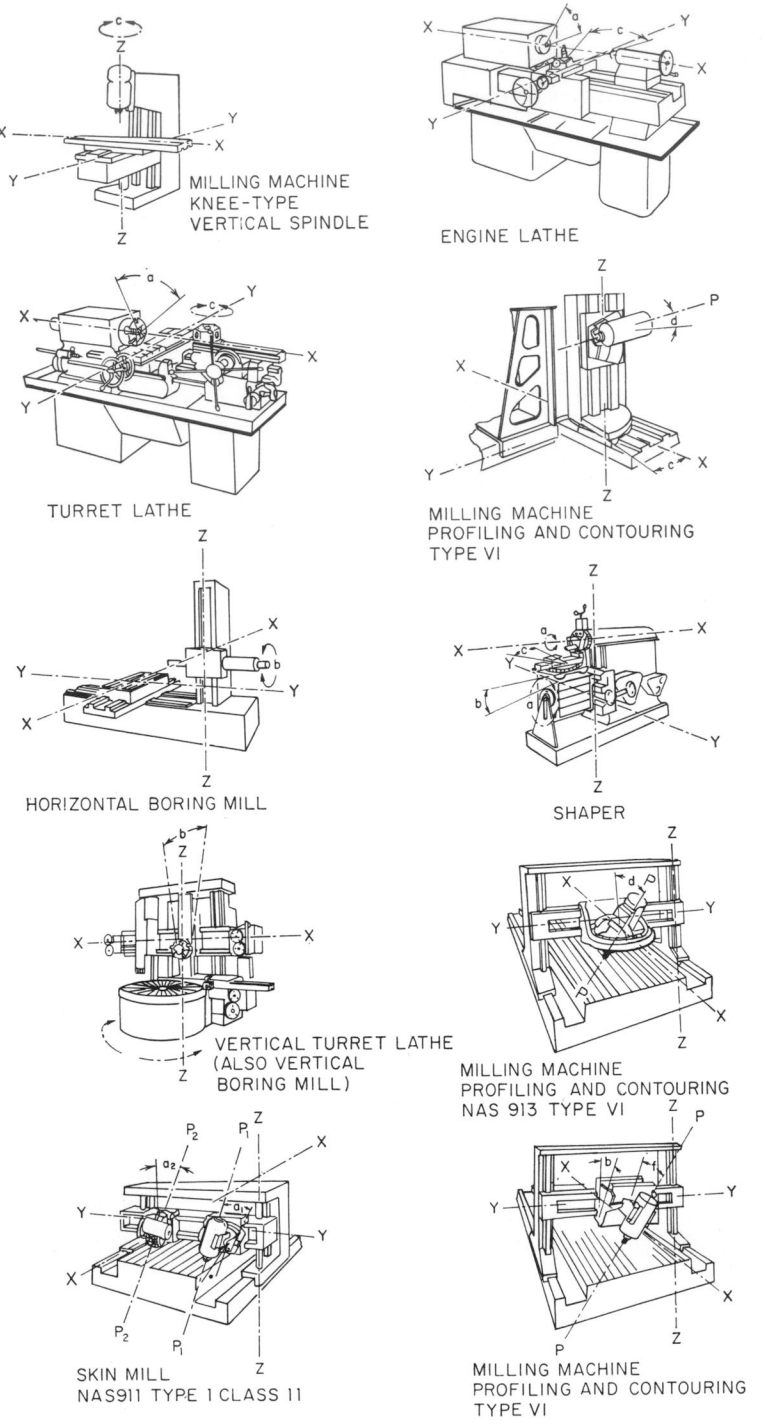

MILLING MACHINE
KNEE-TYPE
VERTICAL SPINDLE

ENGINE LATHE

TURRET LATHE

MILLING MACHINE
PROFILING AND CONTOURING
TYPE VI

HORIZONTAL BORING MILL

SHAPER

VERTICAL TURRET LATHE
(ALSO VERTICAL
BORING MILL)

MILLING MACHINE
PROFILING AND CONTOURING
NAS 913 TYPE VI

SKIN MILL
NAS911 TYPE I CLASS II

MILLING MACHINE
PROFILING AND CONTOURING
TYPE VI

FIG. 4-10. Standard machine-axis nomenclature. (*Courtesy of American Machinist/ Metalworking Manufacturing.*)

Although this nomenclature appears suitable at present, changes will be made as programming techniques and machine tools are advanced—to keep the language consistent with the application.

HOW DOES NUMERICAL CONTROL WORK?

Since point-to-point positioning is the simplest form of numerical control, let us examine the sequence of events leading to the machining of a part by this method.

Figure 4-12 shows that the first step is engineering design. Necessary information for numerical control can often be extracted directly from the engineering drawing with little or no calculation.

FIG. 4-11. Cartesian coordinates with mutual planes and corresponding angles. (*Courtesy of American Machinist/Metalworking Manufacturing.*)

In fact, the amount of calculation required of the person preparing the numerical-control program can be reduced substantially if the design engineer anticipates numerical-control machining and describes the part in the appropriate format.

In all numerical-control systems, whether continuous-path (contouring) or point-to-point (positioning), the part is considered as being in a quadrant of rectangular coordinates. In order that all values be kept positive, the quadrant selected is normally the upper right, as in Fig. 4-13a. If we were to consider a drilling operation, the hole to be drilled would be a distance X from the Y axis and a distance Y from the X axis. The reference point would be at the intersection of the axes.

Conventional blueprint practice of describing center-to-center hole distances appears in Fig. 4-13b. But if the hole locations can be described as distances from a base line or a machined side by positioning the part along one of the axes, as shown in Fig. 4-13c, the problem is simplified. Since the part must first be described in coordinate form, it saves time to designate the dimension in that manner on the original blueprint.

The next step, part-program preparation, is to stipulate the proper machining

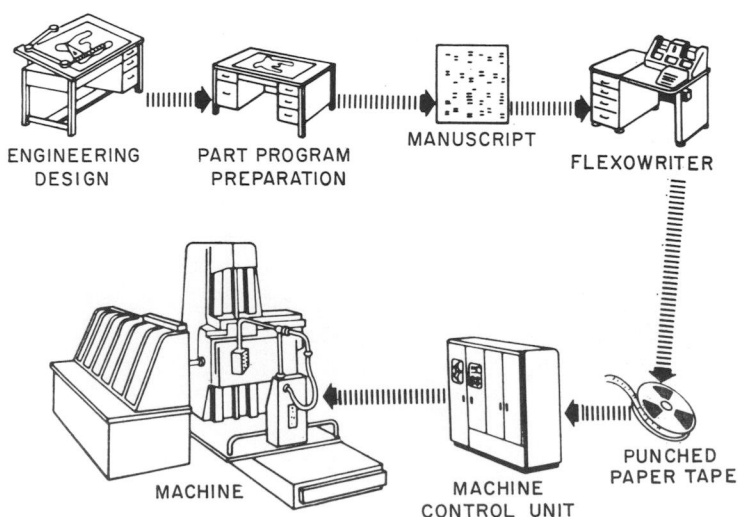

FIG. 4-12. Sequence of events for point-to-point positioning work.

sequence. This information is listed on a format known as a manuscript. The manuscript describes the X and Y positions of each hole, the sequence in which the holes are to be drilled, the speeds and feeds of the cutting head, and auxiliary functions like turning the coolant on and off or clamping and unclamping the part.

After the manuscript is prepared, the information has to be transformed to the control medium, which usually is a punched tape 1 in. wide. Special devices are available for preparing punched tapes, one of the most popular being the Flexowriter (Fig. 4-14).

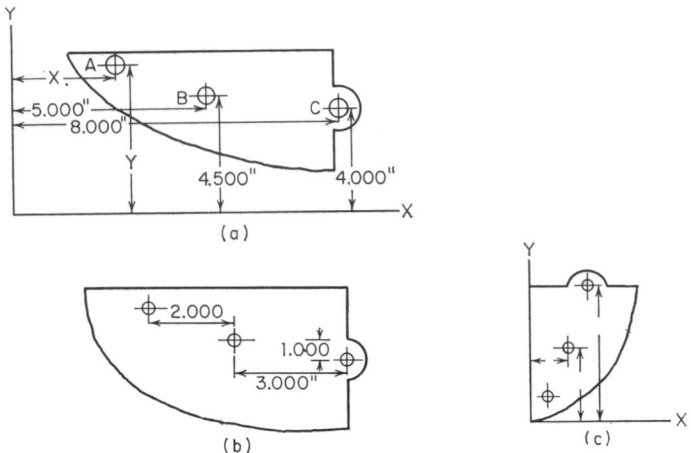

Fig. 4-13. Dimensioning of engineering drawings. (*a*) Hole A is x in. from the Y axis and y in. from the X axis. Holes B and C are assigned numerical values: hole B is 5 in. from the Y axis and 4.5 in. from the X axis; hole C is 8 in. from the Y axis and 4 in. from the X axis. (*b*) The conventional method of dimensioning a part drawing is to state the center distances of the holes. (*c*) Positioning one side of a part against one of the axes reduces the required calculations. (*Courtesy of Machine and Tool Blue Book.*)

Fig. 4-14. Automatic writing and tape perforating machine. (*Courtesy of Friden, Inc.*)

This machine punches the tape while an instruction sheet containing the manuscript information is being typed. The sheet can serve later to check out the original manuscript.

Referring again to Fig. 4-12, it can be seen that the punched tape is directed to the machine control unit, which transforms the digital information on the tape to actual machine movements.

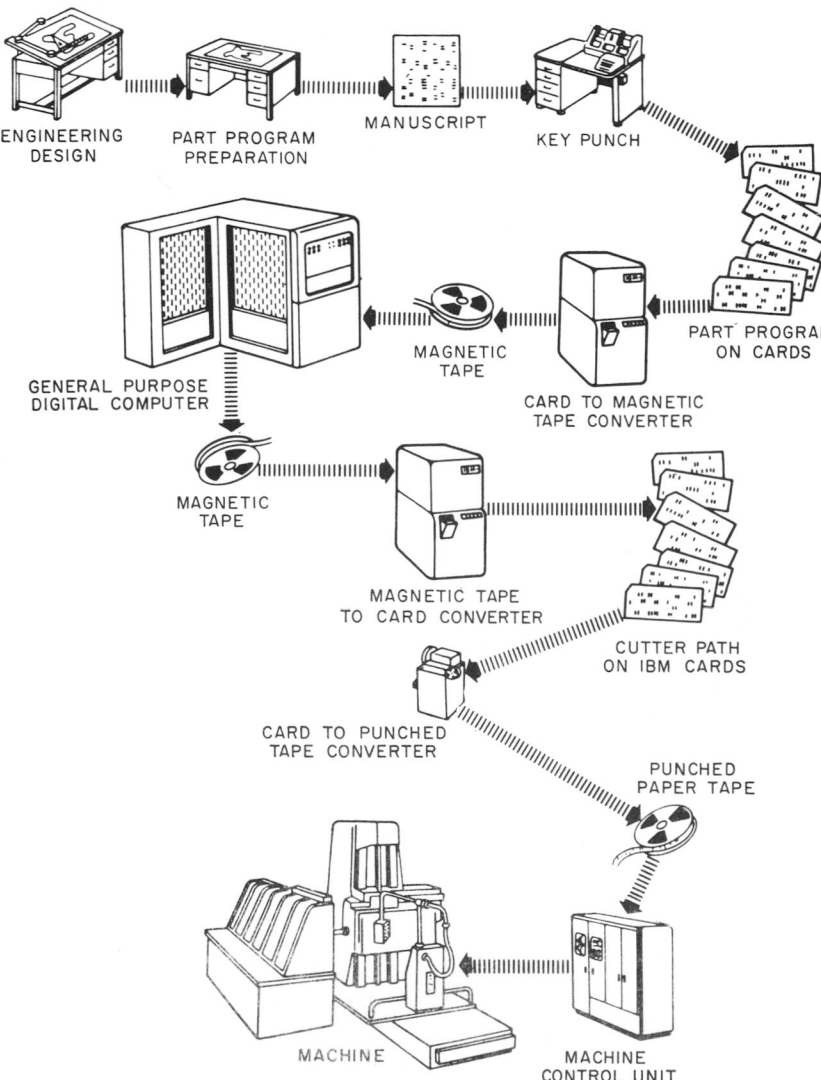

ENGINEERING DESIGN

PART PROGRAM PREPARATION

MANUSCRIPT

KEY PUNCH

PART PROGRAM ON CARDS

GENERAL PURPOSE DIGITAL COMPUTER

MAGNETIC TAPE

CARD TO MAGNETIC TAPE CONVERTER

MAGNETIC TAPE

MAGNETIC TAPE TO CARD CONVERTER

CUTTER PATH ON IBM CARDS

CARD TO PUNCHED TAPE CONVERTER

PUNCHED PAPER TAPE

MACHINE

MACHINE CONTROL UNIT

Fig. 4-15. Sequence of events for contouring work.

An examination of the entire sequence of steps used for point-to-point positioning discloses that a computer is not used. Normally, this is true because most positioning systems are simple enough for any required computations to be handled easily by the desk calculator. This is not the case, however, with contouring machines. Figure 4-15 shows the sequence of steps for contouring work.

In programming or preparing information for continuous-path contouring it is necessary to describe the entire path of the cutting tool within the specified tolerance. To keep the cutter on the prescribed route, thousands of points might be required— hence the need for a computer.

As with any manufactured part, the original source of information is the engineering blueprint. As in point-to-point machining, it would be very helpful to the programmer if the engineering information were in the desired format, namely XY coordinates.

The programmer again prepares a manuscript, except that for contouring work the programmer must use a pseudo-English language, known as APT (Automatically Programmed Tools), instead of the simple descriptions used for programming point-to-point work. The reason for this special language is that most present continuous-path systems describe motions in straight lines. Curves must be broken down into a series of short, straight-line segments. The segments, or chord lengths, must be short enough to allow the cutting tool to remain within specified tolerance requirements. Since the machine control unit must control the path of the center of the cutter, the mathematical description of the part is not sufficient, and the instructions noted on the tape must describe the mathematics of the center path of the cutter. Considering the time required for calculating chord lengths, particularly when taking tolerance and cutter offset into account, it can be realized readily that some sort of automatic data-processing technique is required.

The logical answer is the general-purpose computer. This device has proved extremely helpful in reducing tape-preparation time in the numerical-control field and might be considered as the most significant contribution to the economical operation of continuous-path machines. In order to make use of the high-speed computing attributes of computers it is necessary that the programmer feed information to the computer in a language that the computer will understand. Of equal importance is the necessity of using a simple language that part programmers can understand without years of training, since experience has shown that the best programmers are former machinists who have a background of shop techniques, and who know what speeds and feeds should be used for a particular machining job.

The answer to the problem of a language which a machinist or a computer can understand is APT, which is a special abbreviated form of English. In order for a general-purpose computer to solve specific types of problems, it is necessary for precalculated information, known as programs, to be stored in the computer. As an example, if we wanted to determine the trajectory of an earth satellite, we would be required to feed certain precalculated information, such as formulas for atmospheric influences, into the computer prior to inserting the data for the specific space-flight problem. Similarly, a computer must be primed to accept numerical data describing a particular part to be machined. The APT system consists of a library of pre-programmed routines which is inserted into the computer via a magnetic tape.

The use of APT has replaced many of the conventional numerical data commonly noted on blueprints. In describing a cutting sequence, the abbreviated terms used resemble a verbal description of the operation. If it is required that the cutting tool turn right at a corner on the part, we merely note the abbreviated command "GØ RGT." The symbol Ø is used for the letter O to avoid misinterpretation as a zero. These letters, together with packaged information previously fed into the computer, afford the required instructions for calculating the path of the cutting tool in traveling around the corner of the part. Calculations which would normally require many man-hours of effort are completed in a matter of minutes.

Figure 4-16 illustrates the cutting of a relatively simple two-dimensional part on a profiling-type milling machine.

In place of the conventional part dimensions, specific component characteristics of the part are noted, such as lines, circular arcs, and centers of radii. It is not necessary to calculate most dimensions such as the length of lines, since these will be calculated automatically by the computer. Information required for the computer may be considered in two phases. The first phase describes the geometry of the part and may be noted on the engineering blueprint. The second phase describes the machining instructions; these are normally prepared by the part programmer in the manufacturing department. If the part is described in conventional blue-print dimensions, a conversion into the APT language will be necessary.

Referring again to Fig. 4-16, it will be seen that points, lines, and the circular arc are noted and described in a simple abbreviated form. The Part Description shown below the illustration defines the part characteristics. The "SET PT," which is the starting point of the cutting tool, is noted as having coordinates $x = 1.0$ and $y = 1.0$ in. "PT 1" is defined as a point having coordinates of $x = 1.0$ and $y = 3.0$ in. Line 1 is a line on PT 1 and at an angle of 0° with the horizontal X axis. The circular arc which is noted as "CIR 1" is defined as a circle whose center is "PT 2" and having a radius of 2.0 in. Under Machining Instructions are noted the 1-in. diameter of the cutting tool; the tolerance required, in inches; and the feed rate, in inches per minute. The next instruction specifies turning on the spindle and coolant. The fifth and sixth lines instruct the cutter to go from the "SET PT," in the direction of point 1, to "LINE 1." The eighth line instructs the cutter to make a right turn and go along "LINE 1." "TL RGT" means that the cutting tool is to keep to the right of the part when looking in the direction of travel. The "GØ FWD/CIR 1" and "GØ LFT/LINE 2" mean that the cutter is to continue around the arc and make a left turn along "LINE 2." "GØ PAST/LINE 1" and GØ TØ/SET PT" instructs the cutter to continue along "LINE 2," past the extension of "LINE 1," and then go to the starting point, noted as "SET PT." "ØFF SPIN" and "ØFF KUL" stop the spindle rotation and coolant flow. The notation "END" stops the calculation of the program in the computer and "FINI" designates that the part is completed.

In Figure 4-15 we see that the general-purpose computer has taken the entire machining cycle and broken it down into small segments of time. For each segment of time the computer has calculated the distance that each axis of the machine must travel. The digital magnetic tape, which is the output of the computer, contains all the calculated times and incremental distances.

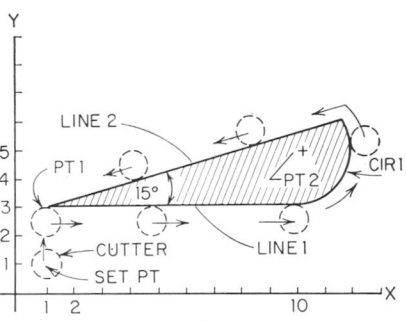

PART DESCRIPTION

```
SET PT = PØINT / 1.0, 1.0
PT 1    = PØINT / 1.0, 3.0
LINE 1  = LINE / PT 1, AT ANGLE O
PT 2    = PØINT / 10.0, 5.0
CIR 1   = CIRCLE / CENTER,
            PT 2, RAD 2.0
LINE 2 = LINE / PT 1,
           AT ANGLE 15
```

MACHINING INSTRUCTIONS

```
CUTTER / 1.0
TØLER / .005
FEDRAT / 20
ØN SPIN, ØN KUL
FRØM / SET PT
IN DIR / PT 1
GØ TØ / LINE 1
TL RGT, GØ RGT / LINE 1
GØ FWD / CIR 1
GØ LFT / LINE 2
GØ PAST / LINE 1
GØ TØ / SET PT
ØFF SPIN, ØFF KUL, END, FINI
```

FIG. 4-16. A simple example of how APT works. In place of the conventional blue-print dimensions, parts are described by part characteristics, such as lines, circles, etc. Next, the machining instructions are described in terms of the characteristics. Calculations required prior to the computer are kept to a minimum. (*Courtesy of Machine & Tool Blue Book Magazine.*)

On most numerical-controlled machines the machine control unit accepts information by means of a punched tape; therefore the magnetic tape must be converted first to punched cards and then to punched tape. On the newer machine tools the magnetic tape can be handled directly by the machine control unit and all the intermediate conversion steps are eliminated.

Now that we have seen the sequence of events leading up to the machining of a part, let us examine the method by which a machine tool carries out the required action.

A drill-press operator is required, according to the blueprint, to drill a hole in a piece of steel plate 10.625 in. to the right of the left edge and 4.256 in. in from the front edge.   He clamps the plate on a positioning table on the drill press and turns a handwheel until the left edge of the plate is located under the spindle center.

Then he turns the handwheel to move the table to the left 10.625 in.   Each full turn of the handwheel is 0.100 in.; hence he turns it 106 full turns and stops at the marking indicating 0.025 in. beyond zero.   Next he locates the front edge of the plate and turns another handwheel to move the table out 4.256 in.   And he is ready to drill.

If the handwheels were replaced by gears having 100 teeth each, so that each tooth was equal to 0.001 in. of travel and a counter was coupled to each gear, the operator would simply zero the counter as each edge was located and then spin the handwheel until the desired dimension appeared on the counter.   But the operator still must observe the counter to know when to stop turning.   He must slow down or overshoot the final thousandth.   He continues to have control responsibility.

Now, let's replace the gears with servomotors.   A servomotor is an electric motor which rotates and aligns itself in response to a distinct signal or command.   The servomotors we have selected have a value of 0.100 in. per revolution.   We attach a common doorbell push button to the servomotor and one push of the button—a discrete signal—turns the motor 1/100 revolution to produce a table movement of 0.001 in.

To move the table 0.010 in., the operator now need only push the button 10 times. However, this system would be less practical than the handwheel if the operator had to push the button 10,625 times for one setting and then 4,256 times for the other dimension.   The point in this theoretical system is that we *now have a control device which can accept numerical values and translate them into physical measurements.*

For a more practical system, we replace this theoretical push-button system with five calibrated dials.   Each dial is divided into ten parts, numbered from zero to nine.   The first dial on the left will provide 90,000 pulses for one full turn—or a total value of 90 in.   To the right of this dial, a second dial will supply 9,000 pulses, or 9 in., in one full turn.   Then we come to an imaginary decimal point.

Decimal fractions are provided by the first dial to the right of the decimal point having a value of 0.900 in. per full turn, followed by a second dial valued at 0.090 in. per full turn and a final dial giving a total range of 0.009 in. divided into increments of 0.001 in. each.   If 0.0001-in. increments are required, a sixth dial can be added.

By setting the left-hand dial to 10 in., the next dial to zero, the dial following the decimal point 0.6, the next dial to the right to 0.02, and the thousandth dial to 0.005 in., the operator releases 10,625 pulses to move the table 10.625 in.

By setting dials to the values called out as numerical symbols on the blueprint, the operator has directed the control to translate these symbols into actual motion of the table for a specific distance.   A second set of dials is used to position the table, and the work, to the 4.256-in. dimension.   Now the hole location has been determined in two dimensions, called X and Y.   A third set of dials could be added to provide the hole depth.   This set provides the vertical, or Z, dimension.

To fully understand the concept, this point is essential: any system that accepts a symbolic numerical value as an input and converts it to a physical value, such as a dimension on the work, as an output, is providing numerical control.   All other elements of the system, such as whether the numbers are put in by punched tape or by push button or by dial, or whether or not the system includes feedback, are secondary functions, not part of the basic concept.

A system does not have to have punched tape, punched cards, or magnetic tape to provide numerical controls.   These devices serve only as information-storage media, as external memories to feed data to the control.

On the other hand, not all preprogrammed machines are numerically controlled. Record-playback systems, in which an operator's procedure in making a "first piece" is recorded on magnetic tape and then is played back to the machine to control manufacture of additional pieces, is not numerical control.   The operator has put in physical movements rather than numerical values.   He has simply used a tape recorder to memorize his motions.

Similarly, machines which are preprogrammed by setting length measures and limit stops or are controlled by tape templets are not *numerically* controlled. In these systems, too, the input data are in physical measurements. (Tape templets, such as are used to control large riveters, have holes physically spaced in the tape in relation to the desired hole location in the work.)

In evaluating control systems, it is important to recognize this distinction. Costs, capability, accuracy, flexibility—all are affected by these differences. Program control is a broad field in which numerical control is only one area, albeit basic and extensive. Program control describes any control system which permits a sequence of two or more functions to be performed automatically according to preset instructions. Thus, except for simple inputs such as the direct dial positioning described earlier, most numerical-control systems provide program control. However, not all program controls are numerical.

Input signals can be electrical, electronic, hydraulic, mechanical, pneumatic, optical, etc. The concept is not limited to any one form. As long as the signal can be applied as a numerical value and converted to a physical value by the system, any energy form may be used.

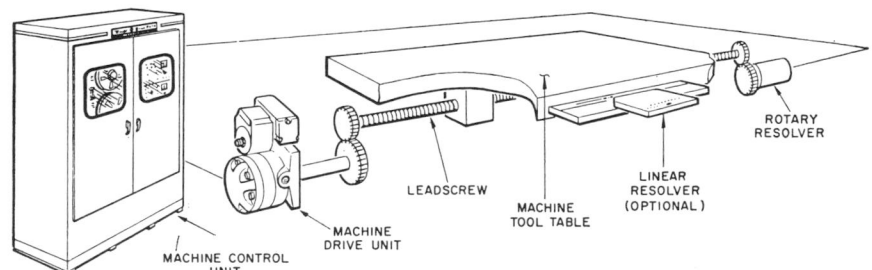

FIG. 4-17. A typical machine control system for one axis. (*Courtesy of Bendix Corporation.*)

Techniques of numerical input, other than the pulse system described earlier, are many and varied. In fact, a method based on comparison is much more common than the system used as an example.

In this method (Fig. 4-17), a signal equal to the desired numerical value is set, by dial or tape, as the input to a comparing device in the machine control unit. A second signal is sent to the comparing device by the object being positioned, in this case the machine-tool table, by means of a transducer such as a rotary or linear resolver. This second signal is proportional to the actual physical position of the table. When the two signals are unequal, the machine control unit causes the machine drive unit to rotate the lead screw, thus changing the position of the machine-tool table. When the physical dimension reached by the table is equal to the numerical value set as an input, the signals are said to "null," or balance, and the table stops.

The second signal previously referred to is known as the "feedback" signal because it feeds back information regarding the actual position of the object being located. Control systems using feedback for self-compensation are called "closed-loop" systems. Without feedback they are termed "open-loop" systems. Feedback is needed in direct proportion to the accuracy and repeatability required of the control system. Generally, feedback is desirable, but it is not always essential.

MACHINE-TOOL CONTROL DEVICES

Numerical control has brought a new family of control devices to the attention of the maintenance technician. These devices have heretofore been used in the computer field and are foreign to most industrial-maintenance people.

The tape reader is the first of these devices which will be discussed here. There are three basic types of tape readers used for numerical control:

1. Mechanical.
2. Photoelectric.
3. Digital magnetic.

The mechanical tape reader (Fig. 4-18) senses the perforations in punched tape by means of five-point star wheels. Spring pressure applied to the star-wheel lever by each pair of movable contacts holds the star wheel lightly against the tape (see A, Fig. 4-19). When a no-hole condition is sensed, the star wheel rides the tape on two of its points, and the movable contact is switched to the upper, normally closed (N/C) position. When a hole is sensed (with the tape moving in either direction), one of the star-wheel points drops through the hole, as shown in B, Fig. 4-19, and the movable contact is switched downward to the normally open (N/C) position. Consequently,

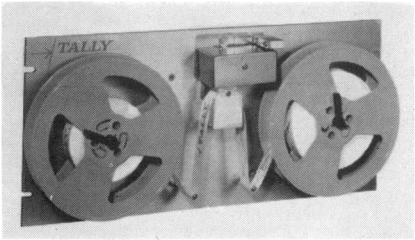

FIG. 4-18. Bi-directional mechanical tape reader. (*Courtesy of Tally Register Corporation.*)

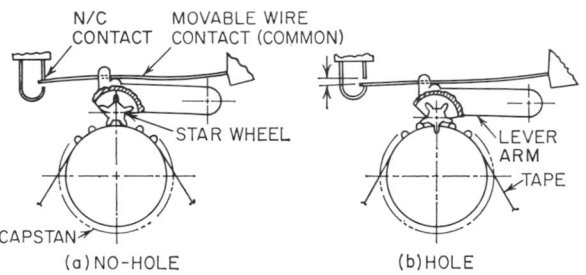

FIG. 4-19. Starwheels reading perforated tape. (*Courtesy of General Electric Company.*)

an electric pulse delivered to the movable contact wire (common) will be conducted to the N/C terminal if a no-hole is sensed or to the N/C terminal if a hole is sensed.

The photoelectric punched-tape reader (Fig. 4-20) is similar in appearance to the mechanical reader. The basic difference is that the star wheels have been replaced by photoelectric cells which sense light or no-light passing through the perforations. This reader is used when faster block-reading times are required. It accommodates tape in the form of a reel, strip, or loop and comes with servo-driven spoolers which will handle 1,000 ft of 1.5-mil Mylar tape. It is provided with automatic or tape-programmed rewind.

The digital magnetic-tape reader (Fig. 4-21) is unlike the previous readers inasmuch as the tape is not perforated. Instead, the plastic tape is coated with an iron oxide. If it were possible to make a visual examination of the magnetic structure of the oxide particles on a piece of demagnetized tape, one would see a very large number of randomly oriented permanent magnets. As the magnetic tape passes under a recording head, all the randomly oriented elementary magnets in the oxide are forced into a different orientation.   This forcing occurs as a result of the unidirectional magnetic field set up by the recording head.   All the elementary magnets within the oxide will align themselves with the external field and will stay in this orientation.   When the magnetic polarity of the recording head is reversed, the oxide magnets will reverse.   Successive reversals of the recording-head polarity cause alternating patterns of oxide magnets.   Upon playback on a machine-tool reader the square waves of flux originally recorded on the

Fig. 4-20. A transistorized photoelectric punched tape reader. (*Courtesy of Digitronics, Inc.*)

Fig. 4-21. A digital magnetic tape reader. (*Courtesy of Kennedy Company.*)

tape (all oxide magnets lined up, alternately in one direction and then the other) produce sharp spikes of voltage.   These voltage spikes are what the control system uses in directing the machine's operation.   Digital magnetic-tape readers have a speed of 1,200 cps, and are compatible with computer tapes, thus eliminating some steps from programming to operation.   These readers also handle the tape by means of cartridges (Fig. 4-22), thereby eliminating manual tape handling since tape threading is replaced by a simple snap-in operation.   Opportunities for tape contamination

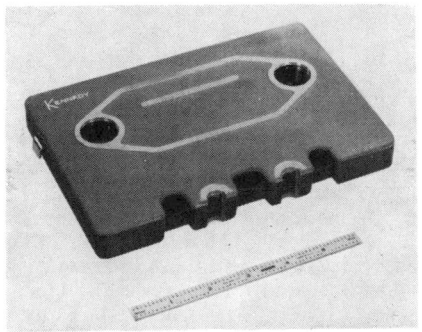

Fig. 4-22. A digital magnetic tape cartridge.   (*Courtesy of Kennedy Company.*)

are greatly diminished, since adverse environments have little effect on the cartridges (Fig. 4-23).

The tape reader tells the control system what to do. The feedback transducer tells the control system the physical location of each particular axis. The simplest form of feedback transducer is the commutator digitizer shown in Fig. 4-24. This device is mechanically coupled to the machine slide being measured. As the slide moves, a

FIG. 4-23. Changing the tape cartridge on a digital magnetic tape reader. (*Courtesy of The Bunker-Ramo Corporation.*)

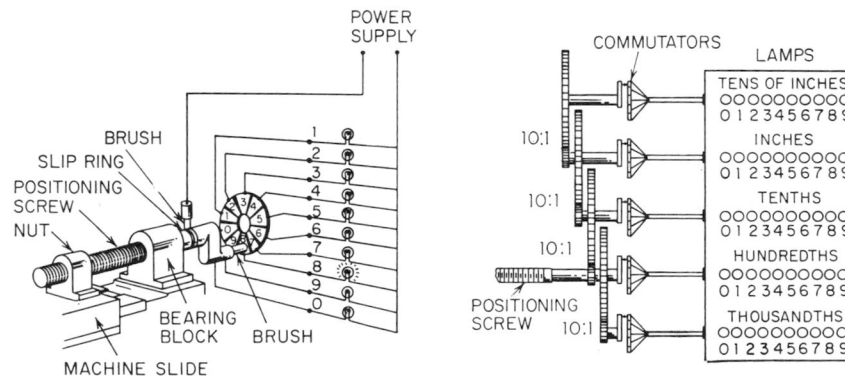

FIG. 4-24. Commutator digitizer is a simple device to translate physical position into a numerical value. (*Courtesy of American Machinist/Metalworking Manufacturing.*)

FIG. 4-25. Gearing commutator digitizers provides measure to any desired fineness. (*Courtesy of American Machinist/Metalworking Manufacturing.*)

rotating brush in the digitizer switches from one commutating segment to another. Obviously, the sensitivity of this device is limited by the number of discrete segments that can be accommodated with one revolution of the rotating brush. To overcome this disadvantage use is made of multiple digitizers, wherein each successive unit is geared to the next unit (Fig. 4-25). With this method any desired fineness can be obtained.

Another type of feedback transducer, and the commonest by far, is the rotary resolver (Fig. 4-26). When rotated, the resolver produces two sinusoidal signals 90° apart in phase. The electronic circuitry in the machine control unit monitors the relative magnitude and phase of each of the resolver signals and thus detects the physical location of the machine member which is geared to the resolver.

The linear resolver shown in Fig. 4-27 is an inductive device with many characteristics of the ordinary two-phase rotary resolver. The basic difference is that the linear resolver does not have to be geared to the moving machine slide and the other part of

FIG. 4-26. The rotary resolver is the position-sensing unit in the servo loop. (*Courtesy of The Bunker-Ramo Corporation.*)

FIG. 4-27. The linear resolver is an inductive device with many of the characteristics of the ordinary two-phase resolver. (*Courtesy of The Bunker-Ramo Corporation.*)

the resolver is fastened to the machine base. As the slide moves, a two-phase voltage is generated. By mounting the stationary portion of the resolver along the entire length of the machine, a very high position accuracy can be achieved.

The machine control unit accepts signals from the tape reader and compares them to signals from the feedback transducer. Although every control system differs in the hardware used in the machine control unit, there are some similarities. All the systems can be characterized by use of modular components. This means that the functional circuitry of the control system is arranged in plug-in printed circuit boards (see Figs. 4-28 and 4-29). Each plug-in board is coded to prevent misplacement when

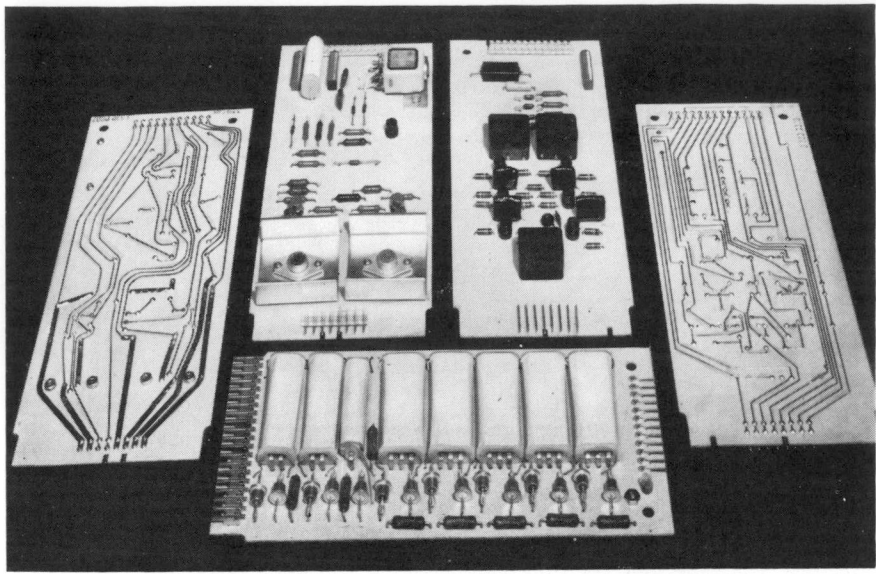

FIG. 4-28.   Typical plug-in printed circuit boards.   (*Courtesy of The Cincinnati Milling Machine Company.*)

FIG. 4-29. A typical control cabinet showing swing-out door containing printed circuit boards.   (*Courtesy of General Electric Company.*)

changing boards, and boards bearing the same identification are interchangeable. Specific details regarding the machine-control-unit circuitry are available from the different manufacturers.

Once the machine control unit has decided that some physical action is required of one of the axes, it is necessary for the machine "muscle" to come into play.   There are

FIG. 4-30. A reversible d-c output solid state power amplifier. *(Courtesy of Norbatro Electronics Corporation.)*

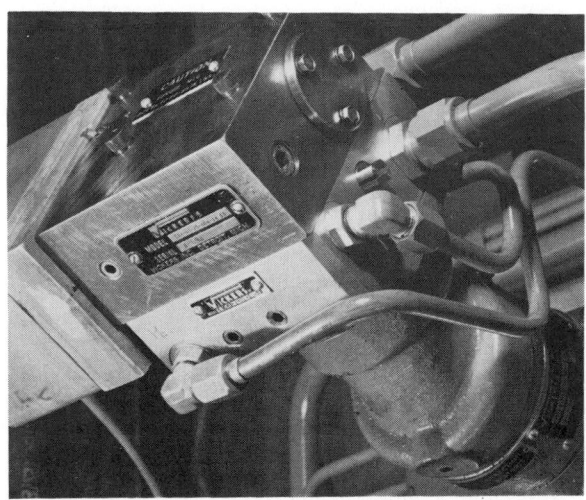

FIG. 4-31. A servo valve integrally mounted on a hydraulic motor.   *(Courtesy of Vickers, Inc.)*

many prime movers in use, including d-c electric motors, two-phase a-c motors, hydraulic motors, and hydraulic cylinders.   Most electric motors are powered by static amplidynes, as shown in Fig. 4-30.   These devices are reversible-output, d-c power amplifiers which respond to milliwatt signals.   They employ magnetic amplifiers providing phase control to fire silicon-controlled rectifiers, achieving fast response, high efficiency, and maximum reliability. Stepless speed control and dynamic braking are inherent features.

Hydraulic motors are controlled by servo valves which control the direction and amount of flow to the fluid motor (see Fig. 4-31 for a typical servo valve integrally fastened to the fluid motor). The primary control unit of the servo valve is a permanent-magnet torque motor. The amount of flow of fluid to the hydraulic motor is directly proportional to the amount of differential current flowing in the torque-motor coil windings. The direction of fluid flow is dependent upon the direction of current unbalance in the coil windings.

THE MAINTENANCE TECHNICIAN

Much has been written about maintenance technicians for numerical-control systems. However, most of it has been written by the manufacturers of the equipment, whose primary function is to sell more equipment. If one were to believe all that has been published on the subject, it would seem that all that is necessary is to take the average maintenance man from the shop, give him a few hours of training along with a set of drawings, and behold—a numerical-control maintenance technician. Unfortunately, such is not the case.

A maintenance technician, in general, should have very special characteristics. Not only must he be technically competent, he must have a natural curiosity about how things work. This curiosity must apply to fields other than his own specialty, because with numerically controlled machines it takes a multiinterested viewpoint to determine whether the trouble is a bad amplifier, a sticky servo valve, or just tight gibs. The technician must also be a diplomat and know how to keep peace with the production department while he is trying to locate a troublesome diode. Lastly, he must not tire of doing the same thing over and over again, because the very nature of the maintenance function is to keep the same machines running day after day—a repetitious chore but a challenge nevertheless. In short, today's numerical-control maintenance technician must possess a combination of skills not usually available in the inventory of average maintenance personnel.

Experience has shown that the numerical-control technician should have an electrical/electronic background, since it is far easier to teach an electrician the mechanical and hydraulic aspects of a machine than to teach a mechanic how electricity works. With an electrical/electronic background as the basic criterion, two sources of manpower are:

1. Television-repair technicians.
2. Electrical-maintenance men.

Falling back on experience again, we have found that most TV repair men do not make good industrial-maintenance technicians. They can repair a specialized piece of electronic equipment satisfactorily, but they have difficulty in comprehending the multitude of overlapping problems that occur with numerically controlled equipment. Electrical-maintenance people seem to possess that special "inner sense" which is so necessary for adequate maintenance of complex equipment.

In addition to maintenance technicians, some larger industrial plants are employing graduate electrical engineers who have specialized in industrial electronics. We are tempted to say that these engineers are used as trouble shooters. However, the maintenance technician prefers to consider himself as doing the "trouble shooting"; therefore let us say that the engineers are maintenance "diagnosticians." When troubles crop up in the more complex equipment and the technician cannot locate the source after a reasonable time, the engineer is called in. Being more thoroughly trained, primarily because he is more capable of being trained, the engineer is more likely to locate the unobvious trouble. These engineers do not replace the technicians, but they do complement them. It should be pointed out that graduate engineers (salaried employees) can be used only when the local craft unions are cooperative and realize that their people alone cannot handle all the problems.

Up until now we have discussed "in-house" maintenance personnel. Large companies can afford specialized technicians and graduate engineers, but what about the small manufacturing concern that uses only a few machines? First of all, the small company would be fooling itself if it were to think that its "handyman" maintenance man could take care of the trouble that can occur with numerical-control equipment. With few exceptions, all the training in the world will not help the man whose background is changing light bulbs or solenoid valve coils and who checks circuit continuities with two moistened fingers of his right hand. These men, capable as they may seem in the work they are doing, just can't handle complex equipment. Furthermore, the same man is usually responsible for all sorts of maintenance problems and, as a result, he doesn't have enough time to concentrate on the maintenance of his numerically controlled equipment. Continuous self-education, continuous surveillance of the equipment, and continuous contact with the equipment are necessary for its care.

For the small plant there are two other sources of outside maintenance assistance. First, there is the equipment manufacturer's factory-trained service man, and second, there is the contract maintenance house, which, for a price, will maintain anything.

The factory man is the better choice if he is available when your machine is in trouble. Unfortunately, he must cover a lot of territory and service many machines. If he is tied up at one plant on a particularly complex problem, your machine will just have to wait. If there is more than one factory man in your area, the problem is not much better because the chances are that there are just that many more machines to be kept running. The advantage of the factory man is that he is exceptionally trained and experienced with your particular machine and is more likely to find the trouble rapidly.

The contract maintenance house can usually offer faster service. In most cases firms of this sort are composed of former factory men who have decided to go into business for themselves. The disadvantage is that they are probably not so well trained on all systems as they profess to be. A man who has spent years working for company "Z" would no doubt have trouble diagnosing troubles on a machine built by company "X." In all fairness to these firms, however, there are isolated instances of well-trained men who are available at reasonable contract prices. The small manufacturer intending to use this source of maintenance would do well to examine the situation very carefully before signing any contract.

TRAINING THE NUMERICAL-CONTROL TECHNICIAN

The numerical-control maintenance technician must have a complete knowledge of mechanics, hydraulics, electrical circuits, and electronic circuits. In addition to this generalized knowledge, the technician must have detailed knowledge of the specific control systems which he must maintain. This knowledge, both general and specific, can be acquired through training and experience.

Table 4-1 outlines a general training course to acquaint an above-average electrical maintenance man with the fundamentals of hydraulic/mechanical maintenance practices and procedures. The course is designed to be presented in 45 hr of classroom instruction and is intended to give more knowledge of the different components used in hydraulic systems, their functions, and how they fit into the over-all machine system.

Table 4-2 presents the suggested outline of a course in basic a-c and d-c electrical theory. This course, which is presented in 25 sessions of $2\frac{1}{2}$ hr each, develops the fundamental principles governing the performance of d-c and a-c equipment and provides a complete background to enable the technician to continue study in electronics.

Table 4-3 outlines a 62-hr training course in basic electronics, including untuned and tuned circuits, reactance, impedance, resonance, vacuum-tube theory, semiconductor theory, basic circuits, circuit analysis, and trouble shooting.

The training courses outlined in these tables cover the *generalized* knowledge which the numerical-control maintenance technician must have if he is to do a good job of keeping the machines running. Larger companies should have no difficulty in providing these courses with their existing training department staffs. For smaller companies, union-company sponsored courses at local trade schools or junior colleges may

Table 4-1. Session Outline for Training Course in Basic Hydraulics*

Session I.   Hydraulic Pumps, 2 hr
  Types, operation, and application
  1. Pump introduction
  2. Centrifugal pump (volute)
  3. Centrifugal pump (diffuser)
  4. Propeller pump (axial)
  5. Gear pump (rotary)
  6. Gear pump (gerotor)
  7. Lobe pump (rotary)
Session II.   Hydraulic Pumps (*cont.*), 2 hr
  Types, operation, and application
  1. Vane pump (unbalanced)
  2. Vane pump (balanced)
  3. Vane pump (double)
  4. Vane pump (two-stage)
  5. Vane pump (combination)
Session III.   Hydraulic Pumps (*cont.*), 2 hr
  Types, operation, and application
  1. Piston pump (radial)
  2. Piston pump (axial)
  3. Reciprocating pump
Session IV.   Hydraulic Pumps (*cont.*), 2 hr
  Review and test
Session V.   Hydraulic Pumps (*cont.*), 2 hr
  Maintenance and repair
  1. Alignment and mounting
  2. Filters and strainers (pump inlet)
  3. Cavitation and noise
  4. Repair and assembly
  5. Use of abrasives
Session VI.   Hydraulic Valves, 2 hr
  Types, operation, and application of pressure-controlling valves
  1. Valve introduction
  2. Relief valve (simple)
  3. Relief valve (compound-balanced piston)
  4. Pressure-reducing valve
  5. Sequence valve
  6. Pressure switch
Session VII.   Hydraulic Valves (*cont.*), 2 hr
  Types, operation, and application of directional-controlling valves
  1. Check valve (poppet)
  2. Prefill check valve (surge)
  3. Foot valve (compound check)
  4. Spool valve (rotary)
  5. Spool valve (sliding)
  6. Four-way valve
  7. Servo valve
Session VIII.   Hydraulic Valves (*cont.*), 2 hr
  Types, operation, and application of volume-controlling valves
  1. Flow-control valve (pressure-compensated)
  2. Control panels
  3. Tracing valves
Session IX.   Hydraulic Valves (*cont.*), 2 hr
  A. Maintenance and repair
    1. Repair and assembly
    2. Causes of malfunction
    3. Fits (tolerances)
  B. Review and test
Session X.   Power Lines, 2 hr
  A. Types of power lines
    1. Pipe
    2. Tubing
    3. Flexible hose

* Courtesy North American Aviation, Inc., Los Angeles Division, Training Department.

Table 4-1. Session Outline for Training Course in Basic Hydraulics (*Continued*)

   B. Application and maintenance of power lines
     1. Size
     2. Wall thickness
     3. Proper bends
   C. Application and maintenance of fittings
     1. Flange fittings (tube and pipe)
     2. Flare fittings (tube)
     3. Flareless fittings (tube)
     4. Hose fittings (pressed-on and reusable)
Session XI.   Power Lines (*cont.*), 2 hr
   A. Joints, couplings, and restrictors
     1. Joints (swivel)
     2. Joints (rotating)
     3. Couplings (self-sealing)
     4. Couplings (quick-disconnect)
     5. Maintenance and repair
     6. Restrictors, orifices, and snubbers
   B. Review and test
Session XII.   Energy and Force Producers, 2 hr
   A. Cylinders, operation and maintenance
     1. Cylinders (single-acting and double-acting)
     2. Cylinder (rotating)
     3. Cylinder (unbalanced and balanced)
   B. Hydraulic motors, operation and maintenance
     1. Gear motor (rotary)
     2. Vane motor (rotary)
     3. Piston motor (rotary)
   C. Intensifiers, operation and maintenance
Session XIII.   Energy and Force Producers (*cont.*), 2 hr
   Review and test
Session XIV.   Packing and Seals, 2 hr
   A. Types, application, and installation
     1. Static and dynamic seals
     2. O rings
     3. Quad rings
     4. V packing
     5. Cup packing
     6. U-cup packing
     7. U packing
     8. Flange packing
     9. Press-in seals (retainers)
     10. Rings (automotive)
   B. JIC packing standards
   C. Packing-replacement methods
Session XV.   Hydraulic Fluids, 2 hr
   A. Types of hydraulic fluids
     1. Hydraulic oil
     2. Nonflammable fluid
   B. Proper use and effects of hydraulic fluids
     1. Heat
     2. Acids
     3. Cleaning and flushing
     4. Checks and handling
Session XVI.   Heat Exchangers, 2 hr
   Types, operation, and application
   1. Single-pass types
   2. Two- and four-pass types
   3. Proper use
   4. Maintenance and repair
Session XVII.   Reservoirs, Strainers, and Filters, 1 hr
   A. Types, operation, and application of reservoirs
     1. Proper Design
     2. Mounting

Table 4-1. Session Outline for Training Course in Basic Hydraulics (*Continued*)

B. Types, operation, and application of strainers and filters
   1. Sump type (immersion)
   2. Line type
   3. Full flow
   4. Proportional
Session XVIII.   Accumulators, 2 hr
  A. Types, operation, and application of accumulators
   1. Dead-weight
   2. Spring-loaded
   3. Bladder
   4. Diaphragm
   5. Piston (free-float)
   6. Free-surface
   7. Maintenance and repair
  B. Test on Sessions XIV to XVIII
Session XIX.   Schematics and Symbols, 2 hr
  A. JIC hydraulic standards
   1. JIC symbols
   2. JIC fluid code
  B. Hydraulic schematics
   1. Purpose
   2. How to read
Session XX.   Hydraulic System, 2 hr
  Building a Hydraulic System
  1. What is needed and why
  2. Making a schematic
  3. Trouble shooting a system
  4. Synchronizing rams
Session XXI.   Bearings, 2 hr
  Maintenance and use of bearings
  1. Installation
  2. Handling
  3. Lubrication
  4. Types
Session XXII.   Gages, Couplings, and Precision Instruments, 2 hr
  A. Miscellaneous components (1 hr)
   1. Gages
    a. Types
    b. Proper use
    c. Protection of
   2. Couplings (drive)
    a. Types
    b. Installation
    c. Maintenance
  B. Precision instruments (1 hr)
   1. Micrometers (inside and outside)
   2. Vernier-scale instruments
   3. Dial indicators
Session XXIII.   General Review and Final Test, 2 hr

Table 4-2. Session Outline for Training Course in Basic Electricity*

Session I. D-C Theory
  1. Composition of matter
  2. Electron theory
  3. Types of electricity
  4. Electron flow
  5. Insulation
  6. Conduction
Session II.   Electrical Terms
  1. Resistance
  2. Voltage

* Courtesy North American Aviation, Inc., Los Angeles Division, Training Department.

Table 4-2. Session Outline for Training Course in Basic Electricity (*Continued*)

    3. Amperage (coulomb)
    4. Power (watts)
    5. Electrical symbols
    6. Principles of circuit drawings
Session III.   Batteries
    1. Basic chemistry
    2. Voltaic cell
    3. Dry cell
    4. Lead-acid battery
    5. Other types
    6. Use of batteries
    7. Care of batteries
    8. Caution in handling
    9. Connection in series
   10. Connection in parallel
Session IV.   Conversions and Resistor-color Code
    1. Conversions
    2. Metric conversion
    3. Powers of 10-principles and use
    4. Resistors—types
    5. Resistor-color coding and tolerance
Session V.   Ohm's Law
    1. Relationship
    2. Statement of Ohm's law
    3. Equations
Session VI.   Series and Parallel Circuits
    1. Series resistance
    2. Formula (series) and problems
    3. Parallel resistance
    4. Formulas (parallel) and problems
Session VII.   Combined Series and Parallel Circuits
    1. Voltage drops
    2. Series-parallel combinations
    3. Kirchhoff's laws
    4. Equivalent series circuit
    5. Problems
Session VIII.   Power
    1. Relationship and definition
    2. Equations
    3. Problems (combined Ohm's law and power)
Session IX.   Magnetism
    1. Magnetic theory and terms
    2. Magnetic measurement
    3. Ohm's law equivalent for magnetic circuits
    4. Electromagnetism
    5. Construction of an electromagnet
    6. Left-hand polarity rule
    7. Left-hand rule for lines of flux
Session X.   D-C Generators and Induced Electromotive Force
    1. Electromagnetic induction by moving conductor
    2. Left-hand generator rule
    3. Electromagnetic induction by moving magnetic field
    4. Determining magnitude
    5. Comparison of generators and motors
    6. Component parts in a generator
    7. Operation of a generator
    8. D-c generator voltage control
    9. Carbon-pile voltage-regulator control circuit
   10. Types of generators (series) (shunt, compound)
Session XI.   D-C Electric Motors
    1. Purpose and types
    2. Operation of component parts
    3. Operation of motor
    4. Determining direction of motor rotation

Table 4-2. Session Outline for Training Course in Basic Electricity (*Continued*)

5. Torque in a motor
6. Shunt-wound motor
7. Shunt-wound motor (speed control)
8. Series-wound motor
9. Compound motor
10. Reversible motor
11. Motor-control principles
12. Counter emf (in motors and generators)
13. Dynamotor

Session XII.   Thermocouples, Switches, Relays, and Solenoids
1. Definition, theory, and construction of thermocouples
2. Typical uses and circuits
3. Thermal switches
4. Purposes of switches
5. Types of switches
6. Construction
7. Purpose of relays
8. Construction
9. Contact symbols
10. Types
11. Solenoids
12. Uses and circuits involving relays

Session XIII.   A-C Theory
1. Principles
2. A-c cycle
3. Sine wave—plotting and generation
4. Alternating frequency
5. Advantages of alternating current
6. Producing voltage
7. Peak (maximum) value
8. Average value
9. Effective or root-mean-square value

Session XIV.   Vectors
1. Quantities
2. Addition and subtraction
3. Addition of vector quantities
4. Pythagorean theory
5. Square-root problems

Session XV.   Inductance and Inductive Reactance
1. Explanation and definition
2. Electrical effect of an inductor (definition of counter emf)
3. Measurement
4. Changing values
5. Symbols
6. Plotting voltage and current-phase angle
7. Inductors in series
8. Inductors in parallel
9. Inductive reactance
10. Calculating inductive reactance (formula and problems)
11. Impedance
12. Series RL circuits (voltage drops)
13. Parallel circuits (current)
14. Formulas and problems

Session XVI.   Capacitance and Capacitive Reactance
1. Basic construction
2. Explanation, definition, and operation
3. General types and characteristics
4. Values and measurement—plotting and phase angle
5. Capacitive reactance
6. Calculating capacitance reactance (formula and problems)
7. Impedance
8. Series RC circuits (voltage drops)
9. Parallel RC circuits (current)
10. Formulas and problems

Table 4-2. Session Outline for Training Course in Basic Electricity (*Continued*)

Session XVII. Impedance, Resonance, and Time Constants
   1. Series LCR circuits
   2. Parallel LC circuits
   3. Series resonance
   4. Parallel resonance
   5. Circuit Q
   6. Bandpass
   7. Resonant circuits as filters
   8. L/R time constants
   9. RC time constants
  10. Formulas and problems
Session XVIII. Transformers and Selenium Rectifiers
   1. Definition, construction, and operation
   2. Types of transformers
   3. Efficiency (hysteresis, saturation, eddy currents, etc.)
   4. Selenium rectifiers
   5. Construction
   6. Operation
   7. Use in power supplies with filters
   8. Half-wave rectification
   9. Full-wave rectification
Session XIX. A-C Generators or Alternators
   1. Comparison of a-c and d-c generators
   2. Lenz's law
   3. Kva
   4. Types of alternators
   5. Voltage control on alternators
   6. Three-phase generation
   7. Y connection
   8. Delta connection
   9. A-c power factor
  10. A-c distribution in aircraft power system
Session XX. A-C Motors
   1. Rotating magnetic field
   2. A-c polyphase motors
   3. Principle of induction motor
   4. Squirrel-cage motor
   5. Slip
   6. Single-phase induction motors
   7. Shaded pole
   8. Split phase
   9. Capacitor start
  10. Repulsion-induction
  11. Repulsion start, induction run
  12. Universal
Session XXI. A-C Synchronous Motors and Inverters
   1. Principles of synchronous motors
   2. Value and use of synchronous motors
   3. Power-factor correction
   4. Inverters—definition
   5. Construction
   6. Operation
Session XXII. Electrical Trouble Shooting
   1. Types of troubles (open, shorts, grounds, etc.)
   2. Test equipment to locate trouble
   3. Servicing techniques
   4. Short, continuity, and voltage test lights
Session XXIII. Meters
   1. Types of meter movements
   2. Moving—iron meters
   3. Moving—coil meters
   4. Dynamometer
   5. Hot-wire ammeter
   6. Thermocouple meter

Table 4-2. Session Outline for Training Course in Basic Electricity (*Continued*)

   7. Multimeters
   8. D-c voltmeter (multirange)
   9. D-c ammeters (multirange)
  10. A-c voltmeter
  11. A-c ammeter
Session XXIV. Ohmmeters
   1. Series ohmmeter
   2. Shunt ohmmeter
   3. Megger
   4. Wheatstone bridge
   5. Slide wire
   6. Hypot
Session XXV. Multimeter
   1. Simpson No. 260
   2. Care and use of test equipment
   3. Safety
   4. Examination—final

Table 4-3. Session Outline for Training Course in Basic Electronics*

Session I. Introduction
   1. Meaning of electronics
   2. Electrical equipment
   3. Parts used in electronic equipment
   4. Types of conduction
   5. Review of Ohm's law, Kirchhoff's law
Session II. Resonance
   1. Inductance
   2. Capacitance
   3. Reactance, impedance
   4. Series- and parallel-resonant defined
Session III. Resonance (*cont.*)
   1. Q factor
   2. How to determine series- and parallel-resonant circuit
   3. Load matching
Session IV. Vacuum Tubes
   1. Type of vacuum tubes
   2. Cathode construction
   3. Classification
Session V. Vacuum Tubes (*cont.*)
   1. Action of vacuum tubes
Session VI. Gaseous Tubes
   1. Types of gas-filled tubes
   2. Operation
Session VII. Gaseous Tubes (*cont.*)
   1. How the thyratron works
   2. How the ignitron works
Session VIII. Tubes as Rectifiers—Vacuum
   1. Theory
   2. Application
Session IX. Voltage Regulation
   1. Theory
   2. Application
Session X. Tube as an Amplifier
   1. Electric characteristics
   2. Voltage amplifier
   3. Power amplifier
Session XI. Tube as an Oscillator
   1. Theory
   2. Types
   3. Application

* Courtesy North American Aviation, Inc., Los Angeles Division, Training Department.

Table 4-3. Session Outline for Training Course in Basic Electronics (*Continued*)

Session XII.   Time-delay Action
  1. D-c time-delay relay
    a. Speed of capacitor discharge
    b. Time constant
    c. Time-delay calculation
  2. A-c time-delay relay
    a. General-purpose timer
    b. Circuit action
    c. Circuit problem
Session XIII.   Simple Welding Control
  1. Ignition contactor
    a. Resistance welding and controls
    b. Ignition-tube ratings
    c. Per cent of duty
    d. Load calculations
Session XIV.   Light and Heat Relays
  1. Photoelectric relay
  2. Room-lighting relay
  3. Heating and light-dimming controls
Session XV.   Automatic Tube Control of D-C Motors
  1. Armature and field-voltage control
  2. Preventing overload
  3. Current-limit control
Session XVI.   Servomechanisms—Closed-loop System
  1. Regulators and servos
  2. Time constant
  3. Position-control servos
Session XVII.   Synchro Systems
  1. Theory
  2. Types
Session XVIII.   Meters
  1. D-c meters
  2. A-c meters
  3. Vacuum-tube voltmeter
Session XIX.   Cathode-ray Oscilloscope
  1. Theory of operation
  2. Uses
Session XX.   Stroboscope, Megger
Session XXI.   Register Controls
  1. Control of printed paper
  2. High speed web-register control
  3. Side register control
Session XXII.   Induction and Dielectric Heating
  1. Induction heating
    a. Purpose
    b. Principles of operation
  2. Dielectric heating
    a Purpose
    b. Principles of operation
Session XXIII.   Field and Bench Test of Electronic Parts
  1. When tests are required
  2. Fixed resistors, variable resistors
  3. Condensers
  4. Power transformers, chokes
Session XXIV.   Transistors
  1. Theory
  2. Uses in circuits
  3. Simple amplifier circuit
  4. Switching circuits
Session XXV.   Circuit Analysis and Trouble Shooting

be the answer.   If there is enough interest, most educational institutions will cooperate in setting up the required training courses.   This interest must be created jointly by the trade union and the company.   The union must take a leading step in encouraging its members to enroll in these courses if its members are to remain economically desirable.   The companies must agree to share the expenses, which may include time off from work to attend the courses.   The technicians, themselves, must give some of their own time if they are not to become technically obsolete.

In many cases, larger companies are willing to present these courses for the benefit of their subcontractors and suppliers at nominal charges.

Specialized training courses for specific control systems are available from all the major manufacturers.   Usually there is no charge for the courses, which are held at the manufacturers' plants, and all attenders are expected to pay their own living and transportation expenses.   These courses usually take a minimum of 1 week and may last as long as 2 weeks.   At the completion of the course, a report is available for each employer regarding the success of each participant the employer has sent.   It has been the practice of many large companies to send representatives of the respective training departments to these courses as well as supervisors and foremen from the maintenance departments.   This is done so that training courses can be established at the user's plant which cover the same material that the manufacturer has presented at his course.   It should be pointed out, if it is not already common knowledge, that although similarities exist between the various control systems, there is enough difference to require separate training courses.   All the specialized training courses should include detailed coverage of the following:

1. Factual knowledge of the equipment, i.e., its capabilities, limitations, and the expected performance.
2. Explanation and demonstration of alignment and adjustments of the equipment.
3. Coverage of *how* the system works, not why.   Coverage of control and interlock circuitry to enable the maintenance personnel to operate the equipment unaided.
4. Study of preventive-maintenance procedures.
5. Study of equipment blueprints and procedures of maintenance peculiar to the specific equipment.
6. Explanation of likely problems which may arise in the equipment.

Adequate training is the key to successful maintenance of numerically controlled equipment and should not be passed over lightly.

TEST EQUIPMENT

A well-qualified technician with the best of training cannot maintain numerically controlled equipment without adequate test equipment.   A simple "wiggy" or test light is not enough.   Instead, more complex and more specialized testing devices are required.

For the purposes of this discussion, there are four classes of test equipment:

1. Built-in test equipment.
2. General-purpose test equipment.
3. Test consoles.
4. "Homemade" test equipment.

Built-in test equipment includes equipment provided by the control manufacturer as an integral part of the machine controls.   Figure 4-32 shows a test panel just below the tape reader.   One of the test operations provided on this panel is power-supply monitoring.   Since most numerical control systems utilize various power supplies, it would be most time-consuming and inefficient for the maintenance technician to have to make a separate connection with a portable voltmeter for each power supply he wishes to check out.   Instead, all the power supplies are connected to a single selector switch, which is permanently connected to a voltmeter.   To check out the various voltages it is necessary only to flip the selector switch from one position to another and observe the meter. Meter-range changing for the various magnitudes encountered is accomplished automatically by the selector switch. Some control panels also incorporate a pair of test jacks in parallel with the meter so that the power-supply output waveshapes can be observed on an oscilloscope. This is important when it is suspected that the filter network may have gone bad.

Figure 4-33 shows another built-in test panel. In addition to the power-supply monitor previously described, this test panel provides a marginal-test feature which enables the maintenance technician to locate marginal components before they actually fail. This is accomplished by operating all the circuit modules under a test routine while the power-supply voltage is decreased below its normal operating point.

Fig. 4-32. Machine control unit with tape reader, test panel, and plug-in circuit modules. (*Courtesy of The Cincinnati Milling Machine Company.*)

The theory is that under weakened power-supply conditions, marginal components will begin to fail. The marginal components, once located, can be replaced before they have a chance to fail during a production run of the machine.

In addition to the equipment previously described, built-in test equipment can include test lights, test jacks, or test meters. In short, any built-in device which will allow the maintenance technician to locate and fix problems rapidly will be appreciated. The exact nature of the built-in test equipment is dictated by the complexity of the numerical-control system which must be maintained.

Two pieces of general-purpose test equipment are usually considered to be indispensable for the maintenance of numerically controlled equipment. The first is a volt-ohm-milliammeter, as shown in Fig. 4-34. This is a relatively inexpensive instrument (under $50), which can be carried easily from one machine to another. It can be used for checking continuity as well as ohms, volts, and milliamperes.

FIG. 4-33. Portion of a machine control unit showing operational test panel.   (*Courtesy of Bendix Corporation.*)

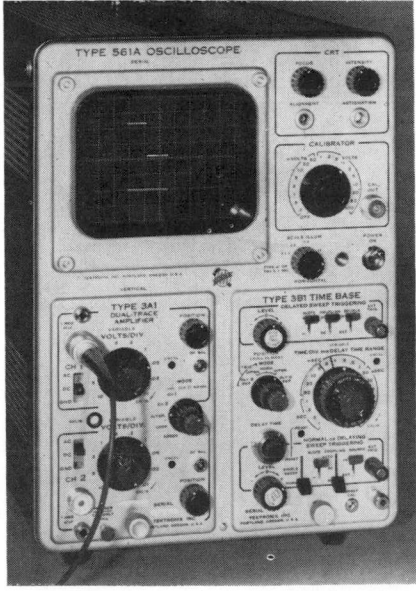

FIG. 4-34. A typical volt-ohm-milliammeter. (*Courtesy of Simpson Electric Company.*)

FIG. 4-35. A typical oscilloscope for maintaining numerical control systems.   (*Courtesy of Tektronix, Inc.*)

The second indispensable instrument is the oscilloscope. A typical "scope" is shown in Fig. 4-35. It features dual trace and triggered sweep operation and its cost is in the neighborhood of $1,000. Since this instrument is rather large and bulky, it is strongly suggested that a portable test stand be used for moving the instrument into the best possible viewing position for the maintenance technician. Figure 4-36 illustrates an oscilloscope on a test stand being used for the checkout of a piece of numerically controlled equipment.

In addition to the two indispensable instruments, various other general-purpose test instruments make life easier for the technician. These include the recording oscillograph, vacuum-tube voltmeter, pulse counter, and function generator.

FIG. 4-36. Checking a numerical control system with an oscilloscope on a portable stand. (*Courtesy of North American Aviation, L.A. Div.*)

In most cases the built-in test equipment and the general-purpose test equipment will allow the maintenance technician to isolate a faulty plug-in module. In this case, the defective module is replaced with a spare module, and the machine is back in operation. The faulty modules can be returned to the control-system manufacturer, where they will be replaced or repaired at a nominal charge. Large companies which have numerous numerically controlled machines may prefer to repair the modules themselves. In this case it becomes necessary to have a means of checking each individual plug-in module. Figures 4-37 and 4-38 show maintenance consoles which provide the means to set up typical operating conditions for each plug-in unit. This functional checking of each unit permits isolation of faulty components within the plug-in module. Complete verification of proper operation may be accomplished before the module is returned to use.

Maintenance consoles, which range in price from $5,000 to $10,000, can also be used for checking plug-in modules which are suspected of being faulty, even though the

built-in test equipment and the general-purpose instrumentation have not clearly indi⁻
cated that they are faulty.

The last class of test equipment to be discussed here depends upon the initiative and
imagination of the individual technicians, coupled with a foresighted management
policy regarding numerical-control-equipment maintenance. "Homemade" test
equipment will usually produce exceptional results because it is designed and built by

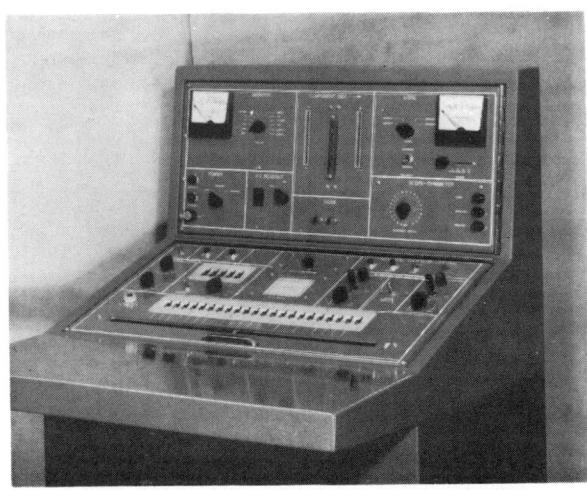

Fig. 4-37. Maintenance console for checking plug-in circuit modules.   (*Courtesy of Bendix
Corporation.*)

Fig. 4-38. Maintenance console for checking power supplies, servo amplifiers, and plug-in
circuit modules.   (*Courtesy of The Bunker-Ramo Corporation.*)

the men who need it, the maintenance technicians.   They have been faced with the
problem and have evolved the answer to it.

Although homemade test equipment for one plant may not solve another plant's
problems, it is worth while discussing some homemade equipment in the hope that
maintenance technicians who are referring to this handbook will be stimulated to build
their own test equipment.   Any technician who builds test equipment will learn more
about the equipment to be maintained than he will learn from attending 10 sessions of
the training school.

FIG. 4-39. Hydraulic component analyzer and test bench. (*Courtesy of Boeing Company, Aero-Space Div.*)

FIG. 4-40. Plug-in circuit board tester. (*Courtesy of Time-Trol, Inc.*)

Figure 4-39 shows a hydraulic component analyzer which includes a servo-valve driving system and differential pressure transducers. Its combined functions resolve servo-valve response and hydraulic-motor condition. This piece of equipment is large and costly because the very nature of the devices being tested requires a hydraulic reservoir along with the associated pumps, valves, and gages. This equipment would be suggested only for very large plants with many machines.

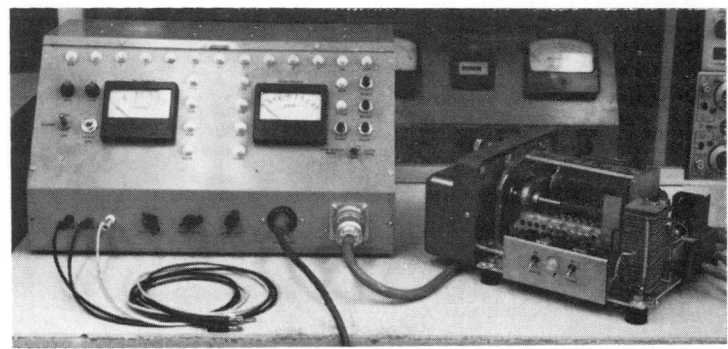

FIG. 4-41. Tape reader analyzer.   (*Courtesy of Boeing Company, Aero-Space Div.*)

FIG. 4-42. D-c amplifier balance checker.   (*Courtesy of North American Aviation, L.A. Div.*)

Figure 4-40 shows a plug-in circuit-board tester which can accomplish almost th^e same testing as the maintenance consoles at a fraction of the cost. The basic difference is that the smaller unit requires each test to be set up with patch cords, whereas the large units have the test automatically programmed.

Figure 4-41 illustrates a tape-reader analyzer which simulates the "read-in" and "reader-control logic" of a machine-control unit. The tape-perforation-sensing and cam-timing sections of the reader are easily checked, allowing repair and/or adjustment.

D-c amplifiers have a tendency to drift. Figure 4-42 shows a homemade test device which can be plugged into a machine and which will automatically check the balance of all the d-c amplifiers. If any amplifiers are out of balance far enough to cause trouble, the tester stops and indicates the troublesome unit, so that the maintenance technician can make the necessary adjustments.

Figure 4-43 illustrates a vibration analyzer which includes both vertical and horizontal accelerometers. These devices can be attached to the machine and will allow oscillograph or oscilloscope presentations of the machine-tool roughness. This test device can detect dull cutting tools or defective bearings.

FIG. 4-43. Vibration analyzer with recording oscillograph. (*Courtesy of Boeing Company, Aero-Space Div.*)

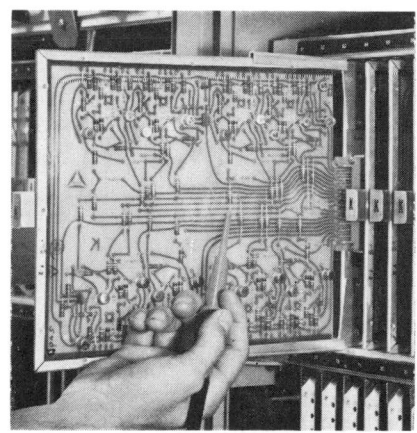

FIG. 4-44. Plug-in circuit board modules can be easily checked with a circuit board extender which allows access to both sides of the board. (*Courtesy of The Bunker-Ramo Corporation.*)

Figure 4-44 shows a very inexpensive device which can save hours of work in detecting a defective component. It is a circuit-board extender which allows accessibility to both sides of a circuit board while it is connected to the machine control unit. In other words, it is a device for allowing in-place testing.

All the test equipment described in this section is intended to make the job easier for the technician. The easier his job is, the faster he can find and fix the troubles. Obviously, the faster he gets the machine back into production, the more money the machine can make.

PREVENTIVE MAINTENANCE[1]

So far as standard machines and equipment are concerned a preventive-maintenance program "would be nice if there is time to carry it out and if it doesn't cost too much." With numerically controlled equipment, preventive maintenance is absolutely necessary!

Since the initial cost of numerically controlled machines is quite high, the machine must be kept producing if it is going to pay for itself, let alone make a profit. Not many breakdowns can be fixed in a few minutes. For example, a shorted transistor, a minor problem in itself, can require hours of trouble shooting before it is located. In other cases transient problems may occur. These are difficulties which occur at random with no apparent rhyme or reason. They may plague a machine for days or weeks before the technician stumbles upon the answer. In other words, there are few minor problems. When a major breakdown occurs, making the machine totally unfit for production, the chances are slight that there is another numerically controlled machine sitting idle to which the job can be transferred.

In essence then, for a numerically controlled machine to make money it must have no unscheduled downtime. All maintenance work must be planned and carried out on a regular schedule; in other words, there must be a preventive-maintenance program.

Most plants provide minor preventive maintenance on a 30-, 60-, 90-day schedule while major overhauls are done on a 6- and 12-month schedule. In addition, a daily "quasi-preventive-maintenance" program is usually carried out by the operator before starting a production run.

Following are recommendations for typical numerically controlled machines in a normal shop environment. In areas that are excessively dusty or dirty, have high humidity, or undergo large temperature changes in short periods of time, the frequency and scope of work performed should be increased. These recommendations should be used only as minimum guides. Most machinery and control manufacturers will recommend specific procedures to be used with their equipment.

Daily

1. Wipe exposed areas of lead screws and ways and flush with light oil to remove dirt and chips.
2. Clean areas around all exposed limit switches. Carefully clean all transducer/resolver racks, gears, or bars.
3. Check oil reservoirs of lubricating and hydraulic systems.
4. Warm up electronic and hydraulic system for a minimum of 30 min.
5. Exercise all axes of motion to insure proper lubrication and prevent stickiness.
6. Visually inspect machine and hydraulic power unit for oil leaks (particularly during rapid reversals of machine motions).

Weekly

1. Perform daily check list.
2. Balance electronic d-c amplifiers.
3. Check all axis reference positions for accuracy, using a test tape.
4. Make a marginal control test (if available) and replace weak components.

Monthly

1. Perform weekly check list.
2. Vacuum clean interior of control cabinets.
3. Check, clean, or replace ventilation-system air filters.
4. Make visual inspection for excessive heating of components.
5. Check all solenoid and limit switches for proper operation.

[1] The author gratefully acknowledges the assistance of L. Lenihan, Maintenance Engineer, North American Aviation, Inc., in the preparation of the preventive-maintenance schedules.

6. Check all push buttons and indicating lights for proper operation.
7. Check and tighten all electrical connections and check for corrosion.
8. Inspect, clean, and adjust the tape reader.
9. Make a general inspection for mechanical secureness.

Bimonthly

1. Perform monthly check list.
2. Check and tighten all hydraulic connections.
3. Check power supplies for proper voltage and absence of ripple.
4. Check all electrical motors and replace brushes as required.
5. Check hydraulic motors for leaks and replace seals as required.
6. With hydraulic power unit operating, open any bleeders to exhaust air from lines and cylinders.
7. Check couplings, sheaves, and belts for looseness and wear.
8. Clean or replace slide and way-wiper felts.

Every Ninety Days

1. Perform bimonthly check list.
2. Drain and flush the coolant tank.   Refill.
3. Clean or replace filters on hydraulic power unit.
4. Clean or replace filters on servo control systems.
5. Drain and flush gear boxes. Refill with oil.
6. Check interlocks, timers, and switches for proper operation.
7. Check relays for proper contact pressure.   Clean points and adjust if required.
8. Check gearboxes and drive units for mechanical backlash.

Every Six Months

1. Sample oil in hydraulic reservoir.   If tests indicate contamination, drain complete system and refill through a filter.   Operate the hydraulic system for 24 hr and replace filters.
2. Check the level of the machine work tables.   Check all hold-down screws and jacks, if any, for tightness.   Relevel as required.
3. Check the settings of the slide gibs and adjust if required.
4. Check and adjust loading on all drive screws.
5. Remove, clean, and lubricate electrical motors.   Check bearings and replace as required.
6. Inspect, clean, and repack all mechanical couplings.
7. Clean, check, and adjust counterbalance system.   Replace cables or wire ropes (annually).

TROUBLE SHOOTING

The numerically controlled machine has been well designed and expertly built. The maintenance technician is well qualified and has been well trained—he knows the equipment.   The best test equipment has been provided and a good preventive-maintenance program is being followed.   Despite all this, the time will come when the machine fails during production and an effective troubleshooting technique must be available.

This handbook cannot attempt to specify the exact means for fixing all problems which can occur on all of the different numerically controlled machines.   Specific trouble-shooting techniques must be provided by the specific machine manufacturers. The best we can do is outline an approach to trouble-shooting which may serve to clear the thinking.

All machine problems can be broken down into three basic classifications:

1. Mechanical problems.
2. Electronic problems.
3. Tape problems.

Of the three, tape problems are usually the easiest to resolve. First, it is necessary to know whether the information on the tape is correct. If the tape has been used before and produced correct parts, then usually it will still be good. Sometimes, however, a punched tape has been used too many times and the holes have become ragged, or a dial-indicator magnetic base has been put down too close to a reel of magnetic tape and erased part of it. In either case the information on the tape is no longer usable. If the tape has never been used, it will be necessary to have some means of verifying that the tape is good. Since tape verification is normally considered a programming problem, it will not be discussed here; however, the maintenance people should be aware that the problem can exist.

Assuming the tape is known to be good, the easiest check to make is of the tape reader. First of all, is the reading head clean? It is surprising how many problems are caused by dirty readers. After cleaning, run the tape reader block by block and verify the reading with scope, tester, or indicating lights.

If it is now established that the reader is satisfactory, the nature of the problem must be known with a little more detail. If the problem is with one particular axis, then further probing should be done with parts of the over-all system that pertain to that axis. If the problem is not concentrated around one axis, then an over-all checkout is in order. Keep in mind that on a multiaxis machine it may be difficult to pin the trouble on one axis. Nevertheless, let us continue our trouble shooting and remember that we are outlining an approach rather than a specific cure for a specific ill.

A general check of the machine's mechanism is fairly easy to accomplish. Look for hydraulic-oil pools, which may suggest leaking lines, valves, or fittings. Check the ways and lead screws for burrs, which may be causing stickiness. Check for excessive backlash by running the machine under manual control with many axis reversals. In short, keep the eyes open and the ears tuned in for nonconforming events.

If the machine's mechanism appears to be good, we are now ready to check out the electronics. First, check the output of the power supplies. Next, be sure all the amplifiers are balanced. Then, operate the controls in a test mode with either the built-in test routine or with a special test tape which has been programmed specifically for maintenance purposes. Finally, check each plug-in circuit module which pertains to the axis causing the trouble.

At all times keep notes of the testing and checkout so that you do not double back on yourself and unintentionally repeat the same tests over and over. Above all, keep in mind that the entire machine system is composed of small, individually functioning subsystems and that these subsystems are easier to check than the over-all system.

One last word regarding trouble shooting. Be sure that any circuit changes are documented on the drawings and be sure that all the drawings are available to all the maintenance men on all the shifts. The cost of a set of reproducible drawings from the manufacturer is negligible when compared to the money that can be saved by having all changes noted on the drawings rather than kept in the back of someone's head.

NUMERICAL-CONTROL GLOSSARY[1]

A

Absolute coordinates. Coordinates measured from a specific reference zero.

Accuracy. Freedom from error. Accuracy is not the same as precision; e.g., a correctly computed four-place decimal number is accurate; a six-place decimal number containing an error in the last place is more precise, but not accurate.

Actuating. The function of performing the motion, physical changes, and adjustments to the positions, actions, or restraints of the workpiece, machine tool, or process.

Actuating signal. (1) A voltage or difference measured with respect to a reference and used for control. (2) The difference at any time between the reference input and a signal related to the controlled variable.

Adder. A device capable of forming the sum of two or more quantities.

AIA. Abbreviation for the Aircraft Industries Association.

Aligning point. An accurately located point of a boss or plug on a fixture or workpiece that is used in aligning a machine tool to coordinate points of director program cards.

[1] Courtesy of North American Aviation, Los Angeles Division, Part-programming Department.

Amplifier buffer. An amplifier used to isolate the output of any device, e.g., oscillator, from the effects produced by changes in voltage or loading in subsequent circuits.

Amplifier, torque. A device which produces an output turning moment wherein the output moment and associated power is supplied by the device, and the device requires an input moment and power smaller than the output moment and power.

Analog. (1) The representation of numerical quantities by means of physical variables, e.g., translation, rotation, voltage, resistance; contrasted with "digital." (2) A signal used for control or computation purposes, continuous in time, and directly proportional to the dimension or function it represents.

Analog input data. Information supplied to a machine control or director in the form of a directly measurable quantity used to represent some other quantity. These data are generally continuously variable quantities, as distinguished from quantities allowed to take on only discrete values.

Angular rotation. Movement or rotation (usually) around an axis of such a nature as to be angular, i.e., by degree of a given arc, angle, or movement.

APT. An automatic computer technique, developed at MIT and implemented by the airframe industry, which utilizes the IBM 704 and 709 computers to aid the part programmer in converting design intent into the coded input required by a numerically controlled machine tool. A major part of this technique is a pseudo-English language.

Automatic. A term applied to machines and processes that are self-acting and can work for an extended time without human intervention.

Automatic controller. Not actually a computer. Called "control panels" by machine builders and industry. Performs, mainly, sequencing and timing functions and some simple programming. Universally used to control automatic machines on a logical digital, or analog basis.

Automation. (1) The entire field of investigation, design, development, application, and methods of rendering or making processes or machines self-acting or self-moving; rendering an automatic theory, art, or technique of making a device, machine, process, or procedure more fully automatic; the implementation of a self-acting or self-moving, hence automatic, process or machine. (2) The use of machines to perform automatically the functions of their design intent.

Auxiliary function. A function of the machine other than the control of the coordinates of the workpiece or cutter. Usually on-off type operations, such as starting and stopping a spindle, coolant pump, lubricating pump, etc.

Axis. (1) An imaginary or real line which passes through an object and about which the object turns, seems to turn, or is oriented. (2) A line around which parts are arranged regularly. (3) A central or principal line of relations.

B

Bang-bang information. Program-card information that is relayed directly from card reader to machine, does not pass through director stores, and is acted upon immediately by the machine.

Basic control functions. *Sensing* the conditions that affect the process; *controlling* the process; *actuating* the process or elements of the process. (*Process* includes machines.)

BCD. Binary-coded decimal (see Binary-coded decimal system).

Below work line. When cutter movement is below work clamped on the table, a safety-circuit light on the director control panel will glow to notify the operator of a critical cutter location. (This safety-switch location is adjustable and should be set by the operator for each workpiece.)

Binary code. A numerical system for expressing data in terms of elements, each capable of assuming one or the other of two states, e.g., on or off, 0 or 1. Several different codes are in use for representing alphabetical and numerical characters in this fashion.

Binary-coded decimal system. A system of number representation in which each decimal digit is represented by a group of binary digits.

Binary number. A single digit or group of characters or symbols representing the total, aggregate, or amount of units utilizing the base 2, usually using only the 0 and 1 digits to express quantity.

Block. A group of words considered or transported as a unit; an item; a message; in flow charts, an assembly of boxes, each box representing a logical unit of programming, usually requiring transfer to and from the high-speed storage; in circuitry, a group of electrical circuits performing a specific function, as in a "block" diagram, in which unit, e.g., oscillator, is represented as a block (symbol).

Block data. Information regarding tool position, feed rate and direction of motion, and auxiliary commands which is stored as a single coded entry of position storage.

Break point. A point in a routine at which the computer may, under the control of a manually set switch, be stopped for a visual check of progress.

Bus. A path over which information is transferred; a trunk; an electrical conductor, channel, or line; a heavy wire or heavy lead.

C

Cable. An electrical conductor designed to provide a common electric potential between two or more points.

Card. Heavy, stiff paper of uniform size and shape, adapted for being punched in an intelligible array of holes. The punched holes are sensed electrically by wire brushes or mechanically by metal feelers. One standard card is $7\frac{3}{8}$ in. long by $3\frac{1}{4}$ in. wide and contains 80 columns, in each of which one or more of 12 positions may be punched.

Carriage, automatic. A typewriting paper-guiding or paper-holding device which is automatically controlled by information and program so as to feed forms or continous paper to a set of impression keys and to provide the necessary space, skip, eject, tabulate, or performing operations.

Cartesian coordinates. An ordered triad of real numbers used to locate a point relative to a system of three mutually perpendicular straight lines, called axes.

Cavity mill. A milling machine primarily designed for cutting out pockets (cavities) in spars and machined parts; a milling machine whose spindle axis is variable or whose depth of cutter (movement) is variable.

Cavity milling. Cutting cavities, pockets, or variable-depth contours in machined parts.

Check, built-in or automatic. Any provision constructed in hardware for verifying the accuracy of information transmitted, manipulated, or stored by any unit or device in a computer. Extent of automatic checking is the relative proportion of machine processes which are checked or the relative proportion of machine hardware devoted to checking.

Check, parity. A summation check in which the binary digits, in a character or word, are added (modulo 2) and the sum checked against a single, previously computed parity digit; i.e., a check which tests whether the number of ones is odd or even.

Check redundant. A check which uses extra digits, short of complete duplication, to help detect malfunctions and mistakes.

Checking, marginal. A system or method of determining computer-circuit weaknesses and incipient malfunctions by varying the power applied to various circuits, usually by a lowering of the d-c supply or filament voltages.

Climb milling. Having the cutter rotating toward the direction of tool (spindle) movement, i.e., with the cutter turning clockwise and the spindle moving from left to right.

Clock frequency. The number of pulses per unit of time supplied by a master or reference pulse generator. Clock frequency is expressed interchangeably in cycles per second or pulses per second.

Closed-loop system. A system in which the output or some result of the output is fed back for comparison with the input to reduce the difference between input command and output function.

Code. A system of symbols and their use in representing rules for handling the flow or processing of information; to prepare problems for solution on a specific computer.

Code, instruction. An artificial language for describing or expressing the instructions which can be carried out by a digital computer. In automatically sequenced computers, the instruction code is used when describing or expressing sequences of instructions, and each instruction word usually contains a part specifying the operation to be performed and one or more addresses which identify a particular location in storage. Sometimes an address part of an instruction is not intended to specify a location in storage but is used for some other purpose. If more than one address is used, the code is called a multiple-address code.

Command. A pulse, signal, or set of signals initiating one step in the performance of a computer operation.

Component. A major section of a unit.

Computer. Any device capable of accepting information, applying prescribed processes to the information, and supplying the results of these processes; sometimes, more specifically, a device for performing sequences of arithmetic and logical operations, as opposed to *calculators*, on which the sequence is impressed manually (desk calculator) or from tape or cards (card-programmed calculator).

Computer, analog. A calculating machine which solves problems by translating physical conditions like flow, temperature, or pressure into electrical quantities and using equivalent electrical circuits for the physical phenomena.

Computer, asynchronous. A calculating device in which the performance of any operation starts as a result of a signal that the previous operation has been completed; contrasted with synchronous computer.

Computer, automatic. A calculating device which handles long sequences of operations without human intervention.

Computer, digital. A calculating device utilizing discrete numbers to express all the variables and quantities of a problem. The numbers are usually expressed as a space-time distribution of punched holes, electrical pulses, sonic pulses, etc.

Computer, synchronous. A calculating device in which the performance of all operations is controlled with equally spaced signals from a master clock.

Contiguous dimension. A dimension that can be measured at a number of points in a system, each point near or touching other points of that dimension.

Continuous data. Data of which the information content can be ascertained continuously in time.

Continuous dimension. Dimensions not broken in time or length. Numerical value of a factor.

Contour. The outline of a figure, shape, or thing.

Contour-control system. A system in which the cutting path can result from the coordinated, simultaneous motion of two or more assemblies.

Control, unit. That portion of the hardware of an automatic digital computer which directs the sequence of operations, interprets the coded instructions, and initiates the proper commands to the computer circuits to execute the instructions.

Controlling. The function of evaluating the input-data information derived from the *sensors* or "controls" and initiating the proper action of the machine on logical or mathematical grounds, or both, in accordance with the designed mode of operation of the machine or process.

Controlling means; controller. Those elements of an automatic-control system which are involved in procuring a corrective action. The servo controller is the limited portion of the numerical-control system which produces the actuating signals used to drive the servomotor.

Conventional milling. Having the cutter rotating away from the direction of tool (spindle) movement, i.e., with the cutter turning clockwise, and the spindle moving from right to left.

Coolant. A material (usually liquid) to keep tools, cutters, and machines cool or within a given variation of temperature.

Coordinates. Any of two or more magnitudes that define the position of a point, line, or plane by reference to a fixed figure, system of lines, etc.

Counter. A device, register, or storage location for storing integers, permitting these integers to be increased or decreased by unit or by an arbitrary integer, and capable of being reset to zero or to an arbitrary integer.

Counter, ring. A loop of interconnected bistable elements such that one and only one is in a specified state at any given time and such that, as input signals are counted, the position of the one specified state moves in an ordered sequence around the loop.

CPS. An abbreviation for cycles per second.

CRT. Cathode-ray tube; a device yielding a visual plot of the variation of several parameters by means of a proportionally deflected beam of electrons.

Cutter compensation. An operational feature of the director which automatically computes and stores the offset (in any one of the planes—XY, XZ, or YZ) necessary to allow use of an undersized or oversized cutter without any change in the program.

Cutter, milling. A rotary cutting tool provided with one or more cutting elements called teeth, which intermittently engage the workpiece and remove material by relative movement of the workpiece and cutter.

Cycling. Periodic change of the controlled variable (oscillation is a synonymous term).

D

Damping. A characteristic built into electrical circuits and mechanical systems to prevent rapid or excessive corrections which may lead to instability or oscillatory conditions; e.g., connecting a resistor on the terminals of a pulse transformer to remove natural oscillations or placing a moving element in oil or sluggish grease to prevent overshoot.

Data. Bits of information concerning the operation or control factors and dimensions of a process.

Data processing. Data processing for numerical machine control includes the encoding of dimensional and other data in a form suitable for computation, the computation of detailed machine instructions, and the writing out of those instructions in a portable, stored form suitable for use in the direct control of the machine. More briefly, data processing is translating numerically descriptive engineering and manufacturing data into a form suitable for machine control.

Dead band. The range of values through which the input can be varied without initiating output response.

Dead time. Any definite delay between two related actions. It is measured in units of time.

Debug. To isolate and remove all malfunctions.

Decade. A group or assembly of 10 units, e.g., a decade counter counts to 10 in one column; a decade resistor box inserts resistance quantities in multiples of powers of 10.

Decoding. Translation from a coded form to an analog or other easily recognized form without significant loss of information.

Diagram. A schematic representation of a sequence of subroutines designed to solve a problem; a coarser and less symbolic representation than a flow chart, frequently including descriptions in English words; a schematic or logical drawing showing the electrical circuit or logical arrangements within a component.

Diagram, logical. In logical design, a diagram representing the logical elements and their interconnections without necessarily expressing construction or engineering details.

Differential analyzer. A general-purpose analog computer used primarily to solve differential equations, usually making use of operational amplifiers and integrators.

Digital. The quality of utilizing numbers in a given scale of notation to represent all the quantities that occur in a problem or a calculation.

Digital computer. A mechanical, electromechanical, or electronic system capable of solving a wide variety of problems by processing data in digital form by an arranged program. It may include memory devices, input-output elements, accumulator, control element, instruction register, and instruction counter.

Digitize. To render an analog measurement of a physical variable into a numerical value, expressing the quantity in digital form.

Dimension. A factor used to characterize properties and attributes of a process or an object. The factors, too, are called "dimensions" at times. Also, the numerical value of the factor.

Director. A unit which provides the path-control signals to direct machine operation, i.e., an interpolator either alone or combined with a controller.

Discrete dimension. A dimension that can be measured only with respect to discrete points in a system.

Discrete units. Distinct or individual units.

Discrimination. Comparing two or more signals and determining their relative amplitude, equality, and sense, difference, or polarity.

Downtime. The period during which a computer is malfunctioning or not operating correctly because of machine failures; contrasted with available time or stand-by time.

E

Eccles-Jordon (trigger). A direct-coupled multivibrator circuit possessing two conditions of stable equilibrium. Also known as a flip-flop circuit or "toggle."

Electronic. Pertaining to the application of that branch of science which deals with the motion, emission, and behavior of free electrons, especially in vacuum, gas or photo tubes, and special conductors. Contrasted with "electric," which pertains to the flow of large currents in wires only.

Elevation. The angular measurement in a vertical plane from a specific reference, usually the horizontal plane.

Encoding. Translation to a coded form from an analog or other easily recognized form without significant loss of information.

End-of-block signal. A symbol or indicator that defines the end of one block of data.

End point (coordinate). The final position of cutter when a span is completed (the information on a card has caused movement of spindle carrier). The end point of any given span is the starting point of the following span.

Error. The amount of loss of precision in a quantity; the difference between an accurate quantity and its calculated approximation; *errors* occur in numerical methods; *mistakes* occur in programming, coding, data transcription, and operating; *malfunctions* occur in computers and are due to physical limitations on the properties of materials; the differential margin by which a controlled unit deviates from its target value.

Error signal. A voltage differential between input signal of program card and actual location of cutter. When error becomes zero, the cutter is at coordinate location specified by card punchings.

External control. The means whereby a machine (or process) is caused to adjust to variable conditions and immediate requirements from outside of the machine.

F

Face. The principal plane or surface of an object.

Feed, card. A mechanism which moves cards serially into a machine.

Feedback control. Negative feedback: causing a system (machine or process) to respond to the difference between the command signal and a portion of the output of the system.

The policy of continuously or continually "checking up" to ascertain that system performance is satisfactory.

Feedback loop. That part of the control system which permits comparison of the output function with the input-signal command.

Feedback sensor. A device to provide a flow of information concerning the machine output.

Feed rate. (1) The speed of cutter movement through workpiece. (2) A velocity expressed in inches per time unit.

Finish cut. The end or last cutter pass for a machined part, usually leaving a very smooth surface and requiring very little material to be removed.

Fixture. A tool used to hold a part during a machine operation.

Flexowriter. The trade name for a line of automatic typewriters operated by or to produce punched tape. The manufacturer is Commercial Controls Corporation.

Flip-flop. A bistable device; a device capable of assuming two stable states; a bistable device which may assume a given stable state depending upon the pulse history of one or more input points and having one or more output points. The device is capable of storing a bit of information; controlling gates, etc.; a toggle.

Flow chart. A graphical representation of a sequence of operations, using symbols to represent the operations. A flow chart is a more detailed representation than a diagram.

Fortran. An automatic-computer program to translate formulas into computer language.

Functional. A device, system, or process which accomplishes a given task.

G

Gate. A circuit having the ability to produce an output which is dependent upon a specified type or the coincidence nature of the input, e.g., an AND gate has an output pulse when there is time coincidence at all inputs; an OR gate has an output when any one or any combination of input pulses occurs in time coincidence; any gate may contain a number of "inhibits," in which there is no output under any condition of input if there is time coincidence of an inhibit or except signal.

Generator. A program for a computer which generates the coding of a problem; a mechanical device which produces an electrical output.

Grid, control. The electrode of a vacuum tube other than a diode upon which a signal voltage is impressed in order to control the plate current.

H

Hardware. The mechanical, magnetic, electronic, and electrical devices from which a computer is fabricated; the assembly of material forming a computer.

Hunting. A continuous attempt on the part of an automatically controlled system to seek a desired equilibrium condition. The system usually contains a standard, a method of determining deviations from standard, and a method of influencing the system such that the difference between the standard and the state of the system is brought to zero.

Hysteresis. The difference between the response of a system to an increasing signal and the response to a decreasing signal.

I

Ignore. A typewriter character indicating that no action whatsoever be taken. (In Teletype or Flexowriter code, when all holes are punched, it is an ignore); an instruction requiring nonperformance of what normally might be executed; not to be executed.

Induction potentiometer. A device, such as Variac, which uses inductance, rather than resistance, to produce a linear voltage drop along a toroidal winding of wire. A "wiper" is used to tap off the voltage existing at various points along the winding.

Inspection. The operation of comparing actual condition of a work piece to standards, manually or automatically.

Instrumentation. The use of indicators or instruments to reveal the quality or quantity of the condition sensed.

Instruments. Devices that usually reveal the extent or level of a variable or parameter that is being measured.

Integrator. A device whose output is proportional to the integral with respect to the input variable.

Intelligence. The power to "think" successfully when specific demands are made by man or machine.

Interpolator. A device which defines in detail the path to be followed and the rate of travel, given a condensed, coded, mathematical description of the same. The interpolator translates tool-center-position instructions (e.g., end points of straight lines or specific circular arcs) into discrete, progressive path positions close enough together to maintain the desired tolerance.

J

Job. A piece of work.

K

Key punching. The process of producing coded, punched cards either manually by a key-punch operator or automatically by computer peripheral equipment. Related processes include verifying, interpreting, reproducing, sorting, and collating.

L

Lag. A relative measure of the time delay between two events, states, or mechanisms.

Language, machine. Information recorded in a form which may be made available to a computer; e.g., punched paper tape may contain information available to a machine, whereas the same information in the form of printed characters on a page is not available to a machine; information which can be sensed by a machine.

Least count. The smallest unit of measure which can be discriminated by a measuring instrument. In most numerical-control systems the least count of the position sensor is equated to the quantization level of the digital circuits.

Left-hand rotation or cut. The clockwise rotation of a cutter when viewed from a position in front of a horizontal milling machine and facing the spindle.

Limit. The extreme tolerable point or points or conditions of a system or process.

Linear. Of or in a line or lines; made of lines; making use of lines; long and narrow.

Logger. A device which automatically records physical processes and events, usually with respect to time.

M

Machine. An assembly of equipment that does a particular type of work.

Machine actuator or servomotor. A power device for directly affecting machine motion.

Magnitude. The absolute value of a number, or the size of a quantity. (Must not be used for "scale.")

Malfunction. A failure in the operation of the hardware of a computer.

Manual. "Done by hand," set up entirely by muscular energy and human skill; not by machine.

Manual control. Manual operation of machine functions by means of the push buttons, switches, and handwheels on the operator's control panel.

Manuscript. A compilation of the engineering data and manufacturing information necessary to make a part, arranged in sequential form suitable for translation into instruction storage. The manuscript corresponds to the usual manufacturing outline or planning sheet and, together with the part drawing, contains all necessary numerical data on the machine tool and cutter specifications, tool path and cutting sequences, work location on the machine table, feeds and speeds, tolerances and other information required for controlling auxiliary machine functions, coolant flow, and chip disposal.

Mathematical operations. Control operations which take place, usually simultaneously, on the basis of the reconciliation of analog or digital representations of the process factors, by means of a computer-type element. Also includes decoding, such as used with numerical control.

Measurement. The process or technique of determining the numerical value of dimensions or factors; determination of the quality, extent, or degree of the dimensions or factors of a process or object.

Measuring means. Consists of those elements of an automatic controller which are involved in ascertaining and communicating to the controlling means the value of the controlled variable.

Mechanized. Descriptive of machines that receive power from an outside source; mechanical means to accomplish physical or mental work.

Microsecond. A millionth part of a second.

Mid-point (coordinate). A coordinate point necessary in the formation of a parabolic span.

Milling. A method of removing material in the form of chips by means of a rotating cutter.

Millisecond. A thousandth part of a second.

Mirror image. In defining the shape of objects, a right-hand part as opposed to a left-hand part; an exact opposite; a reverse image of an object.

Mistake.   A blunder which results in an incorrect instruction in a program or in coding, an incorrect element of information, or an incorrect manual operation.

Motor operator.   A portion of the controlling means which applies power for operating the final control element.

Multivibrator.   A type of relaxation oscillator used for the generation of nonsinusoidal waves in which the output of each of its two tubes is coupled to the input of the other to sustain oscillations.

Multivibrator, astable.   A free-running type of relaxation oscillator used for the generation of nonsinusoidal waves.

Multivibrator, monostable.   A type of relaxation oscillator used to sustain a trigger pulse for a specified time, since the device assumes another state for a specified length of time, at the end of which it returns to its original state, after being pulsed or forced into another state.

N

Negligible.   Factors that have little or no effect on the process and may be disregarded.

Neutral zone.   A predetermined range of values of the controlled variable in which no change of position of the final control element occurs.   It is commonly expressed in per cent of controller-scale range.   A neutral zone is employed in some types of floating controller action.

Number, binary.   A numerical value written in the base 2 system of notation.

Numerical control.   Continuous-path machining, automatically controlled from numerical data.

Numerical-control system.   A system in which actions are controlled by the direct insertion of numerical data at some point.   The system must automatically interpret at least some portion of these data.

Numerical data.   Data in which information is expressed by a set of numbers or symbols that can assume only discrete values or configurations.

O

Open-loop control.   Assumes that a system is always satisfactory and suffers no lack of performance, so that checking up on the system is not needed.   Specifically, "open-loop" means "not closed loop," or "feedback."

Open-loop system.   A system that has no means for self-correction of errors by comparison of the output function with the input demand.

Operator.   The person who actually manipulates the computer controls, places information media into the input devices, removes the output, presses the start button, etc.

OR circuit.   An electrical or mechanical device which will yield an output signal whenever there are one or more inputs on a multichannel input; e.g., an OR gate is one in which a pulse output occurs whenever one or more inputs are pulsed; forward merging of pulses simultaneously providing reverse isolation.

Override control.   The means whereby an automatic function may be reverted by some other (i.e., manual) control to allow for a modification in a given process or procedure.

P

Parallel.   Handled simultaneously in separate facilities; operating on two or more parts of a word or item simultaneously; contrasted with serial.

Park position.   The retracted spindle position of machine.   For a wing-skin miller, both heads will be at outer limits on gantry and within 3 in. of topmost spindle movement.

Part planning.   The machining process planning necessary to prepare the manuscript for each particular part.

Part programming.   The processes of converting an engineering drawing of an object to be machine-formed into that contour which will be equal to the engineering drawing and within the tolerances set forth in it through the use of numerically controlled machines and the format required to run them.

Path storage.   Storage media containing interpolated tool-path data and instructions for auxiliary functions.   Interpolated data usually are recorded on multiple-channel magnetic media during data processing and are then sent into the shop to operate the machine tool.

Peripheral.   On an outer ring; outer contour; pertaining to associated equipment.

Pick-off.   See Pickup and Transducer.

Pickup or pick-off.   Sensors that reveal the on-off or other two-state condition of a process factor; also, devices that reveal process factors in the form of pulses.

Platenize.   To secure parts or fixtures to flat mounting plates for the purpose of establishing and maintaining part position and alignment with respect to reference points on one or more machine tools.

Plug-board.   A removable panel containing an ordered array of terminals which may be interconnected by short electrical leads according to a prescribed pattern and hence designating a specific program.   The entire panel, prewired, may be inserted for different programs.

Position analog unit (PAU).   Feedback of director servo loop.   Includes indicators for visual location of control position.

Position-control system.   A positioning system in which the controlled motion is required only to reach a given end point, with no metalworking occuring during the transition from one end point to the next.

Position sensor.   A device for converting linear or angular mechanical position into a signal form convenient for computation or control.

Potentiometer.   A variable-voltage divider, a resistor which has a variable-contact arm so that any portion of the potential applied between its ends may be selected.

Power actuator or servomotor.   A power device for directly driving the movable machine elements.

Precision.   The degree of exactness with which a quantity is stated; a relative term often based on the number of significant digits in a measurement.

Preset.   The practice of adjusting the process before the work cycle starts, on the basis of the condition of the work piece; the control-system function whereby control is based on the automatic sensing of preprocess conditions.

Process.   All the operations necessary to produce an object or to do a specific job; the equipment used for either.

Process control.   The control of a process as a whole, as distinct from control at a specific point in a process.

Production.   Making or creating a product by manufacturing or processing.

Program.   A plan for the solution of a problem.   A complete program includes plans for the transcription of data, coding for the computer, and plans for the absorption of the results into the system.   The list of coded instructions is called a "routine"; to plan a computation or process from the asking of a question to the delivery of the results, including the integration of the operation into an existing system.   Programming consists of planning and coding, including numerical analysis, system analysis, specification of printing formats, and any other functions necessary to the integration of a computer in any system.

Programmer.   A person who formulates (1) a plan or procedure of an operation of a machine or process; (2) a set of instructions arranged in proper sequence to cause desired operations; and (3) the numerical data pertaining to the operation or process.

Programming.   The analysis and combining of engineering and manufacturing information to provide encoded machine-control instruction.

Programming, automatic.   Any technique in which the computer is used to help plan as well as to help code a problem, e.g., compiling routines, interpretive routines.

Program-sensitive malfunction.   A malfunction which occurs only when some unusual combination of program steps occurs.

Pulse.   (1) A change in the intensity or level of some medium, usually over a relatively short period of time.   (2) A shift in electric potential of a point for a short period of time compared to the time period; i.e., if the voltage level of a point shifts from -10 to $+20$ volts with respect to ground for a period of 2 μsec, one says that the point received a 30-volt 2-μsec pulse.   (3) A pattern of variation of a quantity, such as a voltage or current, consisting of an abrupt change from one level to another followed by an abrupt change to the original level.

Punch, calculating, electronic.   A card-handling machine which reads a punched card, performs a number of sequential operations, and punches the result on a card.

Punch, card.   A device which perforates or places holes in cards in specific locations designated by a program.

Punched tape.   A paper or synthetic (plastic) tape approximately 1 in. wide and varying in length to as much as several hundred feet long.   Round holes are punched in the tape across its width and length to signify various coded bits of information and direction.

R

Rate sensor.   A device producing a signal proportional to the angular or linear velocity of a mechanical member, e.g., a tachometer.

Ratio, operating.   The ratio obtained by dividing the number of hours of correct machine operation by the total hours of scheduled operation; e.g., on a 168-hr week scheduled operation, if 12 hr of preventive maintenance is required and 4.8 hr of unscheduled downtime occurs, then the operating ratio is $(168 - 16.8)/168$, which is equivalent to a 90 per cent operating ratio.

Raw storage. Storage media, such as drawings and specifications containing information (geometry of part, cutter size, allowable feeds and speeds, etc.) necessary for preparation of the manuscript. These raw data are integrated by the combination of skills of the part planner, tool engineer, producibility expert, and machinist in the process of writing the manuscript.

Reader, card. A mechanism that permits the sensing of information punched on cards by means of wire brushes or metal feelers.

Reader, tape, magnetic. A device capable of restoring to a train or sequence of electrical pulses information recorded on a magnetic tape in the form of a series of magnetized spots, usually for the purpose of transferring the information to some other storage medium.

Reader, tape, paper. A device capable of restoring to a train or sequence of electrical pulses information punched on a paper tape in the form of a series of holes, usually for the purpose of transferring the information to some other storage medium.

Regeneration. The process of returning a part of the output signal of an amplifier to its input circuit in such a manner that it reinforces the grid excitation and thereby increases the total amplification.

Regulation, voltage. A measure of the degree to which power source maintains its output-voltage stability under varying load conditions.

Reliability. The probability that an item will perform as intended.

Reset. To return a device to zero or to an initial or arbitrarily selected condition.

Resolver. A device which separates or breaks up a quantity, particularly a vector, into constituent parts or elements, e.g., the three mutually perpendicular components of a space vector.

Response, frequency. A measure of the ability of a device to take into account, follow, or act upon a rapidly varying condition; e.g., as applied to amplifiers, the frequency at which the gain has fallen to the one-half power point or to 0.707 of the voltage-gain factor; as applied to a mechanical controller, the maximum rate at which changes in condition can be followed and acted upon.

Rewind. To return a film or magnetic tape to its beginning.

Rough cut. A primary cut on a workpiece which leaves sharp and deep surface ridges; a cut whose main purpose is the rapid removal of material with little regard for the finish obtained.

Round off. To change a more precise quantity to a less precise one, according to some rule.

Routine. A set of coded instructions arranged in proper sequence to direct the computer to perform a desired operation or series of operations.

S

Safety circuits. Special circuits in the director which check input information and stop the machine when faulty information is entered.

Sampled data. Data in which the information content can be, or is, ascertained only at discrete intervals of time. *Note:* Sampled data can be analog or digital.

Scanner. An instrument which automatically samples or interrogates the state of various processes, conditions, or physical states and initiates action in accordance with the information obtained.

Sense. To examine, particularly relative to a criterion; to determine the present arrangement of some element of hardware, especially a manually set switch; to read holes punched in paper.

Sensors. Devices that detect or sense the condition, level, or extent of process factors.

Servo loop. Closed circuit (electric and/or hydraulic) used in accurate positioning.

Servomechanism. A closed-loop system in which the error or deviation from a desired or preset norm is reduced to zero, and one in which a mechanical position is usually the controlled variable; e.g., a synchronized-drum storage system requires a servomechanism to insure synchronism between a crystal-controlled electronic oscillator and a rotating cylinder; an antiaircraft fire-control gun-positioning system requires a servo to insure that deviations are corrected.

Set point. A point of reference; a position from which directions and dimensions can be determined.

Signals. Data in a form usable by a control system, usually as electrical voltages or pulses, or shaft rotation.

Significance. The arbitrary rank, priority, or order of relative magnitude assigned to a given position or column in a number; the significant digits of a number are a set of digits, usually from consecutive columns, beginning with the most significant digit different from zero and ending with the least significant digit whose value is known to be revelant; e.g., 2,300.0 has five significant digits, whereas 2,000 probably has two significant digits.

Speed (Internal) attenuator. The director control that allows operator to stop and start machine at any location or to adjust to any percentage of the programmed speed (speed override).

Spindle rotation. The movement of turning forward or clockwise, reverse or counter-clockwise as viewed from rear of spindle.

Station. Portion of a machine where a specific operation is performed.

Stock. The substance from which piece parts are made.

Storage. Preferred to memory, any device into which units of information can be copied, which will hold information in the form of arrangements of physical elements, hardware, or equipment; the erasable storage in any given computer.

Storage, magnetic. Any storage system which utilizes the magnetic properties of materials to store information.

Storage, medium. Any device or recording medium into which data can be copied and held until some later time, and from which the complete original data can be obtained.

Straight cut-control system. A system in which the controlled cutting action occurs only along a path parallel to linear, circular, or other machine ways.

Switch, electronic. A circuit which causes a start-and-stop action or a switching action by electronic means.

Switch, function. A circuit having a fixed number of inputs and outputs so designed that the output information is a function of the input information, each expressed in a certain code or signal configuration or pattern.

Switch, manual. Functionally, any manually set device which conveys information.

Symbol. Something that stands for or represents something else, i.e., an emblem, sign, or mark.

Synchro. A class of wound-rotor magnetic-induction transducers (known also as selsyns, autosyns, telesyns, etc.) which are capable of electrically transmitting or receiving angular positional information.

System. (1) The functional and operational devices by which control is accomplished. The process as a whole, considering the mechanisms and controls collectively. (2) An assembly of components united by some form of regulated interactions; on organized whole.

T

Table. (1) The bed or working surface of a machine. (2) A condensed list of tabulated information.

Tabulator. A machine which reads information from one medium, e.g., cards, paper tape, magnetic tape, etc., and produces lists, tables, and totals on separate forms or continuous paper.

Tachometer. An instrument for measuring or indicating the speed of a machine.

Tape channel. A path on numerical-control tape over which information is recorded and read.

Tape, magnetic. A tape or ribbon of any material impregnated or coated with magnetic material on which information may be placed in the form of magnetically polarized spots.

Tape, program. A tape which contains the sequence of instructions required for solving a problem and which can be read by the computer.

Tape transport. That group of equipment directly involved in the reading or recording of numerical control tape (includes the reels, recording and reading heads, and associated controls).

Template. (1) A guide, usually metal, used to check the contour and dimensions of a close-tolerance part. (2) An exact duplicate usually in flat pattern, or a scribed layout of part to be checked for dimensional accuracy as related to its blueprint description.

Threshold sensitivity. The lowest level of the measured variable which produces effective response of the instrument or automatic controller.

Thyratron. A hot-cathode, gas-discharge tube in which one or more electrodes are used to control electrostatically the starting of an undirectional flow of current.

Time, engineering or servicing. All machine downtime necessary for routine testing (good or bad), for machine servicing due to breakdowns, or for preventive-servicing measures, e.g., block-tube changes. Includes all test time (good or bad) following breakdown and subsequent repair or preventive servicing.

Time, idle. Time in which machine is believed to be in good operating condition and attended by service engineers but not in use.

Tolerance. That distance which a product may deviate from a given dimension. The variation allowed between a given dimension and the acceptable final deviation in the end product.

Tool. The object that comes in active contact with the workpiece.

Tool path. (1) The movement, the direction of movement, and the area covered by such movement of a machine tool. (2) The placement or movement of a machine spindle as against the placement or movement of a machine bed.

Transducer. A device which converts energy from one form to another.

Transducers. (1) Sensors that reveal the level or extent of process factors by converting mechanical factors to an equivalent electrical signal, an analog of the factor instrumented. (2) Measuring, detecting, or sensing devices, usually electromechanical.

Transfer, parallel. A system of data transfer in which the characters of an element of information are transferred simultaneously over a set of paths.

Transfer, serial. A system of data transfer in which the characters of an element of information are transferred in sequence over a single path in consecutive time positions.

Transient. A phenomenon experiencing a change as a function of time; something which is temporary; a build-up or breakdown in the intensity of a phenomenon until a steady-state condition is reached; an aperiodic phenomenon; the time rate of change of energy is finite, and some form of energy storage is usually involved.

Transistor. An electronic device utilizing semiconductor properties to control the flow of currents from one source in one circuit by currents from another circuit.

Trouble shoot. To search for a mistake or the cause of a malfunction in order to remove them.

V

Validity. Correctness; the final degree of closeness by which a result approaches the known and correct result.

Variable dimensions. Those dimensions of a process subject to continual change and control to bring about the desired results from the process. Also, the numerical value of variable factor.

W

Wire, magnetic. Wire made of a magnetic material along small incremental lengths of which magnetic dipoles are placed in accordance with binary information.

Work. What is done to the piece part, component, unit, or product.

X

X, Y, Z axis. The three axes along which machine elements move. The X axis is always a longitudinal movement (gantry of wing-skin miller, column along bed of traveling-column hydro-tel and table of vertical hydro-tel); Y axis is always traverse movement (spindle carriers along gantry rail of wing skin, spindle carrier on column of traveling-column hydro-tels, ram of vertical hydro-tel); Z axis is always spindle movement into or away from work.

Z

Zero set. The point of orientation for the machine and workpiece to the part drawing and numerical-control medium, i.e., tape.

Zero suppression. The editing or elimination of nonsignificant zeros to the left of the integral part of a quantity before printing operations are initiated; a part of editing.

Chapter 5

VIBRATION: ITS ANALYSIS AND CORRECTION

By D. L. BERNHARD
International Research and Development Corporation
Worthington, Ohio

Introduction. The vibration which occurs in rotating machinery and the surrounding structure results from mechanical defects in the machine or from causes inherent in the way the machine operates or is transmitted there from some outside source.

Vibrations transmitted from outside sources can be removed as a problem by isolation. Isolation means separating a machine from the vibration source with materials such as rubber, cork, springs, etc. Each material has its own distinct capabilities for refusing to transmit vibration. The transmissibility of vibration-isolation materials is a function of the type of material, the amount and frequency of the vibration, and the load on the material.

The subject of vibration isolation can be quite complex and is beyond the scope of this text. Excellent literature on the subject is available from the many suppliers in this field.

Vibrations in machinery that are inherent in the way a machine operates can rarely be reduced by means other than design changes. Such vibrations will be discussed here so that they can be recognized and separated from those vibrations which can be corrected.

Most machines vibrate because of mechanical defects. Such defects are always present, because there is no such thing as a perfect machine. A well-designed and well-built machine will operate smoothly because the defects are small, but when the defects are large, vibration becomes excessive. Therefore, vibration is an excellent measure of the mechanical condition of machines. Since vibration analysis can tell both the extent of mechanical trouble and what that trouble is, vibration is an excellent source of informance for machinery maintenance.

What Is Vibration? Vibration is the motion of a machine or machine part back and forth from its position of rest.

The simplest way to show vibration is to follow the motion of a weight suspended on a spring (Fig. 5-1). This is typical of all machines since they have weight and spring-like properties.

Until a force is applied to the weight to cause it to move, there is no vibration. Applying a force makes the weight move upward, compressing the spring. Releasing the force makes the weight drop below its neutral position to some bottom limit of travel, where the spring stops the weight. It then travels upward through the neutral position to the top limit of motion and back again through the neutral position. This motion will continue in exactly the same manner as long as the force is reapplied. This is vibration.

The Characteristics of Vibration. By plotting the movement of the weight against time it is possible to study the detailed characteristics of vibration.

The motion of the weight from its neutral position to the top limit of its travel back through neutral to the bottom limit of travel and its return to the neutral position represents one cycle of the motion. The time required for one cycle is the period of the vibration. More useful, however, is the number of cycles for a given period of time, which is the frequency of the vibration. The total distance the weight moves is the peak-to-peak displacement of the vibration.

Since the weight is moving, it must be moving at some speed, but the speed changes depending upon the position of the weight (Fig. 5-2). At the top limit of the motion the speed is zero, as the weight must come to rest before it can go in the opposite direction. The speed or velocity is greatest as the weight passes through the neutral position. Normally the maximum, or peak, velocity is selected for measurement.

The position of the weight at any given instant with reference to some fixed point is the phase of the vibration. Phase is measured by using a stroboscopic light to observe the position of a reference mark on a rotation part.

What the Vibration Characteristics Tell Us. Each characteristic of vibration tells something of significance about the vibration. The characteristics most commonly measured are (1) displacement or velocity, (2) frequency, and (3) phase.

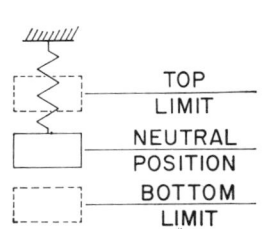

Fig. 5-1. Simple spring mass system.

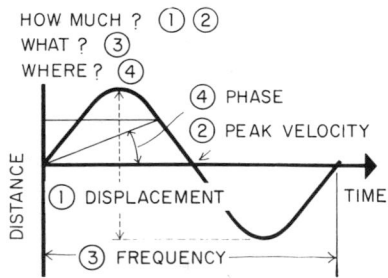

Fig. 5-2. Characteristics of vibration.

Displacement and *velocity tell how much* vibration is present or, in terms of the condition of machinery, *how* bad or *good* its *condition* may be.

The frequency of the vibration tells what is causing the vibration and is therefore the most important characteristic measured. By comparing the frequency of vibration to machinery-rotation speeds and multiples of rotating speeds, we can pinpoint the particular part causing the vibration and determine what the trouble is with that part.

Phase is used in balancing and is also helpful in pinpointing the causes of vibration.

The characteristics of vibration just discussed are those for the vibration coming from a single cause. Machinery is considerably more complex than a weight suspended on a spring. Machines have many weights on many springs. There are many different rotating parts spinning at different speeds and many sources of vibration. As a result the typical machine will have vibration at several frequencies each with different amounts and phase.

Vibration Measurement and Analysis Instruments. Measurements to determine the total amount of vibration at a point on a machine have been common to most industries for a long time. Devices ranging from finger tips and balancing a coin on edge to electronic instruments are in common use. The electronic instruments for vibration measurement developed in recent years provide the first means of obtaining *accurate* results.

A portable battery-operated vibration meter like the one shown in Fig. 5-3 is widely used for accurate, repeatable readings. Such readings are used to obtain early warning of trouble present or impending in rotating machinery.

More important has been the development of electronic instruments for vibration analysis. These remarkable instruments are able to provide measurements of the individual characteristics of vibration even when the vibration is complex. This makes it possible to trouble shoot a machine and, in the case of unbalance, correct it in place.

The vibration analyzer must be able to measure and indicate the amount, frequency, and phase of vibration. Furthermore, when the vibration occurs at several frequencies, it must be able to separate one frequency from another so that each individual vibration characteristic can be measured.

The vibration pickup senses the vibration of a machine and turns it into an electrical signal proportionate to the vibration. This signal goes into the vibration analyzer. The amount of vibration displacement is indicated on the amplitude meter. This is the vibration at the point where the pickup is placed and in the direction in which it is pointed.

FIG. 5-3. Portable vibration meter. (*Courtesy of IRD Corporation, Worthington, Ohio.*)

The frequency meter (Fig. 5-4) shows the frequency of the vibration. It is direct-reading in cycles per minute. It will show the frequency of the strongest or most predominant vibration present. This is usually the rotating speed of the part causing the vibration.

When several frequencies of vibration are present, none of which is the strongest, the frequencies meter cannot determine which frequency to show. Since frequency is needed to tell which part is causing the vibration, some means of separating several frequencies from each other is necessary. A tunable filter separates vibration frequencies for measurement of the displacement and frequency of each to learn which part of the machine is causing them and why. It is tuned to each vibration present in the same way a radio is tuned.

The strob light is used to determine the phase of the vibration for balancing and to pinpoint the part causing the vibration. The strob light flashes at a rate determined by the frequency of the vibration.

For example, the electric motor and pulley illustrated by Fig. 5-5, has vibration. The frequency of the strongest vibration is the same as the rotating speed of the motor.

When the unit is examined with the strob light, the pulley appears stationary or "frozen." A well-defined mark (reference mark) placed on the pulley helps to make it appear frozen under the strob light.

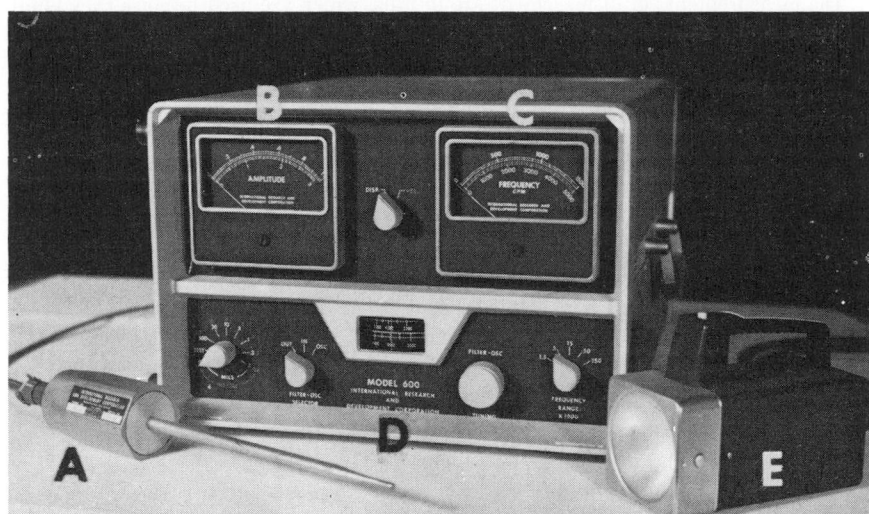

Fig. 5-4. Vibration analyzer: (*A*) vibration pickup; (*B*) amplitude meter; (*C*) frequency meter; (*D*) tunable filter; (*E*) strob light. (*Courtesy of IRD Corporation, Worthington, Ohio.*)

Fig. 5-5. Freezing the reference mark. (*Courtesy of IRD Corporation, Worthington, Ohio.*)

In a more complex system with several frequencies of vibration, none of which is predominant, the strob light flashes at several frequencies so a definite image of the reference mark would not be seen. By using a tunable filter, tuned to the frequency of vibration, the other vibrations are blocked out. The strob light will "freeze" the part responsible.

Terms of Measurement. Most electronic instruments for vibration measurement and analysis indicate the vibration amount in terms of mils peak-to-peak displacement and peak velocity in inches per second.

The measurements of displacement are in mils, which are used because they eliminate handling extra zeros. Thus 1 mil equals 0.001 in., 30 mils equal 0.030 in., and $\frac{2}{10}$ mil equals 0.0002 in., or 200 μin. Microinches are often used for vibrations less than 1 mil. The smallest vibration which can be indicated is approximately 5 μin. (0.000005 in.).

For the most part displacement readings of vibration meet all the requirements for vibration measurement. However, at high frequencies, above 6,000 cpm, velocity measurement is helpful in detecting small displacement vibrations. Velocity is a function of the product of the displacement and frequency, thus providing intelligent reading for even the smallest displacement. This is especially helpful when checking for bad antifriction bearings.

The amount of vibration tells how much vibration is present. This is a measure of the severity of the mechanical trouble in a machine. Comparison with vibration standards tells when correction is required.

The frequency of vibration is commonly measured in cycles per minute (cpm) rather than cycles per second. This makes it easy to compare frequency to rotating speed in revolutions per minute (rpm).

What Causes Vibration? With few exceptions mechanical troubles cause vibration. Since it is impossible to give all the possible troubles in a machine, the following list includes those which most commonly occur:

1. Unbalance of rotating parts.
2. Misalignment of couplings and bearings.
3. Tooth impact, dirt, interference, eccentricity of gears.
4. Bad drive belts and chains.
5. Bad bearings—antifriction type.
6. Torque variations.
7. Electromagnetic forces.
8. Aerodynamic forces.
9. Hydraulic forces.
10. Looseness, rubbing, and resonance.

Regardless of how the causes of vibration are listed, one basic thing must always be true. *The cause of vibration must be generating a force which is changing in either its direction or its amount. It is the force which causes vibration, and the resulting characteristics will be determined by the manner in which the force is generated.* This is why each cause of vibration has its own peculiar characteristics.

The forces which cause vibration are generated through the rotating motion of the machine's parts and thus change their amount and direction as the rotating part changes its position with respect to the rest of the machine. Therefore, the vibration resulting will have a frequency dependent upon the rotating speed of the part which has the trouble. This is why frequency tells which part is at fault.

There are other peculiarities associated with each cause of vibration, which include the relationship of phase observations at different points and the direction in which the vibration occurs. The displacement of vibration tells little regarding the cause of vibration, but it does indicate the severity of the trouble.

Vibration Analysis. The procedure for determining the characteristics of vibration is called vibration analysis. Vibration analysis consists of measuring the vibration present and the characteristics of that vibration. By comparing this information with what is known about the machine, its speed or speeds, what it does, and the various causes of vibration, the trouble can be pinpointed and correction prescribed.

Measuring Vibration. To measure the vibration the pickup must be placed at various points on a machine where the most useful information can be gained (Fig. 5-6). Axial-vibration readings are those taken with the pickup parallel to the center line of the shaft of the machine (A). The pickup is placed on the bearing housing as near to the shaft as possible. Vertical and horizontal readings are taken with the pickup perpendicular to the shaft center line and are generally called radial-vibration measurements (*B* and *C*).   It should be remembered that the pickup measures the vibration occurring in the direction in which it is pointed.

Readings at the base of the machine are taken at any convenient spot, preferably with the pickup in the vertical direction.

It is sometimes useful to know the actual vibration of a shaft to compare with bearing-housing vibrations.   Shaft readings can be taken by using a shaft stick like the one shown in Fig. 5-6*D*.   It is simply a hardwood fishtail-shaped stick with a stud

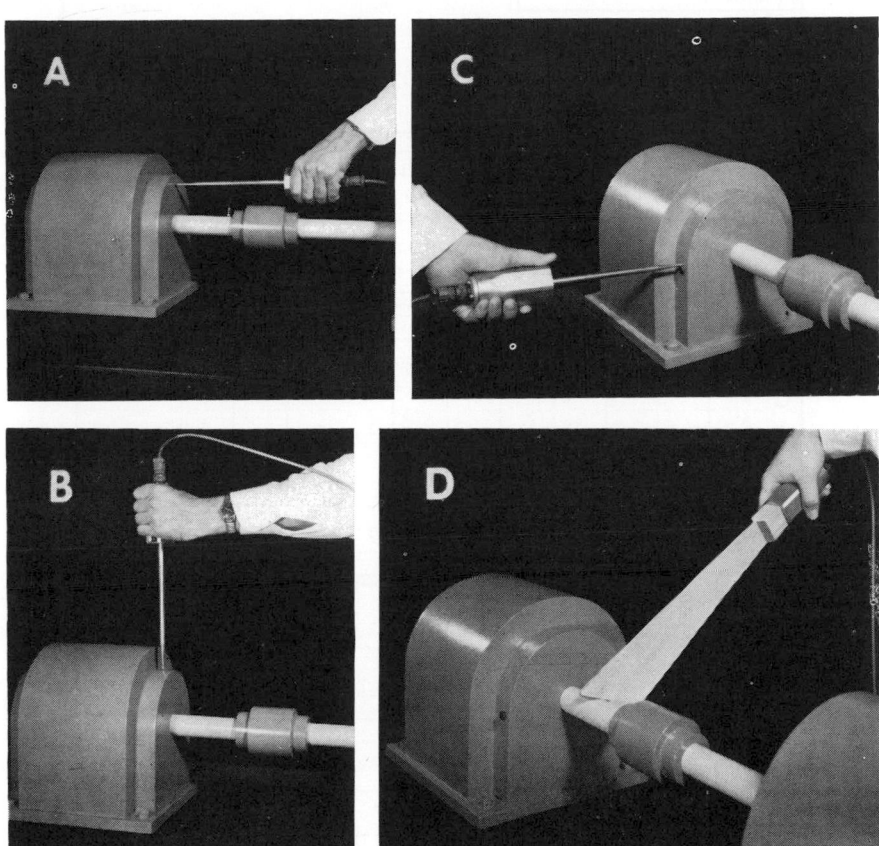

FIG. 5-6. Placing the vibration pickup: (*A*) axial; (*B*) vertical; (*C*) horizontal; (*D*) shaft.

for attaching to a pickup.   When taking shaft readings remember that any eccentricity or runout of the shaft will add to the indicated shaft vibration.

Often the position of the pickup will be dictated by the physical shape of the machine.   In general the pickup should be placed on, or as near as possible to, the bearings, because it is through the bearings that the vibration forces are transmitted.

Recording the Data.   A good vibration analyst keeps good records of his vibration readings.   This helps avoid confusion and provides a historical record for future reference.

The form illustrated in Fig. 5-7 is a typical one.   It furnishes room for a sketch of the machine in question with provisions for coding the listed readings to the point on the machine where vibration was measured, with ample room for measurements at

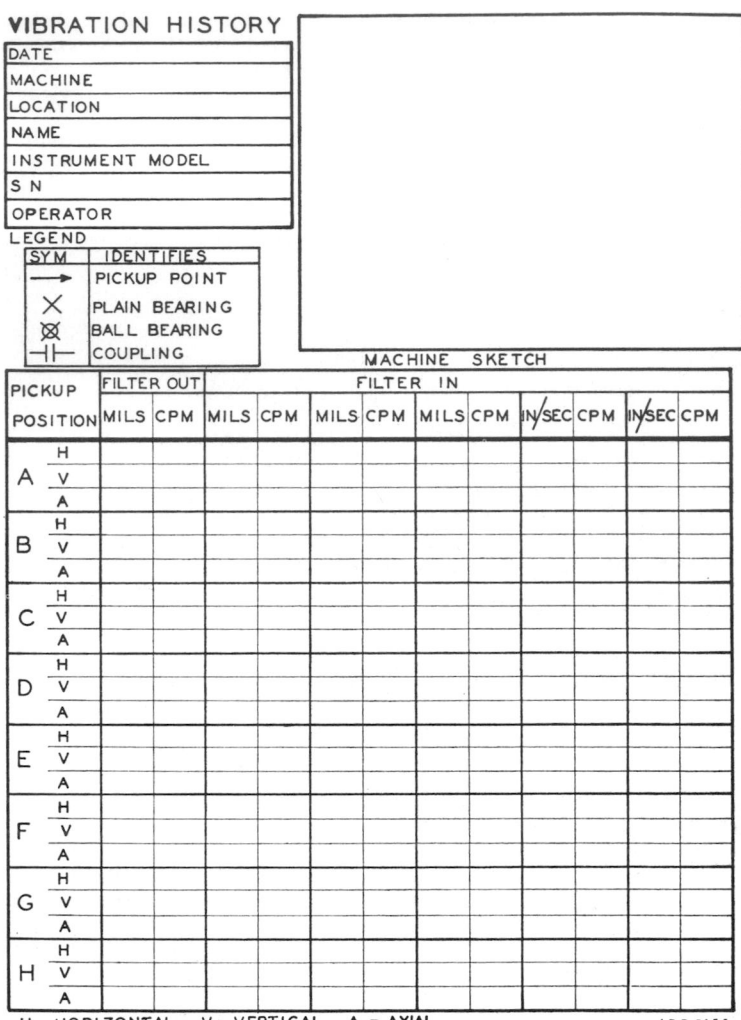

FIG. 5-7. Vibration data sheet.   (*Courtesy of IRD Corporation, Worthington, Ohio.*)

several frequencies.   For each of the pickup positions the operator should observe and record the following:

1. (*a*) Displacement; (*b*) predominant frequency; (*c*) phase or position of reference mark under strob light.
2. Analyzer with filter tuned to rotating speed frequency or predominant frequency observed in 1(*b*) above, record (*a*) displacement; (*b*) frequency; (*c*) phase.
3. Analyzer with filter tuned to each frequency where a steady reading can be observed, record (*a*) displacement; (*b*) frequency; (*c*) phase.

Any peculiarities noted should also be recorded.   After following this procedure, the operator should have a good record of the vibration in the machine.   During these measurements the machine should have been operating as it normally does.

A check for any vibration of the machine should also be made after it has been stopped to assure that the vibration measured is not coming from another machine. If background vibration is present and is occurring at the same frequencies observed previously, then it is likely that the original reading will be misleading, as these vibrations originate outside the machine.

Making the Comparison.   After the characteristics of the vibration have been determined, the next step is to compare the readings with the characteristics of vibration typical of various types of troubles.   The key to this comparison is frequency. The comparison by frequency is made on the basis of the rotating speed of the parts in the machine.

The table in Fig. 5-8 lists the frequency of vibration in terms of rpm of a part and the possible cause of the vibration.   The trouble referred to will be with the part whose rpm is some multiple of the vibration frequency.   The comparison made should indicate without any doubt the part causing the trouble.   After the comparison is made, the part causing the vibration is pinpointed and corrections can be prescribed.

The chart illustrated lists all the common causes of vibration likely to be encountered.   It lists the amplitude, frequency, and phase characteristics for each cause with remarks about any peculiar characteristics.   A few of the commoner ones are discussed in detail.

Vibration Due to Unbalance.   Unbalance is the largest single cause of vibration. Its vibration characteristics are not complicated by any peculiarities.   *The frequency of vibration due to unbalance is equal to the rotating speed of the part.*   The displacement of vibration due to unbalance is proportional to the amount of unbalance present. Even with the filter out, steady vibration readings are obtained and the strob light freezes the part.

Vibration Due to Misalignment.   Misalignment is the second largest cause of vibration.   The reason is quite simple.   In spite of self-aligning bearings and flexible couplings it is most difficult to align two shafts and their bearings properly so that no forces are present which will cause a vibration.   There are two types of misalignment (Fig. 5-9): angular, where the center line of the two shafts meet at an angle, and offset, where the center lines are parallel but offset to each other.   It is, of course, possible to have a combination of the two.

A bent shaft acts very much like angular misalignment so its vibration characteristics are included with misalignment.

Misalignment, even with flexible couplings, results in two forces, axial and radial, which cause axial and radial vibration.   This is true even when the misalignment is within the limits of "flexibility" of the coupling.   The size of the forces, and therefore the amount of vibration generated, will increase with increased misalignment.

The significant characteristic of vibration due to misalignment and bent shafts is that it will be in both the radial and *axial* directions.   This is the reason that axial-vibration readings are taken.   When the misalignment is severe, second- and sometimes third-order vibration frequencies may appear.   It is not possible to predict the conditions under which these higher-order frequencies will occur, because of the large number of possible combinations of couplings, shaft loadings, and bearings.

A condition of misalignment can exist which does not involve a coupling.   This is misalignment of a bearing with its shaft (Fig. 5-10).   In the case of a misaligned sleeve-type bearing no vibration will result unless there is also unbalance.   A radial vibration will be present as well as an axial vibration which results from the reaction of the misaligned bearing to the force due to unbalance.   The real cause of this vibration is unbalance, and both axial and radial readings will be reduced when the part is balanced.

When an antifriction bearing is misaligned with a shaft, then axial vibration will exist even when the part is balanced.   Proper installation of the bearing is necessary to eliminate the vibration.

Axial vibration is the best indicator of misalignment.   *When the axial vibration is one-half of the radial or more, then misalignment or a bent shaft should be suspected.*   A check or correction of this condition by conventional means should be made before any balancing is attempted.

VIBRATION IDENTIFICATION

CAUSE	AMPLITUDE	FREQUENCY	PHASE	REMARKS
Unbalance	Proportional to unbalance. Largest in radial direction.	1 x RPM	Single reference mark.	Most common cause of vibration.
Misalignment couplings or bearings and bent shaft	Large in axial direction 50% or more of radial vibration	1 x RPM usual 2 & 3 x RPM sometimes	Single double or triple	Best found by appearance of large axial vibration. Use dial indicators or other method for positive diagnosis. If sleeve bearing machine and no coupling misalignment balance the rotor.
Bad bearings anti-friction type	Unsteady - use velocity measurement if possible	Very high several times RPM	Erratic	Bearing responsible most likely the one nearest point of largest high-frequency vibration.
Eccentric journals	Usually not large	1 x RPM	Single mark	If on gears largest vibration in line with gear centers. If on motor or generator vibration disappears when power is turned off. If on pump or blower attempt to balance.
Bad gears or gear noise	Low - use velocity measure if possible	Very high gear teeth times RPM	Erratic	
Mechanical looseness		2 x RPM	Two reference marks. Slightly erratic.	Usually accompanied by unbalance and/or misalignment.
Bad drive belts	Erratic or pulsing	1, 2, 3 & 4 x RPM of belts	One or two depending on frequency. Usually unsteady.	Strob light best tool to freeze faulty belts.
Electrical	Disappears when power is turned off.	1 x RPM or 1 or 2 x synchronous frequency.	Single or rotating double mark.	If vibration amplitude drops off instantly when power is turned off cause is electrical.
Aerodynamic hydraulic forces		1 x RPM or number of blades on fan or impeller x RPM		Rare as a cause of trouble except in cases of resonance.
Reciprocating forces		1, 2 & higher orders x RPM		Inherent in reciprocating machines can only be reduced by design changes or isolation.

IRD # 393

FIG. 5-8. Vibration identification chart. (*Copyright IRD Corporation, Worthington, Ohio.*)

COPYRIGHT 1960 INTERNATIONAL RESEARCH AND DEVELOPMENT CORPORATION

Vibration Due to Antifriction Bearings.   Antifriction bearings which have flaws on the raceways, balls, or rolls will cause a high-frequency vibration.   This frequency is usually several times the rotating speed of the part but not necessarily an even multiple.   However, when a bad bearing is present, there will be little doubt, for this is usually the only explanation for such a high frequency of vibration.   The bad bearing is usually the one nearest the point where the greatest vibration of this type occurs.   Illustrated is an antifriction bearing detected by the presence of a high-frequency vibration.   Its only flaw appears on the one ball (see Fig. 5-11).

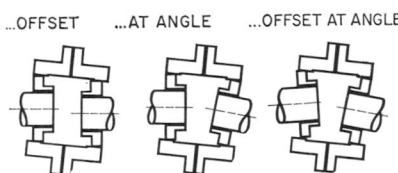

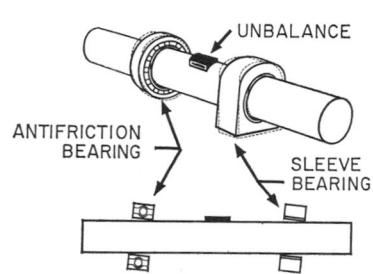

FIG. 5-9. Types of misalignment.   FIG. 5-10. Bearings misaligned with a shaft.

FIG. 5-11. Bad bearing detected by vibration analysis.   (*Courtesy of IRD Corporation, Worthington, Ohio*)

It should be remembered that bearings are one of the most precisely made devices available.   They do not fail prematurely unless some force or forces are responsible. Such forces are often the same as those which cause vibration.   A careful check for other difficulties such as unbalance and misalignment should be made after the bearing has been replaced.

Vibration Due to Sleeve Bearings.   Unlike antifriction bearings, sleeve bearings do not cause vibration except to a very minor degree.   A sleeve bearing with *excessive clearance may allow* unbalance, misalignment, or some other vibratory force to result in mechanical looseness or pounding.   The bearing is not the cause.   When it is suspected that a sleeve bearing is bad, more conventional methods of inspection should be used.

Although no definite conclusions have been reached, there is evidence to indicate that the quality of lubricant film in a bearing has more effect on the vibration *caused* by the bearing than any other factor. A nearly dry bearing has caused vibration at frequencies of one, two, three, four, and more multiples of rotating speed. A nearly dry bearing may also result in an oscillating amplitude of vibration, which increases and decreases periodically. Such vibrations are usually caused by a poor lubricant film and indicate that an inspection of the lubrication system is in order.

Vibration Due to Oil Whirl. On machines which operate at very high speeds or higher than their second critical speed, a vibration may be encountered called oil whip or oil whirl (Fig. 5-12). This vibration is often very severe. Normally it happens only on those high-speed machines where pressure-lubricated sleeve bearings are used.

The position of a shaft inside a bearing is to one side of the bearing center, depending on the direction of rotation. The distance up the side of the bearing the shaft will rise will depend on the rpm, weight, and oil pressure. As the shaft moves upward in the direction of rotation, greater quantities of oil are pumped into the evacuated space. In the case of oil whirl this is a continuing process and results in the shaft's whirling about the center of the bearing at a frequency approximately one-half rotating speed. This vibration is often quite violent, and the best correction is a change in the design of the bearing. For a quick cure, a change in the temperature of the lubricant is often effective.

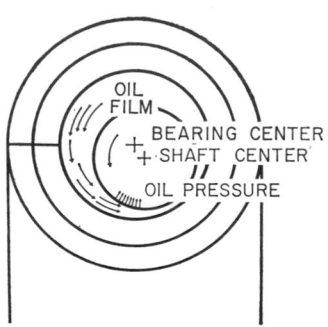

Fig. 5-12. Oil whirl.

Vibration Due to Looseness. Mechanical looseness and the resultant pounding action cause a vibration at a frequency twice the rotating speed of the loose part. This in part explains why misalignment sometimes has a frequency of vibration of twice rotating speed.

An example of looseness would be when a machine's base is free to rock on its foundation. Variations in torque and other forces associated with rotation will result in an impact of the base twice for each revolution. Excessive clearance in bearings results in the same thing. Most often such vibration disappears when the forces due to unbalance or misalignment are corrected.

Looseness often simply allows more vibration to occur than would otherwise appear, especially in antifriction bearings. When there is excessive clearance, even small amounts of unbalance result in large vibrations at first and second orders of the shaft speed. This can be viewed graphically with an oscilloscope attached to a vibration analyzer (Fig. 5-13). The odd-looking waveform which appears is typical of mechanical looseness and is the result of two frequencies of vibration: one at rotating speed and one at twice rotating speed.

Vibration Due to Bad Belts. Bad drive belts on belt-driven machines are often the cause of an undesirable vibration, especially on grinders. Such vibrations are most pronounced in the direction of tension on the belts. They occur at frequencies equal to one, two, three, and four times the rotating speed of the belts depending on the actual cause. Eccentric pulleys, high or low spots on the belts, slippage and unbalance will all result in a vibration of the belts and the machine upon which they are mounted.

The best way to detect belt vibrations is to apply the pickup perpendicular to, or in the direction of, tension of the belts on a bearing housing and then observe the belts under the strob light. A chalk mark on the belts will appear to stand still in one, two, etc. positions depending upon the frequency of the vibration generated. You can expect the vibration readings on the meters to be unsteady as well. This unsteadiness results from the fact that two pulleys run at different speeds and are of different diameters, and a high or low spot will be effective at varying times during the rotation of the belt.   Also with a multiple-belt installation, each belt may slip with a varying degree, so that the faults on the belt will at one time add to each other and another time subtract from each other.   The net result will be an increase and decrease of vibration in a periodic manner.

The only corrections for belt vibrations are *round pulleys and new well-matched* belts properly installed.   Some types of belts minimize vibration by way of their flexibility.

Inherent Vibrations.   *Electrical.*   Some machines have vibrations due to the manner in which they operate.   Electric motors will have vibration due to torque pulses.   The frequency of such a vibration is twice the synchronous frequency, which is the frequency at which alternating current is generated.   Here in the United States, synchronous frequency is usually 60 cps, or 3,600 cpm.   Therefore, the frequency at which the torque-pulse vibrations occur will be 7,200 cpm.

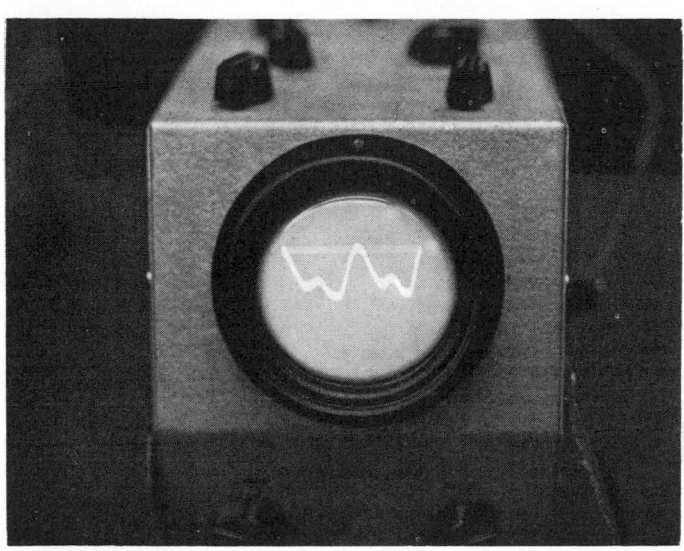

Fig. 5-13. Oscilloscope pattern typical of mechanical looseness.   (*Courtesy of IRD Corporation, Worthington, Ohio.*)

This is rarely a troublesome vibration except on grinders, where extremely low vibration levels are sought.   The best way to detect the presence of this vibration is to place the pickup on the motor housing, as shown in Fig. 5-14.

Electrically excited vibrations such as torque pulses, eccentric motor-armature journals, and others may be pinpointed rather easily.   If a vibration disappears instantly when the electric power is turned off, this is positive evidence that the cause of that vibration is primarily electrical.

Reciprocating Forces.   Reciprocating machines will have vibrations which result from the reciprocating motion.   The forces which cause vibration result from the inertia of the parts and the steam or gas pressure on the pistons which cause torque variations.   In piston-type engines and compressors the amount of vibration and the frequency of the vibration will depend upon the number of pistons and their relationship to each other.   The frequencies of vibration normally found are first- and second-order.   Other orders can also be detected in some engines.   Six- and eight-cylinder in-line engines are generally balanced with regard to the reciprocating forces and respond nicely to mass balancing when required.   The usual procedure is to isolate such machines from their bases to restrict the transmission of vibration to other machines.

Hydraulic Forces.   Machines which handle fluids such as air, water, gas, etc., will have vibrations due to the reaction of the blades or impellers striking the fluid.   As an example, a large, multiple-bladed, induced-draft fan may have vibrations at a frequency equal to rotating speed times the number of blades.   Such vibrations are rarely troublesome unless they excite some part of the machine to resonance.

Rubbing.   Rubbing may cause the vibration to have, in addition to the rotating speed frequency, a frequency at twice rotating speed.   If the rubbing is continuous, it is unlikely that any particular vibration characteristics will be noted.   A very high frequency may be present and be due to friction's exciting a natural frequency of the system.   It has been reported that rubbing in the seals of a steam turbine will cause changes in amplitude and phase from one run to the next when no changes have been made to the system.

FIG. 5-14. Pickup position for measuring electric torque pulses.   (*Courtesy of IRD Corporation, Worthington, Ohio.*)

For example, a steam turbine running at 3,600 rpm will have a certain amount and phase of vibration at rotating-speed frequency.   Reducing the speed to 1,800 rpm and then increasing the speed again to 3,600 rpm will produce a new amount and/or phase. This seems to indicate that the point at which rubbing occurs changes from one run to the next.

Rubbing, when it exists, is usually the result of a bent shaft or some similar distortion of the system that would indicate itself by other vibration characteristics.

Resonance.   The forces which cause vibration vary in their amount or direction or both.   The frequency at which the force varies is called the *exciting frequency*, and it determines at what frequency vibration will occur.

Every part of a machine has a *natural frequency*.   This is the frequency at which the part *likes* to vibrate.   Resonance occurs when the exciting frequency is the same as the natural frequency of the part.   The part will vibrate more at its natural frequency than at any other.   This means that a relatively small exciting force is required to get a lot of vibration when resonance occurs.

For example, one problem involving resonance occurred on a large cooling-tower fan. The fan had four blades and rotated at 300 rpm. An extremely large vibration was measured at a frequency of 1,200 cpm. It was apparent that the exciting force was the hydraulic forces of the fan. The support member which had the largest vibration apparently had a natural frequency close to 1,200 cpm.

Several approaches to solution of the problem were possible: removing the exciting force, changing the frequency of the exciting force, or changing the natural frequency of the support. In this case removing the exciting force was not feasible, since the hydraulic or aerodynamic forces were inherent and necessary if air was to be moved. The frequency of the exciting force could have been changed by changing the speed of the fan or by changing the number of fan blades, but neither of these solutions was desirable. Changing the natural frequency seemed to be the best approach. Two things determine what the natural frequency of a part is, the stiffness and mass or weight of the part. The wooden support was replaced with a stiffer and lighter aluminum one. Vibration at 1,200 cpm was hardly measurable.

Vibration Isolation. Normally it is recommended that the source or cause of vibration be sought and corrected. If a vibration is the result of a mechanical trouble, this should always be done. Since there are many vibrations which are inherent in certain types of machines, vibration isolation is often the only solution. However, care should be exercised in selecting the method and type of materials to be used. Vibration isolation is a job for the expert; however, knowledge of vibration analysis can be used to provide the expert with the right information.

Vibration isolation works both ways. It can be used to isolate a machine from vibration transmitted to it from other machines, or it can be used to isolate a machine so it will not transmit its vibration to other machines and the building around it. Whichever is required or more economical, the principles are the same.

The mass or weight of the machine is the first consideration. What are the disturbing vibration frequencies you wish to avoid or isolate? And last, what degree of isolation is desired? A vibration analyzer can be used to determine the frequencies of the disturbing vibrations and their amplitude and later to evaluate the isolation mounts installed.

The actual job of selecting vibration isolators should be left to someone who understands the engineering principles and is familiar with the commercial isolators available.

Vibration Tolerances. How much is too much vibration? Making the decision to correct a condition of vibration is often a tough one, especially when it involves downtime of critical machinery.

Figure 5-15 shows a vibration-severity chart which is commonly used for maintaining long service life of a machine. Note that the higher the frequency, the smaller the allowable vibration.

Whatever the decision, it should be based on a balance of cost, downtime, service life, and the importance of the machine in carrying out your company's activity.

Precision machine tools are easier to apply tolerances to because they can be based on the machine's ability to produce a certain size or finish tolerance. Figure 5-16 shows some tolerances whose values come from years of experience with vibration analysis of machine tools. They indicate the range in which satisfactory parts have been produced, and will vary depending upon size and finish tolerances.

Sample Problem. Vibration analysis is the process used to learn whether or not the mechanical condition of a machine is acceptable and, if not, to learn what is wrong with the machine so that corrections can be made. In effect, we *measure* the vibration present, *compare* the readings with the identification and tolerance charts to *pinpoint* the trouble and prescribe *correction*. The most vital step is the comparison. Following is a sample problem where the vibration has already been measured. You make the comparison and pinpoint the cause for each vibration and indicate if correction is required. The machine in question is a large motor-driven pump (Fig. 5-17), which has just been overhauled. There were no other noticeable vibrations.

(*a*) What are the possible causes for the vibration which occurs at 1,800 cpm on bearings *A* and *B*?

INTERNATIONAL RESEARCH AND DEVELOPMENT CORPORATION
Worthington, Ohio

GENERAL MACHINERY VIBRATION SEVERITY CHART

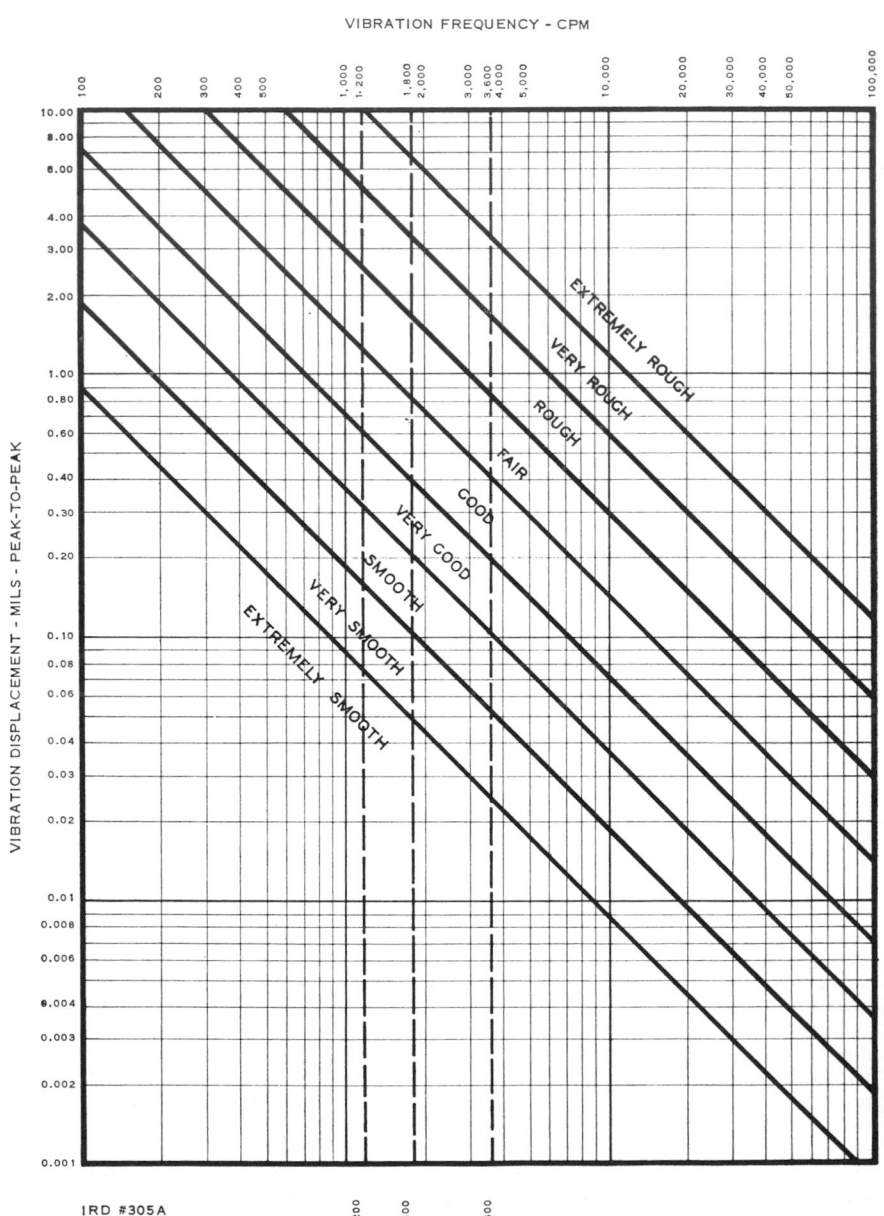

IRD #305A

FIG. 5-15. Vibration severity chart.

TENTATIVE GUIDE TO VIBRATION TOLERANCES FOR MACHINE TOOLS

TYPE OF MACHINE

Displacement of vibrations as read with pickup on spindle bearing housing in the direction of cut.

Grinders   **Tolerance Range**

Thread Grinder   .01   —   .06 mils

Profile or Contour Grinder   .03   —   .08 mils

Cylindrical Grinder   .03   —   .10 mils

Surface Grinder (vertical reading)   .03   —   .2   mils

Gardner or Besly Type   .05   —   .2   mils

Centerless   .04   —   .1   mil

Boring Machine   .06   —   .1   mil

Lathe   .2   — 1.0 `mils

These values come from the experience of IRD personnel who have been troubleshooting machine tools for over 10 years with the IRD equipment. *They merely indicate the range in which satisfactory parts* have been produced and will vary depending upon size and finish tolerances.

IRD #192

FIG. 5-16. Guide to machine tool vibration tolerances. (*Copyright IRD Corporation, Worthington, Ohio.*)

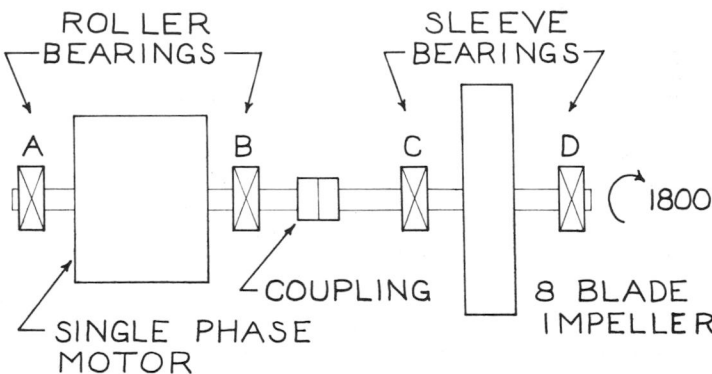

FIG. 5-17. Problem sketch and vibration readings.

Pickup	Location	DISP	FREQ	DISP	FREQ	DISP	FREQ	DISP	FREQ
	Vert	1.8	1800	.3	3600	.05	7,200		
A	Horiz	2.5	1800	.5	3600	.05	7,200		
	Axial	1.3	1800	.09	3600	.01	7,200		
	Vert	2.1	1800	.4	3600	.05	7,200	.08	Variable 45,000
B	Horiz	3.2	1800	.7	3600	.05	7,200	.07	Variable 45,000
	Axial	1.9	1800	.15	3600	.01	7,200		
	Vert	1.1	1800	.2	3600	.05	14,400		
C	Horiz	1.3	1800	.15	3600	.4	14,400	.4	1200
	Axial	1.2	1800	—	—	—	—	.45	1200
	Vert	1.3	1800	.2	3600	.08	14,400	.25	1200
D	Horiz	1.1	1800	.09	3600	.05	14,400	.30	1200
	Axial	1.5	1800	—	—	—	—	.42	1200

Displacement readings are in mils. Frequency readings are in CPM.

(*b*) If more than one cause is possible, how would you check to be positive of what the cause is?

(*c*) What is the cause of the 3,600-cpm vibration on bearings *A* and *B* as well as *C* and *D*?

(*d*) What is the cause of the 7,200-cpm vibration on bearings *A* and *B*?

(*e*) What is the cause of the 45,000-cpm vibration on bearing *B*?

(*f*) What is the cause of the 14,400-cpm vibration on bearings *C* and *D*?

(*g*) What is the cause of the 1,200-cpm vibration on bearings *C* and *D*?

(*h*) How would you know whether or not a correction of the troubles causing these vibrations is necessary?

The answers to the sample problem are on page 13-182.

Balancing. Unbalance has been named the most common cause of vibration in machines. Since this is true, it would be an advantage to correct this condition as easily as possible. Before a part can be balanced with the vibration analyzer, certain conditions must be satisfied. *The vibration must be due to unbalance, and it must be possible to make weight corrections on the rotor and to observe the rotor with the strob light for phase measurements.*

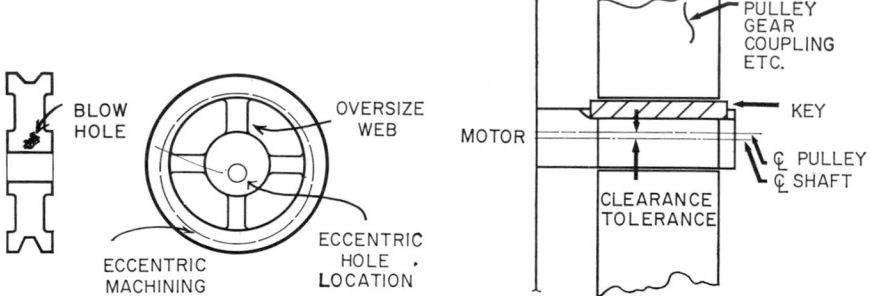

FIG. 5-18. Sources of unbalance.   FIG. 5-19. Stack up of assembly tolerances.

The conditions which must be satisfied can almost always be met with the unbalanced part mounted in its own bearings, operating as it normally does. The process of balancing a part without taking it out of the machine is called *in-place balancing.*

In-place balancing eliminates the need to disassemble the machine, transport the part to a balancing machine, and balance under artificial conditions, and it assures smooth operation of the machine when you are done.

In-place balancing is a straightforward process which involves following a few simple rules. However, before discussing balancing we shall first cover unbalance, where it comes from, and what must be done to correct it.

Unbalance. Unbalance is the unequal distribution of the weight of a part about its rotating center line (Fig. 5-18). Illustrated are some reasons for an unequal weight distribution. The blowhole in the casting, the thicker web, the eccentric hole location, and eccentric machining of the pulley groove all add up to more weight on one side of the rotating center line than on the other. The faults shown are exaggerated but could easily exist in almost every rotating part manufactured.

More important as a source of unbalance is the accumulation of tolerances possible when assembling rotating parts. The example illustrated in Fig. 5-19 is a very common one. The hole in the pulley is necessarily larger than the shaft diameter, and when a key or setscrew is attached, the take-up in clearance shifts the weight of the pulley to one side of the rotating center line of the shaft. Thus the assembly is out of balance.

All the combinations of unequal weight distribution can be considered to be concentrated at one point, called the heavy spot. This heavy spot represents the accumulated results of all of the unbalance of the pulley.   An equal amount of weight at the same radius but opposite the heavy spot will balance the rotor.

The units for measuring unbalance are generally ounce-inches or gram-inches (Fig. 5-20).   Thus 1 oz-in. of unbalance would be a heavy spot 1 oz in weight 1 in. from the rotating center line, and 3 oz located 3 in. from the center would be 9 oz-in.

The effect of unbalance is that it generates a force which causes the part and the supporting bearing and structure to vibrate.   The size of the force generated depends

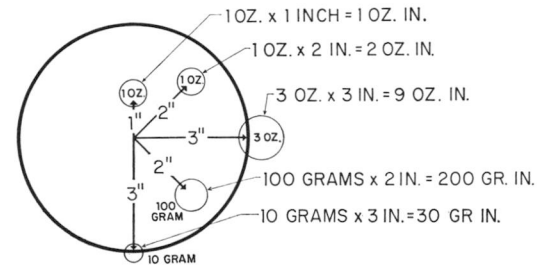

UNBALANCE = WEIGHT x DISTANCE FROM CENTER

Fig. 5-20. Unbalance units of measure.

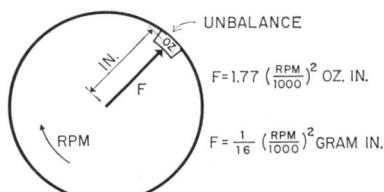

Fig. 5-21. Force due to unbalance.

on the speed of rotation and the amount of unbalance.   In Fig. 5-21 the part has an unbalance represented by a heavy spot located some distance from the center of rotation.   If the heavy spot and distance are in ounces and inches, the force generated can be computed by the formula

$$F = 1.77 \left(\frac{\text{rpm}}{1,000}\right)^2 \times \text{oz-in.}$$

F is the force in pounds; rpm, the rotating speed of the part, ounce-inch the amount of unbalance, and 1.77 a constant required to make the formula dimensionally correct. When the unbalance is given in terms of gram-inches, the formula becomes

$$F = \frac{1}{16} \left(\frac{\text{rpm}}{1,000}\right)^2 \times \text{g-in.}$$

The amount of force generated by 1 oz-in. of unbalance at high speeds is surprising and explains why good balance becomes absolutely necessary for high-speed machines. For instance, at 3,600 rpm nearly 23 lb of force is generated for each ounce-inch of unbalance.

Vibration Related to Unbalance.   The more unbalance present, the greater the force, and therefore the greater the vibration.   The amount of vibration indicates how much unbalance is present.   The position of a reference mark on the unbalanced part as seen by the strob light indicates the location of the unbalance.

The reference mark shifts in the opposite direction to a shift of the heavy spot. The angle the reference mark shifts is used to determine the angle of shift of the heavy spot.

At the start of a balancing operation the size of the heavy spot and its location are unknown. The unbalance in the part at the start is called the *original unbalance*, and the vibration amount and phase which represents that unbalance is called the *original reading*. The original unbalance is changed by adding a *trial weight* to the part. The new total unbalance in the part will be represented by a new amount and phase of vibration. The change caused by the trial weight can be used to learn the size and location of the original unbalance, or where the trial weight must be placed to be opposite the original unbalance and how large the trial weight must be to be equal but opposite the original spot.

When a trial weight is added, three things can happen. *First,* if the trial weight is added right on the heavy spot, the vibration will increase and the reference mark will

Fig. 5-22. The original reading. (*Courtesy of IRD Corporation, Worthington, Ohio.*)

appear in the same position it did on the original run. To balance the part the trial weight is moved directly opposite its first position and the amount adjusted until a satisfactory balance is obtained.

Second, the trial weight may be added in exactly the right place—opposite the heavy spot. If the trial weight is smaller than the unbalance, then the heavy spot will still be the heavy spot, but the vibration will decrease and the reference mark will be in the same place. To balance, add more weight until a satisfactory vibration level is reached.

If the trial weight is larger than the unbalance, its position will now be the heavy spot, and the reference mark will shift 180°, or directly opposite where it was originally. To balance, the trial weight is reduced until a satisfactory vibration level is reached.

Third (and what usually happens) the trial weight is added neither at the heavy spot or opposite it. When this happens, the reference mark shifts to a new position, and the vibration displacement changes. By what angle should the trial weight be shifted, in which direction, and should its amount be increased or decreased to be equal but opposite the original unbalance?

Single-plane Vector Method of Balancing.   An unbalance vector is simply a line whose length represents the amount of the unbalance and whose direction represents the angle of the unbalance.   When a trial weight is added to the part, the original unbalance is changed and the position of the *total* unbalance is some new position between the two.   A new vibration displacement and reference-mark position or phase will be observed.

Note: (1) The position of the reference mark is *not* the location of the heavy spot. (2) The trial weight is added at any convenient location on the part.

Example.   The original unbalance (Fig. 5-22) is represented by 1.8 *mils* and a phase (reference-mark position) of 12:40 *o'clock*.   After adding a trial weight, the unbalance due to both the *original plus the trial weight is represented by* 2.30 *mils and a phase of* 2:30 *o'clock*.

Using polar-coordinate graph paper, plot the original unbalance vector.   Draw a line from the center at the same angle as the reference mark, 12:40 o'clock.   Each hour is equal to 30°.   Select a convenient scale for the length of the line, such as 1 mil equals two divisions.   Call this vector *O* for the *original unbalance*.

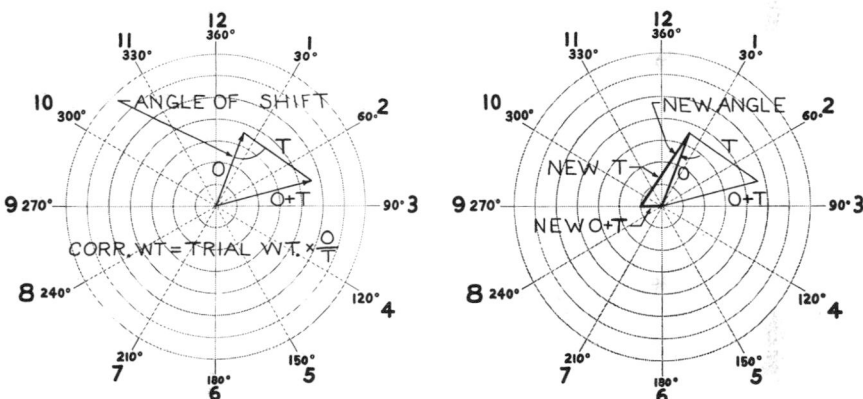

Fig. 5-23. The vector diagram.   Fig. 5-24. Vector diagram for additional corrections.

Next, draw the *original plus the trial-weight* unbalance vector *O + T* to the same scale.   It is drawn at the new angle for the original plus the trial-weight unbalance phase, 2:30 o'clock.   This is all the information needed to solve for the effect of the trial weight alone.

To solve for the trial-weight vector, connect the end of vector *O* to the end of vector *O + T*.   Mark this line *T* (see Fig. 5-23).

The correct balance weight is equal to the trial weight times *O/T*.   The balance weight should be added at an angle equal to angle between *O* and *T* away from where the trial weight was added.   The *direction* of this angle is *opposite* from the shift of the reference mark on the trial run.

Note: The trial weight is moved from its position on the part through the angle determined by the vector diagram.   This is *not* an angle from the reference mark but is the angle from the trial weight's old position to a new one.

Small errors in measuring the phase angle, in shifting the weight, and adjusting the weight to the proper amount can result in some remaining vibration still due to unbalance.

To make further corrections simply observe the new amount and phase of vibration. Plot this reading as a new *O + T* (see Fig. 5-24).   Then connect the ends of *O* and the *new O + T* vector to find the *new T*.   This may be repeated as many times as necessary but *always using the original O line*.

This, then, is the vector method for single-plane balancing. It is simple to use and provides accurate information to balance a part in the fewest number of starts and stops of the machine as possible.

Single-plane Four-step Method of Balancing. Another method for balancing, which is not so precise as the vector method, follows the same basic procedure. The four-step method follows a few simple rules to find the proper location for the correction weight, after which the amount is adjusted to balance the part. Since it generally requires many starts and stops for the machine, it is not very popular, except when the number of balancing runs is not important.

Refer to Figs. 5-25 to 5-27. First observe the amount of vibration and the position of the reference mark when the strob light flashes. For example, 2.4 mils at 5:00 o'clock. This is the original run. All future data will be referred to these readings,

Fig. 5-25. Original reading, 2.4 mils at 5:00 o'clock. (*Courtesy of IRD Corporation, Worthington, Ohio.*)

just as in the vector method. Next, add a trial weight to the part at any convenient location and again observe the amount and phase, 1.8 mils at 7:00 o'clock.

The first goal is to shift the trial weight to a position where the reference mark returns to its original position or 180° away. Do this by shifting the trial weight in a direction opposite the shift of the reference mark. Do not be afraid to move the trial weight by a large angle, because if you move it too far, the phase will direct you to move it back. In the example (Fig. 5-28) the reference mark shifted from 5:00 to 7:00 o'clock after adding the trial weight. This is a clockwise shift of the reference mark. Therefore, move the trial weight in the counterclockwise direction. A new reading might be 2.3 mils at 3:00 o'clock (not illustrated). This would indicate the weight was moved too far because the mark is counterclockwise from the first position of 5:00 o'clock.

Shifting the weight again, the reference mark may be returned to its original position, and the vibration reduced to 0.1 mil. This means the weight is in the proper position and needs only a slight increase in the size of the trial weight. If the reference mark had appeared 180° away from its original position, the weight would have been in the proper place but too large. If the reference mark had returned to its original position

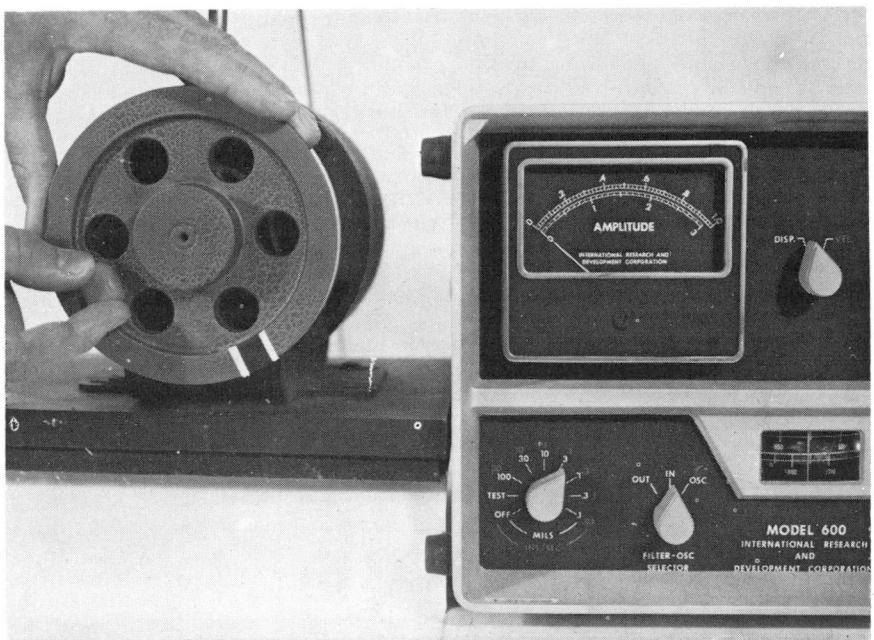

FIG. 5-26. Adding a trial weight.   (*Courtesy of IRD Corporation, Worthington, Ohio.*)

FIG. 5-27. Trial run reading, 1.8 mils at 7:00 o'clock.   (*Courtesy of IRD Corporation, Worthington, Ohio.*)

but with an increased vibration, then the trial weight would have been on the heavy spot.

Sample Problems.   Following are some examples of balancing problems.   You are given the original readings and the readings after a trial weight has been added.   See if you can solve each problem correctly.   Your answer should indicate, first, the direc-

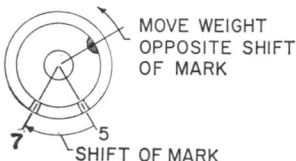

Fig. 5-28. Direction to shift the trial weight.

tion to move the trial weight; second, the angle; and third, the adjustment required to get the correct size of the trial weight.

	Amount, mils	Phase, o'clock
1. Original reading..............	5.0	3:00
First trial reading............	3.0	4:00

Answer.   The reference mark moved from 3:00 to 4:00, a clockwise shift.   The trial weight must be moved *counterclockwise* from its position for the trial run.

Discussion.   The vector diagram was constructed as shown in Fig. 5-29.   The O vector was scaled off to five units long, representing 5 mils vibration.   The $O + T$

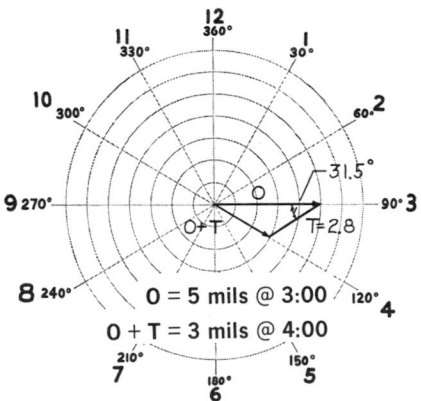

Fig. 5-29. Vector diagram.

vector was scaled off to the same scale as the O vector.   The ends of the O and $O + T$ vectors were connected.   This is the T vector.   The angle between the O vector and the T vector is the angle the trial weight must be moved from its position for the trial run.

The length of the T vector was measured, using the same scale used for the O and $O + T$ vectors.   The effect of the trial weight is smaller than the original unbalance because the T vector is shorter than the O vector.   The amount the trial weight must be increased was calculated using the formula

$$\text{Correct weight} = \text{trial weight} \times \frac{O}{T}$$

The solution is to move the trial weight 32° counterclockwise from its position on the first trial run. At the same time increase the size of the trial weight 1.75 times its original size.

Now you work the rest.

	Amount, mils	Phase, o'clock
2. Original reading...............	3.0	7:00
First trial reading............	4.0	7:00
3. Original reading...............	9.0	10:30
First trial reading............	4.5	4:30
4. Original reading...............	18.0	9:00
First trial reading............	3.0	9:00
5. Original reading...............	9.0	2:00
First trial reading............	1.5	9:00
6. Original reading...............	9.0	2:00
First trial reading............	9.0	12:00

Determine the corrections required. After the corrections indicated by the readings above have been made, a new reading is taken indicating additional correction is required.

Second trial reading......3.0 mils at 4:45 o'clock

What additional correction is required? Check your answers to these problems with the answers on page 13-183.

Dynamic Balancing. Up to this point unbalance and its correction as it occurs in a single plane or disk have been discussed. There are actually two types of unbalance, static and dynamic (Fig. 5-30).

Static unbalance is that condition of weight distribution of a rotor where the center of gravity does not lie on the rotating center line of the rotor. Static unbalance gets its name from the fact that it can be detected by placing the part on level parallel knife edges. The heavy side of the rotor will swing to the bottom. Corrections can be made, and the part is considered balanced when it does not rotate on the knife edges when placed in any position.

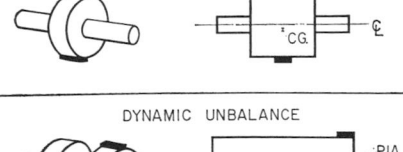

FIG. 5-30. Static and dynamic unbalance.

Static unbalance is sometimes known as force or kinetic unbalance. These names imply rotation of the unbalanced part and are applied by balancing-machine manufacturers who make machines to correct static unbalance by rotating the part. This is, in most cases, a better approach than knife edges because of increased production rates and precision.

The center of gravity of a part is the point about which all the weight of a rotor is equally distributed. If a rotor were sliced into a series of small slices, the line through the centers of gravity of each slice would be the principal inertia axis. This is the axis about which any rotor will try to rotate. When a rotor is restricted in its bearings, vibration results if the principal inertia axis and the rotating center line are not the same.

Dynamic unbalance is that condition of weight distribution of a rotor which causes the principal inertia axis to intersect the rotating center line. The intersection will occur at the center of gravity of the rotor. Such a condition is created by a heavy spot at each end of the rotor but on opposite sides of the center line, so as to produce two forces acting in opposite directions on opposite ends of the rotor.

Dynamic unbalance is also called couple or moment unbalance. These names come from the "couple" of forces or the "moments" they create about the center of gravity. Dynamic unbalance cannot be detected on knife edges, as static can, and doesn't become apparent until the part is rotated. Thus the name dynamic.

These then are the two types of unbalance, static and dynamic. They may be present in a rotor individually, but normally an unbalanced rotor includes some of each.

Consider the rotor illustrated in Fig. 5-31, which is a shaft with two slender disks mounted fairly far apart. The disk at the left has an unbalance at the 12:00-o'clock point. The other disk is unbalanced by the same amount at the 6:00-o'clock point on the opposite side of the rotor. This is dynamic unbalance, and could be corrected only by weight corrections in two planes. When the disks are right next to each other, the two unbalanced weights cancel each other, and for all practical purposes the rotor is balanced. The only significant unbalance would be if one weight were larger than the other. This would be static unbalance and could be corrected by weight added in a single plane.

A rotor whose length is significantly smaller than its diameter will have static unbalance, and a weight correction in a single plane is all that is required.

Separating the disks but with the unbalance weights on the same side of the rotor again results in static unbalance but could only be corrected by weights added in each disk or plane. By moving one weight 90° a combination of static and dynamic unbalance is produced, which could be corrected only by weights added in two planes. This shows that static unbalance is possible in two or more planes.

Balancing problems are divided into two types, single-plane and two-plane. One authority says that the type of correction or balance planes should be based on the length-to-diameter ratio or the length divided by the diameter. The L/D ratio is calculated using the dimensions of the rotor exclusive of the supporting shaft. For L/D ratios *less* than 0.5, single-plane balancing is sufficient for operating speeds from 0 to 1,000 rpm. Above 1,000 rpm, two-plane balancing is required. For L/D ratios *greater* than 0.5, two-plane balancing is required for operating speed greater than 150 rpm. There is no argument with these recommendations, except that smooth operation is the final authority, and corrections should be made on that basis. You will find from your own experience that single-plane balancing is suitable for devices such as single-sheave pulleys and grinding wheels.

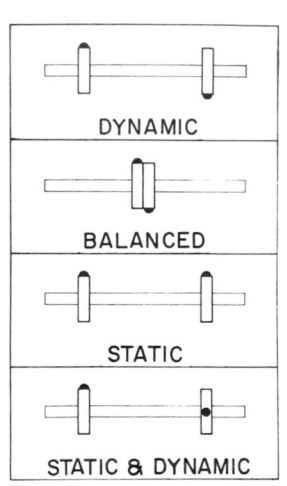

FIG. 5-31. Types of unbalance related to the number of planes of unbalance.

Very few rotors are actually made of one or two simple disks but are usually composed of a large number of disks, sometimes assembled into complex shapes. This makes it impossible to know in which disk the unbalance lies. The unbalance could be in any plane or planes located along the length of a rotor, and there is no way to tell where. Furthermore, it isn't always possible to make weight correction just any place. Therefore, it is necessary to compromise by making weight corrections in the two most convenient planes available. This is fine because *any condition of unbalance can be compensated for by weight corrections in any two balancing planes at a given operating speed.* This is true only if the rotor and shaft are rigid and do not bend or deflect under the forces caused by unbalance.

Rotors which operate below 70 per cent of their critical speed are considered rigid. Those which operate above 70 per cent of their critical speed are considered flexible rotors. Flexible rotors whose unbalance was not corrected in the actual plane of unbalance will distort or bend at high speeds.

Critical Speed and Resonance. Every material has a natural frequency, a frequency at which it likes to vibrate. Some of the best examples of natural-frequency vibration are found in musical instruments. The tuning fork, the violin, drums, and bells all vibrate at their natural frequency when struck or plucked. The natural frequency of most musical instruments is readily changed to give various musical notes. Two things most affect what the natural frequency of a part is: the stiffness or spring constant and the weight or mass of the part. When the natural frequency of some part of a machine is also equal to the rotating speed, there is a condition of resonance. The rotating speed at which resonance occurs is a critical speed.

Starting with a machine at rest, if the speed of the machine is increased at the same time as the vibration is measured, the result is a graph like the one in Fig. 5-32, showing an increase in vibration then a drop back to a fairly constant amount of vibration. The speed at which the peaks occurs is where resonance occurs, and is called the critical speed.

The things which decide the critical speed of a machine are the stiffness and weight of the machine. The bearing housing will have a certain stiffness, which is probably

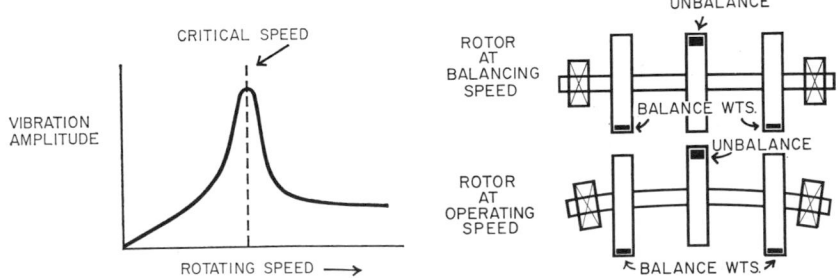

FIG. 5-32. Critical speed curve.   FIG. 5-33. Shaft bending due to unbalance.

different from the shaft stiffness. Therefore, a bearing-housing critical as well as a shaft critical will be observed. In discussing rigid and flexible rotors the shaft critical is referred to.

A rotor which does not operate above 70 per cent of its critical speed is a rigid rotor, and when balanced at one speed, is balanced at any other normal operating speed below 70 per cent of critical speed. A flexible rotor balanced at a speed below its critical speed will not necessarily be balanced when operated above its critical speed. Here's why:

The rotor illustrated in Fig. 5-33 has three planes or disks where unbalance is possible. All the unbalance is in the center disk. At a rotating speed below 70 per cent of critical the rotor can be balanced with weight corrections in the two end planes. Above 70 per cent of the critical speed the rotor would still be balanced if the force in the center disk did not deflect or bend the shaft. The shaft does bend, and the weight of the disk is moved out away from the rotating center line. This adds to the original unbalance, creating a new unbalance for which there is no correction. The rotor can, of course, be balanced at its operating speed by additional corrections in the two end planes. The rotor would then be out of balance at slow rotating speeds, where there is no deflection.

What is the solution to such a problem? Balancing the rotor in the actual plane of unbalance is the answer, but there is no way of knowing in which plane the actual unbalance lies. By increasing the number of planes in which balance corrections are made, a better compromise of balance can be assured. This is actually what is done. It is called multiplane balancing.

Although there are only two kinds of unbalance, static and dynamic, there are actually three kinds of balancing problems, single-plane, two-plane, and multiplane.

Two-plane Balancing. It should be apparent that balancing is a compromise, where at a certain rotating speed balance corrections are made to reduce the vibration at the bearing supports.   Corrections are made in planes where it is convenient and are good only for the conditions under which the part was balanced.   A change in speed is likely to produce a new unbalance condition.   Whenever possible, therefore, a rotor should be balanced or trim-balanced in its own operating environment under normal operating conditions.   By recognizing the facts which effect balance the best compromise can be reached.

Two-plane balancing is done in much the same manner as single-plane.   However, two-plane balancing requires some special attention because of cross-effect.

To show what is meant by cross-effect, begin with a perfectly balanced rotor (Fig. 5-34).   Adding an unbalance in the right-hand correction plane and taking a vibration reading at the right-hand bearing support, we should see, say, 5.0 mils at 3:00 o'clock. This is to be expected.   At the left-hand bearing a vibration of 0.66 mil is also noted with a phase of 10:00 o'clock.   This vibration is due to cross-effect, which is the vibration at the left-hand bearing caused by unbalance in the right-hand correction plane.

To see what this does to two-plane balancing, an unbalance added in the left-hand correction plane changes the amount and phase of vibration at the right-hand bearing to 6.4 mils at 4:00 o'clock.   Therefore, cross-effect results in giving vibration readings which do not exactly represent the unbalance in the correction plane.   The amount and phase of the cross-effect vibration will be different for different machines.

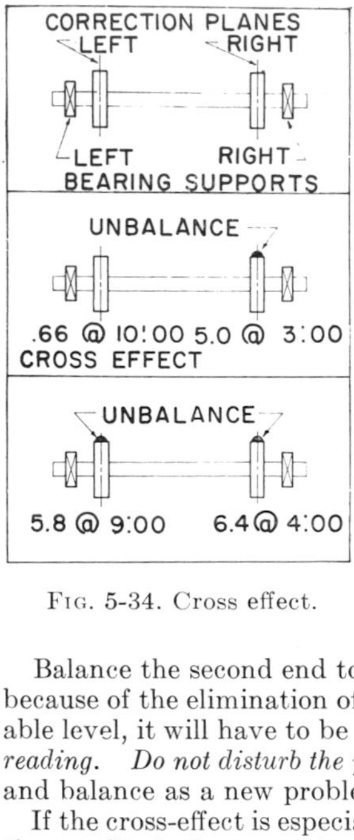

Cross-effect must be taken into account when balancing in two planes.   There are many ways to do this. The most popular is to treat each correction plane as a single-plane problem using the nearest bearing for the vibration readings.   Balancing each correction plane as a single-plane problem is not always 100 per cent effective, however, because of cross-effect.   Here is what must be done:

Observe the amount and phase of vibration at each bearing.   Select the one with the most vibration to balance first.   Balance the first end down to an acceptable level.   This will usually result in a different amount and phase reading at the other end of the rotor, because you have removed most of the cross-effect. This gives you a *new original* reading to be used in balancing the second end.

FIG. 5-34. Cross effect.

Balance the second end to an acceptable level.   The first-end vibration will change because of the elimination of cross-effect.   If the change is an increase to an unacceptable level, it will have to be rebalanced.   *This new reading is once again a new original reading.   Do not disturb the previously applied corrections.   Start with a new trial weight* and balance as a new problem.

If the cross-effect is especially severe, this procedure may have to be repeated several times.   Each time you change correction planes you must start a new problem using the new original readings.   Do not disturb the earlier corrections.

The typical setup for two-plane balancing includes a vibration analyzer with an additional pickup and a two-position selector switch.   A means for accurately measuring phase, a protractor, a straightedge, polar-coordinate graph paper, and a scale for weighing balance weights are also necessary for precise balancing in as few runs as possible.   Here is a step-by-step procedure in common use:

1. First analyze the vibration to determine that the vibration is due to unbalance.

2. Observe and record the amplitude and phase of the vibration at each bearing in the vertical, horizontal, and axial directions.   Select either the vertical or horizontal reading, whichever is larger, for balancing.   It is best if readings from the same direction are used, although it is not absolutely necessary.

3. Attach each pickup at the position to be used for balancing.   Observe and record the amplitude and phase for each pickup location.

4. When the machine is being shut down, watch the vibration as the machine slows down.   If the machine is operating below a critical speed, the vibration will decrease steadily as the speed drops off.   If the machine is operating above critical speed, the vibration will decrease and then increase and then decrease again.   The critical speed will be shown on the frequency meter at the time the vibration peaks.   The amount of vibration at the critical speed should be noted.   If it is more than the vibration at the balancing speed, care in selecting trial weights will have to be taken.

5. With the machine at rest observe and record the presence of any vibration. This is called background vibration.   Special interest should be paid to any background vibration occurring at a frequency equal to the balancing speed.   If it is larger than the level to which you plan to balance, the machine responsible will have to be shut down.   Background vibration at the same frequency as the balancing speed will limit the vibration level to which a machine can be balanced.

6. The next step is to add a trial weight.   The correction plane for which the vibration was largest should be balanced first.   Inspect the rotor to find the best way to add a trial weight.

If there is a flange or recessed area under which modeling clay can be placed, the clay makes an excellent trial weight.   For large induced- or forced-draft fans and blowers, beam clamps, U clamps, or strips of metal stock tack-welded to a fan blade make suitable trial weights.   Bolts, nuts, washers, and similar items make convenient trial weights where holes are available for attaching them.   Hose clamps and metal baling straps may be used on bare shafts and rolls.   Inspection of the rotor may reveal how balance weights were attached by the manufacturer.   Trial weights which can be left on the rotor as permanent corrections will save the final step of replacing trial weights after the rotor is balanced.

The size of the trial weight is important because if it is too small, no change in amplitude or phase will be noticed, and a balancing run will have been wasted.   Too large a trial weight may damage the machine, especially if it operates above critical speed. Here are two formulas for calculating a safe trial weight.   For rotors operating less than the critical speed and less than 1,500 rpm use

$$\text{Trial weight} = \frac{WD}{4R}$$

For rotors operating above critical speed or more than 1,500 rpm use

$$\text{Trial weight} = \frac{2.86(W/100)}{(\text{rpm}/1,000)^2 R}$$

where W = weight of rotor, lb
$\quad\quad D$ = peak-to-peak vibration displacement, in.
$\quad\quad R$ = radius at which weight is to be added, in.
$\quad\text{rpm}$ = the balancing speed

and the trial weight is in ounces.   The trial weight calculated by the second formula may be quite small for *lightweight rotors* and may be doubled or tripled without danger unless the rotor has a severe critical speed.

Attach the trial weight securely so that centrifugal force does not cause it to come off.

7. The position of the trial weight may be at any convenient location in the correction plane.   There is no best position for the trial weight, but there is a rule of thumb which may be helpful.   For rotors being balanced above their critical speed, the trial weight may be added in line with the vibration pickup when the rotor is positioned so the reference mark is in the position observed on the first run.   For rotors being balanced below their critical speed, add the trial weight opposite the vibration pickup.

8. Start the machine and observe the amplitude of vibration as the machine comes up to speed.   Special care should be taken to avoid excessive vibration going through a critical speed.   Make sure the rotor returns to the same speed as on the previous balancing run.

9. Observe the amount and phase of the vibration at each end of the rotor.   Only the one reading will be used for balancing, but it is helpful to know what the vibration is at the other bearing to avoid trouble.

10. The vector diagram for the correction plane to be balanced first can now be constructed. Then make the required correction to the amount and position of the trial weight. Use the rules for single-plane vector diagrams.

11. Start the machine and take the same precautions you did in step 8 and observe the new amount and phase of the vibration for each end of the rotor.

Note: If necessary, repeat the preceding steps until satisfactory balance for the first correction plane is reached. Cross-effect may require a rebalance of the first correction plane, so it is wise to reserve fine balance corrections until that time.

12. Observe the amount and phase of vibration for the other end of the rotor. This reading is probably different than it was before the first plane was balanced, so it will be the original reading for the correction plane.

13. The next step is to add a trial weight in the new plane and proceed as before.

14. After seeing that both ends of the rotor are well balanced, check the vertical and axial readings to see that they were also improved. If they were not reduced to acceptable levels, part of the vibration was caused by other than unbalance. Vibration analysis will help determine the cause.

Summary. Although vibration is generally considered harmful and undesirable, it can be put to good use when supported by the preceding information. Here are some suggestions.

Inspection. Vibration can be used as a check of acceptability of purchased components to prevent excess vibration in finished products. Final-assembly inspection assures that products will operate smoothly and efficiently to guard against customer complaints.

Quality Control. Often vibration may affect the quality of finish, size, and concentricity of machined parts. Periodic checks of vibration for comparison against acceptable standards for good-quality work will safeguard against producing scrap by catching difficulties before they arise. Realistic vibration and balance tolerances can be determined.

Engineering. Vibration often interferes with engineering tests. The ability to recognize and eliminate vibration and balance problems readily will speed up results. Studying prototype machines and manufacturing processes helps iron out bugs early in the stage of development.

Plant Engineering and Layout. Often vibration is unavoidable, and critical machines should be moved to vibrationfree areas. Evaluation of new and overhauled machinery for the usual bugs can be quickly accomplished.

Field Service. Check out new customer installations and satisfy customer complaints at the same time you are pinpointing chronic difficulties for future correction.

Sales. Demonstrate the quality and smooth operation of your product vs. competition.

Maintenance. Vibration means trouble. Finding out what the trouble is is half the battle. Pinpointing mechanical troubles and balancing are the major subjects of this chapter. The application should be obvious.

Preventive Maintenance. The use of your knowledge and equipment for this application can prove to be the most profitable, as it includes or has some bearing on all those just mentioned. Preventive-maintenance procedures can be established to determine normal vibration patterns on each machine in your plant. Then periodic vibration checks can reveal when the vibration starts to increase, a warning of impending trouble. When the vibration increases beyond allowable limits, analysis will reveal what the trouble is and what must be done to repair it. Such a procedure provides a positive protection against unscheduled downtime and unnecessary maintenance costs.

ANSWERS TO PROBLEMS

Answers to Sample Problem of Vibration Analysis, Page 13-167.

(*a*) What are the possible causes for the vibration which occurs at 1,800 cpm on bearings *A* and *B*? Unbalance, misalignment, electrical-eccentric journals, and misaligned bearings. The presence of an axial vibration more than half as large as the radial vibration indicates either misaligned coupling or bearings. Unbalance and/or an eccentric journal, since it is on the motor bearing, may be supplying the exciting force if it is not a misaligned coupling. Further tests are required.

(b) If more than one cause is possible, how would you check to be positive of what the cause is? If vibration is due to an eccentric armature journal, it will disappear when electric power is turned off. If it is not, then unbalance and misalignment of coupling or bearings is the cause. Check coupling alignment. If it is good, then you may assume vibration is due to unbalance with some misalignment of bearings with the shaft. Proceed to balance.

(c) What is the cause of the 3,600-cpm vibration on bearings A and B as well as C and D? May be due to misalignment or mechanical looseness. If the check of misalignment is OK, then proceed to balance motor as indicated. If 3,600-cpm vibration does not reduce by a corresponding amount as you balance, search for some looseness.

(d) What is the cause of the 7,200-cpm vibration on bearings A and B? Torque pulses. They should disappear when electric power is turned off.

(e) What is the cause of the 45,000-cpm vibration on bearing B? Only an anti-friction-bearing noise could explain such a high-frequency vibration on this machine. Note for periodic checks at a later date to see if it is going to get worse.

(f) What is the cause of the 14,400-cpm vibration on bearings C and D? Hydraulic forces. Eight impeller blades times rpm. Might indicate some wear of impellers; note for periodic check.

(g) What is the cause of the 1,200-cpm vibration on bearings C and D? Probably from another machine, so check background vibrations after the machine is shut down.

(h) How would you know whether or not a correction of the troubles causing these vibrations is necessary? Check with the vibration-tolerance chart and use a measure of judgment of the time required to correct and expected service life. Check similar machines to see if there is anything different from what is normally found on good serviceable installations.

Answers to Balancing Problems, Page 13-177

	Amount, mils	Phase, o'clock
2. Original reading.............	3.0	7:00
First trial reading...........	4.0	7:00

Answer. Shift the trial weight 180° and triple its size. A vector diagram is not really necessary to solve the problem. When the position of the reference mark is unchanged, the position of the heavy spot is also unchanged. The increase in vibration then indicates that the trial weight was added right on the heavy spot. Since the vibration increased by 1.0 mil and the trial weight is responsible for the increase, its effect must equal 1.0 mil. The trial weight must be tripled then to compensate for the 3.0-mil vibration due to the original unbalance and shifted 180°.

	Amount, mils	Phase, o'clock
3. Original reading.............	9.0	10:30
First trial reading...........	4.5	4:30

Answer. It is not necessary to move the trial weight, as it is in the proper place. The size of the trial weight is too large and should be reduced to two-thirds its original amount. Once again a vector diagram is not necessary to solve the problem. The reference mark has shifted exactly 180°. The original vibration was 9.0 mils, and the trial weight cancelled that amount plus an additional 4.5 mils. The total effect for the trial weight is 13.5 mils and therefore one-third too large to cancel the 9.0 mils exactly.

	Amount, mils	Phase, o'clock
4. Original reading.............	18	9:00
First trial reading...........	3.0	9:00

Answer. The trial weight is at the proper location but is not large enough. Increase the trial weight 1.2 times its original size. Once again a vector diagram is not required to solve the problem. Since the reference mark has not shifted, the position of the heavy spot is unchanged. The reduction in vibration indicates that the trial weight is properly placed but not large enough to cancel all 18.0 mils of the original vibration. The effect of the trial weight is 15.0 mils, since this is the amount the vibration has been reduced.

	Amount, mils	Phase, o'clock
5. Original reading.............	9.0	2:00
First trial reading...........	1.5	9:00

Answer. Shift the trial weight 4° in the clockwise direction and reduce the size to 0.86 times its original amount. A vector diagram is necessary to solve this problem since the trial weight was not on or directly opposite the heavy spot.

	Amount, mils	Phase, o'clock
6. Original reading.............	9.0	2:00
First trial reading...........	9.0	12:00

Answer. Shift the trial weight counterclockwise 60°. No adjustment in amount is necessary.

Second trial reading........ 3.0 mils at 4:45 o'clock

Answer. Shift the trial weight counterclockwise 28°. No adjustment in weight is required. Note that a new $O + T$ vector is drawn but the same original vector is used to solve for the new effect of the trial weight.

REFERENCES

Den Hartog, J. P.: "Mechanical Vibrations," McGraw-Hill Book Company, New York.
McGoldrick, R. T.: "A Vibration Manual for Engineers," U.S. Department of Commerce, Office of Technical Services, PB 131785.
Thompson, William T.: "Mechanical Vibrations," Prentice-Hall, Inc., Englewood Cliffs, N.J.
Timoshenko, S.: "Vibration Problems in Engineering," D. Van Nostrand Company, Inc., Princeton, N.J.
Tong, Kin N.: "Theory of Mechanical Vibrations," John Wiley & Sons, Inc., New York.
"Vibration Analysis and Dynamic Balancing," International Research and Development Corporation, Worthington, Ohio.

Section 14

SANITATION AND HOUSEKEEPING

Chapter 1

ORGANIZING THE SANITATION PERSONNEL

By Mohe H. Solworth
President
Industrial Sanitation Counselors
Louisville, Ky.

The purpose of the sanitation program is to obtain a clean plant at a reasonable cost. The ultimate responsibility for attaining this objective rests on the man directly in charge of the sanitation program. He may be called a maintenance engineer, sanitation administrator or supervisor, superintendent, or building service director or by some still different title.

The Supervisor. Supervising a modern sanitation program is unlike any other supervisory work. There are many reasons for this difference: the problem of coping with increased soil, disorder, and wear in the increasingly complex modern factory; the comparative underdevelopment of industrial sanitation; the lack of up-to-date operating guideposts; ill-informed management who cannot give better direction; the low status and output of the ordinary sanitation worker; and the low regard in which sanitation is generally held. All these make unusual demands upon the sanitation supervisor and require that he assume responsibilities not usually encountered in ordinary supervisory practice.

Far from being merely a head janitor, the ideal sanitation supervisor should have many executive capacities. He should possess ability to handle people, creativeness, planning ability, initiative, open-mindedness, cost consciousness, improvement-mindedness, articulateness, a knowledge of modern management methods, and the physical capacity and drive to maintain a constant follow-up and vigilance over activities which are more widespread than those in any other department.

The 40 headings on the supervisor's rating form, Fig. 1-1[1], indicate what a sanitation supervisor must know and do if he is to get results. The exact names of these functions do not matter, but mastery of these areas of knowledge is imperative. (Explanations of the headings will be found further along in this and the next chapter.)

The supervisor's rating form is not only a device to measure the worth of the administrator or supervisor but also a guide to enable the supervisor to find both his weak and strong points. Only by periodically giving himself an honest and thorough going-over can he correct his weaknesses and further strengthen his strong points. The rating form may also be used by a superior to evaluate foremen and supervisors and to aid constructively the development of the supervisory staff.

The final scores achieved on such a form correlate closely with the results of the sanitation program: If the supervisor's score is low (under 400), program costs will be high and the quality of the cleaning low. If his score is high (over 640), the program

[1] Illustrations not specifically credited are furnished by Industrial Sanitation Counselors.

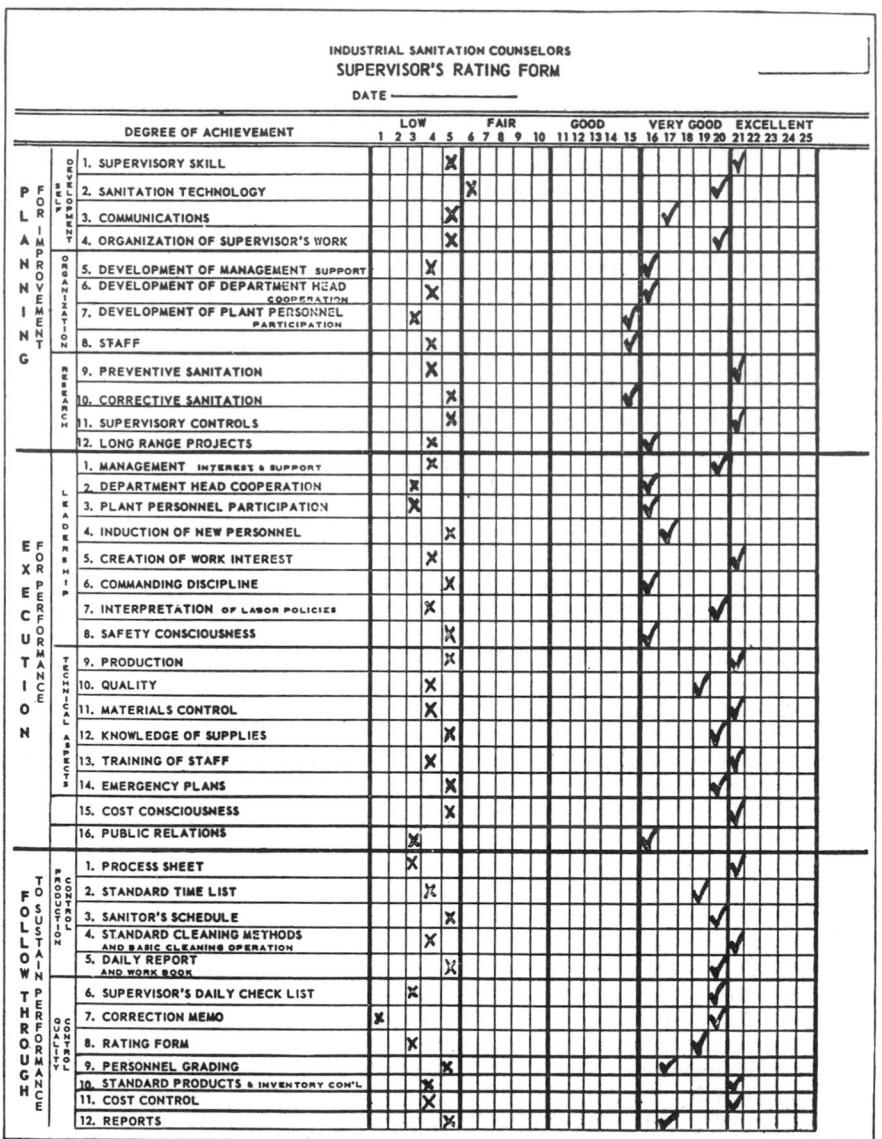

INDUSTRIAL SANITATION COUNSELORS
SUPERVISOR'S RATING FORM
DATE ————

DEGREE OF ACHIEVEMENT	LOW 1 2 3 4 5	FAIR 6 7 8 9 10	GOOD 11 12 13 14 15	VERY GOOD 16 17 18 19 20	EXCELLENT 21 22 23 24 25

FOR IMPROVEMENT — PLANNING

SELF DEVELOPMENT
1. SUPERVISORY SKILL
2. SANITATION TECHNOLOGY
3. COMMUNICATIONS
4. ORGANIZATION OF SUPERVISOR'S WORK

ORGANIZATION
5. DEVELOPMENT OF MANAGEMENT SUPPORT
6. DEVELOPMENT OF DEPARTMENT HEAD COOPERATION
7. DEVELOPMENT OF PLANT PERSONNEL PARTICIPATION
8. STAFF

RESEARCH
9. PREVENTIVE SANITATION
10. CORRECTIVE SANITATION
11. SUPERVISORY CONTROLS
12. LONG RANGE PROJECTS

FOR PERFORMANCE — EXECUTION

LEADERSHIP
1. MANAGEMENT INTEREST & SUPPORT
2. DEPARTMENT HEAD COOPERATION
3. PLANT PERSONNEL PARTICIPATION
4. INDUCTION OF NEW PERSONNEL
5. CREATION OF WORK INTEREST
6. COMMANDING DISCIPLINE
7. INTERPRETATION OF LABOR POLICIES
8. SAFETY CONSCIOUSNESS

TECHNICAL ASPECTS
9. PRODUCTION
10. QUALITY
11. MATERIALS CONTROL
12. KNOWLEDGE OF SUPPLIES
13. TRAINING OF STAFF
14. EMERGENCY PLANS
15. COST CONSCIOUSNESS
16. PUBLIC RELATIONS

TO SUSTAIN PERFORMANCE — FOLLOW THROUGH

PRODUCTION CONTROL
1. PROCESS SHEET
2. STANDARD TIME LIST
3. SANITOR'S SCHEDULE
4. STANDARD CLEANING METHODS AND BASIC CLEANING OPERATION
5. DAILY REPORT AND WORK BOOK

QUALITY CONTROL
6. SUPERVISOR'S DAILY CHECK LIST
7. CORRECTION MEMO
8. RATING FORM
9. PERSONNEL GRADING
10. STANDARD PRODUCTS & INVENTORY CON'L
11. COST CONTROL
12. REPORTS

Fig. 1-1. Supervisor's rating form showing supervisor's initial performance rating of 168 (X) and increased rating of 750 (✓) after one year's development.

costs will be low and the quality high. With such a measuring tool, there can be an objective basis for supervisory advancement and compensation.

Three primary organizational forces are available to the supervisor to help him do his job: (1) a sanitation staff composed of supervisors, foremen, and cleaners; (2) plant personnel; and (3) management. The supervisor's major function is to organize and direct these forces toward the correction, control, and maintenance of sanitation performance.

The Sanitation Staff. The supervisor's chief objective with his staff is to tap the potential productivity that is within each man.   For instance, national average coverage per man of office areas is 6,000 to 8,000 sq ft per day; a trained sanitation worker covers 15,000 to 18,000 sq ft.   All the supervisor's effort should be directed toward high productivity, because it is only through high productivity that program costs can be cut and the quality of cleaning raised.

The organizational chart, Fig. 1-2, illustrates how a successful program builds productivity controls into its very structure.

From the division manager down to the worker, there is a firm chain of command with clearly assigned duties and checks.   Each man is finally responsible to his superior for his performance, but self-policing of the daily job is encouraged throughout and is, in fact, the rule.   The necessary direction of nonroutine jobs always goes through the proper channels.   Although this organizational setup may seem cumbersome at first, in the long run it strengthens the forward progress of the program and prevents retrogression.   Individual effectiveness and productivity rise when each member of the staff knows just where he stands with every other member of the team.   Manager, supervisors, foremen, and crew leaders all help increase worker productivity, but it is the worker who finally does the job.

*The sanitors** are assigned individual area stations.   Large floors or departments may be divided into equal work loads among several workers, headed by a crew leader.   Each worker is given the entire responsibility for keeping his own area clean.   As sanitors try to surpass one another, a healthy and lively competition is aroused among the various crews.   This high work interest invariably leads to high productivity.   Further bolstering each man's production is his intimate knowledge of the base station that he cleans daily.   Every man is familiar with the varying soil loads in his area; he and his crew leader know, for example, which equipment and process areas in his station need thorough daily cleaning because of a heavy daily soil load; he knows which traffic lanes need touching up because of intense daily traffic; he knows what seasons affect the soil loads; and so on.   Such knowledge can help a sanitor clean more units with higher quality.   When the supervisor also becomes acquainted with these short cuts and builds them into the schedule, the man becomes more productive.

Every sanitor in a dynamic program should be shown the organizational chart and should realize that he, too, can rise to crew leader and foremen positions when he consistently achieves superior performance on the personnel grading form, Fig. 1-3.   Periodically, he confers with the supervisory staff about his progress, and his performance is numerically graded on the form.

The grading form is both a control and a measuring stick for determining the comparative value of the sanitors.   It not only serves to measure and reward merit but also strengthens poor workers and weeds out hopeless ones before the entire program suffers.   The information on which it is based is mainly derived from a daily record (daily check list and correction memos).   This gives the final score on an objective basis and avoids the usual charges of unfairness or partiality.   When presented with such a complete factual account, disgruntled employees or unions defending the interests of their members cannot help but be impressed by the lack of bias and by the constructive effort on *recorded* occasions to guide and correct substandard performance.

The numerical weightings indicated for the various sections can be changed to suit particular program needs.   If "Attendance" is not a problem and "Work Interest" is, then the weightings can be reversed.   The standards should all total up to 100 points, as in this scoring 100 points represents a fully efficient, trained worker.   Any sanitor failing to achieve the standard costs the company money.   (If, for example, a 50-man sanitation staff averages 80 points on the grading form, this means a loss of 1,000 points, which amounts to 10 full men.   In effect, that program is working with only 40 men, although paying for 50.   The plant is losing from $25,000 to $40,000 a year, depending on its annual wage.)

Induction. The organizing of sanitation workers in order to tap their full produc-

_____
* Sanitor is the name used in some modern programs for skilled sanitation workers.   Not only do they respond more favorably to such a title, but because they are craftsmen, they deserve a better name than "janitor."

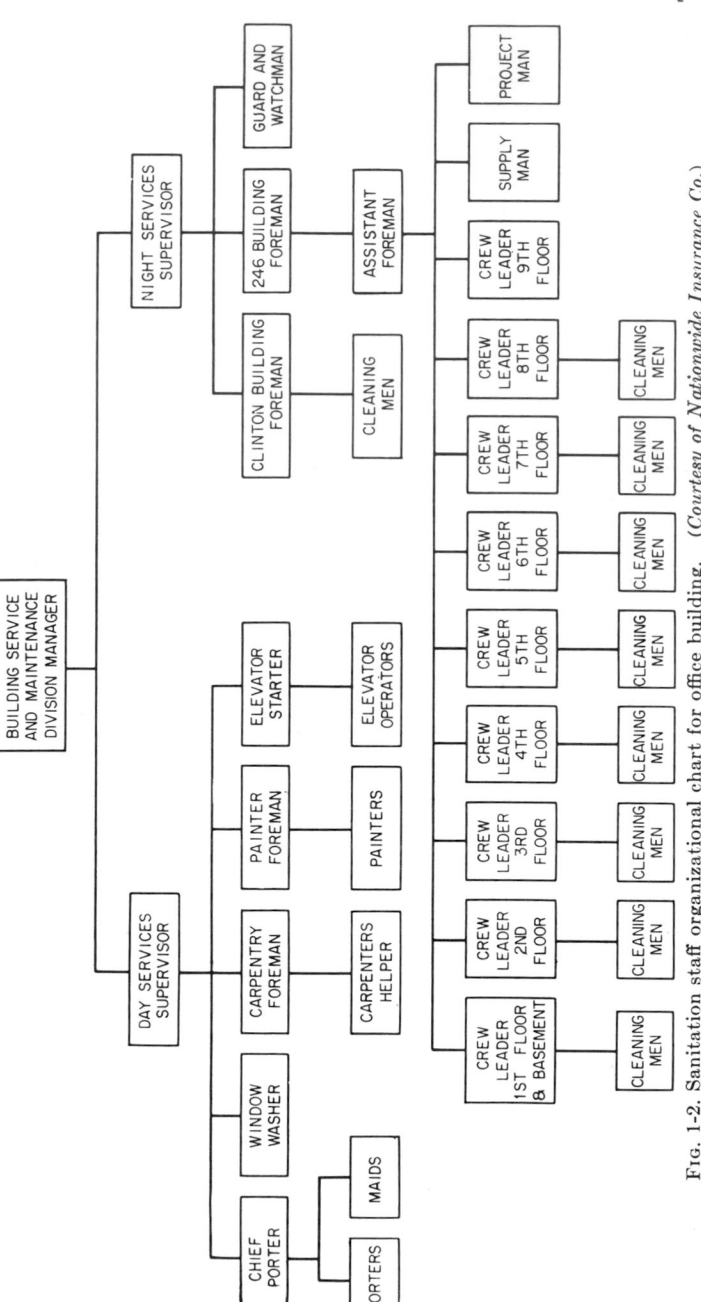

Fig. 1-2. Sanitation staff organizational chart for office building. (*Courtesy of Nationwide Insurance Co.*)

tivity must start from the day of their induction into the program.   New men should be inducted only after a thorough briefing.   The costly, rapid turnover so common in sanitation is often due to sloppy hiring practices: New men do not know what is expected of them, while the supervisory staff often does not know what the new men

---

INDUSTRIAL SANITATION COUNSELORS

PERSONNEL GRADING FORM

Name: Typical Porter

Current Grade _____   Former Grade _____   Improvement _____

Assignment _____   Date _____

		POOR	FAIR	GOOD	EXCELLENT	STD.	SELF GRADE	Supervisor GRADE
PRODUCTION	Habits	6 7 8 9 — Sleeps on job; leaves assignment often; poor work attack.	10 ... (11) — Personal needs interrupt work; telephone calls; visits other workers.	12 ... 13 — Works steadily; work organized.	14 15 — Aggressive attack; self-drive; requires little supervision.	40		
	Pace	6 7 8 9 — Intermittent work flow.	10 ... (11) — Satisfactory until end of evening.	12 ... 13 — Keeps up with schedule.	14 15 — Keeps ahead of schedule.			
	Efficiency of Action	1 2 3 4 — Awkward; non-thinking.	5 ... (6) — Does single, simple job assignments well.	7 ... 8 — Good motion economy.	9 10 — Inventive; skilled in many jobs; improves work methods.			28
QUALITY	Rating	10 11 12 13 14 (15) — Pink Rating	15 ... 16 — Blue Rating	17 ... 18 — Green Rating	19 20 — Gold Rating	30		
	Correction Memos	1 ... 2 — Many (10)	... 3 — Some (5)	(4) — Few (3)	5 — None			
	Supply Closet	1 ... 2 — Unsightly; slovenly; Inefficient.	... 3 — Untidy; improper inventory; caps off containers.	(4) — Neat; proper supplies on hand.	5 — Excellent appearance; supplies well cared for.			23
WORK ATTITUDE	Team Work	1 ... 2 — Reluctant to assist others; always measures personal output.	... 3 — Co-operates to slight extent.	(4) — Accepts extra assignments.	5 — Volunteers to help at all times.	10		
	Foreman Cooperation	1 ... 2 — Poor Respect, courtesy, ability to take directions.	... (3) — Fair Respect, courtesy, ability to take directions.	4 — Good Respect, courtesy, ability to take directions.	5 — High Respect, courtesy, ability to take directions.			7
ATTENDANCE	Attendance −4 Points for Each Unexcused Absence	4 — Frequent absence (4x).	8 — Absence (2x).	12 — Seldom absent (1).	(16) — Never absent.	20		
	Punctuality	1 — Frequent tardiness.	2 — Irregular arrival.	3 — Usually prompt.	(4) — Never tardy.			20
EXTRA MERIT						1–10		
					TOTAL			78

Fig. 1-3. Personnel grading form showing grade of typical porter.

are capable of.   The training of new men and the establishing of proper work habits do not involve great expense, but both time and money can be wasted if newcomers quit before this investment pays off in higher productivity.

When the personnel department first interviews a potential employee, it should have some general knowledge of the sanitation operation as a background for screening. The new man should be introduced to the supervisory staff during a formal conference so that he will be impressed with the importance of his job to the company. This first meeting should make clear to the man how large an area he is to maintain, what quality is expected, the care and maintenance of his tools, the training he will get, the necessity for continuing personal development, the various controls used, the advancement levels open to him, and his responsibility for improving his job, techniques, work patterns, etc., as well as company policy in general.

A trip through the plant where the new man observes the industrious and skillful work attack of the present staff frequently prepares him to meet the high performance desired. Such a tour also provides an opportunity to point out the actual extent of typical areas and the work load in them.

After the explanatory conference, the meeting should shift to a test area where the man is examined for his ability to use cleaning tools. He should be asked to dust mop, sweep, use floor machines, dust equipment, and demonstrate his techniques in washing floors, walls, ceilings, etc. These tests are meant to uncover any muscular deficiencies and to determine his technical knowledge, as it is unlikely that the average worker has been properly trained in efficient basic cleaning techniques.

The test area itself should be furnished with informative displays, exhibits, and charts which give a true understanding of the complexity of sanitation.

Plant Personnel. Few supervisors have taken full advantage of the help that operating personnel can give the sanitation program, and despite the fact that such personnel are the primary source of the soil that accumulates each day (which is called the "daily drop"), very little effort has been made to enlist their positive support in cutting down the soil load (see Fig. 1-4).

Some of the daily drop results from atmospheric conditions or defective machines spilling product or leaking oil, etc. (To counteract this, aid can frequently be obtained from the engineering or maintenance departments.) But the spillage and soil caused by careless, sloppy personnel can be radically reduced by a full-scale educational program that gets at the heart of the problem.

The tendency to be oblivious of the soil we cause stems from the fact that we are comparatively only recently civilized. Our thin veneer of civilization—expressed in this case by sanitary behavior—is a fairly new acquisition in the long history of man. We carry with us a primitive heritage from thousands of centuries of living in dark, dirty caves, hovels, and slums before the discovery that sanitation and health are closely related. In that early primitive period, there were, of course, no machines whose function could be impaired by soil, and there was no such thing as bad public relations because of a dirty plant. Now, when cleanliness is so important that private industry alone spends two and one-half billions of dollars each year to keep its plants clean, man still finds it difficult to refrain from littering, spilling, and leaving work areas disorderly. But it is becoming clearer and clearer that the eternal job of housekeeping will never be reduced until all workers and executives recognize that sanitation is everyone's responsibility. This does not mean that everyone should become a full-time sanitation worker; it does mean that everyone can be expected to stop carelessly dirtying areas which others must spend time and money in cleaning, and it means, also, that operating personnel can be expected to police their immediate areas at least. It is the responsibility of the sanitation supervisor to enlighten these people and lessen the sanitation work load.

The usual objection raised to plant personnel participation in housekeeping is that it is wasteful to use the time of higher paid workers for cleaning. This would be true if the time spent in policing came from productive time. But observation has repeatedly established that plant personnel spend a sizable number of nonproductive minutes each day. It is during this downtime that some elementary policing and clearing up of disorder can be accomplished. Moreover, much soil, litter, or misplacing of production tools, materials, and personal items do not require additional time for disposal or putting away. Of course, this means that facilities—trash cans, waste containers, tool racks, closets, lockers, etc.—should be provided in convenient places so that employees are able to make use of them.

The first step in obtaining plant personnel participation is to convince individual department heads: If department heads want to be clean, the plant will be clean.

Frequently, it is profitable for the sanitation supervisor to spend as much as a whole day in a department; sometimes, at the start of an extensive program, he may spend an entire week in a department, helping organize and set up a departmental program. The department can serve as his temporary headquarters. At this time, the entire sanitation program can be explained: the objectives; the costs of cleaning (exactly what it costs to clean a desk, a piece of equipment, a floor, etc., per year); how obstruction, such as junk or crowding, raises cleaning times and costs; what work load is in the area; what quality is and how it can be raised.   After the introduction, the specific part that can be played by department personnel should be presented so that they can see exactly where they can help.   Emphasis should be placed on what the sanitation

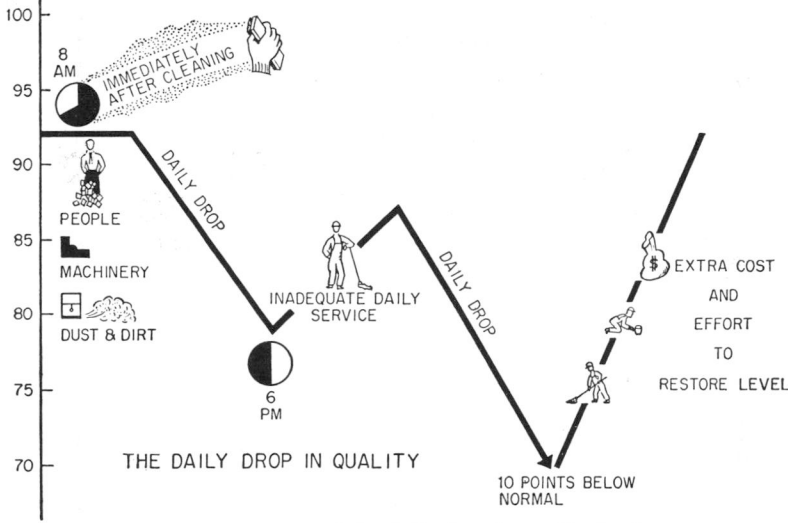

FIG. 1-4. Effects of the daily drop in quality level.

department will provide in the way of aid or direction.   Devices to encourage participation are easy-to-use trash receptacles, simple standard tools (such as rags; disposable, treated tissues; plastic sprayers for spot cleaning; sponge cloths; standard cleaning methods for cleaning all surfaces, and field stations for the easy storage and availability of tools and equipment).

The department head and his department should realize that this educational campaign is going on throughout the company and is under the auspices of top management.   Emphasis should be placed on how participation is socially acceptable and even socially desirable, because everyone is taking part.   Only a few people are needed to start the ball rolling.   Those who first take hold should be publicized immediately in bulletins and meetings.   They should be pointed out as employees who help the company save thousands of dollars a year and who aid in keeping a clean plant which benefits all who work in it.   The contributions of the plant personnel must be on a regular basis, or the educational campaign (which also must be continuous with frequent changes of material) will have been wasted.   Once the personnel get into the habit of policing their areas and maintaining order, it will be easy to keep up the impetus.

Personnel participation should be tied in with the rating system.   The people working in the areas should realize that they can help bring up area scores.

Examples. There are many examples of successful personnel cooperation in housekeeping.

After many years of tolerating an adverse situation, the Revere Sugar Refinery, Boston, Mass., instituted an over-all program of getting its operators into the act. Now highly paid veteran operators, who would once have laughed at the idea of doing janitor work, can be seen policing their areas as a normal part of their daily routine.

In another refinery, the plant personnel campaign caught fire when a union steward, convinced by the able presentation of a sanitation supervisor, led the way by painting during his downtime.

At Joseph E. Seagram & Sons, the vice president was quickly sold on the idea of personnel participation when he found out how much money could be saved. After he sent out a memo asking office personnel to clear all unauthorized material off the floors, desks, and filing cabinets (in order to reduce obstruction and cut down on clean-

```
KEEP CLEAN
BULLETIN NO. 1
                    CLEAN AREAS
1.  In the course of the last six weeks, and with
consideration based on nature of work, size of
area, and number of personnel concerned, the fol-
lowing have been chosen, after reasonable periodic
inspection and attitude of cooperation, to be the
best kept areas:
        1. Manufacturing      - G. Chevalier
        2. Liquid Line No. 1 - B. Novak
        3. Cream Line         - A. Martinat
2.  Other areas deserving of favorable mention be-
cause of satisfactory and co-operative attitude of
personnel are:
        1. Returns & Salvage - F. Conley
        2. Shipping          - W. Burlingham
        3. Plant Yard &
           Building Exterior - Peter Provost

                  SPECIAL NOTICE

   Keep your attention on cream manufacturing and
notice a real attempt to keep a working area
clean.  This area is one of the most difficult to
maintain clean while working, but it is kept in
good condition eighty per cent of the time.
```

FIG. 1-5. Management bulletin encouraging personnel participation in sanitation. (*Courtesy of John H. Breck Co., Inc.*)

ing time), he personally inspected the entire building and collected all material not removed. Those who came to claim their possessions had to face an irate vice president who demanded to know why his orders had been disregarded. It did not take long for the entire plant to catch on.

Another example from Seagram's involves the bottling-line girls. While waiting for bottles to come through, they idly pasted labels on the conveyor belt lines. They were shocked to learn that this practice was costing the company $12,000 a year. After the fact was brought to their attention, the girls eliminated their decorating, and the conveyor lines could be cleaned in half the time at half the cost.

At the Nationwide Insurance Company, Columbus, Ohio, the sanitation administrator amassed some impressive figures and presented them with color slides before all the departments involved. He showed that it took 18,720 hr a year (2 hr a night for each sanitor working a 6-day week) to clean the cluttered desks and files in their area. He then demonstrated how the same desks, cleared and free from obstruction, required only 11,440 hr a year, making it possible to save 7,280 hr each year. Employees did not want to be held responsible for causing the company such needless loss of money, especially when it took less than a minute of their time to clear their desks before leaving in the evening. The results were cleared desks and money saved.

The Simplex Wire and Cable Company conducts good-housekeeping contests among its employees.

The B. F. Goodrich campaigns have long been noted for their effective posters and successful results.

Many companies utilize the house organ to encourage personnel participation in housekeeping.

American Sugar Refinery, Fawcett-Dearing, W. A. Shaeffer Pen Company, National Biscuit Company, and Nationwide Insurance Company publish articles on company-wide efforts and recognition of outstanding performances.

Chance Vought Aircraft of Dallas, Joseph E. Seagram's, and other companies publish housekeeping manuals which are distributed to all personnel to explain company policy on sanitation. Chance Vought also distributes a good-housekeeping award.

See Figs. 1-5 and 1-6 for examples of employee recognition and housekeeping manuals.

Management. Vigorous management support of the supervisor is vital to the success of the sanitation program. Management helps determine the amount of support that the department heads and their operators will contribute; it sets the budget limits and establishes how much will be spent for equipment, supplies, supervisory staff, labor, etc.; its attitudes help decide the amount of cooperation that will be obtained from the building maintenance and machine engineers; and most important, it creates the climate in which sanitation must grow. A program lacking a favorable climate can quickly become stagnant and fail to achieve the goal for which it was set up—a clean plant at a reasonable cost.

But if management does not know what to do or how to do it, the blame

CLUTTERED AISLES

E. *Unstable Piles.*

Top-heavy or unbraced piles, toppling boxes, or poor containers, creating a safety hazard.

F. *Holes or Indentions in Floors.*

Uncovered floor wells, holes in floor not filled or covered, lag lugs not filled with lead.

G. *Misplaced or Blocked Fire Equipment.*

Fire extinguishers or equipment without proper access and clearance around them,

Fig. 1-6. Page from a good-housekeeping manual. (*Courtesy of Chance Vought Aircraft, Inc.*)

must be placed on the supervisor who has failed to keep it informed. Only by sending his boss and other top executives clear, accurate, and concise sanitation reports can the supervisor expect to obtain the necessary support and participation of management. Effective top-level decisions can be made only when management has all the basic information. It is the supervisor who must set up a communication line with management, for this is the life line that the sanitation program hangs on.

Reports to Management. A continuing monthly report enables management to keep its finger on the pulse of the program. The report must present all the necessary information and at the same time be concise and easily understood without taking too much of management's time. "Sight reports," which *show* information at a glance and thus do not require page after page of written detail, fill both these requirements, and it is advisable to use them.

The most commonly used sight reports are statistical graphs. These clarify complex situations and expose facts that might be buried in a written report. Among the simplest and most effective are line graphs, bar graphs, and pictorial graphs. When graphs are varied and photographs and color used, the accomplishments and progress of the program can be brought to management's attention quickly and strikingly.

The length of a monthly report cannot be predetermined. A good rule to follow, however, is: Make all reports as brief as possible. In fact, sometimes the entire monthly report should be fitted into one page and sent to management. If a superior indicates that this is what he wants, the supervisor should make his future reports in the same way.

No subject interests management as much as costs, especially in the light of constantly rising operating costs common to all companies. With cost data management can plan over-all budgets and also understand the financial requirements of the sanitation program. For a service department especially, the price at which that depart-

HOUSE SERVICE INSPECTION

CLASSIFICATION	Poor	Fair	Good	Excellent	Quality Value
	Range of Quality				
Floors	8	12	16	20	
Walls, Doors & Partitions	8	12	16	20	
Washrooms	6	9	12	15	
Furniture, Lockers & Files	4	6	8	10	
Exterior & Grounds	4	6	8	10	
Windows, Shades & V. Blinds	2	3	4	5	
Lighting Fixtures & Fans	2	3	4	5	
Supplies & Tools	2	3	4	5	
Service Quarters	2	3	4	5	
Miscellaneous	2	3	4	5	
Wind Clng. _____	Quality Index				
Wall Wash _____	Clng. Hrs. per M ⬚ per Wk.				
Grounds _____	Pop. Density per M ⬚				

PRINTED IN U.S.A.

City _____ Date _____
Bldg. _____ Yr. Blt. _____
Bldg. _____
No. Flrs. _____
Occupancy _____ Pop. _____
Traf. _____ % Plt. _____ % Off. _____ % Vacant _____ %
Clng. Force M. _____ @ _____ hrs.
Fe. _____ @ _____ hrs.

Bldg. ⬚ Grds. _____
Grds. ⬚

CHECKING LIST

EXTERIOR & GROUNDS EXTERIOR: Flags, Fire Escapes, Roofs, Metalwork, Signs, Shutters, Entrances, Sanitary Napkin, Wall Bases, GROUNDS: Walks, Steps, Toilets, Urinals, Archways, Fences, Lawns, Parking Lot, Shrubbery, Sidewalks, Trees

FLOORS: Asphalt, Carpet - Rugs, Concrete, Linoleum, Marble, Rubber, Terrazzo, Tile, Others

WALLS, DOORS & PARTITIONS: DOORS - Checks, Finish, Frames, Hardware, Kickplates, PARTITIONS, Frames, Glass, WALLS, Bases, Ceilings, Dado, Marble, Painted, Papered, Tile, Others

FURNITURE, LOCKERS & FILES: FILES, FURNITURE, Cabinets, Chairs, Desks, Footings, Tables, LOCKERS

WINDOWS, SHADES & VENETIAN BLINDS: SHADES, VENETIAN BLINDS, WINDOWS, Awnings, Frames, Glass, Screens, Ventilators

LIGHTING FIXTURES & FANS: FANS, LIGHTING FIXTURES

SUPPLIES & TOOLS: Cleaning Supplies, Cleaning Tools, Sanitary Supplies

CONDITIONS TO OBSERVE: Appearance, General, Broken or Loose, Chipped, Clogged, Cracked, Debris, Dirty, spots-overall, Dusty, Fingermarked, Frayed, Hazards, Accident, Fire, Indenting, Floor, Leaks, Marred, Odor, Operation of Facilities, Stained, Streaked, Supplies, approved-storage-quantities, Tarnished, Torn, Unsightly Grounds, Wax, spot-overall-polish, Worn out

WASHROOMS: Dispensers, Paper Towel, Sanitary Napkin, Soap, Toilet Paper, Floors, Mirrors, Partitions, Piping, Shelves, Toilets, Towel Baskets, Urinals, Walls, Wash Basins

MISCELLANEOUS: Bell System Practices, Cleaning Procedures, Drinking Fountains, Elevators, Cabs, Doors, Shafts, Fire Extinguishers, Stairs, Utility Shafts, Radiators, Work Frequencies, Schedules

SERVICE QUARTERS: Basement, Boiler Room, Mechanical Equipment, Service Sink Rooms

When notes are made, number them and write number after item for reference.

FIG. 1-7. Quality inspection form. *(Courtesy of Bell Telephone Co.)*

ment delivers its services is a matter of great concern. Obviously, if the sanitation department had unlimited funds, it could give nearly perfect cleaning. But because of inflated costs, its success must be measured by how much cleanliness it can get at as low a cost as possible. Management can be shown that although the sanitation department may not directly bring in sales, it can hold costs down and even save money over previous years' achievements.

There are many ways of presenting costs visually:

1. Line graphs can show total monthly cleaning costs of the current and past months for quick management comparison.

2. Colored horizontal bar graphs can show the component parts of the total monthly costs: direct and indirect labor costs, supplies, miscellaneous, and contractors' or other services used in plant sanitation.   Pie charts are another way of presenting such information.
3. Vertical bar graphs can depict monthly costs on a cents-per-square-foot basis. National averages of cleaning costs can be included for comparison.   Coins can be used to show the costs in cents.

Management must also be given a report on the cleanliness of the plant.   It should receive a factual, objective representation of the quality of the cleaning achieved during the past month.   Some kind of form, such as the quality inspection forms, Fig. 1-7, should be devised to secure the data from which the management summary can be prepared.

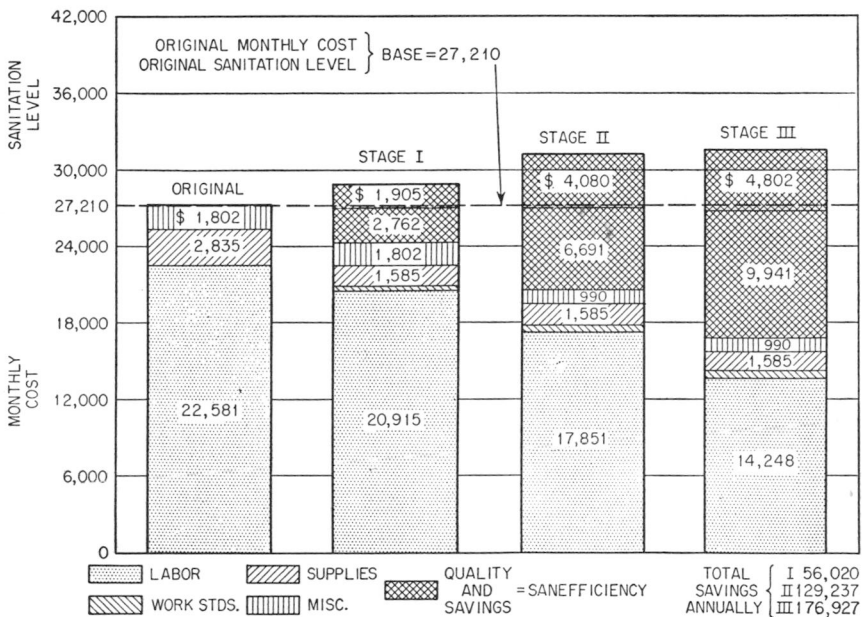

FIG. 1-8. "Sanefficiency" chart showing progressive reduction in cost and increase in savings.

As sending management detailed descriptions of all the areas would make the quality report too long and difficult to understand, area floor maps, indicating the net performance, should be substituted instead.   (These maps can usually be obtained from the plant engineer, or he can help draw them up.   The only details needed are the correct outlines of the buildings and walls so that each area can be easily recognized.) Using a color key to represent net performances aids quick visual comprehension and enables management to see how the various areas compare with one another.   A single, reduced plant-wide map is usually sufficient to cover all the areas for which the sanitation department is responsible.   Occasionally, when a particular area shows a radical change, it is a good idea to include the rating form along with the map to help show the cause.

Another part of the quality report should average all the actual sanitation levels to obtain the total plant level.   If desired, a more accurate plant level can be obtained by weighting each area according to size and sanitation importance.   Still another section can be devoted to the changes in plant levels that have taken place in the past months or years.   Photographs that picture the actual changes can be very effective.

A good way of pointing up quality improvements is to include a best area list.   The sanitation supervisor might even suggest that these areas be publicly recognized by management to stimulate competition among the departments.

A progress graph, called the "Sanefficiency" chart, Fig. 1-8, combines cost and quality figures for the past year on one page.   Based upon the original monthly cost and original sanitation level, this graph measures the advances made in cost reduction and quality improvement (which is also expressed in dollars) by showing the spread between original and current figures.   The use of various colored tapes (or gummed paper) facilitates making the chart and dramatizes the final effect.   After some practice, supervisors will find it easy to fit all the dollar results of their program into this chart.

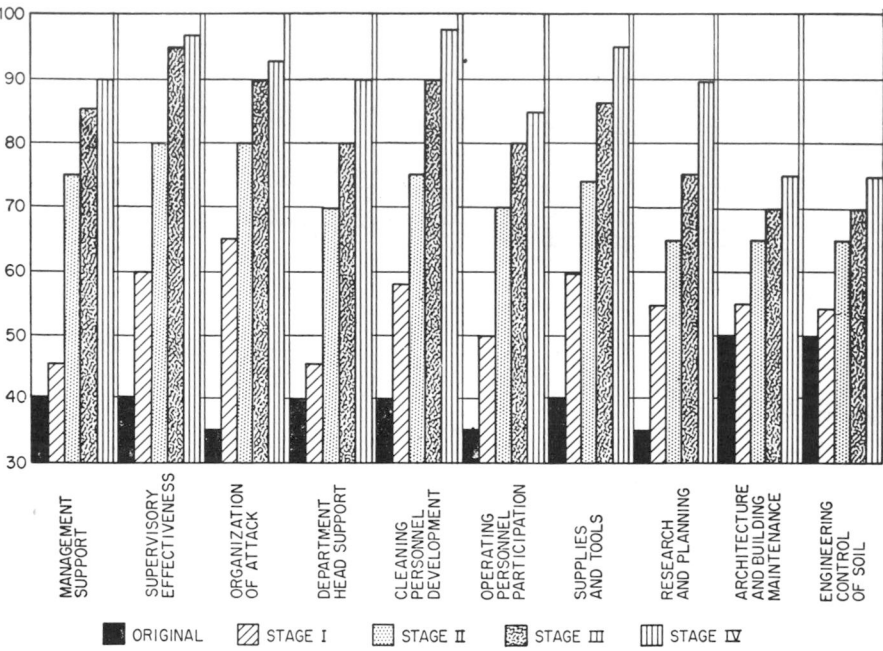

Fig. 1-9. Development of sanitation program through works standards system of cost control.

The Sanitation Factors.   Recording the results of the sanitation program is only a part of the complete report.   It is also necessary to report on the effort that went into getting these results.   For this, an analysis of the basic program factors must be presented in order that management can see which operating cylinders are not functioning properly and are thus adversely affecting costs and quality.   With such knowledge, it can turn its executive attention toward bolstering them and seeing that they are strengthened.   The chart of Fig. 1-9 is one example of how the sanitation factors can be illustrated (modifications can be made to suit particular needs).

The sanitation-factor check list, Fig. 1-10, is a guide for determining the particular score on the chart for each factor; the various headings are the different elements that make up the major factor and explain what goes into each one.

The chart also helps management anticipate future results.   When some factors are low and remain that way, the next reporting period will show high costs and low quality.   Such an X ray amounts to a behind-the-scenes analysis of just what is making the sanitation program sick or healthy.

SANITATION FACTOR CHECK LIST

This Check List is a guide to the development of the Sanitation Factors (such as, **MANAGEMENT PARTICIPATION & SUPPORT.**) It shows to what degree the Sub-factors (such as, **LEADERSHIP WITH DEPARTMENT HEADS**) have been put into practice. Following the Components (such as, **Formal Meetings**) there are numbers between parenthesis; these are the values on which you base your numerical estimation of the Components in your program. Your estimation is entered in the boxes following the parenthesis. The boxes under each Sub-factor are then added and the total entered in the Current column. When the totals in the Current column are added, the result will indicate how high that Factor will be on the Sanitation Factor Chart.

FACTORS—SUB-FACTORS—COMPONENTS WITH VALUES	POSSIBLE	PREVIOUS	CURRENT
MANAGEMENT PARTICIPATION & SUPPORT To what degree is management participating in the sanitation program?	100		
LEADERSHIP WITH DEPARTMENT HEADS Attitude toward Sanitation (5) ☐ Active Direction: Formal Meetings (5) ☐ Follow-up on Departmental Performance (4) ☐ Conferences (3) ☐ Informal Discussions (2) ☐ Recognition of Outstanding Performance (1) ☐	20		
DIRECT SUPPORT OF SANITATION SUPERVISOR Action Based on Supervisor's Reports (5) ☐ Status in Organization (5) ☐ Conferences (2) ☐ Guidance (2) ☐ Providing Adequate Workers and Staff (2) ☐ Clerical Assistance (2) ☐ Office (2) ☐	20		
WORK TOOLS (PRODUCTS AND EQUIPMENT) Provided for: Cleaning Staff (1) ☐ Departmental Cleaners (1) ☐ Operators (1) ☐ Manual (1) ☐ Mechanical (1) ☐ Central Storage Facilities (1) ☐ On-Job Storage Facilities (1) ☐	10		
PERSONAL INSPECTION OF PLANT Weekly (3) ☐ Monthly (2) ☐ Bi-Monthly (1) ☐ Consultations with Personnel (2) ☐ Supervisory Staff (2)	10		
BUILDING MAINTENANCE Repairs (8) ☐ Painting (6) ☐ New Installations (6) ☐	20		
ENGINEERING CONTROL OF SOIL Repair of Equipment (7) ☐ Spillage Control Devices (5) ☐ Dust Control Devices (4) ☐ New Equipment (4) ☐	20		
SUPERVISORY EFFECTIVENESS How well is the supervisor functioning as the key man in the sanitation program?	100		
PLANNING FOR IMPROVEMENT Supervisor's Self-Rating Form (5) ☐ Organizational Development (2) ☐ Self Development (1) ☐ Research (1) ☐	10		
LEADERSHIP With Management (5) ☐ Sanitation Workers (5) ☐ Department Heads (4) ☐ Plant Personnel (1) ☐	15		
TECHNICAL KNOWLEDGE OF JOB Production (5) ☐ Quality (5) ☐ Cost Consciousness (2) ☐ Materials Control (1) ☐ Supplies (1) ☐ Training of Staff (1) ☐	15		
PUBLIC RELATIONS Letters of Commendation (2) ☐ Published Articles (1) ☐ Talks (1) ☐ Favorable Comments from Visitors (1) ☐ Articles in House Organ (1) ☐	5		
UNION RELATIONS Definite Union-Sanitation Program (2) ☐ Orientations Before Major Program Changes (2) ☐ Conferences with Union Officials (1)	5		
QUALITY CONTROL Rating System (10) ☐ Supervisor's Daily Check List (4) ☐ Correction Memo (1) ☐	15		
PRODUCTION CONTROL Schedules (5) ☐ Adequate Supervision (3) ☐ Standard Times (3) ☐ Minimal Make-Ready, Transportation, and Put-Away Times (2) ☐ Emergency Plans (2) ☐	15		
PERSONNEL GRADING Periodic (2) ☐ Conferences (1) ☐ Promotions (1) ☐ Demotions (1)	5		
STANDARD SUPPLIES AND INVENTORY CONTROL (5) ☐	5		
REPORTS Sanitation Factors (2) ☐ Weekly (2) ☐ Monthly (1) ☐ Quality (1) ☐ Costs (1) ☐ Production (1) ☐ Use of Graphs (1) ☐ Photographs (1) ☐	10		
ORGANIZATION OF ATTACK To what extent has the Work Standards System been put into effect?	100		
AREA WORK LOAD EVALUATION Daily (10) ☐ All Shifts (5) ☐ Project (5) ☐	20		
STANDARD CLEANING RATES Floors (5) ☐ Equipment (5) ☐ Walls and Ceilings (2) ☐ Windows (2) ☐ Lights (1) ☐	15		
STANDARD CLEANING METHODS Floors (4) ☐ Equipment: Office (2) ☐ Factory (2) ☐. Walls and Ceilings (2) ☐ Lavatories (2) ☐ Windows (1) ☐ Lights (1) ☐ Pest Control (1) ☐	15		
RATING PROGRAM Used with: Department Heads (6) ☐ Plant Personnel (5) ☐ Management (3) ☐ Sanitation Staff (2) ☐ Incentives (4) ☐	20		

FIG. 1-10. Sanitation factor check list providing an analysis of the basic program factors.

FACTORS—SUB-FACTORS—COMPONENTS WITH VALUES	POSSIBLE	PREVIOUS	CURRENT
COST CONTROL Labor (8) ☐ Computed on Square Foot Basis (3) ☐ Materials (2) ☐ Equipment (2)	15		
WORK SCHEDULES Daily (5) ☐ Sanitation Staff (3) ☐ . Departmental Cleaners (3) ☐ All Shifts (2) ☐ Operators (1) ☐ Project (1) ☐	15		
DEPARTMENT HEAD PARTICIPATION To what degree are the department heads participating?	100		
MEETINGS WITH FOREMAN (15) ☐	15		
STIMULATION OF OPERATING PERSONNEL Meetings (8) ☐ Appointment of Department Spark Plug (4) ☐ Conferences (3) ☐	15		
ACTION ON RATINGS REPORTS (20)	20		
ADEQUATE SUPPLIES AND TOOLS Departmental Cleaners (5) ☐ Operators (3) ☐ Storage Facilities (2) ☐	10		
PERSONAL INSPECTION Daily (3) ☐ Semi-Weekly (1) ☐ Weekly (1)	5		
CONTROL OF PROCESSING SOIL LOAD Spillage (4) ☐ Dust Control (1) ☐	5		
AREA MAINTENANCE Repairs (4) ☐ Painting (3) ☐ New Installations (3) ☐	10		
COMPUTING SANITATION FACTORS CHART Posted in Office (3) ☐ Discussions (2) ☐	5		
SETTING STANDARDS Sanitation Level (2) ☐ Work Load (1) ☐ Schedules (1) ☐ Costs (1) ☐	5		
SUPERVISION OF DEPARTMENTAL CLEANING PERSONNEL (10)	10		
DEVELOPMENT OF CLEANING PERSONNEL What is the effectiveness of sanitation personnel?	100		
TRAINING Basic Cleaning Techniques (7) ☐ Standard Cleaning Methods (7) ☐ Meetings Schedules (4) ☐ Care and Maintenance of Equipment (2) ☐	20		
WORK INTEREST Attitudes and Morale (10) ☐ Incentives (6) ☐ Recognition (5) ☐ Co-operation (5) ☐ Team Work (4) ☐	30		
PRODUCTIVITY Meet Schedules (13) ☐ Dependability (6) ☐ Efficiency of Action (6) ☐ Work Flow (5) ☐	30		
QUALITY SENSITIVITY Self-Rating (9) ☐ Progressive Improvement (4) ☐ Quality Work (2) ☐ Corrections memos (2) ☐ Corner Cleaning (1) ☐ Care of Equipment (1) ☐ Personal Appearance (1) ☐	20		
OPERATING PERSONNEL PARTICIPATION How much are the operating personnel on all shifts contributing to high sustained sanitation levels?	100		
CLEANING MACHINES AND EQUIPMENT (25) ☐	25		
POLICING OWN AREAS Spillage (8) ☐ Trash (8) ☐ Personal Storage Lockers (4) ☐	20		
CONTROLLING DISORDER Tools (4) ☐ Boxes (3) ☐ Junk (3) ☐ Clothes (2) ☐ Miscellaneous (2) ☐ Sanitation Equipment (1) ☐	15		
INTEREST IN AREA RATING PERFORMANCE Actions (6) ☐ Attitude (4) ☐	10		
SANITARY HANDLING OF PRODUCT Contamination (8) ☐ Quality Control (7)	15		
PERSONAL HABITS Locker Rooms (5) ☐ Toilets (5) ☐ Spitting (3) ☐ Lunch Debris (2) ☐	15		
ADEQUATE SUPPLIES AND TOOLS Are modern sanitation supplies and tools being fully utilized to increase productivity?	100		
QUANTITY AND QUALITY Sweeping Tools: Manual (7) ☐ Mechanical (3) ☐. Mopping Tools: Mops (5) ☐ Buckets (5) ☐ Scrubbing or Buffing Tools (2) ☐. Equipment Cleaning (4) ☐ Wall Washing (2) ☐ Window Washing (2) ☐ Light Fixture (1) ☐ Ladders and Scaffolding (2) ☐ Miscellaneous (3) ☐ Supplies: Floor Cleaners (4) ☐ Finishes (3) ☐.	40		
DISTRIBUTION OF TOOLS Sanitation Workers (15) ☐ Departmental Cleaners (15) ☐ Operating Personnel (5) ☐	35		
RESERVE SUPPLIES (5) ☐	5		
STORAGE FACILITIES (5) ☐	5		
DISPENSING SYSTEM Reduced Transportation Time (3) ☐ Control Records (2) ☐	5		

FIG. 1-10. (*Continued*).

FACTORS—SUB-FACTORS—COMPONENTS WITH VALUES	POSSIBLE	PREVIOUS	CURRENT
CARE AND MAINTENANCE Daily (3) ☐ Weekly (2) ☐ Periodic (1) ☐	5		
MACHINE SHOP AID Repair (3) ☐ Creating Designs (2) ☐	5		
RESEARCH AND PLANNING What steps are being planned and what research is being done to improve the sanitation program?	100		
MANAGEMENT EDUCATION (15) ☐	15		
STRENGTHENING SUPERVISION (15) ☐	15		
IMPROVEMENT OF ATTACK (15) ☐	15		
PARTICIPATION OF DEPARTMENT HEADS (10) ☐	10		
TRAINING OF CLEANING PERSONNEL (10) ☐	10		
STIMULATION OF OPERATING PERSONNEL (10) ☐	10		
IMPROVING SUPPLIES AND TOOLS (5) ☐	5		
ARCHITECTURE AND MAINTENANCE (10) ☐	10		
ENGINEERING CONTROL (10) ☐	10		
ARCHITECTURE AND MAINTENANCE What improvements have been made in the repair, maintenance, and painting of the plant?	100		
FLOORS Repairs (10) ☐ Leaks (8) ☐ Replacements (5) ☐ Floor Drains (3) ☐ Pitched (2) ☐ Seals (2) ☐	30		
WALLS Painting (12) ☐ Repairs (8) ☐	20		
CEILINGS Paintings (9) ☐ Repairs (6) ☐	15		
WINDOWS Sashes (4) ☐ Frames (4) ☐ Screening (2) ☐	10		
LIGHTS Replace burned-out bulbs (4) ☐ Adequate Light (4) ☐ Reflectors (2) ☐	10		
RODENT AND INSECT PROOFING (15) ☐	15		
ENGINEERING CONTROL What process has been made in eliminating or reducing leaks from processing equipment?	100		
SPILLAGE CONTROL Liquid leaks from: Tanks (10) ☐ Pipes (10) ☐ Pumps (7) ☐ Miscellaneous (8) ☐	35		
DUST CONTROL Powder leaks from: Mixers (5) ☐ Fillers (5) ☐ Pipes (10) ☐ Conveyors (5) ☐ Elevators (5) ☐ Miscellaneous (5) ☐	30		
SANITARY DESIGN OF EQUIPMENT To prevent contamination: Covers (8) ☐ Drip Pans (8) ☐ Smooth Impervious Metal (4) ☐	20		
SANITARY DESIGN OF EQUIPMENT To aid in cleaning: Round Corners (4) ☐ No Ledges (4) ☐ Ease of reaching (3) ☐ Flushable (4) ☐	15		

FIG. 1-10. (*Continued*).

Other parts of the report to management can include charts and analyses of production figures, personnel development, research, and public relations.   The administrator must get to know what his management is interested in and provide it with information on that subject.   But one thing is clear: Only attention-getting reports can convince management quickly and easily that the sanitation department deserves support.

Chapter 2

WHAT TO DO TO MAINTAIN SANITATION

By Mohe H. Solworth
President
Industrial Sanitation Counselors
Louisville, Ky.

Measuring the Sanitation Level. Since the cleanliness of the plant is the end product of all the sanitation effort, the most important question that the supervisor must answer is, "How clean is clean?"

No other department operates without an exact accounting of the units of production or of the end product of the investment. The sanitation department spends its budget to gain a clean plant, but judgments of cleanliness vary so widely that in the last analysis the supervisor can justify this expenditure only by an organized, detailed inspection that numerically measures cleanliness in as objective a manner as possible.

One of the major controls in maintaining sanitation is a quality-rating system that convinces sanitation workers, plant personnel, and top management of its fairness and thoroughness. With such a system the supervisor can make sense when he talks about costs; translate quality into dollars; show management exactly what the company is receiving for its money; obtain plant personnel participation; produce tangible evidence, in union discussions for instance, of workers' effectiveness; fix responsibility for substandard conditions; prevent quality from deteriorating; and provide for remedial action.

The inspection service rating form, Fig. 2-1, is an example of a tool that describes the degree of sanitation achieved in a specific area. The area is broken down into its physical elements (floors, equipment, walls, ceilings, lights, and windows). These are inspected and given scores for their cleanliness, order, and repair and finish, which are all part of the over-all sanitation effect. (Even though the last two are not directly related to cleaning, they contribute to the sanitation appearance of an area.) In a food plant, for which a different form would be used, Fig. 2-2, a fourth consideration and score would be added for the evaluation of evidences of insects and rodents.

Different weightings are alloted to the elements on the basis of their sanitation importance. Floors in a mechanical production area would have a possible total score of 40 points for the three considerations. Since walls are less important, they are weighted only 10 points in this type of area. (In a lavatory without windows, walls would receive 18 points.)

The cleanliness chart, Fig. 2-3, is a reference aid, used in rating floors, for showing how many points should be deducted from the possible score of 32 points (which is perfect cleanliness). (Note that the number of deducted points increases, as the negative conditions increase in intensity and distribution. The same principles are applied when rating other elements.)

For example, if a little dust, scuffing, spillage, or litter is found in one corner of the floor, only ½ point is taken off the 32 points; if the same kind of soil is found in several places, then 1 to 2 points are deducted; if it is found in all previous areas and in all the traffic lanes, then 4 points are deducted; if found over all, 8 points are deducted.

INSPECTION SERVICE RATING FORM
LOBBY AND CORRIDOR

Unit Area_____   Unit Standard_____

Plant_____Dept._____   Actual San. Level_____

Area Number_____Bldg._____Date_____   Net Performance_____

ELEMENTS	CONSIDERATIONS						
	CLEANLINESS		ORDER		REPAIR AND FINISH		
FLOORS Baseboards	Possible Score **28** Actual	☐ Dust ☐ Litter/Glass ☐ Scuff Marks ☐ Buff Floor ☐ Dirt Film ☐ Spillage ☐ Grease—Oil ☐ Needs Waxing ☐ Needs Scrubbing ☐ Stains	☐ Corners ☐ Base Boards ☐ Under Equip. ☐ Overall ☐ Insects ☐ Rodents	Possible Score **6** Actual	☐ San. Equip. ☐ Clothing ☐ Cartons/Boxes ☐ Uncoiled Hose ☐ Tools ☐ Junk ☐ Aisles Blocked ☐ Area Crowded ☐ Misc. Items	☐ In Corners ☐ Behind Equip. ☐ Under Equip. ☐ Behind Door	Possible Score **10** Actual	☐ Worn ☐ Baseboards ☐ Traffic Lanes ☐ Decayed ☐ Stained ☐ Finish Gone ☐ Cracked ☐ Gouged ☐ Warped ☐ Splintered ☐ Broken Boards ☐ Tiles Missing ☐ Tile Loose	Possible Score **44** Actual

EQUIPMENT
Piping
Storage &
Inventory
Items
Furniture
Files
Lockers
	10	☐ Dust
		☐ Marks
		☐ Streaks
		☐ Product Spillage
		☐ Dirt Film
		☐ Grease—Oil
		☐ Cobwebs
		☐ Stains
		☐ Tarnish
		☐ Insects
		☐ Rodents
			☐ Upper Surfaces
			☐ Sides
			☐ Low Areas
			☐ Rails
			☐ Hardware
			☐ Overall
			☐ Inside
				2	☐ Pictures Crooked
					☐ Tools
					☐ Clothing
					☐ Furniture
					   Out of Place
					☐ Misc. Items
					☐ Junk
					☐ Improper
					   Stacking
						☐ On Top
						☐ Hanging
						☐ Inside
							4	☐ Marred
								☐ Worn
								☐ Stained
								☐ Spot Paint
								☐ Refinish
								☐ Leaks
								☐ Legging
								☐ Broken
								☐ Guards Off
									16

WALLS Doors Woodwork Wainscoting	**12**	☐ Dust ☐ Marks ☐ Finger Prints ☐ Streaks ☐ Spillage ☐ Dirt Film ☐ Cobwebs ☐ Stains	☐ Insects ☐ Rodents ☐ Corners ☐ Ledges ☐ Fixtures	**1**	☐ Tools ☐ Clothing ☐ Notices ☐ Nails ☐ Hooks ☐ Misc. Items	Hanging on ☐ Hooks ☐ Nails	**7**	☐ Marked ☐ Scratched ☐ Spot Paint ☐ Discolored ☐ Refinish ☐ Stained ☐ Holes	**20**
CEILINGS	**5**	☐ Dust ☐ Spots ☐ Cobwebs ☐ Dirt Film ☐ Stains ☐ Insects	☐ Corners ☐ Overall	NOT RATED			**3**	☐ Discolored ☐ Spot Paint ☐ Refinish ☐ Cracks ☐ Stains ☐ Holes	**8**
WINDOWS Skylights Blinds Sills		☐ Dusty ☐ Streaked ☐ Cobwebs ☐ Dirty ☐ Insects ☐ Rodents	☐ Few ☐ Several ☐ All	☐ Personal Items ☐ Misc. Items	☐ Hanging ☐ On Sills			☐ Paint Frames ☐ Etched ☐ Cracked ☐ Broken	
LIGHTING **FIXTURES**	**8**	☐ Dusty ☐ Dirty ☐ Cobwebs	☐ Few ☐ Several ☐ All	NOT RATED			**4**	☐ Light Poor ☐ Shade/Globe Gone ☐ Tubes/Bulbs Out ☐ Paint Fixtures ☐ Switch Broken	**12**

COLOR KEY
Gold..........Above Std., 5 Pts
Green..............Std. to +5.0
Blue...............—0.5 to —5.0
Pink.............—5.0 to —10.0
Red...............Below —10.0

Comments:

Time_____ (A.M.) (P.M.)

Inspector_____

FIG. 2-1. Rating form for lobby and corridor.

When more intensive soil, such as dirt film and incrustations, is found in a single place, the graduations start with a ½-point deduction and go as high as 32 points off for over-all distribution. When stains are widespread, as many as 32 points should be deducted—starting with 4 points and adding 4 more points for each additional area the stains are found in.

FOOD PLANT RATING FORM

Unit Area _____   Plant _____   Dept _____   Bldg _____   Std _____

Area No. _____   Date _____   Time _____   (A.M.) (P.M.)   Act _____   Net _____

LOCATION		CLEANLINESS		ORDER		REPAIR AND FINISH		INSECTS—RODENTS		Possible Score
FLOORS	Possible Score 20 / Actual	Dust, Dirt/Glass, Buff/Wax, Dirt Film, Spillage, Grease–Oil, Needs Scrubbing, Stains, Mold, Odors	Corners, Base Boards, Under Equip., Overall	Possible Score 10 / Actual	San. Equip., Clothing/Shoes, Cartons/Boxes, Tools/Hose, Junk, Aisles Blocked, Area Crowded, Misc. Items	In Corners, Behind Equip., Under Equip., Behind Door, Along Walls	Possible Score 5 / Actual	Worn, Traffic Lanes, Stained, Finish Gone, Cracked, Gouged, Warped/Splintered, Nails, Broken Boards/Tiles, Tiles Missing/Loose, Decayed	Baseboards	Possible Score 5	EXCRETA: Rodent, Bird, Insect / INSECTS: Live–Dead, Adult–Larvae, Webbing / TRACKS: Insect, Rodent	Corners, Baseboards, Under Equip.	40
Baseboards												3
EQUIPMENT Piping, Storage & Inventory Items, Furniture, Files & Lockers, Machinery	10	Dust, Marks, Seepage, Spillage, Dirt Film, Grease–Oil, Cobwebs, Stain–Rust, Tarnish, Mold, Odors	Upper Surfaces, Sides, Low Areas, Rails, Hardware, Overall, Inside/Outside	3	Tools, Clothing–Shoes, Furniture/Equip. Out of Place, Personal Items, Misc. Items, Junk, Improper Stacking	On Top, Hanging, Inside	6	Marred, Worn, Stained, Spot Paint, Refinish, Leaks, Lagging, Broken, Guards Off		5	EXCRETA: Rodent, Bird, Insect / INSECTS: Live–Dead, Adult–Larvae, Webbing / TRACKS: Insect, Rodent	Inside, Outside	24
WALLS Doors, Woodwork, Wainscoting	5	Dust, Marks, Finger Prints, Streaks, Spillage, Dirt Film, Cobwebs, Stains, Mold	Upper Surfaces, Corners, Ledges, Fixtures, Overall	1	Tools, Clothing, Notices, Nails, Hooks, Misc. Items, Personal Items	Hanging on Hooks, Nails	5	Marked, Scratched, Spot Paint, Discolored, Refinish–Peeling, Stained, Cracks, Holes	Wires, Nails	5	EXCRETA: Rodent, Bird, Insect / INSECTS: Live–Dead, Adult–Larvae, Webbing / TRACKS: Insect, Rodent	TRACKS: Insect, Rodent	16
CEILINGS	4	Dust, Spots, Cobwebs, Dirt Film, Stains, Mold	Beams, Corners, Overall	1	NOT RATED		3	Discolored, Spot Paint, Refinish–Peeling, Cracks, Stains, Holes	Wires, Nails	1	EXCRETA: Rodent, Bird, Insect / INSECTS: Live–Dead	Adult–Larvae, Webbing, TRACKS: Insect, Rodent	8
WINDOWS Skylights, Screens, Blinds, Sills	2	Dusty, Streaked, Cobwebs, Dirty, Mold, Rust	Few, Several, All	1	Personal Items, Misc. Items, Tools	Hanging, On Sills	2	Paint Frames, Paint Peeling, Cracked, Broken, Holes, Screens Missing		2	EXCRETA: Rodent, Bird, Insect / INSECTS: Live–Dead	Adult–Larvae, Webbing, TRACKS: Insect, Rodent	7
LIGHTING FIXTURES Switch Boxes	2	Dusty, Dirty, Cobwebs, Mold	Few, Several, All		NOT RATED		2	Light Poor, Shade/Globe Gone, Tubes/Bulbs Out, Paint Fixtures, Switch Broken–Wires Exposed		1	EXCRETA: Rodent, Bird, Insect / INSECTS: Live–Dead	Adult–Larvae, Webbing, TRACKS: Insect, Rodent	5

COMMENTS _____

Gold — Above Std. 5 Points   Green — Std. to + 4.5   Blue — 0.5 to − 4.5   Pink — Below − 5.0   Inspected By _____

Fig. 2-2. Rating form for food plant.

The reasons behind the weights assigned to these numbers are based on two factors: the amount of time it would take to rectify such negative conditions (based on the standard cleaning times for the various operations considered necessary) and how disfiguring such conditions in the area are.

The points to be deducted are totaled and subtracted from 32. The answer will be the cleanliness score for the floor.

Unit Standard. Although the total of all the actual scores is the actual sanitation level (rated on the basis of 100 per cent), area net performance scores are usually determined by measuring the actual against a standard. Thus, fair comparisons can be

POSSIBLE SCORE 32		CLEANLINESS				
	Condition	DISTRIBUTION				
		SLIGHT	LIMITED	FAIRLY WIDESPREAD	WIDESPREAD	OVERALL
FLOORS — Baseboards	scuffing	-½	-1	-2	-4	-8
	dust	-½	-1	-2	-4	-8
	litter	-½	-1	-2	-4	-8
	soil film — damp mop	-½	-1	-2	-4	-8
	soil film — wet mop	-1	-1½	-3	-6	-12
	soil film — machine scrub	-1½	-3	-6	-12	-18
	soil film — incrustations	-2	-4	-8	-16	-32
	stains incrust-ations	-4	-8	-16	-32	

FIG. 2-3. Cleanliness chart for floors.

made between different types of areas within a single program. An area standard is usually assigned by a committee composed of the department head in charge of the area, the sanitation administrator, and an engineering department representative. Each standard is an expression of the desired sanitation level. It is based on the considerations of what level is possible under existing circumstances (such as operations, age of area, layout) and what budget is allotted for maintenance in that area. By using practical, feasible standards, the area personnel are not penalized for conditions over which they have no control, and attainable company goals are achieved.

For example, a powerhouse equipped with defective coal-handling equipment which leaks coal dust might be assigned a standard of 70 or 75. Its net performance would then be measured by a plus or minus deviation from this standard. A plant cafeteria would be assigned a standard of 90—a relatively high standard. However, the level of a cafeteria has a close bearing upon the physical health of the personnel, and its appearance affects the morale of employees who eat or spend their relief periods there. Also, this area is frequently under observation by visitors and therefore bears a strong public relations value.   Moreover, a clean cafeteria sets a pattern of behavior for the personnel when they return from the cafeteria to work in their production area.

Executive offices should have standards of 87.5 to 90 points, because visiting clients and executives often form part of their impressions about a company from the condition of the offices they see.   Lower-echelon office areas can have standards of 80 to 85.

Warehouses are usually given standards of 65 to 75 because the condition of storage areas does not measurably affect production, the health of the people working there, or public relations.

In food plants especially, or in sensitive areas where a slight amount of dust can cause great damage, as in some electronics plants, the standards should be set very high.

When rating, the time of day and of the week should be taken into consideration, as the ratings are comparative tools that are used to indicate the amount of progress or retrogression in different rating periods.   It would not be fair to compare a rating taken early in the day before production starts with a rating taken after production has got under way.   Similarily, different times of the week or month radically change conditions and, hence, final scores.   When possible, the preferable time to rate is just after cleaning on the same day of the week and about the same time of the month as the previous rating.

The most helpful frequency for taking ratings is once every 2 months, although department heads and the sanitation supervisory staff should conduct their own spot ratings in between.   The 2-month interval is usually best because it allows sufficient time for correction of the deficiencies revealed in the inspection. At the same time, the interval is not long enough to permit a serious drop in the sanitation level.

Inspector or Rater.   In rating, it is extremely important that subjectivity be reduced to a minimum.   For all ratings to be impartial, the same conditions should be scored equally in all areas and in all rating periods.   Each rater should be part of a team that is thoroughly trained in an understanding of what constitutes cleanliness, order, and repair of each element.   For example, some companies do not regard as disorder the placing of books and boxes on filing cabinets or the storage of boxes under tables.   In such cases, all raters should know this and score the same for it.

The raters should be intimately acquainted with one another's scoring standards and methods for taking off points; how many points each deducts for a little dust, a great deal of dust, and so on down the line; how much off for a little disorder, some gouged sections, a broken switch, etc.; how much off for light, medium, and heavy soil films.   Maintaining the same rating team and having them work together for a time will ensure a close correspondence of final scores and a greater amount of objectivity.

Time Required for Rating.   The amount of time required to rate various areas depends on the rater's familiarity with the areas and his rating tools.   The second time a rater inspects an area he might find it convenient to score with the previous rating alongside to help him.   After a few complete ratings, he will notice many repetitions and will discover key places to check in each area.   As his intimacy with these conditions grows, he can score more rapidly and cover more areas in less time. Experience makes him more facile in scoring.   Also numerical standards begin to translate automatically into acutal conditions, and he quickly recognizes a 28-point floor, a 24-point piece of equipment, and so on.   The rater also learns to start rating an area in one corner and check all the elements there at one time—floors, equipment, walls, etc.—and then move into other sections where he does the same thing.   This eliminates walking around the area five or six times inspecting each element separately.   Furthermore, as the rating system gains greater acceptance, the areas become cleaner, which means that the rater does not need to make so many notations and can move more quickly.

A rough estimate of how long it takes an experienced inspector, after the first time, to rate various areas is as follows:

Small production areas (1,000 sq ft)......... 5 min approx.
Medium production areas (2,500 sq ft)....... 8 min approx.
Large production areas (5,000 sq ft)......... 12 min approx.
Factory (550,000 sq ft)..................... 1 man-day
Food-processing plant (1,300,000 sq ft)....... 4 man-days
Office building (325,000 sq ft).............. 1 man-day
Office areas:
    Small (500 sq ft)........................ 8 min
    Large (2,000 sq ft)...................... 12 min
    Very large (5,000 sq ft)................. 15–17 min

Work-load Determination. The determination of the entire sanitation work load is one of the first and most basic steps in setting up and maintaining a sanitation program. Without knowing how much cleaning has to be done, no one can operate a program efficiently, control it intelligently, or improve it progressively. Only an exact knowledge of the amount of work necessary can provide the information for knowing how many sanitation workers are needed, how to make up and distribute fair and equal work schedules, how to arrive at fair productivity levels, how to compare costs with other programs, what research should be made for improvements, what goals can be set up as incentives.

In order to determine the work load, certain factors must be taken into consideration:

1. The sanitation level to be maintained. If a high level is established, greater intensity of cleaning (washing or scrubbing rather than dusting) and more frequencies will be necessary.
2. The ability of available manpower: male or female workers, standard or substandard personnel, age of workers, etc.
3. The effectiveness and amount of available supervision.
4. Conditions in the area. The degree of obstruction; traffic problems (specific times when an area can be serviced); age, repair, and finish of various surfaces; and the rate of soil deposition.
5. Cleaning methods used.
6. Available tools and their location for use in the area.
7. Possibilities for reduction or prevention of soil.
8. Initial or temporary work load. Usually the soil to be removed initially results from build-up and firmly bonded accumulations that are caused by neglect; once they are removed, they will not reappear, since scheduled maintenance will prevent recurrence and serve to sustain the level. Hence, this temporary work load should be considered a one-time operation and ignored when determining the regular, daily, or project load.

The work-load determination form, Figs. 2-4 and 2-5, is one type of system for determining how much sanitation work there is in a given area. (Other special systems have been created by F. L. Gilbert of Lincoln-Liberty, D. Granato of Sharpe and Dohme, and A. Burner of the New York Port Authority.)

In the Industrial Sanitation Counselors' system, all areas that require cleaning are broken down into integral areas. (Normally one sheet is sufficient for entering all the units that require cleaning in any area.) Sometimes an entire floor or station is entered on one sheet. Areas are processed in ordered sequence as the processor moves from one adjacent area to another and from one floor to another, listing and describing each unit. For this part of the operation, help can be enlisted from department heads, foremen, or almost anyone who works in the particular area, as all that is necessary is a complete inventory of everything that must be cleaned: machines, motors, tanks, piping, desks, tables, chairs, walls (square footage), windows, ceilings, lights, and floors. In fact, the processing can be done without even seeing areas, provided the inventory data are correctly assembled and there is sufficient knowledge of the area operation to determine the soil loads for standard cleaning rates and frequencies.

After entering the description of unit and the total units in the areas, the required cleaning operations must be chosen and indicated for each unit on a daily, weekly,

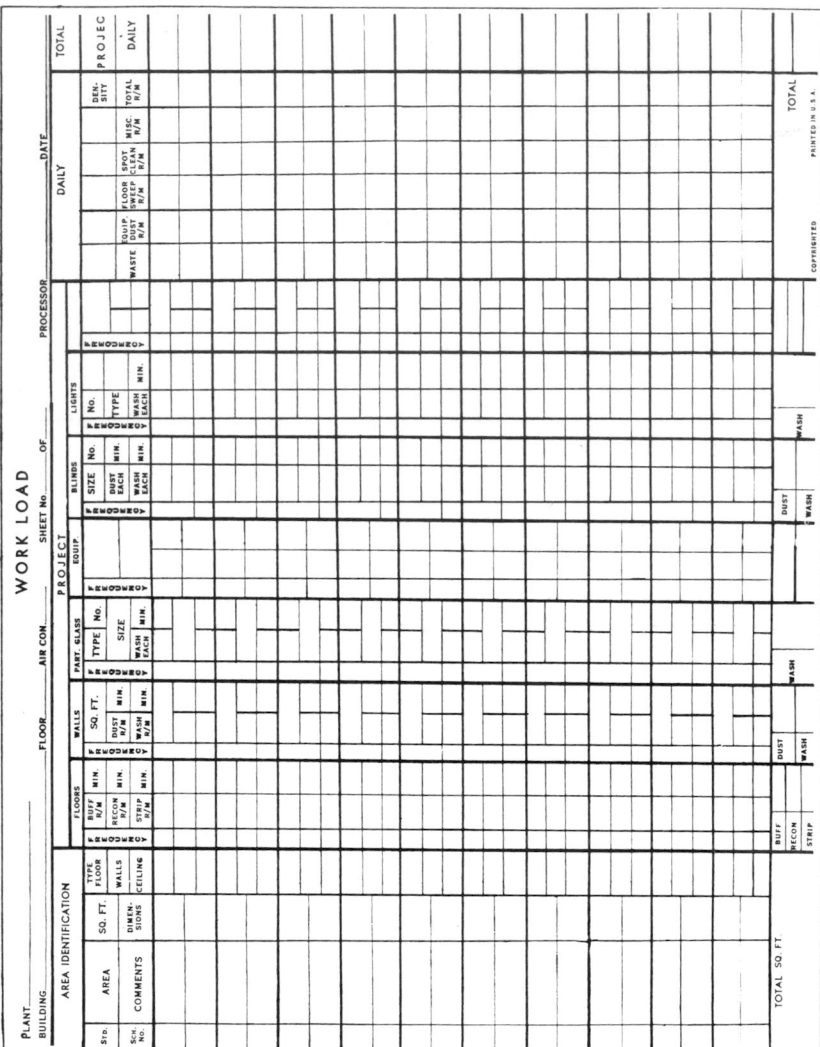

FIG. 2-4. Work-load determination form used in setting up a sanitation program.

monthly, or annual frequency (*F*). (Employing different-colored pencils for the operational entries helps to identify the frequencies easily and facilitates the final step of scheduling.) The operation that is selected depends on the standard that is set for the area. For example, in a shipping area where the standard would most likely be 75, there would be no polishing, hardly any complete dusting, and little horizontal dusting of equipment. If the same area had a standard of 80, there would have to be more dusting of both types to keep up the sanitation level.

In selecting operations, area conditions must be carefully examined, and unnecessary cleaning avoided. If dust settling is light, complete dusting, which includes dusting of vertical surfaces of equipment, can be done once every 2 or 3 weeks. In offices particularly, some complete dusting should be scheduled each day. One-fifth of the equipment dusted daily in a 5-day work week would complete the entire area in a week; one-tenth daily (for air-conditioned offices) would complete the cycle in

AREA WORK UNIT NOTES	
PROBLEMS SPECIFIC TO AREA	
DEGREE OF OBSTRUCTIONS	UNOBSTRUCTED ☐ SLIGHTLY OBSTRUCTED ☐ OBSTRUCTED ☐ HEAVY OBSTRUCTION ☐
INTENSITY OF USE MOUNT OF TRAFFIC HEAVY DAYS LIGHT DAYS	
DAYS CLOSED	
VARYING SOIL CONDITIONS	
WORK AID PREVENTIVE SAN. DAY WORK MACHINES	
SPECIAL SUPPLIES REQUIRED	
TIME AVAILABLE FOR SERVICING	

FIG. 2-5. Reverse of work-load determination form.

2 weeks; etc. It should also be remembered that judicious spot cleaning can frequently be substituted for over-all cleaning. Generally, it is better to employ several fast, light operations than to wait until a vigorous, time-consuming washing operation is necessary because the soil has become bonded to the surface. For example, wall dusting a few times a year will frequently stretch wall washing to every 18 months rather than once a year.

"No. of Units" indicates how many units receive that operation. "Unit Time Sec." is the rate of time in seconds (this may, of course, be changed to minutes) that is required to do the particular cleaning operation. Many of these rates for standard units can be found in standard time lists. Since the rate for accomplishing a certain operation depends on many factors, such as the worker's interest in his job, the methods and tools used, and the supervision, care must be exercised in using established production times. The rates shown in this list are for average sanitation workers. They are maximum times that can easily be surpassed by more highly developed and trained workers, and they should be used only as beginning rates which will shortly be replaced by tighter times, such as given later in this chapter.

When applicable, standard times lists can save a great deal of work by eliminating the necessity of conducting dozens of time studies to find the standard cleaning time for each type of unit. Those units for which standard rates cannot be found or which are nonstandard items must, of course, be assigned rates. These are formulated by (1) providing workers with appropriate methods, tools, and materials; (2) having them

MASTER OUTPUT CHART

DRY FLOOR CLEANING

DEGREE OF OBSTRUCTION (Area / Soil)	Cond.	UNOBSTRUCTED LIGHT L	M	S	MEDIUM L	M	S	HEAVY L	M	S	SLIGHT LIGHT L	M	S	MEDIUM L	M	S	HEAVY L	M	S	MEDIUM LIGHT L	M	S	MEDIUM L	M	S	HEAVY L	M	S	VERY HEAVY LIGHT L	M	S	MEDIUM L	M	S	HEAVY L	M	S
DUSTING / SOFT	a	4	6	7	4.5	6	7	8	9	9	4.5	7.5	9	5	8	9	9	9	10	10	10	11	11	11	12	13	13	14	14	14	15	15	15	16	17	17	18
DUSTING / SOFT	b	4	6	7	4.5	7	8	9	10	11	4.5	8	9	5	9	10	10	10	11	11	11	12	12	13	14	14	15	15	15	16	16	17	18	18	18	18	19
DUSTING / SOFT	c	7	8	9	8	9	10	10	11	12	8	10	11	9	11	12	12	13	15	13	13	14	14	14	16	16	16	17	17	17	18	19	19	20	21	21	22
DUSTING / HARD	a	4	6	7	4.5	7	8				4.5	8	9	5	9	10				11	11	12	12	12	13				15	15	16	16	16	17			
SWEEPING / SOFT	a	5	6.5	7.5	6	7	8	8	9	10	8.5	9.5	10	9	10	11	11	10	11	12	12	13	12	13	13	13	13	14	15	15	16	16	16	17	19	19	20
SWEEPING / SOFT	b	5	6.5	7.5	6	7	8	8	9	11	8.5	9.5	11	9	10	11	10	11	12	12	12	13	12	13	13	13	14	15	15	16	16	16	17	19	19	20	
SWEEPING / SOFT	c	6	7	8	7	8	9	9	11	12	9.5	11	12	10	11	13	11	12	13	13	13	14	13	14	14	14	15	16	16	17	17	17	18	20	20	21	
SWEEPING / HARD	a	5	6.5	7.5	5.5	7	8	8	9	10	6	8	9	6	8	9	9	10	10	11	11	12	13	13	14	14	14	15	15	15	16	17	17	18			
SWEEPING / HARD	b	7	8.5	9.5	7.5	9	10	9	10	11	7.5	9	10	7.5	10	11	10	12	13	11	11	12	12	13	14	14	15	15	15	16	16	16	17	19	19	20	
SWEEPING / HARD	c	8	10	11	9	12	13	11	13	14	9	11	12	9.5	12	13	12	14	13	13	14	15	15	16	17	17	18	17	17	18	18	18	19	24	24	25	
SWEEPING / STAIRS	a	28	30	33	30	32	35	32	34	37																											
SWEEPING / STAIRS	b	30	32	35	32	34	37	34	36	39																											
SWEEPING / STAIRS	c	33	35	38	35	37	40	37	39	42																											
MANUAL SWEEPER / HARD	a	2.5			3			4			3			4			5																				
MANUAL SWEEPER / HARD	b	2.5			3			4			3			4			5																				
MANUAL SWEEPER / HARD	c	2.5			3			4			3			4			5																				
MECHANICAL SWEEPER / HARD	a	1			1.1			1.3																													
MECHANICAL SWEEPER / HARD	b	1			1.1			1.3																													
MECHANICAL SWEEPER / HARD	c	1			1.1			1.3																													
MECHANICAL DRY CLEANING / SOFT LIGHT BUFFING	a	14	16	18	40	40	40				16	18	20	40	40	40				21	23	25	40	40	40				27	30	33	45	45	45			
MECHANICAL DRY CLEANING / SOFT LIGHT BUFFING	b	15	17	19	40	40	40				17	19	21	40	40	40				22	24	26	40	40	40				29	32	35	45	45	45			
MECHANICAL DRY CLEANING / HARD	a																																				
MECHANICAL DRY CLEANING / HARD	b																																				
MECHANICAL DRY CLEANING / HARD	c																																				
MECHANICAL DRY CLEANING / WOOD	a	40	45	60	45	50	70	50	55	70	44	49	65	49	55	77	55	61	73	60	60	72	65	65	77	70	70	82	90	90	95	105	105	110	120	120	129
MECHANICAL DRY CLEANING / WOOD	b	46	52	69	52	58	80	58	63	80	51	57	74	57	63	88	63	70	83	69	69	82	74	74	88	80	80	94	103	103	109	120	120	126	138	138	143
VACUUM / CARPETS	a	15	16	20	16	17	21	16	18	23	16	17	21	17	18	22	19	21	24	20	24	25	23	24	28	25	26	30	25	26	30	28	29	33	30	31	33
VACUUM / WOOD	a	15	16	20	17	18	22	18	20	25	16	17	21	18	19	23	20	22	25	21	22	26	22	25	29	27	28	32	27	28	32	30	31	35	32	33	37
VACUUM / WOOD	b	17	18	22	19	20	24	20	22	27	18	19	23	20	21	25	22	24	27	23	24	28	24	27	31	29	30	34	29	30	34	32	33	37	34	35	39
VACUUM / WOOD	c	21	22	26	23	24	28	24	26	31	22	23	27	24	25	29	26	28	31	27	28	32	28	31	35	33	34	38	33	34	38	36	37	42	39	40	44

RATES GIVEN IN MINUTES PER 1000 SQUARE FEET

Fig. 2-6. Master output chart for dry floor cleaning.

perform the operation many times at a normal pace; (3) clocking each complete operation, including make-ready, transportation, and put-away times; (4) reproducing on-job conditions for each time study, such as actual soil load, production interference and traffic.

MASTER OUTPUT CHART

WET FLOOR CLEANING

		COND.	UNOBSTRUCTED LIGHT			UNOBSTRUCTED MEDIUM			UNOBSTRUCTED HEAVY			SLIGHT LIGHT			SLIGHT MEDIUM			SLIGHT HEAVY			MEDIUM LIGHT			MEDIUM MEDIUM			MEDIUM HEAVY			HEAVY LIGHT			HEAVY MEDIUM			HEAVY HEAVY		
			L	M	S	L	M	S	L	M	S	L	M	S	L	M	S	L	M	S	L	M	S	L	M	S	L	M	S	L	M	S	L	M	S	L	M	S
DAMP MOP — SOFT SEALED WOOD		a	10	10	12	11	11	13	METHOD			11	11	13	12	12	14	METHOD			13	13	15	15	15	17	METHOD			18	18	21	20	20	23	METHOD		
		b	10	10	12	11	11	13				11	11	13	12	12	14				13	13	15	15	15	17				18	18	21	20	20	23			
		c	11	11	13	12	12	14				12	12	14	13	13	15				14	14	16	17	17	19				21	21	24	23	23	26			
DAMP MOP — HARD		a	10	10	12	11	11	13	UNSUITABLE			11	11	13	12	12	14	UNSUITABLE			13	13	15	15	15	17	UNSUITABLE			18	18	21	20	20	22	UNSUITABLE		
		b	12	12	14	13	13	15				13	13	15	14	14	16				15	15	17	18	18	20				21	21	24	24	24	26			
		c	14	14	16	15	15	17				15	15	17	16	16	18				17	17	19	20	20	23				24	24	27	27	27	29			
WET MOP — SOFT		a	15	15	17	18	18	20	35	35	39	18	18	20	20	20	23	38	38	41	21	21	23	24	24	26	45	45	49	27	27	30	30	30	33	55	55	60
		b	15	15	17	18	18	20	35	35	39	18	18	20	20	20	23	38	38	41	21	21	23	24	24	26	45	45	49	27	27	30	30	30	33	55	55	60
		c	17	17	19	20	20	22	39	39	43	22	22	24	24	24	27	42	42	46	25	25	28	28	28	31	50	50	55	31	31	34	34	34	38	61	61	66
WET MOP — HARD AND UNSEALED WOOD		a	13	15	17	17	18	20	35	35	39	16	18	20	19	20	22	40	40	44	19	21	23	23	24	26	48	48	52	25	27	30	29	30	33	55	55	60
		b	15	17	19	19	20	22	40	40	44	18	20	22	21	22	24	44	44	48	22	23	25	26	27	29	53	53	56	30	30	33	33	33	36	60	60	65
		c	18	20	22	23	24	26	50	50	54	20	22	24	25	26	28	52	52	56	26	27	29	30	31	33	62	62	65	34	34	37	37	37	40	68	68	73
WET MOP — STAIRWAY		a	46	43	40	48	45	42	51	48	45																												
		b	48	45	42	50	47	44	53	50	47																												
		c	51	48	45	53	50	47	56	53	50																												
MACHINE SCRUB — SOFT STRIP WAX		a	16	50	54	18	100	107	36	170	180	26	60	65	28	110	117	46	180	190	85	85	90	140	140	148	205	205	215	100	100	107	170	170	180	230	230	240
		b	16	50	54	18	100	107	36	170	180	26	60	65	28	110	117	46	180	190	85	85	90	140	140	148	205	205	215	100	100	107	170	170	180	230	230	240
		c	18	55	60	20	105	112	40	180	190	28	65	70	30	115	122	48	185	195	90	90	95	145	145	153	210	210	220	105	105	112	175	175	185	240	240	250
MACHINE SCRUB — HARD		a	16	45	49	16	65	70	30	80	85	21	54	60	21	74	80	30	90	95	77	77	83	99	99	106	125	125	132	91	91	98	113	113	120	130	130	137
		b	16	50	54	17	70	75	30	85	90	21	60	65	21	80	85	30	95	102	83	83	89	105	105	112	130	130	137	97	97	104	120	120	127	138	138	145
		c	18	55	60	19	77	83	34	93	100	24	65	72	24	88	93	35	105	112	89	89	97	116	116	123	143	143	151	103	103	110	133	133	141	152	152	160
HOSE SQUEEGEE — HARD		a	8	10	15	14	16	20	15	18	22	10	12	17	15	18	23	21	24	30	15	18	24	21	25	30	30	34	40	21	25	30	28	32	38	34	40	48
		b	10	12	17	16	18	23	19	22	26	12	14	19	19	22	28	26	29	35	19	22	28	25	30	37	34	40	48	25	30	37	33	38	46	40	48	56
		c	12	14	19	18	20	25	23	26	30	14	16	21	23	26	32	30	35	42	39	46	54	30	35	42	39	46	54	30	35	42	38	43	52	46	54	62
STEAM — HARD		a																																					
		b								25			50																										
		c																																					

RATES GIVEN IN MINUTES PER 1000 SQUARE FEET

FIG. 2-7. Master output chart for wet floor cleaning.

F designates the frequency, the number of times that the operation is to be performed during the period indicated by the color in which the entry is made. If the entry is in red and a 2 is put in the *F* column, it means that the operation is performed twice a week.

"Total Min." is the result in minutes of multiplying the number of units by the rate per unit by the frequency. The column designated "M.R., Trans., Per., P.A.," is for entering *additional* make-ready, transportation, personal, and put-away times; the normal allotment for these nonproductive activities is included in the rates or unit time in seconds.

Since floors require different types of operations from other elements in an area, a separate section is necessary. Here the floors are described as asphalt tile, linoleum, wood, terrazzo, concrete, etc., and the square footage of each type is noted. (The square footage can usually be secured from plant floor plans or the plant engineer. It is measured as gross square footage and includes the floor space under machines or equipment but excludes the space occupied by walls, partitions, or storage space that is usually occupied.)

The rates in minutes for cleaning each thousand square feet of floor for a particular operation are also found in various standard time lists. The master output charts for dry and wet floor cleaning, Figs. 2-6 and 2-7, are practical comparative tools, compiled from actual operations, to help the user see at a glance what floor-cleaning rates are standard in every type of industry for almost every type of area condition.

Each chart contains up to 216 rates which tell how long every major floor-cleaning operation (dusting, sweeping, vacuuming, etc.) should take in minutes to service a thousand square feet. They are arranged to meet:

1. Four degrees of obstruction (Obstruction is anything which interferes with the rhythmic application of the cleaning tool. It includes machinery, desks, chairs, furniture, partitions, columns and people): Unobstructed, slight, medium, heavy.
2. Three degrees of soil:
   a. Light—dust.
   b. Medium—retentive, traffic soil, litter.
   c. Heavy—production types, food soils, spillage. (For some industries, very heavy may be added by increasing the rate.)
3. Area size:
   a. L—large area over 2,000 sq ft.
   b. M—medium area, 250 to 2,000 sq ft.
   c. S—small area, up to 250 sq ft.
4. Condition of floor:
   a. a—excellent condition: very smooth finish, sealed or waxed.
   b. b—good condition, but unsealed or unwaxed.
   c. c—poor condition: cracks, holes, porous, rough.
5. Two main divisions of floors:
   a. Soft—asphalt tile, rubber, vinyl, wood, cork, linoleum.
   b. Hard—concrete, quarry tile, marble, terrazzo, ceramic tile.

When the five conditions operative in a specific area are determined, the standard rate can quickly be found. For example, to sweep a production area of 3,000 sq ft of unsealed, cracked concrete floor whose traffic lanes are narrow, blocked with trucks, and covered with a great many metal shavings and chips would take 24 min per 1,000 ft or 84 min for the entire area.

Both these rates and those in the standard time list, Fig. 2-8, are based on the physical capacity of the average sanitation worker, average-sized floor tools and products, average supervision, and average work interest. If any of these work factors is improved, the times can be reduced. The rates also include normal make-ready, personal, transportation, and put-away times. This covers the securing of tools and supplies for a complete day's schedule at the beginning of the workday or the provision of a field station, containing all equipment and supplies and conveniently located in the work area.

The total minutes for each unit, type of floor, and all time periods are totaled and entered in the extreme right column under the heading "Totals (Min.)." The totals for each operation are also totaled and entered in the daily and weekly "Operational Total." The totals enable the program administrator to see how many minutes or hours are needed to maintain an area. When all the area times are added, they indicate how many sanitation workers are required for the entire program.

Although determining the work load is a rather long job, the time required for

STANDARD TIME LIST

DUSTING — Time in Seconds

Item	Time in Seconds
Accounting Mach. Extra Large	165
Ash Tray (Empty & D.W.)	15
Billing Mach. & Table	52
Book Cases	
13"x35"x12"	22
36"x30"x8"	33
12"x40"x12"	216
3 Section Glass Front	22
42"x24"x11" Open Front	49
Bulletin Boards –Open	13
Glass	T.S.*
Cabinets	
Wardrobe 36"x65"x24"	34
Supply 36"x77"x18"	106
Supply 30"x66"x18"	42
Calculators --- Small	7
Large	9
Card Rack	
72"x40"x6"	211
12"x30"x6"	46
15"x36"x6"	100
15"x120"x6"	187
Card Sorting Machine	147
Chairs, Lounge — Large	63
Medium	35
Steno. Fold. Stool, Etc.	22
Cigarette Stand	25
Clock, Desk	8
Clock, Wall	20
Clothes Tree	22
Desk Items (Small) Misc.	3
Desks, Large, Office	48
Medium Office	43
Small Office	38
Writing, Small	51
" Large	69
Dictionary Stand	35
Doors, Without Glass	25
With Glass	40
Elevator, Outside	66
Elevator Cabs (Inside Only)	196
Files -- 4 Drawer — Single	
Side 7 secs.	
Front 11 "	
Top 4 "	29
Files -- 5 Drawer	
Side 8 secs.	
Front 14 "	
Top 5 "	
File, Card Index	11
Upright Reference	10
Fire Extinguishers	16
In and Out Trays	8
Lamps & Lights	
Wall Fluorescent (CJ)	8
Desk Lamp Fluorescent (CJ)	18
Table Lamp w/shade	35
Floor Lamp w/shade	35

*Time study required because of variations.

Item	Time in Seconds
Lockers	
12"x60"x12"	12
15"x66"x18"	T.S.*
Mail Box	40
Mail Sorter	
36"x8"x2"	22
28"x8"x6"	19
Multigraph	65
Partitions, Glass	
Dusting Rate 50 sq. ft.	60
Pencil Sharpener	15
(Empty and Dusting)	
Pictures & Photos	
3'x5'	45
Medium	15
Small	15
Rack, Coat & Hat (6' long)	90
Radiator & Window Ledge	
124"x15"	45
Radiator (Metal Flush)	
40"x36"x6"	21
Sand Urns	60
Spittoons	180
Tables	
Small — Plain	22
Medium — Plain	35
Large — Plain	60
Restaurant	T.S.*
Cocktail Lounge	T.S.*
Fancy	T.S.*
Telephone	9
Telephone Switchboard	101
Teletype Receiver	50
Typewriter (Covered)	7
Typewriter Stand	35
Typing Aid	5
Vending Machines	60
Venetian Blinds	
Conventional Size	210
Waste Baskets	
(Plus M.R. & Trans.)	15

LAVATORY ITEMS

Item	Time in Seconds
Cleaning Commode	
w/partition	180
Door — Spot Wash both sides	50
Door Checks	10
Mirrors, Damp Wash, Dry	
25"x49"	20
60"x21"	20
88"x31"	40
Napkin Dispenser	13
Napkin Disposal	10
Paper Towel Dispenser	7
Disposal	10
Shelving 20" Long	8
126"x6"	60
Urinals — Complete	120
Wainscotting	
75-100 ft. long	25
Wash Basin & Soap Dispenser	
Complete Wash	120

FLOOR RATES

Item	Rate
Sweeping	
Unobstructed	9 Min/M Sq. Ft.
Slightly Obst.	10 " " "
Obstructed	12 " " "
Heavily Obst.	16 " " "
Dust Mopping	
Unobstructed	7 Min/M Sq. Ft.
Slightly Obst.	9 " " "
Obstructed	12 " " "
Heavily Obst.	16 " " "
Wet Mopping	
Unobstructed	35 Min/M Sq. Ft.
Slightly Obst.	45 " " "
Obstructed	50 " " "
Heavily Obst.	55 " " "
Vacuuming	
Unobstructed	23 Sq. Ft./Min.
Slightly Obst.	19 " "
Obstructed	17 " "
Heavily Obst.	14 " "
Spot Vacuuming	
All degrees of obstruction	80 Sq. Ft./Min.
Buffing	
Unobstructed	25 Min/M Sq. Ft.
Slightly Obst.	35 " " "
Obstructed	40 " " "
Heavily Obst.	40 " " "
Strip and Rewax	
Unobstructed	100 Min/M Sq. Ft.
Slightly Obst.	120 " " "
Obstructed	140 " " "
Heavily Obst.	180 " " "
Standard Maintenance Method	
All degrees of obstruction	40 Min/M Sq. Ft.

WASHING

Item	Rate
Glass Partitions	
Clear	8 Sq. Ft./Min.
Opaque	20 " "
Whisking Upholstery	
Same as dusting Time	

MISCELLANEOUS

Item	Time in Seconds
Door (Washing)	150
Partition (Washing)	
Clear Glass	8 Sq. Ft./Min.
Opaque Glass	20 " "
Drinking Fountain (Clean)	
Stainless Steel	60
Ceramic	120
Vacuuming	
Large Divan Complete	190
" " (Exterior back omitted)	130

FIG. 2-8. A standard time list for dusting, lavatory items, floor rates, and washing.

processing each area decreases substantially as one proceeds from area to area. This is true because the research on the necessary tools, methods, and actual time studies in one area leads to common standards that are applicable to many of the remaining areas.

Scheduling: Distribution of the Work Load. Loose, informal work assignments are responsible for much loss of productive time. As much as 2 hr a day can be gained in production by instituting schedule controls that assign sanitation workers a written guide of what areas they are expected to clean, what to do in each area, and how long each operation takes. This ensures the meeting of area quality standards.

When based upon a thorough work-load determination, full work routines can gain easy acceptance among all personnel. Since schedules organize the work in the most effective way, divide the work load equally, and encourage self-policing, workers can easily be led to see the many advantages for them.

Supervisors like schedules because they eliminate friction among workers, who otherwise may be inclined to argue that some men have less work than others. Also, written schedules prevent the misunderstanding and confusion that sometimes arise from oral assignments. Their chief advantage for supervisors is that when workers know what they have to do, they do not require constant supervision and checking. This releases supervisors from the drudgery of perpetual surveillance and allows them time for research and the development of higher worker productivity.

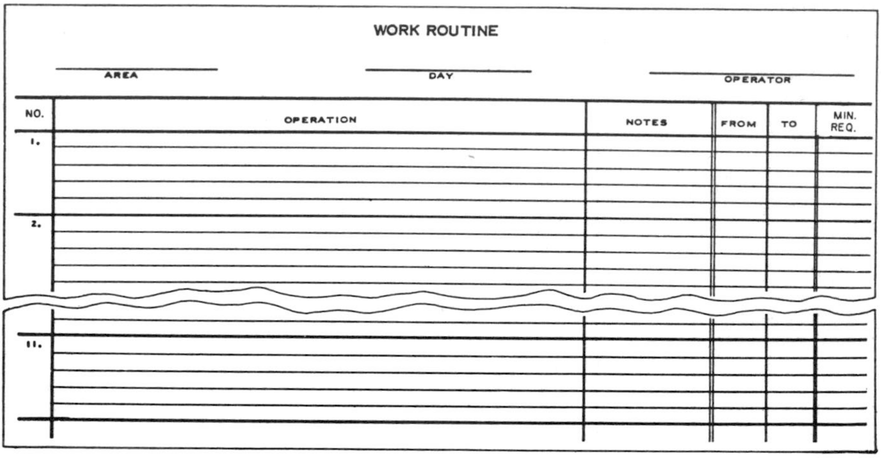

FIG. 2-9. Work-routine chart providing an easy-to-follow schedule for the worker.

The work-routine form, Fig. 2-9, is an easy-to-follow schedule for sanitation workers. All the data required to fill out the work routines are secured from the work-load determination forms. One method of filling out the work routine is to enter the necessary information from each work-load form into each work-routine form box. The name of the area is listed, the operations (indicated by code numbers) to be performed, the time required for each operation, the starting time to service the area, and the area completion time.

Sufficient areas are included to make a full day's work load with the exception of a 15-min cushion at the end of the day, called supplementary time, for emergencies, heavy days, absenteeism (where several supplementary times may be employed to fill a vacancy), etc. For example, in an 8-hr day the company-allotted rest periods of two 10-min periods a day are deducted from the total possible paid time of 480 min. From this possible work time of 460 min, approximately 15 min are allocated to supplementary time, leaving a total scheduled time of 445 min. Individual work-load determination sheets are selected in a convenient work sequence until they meet this figure, which constitutes a day's scheduled work. While the supplementary time is not scheduled, it is, on average days, used for minor project work (periodic cleaning requiring small amounts of time) and area inspection.

The Production. In most industries, rising wages have pushed the cost of sanitation service higher and higher. In the face of such a trend no sanitation program can afford to remain static. Only by following the successful example of American production can administrators of sanitation programs keep up with or reduce the growing annual cleaning cost per square foot—a cost which has risen from an average of 17 cents (in office area cleaning) in 1940 to over 60 cents in 1965. The rising cost of sanitation is even greater in manufacturing areas.

American industry meets the challenge of increased wages by increased worker productivity. Similarily, the supervisor must increase his sanitation workers' productivity so that they will do more cleaning—more floors, more desks, more walls, more pipes, more machines—for each dollar being spent.

The most direct way of increasing worker output is by plugging up the leaks in existing productivity. The supervisor's daily check list, Fig. 2-10, provides an orderly procedure for accomplishing this task.

This type of control is not meant for a desk-bound supervisory staff who believe that sanitation programs can be run by remote control. It is made for supervisors who know that every worker and every area should be inspected each day so that

SUPERVISOR'S DAILY CHECK LIST

DATE

		ATTENDANCE		WORK QUALITY												WORK OUTPUT			WORK ATTITUDE			SUPPLIES			
	NAME	ABSENT	TARDY	WASTE BASKETS	FLOORS	FURNITURE & EQUIPMENT	LAVATORIES	SANITOR'S CLOSET	WALLS & CEILINGS	GLASS PARTITIONS	LIGHT FIXTURES	AIR CONDITION DUCTS	WINDOWS			ON-JOB	ON-SCHEDULE		TEAM COOPERATION	WORK IMPROVEMENT	PERSONAL PROBLEMS	PRODUCTS	EQUIPMENT	TIME CHECKED	NOTES
1																									
2																									
3																									
4																									
5																									
28																									
29																									
30						ARE YOU CONSTRUCTIVE?																			

FIG. 2-10. Supervisor's daily check list to aid supervisory inspection.

minor deficiencies do not grow worse and become chronic. For conscientious supervisors this form does not represent more work but is an aid in organizing a normal daily supervisory job.

The names of the sanitation staff are mimeographed or otherwise reproduced in the left column. As the supervisor or foreman inspects each man's performance and station, he checks off the items which are up to par.

Attendance, of course, is a major concern in any efficient organization. When all sanitation workers are given full schedules, the repeated absence of one person can leave large gaps in the over-all program, even though the administrator is always prepared with plans to fit occasional emergencies. Tardiness, too, can be serious when a worker makes a practice of being late, since he cannot maintain the necessary quality of his entire area when he starts servicing it behind schedule. Moreover, chronic tardiness affects the morale of the entire organization.

The *work-quality* section prevents the "daily drop" in quality from degenerating into a heavy work load requiring an intensive cleanup operation. It is a quick spot check that supplements the rating system. When a negative condition is observed, a correction memo, Fig. 2-11, is filled out in duplicate and the number of the memo, instead of a check mark, is entered in the appropriate box. One copy of the memo indicating what needs correction is handed to the area sanitation worker. The memo has a red border to attract the worker's attention and to help him remember it. The duplicate is kept by the supervisor until the next day, when the negative condition is again checked to see if it has been corrected. Then the duplicate is filed with the worker's permanent record of performance and used in determining his personnel grading score.

Work output is here divided into only two phases: *on-job* and *on schedule*. Not being on the job is a grave matter in a well-run sanitation program because the very nature of cleaning dictates that men work in widely dispersed areas, and this condition makes supervision difficult. If constant overseeing of each man were necessary, an exhorbitant number of supervisory personnel would be required. Sanitation workers must be trusted to stay on their jobs, and all reasons for leaving their areas should be eliminated. When a worker is not on schedule, there is something wrong with either the schedule or the man's performance; in either case the supervisor should find out what is wrong and start correcting it immediately. A typical schedule control sheet is shown in Fig. 2-12.

Work attitude is not an easy quality to pin down, but it affects the way workers perform their jobs, and the supervisor must learn how to instill it into his staff. *Team cooperation* is a "must" in an operation where one man can sour the entire organization. *Work improvement* is a constant process that keeps each worker alert and thinking and helps him advance up the organizational ladder. *Personal problems* should

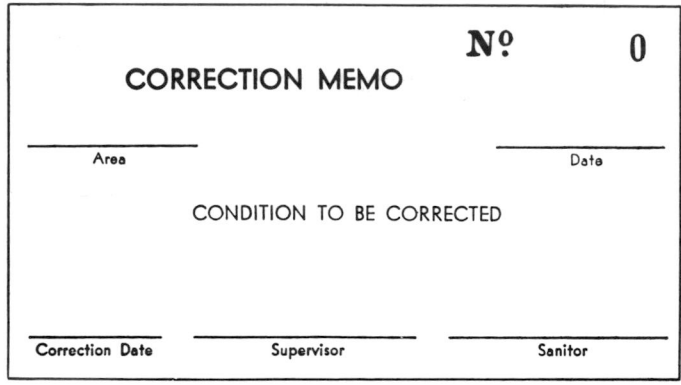

FIG. 2-11. Sample correction memo.

receive sympathetic attention from supervisors because they can affect the work and because all workers, especially those in sanitation, want to feel that they are recognized for more than their hands or their backs. This does not mean that supervisors need to coddle their men or engage them in long, private discussions during working hours. It does mean that supervisors can occasionally ask about the worker's family, for example, or express some kind of interest in his personal welfare.

Supplies must be checked because a great deal of productive time can be wasted in looking for the proper tools or materials after the job is started. A daily inspection serves to keep the sanitation worker's supply requirements ahead of him so that he does not run out when they are most needed.

A complete file of daily check lists comprises a factual body of documentation that backs up the supervisor. With such objective and substantial proof, he can recognize outstanding performance, advance or demote workers according to their merit, and have confidence in dealing with unions.

A copy of the daily check list left by the foreman or supervisor for his superior's attention keeps the supervisor actively aware of what is going on in the program and will often encourage executive direction from him.

Development of Work Interest. The most promising source of job productivity is to develop the will-to-work of the man on the job. His willingness to produce can do more for the sanitation program than any other single factor. On the other hand, if his work interest is low, if he must be compelled to produce, he can circumvent all job aids and controls. The supervisor's task is to bring out the sanitor's will-to-work.

High morale, however, does not develop spontaneously or overnight. It must be

DEPT. _39–24_   NAME _____

WEEK ENDING_____   EMPLOYEE NO._____

ASSIGNMENT SCHEDULE, CHECK OFF LIST & PERFORMANCE RECORD

LOCATION	OPERATION	OPER. MINS.	SCHED. COMPL.	MON.	TUES.	WED.	THURS.	FRI.
5D	Service restroom	17	7:27					
5C	Service restroom	17	7:44					
5A	Service restroom	17	8:01					
	Sterilize & Mop	27	8:28					
HH5	Service restroom							
	Sweep, sterilize							
	& mop, clean foun-							
	tain	13	8:41					
Stairway to								
B-6 Bldg.	Sweep	5	8:46					
5A	Sweep & clean foun-							
	tain	8	8:54					
Elev. #5								
First Aid	Sweep & empty trash	7	9:01					
5B	Sweep stairs	12	9:13					
5C	Sweep stairs & lobby	16	9:29					
	BREAK	10	9:40					
5C	Mop vending machine							
	area & clean fountain	7	9:47					
5D	Sweep stairs & lobby	16						
	Mop vending machine							
	area & clean foun-							
	tain	7	10:10					
5E	Sweep stairs & clean							
	fountain	13	10:23					
Cafeteria #5	Sweep	27	10:49					
5D	Restroom pick-up							
	trash	5	10:54					
5C	Restroom pick-up							
	trash	6	11:00					
	LUNCH	45	11:45					
5D	Pick-up trash, check							
	& supply	3	11:48					
5D	Spot clean lobby &							
	stairs	6	11:54					
5D	Spot mop vending							
	machine area	3	11:57					
5C	Pick-up trash, check							
	& supply	3	12:00					
5C	Spot clean lobby &							
	stairs	6	12:06					
5C	Spot mop vending							
	machine area	3	12:09					
5B	Sweep stairway from							
	top to bottom	20	12:29					
Training Rooms								
#8, 9, 10, 32, 34	Sweep	50	1:19					
Tunnel 4 1/2	Sweep & empty trash	25	1:44					
	vending machine area							
			2:00					
	BREAK	10	2:10					
Cafeteria #5	Sweep	50	3:00					
5D	Service restroom	17	3:17					
5C	Service restroom	17	3:34					
	Clean up stock							
	room & equipment	11	3:45					

FIG. 2-12. Typical schedule control sheet.

built up by the supervisory staff over a long period of time.   There are no magic wands to wave or sure-cure panaceas.   Trial and error, persistence and understanding, imagination, and an open mind must accompany all efforts to foster the growth of work interest.

The following successful examples, culled from actual programs, may or may not work in other programs, but they can serve as starting points or suggestions for other types of morale boosters.

Organizational Climate.   The climate in which an organization functions usually sets the tone for the new men who enter it.   Many potentially good sanitation workers have become discouraged and inefficient because the new operation they enter is loosely knit, poorly directed, or haphazard.   But in a strong program, such as the night cleaning program at the Waldorf Astoria, clockwork efficiency helps maintain morale.   Here the new worker is exposed to a businesslike climate from the very beginning.   When the new man begins his night's work, he starts servicing his station on time because everyone else does.   He respects the supervisory staff because everyone else does.   He cleans a larger area with a much greater work load than is standard practice because here it is standard for everyone.   His quality is high because it is an expression of the high sensitivity of the entire crew.   In other words, new men fit in with a highly advanced program because it operates as everyday routine.   They have no reason or excuse for working any differently, even though output and quality are higher than most programs.

Recognition.   Little recognition has been given the sanitation worker for the role he plays in the industrial operation.   While the contributions of other workers receive notice and even prominence, the worker in sanitation has frequently become a second-class employee.

An easy way to accord him his deserved recognition is to place articles in the company house magazine mentioning names and describing the job that is being done. Most of the time it is not necessary for the administrator to write these articles, as editors are usually looking for copy and are glad to write up articles from a few notes.

Labeling workers' equipment with their own names can prove a stimulus to recognition, as workers tend to respect a job which can be identified with their own tools. A side effect of labeling equipment is that it leads to better care and maintenance, as misuse or lack of care cannot be blamed on someone else.

Providing uniforms and better personal facilities such as locker rooms, can be an expensive investment, but it can also pay off in increased work interest and productivity.   When workers see that the company takes an interest in them, they start taking an interest in their work.   From the company's point of view, uniformed sanitation workers can create good public relations for the firm.   And when workers can wear decent, clean clothes to work and then change to company-provided uniforms, they will not have to be ashamed of their appearance as they come and go.   In addition, uniforms avoid the common pitfall of the double standard that expects sensitivity to quality cleaning from sanitation workers who are themselves dirty.

Letters of commendation from top management for especially well-done jobs often give workers the satisfaction of knowing that their efforts are not going unwatched or unappreciated.   Although a small thing in itself, such a letter adds another little incentive for doing good jobs again.

Social Position.   There is hardly a job so down-graded in the social hierarchy as that of the sanitation worker.   People outside the field regard it as one of the most unattractive occupations and consider a sanitation job as one to be taken temporarily or only in an emergency.   Those who have sanitation jobs are too often waiting for opportunities to open in other fields.   This misconception of sanitation work is based primarily on the idea of the work performed by the old-fashioned janitor, from whom nothing was demanded or expected except some desultory sweeping and mopping.

Today, however, workers in modern sanitation programs need skill, judgment, and knowledge (and since the majority of them in industry receive from $1.50 to $2.00 an hour, employers have a right to expect these qualities in them).   They must, at all times, be convinced of the inherent dignity and worth of their craft.   One of the best ways of manifesting this is to dissociate the job from the derogatory name of "janitor."

Many companies are following the trend of changing the titles of sanitation workers. Among the most popular of the new ones are sanitors, service workers, building service men, and custodians.   It has been found that almost anything is better than janitor.

At Joseph E. Seagram & Sons, a sanitation society was formed among the workers and run by them.   It very shortly became an exclusive club which was very difficult to join.   Candidates had to pass a highly technical examination in sanitation technology and methods; they had to achieve certain high-quality ratings and meet other requirements.   (When they did, a certificate, Fig. 2-13, was awarded.)   The society met on its own time and was addressed by visiting experts and professors on various aspects of sanitation.   There was no doubt in the minds of these workers of the dignity of their craft, and they were anxious to stay on their jobs.

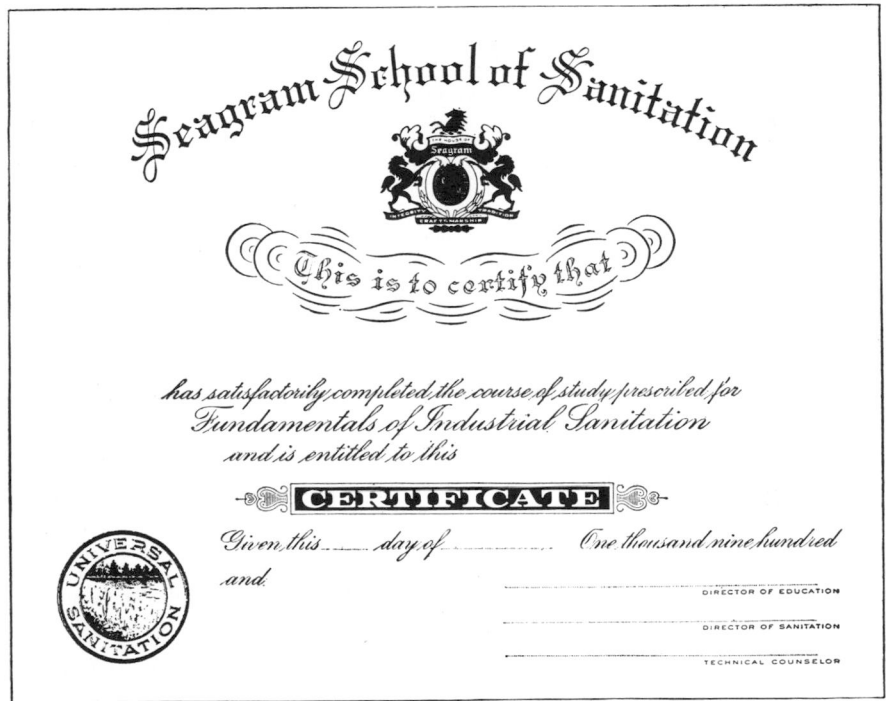

FIG. 2-13. Diploma awarded to sanitors for completing course of study satisfactorily.

Opportunity to Grow.   A major reason for apathy in sanitation is that the workers are seldom given an opportunity to advance to levels commensurate with their ability. Advancement levels must be provided for superior workers if they are to be kept in the organization.   Among the possible levels are test operator, swing man, project man, master sanitor, assistant crew leader, crew leader, and foreman (or supervisor).   Each of these positions requires special qualifications and higher compensation.   If promotions are provided, the entire staff will be stimulated to increased productivity and higher caliber workers will be attracted to the organization.   (The personnel grading form can be the means of determining superior performance.)

With the entrance of more and better work measurement into sanitation, increased compensation and incentives can be tied in with cleaning work.   This area represents one of the hopeful fields for raising worker productivity and as yet has scarcely been touched.

At the Fawcett Dearing Printing Company of Louisville, a bonus system, based on the rating system, was arranged with the union.   This plan called for 5-cents-an-hour increase for every sanitation worker whose areas reached standard and for an additional 3-cents-an-hour increase for every worker whose areas attained 5 points above standard. It was further arranged that when workers' scores dropped, they would no longer get the additional bonuses. This system, of course, was adopted by the union only because the union was convinced of the fairness of ratings with which they had long been familiar.

Other companies reporting success with bonus systems are Oscar Mayer of Chicago, Eastman Kodak of Rochester, and Kwikset Lock Company of Anaheim, Calif.

Training. The old saying, "Anyone can swing a mop," is totally out of date in a department which is trying to tap the full productivity of each man.

Close observation of sanitation workers on the job would reveal that most of them do not know how to swing a mop properly and that a great number of workers are awkwardly *pushing* their mops. It would also reveal men using floor brushes improperly and, as a result, getting low output with high effort. Few workers know the correct patterns for sweeping areas and are therefore doing a great deal of unnecessary walking. There are men waxing floors who do not know how to "feather in" wax or reduce stripping frequencies, and others are dusting equipment with many waste motions. The number of things the average sanitation worker does not know is filling cost books with red ink and causing much unnecessary fatigue.

A further drawback of the average sanitation worker is the mountain of tools that he "abuses out" rather than uses out. Not only do his neglect and misuse raise maintenance costs, but they also reduce productivity, for equipment that is out of action or only half effective cannot play its full part in getting the job done. This principle applies to matted floor brushes which have not been turned or combed often enough, to wet mop heads which have not been rinsed and are giving off objectionable odors, to overtreated dust mops which leave streaks on the floors, to mop wringer levers that have been broken because too much force was used in wringing, and to all the other man-handled tools that were purchased to help save time and effort.

Obviously, in order to produce more effective and productive workers it is necessary to train them in proper techniques and methods. This is not an occasional job, but a fully planned program which is constantly in progress. The entire supervisory staff should be instructed to include some on-job training in their daily work load. They should be on the alert for bad work habits, and each supervisor should be able to show workers exactly how the job can be performed better. (Every member of the staff should be more adept in all the basic cleaning techniques than the sanitation workers.)

Formal training classes should be conducted periodically. All the modern aids of audio-visual education should be brought to bear so that the workers will clearly understand what is being presented. Slides, charts, motion pictures, and demonstrations will hold the interest of the workers and drive home the message. Classes need not be long, but they should be carefully prepared and organized. Their tone should be crisp and down to earth. Naturally, the material should be thoroughly researched and up to date. Some suggested topics are:

1. What Happens When We Clean (The Mechanics of Cleaning).
2. The Cleaning of Soft Floors.
3. The Cleaning of Hard Floors.
4. The Care and Maintenance of Waxed Floors.
5. The Cleaning of Carpets and Rugs.
6. The Cleaning of Equipment.
7. The Cleaning of Lavatories.
8. The Cleaning of Walls and Ceilings.
9. The Cleaning of Glass.
10. How to Use Schedules.
11. What to Do in Emergencies.
12. How to Secure High Quality.

Another elementary series can be devoted to basic techniques. Workers, for example, can be shown why the proper wet-mopping method is less fatiguing; why a rhythmical, side-to-side, 9-ft stroke is best in open areas; why the body weight should shift from one foot to the other; why the stroke should be continuous; why the mop strands should be well spread out with the heel on the floor; why the mop handle should be as tall as the operator; why it should be held close to the body; why the back should be straight; and all the other numerous points in mopping that make the job easier and the worker more productive. Every cleaning technique can be broken down into separate motions, each one of which should be performed in certain ways under particular conditions in order to make the over-all operation as efficient as possible.

Training Aids. There are many sources of training aids. A number of manufacturers and sanitary suppliers issue pamphlets, job instructions, and films. The salesmen of these companies are often highly proficient in the use of their products and equipment, and they can give valuable free assistance in the best methods to be followed.

Every sanitation program should compile a standard cleaning manual that can be used as a training aid and as a follow-up to training. A standard cleaning manual is a collection of step-by-step descriptions of the cleaning techniques and standard methods for cleaning various surfaces. The manual should be written clearly and simply, as it is intended for use by the sanitation worker. Each method should specify all the materials (and their use-dilution when necessary) and equipment which are to be employed for that job. Concise, easy-to-read directions should be listed in the sequence in which they will be followed on the job. Practical alternatives to suit varying conditions that the worker might encounter should also be noted. Explanations need not be included in the directions but can be printed on the back of the page or elsewhere. Frequently, it is helpful to state the standard time rate for performing the operation.

Sometimes manuals can be secured from various sanitation-minded companies who have studied and created standard methods for their own operations. The Nationwide Insurance Company has put out an extremely useful standard cleaning manual which contains many up-to-date methods as well as the entire story of their eminently successful program. This manual may be secured by writing to Superintendent of Properties, Nationwide Insurance Company, 246 N. High Street, Columbus, Ohio.

Other organizations that have issued manuals are Port of New York Authority; Veteran's Administration, Washington, D.C.; Carbide and Carbon, Charleston, W. Va.; Esso Standard Oil Company, Linden, N. J.; General Services Administration, Washington, D.C.

Simplified maintenance charts which indicate proper care of tools can help the problem created by careless or unknowing workers. These inexpensive charts can be handed to workers, be posted in lockers or on bulletin boards, or provide subject matter for classes. Similar charts can be obtained from manufacturers or suppliers who have established the correct procedures for taking care of their tools.

Purchasing Products and Tools. The selection and purchasing of specific supplies for the sanitation program depend on the needs of the particular program. There are, however, some general considerations that should be kept in mind.

Supplies are purchased to help the worker accomplish his job in the easiest and fastest way possible. However, in practice this elementary consideration is too often overlooked. In their desire to hold down mounting costs, many sanitation administrators have turned to saving pennies on supplies and, as a result, are losing dollars in decreased or wasted output. (Since only 5 per cent of the average sanitation budget is spent on supplies—as opposed to 95 per cent on labor—the little that can be saved on supplies amounts at best to only a small fraction of the total budget.)

Penny-pinching on supplies leads to two dangerous purchasing policies: buying fewer supplies or buying them at a low price. Insufficient supplies mean that the worker does not have all the tools and products that can get his job done. Low-price tools mean that the worker has to work harder and longer to accomplish his job. Low-price products mean that results do not last so long and that consequently the job must be done more often, which in turn may be translated as more man-hours spent in getting the desired results. Low price squeezes the profits of the supplier so that he cannot afford to train his salesmen to give better service or afford the research that

Industrial Sanitation Counselors

FLOOR FINISH
RESEARCH & TEST REPORT

Company ____________

Product ____________ Area & Bldg. ____________ Type/Color Floor ____________ Condition of Floor ____________

Traffic & Congestion ____________ Square Feet ____________ Size of Machine ____________ Researcher or Supervisor ____________

Scoring	
Excellent	1
Very Good	2
Good	3
Fair	4
Poor	5
Very Poor	6

- Initial Spread ☐
- Subs. Coat Spread ☐
- Water Resist. ☐
- Chemical Resist. ☐
- Removability ☐

Date	Inspection	Service Required	Service Time	Gloss	Scuff	Scratch	Slip	Soil Retention	Wear	Discolor	Notes

Fig. 2-14. Floor finish research and test report

makes for better supplies.   A great many of the difficulties encountered in industrial sanitation today are caused by a combination of these forces.

On the other hand, every dollar-saving sanitation program in the last 10 years began its successful cutting of costs per square foot by providing workers with a full range of quality supplies and work tools.   These programs have proved that fully equipping sanitation workers can help to almost double their productivity.

High-quality labor-saving tools are constructed to give maximum efficiency.   Care goes into the manufacture of each part to insure top levels of performance, and each part is tested and retested to eliminate flaws.   Each year research brings new and improved tools into the market.   Battery-operated floor machines and vacuums, and improved combination auto scrubbers, for example, have joined the group of mechanized equipment which can multiply worker productivity so greatly that it is short-sighted economy to buy anything but the best.

Most impressive gains have been made in the manufacture and marketing of quality products.   Advances have taken place in the field of detergency, particularly in synthetics and biodegradable materials to eliminate sewerage problems.   New and better disinfectants, abrasive cleansers, floor finishes, and wax strippers are continually being developed.   Supervisors should investigate new materials constantly to determine whether they can be used profitably in the supervisor's own program.

One difficulty encountered by supervisors is determining the comparative over-all effectiveness of products for on-job conditions.   When we test floor finishes, for example, the performance of the finishes can vary tremendously under different conditions.   Only through broad and comprehensive testing can the many variables be controlled.   Over-all results are only as good as each individual's original application of the test finish, care, and frequency of servicing, and accurate recording of performance.

After the proper reconditioning at the proper time is provided, the results may be recorded on a form similar to that in Fig. 2-14.   The supervisor should check the finish on a daily to semiweekly basis, depending on how the finish is holding up. (These checks should require only a few minutes for each test area.)   He must record the results on the form and note his observations and evaluations.   He must also record the exact time and manning required to maintain the desired level.   After a while, it will be apparent which test finishes stand up and require less frequent servicing under equal conditions of soil and wear.

Chapter 3

SANITATION IN FOOD PLANTS

By J. S. HUTCHISON[1]
Chief Engineer
Lemon Products Division, Sunkist Growers
Corona, Calif.

In a food plant, sanitation may include, in addition to the usual procedures for effectively maintaining a clean plant, such diversified tasks as testing the plant water supply, bacteriological determinations on product and equipment, rodent and insect control, and advising the engineering department on building and equipment design. A good organization, actively supported by management, supervised by a well-qualified, hard-working sanitarian is necessary to produce the desired results. The plant sanitarian should report directly to management rather than to production or quality-control personnel. This maintains the independence of the sanitation function without the direct influence of production costs. The size of his crew will fall between a ratio of 1 to 12 and 1 to 25 employees. It is well to include the worker in planning the sanitation program. His interest will take on new life if he is asked for suggestions.

Edwin S. Doyle states: "The food industry is becoming increasingly aware that good plant sanitation is one of its best investments, because it results in more efficient operation, better workmanship, fewer accidents, better employee relations, better public relations, easier and better maintenance of equipment, and the production of quality products."[1]*

A sanitation-procedures manual is a must in any sanitation organization, and it must be kept up to date. The foremen should be familiar with everything in the manual, and new employees must be thoroughly trained in all phases of the work they are to perform. A sense of pride should be instilled in the workman—pride in maintaining a clean, orderly, and safe plant in which he and his fellow employees may work. Some of the many ways to arouse employees' interest in good housekeeping will include meetings where the plant sanitarian explains the purpose and necessity of keeping the plant clean and orderly, posters, competition between departments, suggestion boxes, an occasional "pat on the back" for a job well-done, etc. Workmen should be trained to throw no trash on the floor, walks, or roadway. Trash containers should be conveniently located to discourage "litter bugs." Production areas should be swept or vacuumed at least daily. Some areas will need scrubbing with detergent frequently. Clean up oil and grease spots immediately or at least cover with sand or sawdust to reduce the hazard. There is no place in a food plant for a drippy oil pan or an inadequate splash guard.

[1] For valuable assistance the author wishes to give credit to Clayton L. Baldwin, Jr., plant sanitarian of Lemon Products Division, Sunkist Growers, Corona, Calif.
* Superior numbers refer to references listed at end of chapter.

Designed to be Kept Clean. If every piece of process equipment in a food plant were designed to be easily and quickly cleaned, less time would be required by the sanitation crew and more effective cleaning would result. What if every tank in your plant had a name plate attached reading "Designed To Be Kept Clean?" Chances are that the operators and cleanup men would take more pride in maintaining those tanks in a sanitary condition.

Bacteria are killed in the canning process by pasteurization and retorting. It is just as important, however, to prevent contamination of food as it is handled in pipelines, pumps, tanks, and process equipment. The sanitation program is designed to prevent this contamination by reducing bacterial growth all along the line. Equipment must first be cleaned of all food particles. Steam guns, high-pressure water sprays and brushing will usually accomplish this. Then the equipment must be sanitized by flushing with a germicide, followed by flushing with fresh water prior to using.

To be easily cleaned, all vessels should have corners with a generous radius, a rolled and welded edge around the top, ground and polished welds, strategically located cleanouts and drains in a dished or sloping bottom, and no riveted and calked seams to work loose. The inside should be kept as free as possible of appurtenances such as ladders, brackets, and supports, since these may present blind spots to the cleaning solutions. In many cases heating or cooling coils can be replaced by jackets or an outside heater. Agitators should be simple and streamlined.

Packing glands may present a problem of contamination unless properly designed. The use of nylon or other synthetic materials to take radial and thrust loads at stuffing boxes and flax packing with paraffin lubricant has proved quite acceptable. If located where dripping oil would contaminate the product, all bearings must be well-sealed. Foot valves, drain plugs, and manholes, should have flush surfaces to present a smooth interior.

The outside of the process equipment should have as few attachments as possible. Manholes and other openings must have easily removed covers or lids, kept in place except when necessary to remove. The cover should overlap the inlet collar so that the vessel or machine can be washed without water entering. Supporting members of welded tubular construction and platforms of open steel grating contribute to ease in maintaining equipment clean. Elevating the equipment well off the floor and keeping its underside smooth are conductive to cleanliness. A machine or vessel which must be set directly on the floor should be sealed to the floor with grout, mastic, or one of the new resins.

The responsibility for incorporating all the desirable characteristics just mentioned and for eliminating any poor design features should fall upon the engineering department. Others, however, have a share in this responsibility, namely, the production department, the sanitation department, the purchasing department, and last but not least the sales engineers who represent the manufacturers. All drawings of plant layout and equipment design should be regularly routed to these departments for comments and criticisms. A poor design feature or a serious omission overlooked by one group has a good chance of being detected by one of the other groups.

The choice of materials of construction is of vital importance in food-processing equipment. Most food products can be handled in type 304 stainless steel vessels and pipelines. If their surfaces are polished, they can be maintained in sanitary condition, and their appearance is very attractive. Welding techniques must be right and carefully controlled, using the correct welding rods and temperatures for sound welds and a minimum of carbide precipitation. Even though stainless steel has some disadvantages, such as its lower heat conductivity compared with that of copper, its inability to turn against similar metal as in the case of a journal in a bearing, its nonmagnetic property, and its high price, it has many advantages which make it desirable for most processing apparatus. The corrosive nature of some processes will dictate the use of types 316 and 317 stainless steel, at an increase in price of about 15 to 25 per cent.

Stainless steels are being used more extensively all the time. Their consumption per person in the United States has increased nearly six times as rapidly as has consumption of all steels during the past 27 years. The yearly figure now stands at about 8 lb of stainless steel used for all purposes per person. Whereas processing equipment of ordinary steel will cost from $0.50 to $1 per pound, stainless steel equipment will cost from $1.50 per pound for simple flat work to $4.25 per pound for items requiring considerable machining and fitting. The use of stainless-clad plate will reduce first cost somewhat if the plate is $\frac{3}{16}$ in. or thicker, in which case the cladding might be 15 to 25 per cent of the total thickness. Minimum cladding is about 0.03 in. For heavier plate used in pressure vessels, the cladding will be from 5 to 15 per cent of the total thickness. It must be remembered, however, that the mild steel outside of the vessel will have to be painted for protection, whereas stainless steel outer surfaces need no paint, are attractive, and are easily maintained in sanitary condition. If all the economic factors are carefully weighed, the high first cost of stainless-steel equipment may prove to be the most economical in the long run. Many food plants find that for certain food products they must use Monel, copper, brass, rubber-lined vessels, or wood. The precautions mentioned at the beginning of this section should be exercised in their construction and use.

To be cleaned in place, pipelines should have smooth interiors, including all joints, couplings, and fittings. Stainless-steel piping should be of sanitary-type construction. Glass piping lends itself to in-place cleaning and is used in many dairies and wineries. There must be no pockets where food may collect. There are a number of CIP systems available on the market, utilizing specialized equipment, such as steam guns, rotary sprays, interior tank cleaners, foaming devices, and the like. Pipelines carrying different fluids should be plainly marked or painted for easy identification.

Using In-plant Chlorination. In-plant chlorination may be defined as "chlorination beyond the break point of almost all water in a food plant."[2] As chlorine is added to water, the chlorine residual will rise with the chlorine added but at a lower rate, except in the case of a water of zero chlorine demand.[3] Continued application may result in a decreasing residual until a point is reached at which the chlorine demand of the water is satisfied. At this point the residual will again rise nearly in proportion to the rate of application. This latter point is described as the break point. The chlorine residual just beyond the break point is considered the optimum dosage of chlorine to reduce objectionable tastes, odors, and bacterial content to a minimum. A residual of 0.1 ppm (parts per million) after 30-min contact is considered an effective dosage.[3]

Many food plant sanitarians prefer, however, to chlorinate well beyond the break point, and 10 to 25 ppm of chlorine applied is not uncommon, although the chlorine demand may be much below these figures. Chlorinators are on the market for treating plant water supplies to any desired concentration. There are manual and automatic models requiring a minimum of attention. Some idea of the quantity of chlorine necessary for any application may be gained from the following statement: A plant using 1 million gallons of water per day (8,330,000 lb) would require 8.33 lb chlorine per day to maintain a concentration of 1.0 ppm. The quantity varies, of course, directly with parts per million of chlorine added and water consumption.

Even with low residuals, in-plant chlorination does an admirable job of controlling bacterial growth, preventing the formation of slime and algae, and reducing odors. The extent to which all water is chlorinated within a food plant is dependent upon the analysis of the water, its potability, and the products being processed. Water with a residual of much above 0.1 ppm may have an objectionable chlorinous taste. In plants where a residual considerably higher than this is maintained, it is customary to provide other water for drinking purposes. Likewise, to prevent off-flavors, syrup and brine are usually not chlorinated, nor is boiler feed water.

In-plant chlorinated water is used during normal operations for: fruit and vegetable washers; sorting belts; top and underside of belt conveyers; can coolers where cans are submerged; periodic quick rinses of tanks, screens, and reels; elevators; floors; platforms; flumes; and gutters. It has been proved that much time can be saved in plant cleanup by the effectual use of chlorinated water to reduce the formation of slime.[4] It should be interesting to plant managers and engineers that no increase in corrosion is attributed to chlorination where a residual of 5 ppm is maintained during operations and 20 ppm during cleanup.[4]

During the cleanup period, chlorination may be increased to a residual of 20 to 100 ppm applied either at the usual pressures of 50 to 100 psi or by means of guns with a nozzle pressure of 300 to 800 psi.   It is a good idea to distinguish chlorinated-water piping from process-water piping by marking lines, valves, and hoses a distinct color.

The reader is referred to two splendid articles on the subject of chlorination of plant water which appeared in *Food Technology*.[4,5]   The former deals with vegetable and fruit canneries; the latter covers work with citrus juices.   Studies are under way testing the new iodine compounds which hold considerable promise as sanitizing and disinfecting agents in the presence of organic matter.

Preventing Bacterial Contamination.   Nothing takes the place of a thorough cleanup program carried out by an efficient and well-equipped organization and followed up with adequate inspection.   The Federal Food and Drug Administration enumerates as sources and routes of contamination in a food plant the factors shown in the following list:

1. Poor personal hygiene on the part of employees.
2. Prevalence of rats, mice, and other vermin.
3. Incidence of flies.
4. Use of unclean equipment.
5. Polluted water or ice supplies.
6. Use of unfit raw materials.
7. Inadequate service facilities, toilets, and washrooms.
8. Undesirable structural features of the buildings, lighting, and ventilation.
9. Improper waste and sewage disposal.[6]

Employees should be provided with readily accessible washrooms and adequate toilets.   The dressing rooms should be roomy, well lighted, and ventilated.   Drinking fountains and eating facilities should be located away from machines and working areas.   Floors should be easy to wash down and sloped to drain well.   Elevated benches and lockers supported by a minimum number of sturdy legs, leaving the floor clear, allow thorough floor cleaning and discourage throwing trash behind lockers or under benches.   Lockers with sloping tops prevent unsightly stacking of articles on top.   Toilet rooms need to be screened and to have tight doors and walls.   Toilets and urinals which are wall-hung present no hard-to-clean spots on the floor.

The cleaning of open equipment accessible to hosing down is generally done by spraying first with water to remove particles of food and debris, followed by a rinse of clear or chlorinated water.   If the equipment has inaccessible spots, high-pressure water may be used, the pressure being as high as 500 to 800 psi to clean the equipment more thoroughly and quickly.   Often steam will be used, and if the debris is persistent, detergent solutions may have to be used with brushes and scrapers, the strength depending upon the type and tenacity of the scale.   The following comments are gleaned from an article by Dr. G. Robert DiMarco, Chairman, Department of Food Science, Rutgers University, College of Agriculture, New Brunswick, N.J.

Alkaline detergents are commonly used, such as caustic soda, silicates, phosphates, and carbonates.   Acid compounds are sometimes used, especially the milder organic acids like citric, lactic, and propionic.   To the cleaning solutions, surfactants are often added as wetting agents.   The cleaning operation should then be followed by a sanitizer or germicide, consisting of chlorine-water rinse or one of the hypochlorites. The quaternary ammonium compounds are used extensively, but they must be selected carefully for the job they are to do.   Iodine-type sanitizers and detergents are effective for cleaning and bacterial control in both hard and soft water, warm or cold.   They will soften milkstone and lime deposits.[7]

Some closed vessels are cleaned without opening by circulating detergent solutions through spray coils located to allow the cleaning solution to reach all parts of the vessel.   A good example of this is a sanitary evaporator or vacuum pan with its tube bundles, heat exchangers, vapor separator chambers, condensers, pumps, and piping system. After about 30 min the detergent is pumped back to its storage tank, the lines and vessels rinsed with clear water and then with chlorine water. It is well to open part of the system for a visual inspection at the end of the cleaning operation. Warning signs should be posted at entrances to areas being cleaned with detergents.

At times it will be necessary to aid the cleaning by means of brushes, brooms, scrapers, or sponges. Steam should be used sparingly so as not to fill the room with fog, thus creating a hazard to the men. Many transfer pipelines are cleaned in place by circulating strong detergent solutions through them. Time and labor can be saved if the sanitation crew is provided with proper tools, equipment, and space for orderly storage of their tools and supplies. Mechanical scrubbers, sweepers, steam guns, high-pressure pumps, hoses and nozzles, brooms, brushes, scrapers, rubber boots and gloves, suits, hats, and face shields all have their place in any sanitation program.

Frequent inspections will encourage a thorough cleaning job, and an occasional reprimand from the inspection team will serve to point up some deficiency. The inspection team may be composed of the plant sanitarian, sanitation foreman, the operating foreman of the department being inspected, an operator in this department, and a chemist or member of the technical staff. The operator and chemist should be rotated periodically to allow more men in the organization to become familiar with the objectives and function of the sanitation department. A term of serving on this team will make an employee more sanitation-conscious and give him an insight into the problems to be overcome. The purpose of these periodic inspections is to observe the efficiency of cleaning tools and methods used, tidiness, safety conditions of equipment, sources of contamination, and anything else concerning sanitation. The committee then makes recommendations to the plant superintendent, with a copy to the plant manager, for changes and commendations for work well done. Doyle lists the following areas and equipment to be inspected and conditions to be considered in a complete inspection.

Plant surroundings.
Construction and arrangement of buildings.
Equipment and machinery.
Storage and warehousing.
Rodent infestation.
Insect infestation.
Lighting, ventilation, and temperature control.
Water supply.
Cleanup procedures.
Sewers and sewage disposal.
Waste disposal.
Sanitation of employees.
Sanitary facilities.
Dressing rooms.
Drinking fountains.
Plant feeding facilities.[1]

A properly functioning sanitation department, guided by an alert inspection committee, will keep the plant and the management in the good graces of both local and federal health departments.

Determination of bacterial contamination may be made by several methods, including total plate count, direct counts, and microscopic examination of stained smears. Not only should the final product be examined, but line checks should be made on washers, conveyers, peelers, pulpers, juicers, filling equipment, and pipelines. City water is usually safe from a bacterial standpoint, but water pumped by plant wells should be checked regularly. This source may be contaminated by surface drainage, animal or waste-disposal pollution, or cesspool seepage.

Efforts have been renewed recently to use electronic radiation and cathode rays for cold sterilization of certain foods.   Results heretofore have not been very promising because of changes in flavor and color and incompleteness of the sterilization. Several years ago, the Quartermaster Food and Container Institute for the Armed Forces launched its Radiation Sterilization Research Program to study this process further.   Having much to gain from the perfection of such a method of pasteurization, the QMI has obtained the cooperation and assistance of several other governmental agencies and some large industrial firms to aid in the research and experimental work. The X-ray department of the General Electric Company has experimented with electron-beam generators for irradiating samples of food in cooperation with industries that wish to test this method on their products.

In Gloucester, Massachusetts, the first large-scale fish irradiator is holding fish fresh for 30 days by a combination of irradiation and normal refrigeration.   The Atomic Energy Commission combined its efforts with the Bureau of Commercial Fisheries to turn this long-time dream into a reality.   This unit utilizes gamma rays from a cobalt-60 source.   The next step which Marine Products Development Irradiator in Gloucester is working on is putting the irradiator right in the fishing boat.[8]

Studies are also under way using ultraviolet light and ultrasonic waves as means of sterilizing food products.   Ultraviolet light has been used in many food plants to kill air-borne bacteria.   Its usefulness is more effective in rooms where food is actually exposed to the air, such as meat-storage cabinets, dough-mixing kitchens, juice-extraction rooms, and fruit- and vegetable-peeling stations.   The air should have active circulation and effective filtration, including an air washer.

Install Proper Floors and Walls.   Most food plants have floor conditions which alternate between acid and alkaline reactions.   Fruits, juices, sugar, milk, and many vegetables are sufficiently acid to cause serious corrosion to concrete floors.   During the cleanup period these floors are subjected to alkaline cleaning solutions.   Prolonged treatment like this will eat away the cement in the floor, leaving the rock protruding on the surface.   Soon the floor becomes a hazard to operators and equipment, unsightly in appearance, and impossible to maintain clean.   Application of one of the commercial concrete hardeners adds but little to the resistance of concrete under such conditions.   Our plant has been quite satisfied with $\frac{1}{8}$ in. epoxy coatings with sand as an extender, applied by our own personnel to areas subjected to moderate or light lemon-juice spillage, and costing about $0.90 per square foot, including floor preparation.   Where heavy trucking is encountered, the epoxy should be $\frac{1}{4}$ in. thick, as described in *Plant Engineering Magazine*.[9]   Polyurethane formulations are now used for resilient floor topping and as a sealer.   Wood floors, whether of wood blocks, laminated flooring, flat planking, or hardwood, are serviceable but require considerable maintenance.   Periodically a good scraping or sanding will renew the surface and with the application of a sealer will aid in keeping the floor clean.   Hot mastic about $1\frac{1}{4}$ to $1\frac{1}{2}$ in. thick applied over concrete will satisfactorily resist most acids and alkalies and is reasonable in price.   The binder being asphalt, the surface will not support heavy loads.   A barrel chime, for instance, will sink into it in warm weather, making it difficult to clean the floor and maintain it dry.   Machinery and equipment legs must penetrate the mastic and rest on concrete.   Patching around these legs must be tight and vibration kept to a minimum to prevent acids from seeping down to the concrete, where corrosion will take place.

Vitrified quarry tile or acidproof brick laid in acidproof cement over concrete offers the most satisfactory type of floor for a food plant.   Costing about $2.50 per square foot installed, it is rather expensive but offers many advantages over concrete or wood. It is permanent, is easily maintained clean, will take heavy traffic, is equally good wet or dry, can be sanitized with detergents or chlorinated water, and looks attractive. In areas where the floors must be washed, they should slope $\frac{1}{4}$ in. per ft.   This permits the water to drain readily, and small inaccuracies in the surface will not leave puddles of water to become stagnant.   The quarry tile can be applied to the sides of ditches and flumes.   The bottoms should be made of a half section of round vitrified clay pipe bedded in the same cement used on the floor tile.   The ditch should slope $\frac{1}{8}$ to

¼ in. per ft, which will make it largely self-cleaning. Quarry tile is made in a variety of shapes, so that regardless of irregularities in walls, curbs, foundations, or obstructions, there need be no sharp corners to hinder cleaning.

Ceramic tile for walls is a good match for quarry-tile floors, being easy to maintain clean. Smooth-surface asbestos board and Keene cement plaster make very good walls. Plywood, if kept well protected with paint, provides a good surface. Glass block has the advantage of admitting diffused light but can be set so there is no sill to catch dust as there is with most windows.

Ceilings should be high in a food plant to accommodate tall equipment and to allow piping to be well out of the way and yet exposed for easy cleaning, inspection, and servicing. Gravity flow of materials will be aided also. Floors should not be crowded with equipment or stored materials because cleaning costs will surely rise under congested conditions and a much less effective performance will result. Sharp corners and inaccessible spots should be eliminated. Adequate aisle space is essential for cleaning.

Ensure Proper Lighting. Food plants are deserving of good lighting the same as an aircraft assembly line or a shoe-manufacturing plant. The actual amount of light or brightness that should be provided in any area depends upon the task being performed. The Illuminating Engineering Society recommends, and the American Standards Association has approved, the following specific recommended values of illumination for the canning and preserving industries.

Seeing Task	Current Recommended Practice, Ft-c in Service (On Task or 30 In. above Floor)
Receiving:	
Grading raw-material samples	50
Tomatoes	100
Color grading (cutting rooms)	200
Preparation:	
Preliminary sorting:	
Apricots and peaches	50
Tomatoes	100
Olives	150
Cutting and pitting	100
Final sorting	100
Canning:	
Continuous-belt canning	100
Sink canning	100
Hand packing	50
Olives	100
Examination of canned samples	200
Container handling:	
Inspection	200
Can unscramblers	70
Labeling and cartoning	30
Storage warehouses	10[10]

From this table an idea may be gained as to the light required for almost any operation, whether the food plant be cannery, dairy, or bakery.

Direct glare should be avoided by reducing the brightness of the light source, elevating it out of direct view, or increasing the brightness of the area behind the light source. If the glare is from natural light sources, shades or blinds should be installed. On light fixtures of low mounting height it is good practice to install louvers which block out the lamp from the vision of the worker below 45 degrees. A program of periodic cleaning of all lighting equipment should be established. Two cleanings per year are recommended for average locations. In dusty places more frequent cleaning is justified in order to keep lighting equipment near peak efficiency. The fact is often overlooked that lack of cleaning fixtures and lamps may easily reduce their efficiency to 50 per cent of the initial value.

Among the advantages of good illumination the following may be listed:

1. Increased production.
2. Better workmanship.
3. Better utilization of floor space.
4. Greater ease of seeing:
     a. Continued production by older employees.
     b. Less eye strain among all employees.
5. Better housekeeping.
6. Better supervision of workers.
7. Improved morale among employees.
8. Greater safety.

An installation of incandescent lamps in good reflectors, if well designed, can be satisfactory.   Fluorescent lamps are some two to three times as efficient as incandescent lamps, which means that operating costs are reduced.   Installation costs are also reduced because less copper and a smaller conduit need to be used.   Lamp life is many times that of the incandescent lamps.   The slim-line, rapid-start, high-output, and power-groove lamps eliminate the objectionable, slow, uncertain starting and the flicker so prevalent with the older F40T12 lamps with starters.   Mercury lighting is very satisfactory for high-bay installations, and the new metallic vapor lamps show promise of yet greater efficiencies.

Industrial lighting is certainly headed for higher foot-candle levels.   Lighting intensities have been doubling about every 10 years, and this trend has been going on for over 50 years.   Considerable research is being conducted in the field of light intensities versus worker-efficiency concepts and points to higher foot-candle levels to increase the efficiency of workmen.[11]

Should modernization or expansion become necessary and it is found that wire sizes and conduits are inadequate for the new lighting load, the following facts should be kept in mind: New insulating materials reduce the OD of the wire so that more or larger conductors may be installed in existing conduits.[12]   Wiring capacities may also be increased by changing the type of distribution system in use.   A change from a two-wire 115-volt to a three-wire 115/230-volt system results in 100 per cent increase in capacity.   A change from a three-wire single-phase to a four-wire three-phase system results in a correspondingly large increase.   Consideration should also be given to high-frequency lighting systems.   Lamp efficiencies are increased with no adverse effect upon lamp life.   For a given illumination level, fewer fixtures are needed with high frequency because of improved lamp efficiency.[13]

Insect and Rodent Control.   The battle against insects and rodents is ever present in a food plant, and to slacken off anywhere along the line is to lose ground rapidly. It is the persistent day-by-day control procedures that produce results rather than the frantic weekly or monthly eradication campaign.

Any program, to be successful, must incorporate these four major phases of rodent control: destruction of rats, elimination of rat harborages, elimination of food supply for rats, and rat proofing of buildings.   For the destruction of rodents, there are a number of reliable rodenticides such as red squill, zinc phosphide, ANTU (alpha-naphthylthiourea) and 1080 (sodium fluoracetate).[14]   All of these are quite effective. Except for red squill their toxicity to man is rather high, and they should be used only where extreme caution is exercised.   1080 should not be used about a food-processing plant.   Warfarin, Pival, Fumarin, Diphacinone, and PMP are known as anticoagulant poisons, because they prevent the normal clotting of blood and cause rats and mice to die by internal bleeding.   They should be provided in small quantities over a period of 2 to 3 weeks.   Rats seem to be unable to detect these poisons in the food; thus they do not arouse bait shyness in the colony.   A new, fast-acting raticide has been shown to act specifically against rats only—the new compound kills the common Norway rat in a single dose containing only 5 mg of the active ingredient—yet produces no deaths when submitted at high dose levels to chickens, turkeys, ducks, geese, sheep, swine, cattle, horses, rabbits, cats, dogs, squirrels, mice, mink, monkeys, and chimpanzees.[15]

Junk piles, old unused buildings or sheds, weed patches, and banks of ditches or railroads provide harborage for rats and mice. These should be cleaned up, weeds cut or killed, and the burrows in dirt banks treated with poison or gas. If the plant sanitarian has eliminated all breeding places on his own property and rodents still enter from neighboring properties, he may resort to bait boxes along the routes traveled by the rats. Well-trimmed lawns discourage rats from crossing from fence to building, whereas rubbish piles furnish good protection for them on their nightly invasions.

Good plant sanitation practices will include measures necessary to eliminate sources of food for rodents. This is just as important in storage of raw materials as it is in protecting materials in process or the final product. Prevent rodents from feeding, and they will move elsewhere. The best control of rats and mice is to take away the food and shelter that permits them to survive. Traps, gases, and poisons will only temporarily halt a growing rat population.[16] With the above preventive measures and an active program of eradication, rodent problems can be solved.

Most of the comments above are applicable to the elimination of flies and other insects from a food plant. All openings should be screened or have a fan blowing air across the open area. A knockdown type of spray is effective and safe inside buildings provided all tanks are covered during the spray period. It is generally safe to use a residual spray outside the buildings. If vigorous sanitation measures are not continually practiced, insects, especially flies, can easily become a terrific nuisance and a source of serious contamination.

REFERENCES

1. D. K. Tressler and M. A. Joslyn, "The Chemistry and Technology of Fruit and Vegetable Juice Production," pp. 276–277, Chap. 8, "Plant Sanitation," by Edwin S. Doyle. The Avi Publishing Company, Inc., 1954.
2. *Ibid.*, p. 284.
3. Solvay Process Div., Allied Chemical and Dye Corp., Solvay Technical and Engineering Service Bulletin 8, pp. 62–66.
4. Ira I. Somers, Studies on In-Plant Chlorination, *Food Technol.*, vol. 5, no. 2, p. 51.
5. Charles H. Brokaw, The Role of Sanitation in Quality Control of Frozen Citrus Concentrates, *Food Technol.*, vol. 6, no. 9, p. 344.
6. Microanalysis of Food and Drug Products, Food and Drug Circ. 1, pp. 4–8.
7. *Food Engineering*, vol. 36, no. 10, p. 54.
8. *Canner/Packer*, vol. 133, no. 12, p. 30.
9. *Plant Engineering*, vol. 15, no. 6, p. 110.
10. The Illuminating Engineering Society, "American Standard Practice For Industrial Lighting."
11. Industrial Lighting—Present and Future, *Plant Engineering*, vol. 17, no. 3.
12. The Illuminating Engineering Society, "American Standard Practice for Industrial Lighting," pp. 34, 35.
13. *Plant Engineering*, vol. 17, no. 10, p. 131.
14. U.S. Fish and Wildlife Service, Leaflets 317, 318, 319, District Agent, Purdue University.
15. *Food Processing*, vol. 25, no. 11, p. 156.
16. U.S. Fish and Wildlife Service, Leaflet 316, District Agent, Purdue University.

Chapter 4

INDUSTRIAL HOUSEKEEPING

By JAMES E. THOMPSON[1]
Stanford Research Institute
Southern California Laboratories
South Pasadena, Calif.

Industrial housekeeping is the process of maintaining all work and storage areas clean, neat, and orderly combined with elimination of all nonessential material and equipment. When this condition is maintained, then good housekeeping will prevail —in the factory, in the office, in material storage yards, and in all other work areas.

The quality of housekeeping in a department or company is an excellent indication of the efficiency of its operation and of the effectiveness of maintenance. Good housekeeping and profitable operation are inseparable companions. Production efficiency and effective maintenance are not guaranteed by good industrial housekeeping, but it is certain that effective operation cannot be achieved in the midst of disorder and confusion.

Maintaining good housekeeping makes it possible for each worker to devote full attention to his assigned job. Tools and material are readily available and always in the same place. There is adequate working area, and the worker's efforts are not obstructed by irrelevant objects.

Housekeeping in an industrial organization is not essentially different from housekeeping at home. Good housekeeping ensures a pleasant, safe, and efficient area in each case.

A considerable portion of the responsibility of maintaining good industrial housekeeping falls upon maintenance. Unfortunately, maintenance cannot do the entire job and often must "sell" operating personnel on the desirability of cooperating in the housekeeping effort.

Selling Good Housekeeping. Some foremen and supervisors may question the value of effort spent in maintaining good housekeeping. These objections are usually encountered in cases where good housekeeping has been absent for such a long period that filth and disorder have become accepted as normal.

In the absence of contrast or standards, it is only too easy for serious deterioration to be accepted as normal. In the case of a cement mill that came to the author's attention, housekeeping was apparently absent during the plant's twenty-odd years of operation—other than to push rubbish accumulations aside when they reached the point of obstructing passage. In fact, even elementary housekeeping was neglected to the absurd point that a section of the mill roof collapsed from the weight of cement dust accumulated over a period of years.

A definite "selling" job is involved when confronted with conditions such as this— selling good housekeeping to supervisors and foremen who, in the absence of comparisons, may find it difficult to realize how seriously their workplaces have deterior-

[1] The author is now Consulting Engineer, Lake Havasu Irrigation and Drainage District, Lake Havasu City, Ariz.

ated.   These men can, of course, be shown that over a period of time the total effort required to operate each group or department is less when good housekeeping is present.   However, this does not break down their sales resistance and provide the necessary initial cooperation to begin housekeeping improvement.

It must not be overlooked for a single moment that obtaining good housekeeping in an office or factory requires the cooperation of all supervisors and foremen and that

(a)

(b)

FIG. 4-1. Inspection area, sheet-metal department (a) before, (b) after application of basic factors of good housekeeping.   (*Courtesy of San Diego Plant of Convair Div., General Dynamics Corp.*)

obtaining this requires a "selling" job sponsored by top management.   People cannot be forced into being neat and orderly, although they can be "bribed" to maintain good-housekeeping standards through an incentive bonus.

The best possible means of selling good housekeeping is by demonstrating the difference between a disorderly department and one where good-housekeeping standards are maintained.   Demonstrating should be done preferably by actual physical example, otherwise by means of photographs such as those reproduced as Figs. 4-1 through 4-6.

The advantages of a cleaned-up, neat, orderly department are so obvious that words are generally superfluous, and in practically every case the "sales resistance" of the objecting supervisor or foreman will be overcome. Only in rare cases will an individual be encountered who is disorderly by nature, rather than circumstance, and who

(a)

(b)

Fig. 4-2. Office (a) before, (b) after conformance to layout and equipment standards. (*Courtesy of San Diego Plant of Convair Div., General Dynamics Corp.*)

is unable to see the advantages of good housekeeping even when shown actual physical results. These unfortunate individuals probably require the assistance of a psychiatrist rather than of maintenance.

In most cases it is possible to locate at least one supervisor or foreman who is easily sold on the advantages of good housekeeping. His department or group can be used as a proving ground. All effort should be concentrated on establishing the highest possible standards of housekeeping, neglecting, for the moment, the other departments. After the one department is cleaned up, with good-housekeeping practices firmly established, it will be comparatively easy to sell the others, for the comparison between order and disorder will be painfully obvious as will the fact that little effort is required to maintain good housekeeping.

Typical photographs should be obtained of each "cleaned-up" group or department, showing conditions before and after establishment of good housekeeping. These will be invaluable in selling good housekeeping to other supervisors and foremen.

(a)

(b)

Fig. 4-3. Material preparation area (a) before, (b) after application of basic factors of good housekeeping. (*Courtesy of San Diego Plant of Convair Div. General Dynamics Corp.*)

Suppose, however, that neither photographs nor a cleaned-up department is available to aid in selling good housekeeping. What can then be done? It becomes necessary to rely upon words—persuasiveness and logic. A feeble substitute for actual demonstration, it must be admitted, but this is the only remaining solution to the problem.

Obvious comparisons in other fields where the value of orderliness is without question can be pointed out. A simple analogy is that of a reference book without an index.   The desired information may be in the book, but the effort of locating the data usually prevents their being applied.   Another analogy is the obvious advantage of driving through city streets provided with well-synchronized traffic signals in contrast to the confusion and waste of unregulated traffic.

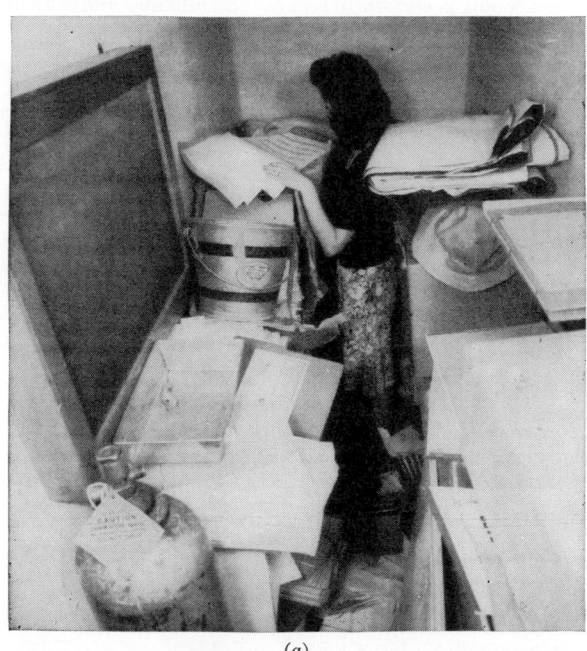

(a)

(b)

FIG. 4-4. Office, material handling and storage, (a) before, (b) after application of basic factors of good housekeeping. (*Courtesy of San Diego Plant of Convair Div., General Dynamics Corp.*)

The evident deduction to be drawn from these and other everyday examples is that if orderliness provides greater efficiency in these cases, then certainly the same thing should be true in a factory section or department.

Factors Governing Housekeeping.   It may appear that establishing good housekeeping is a formidable task.   Quite the contrary.   There are not many requirements for obtaining good housekeeping.   In fact, there are only three: (1) proper layout and equipment, (2) correct material handling and storage, and (3) cleanliness and orderliness.   These are the factors to be considered when evaluating the degree of housekeeping in a department, irrespective of its being a factory or office group.

When proper attention is given to establishment and maintenance of these three factors, good housekeeping is certain to result.   Should any one of them be neglected, deterioration will begin.

(a)

(b)

FIG. 4-5. Saw section, sheet-metal department, (a) before, (b) after application of basic factors of good housekeeping. (*Courtesy of San Diego Plant of Convair Div., General Dynamics Corp.*)

Good housekeeping and its effect upon industrial efficiency have received sufficient discussion.   More can be accomplished by showing how good-housekeeping principles were actually applied in one industrial plant.

In Figs. 4-1 through 4-6 are shown actual typical views of various factory and office departments.   In each case there is a "before" (identified as a) view and an "after"

(b) view.   These are not hand-picked exceptions, but typical views illustrating the three basic factors of good housekeeping and showing the results obtained by applying these factors.

Proper Layout and Equipment.   Plant layout controls the ease of maintaining good housekeeping, while proper handling and storage equipment affects the degree of housekeeping attainable.   Even the most sincere efforts to maintain order will pro-

(a)

(b)

FIG. 4-6. Office (a) before, (b) after conformance to principles of cleanliness and orderliness. (*Courtesy of San Diego Plant, Convair Div., General Dynamics Corp.*)

duce mediocre results when handicapped by insufficient space to move and store material or when frustrated by lack of tool and material storage racks and skids.

This does not mean that good housekeeping can be attained only by starting from scratch, that is, the original layout of a plant.   It is true that less effort would then be required to establish order, but adjustment of the plant layout can be made at any time.

Each department or section should be examined to determine what should be done to provide ample working space, adequate and proper storage for all tools and material, and proper facilities for moving material. The machines, benches, and other equipment should then be arranged to provide straight-line uninterrupted flow of material through the area.

All tendencies toward unnecessary accumulations of material should be eliminated. If material must be accumulated while awaiting processing or movement to the next operation, accumulation areas should be provided at each end of the department or section. The only material in the work area should be that actually in work.

A natural question at this point might be, "That sounds swell, but where can I get the additional floor space required for all this?" In most cases additional floor area cannot be obtained and is not actually necessary. There is probably ample space now, but it is not being properly used. All unnecessary secondary factors should be eliminated, either by complete removal or by moving to locations that will not interfere with material flow. Secondary factors are equipment that does not contribute directly to the work in progress: tool storage racks, stock bins, even lavatory facilities. Many of these secondary factors may be necessary, but they are not in continuous use as part of the production flow. These should be removed from the production flow, and the space used for production instead of service.

Eliminating unnecessary accumulation of material is another means of gaining floor space. Material should always be flowing through the plant, rather than accumulating in quantity at each department or section. The only places that material should accumulate in quantity are storerooms and warehouses.

The views of a typical inspection area shown in Fig. 4-1 are fine examples of housekeeping problems and their solution. In Fig. 4-1*a* is an excellent case of what should *not* exist—benches and aisles piled with material awaiting inspection or movement to the next operation, material stacked on benches or tossed into paper cartons rather than being on skids or pallets or in tote pans—a disorderly array, where no one can be certain what is going on, and an excellent example of poor housekeeping.

Study the contrast presented by Fig. 4-1*b*. In particular, note that approximately the same floor space is required. The trouble was not lack of space but failure to use the existing area properly.

Proper material-handling facilities have been provided. Material is no longer permitted to accumulate in the area; it is received, inspected, and moved to the next operation. It is evident that good housekeeping prevails and equally apparent that little effort will be required to maintain order and cleanliness.

Identical principles of industrial housekeeping can be applied to both direct labor and indirect labor departments. Only the equipment and operations are different—not the basic problems and their solutions. In Fig. 4-2 is shown a typical office department where the same principle of proper layout and equipment has been applied.

Poor housekeeping and its causes are both obvious in Fig. 4-2*a*. In the after view of Fig. 4-2*b* the office is neat and clean. Desks are properly spaced and aligned. All filing cabinets are collected in one corner of the office. Books and catalogs not in constant use have been placed in a bookcase. Straggling telephone cords have been replaced by properly installed extensions. Only a small effort was required to effect the change. An untidy, undesirable workplace became a neat, cheerful area. Similar results can be obtained in any office by applying good layout and equipment practices.

Material Handling and Storage. Good housekeeping begins with proper facilities for handling and storing material. Another advantage accrues when material handling and storage is properly arranged—a sharp reduction in material handling *time*, with a corresponding labor saving. The largest single item in the production cost of any article is material handling time. This must not be confused with machine or processing time. Time actually spent in moving material from one operation to another is material handling time. Reduction in material handling time always produces an immediate, definite saving.

In fact, reducing material handling time is the best possible means of increasing production and profit. The expense of rearranging and handling equipment required to achieve good housekeeping can often be rapidly liquidated by the saving in handling time.

In Figs. 4-3 and 4-4 are excellent cases of improvement realized through correction of material handling and storage. In each case the before views (Figs. 4-3*a* and 4-4*a*) reflect lack of storage facilities, working areas cluttered with unnecessary items, and inadequate handling equipment. It is obvious that the time and effort required to receive, store, and disburse material will be much less with the "after" arrangements shown in Figs. 4-3*b* and 4-4*b*.

Yet in each case nothing unusual has been accomplished—simply accomplishment of the obvious. Junk and trash have been cleaned up. Simple, practical storage racks and cabinets and inexpensive skids have been provided for handling material in the factory storage area.

Special material handling equipment should be avoided except when standard equipment cannot be used without damage to the material being transported. Such cases are infrequent but should be recognized. Production changes frequently render special handling equipment obsolete and useless. Considerable financial loss can result from this obsolescence. Standard handling equipment, on the other hand, can ordinarily be used for each product, and by every department.

The preceding examples have shown both direct and indirect labor departments. Identical principles were applied to both, and identical results obtained in each case.

Cleanliness and Orderliness. The third and final requirements for establishing and maintaining good housekeeping are cleanliness and orderliness. The metal sawing department shown in Fig. 4-5*a* is an example of lack of these requirements. It is obvious that housekeeping would be difficult to maintain, even with the most sincere effort, in the congested conditions prevailing in this work area.

On the other hand, the cleaned-up department shown at Fig. 4-5*b* epitomizes the third requirement of good housekeeping—cleanliness and orderliness. It hardly seems possible that it is the same department, but such is the case. It is apparent that the men and machines will produce more with the arrangement shown in Fig. 4-5*b* to say nothing of the fact that the janitorial effort required by maintenance will be much less.

In Fig. 4-6*a* and *b* are shown the before and after results of applying the third requirement of good industrial housekeeping to an office area. Careful study of these views will reveal that in reality only minor changes have been made. Personnel have been taught to place inactive equipment and material promptly in designated storage spaces, keeping upon desks and drawing boards only those items actually in use on current jobs. Emphasis has been placed upon keeping the workplace neat and clean at all times.

This office area was cleaned up by applying the same principles used for the factory area shown in Fig. 4-5. The only difference encountered was that the task was easier in the case of the office area.

Maintenance of Housekeeping. This scheme for establishing good industrial housekeeping will always obtain the desired results when properly applied. However, this is only half the battle, perhaps less than half. The problem of *maintaining* good housekeeping will always be present, and a definite plan must be provided to prevent deterioration.

The deterioration problem can be eased by "dressing up" work areas to emphasize good housekeeping. A simple and effective means is the use of painted floor markings to indicate all aisles, accumulation areas, departmental and section boundaries, machine locations, and storage stations for movable equipment. Effective use of floor markings is shown in Figs. 4-3*b* and 4-5*b*.

A well-planned educational program will assist in selling the necessity for maintaining housekeeping. Propaganda, in the form of suitable items in the company's house organ, also will help.

Periodic inspection by a housekeeping committee is a vital part of every good-housekeeping program. The knowledge that each work area is frequently subject to a critical housekeeping inspection keeps all supervisors and foremen alert to the necessity for housekeeping and retards deterioration.

Housekeeping Incentive Plan.   All these devices will aid in preventing deterioration but will not ensure maintenance of good housekeeping.   It may be found that this can best be done by providing a definite, concrete incentive to spur all supervisors and foremen to constant awareness of the necessity of maintaining good housekeeping.

One excellent incentive is a bonus payment to supervisors and foremen who excel in maintaining good housekeeping within their departments and sections.   This should be part of a general supervisory incentive plan but can be operated as an individual bonus in the absence of an over-all incentive plan.

ELIMINATE
PHILTHY PHILBERT!

HIS CLUTTER OF TOOLS & PARTS ARE A MENACE TO EVERYONE.

(a)

FIG. 4-7. (a), (b), and (c)—posters used to publicize a good housekeeping program.   (*Courtesy of North American Aviation, Inc.*)

When an over-all incentive plan is in operation, poor housekeeping becomes a factor that may decrease the bonus paid to a particular supervisor or foreman irrespective of the actual increase in production realization obtained by his department or section. In the case of a separate housekeeping bonus, small payments are made each month to supervisors and foremen who maintain their housekeeping above a designated minimum.   The amount of this payment is a matter for top-management decision.   Two per cent of the supervisor's or foreman's salary during the preceding month is a value used by some companies.

The Derision-campaign Plan.   In contrast to an incentive bonus for good housekeeping is the plan of focusing attention upon the department or group showing the lowest housekeeping score.   A definite campaign along these lines was launched by North American Aviation, Inc., a few years ago and obtained remarkable results in improving and maintaining housekeeping in their plants.

The first phase of the North American campaign involved a 6-week publicity campaign, using the company house organ and large posters at each time-clock station, to emphasize the drive to improve housekeeping. A slovenly character, identified as "Philthy Philbert," was created by their art department and used as the principal of a

PHILTHY PHILBERT –

> Philthy doesn't believe in signs – especially those to maintain order. He tosses everything away (except money), and never in the right place. Philthy always floors it – never cans it.

HE'S UNSANITARY-DONT TOUCH HIM

(b)

FIG. 4-7 *(Continued)*.

series of cartoon posters (Fig. 4-7). All trash cans were repainted and stenciled with the slogan, "Can it, don't floor it!" (see Fig. 4-8). A housekeeping committee was appointed to make periodic inspection of all office and factory areas.

At the end of the 6-week campaign the first housekeeping inspection was made, and the department showing the lowest rating awarded the "booby prize"—a large poster showing "Philthy Philbert" enthroned upon a pile of rubbish and bearing the slogan "Philthy Philbert Lives Here." It was required that this poster remain above the entrance to the department foreman's office until the next monthly housekeeping review. At that time the "prize" was reawarded to the department that then received the lowest housekeeping score.

The results of the "Philthy Philbert" plan were so satisfactory that the scheme has continued in operation, with only minor additions and alterations. A member of the North American Aviation methods department now has the responsibility for periodically roving through all office and factory areas, armed with a camera with which to record instances of poor housekeeping. Prints of the photographs are sent to the fore-

Fig. 4-7 (*Continued*).

man of the erring department with a request to correct the unsatisfactory condition. The poster of "Philthy Philbert" has been replaced by a small statue, and this is awarded to the department showing the lowest monthly housekeeping score.

Housekeeping Inspection Plan. A housekeeping inspection plan begins with the establishment of a housekeeping committee. This group should meet at least once a month to inspect plant-wide housekeeping conditions and will normally comprise the following department heads, their designated alternates, or equivalents: plant engineer, safety engineer, chief of plant fire department, material control manager, office manager, and works manager. Some of these positions may not exist in some companies, but the committee should still comprise the men responsible for these or similar functions, irrespective of their actual job titles.

FIG. 4-8. Trash can placard used in good housekeeping campaign. (*Courtesy of North American Aviation, Inc.*)

```
                    HOUSEKEEPING  INSPECTION  AND  RATING  SHEET

    DEPT. NUMBER_____31_____          INSPECTION  MONTH_____March_____
    DEPT. NAME  Subassembly                CURRENT RATE_____81_____
    OFFICE___SHOP x BUILDING  1            PREVIOUS RATE_____86_____
```

	POOR		FAIR		NORMAL		EXCELLENT
CONFORMANCE TO LAYOUT AND EQUIPMENT STANDARDS	○	○	○	✗	○	○	○

REASONS: *Department does not conform to layout at C–17 & 19, Q–18 to 20.*
Clearance nil on south side nose buck platform station 1,
when the arms open – a safety hazard.

	POOR		FAIR		NORMAL		EXCELLENT
MATERIAL HANDLING AND STORAGE	○	○	○	○	○	✗	○

REASONS:

	POOR		FAIR		NORMAL		EXCELLENT
CLEANLINESS AND ORDERLINESS	○	○	○	✗	○	○	○

REASONS: *Some dirty benches and tool box racks.*
Miscellaneous items parked on the floor consisting of insulation,
drills, questionable parts, air motors, "C" clamps and rope.

PLANT HOUSEKEEPING COMMITTEE BY ___C. E. Y.___

FIG. 4-9. Rating sheet used by housekeeping committee.

Following the establishment of a housekeeping committee, it is necessary to provide housekeeping standards and a means of evaluating the relative degree of housekeeping found in each department and section of the company. In Fig. 4-9 is presented a housekeeping inspection and rating sheet, and in Fig. 4-10 a schedule for converting the inspection results into a point-value score.

A score of 85 represents normal, standard housekeeping. When housekeeping is part of an over-all supervisory incentive plan, a penalty is assessed against departments and sections failing to realize a housekeeping score of 85 or better, but additional credit is not given for exceeding the 85 norm. It usually is considered that maintenance of established housekeeping standards is a routine obligation of those participating in a supervisory incentive plan.

It will be observed that the housekeeping inspection form shown in Fig. 4-9 is based upon the three basic housekeeping factors of *layout and equipment standards, material handling and storage,* and *cleanliness and orderliness.* It is necessary to determine the

FACTOR	POOR	FAIR	NORMAL	EXCELLENT
CONFORMANCE TO LAYOUT AND EQUIPMENT STANDARDS	○ ○	○ ○	○ ○	○
OFFICE :	9 13	16 19	21 23	25
SHOP :	11 16	20 23	26 28	30
MATERIAL HANDLING AND STORAGE	○ ○	○ ○	○ ○	○
OFFICE :	5 8	10 11	13 14	15
SHOP	10 15	19 22	25 28	30
CLEANLINESS AND ORDERLINESS	○ ○	○ ○	○ ○	○
OFFICE :	21 30	39 45	51 56	60
SHOP	14 20	26 30	34 37	40

NOTE : THESE VALUES ARE USED TO CONVERT THE FINDINGS OF THE HOUSEKEEPING COMMITTEE'S INSPECTION INTO A POINT SCORE REPRESENTING THE COMPARATIVE DEGREE OF HOUSEKEEPING PRESENT IN THE AREA INSPECTED (SEE FIG.   4-9)

FIG. 4-10. Housekeeping rating values.

conditions to be considered when evaluating each factor during housekeeping inspections. Unless this is done, there is a possibility of unequitable evaluation of different departments or sections, resulting from the influence of extraneous factors having no actual relation to basic housekeeping.

The conditions to be established as representing poor housekeeping will vary somewhat with different industries and must be tailored to fit the conditions existing in the company inaugurating a housekeeping program. The following schedule has been found acceptable in various phases of heavy industry and can be modified to suit conditions present in a particular company.

1. Conformance to layout and equipment standards:
    a. Unauthorized rearrangements: Unauthorized movement of equipment from location established in approved plant layouts.
    b. Damaged or obsolete equipment: Improperly guarded, unsightly, damaged, unpainted, or defaced equipment, machines, and fixtures.
    c. Congested portable equipment: Air guns, drill motors, or office equipment placed in a manner that hampers operations.
    d. Leaks: Air, gas, water, oil, or coolant hazards; leakage from pipes, tanks, or other containers.

2. Material handling and stores:
   a. Protrusions: Hazardous protrusions from racks, bins, benches, file cabinets, or desks.
   b. Unstable piles: Top-heavy or unbraced piles, toppling boxes or containers.
   c. Cluttered aisles: Boxes, waste baskets, storage racks, pieces or piles of material, tote pans, and skids left in aisles and walkways in a manner that creates a hazard or retards operations.
   d. Overloaded equipment: Structures, frames, racks, shelves, tote-pans, and skids improperly loaded or loaded beyond capacity.
   e. Makeshift equipment: Improper use of standard equipment; use of makeshift equipment when standard equipment is available.
3. Cleanliness and orderliness:
   a. Dirty floors and walls: Dirt or oil accumulation in aisles and work areas; under benches, machines, racks, and desks; and in corners.   Misuse of cuspidors.
   b. Needlessly unclean equipment: Dirty benches, racks, machines, tote pans, and the like.   Dust filings, chips, scraps of work, and rubbish allowed to accumulate.
   c. Unclean restrooms: Restroom and fountain facilities adjacent to the area unclean.   Lack of use of disinfectants.   Lack of available soap, paper, towels, and the like.
   d. Personal items: Clothing, lunch boxes, or packages hung or lying on benches, machines, or desks and not in spaces provided or on coat racks.
   e. Rubbish and scrap: Cigarette butts, papers, bottles, or other rubbish on floors, on machinery benches, in yards, or in any location except *proper* containers. Use of other than *proper* containers for rubbish accumulation.
   f. Projections and hazards: Nails, rough jagged corners, broken glass, hanging wires, broken flooring or paving, and the like.

Maintenance Responsibility for Improving Housekeeping.   Maintenance should not be charged with total responsibility for establishing and maintaining good housekeeping.   However, it is proper for top management to assign to plant engineering and maintenance the joint responsibility of planning and conducting a good-housekeeping campaign.

In such cases plant engineering has the responsibility of planning the housekeeping campaign, preparing instructions and work orders for its execution, working with the company public relations activity to obtain necessary intraplant publicity for the campaign, and monitoring the housekeeping inspections.   Equally important is plant engineering's task of assisting maintenance in setting an example of good housekeeping in its shops and work areas.

Maintenance always has a basic responsibility to maintain excellent housekeeping within its own shops and areas.   In addition, maintenance must always strive to provide the maximum of plant-wide janitorial and cleanup services that are possible within budget allowances for this work.   A condition should never be permitted where an office or factory supervisor can escape censure for poor housekeeping in his area by claiming that janitorial and cleanup services were deficient.

Housekeeping Work Standards.   Strictly repetitive phases of janitorial and cleanup services performed by maintenance as part of the routine plant housekeeping program should be reduced to written instructions and checkoff lists which together comprise operational standards for accomplishment of the work.   Only in this manner can there be some assurance of the work being consistently accomplished in the proper manner and can new employes be quickly indoctrinated into the proper routines.

It might appear upon superficial consideration that formalized work standards would be required only in large maintenance departments and that small departments could depend upon the foreman to define verbally housekeeping rules and procedures wherever the need arose.   This is not considered desirable, as conflicting instructions may be given when long periods elapse between recurrences of similar questions. Also, too much of the foreman's time may be spent in giving instructions on routine matters.   The time spent in explaining a particular matter *once* is little greater than that required to prepare the information as a written *work standard*, which can then be made available to all concerned to answer the particular question permanently.

An example of a work standard applicable to janitorial and cleanup work is given as follows:

Technique of Mopping

Wet mopping: Dip mop into pail, and allow to soak in solution at least ½ min. Lift mop out of solution, and mop an area from left to right, allowing a thin film of water to remain on the floor area. Redip mop in solution, and repeat the mopping operation on an adjacent area. Continue doing this until the entire floor area is "wet mopped."

Dry mopping: Dip mop in clean rinse water, and wring out dry. Mop a small area, blotting up the moisture left from the wet mopping. Continue dipping and wringing out the mop and mopping up until the entire area is finished in this manner.

Spots and marks: If spots or marks do not disappear in mopping, study the type of spot or mark and use for:

Oil spots: Approved abrasive compound.
Chewing gum: A dull knife blade, taking care not to scratch the floor surface.
Heel marks: Steel wool.
Ink spots: Steel wool and approved abrasive compound.
Paint spots: Same as ink spots.

Cautions:

1. Do not splash baseboards while mopping.
2. Do not allow any solution or water to stand on floor too long.
3. Do not use solution or rinse water when it becomes heavily contaminated with dirt or oil.
4. Do not neglect to overlap in both wet and dry mopping.
5. Do not pour dirty solution or rinse water into urinals, toilet bowls or basins, but always empty into janitor sink.

Table 4-1. Time Standards for Factory-area Sweeping

Allowance in minutes for listed combinations of trash, density, and floor conditions*

Floor area, sq ft	1-1		1-2		1-3		2-1		2-2		2-3		3-1		3-2		3-3	
	W	C	W	C	W	C	W	C	W	C	W	C	W	C	W	C	W	C
500	10	11	11	12	12	14	12	15	13	16	14	17	14	18	15	19	16	20
1,000	20	22	21	24	23	27	24	29	26	31	27	33	28	36	30	38	31	40
1,500	30	33	32	36	35	41	36	44	39	47	41	50	42	54	45	57	47	60
2,000	40	44	42	48	46	54	48	58	52	62	54	66	56	72	60	76	62	80
2,500	50	55	53	60	58	68	60	73	65	78	68	83	70	90	75	95	78	100
3,000	60	66	63	72	69	81	72	87	78	93	81	99	84	108	90	114	93	120
3,500	70	77	74	84	81	95	84	102	91	109	95	116	98	126	105	113	109	140
4,000	80	88	84	96	92	108	96	116	104	124	108	132	112	144	120	152	124	160
4,500	90	99	95	108	104	122	108	131	117	140	122	149	126	162	135	171	140	180
5,000	100	110	105	120	115	135	120	145	130	155	135	165	140	180	150	190	155	200
5,500	110	121	116	132	127	140	132	160	143	171	149	182	154	198	165	209	171	220
6,000	120	132	126	144	138	162	144	174	156	186	162	198	168	216	180	228	186	240
6,500	130	143	137	156	150	176	156	189	169	202	176	215	182	234	195	247	202	260
7,000	140	154	147	168	161	189	168	203	182	217	189	231	196	252	210	266	217	280
7,500	150	165	158	180	173	203	180	218	195	233	203	248	210	270	225	285	233	300
8,000	160	176	168	192	184	216	192	232	208	248	216	264	224	288	240	304	248	320
8,500	170	187	179	204	196	230	204	247	221	264	230	281	238	306	255	323	264	340
9,000	180	198	189	216	207	243	216	261	234	279	243	297	252	324	270	342	279	360
9,500	190	209	200	228	219	257	228	276	247	295	257	314	266	342	285	361	295	380
10,000	200	220	210	240	230	270	240	290	260	310	270	330	280	360	300	380	310	400

* 1st numeral: light (1), medium (2), or heavy (3), degree of trash accumulations.
2d numeral: light (1), medium (2), or heavy (3), density of floor installations.
W—wood floor.
C—concrete floor.

Table 4-2. Time Standards for Janitor Operations

Quantity

Janitor standards, allowed min

Item or operation	1	2	3	4	5	6	7	8	9	10	11	12	13	14	15	16	17	18	19	20	21	22	23	24	25	26	27	28
Bradleys*	7	12	17	22	27	32																						
Wash basins*	5	8	12	15	19	22	26	29	33	36																		
Toilet bowls*	3	6	8	11	13	16	18	21	23	26	28	31	33	36	38	41	43	46	48	51	53	56	58	61	63	66	68	71
Urinals*	2	3	4	5	6	7	8	9	10	11	12	13																
Mirrors*	3	5	7	9	11	13																						
Drinking fountain, cabinet																												
Drinking fountain, bubbler																												
Windows, 42 × 76 in, wash (inside only)	9	18	27	36	45	54	63	72	81	90	99	108	117	126	135	144	153	162	171	180								
Venetian blinds, 42 × 76 in., wash	31	61	91	121	151	181	211	241	271	301	331	361	391	421	451	481	511	541	571	601								
Venetian blinds, 42 × 76 in., dust	12	24	35	46	57	68	79	90	101	112	123	134	145	156	167	178	189	200	211	222								
Venetian blinds, 42 × 76 in., vacuum	11	21	31	41	51	61	71	81	91	101	111	121	131	141	151	161	171	181	191	201								
Office cleaning (per desk or table)	5	8	12	15	19	22	26	29	33	36	40	43	47	50	54	57	61	64	68	71	75							
Desk top, wash	6	12	18	24	30	36	42	48	54	60																		
Desk top, clean and dust	3	5	7	9	11	13	15	17	19	21																		
Desk top, wax	4	8	12	16	20	24	28	32	36	40																		

Area, sq ft

Janitor standards, allowed min

Item or operation	50	100	150	200	250	300	350	400	450	500	550	600	650	700	750	800	850	900	950	1,000
Sweep stairs (treads 1 ft wide)	5	6	9	12	15	18	21	24	27	30	33	36	39	42	45					51
Wax and buff floors	5	6	8	11	13	16	18	21	23	26	28	31	33	36	38	41	43	46	48	51
Wet mop, concrete	5	6	8	11	13	16	18	21	23	26	28	31	33	36	38	41	43	46	48	51
Dry mop, concrete, wood, or tile	3	3	4	5	6	7	8	9	10	11	12	13	14	15	16	16	17	18	19	20
Wet mop, wood or tile	2	2	3	4	5	6	7	8	9	10	11	12	13	14	15	16	17	18	19	20
Sweep and wet mop, concrete	7	7	12	15	22	26	29	33	36	40	43	47	50	54	57	61	64	68	71	71
Sweep and wet mop, wood or tile	4	4	6	8	10	12	14	16	18	20	22	24	26	28	30	32	34	36	38	40
Vacuum rugs	4	5	7	8	11	13	15	17	19	21	23	25	27	29	31	33	35	37	39	41

* Add 5 min per rest room for each 100 sq ft for miscellaneous cleaning, dispenser service, etc.

Housekeeping Time Standards. The majority of routine janitorial and cleanup operations lend themselves to establishment of time standards for measuring efficiency and estimating detailed personnel requirements. Some operations not practical for accurate time study often can be placed under synthetic (estimated) standards, and criteria established for measuring trends in efficiency. Information of this type is equally important to actual efficiency data because the efficiency trend of employees is usually an accurate index of the effectiveness of supervision.

The data shown in Tables 4-1 and 4-2 are summations of actual standards established through detailed time study by two large West Coast manufacturing plants, Lockheed Aircraft Corp. and North American Aviation, Inc.

These data can be modified, as necessary, to establish janitorial work standards for a specific facility or installation. They should *not* be used verbatim without careful verification, as the conditions influencing time requirements may vary greatly in different plants.

Chapter 5

CLEAN ROOMS—
CONSTRUCTION AND MAINTENANCE

By C. E. Schmid
Director, Plant Engineering and Facilities
Aerospace Group
General Precision, Inc.
Little Falls, N.J.

Clean rooms are also called "white," "ultraclean," "superclean," "environmentally controlled," "dust-controlled," or "dust-free" rooms. The term "dust-free," however, is a misnomer; there is no such thing as a room that is dust-free.

EVALUATION OF REQUIREMENTS

If you underdesign the room, you may not provide an adequate facility. If you overdesign it, you may have to spend more than can be justified. Before proceeding, the following questions must be answered:

1. What type of environment does the product that is to be produced or assembled in the area require?
2. How constant must the temperature be held?
3. What is the maximum humidity allowable?
4. What should the rate of air change be?
5. How much contamination can the product live with?
6. How large is the product?
7. Must exhaust systems be provided?
8. What changes in specifications, size, design, or production schedules are planned for the future or are likely to occur?
9. Must the facility be autonomous? That is, must it be entirely independent of plant services (air conditioning, filtration, compressed air, vacuum, power, rest rooms, and so on)?

Clean rooms cost us from $28 to $50 per square foot installed in an existing building. The $28 facility drew air conditioning, compressed air, and vacuum from the main plant; the $50 facility was an autonomous setup.

General decor affects cost. For example, covering the walls and ceiling with vinyl Sanitas costs approximately 41 cents per square foot, whereas the use of Kalistron, Noltawall, or Marlite runs about $1 per square foot. These prices include labor and material and may vary, depending upon the geographical location. The price range of $28 to $50 does not include cost of benches, stools, pressurized assembly hoods, test equipment, ultrasonic cleaners, and tools.

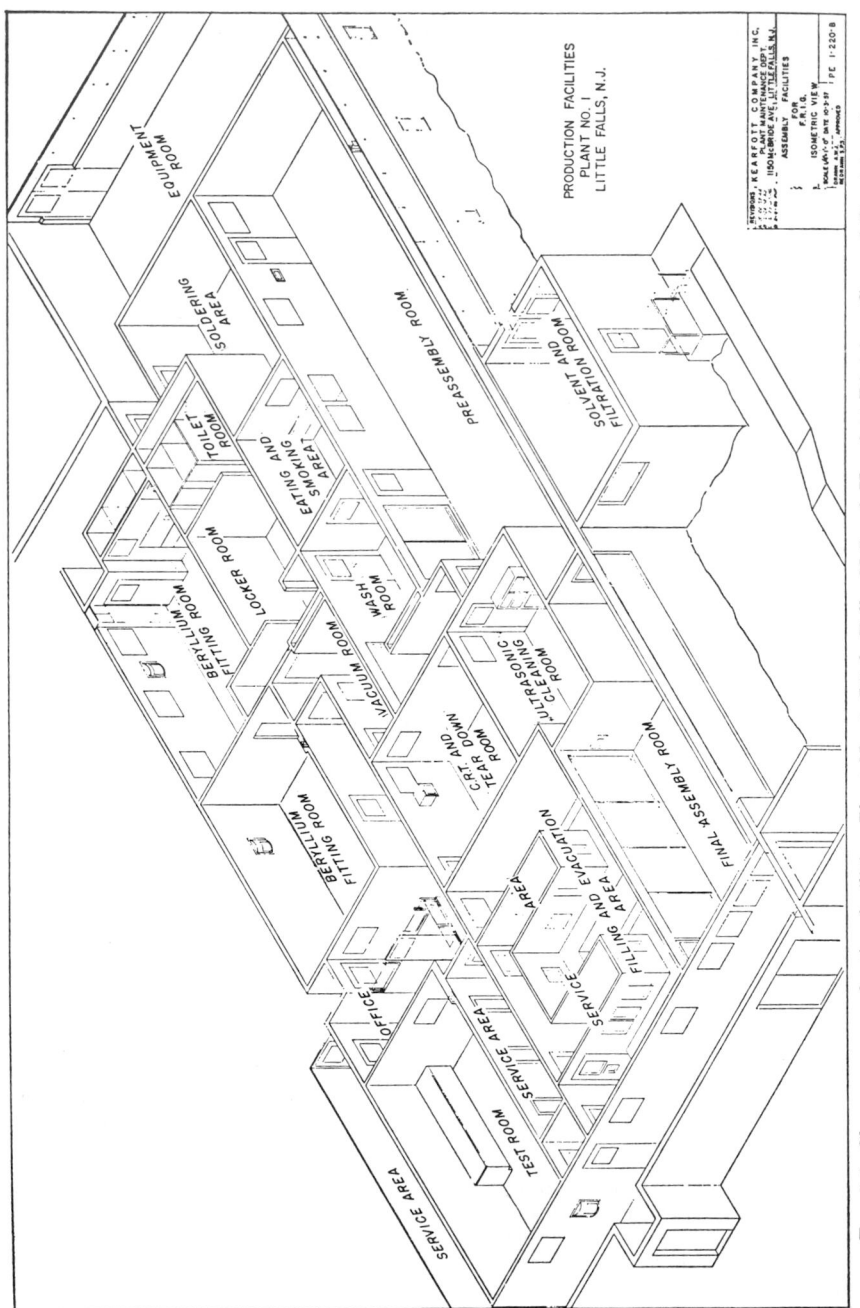

FIG. 5-1. Clean room production facilities, Plant No. 1, Little Falls, N.J., of Kearfott Division, General Precision, Inc.

The facility at the Kearfott Division, General Precision, Inc., which Kearfott designed, built, and financed, cost $46 per square foot to construct. This price included air conditioning, air filtration, vacuum systems, an air compressor, fluid filtration, a rest room, a locker room, washroom facilities, and all material and labor. The cost of the equipment in the rooms, not including the test equipment, amounted to $47 per square foot. The facility consists of 3,780 sq ft and contains ten rooms (see Fig. 5-1).

GENERAL DESIGN FEATURES

There are many types of design available for purchase as packaged units, both as complete rooms (conventional design or laminar flow) and as laminar-flow work stations; the measure of design perfection is its effectiveness in use. There are basic items that must be incorporated, aside from special features that are required for specific operations. All dust-generating and dust-retaining items must be eliminated from the design. This means that there must be no painted surfaces, exposed wood, exposed light fixtures, ledges on windows, waxed asphalt-tile floors, wooden cabinets, electric motors, foot rests on benches, fibrous wire insulation, or electric wall switches, among other things.

It is also important to consider the number of rooms, the number of employees per room, and the size of each room. Generally speaking, we at Kearfott have found that a room larger than 700 sq ft or with more than 50 occupants is very difficult to keep clean. Complete perimeter access should be provided to enable maintenance or other personnel to service and repair equipment from outside the clean areas. Walls in test areas should be designed for flush mounting of test equipment and servicing from outside the clean area.

Air locks or dedusting corridors should provide a high-velocity filtered air blast and a high-velocity exhaust to remove all dust and lint quickly. Doors in the air lock should be designed to lock automatically when the air blast is in operation and to unlock at the completion of the dedusting cycle. This applies to both the initial dedusting of street clothing and the final dedusting of protective garments. If rest rooms, eating rooms, or smoking rooms are provided, exit doors from the critical areas to these noncritical areas should be one-way, to compel each employee to go through the washroom and the dedusting air blast before returning to his work station. Drinking fountains may be installed in the area, but the refrigerant unit should be mounted outside the wall or over the hung ceiling. An intercom should be provided between each room and the outside of the clean area to eliminate travel.

Lighting fixtures should be hung over glass that is a tightly sealed, integral part of the ceiling, and the lamps should be changed from overhead. The same result can be achieved with a plastic panel ceiling which also permits the elimination of sprinklers from the clean room. A minimum of 100 ft-c at bench level is recommended.

Benches should be approximately 30 in. high to eliminate the need for dust-catching foot rests. Plastic-covered power distribution should be mounted under the benches. Nonshedding tubing, such as Tygon, should be used for individual vacuum lines. Such things as vacuum, compressed air, exhaust and filtered air-supply ducts, and power should be built into the walls at the time of construction, and an outlet panel containing all these services should be provided at the end of each row of benches. It is possible that only part of these services will be required initially, but should the need arise, it is a simple matter to plug into the panels and eliminate the intolerable disturbances caused by cutting through the wall.

Most clean rooms have a temperature specification of 75 deg $\pm$ 2 and humidity not to exceed 40 per cent RH. Rates of air change per room range from 2 per min to 1 per 3 min. Room pressures in inches of water above atmospheric pressure range from a high of 0.3 to a low of 0.04 in. This is required since it is obvious that the more critical the room the higher the pressure must be because the basic desire is to have air move out of the critical room as a person enters from a less critical area. The rates of air change vary with the type of activity conducted. For example, an ultrasonic cleaning room must have a high rate of air change to ensure removal of chemical fumes as well as to maintain the dust count as low as possible. The same applies to the critical-assembly or final-operations rooms.

During the process of constructing a clean-room facility, it is imperative that all surfaces be constantly vacuum cleaned to insure that no dust is left between the walls, in the ceiling, or under the floor covering.

Another very important design feature to consider is the installation of an ultrasonic cleaning room within the facility. It should be located in accord with the planned work flow and, if possible, should be attached to an outer wall so a remote means of draining and refilling the ultrasonic tanks can be provided. This prevents the contamination caused by rolling drums of solvents into the critical area. Combination pressurized-exhausted hoods are available that can be used in place of an ultrasonic cleaning room.

Prior to inspection, all incoming parts can be vapor degreased and accepted parts coated with antirust material and put into the stockroom like any other parts. When the parts are withdrawn for use in the white rooms, they are ultrasonically cleaned and placed in ultrasonically cleaned lint-free trays. These trays with the parts on them are then stored in dust-controlled areas in the white room. Immediately prior to use they are again ultrasonically cleaned in the final clean room.

Wide, continuous-strip vinyl or conductive linoleum floor covering should be used to eliminate the dust-catching cracks in a floor covered with conventional 9-in. tile. Electrostatically conductive flooring should be grounded to eliminate the static attraction of dust. Where the floor joins the wall, a cove, or radius, should be provided, tying the floor to the wall in one unbroken sweep. The same applies where the ceiling joins the wall.

Doors made of stainless steel or glass or clad with hard plastic, with concealed or ball-bearing-type nonmilling buck hinges, are essential. If the clean rooms are narrow, the generous use of windows or plate-glass walls will tend to minimize claustrophobia.

As to filtration of air supply to the clean rooms, the degree of purification is determined by the needs of the end product. It is needless to filter air to 0.3 micron if you can live with 5 microns. In the general language of clean rooms, however, the specification of 0.3 micron seems to be standard throughout the industry. This is achieved by use of Cambridge filters that remove 99.95 per cent of all particles of 0.3 micron and larger from the air supply. With this type of equipment, the cleanest possible air can be provided.

All screws used for securing metal moldings, and so on, to wooden studs or joists should be dipped in liquid vinyl to prevent shedding of wood particles or dust into the room.

If a rest room is part of the facility, steel partitions and fixtures should be wall-hung for easier cleaning and elimination of dust-catching crevices.

Assembly stools should be of the ball-bearing-caster type to prevent an employee from using his hands to move the stool away from or toward his work station, and thereby possibly contaminating the parts he is working on.

Access doors should be placed in the supply- and filtered-air ducts to give access for periodic duct vacuuming as required.

HOUSEKEEPING STANDARDS

Housekeeping standards must be the highest attainable. Despite design for dust control, the introduction of personnel is accompanied by the introduction of dust, and removal of this dust is the responsibility of the housekeeping section of maintenance. It is essential that a detailed procedure be established, and that the employees who do the cleaning be given thorough training in the use of the cleaning equipment and the frequency of cleaning and extent of cleanliness necessary. Despite this training, continual spot checking will be necessary to make sure the procedures are being adhered to. A central vacuum system should be installed with conveniently located outlets in each room so plastic vacuum lines can be used to clean floors. Housekeeping personnel should wear the same type of clothing worn by other employees in the area and enter the facility by the same procedures. Nonshedding materials, such as nylon mops and plastic sponges, should be provided. Housekeeping personnel should be present during all hours the other occupants of the white room areas are working there.

The cost of housekeeping, in terms of janitorial labor and materials, runs high. We operate our clean room seven days a week, 24 hours a day; housekeeping costs amount to slightly less than $10 per square foot per year.

Further control of the housekeeping standards is maintained by the quality-control department, which performs a daily inspection covering some 70 items on a check list. Any unsatisfactory conditons are noted, and a copy of the list is forwarded to the plant engineering office for corrective action. Quality-control personnel are rotated periodically, because it has been found that severity of inspection decreases with prolonged exposure to the area.

EMPLOYEE TRAINING

In addition to possessing the necessary skills and technical qualifications, employees assigned to clean rooms must be given pretraining and indoctrination. These people will be exposed to many new methods and procedures and to regulations that impose restrictions very different from those they have been accustomed to in other areas. One way to prevent resentment is to issue periodic bulletins to the potential occupants of the clean room during the course of construction, explaining what is being built, why it is being built, and what the function of each room and its equipment is to be. The final bulletin should contain a message to this effect: "We have told you so far what the clean rooms are and what they will do for you. Now we will tell you what you must do for the clean rooms." The average employee who watches the construction of a clean room facility that he is scheduled to occupy somehow gets the impression that when he passes through the doors of this "shrine" his troubles will be over. Nothing could be further from the truth. If an employee does a fair assembly job in the normal assembly area, he will not do a better job in the clean room.

In addition to issuing the bulletins, we at Kearfott transferred five employees per day into our new clean-room facility to prevent any possible confusion or resentment. All the elaborate, costly equipment installed to provide clean work areas will be to no avail if the employees assigned to these areas do not cooperate and show a willingness to comply with the strict requirements.

There are general regulations that apply to any clean room; they should be given to each employee in writing prior to assignment to the area:

1. Do not wear nail polish.
2. Thoroughly wash hands and scrub fingernails.
3. Do not walk about unnecessarily. Use intercom.
4. Always wear required garments.[1]
5. Haircuts are to be as short as socially tolerable.
6. Female employees are to tuck hair inside head covering.
7. Never comb hair in a clean room.
8. Do not wear wrist watches or rings in pressurized hoods.
9. Pencils and/or erasers must not be used. Ball-point pens will be provided.
10. No papers of any kind will be allowed in these areas. Glasine or acetate writing sheets will be provided.
11. Only test fixtures, tools, jigs, and assembly fixtures needed to perform the work required will be permitted.
12. No abrasive instruments such as crocus cloths, files, etc. are permitted.
13. Each employee is responsible for a high degree of cleanliness and neatness in his work station.
14. Foods of any kind are prohibited.

[1] Whether garments are owned or rented, they should be free from static. (An outside company, which owns our garments, does all the laundering. A destaticizer is put into the detergent and final rinse, which delivers the garments to us static-free. After 3 or 4 days, the static seems to build up very slowly. Because we change our garments every 5 days, this is not a problem.)

15. No smoking.
16. No shredding or masking tapes are permitted.
17. Boots, garments, and hats must be thoroughly tied and buttoned at ankles, collars, and wrists.
18. No painted materials are allowed in the area.
19. No personal items, such as handkerchiefs, tissues, and keys, are permitted in clean rooms.
20. Use protective finger covering as instructed.
21. Never leave exposed parts on work benches.
22. Store surplus materials in containers provided.
23. Follow prescribed procedures on entering and leaving the clean room.
24. Materials are to be transferred through pass-throughs provided.
25. Check your uniform, hat, and boots for raveled or frayed edges.
26. Enter and leave rooms at a slow gait.
27. Report any irregularities to your supervisor.
28. If you have a cold or are developing a skin condition, notify your supervisor.

Section 15

WELDING

Chapter 1

ARC WELDING IN MAINTENANCE

By ROBERT WILSON
Vice President, Director of Application Engineering
The Lincoln Electric Company
Cleveland, Ohio

Among the most important uses of welding in the plant maintenance department are repairing and making machinery and plant equipment. In this respect, welding is an indispensable tool without which production operations would soon shut down. Fortunately, welding machines and electrodes have been developed to the point where reliable welding can be accomplished under the most adverse circumstances. Frequently, welding must be done under something less than ideal conditions, and therefore equipment and men for maintenance welding should be the best.

FIG. 1-1. Steel replacement and the cast-iron cover it replaced.

Besides the quick on-the-spot repairs of broken machinery parts, welding offers the maintenance department a means of making many items needed to meet a particular demand in a required minimum of time. Broken castings, when new ones are no longer available, can be replaced with steel weldments fashioned out of standard shapes and plates. Special machine tools, required by production for specific operations, can be designed and made for a fraction of the cost that might be needed to buy a standard machine that would have to be adapted to do the job. Material-handling devices can be made to fit the plant's physical dimensions. Individual jib cranes can be installed. Conveyors, either roll-down or pallet-type, can be tailor-made for the application. Containers and other handling devices can be made to fit products. Grabs, hooks, and other handling equipment can be made for shipping and receiving.

Jigs and fixtures, as well as other simple tooling, can be made in the maintenance department, as either permanent tooling or temporary tooling for a trial lot.

The almost infinite variety of this type of welding makes it impossible to do more than suggest what can be done. Figures 1-1 to 1-5 show what the imaginations of

FIG. 1-2. Long delivery prompted welding of this cast-iron punch-press frame.

FIG. 1-3. Plant-made racks for holding steel.   FIG. 1-4. Typical welding jig and positioner that can be readily fabricated.

some maintenance men have accomplished in this field. As for the welding involved, it should present no particular problems if the welders have the necessary training and background to provide them with a knowledge of the many welding techniques that can be used.

With welding, a maintenance crew can fabricate and erect many of the structures

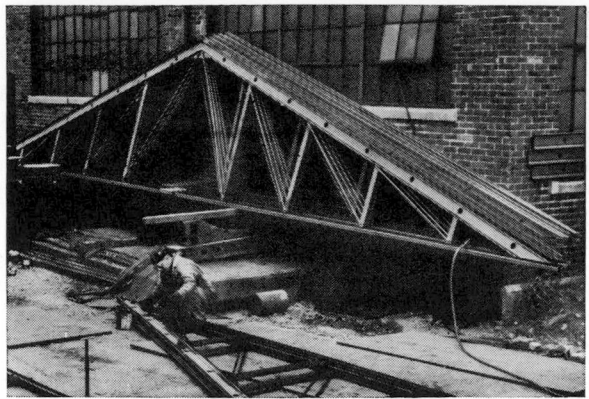

FIG. 1-5. Maintenance-department fabricating trusses for plant expansion. Trusses made from channels and angles. A jig was laid out on plate in the plant yard.

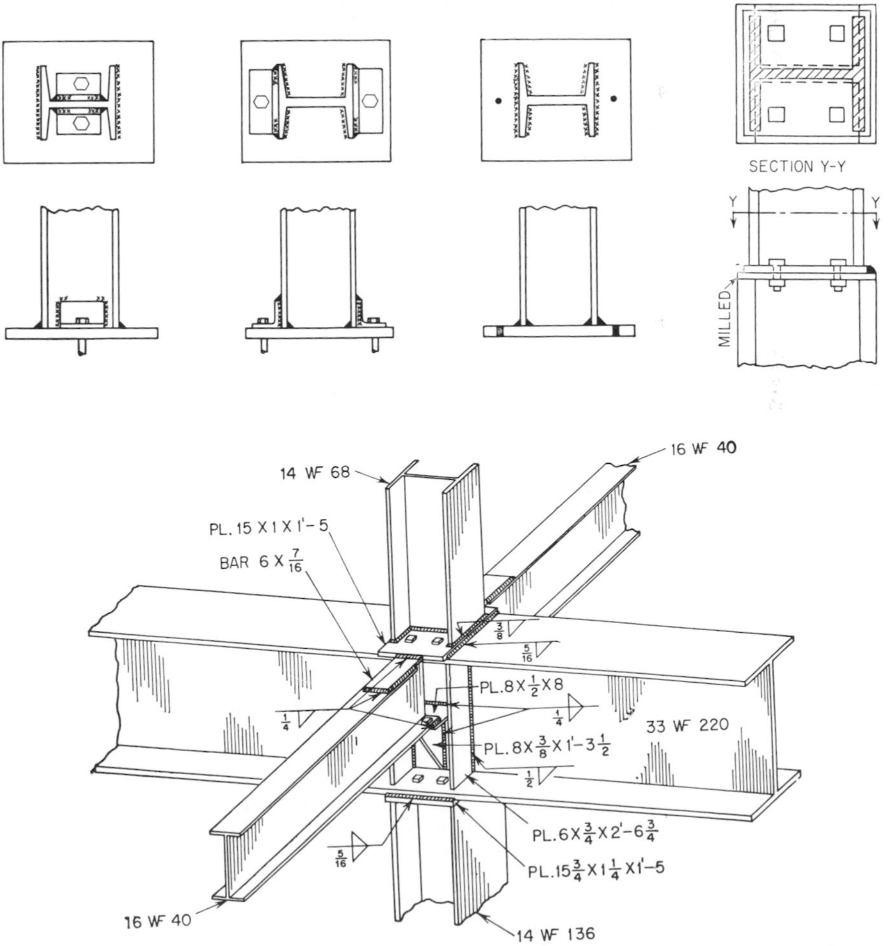

SECTION Y-Y
Y
Y
MILLED
16 WF 40
14 WF 68
PL. 15 X 1 X 1'-5
BAR 6 X $\frac{7}{16}$
$\frac{3}{8}$
$\frac{5}{16}$
PL. 8 X $\frac{1}{2}$ X 8
$\frac{1}{4}$
$\frac{1}{4}$
33 WF 220
PL. 8 X $\frac{3}{8}$ X 1'-3$\frac{1}{2}$
$\frac{1}{2}$
PL. 6 X $\frac{3}{4}$ X 2'-6$\frac{3}{4}$
$\frac{5}{16}$
PL. 15$\frac{3}{4}$ X 1$\frac{1}{4}$ X 1'-5
16 WF 40
14 WF 136

FIG. 1-6. Typical column bases, column splices, and beam-to-column connections that can be used in structural welding.

required by a plant, even to the extent of making structural steel for a major plant expansion. Welding can be done either in the plant maintenance department or on the erection site. Structures must, of course, be adequately designed to be able to withstand the loads to which they will be subjected. Such loads will vary from those of wind and snow in a simple shed to dynamic loads of several tons where a crane is involved.

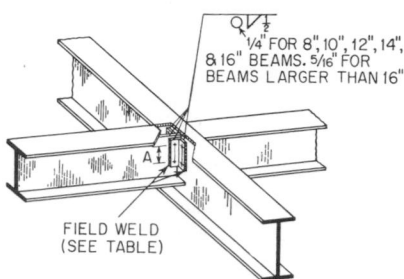

FIELD WELD
(SEE TABLE)

STANDARD CONNECTION FOR SIMPLE
BEAM-TO-BEAM FRAMING

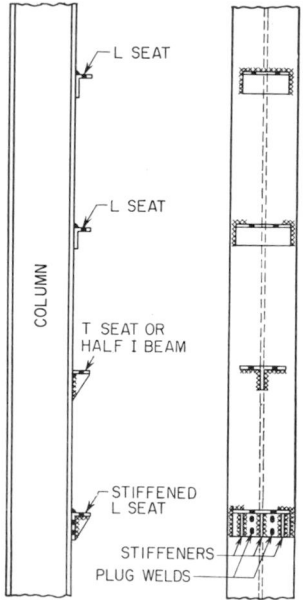

Materials and joint design must be selected with a knowledge of what each can do. Then the design must be executed with the use of properly trained welders only. Structural welding involves out-of-position work, frequently under awkward conditions, so that a welder must be able to put in good welds under all kinds of conditions.

Standard structural shapes can be used. Frequently pipe makes an excellent structural shape. Scrap materials often can be put to good use. In using scrap, however, it is best to weld with a low-hydrogen E6018 type of electrode, since the analysis of the steel may be unknown and some high-carbon steel may be encountered. The low-hydrogen electrodes will minimize the tendency to crack. This structural scrap frequently comes from old structures, such as elevated railroads being dismantled, which used riveted-quality steel that takes little or no account of the carbon content. Where the quality of the steel is known, an E6010 electrode is used for erection welding. An E6012 or E6013 electrode can be used for fabricating in the shop. Typical joints that are used in welded structures are shown in Figs. 1-6 to 1-9.

WELDING PROCESSES

Electric Arc Welding. Electric arc welding employs the heat of an electric arc to bring metals to be welded to a molten state. In electric arc welding, the work to be welded is made part of an electric circuit, known as the welding circuit, which has its power source in a welding generator or transformer. One cable carrying current from the power source is attached to the work, and another cable is attached to an electrode holder. An arc is established between the electrode and the work. The arc is moved along the work, melting and fusing the metal as it progresses. Since the arc is one of the hottest commercial sources of heat, this melting takes place almost instantaneously as the arc is applied to the metal.

Fig. 1-7. Beam-to-beam framing and methods for seating beams on columns.

A variety of welding processes are in common use, employing the electric arc to obtain the welding heat. Each has its particular advantage. All, however, have one problem in common—that of shielding the arc. Molten steel has a strong affinity for oxygen and nitrogen. If the arc and molten-metal pool are exposed to the atmosphere during welding, the metal will pick up oxygen and nitrogen, forming oxides and nitrides in the weld as it solidifies. These are impurities which will embrittle the weld and thus weaken it.

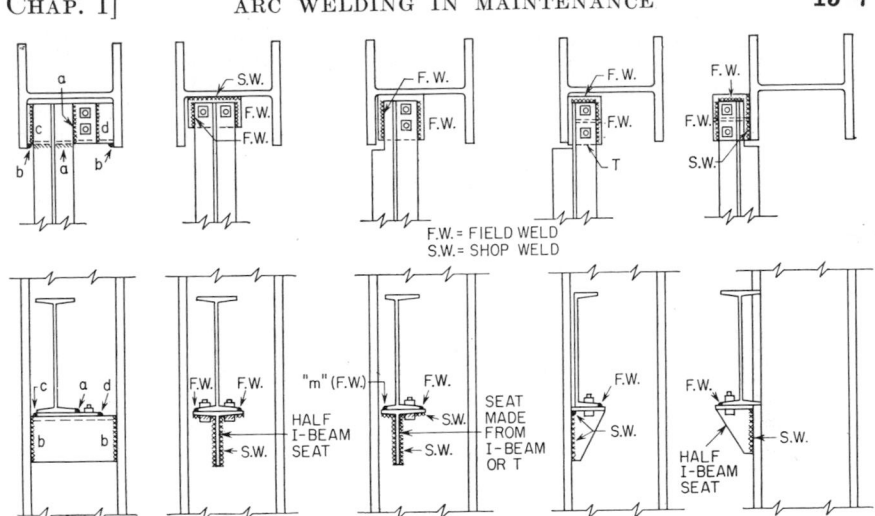

Fig. 1-8. Different ways of connecting beams to columns when an offset is required.

Most of the welding processes familiar to the maintenance welder use some method of shielding the arc and molten pool from the atmosphere, obtaining welds, when correctly made, that are as strong as, or stronger than, the metal being welded. These processes are variations of shielded metal arc welding.

Manual and Automatic Welding. Manual welding, also called hand welding, is welding where the entire welding operation is performed and controlled by hand. Automatic welding differs from hand welding in that welding equipment mechanically performs the welding operation. The terms "semi" and "fully" are also used to further identify automatic welding in respect to the degree of automation. With semiautomatic welding, the welding equipment is traveled manually along the joint. With fully automatic welding, the welding equipment is traveled mechanically along the joint.

SHIELDED ARC WELDING[1]

Shielded arc welding is by far the most widely used method of arc welding. With

[1] Recent welding-process developments and modifications in existing processes are tending to confuse the process classifications established by the American Welding Society. For the most part, the "family grouping" and process name are the same as present American Welding Society designations. In a few instances, however, minor modifications in family-group identification and process name have been made in an attempt to improve clarity and continuity.

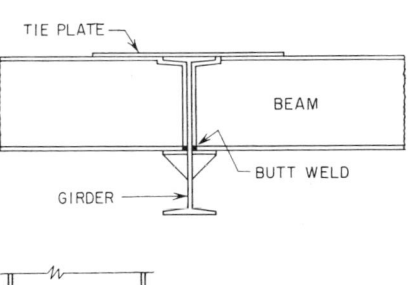

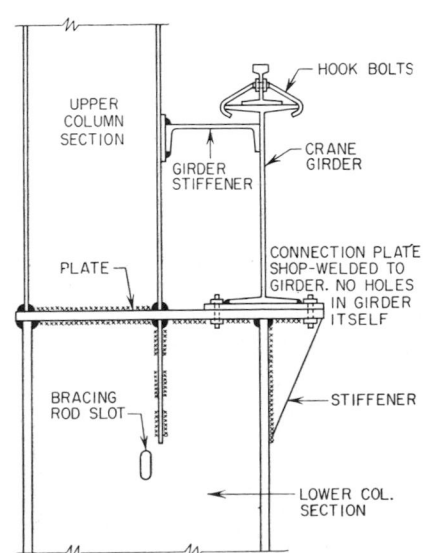

Fig. 1-9. A beam-and-girder connection and a column detail showing craneway.

this welding method, an electric arc is formed between a consumable metal rod and the work. The intense heat of the arc, which has been measured at temperatures as high as 13,000°F, melts the electrode and the surface of the work adjacent to the arc. Tiny globules of molten metal rapidly form on the tip of the electrode and transfer through the arc, in the "arc stream" into the molten "weld pool," or "weld puddle," on the work's surface. The actual transfer is induced by the force of gravity, molecular attraction, and surface tension, if the welds are flat or horizontal. Molecular attraction and surface tension are the forces that induce metal transfer from the electrode to the work when the weld is being made in the vertical or overhead position.

In addition to supplying filler metal for the weld deposit, other materials are usually introduced into and/or around the arc which perform one or all three of the following functions, depending upon the material being welded and the process being used: (1) "Shielding the arc" and preventing atmospheric contamination of the molten metal in the arc stream and the weld puddle. (2) Providing scavengers and deoxidizers to refine the grain structure of the weld. (3) Producing a slag blanket over the very hot but solidified weld. All these functions are necessary to assure the strength and quality of the weld being made.

Self-shielded Arc Welding. The electrodes for the shielded-arc-welding process are manufactured by extruding, dipping, or fabricating. The extruded and dipped electrodes, more often referred to as coated, or covered, electrodes, contain the shielding, scavenging, and deoxidizing materials in the coating that surrounds a solid metal core. The fabricated, or cored, electrodes contain the shielding, scavenging, and deoxidizing materials compacted in the electrode core surrounded by a metal sheath. Since both the coated and the fabricated electrodes contain all the materials to accomplish complete arc shielding, they are called "self-shielding" electrodes.

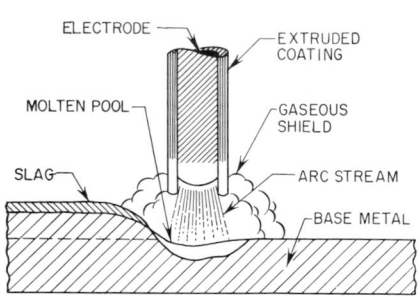

ELECTRODE — EXTRUDED COATING

MOLTEN POOL — GASEOUS SHIELD

SLAG — ARC STREAM

BASE METAL

FIG. 1-10. Shielded-metal arc-welding process.

The arc-shielding action is essentially the same for both the coated electrodes, as illustrated in Fig. 1-10, and the fabricated electrodes. But the actual method of arc shielding and volume of slag produced will vary with different electrodes types.

The bulk of the core or coating materials in some electrodes is converted to a gas by the heat of the arc, and only a small amount of slag is produced. This type of self-shielding electrode, depending largely upon a gaseous shield to prevent atmospheric contamination, can be identified by the incomplete or light slag covering of the completed weld.

The other extreme in self-shielding electrode design is the type where the bulk of the coating material is converted into slag in the arc heat with only a small volume of the gas being produced. With this type, the tiny globules of metal being transferred in the arc stream are entirely coated with a thin film of molten slag. This slag floats to the surface of the molten weld puddle before solidifying. These electrodes are identified by the heavy slag deposit that completely covers the surface of the finished weld.

In between these extremes there is a wide variety of electrode types having the ability to produce various combinations of gas and slag shielding. These variations in slag action and arc shielding also influence the "performance characteristics" of the many different types of self-shielding electrodes available for use in maintenance and manufacturing. For example, an electrode that has a heavy slag action is also one which has a high deposition rate and is suited for making large welds in flat position. An electrode that develops a gaseous arc shield is one which also has a low deposition rate and smaller molten weld puddle and therefore is suited for making welds in the vertical and overhead positions. These and many other performance characteristics are the reasons why one type of self-shielded electrode is preferred over all others for a specific weld in a specific position.

Manual Self-shielded Arc Welding. Extruded, dipped, and fabricated electrodes are used for manual self-shielded arc welding. These electrodes range in length from 9 to 18 in. The consumable welding electrode is placed in a hand-held clamping device called the electrode holder. Welding begins by touching the tip of the electrode to the work to complete the electric welding circuit, then withdrawing the tip, establishing the arc. As the heat of the arc melts the tip of the electrode, the welding operator, called the welder, manually lowers the tip of the electrode, maintaining a uniform distance between it and the work, thereby maintaining a steady arc. Simultaneously, the welder manually moves the electrode along the work at a rate of speed that deposits sufficient filler metal to create the needed weld size.

Fig. 1-11. Semiautomatic self-shielded arc welding.

Semiautomatic and Fully automatic Self-shielded Arc Welding. The electrode used for semiautomatic and fully automatic self-shielded arc welding is mechanically fed through a welding gun or welding jaws into the arc from a continuously wound coil that weighs approximately 50 lb. Only the fabricated self-shielding electrodes are suited for this method of welding, since coiling the extruded or dipped electrodes would damage the coating. In addition, metal-to-metal contact at the electrode's surface is necessary to transfer the welding current from the welding gun or welding jaws into the welding electrode. This is impossible if the electrode is coated.

Typical applications of semiautomatic and fully automatic equipment for self-shielded arc welding are shown in Figs. 1-11 and 1-12. For a given cross-sectional area of electrode wire, much higher welding amperage can be applied with semiautomatic and fully automatic welding. This is because the current travels only a very short distance along the bare metal electrode, since contact between the current-carrying jaws and the bare metal electrode occurs close to the arc. In hand welding, the welding current must travel the entire length of the electrode, and the amount of current is limited to the current-carrying capacity of the wire. The higher currents used with automatic welding result in a high weld-metal deposition rate. This increases welding speed, reduces welding time, and lowers welding costs.

Submerged Shielded Arc Welding. With submerged shielded arc welding the arc is completely hidden under a small mound of granular inorganic flux which is automatically deposited around the electrode wire as it is fed to the work (Fig. 1-13). The arc and molten pool are completely blanketed with flux at all times, and there are

FIG. 1-12. Fully automatic self-shielded arc welding.

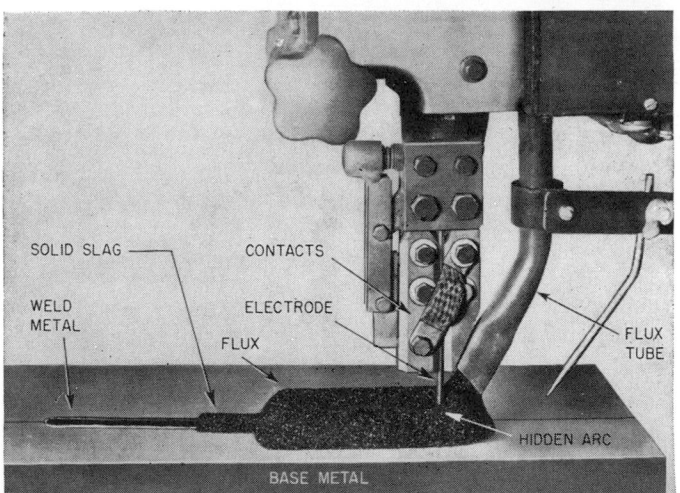

FIG. 1-13. Elements of the submerged-arc-welding process.

no visible arc rays or weld spatter. This process is more commonly called submerged arc welding, for obvious reasons.

Under usual welding conditions, the quantity of flux melted weighs approximately the same as the electrode consumed. The unfused flux may be collected and reused. Precautions should be taken to keep the flux and the work clean in order to prevent weld contamination and to maintain weld quality.

The high currents used with submerged arc welding also develop a deep-penetrating-arc characteristic. Consequently, no groove or a small groove may be used, depending upon the thickness of the base metal, with correspondingly smaller additions of filler metal.   For example, no chamfering is necessary for two-pass butt joints in steel up to ⅝ in. thick.   Complete penetration can also be obtained in fillet welds for material up to ¾ in. thick without chamfering.   For joints in thicker material, a double V-groove weld is used.   The graph of Fig. 1-14 shows typical relations between penetration and applied current.

With submerged arc welding, distortion is minimized because of the high welding speeds, minimum number of passes, and efficient application of heat.   This means that less heat is applied to the weld area and, furthermore, that the heat is applied more uniformly than with hand welding.   Distortion due to an unbalanced heat condition, as in single-groove multiple-pass welded joints, can be corrected by presetting the base-metal parts to offset angular movement.   The other methods of controlling distortion, discussed later in this chapter, can also be applied.

Although the submerged-arc-welding process is used primarily for production welding, it also has potential maintenance use which even to this day has been only partially exploited.   The process is particularly suited to rebuilding worn surfaces and developing abrasive-resistant surfaces for manufacturing operations encountering severe metal-erosion problems.

Gas-shielded Arc Welding.   In gas-shielded arc welding, the arc and weld region is shielded from the air by a protective gas.   This gas may or may not be inert.   The gases experiencing greatest industrial use are argon, helium, and CO_2.   Two variations of the gas-shielded arc-welding process are gas tungsten arc welding and gas metal arc welding.

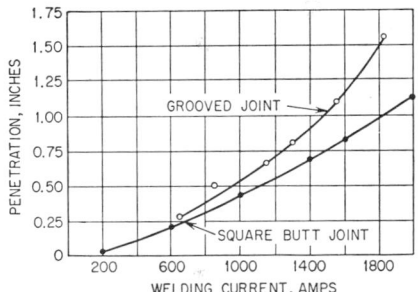

Fig. 1-14. Penetration vs. applied current for submerged arc welding.

Gas-shielded Tungsten Arc Welding. Gas-shielded tungsten arc welding with an inert gas was originally developed to weld the corrosion-resistant and other difficult-to-weld metals such as aluminum and copper.   Over a period of years, however, its application has expanded to include welding and surfacing operations on practically all commercial metals.

The gas arc-welding process obtains the necessary heat for welding by a very intense electric arc which is struck between a virtually nonconsumable tungsten electrode and the metal workpiece (Fig. 1-15).   On joints where filler metal is required, a welding rod is fed into the weld zone and melted with the base metal in the manner used with oxyacetylene welding.   The weld zone is shielded from the atmosphere by an inert gas fed through the welding torch.   Either argon or helium may be used.

Inert-gas-shielded tungsten arc welds, because of 100 per cent protection from the atmosphere, are stronger, more ductile, and more corrosion-resistant than welds made with ordinary arc-welding processes.   Corrosion due to flux entrapment does not occur, and postwelding cleaning operations are reduced to a minimum.   The entire welding action takes place practically without spatter, sparks, or fumes.   Fusion welds can be made in nearly all metals used industrially.   These include aluminum alloys, stainless steel, magnesium alloys, nickel and nickel-base alloys, copper, silicon-copper, copper nickel, brasses, silver, phosphor bronze, plain-carbon and low-alloy steels, cast iron, and others.   The process is also widely used for welding various combinations of dissimilar metals and for applying hard-facing and surfacing materials to steel.

The power supply for inert-gas-shielded tungsten arc welding may be either alternating or direct current.   However, certain distinctive weld characteristics obtained with each type often make one or the other better suited to a specific application.

In d-c welding, the welding current circuit may be hooked up as either "straight polarity" or "reverse polarity."   The connection for d-c *straight-polarity* (DCSP) welding is electrode-negative and work-positive. In other words, the electrons flow from the electrode to the plate or workpiece, as shown in Fig. 1-16. For d-c *reverse-polarity* welding (DCRP), the connections are just the opposite; electrons flow from the plate to the electrode, as shown in Fig. 1-17.

In straight-polarity welding, the electrons hitting the plate at high velocity exert a considerable heating effect on the plate. In reverse-polarity welding, just the opposite occurs; the electrode acquires this extra heat, which then tends to melt off the end of the electrode. Thus, for any given welding current, DCRP requires a

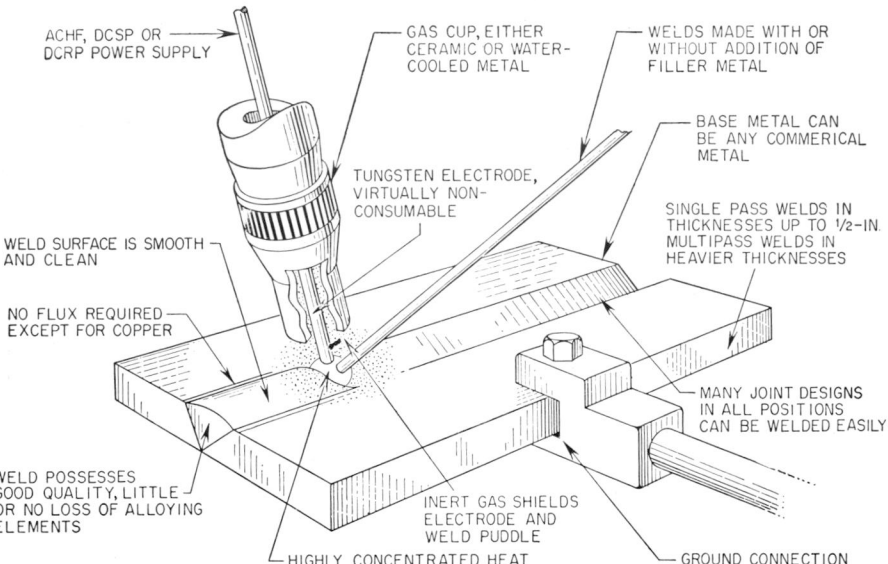

FIG. 1-15. Inert-gas shielded arc welding with a nonconsumable electrode.

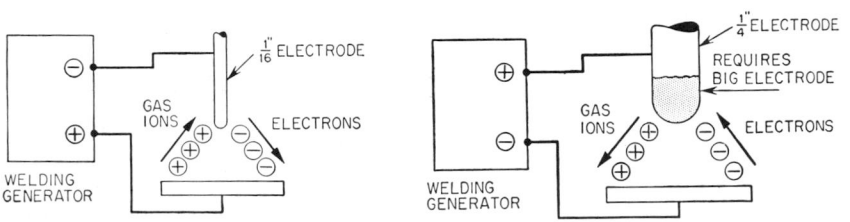

FIG. 1-16. Direct-current straight polarity.   FIG. 1-17. Direct-current reverse polarity.

larger-diameter electrode than does DCSP. For example, a $1/16$-in.-diameter pure-tungsten electrode can handle 125 amp of welding current under straight-polarity conditions. If the polarity were reversed, this amount of current would melt off the electrode and contaminate the weld metal. Hence a $1/4$-in.-diameter pure-tungsten electrode is required to handle 125 amp DCRP satisfactorily and safely.

These opposite heating effects influence not only the welding action but also the shape of the weld obtained. DCSP welding will produce a narrow, deep weld; DCRP welding, because of the larger electrode diameter and lower currents generally employed, gives a wide, relatively shallow weld.

One other effect of DCRP, the so-called plate-cleaning effect which seems to occur, is worth mentioning. Although the exact reason for this surface-cleaning action is not known, it seems probable that either the electrons leaving the plate or the gas ions striking the plate tend to break up the surface oxides, scale, and dirt usually present.

Welding with an alternating current is theoretically a combination of DCSP and DCRP welding, since the current flows in one direction and then in the other, or reverse, direction. However, moisture, oxides, scale, etc., on the surface of the plate tend to prevent (partially or completely) the flow of current in the reverse-polarity direction. To ensure proper current flow in the reverse direction when welding with alternating current, it is common practice to introduce into the welding current a high-voltage high-frequency low-power current. This high-frequency current jumps the gap between the electrode and the workpiece and pierces the oxide film, thereby forming a path for the welding current to follow. Superimposing this high-voltage high-frequency current on the welding current gives the following advantages:

1. The arc may be started without touching the electrode to the workpiece.
2. Better arc stability is obtained.
3. A longer arc is possible; this is particularly useful in surfacing and hard-facing operations.
4. Welding electrodes have longer life.
5. The use of wider current ranges for a specific-diameter electrode is possible. ·

A typical weld contour produced with high-frequency stabilized alternating current is shown in Fig. 1-18, together with DCSP and DCRP welds for comparison.

Tungsten-arc-welding   Equipment. Basic equipment requirement for manual inert-gas tungsten arc welding is a welding torch plus additional apparatus to supply (1) electric power, (2) argon, and (3) water. Also, certain protective equipment should be employed to protect the operator from the arc rays during welding operations.

D.C.
STRAIGHT
POLARITY

D.C.
REVERSE
POLARITY

A.C.
WELDING

Fig. 1-18. Comparison of weld penetration for the three types of welding current used with inert-gas tungsten arc welding.

The welding current is supplied either by a welding generator or rectifier for d-c welding or by a welding transformer for a-c welding. When selecting a generator or rectifier, it is important to obtain one which has good current control at the lower end of its current range. This ensures the arc stability required for efficient operation. If you plan to use an older d-c welding machine which operates inefficiently in the lower current range, a resistor should be used in the ground line between the generator and workpiece. These resistors are marketed by most manufacturers of d-c generating equipment. Several firms manufacture transformers which are suitable for tungsten arc welding, some with built-in high-frequency stabilization. Bear in mind that some transformers are designed to produce a balanced wave and can be used at the full rated capacity. Others are not, and should not be used at over 70 per cent maximum capacity to avoid overloading the primary. Be certain you know which type you are using. A high-frequency generator used with a-c welding can also be obtained from any reputable dealer.

High-purity argon is supplied in steel cylinders, each containing approximately 240 cu ft of argon at a pressure of 2,000 psi. A regulator is needed to reduce this pressure down to that required for welding, generally around 20 psi. In addition, a flow meter is required at every welding station, since different materials need different flows or amounts of argon for adequate protection. Where a large amount of welding is being done continually, it is advisable to connect a manifold to a bank of cylinders and pipe the argon to each individual work station. Again, a flow meter is required for each station.

When currents above 130 amp are used, water cooling of the torch and power cable is required. The cooling water for water-cooled torches must be clean; otherwise restricted or blocked passages may cause excessive overheating and damage to the equipment. Most shops have an adequate supply of cooling water available. However, where welding is done in large shops or outdoor locations, completely self-contained units are available. A typical portable installation is shown in Fig. 1-19.

An inert-gas tungsten-arc-welding torch feeds both the welding current and the inert gas to the weld zone, as shown in Fig. 1-20. The current is fed to the weld zone through the tungsten electrode, which is held firmly in place by the electrode holder. The argon (or helium) is fed to the weld zone through a gas cup at the head of the torch.

The electrode should extend about $\frac{1}{8}$ to $\frac{3}{16}$ in. beyond the end of the gas cup for butt welding and about $\frac{1}{4}$ to $\frac{3}{8}$ in. for fillet welding.

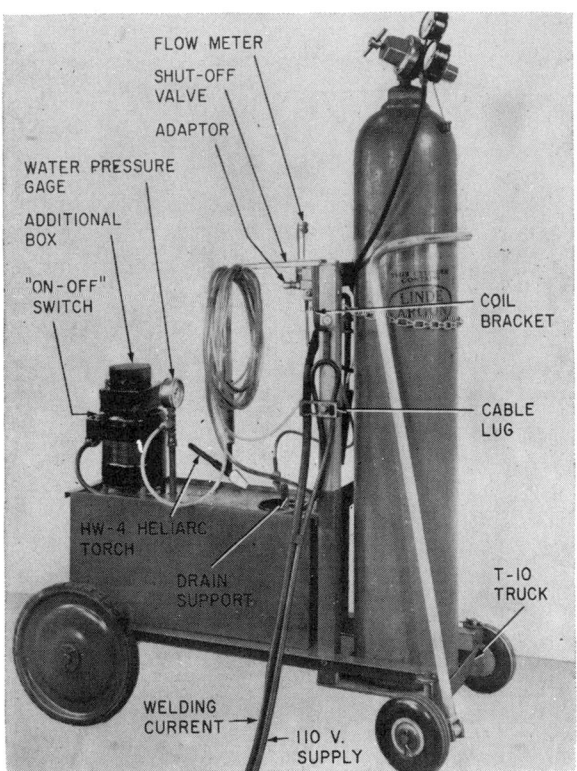

FIG. 1-19. Typical portable installation for inert-gas tungsten arc welding.

Recommended gas cup sizes for the various torches and electrode diameters are specified by the manufacturer. Ceramic cups are generally acceptable when the welding current is less than 250 amp. With higher currents, or where welding conditions are unusually severe, water-cooled, metal gas cups must be used to prevent overheating. Water-cooled cups should never come into contact with the workpiece when the welding current is *on*. Conductivity of the hot gases may cause the arc to jump from the electrode to the cup rather than to the workpiece, thus damaging the cup.

As with all industrial equipment, certain common-sense precautions should be observed. In the case of tungsten arc welding, the operator should be properly protected from the arc rays. This requires suitable clothing to cover all exposed skin surfaces and a welder's helmet with the proper shade of glass to protect the eyes and face. The shade of the glass lens will depend upon the intensity of the arc. The recommended shades for various current ranges are listed in Table 1-1.

Gas-shielded Metal Arc Welding. Gas-shielded metal arc welding is commercially called MIG welding when an inert gas is used. An arc between the consumable wire electrode and the workpiece (Fig. 1-21) is maintained in an atmosphere of inert gases, principally argon. The gases shield the weld zone from possible contamination by the atmosphere and eliminate the need for flux. Quality welds can be produced by either manual or machine welding. Welds made by this process are relatively clean and require little or no postweld finishing.

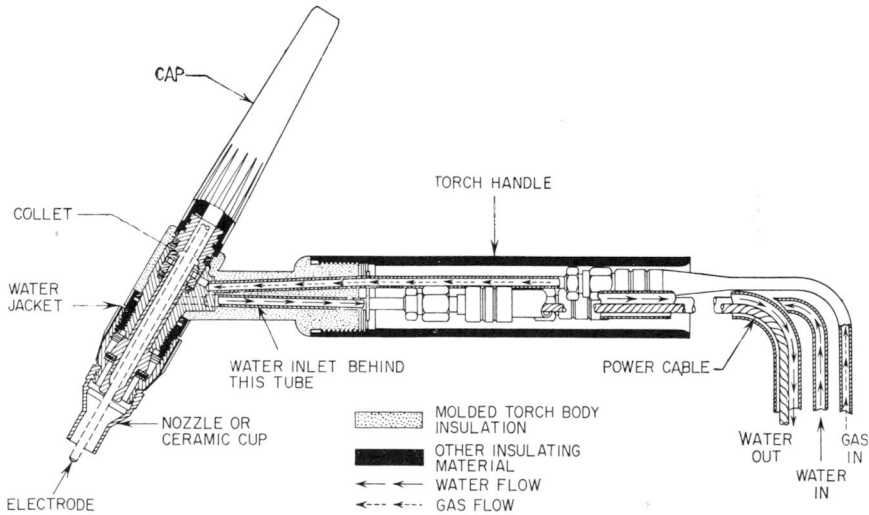

Fig. 1-20. A water-cooled torch for inert-gas tungsten arc welding.

With inert-gas shielded arc welding, you can weld such metals as aluminum, magnesium, copper, nickel, silicon bronze, aluminum bronze, stainless steel, low-alloy steel, and carbon steel. A consumable electrode similar to the metal being welded is used.

The average current density used is about twenty times that recommended for carbon arc welding and about six times that recommended for coated-metal arc welding. This high current density results in concentrated heat that produces narrow welds with deep penetration, a small heat-affected zone, and reduced distortion. Conventional d-c-welding or constant-potential power supplies may be used.

Table 1-1. Lens Shades for Current Ranges

Glass No.	Welding Current, Amp
6	Up to 30
8	30 to 75
10	75 to 200
12	200 to 400
14	Above 400

Constant-potential power offers many advantages for inert-gas shielded arc welding with continuously fed, bare-wire electrode. As shown in the accompanying graph (Fig. 1-22) constant potential has a flat volt-ampere characteristic rather than the drooping characteristic of conventional d-c power. Since the welding voltage remains essentially constant, the speed of wire feed controls the welding current.

A manual welder for inert-gas shielded arc welding with a consumable electrode is shown in Fig 1-23. This particular unit, a portable welder, uses welding currents as high as 500 amp.   The electrical control box contains the various control circuits for wire feed, gas flow, and application of welding current.   The wire drive unit feeds the consumable wire electrode at the required speed.   Once the welding conditions have been set up, the trigger switch on the water-cooled torch stops and starts welding. The remote-control box permits the operator to adjust arc length and to inch out wire electrode for arc striking without leaving his welding position.   Source of welding

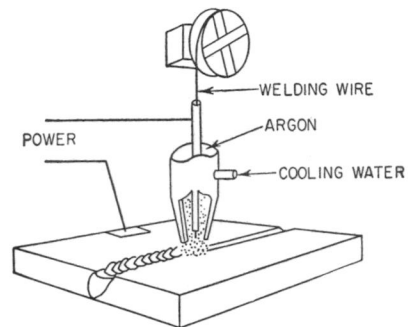

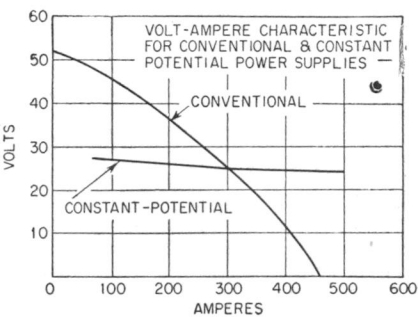

FIG. 1-21. Inert-gas shielded arc welding with a consumable electrode.

FIG. 1-22. Ampere-volt characteristic of constant-potential and conventional power supplies.

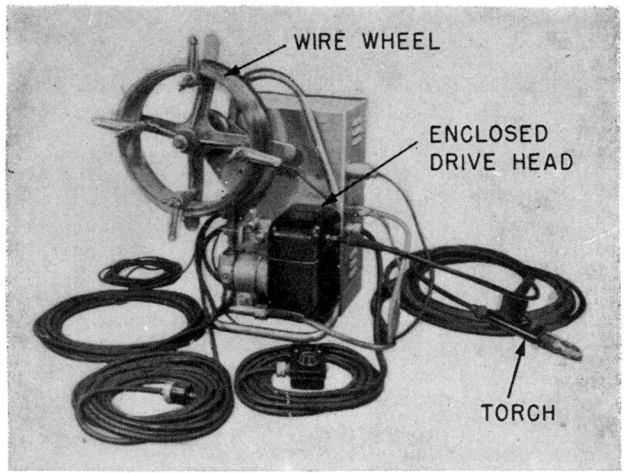

FIG. 1-23. A manual welder for inert-gas shielded arc welding with a consumable electrode. (*Courtesy of Linde Division, Union Carbide Corporation, New York.*)

current, supply of inert shielding gas (argon, helium, or a mixture of approximately 95 per cent argon and 5 per cent oxygen), and a supply of cooling water also are required.

The gas-shielded arc-welding processes can successfully weld plain carbon steel, but in most instances, when compared with other arc-welding processes, the cost has prohibited their use.

Gas-shielded Metal Arc Welding—CO_2. Another version of gas-shielded metal arc welding uses CO_2 (carbon dioxide) rather than an inert gas to blanket the arc and surrounding weld area.   A typical production welding installation is illustrated by Fig. 1-24.   There are three variations of this process.   The first uses a solid electrode;

the second, a fabricated flux-cored electrode; the third, a flux-coated electrode.   In addition to providing filler metal, these electrodes or the flux contain elements which perform a scavenging and deoxidizing action in the crater to improve weld quality.

The flux-cored-electrode process has the flux wrapped within an outer steel sheath.

The flux coating of the electrode is accomplished by feeding a magnetic flux material into the arc area, where it magnetically attaches to the bare solid electrode being mechanically fed into the arc.

The gas-shielded metal-arc-welding process with CO_2 is used for production-welding the carbon steels and for fabricating industrial piping and sheet metal.

Gas-shielded-arc Spot Welding.   This method of welding combines either gas-shielded tungsten-arc-welding or gas-shielded metal-arc-welding equipment with an electrical timing-control system that automatically starts and maintains the arc for a

FIG. 1-24. Gas-shielded metal arc welding.

controlled time period.   Two lapped pieces of metal are spot-welded together by applying heat from an electric arc to the top surface of the joint.   Welding action is controlled by the current input to the arc and the time the arc dwells on the material being welded.

Shielding of the arc, electrode (consumable metal or nonconsumable tungsten), and fluid weld puddle are similar to those of conventional gas-shielded arc welding.

The resulting spot weld parallels that produced by resistance-welding techniques; however, no electrode pressure is required, and the welding is done from one side of the plate without requiring any weld backup.   Both inert-gas and CO_2 spot welding are experiencing expanding industrial use.

RESISTANCE WELDING

Resistance-welding processes are primarily designed for production-welding usage. Nevertheless, a few of the processes can be used effectively by the maintenance department.   With this method of welding, the joining of the parts being welded is accomplished by the heat obtained from resistance of the work to the flow of electric current in a circuit of which the work is a part and by the application of pressure.

Spot Welding.   Spot welding is the most common resistance-welding process.   It is usually employed in the welding of thin metal sheets and is accomplished by placing the sheets between movable copper-alloy electrodes.   The electrodes carry the welding current, and can be actuated to apply the proper pressure during the welding cycle. A typical production installation in a sheet-metal shop is illustrated by Fig. 1-25. Aluminum presents a special problem because of its high electrical conductivity.   So does copper, which has practically the same conductivity as electrode material.

Although maintenance welding departments occasionally have the larger floor-mounted equipment, more often the small portable hand-held spot-welding guns are used for fabricating sheet metal.

Fɪɢ. 1-25. This resistance spot welder is being used to fabricate sheet metal.

OTHER WELDING PROCESSES

The welding processes and equipment described up to this point have potential use in the typical maintenance welding department.   Many other welding processes are being used which, admittedly, have limited maintenance use.   These will be summarized briefly.   Additional information about specific processes can be obtained from the American Welding Society (see Bibliography at the end of this chapter).

Atomic-hydrogen Welding.   Atomic-hydrogen welding differs from the other arc-welding methods in that the arc is formed between two tungsten electrodes and the work is not part of the welding circuit.   A stream of hydrogen gas is passed through the arc and, in the heat of the arc, changes from molecular to atomic form, giving off an intense heat.   The hydrogen acts as an effective heat-transfer medium and results in high heat being applied close to the work.   A filler rod is used to supply additional metal to the joint.   The process has some advantages in welding thin sheet where a high finish is needed.

Electroslag Welding.   Electroslag welding is the metal-arc-welding process employing the principles of submerged arc welding.   This process involves fusion of the base metal and continuously fed filler metal under a substantial layer of high-temperature, electrically conductive molten flux.   By feeding one or a combination of two or three electrodes simultaneously into the arc, plates ranging from 1 to 14 in. thick can be joined in a single pass.   Application is generally limited to very heavy weldments.   Welds are usually made with the joint vertical and with welding progressing from bottom to top.

Impregnated-tape Shielded Arc Welding.   Impregnated-tape shielded arc welding parallels self-shielded arc welding with coated electrodes.   But in this case the arc shield is obtained from the decomposition of tape that is wrapped around the electrode. This method is rarely seen in industry today.

Plasma Arc Welding.   Plasma arc welding exists in several forms.   The basic principle is that of an arc or jet created by heating electrically a plasma-forming gas (such as nitrogen or hydrogen) to such a high temperature that its molecules become ionized atoms possessing extremely high energy.   When properly controlled, this process results in very high melting temperatures.   Plasma arc welding holds a potential solution to the easier joining of many hard-to-weld materials.   When modified for metal cutting, this process achieves unusually high cutting speeds.   Another application is the depositing of materials having high melting temperatures to produce surfaces of high resistance to extreme wear, corrosion, or temperature.

Stud Welding.   Stud welding is the end welding of a stud, ordinarily a machine screw, at a particular spot on the work by fusion.   An electric arc, struck between the stud serving as the electrode and the base plate, brings the tip of the stud and the surface of the work adjacent to the stud to a molten state.   A light pressure is applied, forcing the stud into the molten weld puddle.   Current flow is discontinued, and the stud fuses to the work surface as it cools.   A compact portable unit, called a stud welder, supplies the welding current.   The arc may be shielded or unshielded.

Carbon Arc Welding.   Carbon arc welding employs a carbon rod as an electrode.   The arc is formed between the carbon and the work, creating a molten pool on the work surface.   This pool is kept molten by playing the arc across it.   If extra filler metal is needed to make the weld, it is supplied by introducing a filler rod into the arc, where it is melted into the molten pool.   This is a puddling process, and is not applicable to vertical or overhead welding.   Shielding may be obtained if desired by introducing a paste, powder, or fibrous flux into the arc.

Carbon arc welding is used only for specialized applications and with automatic equipment.   The carbon arc is also used for cutting where a precision cut is not necessary or on alloys that cannot be cut by the gas process.

Flash Welding.   Flash welding is a resistance-welding process in which fusion is produced by a high localized heat obtained from the electrical resistance existing between two touching surfaces.   This type of resistance is evidenced by a flashing, or shower, of sparks produced by the arcing of current at the joining surfaces.   When the temperature of the metal has increased to where the joining surfaces have plasticized, the parts are forced together under pressure to make the weld.   A portion of the metal squeezes out (upsets) to form the "flash."   This must be trimmed off, and the joint then ground or otherwise finished to the section desired.

Percussion Welding.   Percussion welding is a process in which fusion temperature results from an arc created across a gap between two surfaces to be joined, the arc being caused by rapid discharge of electrical energy.   A percussive (impact) force is applied during or immediately following the electrical discharge.

Projection Welding.   Projection welding is another method of resistance welding.   It differs from those previously described, since it uses projections, or embossments, to localize the current flow and welding heat at predetermined points.   These projections, which serve as points of contact, are a part of one or both of the parts to be joined.   The parts are supported and pressed together by special dies during welding.

Seam Welding.   Seam welding is fundamentally a spot-welding process.   One or two electrode wheels running along a straight line at a fast rate of travel make a series of closely spaced spot welds.   When the welded spots are so close that they actually overlap, they form a gastight or watertight seam, as required for a vessel.   In other cases, the series of spots may be so spaced that the process becomes a mere tack welding operation in the assembly of a unit.   This is called roll-spot welding and is used to speed up standard spot welding.

Upset Welding.   Upset welding is a process in which fusion is produced by the heat obtained from electric resistance through the area of contact of two surfaces held together under pressure.   In this case, the force is applied prior to introduction of the electric current and is continued until heating is complete.   The continued force produces an upsetting as in flash welding, but since the surfaces are in solid contact with one another, there is no arcing or flashing effect.

Electron-beam Welding.   Electron-beam welding directs a bombardment of electrons at the workpiece placed in a vacuum.   Electrons are admitted from a filament, acting as a type of nonconsumable electrode, and are highly accelerated by high-voltage potential between the electrode and the work. The high-velocity energy of the electrons converts to heat when they strike the work. The electron flow is electrically concentrated into a beam by means of an electron gun. Since the operation is carried on in a vacuum, the process can be used to weld highly reactive metals without contamination.

Explosive Welding. Explosive welding is a process wherein a surface-to-surface bond is achieved by the compressive force of a controlled explosion.

Flow Welding. This is a process where fusion is produced by heating with molten filler metal poured over the joint until the welding temperature is attained and the required filler metal has fully penetrated the joint.

Hammer Welding. Hammer welding was commonly employed by the blacksmith of yesteryear; it sees very little industrial usage today. It is also called forge welding.

Friction Welding. Friction welding is based on the fact that a rapidly moving part in pressure contact with a stationary part generates heat in contacting surfaces. When the fusion temperature is reached, movement is stopped and pressure maintained or increased until the weld is completed.

Induction Welding. Induction welding depends upon the resistance of the workpiece to the flow of an induced electric current to create heat for fusion. The pieces to be joined are placed within a radio-frequency field, usually developed to the inside of a radiating coil that has been designed to approximate the shape of the intended assembly. Filler metal having a low melting temperature is prepositioned at the joint and distributes through the heated joint by capillary action.

Pressure Welding. Pressure welding is a process in which two pieces of ductile metal are butt-welded or lap-welded by the application of pressure only, without any of the metal reaching the melting point. Heat, if applied, is sufficient only to facilitate plastic flow of the metal under pressure. Bonding depends upon the ability to bring a large number of atoms on the two surfaces being joined into immediate contact. This requires perfect cleanliness of the surfaces, good alignment, and application of high pressures. The pressure is a squeezing action rather than impact.

Thermit Welding. Thermit welding is based on the chemical reaction between aluminum and iron oxide. The members to be welded are aligned in proper relation, and a mold is built around the ends to be joined. A pouring gate in the top of the mold receives the molten metal. The Thermit charge is placed in a crucible which has a pouring hole in its bottom. The charge is a mixture of iron oxide and granulated aluminum together with small quantities of alloying elements in the iron oxide. Ignition of the mixture produces a reaction between the iron oxide and aluminum, liberating a large amount of heat. The aluminum combines with the oxygen in the iron oxide and releases free molten steel, which flows into the mold, thus producing the weld.

WELDABILITY OF METALS

The term "weldability" is a relative one. Practically all metals are weldable. Some, however, require special welding procedures in order to preserve the properties and characteristics of the metal for which it was originally alloyed.

Special welding procedures are variants within a limited range of possibilities. If a metal cannot be welded with the regular mild-steel electrodes, E6010 and E6012, etc., some degree of preheat with these electrodes is the next step. Following this, the next alternative is to use a low-hydrogen electrode and finally a stainless-steel type of electrode.

The first aspect of any maintenance welding job is to consider the metal being welded. The behavior of the metal under the heat cycle of welding may or may not be critical. The economy and quality of welding on various metals may be affected by any one or more of the following factors:

1. *Oxidation.* (a) Oxidation producing a gaseous oxide of some one of the elements causing gas holes in the weld metal. (b) Oxidation producing solid oxides which have a melting temperature higher than the metal, thus causing slag inclusions.

(c) Oxidation producing oxides which are soluble or which are heavier and sink in the molten metal and which render the weld metal brittle or of low strength.

2. *Vaporization.* Vaporization of some element in the metal which vaporizes at a temperature lower than the melting point of the metal.

3. *Nonmetallic inclusions.* Some metals may contain finely divided nonmetallic inclusions which have a melting point higher than that of the metal and therefore did not coalesce when the metal was refined but do melt and coalesce under the high temperature of the arc and then form visible slag inclusions.

4. *Change of structure.* Change of structure or arrangement of elements within the metal may take place during arc welding, causing change of physical properties or change of resistance to corrosion, etc.

5. *Gas solubility of metal.* (a) Different elements may affect the solubility of various gases at different temperatures, and a decrease in solubility of a gas with a decrease in temperature at the freezing point may cause porosity in weld metal. (b) The fluxing out or elimination of an element during welding may cause the capacity of the metal for a given gas to decrease and thus cause the gas to be given up, producing porosity in the weld metal. (c) Gases are absorbed during welding to form stable compounds with elements in the metal and thus alter the composition and physical properties of the weld metal.

6. *High coefficient of thermal expansion,* or high contraction of weld metal upon cooling.

7. *Hot shortness,* or low strength of the metal at high temperatures.

8. *Thermal conductivity,* or rate of transfer of heat from fusion zone.

9. *Hardenability.* Tendency of metal to become hard and brittle in the weld or fusion zone during heat cycle of welding.

The foregoing list indicates why some metals are more satisfactory than others. A careful study of the factors listed indicates that most of the possible undesirable characteristics can be corrected by one or more of the following methods:

1. Selection of metal within the permissible class most suitable for arc welding.
2. Use of proper shielded arc.
3. Use of proper fluxing material.
4. Use of proper electrode or filler metal.
5. Proper welding procedure.
6. In some cases, subsequent heat-treatment.

In considering the weldability of any metal, it should be borne in mind that the weld largely depends upon the characteristics of the weld metal which may come from two sources, viz., base metal and electrode or filler metal.

If little or no electrode or filler metal is used, the proper selection of the base metal becomes of prime importance.   If the weld metal comes mostly from the electrode or filler metal, then selection of the proper filler metal or electrode becomes of prime importance.   However, both electrode and base metal are subjected to similar requirements during arc welding, and both should be of best arc-welding quality, although in many cases the electrode or filler metal serves as a corrective for the base metal.

THE CARBON STEELS

The carbon steels are widely used in all types of manufacturing.   The weldability of the different types (low, medium, and high) varies considerably.   The preferred analysis range of the common elements found in the carbon steels is shown in Table 1-2.   Welding metals whose elements vary above or below the range usually call for special welding procedures.

Low-carbon Steels (0.10 to 0.30 Per Cent Carbon).   Steels of low-carbon content represent the bulk of the carbon-steel tonnage used by industry.   These steels usually are more ductile and easier to form than higher-carbon steels, and for this reason are used in most applications requiring considerable cold forming such as stampings and rolled or bent shapes in bar stock, structural shapes, or sheet.   Steels with less than 0.13 per cent carbon and 0.30 per cent manganese have a slightly greater tendency for internal porosity than steels of higher carbon and manganese content.

Medium-carbon Steels (0.30 to 0.45 Per Cent). The increased carbon content in medium-carbon steel usually raises tensile strength of the material and also hardness and wear resistance. These steels experience selective use by manufacturers of railroad equipment, farm machinery, construction machinery, material-handling equipment, and other similar products. The medium-carbon steels can be successfully welded with the E60XX electrode if certain simple precautions are taken, and the cooling rate is controlled to prevent excessive hardness.

High-carbon Steels (0.45 Per Cent and Higher). The high-carbon steels are generally used in a hardened condition. In this group are most of the steels used in tools for forming, shaping, and cutting. Tools used in metal-working, woodworking, mining, and farming, such as lathe tools, drills, dies, knives, scraper blades, and plow

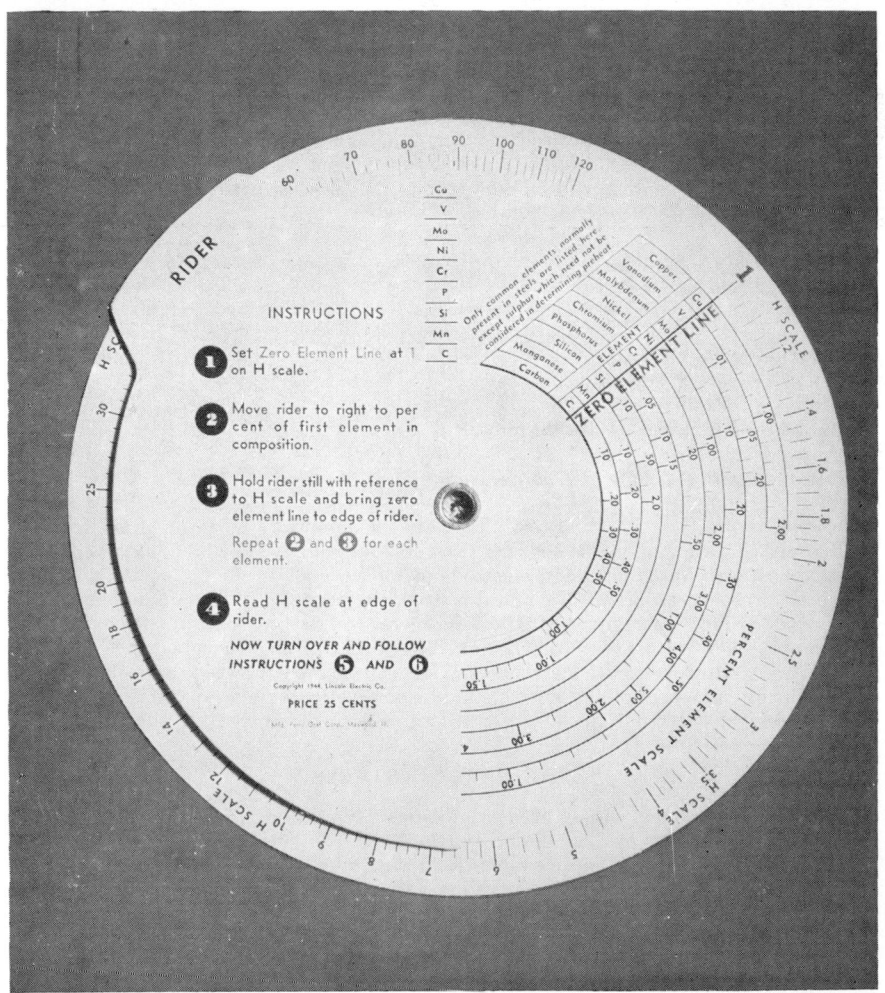

(*A*)

Fig. 1-26. (*A* and *B*). Calculator for determin-

shares, are typical examples. The high-carbon steels are often described as being "difficult to weld," and are not suited to mild-steel welding procedures. Usually, low-hydrogen or other special electrodes are required, and controlled welding procedures, including preheating and postheating, are needed to produce welds that are crack-free.

The higher the content of the carbon in a steel, the harder it becomes when it is quenched from above the critical temperature. Welding raises steel above the critical temperature, and the cold mass of metal surrounding the weld area creates a quench effect. Hardness and absence of ductility result in cracking as the weld cools and contracts. Preheating to 400 to 600°F and slow cooling will prevent cracking. Figure 1-26A and B shows a calculator for determining preheat and interpass temperatures.

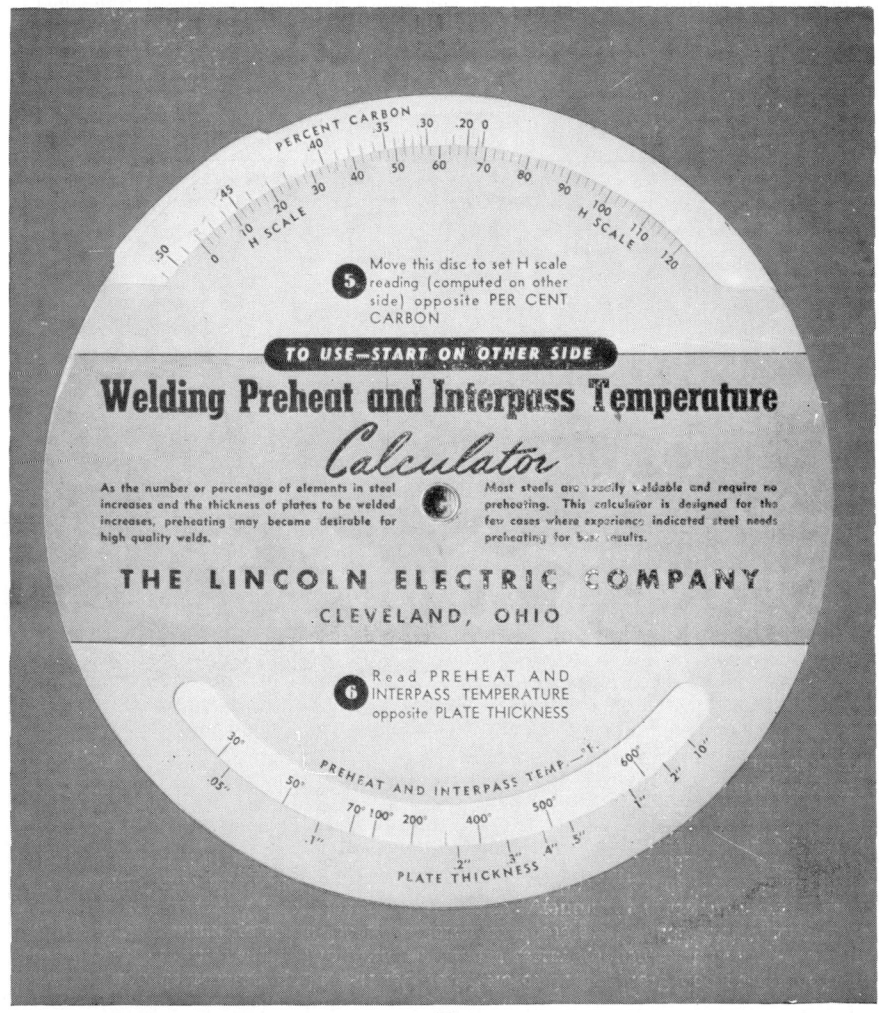

(B)

ing preheat and interpass temperatures.

For steels in the higher-carbon ranges (over 0.30 per cent) special electrodes are recommended. The lime-ferritic low-hydrogen electrodes (E60 or E7015, E7016, or E7018) can be used to good advantage in overcoming the cracking difficulties in high-carbon steels. These electrodes deposit a more ductile weld because of the absence of hydrogen in the deposit. An 18-8 stainless-steel electrode can also be used to give good physical properties to a weld in high-carbon steel.

Cast Iron. Cast iron is a complex alloy in which the most important element in welding is the very high carbon content. Quickly cooled cast iron is harder and more brittle than slowly cooled cast iron. The metal also naturally has a low ductility, which results in considerable strain on parts of a casting when one local area is heated. The brittleness and the uneven contraction and expansion of cast iron are the principal concerns in welding it.

Each job must be analyzed to predetermine the effect of welding heat, and procedures correspondingly adopted. A curved bead will reduce the cumulative effect of the strain of contraction that would be effective in a straight weld. Welds can be deposited in short lengths, allowing each to cool. Peening of the weld metal may be used to stretch the weld deposit.

Table 1-2. Preferred Analysis Range of Carbon Steels

	Low, %	Preferred, %	High, %
Carbon	0.10	0.13 to 0.20	0.25
Manganese	0.30	0.40 to 0.60	0.90
Silicon	....	0.10 or under	0.15 max.
Sulfur	....	0.035 or under	0.05 max.
Phosphorus	....	0.03 or under	0.04 max.

Either steel or cast-iron electrodes may be used as well as carbon electrodes and nonferrous rods. All oil, dirt, and foreign matter must be removed from the joint before welding. With steel electrodes, intermittent welds no longer than 3 in. and light peening should be used. To reduce contraction, the work should never be allowed to get too hot in one spot. Preheating will help to soften the deposit to make it more machinable.

For welds of such machinability, a nonferrous-alloy rod should be used. A two-layer deposit will have a softer fusion zone than a single-layer deposit. When it is practical, heating of the entire casting to a dull-red heat is recommended, further to soften the fusion zone and burn out dirt and foreign matter. A lower heat can be used if necessary. When the weld to be made is in a deep groove, it is general practice to use a steel electrode for welding cast iron to fill up the joint to within approximately ⅛ in. of the surface and then finish the weld with the more machinable nonferrous deposit.

THE ALLOY STEELS

High-tensile Low-alloy Steels. This group of steels is being used increasingly in metal fabricating because their high physical properties permit the use of thinner sections, thus saving metal and reducing weight. They are made with a number of different alloys and can be readily welded with the proper type of electrode designed especially for these metals. Excellent joints of the same high physical properties as the base metal are obtained by the use of these electrodes. It is not necessary, as might be suspected, to have a coated electrode of composition similar to each of the alloys. In some cases, this may even be undesirable, since the electrode metal, in going through the arc, frequently has its analysis and characteristics changed.

Stainless Steels. Electrodes are made to match various types of stainless steels so that corrosion-resistance properties are not destroyed in welding. The most commonly used types of stainless steels for welded structures are the 18-8, 25-12, and 25-20 groups.   Group 18-8, with 0.08 per cent carbon maximum, is a commonly specified type of stainless steel used for welding, in which the carbon content is reduced to a low value so that no carbides can be precipitated during the welding heat cycle.   Electrodes are used which contain 0.05 to 0.07 per cent carbon.

The general mild-steel welding procedures are used, taking into account the fact of higher electrical resistance, lower thermal conductivity, and higher thermal expansion of the stainless steels.   It is important to fit work carefully and clean all edges of foreign material.   Light-gage work must be clamped firmly to prevent distortion and buckling.   Small-diameter and short electrodes should be used to prevent loss of chromium and undue overheating of the electrode.   The core-wire deposit should be approximately the same analysis as the plate.

Stainless Clad Steel.   The significant precautions in welding this material are in joint design, including edge preparation, procedure, and choice of electrode.   An electrode should be used of the correct analysis for the cladding being welded.   The joint must be prepared and welded to prevent dilution of the clad surface by the steel-backing material.   The backing material is welded with a mild-steel electrode but in multiple passes to prevent penetration into the cladding.   The clad side is also welded in small passes to prevent penetration into the backing material and resulting dilution of the stainless joint.   Where in thin-gage material it is necessary to make the weld in one pass, a 25-12 stainless electrode should be used for the steel side as well as the stainless side.   The design and preparation of the joint can do much to prevent iron pickup as well as reduce labor costs in making the joint.

Chromium Steels.   The intense air-hardening property of these steels, which is proportional to the carbon and chromium content, is the chief consideration in establishing welding procedures.   Considerable care must be taken to keep work warm during welding and annealed afterward; otherwise the welds and area adjacent to the welds will be brittle.   It is well to consult steel suppliers for specific heat-treatment, temperatures, and treatment.

High-manganese Steel.   The tough work-hardening characteristic of this material recommends it for surfaces which must resist abrasion or wear, as well as shock.   For building up parts of high-manganese steel, an electrode should be used of such type that the physical characteristics of the deposited metal will be approximately the same as the base metal.

THE NONFERROUS METALS

Aluminum.   Pure aluminum and various aluminum alloys in sheet, forged, extruded, and cast forms can be welded with either self-shielded carbon arc welding or gas-shielded arc welding, the latter being in most common use.

With arc welding, the high melting rate of the aluminum electrode necessitates rapid welding and presents the problem of getting enough heat into the work.   The rapid freezing rate of the metal may also trap gases in the weld and cause porosity.   For self-shielded arc welding, the minimum thickness of metal is generally recommended to be $\frac{1}{8}$ in., although thinner sections are successfully welded.   Material $\frac{1}{4}$ in. thick is generally regarded as the minimum thickness for gastight arc welds in aluminum.

Arc welding has usually proved unsatisfactory for joining extremely thick sections, because of the quench effect resulting from the high thermal conductivity of the material.   When arc welding is called for on applications involving thick pieces or complicated welds, the problem of thermal conductivity can be partially solved by preheating from 250 to 400°F.   Preheating also helps prevent porosity since the gases developed in the molten metal during welding are permitted to escape before the crater solidifies.

Self-shielded arc-welding techniques differ little from those of welding steel, except that there is no necessity for weaving, and striking the arc must be accomplished by a match-striking motion rather than simply tapping the work.   Direct current with electrode positive is used.

Inert-gas arc welding of aluminum generally employs both 60-cycle and high-frequency alternating current. No flux is used with this process, since all shielding is accomplished by the gas. Argon gas is used for a-c welding, and it must be of a high purity. The method has proved to be of particular advantage in welding thin sheet.

Copper and Copper Alloys. Copper and its alloys can be welded with self-shielded, gas-shielded, or carbon arc welding. Of the three, gas-shielded arc welding with an inert gas is preferred.

Decrease in tensile strength as temperature rises and high coefficient of contraction may make welding of copper complicated. Preheat usually is necessary on thicker sections because of the high heat conductivity of the metal. Keeping the work hot and pointing the electrode at an angle so the flame is directed back over the work will aid in permitting the gas to escape. It is also advisable to put as much metal down per bead as is practical.

CONTROL OF DISTORTION

Distortion in the metal being welded, caused by the heat of welding, may be a problem in welding sheet metal or unrestrained large sections. The following suggestions will help overcome problems of distortion, based on three simple rules applied singly or together:

1. Reduce the effective shrinkage force.
    a. Avoid overwelding. Use as little weld metal as possible by taking full advantage of penetrating effect of arc force.
    b. Use correct edge preparation and fit-up to obtain required fusion at root of weld.
    c. Use few passes.
    d. Place welds near neutral axis.
    e. Use intermittent welds.
    f. Use back-step welding method.
2. Make shrinkage forces work to minimize distortion.
    a. Locate parts out of position so that when weld shrinks they will be in correct position.
    b. Space parts to allow for shrinkage.
    c. Prebend parts so that contraction will pull parts into alignment.
3. Balance shrinkage forces with other forces (where natural rigidity of parts is insufficient to resist contraction).
    a. Balance one force with another by correct welding sequence so that contraction caused by weld counteracts forces of welds previously made.
    b. Peen beads to stretch weld metal. Care must be used not to damage weld metal.
    c. Use jigs and fixtures to hold work in a rigid position with sufficient strength to prevent parts from distorting. Fixtures actually cause weld metal to stretch, thus preventing distortion.

ELECTRODE SELECTION

Self-shielded Arc Welding. There are two aspects to the problem of selecting the correct electrode for making a good weld under given conditions. The selection must be made according to (1) electrode type as to coating and core-wire analysis and (2) electrode diameter size. In selecting the type of electrode it is necessary to know:

1. The position in which the work is to be welded.
2. The type and thickness of the metal being used.
3. The preparation of the work with regard to fit-up.
4. The type of available welding current.
5. The class of work, that is, whether deep penetration, surface quality, required physical properties, or code requirements is the chief essential.

The American Welding Society and the American Society for Testing Metals have jointly established specifications for the manufacture of welding electrodes to fulfill the

Table 1-3. Steel-electrode Classification, Characteristics, and Uses

Class No.	Work position	Current supply	Basic application
EXX10	All	D-C+	Designed to produce good mechanical properties consistent with good radiographic inspection quality. Application is usually structural where multipass welding is employed, such as shipbuilding, bridges, buildings, and piping and pressure vessels.
EXX11	All	A-C (D-C+)	Designed to do the work of XX10, but to employ an a-c current source. Slightly higher tensile and yield strength.
EXX12	All	D-C− A-C	Especially recommended for single-pass, high-speed, high-current, horizontal fillet welds. It is characteristically easy to handle and useful in cases of poor fit-up, both groove and fillet, where a wide range of currents is used. Class 12 has reduced penetration but can meet radiographic standards with single-pass welds.
EXX13	All	A-C (D-C−)	Designed for light-sheet-metal work, but now used widely as an electrode having light penetration. Frequently used in vertical downwelding, even though it produces a flat bead. Particularly well designed for use with low-voltage A-C transformers.
EXX14	All	A-C (D-C−)	An iron-powder electrode designed to do the work of 13 with increased deposit rate, although 14 has lower deposition rates than 24 and 27. In the fixed position, 13 and 14 have similar welding speeds. Has improved weld appearance and ease of welding in drag technique.
EXX15	All	D-C+	Offers exceptional physical properties and best X-ray quality. A "low-hydrogen" electrode for difficult-to-weld material such as high-carbon or low-alloy steel. Also, free machining, high-sulfur-bearing steel and armor plate. Frequently pre- and postheating may be eliminated or reduced by using low-hydrogen rod. Rod coating cannot perform properly with included moisture. Electrode should be heated before use as recommended by the manufacturer, or stored in a moisture-free area.
EXX16	All	A-C D-C+	A rod similar to 15 designed to be used with a-c and d-c+ current supply.
EXX18	HF-F	A-C D-C−	A 30% iron-powder titania-type electrode. A rod similar to 15 with a higher deposition rate but an improved weld appearance. Offers better slag removal and higher usable current than the E6016 type.
EXX20	HF-F	D-C− A-C	A high-production electrode designed for heavy sections, such as pressure vessels, heavy machine bases, and structural parts; in flat or horizontal fillet position. The weld has good quality and is frequently used where deep-fillet techniques are required.
EXX24	HF-F	A-C (D-C−)	An iron-powder-type electrode ideal for fillet welds. The iron powder in the electrode coating assists in increasing the deposit rate over the 12 class. Electrode can be used in drag technique with ease of handling and good weld appearance. Requires better fit-up than 12, but is of similar application, although limited as to position.
EXX27	HF-F	D-C− A-C	When this high-iron-powder electrode is used in the drag technique, it is 50% faster than the 20 electrode. It is primarily a downward deep-groove rod, well suited for heavy sections. Second only to 24 in welding speed, but with properties superior to it. Both are equally easy to handle.

Table 1-3. Steel-electrode Classification, Characteristics, and Uses (*Continued*)

Class No.	Work position	Current supply	Basic application
EXX28	HF-F	D-C– (A-C)	A 50% iron-powder lime-type electrode. This one yields the highest deposition rates of the low-hydrogen group. The coating also produces an easy-to-maintain arc with a smooth, wide bead; can be used only in the flat position.
EXX30	F	D-C– A-C	Capable of higher deposition rates than 20. Designed for welding of heavy plate in the flat position and good in deep-groove welding. Has less fluid slag than 20.

HF—horizontal fillet position; F—flat position.

above job requirements. The following specifications have been issued, classifying electrodes as follows:

Mild Steel Covered Arc Welding Electrodes, A5.1-64.
Low Alloy Steel Covered Arc Welding Electrodes, A5.5-64.
Corrosion-resisting Chromium and Chromium-Nickel Steel Covered Welding Electrodes, A5.4-62.
Copper and Copper-alloy Arc Welding Electrodes, A5.6-57.
Nickel and Nickel-alloy Covered Welding Electrodes, A5.11-64.

In addition to these classifications, electrodes are also manufactured for hard surfacing, welding cast iron, and other miscellaneous applications.

The mild- and low-alloy-steel electrodes are classified with a numbering system for simple identification. E6010 is a typical four-digit classification number. The prefix E designates a metal-arc-welding electrode; the first two digits stand for the minimum allowable tensile strength of stress-relieved deposits in thousands of pounds per square inch. The third digit stands for the welding position or positions in which the electrode will make a satisfactory deposit, and the last digit indicates various arc characteristics, among them polarity.

Since at least 90 per cent of all arc welding is done in mild steel, the following brief descriptions of mild-steel electrode types are included. The significance of the various classification digits as explained for these electrodes is consistent throughout the E70, E80, E90, E100, and E110XX series of steel electrodes. Table 1-3 gives classification characteristics and uses for steel electrodes.

Cellulose-coated Electrodes EXX10 and EXX11. The relatively thin coatings of these electrodes contains a high percentage of cellulose. This type of coating produces a small volume of molten slag in the weld crater and light slag coverage of the solidified weld bead. The EXX10 and EXX11 electrodes can be used in all welding positions, as illustrated in Fig. 1-27.

Types E6010 and E6011. These types may be classified as general-purpose electrodes, since they are used for a wide variety of work and possess high average mechanical characteristics. E6010 is best suited for direct current, electrode positive. In sizes of $\frac{3}{16}$ in. and smaller, in any type of weld, it is suitable in all positions—flat, horizontal, vertical, and overhead (Fig. 1-28). It has deep-penetration qualities and is used very satisfactorily on square-groove butt joints where the electrodes actually scarf or melt the plates. It produces a rather flat bead shape.

The E6010 electrode has a high cellulose content in the coating. The arc is very penetrating, with a relatively quick solidifying slag and weld-crater action. Protection of the molten metal is obtained principally by gases since only a small amount of slag is produced. The weld metal has excellent physical qualities. Some of the applications are welding pipe, ships, machinery, structures (especially field or erection), and jigs and fixtures.

FIG. 1-27. EXX10 and EXX11 electrodes are used for all-position welding.

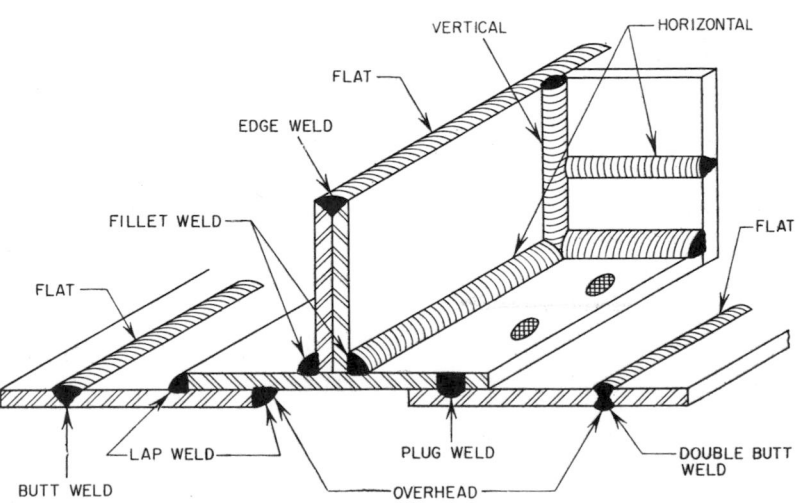

FIG. 1-28. Types of welds encountered in structural and general maintenance welding.

The E6011 electrode is similar to the E6010 but is designed for a-c or either-polarity d-c operation. The d-c polarity (electrode negative) or reverse (electrode positive) depends upon the type of work being performed. The characteristics of E6011 electrode design are also high-cellulose coating, penetrating arc, quickly solidifying slag action, similar to E6010, and protection of molten metal obtained principally by gases. As in the case of E6010, this electrode is well suited for making vertical and overhead fillet and butt welds. The applications are the same as for E6010.

These electrodes are generally recommended for use where the weld metal cannot be deposited in the flat, or downhand, position. The deposited metal has good strength and high elongation.

Of the same general characteristics are several electrodes for welding the low-alloy high-tensile steels (E7010, E9010, etc.).

Titania-coated Electrodes (EXX12, EXX13). The medium-thick coatings of these electrodes contain a relatively high titania content. This type of coating produces a medium volume of molten slag in the weld crater which simply covers the weld bead when it solidifies. These electrodes can be used in all positions, but are more difficult to control out of position than the cellulose types.

Types E6012 and E6013. The 6012 electrode has a medium-thick coating and is used with direct current with the electrode negative or may be used with alternating current. Sizes of $\frac{3}{16}$ in. and smaller are suitable for all positions, and larger sizes for welding in flat positions. The electrode may be used for fillet welding, single- or multiple-pass, and can be used for butt welds of the V-groove or U-groove type. Because of its deposition characteristics and ability to build up, it is used to fill gaps in cases of poor fit-up. E6012 coatings are high in titania and low in cellulose. The arc is less penetrating than that of E6010 and E6011, but adequate when correct welding procedures are used. The larger amount of slag gives a better coverage, producing a finer ripple with a more pleasing bead surface.

The E6012 electrode has higher melting rate with lower spatter than E6010 or E6011. It is ideally suited for horizontal and flat fillet welds, for applications where fit-up may be poor, and on steel having characteristics which give poor welding action with electrodes producing greater penetration. It can be used for butt welds of the V-groove or U-groove types. Because it does not penetrate deeply, it is used in cases where dilution of weld and base metal is not desirable. It produces a somewhat convex bead. The weld metal has higher tensile strength and slightly lower elongation than have E6010 and E6011. Some typical applications are welding sheet-metal ducts, tanks, machine guards, and structural work.

E6013 has better a-c operation than E6012 and develops a smoother bead appearance. Penetration is similar to that of E6012, so that it works well for poor fit-up. E6013 is more suitable for light-gage metals than E6012. The bead has a tendency to be convex in making horizontal fillets. The applications are similar to those for E6012.

Mineral-coated Electrodes EXX20 and EXX30. The thick coatings of these electrodes contain a relatively high percentage of minerals. They are characterized by a high deposition rate and substantial volume of molten and solidified slag. These electrodes are limited to horizontal and flat position welding.

Mineral-coated Electrodes Types E6020 and E6030. These types have a heavy coating and can be used with direct current with either positive or negative polarity and can also be used with alternating current. They are used in the flat position only and are not suitable for vertical or overhead work, although under special conditions as to setup, such as 30° from vertical, they may be used for fillet, welding downward. These types are used for fillets or butt joints of the V-groove or U-groove types. They flow very readily with a heavy slag covering the weld. They sometimes are known as the "hot-rod" type. They produce a very smooth bead, slightly concave and in some cases very concave. There is exceptionally low spatter loss. This type of electrode gives fine performance for single-pass fillet welds where strength is not based on the size of the fillet but on the actual amount of the fused base metal. The fit-up must be good to realize the full benefits of a fine combination of strength and elongation. The applications are numerous, i.e., production welding of ships, oil-field equipment, pressure vessels, machine bases, and fabricated I-beams and girders. These are essentially production electrodes.

Iron-powder Electrodes. The iron-powder-coated electrodes have an exceptionally heavy coating containing a large quantity of iron powder (Fig. 1-29). This type of coating makes welding with these electrodes faster and easier. Welding speeds are increased as much as 50 per cent. Weld appearance is smoother; slag is practically self-cleaning; spatter is eliminated almost completely.

All these advantages result from the nature of the iron-powder coating. The coating more efficiently utilizes the heat of the arc in melting. Welding currents can be increased for a given-diameter electrode, providing greater deposition rates without the difficulties of excessive penetration, gouging, undercutting, and spatter normally encountered when welding with higher currents.

The electrodes operate on either alternating or direct current, but alternating current is preferred. Slightly higher currents than those used with conventional electrodes are required. Also, an electrode one size smaller in diameter is generally used.

They are ideally suited for contact or drag welding techniques, although an arc may be held if desired.

Type E6024. This type of electrode has been designed especially for welding flat and horizontal fillets with either alternating or direct current. It is widely used for production welding in making machinery and structures.

Type E6027. This type of iron-powder electrode has been designed especially for welding flat, deep-groove butt welds with either alternating or direct current. It is also used for flat and horizontal fillets. It

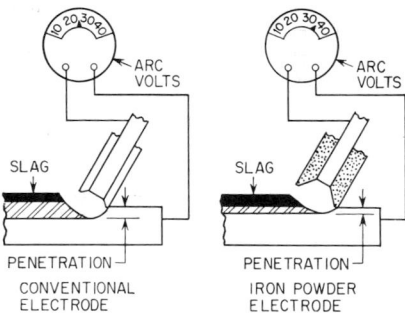

FIG. 1-29. Essential difference between iron-powder and conventional electrodes.

is used for code work normally calling for an E6020 type of electrode. The bead has excellent wash-in properties and makes a smooth cover pass. The slag is extremely friable, and therefore easily removable under all conditions.

Type E6014. Iron powder has been added to the coating to produce this modified version of an E6013 type of electrode. The result is an excellent electrode having the iron-powder characteristics plus the feature of being suited to out-of-position use up to 45° downhill. Although classified as all-position, it is rarely used for vertical and overhead welding.

Build-up and Manganese-steel Electrodes. Several manufacturers are making iron-powder maintenance electrodes for build-up work on worn machinery parts and welding manganese steel. These electrodes do not, as yet, carry an official AWS classification, but are usually descriptively named. The high deposition rate of the electrodes results in depositing 35 to 45 per cent more metal per minute than is possible with conventional electrodes. This means considerable saving in time when areas being restored to size require the deposition of a large quantity of metal. Properties and characteristics of the electrodes are varied to meet particular service requirements.

Lime-coated "Low-hydrogen" Electrode Types. The low-hydrogen electrode consists essentially of a rimmed-steel core wire upon which a covering of the carbonate of soda and lime type is applied, using other compounds low in hydrogen. This covering is slightly thicker than normal, for each diameter, and the electrode is slightly more difficult to use, because of the shortness of the arc which must be maintained. A typical analysis of the deposit from this electrode is 0.08 per cent carbon, 0.56 per cent manganese, and 0.25 per cent silicon. The arc is moderately penetrating; the slag heavy, friable, and easily removed; and the deposited metal lies in a flat bead or may be even slightly convex.

The as-welded mechanical and impact properties of deposits made using the low-hydrogen-type electrodes have been found to be superior to those of E6010 and E6011 electrodes depositing weld metal of the same composition. Numerous tests have indicated that the as-welded mechanical and impact properties of deposits from these electrodes approach the properties of stress-relieved deposits of conventional electrodes. Whereas the properties of deposits of conventional electrodes are materially improved when they are stress-relieved, the deposits of low-hydrogen electrodes are changed only slightly. The reduced tendency for underbead cracking and the high quality of as-welded deposits of these electrodes should materially reduce the preheat and postheat of weldments, thus making for better welding conditions and reductions in the cost of thermal treatments.

Low-hydrogen electrodes operate best on d-c reversed polarity, but some types can also be used with alternating current. They were developed for welding higher-strength high-carbon alloy steels in which the ordinary electrodes are subject to developing "underbead cracking." These underbead cracks occur along the line of fusion between the parent metal and the weld metal, and are caused by the hydrogen present in the conventional electrode coating. Naturally, eliminating the hydrogen tends to help control underbead cracking and permits the welding of the "difficult-to-weld steels" with little or no preheat, thus making for better welding conditions. Although these cracks do not occur in ordinary steels, they may occur whenever an ordinary electrode is used on high-tensile steels.

Another use for the low-hydrogen-type electrode is the welding of high-sulfur steels. The ordinary electrode deposit on these steels (which contain 0.10 to 0.25 per cent sulfur) is badly honeycombed. Low-hydrogen-type electrodes can be used to weld these steels without any difficulty.

Many of the newer high-tensile steels being produced today call for low-hydrogen electrodes ranging up to 110,000 psi tensile strength (E110XX).

The low-hydrogen electrode was developed during the war for the welding of armor plate, and in addition to its use on alloy steels, high-carbon steels, and high-sulfur steels, it has been found useful on malleable iron, on spring steels, and for welding the mild-steel side of clad plates. Another extensive use has been in the welding of steels which will subsequently be enameled and in all those steels which contain selenium. It is an excellent maintenance electrode, since it can be used with assurance of good welding on steels whose analysis is unknown or may be questioned.

Type E6015. The E6015 electrode was the first of the low-hydrogen types for welding the carbon steels. It was designed exclusively for d-c electrode-positive operation. The E6015 electrode can be used in all positions up to and including $\frac{5}{32}$-in.-diameter. The larger diameters are useful for fillet and butt welds in the horizontal and flat positions.

Type E6016. The E6016 classification of electrode has all the characteristics of the E6015 classification. The core wire and coating are very similar, except for the use of a certain amount of potassium silicate or other potassium salts on the E6016 classification to facilitate its use on alternating current. All that has been said of the E6015 electrode applies equally well to the E6016.

Type E6018. Iron powder has been added in the E6018 type of electrode, thus producing the iron-powdered, low-hydrogen electrode manufactured under this classification. The electrodes have the advantage of low-hydrogen properties plus the excellent operating characteristics associated with iron powder. All that has been said of the E6015 and E6016 applies equally to the E6018. This is an excellent maintenance electrode.

Type E6028. The E6028 classification of electrode combines the advantages of the low-hydrogen types and the heavy-coated powdered-iron types. The electrode manufactured under this classification has a high deposition rate, and is limited in application to horizontal- and flat-position welding.

SUBMERGED ARC WELDING—EQUIPMENT, ELECTRODES, AND FLUX

Welding Equipment. The welding heads normally used for fully automatic submerged arc welding perform the triple function of progressively depositing flux along the joint, feeding the electrode, and transmitting welding current to the electrode. The flux is usually supplied from a hopper either mounted directly on the head or connected to the head by tubing. The bare electrode or wire is fed into the welding head from a coil mounted on a reel. The distance between the end of the electrode and the base metal is maintained constant by special controls which automatically regulate the electrode-feed motor speed or welding current.

Equipment manufactured for semiautomatic submerged arc welding performs the same functions as that for fully automatic welding. The welding head, however, now consists of a welding gun and wire feeder unit. The flux for semiautomatic welding is supplied by a canister mounted on the welding gun or a "continuous-flow" flux feed from a pressurized flux tank. With semiautomatic welding equipment, the electrode wire is mechanically fed to the work but the welding gun is manually moved along

FIG. 1-30. Semiautomatic submerged arc welding.

the joint being welded. This procedure gives added flexibility to this method of welding by permitting its use on irregular shapes and contours, thereby promoting expanded use.

Direct current is used with both semiautomatic and fully automatic submerged arc welding, whereas alternating current is usually limited to fully automatic submerged arc welding. The welding voltage for submerged arc welding will range from 28 to as high as 55 volts. Currents generally used for submerged arc welding are higher than those used for the other arc-welding processes. They range from a low of 200 amp up to as high as 4,000 amp.

Alternating current may be supplied from one or more heavy-duty welding transformers. Direct current may be supplied by one or more motor-generator or rectifier welding machines having capacity suitable for the application. The d-c power supplies can be constant-potential or variable-voltage types, depending upon the application and manufacturer's recommendations. Installations of semiautomatic and fully automatic welding equipment are illustrated by Figs. 1-30 and 1-31.

Electrodes and Fluxes.   The ferrous and nonferrous electrodes commonly used for submerged arc welding are bare rods or wires with clean, bright surfaces to facilitate the introduction of relatively high currents.   Electrodes are normally used in the form of coils ranging in weight from a minimum of 25 to 200 lbs.   On very high-production welding installations, the electrode is frequently fed from a coil in a drum.   These drums range up to as high as 1,000 lb in weight.   Ferrous wire of composition that might readily rust is coppercoated to retard rusting and improve the contact surfaces.

The fluxes used with submerged arc welding are granulated fusible mineral materials which are essentially free from substances that would create large amounts of gases during welding.   These fluxes are made to a variety of chemical specifications which develop particular performance characteristics.   The flux has a number of functions to perform, including prevention of atmospheric contamination and performing a

Fig. 1-31. Fully automatic submerged arc welding.

scavenging-deoxidizing action on the molten metal in the weld crater.   Some special fluxes perform the additional function of contributing alloying elements to the weld deposit, thereby developing specific weld-metal characteristics of higher strength or even abrasion resistance.   The choice of flux depends on the welding procedure to be employed, the type of joint, and the composition of the material to be welded.

SPECIAL APPLICATIONS

Sheet-metal Welding.   The welding of sheet metal, as illustrated by Fig. 1-32, has frequent application in plant maintenance.   The principles of good welding practice apply in welding sheet metal as elsewhere, but the nature of the work places special emphasis on several aspects.   The problem of distortion requires special consideration in welding thin-gage metals as well as the problems of burning through the metal. Special attention should therefore be given to all the factors involved in controlling distortion: the speed of welding, the choice of proper joints, good fit-up, position, selection of proper current, use of clamping devices and fixtures, number of phases, and sequence of beads.

Fig. 1-32. Typical sheet-metal welding using the self-shielded arc-welding process.

Within the limits of good welding appearance, the highest arc speeds and the highest currents should be used. In sheet-metal work, however, there is always the limitation imposed by the threat of burn-through. As the gap in the work increases in size, the current must be decreased to prevent burn-through, which, of course, will reduce welding speeds. A clamping fixture will improve the fit-up of joints and thus make possible the higher speeds. If equipped with a copper backing strip, the clamping fixture will make for easier welding by decreasing the tendency to burn through and will also remove some of the heat which causes warpage. Where possible, sheet-metal joints should be welded downhill at about a 45° angle with the same currents as are used in the flat position, or slightly higher. Tables 1-4 and 1-5 offer a guide to the selection of the proper current, voltage, and electrodes for the various types of joints used with sheet metal ranging from 20- to 8-gage.

Hard Surfacing. The building up of a layer of metal or a metal surface by electric welding, commonly known as arc-weld surfacing, has an important and useful application in equipment maintenance. Applications of the process are varied and many,

Table 1-4. Welding Currents for Sheet Metal

Type of welded joint	20 ga			18 ga			16 ga			14 ga			12 ga			10 ga			8 ga		
	F*	V*	O*	F	V	O	F	V	O	F	V	O	F	V	O	F	V	O	F	V	O
Plain butt......	30†	30†	30†	40†	40†	40†	70†	70†	70†	85†	80	85†	115	110	110	135	120	115	190	130	120
Lap............	40†	40†	40†	60†	60†	60†	100	100	100	130	130	130	135	120	120	155	130	120	165	140	120
Fillet..........				40†	40†	40†	70†	70†	70†	100	90	85	150	140	120	160	150	130	160	160	130
Corner........	40†	40†	40†	60†	60†	60†	90†	90†	90†	90	80	75	125	110	110	140	130	125	175	130	125
Edge..........	40†	40†	40†	60†	60†	60†	80†	80†	80†	110	80	80	145	110	110	150	120	120	160	120	120

* F—flat position; V—vertical; O—overhead.

† Electrode negative, work positive.

Table 1-5. Sizes of Electrodes for Sheet Metal

Type of welded joint	20 ga			18 ga			16 ga			14 ga			12 ga			10 ga			8 ga		
	F*	V*	O*	F	V	O	F	V	O	F	V	O	F	V	O	F	V	O	F	V	O
Plain butt	3/32	3/32	3/32	3/32	3/32	3/32	1/8	1/8	1/8	1/8	1/8	1/8	5/32	5/32	5/32	5/32	5/32	5/32	3/16	5/32	5/32
Lap	3/32	3/32	3/32	3/32	3/32	3/32	1/8	1/8	1/8	5/32	5/32	5/32	5/32	5/32	5/32	3/16	3/16	5/32	3/16	3/16	5/32
Fillet				3/32	3/32	3/32	1/8	1/8	1/8	1/8	1/8	1/8	5/32	5/32	5/32	3/16	5/32	5/32	3/16	5/32	5/32
Corner	3/32	3/32	3/32	3/32	3/32	3/32	1/8	1/8	1/8	1/8	1/8	1/8	3/16	5/32	5/32	3/16	5/32	5/32	3/16	5/32	5/32
Edge	3/32	3/32	3/32	3/32	3/32	3/32	1/8	1/8	1/8	1/8	1/8	1/8	3/16	5/32	5/32	3/16	5/32	5/32	3/16	5/32	5/32

* F—flat position; V—vertical; O—overhead.

such as restoring worn cutting edges and teeth on excavators, building up worn shafts with low- or medium-carbon deposit, lining a carbon-steel bin or chute with stainless-steel corrosion-resistant alloy deposit, putting a tool-steel cutting edge on a medium-carbon-steel base, and applying wear-resistant surfaces to metal machine parts of all kinds. The dragline bucket of Fig. 1-33 is being returned to "new" condition by rebuilding and hard surfacing.

Arc-weld surfacing includes, but is not limited to, hard surfacing. There are many building-up applications where hard surfacing is not required.

Wear is the gradual impairment of machinery parts through use. Excluding corrosion, wear results from various combinations of abrasion and impact. Abrasive wear results from one material scratching another, and impact wear from one material hitting another.

FIG. 1-33. Self-shielded arc welding is used to rebuild and to hard-surface worn areas of a dragline bucket.

How to Resist Abrasive Wear. Abrasive wear is resisted by materials with a high scratch hardness. Sand wears metals with a low scratch hardness at a high rate, but under the same conditions it will wear a metal of high scratch hardness very slowly. Scratch hardness, however, is not necessarily measured by standard hardness tests. Brinell and Rockwell hardness are not reliable measures for determining the abrasive-wear resistance of a metal. A hard-surfacing material of the chromium-carbide type may have a hardness of 50 Rockwell C. Sand will wear this material at a slower rate than it will a steel hardened to 60 Rockwell C. The sand will scratch all the way across the surface of the steel. On the surfacing alloy the scratch will progress through the matrix material and then stop when the sand grain comes up against one of the microscopic crystals of chromium carbide, which has a higher scratch hardness than sand. If two metals of the same type have the same kind of microscopic constituents, however, the metal having the high Rockwell hardness will be more resistant to abrasive wear.

How to Resist Impact Wear. Whereas abrasive wear is resisted by the surface properties of a metal, impact wear is resisted by the properties of the metal beneath the surface. To resist impact, a tough material is used, one which does not readily bend, break, chip, or crack. It yields so as to distribute or absorb the load created by impact, and the ultimate strength of the metal is not exceeded. Included in impact wear is that caused by bending or compression at low velocity without impact, resulting in loss of metal by cracking, chipping, upsetting, flowing, or crushing.

Types of Surfacing Electrodes. Many different kinds of surfacing electrodes are available. The problem is to find the best one to do a given job. Yet because service conditions vary so widely, no universal standard can be established for determining the ability of surfacing to resist impact or to resist abrasion. Furthermore, there is no ideal surfacing material that resists both impact and abrasion equally well. In manufacturing surfacing electrodes, it is necessary to sacrifice somewhat one quality to gain the other. A material that has a high resistance to abrasion will have a low resistance to impact. High impact resistance is gained by sacrificing abrasion resistance.

Price is no index to quality of electrodes. Simply because an electrode contains an expensive ingredient does not necessarily make it superior for wear resistance. Thus the user of surfacing materials must rely upon the manufacturer's recommendations and his own tests to determine the best surfacing material for his purpose.

How to Choose Hard-facing Material. The chart of Fig. 1-34 lists the relative characteristics of manual hard-surfacing materials. It shows in the various columns the ability of each of the materials to resist abrasion, metallic friction, impact, and corrosion. It also gives the relative hardness, ductility, and cost of depositing the material, as well as the physical limitations of weld size in applying each one. This chart is a guide to selecting:

1. The hard-surfacing electrode best suited for a job not hard-surfaced before.
2. A more suitable hard-surfacing electrode for a job where present material has not produced desired results.

Example 1. application: Dragline bucket tooth, as illustrated by Fig. 1-35. service: Sandy gravel with some good-sized rocks.

Maximum wear that can be economically obtained is the goal of most hard-surfacing applications. Try to use a material that rates as high as possible in the resistance-to-abrasion column unless some other characteristics shown in the other columns make it unsuited for this particular application.

First, consider the tungsten-carbide types. Notice that they are composed of very hard particles in a softer and less abrasion-resistant matrix. Although such material is the best for resisting sliding abrasion on hard material, in sand the matrix is apt to scour out slightly, and then the brittle particles are exposed. These particles are rated poor in impact resistance, and they may break and spall off when they encounter the rocks.

Next best in abrasion, as listed in the chart, is the high-chromium carbide type shown in the electrode-size column to be a powder. It can be applied only in a thin

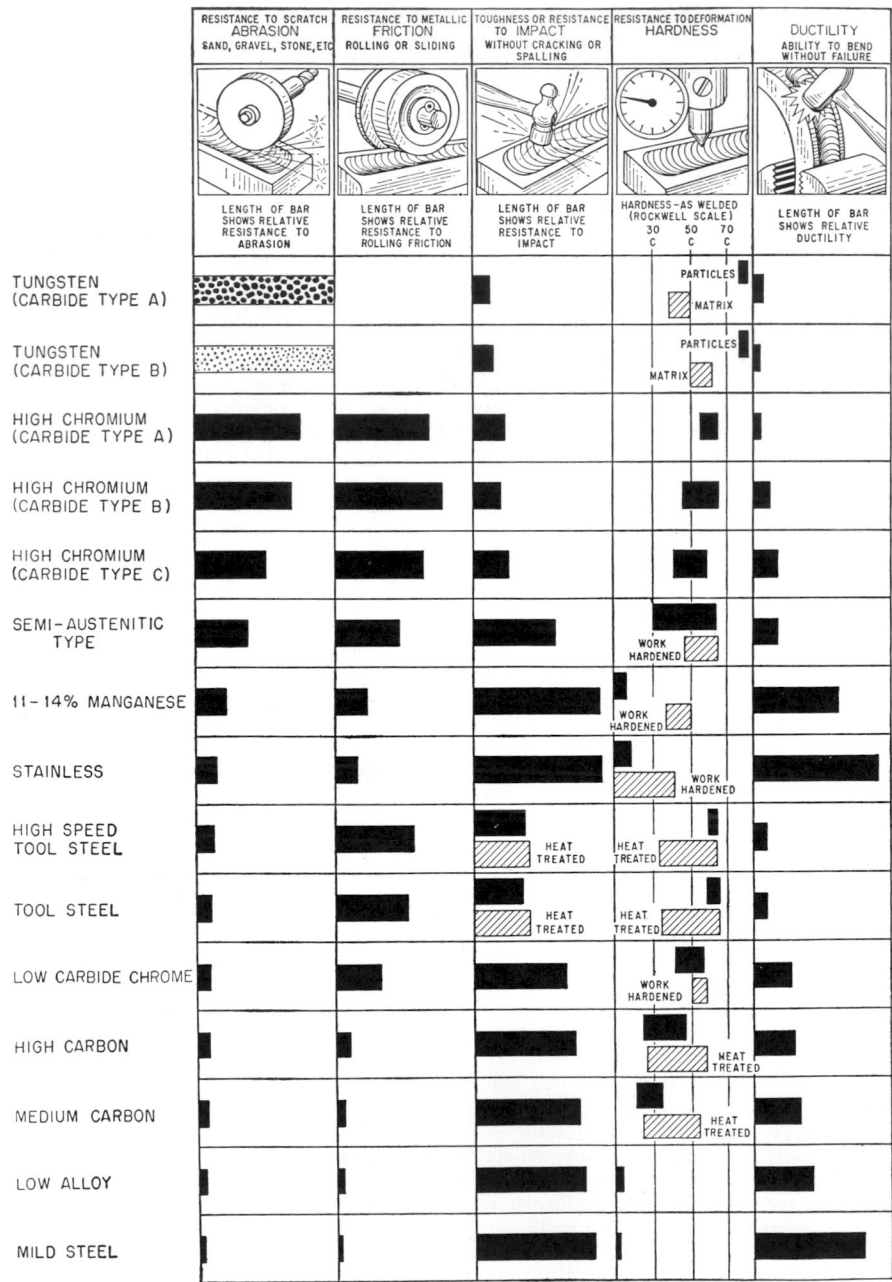

Fig. 1-34. Hard-

MACHINABILITY		RESISTANCE TO CORROSION RUST, PITTING, HIGH TEMPERATURE SCALING	WELD SIZE	COST	ELECTRODE SIZE AVAILABLE

surfacing guide.

layer, and also is not rated high in impact resistance. This makes it doubtful for use in this rocky soil.

The rod-type high-chromium carbides also rate very high in abrasion resistance, but do not rate high in impact resistance. However, the second does show sufficient impact rating to be considered if two or three different materials are to be tested in a field test. Since there is a chance that it has enough impact resistance to do this job, we should not like to pass up its very good wearing properties.

Nevertheless, the semiaustenitic type is balanced in both abrasion and impact resistance. It is much better in resistance to impact than the materials that rate higher in abrasion. Thus semiaustenitic is the first choice on this job, considering that the added impact resistance of the austenitic type is not necessary, since the impact in this application is not extreme.

Example 2. APPLICATION: Same dragline tooth used in Example 1. SERVICE: Soil changed to clay and shale.

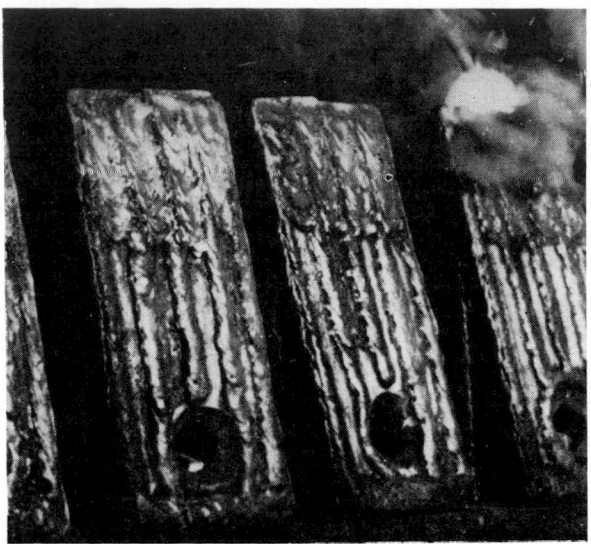

FIG. 1-35. Bucket teeth have been rebuilt and hard-surfaced.

The semiaustenitic type selected in the first example stands up well, but the teeth wear only half as long as the bucket lip. With double the wear on the teeth, only half the downtime periods for resurfacing would be needed, and both teeth and bucket could be done together.

Since the impact is now negligible with the new soil conditions, go to a material higher in the abrasion column. Choose a material such as the first high-chromium carbide rod, which could give twice the wear by controlling the size bead applied and still be within reasonable cost.

Example 3. APPLICATION: Same dragline tooth used as in Examples 1 and 2. SERVICE: Soil changed to contain large rocks.

If the earth has been changed so that it contains many hard and large rocks and the teeth are failing because of spalling under impact, move down in the abrasion-resisting column to a better impact-resistant material, such as the semiaustenitic type.

From the above, it can be seen that where a dragline operates in all kinds of soils, a material that is good in both abrasion and impact, such as a semiaustenitic type, is the best choice when in doubt as to the conditions that will be met.

When this same type of reasoning is followed in checking the important characteristics, a material can be chosen for any application. And if, for any reason, the first choice does not prove satisfactory, it is usually a simple matter to improve the next application by choosing a material that is rated higher in the characteristic that has caused difficulty.

Where failures occur because of cracking or spalling, it usually indicates that a material higher in impact or ductility rating should be used. Where normal wear alone seems too rapid, a material higher in abrasion rating is indicated.

Check Welding Procedure. Often hard-surfacing failures due to cracking or spalling may be caused by improper welding procedures rather than by improper choice of hard-surfacing material. Before changing to a different hard-surfacing material, serious consideration should be given to the question of whether or not the material has been properly applied.

For almost any hard-surfacing application, very good results can be obtained if the following precautions are observed:

1. Do not apply hard-surfacing material over cracked or porous areas. Remove any defective areas down to sound base metal.
2. Preheat. Preheating to 400 to 500°F improves the resistance to cracking and spalling. This minimum temperature should be maintained until welding is completed. The exception to this rule is 11 to 14 per cent manganese steel, which should be kept cool.
3. Cool slowly. If possible, allow the finished weldment to cool under an insulating material such as lime, asbestos, or sand.
4. Do not apply more than the recommended number of layers.

When more than normal build-up is required, apply intermediate layers of either medium carbon or stainless steel. This will provide a good bond to the base metal and will eliminate excessively thick layers of hard-surfacing material which might otherwise spall off.

Stainless steel is also an excellent choice for intermediate layers on manganese steels or for hard-to-weld steels where preheating is not practical.

Check before Total Wear. Whenever possible, examine a surfaced part when it is only partly worn. Examination of a part after it is completely worn is unsatisfactory. Did the surface crumble off, or was it scratched off? Is a tougher surface needed, or is additional abrasion resistance required? Should a heavier layer of surfacing be used? Should the surfacing be reduced? All these questions can be answered by examination of a partly worn part and with a knowledge of the surfacing costs and the service requirements.

In case it is impossible to analyze carefully the service conditions, it is always on the safe side to choose a material tougher than is thought to be required. A tough material will not knock or chip off and will offer some resistance to abrasion. A hard abrasion-resistant material is more susceptible to chipping, and surfacing material does not do any good when it is knocked off in large pieces.

After some experience is gained in the use of surfacing materials, various combinations of materials can be tried out to improve product performance. For example, on a part which is normally surfaced with a tough, semiaustenitic electrode, it may be possible to get additional abrasion resistance without sacrificing resistance to cracking. Fuse a little of the powdered chromium-carbide material on critical areas where additional protection is needed.

Many jobs that are badly worn are first built up to almost finished size with a high-carbon electrode. They are then surfaced with an austenitic rod, and finally a few beads of chromium-carbide deposit are placed in spots requiring maximum protection against abrasion.

Regardless of the circumstances, careful analysis of the surfacing problem is well worthwhile. For examples of jobs see Figs. 1-36 to 1-38.

Hard Surfacing with Submerged-arc Process. The submerged-arc process offers several advantages for hard surfacing. The greater uniformity of the surface makes for better wearing qualities. The speed of submerged arc welding creates major economies in hard-surfacing areas which require the deposition of large amounts of metal. These areas may be either flat or curved surfaces. Mixer bottom plates, scraper blades, fan blades, chutes, and refinery vessels are examples of flat plate to be surfaced. Shafts, blooming-mill spindles, skelp rolls, crane wheels, tractor idlers and rollers, and rams are examples of cylindrical surfaces (Figs. 1-39 to 1-42).

The process can be used with either fully automatic equipment or with semiautomatic equipment, the choice depending upon the economics of the application. It is a relatively simple calculation to determine the savings that will result from using the submerged-arc process and thus arrive at a decision as to which type of equipment is warranted. Fully automatic equipment can be quickly fitted with auxiliary accessories which result in more economical metal deposition. An oscillating device can be added to an automatic head to create a bead up to 3 in. wide in a single pass. Another attachment permits the feeding of two electrode wires through a single head and single contact jaw. Both of these attachments are useful in hard surfacing.

FIG. 1-36. Mild-steel die, on the edge of which tool steel has been deposited by means of tool-steel electrode.

Hard surfacing with the submerged arc can be done with several different types of materials. The hard-surfacing deposit can be created by using solid alloy wires and a neutral granular flux. It can also be created by using a solid mild-steel wire and an agglomerated alloy flux, the alloys being added to the deposit through the

FIG. 1-37. Cone used for uncoiling steel. Tool-steel electrode has been deposited on mild-steel base. Surface is ready for grinding.

FIG. 1-38. Using mild-steel electrode to build up inside diameter and all teeth of 25-year-old cast-steel gear that could not be replaced.

flux rather than through the wire. Also available are tubular wires which contain alloying material in the hollow portion of the mild-steel tube. All the methods have particular advantages. In considering the submerged-arc process, it is well to consult a qualified field engineer who can recommend methods and procedures. With submerged arc welding, considerable variation in the hard-surfacing deposit can be made by changing the welding procedure to control admixture and the heat-treatment effect of the welding cycle. Procedures should be established with the help of qualified engineers.

Fig. 1-39. Steel-mill coke pushers being hard-faced by submerged-arc process. Mild-steel wire and alloy flux. Fully automatic equipment in foreground, semiautomatic in background.

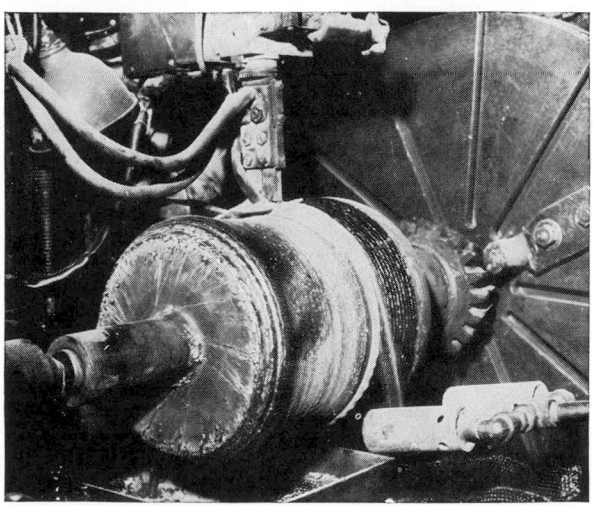

Fig. 1-40. Hard-surfacing wire-mill roll by submerged-arc process. Mild-steel wire and alloy flux. Gas torch keeps roll up to temperature.

Carbon Arc. Manual carbon arc welding can be used to good advantage for welding of copper and its alloys, cast iron, and galvanized sheets and hard surfacing with alloy powder. The hand carbon can also be used for the cutting of steel, cast iron, and the stainless steels, the last two of which cannot be readily cut with the oxyacetylene torch.

The procedures to be used in welding any particular material will vary with the application. In making an edge weld where no filler metal is to be added, the average speeds given in Table 1-6 should be obtained.

FIG. 1-41. Automatic head adapted for oscillating and for two electrodes, being used to deposit 3-in. beads on a flat mixer bottom plate.

FIG. 1-42. Submerged arc welding being used to hard-surface a cylindrical surface.

Pointing of the Carbons. The diameter of the point should be approximately half the diameter of the carbon used. The taper should be gradual back to the point where it is gripped in the holder.

Position of the Carbon in the Holder. The carbon should be gripped as close to the arc as practical because, if a long length of carbon is exposed, the heating causes the carbon to vaporize and burn very rapidly, resulting in excessive wastage.

Table 1-6. Average Conditions for Welding

Metal thickness	Arc volts	Arc amp	Carbon size, in.	Welding speed, fph
16 ga. (0.0598 in.)	25	90–100	$\frac{3}{16}$	135
14 ga. (0.0747 in.)	25	125–135	$\frac{1}{4}$	125
12 ga. (0.0146 in.)	25	200–250	$\frac{1}{4}$–$\frac{5}{16}$	110
10 ga. (0.1345 in.)	25	250–275	$\frac{1}{4}$–$\frac{5}{16}$	100

Table 1-7. Maximum Currents for Hand Carbon Arc

Size of Carbon Electrode, In.	Maximum Current
$\frac{5}{32}$	50
$\frac{3}{16}$	100
$\frac{1}{4}$	200
$\frac{5}{16}$	350
$\frac{3}{8}$	450
$\frac{1}{2}$	700

Polarity. Carbon negative should be used in almost all cases.

Currents. The proper current to be used depends upon the work to be done. Table 1-7 will serve as a guide. The currents given are about the maximum which should ever be used. Smaller currents may be used, depending upon the weight or thickness of the base metal.

Arc Torch. The development of the carbon arc torch (Fig. 1-43) has further extended the use of the carbon-arc-welding technique to jobs where the application of heat is desired without melting the base metal. With the arc torch, a high-temperature flame is held between the two carbon electrodes clamped in adjustable jaws. The flame is played over the surface of the work, similar to a gas flame, and as the carbons are consumed, they can be adjusted to maintain a constant distance between them.

The torch is useful for all brazing, soldering of light or heavy copper and galvanized or tinned parts, preheating localized areas prior to welding, and general heating for bending or straightening.

The carbon arc torch operates at 35 to 40 volts, and since most welder controls are calibrated in amperes at the average metallic arc of 25 to 30 volts, the machine controls should be set 20 per cent above recommended current settings. Copper-coated and copper-cored carbons are generally used in $\frac{1}{4}$ to $\frac{3}{8}$ in. diameter. The current

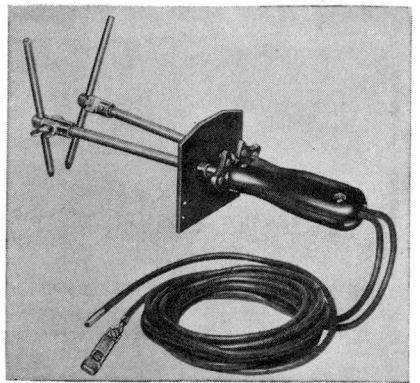

Fig. 1-43. Typical carbon arc torch.

should never be set so high that the copper coating is burned away more than $\frac{1}{2}$ in. ahead of the arc. Only enough current should be used to cause the filler material to flow freely on the work. This will avoid consuming carbons too rapidly. The recommended current is between 50 and 75 amp on $\frac{5}{16}$-in. carbons. Best results in brazing are obtained when carbons are $\frac{1}{4}$ to $\frac{3}{8}$ in. away from the work. When possible, have the joint lying horizontal to secure the best flow of molten filler rod.

Cutting. Steel can be readily cut with great accuracy by means of the oxyacetylene torch. Not all metals cut as easily as steel. Cast iron, stainless steels, manganese steels, and nonferrous materials cannot be satisfactorily cut and shaped with the oxyacetylene cutting process because of their reluctance to oxidize. In these cases, arc cutting is often used to good advantage.

The cutting of steel is a chemical action. The oxygen combines readily with the iron to form iron oxide. In cast iron, this action is hindered by the presence of carbon in graphite form. Thus cast iron cannot be cut as readily as steel. Higher temperatures are necessary, and cutting is slower. In steel, the action starts at bright-red heat, whereas in cast iron, the temperature must be nearer the melting point in order to obtain a sufficient reaction.

Because of the very high temperature, the rate of cutting is usually fairly high. However, as the process is essentially one of melting without any great action, tending to force the molten metal out of cut, some provision must be made for permitting the metal to flow readily away from the cut. This is usually done by starting at a point from which the molten metal can flow readily. This method is followed until the desired amount of metal has been melted away.

As an example, the general method is to apply the electric arc on the underside of the work, starting at a lower corner, working toward the center on the lower surface and then up the side, and repeating this action as many times as necessary. This will allow the molten metal to flow out of the cut.

A carbon electrode is generally used. Graphite electrodes are used to some extent because they permit use of higher currents. Shielded-arc-type electrodes are also effective. In starting a cut, the arc is held at the point selected for the initial cut, as, for example, a lower corner. When the metal begins to flow and run off, the arc is moved along at a rate to permit metal to flow continuously out of the cut.

The width of the cut is dependent upon the ability of the operator to follow a straight line, the size electrode used, and the thickness of material. The width of the cut is greater on thick sections than on thin.

A process which has come into use for the cutting of materials not readily cut with the oxyacetylene flame is the "oxyarc" cutting process. It cuts by directing a stream of oxygen into a pool of molten metal. The pool is made and kept molten by an arc established between the base metal and the coated tubular cutting rod, which is consumed during the cutting operation. In addition to providing the arc, the rod also provides an oxidizing flux and a means of conveying oxygen to the surface being cut.

The tubular cutting rod is made of mild steel. This is not a detriment when the rod is used for cutting materials other than mild steel because no contamination of the base metal adjacent to the cut occurs. The possibility of contamination is eliminated by the combination of extremely high heat and oxygen under pressure, which act together to oxidize the rod and coating at the point of the arc before the rod metal can fuse with the base metal. The rod coating helps to maintain arc stability by confining and directing the arc. When in use, it acts as an insulator to prevent the arcing of the rod at undesirable areas.

Quite simple equipment is required for metal cutting by this arc-oxygen process. There is, first of all, a special electrode which is not unlike an arc-welding electrode holder in appearance. This holder serves the double function of conducting current and feeding oxygen for the cutting operation. The tubular cutting rod can be inserted or removed from the holder with ease. The only other equipment required is an a-c or d-c arc welder and an oxygen source with usual regulators.

The arc-oxygen process has been used successfully to cut high-chrome and chrome-nickel stainless steels, nickel, cupronickel, Monel, nickel-clad or stainless-clad steel, bronze, copper, brass, aluminum, cast iron, and mild and low-alloy steels. It has not supplanted, however, the oxyacetylene flame for cutting mild steel and other readily oxidized materials because it is somewhat more expensive.

SELECTION AND MAINTENANCE OF EQUIPMENT

Machines. Satisfactory welding can be accomplished with either alternating or direct welding current. Each type of current, however, has a particular advantage which makes it best suited for certain types of welding and welding conditions. The chief advantage of alternating current is its elimination of arc blow, which may be encountered when welding in heavy plate or into a corner. The magnetic fields set up in the plate deflect the path of the arc. Alternating current tends to minimize this deflection and will also sometimes increase the speed of welding with larger electrodes, over $\frac{3}{16}$ in., and with the iron-powder type of electrodes.

The chief advantages of direct current are the stability of the arc and the fact that the current output of the motor-generator-type welder will remain constant in spite of variations of input current which affect a transformer-type welder. Direct current, therefore, is a more versatile welding current. Certain electrodes, such as stainless, require a very stable arc, and as yet these electrodes operate much better with direct

FIG. 1-44. Compact portable welder designed especially for maintenance work. Shows temporary work table for welding angle-iron frame.

current. Direct current, because of its stability, is also better for sheet-metal welding where danger of burn-through is present. The d-c arc can also be more readily varied to meet different welding conditions. A wider range of control over both voltage and current permits closer adjustment of the arc for difficult welding conditions, such as might be encountered in vertical or overhead welding. Because of its versatility, direct current should be available for maintenance welding.

Direct-current welders (Figs. 1-44 and 1-45) are made either as motor-generator sets or as transformer-rectifier sets. Motor-generator sets are powered by a-c or d-c motors.

Generators are also powered by small air-cooled gasoline engines (Fig. 1-46). The advantage of this type of set is that, for on-the-spot maintenance welding, it is not necessary to string electric power lines to the welding set, which may have to be used in a location some distance from a power line.

Engine-driven welders powered by gasoline engines are also available and come in larger sizes than the air-cooled engine sets. These are suitable where the size of the plant maintenance operation warrants a larger welder.

For most general maintenance welding, 180- or 250-amp output capacity is ample. Several manufacturers make machines especially for this type of welding, which are compact and readily portable. Larger amperages may be required in particular applications, and for these, heavy-duty machines should be used. Such a machine is shown in Fig. 1-47.

A new development in welding machines is one which produces both alternating and direct welding current, either of which is available at the flip of a switch (Fig. 1-48). This type of equipment is ideal for maintenance welding, since it makes any kind of welding arc available, giving complete flexibility to the maintenance welding.

Figure 1-49 shows a self-propelled truck with welder driven from power take-off.

Automatic submerged arc welding is increasingly used as a maintenance process. Both fully automatic and semiau-

FIG. 1-45. Motor-generator d-c maintenance welder.

FIG. 1-46. Small engine-driven combination welder and power supply promotes speedy on-the-spot repair.

FIG. 1-47. Mobile 300-amp d-c motor generator set for work in power plant. Welding cables are fed through wall to weld pipe several hundred feet away. Cable reel is mounted on rear of welder platform. Dual-voltage switch permits use of 220 or 440.

tomatic equipment can be used with the process. The chief use of the process in maintenance is for hard surfacing. It permits the rapid deposition of large amounts of uniformly excellent weld metal. Where the maintenance work includes hard surfacing, it is well to consider the use of this process. Semiautomatic equipment is relatively inexpensive, and can be adapted to existing welding equipment of larger amperage outputs. Fully automatic equipment is more expensive, and only a large volume of work will justify its installation.

Accessory Equipment. The varied and severe service demands made on equipment for maintenance welding require that the best in accessories be used for maximum efficiency. Most maintenance welders make racks for themselves, or other storage conveniences, which they attach directly to the welding machine for storing and transporting electrodes and accessories. These arrangements will vary to suit individual tastes and needs. The end result of all of them, however, is to have everything immediately available for use.

A part of such accessory equipment mounted on welders should be a fire extinguisher. Maintenance welding may be required in an area containing a fire hazard. At all times, the possibility of fire should be the welder's concern, and in addition to having the proper fire-extinguishing equipment at hand, he should police the area for flammable materials.

FIG. 1-48. Unit which produces both alternating and direct welding current.

Many electrode holders are available, but only a few combine all the desired features. The operator holds the electrode clamped in the holder, and the current from the welding set passes through the holder to the electrode. The clamping device should be so designed as to hold the electrode securely in position and yet permit quick, easy change of electrodes. It should be light in weight, properly balanced, and easy to handle, yet sturdy enough to withstand rough usage. It should be designed so that it will remain cool enough to be handled comfortably (Fig. 1-50).

Care should be taken in the selection of face or head shields to ensure maximum protection to the operator.   These shields are generally constructed of some kind of pressed-fiber insulating material, usually black to reduce reflection.   The shield should be light in weight and designed to ensure greatest comfort to the welder.   The glass windows in the protective shields should be of such composition as to absorb the infrared rays, the ultraviolet rays, and most visible rays emanating from the arc.   The welding lens in the head or face shield should be protected from molten-metal spatter

FIG. 1-49. Self-propelled truck with welding generator driven from power take-off.   Has cable reel and cutting torches.

and breakage by a chemically treated clear "nonspatter" glass covering the exposed side of the lens.

A good protective lens and shield should be used by the operator, and the arc should never be looked at with the naked eye at close quarters.   When a new lens is put into the shield, care should be taken that no light leaks in around the glass.   If practical, the welding room should be painted a dead black or some other color to prevent reflection.   Other workmen around an arc can be readily protected by movable or portable screens.

Special goggles are used by welders' helpers, foremen, supervisors, inspectors, and others working close to a welding arc, to protect their eyes from occasional flashes. A good goggle has adjustable elastic headbands and is light, cool, well ventilated, and comfortable.   Clear cover glasses and greenish-tinted lenses in various shades are available for this type of goggle.

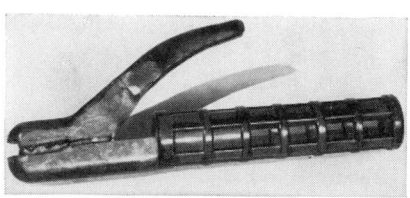

FIG. 1-50. Fully insulated electrode holder designed especially for cool operation.

During the arc-welding process, some sparks and globules of molten metal are thrown out from the arc.   For protection from possible burns, it is advisable that the operator wear an apron of leather or other protective material.   Some operators also wear spats or leggings and sleevelets of leather or other fire-resistant material. Some sort of protection should be provided for the operator's ankles and feet since a globule of molten metal can cause a painful burn before it can be extracted from the shoe.

A gauntlet type of glove, preferably of leather, is generally used by operators to protect the hands from the arc rays, spatter of molten metal, sparks, etc.   Gloves also provide protection when handling the work.

As a means of protection to other workers from the arc rays, spatter of molten metals, and sparks, the scene of each welding operation should be enclosed by a portable or permanent structure, booth, or screen.   Where the welding machine must be taken to the work, it is advisable to surround the scene of the welding operation with portable screens painted dead black to prevent reflection of the arc rays.

Other tools which will prove of value in any shop where welding is done include wire brushes for cleaning the welds, cold cuts for chipping, clamps for holding work in position for welding, wedges, and, where work is large or heavy, a crane or chain block.   A drill, air hammer, and grinder are also of value.

Table 1-8. Recommended Wire Sizes for Input Power Cable for Typical Motor-generator-type Welder
(Based on National Electrical Code)

Welder size	Input voltage	Ampere rating	3 wires in conduit or 3-conductor cable, Type R	Grounding conductor
200	220	44	8	8
	440	22	12	12
	550	18	12	14
300	200	58	6	8
	440	29	10	10
	550	23.4	10	12
400	220	74	4	6
	440	37	8	8
	550	29.6	10	10
600	220	106	2	6
	440	53	6	8
	550	42.5	8	8
900	220	160	00	4
	440	80	3	6
	550	64	4	8
Dc-dc 200	230	60	6	8
	440	31.5	10	10
	550	25	10	12
Dc-dc 300	230	90	2	6
	440	47	6	8
	550	38	8	10
Dc-dc 400	230	120	1	6
	440	63	4	8
	550	50	6	8

INSTALLATION

Good welding begins with proper installation of equipment.   Installations should be made in locations that are as clean as possible, and there should be provisions for a continuous supply of clean air for ventilation.   It is important to provide separate enclosures if the atmosphere is excessively moist or contains corrosive vapors.   If welding must be done where the ambient temperature is high, place the equipment in a different location.   Sets operated out of doors should be provided with protection against inclement weather.

When making an installation, keep the following points in mind:

1. Consult the local power company to ensure adequate supply of the right type of power.
2. Provide adequate and even support for the set.
3. See that there is adequate protection against mechanical abuse and atmospheric conditions.

Table 1-9. Input Cable Sizes for A-C/D-C Welder

Welder	Volts input	Amp input		Wire size (3 in conduit)			Wire size (3 in free air)		
		With condsr.	Without condsr.	With condsr.	Without condsr.	Ground conduct.	With condsr.	Without condsr.	Ground conduct.
300	200	84	104	2	1	1	4	4	4
	440	42	52	6	6	6	8	8	8
	550	38	42	8	6	6	10	8	8
400	220	115	143	0	00	00	3	1	1
	440	57.5	71.5	4	3	3	6	6	6
	550	46	57.2	6	4	4	8	6	6
500	220	148	180	000	0000	0000	1	0	0
	440	74	90	3	2	2	6	4	4
	550	61	72	4	3	3	6	6	6

Table 1-10. Welding Cable Sizes, Motor-generator Welder

Machine sizes, amp	Cable sizes for lengths		
	Up to 50 ft	50–100 ft	100–250 ft
200	2	1	2/0
300	0	2/0	4/0
400	2/0	3/0	4/0*
600	2/0	4/0	4/0*
900	Automatic application only		

* Recommended longest length of 4/0 cable for 400-amp welder, 150 ft; for 600-amp welder, 100 ft. For greater distances, cable size should be increased; however, this may be a question of cost—consider ease of handling vs. moving of welder closer to work.

Table 1-11. Welding Cable Sizes 11 A-C/D-C Welder—for Combined Lengths of Electrode and Ground Cable

Machine size, amp	Lengths up to 70 ft	70–150 ft	150–250 ft
300	0	2/0	4/0
400	2/0	3/0	4/0*
500	2/0	3/0	4/0*

* Recommended longest length of 4/0 cable for 400-amp welder is 150 ft and for 500-amp welder, 120 ft. For longer lengths, cable size should be increased; however, it may be a question of cost and flexibility, so that the welder should be moved closer to the work.

4. Make proper provisions for large quantities of fresh air for ventilation and cooling.
5. Ground the frame of the welding set solidly.
6. Check electrical connections to make sure they are tight.
7. The fuses for a motor-generator welder should be of the "high-lag" type and be rated two or three times the input current rating of the welder.
8. Make sure that the line and welding leads are of sufficient capacity to handle the required current and are well insulated (Tables 1-8 to 1-11).
9. Check over the set before operating to make sure that no parts are visibly loose or not in good condition.

OPERATION AND MAINTENANCE

Careful observance of the following precautions and principles will do much to ensure the maximum of satisfactory service from arc welders.

Keep Machine Clean and Cool. Because of the large volume of air pulled through welders by the fans in order to keep the machines cool, the greatest enemies of continuous, efficient performance are air-borne dust and abrasive materials. Where machines are subjected to ordinary dust, they should be blown out at least once a week with dry, clean compressed air at a pressure not over 30 psi. Higher pressures may damage windings.

In foundries or machine shops, where cast-iron or steel dust is present, substitute vacuum cleaning for compressed air. Compressed air under high pressure tends to drive the abrasive dust into the windings. If vacuum-cleaning equipment is not available, compressed air may be used at low pressure.

Abrasive material in the atmosphere grooves and pits the commutator and wears out brushes.

Greasy dirt or lint-laden dust quickly clogs air passages between coils and causes them to overheat. Since resistance of the coils is raised and the conductivity lowered by heat, it reduces the efficiency and can result in burned-out coils if the machine is not protected against overload. Overheating makes the insulation between coils dry and brittle.

Do not block the air intake or exhaust vents, because doing so will interrupt the proper flow of air through the machine.

Keep the covers on the welder. Removing them destroys the proper path of ventilation.

Do Not Abuse It. *Never Leave the Electrode Grounded to the Work.* This condition creates a "dead" short circuit. The machine is forced to generate much higher currents than it was designed for, which can result in a burned out machine.

Do Not Work the Machine over Its Rated Capacity. A 200-amp machine will not do the work of a 400-amp machine. Operating above capacity causes overheating, so that the insulation may be destroyed or the solder in the commutator connections melted.

Use extreme care in operating a machine on a steady load other than arc welding, such as thawing water pipes, supplying current for lighting, running motors, charging batteries, or operating heating equipment. For example, a d-c machine, NEMA-rated 300 amp at 40 volts or 12 kw should not be used for any continuous load greater than 9.6 kw, and not more than 240 amp. This precaution applies to machines with a duty cycle of at least 60 per cent. Machines with lower load-factor ratings must be operated at still lower percentages of the rated load.

Do Not Handle Roughly. A welder is a precisely aligned and balanced machine. Mechanical abuse, rough handling, or severe shock may disturb the alignment and balance of the machine, resulting in serious trouble. Misalignment can cause bearing failure, bracket failure, unbalanced air gap, or unbalance in the armature.

Never pry on the ventilating fan or commutator to try to move the armature. To do so will damage the fan or commutator. If the armature is jammed, inspect the unit for the cause of the trouble. Check for dirt or foreign particles between the armature and frames. Inspect the banding wire on the armature. Look for a frozen bearing.

Do not neglect the engine if the welder is an engine-driven unit. It deteriorates rapidly if not properly cared for. Follow the engine manufacturer's recommendations. Change oil regularly. Keep air filters and oil strainers clean.

Do not allow grease and oil from the engine to leak back into the generator. Grease quickly accumulates dirt and dust, clogging the air passages between coils.

Maintain It Regularly. *Bearings.* Many bearing failures may be traced directly to overgreasing. Welders equipped with ball bearings have sufficient grease to last one year under the most severe service. An ounce of grease each year is sufficient for each bearing. A pad of grease, approximately 1 cu in. in volume, weighs close to 1 oz.

Dirt is responsible for more bearing failures than any other cause. This dirt may get into the grease cup when it is removed to refill, or it may get into the grease in its original container. Before the grease cup or pipe plug is removed, it is important to wipe it absolutely clean. A piece of dirt no larger than the period at the end of this sentence may cause a bearing to fail in a short time. Even small particles of grit that float around in factory atmosphere are dangerous.

If too little grease is applied, bearings fail.

Too light grease will run out. Grease containing solid materials may ruin antifriction bearings; rancid grease will not lubricate.

Dirty grease or dirty fittings or pipes cause bearing failures.

Bearings do not need inspection. They are sealed against dirt, and it is inadvisable to open them unless necessary.

If it is necessary to pull bearings, it should be done with a special puller designed to act against the inner race. These pullers can be bought.

Never clean new bearings before installing. Handle them with care. Put them in place by driving against the inner race. Make sure that they fit squarely against the shoulders.

Brackets or End Bolts. If it becomes necessary to remove a bracket, to replace a bearing, or to disassemble the machine, do so by removing the bolts and tapping lightly and evenly with a babbitt hammer all around the outside diameter of the bracket ring. Do not drive off with a heavy steel hammer.

The bearing housing may become worn oversize, caused by the pounding of the bearing when the armature is out of balance. Bracket bearing housings may be checked for size by trying a new bearing for fit. The bearing should slide into the housing with a light drive fit. Replace the bracket if the housing is oversize.

Brushes and Brush Holders. Set brush holders approximately $\frac{1}{16}$ to $\frac{1}{8}$ in. above the surface of the commutator. If brush holders have been removed, be certain that they are set squarely in the rocker slot when replaced. Do not force the brush holder into the slot by driving on the insulation. Check to ensure that the brush-holder insulation is squarely set.

Tighten brush holders firmly. When properly set, they are parallel to the mica segments between commutator bars.

Use the grade of brushes recommended by the manufacturer of the welding set. Brushes may be too hard or too soft and cause damage to the commutator. Brushes will be damaged by excessive clearance in the brush holder or uneven brush spring pressure. High commutator bars, high mica segments, excessive brush spring pressure, and abrasive dust also will wear out brushes rapidly.

Inspect brushes and holders regularly. A brush may wear down and lose spring tension. It will then start to arc, with damage to the commutator and other brushes.

Keep the brush contact surface of the holder clean and free from pit marks. Brushes must be able to move freely in the holder. Replace them when the pigtails are within $\frac{1}{8}$ in. of the commutator or when the limit of spring travel is reached.

New brushes must be sanded in to conform to the shape of the commutator. This may be done by stoning the commutator with a stone or by using fine sandpaper (not emery cloth or paper). Place the sandpaper under the brush, and move it back and forth while holding the brush down in the normal position under slight pressure with the fingers.

See that brush holders and springs seat squarely and firmly against the brushes and that the pigtails are fastened securely.

Commutators. Commutators normally need little care. They will build up a surface film of brown copper oxide, which is highly conductive, hard, and smooth. This surface helps to protect the commutator. Do not try to keep a commutator bright and shiny by constant stoning. The brown copper oxide film prevents the build-up of a black abrasive oxide film that has high resistance and causes excessive brush and commutator wear.

Wipe clean occasionally with a rag or canvas to remove grease discoloration from fumes or other unnatural film.

If brushes are chattering because of high bars, high mica, or grooves, stone by hand or remove and turn in a lathe if necessary.

Most commutator trouble starts because the wrong grade of brushes is used. Brushes that contain too much abrasive material or have too high a copper content usually scratch the commutator and prevent the desired surface film from building up. A brush that is too soft may smudge the surface with the same result as far as surface film is concerned. In general, brushes that have a low voltage drop will give poor commutation. Conversely, a brush with high voltage drop commutates better but may cause overheating of the commutator surface.

If the commutator becomes burned, it may be dressed down by pressing a commutator stone against the surface with the brushes raised. If the surface is badly pitted or out of round, the armature must be removed from the machine and the commutator turned in a lathe. It is good practice for the commutator to run within a radial tolerance of 0.003 in.

The mica separating the bars of the commutator is undercut to a depth of $\frac{1}{32}$ to $\frac{1}{16}$ in. Mica exposed at the commutator surface causes brush and commutator wear and poor commutation. If the mica is even with the surface, undercut it.

When the commutator is operating properly, there is very little visible sparking. The brush surface is shiny and smooth with no evidence of scratches.

Generator Frame. The generator frame and coils need no attention other than inspection to ensure tight connections and cleanliness. Blow out dust and dirt with compressed air. Grease may be cleaned off with naphtha. Keep air gaps between armature and pole pieces clean and even.

Armature. The armature must be kept clean to ensure proper balance. Unbalance in the set will pound out the bearings and wear the bearing housing oversize. Blow out the armature regularly with clean, dry compressed air. Clean out the inside of the armature thoroughly by attaching a long pipe to the compressed air line and reaching into the armature coils.

Motor Stator. Keep the stator clean and free from grease. When reconnecting it for use on another voltage, solder all connections. If the set is to be used frequently on different voltages, time may be saved by placing lugs on the ends of all stator leads. This eliminates the necessity for loosening and resoldering to make connections, since the lugs may be safely joined with a screw, nut, and lock washer.

Exciter Generator. If the machine has a separate exciter generator, its armature, coils, brushes, and brush holders will need the same general care recommended for the welder set.

Keep the covers over the exciter armature, since the commutator can be damaged easily.

Controls. Inspect every time the welder is used to ensure that the ground and electrode cables are connected tightly to the output terminals. Loose connections cause arcing that destroys the insulation around the terminals and burns them.

Do not bump or hit the control handles. It damages the controls, resulting in poor electrical contacts. If the handles are tight or jammed, inspect for the cause.

Check the contact fingers of the magnetic starting switch regularly. Keep the fingers free from deep pits or other defects that will interfere with a smooth, sliding contact. Copper fingers may be filed lightly. All fingers should make contact simultaneously.

Keep the switch clean and free from dust. Blow out the entire control box with compressed air.

Connections of the leads from the motor stator to the switch must be tight. Keep

Table 1-12. Arc-welding Trouble-shooting Chart

Trouble	Cause	Remedy
Welder will not start	Power circuit dead	Check voltage
	Broken power lead	Repair
(Starter not operating)	Wrong supply voltage	Check name plate against supply
	Open power switches	Close
	Blown fuses	Replace
	Overload relay tripped	Let set cool. Remove cause of overloading
	Open circuit to starter button	Repair
	Defective operating coil	Replace
	Mechanical obstruction in contactor	Remove
Welder will not start	Wrong motor connections	Check connection diagram
(Starter operating)	Wrong supply voltage	Check name plate against supply
	Rotor stuck	Try turning by hand
	Power circuit single-phased	Replace fuse; repair open line
	Starter single-phased	Check contact of starter tips
	Poor motor connection	Tighten
	Open circuit in windings	Repair
Starter operates and blows fuse	Fuse too small	Should be two to three times rated motor current
	Short circuit in motor connections	Check starter and motor leads for insulation from ground and from each other
Welder starts but will not deliver welding current	Wrong direction of rotation	Check connection diagram
	Brushes worn or missing	Check that all brushes bear on commutator with sufficient tension
	Brush connections loose	Tighten
	Open field circuit	Check connection to rheostat, resistor, and auxiliary brush studs
	Series field and armature circuit open	Check with test lamp or bell ringer
	Wrong driving speed	Check name plate against speed of motor or belt drive
	Dirt, grounding field coils	Clean and reinsulate
	Welding terminal shorted	Electrode holder or cable grounded
Welder generating but current falls off when welding	Electrode or ground connection loose	Clean and tighten all connections
	Poor ground	Check ground-return circuit
	Brushes worn off	Replace with recommended grade. Sand to fit. Blow out carbon dust
	Weak brush spring pressure	Replace or readjust brush springs
	Brush not properly fitted	Sand brushes to fit
	Brushes in backward	Reverse
	Wrong brushes used	Renewal part recommendations
	Brush pigtails damaged	Replace brushes
	Rough or dirty commutator	Turn down or clean commutator
	Motor connection single-phased	Check all connections
Welder runs but soon stops	Wrong relay heaters	Renewal part recommendations
	Welder overloaded	Considerable overload can be carried only for a short time
	Duty cycle too high	Do not operate continually at overload currents
	Leads too long or too narrow in cross section	Should be large enough to carry welding current without excessive voltage drop

Table 1-12. Arc-welding Trouble-shooting Chart (*Continued*)

Trouble	Cause	Remedy
	Power circuit single-phased	Check for one dead fuse or line
	Ambient temperature too high	Operate at reduced loads where temperature exceeds 100°F
	Ventilation blocked	Check air inlet and exhaust openings
Welding arc is loud and spatters excessively	Current setting too high	Check setting and output with ammeter
	Polarity wrong	Check polarity; try reversing or an electrode of opposite polarity
Welding arc sluggish	Current too low	Check output and current recommended for electrode being used
	Poor connections	Check all electrode-holder, cable, and ground-cable connections Scrap iron is poor ground return
	Cable too long or too small	Check cable voltage drop and change cable
Touching set gives shock	Frame not grounded	Ground solidly
Generator control fails to vary current	Any part of field circuit may be short-circuited or open-circuited	Find faulty contact and repair

the lugs in a vertical position. The line voltage is high enough to jump between the lugs on the stator leads if they are allowed to become loose and cocked to one side or the other.

Keep the cover on the control box at all times.

CONDENSERS

Condensers may be placed in an a-c welder to raise the power factor if required. When condensers fail, it is not often apparent from the appearance of the condenser. Consequently, if it is desired to check to see if they are operating correctly, the following should be done: At rated input voltage and with the welder drawing the rated output load current, the input current reading should correspond to the name-plate amperes. If the reading is 10 to 20 per cent more, at least one condenser has failed.

Caution: Never touch the condenser terminals without first disconnecting the welder from the input power source, then discharge the condenser by touching the two terminals with an *insulated* screwdriver.

DELAY RELAYS

The delay relay contacts may be cleaned by passing a cloth soaked in naphtha between them. Do not force the contact arms or use any abrasives to clean the points. Do not file the silver contacts. The pilot relay is enclosed in a dustproof box and should need no attention. Relays are usually adjusted at the factory and should not be tampered with unless faulty operation is obvious.

Table 1-12, a trouble-shooting chart, may prove to be a great timesaver.

BIBLIOGRAPHY

1. "Procedure Handbook of Arc Welding Design and Practice," 11th ed., The Lincoln Electric Company, Cleveland, 1957.
2. "New Lessons in Arc Welding," The Lincoln Electric Company, Cleveland, 1957.
3. Jefferson, T. B., and Gorham Woods: "Metals and How to Weld Them," The James F. Lincoln Arc Welding Foundation, Cleveland, 1962.
4. Rossi, Boniface E.: "Welding Engineering," McGraw-Hill Book Company, New York, 1954.

5. Austin, John Benjamin: "Electric Arc Welding," American Technical Society, Chicago, 1952.
6. Morris, Joe Lawrence: "Welding Principles for Engineers," Prentice-Hall, Inc., Englewood Cliffs, N.J., 1951.
7. "Welding Handbook," American Welding Society, New York, 1964.
8. American Welding Society Publications, 1354 East 47th St., New York, N.Y. 10017:

  Safe Practices for Welding and Cutting Containers That Have Held Combustibles, A6.0-65.
  Recommended Safe Practices for Inert-gas Metal-arc Welding, A6.1-58.
  Safety in Electric and Gas Welding and Cutting Operations—American Standard, Z49.1-58.
  Code of Minimum Requirements for Instruction of Welding Operators: Part A— Arc Welding of Steel, B2.1-45.
  A Test Program on Welding Iron Castings, D11.1-65.
  Recommended Practices for Repair Welding of Cast-iron Pipe, Valves, and Fittings, D10.2-54.

9. Henry, O. H., G. E. Claussen, and G. E. Linnert, "Welding Metallurgy," American Welding Society, New York, 1949.
10. Sosnin, H. A.: "Arc Welding Instructions for the Beginner," The James F. Lincoln Arc Welding Foundation, Cleveland.

Chapter 2

GAS WELDING IN MAINTENANCE

By Engineers of
Union Carbide Corporation
Linde Division
New York, N.Y.

AIR-ACETYLENE SOLDERING, HEATING, AND BRAZING

An air-acetylene appliance produces a flame with a temperature of approximately 4000°F by mixing acetylene with atmospheric air in much the same way that air is mixed with city gas in a kitchen range. The correct mixture produces a pale blue flame with a bright, sharp inner cone that is hot enough for light silver soldering (brazing), for most soft soldering, and for hundreds of heating jobs. Air-acetylene appliances are used throughout industry as companion equipment to the oxyacetylene blowpipe for applications requiring clean, ready-to-use heat but not the extremely high temperatures of the oxyacetylene flame.

An air-acetylene outfit consists of torch handle, a torch stem or tip, a pressure-reducing regulator, a cylinder of acetylene, and a hose for connecting the torch to the regulator and tank. Interchangeable stems or tips that give various sizes and types of flames are available (see Fig. 2-1). The acetylene cylinders themselves come in all sizes, including small portable units (see Fig. 2-2).

Soldering. The air-acetylene torch is extensively used for all kinds of soldering with both soft and silver (hard) solder. Although soft soldering is more widely used, silver soldering (also referred to as brazing) is sometimes used for soldering sweat-type fittings in addition to the more precise soldering associated with jewelry and instrument manufacturing. With an air-acetylene torch, the silver solder used must have a melting point lower than 1500°F. If sweat-type fittings being silver soldered are larger than $1\frac{1}{2}$ in. in diameter, or if a great number of joints are being made, an oxyacetylene torch is recommended, since its greater flame temperature speeds the work. Silver-soldering commercial metals over $\frac{1}{32}$ in. thick is also best done with an oxyacetylene torch. In contrast to silver soldering, practically all soft soldering can be done with an air-acetylene torch.

Caution: Silver soldering requires a special rod and a special flux, usually in paste form. Care should be taken to follow the manufacturer's directions. The fumes from some silver solders are toxic; therefore, special ventilating precautions are necessary.

When using air-acetylene appliances, you have a choice of two soldering methods:

1. The open (direct) flame method. The flame heats the workpiece, and the workpiece melts the solder in conjunction with the flame. The advantages of the open (direct) flame method include

   a. Speed (no copper intermediary to be heated).

   b. Greater diversity in the uses to which the flame can be put.

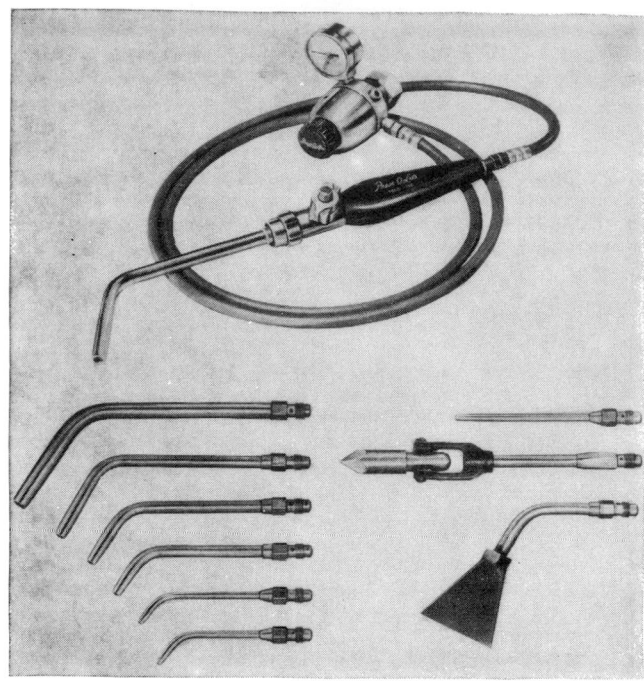

Fig. 2-1. A typical air-acetylene outfit consisting of a regulator, torch handle, and attached torch stem with interconnecting hose.   Also shown are some of the typical interchangeable torch stems available.   Notice the special-purpose stems—the hatchet-shaped paint-burner stem and the soldering-iron stem.

    c. Greater efficiency in the use of fuel (the gas goes further because it is applied directly to the workpiece).

    d. More heat because of direct application of the flame.

I. ATTACH REGULATOR TO TANK. TIGHTEN NUT WITH WRENCH.

2. ATTACH HOSE ASSEMBLY TO REGULATOR AND HANDLE. TIGHTEN NUTS WITH WRENCH.

3. ATTACH STEM TO HANDLE. TIGHTEN THE CONNECTION NUT WITH YOUR FINGERS.

Fig. 2-2. Connecting a typical air-acetylene outfit. The standard type of portable outfit is shown. Smaller tanks also are available.

2. The enclosed (indirect) flame method. The flame is applied to the soldering copper.   The copper in turn heats the workpiece.   The workpiece, in conjunction with the soldering copper, melts the solder where it is needed.   The advantages of the enclosed (indirect) flame method include:

    a. Heat is better controlled.

    b. Less experience is needed on the operator's part.

    c. More delicate work is possible, especially where damage to the adjacent materials might result from the use of an open flame.

    See Table 2-1 for commonly used soft solders and Table 2-2 for soldering fluxes.

    Sheet-metal Working.   Sheet-metal soldering can be done with either the enclosed (indirect) flame method or the open (direct) flame method depending on the choice of the operator.   Many types of joints can be made in sheet metal.   Joints described on the following pages are most widely used.

Table 2-1. Commonly Used Soft Solders

Composition, per cent	Melting point, °F	Flowing point, °F	Gives best results when used for
Tin, 15–35; lead, 85–65	415–360	560–475	Filling dents in automobile bodies. Apply by wiping
Tin, 38–40; lead, 62–60	360	460	Automobile radiator cores, roofing seams, and wiped joints in lead pipe
Tin, 50; lead, 50	360	420	General purposes
Tin, 50; lead, 32; cadmium, 18	293	293	Pewter and similar alloys that are readily fusible. Not good for lap joints
Tin, 95; antimony, 5	450	464	Electrical work and copper tubing joints. Do not use on zinc or galvanized iron
Tin, 5; lead, 95	540	600	Where the higher melting point solder is required or desirable

Table 2-2. Soldering Fluxes

Metal	Flux to Use*
Aluminum	Usually none required. Sometimes paraffin helps after surfaces have been tinned
Block tin	Rosin or zinc chloride
Brass	Zinc chloride, rosin, or sal ammoniac
Cast iron	Zinc chloride or sal ammoniac. Also zinc chloride added to melted tallow and heated until it foams and turns reddish brown
Copper	Zinc chloride, rosin, or sal ammoniac
Gun metal	Zinc chloride, rosin, or sal ammoniac
Iron (black)	Sal ammoniac
Iron (galvanized)	Muriatic acid†
Iron (tin-coated)	Zinc chloride or rosin
Inconel	Strong zinc chloride
Lead	Tallow, rosin, or zinc chloride
Monel	Zinc chloride
Nickel	Zinc chloride
Pewter	Turpentine
Stainless steel	Zinc chloride
Steel (plain)	Sal ammoniac
Steel (galvanized)	Muriatic acid
Steel (tin-coated)	Zinc chloride or rosin
Zinc	Muriatic acid

* Nearly all of these fluxes are available commercially in paste form. Pastes are usually preferred because they give excellent results on most jobs and are easy to use.
† Muriatic acid is a mild form of hydrochloric acid.

1. The lap joint (see Fig. 2-3):
   a. Thoroughly clean the edges to be joined.
   b. Flux the edges by dipping them in a bath of hydrochloric (muriatic) acid, or using a brush, paint them with it.
   c. If you are using a soldering iron, tin the iron first and then tin the edges. If you are using a soldering torch, tin the edges. The edges should be tinned along their entire length and then placed so that the tinned edges overlap. Use C clamps to hold them together if you have them.
   d. Next, pressing down on the soldering iron, run it up and down over the seam until a fillet of solder is visible. If you are using a soldering torch, move it back

and forth with the flame touching the work until the fillet appears. In both cases, where no fillet appears, add more solder.

    e. When making a long seam with a plain lap joint, it is best to "tack" the seam first. Tacking means applying drops or spots of solder at intervals along a seam to hold it in place. Clean, flux, and tin the entire job. Heat the seam, and

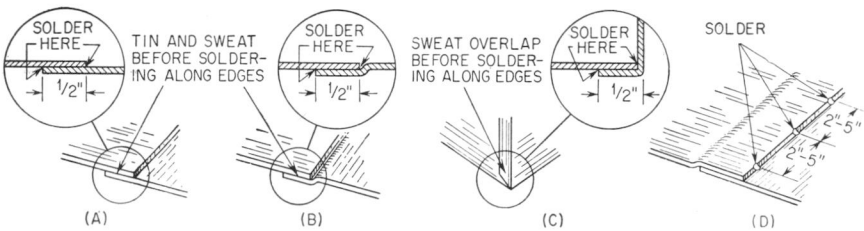

Fig. 2-3. Three variations of the lap joint (*A*, *B*, and *C*); at the right, (*D*), how to tack a long seam by applying spots of solder at intervals.

apply solder spot by spot. Then do the regular soldering job on the whole seam. If the "tacks" tend to melt or the seams to pull apart when you near them with the torch, proceed as follows:

    (1) Press the pieces of metal together at the "trouble spot" with a stick.

    (2) Reheat the "tacks" and the solder that has been previously applied as timing. Keep pressing the heated area together with the stick until the solder has cooled and formed a bond. Proceed with the soldering job.

    f. When the joint is finished, wipe off all excess solder with a stiff bristle brush and wash off the excess flux with hot water.

2. Lock joint (see Fig. 2-4):

    a. Thoroughly clean surfaces that will form the joint.

    b. Form the lock joint between the two sheets.

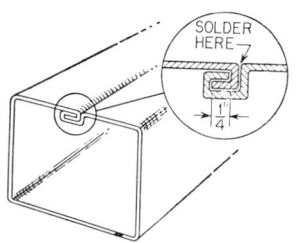

Fig. 2-4. A lock joint where mechanical strength is provided by the joint rather than the solder bond.

    c. Pound the joint tight with a composition mallet, or use a block of wood between the sheets and a steel hammer. Try to get the joint as flat and tight as possible.

    d. Apply acid flux along the seam, and heat the seam.

    e. Apply just enough solder to seal the seam. (You have already made the seam mechanically strong by hammering and forming the lock joint.)

    f. If the seam is fairly long, you can run the flame a few inches ahead of the solder instead of heating and soldering a section at a time.

    g. Remove all excess solder with a stiff bristle brush, and wash off excess flux with hot water.

3. Flange joint:

    a. A flange joint is generally used in conjunction with rivets or spot welds. The solder is used to make the seam tight to air, gas, or water.

    b. Before the joint is formed, the area to which the solder will be applied must be thoroughly cleaned and must remain clean until the seam is finished.

    c. A tinning coat of solder can be applied to the seam before it is riveted or spot welded.

    d. Either use acid core solder, or flux the joint with hydrochloric (muriatic) acid.

    e. Heat the joint with either a torch or soldering iron. Capillary attraction will draw the solder into the seam. Fill the joint with the desired amount of solder.

    f. Remove all excess solder with a stiff bristle brush; wash off excess flux with hot water.

    Automobile-body Soldering. Automobile-body soldering is done to fill in dents that cannot be hammered out completely, rough spots, and welded seams. Either soldering method can be used, direct (open) flame or indirect (closed) flame. Where, the deposits of solder to be made are considerable or in places where an open flame would not damage chrome finishes or glass, we recommend the open (direct) flame method because of its speed and the rapidity with which the solder can be deposited. For the places adjacent to glass or chrome finishes, use the enclosed (indirect) flame method. When you have decided which method to use, proceed as follows:

1. Grind away the paint from the dented area, and polish with steel wool or emery cloth.
2. Flux thoroughly, and after heating, apply enough solder to tin the dent.
3. Fill in the dent by adding solder from a bar and smoothing with a maple paddle. Take care not to melt the solder until it runs. Melt it just enough to make it pasty, then smooth with the paddle.
4. When the dent is filled in, heat the solder slightly and smooth it again before letting it cool.
5. Finish the job with rasps, body files, and emery cloth. Clean, prime, and paint.

Electrical Connections. For soldering electrical connections, Fig. 2-5, the enclosed (indirect) flame method is preferred. Prepare the electrical connections the way you usually do, and proceed as follows:

1. Thoroughly clean the connections.
2. Apply a noncorrosive flux paste.
3. Tin the soldering iron with a thin coat of solder.
4. Tin the wires, and melt enough solder on to them to be sure you have a good electrical connection.

(A) TWIST WIRE ENDS AND FLUX

(B) SOLDER THE SPLICE

(C) FLOW SOLDER INTO ALL SPACES

FIG. 2-5. Soldering electrical connections.

Note: Where very large connections are to be made, an open-flame stem can be used.

Installing Sweat-type Fittings. The following is the most efficient method for making sweat-type joints as recommended by two of the leading copper-tube manufacturers. The air-acetylene torch with a direct (open) flame is used by literally thousands of plumbers and is universally recognized as the best means of making these joints. The torch saves time and money, and a relatively inexperienced workman can do a good job with very little training and practice.

There are two basic types of sweat-type fitting: the "plain type" and "cast type." With the plain type the solder is fed at the point where the fitting and the tube join. With the cast type the solder is fed in through precast holes in the fitting itself. The instructions below will work equally well with both types (see Figs. 2-6 and 2-7).

1. Cut the tube to the length required with a hack saw (32 teeth to the inch), or a disk cutter. Make certain that the tube ends are cut square. Special vises which hold the tube securely and guide the saw blade are furnished by a number of manufacturers.
2. Ream the tube, and remove burrs on the outside. Use a sizing tool if necessary to correct any possible distortion of the tube from handling. The point of a sizing tool is inserted in the end of the tube and is hammered until the tube is again round.
3. Clean the outside surface of the tube and the inside surface of the fitting until the metal is bright. All traces of discoloration must be removed. This must be done even though the tube may appear to be perfectly clean, and it is particularly important when soldering larger size joints. No. 00 steel wool is very satisfactory for cleaning tubes and fittings. Do not use files or rough sandpaper, etc., as they score the surface and may result in a poor joint.
4. Apply a thin, uniform, and complete coating of a reliable brand of soldering flux or paste to the cleaned portion of both tube and fitting. Do not apply the flux too

thickly, as excess flux may form bubbles when heated and prevent the solder from creeping into the joint. After the tube has been inserted into the fitting as far as it will go, revolve the fitting once or twice to spread the flux evenly.

5. Apply the flame evenly all around the circumference of the fitting, and as it becomes heated, move the flame back and forth to prevent overheating. Occasionally test the heat by touching the fitting with solder where the tube and fitting join. Do not let the flame touch the solder while testing the temperature of the joint.

It is important not to overheat the joint. If the connection is heated too much, the flux may be burned out from inside the joint and the solder will not spread properly. An overheated joint causes the solder to seep through the joint and run away.

During the heating operation, adjacent wood surfaces should be protected from the heat by means of sheet asbestos. Because of its narrow, concentrated flame, the air-acetylene torch can be used very close to wood surfaces without scorching them.

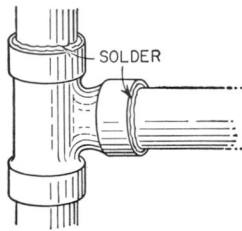

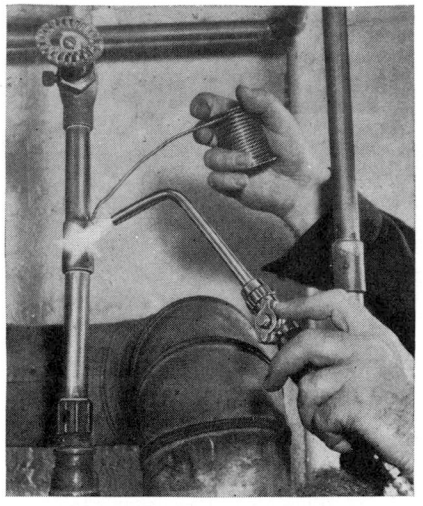

Fig. 2-6. Where to solder plain-type sweat fittings.

Fig. 2-7. Soldering 1-in. copper tubing and fitting with precast holes.

6. Remove the flame, and apply solder to the edge of the fitting where it comes in contact with the tube as soon as the fitting has reached the correct temperature to melt the solder. Be sure that enough solder is used.

Enough solder to make an efficient joint will be automatically sucked in by capillary attraction. When a line of solder shows completely around the fitting, that is, a fillet of solder appears in the chamfer at the end of the fitting, the joint has all the solder it will take. Wipe off any excess solder or flux.

7. Slightly reheat the connection in order to help the solder permeate the metal. Remove the flame, and continue to feed solder to make certain the joint is filled.

8. Permit the connection to cool for a fraction of a minute. A rag or wad of waste saturated with water will hasten the cooling. Remove all surplus solder from around the edges with a brush. This operation will show whether or not the solder has filled the joint.

9. When disconnecting a soldered tube from a fitting on which other soldered connections are to be left intact, the application of wet cloths to the parts which are not to be disconnected will prevent melting of the solder at such connections.

10. More than ordinary care should be exercised in soldering fittings 2½ in. in diameter and larger. It is essential that the heat should be uniformly distributed around the entire circumference of the fitting and not concentrated in one spot.

When making large-diameter joints, a tip producing a large flame should be used. The flame should be directed on the fitting to avoid any unnecessary annealing of the tube.

For assembling lines 3 in. in diameter or over, it may be advisable to use two or three torches. Solder should then be applied simultaneously at two or more points.

11. In applying solder to a T, feed solder from both ends of the fitting.

12. Solder when confined between two surfaces will run up hill (by capillary attraction), and joints can be made in almost any position.

13. In sweating male and female adaptors, care should be taken to allow more time for the solder to set, as these heavier fittings do not cool so quickly.

Paint Burning. An air-acetylene torch with a paint-burning stem is a quick, easy, and economical means for removing old, cracked, and checked paint from a surface that can stand a moderate amount of heat. The number of coats of paint is not important; it just takes a little more time to remove them. Paint can be removed from wood, canvas, brick, stone, or metal.

Caution: Avoid inhaling any dust or fumes that may be given off in the paint-burning operation. Such dust and fumes may be toxic, particularly if the paint being removed contains lead or cadmium compounds.

There are two methods of removing paint. They are listed below as Method A and Method B. We suggest you try both methods. You can then use the one that suits your particular type of work. Once the old paint is removed and rough spots smoothed, the surface is ready for a new coat of paint.

Method A (Fig. 2-8):

1. Hold the paint burner in your left hand. Hold the putty knife (with a stiff blade about 3 in. wide) in your right hand.

2. Move the torch backward and forward 1 in. from the painted surface about 6 in. at a stroke. Follow the movements of the torch with a steady forward movement of the putty knife, keeping the putty knife hot with the flame.

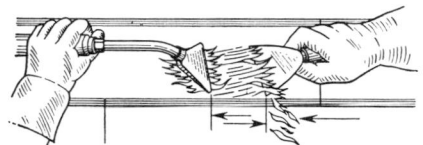   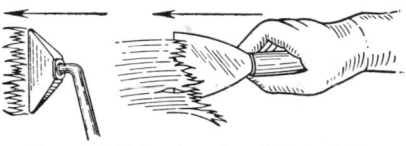

FIG. 2-8. Paint burning (Method A).   FIG. 2-9. Paint burning (Method B).

Note: You will find it advisable to wear asbestos or other heavy flame-resistant gloves when burning paint. The putty knife gets very hot after a while, so you should protect your right hand. Cloth (cotton) gloves are not satisfactory.

3. Moving the torch back and forth changes the paint to a plastic state and keeps the putty knife blade hot. A hot blade reduces the tendency of the paint to stick to it.

Method B (Fig. 2-9).

1. Move the torch more or less steadily from right to left over the painted surface. Bring the paint to a bubbly plastic state. Scrape off the paint as soon as it bubbles. Do not let the flame touch the blade of the putty knife.

2. The putty knife should have a back-and-forth motion which will intermittently expose the scraped area to the flame. This method is recommended for particularly heavy or stubborn paint.

Miscellaneous Air-acetylene Applications. There are many repair and maintenance jobs aside from soldering and brazing that can be done efficiently with an air-acetylene torch. A few of these applications are given below.

Loosening Nuts and Bolts. Frequently you come across a bolt that resists all attempts to loosen it with a wrench. Heat the nut for several minutes and let it cool; then try the wrench again. Generally, you will now find the nut ready to turn.

Freeing Frozen Shafts. A frozen shaft of small diameter can be freed by heating the collar that holds it. Heat the collar, not the shaft. You will find that you can separate the parts quite quickly no matter how tightly they are frozen together.

Lead Working. The air-acetylene torch can be used to build up lead battery terminals. Any of the standard stems can be used depending on the amount of work to be done and the speed with which you want to do it.

It is recommended that you use a form, where possible, to keep the lead in the shape of a battery terminal and to prevent it from running on the battery. Put the form over the old terminal and keep adding melted lead until the desired height and shape of the terminal are attained.

The air-acetylene torch can be used to repair lead-lined vats, wipe joints in lead pipe and lead-covered cable, and solder battery-cable lugs.

Caution: When working with lead in a confined space, be very sure of your ventilation and, if possible, use a suitable air-line mask.

Anchoring Bolts in Concrete or Stone. Firmly anchoring a large bolt in concrete or stone can be solved as follows:

1. Drill a hole in the concrete or stone with a star or other type drill. It is best to dish or widen the bottom of the hole slightly to increase the stability of the bolt after the solder sets. Make certain all free moisture or water is removed from the cavity.
2. Heat the solder (bar solder is best) in a ladle with an air-acetylene torch until the solder is molten.
3. Place the bolt in the hole thread-end up, and pour molten solder around it until the solder is level with the floor.
4. This type of mounting will give years of satisfactory service; if it should become loose, just reheat the solder with the torch and it will be as tight as ever.

Cutting Asphalt Tile. The air-acetylene torch has been used with good success by asphalt tile contractors for heating tiles that have to be bent, formed, or cut. After a few seconds of heating, the tile can be shaped or cut with great ease.

Cutting Safety Glass. Using an air-acetylene torch with a medium-size stem, the following procedure can be used when cutting safety glass.

1. Score both sides of the glass with a glass cutter and break the glass.
2. Soften the plastic filler by running the torch back and forth along the line of the cut.
3. Wobble the glass from side to side several times. Then hold the glass to one side while you cut the heat-softened plastic filler with a razor blade.

Precautions and Safe Practices

1. Do not let acetylene escape near any possible source of ignition. Accumulations of acetylene in certain proportions may explode if ignited.
2. *Never* store acetylene tanks in a closed or confined space, such as a closet.
3. *Never* solder a container that contains or has contained flammable liquids or vapors (including gasoline, benzene, solvents, and other similar or dissimilar materials) unless the container has been thoroughly purged of all traces of flammable material and vapors. Be sure that any container you work on is vented. We urge that before you do work of this kind, you get Booklet A-6.0.40 from the American Welding Society, 345 E. 47th Street, New York, N.Y. 10017.
4. *Never* use a tank with a leaking valve.
5. *Do not* make any repairs to an acetylene tank, except to tighten the packing-gland nut on the valve.
6. *Do not* abuse or drop tanks or handle them roughly.
7. *Never* use a tank as a roller. Never use a wrench or pliers on the tank valve. Always use a valve key.
8. *Never* allow full tank pressure to enter a stopped hose. Always use a **regulator** when there is a needle valve on the torch handle.

9. Examine your hose for leaks frequently.   Dipping it in a bucket of clean water, with the pressure in the hose, is the quickest and easiest way.
10. *Do not* use hose that is worn or any equipment that is in need of repair.

OXYACETYLENE WELDING, CUTTING, GOUGING, AND HARD FACING

Metal production, fabrication, and repair, as they are known today, would be impossible without the oxyacetylene process and its flame of approximately 6000°F. The oxyacetylene process is built on two principles: (1) Acetylene burned with an equal amount of oxygen produces an intensely hot flame that will melt and fuse most metals, and (2) a jet of oxygen striking a piece of ferrous metal that has been heated to its kindling temperature will rapidly burn the metal away.

Welding and Brazing.   Welding with an oxyacetylene blowpipe is simple.   You put two pieces of metal together, then melt the edges with an oxyacetylene flame. The molten metal flows together and forms a single, solid piece of metal.   Welding rod similar to the base metal is usually added to strengthen the joint.   This is known as *fusion welding*.   If you use a steel rod, the process is sometimes called *steel welding*.

Braze welding is another method.   In braze welding, the two pieces being joined are heated to a dull red.   They are not melted.   A flux is added to clean the metal and protect it from the air.   When the pieces are dull red, molten-bronze welding rod is added to form a strong bond.   This bronze weld is generally as strong as the base metal.

Building up worn parts with bronze or steel welding rod, heating and forming of metals, gouging, hard facing, and soldering are other jobs done by the oxyacetylene flame.

Cutting.   Oxygen cutting is similar to the eating away of steel by ordinary rusting, only it is very much faster.   In rusting, the oxygen—in the air or in water—affects the metal slowly.   Directing a jet of pure oxygen at metal heated almost to the melting point actually speeds up chemical reaction of rusting to such an extent that the metal ignites and burns away.   The iron oxide melts and runs off as molten slag to expose more iron to the action of the oxygen jet.   This makes it possible to cut iron and steel leaving a smooth, narrow cut.   An oxyacetylene outfit is shown in Fig. 2-10.

Setting up an Outfit.   Suggestions and recommendations for safe handling of oxyacetylene equipment have been set forth by the International Acetylene Association. They are included here in brief form:

1. Fasten your cylinders.
    a. Use a cylinder truck, or tie them to a post or bench with a chain, wire, or strap iron.
2. "Crack" the cylinder valves.
    a. Stand behind them; open each a fraction of a turn and close immediately. This blows out any dirt that may have collected in the valve.
3. Connect the regulators.
    a. Oxygen connections have right-hand threads.
    b. Acetylene connections have left-hand threads.
4. Loosen the pressure-adjusting screws on the regulators.
5. Open the oxygen cylinder valve slowly, then as far as you can.
6. Open the acetylene cylinder valve only 1½ turns.
    a. Stand to one side of the regulator gages when opening these valves.
    b. Leave the T wrench in the acetylene cylinder in case you have to shut it off quickly.
7. Attach the hoses to the regulators, then to the blowpipe.
    a. Use oxygen to blow out new hoses.
8. Attach a welding head to the blowpipe.
    a. Tighten the connection nut.
9. Turn off valve at blowpipe, admit pressure to hose, and test for leaks.

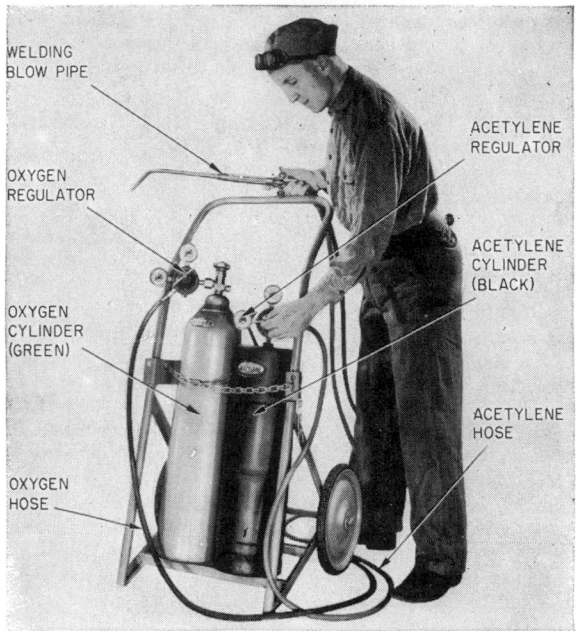

FIG. 2-10. A complete oxyacetylene outfit.   The welding blowpipe shown may be adapted for cutting by exchanging welding tip with a cutting attachment.   Blowpipes designed especially for cutting only are also available.

10. Adjust the oxygen pressure.
    a. Open the blowpipe oxygen valve.
    b. Turn in the regulator pressure-adjusting screw until the regulator gage shows desired pressure.
    c. Close the blowpipe valve.
11. Adjust the acetylene pressure.
    a. Same procedure as for oxygen.

Flame Adjustment.   The three basic types of flames for an oxyacetelene blowpipe are shown in Fig. 2-11.

1. To adjust to an excess acetylene (carburizing) flame, start with both blowpipe valves closed.   Then:
    a. "Crack" the blowpipe oxygen valve, open the acetylene valve about a full turn. Light the blowpipe.
    b. Increase the oxygen supply until you see three distinct parts to the flame: a brilliant inner cone, a whitish acetylene feather, and a bluish outer envelope. This is a carburizing flame.
    c. The amount of excess acetylene in the flame is expressed as a ratio of the total length of the feather to the total length of the inner cone.   Thus, in a 2X flame, the acetylene feather is twice as long as the inner cone.
2. To adjust to a neutral flame:
    a. Proceed as above, but keep adding oxygen until the acetylene feather just disappears.
    b. This leaves two parts to the flame: a brilliant white inner cone and a bluish outer envelope.
    c. At this point, the blowpipe is burning equal amounts of oxygen and acetylene. This is a neutral flame.

3. To adjust to an oxidizing flame:
   a. Proceed as above until a neutral flame is obtained.
   b. Keep adding oxygen beyond the point where the acetylene feather disappears until the inner cone shortens (about 20 per cent shorter than a neutral **inner cone**) and becomes "necked-in."
   c. A harsh sound also characterizes this oxidizing flame unless a very low flow is used.

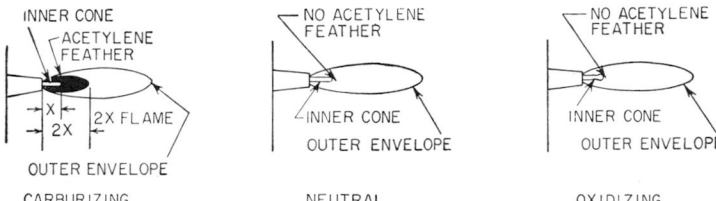

Fig. 2-11. The three basic types of flames for an oxyacetylene blowpipe.

4. Carburizing, neutral, and oxidizing flames can be harsh or soft. You get a harsh flame when using almost the maximum flow through a tip; you get a soft flame when using less than normal flow.
   a. In a harsh flame, the pressures approach "blowoff"; that is, a slight increase in pressure causes a gap to appear between the flame and the tip.
   b. In a soft flame, the gas flow is reduced with the blowpipe valves. The inner cone is about half as long as that in a harsh flame.

Braze Welding (see Fig. 2-12). Braze welding is a process which enables you to weld various metals and alloys without melting the base metal. Using a bronze rod (which melts between 1500 and 1650°F) as a filler metal, you can make strong joints in many metals and alloys. The process is similar to soldering, the difference being that solder melts at a much lower temperature than the bronze rod does and is of much lower strength.

In braze welding, a slightly oxidizing flame is generally used, since a carburizing flame gives off certain gases that dissolve in the molten puddle and leave weak, porous spots in the weld.

You can braze-weld cast, malleable, wrought, and galvanized iron; carbon steels and alloy steels; copper; brass and bronze; nickel; Monel; Inconel; and other metals. Here are some of the features and advantages of braze welding:

1. Braze welding can be used for many repair and fabrication jobs.
2. It is faster than fusion welding because less heat is required to melt the filler metal.
   a. This means that you use less gas, so costs are lower.
   b. Less heat means less distortion in the piece being braze-welded.
   c. More work can be done in less time with this fast process.
3. Braze welding produces good strong joints.
   a. Bronze rod, properly deposited, can have a tensile strength up to 56,000 psi.
   b. Tensile strength of plain low-carbon steel is about 52,000 psi.
4. Braze welding can be used for joining dissimilar metals: cast iron to steel, iron to copper, etc.
5. Braze welding can be used to join malleable iron parts and to repair large castings.

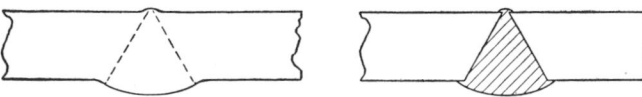

Fig. 2-12. A braze weld.   Fig. 2-13. A fusion weld.

Fusion Welding (see Fig. 2-13). Fusion welding is the joining of metal by melting and fusing the edges together. The joint is a thorough mixture of the base metal and the welding or filler rod used to build up the seam. There is no sharp line of demarcation as with a braze weld. The filler rod is used in all cases, except when you are welding sheet metal, and should be about the same composition as the base metal. For example, you use steel rods when welding various plain-carbon or alloy steels while cast-iron rod is used for welding iron castings.

Fusion welding is used mainly where you cannot use braze welding. It has a wide appeal to small users for light-gage, mostly nonproduction work and for maintenance jobs, although it has largely been displaced for large-scale production work by electric arc welding. Fusion welding, rather than braze welding, is necessary for parts that will be in use at high temperatures. As a braze-welded joint becomes heated, it loses its strength rapidly, since the filler metal will melt at about 1650°F.

Parts subjected to great tensile stresses, i.e., great pulling loads, should be fusion-welded. For example, some steels have tensile strengths up to 90,000 psi and more. These exceed the tensile strength of a braze weld (up to 56,000 psi) and must be fusion-welded with a special steel rod if the joint strength is to equal or exceed the strength of the base metal.

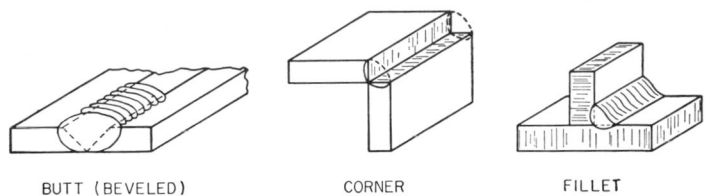

BUTT (BEVELED) CORNER FILLET

Fig. 2-14. Butt, corner, and fillet joints.

Fusion welding can also be used where an approximate color match between welded parts is necessary.

Fusion welding uses a neutral or slightly oxidizing flame, since a carburizing flame can cause entrapments in the filler metal.

Weld Preparation

1. As a part of your preparation for welding, you should select and prepare the proper joint design for your work (see Fig. 2-14).
   a. Square-edge butt and flange welds are commonly used in sheet-metal work. In the latter, the edges are turned up and melted to form the joint and no filler rod is needed.
   b. Lap joints are rarely used except where one cylindrical section fits inside another.
   c. The butt joint with beveled edges (the V) is most widely used. For plate over $\frac{3}{16}$ in., bevel the edges by oxygen cutting, grinding, or machining to an included angle of 90°.
   d. The corner fillet and double-V joints can also be used, depending on the demands of the job.
   e. In the double-V joint, the plates are welded from both sides. It is generally used for work thicker than $\frac{1}{2}$ in.
2. The second step in preparation is to clean the edges of any oil or grease, dirt, scale, or rust with steel wool, a wire brush, or some other means.
3. Before welding, the pieces must be properly spaced, since they will tend to expand during welding. Two types of spacing are used to counteract expansion. On material $\frac{1}{8}$ in. thick or less, the edges are generally placed parallel to each other about $\frac{1}{8}$ in. apart. They should then be tack-welded every 6 in. or so to prevent undue distortion. This space between the plates allows the molten filler metal to flow to the bottom of the joint. Good penetration is thus assured. For material over $\frac{1}{8}$ in. thick, a progressive method of spacing is used (see Fig. 2-15). For every foot of weld length, the pieces should be spread apart about $\frac{1}{8}$ in. For example, welding pieces 2 ft long, you would leave the pieces approximately $\frac{1}{4}$ in. apart at

the finishing end of the weld. At the starting end, the pieces should be spaced about $\frac{1}{16}$ in. Slightly more spacing is required for unbeveled edges.

4. Tack-weld the pieces at start and finish. In sheet metal, tack-weld about every 6 in. This keeps the pieces in alignment and prevents them from drawing too close together as they are heated during welding. There is a great deal of strain on a tack weld as a result of these internal expansion and contraction stresses. So make your tack welds carefully, and make them strong.

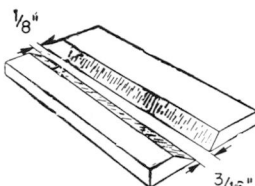

FIG. 2-15. When making a butt weld of pieces over $\frac{1}{8}$ in. thick, "progressive spacing" will counteract distortion caused by expansion.

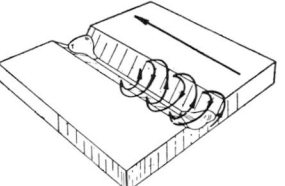

FIG. 2-16. Blowpipe motion for fusion and braze welding.

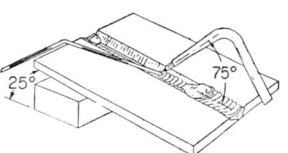

FIG. 2-17. Braze or fusion welding of two pieces thicker than $\frac{3}{16}$ in. is best done with two passes. Notice that the weld proceeds in stages.

Blowpipe Motion. There is no hard-and-fast rule which will tell anyone exactly how to move a blowpipe when welding. Each weldor develops a natural motion after a little practice. Figure 2-16 gives a suggested pattern for moving the blowpipe while welding. The motion is effectively a series of semicircles, wide enough to ensure heating beyond the limits of beveling and moving forward to a slight extent in each blowpipe swing. For fusion welding, it is important to try to move the flame around in front of the rod at the end of each sweep so that complete melting of the edges is obtained. With braze welding, it is not necessary to melt the edges of the joint, so the blowpipe motion is generally faster.

Making a Weld. The procedures for making a braze or fusion weld are essentially the same except that for fusion welding, the edges of pieces being joined are actually melted while for braze welding, the edges of the pieces being joined are heated to a dull red. In both fusion and braze welding, the filler rod is melted to furnish the filler metal for the seam. The following brief discussion applies to both fusion and braze welding. Nevertheless, the difference between the two welding methods should always be remembered.

1. Steel thicker than $\frac{5}{16}$ in. can be welded in two or more passes, while material over $\frac{1}{2}$ in. should always be multipass welded (see Fig. 2-17).
2. Lay in the first pass or root weld from 2 to 3 in. long. After making this beginning section of the root weld, go back and build up the finishing weld to the desired reinforcement.
3. There are two reasons for making a root weld for about $2\frac{1}{2}$ in. and then returning for the second pass or finishing weld before continuing with the root weld (see Fig. 2-18).

16	6	4	2
15	5	3	1

LAYER SEQUENCE

FIG. 2-18. Sequence of root and finishing welds for a weld made in two passes (layers).

   a. You take advantage of the heat left in the plate when you made the beginning section of the root weld. If you continued all the way across the plate, this heat would be lost when you returned for a second pass.
   b. Experience shows that best results in strength, uniformity, and appearance are achieved when this system is used.
4. The following points are important in making a good weld.
   a. Do not add filler rod until you have formed a molten puddle (fusion welding) or heated to a dull red (braze welding).
   b. Keep the rod in the puddle.

c. Keep your eye on the leading edge of the puddle to ensure that you always have thorough fusion or heating.

d. Remember that the rod is deposited evenly by constantly melting it into the molten puddle, not by applying the flame directly to the rod.

5. The blowpipe should be tilted slightly, to an angle of 75° with the plate surface, to ensure a certain amount of preheat as the weld proceeds. The plate may be tilted upward to an angle of perhaps 25° to aid an even build-up.

6. The blowpipe should be directed squarely into the V between the plates so that both sides will be heated evenly.

7. Proper weld sequence is shown below. The first root weld is made for about $2\frac{1}{2}$ in.; the first finishing weld is about half this length. Each successive pass, both root and finishing, is about the same length as the first section. The final section of finishing weld will be a bit longer than any other part to make up for the shortness of the first finishing weld.

8. Never make a flush weld if maximum strength is desired. Always provide reinforcement; i.e., make sure that the lowest ripple is $\frac{1}{16}$ in. above the surface of the plate.

Heavy Braze Welding. The following points apply to such heavy jobs as repairing heavy steel or iron castings.

1. Preparation of the work is important. First, vee out the crack with your gouging nozzle on steel parts or by chipping, grinding, or machining if the piece is cast iron. Be sure to clean thoroughly a generous space on each side of the V to permit the crown of the weld to lap over and give additional strength.

2. On cast-iron pieces, it is fairly certain that graphite (pure carbon) flakes are embedded in the surface and have been smeared by machining or grinding. In the presence of an oxidizing flame, this carbon will unite with oxygen and burn off as a gas. Use steel wool or a wire brush on the surface to complete the cleaning job.

3. Choose a location where it will be possible to set up a temporary preheat furnace. The reasons for preheating are:

    a. It is easier to braze-weld if heat is stored up in heavy pieces. A fairly small and convenient welding flame can be used if the pieces are at about 500°F.

    b. If the pieces are cold, heat from the welding flame would be rapidly drawn away.

    c. Preheating will help prevent excessive internal stresses from occurring as the piece cools.

4. Depending on the shape of the piece, it may be possible to make a double V and have a weldor work on each side of the joint.

5. Since it is easier to build up a weld in successive horizontal layers, position the work if possible so that your weld line is flat.

    a. If possible, it is desirable to support your starting weld on a carbon block or piece of fire brick. If this cannot be done, use a piece of 10-gage sheet or carbon plate fitted to the bottom of the abutting pieces. When the weld is finished and the casting is cool, you can remove the sheet if necessary by chipping.

    b. Use plenty of flux or flux-coated rod so the tinning action will take place automatically and stay well ahead of the weld itself.

6. When completed, the weld can be cleaned by starting at the top and working downward with a large oxidizing flame, melting the runovers.

7. In cases where the castings are spread out, be sure that they are well supported, since cast iron is weakened when heated to a high temperature.

Fusion-welding Cast Iron

1. Cast iron does not have the strength and ductility that steel has. Without careful cleaning before and proper cooling after welding, a casting may become hard and brittle and possibly crack.

    a. Clean off any dirt, scale, and grease that might weaken the final weld with a wire brush, a grinder, or a file.

    b. In order to equalize internal expansion and contraction stresses introduced

Table 2-3. Recommended Welding Methods (Ferrous)

Metal	Welding method	Flame adjustment	Recommended welding rod	Flux
Steel, cast..........	Fusion weld	Neutral	High-test steel	None
Steel pipe...........	Fusion weld	Neutral	High-test steel	None
	Steel welding	Carburizing	CMS steel	
Steel plate..........	Fusion weld	Neutral	Drawn iron	None
	Steel welding	Carburizing	High-test steel	
			CMS steel	
Steel sheet..........	Fusion weld	Neutral	Drawn iron	None
	Bronze weld	Slightly oxidizing	High-test steel	Brazing
			Bronze	None
			Cupro	
High-carbon steel....	Fusion weld	Carburizing	High-test steel	None
			CMS steel	
Manganese steel.....	Fusion weld	Slightly oxidizing	Same composition as base metal	None
Cromansil steel......	Fusion weld	Neutral	High-test steel	None
			CMS steel	
Wrought iron.......	Fusion weld	Neutral	High-test steel	None
Galvanized iron.....	Fusion weld	Neutral	Drawn iron	None
	Fusion weld	Neutral	High-test steel	None
	Bronze weld	Slightly oxidizing	Bronze	Brazing
Cast iron, gray......	Fusion weld	Neutral	Cast iron	Ferrous
	Bronze weld	Slightly oxidizing	Bronze	Brazing
Cast iron, malleable..	Bronze weld	Slightly oxidizing	Bronze	Brazing
Cast-iron pipe, gray..	Fusion weld	Neutral	Cast iron	Oxweld ferrous
	Bronze weld	Slightly oxidizing	Bronze	Brazing
Cast-iron pipe.......	Fusion weld	Neutral	Cast iron	Ferrous
			Same composition as base metal	
Chromium-nickel....	Bronze weld	Slightly oxidizing	Bronze	Brazing
Chromium-nickel steel castings	Fusion weld	Neutral	Same composition as base metal	Stainless steel
			25-12 chromium-nickel steel	
			Columbium-bearing 18-8	
			Stainless steel	
Chromium-nickel steel (18-8)	Fusion weld	Neutral	Columbium-bearing 18-8	Stainless steel
			Stainless steel	
Chromium-nickel steel (25-12)	Fusion weld	Neutral	Same composition as base metal	Stainless steel
Chromium steel.....	Fusion weld	Neutral	25-12 chromium-nickel steel	Stainless steel
			Columbium-bearing 18-8	
			Stainless steel	
Chromium steel (4–6 per cent)	Fusion weld	Neutral	Columbium-bearing 18-8	Stainless steel
			Stainless steel	
Chromium iron......	Fusion weld	Neutral	25-12 chromium-nickel steel	Stainless steel
			Columbium-bearing 18-8	
			Stainless steel	
			Same composition as base metal	

during welding, preheat small castings locally with your blowpipe. Large castings should be placed entirely in a preheat furnace and raised to a temperature of approximately 500°F. The stresses of concentrated welding heat might crack the casting without this preheating.

2. Molten cast iron is very fluid and may tend to fall through. It is also a good idea to weld "in the flat" with some sort of backup where possible. Carbon blocks may be removed after the weld has cooled.

3. Bevel the edges, by chipping or grinding, to an included angle of about 90°.

Table 2-4. Recommended Welding Methods (Nonferrous)

Metal	Welding method	Flame adjustment	Recommended welding rod	Flux
Aluminum........	Fusion weld	Slightly carburizing	Aluminum	Aluminum
Brass.............	Fusion weld	Oxidizing	Bronze	Brazing
	Bronze weld	Slightly oxidizing	Bronze	
Bronze..........	Fusion weld	Neutral	Bronze	Brazing
	Bronze weld	Slightly oxidizing	Bronze	
Copper (deoxidized)	Fusion weld	Neutral	Deoxidized copper	None
	Bronze weld	Slightly oxidizing	Bronze	Brazing
Copper (electrolytic)	Fusion weld	Neutral	Cupro	None
	Bronze weld	Slightly oxidizing	Bronze	Brazing
Everdur bronze....	Fusion weld	Slightly oxidizing	Everdur bronze	Silicon bronze
Nickel...........	Fusion weld	Slightly carburizing	Same composition as base metal	None
Monel metal......	Fusion weld	Slightly carburizing	Same composition as base metal	Monel
Inconel..........	Fusion weld	Slightly carburizing	Same composition as base metal	Inconel
Lead.............	Fusion weld	Slightly carburizing	Same composition as base metal	None

4. To help further in cleaning the edges so that a clean, sound weld will be obtained, use a flux that will chemically float out dirt, slag, and oxide inclusions.

5. Add just enough flux so that all the impurities are cleaned and fluxed out of the weld zone.

6. Use only one pass. It is not necessary to fill in a root weld and then a finishing weld as was the case with steel.

7. Cast iron must be cooled slowly after welding. Sudden chilling of a recently welded cast-iron part can cause it to crack. Fast cooling also makes a casting hard, brittle, and subject to being cracked easily; slow cooling imparts softness and ease of machinability. Small parts can be placed into a can of lime or cement or some similar material so that they will cool properly. Larger castings can be left in the preheat furnace for slow, even cooling.

For recommended welding methods see Tables 2-3 and 2-4.

Oxygen Cutting. Iron burns (all burning is an oxidation process) as readily as wood or paper if it is heated to the right temperature and is exposed to a large amount of pure oxygen. Metals like aluminum, stainless steel, and magnesium also oxidize, but it takes even more heat to melt their oxides than it does for iron oxide. Other means must be used to cut them. Oxygen cutting is primarily intended for cutting ferrous metals (iron or steel).

The first step in oxygen-cutting ferrous metals is to preheat the metal until it is red hot. At this point, the metal is said to be at its kindling or ignition temperature—it is ready to burn away. The actual cut in the metal is started by directing the pure oxygen stream from a cutting blowpipe at the preheated metal. The hot iron and the oxygen react instantly, producing so much heat that the oxide formed melts and flows or is blown away. As the oxide flows away, the cut progresses through the metal as the next layer of metal is exposed to the oxygen. When the blowpipe is moved along the line of cut, the heat of the reaction between the iron and oxygen raises the temperature of these successive layers of metal.

Oxygen cutting is used almost everywhere—for cutting straight lines and circles in plate, for cutting shapes to accurate dimensions in single pieces and in stacks, for trimming plate to size and beveling it for welding, for piercing holes, for cutting I beams and other structural members to size, and for many other uses. The oxygen-cutting blowpipe is also a prime fabricating tool in industry for preparing plates and cutting structural members in the shipbuilding, heavy-machinery, and building-construction industries. Oxygen cutting is also extensively used for demolishing and scrapping of machinery,

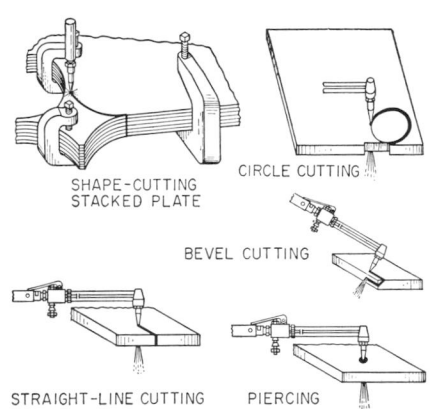

SHAPE-CUTTING
STACKED PLATE

CIRCLE CUTTING

BEVEL CUTTING

STRAIGHT-LINE CUTTING   PIERCING

FIG. 2-19. Some of the jobs done by oxygen cutting.

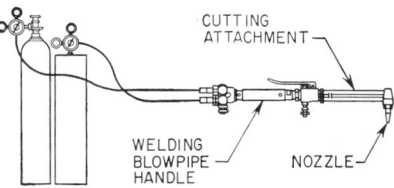

CUTTING ATTACHMENT

WELDING BLOWPIPE HANDLE   NOZZLE

FIG. 2-20. Oxygen-cutting equipment.

obsolete equipment, unsafe or unwanted structures; for cutting heavy scrap to smaller size; for removing bolts and rivets; and for similar work (see Fig. 2-19).

Oxygen cutting is very versatile in that steel, wrought iron, and cast iron can be cut in almost any form, of almost any thickness. Hand cutting is restricted to thicknesses of about 1 ft. Machine cuts have been made, however, in material of about 6 ft in thickness.

The process is inexpensive. Initial equipment cost and subsequent upkeep costs are very low compared with other means of doing the same job. The gas costs are almost negligible when you consider the variety and quality of the work done. The equipment needed for oxygen cutting is easily portable and can be taken almost anywhere for "on-the-job" use. The process is very fast. Depending on the thickness of the material, speeds up to 500 fph can be attained. The process is easily learned. The correct techniques can be studied and picked up in a few minutes.

Oxygen-cutting Equipment (see Fig. 2-20). Oxygen cutting requires the same equipment needed for welding, including a welding blowpipe fitted with a cutting attachment and a special nozzle. Where you are going to do oxygen cutting for long periods, a cutting blowpipe is more desirable than a cutting attachment. The cutting nozzles come in various sizes. The thickness of the metal and its surface condition determine the size of the nozzle needed. For example, five different-sized nozzles handle all thicknesses up to 12 in.

Various accessories, which supplement basic equipment, are available for making special types of cuts. In free-hand "guided" cutting, the blowpipe head can be drawn along a bar or straightedge. This will assure an accurate square or beveled straight-line cut. Circles or disks with 2 in. or greater diameters can be accurately made with circle-cutting attachments. Where high accuracy is required in cutting straight lines, circles, or shapes, special machines are available which mechanically hold, guide, and advance the blowpipe over the work. Little or no finishing is required on these high-quality machine cuts.

Preparation for Cutting

1. First, select a suitable place for working—make sure there is no combustible material at hand. Use asbestos or sheet-metal shields to protect wood floors, etc., where necessary. Protect your legs and feet from sparks and slag.
2. A clean metal surface means lower gas consumption and a good-quality cut. So remove all the dirt, paint, etc., you can by scraping or wire brushing.
3. Look at the instruction sheet for your cutting attachment or blowpipe to find out what size nozzle to use for the thickness of metal you are cutting.

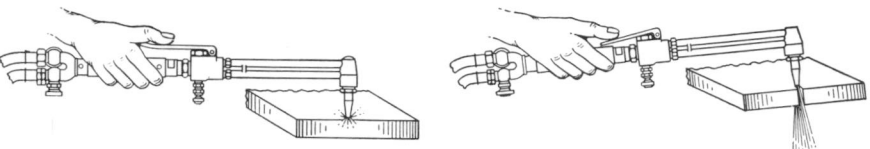

FIG. 2-21. Preheating.   FIG. 2-22. Beginning a cut.

4. The adjustment of the flame for a cutting attachment or blowpipe is different from that for a welding blowpipe because the latter has no cutting oxygen stream.
    a. If the cutting oxygen valve is opened after the preheat flames are adjusted to neutral, the preheat flames will lack oxygen. This is because both preheat and cutting oxygen come from the same source and part of the preheat supply has been diverted to form the cutting-oxygen stream.
    b. To correct this, the preheat flames should be adjusted with the cutting oxygen lever down.
    c. Also, oxygen-flow adjustments must always be made with the needle valve on the cutting attachment. Open the blowpipe oxygen valve wide, leave it that way while cutting, and adjust the flame with the other valve.

Making the Cut

1. During cutting, hold the blowpipe in one hand and guide the blowpipe by resting it on your other hand.
    a. A piece of firebrick on the plate will provide a rest for your hand as well as indicate the proper spacing of the blowpipe from the work.
    b. Make sure nothing will prevent you from finishing the cut without interruption.
2. Hold the blowpipe so that the preheat cones just lick the work surface. Preheat the starting point on the edge to a bright red (see Fig. 2-21).

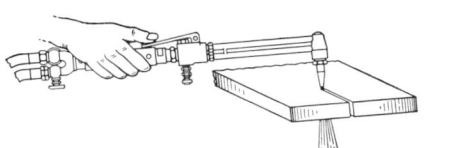

FIG. 2-23. Cutting.

3. Start the cut by slowly pressing down the cutting-oxygen lever (see Fig. 2-22).
    a. Keep the tip vertical and always the same height above the work.
    b. Do not advance the blowpipe until the cut is completely through the metal.
    c. Continue the cutting action by moving the blowpipe along the line of cut at a uniform rate (see Fig. 2-23).
4. If you move the blowpipe too slowly, you will melt over the edges of the cut and give it a ragged appearance.
5. If you move the blowpipe too fast, the cutting jet will not penetrate the metal completely and you will "lose the cut." In this case, release the cutting oxygen lever, go back to where you "lost the cut," and start over again.
    a. Experience is the only way to learn exactly how fast to move the blowpipe.

b. When the cut is finished, release the cutting-oxygen lever and turn off the preheat flames.

Gouging. Gouging or grooving is merely a special type of oxygen cutting. It is a means of removing a narrow strip of metal from the surface of a plate. You use the same equipment for gouging that you use for cutting, except that you must have a large-bore, low-velocity nozzle. As in cutting, the operation centers around three main steps: preheating, starting the groove, and progressing. Other things to be watched during gouging include:

1. Pulling the nozzle back along the plate surface after preheating, then opening the cutting oxygen lever. This ensures that the stream will fall on hot metal, not on relatively cold metal ahead of the preheated spot.
2. Keeping the flames low. If the inner cones of the preheat flames on the lower side of the nozzle are just barely touching the work, you will get maximum efficiency from the preheat flames.
3. Keeping the blowpipe moving in a straight line. When making a long groove, there is a tendency to move the blowpipe toward you as the groove proceeds and describe a long arc instead of a straight line in the plate.

With the "step-back" method of gouging, you will have less tendency to lose the cut or swing out of line than if you gouge in one continuous pass.

1. The groove is carried progressively across the plate in a series of short gouges.
2. Start the groove, then continue it for about 3 in. Lift up the blowpipe, bring it back about $\frac{1}{2}$ in., and restart the groove.
3. As each short pass is completed, the nozzle is drawn back slightly to restart the groove.
4. Repeat these steps until you have reached the full length of the desired groove.

Gouging is used in three main applications:

1. Removing defective welds. When a weld does not have a good appearance or is not so strong as it should be, it can be removed by gouging and replaced. You can also remove the old weld and have the piece ready to be rewelded all in one operation by gouging.
2. Opening up cracks in castings so that sound repairs can be made by welding.
3. Dismantling welded structures to permit reuse of most of the parts, thus obtaining maximum salvage.

Using a special gouging nozzle, you can cut grooves from $\frac{3}{8}$ to $\frac{1}{2}$ in. wide by $\frac{1}{8}$ to $\frac{7}{16}$ in. deep. These variations in groove dimensions are controlled by three factors:

1. By the angle of the nozzle with respect to the work (see Fig. 2-24). A flat angle gives a shallow groove, and a steeper angle a deep groove.
2. By the speed of travel of the blowpipe. The faster you move, the shallower the gouge becomes.
3. By the oxygen pressure. High pressures wash a bit more metal out of the groove than lower pressures.

Hard Facing. Hard facing is the process of applying a layer of special alloy on a metal part or surface to protect it from wear. The big difference between hard facing and the fusion welding is that the hard-facing alloy does not mix with the base metal to any extent. In fusion welding, complete penetration is necessary, but in hard facing, it should be avoided. This is important because mixing of the base metal with the hard-facing alloy would dilute and soften the deposit. In hard facing, the surface of the steel picks up carbon from an excess acetylene flame. The carbon lowers the melting point of the steel and causes it to melt quickly to a depth of only a few thousandths of an inch. This very thin film of melted steel fuses with the hard-face deposit to make a strong bond between the deposit and the steel.

Metals that can be hard-faced include carbon and low-alloy steels (covering 95 per cent of the wear problems you will normally encounter), all forms of cast iron (except chilled), and many other special alloys.

With the longer life of hard-faced parts (2 to 25 times longer), the reduction of maintenance labor and of replacement parts used is dollars saved. Here are a few typical examples of how hard facing increases the life of parts:

Part Hard-faced	Times Longer Life
Pump shaft	3
Clutch plate	7
Valves, valve seats	7
Valve-seat inserts	15
Hand shovels	3
Spray nozzle disks	12
Cams	6
Shear blades	10
Mill hammers	5
Punches	13

Hard-facing Rods. There are a number of hard-facing rods available to help you solve particular wear problems resulting from such factors as abrasion, impact, corrosion, and heat. Very often more than one cause of wear is present. Your problem

Table 2-5. Characteristics of Hard-facing Rods

Hard-facing rod	Tensile strength, psi	Hardness on Rockwell C scale	Melting point, °F	Contains:
Haynes:				
90	63.000	45–55˙	2390	Iron, chromium, carbon
92	25,000	64	2012	Iron, molybdenum, carbon
93	43,000	57–62	2225	Iron, chromium, molybdenum, cobalt, vanadium, carbon
94	60,000	50–61	....	Iron, chromium, boron, cobalt, carbon
Haynes Stellite:				
1	47,000	46–54	2828	Cobalt
6	105,000	33–44	2327	Chromium
12	76,000	37–47	2306	Tungsten
1016	....	58	....	Cobalt, chromium, tungsten, carbon
Hascrome	40,000	28–43	2500	Iron, chromium, manganese

then is to choose the hard-facing alloy best suited to combat the combination of factors. You should consider every job as a special problem. The same rod used for one job will not necessarily work on the same or similar part in another instance. If you are in doubt about which rod to select, test several under actual conditions. Manufacturer's data will usually help you select the proper rod, but often you must make the final decision in the light of what you can find out about the wear conditions involved. Tables 2-5 and 2-6 show the particular characteristics of some of the hard-facing rods available.

How to Hard-face Steel

1. Clean the surface to be hard-faced by filing, wire-brushing, or grinding. Edges or corners that might become overheated during hard facing should be grooved out as shown and filled with hard-facing deposit. Use your cutting blowpipe or attachment and grooving nozzle for this (see Fig. 2-25). If an edge or corner of the part takes a lot of pounding or impact in use, machine the corner or edge as shown in Fig. 2-26. The dotted lines in the illustration show how the hard-face deposit should be built up to the original contour of the part.

2. Parts more than 2 in. in thickness should be preheated throughout to prevent the deposit or the part itself from cracking when it cools.   You can preheat medium-size parts with your blowpipe.   Use a neutral flame.   Move the flame in a wide circle over the part.   Gradually make the circles smaller and smaller until the

Table 2-6. Characteristics of Hard-facing Rods

Hard-facing rod	Resistance to:			
	Abrasion	Impact	Corrosion	Hot abrasion
Haynes:				
90	A	C	C	NR
92	A	NR	NR	NR
93	A	D	C	NR
94	A	D	D	NR
Haynes Stellite:				
1	A	NR	A	A
6	B	A	A	B
12	A	B	A	A
1016	A	NR	C	A
Hascrome	C	A	D	NR

A, excellent; B, high; C, good; D, fair; NR, not recommended.

part turns a dull red color.   Large surfaces or bulky parts should be preheated in a furnace.   Heat the part until it turns a dull red color.

3. Deposits up to $\frac{1}{8}$-in. in thickness can be made in one pass.   Best impact resistance is obtained from deposits $\frac{1}{16}$ in. in thickness, never over $\frac{1}{8}$ in.   If you want to build up a badly worn surface with hard facing to a depth greater than $\frac{1}{8}$ in., you should use more than one deposit.

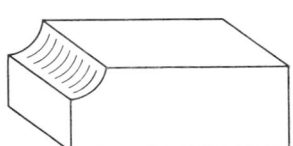

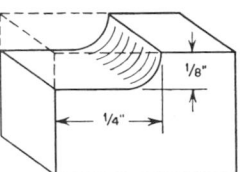

Fig. 2-24. The angle of the nozzle with respect to the work controls the depth of the groove.

Fig. 2-25. A grooved edge for hard facing.

Fig. 2-26. A machined edge for hard facing.

4. Hard-facing rods are applied with a carburizing flame—a flame using more acetylene than oxygen.   The extra acetylene shows up as a whitish "feather" around the inner cone.   Use the amount of excess acetylene specified by the rod manufacturer.

5. Low- and medium-carbon steels are the most widely used metals and are the easiest to hard-face.   The following instructions are for the hard facing of these steels.

6. If you have selected a rod, prepared the part, and set up your welding outfit, you are ready to start hard-facing.   Begin by heating the part (see Fig. 2-27).

7. Now adjust to a carburizing flame.   Reduce the amount of oxygen until you have the proper flame, depending on the rod you are using.

8. Hold the carburizing flame over the heated area.   The tip of the inner cone should be just off the steel surface—about $\frac{1}{8}$ in. as shown.   Hold the flame there until the metal under the flame starts to "sweat."

9. Next lift the welding blowpipe a little and put the rod into the flame so that it just touches the "sweating" surface. Lower the blowpipe until the inner cone of the flame just touches the rod and is about 1/8 in. from the steel surface, as shown in Fig. 2-28. A small puddle of melted rod will form on the sweating surface. If the first few drips of the melted rod foam or bubble or do not spread evenly, the surface is too cold. Take the rod away and start over again.

10. Next take the rod out of the puddle. Spread the puddle over the "sweating" surface by pointing the flame into it—do not use the rod to spread it. If there is not enough hard-facing deposit to cover the wearing surface, continue the process.

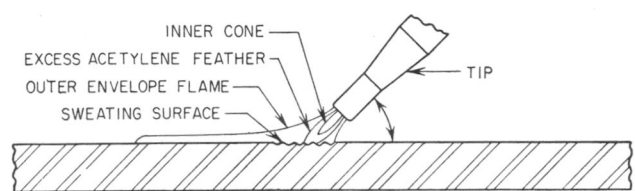

FIG. 2-27. Heating the surface before depositing the hard-facing rod.

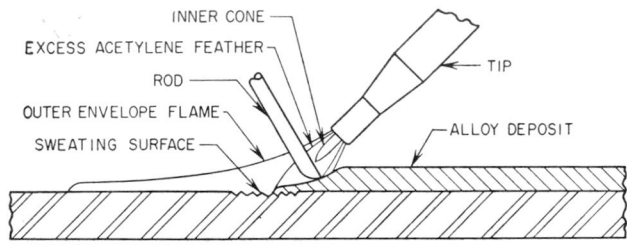

FIG. 2-28. Depositing the hard-facing rod.

11. Point the flame so that it touches the forward end of the puddle and the steel surface.

12. When the surface sweats, add more metal to the puddle from the rod. Then, as you did before, remove the rod and spread the puddle with the flame. Repeat until the entire surface is covered.

13. Allow the part to cool slowly to prevent cracks and stresses in the hard face. Small and medium-size parts can be cooled in air. Large or bulky parts should be wrapped in asbestos paper or buried in asbestos, slaked lime, wood ashes, or some other insulating material until they cool. Parts that are liable to crack should be put in the preheating furnace while they are still hot from hard facing. Then they should be brought to an even red heat and, with the heat turned off, allowed to cool overnight in the furnace with the door closed.

Hard-facing Cast Iron

1. Cast iron does not sweat like steel, and it melts at about the same temperature as the rod. So *be careful*—do not melt the base metal too deeply.

2. Use a little less acetylene in the flame than you would for steel.

3. Use cast-iron brazing flux when you apply the rod.

4. A crust will form over the surface of the cast iron when it is heated. To get a good bond, you will have to break the crust with the end of your rod.

5. Very thin cast-iron parts should be backed up with wet asbestos or carbon paste to keep them from melting.

Finishing the Hard-facing Deposit

1. *Heat-treating* of the hard-faced part is *usually not necessary*. The only time you will heat-treat a part after hard-facing it is when you want to toughen the base

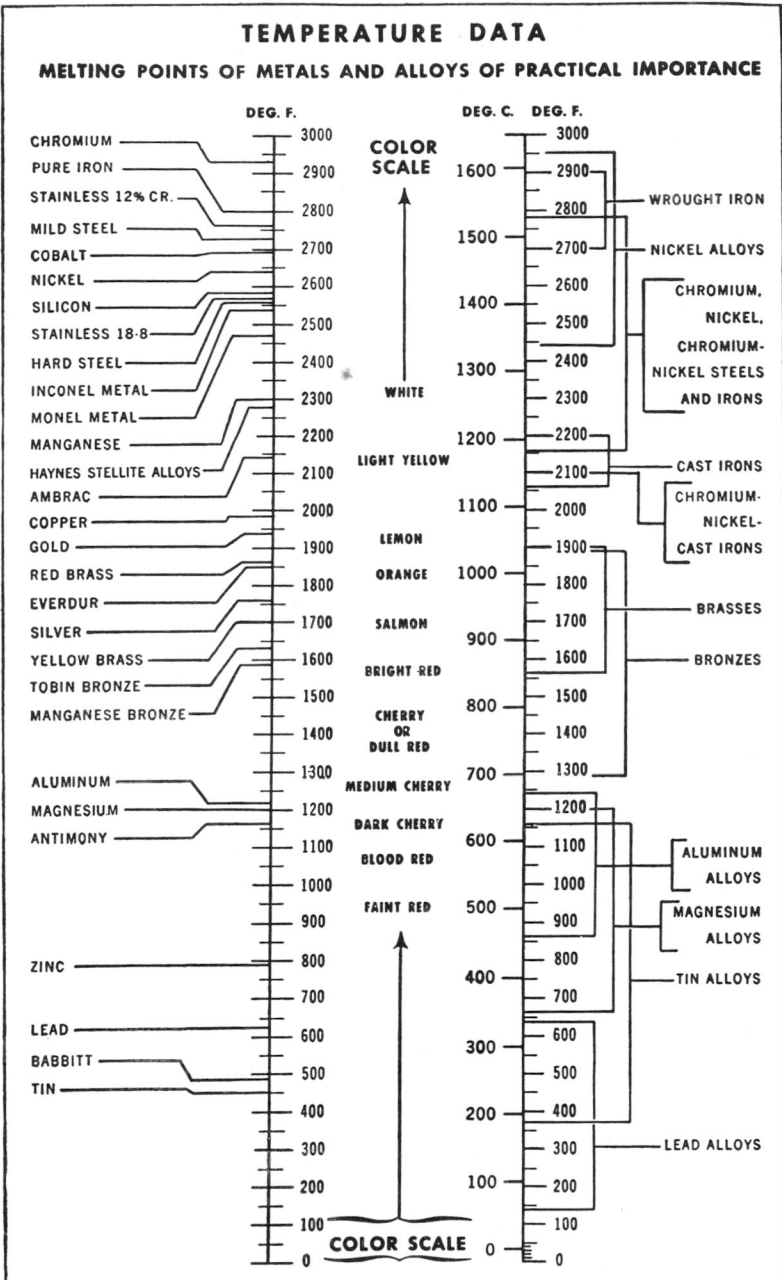

FIG. 2-29. Melting points of metals and alloys.

Codes, Specifications, and Welding Standards*

Title	Published by:	Field of application	Source
General:			
Accident Prevention Manual No. 3, Gas and Electric Cutting and Welding	API,† 1953, 20 pp.	Petroleum industry	API†
AWS Definitions—Welding and Cutting	AWS,‡ 1961, 59 pp.		AWS‡
Controls for Resistance Welding Machines, B88.1	ASA,¶ 1963	General welding	ASA¶
Definitions of Electrical Terms, Electric Welding and Cutting (Group 50), C42.50	ASA,¶ 1958	General welding	ASA¶
Graphical Symbols for Welding, Y32.3	ASME,§ 1959	Engineering-shop drawings	ASA¶
Master Chart of Welding Processes	AWS,‡ 1961	Wall size 22″ × 28″	AWS‡
		Desk size 8½″ × 11″	AWS‡
Requirements for Electric Arc-welding Apparatus, B87.1	National Electrical Manufacturers Association, 1963	General welding	ASA¶
Safety in Welding and Cutting, z49.1	ASA,¶ 1958	General welding	ASA¶
Safety Standard for Transformer-type Arc-welding Machines, C33.2	Underwriters' Laboratories, 1956	General welding	ASA¶
Standard Welding Symbols	AWS,‡ 1958, 87 pp.	Engineering-shop drawings	AWS‡
Welding Symbols Chart	AWS,‡ 1958	Wall size 22″ × 28″	AWS‡
		Desk size 8½″ × 11″	AWS‡
Boilers and pressure vessels:			
ASME Codes for Construction			
Sec. I, Power Boilers	ASME,§ 1962, 154 pp.	Power boilers in stationary service	ASME§
Sec. III, Nuclear Vessels	ASME,§ 1962, 144 pp.	Nuclear power plants	ASME§
Sec. IV, Low-pressure Heating Boilers	ASME,§ 1962, 36 pp.	Boilers in operation at less than 15 psig and for hot-water heating and supply	ASME§
Sec. VIII, Unfired Pressure Vessels	ASME,§ 1962, 228 pp.	Unfired pressure vessels	ASME§
Inspection and testing:			
Inspection of Welding, Appendix	API,† 1959	Refinery equipment	API†
Standard Methods for Mechanical Testing of Welds	AWS,‡ 1942 (with 1945 Supplement)	Welding shops and fabricators of welded structures	AWS‡
Piping:			
ASA Code for Pressure Piping	ASME,§ 1942, 227 pp.	Pressure piping systems	ASME§
Standard for Field Welding of Pipelines (Std. 1104)	API,† 1961	Cross-country petroleum and natural-gas pipelines	API†
Structural (building):			
Code for Welding in Building Construction	AWS,‡ 1963, 72 pp.	Buildings	AWS‡
Rules Covering the Specifications for Design, Fabrication, and Inspection of Fusion Welded Structures and Qualification of Welders and Supervisors (New York City Building Code)	Boards of Standards and Appeals, New York	Buildings in New York	Boards of Standards and Appeals, Municipal Bldg., New York
Specifications for Welded Highway and Railway Bridges	AWS,‡ 1963, 94 pp.	Highway and railway bridges	AWS‡

Codes, Specifications, and Welding Standards (*Continued*)

Title	Published by:	Field of application	Source
Structural (tanks):			
Safe Practices for Welding and Cutting Containers That Have Held Combustibles	AWS,‡ 1952, 10 pp.	Shops engaged in welding or cutting operations on containers of combustible solids, liquids, or gases	AWS‡
Specifications for Large Welded Production Tanks (Std. 12D)	API,† 1957	Oil-field service—capacities over 500 bbl	API†
Specifications for Small Welded Production Tanks (Std. 12F)	API,† 1961	Oil-field service—capacities to 440 bbl	API†
Design and Construction of Large, Welded, Low-pressure Storage Tanks (Std. 620)	API,† 1963	Petroleum-products storage—for internal pressures of 15 psig or less	API†
Welded Steel Tanks for Oil Storage (Std. 650)	API,† 1964	Oil storage at atmospheric pressure	API†
Standard Specifications for Steel Tanks, Standpipes, Reservoirs, and Elevated Tanks for Water Storage	American Water Works Association and AWS,‡ 1959, 47 pp.	Elevated steel water tanks, standpipes, and reservoirs	AWS‡
Standards of the National Board of Fire Underwriters for the Construction and Installation of Tanks, Gravity and Pressure Towers, etc.	National Board of Fire Underwriters	Field-welded tanks, gravity and pressure towers, etc.	National Board of Fire Underwriters, 85 John St., New York
Specifications of the Associated Factory Mutual Fire Insurance Companies for Gravity Water Tanks and Steel Towers	Associated Factory Mutual Fire Insurance Companies	Field-welded gravity water tanks and steel towers	Associated Factory Mutual Fire Insurance Companies, 184 High St., Boston
Specifications of the AREA for All-welded Steel Tanks for Railway Water Service	American Railway Engineering Association	Field-welded water-storage tanks	American Railway Engineering Association, 59 E. Van Buren St., Chicago
Rules for Field Welding of Steel Tanks	AWS,‡ 1947, 19 pp.	Storage tanks for liquids at atmospheric pressure	AWS‡
Qualifications:			
Qualifications Test for Gas Welders (General Specifications for Inspection of Material, Appendix VII, Welding, Part E, Sec. E-2)	Bureau of Supplies and Accounts, Navy Department	All gas welding done for the Navy Department	Bureau of Supplies and Accounts, Navy Dept. (available only to contractors or prospective contractors for Navy work)
Standard Qualification Procedure	AWS,‡ 1941, 39 pp.	Industry, welding instructors, and code-writing bodies wishing to prescribe methods	AWS‡
Welding Qualifications	ASME,§ 1964, 65 pp.	Boilers and pressure vessels fabricated to ASME codes	ASME§

* All are available from sponsoring organization. For convenience, AWS is given as source when possible.

† American Petroleum Institute, Publications Section, 1271 Avenue of the Americas, New York, N.Y. 10020.

‡ American Welding Society, United Engineering Center, 345 East 47th St., New York, N.Y. 10017.

§ The American Society of Mechanical Engineers, Order Department, United Engineering Center, 345 East 47th St., New York, N.Y. 10017.

¶ American Standards Association, 10 East 40th St., New York, N.Y. 10016.

metal. To do that, heat the whole part to a dull red heat. Then dip it in oil. Do not use water for the quench because it may crack the deposit and base metal.

2. *Surface cracks* are usually caused by insufficient preheat or by cooling the part too quickly. You will find, however, that a surface crack will not harm the properties of the hard face or the strength of the part. If you want to repair a cracked surface:

   a. Preheat the piece as for hard facing.

   b. Heat the metal around the crack to a dull red.

   c. Then melt the edges down into the crack.

   d. Add a little metal from the rod.

   e. Now slowly move the flame away from the hot spot to prevent quick cooling.

3. You can grind a hard-faced part to exact size or remove high spots on the surface. Use a grinding wheel not coarser than 46 or finer than 60 in Grade I or J of the Norton system. The speed of the wheel should be between 2,800 and 4,200 sfpm. Higher speeds might crack the hard-face surface.

See Fig. 2-29 for melting points of metals and alloys.

References

"The Oxy-Acetylene Handbook," Union Carbide Corporation, Linde Division.

"Welding and Cutting Manual," Union Carbide Corporation, Linde Division.

"Welding Metallurgy," American Welding Society.

"Welding Aluminum," Reynolds Metal Company.

"Welding and Brazing Alcoa Aluminum," Aluminum Company of America.

"Haynes Hard-facing Alloys," Union Carbide Corporation, Stellite Division.

"Welding and Cutting in the Mining Industry," Canadian Liquid Air Company, Ltd.

Groth, L. A.: "Welding and Cutting Metals,"

MacKensie, L. B., and H. S. Card: "The Welding Encyclopedia."

"Welding Handbook," American Welding Society.

Section 16

CORROSION AND CHEMICAL CLEANING

Chapter 1

CORROSION CONTROL BY SELECTION OF EQUIPMENT AND MATERIALS

By L. R. Honnaker
Engineering Department
Engineering Service Division
E. I. du Pont de Nemours & Company, Inc.
Wilmington, Del.

Importance of Corrosion Control. The direct cost of corrosion to American industry today is estimated to be approximately six billion dollars annually. An even greater sum of money may be involved in the hidden cost of corrosion if it is considered that in many instances the value of the lost production incidental with equipment repairs or replacements is greater than the maintenance and replacement costs. Modern manufacturing steps are highly integrated, and techniques have largely changed from batch- to continuous-type operations. This means that practically none of the equipment can be out of service for repairs or replacement without seriously curtailing production, and it is important in these days of expensive materials and high construction costs that minimum facilities be installed to meet operating requirements. These conditions require careful consideration of corrosion and selection of materials of construction. Corrosion control and prevention warrant serious attention by management and all others responsible for the building and maintenance of plants.

Considerable advancement has been made in the last 20 years in increasing the knowledge and understanding of corrosion and developing new materials to withstand severely corrosive conditions. A great amount of information is now available, and it is no longer necessary to assume that frequent failures and high maintenance costs are a necessary evil. This does not mean that corrosion can be eliminated, but it can be minimized by study and application of available information on the subject of corrosion.

Role of Corrosion Engineer. It is believed the best possible approach, if not the answer, to industrial corrosion problems is to assign personnel to corrosion engineering work. They should acquire a good background in the knowledge of corrosion. This includes a knowledge of the corrosive characteristics of chemicals as well as the corrosion-resisting characteristics of materials of construction. They should become familiar with the physical and mechanical properties of materials of construction, the physical properties and characteristics of the chemical materials to be handled, availability and cost of materials of construction, and fabrication techniques and limitations.

A corrosion engineer's work should involve more than acquiring a background of information and simply selecting materials of construction for design and maintenance work. He should investigate cases of failure on high-maintenance items and arrive at a decision or recommendation to effect an improvement. This may involve an experimental program or changes in design or fabrication procedure and not necessarily in materials of construction. He should set up specifications covering materials, procedures, heat treatment, etc., for new or repaired equipment. He should make inspections of new equipment to see that specifications have been met and existing equipment to see that corrosion difficulties are not developing. He should help establish improved maintenance methods and preventive-maintenance programs. Records should be maintained for future reference, and standards should be set up for spare parts and materials. A very important part of his work should be in maintaining contact with research, operation, and design personnel to see that corrosion-engineering principles are considered in their work.

The science and technology of corrosion control and prevention have now reached the point where impressive reductions in cost and annual losses can be guaranteed by study and application of known corrosion-engineering principles and information. Improvements in product quality and operating conditions with respect to housekeeping and safety hazards can also be obtained through corrosion-engineering work. The cost of applied corrosion-engineering work will almost always be regained severalfold as the result of better control or prevention of corrosion and reduced maintenance.

Although most corrosion problems are too specific to be solved by the direct application of general corrosion data, it is frequently possible to obtain leads to a course of action or study that will provide a solution. There is a great deal of published literature that treats the subject of corrosion and its many facets from both a practical and a theoretical standpoint, and reference to it through one of the abstract reviews will generally prove worth while. Technical service assistance is available from many of the corrosion-resistant-materials vendors, and the experience from these sources can frequently contribute to the elimination or control of corrosion under specific conditions.

Selection and Use of Materials. Good corrosion control requires proper selection, specification, design, fabrication, installation, and maintenance of equipment and structures. These factors are all related, and attention should be given to each for both new and replacement items in order to obtain maximum economy and performance.

Selection of materials should preferably be based on experience. Where specific experience is not available, it is frequently possible for experienced persons to make adequate selections based on knowledge of chemical-resistance characteristics and limitations of materials of construction. It is, however, generally desirable to conduct corrosion- or chemical-resistance tests to determine the suitability of proposed materials. It is most important that the test conditions employed be the same as or similar to those to be involved in the installation being considered. Test procedures and conditions should be as realistic as is practical to simulate operating or exposure conditions with respect to temperature, aeration, and velocity. Hot-wall effects should be considered where heating equipment is involved. The possibility of crevice corrosion, stress corrosion, intergranular corrosion, pitting, and other forms of corrosion occurring should be considered, and tests designed and made to determine suitability of materials where they are known or suspected to be susceptible to a particular type of corrosion under the environmental condition being considered.

Specifications should be sufficiently complete to ensure that the composition or type of material desired will be used and the right condition of heat treatment and surface finish will be provided. Materials should be inspected by the user or his representative.

Design consideration should include the desirability for free and complete drainage, ease of cleaning and inspection, and the possibility of galvanic corrosion of dissimilar metals if used in contact with each other. Crevices generally should be avoided. The following general rules should be considered from the standpoint of minimizing likelihood and extent of corrosion difficulties:

Butt joints should be used wherever possible. If lap-type joints employing fillet welds are used the welds should be continuous on the process side.

The installation of baffles, stiffeners, drain nozzles, and the location of valves and pumps should be such that free drainage will occur and washing can be accomplished without holdup. Means of access for inspection and maintenance should be provided where it is practical.

The use of dissimilar metals in contact with each other should generally be avoided, particularly if they are widely separated in their nominal position in the electrochemical series. If they are to be used together, consideration should be given to making the largest area of the anodic material or insulating them from each other.

Localized areas of turbulence and high velocities at feed and drain connections and at fittings in lines should be minimized where possible.

Equipment should be supported in such a way that it will not rest in pools of liquid- or damp-supporting material. Porous insulation should be weatherproofed or otherwise protected from moisture or spills to avoid contact of the wet material with the equipment.

Fabrication methods used should cause a minimum of surface roughness, welds should be sound, and heat-treating procedures and requirements should be followed closely. Inspection during fabrication and prior to acceptance is desirable.

During installation care should be taken to avoid overstressing of parts and adequate access should be left to permit inspection and maintenance. Frequent inspection should be made, particularly of new equipment, to check its condition and determine if corrosion is occurring or if preventive maintenance is required. It is always desirable to be aware of and to follow the progress of corrosion or chemical attack so that corrective treatment can be made to avoid excessive or irreparable damage.

Corrosion control and prevention will minimize loss of investment value in equipment and structures, reduce plant maintenance costs by extending service life, reduce product loss from shutdowns and leaks in equipment, reduce over-all plant operating costs, and maintain product quality. It is of such importance that personnel should be designated for responsibility of this aspect of plant design, operation, and maintenance.

METALLIC MATERIALS

In corrosion-control work it is fundamentally important to have a knowledge and understanding of corrosion processes and the materials available to handle the many corrosive conditions and environments that are to be encountered. Information relative to the technical details of corrosion processes and the chemical resistance of the many materials of construction to specific corrosive media is beyond the scope of this chapter. Such information is available in existing literature. Suggested references are given at the end of this chapter. It is also important to recognize the type or form of corrosion that occurs in order to apply available information. The most common forms of corrosion of metals are described briefly in the following paragraphs. For purpose of this review they are summarized as 14 forms of corrosion, almost all of them being electrochemical in nature. Their characteristics are well known, they are generally easily recognized, and information regarding corrective measures or resistant materials is generally available in the literature. These forms of corrosion are as follows:

General or Uniform Corrosion. Here thinning and loss of metal is not accompanied by any definite manifestation of pitting, cracking, or erosion. This form of corrosion causes the greatest amount of damage or loss to metals. It is not of as great concern as other forms, because it can be observed. Also the life of equipment can generally be determined or estimated well enough to permit a scheduled maintenance replacement. In most cases where this form of corrosion occurs, it will be necessary to use material with greater resistance to corrosion where it is desired to reduce corrosion and loss of thickness. Occasionally it will be practical and economical to use inhibitors to minimize corrosion or protective coatings or linings as an economical change and improvement. These changes will frequently be useful to correct an existing condition as well as to provide protection in a new installation, particularly where protection against contamination is desired. If problems are encountered, consideration should be given to reducing temperature, acidity, velocity, and aeration and to the use of an inhibitor as a means of minimizing corrosion. Such changes in environmental conditions are sometimes practical and effective.

Pitting. Where electrochemical action results in loss of metal at anodic areas. It is usually highly localized, and general corrosion is frequently slight, even in instances where perforation of the metal occurs as a result of pitting. It is one of the most serious forms of corrosion because it can, and frequently does, occur very rapidly and may not be detected until failure occurs. This form of corrosion can occur in any metal, but the most common occurrence is with aluminum and stainless alloys in aqueous environment containing metal chlorides in solution. The amount of chloride required is small, and in some instances a few parts per million can cause serious pitting attack. In many instances it can be prevented or at least minimized by use of an inhibitor, such as sodium or potassium dichromate.

Stress-corrosion Cracking. Here cracking occurs as the result of the combined effects of residual or applied stresses and corrosion and generally without noticeable loss of metal or uniform corrosion. This form generally occurs rapidly once action has started and is frequently not detected until failure occurs. The period of time required for cracking varies from a few minutes to several years after initial exposure. It usually takes the form of rapid penetration or cracking along grain boundaries, although many alloy systems exhibit transgranular stress-corrosion cracking. It has been observed in almost all metals or their alloys, but each metal or alloy requires certain environmental conditions to produce this form of corrosion. It has been found that only tensile stresses cause stress-corrosion cracking.

Typical examples of this form of corrosion include the "season cracking" of cold-formed or rolled brass in environments containing ammonia, the cracking of the austenitic stainless alloys in the presence of chlorides, the cracking of Monel in hydrofluosilicic acid, and the cracking or "caustic embrittlement" failure of steel in caustic solutions.

This form of corrosion can be prevented by the effective elimination of high stresses. Fabricating stresses, including welding, are the most frequent sources of trouble, and stress-relieving or annealing heat treatment after fabrication should always be considered where these materials are going to be exposed to such environments. Temperature and concentration are important factors in all cases. Experience with handling caustic in steel, for example, indicates that if temperature is held to about 120°F, as-welded steel equipment can be used without stress-corrosion cracking difficulty. If temperature is higher, and particularly if concentration is above 30 per cent by weight, cracking at and adjacent to non-stress-relieved welds frequently occurs and the time to failure decreases with increase in temperature.

Hydrogen Embrittlement. Here atomic hydrogen enters the metal and causes microcracking, blistering, and apparent loss of ductility. This form is closely related to, if it is not a type of, stress-corrosion cracking. Aqueous solution containing hydrogen sulfide frequently causes cracking-type failure in plain-carbon and low-alloy steel as the result of such effects. Where it occurs in hydrogen sulfide, it is also called sulfide cracking. Typical of this form of corrosion is the failure of bolting materials. As in the case of other types of stress corrosion cracking, reduction of total tensile stresses by heat treatment or decreasing the applied load will prevent this type of corrosion. It has been found in the case of bolting used in hydrogen sulfide exposures that low-alloy material, such as AISI 4140, will fail at lower applied loads when hardened to high-yield strength values than when used in a lower or intermediate-yield-strength condition. Maximum usable strength is indicated to be at a hardness value of about 28 Rockwell C. Amine-type inhibitors are effective in minimizing corrosion and cracking of steel in solutions containing hydrogen sulfide.

Crevice Corrosion. Here localized corrosion occurs on surfaces partially shielded from contact with the corroding solution. This is closely related to pitting corrosion and includes concentration cell and differential aeration effects. The cause is electrochemical in nature, and it results from a difference in composition of solution within the crevice as compared with that just outside or adjacent to the crevice. The difference in solution composition or electrolyte results in a difference in potential of adjacent surfaces and causes the corrosion. All metals and alloys are susceptible to this form of corrosion, but fortunately the specific conditions required are encountered relatively infrequently. It can generally be avoided in gasketed joints by using a nonporous gasket material.

Galvanic Corrosion. Here the more noble of two metals in contact in an electrolyte causes electrochemical attack of the less noble metal. Perhaps the best example of this form is the use of zinc to protect steel equipment. Being anodic, or less noble than the steel, in most water and atmospheric exposure conditions, the zinc corrodes, while the steel, being cathodic, or more noble than the zinc, is protected. This protection of the steel is obtained as the result of the sacrificial corrosion of the zinc. The extent or severity of galvanic corrosion depends not only on the difference in potential of the two metals but also upon the relative surface areas involved. If the area of the cathodic metal is large compared with that of the anodic metal, the rate of galvanic or accelerated corrosion of the anodic metal will be much greater than if the relative areas were reversed. Bronze valves and fittings are commonly used in steel water lines without much difficulty due to localized corrosion of the steel at the fitting, but when a steel fitting is used in a copper line, relatively rapid corrosion of the steel fitting occurs. Although galvanic corrosion is frequently troublesome, the principle of galvanic corrosion is used to advantage to protect a large amount of equipment. Typical of this is the use of magnesium, aluminum, and zinc anodes to protect buried steel and iron pipelines.

Dezincification. Here the zinc constituent in brass alloys is selectively removed, leaving sponge copper behind in essentially the original shape and volume of the uncorroded piece. This effect is generally limited to brass compositions containing more than 15 per cent zinc. The addition of small amounts of arsenic, antimony, or tellurium to the alloy will effectively inhibit, if not prevent, this form of corrosion in brass. Brass-alloy tubing used for heat-exchanger services should be of one of the inhibited grades.

Graphitization. Here galvanic corrosion occurs between the graphite and iron constituents in cast iron with resultant formation of a spongy mass of corrosion products. The original shape and volume are generally retained, but the strength of the material is essentially lost as the corrosion proceeds through the cross section. This form of corrosion is rather common in buried cast-iron lines, particularly where moist and slightly acidic conditions prevail. Its rate is generally sufficiently low, however, that more expensive materials cannot be justified.

Intergranular Corrosion. Here attack is concentrated at grain boundaries without appreciable general corrosion. Most of the metals and alloys are susceptible to this form of corrosion under specific conditions, but the materials that are most frequently involved are the austenitic stainless steels, high-nickel alloys, and aluminum alloys.

This form of corrosion was a common occurrence in austenitic stainless-steel equipment 15 to 20 years ago before the effects of carbide precipitation were understood. It has been found, in the case of the austenitic stainless steels, that some of the chromium combines with the carbon to form chromium carbide, which is precipitated at the grain boundaries when the alloy is heated in or cooled slowly through the range of 800 to 1500°F. The rate and extent of formation of the chromium carbide are functions of time, temperature, and carbon content. It occurs during welding in the base material adjacent to the deposited metal. As the result of the localized impoverishment of chromium at the grain boundaries, preferential corrosion may occur at the grain boundaries in some acidic environments.

This form of corrosion can be prevented in stainless-steel materials by annealing the equipment (heating at 1950 to 2050°F followed by quenching) after welding operations, by the use of the low-carbon (0.03 per cent maximum) grades of stainless steel, or by the use of columbium or titanium stabilized grades of stainless steel. Critical amounts of chromium carbides do not precipitate at the grain boundaries in the low-carbon or the stabilized grades during welding, and annealing after welding is not required as a precaution against this form of corrosion.

Erosion Corrosion. Here the effects of velocity remove normally protective films and cause increased rate of corrosion. This form is most likely to occur in liquid systems that contain solids. Items such as pump impellers, agitator blades, and pipeline fittings are particularly subject to this form of corrosion. It can be minimized by reducing velocity, by changes in environment to reduce the corrosiveness of the solution, by addition of an inhibitor, or by the use of more corrosion-resistant material. Hard-surfacing materials have also been found to be an effective means of minimizing difficulty due to this form of corrosion.

Impingement. This is similar to erosion corrosion except that solids are generally not involved and specific effects are more localized. Perhaps the most common occurrence of this form of corrosion is in nonferrous-alloy condenser tubes, particularly near the inlet ends. A reduction in velocity or turbulence will prevent or minimize this difficulty. It can also be overcome by the use of alloy materials having greater resistance to this type of attack. The use of ferrules of plastic or alloy materials, inserted in the ends of the condenser tubes, has been effective where the attack was confined to an area near the inlet end.

Fretting Corrosion. Here corrosion between two surfaces is accelerated or results from the mechanical removal of protective film or corrosion products. It sometimes occurs at the interface of metals when they are clamped or fitted closely together and subjected to small vibrating motion. Its most common occurrence is on machine parts with small relative motions and high unit loads. Use of rust-inhibitive oils or greases is generally beneficial.

Oxidation. Here, generally at elevated temperatures, metal oxides are formed by direct chemical reaction and losses occur in form of scaling. Loss of metal is greater under cyclic fluctuations in temperatures as a result of loosening of scale and loss of its protective value. Maximum resistance to oxidation is provided by alloys containing a minimum of about 25 per cent chromium and 20 per cent or more nickel. Some further improvement can be obtained, in some instances, by surface treatment and alloying with aluminum.

Sulfidation. Here, at elevated temperatures, sulfur-bearing atmospheres cause intergranular attack. This is limited for the most part to nickel and alloys of high-nickel content. The sulfur reacts along the grain boundaries to form a low-melting eutectic which results in loss of ductility. The rate of attack is somewhat greater under reducing conditions than under oxidizing conditions. Nickel is not considered suitable for use in sulfur-bearing atmospheres at temperatures above about 600°F. The addition of chromium greatly improves the resistance of nickel alloys to sulfur-bearing gases.

These various forms of corrosion may overlap or occur in combination with one another. They are not always clearly defined by simple visual observation, and metallographic examination may be necessary for positive identification. The field of study of corrosion of metals is a large one, and it may be complicated by many ramifications. A good understanding of the corrosion of metals can, however, be obtained by study of information available in published form, and means of controlling or preventing corrosion may be determined.

NONMETALLIC MATERIALS

Metallic contamination of product has become a very important consideration and, in some instances, is responsible for limiting the use of metals for process equipment. The use of nonmetallic materials, in particular the plastics and elastomers, has proved to be very successful in avoiding metallic contamination as well as corrosion, and in many instances nonmetallic materials will provide greater chemical resistance at lower cost than metallic construction. Again, it is beyond the scope of this chapter to give detailed chemical-resistance data, and the reader is referred to the technical and trade literature publications for specific information.

Plastics. The use of plastics is, for the most part, limited to relatively low-temperature services and to low-pressure applications except where they may be used as a lining bonded to or otherwise supported by a strong material. There are a number of types of plastic materials that have proved to be economical improvements over metals for a number of corrosive conditions. Notable among these are polyethylene, the unplasticized polyvinyl chlorides, the styrene–synthetic-rubber blends, the polyesters and epoxy resin laminates, and the phenolic and furan resin impregnated, molded, and extruded materials. All these materials are available as piping, sheet stock, and miscellaneous molded and fabricated items. These materials, particularly polyvinyl chloride, are now being used extensively for ventilating ductwork for handling corrosive fumes, and they have proved to be economical improvements over metals, such as stainless steel, lead, aluminum, and galvanized steel, in many instances. They generally are not subject to pitting, stress-corrosion cracking, and other forms of corrosion common to metals. A point of merit that should not be overlooked is that they do not require painting for protection against external corrosion. Plastic materials are replacing metals in many applications because of their better resistance to chemical exposures and the improved service life and economy.

The most chemical-resistant plastic commercially available today is tetrafluoroethylene (Teflon). This is a thermoplastic material which is practically unaffected by all acids and alkalies at temperatures up to about 500°F. It has proved to be an outstanding material for gaskets, packing, diaphragms, and other relatively small molded items. Its chemical inertness makes normal bonding and cementing operations impractical, but it can be cemented to metals and other materials by using special sheets that have rough backing surfaces which provide mechanical adherence through any one of a number of resin cements. Techniques have also been worked out that make it possible to heat-seal sheets of the material together, and loose linings, including nozzle linings, may now be installed in small tanks, ductwork, and other straight-sided and nonintricate equipment.

Chlorotrifluoroethylene (Kel-F) also possesses excellent chemical resistance to almost all acids and alkalies at temperatures up to about 350°F and is second only to the tetrafluoroethylene material in this respect. It, too, is difficult to bond to itself and other materials, and fabrication is limited accordingly.

Polyethylene is the lowest cost plastic that has excellent resistance to a wide variety of chemicals. Its greatest use to date has been as piping and tubing in corrosive services, but large quantities are also used as thin sheet or film liners in drums and other packages. Polyethylene tape, with pressure-sensitive adhesive on one side, is receiving increasing attention and use as a wrapping material to protect conduit and pipe from corrosion. Unfortunately, its mechanical properties are relatively poor, particularly at temperatures of about 120°F, and it must be fully supported for most applications. Cements have not been developed, to date, that are suitable for use with polyethylene, but it can be readily joined to itself by heat sealing or fusing, and a wide variety of equipment has been made satisfactorily using heat-sealing techniques. Weathering resistance of the unfilled grades is poor, but the carbon-filled grades have good resistance to sunlight and are satisfactory for outdoor use.

The unplasticized polyvinyl chloride materials have excellent resistance to oxidizing acids, other than concentrated nitric and sulfuric, and to nonoxidizing acids in all concentrations and are satisfactory for use at temperatures up to about 150°F. They are also resistant to both weak and strong alkaline materials and solutions of most chemical salts. Their resistance to aromatic and aliphatic hydrocarbons is generally good, but resistance to chlorinated hydrocarbons is poor. They are not satisfactory for use with ketone and ester solvents. They are self-extinguishing with respect to flame resistance and have good resistance to sunlight and outdoor weathering.

Two general types are available, the regular and the high-impact. The latter has appreciably better impact resistance but somewhat lower strength and over-all chemical resistance. They are readily fabricated and can be joined by fusion and solvent-welding techniques.

The styrene–synthetic-rubber-blend materials, which are a mixture of styrene-acrylonitrile copolymer with butadiene-acrylonitrile copolymer, have good resistance to nonoxidizing and weak acids but are not satisfactory for handling oxidizing acids. Upper useful temperature limit is about 150°F. Resistance to strong alkaline solutions is fair and to weak alkaline and chemical salt solutions generally good. They are not satisfactory for use with aromatic and chlorinated hydrocarbons, and they possess only fair resistance to aliphatic hydrocarbons. They are not satisfactory to use with ketone and ester solvents. These materials normally will burn, but fire-retardant grades are commercially available. Resistance to sunlight and outdoor weathering is generally good. They can be readily fabricated and can be joined with solvent-welding technique.

The epoxy resin laminate materials are relatively new developments. They possess very good strength and chemical resistance, and it appears that they will be widely used for corrosion-resistant equipment. They are generally laminated with glass-fiber cloth, but for many chemical services, over-all resistance can be improved by using chemically resistant synthetic-fiber cloth, such as Orlon acrylic fiber, for laminating. The glass-fiber laminates are not satisfactory for use in hydrofluoric acid, and it has been found that they are subject to attack and penetration in other acid and alkaline solutions where cut edges are used with exposure of the glass fiber. Chemical resistance of the epoxy resin material is excellent to nonoxidizing and weak acids, but resistance to strong oxidizing acids is generally not satisfactory. Upper temperature limit for these materials is about 200°F. Resistance to alkaline and most chemical salt solutions is good. They also have good resistance to aromatic and aliphatic hydrocarbons but only fair resistance to chlorinated hydrocarbons and ketone and ester solvents. These materials will burn, but flame-retardant grades are being developed. Resistance to sunlight and outdoor weathering is generally good. Satisfactory cements are available for fabrication purposes.

There are a number of polyester resin materials being used for laminates, and their chemical resistance varies appreciably. In general, the chemical resistance of the polyester laminated materials is not so good as that of the epoxy laminated materials. They should not be used for alkaline materials. Temperature limit is about 150°F for most chemical services. The regular grades will burn, but flame-resistant grades are available. Resistance to sunlight and outdoor weathering is generally good, and large quantities of this type of material are now being used for skylights, siding, etc., in buildings where a translucent material is desirable.

Rubber and Elastomers. Natural rubber has been used for many years as a material for molded and lined equipment for chemical service. It can be compounded for maximum resistance to a number of service conditions and has proved to be a very useful material for many conditions that are highly corrosive to metals. Natural-rubber compounds will resist a wide variety of chemical solutions, including all concentrations of hydrochloric, acetic, and phosphoric acids; sulfuric acid up to about 50 per cent concentration; saturated salt solutions, such as ferric chloride; brine; bleaching solutions; and most plating solutions. They are readily attacked by strong oxidizing acids such as nitric and chromic and the aliphatic, aromatic, and chlorinated solvents. Maximum temperature at which rubber compounds can be used varies with the chemical and the strength of solution. The temperature limitation for continuous exposure for most soft-rubber compounds is about 140°F, and that for hard rubber is about 180°F. However, there are heat-resisting compounds available which may be used at somewhat higher temperatures. Soft rubber, specifically compounded for maximum temperature resistance, may be used for continuous exposures under some chemical conditions at temperatures as high as 200°F, and hard rubber may be compounded for service temperatures as high as 230°F.

A number of synthetic rubber and other elastomeric materials have been developed with special characteristics that extend the over-all usefulness of elastomers for corrosion-resistant equipment. Notable among these are the buna S (GR-S), buna N (GR-A), butyl (GR-I), neoprene (GR-M), "Hypalon" Chlorosulfonated Polyethylene and Thiokol compounds. Like natural rubber, each of these may be compounded in several ways for maximum resistance to specific chemical exposures. Natural rubber and other elastomer materials are frequently used in combination with brick linings where temperature conditions are above the limit for the elastomer materials, and they have proved to be excellent membrane linings for such construction.

Brick Linings. Brick-lined construction can be used for many conditions that are severely corrosive even to high-alloy materials, and it should be considered where tanks, vats, stacks, and similar equipment items are required. Brick shapes commonly used for such construction are made from carbon, red shale, and acidproof refractory materials. Carbon bricks are useful for handling alkaline conditions as well as acid, while the shale and acidproof refractory materials are used primarily for acid solutions. Carbon can also be used where sudden temperature changes are involved that would cause spalling of the other two materials. Red shale brick generally are not used at temperatures over about 350°F because of poor spalling resistance. Acidproof refractories are used at temperatures up to about 1600°F.

There are a number of cement materials that are regularly used for brick-lined construction, the most commonly used being the resin, sulfur, and silicate-base materials. The resin cements include the phenolic and the furan resin-base materials, which can be used at temperatures up to about 350°F. The carbon-filled phenolic resin cements have excellent resistance to all nonoxidizing acids, salts, and most organic solvents. The carbon-filled furan resin cements have excellent resistance to all nonoxidizing acids and alkalies, salts, and most organic solvents. Silica-filled resin compositions are available in both types of resin cements and are almost equally resistant except to hydrofluoric acid and alkaline solutions. The sulfur-base cements are limited to a maximum service temperature of about 200°F. In general, they have excellent chemical resistance to nonoxidizing acids and acid or neutral salts but are not suitable for use in the presence of alkalies or organic solvents. The sodium silicate-base cements have good resistance to all inorganic acids (except hydrofluoric) at temperatures up to about 750°F. The potassium silicate-base cements are useful at somewhat higher temperatures, the upper limit depending upon specific conditions and requirements.

Protective Coatings. Protective coatings are probably the most widely used and also the most controversial materials employed for minimizing corrosion of steel and certain other materials. Because of its importance, the subject of protective painting is discussed in a separate chapter in this handbook. It is in order to emphasize here, however, that it is unwise and generally uneconomical to try to use steel equipment with chemically resistant coatings for containing chemicals that are quite corrosive to steel. This results from the fact that it is almost impossible to avoid some pinholes or holidays in the coatings. Rapid attack of the steel will occur at such points, and continued maintenance attention will be required. The chemical-resistant coatings, such as the baked phenolics and the epoxy-, vinyl-, and neoprene-base coatings, are ideal for minimizing contamination of chemicals handled in steel equipment, but they should not be used where 100 per cent protection against corrosion is required.

Glass Linings. Glass-lined equipment is available that is satisfactory, from a chemical-resistance standpoint, for handling all acids (except hydrofluoric and some concentrations of phosphoric) at ambient and elevated temperatures and many alkaline conditions at ambient and slightly higher temperatures. The glass lining is resistant to all concentrations of hydrochloric acid at temperatures up to 300°F, to dilute concentrations of sulfuric acid to their boiling points, to concentrated solutions up to about 450°F, and to all concentrations of nitric acid up to their boiling points. A newly developed acid-resistant glass with improved alkali resistance is now commercially available for use under alkaline conditions up to 12 pH at about 200°F. Equipment items such as tanks, pressure reactors, lines, valves, and accessory equipment are available. Methods for field repair of damaged glass linings have been developed. These include the use of plugs and cover plates of tantalum and other metals alone or in combination with resin cements and Teflon.

Wood. Wood continues to be used as a material of construction for tanks, vats, filter presses, cooling towers, and other items. The woods most commonly used now are yellow pine, cypress, redwood, and maple. The choice depends largely on service conditions and type of equipment involved. All woods are affected adversely by acids, particularly the strongly oxidizing ones, but they are regularly used in dilute sulfuric and hydrochloric acid solutions at ambient temperatures. Acetic acid has very little effect on wood, although its use may impart some discoloration to the acid. Strong alkaline solutions, particularly caustic, generally cause disintegration and cannot be used in wood. Weak solutions can, however, be used with wood equipment with reasonably good service life.

INHIBITORS

The corrosion of iron and other metals in aqueous solutions can frequently be inhibited and controlled by the addition of soluble chromates, phosphates, silicates, amines, and other chemicals. They are generally more attractive for use in recirculating systems than in nonrecirculating systems because of the quantity and the cost of the inhibitor required. They are also most attractive for use in neutral or very slightly acid solutions rather than in alkaline solutions, since corrosion in alkaline solutions is generally low.   One exception to this is the use of aluminum in alkaline environments where sodium silicate has been used effectively as an inhibitor.   The concentration of an inhibitor required for optimum control depends upon solution composition, temperature, velocity, the metal system, and the presence of dissimilar metals in contact in the solutions.   Care should be taken in the selection and application of inhibitors, since in some instances they can cause increased localized attack. Although the chromate treatment is widely used, it does require attention to keep concentration at the required minimum for specific environmental conditions.   Thorough testing or reference to technical literature should be made where experience under similar conditions is not available.

One of the most common uses of inhibitors is in brine systems.   Where calcium or sodium chloride brines are used in steel equipment, it is generally recommended that sodium dichromate ($Na_2Cr_2O_7 \cdot 2H_2O$) be used.   Where chromates cannot be used, disodium phosphate ($Na_2HOP_4 \cdot 12H_2O$) is recommended for sodium chloride brines.

Where aluminum equipment is used in brine service, it is recommended that 1 per cent as much sodium dichromate be used as there is chloride present.

For recirculating water systems made of steel, it has been found that 0.2 ml of sodium silicate (40°B) per liter is effective in inhibiting corrosion.   Sodium dichromate at 0.01 per cent concentration is also effective and can be used where toxicity effects are not important.   Where aluminum is used for recirculating water systems, it has been found that 0.1 per cent sodium chromate is effective.   If aluminum is in contact with other metals, it may be necessary to use as much as 1 per cent of the sodium chromate.

One of the more recent developments in inhibitors is the use of the volatile (VCI) or vapor-phase (VPI) corrosion inhibitors.   These materials are amine nitrite salts. They have proved to be very effective in preventing corrosion of steel and ferrous-base materials and are ideal for protecting machined parts in storage or shipment.   They can also be used to protect steel process equipment when idle or in stand-by condition. The materials are available as crystals or as impregnated paper.   The form to be used will depend upon the physical characteristics of the item to be protected.   The inhibitors are slightly volatile at atmospheric temperatures, and the protection obtained results from the diffusion and condensation of the vapors on the surface of the items being protected.

CATHODIC PROTECTION

Fundamentally, cathodic protection is the use of an impressed current from an auxiliary anode to prevent or minimize the corrosion of a metal by making it a cathode in the system.   This current is provided by use of rectifiers or sacrificial galvanic anodes.   Graphite, aluminum, and high-silicon iron are used as anodes in conjunction with rectifiers.   The most commonly used sacrificial materials are magnesium, zinc, and aluminum.   Cathodic protection is now recognized as a proved method of controlling corrosion of steel and other metals under some environmental conditions. Although it should, theoretically, be possible to use cathodic protection under most conditions where metals are used with electrolytes present, it has been found that practical limitations and cost make it attractive for only a few.   It is now being used successfully for minimizing corrosion of equipment, such as buried pipelines, water-storage tanks, condensers, and heat exchangers, water boxes, and dock piling.   The factors involved in the design and application of cathodic protection are rather complex, and assistance should be obtained from persons experienced in this field before application of this type of corrosion control is attempted.

BIBLIOGRAPHY

"Surface Protection Against Wear and Corrosion," American Society for Metals, 1954.
Robertson, W. D.: "Stress Corrosion Cracking and Embrittlement," John Wiley & Sons, Inc., New York, 1956.

De Paul, D. J. (ed.): "Corrosion and Wear Handbook," McGraw-Hill Book Company, New York, 1957.

Miller, V. D. (ed.): "Proceedings Short Course on Process Industry Corrosion," (Ohio State University, Sept. 12–16, 1960) National Association of Corrosion Engineers, Houston, Tex.

Nelson, G. A.: "Corrosion Data Survey," 1960 ed., Shell Development Company, Emeryville, Calif.

Shreir, L. L.: "Corrosion," vols. 1–2, John Wiley & Sons, Inc., New York, 1963.

Perry, J. H. (ed.): "Chemical Engineers' Handbook," 4th ed., McGraw-Hill Book Company, New York, 1963.

Uhlig, H. H. (ed.): "The Corrosion Handbook," sponsored by the Electro-Chemicals Society, John Wiley & Sons, Inc., New York, 1958.

Bregman, J. I.: "Corrosion Inhibitors," The Macmillan Company, New York, 1963.

Seymour, R. B., and R. H. Steiner: "Corrosion Resistant Plastics," Reinhold Publishing Corporation, New York, 1955.

Atkinson, H. E.: "Designing Reinforced Plastics for Chemical Resistance," *Mech. Eng.*, vol. 84, no. 6, June, 1962.

Chapter 2

CHEMICAL CLEANING

By CHARLES M. LOUCKS
Consulting Chemist
Cleveland, Ohio

If fouling has occurred on heat-exchange surfaces and in flow channels and cleaning needs to be done, it may be accomplished with chemicals. Methods, equipment, and procedures are discussed in this chapter. The chemistry of chemical cleaning is not.[1]

One method of chemical cleaning is to use tanks, some holding hot detergent solutions and rinse water, others holding organic solvents for removing greasy soils. Objects to be cleaned may be put in by hand or by mechanized lift equipment. Another method is to use the steam jenny to deliver wet steam plus detergents through a hose and nozzle to remove oil, grease, and general soil. The jenny can be mounted on wheels for mobility. To clean surfaces of oil and grease, *vapor degreasing* can be used. It is a process for washing small parts with organic solvent made continuously clean by distillation. The clean vapor condenses on cool parts, dissolves oil and grease, and returns to the reservoir to be redistilled. *Electrolytic cleaning* is done by hanging the part on the anode or cathode bar of an electrolytic cleaning tank. The action at the electrode helps with the cleaning. In the *ultrasonic cleaning bath*, electrical energy is converted to sound waves by devices called transducers. They, and the parts to be cleaned, are submerged in a liquid within the tank. The liquid conveys the sonic vibrations from the source of the energy to the parts where particles of soil are disturbed physically in a manner that assists the cleaning operation. Neither electrolytic nor ultrasonic cleaning has been useful for large or complex equipment. There are limitations on arrangements of anodes and cathodes in one case and limitations on the proximity of transducers and parts to be cleaned in the other.

CLEANING MATERIALS

Synthetic Detergents. Because they are attracted to surfaces that separate different phases, like oil and water, detergents are called surface-active agents, or surfactants.

Organic Solvents. They are nonwater solvents used primarily for removing oil and grease when cleaning engines and small parts. The solvents are kerosene, diesel fuel, Stoddard solvent, carbon tetrachloride, trichloroethylene, and perchloroethylene. The chlorinated solvents will not burn. They are more expensive than the flammable solvents but safer in this one respect. In another respect they are less safe: the vapors are toxic. "Trichlor" is used widely in degreasing machines. Relatively new solvents that have chlorine atoms or both chlorine and fluorine atoms in the molecule are gaining acceptance because they are both nonflammable and relatively nontoxic.

Emulsion Cleaners. If an organic solvent contains a surfactant, the solvent will dissolve oil and grease and, when water is applied, the solvent and soil disperse as an emulsion and everything washes away. An example is the paint brush cleaner. Put paint brushes in a solvent plus a surfactant; then wash the brushes under the water faucet.

Rust and Scale Removers. Rust and scale do not respond to the use of detergents or organic solvents. A different kind of solvent is needed. In this case acid will work. There are liquid acids, like muriatic and sulfuric, which may be bad smelling, corrosive, and require careful handling. There are solid or "dry" acids that are crystalline materials, easy to handle and exhibiting no acid properties until dissolved in water. *Sulfamic* acid is used for removing rust and scale from engine jackets and heat exchangers. *Citric* acid has been used for cleaning large power and process systems. Acids that are used for cleaning metal surfaces need to be inhibited. Inhibitors reduce the natural corrosive action of the acid. Acid solutions can be put into a tank for dipping parts, pipe sections, sheets, etc. The solution can be pumped into a vessel that is to be cleaned internally. Or the acid can be thickened and applied to accessible surfaces as a paste or gel.

Paint Strippers. Metal parts are stripped with strong solutions of *caustic soda*. *Methylene chloride*, nonflammable, is a modern stripping material used on metal or wood surfaces. Thickening agents are added to make a paste which will adhere to vertical surfaces. Surfactants are included in the flush-off formulations.

Sequestrants. They are also called chelates and chelating agents. To sequester means to isolate. Sequestrants isolate the hardness ions in water to make it soft. They can be used for dissolving some of the things that acids dissolve, without the corrosion and handling problems involved in using acids. They can clean boilers and cooling systems.

Specialty Cleaning Products. Chemical specialties are formulated cleaning products like floor waxes and disinfectants. Included is any product especially formulated for a certain purpose and packaged and sold under a trade name. The largest single use for chemical specialties involves cleaning and related housekeeping chores. Many chemical specialties are purchased for the maintenance of buildings and equipment. However, the chemical cleaning contractors, using large quantities, prefer to purchase the ingredients and do their own formulating. They use tank trucks of up to 2,000-gal capacity, mix off the site, and drive to the plant site.

APPLICATION OF CLEANING MATERIALS

Cleaning Outside Surfaces of Large Equipment. The cleaning of things too large to be put into a tank, too complex to be disassembled, and requiring quantities of cleaning materials that suggest the use of a truck has become a common problem of maintenance. The outsides of automobiles, airplanes, railroad cars, etc., are washed with hoses and long-handled brushes, with semiautomatic washing facilities. Increase the size to that of a tank 80 ft in diameter and 40 ft high, change the material to a paint stripper or rust remover, and the problem changes. The goal has been to apply paint stripper or acid without having to resort to scaffolding and essentially hand methods. Attempts have been made to use spray headers around the top of a tank and solvent recovery gutters around the bottom. There have been vertical spray assemblies that could be rolled around the circumference. Both thickened paint stripper and thickened acids have been applied with special lances and long-handled spreaders. Success by these methods has not been spectacular. Much remains to be done.

Cleaning Insides of Large Hollow Vessels. The job may require removal of oil and wax from a crude-oil storage tank or rust from a tank going into refined-product storage. The cleaning material will be detergent, acid, organic solvent, or paint remover. The confinement provided by the walls and roof of the vessel allows the use of stationary or mechanized robot spray devices that apply liquid cleaning solutions to the interior surfaces while it protects adjacent structures, people, and equipment. Any of the materials to be used can be sprayed, collected, and used again while workmen who operate the pump and control a robot sprayer remain outside the vessel. If inhibited acid is used for rust removal, it soon becomes very corrosive to the spray equipment, so reuse may be unwise. When flammable organic solvents are sprayed, there is a static electricity hazard. One remedy has been to blanket the tank interior with carbon dioxide.

Vapor cleaning has had some application on vessel interiors. Perhaps it is worth more consideration. One report[2] tells how steam and nitric acid were used to clean the stainless steel interiors of two atomic reactor vessels. The method was successful, and the saving in time, material, and labor, over any conventional method, was significant. In another case, steam plus detergent solution were used to remove oil from the interior of a large gas storage sphere. Any accessible surfaces may, of course, be cleaned by using chemicals applied by essentially hand methods. The usual safety methods are in order, and if workmen are to be in a confined space, special precautions are necessary before and after entry.

Much large and/or complex equipment has inaccessible surfaces. This is the area in which chemical cleaning technology has proved most useful. To the chemical cleaning engineer there are two types of such equipment.

One type is equipment that can be filled with a liquid solvent and then, at the proper time, emptied by opening a drain valve. The vessel is pumped full of inhibited acid, for example; the acid cleans fouled surfaces, then the drain is opened, and the solvent is removed. The rinses and neutralizing solutions are handled in the same way. The mechanical requirements are simple. There is need for tank trucks to bring liquid solvents, such as inhibited muriatic acid, to the site. Water is needed for diluting the concentrated solvent. A pump and pipe line to the vessel allow the solvent to be put in. Usually there is need for a steam supply sufficient to heat the diluted solvent to the specified temperature. The heating is done by admitting live steam through a Y-connection on the fill line. Other mechanical facilities will include sample connections, a vent line from the highest point on the vessel, and temporary piping, if necessary, for disposing of the used solvent.

To perform the cleaning service with a solvent such as inhibited acid, the warm solvent is pumped into the warm vessel. During the reaction time, the service engineer takes samples, runs analyses, records temperatures, and decides when the reaction period is completed. The solvent is drained to waste. The vessel is pumped full of water once or twice, then full of an alkaline solution. In the case of a boiler, the last solution may be boiled by firing the boiler for a few hours. The boiler is then cooled, rinsed with water, and opened for inspection and removal of loose debris that almost invariably remains. Vessels that cannot be fired are nonetheless rinsed, neutralized, and made free of loose debris.

The other type is equipment designed to handle mass flow of fluid. It may be a condensed fluid, a liquid, or a noncondensed fluid (a gas or vapor). For example, a boiler is built to produce 100,000 lb of steam per hour. The steam flows from the steam drum through a superheater. The common pendant superheater consists of many parallel tubes which make several down and up loops, with both ends higher than the loops. At 100,000 lb/hr steam flow, the steam enters one end of all parallel paths, gets superheated, and comes out at the other end into an outlet header. The pendant superheater cannot be filled with a liquid cleaning solvent and then drained at will.

There are many other examples. Certain modern boilers, called monotube steam generators, cannot be filled and drained. Some heat exchangers have U-shaped tubes, and whether the open end is up or down, there is a problem. Large surface condensers on steam turbine generators often have tubes that arch slightly in the center. When cooling water is pumped through the tubes at the design flow, all the tubes are full. But if a cleaning solvent is merely pumped in, the two ends of each tube are submerged while air is still trapped in the arch. Draining, of course, is no problem. Refinery process stream heaters frequently have up and down loops. Pipe lines may change elevations several times, leaving high loops and low stretches. For all these kinds of equipment, the fill-and-empty technique is possible only if vents are installed at all high points and drains at all low spots.   This has been done with pipe lines, but in many cases is impractical.

Greater ingenuity is required in planning chemical service for this type of equipment.   The pendant superheater is a good example, not because a superheater is cleaned frequently, but because it is a fairly familiar piece of equipment that represents about the ultimate in awkwardness to the service engineer.   Theoretically, there is an easy way.   A general rule that may be applied to all types of equipment is this: the easiest method is the one that comes closest to having the system do what it was designed to do.   The easiest way to clean a boiler is to put a chemical reactant into the boiler water and fire the boiler.   This would be the fill-and-empty method much simplified.   It has been done, but with reactants other than the aggressive mineral acids.

The superheater, then, would be no problem if the cleaning reactant could be put into the normal flow of steam through the pendant loops.   This procedure will not come into general use until someone demonstrates conclusively that it is safe, effective, and economical.   In the meantime, one method has been to pump solvent through one

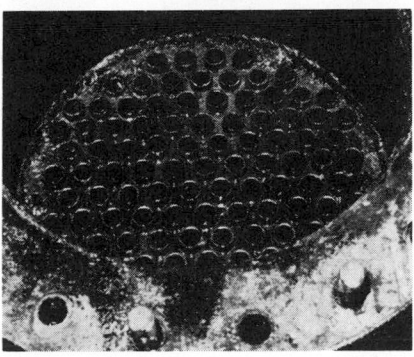

Fig. 2-1. Tube and shell heat exchanger after cleaning with hot 10 per cent inhibited sulfamic acid in 4 hr circulation.   River water clogs this exchanger with mud and carbonate scale in 4 months.   Before cleaning, the ends of the tubes were not visible.   (*Courtesy of E. I. du Pont de Nemours & Co., Inc., Niagara Falls, N.Y.*)

superheater tube at a time by means of a special fitting placed in one end.   When a single tube is used, the mass flow of solvent is sufficient to push the air out; then the solution is pushed out by rinse water, the water by neutralizer solution, and the neutralizer by water.   It is not a method that can be used if superheater headers are so constructed that the ends of the tubes are not accessible.

Another approach is to try to pump through all the parallel paths with as great a mass flow as it is practical to achieve, or as is necessary to make sure of displacing one air or fluid with the next.   For a relatively small U-tube heat exchanger with U-tubes open upward this is not difficult.   If the U-tubes open down, the tubes cannot be filled anyway.   Larger systems with multiple loops and many parallel paths may have large volume pumps in the system; for example, the boiler feed pumps in a monotube boiler system.   If these may not be used for fear of solvent or abrasion damage, large temporary pumps may be installed at considerable expense.

When circulation of any system, large or small, seems necessary to accomplish satisfactory cleaning, there are some things to consider.   Corrosion problems are aggravated.   Experience suggests that aggressive mineral acids be circulated as little as possible.   The so-called organic acids, like citric or formic, may be circulated with greater safety.   So if a weak acid will accomplish the cleaning job, it may be worth considering.   The weak acids normally are used at higher temperatures than the mineral acids, so it will be necessary to provide for adding heat to the circulating system.

Interesting New Ideas. Recently at least two new methods of application have helpful with some of the old cleaning problems. (*a*) The use of noncondensed fluids. Steam has been used in two ways: (1) with nitric acid to vapor-clean large hollow atomic reactor vessels, where condensation on the cool walls performed the cleaning; (2) with a reactant in the normal steam flow to clean superheaters. There needs to be some liquid phase to do the cleaning, but the bulk of the steam flow serves as the transport medium. This has had limited use for cleaning superheaters, but the

FIG. 2-2. Typical pipe-line pig. It is equipped with disks to propel it with the fluid flow and with stiff wire brushes for mechanical cleaning. Pigs sometimes are used in connection with chemical cleaning solutions for pipe-line cleaning. (*Courtesy of T. D. Williamson Co., Tulsa, Okla.*)

FIG. 2-3. Pipe crawlers are available in sizes $1\frac{1}{2}$ in. to 36 in. They are made of reinforced rubber and have an air valve for easy inflation. The scraper chain cleans pipe walls mechanically as crawler moves with the fluid flow. (*Courtesy of Rotary Pipe Crawlers, Corona, Calif.*)

method[3] has had considerable use in solving the awkward pipe-line problems. Results have been good, with substantial savings in time, materials, and cost. (*b*) Use of foamed solvents. Any solvent, including the strong mineral acids, can be made into a foam[4] resembling the push-button shaving creams. The foam can be made to have one-twentieth the density of the corresponding liquid. The first use was in an elevated gas-pipe line, on supports that would not hold up when the line was full of liquid. The flow characteristics are such that foamed acid if put into one water box of a large surface condenser will travel through each arched tube like a solid slug, pushing the air out ahead of it into the empty water box on the opposite end.

Pigs, Plugs, Balls. Mechanical devices often are used, alone or in connection with chemical solvents. In pipe-line work, tools can be made to travel through the line by the force of a fluid behind them. The fluid may be water, oil, gas, or a chemical cleaning solution. The tool may have rubber disks that fit the inside of the line, the disks being attached to a central shaft to which scrapers and brushes may also be attached. Even a radioactive capsule may be attached to assist in showing the location of the tool if the radiation can be detected outside the line. Sometimes the rubber stoppers are used to separate a slug of one fluid from the next. In this manner, cleaning, rinsing, and neutralizing solutions have been put through long lines in proper sequence to avoid filling the line entirely with first one fluid, then the next. There are rubber balls, of any diameter, with chain mesh to fit them when inflated. The balls move with the fluid flow as do the pigs and plugs.

DATA AND DECISIONS

To summarize the kinds of information needed and the decisions that must be made in planning a chemical cleaning job:

It is necessary to know the nature of the deposit phases. The chemical cleaning involves chemical reactions between the substances that foul the equipment (corrosion products and scale) and chemicals that are chosen to correct the fouling condition. As the reaction goes on, new substances will be formed. Knowledge of the deposit phases reveals what has been going on in the system to cause the fouling. It helps select the solvent to be used for cleaning. It helps anticipate the identity of the reaction products, which must be soluble in the cleaning solution to be removed from the system. Reaction products that are flammable, toxic, or corrosive must be anticipated. In addition to identifying the deposit ingredients, it is common practice to use deposit samples for solvent trials and corrosion tests.

It is necessary to know engineering materials and design. What engineering materials will be exposed to the cleaning solvent? What are the details of design? Both materials and design are described in prints and descriptive bulletins furnished by equipment vendors. If there is any doubt about the chemical properties of a material versus the solvents to be proposed, laboratory trials should be made. Specimens of materials can be exposed to solvent and deposits under conditions that simulate the cleaning conditions that are being planned.

After securing the information indicated, there are decisions to be made. If an outside contractor is employed, the decisions may be left to him or they may be reached by consultation between contractor and owner. If the plant is to do the job, someone in the plant must make the decisions. What decisions must be made?

1. What reactants, inhibitors, surfactants, neutralizers should be used?
2. What reactant concentrations and temperatures are necessary? What mixing and heating facilities will provide the chosen conditions?
3. What precautions are necessary to protect people and equipment? This involves safety instructions, clothing, and special protective devices for workmen. It involves isolating the equipment to prevent dispersion of the solvent to other equipment and surroundings. It may mean roping off the work area and posting safety signs. Perhaps most important, it means providing for reaction products that may be hazardous. Hydrogen gas always is anticipated when the cleaning involves acids and steel; providing a suitable vent for hydrogen should be routine. If there is any possibility of toxic gases such as hydrogen sulfide or chlorine, this must be anticipated, either to prevent the reaction or dispose of the product. These are typical reaction problems—there may be others.
4. What supervision is needed during the operation? What people are needed, and what engineering and chemical data are needed so the people can follow the progress? Someone must decide when each step has been completed and it is time to go on to the next, until everything has been done and the system is ready to be put back into use.
5. What records should be kept, and by whom? There are data and records to be kept during the planning, the doing, and the evaluating of the results.

MECHANICAL VERSUS CHEMICAL CLEANING

To compare the costs of mechanical and chemical methods, consider outage time, lost production; man-hours, tools, equipment, materials needed; degree of restored efficiency to be expected; and safety to equipment and personnel.

In any case, the objective is to get the most cleaning per dollar spent. If the system is too large or complex to allow mechanical methods to be used, the answer is the chemical method. Still the question is how to get the most for the money. Can plant personnel do the work, or is it better to seek outside contracting? Are outside services bought by bids? On what are the bids based? Who specifies procedures, materials, results? What assurance is there of competent planning and performance? Some of the answers depend upon whether or not the purchaser has men who know the chemical cleaning technology well enough to furnish specifications describing what is being purchased and to judge the competence of the service that is offered for hire. In the absence of such knowledge, the purchaser is in the position of the layman seeking the advice of medical experts. Bids and lowest prices are not necessarily the greatest bargain. The experience and qualifications of the man who will be responsible for the service are most important.

REFERENCES

1. (a) Loucks, C. M.: Chemistry Tackles Plant Maintenance, *Chem. Eng.*, vol. 69, no. 5, pp. 103–120, Mar. 5, 1962. (b) Loucks, C. M.: "The Chemistry Professor in Industrial Plant Maintenance," C. D. Horn Associates, Caxton Bldg., Cleveland, Ohio, 1963.
2. Loucks, C. M., and W. B. Brown: Reactor Vessels Cleaned with Nitric Vapor, *Chem. Eng.*, vol. 68, p. 166, Feb. 20, 1961.
3. (a) Loucks, C. M.: Something New in Chemical Cleaning, *Power Eng.*, vol. 65, pp. 58–59, June, 1961. (b) U.S. Patent 3,084,076.
4. (a) Carroll, D. B., C. L. Eddington, and J. P. Engle: "Chemical Cleaning with Foamed Solvents," Proceedings of the 22d Annual Water Conference, Engineers Society of Western Pennsylvania, pp. 35–40, 1961. (b) U.S. Patent 3,037,887.

INDEX